C000104284

PUMA®

An Introduction

In 1948, Rudolf Dassler founded PUMA in Herzogenaurach, Germany. Puma is synonymous with sport, particularly running shoes and football boots featuring the now globally recognized 'form stripe;

Olympic Champions ranging from Tommy Smith to Heike Drechsler; and football legends such as Eusebio, Pele, Cruyff and Maradonna as well as Paul Gascoigne and Kenny Dalglish in the UK have worn the famous boots on the international football field.

Through the 70's, the leaping cat logo became synonymous with urban cool, immediately identifying its wearer as an individual with a distinct attitude about both life and sport.

The definition of a new category 'sportslifestyle' was born.

In 2008 Puma is one of the key brands in global football.

Puma sponsors the current World Champions, Italy as well as other key football federations such as The Czech Republic, Poland , Austria, and Uruguay as well as key African Nations teams such as The Ivory Coast, Ghana, and Cameroon. In the World Cup 2006 in Germany, Puma had more teams on pitch from the qualifying teams than any other brand.

Puma is also well represented in terms of global club football teams: Lazio, Monaco, Sporting Lisbon and Villarreal providing international kudos whereas in the UK Puma sponsor Tottenham Hotspur in the English Premier League and a licensee agreement sees brand associations with: Reading, Coventry City, Bristol City, Plymouth Argyle, Brentford, and Luton.

In the modern era, Puma has key player icons such as Samuel Eto'o of Barcelona and Cameroon as well as GianLuca Buffon the Juventus and Italian Goalkeeper. In the UK, Puma is very well represented with key players such as David Bentley, Peter Crouch, Shay Given and Aiden McGeady.

In the UK Puma has a key Grass Roots strategy aimed at specific markets. The Non League market is identified as a key focus hence the sponsorship of the Non League Directory, as well as a plan to target key clubs and coaches throughout the country.Puma has a contract with the Football League which exists under the title of Technical Partner.

Puma supplies the majority of the Football League clubs' Football in the Community Schemes with uniforms, balls, bibs etc. Also as part of the agreement Puma supplies all apprentices at Football League Clubs with football boots and goalkeeper gloves for the 'keepers.

Puma is an undoubted force in football worldwide and the relationship with Non League Football is identified as a key focus in maintaining and building the brand.

PUMA has continued its sporting heritage by being involved in numerous other sporting categories in addition to Football thus underpinning its overall strength in Sport.

With performance products being worn at the highest level PUMA is seen on the field of play extensively in both Rugby Union and Rugby League.

- In Rugby Union PUMA sponsor the Samoan Rugby Federation but also have an extensive portfolio within the UK from both a Clubs and players perspective.

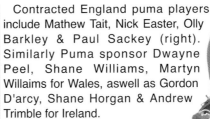

Contracted England puma players include Mathew Tait, Nick Easter, Olly Barkley & Paul Sackey (right). Similarly Puma sponsor Dwayne Peel, Shane Williams, Martyn Willaims for Wales, aswell as Gordon D'arcy, Shane Horgan & Andrew Trimble for Ireland.

Within Rugby League the Brand is represented by Great Britain who are sponsored by PUMA as well as St Helens and numerous Rugby League players.

More recently PUMA has moved into new categories of both Golf and Cricket and therefore the Brand is represented within these Sports at the very highest level as well.

Within Golf Puma sponsors both Geoff Ogilvy (pictured) and Johan Edfors, as well as representing new & exciting talent such as Kiran Matharu & Zane Scotland.

- Within Cricket the Brand is endorsed by players of the calibre such as Geraint Jones and Simon Jones as well.

In more recent years the Brand has moved into new sports Categories such as Motorsport and therefore the Cat logo can also be seen extensively within Formula One !

The passion for desirability will also ensure that the Brand continues to strive for new and innovative ways to ensure that PUMA is at the forefront all all things Sport.

customise your kit
club crest •
sponsor •
name •
number •
PUMA® teamwear
0161 947 2413
kit@teamwearstore.co.uk
PUMA TEAMWEAR by Genesis Group International Ltd, Unit 4 Alpha Point
Bradnor Road, Sharston Industrial Estate, Manchester, M22 4TE
PUMA®

The Association o

History

The Association of Football Coaches was established in 2006 as part of the grassroots initiative by PUMA. It is services by a small team of sports enthusiasts who are always looking at ways of developing and evolving the 'Beautiful Game', especially among the non-league and grassroots fraternity.

The initial growth of the Association came through contact with the English Schools FA, along with other partners now involved, namely World Soccer Magazine, the Football League and PUMA.

About the Association

"Helping the coaches and teachers of today to produce the players and teams of tomorrow"

What is it?

It is an independent Association, fully supported by PUMA, consisting of coaches of all abilities who are involved in coaching football to players of all levels, ages and gender.

This unique Association provides opportunities to access the world of professional sport. It utilises key professional football coaches and professional football players to enhance members' education and broaden their football experience.

Who are its members?

Anyone can join the scheme as it is not restricted to coaches with previous qualifications. Therefore membership is open to everyone including teachers, youth team coaches, managers and any individuals coaching football.

There is specific advice and encouragement for members taking their coaching qualifications and bespoke lesson and session plans in a downloadable format, available for members only.

Each member is presented with their own individual membership number and access to the website. Upon joining, there is a free gift on annual subscription along with a membership card and pen.

Contact Us

You can contact us by e-mail, phone or post.
We look forward to hearing from you.

ootball Coaches

What are the benefits of joining?

In addition to the support and encouragement already stated, there is the opportunity to attend one or more of the 6 (minimum) coaching events per year which will be attended (where possible) by PUMA professional players and top class coaches. Discretionary prices on PUMA/AFC products – up to 40% less than retail price in some cases and an onus on shared experiences and information exchange between each member. In addition to this, there is the chance to enter the on-line competitions.

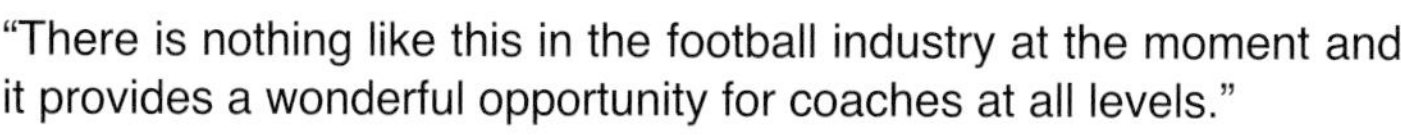

"There is nothing like this in the football industry at the moment and it provides a wonderful opportunity for coaches at all levels."

Peter Crouch (Portsmouth and England)

The events

The highly successful launch event at Reading's Madejeski stadium, saw Kevin Doyle and Graeme Murty (of Reading) come along in support with an extremely high calibre of coaching professionals – Lawrie Sanchez, Mike Kelly and Wally Downes (pictured below).

Since then events have been held at such venues as Tottenham Hotspurs, Wycombe Wanderers, Leicester City and Newcastle upon Tyne. There are more coaching events coming up with scheduled venues in Birmingham and Bristol to finish off 2008. Get in touch for more details and we look forward to welcoming you on board as a member soon!

E - info@thecoachesassociation.com P - 07980 593325
The Coaches Association, PO BOX 5623, London, W1A 6AN
www.thecoachesassocation.com

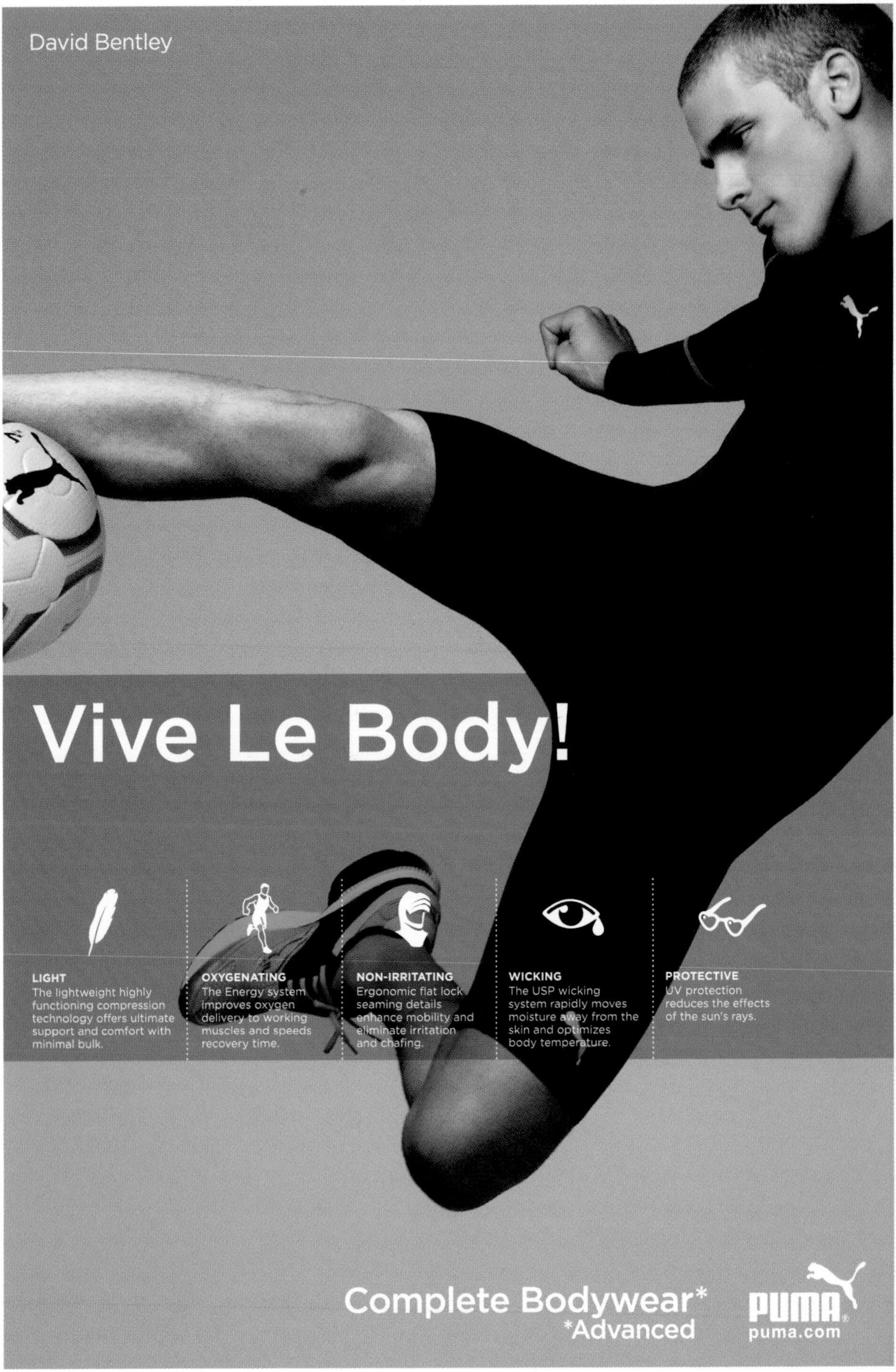

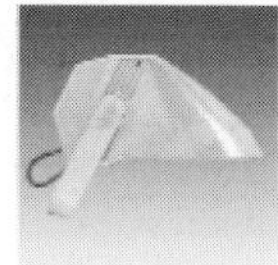

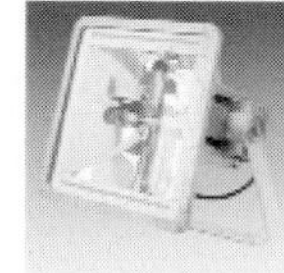

NON-LEAGUE CLUB DIRECTORY 2010

ISBN 978-1-869833-66-4

Editors
Tony Williams
(Tel: 01823 490 684)
Email: t.williams320@btinternet.com
James Wright
6 Harp Chase, Taunton, Somerset TA1 3RY
(Tel: 07786 636659 Fax: 0800 048 8641)
Email: james@nlnewsdesk.co.uk

Published by Tony Williams Publications Ltd
(Tel/Fax: 01548 531 339)
Email: twpublications@mcsolutions.org.uk

Printed by L.E.G.O. S.p.a. (Italy)

Sales & Distribution
T.W. Publications (01548 531 339)

Front Cover:
Action from the 2009 F.A. Vase final between Whitley Bay and Glossop North End.
Photo: Peter Barnes.

NON LEAGUE CLUB DIRECTORY 2010

(32nd Edition)

EDITORS
TONY WILLIAMS & JAMES WRIGHT

EDITORIAL ASSISTANTS
MIKE WILLIAMS, CRAIG POTTAGE AND SARA WILLIAMS

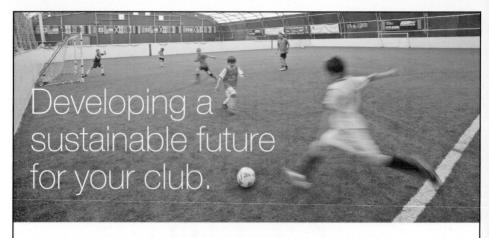

MIKE APPLEBY
THE F.A.'S LEAGUES AND CLUBS MANAGER.

FOREWORD

Having enjoyed a North Easterner's love of football all my life I find it a privilege to be working within The Football Association in close contact with the vast pyramid of leagues that make up steps one to seven throughout non-league football.

With a happy working relationship with the England C international squad who represent the cream of talent outside the Football League I consider myself to be extremely lucky to be working so closely with the game and have recently enjoyed my involvement with the England team that has done so well in The International Challenge Trophy. Paul Fairclough and his excellent supporting colleagues have produced an atmosphere which undoubtedly benefits the talented young players who have graduated through non-league football's international team.

Everyone on and off the field is immensely proud of their involvement with this special representative squad whose progress has been well documented by the Directory, and we look forward to 'Playing for England' a book which will record the development of England's internationals outside The Football League.

The Non-League Club Directory, which started life as a little pocket book in 1978, has always had the encouragement and support of The Football Association. It has given the non-league world a prestigious annual of its own and has recorded the development of our well run leagues who provide such a competitive challenge for non-league clubs throughout the country.

I am particularly pleased with the success of The National League Systems Cup and when you see the pride shown by the winners when representing England in Europe, the importance of International honours for the best players outside the full professional ranks is very clearly understood.

This pride in one's club, league and country is considered very special throughout non-league football and is something that The Football Association is pleased to have seen regularly promoted by the Non-League Club Directory over its first thirty two years.

CONTENTS

FRONT SECTION

THE EDITORS 8
EDITORIALS 12
ANNUAL AWARDS 15
PECKING ORDER 21
PYRAMID 22

NON-LEAGUE CLUB DIRECTORY

STEP 1
Blue Square Premier 23

STEP 2
Blue Square North 173
Blue Square South 297

STEP 3
Northern Premier League Premier 425
Southern League Premier 514
Isthmian Premier 609

STEP 4
Northern Premier League Div. 1 North 470
Northern Premier League Div. 1 South 492
Southern Division One Midlands 564
Southern Division One South & West 586
Isthmian Division One North 658
Isthmian Division One South 680

STEP 5/6
Combined Counties League 702
East Midlands Counties 715
Eastern Counties 717
Essex Senior League 730
Hellenic League 737
Kent League 755
Midland Combination 761
Midland Football Alliance 769
North West Counties 776
Northern Counties East 788
Northern League 800
South West Peninsula League 813
Spartan South Midlands League 822
Sussex County League 836
United Counties League 851
Wessex League 863
West Midlands Regional League 876
Western League 880

STEP 7
step 7
Anglian Combination 893
Bedford & District 898
Cambridgeshire County League 899
Central Midlands League 903
Cheshire Association League 905
Dorset Premier League 907
Essex & Suffolk Border League 908
Essex Olympian 910
Gloucestershire County League 914
Hampshire League 916
Herts Senior County League 917
Kent County League 919
Leicestershire League 926
Liverpool Combination 928
Manchester League 931
Middlesex County League 933
North Berkshire League 935
Northamptonshire Combination 937
Northern Alliance 939
Oxfordshire Senior 942
Peterborough & District League 944
Reading League 946
Somerset County League 948
Staffordshire League 952
Suffolk & Ipswich 955
Surrey Elite Intermediate 957
Wearside League 958
OTHER LEAGUES
Cornwall Combination 967
Dorset County League 969
East Cornwall League 970
Hampshire League 972
Humber Premier League 973
Lincolnshire League 975
Shropshire League 976
Teeside League 978
West Riding League 980
West Yorkshire League 983
Minor League Tables 986

F.A. COMPETITIONS **1033**
NATIONAL GAME XI 1035
THE F.A. CUP 1045
THE F.A. TROPHY 1065
THE F.A. VASE 1081
THE F.A. YOUTH CUP 1101
THE F.A. COUNTY YOUTH CUP 1104
THE F.A. SUNDAY CUP 1105
THE F.A. NATIONAL LEAGUE CUP 1106
THE F.A. WOMEN'S CUP 1107
THE F.A. FUTSAL CUP 1110

BACK SECTION
COUNTY FOOTBALL ASSOCIATIONS 1112
COUNTY CUPS 1116
WELSH FOOTBALL 1015
SCOTTISH NON-LEAGUE FOOTBALL 1027
ISLAND'S FOOTBALL 1031
AMATEUR FOOTBALL 1136
ARMED FORCES 1138
BRITISH UNIVERSITIES 1140
SCHOOLS FOOTBALL 1141
WOMEN'S FOOTBALL 1144
PROGRAMME AWARDS 1147
NON-LEAGUE PUBLICATIONS 1152

THE DIRECTORY'S 'TEAM SHEET'

TONY WILLIAMS
Editor

Educated at Malvern College, one of the country's best football schools in the late sixties, he represented England Under 18 against Scotland at Celtic Park before serving as an administrative officer in the Royal Air Force for five years.

He was on Reading's books from the age of 16 to 22, but also represented F.A. Amateur XI's and the R.A.F. while playing mainly in the old Isthmian League for Corinthian Casuals, Dulwich Hamlet and Kingstonian and joining Hereford United and Grantham during R.A.F. postings.

After taking an F.A. Coaching badge he coached at Harrow Borough, Epsom & Ewell and Hungerford Town and was asked to edit Jimmy Hill's Football Weekly after initial experience with the Amateur Footballer. Monthly Soccer and Sportsweek followed before he had the idea for a football Wisden and was helped by The Bagnall Harvey Agency to find a suitable generous sponsor in Rothmans.

After launching the Rothmans Football Yearbook in 1970 as its founder and co-compiler with Roy Peskett, he was asked to join Rothmans (although a non-smoker!) in the company's public relations department and was soon able to persuade the Marketing Director that Rothmans should become the first ever sponsor of a football league.

After a season's trial sponsoring the Hellenic and Isthmian Leagues, it was decided to go national with the Northern and Western Leagues and for four years he looked after the football department at Rothmans, with Jimmy Hill and Doug Insole presenting a brilliant sponsorship package which amongst many other innovations included three points for a win and goal difference.

So Non-League football led the way with league sponsorship and two, now well accepted, innovations.

Sportsmanship and goals were also rewarded in a sponsorship that proved a great success for football and for Rothmans. Indeed the sportsmanship incentives could be of great value to-day in the Football Association's bid to improve the game's image by ridding the game of dissent and cheating.

After the cigarette company pulled out of their sports sponsorship Tony produced the first Non-League Annual and later The Football League Club Directory, launching 'Non-League Football' magazine with "The Mail on Sunday" and then "Team Talk."

After his ten years with Hungerford Town, he moved West and served Yeovil Town as a Director for seven years but was thrilled when David Emery's plans for the exciting Non-League Media emerged and came into reality, thus giving the grass roots of the game the publicity and promotion that he and his team had been attempting to set up since the Annual (now Directory) was launched in 1978.

T.W. Publications continues to help promote non-league football throughout the country and is providing information for the exciting 'Goalrun' website. The modern history of representative football outside the Football League titled 'Playing for England' is being finalised and this season Tony has also been invited to help with the new 'NonLeagueNews24.com' website and 'TheNonLeague24' magazine as Consultant Editor.

The aim of the company has always been to promote the non-league 'family,' its spirit and its general development. So a plaque from The Football Association inscribed 'To Tony Williams for his continued promotion of all that's good in football' was greatly appreciated as was the trophy to commemorate the thirtieth edition of the Directory and the recent GLS "Lifetime Award' for promoting non-league football.

CRAIG POTTAGE
Editorial Assistant

Craig has been a football aficionado since an early age and has always had an interest in players' careers. Craig has kept detailed records of non league players for the last few years and this is his fourth year involved in this publication.

Started work in Golf Course Design and Project Management moving onto his present career in Business Development for an IT Facilitation Company in Stevenage twelve years ago. Lives in the town with his wife and daughter. Has been an Arsenal season ticket holder for over twenty years and also goes to watch Stevenage Borough when time allows. Also been known to enjoy a beer or two.

JAMES WRIGHT
Editor

James Wright, brought up on the tiny island of St Agnes on the Isles of Scilly and, like his Midlands parents, a life-long Wolves fan, began his career in non-League journalism when joining Tony Williams's editorial staff at the Mail on Sunday Non-League Football magazine in August 1990. James soon assumed from Tony responsibility for the compilation of the Non-League Club Directory and edited the 1992, 1993, 1994 and 1995 editions of the best-selling annual. During this period, James was a founder member of the editorial team of Team Talk magazine, the top non-League periodical of the 1990s, and collated the acclaimed FA Cup Post War Club-by-Club Records. In 1995 James launched Non-League Newsdesk, a newsletter carrying up-to-date league tables and the week's results.

Over the six seasons James published the title, Newsdesk became an immensely popular, no frills, weekly. However, the 2000 launch of The Non-League Paper coupled with the proliferation of information on the internet saw Newsdesk sales dwindle. James decided to team up with the Paper, and for the past nine seasons has collected and collated the four or five pages of minor results and tables that appear each Sunday. The challenge has proved immensely enjoyable despite the fact that it prevents James from following his beloved Taunton Town on away days.

But James regards the highlight of his career to date as the 2000 launch of the Non-League Newsdesk Annual. During his years compiling the Directory he recognised the need for a much smaller publication to be available much earlier, i.e. in pre-season. The first edition of the Non-League Newsdesk Annual filled this void and was an immediate success outselling Alex Ferguson's official autobiography in the Sunday Times chart in its first week. The 2002 edition surpassed all others by reaching the number one slot - staying there for a further week.

This year's merger of the Non-League Directory and the Newsdesk Annual sees James return to his journalistic roots. After publishing nine editions of the Annual independently, he is relishing the challenge of implementing some of the popular features of the Annual into future editions of the Directory.

James attends 100+ matches each season, and covers Taunton Town for the Somerset County Gazette. Outside football he is a qualified marine cartographer, and a keen long distance runner and local league tennis player. He also enjoys fishing, boating and gigging. He lives in the West Country with long-time partner Karen and ten year old daughter Rosie.

MIKE WILLIAMS
Editorial Manager/Publisher

What started out as a holiday job in 1988 helping put together (literally in those days) the Non-League Club Directory and League Club Directory, in the end forged a career which saw him work for Coventry City Football Club, e-comsport in London and finally return to T.W. Publications in 2003.

During his eight year spell with TW Publications he learned the ropes of all aspects of publishing culminating in the roll of production manager for the Non-League Club Directory, Team Talk Magazine, the League Club Directory and many more publications published by the company.

1995 saw the opportunity to take up the post of Publications Manager at Coventry City Football Club, and the transfer was made in the April of that year. Sky Blue Publications was formed and the League Club Directory became their leading title. Re-branded as the Ultimate Football Guide he was to deal with all aspects of the book, from design to sales and was also put on a steep learning curve into the world of Premiership programme production. The three years spent at the Midland's club gave him a great insight into all departments of a Premiership club, having produced publications for them all.

Leaving Coventry F.C. in 1998, and after a spell working on a world wide football player database for e-comsport in London, he returned to the West Country in 2001 to set up his own design/publishing company, which incorporated working on the Directory again. 2009 saw the full time switch to TW Publications and the responsibilities of publishing the Directory.

Having gone to a rugby school his football playing career was delayed. However, becoming the youngest player to have played for the First XV and representing Torbay Athletics club at 100 and 200m proved his sporting background. At the age of 20 he begun his football career which, at it's height, saw him playing for Chard Town in the Western League Premier Division.

Although hampered by a back injury he still hopes to turn out for Loddiswell Reserves in South Devon League this season, and as Club Secretary, is very much enjoying helping the club achieve their goal of promotion to the Premier League, and maybe beyond.

SARA WILLIAMS
Editorial Assistant

Sara has been working behind the scenes at T.W. Publications for the past three years and has had her eyes firmly opened to the wonderful world of non-League football. From the administrative side to actually playing for Totnes & Dartington Ladies, she has experienced every part of the game at our level.

Born in Carshalton, Surrey, Sara showed an early interest in football and craved a Liverpool shirt, only to be bought a Chelsea top! (She has since made amends for this). Excelling in middle distance running, ultimately she represented her county at youth level, and often came up against her nemesis of the time, Donna Frasier.

Having worked in many different jobs Sara found her vocation in the animal care industry and qualified as a Vet Nurse in 2000 having worked for the P.D.S.A. Sara had 10 years working for Veterinary Surgeries in Surrey and Devon before leaving in 2007 to concentrate on T.W. Publications and her own line of children's books based on her experiences as a Vet Nurse.

Sara recently re-ignited her love of running by qualifying to run for the World Wildlife Fund in the London Marathon. No mean feat considering the last time she ran she was a teenager. However, she completed the event in a very respectable 4hrs 33mins.

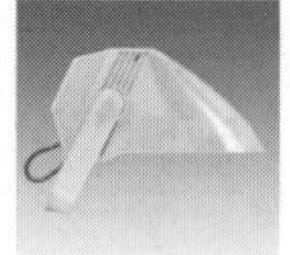
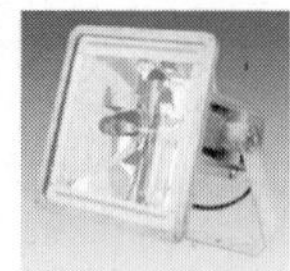

ACKNOWLEDGMENTS

It is particularly pleasing to welcome James Wright back as co-editor of our Directory this year. James worked with us on 'Team Talk' magazine for many years and was editor of the Non-League Club Directory from 1993 to 1995. He is a dedicated football follower at all levels of the game with a special loyalty to Wolves and Taunton Town. James compiles the wonderful results and league table pages for The Non-League Paper every Saturday night. For the last nine years he has also edited the comprehensive non-league statistical review of the season sponsored enthusiastically by Iain McNay's Cherry Red Records company. Iain, who is a lifelong Wimbledon supporter and chairman of their Fans Trust, gives fine support to the non-league game especially at the lower levels.

James is a very genuine football man and friend, and it is a pleasure to be working with him again. **TW.**

++++

I too would like to say how good it is to have James back involved with the Directory. He has been a great help this year and I look forward to improving the Directory further over the coming years.

As always I would also like to extend my thanks to everyone else who has helped with this year's Directory. From the Football Association, club secretaries, programme editors and league officials who have all shown their support, to the contributors and photographers who dedicate a lot of their spare time to their particular interests within the non-League game. In particular:

'OUR TEAM' OF PHOTOGRAPHERS

Peter Barnes, Graham Brown, Keith Clayton, Alan Coomes, 'Uncle Eric' Marsh,
Roger Turner, Bill Wheatcroft and Gordon Whittington.

FA COMPETITIONS DEPARTMENT

Steve Clark, Chris Darnell and Scott Bolton

CONTRIBUTORS

Alan Allcock (Unibond League).
Mike Brown (AFA). Arthur Evans (Photographer & reports).
Stan Journeaux (Channel Islands).
Bill Mitchell & Stewart Davidson (Scottish Scene).
Craig Pottage & John Harman (Blue Square Players records).
Dr. Andrew Sarnecki (Pecking Order). Mike Simmonds (Schools).
And not forgetting Sara and Dad.

Thanks everyone, Mike Williams.

Two gentlemen who have contributed massively to the popularity of our level of the game were **Tony Kempster** and David Stacey who both sadly died recently. Tony provided a website that gave a fantastic amount of information on all aspects of the game and must have given thousands of enthusiasts hours of enjoyment and a wonderful supply of knowledge. I am sure he has inspired many non-league enthusiasts to experiment with ideas of their own and will be greatly missed. .

David Stacey's Football Programme Directory showed his love of the game and its programmes and publications, he was always prepared to help anyone in the game and he loved his work around the country programme fairs and his own special annual 'party' in London.

These two men were very special football people who were valuable members of that non-league football 'family' that means so much to so many. They will be sadly missed.

A SPECIAL THANK YOU TO OUR MAIN SPONSOR

Just another little thank you to Puma for their continued support.

To all of you involved in coaching at any level I highly recommend you get in contact with the Puma Association of Football Coaches and of course make Puma your first choice when replacing kit or footballs.

Editorial....

A RECORD EIGHT NON-LEAGUE CLUBS IN F.A.CUP 3RD ROUND

The Third Round Proper of The F.A. Cup contained a record eight non-league clubs last season and it was a competition brilliantly presented by Setanta T.V. all the way through the qualifying rounds to the climax, which was covered by an excellent day long programme dedicated to the complete competition and of course The F.A. Cup Final itself.

Many of the record eight clubs had already featured in live T.V. matches, with the highlight probably being Histon's 1-0 victory over Leeds United. But just look at the scalps those eight clubs collected last season:

Kettering Town	Lincoln City	(H)	1-1
		(A)	2-1
	Notts County	(A)	1-1
		(H)	2-1
Blyth Spartans	Shrewsbury Town	(H)	3-1
	Bournemouth	(A)	0-0
		(H)	1-0
Forest Green Rovers	Rochdale	(H)	2-0
Barrow	Brentford	(H)	2-1
Eastwood Town	Wycombe W.	(H)	2-0
Histon	Swindon Town	(H)	1-0
	Leeds United	(H)	1-0
Torquay United	Blackpool	(H)	1-0

Only Kidderminster Harriers of the eight didn't beat a Football League club last season but of course they have had that pleasure on some memorable occasions, especially in the 1993-1994 campaign.

Two clubs outside The Blue Square Premier really enjoyed substantial cup runs with Blyth playing eight games in the competition and Eastwood Town, who unfortunately missed the big names in the Third Round and were drawn against Kettering Town, but played nine F.A. Cup ties.

Droylsden knocked out Darlington in the First Round at the second attempt, and then thought they had eliminated Chesterfield before they were disqualified for playing an ineligible player. However, the League scalp obtained by the lowest level non league club was Exeter City's, and they lost a thriller by the odd goal in five at Northern Premier League's Curzon Ashton from Division One North.

The F.A. Cup successes certainly provided the highlights, and even in defeat the wonderful game between Kettering Town and Premier League Fulham will be remembered as a very special match in which 'The Poppies' made a memorable contribution which was sent round the world in style by Setanta.

BEWARE OF 'THE EGO'

At a time when huge sums of money in football's national premier competitions dominates the headlines, it is sometimes difficult to realise we are dealing with the same sport at our levels of non-league football. However, it will probably be money, or the lack of it, at this time of serious recession, that will test the character of our senior club officials.

Clubs who have cut their budgets realistically will worry about losing their ability to attract good players in their area. Much of the available talent will indeed be looking around for the best offers and may not consider loyalty or the integrity of the club officials who may wish to sign them.

The most worrying aspect will be created by a few ambitious chairmen, who may be more worried about their own egos and their standing in the local community rather than the well being of their clubs and loyal supporters. We have all seen them and the terrible state in which they often leave their clubs and supporters. Having signed big name players, who are not always successful, the club fails to receive expected income and the ambitious officials walk away from the club leaving it in serious debt with the long-term supporters stranded and their club in the hands of receivers.

Have a look across the country at the clubs who have changed their names and started again in recent years plus a few that didn't even survive - they just died like Moreton Town, the well respected Hellenic outfit of the seventies.

Clubs who have worked their way up the pyramid within the non-league game without irresponsible spending may not race through the divisions, but by consolidating step by step they gain stability and build on sound foundations. Clubs which I have seen achieve just that have been Histon and Tiverton Town, whose steady impressive progress has been achieved without developing huge debts.

With the state of the country as it is at present, it will be interesting to see which clubs have real leaders.

FAST TRACKED REFEREES

The loss of hundreds of referees every season makes it understandable that County F.A.s and Senior leagues are encouraging keen junior officials by fast tracking their best youngsters. We know they can learn the rules of the game by heart, but have they had time really to understand the game itself?

With guidance to senior referees encouraging immediate 'cautions' for dangerous or wild tackles, we have seen top level games ruined early on with quite unnecessary yellow cards handed out to players, who have challenged with no intent or malicious attitude - just a tackle mistimed by a fraction of a second. If referees cannot tell the difference but just hand out yellow card after yellow card, the game is soon ruined with players being sent off and others not prepared to tackle at all. At non-league level hardly any tackles are perfect but most are well meant and are fair tackles that may catch the opponent a fraction of a second late.

In non-league football nothing is more infuriating for a spectator, player or manager than a bossy young referee doing what he has been told to do, and handing out a free kick and often a yellow card for innocent well meant tackles. It is difficult for young officials really to know or understood the game with their limited experience, but they can very easily ruin a match between two competitive but fair sides.

Deliberate fouls, such as holding a shirt, chopping a player down from behind as he goes away in possession, blocking off a player without attempting to play the ball especially at corners and free kicks, and also holding an opponent without looking at the ball at set pieces, all obviously show intent. The player has deliberately decided to foul and no one will argue that at least a yellow card would be deserved.

The argument in defence of the young official is that he has been instructed to be strict and he has to please the assessor in the stand. Well, if this is ruining a high percentage of non-league football, it must surely be common sense that young referees should be educated into understanding the game a little better and should be encouraged to use common sense by the assessors.

A MAN'S GAME?

When I was a teenager training with senior professionals and coached by ex-Internationals at Reading it was stressed that if I was kicked or fouled by an opponent I shouldn't give him the satisfaction of knowing he had hurt me. There should be no immediate retaliation or loss of control just a check to see who it was and if the opportunity occurred tackle him hard later in the game.

How the game has changed! All those youngsters and non-league players watching our finest in the Premier League see stars, diving, screaming and rolling about if there is a chance of a free kick, penalty or a booking for an opponent.

In their hearts, the British supporters despise the cheats but the stars are copied. One has to admire the professional rugby codes both Union and League, who give and take the toughest of tackles without a murmur and referees' decisions are normally accepted without the embarrassing whingeing of so many in the round ball game.

Having been involved in many a sporting discussion regarding comparisons between the codes, we know our sport is more beautiful and flows better with goals bringing all types of excitement, and when fair tackling is allowed it is also a tough, manly game. However, we cannot be proud of the cheats, the lack of respect for the officials and the general whingeing.

It is apparent that standards in non-league football have improved, but there are so many bad habits copied there is a long way to go and I still feel pleasantly surprised and uplifted when I watch a non-league game played within a sporting atmosphere.

ENGLAND INTERNATIONALS

Another good season was enjoyed by the England team representing non-league football. Now known as 'England C', the Under 21 squad (with ages judged on when the two year competition kicked off) qualified for their second International Challenge Trophy Final but found the Belgian's senior Under 21 squad just a little too strong on the night at Oxford and lost by the only goal of the game.

This team is extremely well run by Paul Fairclough and Steve Burr with an excellent back up team, but the full side's four nations end of season tournament has not been continued. Although the excellent European Under 21 challenge Tournament will hopefully be expanded, it will probably be dominated by full-time professional youngsters mainly from the Blue Square Premier Division.

The idea of internationals for non-league players was introduced to give footballers who were not making a living from the game an opportunity to reach the top of their level of football and represent their country. The amateurs and semi-professionals did just that, but now the only international team available is England C Under 21s and that is filled with young professionals from the fifth level of full-time football. It is one of the most successful of England's teams and produces quality players with an excellent team spirit and high standards, encouraged by their top class managerial team who are preparing them successfully to return to the Football League.

Hopefully The Football Association will also set up a lower level of International games for the real part-timers in non league football for, as we all know, this is the section of the game that represents 95% of the footballers in our country and as experience in the past has shown, they do deserve, and would appreciate, the chance to play for their country.

At a time when many people in all walks of life are feeling the financial credit crunc,h let's hope club managements conduct their financial dealings within their budgets and players realise they have to play well and successfully to earn their money.

JOINED FORCES

In writing this editorial I imagine I find myself addressing two different readerships – those of the "old" Non-League Directory, and those of the "Cherry Red." Consequently, I need to start by saying a few words about the merger.

The Cherry Red was launched as a pre-season handbook. I emphasise - pre-season. It was never intended to rival the Non-League Directory.

A number of readers (and don't get me wrong, I thank them for it) have told me that they are disappointed by my decision to discontinue the Cherry Red. There was no decision. It is now impossible to produce the annual in advance of the new campaign, therefore its raison d'être is compromised.

There are a number of reasons why I can no longer publish in pre-season, of which by far the most significant is the fact that virtually the whole of Step Five now kicks off at the end of the first week in August (I'll spare you my opinion of this!). This compresses unsustainably an already very narrow window for compilation which, naturally, has to include time for verification, printing and dispatch.

Being able to incorporate pretty much all the material which appeared in the Cherry Red into The Puma Non-League Club Directory is, in my opinion, a massive bonus and I am extremely grateful that Tony and Mike Williams accepted my proposal for an amalgamation.

Over the nine years I published the Cherry Red, thousands (literally) of people helped me out either with factual content, or simply by purchasing the book. I thank them all, but two individuals must receive special mention – Nigel Davis and Iain McNay. Thank you, gentlemen – you were both awesome.

So, on to the new book, and I hope it will be viewed as such. With the joining of forces being agreed quite late in the day I have to confess that – for this year anyway - it has been compiled largely as two separate books. Coverage of Step Seven downwards - plus the statistical elements of Steps Five and Six - is along the lines of the former Cherry Red. The remainder of the publication follows the tried and tested Non-League Directory format.

So for those who never saw the Cherry Red some explanation of my pages is perhaps required. The inter-league movements (Ins and Outs) were a very popular feature of the Annual and have been retained throughout (E expelled, F folded, P promoted, R relegated, S switched, W withdrew after end of season, WN withdrew without playing a game, WS withdrew during the course of the season).

In cup ties, penalty shoot-out scores are indicated in parentheses, the first listed side's score preceding the second listed team. So "aet, (3-4p)" means the second listed side won 4-3 on penalties after extra-time. All league tables are "final" even where games remained unplayed.

I would like to extend grateful thanks to all the league officials who submitted data to me throughout the course of the season, and to Richard Rundle of the Football Club History Database for supplying most of the minor league tables. Thank you also to Mark Broom, Nick House and Rowland Lyons who have given me considerable help this summer.

I intend to keep open the Annual (www.nlnews-desk.co.uk) website from where you can still purchase back issues of the Cherry Red Annual, some at heavily discounted prices. I intend to put some of the newly freed up space to good use by posting items of interest, in particular concerning any future developments of the Directory.

So please feel free to contact me through the site if you would like to make any comments about this book or, indeed, the future direction of the publication. Tony, Mike and myself intend to meet regularly during the course of the winter to plan for next year, so any commonly recurring messages will be acted upon.

Thank you for continued support.

James Wright

The Non-League Club Directory

2008-2009 AWARDS

• ROLL OF HONOUR •

FOOTBALLER OF THE YEAR
Aaron Webster (Burton Albion)

MANAGER OF THE YEAR
Steve Fallon (Histon)

ENGLAND PLAYER OF THE YEAR
Russell Penn

MERIT AWARDS
Kettering Town
Eastwood Town
Leamington
Stevenage Borough

• MERIT AWARDS 2008-09 •

KETTERING TOWN

It was impressive to remain unbeaten in their first ten fixtures back in the Blue Square Premier. But this merit Award is really for The Poppies' F.A.Cup run of seven ties, which included victories over Lincoln City and Notts. County after replays and, after the luck of the third round draw had brought a home tie against Eastwood Town, a tremendous Fourth Round match against Premier Divison Fulham was televised live. Two very late goals gave the London club a 4-2 victory but Kettering had brought much pride to the Non-League game by providing a wonderful example of quality and spirit against top class opposition.

EASTWOOD TOWN

A dream season was enjoyed by 'The Badgers' of Eastwood. Who would have thought in October, when the club had played five consecutive cup matches and sunk to tenth position in the League that the season would not only bring them the F.A.Cup Second round scalp of unbeaten Wycombe Wanderers but also promotion? Unluckily the Third Round draw brought them an away game agaisnt another non-league side, but the confidence had been strengthend throughout the club. After losing a hard fought tie at Kettering, Eastwood took over the leadership of The Unibond Premier Division and they lost only three more games in a season that brought the championship and promotion to Blue Square North.

LEAMINGTON

Supporters of the A.P. Leamington club that qualified as one of the founder members of the Alliance Premier League in 1979 will have suffered agonies as their favourites dropped down through the Premier to the Southern Division One in 1985 and disbanded having lost the backing of Automatic Products. Many of those supporters have worked tirelessly to rebuild a town club for Leamington and last season they achieved another step up the non-league pyramid when manager Jason Cadden's squad won promotion back to the Southern Premier with The Division One Midlands championship and a wonderful 101 points and 114 goals. This is truly one of non-league's football's happiest stories!

STEVENAGE BOROUGH

The powerful Hertfordshire club seems to have been favourites for promotion for most recent seasons and, after a change of manager in mid season, Graham Westley's return to Broadhall Way very nearly brought the league success their supporters are sure will soon be theirs. In the second half of the season they suffered just two defeats and only failed to score on two occasions. The F.A.Trophy was enjoyed at the same time and very few clubs have managed to succeed at both. A place in the Play-Offs was a magnificent achievement as Borough had to chase the leaders throughout the season but sadly their thrilling two legged Semi-Final was lost to Cambridge United before supporters were at least able to celbrate a deserved F.A.Trophy success after a comprehensive Wembley victory against York City. Who will bet against Stevenage Borough for the season ahead?

NON LEAGUE FOOTBALLER OF THE YEAR

AARON WEBSTER

(Burton Albion)

Aaron Webster has served Burton Albion loyally for ten years, and was an integral part of the squads that helped Albion through the ranks from The Southern Premier League and then The Northern Premier League from where 'The Brewers' stepped up to The Football Conference in 2002. Aaron is a versatile defender who won three caps for England's Semi-Professionals and has acted as a wonderful example to the local youngsters with loyal service to his home town club. The club's fans have appreciated his whole hearted attitude and club loyalty and no one deserved a championship medal and a chance to play in the Football League more than Aaron.

PAST WINNERS

2007-08 Sean Canham (Team Bath)
2006-07 Jon Main (Tonbridge Angels)
2005-06 Stuart Thurgood (Grays Athletic)
2004-05 Terry Fearns (Southport)
2003-04 Andrew Forbes (Winchester City)
2002-03 Darren Way (Yeovil Town)
2001-02 Daryl Clare (Boston United)
2000-01 Ray Warburton (Rushden & Dia)
1999-00 Gary Abbott (Aldershot Town)
1998-99 Neil Grayson (Cheltenham Town)
1997-98 Phil Everett (Tiverton Town)
1996-97 Howard Forinton (Yeovil Town)
1995-96 Barry Hayles (Stevenage Boro)
1994-95 Kevan Brown (Woking)
1993-94 Chris Brindley (Kidderminster H.)
1992-93 Steve Guppy (Wycombe Wndrs)
1991-92 Tommy Killick (Wimborne Town)
1990-91 Mark West (Wycombe Wndrs)
1989-90 Phil Gridelet (Barnet)
1988-89 Steve Butler (Maidstone Utd)
1987-88 David Howell (Enfield)
1986-87 Mark Carter (Runcorn)
1985-86 Jeff Johnson (Altrincham)
1984-85 Alan Cordice (Wealdstone)
1983-84 Brian Thompson (Maidstone Utd)

NON LEAGUE MANAGER OF THE YEAR

STEVE FALLON

(Histon F.C.)

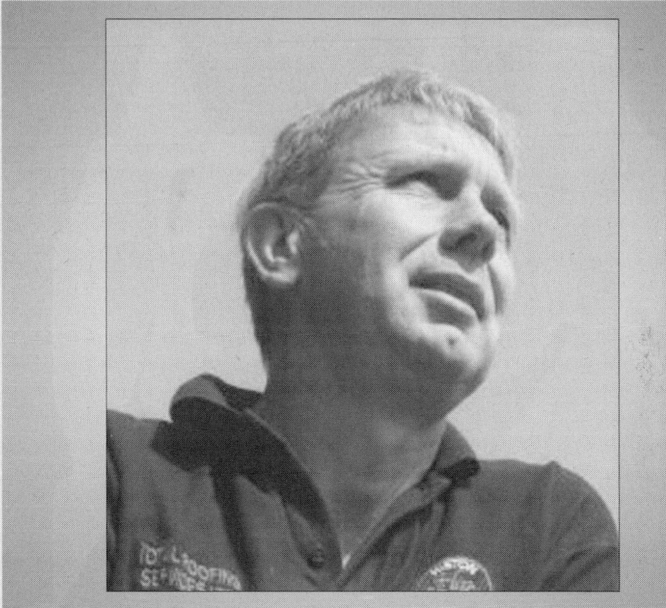

Managers who can attract star players to their clubs by offering attractive financial packages may also be good at coaching, but someone who achieves success against the wealthy clubs, backed by good housekeeping, old fashioned club standards with club spirit and dedicated coaching, deserves special congratulations. Steve Fallon is backed by John Beck a dedicated coach and assistant within a club that is run as well as any in the country, but he is still ultimately responsible for his team and its results. Last season Histon, representing a village on the edge of Cambridge, qualified for the play-offs contesting a place in The Football League and also beat Swindon Town and Leeds United in an F.A.Cup campaign, the memory of which will be treasured by everyone involved with Histon Football Club.

PAST WINNERS

2007-08 Tony Greenwood (Fleetwood Town)
2006-07 John Still (Dagenham & Redbridge)
2005-06 Steve Burr (Northwich Victoria)
2004-05 Paul Fairclough (Barnet)
2003-04 Graham Turner (Hereford United)
2002-03 Gary Johnson (Yeovil Town)
2001-02 Nigel Clough (Burton Albion)
2000-01 Jeff King (Canvey Island)
1999-00 Jan Molby (Kidderminster Harr.)
1998-99 Brendan Phillips (Nuneaton Boro)
1997-98 Steve Cotterill (Cheltenham Town)
1996-97 Paul Futcher (Southport)
1995-96 Paul Fairclough (Stevenage Boro)
1994-95 Sammy McIlroy (Macclesfield T)
1993-94 Bill Punton (Diss Town)
1992-93 Martin O'Neill (Wycombe Wndrs)

ENGLAND PLAYER OF THE YEAR

(Nominated by Manager Paul Fairclough)

RUSSELL PENN

(Kidderminster Harriers)

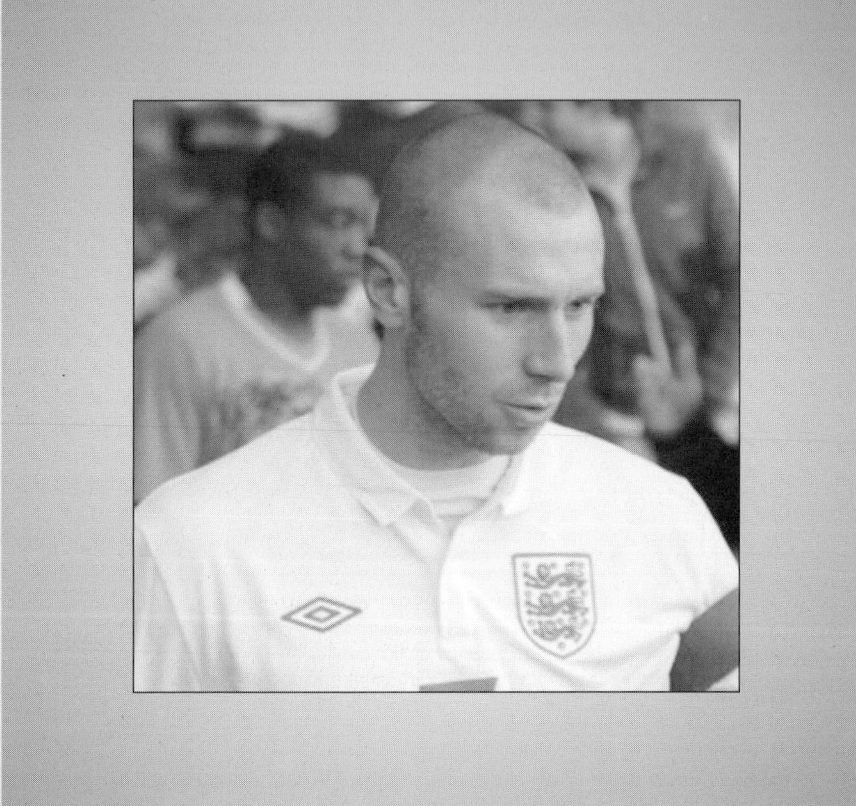

Some players have a natural charisma which commands respect. Russell Penn's character has long been appreciated by club and country, and last season Harriers' steady midfield player was selected for England's two vital European Tournament ties and had the honour of wearing the captain's arm band. His international manager was impressed by his skipper's true English qualities being an example on and off the field with an honourable attitude and being completely reliable. In fact a manager's dream! Burton Albion obviously knew all about his qualities and he has now joined them in the Football League.

PECKING ORDER 2008-2009 by A J Sarnecki

Position in Season				Lge	League	FA Cup			FA Trophy			FA Vase			C	T	V	Total
05-06	06-07	07-08	08-09	Code	League	ent	xmt	won	ent	xmt	won	ent	xmt	won	pts	pts	pts	pts
						1		1	3	2/8		1	4/6					
1	1	1	1	fcp	FOOTBALL CONFERENCE Premier	24	240	29	24	192	37		0		293	301		594
2	3	3	2	fcn	FOOTBALL CONFERENCE North	22	132	31	22	132	21		0		185	219		404
3	2	2	3	fcs	FOOTBALL CONFERENCE South	22	132	22	22	132	16		0		176	214		390
5	4	5	4	soa	SOUTHERN Premier	22	88	30	22	44	37		0		140	147		287
6	6	6	5	npa	NORTHERN PREMIER Premier	22	88	28	22	44	30		0		138	140		278
4	5	4	6	isa	ISTHMIAN Premier	22	88	32	22	44	17		0		142	127		269
new	9	7	7	sobm	SOUTHERN First Midland	22	44	34	22	0	22		0		100	88		188
new	8	10	8	isbs	ISTHMIAN First South	22	44	41	22	0	14		0		107	80		187
	new	11	9	npb	NORTHERN PREMIER First North	21	42	33	21	0	19		0		96	82		178
new	11	9	10	sobs	SOUTHERN First South & East	22	44	23	22	0	17		0		89	83		172
new	10	8	11	isbn	ISTHMIAN First North	22	44	20	22	0	19		0		86	85		171
	new	12=	12	npb	NORTHERN PREMIER First South	20	40	27	20	0	13		0		87	73		160
14	12	12=	13	nora	NORTHERN First	22	0	29		0		22	22	36	51		80	131
11	13	14=	14	mda	MIDLAND ALLIANCE	22	0	25		0		22	26	35	47		83	130
12=	14	16	15	ecoa	EASTERN COUNTIES Premier	19	0	26		0		19	30	33	45		82	127
19	21	18	16	ucoa	UNITED COUNTIES Premier	20	0	20		0		21	32	30	40		83	123
12=	16	24	17	nwca	NORTH WEST COUNTIES First	20	0	21		0		20	24	29	41		73	114
18	22	19	18	ssma	SPARTAN SOUTH MIDLANDS Premier	21	0	16		0		21	22	29	37		72	109
15	19	14=	19	wsxa	WESSEX Premier	18	0	17		0		21	24	27	35		72	107
17	15	17	20	wesa	WESTERN Premier	20	0	14		0		21	24	25	34		70	104
16	17	21	21	ncea	NORTHERN COUNTIES EAST Premier	20	0	17		0		20	18	23	37		61	98
25	18	20	22	coca	COMBINED COUNTIES Premier	21	0	12		0		22	18	23	33		63	96
20	23	22=	23	hela	HELLENIC Premier	19	0	14		0		21	20	21	33		62	95
23	20	22=	24	ssxa	SUSSEX COUNTY First	18	0	11		0		20	16	19	29		55	84
22	24	25	25	kena	KENT First	13	0	14		0		14	10	11	27		35	62
29	27	30	26	ecob	EASTERN COUNTIES First	16	0	11		0		18	0	16	27		34	61
26=	25	29	27	norb	NORTHERN Second	17	0	6		0		18	0	17	23		35	58
24	26	26	28	esxs	ESSEX SENIOR	11	0	6		0		13	12	9	17		34	51
28	31	27	29=	nwcb	NORTH WEST COUNTIES Second	15	0	6		0		15	0	14	21		29	50
35	33	32	29=	mdca	MIDLAND COMBINATION Premier	14	0	8		0		17	0	11	22		28	50
32=	32	31	29=	wmda	WEST MIDLAND REGIONAL Premier	13	0	6		0		17	6	8	19		31	50
26=	28	28	32	nceb	NORTHERN COUNTIES EAST First	12	0	4		0		14	0	12	16		26	42
31	30	33	33	wesb	WESTERN First	10	0	8		0		13	0	9	18		22	40
		new	34	emdc	EAST MIDLAND COUNTIES	6	0	3		0		18	0	12	9		30	39
	new	34	35	swa	SOUTH WESTERN PENINSULAR Premier	8	0	4		0		12	0	11	12		23	35
34	34	36	36	ssxb	SUSSEX COUNTY Second	9	0	3		0		12	0	8	12		20	32
37	37	35	37	ssmb	SPARTAN SOUTH MIDLANDS First	6	0	4		0		12	0	5	10		17	27
38	40	41	38	wsxb	WESSEX First	4	0	3		0		12	0	7	7		19	26
40=	41=	39	39	ucob	UNITED COUNTIES First	4	0	0		0		10	0	8	4		18	22
42=	38	42=	40	cocb	COMBINED COUNTIES First	4	0	2		0		6	0	4	6		10	16
42=	41=	44	41	hebw	HELLENIC First West	1	0	0		0		6	0	7	1		13	14
36	36	37	42	cmda	CENTRAL MIDLANDS Supreme	0	0	0		0		8	0	3	0		11	11
45	44=	40	43	hebe	HELLENIC First East	2	0	0		0		4	0	2	2		6	8
	new	42=	44=	swbw	SOUTH WESTERN PENINSULAR First West	0	0	0		0		4	0	2	0		6	6
32=	35	38	44=	lesa	LEICESTERSHIRE SENIOR Premier	0	0	0		0		5	0	1	0		6	6
47=	47=	47	46=	ssxc	SUSSEX COUNTY Third	0	0	0		0		3	0	0	0		3	3
	49=		46=	mdcb	MIDLAND COMBINATION First	0	0	0		0		1	0	2	0		3	3
		52	46=	wmdb	WEST MIDLAND REGIONAL First	0	0	0		0		2	0	1	0		3	3
		48=	49=	hrta	HERTS SENIOR COUNTY Premier	0	0	0		0		1	0	1	0		2	2
46	49=	49=	49=	wea	WEARSIDE	0	0	0		0		2	0	0	0		2	2
47=	46		49=	nala	NORTHERN ALLIANCE Premier	0	0	0		0		1	0	1	0		2	2
	new	46	52=	swbe	SOUTH WESTERN PENINSULAR First East	0	0	0		0		1	0	0	0		1	1
			52=	exoa	ESSEX OLYMPIC	0	0	0		0		1	0	0	0		1	1
			52=	nbea	NORTH BERKSHIRE Premier	0	0	0		0		1	0	0	0		1	1
40=	39	49=	52=	wcha	WEST CHESHIRE First	0	0	0		0		1	0	0	0		1	1
					no league	1	0	0		0		1	0	0	1		1	2

Points are given for status (acceptance into each of the three competitions), for prestige (exemption from early rounds) and performance (number of wins, however achieved, even by walkover). Entry to the Vase is valued at one point, that to the Trophy at 3. Cup entry gives a further bonus of one point. The number of entries from each league is shown in the appropriate column. Points for exemptions are valued at two for each round missed. The entry in the table is of the total points so gained by the given league, not the number of teams given exemptions. Finally, all wins are valued at one point, regardless of opposition: giving extra points for defeating 'stronger' opponents would be too arbitrary. After all, if they lost then they were not stronger on the day!

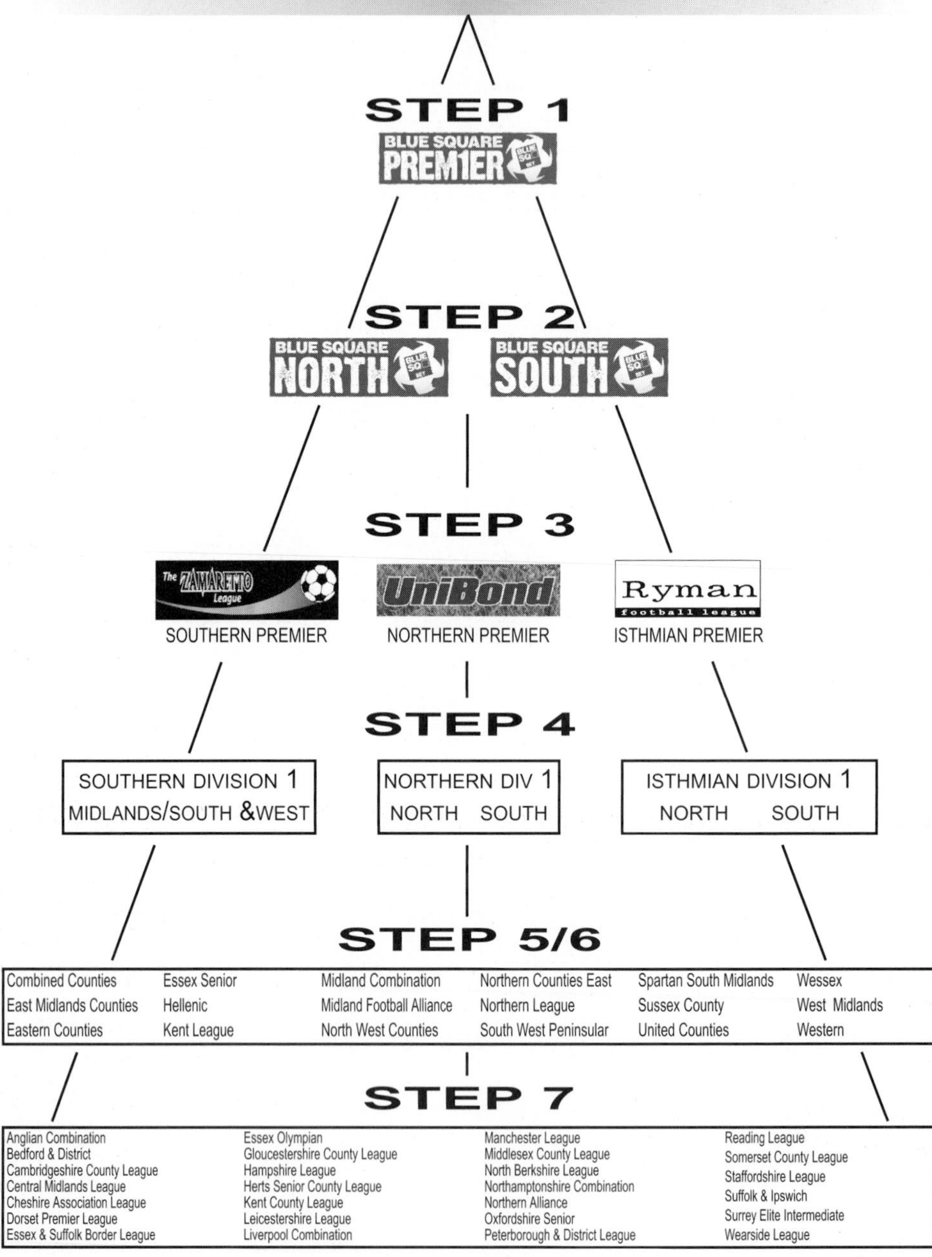

FOOTBALL LEAGUE
STEP 1
BLUE SQUARE PREM1ER
STEP 2
BLUE SQUARE NORTH
BLUE SQUARE SOUTH
STEP 3
The ZAMARETTO League
SOUTHERN PREMIER
UniBond
NORTHERN PREMIER
Ryman football league
ISTHMIAN PREMIER
STEP 4
SOUTHERN DIVISION 1
MIDLANDS/SOUTH &WEST
NORTHERN DIV 1
NORTH SOUTH
ISTHMIAN DIVISION 1
NORTH SOUTH
STEP 5/6
Combined Counties
East Midlands Counties
Eastern Counties
Essex Senior
Hellenic
Kent League
Midland Combination
Midland Football Alliance
North West Counties
Northern Counties East
Northern League
South West Peninsular
Spartan South Midlands
Sussex County
United Counties
Wessex
West Midlands
Western
STEP 7
Anglian Combination
Bedford & District
Cambridgeshire County League
Central Midlands League
Cheshire Association League
Dorset Premier League
Essex & Suffolk Border League
Essex Olympian
Gloucestershire County League
Hampshire League
Herts Senior County League
Kent County League
Leicestershire League
Liverpool Combination
Manchester League
Middlesex County League
North Berkshire League
Northamptonshire Combination
Northern Alliance
Oxfordshire Senior
Peterborough & District League
Reading League
Somerset County League
Staffordshire League
Suffolk & Ipswich
Surrey Elite Intermediate
Wearside League

BLUE SQUARE PREM1ER

		P	W	D	L	F	A	GD	Pts
1	Burton Albion	46	27	7	12	81	52	29	88
2	Cambridge United	46	24	14	8	65	39	26	86
3	Histon	46	23	14	9	78	48	30	83
4	Torquay United	46	23	14	9	72	47	25	83
5	Stevenage Borough	46	23	12	11	73	54	19	81
6	Kidderminster Harriers	46	23	10	13	69	48	21	79
7	Oxford United (-5)	46	24	10	12	72	51	21	77
8	Kettering Town	46	21	13	12	50	37	13	76
9	Crawley Town (-1)	46	19	14	13	77	55	22	70
10	Wrexham	46	18	12	16	64	48	16	66
11	Rushden & Diamonds	46	16	15	15	61	50	11	63
12	Mansfield Town (R) (-4)	46	19	9	18	57	55	2	62
13	Eastbourne Borough	46	18	6	22	58	70	-12	60
14	Ebbsfleet United	46	16	10	20	52	60	-8	58
15	Altrincham	46	15	11	20	49	66	-17	56
16	Salisbury City	46	14	13	19	54	64	-10	55
17	York City	46	11	19	16	47	51	-4	52
18	Forest Green Rovers	46	12	16	18	70	76	-6	52
19	Grays Athletic	46	14	10	22	44	64	-20	52
20	Barrow	46	12	15	19	51	65	-14	51
21	Woking	46	10	14	22	37	60	-23	44
22	Northwich Victoria	46	11	10	25	56	75	-19	43
23	Weymouth	46	11	10	25	45	86	-41	43
24	Lewes	46	6	6	34	28	89	-61	24

PROMOTION PLAY-OFFS - SEMI-FINALS

1st Leg	Stevenage Borough	3 - 1	Cambridge United
2nd Leg	Cambridge United	3 - 0*	Stevenage Borough
1st Leg	Torquay United	2 - 0	Histon
2nd Leg	Histon	1 - 0	Torquay United

PROMOTION PLAY-OFF - FINAL

At Wembley	Cambridge United	0 - 2	Torquay United	Att: 35,089

	1	2	3	4	5	6	7	8	9	10	11	12	13	14	15	16	17	18	19	20	21	22	23	24
1 Altrincham		3-4	1-3	1-0	2-2	2-2	2-0	2-5	2-0	0-1	1-1	2-2	1-0	1-0	1-0	1-0	0-4	0-0	1-2	0-1	4-0	1-0	1-1	1-1
2 Barrow	2-2		0-0	0-2	3-3	3-1	0-3	3-1	1-1	1-0	2-4	1-0	2-0	2-1	0-0	3-0	1-1	0-0	1-3	1-1	0-1	0-1	1-1	0-0
3 Burton Alb.	1-1	2-1		3-1	2-1	2-0	3-1	4-2	4-0	3-1	1-1	2-2	5-2	1-0	1-1	0-1	3-0	1-2	2-0	0-1	1-1	3-2	2-1	2-1
4 Cambridge	0-0	2-1	2-0		1-1	2-1	1-0	0-1	1-0	2-2	0-2	2-1	1-0	2-1	4-1	1-1	0-0	4-0	1-1	0-1	1-0	4-1	2-0	1-0
5 Crawley	4-0	4-0	4-0	2-2		1-0	1-2	2-2	2-1	3-3	1-0	2-0	5-1	2-1	5-2	0-1	0-0	0-3	0-2	3-1	4-2	2-2	1-0	0-1
6 Eastbourne	1-0	0-2	1-2	0-3	2-1		0-1	1-0	2-1	1-1	1-2	2-3	1-0	1-2	4-1	0-3	0-1	0-0	2-1	4-2	3-0	0-0	1-0	2-1
7 Ebbsfleet	1-0	1-0	2-1	1-1	4-4	1-1		0-1	0-1	0-1	0-0	1-1	2-1	2-2	1-0	1-1	1-0	2-2	4-0	0-2	1-0	2-0	1-0	0-0
8 Forest G.R.	1-3	2-1	2-3	2-2	1-0	1-2	1-4		1-1	2-2	0-2	2-2	4-1	1-0	3-0	3-3	4-0	1-2	0-3	1-2	4-1	0-2	2-3	1-1
9 Grays Ath.	2-1	2-1	0-1	0-1	1-0	0-1	3-1	2-1		1-4	1-1	3-2	0-0	2-1	2-1	2-0	0-0	3-1	1-2	1-2	1-1	1-1	2-1	1-0
10 Histon	1-0	2-0	4-3	1-1	1-0	3-3	5-2	0-1	4-1		1-0	1-1	1-1	3-0	2-1	5-2	0-0	2-0	0-0	1-1	1-0	1-0	1-0	1-1
11 Kettering	3-1	0-0	0-1	1-2	1-1	0-1	2-1	1-1	0-0	1-0		1-0	1-0	1-3	2-1	1-2	1-1	1-0	1-0	2-1	0-1	1-0	1-0	4-2
12 K'minster	4-0	0-1	2-1	1-3	2-0	2-0	3-1	1-1	2-0	2-0	0-1		1-1	2-0	1-2	1-0	2-1	3-2	4-2	1-0	0-2	3-0	1-0	2-0
13 Lewes	2-0	0-3	0-1	0-2	0-3	0-2	0-0	3-2	2-0	0-3	1-2	0-1		0-1	2-3	2-1	0-4	1-4	0-2	0-2	1-0	0-2	0-2	1-1
14 Mansfield	2-0	2-2	0-2	1-1	1-0	3-1	2-0	3-0	1-0	1-0	0-0	4-2	1-0		3-2	1-3	0-0	3-0	2-1	1-1	2-1	0-1	1-2	1-0
15 Northwich	0-1	2-1	0-1	0-1	0-1	1-2	2-0	0-0	2-0	1-2	0-0	1-1	3-0	2-0		1-2	4-2	1-1	0-1	2-3	2-3	2-0	1-2	2-2
16 Oxford Utd	1-0	3-0	2-1	3-1	1-2	6-3	5-1	2-1	4-1	2-1	1-1	1-0	2-1	1-0	1-2		2-1	2-0	1-1	0-2	0-1	0-0	1-0	1-0
17 Rushden	1-1	1-1	2-1	1-2	0-1	2-0	2-0	2-2	1-0	1-2	1-0	0-1	2-1	0-1	2-1	1-3		2-1	1-1	1-3	1-0	3-1	1-1	2-0
18 Salisbury	1-3	3-0	0-1	1-2	2-0	2-0	1-0	2-2	1-0	0-4	1-2	0-0	1-2	2-3	1-1	2-1	1-1		2-4	2-2	1-0	1-0	1-4	1-1
19 Stevenage	3-0	3-0	4-1	2-1	1-1	1-3	1-0	1-1	0-0	1-3	2-1	3-1	3-0	3-2	1-1	1-1	3-1	2-0		0-0	1-1	1-0	1-2	3-3
20 Torquay	3-1	4-1	2-1	0-0	0-2	2-0	0-2	3-3	1-1	4-1	2-0	0-1	4-1	2-0	2-1	1-1	1-1	0-1	3-0		0-2	2-1	1-1	1-1
21 Weymouth	2-0	0-3	0-5	2-2	2-2	3-2	0-2	1-1	3-1	2-5	0-2	1-2	2-0	1-1	3-0	2-2	0-9	0-4	0-3	0-1		1-1	1-3	1-2
22 Woking	1-2	1-0	0-0	0-1	0-0	0-4	1-0	0-1	3-1	1-0	0-1	1-5	1-1	2-2	4-1	0-2	1-1	1-0	0-1	2-2	1-1		1-1	0-2
23 Wrexham	0-1	1-1	0-1	2-0	0-2	5-0	3-2	1-1	3-2	0-0	2-1	0-1	2-0	2-0	3-3	2-0	0-3	1-1	5-0	1-1	2-0	1-1		3-1
24 York City	1-2	1-1	1-3	0-0	2-2	1-0	3-1	2-1	0-1	1-1	0-0	0-0	3-0	1-1	1-2	0-0	2-0	1-1	0-2	1-2	2-0	2-0	1-0	

		P	W	D	L	F	A	GD	Pts
1	Tamworth	42	24	13	5	70	41	29	85
2	Gateshead	42	24	8	10	81	48	33	80
3	Alfreton Town	42	20	17	5	81	48	33	77
4	AFC Telford United	42	22	10	10	65	34	31	76
5	Southport	42	21	13	8	63	36	27	76
6	Stalybridge Celtic	42	20	10	12	71	50	21	70
7	Droylsden	42	18	14	10	64	44	20	68
8	Fleetwood Town	42	17	11	14	70	66	4	62
9	Harrogate Town	42	17	10	15	66	57	9	61
10	Hinckley United	42	16	9	17	56	59	-3	57
11	Vauxhall Motors	42	14	11	17	51	67	-16	53
12	Workington	42	13	12	17	54	55	-1	51
13	Gainsborough Trinity	42	12	14	16	57	63	-6	50
14	Redditch United	42	12	14	16	49	61	-12	50
15	Blyth Spartans	42	14	7	21	50	58	-8	49
16	Solihull Moors	42	13	10	19	49	73	-24	49
17	Kings Lynn	42	10	18	14	50	60	-10	48
18	Stafford Rangers	42	12	12	18	41	56	-15	48
19	Farsley Celtic	42	14	5	23	58	65	-7	47
20	Hyde United	42	11	9	22	57	80	-23	42
21	Burscough	42	10	6	26	43	80	-37	36
22	Hucknall Town	42	5	13	24	39	84	-45	28

PROMOTION PLAY-OFFS - SEMI-FINALS

1st Leg	AFC Telford United	2 - 0	Alfreton Town
2nd Leg	Alfreton Town	4 - 3	AFC Telford United
1st Leg	Southport	0 - 1	Gateshead
2nd Leg	Gateshead	1 - 1	AFC Telford United

PROMOTION PLAY-OFF - FINAL

Gateshead 1 - 0 AFC Telford United

	1	2	3	4	5	6	7	8	9	10	11	12	13	14	15	16	17	18	19	20	21	22
1 AFC Telford U.		0-0	2-1	3-0	2-0	2-0	0-0	2-1	1-0	3-1	4-2	3-1	2-3	1-1	1-1	3-0	1-0	0-1	1-0	0-0	5-1	0-0
2 Alfreton Town	3-1		1-1	2-0	2-3	3-1	3-3	1-4	1-3	4-1	1-1	5-0	3-2	1-1	2-0	4-1	2-0	2-0	2-1	1-1	3-1	0-0
3 Blyth Spartans	2-0	2-2		0-2	0-2	5-0	3-0	1-1	0-1	3-4	1-0	3-0	3-0	2-4	1-0	3-0	1-0	2-1	0-0	0-4	0-1	3-1
4 Burscough	0-2	1-3	2-3		0-1	0-0	1-1	0-2	2-4	0-2	1-1	2-3	2-2	1-1	1-0	1-2	2-3	2-0	0-2	0-1	0-1	2-1
5 Droylsden	1-0	2-0	2-0	3-1		2-0	1-3	3-2	0-0	2-1	3-0	5-1	2-1	1-0	2-2	2-1	0-0	0-1	1-1	1-1	1-2	1-1
6 Farsley Celtic	1-0	3-3	3-0	5-1	1-1		4-1	2-1	0-1	1-0	2-3	4-0	2-1	1-1	1-2	0-1	5-1	4-0	2-3	1-3	0-1	0-5
7 Fleetwood T.	1-0	1-1	1-0	3-1	2-1	2-1		2-2	0-2	1-0	1-0	1-3	1-3	3-0	3-1	2-1	1-1	2-2	1-2	1-2	2-0	1-0
8 Gainsborough	1-2	0-2	0-0	0-4	1-0	0-0	3-4		0-0	3-2	3-1	2-2	0-1	2-0	4-1	1-1	0-1	0-3	3-3	0-1	1-1	1-2
9 Gateshead	1-1	3-0	3-0	4-1	1-1	3-0	2-2	1-0		1-3	5-0	1-0	6-3	3-2	2-0	3-0	1-1	0-1	1-0	5-1	2-2	2-1
10 Harrogate Town	2-0	2-2	3-1	2-0	1-1	1-0	5-2	0-3	1-0		2-2	2-0	2-1	4-0	1-1	4-0	0-3	3-3	0-1	2-2	2-0	0-1
11 Hinckley United	0-2	1-1	2-1	0-1	1-0	1-2	2-1	0-2	2-0	2-0		4-0	0-1	1-0	4-2	0-0	1-1	4-0	0-1	1-3	2-3	1-0
12 Hucknall Town	0-5	1-1	1-1	0-2	1-1	1-2	3-2	1-2	2-2	1-1	1-2		0-1	1-2	0-2	0-2	0-0	3-1	2-3	2-3	0-1	0-0
13 Hyde United	0-4	1-1	1-0	0-1	1-3	3-1	5-3	0-0	2-5	2-3	0-0	2-0		0-1	1-2	3-1	1-1	1-1	0-2	1-2	3-1	4-4
14 Kings Lynn	1-1	0-4	2-3	0-0	2-2	1-4	1-0	2-2	2-0	2-3	1-1	0-0	4-1		1-1	3-0	0-0	2-2	1-0	1-2	1-1	1-3
15 Redditch United	0-1	2-2	2-0	1-2	0-4	3-1	1-1	1-1	0-2	2-1	0-2	2-2	1-0	1-2		0-0	0-2	2-2	0-1	1-1	2-1	2-0
16 Solihull Moors	1-3	2-2	2-0	3-2	2-1	2-1	2-2	2-3	2-0	1-1	1-3	3-1	2-2	1-1	2-1		0-2	0-1	0-2	1-1	3-2	2-0
17 Southport	1-1	0-1	2-1	3-0	3-1	1-0	1-1	5-3	2-3	1-0	0-0	3-0	2-0	2-1	2-3	3-0		3-2	2-0	0-1	5-2	0-0
18 Stafford R.	1-3	0-2	1-0	0-2	0-0	1-0	1-2	2-0	4-1	0-0	3-1	0-0	2-0	0-0	0-1	0-2	0-3		0-1	0-1	0-1	0-0
19 Stalybridge C.	2-2	0-2	2-0	4-0	2-2	1-0	0-5	1-2	1-2	1-3	7-1	2-2	4-1	1-1	3-3	5-0	0-1	2-0		2-2	1-0	1-4
20 Tamworth	0-1	1-2	1-1	6-2	2-0	2-1	2-1	0-0	2-1	3-1	1-0	1-1	2-0	2-0	1-1	1-0	1-1	1-2	0-3		2-0	1-0
21 Vauxhall Motors	2-0	1-1	2-1	2-0	1-4	2-0	0-2	1-1	1-2	1-0	0-4	2-3	2-1	1-3	1-1	2-2	0-0	1-1	1-1	2-2		3-0
22 Workington	1-0	0-3	0-1	4-1	1-1	0-2	3-2	5-0	4-2	0-0	1-3	1-0	2-2	1-1	0-1	2-1	0-1	2-2	0-2	1-4	3-1	

		P	W	D	L	F	A	GD	Pts
1	AFC Wimbledon	42	26	10	6	86	36	50	88
2	Hampton & Richmond Boro'	42	25	10	7	74	37	37	85
3	Eastleigh	42	25	8	9	69	49	20	83
4	Hayes & Yeading United	42	24	9	9	74	43	31	81
5	Chelmsford City	42	23	8	11	72	52	20	77
6	Maidenhead United	42	21	8	13	57	46	11	71
7	Welling United	42	19	11	12	61	44	17	68
8	Bath City	42	20	8	14	56	45	11	68
9	Bishop's Stortford	42	17	8	17	60	60	0	59
10	Newport County	42	16	11	15	50	51	-1	59
11	Team Bath	42	16	7	19	62	64	-2	55
12	St Albans City	42	14	12	16	56	50	6	54
13	Bromley	42	15	9	18	60	64	-4	54
14	Braintree Town	42	14	10	18	57	54	3	52
15	Havant & Waterlooville	42	11	15	16	59	58	1	48
16	Worcester City	42	12	11	19	38	53	-15	47
17	Weston Super Mare	42	12	11	19	43	68	-25	47
18	Basingstoke Town	42	10	16	16	36	55	-19	46
19	Dorchester Town	42	10	12	20	39	61	-22	42
20	Thurrock	42	9	13	20	54	60	-6	40
21	Bognor Regis Town (-7)	42	7	12	23	33	68	-35	26
22	Fisher Athletic	42	5	3	34	22	100	-78	18

PROMOTION PLAY-OFFS - SEMI-FINALS

1st Leg	Hayes & Yeading Utd	2 - 4	Eastleigh
2nd Leg	Eastleigh	0 - 4	Hayes & Yeading United
1st Leg	Chelmsford City	1 - 3	Hampton & Richmond
2nd Leg	Hampton & Richmond	0 - 0	Chelmsford City

PROMOTION PLAY-OFF - FINAL

Hampton & Richmond 2 - 3 Hayes & Yeading United

	1	2	3	4	5	6	7	8	9	10	11	12	13	14	15	16	17	18	19	20	21	22
1 AFC Wimbledon		1-0	3-2	4-1	3-1	5-1	3-1	3-1	2-0	0-2	3-0	1-1	3-0	2-0	3-1	3-0	3-0	2-0	2-1	0-1	1-1	2-0
2 Basingstoke T.	0-1		1-0	1-1	0-0	2-2	2-0	1-2	0-0	1-0	2-2	1-1	2-2	1-1	0-1	0-0	1-2	1-3	1-0	0-0	0-1	0-0
3 Bath City	2-2	1-0		2-3	0-1	3-2	1-3	2-1	2-0	1-1	1-0	0-1	2-1	0-1	1-0	2-1	1-0	1-1	2-2	0-4	3-0	1-0
4 Bishop's S'ford	0-1	3-2	0-2		2-0	0-3	1-1	2-1	0-2	3-4	0-1	1-3	1-0	0-0	2-0	1-1	1-1	4-3	2-1	0-1	2-1	3-0
5 Bognor Regis T.	1-5	2-3	0-2	0-2		0-2	1-1	2-1	0-0	1-0	2-1	0-1	1-5	1-1	2-4	0-1	0-5	3-0	1-1	0-0	1-1	1-2
6 Braintree Town	0-1	0-1	0-4	2-0	1-1		2-0	1-2	0-1	1-1	2-0	1-2	1-0	0-1	0-2	3-2	1-0	4-1	1-2	1-1	1-1	1-1
7 Bromley	2-2	0-2	1-1	1-0	1-0	1-4		2-2	1-0	5-1	3-0	0-2	2-2	1-0	1-2	2-1	2-3	4-0	3-3	1-3	3-0	0-2
8 Chelmsford C.	3-2	2-2	2-3	3-3	2-0	1-1	0-1		2-1	3-0	3-0	3-2	1-2	2-1	2-1	0-0	1-1	1-1	3-2	2-0	4-1	2-0
9 Dorchester T.	1-1	0-0	0-2	0-2	1-0	2-2	2-1	0-1		0-4	3-0	0-1	1-0	1-2	0-3	0-1	1-1	2-2	4-3	1-1	1-2	3-1
10 Eastleigh	2-1	1-0	2-0	1-1	2-1	2-1	1-0	2-1	0-1		3-0	2-1	2-0	3-3	0-0	3-2	3-0	1-3	1-1	4-2	1-0	1-0
11 Fisher Athletic	0-3	1-0	1-0	0-3	0-1	0-2	0-2	0-1	4-0	1-2		0-2	1-1	0-5	0-1	1-3	0-4	0-6	0-3	0-5	0-2	0-1
12 Hampton & R.	1-1	0-0	3-1	2-1	0-0	2-1	1-1	4-1	2-0	2-1	3-0		2-1	2-3	1-0	0-1	0-0	3-0	3-1	2-0	4-1	1-2
13 Havant & W.	0-0	5-1	0-0	3-0	2-2	1-1	0-1	1-1	1-2	2-2	3-0	1-4		2-2	3-3	1-1	2-0	2-1	2-2	1-0	2-3	0-2
14 Hayes & Yeading	2-1	5-0	2-2	1-0	3-1	0-1	2-1	0-1	2-1	0-1	3-4	0-0	2-1		2-0	2-0	2-1	1-1	2-1	2-1	3-0	3-1
15 Maidenhead U.	0-4	1-2	0-0	3-2	2-0	2-1	4-0	0-2	2-1	1-4	1-0	0-3	1-0	2-0		0-1	1-0	0-2	1-1	2-0	0-0	5-0
16 Newport Co.	1-4	3-0	0-4	0-1	2-1	2-1	3-0	3-1	4-4	0-1	4-0	1-0	0-2	1-5	0-1		0-1	4-2	1-1	0-0	1-0	1-0
17 St Albans City	0-0	3-0	2-1	2-0	1-0	0-3	4-5	1-2	2-0	5-0	4-1	2-2	1-1	1-1	1-2	1-1		0-0	0-2	2-3	3-0	0-2
18 Team Bath	1-2	1-2	0-1	2-2	1-0	0-3	0-3	2-0	4-1	1-3	4-1	0-2	1-0	4-1	0-2	2-0	2-0		4-1	0-1	1-2	0-2
19 Thurrock	0-1	6-0	2-0	1-3	1-1	1-0	1-1	0-1	1-0	0-1	2-1	3-3	2-3	0-1	1-2	0-0	0-0	1-2		1-2	0-1	2-0
20 Welling United	2-2	1-1	2-1	1-3	4-1	1-0	3-1	1-3	0-0	3-2	3-0	4-0	2-1	0-2	1-1	0-2	0-1	1-1	0-0		2-0	1-3
21 Weston-S-Mare	1-1	0-3	0-1	2-1	1-2	3-1	2-1	1-4	2-2	1-1	3-1	0-3	0-1	1-2	2-2	1-1	1-1	0-1	2-1	0-3		1-1
22 Worcester City	3-2	0-0	0-1	1-3	1-1	2-2	1-0	0-1	0-0	0-1	1-1	1-2	2-2	0-3	1-1	0-0	2-0	0-2	2-0	0-1	1-2	

PLAY-OFF FINAL ACTION...

Top: Cambridge United 'keeper collects the ball cleanly from this Torquay corner.

Above: Torquay United's Hargreaves scores despite the challenge from the Cambridge defender.
Photos: Peter Barnes.

Above right:
Cambridge's, Willmott, knocks the ball past Torquay's Nicholson.

Right: Rendell gets his shot away before the Torquay defence can challenge him.
Photos: Keith Clayton.

A.F.C. WIMBLEDON

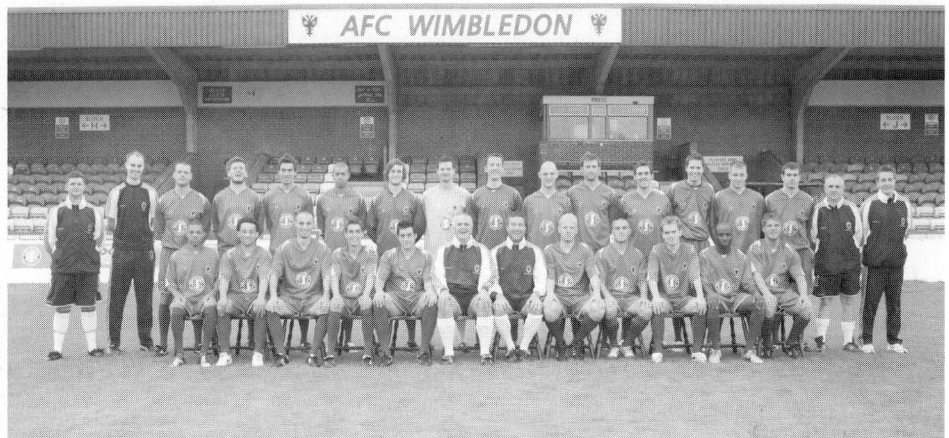

Back row (standing) Simon Bassey (coach) Mike Rayner (physio) Steve Watson, Luke Garrard, Steve Wales, Simon Sweeney, Paul Smith, Josh Lennie, Andy Little, Darren Grieves, Antony Howard, Mark Rooney, Michael Haswell, Jon Boswell, Stephen Goddard, John Morris (Reserve manager) Steve West(kit man)
Front row (seated) Byron Bubb, Wes Daly, Simon Sobihy, Paul Barnes, Lee Kersey, Dave Anderson (manager) Jon Turner (assistant manager) Steve Butler, Chris Gell, Joe Paris, Roscoe Dsane, Richard Butler.

CLUB PERSONNEL

Chief Executive & Company Secretary:

Erik Samuelson.

Directors: Ivor Heller, Nigel Higgs.

Secretary: David Charles

(M): 07712 295266

(B): 020 8547 3528

Correspondence C/o Club

Email: david.charles@afcwimbledon.co.uk

Commercial Manager: Keith McGuiness

(B): 020 8547 3528

Email: commercial@afcwimbledon.co.uk

Manager: Terry Brown.

Club therapist: Mike Rayner.

What a season! Everyone involved with the 'new ' Wimbledon will have wonderful memories of a glorious campaign as Terry Brown's squad was roared on by a regular support of over 3,000. The club were never out of the top four and a start of five consecutive victories with a 13-3 goal difference set the standards for superb season.

Jon Main started the campaign with a hat trick and finished with an impressive 34 goals and there were only five of fifty senior games contested in which The Dons failed to score. An exciting F.A.Cup run brought back plenty of memories for the older Wimbledon supporters as Bedford Town, Dover Athletic and Maidstone United were beaten before old Isthmian rivals Wycombe Wanderers won in front of 4,528 and the television cameras at Kingston.

Following a surprising F.A.Trophy defeat at Uxbridge, the club seemed to move up a gear and just one draw amongst thirteen victories and a goal tally of 36-6 gave Wimbledon the leadership of the Blue Square South, a position they never looked likely to lose despite a slight end of season tension that appeared to effect the goalscorers.

For all the old Wimbledon fans, the club's exciting and satisfying progress must be particularly thrilling and satisfying, but they know there is a long way to go and the loyal support and hard working officials will be determined that the club's progress continues at a sensible and controllable pace in the future.

AFC WIMBLEDON

BEST LGE ATT.: **4,722** v St Albans City
LOWEST: **2,358** v Eastleigh

No.	Date	Comp	H/A	Opponents	Att:	Result	Goalscorers	Pos
1	Aug 9	BSS	A	Newport County	2546	W 4 - 1	**MAIN** 3 (40 55 71) Godfrey 74	
2	12		H	Thurrock	2786	W 2 - 1	Godfrey 86 Garrard 89	
3	16		H	Bognor Regis Town	2741	W 3 - 1	Finn 24 **Main** 88 Mason 90	2
4	23		A	Basingstoke Town	1509	W 1 - 0	Watkins 19 (og)	1
5	25		H	Bromley	3149	W 3 - 1	Finn 44 **Main** 89 (pen) 90	
6	30		A	Bath City	1675	D 2 - 2	Godfrey 25 Inns 85	1
7	Sept 2		A	Braintree Town	1123	W 1 - 0	Hussey 75	
8	6		H	Weston-s-Mare	2934	D 1 - 1	Comyn-Platt 15 (og)	1
9	**8**	**SS S1**	**A**	**Chelmsford City**	**575**	**L 0 - 1**		
10	13		H	Maidenhead United	3039	W 3 - 1	**Main** 25 (pen) 73 (pen) Davis 68	1
11	20		A	Hayes & Yeading	1526	L 1 - 2	Godfrey 27	3
12	**27**	**F.A.C. 2Q**	**A**	**Bedford Town**	**1296**	**D 2 - 2**	**Main 44 (pen) Aiteouakrim 81**	
13	**30**	**F.A.C. 2Q r**	**H**	**Bedford Town**	**1370**	**W 3 - 0**	**Hatton 39 Davis 53 Kedwell 87**	
14	Oct 4		A	Worcester City	1725	L 2 - 3	Davis 30 Hatton 54	4
15	**11**	**F.A.C.3Q**	**A**	**Dover Athletic**	**2710**	**D 0 - 0**		
16	**14**	**F.A.C. 3Q r**	**H**	**Dover Athletic**	**1939**	**W 2 - 0**	**Finn 45 Kedwell 62**	
17	18		H	Bishop's Stortford	3072	W 4 - 1	Hatton 24 **Main** 54 65 Kedwell 83	
18	21		H	Havant & Waterlooville	2711	W 3 - 0	Kedwell 48 80 **Main** 53	2
19	**25**	**F.A.C. 4Q**	**A**	**Maidstone United**	**1710**	**W 1 - 0**	**Hatton 32**	
20	Nov 1		A	Chelmsford City	2318	L 2 - 3	Kedwell 68 **Main** 90	3
21	**10**	**F.A.C. 1R**	**H**	**Wycombe Wanderers**	**4528**	**L 1 - 4**	**Hatton 56**	
22	15		A	Welling United	1625	D 2 - 2	**Main** 6 Judge 24	4
23	**22**	**F.A.T. 3Q**	**A**	**Worcester City**	**895**	**W 3 - 1**	**Godfrey 5 Aiteouakrim 41 68**	
24	29		H	Hampton & Richmond B	3366	D 1 - 1	Hatton 53	6
25	Dec 2		H	Eastleigh	2358	L 0 - 2		
26	6		A	Team Bath	607	W 2 - 1	Hatton 15 Kedwell 44	4
27	**13**	**F.A.T 1R**	**A**	**Uxbridge**	**582**	**L 1 - 2**	**Aiteouakrim 19**	
28	20		H	Newport County	2945	W 3 - 0	Kedwell 23 45 **Main** 62	3
29	26		A	Fisher Athletic	1108	W 3 - 0	**MAIN** 3 (22 pen 39 69)	2
30	Jan 1		H	Fisher Athletic	3190	W 3 - 0	**Main** 28 Hatton 63 Kedwell 79	
31	3		A	Bognor Regis Town	1000	W 5 - 1	Adjel 32 Pearce 35 (og) Kedwell 60 89 Leberl 84	2
32	13		A	Dorchester Town	738	D 1 - 1	Lee 66	
33	17		A	Maidenhead United	1296	W 4 - 0	Hatton 17 Kedwell 37 **Main** 47 78	2
34	24		H	Braintree Town	3229	W 5 - 1	**MAIN** 3 (30 37 47) Hatton 6 Lee 86	2
35	27		A	Bishops Stortford	1003	W 1 - 0	Kedwell 57	1
36	31		H	Chelmsford City	4690	W 3 - 1	**Main** 18 28 Davis 90	1
37	Feb 10		H	Hayes & Yeading	2621	W 2 - 0	**Main** 14 42 (pen)	1
38	14		H	Bath City	3043	W 3 - 2	**Main** 45 (pen) 60 Godfrey 83	1
39	21		A	Thurrock	1173	W 1 - 0	Hatton 85	1
40	24		H	Worcester City	2695	W 2 - 0	Inns 53 **Main** 55	
41	28		A	Havant & Waterlooville	1756	D 0 - 0		1
42	Mar 7		A	Weston-s-Mare	1238	D 1 - 1	**Main** 2	
43	10		A	St Albans City	1105	D 0 - 0		
44	14		H	Dorchester Town	3554	W 2 - 0	**Main** 45 Kedwell 48	1
45	21		H	Welling United	3327	L 0 - 1		1
46	28		A	Eastleigh	2283	L 1 - 2	Godfrey	1
47	April 4		H	Team Bath	3290	W 2 - 0	Ibe 52 Davis 90	1
48	11		H	Basingstoke Town	4136	W 1 - 0	Inns 20	1
49	13		A	Bromley	2177	D 2 - 2	Godfrey 2 88	1
50	18		A	Hampton & Richmond	3225	D 1 - 1	**Main** 82	
51	25		H	St Albans City	4722	W 3 - 0	Adjel 48 Hatton 68 Goodliffe 88	1

Average Home Att: 3219 (2603) **Goals** 99 46

Best Position: 1st **Worst:** 6th

Goalscorers: Main 34, Kedwell 15, Hatton 12, Godfrey 9, Davis 5, Aiteouakrim 4, Finn 4, Inns 3, Lee 2, Adjel 2, Garrard 1, Hussey 1, Ibe 1, Judge 1, Leberl 1, Mason 1, Goodliffe 1. Own Goals 2.

LITTLE	GARRARD	HASWELL	ADJEI	JUDGE	INNS	HATTON	DAVIS	GODFREY	MAIN	FINN	LEBERL	MASON	PIGDEN	PEACOCK	HUSSEY	PULLEN	GOODLIFFE	SULLIVAN	GILBERT	KEDWELL	AITEOUAKRIM	TURNER	LEE	STAFFORD	SAMBROOK	GINDRE	CONROY	SAUNDERS	IBE	BAPTISTE	TAYLOR	
X	X	X	X	X	X	X	X	X	X	X	S	S	S	U	U																	1
X	X	X	X	X	X		X	X	X	X	X	S	U	U	S	U																2
X	X	X	X	X	X	X	X	X	X	X	S	S		U	S	U																3
X	X	S	X	X	X	X	X	X	X	X	S	S			X	U	U															4
X	X	X	X	X	X	X	X	X	X	X	S	S			S	U	U															5
X	X		X	X	X	X	X	X	X	X	U	S			X	U	S	U														6
X	X		X	X	X	X	X		X	X	X		S		X	U	S	S	U													7
X	X		X	X	X	X	X	X	X	X	S	S	S		X		U	U														8
U	U		X	S		S	S	X		X		X	X	X	X	X	X	X	X													9
X	X		X	U	X	X	X	X	X	X	S	U			X	U	X			S												10
X	X	U	X	S	X		X	X	X	X	S	S			X	U	X			X												11
U	X	X	X	X		X	X		X	X	X		S		U	X		S		X	S											12
U	X	U	X	X		X	X		X	X	X	S	S		X	X		U		X	S											13
	X	U	X	X	X	X	X		X	S	X		U		X	X				X	S	U										14
X	X	U	X	X		X	X		X	X	X	U	U		X	U		U		X	S											15
X	X	S	X	X		X	X		X	X	X	U	U		X	U	U	S		X	U											16
X	X	S	X	X		X	X	S	X	X	X				X	U	S			X	U											17
X	X	S	X	X		X	X	S	X	X	X				X	U	U			X	S											18
X	X	U	X	X	S	X	X	U	X	X	X				X	U	U	S		X												19
X	X	U	X	U	X	X	X	S	X	X	X				X	U	S			X												20
X	X	X	X	U	X	X	X	X	X	S	X	S			S	U	U			X	U											21
X	X	U	X	X	S	X	X	X	X	S	U				X	U	X			X												22
X		U	X	X	X	X	X	X		X	S	S	S		X	U	X				X											23
X		S	X	X	X	X		X	S	X	X		U		X	U	X			S	X											24
X		U		X	X	X	X	S	X	X	U				X	U	X			X	S		X									25
X			S	X	X	X	X	X	S	X	S				X	U	X			X	U		X									26
X		X	U	U	X	X	U	S	S	X	X				X		X			X	X		X									27
U			X	X	U	X	X	X	X	S	X				X	X	U			X	S		X									28
U		S	X	X	U	X	X		X	X	X				X	X	S			X	S		X									29
U		X	X	X		X	X		X	X	X				S	X	X			X	S		U	S								30
X		S	X	X		X	X	X	X		X				X	U	U			X	S		X	S								31
U		S	X	X		X	X	X		S	X	U			X	X	S			X	X		X									32
U			S	X	S	X	X	X	X	X	X				X	X	S			X	U		X									33
U		S	X	X	S	X	X	X	X	S		U			X	X	X			X			X									34
X		X		X	X	X	X	S	X	X	S	S			U	U	X			X			X									35
U		U		X	U	X	X	X	X	S	S				X	X	X			X			X		X							36
U		S		X	U	X	X	X	X	S	X	U			X	X	X			X					X							37
U		X		X	S	X	X	X	X	S	X					X	X	U		X				U	X							38
U		U		X	S	X	X	X	X	S	X		U		X	X	X			X					X							39
X		U		X	X	X	X	X	X	S	X		U		X	S	S			X					X							40
		U	U	X	S	X	S	X	X	X	X				X	X	X			X					X	U						41
		S	U	X	X	X	X	X	X	S					X	X	X			X			X			U						42
		X	S	X	X	X	X	S	X	X	X	U			S	X				X						U	X					43
			X	X	X	X	X	X	X		S				X	X				X		U		U			X	S	S			44
			X		X	X	U	X	X	S	U				X	X	X			X			X				X	S	S			45
		U		X	X	X	X	S	X	U					X	X				S			X			U	X	X	X			46
		S		X		X	X	S	X	S	X				X	X				X			X			U	X	U	X			47
		U		X	X	X	X	X	X	X					X	X				S			S			U	X	S	X			48
		U		X		X	X	X	X	S	X				X	X				X			X			U	X			S	S	49
		X		X		X	U	X	S	S	X				S	X	X			X			X			U	X				X	50
		X	X	U		S	X	S	X	X	X				S	U	X			X					X	X					X	51
Total League Appearances																																
20	15	10	25	37	23	39	38	29	38	24	23	0	0	0	32	21	18	0	0	30	2	0	16	0	7	1	8	1	3	0	2	X
0	0	11	3	1	6	1	1	9	3	15	11	9	3	0	7	1	8	1	0	4	7	0	1	2	0	0	0	3	2	1	1	S
10	0	12	2	3	4	0	2	0	0	1	4	5	5	3	2	18	6	3	1	0	3	2	1	2	0	8	0	1	0	0	0	U
Total Cup Appearances																																
6	6	3	8	6	3	8	7	3	6	8	7	1	1	1	7	3	3	1	1	7	2	0	1	0	0	0	0	0	0	0	0	X
0	0	1	0	1	1	1	1	1	1	1	1	3	3	0	1	0	0	3	0	0	3	0	0	0	0	0	0	0	0	0	0	S
3	1	4	1	2	0	0	1	1	0	0	0	2	2	0	1	5	3	2	0	0	2	0	0	0	0	0	0	0	0	0	0	U

AFC WIMBLEDON

CURRENT SQUAD AS OF BEGINING OF 2009-10 SEASON

GOALKEEPERS	SQ NO.	HT	WT	D.O.B	AGE	P.O.B	CAREER	APPS	GOA
Seb Brown		6'00"	12 12	24/11/89	19	Sutton	Brentford Rel c/s 09, St Albans (WE) 10/07, AFC Wimbledon 8/09		
Andy Little	13	6'03"	13 10	3/10/74	34	Sheffield	Sheff Wed (Jun), Croydon 9/94, Sutton U 9/99, Banstead A 10/99, Crawley 11/99, Basingstoke (L) 2/05, AFC Wimbledon 6/05	20	0
James Pullen	1	6'02"	14 00	18/3/82	27	Chelmsford	Heybridge Swifts, Ipswich 10/99 Rel c/s 03 Re-signed, Blackpool (SL) 8/01, Dag & Red (3ML) 8/03, Peterborough (L) 10/03 Perm 11/03, Heybridge S (2ML) 2/04, Hornchurch (L) 9/04, Welling (L) 10/04, Gravesend 11/04, Fisher 8/05, Dulwich (L) 8/06, Eastleigh 10/06, AFC Wimbledon (L) 1/08 Perm 2/08	22	0
Jack Turner	20			17/9/92	16		AFC Wimbledon		
DEFENDERS									
Jay Conroy	2	6'02"	12 02	2/3/86	23	Ryegate	C.Palace, AFC Wimbledon (L) 9/04, AFC Wimbledon (3ML) 11/04, Aldershot (Trial) c/s 05, Canvey Island 8/05, Sutton U (3ML) 12/05, Chelmsford 6/06, Lewes 7/07 Rel 5/08, Havant & W 5/08 Rel 1/09, Northwich 1/09 Rel 2/09, AFC Wimbledon 3/09	8	0
Luke Garrard	12	5'10"	10 09	22/9/85	23	Barnet	Tottenham (Scholar), Swindon 7/02 Rel c/s 05, Bishops Stortford 7/05, Boreham Wood 10/05, Northwood 11/05, AFC Wimbledon 3/06	15	1
Chris Hussey	3			2/1/89	20	Hammersmith	Woking (Yth), AFC Wimbledon, Windsor & E (L) 8/07, Windsor & E (L) 12/07	39	1
Brett Johnson	16	6'01"	13 00	15/8/85	24	Hammersmith	Ashford T (Midd), Reading (Trial), Aldershot 2/04, Northampton £30,000 6/05 Rel c/s 08, Gravesend (L) 11/05, Grays (6ML) 1/06, Luton (Trial) 3/08, Brentford 8/08 Rel c/s 09, AFC Wimbledon 8/09		
Ben Judge	6			22/5/77	32	Redhill	C.Palace (Jun), Croydon (94), Crawley 11/01 Rel 8/07, Bromley 9/07 Rel 3/08, AFC Wimbledon 3/08	38	1
Paul Lorraine	22			12/10/83	25		Welling, Dartford (L) 1/03, Erith & B 3/04, Braintree 5/04, Fisher 5/06, AFC Wimbledon (L) 12/06, Perm 1/07, Woking 5/07, AFC Wimbledon 5/09		
Jack Stafford							AFC Wimbledon	2	0
MIDFIELDERS									
Kennedy Adjei	4			10/2/88	21	Accra, Ghana	Croydon A, AFC Wimbledon 7/08	28	2
Derek Duncan	14	5'10"	10 11	23/4/87	22	Newham	L.Orient Rel 5/07, Lewes (L) 9/06, Grays 5/07, Wycombe 7/07, Lewes (2ML) 11/07, Ebbsfleet 1/09, AFC Wimbledon 6/09		
Elliott Godfrey	11	5'08"	11 03	22/2/83	26	Toronto, Can	Watford Rel c/s 04, Colchester (Trial) 7/04, Hampton & R 9/04, AFC Wimbledon 6/08	38	7
Steven Gregory	15	6'01"	12 04	19/3/87	22	Aylesbury	Wycombe Rel 5/08, Hayes & Yeading (3ML) 8/07, Havant & W (L) 1/08, Hayes & Yeading 7/08, AFC Wimbledon Undisc 5/09		
Sam Hatton	7			7/2/88	21	St Albans	St Albans (Yth), Stevenage, Northwood (L) 3/06, Yeading (2ML) 8/06, Maidenhead (L) 11/06, Yeading (L) 2/07, AFC Wimbledon 5/07	40	9
Alan Inns	5			5/6/82	27	Reading	Oxford C (Jun), Wokingham, Hampton & R 9/02, AFC Wimbledon 5/08	29	3
Lewis Taylor	8	6'00"	11 07	1/8/86	23	Sutton	AFC Wimbledon, Whyteleafe c/s 04, Horsham c/s 06, AFC Wimbledon 5/08	3	0
Ricky Wellard	17						Ashford T, AFC Wimbledon 6/09		
FORWARDS									
Danny Kedwell	9			22/10/85	23	Kent	Chatham, Tonbridge A 7/02, Fisher 10/02, Lordswood 3/03, Maidstone U 5/03 Rel 2/04, Gillingham (Trial) 1/04, Chatham 3/04, Herne Bay 7/04, Kidderminster (Trial) 12/04, Welling 7/05, Grays 5/07, AFC Wimbledon 9/08	34	13
Jon Main	10	5'10"		7/3/81	28	Greenwich	VCD Ath, Cray W, Tonbridge A 1/06, Wolves (Trial) 3/07, Norwich (Trial) 3/07, AFC Wimbledon Undisc 11/07	41	33
Luke Moore	18	5'11"	11 07	27/4/88	21	Gravesend	Gravesend/Ebbsfleet, AFC Wimbledon 6/09		
Peter Rapson	21			5/2/92	17		AFC Wimbledon		

LOANEES	SN	HT	WT	DOB	AGE	POB	From - To	APPS	GOA
(M)Rob Saunders				18/12/81	27	Ashford, Middx	Farnborough (SL) 3/09 -	4	0
(F)Kezie Ibe		5'10"	12 00	6/12/82	26	London	Ebbsfleet 3/09 - Farnborough 7/09	5	1

DEPARTURES	SN	HT	WT	DOB	AGE	POB	From - To	APPS	GOA
(D)Steve Gilbert				3/11/89	19	Kingston	Fulham (Yth) - Rel 1/09, Walton & H 1/09	0	0
(D)Jason Goodliffe				7/3/74	35	Hillingdon	Rushden & D 5/07 - Rel 5/09, Sutton U 6/09	26	1
(M)Tom Davis		5'10"	11 07	17/2/84	25	Bromley	Lewes 5/08 - Rel 5/09, Dover 7/09	39	4
(M)Anthony Finn				27/11/82	26	Manchester	Met Police 6/07 - Rel 5/09, Welling U 6/09	39	2
(D)Michael Haswell				23/8/83	26	London	Chelmsford 6/06 - Rel 5/09, Grays 6/09	21	0
(F)Chris Sullivan				26/9/87	21		Braintree £3,500 6/08 - Rel 5/09, Tooting & M (2ML) 11/08, Billericay 7/09	1	0
(F)Belal Aiteouakrim				12/4/85	24	London	Hendon 6/08 - Rel 5/09, Maidenhead (L) 3/09	9	0
(D)Michael Peacock				16/8/88	21	Hillingdon	North Greenford Undisc 5/08 - Rel 5/09, Northwood (L) 12/08, Ashford T (Middx) (L) 3/09, Northwood 6/09	0	0
(F)Dean Mason				28/2/89	20	Islington	Barnet 8/08 - Rel 5/09, Northwood (L) 10/08, Northwood (L) 12/08, Walton Casuals (L) 3/09	9	1
(M)Luke Pigden				18/9/89	19	Epsom	Yth - Rel 5/09, Godalming (L) 12/08, Ashford T (Middx) (L) 3/09	3	0
(M)Jake Leberl				2/4/77	32	Morden	Dag & Red 7/07 - Rel 5/09, Dover 6/09	34	1
(D)Andrew Sambrook		5'10"	11 09	13/7/79	30	Chatham	Thurrock 1/09 - Welling 5/09	7	0
(M)Dwane Lee		6'03"	13 09	26/11/79	29	Hillingdon	Kettering 12/08 - Rel 7/09	17	2
(G)Nick Gindre				24/7/84	25	Leatherhead	Woking 2/09 -	1	0
(F)Rocky Baptiste		6'02"	11 11	7/7/72	37	Clapham	Maidenhead 3/09 -	1	1

A.F.C. WIMBLEDON

Formed: 2002

Nickname: Dons.

Club Colours: Dark blue shirts, shorts and socks.

Change Colours: Yellow shirts, shorts, socks.

Club Sponsor: Sports Interactive

Previous League: Isthmian League

Ground address: The Cherry Red Records 'Fans' Stadium, Kingsmeadow, 422A Kingston Rd., Kingston upon Thames, Surrey KT1 3PB.

Telephone: 020 8547 3528

Fax: 0808 280 0816

Email: info@afcwimbledon.co.uk

Website: www.afcwimbledon.co.uk

Simple Directions: From town centre Cambridge Rd on to Kingston Rd (A2043) to Maiden Road. From A3 turn off at New Malden and then left onto A2043. Ground one mile on left.

Capacity: 4,500 **Seats** 1,047 **Covered Terrace**: 2,700 **Floodlights:** Yes

Clubhouse: Open matchdays and evenings. Two function rooms for hire.

Club Shop: Yes, fully stocked

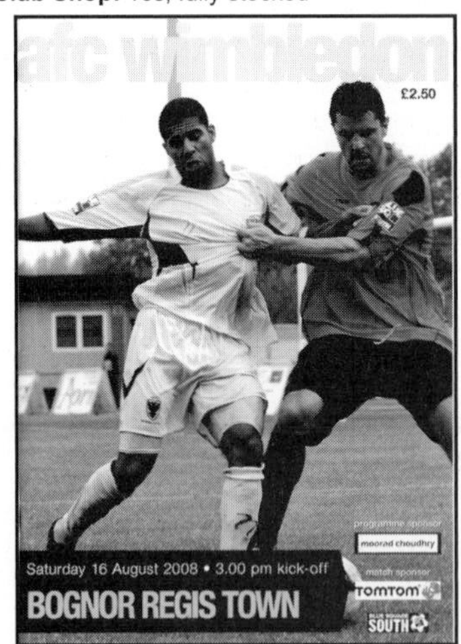

PROGRAMME EDITOR

David Charles

(M) 07712 295266 (B) 020 8547 3528

Email: david.charles@afcwimbledon.co.uk

CLUB STATISTICS

Records

Attendance: 4,722 v St. Albans City 25.04.09.

Victory: 9-0 v Slough 2006-07

Defeat: 0-4 v Hampton & Richmond B. (H) - 01.04.06.

0-4 v Walton & Hersham (A) - 02.04.05

Goalscorer:

Kevin Cooper - 107 in 105 appearances - July 04 - May 07

Career Appearances: Anthony Howard - 148

Record Transfer Fee Paid: Undisclosed for: Michael Haswell (Chelmsford C) , Richard Butler (Ashford Town Middx),Paul Barnes (Bristol Rovers), Simon Sweeney (Chesham U) & Steves Wales (Yeading)

Received: Undisclosed from Halifax Town for Shane Smeltz

SENIOR HONOURS

Combined Counties League & Cup winners 2003-04

Isthmian Division 1 Champions 2004-05

Surrey Senior Cup 2004-05

Conference South Champions 2008-09

PREVIOUS

League: Combined Counties 2002-04. Isthmian 2004-08.

ALTRINCHAM

Back Row (L-R): Mark McGregor, Dale Johnson, Stuart Coburn, Andy Ralph, Greg Young, Chris Lane.
Middle: Danny Heathcote (kitman), Charles Heathcote (kitman), Joe O'Neill, Alex Meechan, Graham Heathcote (manager), Lee Elam, Robbie Lawton, Ian Senior (goalkeeping coach), Graham Barrow (assistant manager).
Front: Anthony Danylyk, Kevin Street, Chris Denham, George Heslop (company secretary), Geoff Goodwin (chairman), Grahame Rowley (vice-chairman), Colin Little, Chris Senior, Matt Doughty.

CLUB PERSONNEL

Chairman: Geoffrey Goodwin.

Vice-Chairman: Grahame Rowley.

Company Secretary: George Heslop.

President: Noel White.

Directors: Andrew Shaw, Derek Wilshaw.

Secretary: Derek Wilshaw

c/o of the Club.

Tel Nos: 01625 928 1045

e-mail: dwilshaw@altrinchamfootball.co.uk

Commercial Director: TBA

Press Officer: Brian Flynn

Tel: 07860 561 011

Manager: Graham Heathcote.

Previous Clubs as Manager: None

Assistant Manager: Ken McKenna.

Club therapist: Sean Riley

Looking back at their away victory at Woking on the first day of the season, 'Alty' supporters couldn't have been blamed for raising their hopes for an improved season after three desperate campaigns. Colin Little, their veteran striker, had scored and went on to collect an impressive 16 goals with the club finishing in a greatly improved fifteenth position.

But an opening day victory was followed by just three points in the next eight games and their second victory was a 1-0 home success over luckless Lewes. However, charismatic manager Graham Heathcote, who had served the club in all roles throughout his football career, found the right blend and six wins in the next eight games with Little scoring in five of them, saw 'Alty into the top ten with confidence high for a victory in their first F.A.Cup tie away to Newcastle Blue Star.

In The First Round Proper a draw against Luton Town, a club in deep depression, was followed by a tough battle and defeat after the dreaded penalty shoot out and their was no progress in the F.A.Trophy, losing heavily to Southport at Moss Lane.

Although only seven league victories were earned in the second half of the season, a comfortable position was enjoyed, and the manager was in a position to introduce new faces and enjoy the England success of Shaun Densmore who won the 'man of the match' award in the International Challenge Trophy Final.

ALTRINCHAM

BEST LGE ATT.: **2,619** v Wrexham
LOWEST: **605** v Eastbourne Borough

No.	Date	Comp	H/A	Opponents	Att:	Result	Goalscorers	Pos
1	Aug 9	BSP	A	Woking	1645	W 2 - 1	Meechan 45 Little 90	4
2	12		H	Barrow	1312	L 3 - 4	Little 64 77 Denham 73	12
3	16		H	Kettering Town	1045	D 1 - 1	McGregor 83	10
4	23		A	Kidderminster Harriers	1335	L 0 - 4		18
5	25		H	Wrexham	2619	D 1 - 1	Senior 5	17
6	30		A	Eastbourne Borough	1170	L 0 - 1		19
7	Sept 2		A	Histon	692	L 0 - 1		
8	6		H	Salisbury City	1002	D 0 - 0		19
9	13		A	Stevenage Borough	1804	L 0 - 3		21
10	20		H	Lewes	827	W 1 - 0	Peyton 88	
11	23		H	Mansfield Town	1005	W 1 - 0	Senior 1	
12	29		A	Rushden & Diamonds	1341	D 1 - 1	Little 44	19
13	Oct 4		H	Ebbsfleet United	967	W 2 - 0	Little 28 Senior 45	17
14	7		A	Salisbury City	950	W 3 - 1	Little 45 Johnson 85 O'Neill 90 (pen)	
15	12		H	Oxford United	1806	W 1 - 0	Little 64	9
16	**14**	**SS N2**	**H**	**Farsley Celtic**	**259**	**D 1 - 1***	**Peyton 111 (won 4-2 on pens)**	
17	18		A	Weymouth	926	L 0 - 2		13
18	**26**	**F.A.C. 4Q**	**A**	**Newcastle Blue Star**	**305**	**W 2 - 1**	**Little 29 Lane 45**	
19	Nov 1		H	Histon	953	L 0 - 1		16
20	**4**	**SS N3**	**H**	**Wrexham**	**537**	**L 1 - 2***	**Meechan 54**	
21	**8**	**F.A.C. 1R**	**A**	**Luton Town**	**3200**	**D 0 - 0**		
22	15		A	Forest Green Rovers	851	W 3 - 1	Little 4 Senior 29 32	
23	**18**	**F.A.C. 1R r**	**H**	**Luton Town**	**2397**	**D 0 - 0***	**Luton Town won 4-2 after penalties**	
24	22		H	Cambridge United	1123	W 1 - 0	Lawton 45	11
25	29		H	Rushden & Diamonds	924	L 0 - 4		12
26	Dec 6		A	Crawley Town	978	L 0 - 4		14
27	9		A	Barrow	976	D 2 - 2	Meechan 31 Little 36	
28	**13**	**F.A.T 1R**	**H**	**Southport**	**609**	**L 1 - 4**	**Senior 82**	
29	20		H	Burton Albion	931	L 1 - 3	Johnson 56	15
30	26		A	Northwich Victoria	1400	W 1 - 0	Young 74	12
31	28		A	York City	2389	W 2 - 1	Senior 52 Johnson 89	11
32	Jan 17		A	Oxford United	4249	L 0 - 1		14
33	24		A	Burton Albion	2124	D 1 - 1	O'Neill 24	14
34	27		H	York City	1027	L 1 - 2	Densmore 14	
35	Feb 3		H	Northwich Victoria	1209	W 1 - 0	Banim 27	
36	14		A	Torquay United	1760	L 1 - 3	Doughty 87	15
37	21		H	Woking	943	W 1 - 0	Senior 27	13
38	28		H	Stevenage Borough	958	L 1 - 2	Little 22 (pen)	14
39	Mar 3		A	Kettering Town	1036	L 1 - 3	Densmore 63	
40	7		A	Grays Athletic	710	L 1 - 2	Doughty 90 (pen)	14
41	10		H	Torquay United	735	L 0 - 1		14
42	14		H	Weymouth	770	W 4 - 0	Welch 2 Little 8 Johnson 14 O'Neill 53	
43	21		H	Forest Green Rovers	852	L 2 - 5	Little 2 21	15
44	28		H	Crawley Town	960	D 2 - 2	Welch 27 Densmore 57	15
45	31		A	Ebbsfleet United	774	L 0 - 1		15
46	April 4		A	Lewes	337	L 0 - 2		17
47	7		H	Eastbourne Borough	605	D 2 - 2	Little 44 Densmore 70	16
48	11		H	Kidderminster Harriers	1142	D 2 - 2	Welch 38 Little 90 (pen)	15
49	13		A	Wrexham	2554	W 1 - 0	Young 52	
50	18		H	Grays Atletic	1148	W 2 - 0	Litle 23 Denham 80	14
51	21		A	Mansfield Town	1682	L 0 - 2		
52	26		A	Cambridge United	7090	D 0 - 0		15

Average Home Att: **1081 (1084)** **Goals** **54 72**

Best Position: 4th **Worst:** 21st

Goalscorers: Little 17, Senior 8, Densmore 4, Johnson 4, Meechan 3, O'Neill3, Welch 3, Denham 2, Doughty 2, Peyton 2, Young 2, Banim 1, Lane 1, Lawton 1, McGregor 1.

COBURN 1	LANE 2	YOUNG 5	MCGREGOR 4	DOUGHTY 3	STREET 6	LAWTON 7	LITTLE 9	MEECHAN 15	DENHAM 10	JOHNSON 14	ELAM 18	DANLYK 16	O'NEILL 12	RALPH 13	SENIOR 19	PEYTON 11	BATTERSBY 17	TIERNEY 20	DENSMORE 21	WATERFALL 17	BROWNHILL 20	HEFFERNAN 20	OWEN 8	SMITH 22	ACTON 23	HADFIELD 8	BANIM 24	WELCH 18	WILKINSON 17	MCFADDEN 15	THORNLEY 26	
X	X	X	X	X	X	X	X	X	X	X	S	S	S	U	U																	1
X	X	X	X	X	X	X	X	X	X	X	S	S	U	U	S																	2
X	X	X	X	X	X	X	X	U	X	X	X	S	U		S	S																3
X	X	X	X	X		X	X	S	X	X	U	X	S	U	S	X																4
X		X	X	X	S	X	X	X	S	S	U	X		U	X	X	X															5
X	U	X	X	X	U	X	S	X	X	S	S	X			X	X	X															6
X	X	X	X		U	X	X		X	X	S	X	S	U		X	X	S														7
X	X	X	X		S	X	X	S	X	X	U	X	U			X	X	S														8
X	X	X	X	U	U	X	X		X	S	X	X			S	X	X	S														9
X	X	S	X	S	U	X	X	X		U	X	X	X		S	X			X													10
X	X	X	X	X	U	X	X	S			X	X	S	U	X	S			X													11
X	X	X	X	X	U	X	X	U	S	S	X	X			X	S			X													12
X	X	X	X	X	U	X	X	U		S	X	X	S		X	S			X													13
X	X	X	X	X	U	X	X	S	U	S	X	X	S		X				X													14
X	X	X	X	X	U	X	X	U		S	X	X	S		X	S			X													15
		X	**X**	**X**	**U**	**X**	**X**	**U**		**S**	**X**	**X**	**S**	**X**	**X**	**S**			**X**	**X**												16
X	X	X	X	X		X	X			S	X	X	U	U	X	S			X	S												17
X	**X**	**X**	**X**	**X**			**X**	**S**		**X**	**X**	**X**		**U**	**S**	**X**			**X**		**U**											18
X	X	X	X	X		X	X	S		S	X	X		S	X	U			X	U												19
	X	**S**	**X**	**X**		**X**	**X**	**X**		**X**		**S**		**X**	**U**	**X**			**X**	**X**		**S**	**U**									20
U	**X**	**X**	**X**	**X**		**X**	**X**	**S**		**S**	**S**	**X**		**X**	**X**	**X**			**X**				**U**	**U**	**U**							21
U		X	X	X		X	X	S		X	S	X		X	X	S			X				U	X								22
U	**S**	**X**	**X**	**X**		**X**	**X**	**S**		**X**	**S**	**X**	**U**	**X**	**X**	**X**			**U**				**U**	**X**								23
U	S	X	X	X		X	X	U		X	S	X		X	X	S			X					X								24
U	U	X	X	X		X	X	S		X	S	X		X	X	S			X					X								25
U	X	X	X	X		U	X	S		S	X	X	S	X	X	X								X								26
X	X	X	X	X		U	X	X		X	U	X	S	U	S	X								X								27
X	**X**	**X**	**X**	**X**			**X**	**X**		**X**	**S**	**X**	**S**	**U**	**S**	**X**						**U**		**X**								28
X	U	X	X	X			X	X		S	S	X	S	U	X	X			X					X								29
X	U	X	X	X			X	S		X	S	X	S	U	X	X			X					X								30
X	X	X	X	X			S	S		X	S	X	U	U	X	X			X					X								31
X	X	X	X	X		S	X	U	S	X		X	S		X	X			X					U								32
X	X	X	X	X		X	X	U	S	X			S	U		X			X					X		S						33
X	U	X	X	X		X			X	X		X	X	U		S			X					X		S	S					34
X	X	X	X	X		X			U	X		U	S	U	X	S								X		X	X					35
X	X	X	X	X		X			U	S		X	U		S	X			X					X		S	X					36
	U	X	X	X		X	X			X		X	S		X	S			X					X	X		U	S				37
X		X	X	X		X	X		U	X		X	S		X	S			X					X	U			S				38
X	U	X	X	X		X	X	S		X		X	U		X	S			X					X				U				39
X	U	X	X	X		X	X	U		X		X	S		X	S			X					X				S				40
X	U	X	X	X		X	X			X		X	S		X	S			X					X	U			S				41
X	S	X	U	X		X	X	S		X		X	X			S			X					X	U			X				42
X	S	X	X	X		X	X	S		X		X	U			X			X					X	U			U				43
X	X	X	X	X		X	X			X		X	U			S			X			U			U			X	S			44
X	X	X	X	X		U	X		U	X		X	S		U	X			X										X	U		45
X	X	X	X	X		U	X		U	X		X	X		U	S			X									X	S			46
X	X	X	S	X			X			X			S			X			X			U		X	U			X	X		S	47
X	X	X	X	X		X	X		S	S			U						X					X	U			X	X		S	48
X	X	X	U	X		X	X		S	X		X	S											X	U			X	X		S	49
X	X	X	U	X			X		S	X		X	S			S			X					X	U			X	X			50
U	X	X	U	X			X		S	X		X	S			S			X					X	X			X	X			51
X	S	U	X	X		X	X		X	X		X	S			X			X						U			X	S			52
Total League Appearances																																
40	30	44	41	42	3	35	41	7	10	31	11	39	4	4	23	19	5	0	33	0	0	0	0	24	2	1	2	9	6	0	0	X
0	4	1	1	1	2	1	2	13	8	13	10	3	24	1	7	21	0	3	0	1	0	0	0	0	0	3	1	4	3	0	3	S
5	9	1	4	1	9	4	0	8	6	1	4	1	10	14	3	1	0	0	0	1	0	2	1	1	10	0	1	2	0	1	0	U
Total Cup Appearances																																
2	4	5	6	6	0	4	6	2	0	4	2	5	0	4	3	5	0	0	4	2	0	0	0	2	0	0	0	0	0	0	0	X
0	1	1	0	0	0	0	0	3	0	2	3	1	2	0	2	1	0	0	0	0	0	1	0	0	0	0	0	0	0	0	0	S
2	0	0	0	0	1	0	0	1	0	0	0	0	1	2	1	0	0	0	1	0	1	1	3	1	1	0	0	0	0	0	0	U

ALTRINCHAM

CURRENT SQUAD AS OF BEGINING OF 2009-10 SEASON

GOALKEEPERS		SQ NO.	HT	WT	D.O.B	AGE	P.O.B	CAREER	APPS	GOA
Richard	Acton	23	6'02"	14 00	16/10/79	29	Manchester	Man City Rel 98, Woodley Sports, Runcorn c/s 99, Hyde 3/01, Altrincham 9/02, TNS 3/04, Altrincham c/s 04, Woodley Sports (Dual) 8/04, Bangor C 9/04, Altrincham 2/05, Woodley Sports (Cover) 2/05, TNS 7/05, Altrincham c/s 05 Rel c/s 08, Altrincham 11/08	2	0
Stuart	Coburn	1	6'01"	14 00	5/5/75	33	Manchester	Maine Road, Irlam, Trafford 94/95, Altrincham 3/97, Leigh RMI 5/02, Altrincham 10/03	40	0
Russell	Saunders	13	6'02"	12 06	3/1/89	20	Bury	Wigan Rel 5/08, Altrincham (L) 9/07, Gainsborough (L) 3/08, Stalybridge 7/08, Ashton U 1/09, Altrincham 7/09		

DEFENDERS										
Matt	Doughty	3	5'11"	11 00	2/11/81	27	Warrington	Chester, Rochdale 7/01 Rel 5/04, Halifax 5/04, Altrincham 6/08	43	2
Danny	Heffernan	20	6'02"	11 08			Bolton	Fletcher Moss, Altrincham Reserves, Abbey Hey, Altrincham (Dual) 11/08, Ashton U 3/09, Altrincham (Dual) c/s 09	0	0
James	Smith	2	5'10"	11 08	17/10/85	23	Liverpool	Everton (Sch), Liverpool, Ross County (3ML) 1/07, Stockport (3ML) 8/07 Stockport 1/08, Altrincham (Trial) 9/08, Vauxhall Motors 10/08, Altrincham 11/08	24	0
Michael	Welch	18	6'03"	11 12	11/1/82	27	Crewe	Barnsley (Scholar), Macclesfield 8/01, Accrington 8/05 Rel 5/07, Northwich 7/07, Altrincham (2ML) 2/09, Altrincham c/s 09	13	3
Robbie	Williams	12	6'05"		6/7/87	22	Blackpool	TNS/The New Saints Rel c/s 09, Newtown (3ML) 11/06, Caersws (4ML) 9/08, Altrincham 7/09		
Greg	Young	5	6'02"	12 03	24/4/83	26	Doncaster	Sheff Wed (Scholar), Shrewsbury (Trial) 3/02, Grimsby 7/02, Northwich (L) 10/04, Northwich (L) 12/04, Halifax 2/05, Northwich (L) 11/06, Alfreton (L) 8/07, Altrincham 1/08	45	2

MIDFIELDERS										
Nicky	Clee	11			30/8/83	26	Huddersfield	Local, Ossett A 12/02, Ashton U 8/04, Hyde U 6/05, Altrincham 7/09		
Matthew	Crowell	8	5'09"	10 10	3/7/84	25	Bridgend	Southampton, Bristol C (Trial) 3/03, Wrexham 7/03 Rel 12/07, Northwich 1/08, Central Coast Mariners (Trial) 5/09, Altrincham 7/09		
Anthony	Danlyk	16	5'08"	11 08	1/2/83	26	Stoke	Stoke (Jun), Stone Dominoes, Leek T 3/02, Belper 8/04, Leek T 6/05, Witton 5/07, Leek T 9/07, Altrincham 6/08	42	0
Shaun	Densmore	6	6'03"	14 09	11/11/88	20	Liverpool	Everton Rel c/s 08, Bradford C (Trial) 7/08, Altrincham 9/08	33	4
Tom	Kearney	4	5'09"	10 12	7/10/81	27	Liverpool	Everton, Bradford C 3/02 Rel 5/06, Halifax c/s 06, Wrexham 6/08 Rel 7/09, Altrincham 7/09		
Robbie	Lawton	7	6'00"	11 08	14/6/79	29	Liverpool	Marine, Vauxhall Motors, Caernarfon, Vauxhall Motors 7/99, Altrincham 6/0636		1

FORWARDS										
Chris	Denham	10	6'00"	12 11	14/9/82	26	Manchester	Prestwich Heys, Stand Ath c/s 01, Bamber Bridge (2ML) 10/01, Stalybridge 8/02, Radcliffe 7/03, Stalybridge 12/03, Droylsden 6/05, Ashton U 8/05, Droylsden 10/05, Altrincham 6/08, Stalybridge (L) 3/09	18	2
Dale	Johnson	14	6'00"	11 08	3/5/85	24	Ashton	Woodley Sports, Hyde U 2/04, Droylsden (6WL) 3/08, Altrincham 6/08	44	4
Colin	Little	9	5'10"	11 00	4/11/72	36	Wythenshawe	Rossendale, Hyde c/s 94, Crewe £50,000 2/96 Rel c/s 03, Mansfield (2ML) 10/02, Macclesfield (L) 12/02, Macclesfield (L) 3/03, Macclesfield 5/03 Rel 3/04, Halifax 3/04, Altrincham 7/04	43	16
Chris	Senior	19	5'06"	9 01	18/11/81	27	Huddersfield	Huddersfield, Wakefield-Emley 7/02, Scarborough 8/03 OOC 5/05, Halifax 8/05 Rel 5/07, Altrincham (SL) 1/07, Altrincham 7/07	30	7

LOANEES		HT	WT	DOB	AGE	POB	From - To	APPS	GOA
(D)Luke	Waterfall	6'02"	12 11	30/7/90	19	Sheffield	Tranmere 10/08 - Rel 6/09, Oxford U (Trial) 7/09, Ilkeston 8/09	1	0
(M)Jordan	Hadfield	5'10"	11 04	12/8/87	22	Swinton	Macclesfield 1/09 - Rel 5/09	4	0
(F)Jody	Banim	5'09"	13 01	1/4/78	31	Manchester	Burton 1/09 - Droylsden (SL) 3/09, Rel 4/09, Salford C 7/09	3	1
(M)Ben	Wilkinson	5'11"	12 01	25/4/87	22	Sheffield	York C (SL) 3/09 - Rel 7/09, Chester 7/09	9	0
(F)Ben	Deegan			13/7/88	21		Ashton U (Dual) 3/09 - FCUM 5/09		
(D)Alex	Frost			18/9/85	23		Ashton U (Dual) 3/09		
(F)Pat	McFadden			4/4/87	22		Ashton U (Dual) 3/09	0	0
(F)Rod	Thornley			2/4/77	32	Bury	Ashton U (Dual) 3/09	3	0

DEPARTURES		HT	WT	DOB	AGE	POB	From - To	APPS	GOA
(F)Tom	Bailey			19/8/90	19		Yth - Curzon Ashton, Glossop NE		
(D)Paul	Tierney	5'10"	12 11	15/9/82	26	Salford	Blackpool 9/08 - Rel 9/08	3	0
(D)Richard	Battersby	5'08"	10 03	13/6/79	30	York	Northwich 1/08 - Rel 9/08, Radcliffe B 10/08, Stalybridge 10/08, Salford C (L) 3/09, New Mills (L) 3/09	5	0
(D)Danny	Browne			6/2/90	19		Yth - Woodley Sports 10/08		
(M)Val	Owen	5'11"	11 08	11/2/71	38	Manchester	ex Halifax 10/04 Rel 12/08, Witton (L) 10/08	0	0
(M)Lee	Elam	5'08"	10 12	24/9/76	32	Bradford	Exeter 7/08 - Rel 1/09, Northwich 1/09	21	0
(G)Andy	Ralph	6'01"	14 01	25/5/83	26	Manchester	Marine 7/08 - Abbey Hey (L) 9/08, Trafford (Dual) 1/09, Redland City Devils (Aust) 2/09	5	0
(F)Alex	Meechan	5'08"	10 10	29/1/80	29	Plymouth	Stalybridge 6/08 - Rel 3/09, Stalybridge (L) 1/09, Stalybridge 3/09, Droylsden 7/09	20	2
(M)Warren	Peyton	5'09"	11 03	13/12/79	29	Manchester	ex Leigh RMI 11/05 - Rel 5/09, Stalybridge 6/09	40	1
(F)Joe	O'Neill	6'00"	10 05	28/10/82	26	Blackburn	York 6/06 - Rel 5/09, Stalybridge 6/09	28	3
(D)Chris	Lane	6'00"	12 10	24/5/79	30	Liverpool	Southport 6/07 - Rel 5/09, Vauxhall Motors 7/09	34	0
(M)Kevin	Street	5'10"	10 08	25/11/77	31	Crewe	Stafford R 5/08 - Nantwich (Ass Man) 7/09	5	0
(D)Mark	McGregor	5'11"	11 05	16/2/77	32	Ellesmere Port	Port Vale 7/08 - Rel 7/09, GAP Connahs Quay (Pl/Man) 7/09	42	1
(M)Joel	Brownhill						Yth -	0	0

ALTRINCHAM

Founded: 1903

Nickname: The Robins.

Club Colours: Red/white striped shirts, black shorts, red socks.

Change Colours: Yellow/royal blue shirts, royal blue shorts, yellow socks.

Club Sponsor: Go Goodwins Coaches

Previous League: Conference North

Ground Address: Moss Lane, Altrincham,Cheshire WA15 8AP
Tel No: 0161 928 1045
Fax: 0161 926 9934
General email address: office@altrinchamfootballclub.co.uk
Official website: www.altrinchamfc.com

SIMPLE DIRECTIONS
By Road From M6 junction19, turn right towards Altrincham into town centre (approx 15 minutes). Turn down Lloyd Street, past Sainsburys on the right. Tesco Extra on left. Then follow signs for Altrincham F.C.
Parking: Carpark adjoining ground.

MATCH TICKETS
Ticket office Telephone: 0161 928 1045
Ticket Prices: Standing - Adults £12; Concessions £7
Seating - Adults £14; Concessions £8
Aged 12 to 16 seated or standing - £5
Under 12s seated or standing - £2
Season Ticket Prices: Standing - Adults £209; Concessionaries £99
Seating - Adults £249; Concessionaries £109
Aged 12 to 16 seated or standing - £50
Under 12s seated or standing - £25
Capacity: 6,085
Seats: 1,154
Covered: Three sides
Clubhouse: Bar under the stand open on matchdays only.
Refreshments: Two snack bars on the ground
Club Shop: Yes.

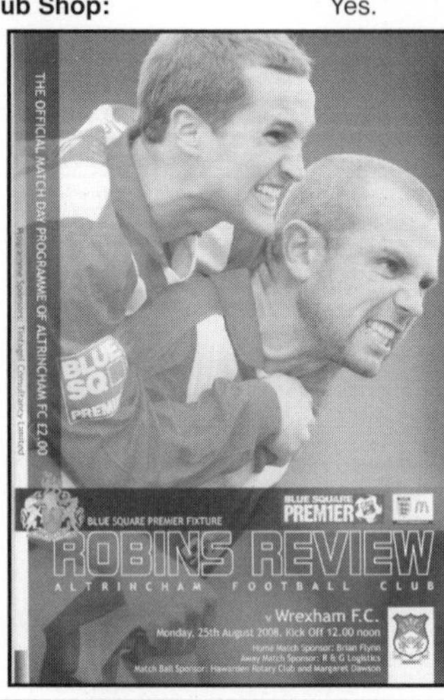

PROGRAMME EDITOR
Grahame Rowley
Telephone: Home: 0161 9801741
Mobile: 07720 606897
E-mail: altrinchamprog@yahoo.co.uk

CLUB STATISTICS

RECORDS

Attendance: 10,275 Altrincham Boys v Sunderland Boys English Schools Shield 1925

Victory (Lge): 9-2 v Merthyr Tydfil Conference 1990-1991

Defeat: 1-13 v Stretford (H) - 04.11.1893.

Career Goalscorer: Jack Swindells 252 1965-71

Career Appearances: John Davison 677 1071-86

Transfer Fee Paid: £15,000 to Blackpool for Keith Russell

Transfer Fee Received:
£50,000 for Kevin Ellison from Leicester City (Feb. 2001).

SENIOR HONOURS

F.A.Trophy Winners 77-78 85-86
Football Alliance Champions 79-80 80-81
Condference North v South Play Off Winners 2004-05
Northern Premier League Champions 98-99
Cheshire Senior Cup Winners 04-05 33-34 66-67 81-82

PREVIOUS

Leagues: Manchester 03-11, Lancashire Comb.11-19, Cheshire County 19-68, N.P.L. 68-79 97-99 Conference 79-97 99-00 Conference North 2004-2005

Grounds: Pollitts Field 1903-1910

BARROW

BackRow (L-R): Barry Postlethwaite (Kit Man); Lee Woodyatt; Carlos Rogan; Lee Hunt; Paul Tait; Tim Deasy; Aaran Walker; Paul Jones; Andy Bond; Steve McNulty; Liam Enright (Physio); Les Potter (Asst Physio)
Front Row; Jason Walker; Ryan Elderton; Nick Rogan; Mark Boyd; Ashley Winn; Dave Bayliss (Joint Mgr); Brian Keen (Chairman); Darren Sheridan (Joint Mgr); Matt Henney; Mike Pearson; Paul Brown; Chris Thompson.

CLUB PERSONNEL

Chairman: Brian Keen.

Vice Chairman: N McDonald.

Company Secretary: D Ingham.

Directors: T Keen, K Allen, N Chalker, R Dodd, M Duffy, I Laird, D Ryder.

Secretary: Russell Dodd.
9 Keswick Avenue, Barrow -in- Furness, Cumbria LA14 4LL
(H) 01229 827 286
(M) 07789 757 639

Commercial Manager: Martin Lewis
(M): 07780 003 839
(B): 01229 823 061

Press Officer: Bob Herbert
(B): 01229 829 133

Managers: Dave Bayliss & Darren Sheridan.
Club therapist: Liam Enright.

A crowd of 2,790 for their first home fixture back in the top level of Non-league football showed how the Cumbrians' promotion had been appreciated by the local football public. A wonderful 3-0 victory over much fancied Oxford United certainly raised expectations for the campaign ahead.

After eight games Barrow were nicely placed in fifth position but perhaps the opposition were beginning to appreciate the strengths and weaknesses of the side brought together by Darren Sheridan and Dave Bayliss. By the new year 'The Bluebirds' had sunk to 20th place in the table but had enjoyed wonderful experiences in the F.A.Cup.

Two 4-0 victories over Tamworth, and Eastbourne Borough in a replay, were rewarded by a home tie against high flying Division Two club Brentford. A memorable 2-1 victory in front of 3,535 then brought an exciting trip to Middlesbrough and a creditable performance which resulted in a 2-1 defeat and another goal for Jason Walker which meant he had scored in six of his club's last seven games.

With the excitement of the F.A.Cup over, the F.A.Trophy was an anti climax bringing a 0-3 home defeat in the very next game and then the battle for survival really began in earnest. Walker, with three singles, was the only scorer in the next ten league games and Barrow found themselves in 22nd position. The battle was on, but just one defeat and six draws in the last ten games ensured another season in The Blue Square Premier and a very satisfying campaign had been thoroughly enjoyed.

BARROW

BEST LGE ATT.: 2,790 v Oxford United
LOWEST: 965 v Histon

No.	Date	Comp	H/A	Opponents	Att:	Result	Goalscorers	Pos
1	Aug 9	BSP	H	Oxford United	2790	W 3 - 0	Boyd 71 McNulty 76 (pen) P.Brown 82	
2	12		A	Altrincham	1312	W 4 - 3	Walker 21 74 Logan 54 P.Brown 80	
3	16		A	Cambridge United	2663	L 1 - 2	Tait 36	6
4	23		H	Mansfield Town	2063	W 2 - 1	O'Hare 44 (og) Walker 88	3
5	25		A	York City	2664	D 1 - 1	Hunt 10	3
6	30		H	Stevenage Borough	1764	L 1 - 3	McNulty 12 (pen)	10
7	Sept 2		H	Rushden & Diamonds	1663	D 1 - 1	P.Brown 90	
8	6		A	Lewes	679	W 3 - 0	P.Brown 39 McNulty 45 (pen) Rogan 71	5
9	13		A	Salisbury City	1116	L 0 - 3		10
10	20		H	Kettering Town	1596	L 2 - 4	Henney 65 Tait 75	13
11	23		A	Northwich Victoria	906	L 1 - 2	Henney 2	
12	27		A	Ebbsfleet United	1378	L 0 - 3		16
13	Oct 4		A	Kidderminster Harriers	1686	W 1 - 0	Boyd 5	16
14	7		H	Burton Albion	1466	D 0 - 0		
15	11		A	Crawley Town	1601	L 0 - 4		16
16	**14**	**SS N2**	**H**	**Fleetwood Town**	**618**	**W 3 - 2**	**Walker 3 (10, pen 26, pen 37)**	
17	18		H	Eastbourne Borough	1206	W 3 - 1	D.Brown 4 Logan 31 Henney 90	15
18	**25**	**F.A.C. 4Q**	**A**	**Tamworth**	**1012**	**W 4 - 0**	**McNulty 39 Brodie 46 82 D.Brown 59 (pen)**	
19	Nov 1		H	Forest Green Rovers	1440	W 3 - 1	D.Brown 2 (pen) Henney 63 Walker 88	11
20	**4**	**SS N3**	**H**	**Gateshead**	**551**	**W 3 - 1***	**Brodie 41, Tait 110, Walker 120**	
21	**8**	**F.A.C. 1R**	**A**	**Eastbourne Borough**	**1216**	**D 0 - 0**		
22	15		A	Ebbsfleet United	1187	L 0 - 1		13
23	**18**	**F.A.C. 1R r**	**H**	**Eastbourne Borough**	**2031**	**W 4 - 0**	**Brodie 45 P.Brown 47 Henney 57 Logan 76**	
24	22		H	Weymouth	1350	L 0 - 1		15
25	**28**	**F.A.C. 2R**	**H**	**Brentford**	**3535**	**W 2 - 1**	**D.Brown 39 (pen) Henney 71**	
26	Dec 6		A	Rushden & Diamonds	1120	D 1 - 1	Walker 11	16
27	9		H	Altrincham	976	D 2 - 2	Walker 9 Jones 69	
28	**13**	**F.A.T 1st Rd**	**H**	**Skelmersdale United**	**743**	**W 2 - 1**	**Walker 34 Joyce 62**	
29	20		A	Grays Athletic	502	L 1 - 2	Walker 26	
30	26		H	Wrexham	1250	D 1 - 1	Walker 30	19
31	28		A	Forest Green Rovers	747	L 1 - 2	D.Brown 45	19
32	**Jan 3**	**F.A.C. 3R**	**A**	**Middlesbrough**	**25132**	**L 1 - 2**	**Walker 60**	
33	**13**	**F.A.T 2R**	**H**	**Workington**	**1614**	**L 0 - 3**		
34	17		A	Stevenage Borough	2205	L 0 - 3		20
35	**20**	**SS N4**	**H**	**York City**	**596**	**W 3 - 1**	**Curtis 2 (24, 83), P Brown 40**	
36	24		H	Kidderminster Harriers	1532	W 1 - 0	Walker 87	
37	26		A	Burton Albion	1939	L 1 - 2	Walker 70	
38	31		H	Salisbury City	1613	D 0 - 0		19
39	**Feb 3**	**SS QFN**	**H**	**Southport**	**678**	**W 3 - 1**	**Bond 52, Rogan pen 66, McGill 83**	
40	14		A	Oxford United	4532	L 0 - 3		19
41	21		H	Grays Athletic	1515	D 1 - 1	Walker 59	21
42	24		A	Histon	541	L 0 - 2		
43	28		H	Northwich Victoria	1437	D 0 - 0		21
44	Mar 7		A	Woking	1529	L 0 - 1		22
45	10		H	Histon	965	W 1 - 0	Boyd 88	20
46	14		A	Torquay United	2269	L 1 - 4	P.Brown 12	21
47	17		H	Cambridge United	1341	L 0 - 2		
48	21		H	Lewes	1390	W 2 - 0	McEvilly 7 Hunt 64	18
49	**26**	**SS SFN**	**H**	**AFC Telford**	**2109**	**L 0 - 1**		
50	29		A	Weymouth	1264	W 3 - 0	Boyd 51 Jones 54 61	17
51	April 2		A	Wrexham	2272	D 1 - 1	Rogan 90	
52	4		H	Woking	1424	L 0 - 1		18
53	7		A	Kettering Town	976	D 0 - 0		
54	11		A	Mansfield Town	2122	D 2 - 2	Bond 52 (pen) Rogan 90	19
55	13		H	York City	2168	D 0 - 0		
56	18		H	Crawley Town	1456	D 3 - 3	Rogan 53 90 McNulty65	18
57	21		H	Torquay United	1918	D 1 - 1	Walker 12	
58	26		A	Eastbourne Borough	1584	W 2 - 0	Boyd 70 Bond 87	20

Average Home Att: 1552 (1084) **Goals 76 77**

Best Position: 3rd **Worst:** 22nd

Golascorers: Walker 18, Brown P 8, Henney 6, Brown D 5, Boyd 5, McNulty 5, Rogan 5, Brodie 4, Bond 3, Jones 3, Logan 3, Tait 3, Curtis 2, Hunt 2, Joyce 1, McEvilly 1, McGill 1. Own Goals 1.

DEASY 1	BOYD 8	MCNULTY 5	JONES 4	HENNEY 6	PEARSON 18	BOND 7	LOGAN 20	ELDERTON 3	HUNT 17	WALKER 9	TAIT 12	P BROWN 11	TAYLOR 21	BAYLISS 16	SHERIDAN 14	ROGAN 10	BLACK 22	A WINN 19	JAMES 3	MARTIN 21	D BROWN 23	KERR 3	BRODIE 24	THOMPSON 15	GAY 25	JOYCE 25	CURTIS 24	HOLNESS 27	SHARRY 26	MCGILL 25	HORNE 19	STEELE 24	P WINN 19	SPENDER 26	WOODYATT 2	MCEVILLY 29	JELLEYMAN 19	
X	X	X	X	X	X	X	X	X	X	X	S	S	U	U	U																							1
X	X	X	X	X	X	X	X	X	X	X	S	S	U	U	U																							2
X	X	X	X	X	X	X	X	X	X		X	S	U	U	U	S																						3
X	X	X	X	X		X	X		X	X		S	U	U	U	S	X	X																				4
X	X	X	X	X	U	X	X		X	X		U	U		U	S	X	X																				5
X	X	X	X	X	S	X	X		X	X	S	U	U			S	X	X																				6
X	X	X	X	X	X	X	X		X	X	S	X		U	U	S		S																				7
X	X	X	X	X	X	X	X		X	X	S	X			U	S		S	U																			8
X	X	X	X	X	X	X	X		S	X	S	X			U	X		S	U																			9
X	X	X	X	X	X	X	X		U	X	S	X			U	X	S	S																				10
	X	X	X	X	X	X	X		X	S	S	U			U	X	X	U		X																		11
	X	X	X	X	X	X	X		U	X	X	S			U	S	X	S		X																		12
	X	X	X	X	X	X	X		X		S	U			U	S	U	X		X	X																	13
	X	X	X	X	X	X	X		X	S	S	U			U		U	X		X	X																	14
	X	X	X	X	X	X	X		X	S	U	U			U		S	X		X	X																	15
X	S		X	X	X	X	X		U	X	S	X			X	X		U			S	X																16
	X	X	X	X	X	X	X		S	X	S	S			U			U		X	X	X																17
U	X	X	X	X	X	X	X		U	S	S	S		U	U			X		X	X		X															18
	X	X		X	X	X	X		U	S	S	X			U			X		X	X	S	X															19
	X	X		U	X	X	X		S	X	S	X		U				X		X	X	S	X															20
U	X	X	S	X	X	X	X		U	S	S	X		U	U			X		X	X		X															21
S		X	X	X	X		X			S	X	U			X			X		X	X	U	X	U														22
X	X	X	X	X	X	U	X			S	S	X		U	U			X			X		X		U													23
X	X	X	X	X	X		X			S	S	X			U			X			X	S	X	U														24
U	X	X	X	X	X		X			X	S	X		U	U	U		U		X	X			U		X												25
U	X	X	X	X	X		X			X	S	X			U	S				X	X	U				X												26
	X	X	X	X	X		X			X	S	X			U	S				X	X	S		U		X												27
U	X	X	X	X	X	U	X			X	X	S			U	S				X		X				X												28
	X	X	X	X	X	S	X		S	X	X	X				U				X	U	S				X												29
	X	X	X		X	S	X		U	X	S	X			U	U				X	X	X				X												30
U	X	X	X		X	S	X			X	U	X			U	S				X	X	X				X												31
U	X	X	X	X	X	S	X			X	U	X		U	U	U				X	X					X	S											32
		X	U	X		X	X			X	S	S			U	S				X		X					X	X	X	X								33
X	X	X	X	X		X	X			X	U	S				S		X				S					X	X		U								34
X	X		X	X			X			X	U	X		S	X	S						X					X	X	U	S								35
U	X	U	X	X			X			X	U	X				S				X		X					X	X	X	S								36
U	X	U	X				X			X	X	X		U		S				X		X		S				X	X	X								37
X	X	U	X	U		S	X			X	U	X			U	X						X						X	X	X								38
U		S	X			X	X				X	X		U	U	X				X		X			U			X	X	X								39
U		U	X	X		X				X	S			U	U	X				X		X						X	X	X	X							40
U		U	X	S		X	X			X	S	X			X	S				X		X						X		X		X						41
	U	S	X	X		X	X			X	U	X			X	S				X		X						X		U		X						42
	X	X	X	X		U	X			X	S	U			X	X				X		X						S		U			X					43
	X		X	X		S	X			X	X	U			X	S				X		X						X		U		S	X					44
X	X		X	U		X	X		X	X		X		U	U							U						X		X		U		X				45
X	X		X			X	X		X	X		X		U	U							S						X		X		S		X	U			46
X	X		X	U		X	X		X			X		U	U							U						X		X		X		X	U			47
X	X	X	X	U		X	X		X			S				S						U								X		S	X	X		X		48
X	X	X		U		X	X		X		U	S				S						U						X		X		X		X			X	49
X	X	X	X			X	X		U			S				S						U						U		X		X		X		X	X	50
X	X	X	X			X	X		X	X		S			U	S						X								X		U			U		X	51
X		X	X			X	X		S	X	U	S			X	X						S								X		U		X			X	52
X		X	X			X	U		U	X		X			X	U				U		U								X				X		X	X	53
X		X	X			X	S		S	X		X			X	S				U		U								X				X		X	X	54
X	X	X	X			X	X		S	X		S				S				U		U								X				X		X	X	55
X	X	X	X			X	X		S	X		S				S				U		U								X				X		X	X	56
X	X	X	X			X	X		S	X		U				X				U		U								X				X		U	X	57
X	X	X		S		X	X		X	X		U				S				S		U								X				X	X		X	58
Total League Appearances																																						
26	39	36	44	28	21	34	43	3	18	35	6	21	0	0	8	8	5	10	0	20	11	12	3	0	0	5	2	11	4	17	1	4	3	12	1	6	9	X
1	0	1	0	2	1	5	1	0	8	6	19	13	0	0	0	24	2	5	0	1	0	7	0	1	0	0	0	1	0	1	0	3	0	0	0	0	0	S
6	1	5	0	4	1	1	1	0	6	0	7	11	6	10	27	3	2	2	2	5	1	12	0	3	0	0	0	1	0	4	0	3	0	0	3	1	0	U
Total Cup Appearances																																						
4	9	9	8	9	8	7	12	0	1	7	2	8	0	0	2	2	0	4	0	8	6	5	4	0	0	3	2	4	2	3	0	1	0	1	0	0	1	X
0	1	1	1	0	0	1	0	0	1	3	7	4	0	1	0	4	0	0	0	0	1	1	0	0	0	0	1	0	0	1	0	0	0	0	0	0	0	S
6	0	0	1	2	0	2	0	0	3	0	3	0	0	7	8	2	0	2	0	0	0	1	0	1	2	0	0	0	1	0	0	0	0	0	0	0	0	U

BARROW

CURRENT SQUAD AS OF BEGINING OF 2009-10 SEASON

GOALKEEPERS		SQ NO.	HT	WT	D.O.B	AGE	P.O.B	CAREER	APPS	GOA
Tim	Deasy	1	6'01"	13 05	1/10/85	23	Salford	Macclesfield Rel c/s 06, Stockport Rel c/s 07, Barrow 8/07	27	0
Stuart	Tomlinson	21	6'01"	14 07	10/5/85	24	Ellesmere Port	Crewe Rel c/s 09, Stafford R (L) 12/04, Stafford R (L) 2/05, Burton (L) 7/06, Burton (L) 2/08, Port Vale (Trial) 7/09, Barrow 8/09		
DEFENDERS										
Dave	Bayliss	16	6'00"	12 11	8/6/76	33	Liverpool	Rochdale, Luton 12/01 Rel c/s 05, Chester (2ML) 12/04, Bristol R (Trial) 4/05, Oxford U (Trial) 5/05, Wrexham 7/05 Rel c/s 06, Rochdale (L) 2/06, Lancaster 7/06, Barrow 11/06 Joint Man	0	0
Phil	Bolland	5	6'02"	13 08	26/8/76	33	Liverpool	Altrincham, Salford C 10/95, Trafford 3/96, Knowsley U 8/96, Southport c/s 97, Oxford U 7/01, Chester (2ML) 1/02 £15,000 3/02, Peterborough 1/06 Rel c/s 06, Chester 6/06, Wrexham 1/08, Cambridge U 7/08 Rel 6/09, Barrow 7/09		
Adam	Dugdale	17	6'03"	12 07	12/9/87	21	Liverpool	Liverpool (Jun), Crewe Rel c/s 07, Accrington (L) 11/06, Southport (2ML) 1/07, Clyde (Trial), Livingston (Trial), Southport 10/07, Droylsden 1/08, Royal Racing Football Club Montegnee (Bel) 2/09, Barrow 7/09		
Paul	Jones	4	6'01"	11 09	3/6/78	31	Liverpool	Tranmere Rel c/s 97, Blackpool (L) 2/97, Barrow 8/97, Leigh RMI 8/99, Oldham 11/99 Rel c/s 02, Colwyn Bay 8/02 Rel 8/02, Hyde 3/03, Barrow 6/06	44	3
Phil	Morris	18						Barrow, Holker Old Boys (Dual)		
Sean	Newton	3	6'02"	13 00	23/9/88	20	Liverpool	Chester, Southport (3ML) 8/07, Droylsden (SL) 2/08, Droylsden 8/08, Barrow 7/09		
Simon	Spender	2	5'11"	11 00	15/11/85	23	Mold	Wrexham Rel 4/09, Barrow (SL) 3/09, Barrow 5/09	12	0
MIDFIELDERS										
Andrew	Bond	7	5'10"	11 06	16/3/86	23	Wigan	Crewe Rel c/s 06, Lancaster (SL) 8/05, Barrow 7/06	39	2
Marc	Boyd	8	5'10"	12 04	22/10/81	27	Carlisle	Newcastle Rel c/s 02, Carlisle (Trial) 3/02, Port Vale 7/02, Carlisle 3/04 Rel c/s 04, Gretna 7/04 Rel 1/06, Macclesfield (SL) 1/05, Accrington 2/06, Southport 6/06, Sligo R c/s 07, Barrow 1/08	39	5
Robin	Hulbert	6	5'10"	12 02	14/3/80	29	Plymouth	Swindon, Newcastle (SL) 2/98, Bristol C £25,000 3/00, Shrewsbury (SL) 3/03, Telford 11/03, Port Vale 7/04 Rel c/s 08, Darlington 8/08 Rel c/s 09, Barrow 6/09		
Carlos	Logan	11	5'07"	11 00	7/11/85	23	Wythenshawe	Man City Rel c/s 05, Chesterfield (SL) 3/05, Darlington 8/05 Rel c/s 07, Bradford C (L) 1/07, Altrincham 8/07 Rel 2/08, Drogheda U (Trial) 2/08, Flixton 3/08, Barrow 8/07	44	2
Michael	Pearson	12	5'11"	11 01	19/1/88	21	Bangor	Liverpool (Sch), Oldham Rel c/s 08, Farsley Celtic (2ML) 10/07, Barrow 7/08	22	0
Paul	Rutherford	15	5'08"	10 11	10/7/87	22	Moreton	Liverpool (Yth), Greenleas, Chester 10/05 Rel c/s 09, Barrow 7/09, Bournemouth (Trial) 7/08		
Darren	Sheridan	14	5'05"	11 05	8/12/67	41	Manchester	Leeds U (Trainee) Rel c/s 86,Local, Maine Road, Mossley, Curzon Ashton, Winsford, Barnsley £10,000 8/93, Wigan 7/99 Rel c/s 01, Oldham 7/01 Rel c/s 04, Clyde 6/04, St Johnstone 7/05, Barrow 1/07 Joint Man	8	0
FORWARDS										
Darren	Green	10	6'00"	11 00	15/5/89	20	Preston	Stockport Rel c/s 09, Farsley Celtic (L) 3/09, Barrow 8/09		
Aaron	Taylor	19			9/3/90	19		Morecambe, Barrow (5WL) 8/09		
Jason	Walker	9	6'02"	14 04	21/3/84	25	Barrow	Dundee, Morton 7/04, Morecambe 1/07, Barrow 3/07, Doncaster (Trial) 7/09	41	12

LOANEES		SN	HT	WT	DOB	AGE	POB	From - To	APPS	GOA
(D)Paul	Black		6'00"	12 10	18/1/90	19	Middleton	Oldham (5ML) 8/08 -	7	0
(G)Alan	Martin		6'00"	11 11	1/1/89	20	Glasgow	Leeds (2ML) 9/08, 11/08, (SL) 1/09 -	21	0
(F)Richard	Brodie		6'02"	12 13	8/7/87	22	Gateshead	York C 10/08 -	3	0
(M)Luke	Joyce		5'11"	12 03	9/7/87	22	Bolton	Carlisle (6WL) 11/08 - Northwich (SL) 3/09, Rel 5/09	5	0
(F)Wayne	Curtis		6'00"	12 00	6/3/80	29	Barrow	Morecambe 1/09 -	2	0
(D)Marcus	Holness		6'00"	12 01	8/12/88	20	Oldham	Rochdale (3ML) 1/09 -	12	0
(M)Luke	Sharry				9/3/90	19	Leeds	Bradford C 1/09 -	4	0
(M)Louis	Horne			12 12	28/5/91	18	Bradford	Bradford C 2/09 -	1	0
(F)Lee	Steele		5'09"	12 05	8/12/73	35	Liverpool	Northwich (SL) 2/09 - Oxford C 6/09	7	0
(F)Peter	Winn		6'00"	11 09	19/12/88	20	Cleethorpes	Scunthorpe 2/09 -	3	0
(F)Lee	McEvilly		6'00"	13 00	15/4/82	27	Liverpool	Rochdale 3/09 - Rel 5/09, Grays 8/09	6	1
(D)Gareth	Jelleyman		5'10"	10 06	14/11/80	28	Holywell	Rushden & D (SL) 3/09 - Rel 5/09, AFC Telford 6/09	9	0

DEPARTURES		SN	HT	WT	DOB	AGE	POB	From - To	APPS	GOA
(D)Ryan	Elderton		5'10"	12 06	3/11/83	25	Morecambe	Lancaster 8/07 - Rel 8/08, Lancaster 9/08, Fleetwood 1/09	3	0
(G)Aaron	Taylor							Workington 7/08 - Rel 9/08, Penrith, Workington (Trial) 2/09, Workington 3/09	0	0
(D)Craig	James		6'00"	13 00	15/11/82	26	Middlesbrough	Livingston 9/08 - Rel 10/08, Darlington (Trial) 7/09	0	0
(F)David	Brown		5'10"	12 06	2/10/78	30	Bolton	ex Accrington 10/08 - Rel 1/09, Forest Green 1/09	11	3
(M)Ashley	Winn		5'11"	11 02	1/12/85	23	Stockton	Stalybridge 7/08 - Southport (L) 12/08, Southport 1/09	15	0
(F)Chris	Thompson		5'10"	11 12	7/2/82	27	Warrington	Scarborough 6/07 - Fleetwood (L) 9/08, Hyde U (L) 10/08, Leigh Genesis (SL) 1/09 Perm 3/09	1	0
(M)Paul	Brown		5'11"	12 00	10/9/84	24	Liverpool	Kingston City (Aus) 8/07 - Rel 5/09, Droylsden 6/09	34	5
(M)Matt	Henney		6'00"	11 08	9/8/76	33	Carlisle	Workington 6/07 - Rel 5/09, Workington 5/09	30	4
(F)Lee	Hunt		6'01"	13 01	5/6/81	28	Chester	Rhyl 5/08 - Rel 5/09, Fleetwood (L) 11/08, Droylsden (L) 1/09, Rhyl 6/09	26	2
(D)Nat	Kerr		6'00"	10 10	31/10/87	21	Manchester	Rotherham NC 10/08 - Rel 5/09, Northwich 7/09	19	0
(M)Brendon	McGill				22/3/81	28	Dublin	Bohemians (Ire) 1/09 - Rel 5/09, Drogheda 7/09	18	0
(F)Paul	Tait		6'01"	11 00	24/10/74	34	Newcastle-u-Lyme	Northwich 3/08 - Rel 5/09	25	2
(D)Lee	Woodyatt				16/7/83	26	Chester	Vauxhall Motors 6/07 - Rel 5/09, Droylsden 7/09	1	0
(F)Nick	Rogan				15/10/83	25	Blackpool	Southport 2/06 - Rel 5/09, Vauxhall Motors (L) 10/08, Fleetwood 6/09	32	5
(D)Steve	McNulty				26/9/83	25	Liverpool	Vauxhall Motors 6/07 - Fleetwood £17,000 6/09	37	4
(M)Josh	Gay							Barrow	0	0

BARROW

Founded: 1901

Nickname: Bluebirds.

Club Colours: White shirts, royal blue shorts, white socks.

Change Colours: Yellow shirts, yellow shorts, yellow socks.

Club Sponsor: Chas Kendall (Turf Accountants).

Previous League: Northern Premier League.

Ground Address: Holker Street Stadium, Wilkie Road, Barrow-in-Furness, Cumbria LA14 5UW.

Tel No: 01229 823 061

Fax No: 01229 823 061

Official website: www.barrowafc.com

SIMPLE DIRECTIONS

By Road M6 to junction 36. A590 to Barrow. Enter the town on Park Road and after two miles turn left into Wilkie Road.

MATCH TICKETS

Ticket Prices: £12 stand, £11 ground.
Concessions: £9 stand, £8 ground.
£4 under 16's (with pass).

Capacity: 4,500

Seats: 1,000

Covered: 2,200

Clubhouse: Yes.

Club Shop: Yes.

No image available

PROGRAMME EDITOR

Programme Editor: Bob Herbert

Tel: 01229 829 133

E-mail: robertbobherb@aol.com

CLUB STATISTICS

RECORDS

Attendance: 16,854 v Swansea Town F.A. Cup 3rd Rd 1954.

Victory (Lge): 12-0 v Cleator F.A. Cup 1920.

Defeat: 1-10 v Hartlepool Utd. Football League Div 4 1959.

Career Goalscorer: Colin Cowperthwaite 282 Dec.1977 - December 1992.

Career Appearances: Colin Cowperthwaite 704.

Transfer Fee Paid:
£9,000 to Ashton United for Andy Whittaker. July 94.

Transfer Fee Received:
£40,000 from Barnet for Kenny Lowe. Jan. 91.

SENIOR HONOURS

F.A. Trophy Winners 89-90.
Northern Premier League 1997-8, 88-89, 83-84.
Lancs Senior Cup 1954-55.
Lancs Challenge Trophy 1980-81.

PREVIOUS

Leagues: Lancs Comb 01-21 Football Lg. 21-72
N.P.L. 72-79, 83-84, 86-89, 92-98, 99-04.
Conference: 79-83, 84-86, 89-92, 98-99.

Grounds: Strawberry & Little Park,Roose.

CAMBRIDGE UNITED

Back Row (L-R): Anthony Tonkin, Dan Gleeson, Wayne Hatswell, Jai Reason, Mark Beesley, Chris Holroyd.
Middle row: James Wynne (kit manager), Darryl Coakley, Josh Coulson, Danny Potter, Rory McAuley, Ben Farrell, Greg Reid (physio).
Front row: Andy Parkinson, Courtney Pitt, Sam Ives, Dan Crick (sponsor), Paul Carden (player assistant-manager), Jordan Patrick, Adam Marriott, Robbie Willmott. Not pictured: Martin Ling (manager), Danny Crow, Lee Phillips.

CLUB PERSONNEL

Chairman: Paul Barry.

Directors: Jez George, Adrian Hanauer,

Renford Sargent.

Fans Elected Director: Colin Proctor.

Associate Directors: Brian Attmore, Richard Smith

Club Secretary: Wayne Purser.

c/o the club.

Tel Nos: (B) 01223 729 203

Commercial Manager: Gary Atyes

Telephone: 07590 734 968

Press Officer: Will Jones

Manager: Martin Ling

Assistant Manager: Paul Carden.

Club therapist: Greg Reid.

A perfect start, with big striker Lee McEvilly in great goalscoring form with six in the first seven games, gave Gary Brabin an excellent introduction as the new manager who had taken over from Jimmy Quinn, a surprise departure from The Abbey Stadium. After many changes of playing personnel, four victories took United to the top and when the league settled down in October they were comfortably placed amongst the leaders.

A win at Boston and a defeat at Kidderminster brought little F.A.Cup excitement and a shock 0-5 F.A.Trophy defeat at home to Crawley was a big disappointment after a much enjoyed 3-2 victory over neighbours Histon in the First Round.

With rumours of discontent concerning the management, Brabin showed his character by setting up a brilliant second half to the season in which a steady and consistent attack on Burton Albion's huge lead brought United to within one big victory of top place.

Unbeaten in February and March, the club had benefited from the loan of Scott Rendell who returned from Peterborough United to score seventeen goals. Although the chase behind Burton was realistically just one victory too much, the play-off success was well within the club's ambitions. After a wonderful come back against Stevenage Borough in the Semi-Finals, a second consecutive Wembley play-off final was sadly lost to Torquay United.

CAMBRIDGE UNITED

BEST LGE ATT.: **7,090** v Altrincham
LOWEST: **2,662** v Northwich Victoria

No.	Date	Comp	H/A	Opponents	Att:	Result	Goalscorers	Pos
1	Aug 9	BSP	A	Northwich Victoria	1445	W 1 - 0	Jardim 28	
2	12		H	Kidderminster Harriers	3008	W 2 - 1	McEvilly 27 61	
3	16		H	Barrow	2663	W 2 - 1	McEvilly 29 Hatswell 40	1
4	23		A	Eastbourne Borough	3105	W 3 - 0	McEvilly 22 Farrell 39 Holroyd 84	1
5	25		H	Kettering Town	3489	L 0 - 2		2
6	30		A	Weymouth	1387	D 2 - 2	McEvilly 42 Beasley 45	
7	Sept 2		A	Ebbsfleet United	1832	D 1 - 1	McEvilly 45	
8	6		H	Wrexham	3076	W 2 - 0	Beesley 28 64	2
9	13		H	Torquay United	4041	L 0 - 1		
10	20		A	Mansfield Town	3171	D 1 - 1	Brown 33	6
11	23		A	Oxford United	4170	L 1 - 3	Jardim 57	
12	28		H	Grays Athletic	2971	W 1 - 0	McEvilly 90 (pen)	5
13	Oct 4		A	York City	2608	D 0 - 0		6
14	7		H	Lewes	3194	W 1 - 0	Challinor 90	5
15	11		H	Weymouth	3981	W 1 - 0	Challinor 11	3
16	16		A	Forest Green Rovers	789	D 2 - 2	Hatswell 33 Crowe 65	
17	**25**	**F.A.C. 4Q**	**A**	**Boston United**	**1956**	**W 3 - 2**	**Crow 9 Wilmott 48 Bloomer 83 (og)**	
18	Nov 1		H	Rushden & Diamonds	3547	D 0 - 0		7
19	**4**	**SS N3**	**A**	**AFC Telford**	**941**	**L 3 - 4**	**McEvilly 3 (15, pen 78, 90+3)**	
20	**8**	**F.A.C 1R**	**A**	**Kidderminster Harriers**	**1717**	**L 0 - 1**		
21	15		A	Crawley Town	1570	D 2 - 2	McEvilly 54 (pen) Convery 90	7
22	18		H	York City	2914	W 1 - 0	Purkiss 50 (og)	
23	22		A	Altrincham	1123	L 0 - 1		5
24	29		H	Ebbsfleet United	2807	W 1 - 0	**Rendell** 45	
25	Dec 6		A	Torquay United	2310	D 0 - 0		6
26	9		A	Burton Albion	1804	L 1 - 3	**Rendell** 63	
27	**13**	**F.A.T. 1R**	**A**	**Histon**	**1332**	**W 3 - 2**	**Rendell 46 52 Willmott 90**	
28	20		H	Salisbury City	3340	W 4 - 0	Willmot 25 **Rendell** 50 Holroyd 62 Pitt 63	
29	26		H	Histon	6488	D 2 - 2	Hatswell 15 **Rendell** 41	6
30	28		H	Stevenage Borough	3351	D 1 - 1	**Rendell** 3	6
31	**Jan 14**	**F.A.T 2R**	**H**	**Crawley Town**	**1233**	**L 0 - 5**		
32	17		H	Woking	2696	W 4 - 1	Crow 3 21 Beesley 66 Wilmott 83	
33	22		A	Wrexham	3103	L 0 - 2		
34	29		H	Oxford United	3774	D 1 - 1	Carden 72	
35	Feb 1		A	Rushden & Diamonds	2058	W 2 - 1	Holroyd 21 (pen) Bolland 88	
36	17		A	Kidderminster Harriers	1361	W 3 - 1	**Rendell** 20 (pen) Holroyd 30 56	3
37	21		H	Lewes	962	W 2 - 0	**Rendell** 83 (pen) Willmott 87	3
38	24		A	Grays Athletic	754	W 1 - 0	**Rendell** 42	
39	28		H	Crawley Town	3231	D 1 - 1	Pitt 82	3
40	Mar 2		A	Cambridge United	2579	D 1 - 1	Hatswell 74	
41	7		H	Burton United	4377	W 2 - 0	**Rendell** 55 Willmott 70	2
42	10		H	Mansfield Town	2781	W 2 - 1	**Rendell** 49 Reason 90	
43	14		H	Northwich Victoria	2662	W 4 - 1	Holroyd 24 **Rendell** 31 37 Parkinson 80	
44	17		A	Barrow	1341	W 2 - 0	Holroyd 63 83	2
45	30		A	Woking	1775	W 1 - 0	Reason 82	
46	April 4		H	Forest Green Rovers	3245	L 0 - 1		2
47	7		A	Stevenage Borough	3408	L 1 - 2	Willmott 16	3
48	11		H	Eastbourne Borough	3391	W 2 - 1	Phillips 66 Holroyd 71 (pen)	2
49	13		A	Kettering Town	2340	W 2 - 1	Holroyd 14 (pen) Willmott 74	2
50	18		A	Salisbury City	1031	W 2 - 1	**Rendell** 20 Martin 43 (og)	2
51	26		H	Altrincham	7090	D 0 - 0		2
52	**30**	**Play Off S-F1**	**A**	**Stevenage Borough**	**4446**	**L 1 - 3**	**Phillips 49**	
53	**May 4**	**Play Off S-F2**	**H**	**Stevenage Borough**	**6507**	**W 3 - 0***	**Willmott 55 Rendell 72 119 Won 4-3 on aggregate**	
54	**17**	**Play Off F**	**N**	**Torquay United**	**35089**	**L 0 - 2**		

Average Home Att: **3570 (3547)** **Goals** **78 548**

Best Position: 1st **Worst:** 7th

Goalscorers: Rendell 17, McEvilly 11, Holroyd 10, Wilmott 9, Crow 4, Beasley 4, Hatswell 4, Challinor 2, Jardim 2, Phillips 2, Pitt 2, Reason 2, Bolland 1, Brown 1, Carden 1, Convery 1, Farrell 1, Parkinson 1. Own Goals 3.

POTTER 1	TONKIN 3	GLEESON 2	BOLLAND 5	HATSWELL 6	JARDIM 20	CHALLINOR 10	CARDEN 15	PARKINSON 8	MCEVILLY 9	BEESLEY 7	FARRELL 16	JONES 19	HOYTE 17	COULSON 12	WILLMOTT 18	QUINTON 23	HOLROYD 21	DRENCH 30	CONVERY 14	MCAULEY 26	BROWN 4	CROW 28	COLLINS 24	RENDELL 27	PITT 11	IVES 19	MCMAHON 4	RENDELL 9	REASON 25	PHILLIPS 27	GRUNDY 30	AINGE 17	BARTLETT 20	
X	X	X	X	X	X	X	X	X	X	X	S	S	U	U	U																			1
X	X	X	X	X	X	X	X		X	X	U	S	U	U	X	U																		2
X	X	X	X	X	X	X	X		X	X	S	S	U	U	X		U																	3
X	X	X	X	X	X	X			X	X	X	S	U	U	X		S	U																4
X	X	X	X	X	X	X			X	X	X	X	U	U	S		S	U																5
X	X	X	X	X	X	X	X		X	X		S		S	X		U	U	S															6
X	X		X	X		X	X		X	X		X		U	X		S	U	U	X	U													7
X	X		X	X	U	X	X		X	X		U		U	U		X	U	X		X													8
X	X		X	X	U	X	X		X	X	U	S					X	U	X		X	S												9
X	X	X	X	X	X	X	X		X			U		U			X	U	U		X	S												10
X		X	X	X	X	X	X		X			U		U	X		S	U	S		X	X												11
X		X	X	X	X	X	X		S			U		U	S		X	U	X		X	X												12
X	X	X	X	X	S	X	X		X	U					U		X	U	X		U	X												13
X	X	X	X	X	X	X	X		X	X	S	U			X		S	U				U												14
X		X	X	X	U	X	X		X	X	X				X		S	U	U			U	X											15
X	X	X	X	X	U	X				X	X				X		S	U	U		X	X	U											16
X	X	X	X	X	X	X	X			X	U	U		U	X		S	U	U		U	X												17
X	X	X	X	X	X	X	X			X	U			U	X		S	U	U			X												18
U	S		X		X		S		X		X	X		X	U	X	X	X	X			S	X											19
X	X	X	X	X	S	X	X		X	S	S			U	X		X	U	U			X	U											20
X	X	X		X	S	X			X	X	X			X	X		U	U	X	U		S												21
X	X	X	X	X	X		X		X	X				S	X		U	U	X			S		S										22
X	X	X	X	X	S	X	X		X	X					U		S	U	X			S		X										23
X	X	X	X	X	X	U	X			S					X		U	U	X			X		X	S									24
X	X		X		X	X	X			S	S			X			U	U	X	X		X		X	S									25
X	X	X	X	X	S	S	X			U					X		U	U	X			X		X	X									26
X	X	X	X	X	U	X	X				X			U	X		X	U				U		X	S									27
X	X			X	S	X	X			S	X			X	X		X	U				U		X	X									28
X	X	U		X	S	X	X			S	X			X	X		X	U				U		X	X									29
X	X	X	X	X	S	S	X			U	X			U	X		X					U		X	X									30
X	X		X	X	X	X	X			X	X		U	U	X		X					S			S	S								31
X	X		X	X	U					X	X		U	X	S		X			X		X			S	S	X							32
X	X	X	X	X	S	U				X	X			U	X		S					X			U		X	X						33
X	X	X	X			S	X			S	U			X	X		U			U		X			X		X	X						34
X		X	X	X	U	X	X			X	U		U	X	S		X			U		X			X									35
X	X	X	X	X		S	X			X				U	U		X			U					U		X	X	X					36
X	X	X	X	X		U	X			X				U	S		X			U					S		X	X	X					37
X	X	X	X	X		X	X			X				U	S		X					U			U		U	X	X					38
X	X	X	X	X		U	X			X				U	S		X					U			S		X	X	X					39
X	X	X	X	X		U	X							U	X		U					U			X			X	X	X	U			40
X	X	X	X	X		U	X	S						U	X		X								X		U	X	X		U			41
X	X	X	X	X		U	X	S						U	X		X					S			X		U	X	X					42
X	X	X	X	X		S	X	S						U	X		X					S			X		U	X	X					43
X	X	X	X	X		S	X							U	X		X					U			X		U	X	X	U				44
X	X		X	X		X	X	S							X		X					U			X		U	X	X	U		S		45
X	X		X	X		S	X	X							X		X					S			U		S	X	X	U		X		46
X	X	X		X		U	X	S						X	X		X					U					X	X	X	S		U		47
X	X	X		X		X	X	X						X			S					X			S		X	S	U	X		U		48
X	X	X		X		U	X	S						X	X		X								X		U	X	X	S		U		49
X	X	X	X	X		U	X	X						U	X		X					U					U	X	X	U				50
X	X	X	X	X			X	X						U	X		X					S			S		U	X	X	S				51
X	X	X	X	X		X	X							X	S		S					X			S		U	U	X	X				52
X	X	X	X	X		U	X	S							X		S					U			X		U	X	X	X				53
	X	X	X	X		S	X	S							X		S					U			X		U	X	X	X			X	54
Total League Appearances																																		
46	42	37	40	44	14	26	40	5	17	23	10	2	0	10	30	0	24	0	10	3	6	13	1	7	13	0	8	17	15	2	0	1	0	X
0	0	0	0	0	8	7	0	6	1	5	4	6	0	2	7	0	11	0	2	0	0	9	0	1	7	1	1	1	0	3	0	1	0	S
0	0	1	0	0	6	10	0	0	0	3	5	5	7	24	5	1	9	22	5	5	2	12	1	0	4	0	9	0	1	4	2	3	0	U
Total Cup Appearances																																		
6	7	6	8	7	3	5	7	0	2	2	3	1	0	2	6	1	4	1	1	0	0	3	1	1	2	0	0	2	3	3	0	0	1	X
0	1	0	0	0	1	1	1	2	0	1	1	0	0	0	1	0	4	0	0	0	0	2	0	0	3	1	0	0	0	0	0	0	0	S
1	0	0	0	0	1	1	0	0	0	0	1	1	1	4	1	0	0	3	2	0	1	3	1	0	0	0	3	1	0	0	0	0	0	U

CAMBRIDGE UNITED

CURRENT SQUAD AS OF BEGINING OF 2009-10 SEASON

GOALKEEPERS		SQ NO.	HT	WT	D.O.B	AGE	P.O.B	CAREER	APPS	GOA
Danny	Potter	1	5'11"	13 00	18/3/79	30	Ipswich	Chelsea (Trainee), Colchester 10/97 Rel c/s 98, Exeter 8/98 Rel c/s 00, Weymouth (L) 11,99, Salisbury (L) 1/00, Weymouth 6/00, Chelmsford 2/02, Canvey Island 8/02, Stevenage 6/06, Cambridge U 5/07	46	0
Laurie	Walker	31	6'00"	11 09	8/2/90	19		MK Dons Rel c/s 09, Cambridge U		
DEFENDERS										
Darryl	Coakley	21			9/2/91	18	Bury St Edmunds	Ipswich (Yth), Cambridge U (Yth) Pro c/s 09		
Josh	Coulson	4	6'03"	11 11	28/1/89	20	Cambridge	Cambridge C (Yth), Cambridge U c/s 06	12	0
Dan	Gleeson	2	6'03"	13 02	17/2/85	24	Cambridge	Cambridge U Rel 5/06, Welling (L) 9/03, Notts County 7/06, Cambridge U (SL) 3/07, Cambridge U 5/07	37	0
Wayne	Hatswell	6	6'00"	13 10	8/2/75	34	Swindon	Cinderford T, Witney T, Cinderford, Forest Green 7/99, Oxford U £35,000 12/00 Rel 4/02, Chester Free 5/02, Kidderminster £15,000 10/03, Rushden & D 1/06, Cambridge U Undisc 1/08	44	4
Anthony	Tonkin	3	5'11"	12 01	17/1/80	29	Newlyn	Plymouth, Liverpool, Falmouth 7/97, Yeovil 7/98, Stockport £50,000 9/02, Crewe £150,000 8/03 Rel 5/06, Yeovil 8/06, Grays (SL) 3/07, Forest Green 7/07 Rel 4/08, Cambridge U 7/08	42	0
MIDFIELDERS										
Paul	Carden	15	5'09"	11 10	29/3/79	30	Liverpool	Blackpool, Rochdale (Trial) 2/98 Perm 3/98, Hull C (Trial), Chester 3/00, Doncaster £10,000 7/01, Chester 11/01 Rel c/s 05, Peterborough 7/05 Rel 10/06, Burscough 10/06, Burton (3ML) 10/06 Perm 1/07, Accrington 5/07 Rel 5/08, Cambridge U (6WL) 11/07, Camb	40	1
Jon	Challinor	25	5'11"	11 11	2/12/80	28	Northampton	Rushden & D, Stamford 4/99, Cambridge C 2/01 , Kalamazoo Kingdom (USA), St Albans 5/02, Aldershot 8/03 Rel 5/05, Exeter 5/05, Rushden & D 5/07, Cambridge U £15,000 8/08, Forest Green (L) 8/09	33	2
Ben	Farrell	16	6'00"	11 11	20/7/86	23	Cambridge	Bedford, Cambridge U 1/08, Cambridge C (L) 3/09	14	1
Sam	Ives	20			24/6/91	18	Cambridge	Cambridge C (Yth), Cambridge U	1	0
Rory	McAuley	12	5'10"	12 06	16/10/89	19	Blackpool	Cambridge U	3	0
Jordan	Patrick	23			3/2/91	18	Honolulu	Cambridge C (Yth), Cambridge U (Yth) c/s 06 Pro c/s 09		
Courtney	Pitt	26	5'07"	10 08	17/12/81	27	Paddington	Chelsea, Portsmouth £200,000 7/01, Luton (3ML) 8/03, Coventry (L) 12/03, Oxford U 3/04 Rel c/s 04, Luton (Trial) 7/04, Boston U 8/04 Rel c/s 05, Colchester (Trial) 7/05, Port Vale (Trial) 8/05, Cambridge U 9/05, CRC (L) 10/08	20	2
Jai	Reason	14	5'11"	13 01	9/1/90	19	Southend	Ipswich Rel 5/09, Cambridge U (SL) 2/09, Cambridge U 7/09	15	2
Robbie	Willmott	11	5'09"	12 01	16/5/90	19	Harlow	Cambridge U	37	6
FORWARDS										
Mark	Beesley	7	5'10"	11 10	10/11/81	27	Burscough	Preston Rel c/s 00, Chester 7/00, Southport (L) 9/03, Hereford 12/03 Rel 5/04, Forest Green 6/04, Lancaster (L) 8/06, Cambridge U Undisc 1/08	28	4
Danny	Crow	10	5'10"	11 00	26/1/86	23	Great Yarmouth	Norwich, Northampton (2ML) 2/05, Peterborough 8/05 Rel 9/08, Notts County (L) 10/08, Notts County (SL) 2/09, Cambridge U 9/08	22	3
Chris	Holroyd	9	5'11"	12 03	24/10/86	22	Macclesfield	Crewe (Yth), Chester Rel 7/08, Cambridge U 8/08	35	10
Adam	Marriott	22			14/4/91	18	Brandon	Norwich (Yth), Cambridge C (Yth), Cambridge U (Yth) c/s 06 Pro c/s 09		
Andy	Parkinson	8	5'10"	12 12	27/5/79	30	Liverpool	Liverpool (Trainee), Tranmere 4/97 Rel c/s 03, Aberdeen (Trial) 5/03, Sheff Utd 7/03, Notts County (L) 1/04, Notts County (SL) 3/04, Grimsby 7/04, Notts County 6/06 Rel c/s 08, Cambridge U 7/08	11	1
Lee	Phillips	27	5'10"	12 00	16/9/80	28	Penzance	Plymouth, Weymouth (3ML) 12/00 Perm 3/01, Exeter 2/05, Torquay £17,500 6/07, Rushden & D Undisc 5/08, Weymouth 1/09 Rel 2/09, Cambridge U 3/09	5	1

LOANEES		HT	WT	DOB	AGE	POB	From - To	APPS	GOA
(F)Chris	Jones	5'07"	10 00	12/9/89	19	Swansea	Swansea (4ML) 8/08 - Grimsby 7/09	8	0
(G)Steven	Drench	6'01"	12 09	11/9/85	23	Salford	Southport (4ML) 8/08 - Leigh Genesis 3/09	0	0
(F)Scott	Rendell	6'01"	12 09	21/10/86	22	Ashford	Peterborough (6WL) 11/08, (SL) 1/09 - Torquay (SL) 7/09 -	26	13
(D)Simon	Ainge	6'01"	12 02	18/2/88	21	Shipley	Bradford C (SL) 3/09	2	0
(G)Adam	Bartlett	6'00"	11 10	27/2/86	23	Newcastle	Kidderminster 5/09 - Rel 5/09, Hereford 6/09	0	0

DEPARTURES		HT	WT	DOB	AGE	POB	FROM - TO	APPS	GOA
(F)Lee	McEvilly	6'00"	13 00	15/4/82	27	Liverpool	Accrington 6/08 - Rochdale (6WL) 11/08 Undisc 1/09 Rel 5/09, Barrow (L) 3/09, Grays 8/09	18	8
(M)Danny	Brown	6'00"	12 06	12/9/80	28	Bethnal Green	Crawley 11/06 - Eastbourne B (2ML) 11/08, Perm 1/09	6	1
(D)Gavin	Hoyte	6'04"	12 06	24/6/86	23	Bedford	Bedford T 5/07 - Rel 2/09, Halesowen T (3ML) 10/08, Weymouth 2/09, Grays 7/09	0	0
(F)Felino	Jardim			10/8/85	24	Rotterdam	Sparta Rotterdam (Holl) 8/08 - Rel 2/09	22	2
(M)Mark	Convery	5'06"	10 05	29/5/81	28	Newcastle	York 7/07 - Rel 3/09, CRC (L) 3/09, Newcastle Blue Star 3/09	12	1
(M)Darren	Quinton	5'08"	9 11	28/4/86	23	Romford	Yth - Rel 3/09, Braintree 3/09, St Albans 8/09	0	0
(M)Craig	Bussens			28/10/89	19		Norwich (Yth) c/s 06 Pro c/s 08 Rel 5/09, AFC Sudbury (L) 9/08, Lowestoft T 7/09		
(M)Jordan	Collins			7/12/88	20		Yth - Rel 5/09, Weymouth (SL) 11/08, Ebbsfleet 7/09	1	0
(D)Phil	Bolland	6'02"	13 08	26/8/76	33	Liverpool	Wrexham 7/08 - Rel 6/09, Barrow 7/09	40	1
(G)Aaron	Grundy	6'01"	12 07	21/1/88	21	Bolton	Warrington NC 3/09 - Fleetwood 8/09	0	0
(M)Daryl	McMahon	5'11"	12 02	10/10/83	25	Dublin	Stevenage - 1/09 Rel c/s 09	9	0

CAMBRIDGE UNITED

Founded: 1912

Nickname: The 'U's

Club Colours: Amber & Black shirts, amber & black shorts, amber & black socks.

Change Colours: White shirts, white shorts, white socks.

Club Sponsor: Kershaw

Previous League: Football League

Ground Address: Abbey Stadium, Newmarket Road, Cambridge CB5 8LN
Telephone: 01223 566 500
Fax: 01223 729 220
Official website: www.cambridge-united.co.uk

MATCH TICKETS:
Ticket office Telephone: 01223 566 500

Ticket Prices
Adults £15.00 - £18.00
Concessions £11.00 - £13.00
Under-16s £6.00 - £10.00
Junior U's £2.00

Capacity: 9,217
Seats 2,500
Cover 5,000

Clubhouse: Open matchdays
Club Shop: Yes.
Refreshments Restaurant and burger bars

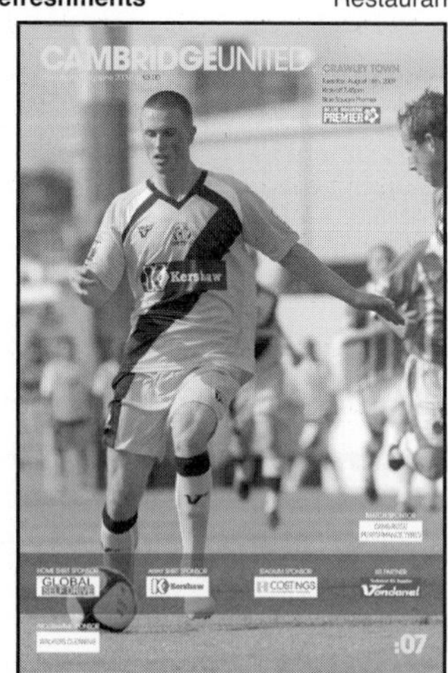

PROGRAMME EDITOR
Mark Johnson & David Gray
mark.johnson.6@btinternet.com

CLUB STATISTICS

RECORDS

Attendance: 14,000 v Chelsea, Friendly 1st May 1970

Victory: 5-1 v Bristol City F.A.Cup 5th Rd 89-90

Defeat: 0-7 v Sunderland League Cup 2nd Rd 02-3

Career Goalscorer: John Taylor 86 1988-92 1996-2001

Career Appearances: Steve Spriggs 416 1975-87

Transfer Fee Paid:

£192,000 Nov. 92 to Luton Town for Steve Claridge

Transfer Fee Received: £1,000,000 from Manchester United for Dion Dublin August 92 from Leicester City for Trevor Benjamin July 2000

SENIOR HONOURS

Football League Div 3

Champions 1990-91, Runners-Up 77-78 98-99

Football League Division 4

Champions 1976-77 Promoted from Play offs 89-90

PREVIOUS

Leagues: United Counties, Eastern Counties 1951-58 Southern League 1958-1970 Football League 1970-2005

Name: Abbey United: 1919-1951

CHESTER CITY

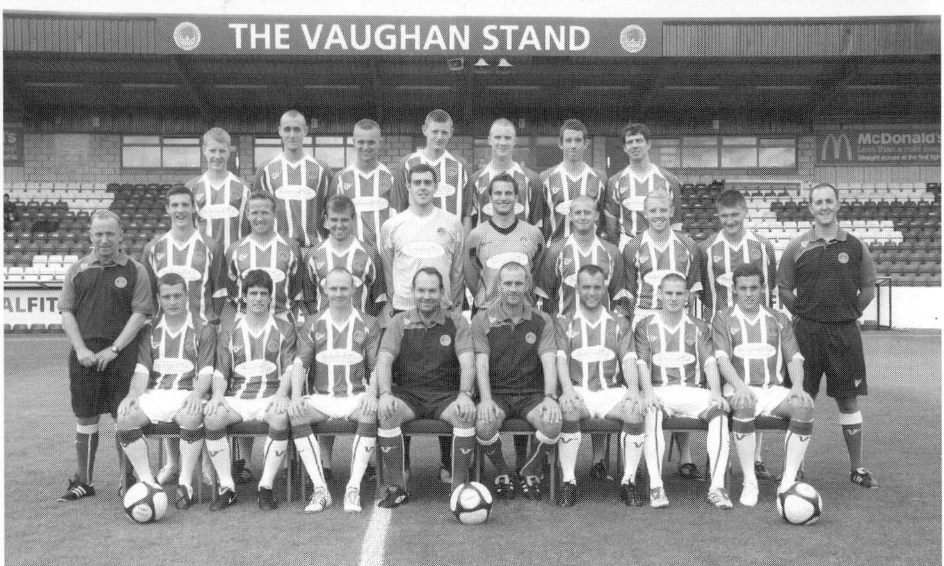

CLUB PERSONNEL

Chairman: Stephen Vaughan.

Directors: Ish Malleck (Company Secretary),

Tony Allan, Rob Gray, Ian Anderson.

Club Secretary: Tony Allan.

c/o the club.

Tel Nos: (B) 01244 371 376.

(M) 07988 646 921

email: ccfctony@aol.co.uk

Commercial Manager: Shaun Piercy.

Tel: 07840 783 539.

Press Officer: See secretary.

Manager: Mick Wadsworth

Club therapist: Ben Holt.

After a distressing season in Division Two, the loyal Chester supporters, who must by now be wondering when there beloved club will ever again benefit from some effective leadership, were possibly relieved to be returning to the comparative peace and quiet of the Blue Square Premier.

Their memories of the old Conference will be happy ones as their battered club recovered once before to restore pride by winning the championship in 2004. This time only the loyalty of the Conference Board and the member clubs saved them and has given them another chance, although they are starting with a deficit of 25 points - at least they were starting.

Although guided by an experienced and well respected manager in Mick Wadsworth, Chester City and their loyal supporters will still find it extremely difficult to avoid relegation. So their recovery may have to be planned over a five year campaign in which only the very dedicated may cope with the pressure.

What a test for all involved !

CHESTER CITY

BEST LGE ATT.: **3,349** v AFC Bournemouth
LOWEST: **1,235** v Rotherham United

No.	Date	Comp	H/A	Opponents	Att:	Result	Goalscorers
1	Aug 9	FL2	A	Dagenham & Redbridge	1434	L 0-6	
2	**12**	**LC 1**	**H**	**Leeds**	**3644**	**L 2-5**	**Lowe 15 75(p)**
3	16	FL2	H	Wycombe	1419	L 0-2	
4	23	FL2	A	Rotherham	3462	L 1-3	Ellison 18
5	30	FL2	H	Barnet	1295	W 5-1	Ellison 32 **Lowe** 57 79 Linwood 62 Roberts 65
6	Sept 6	FL2	H	Bury	2327	D 1-1	Mozika 38
7	13	FL2	A	Grimsby	2950	W 3-1	ELLISON 3 (3 80 87)
8	21	FL2	H	Shrewsbury	2891	D 1-1	McManus 43
9	27	FL2	A	Luton	5731	D 1-1	McManus 77
10	Oct 4	FL2	H	Lincoln	1962	L 0-2	
11	**7**	**FLT**	**H**	**Morecambe**	**926**	**D 1-1**	**Ellison 82 Lost 1-3 on penalties**
12	11	FL2	A	Chesterfield	3042	D 1-1	Linwood 17
13	19	FL2	H	Port Vale	3102	L 1-2	**Lowe** 85
14	21	FL2	A	Rochdale	2162	L 1-6	McArdle 53 (og)
15	25	FL2	A	Gillingham	4852	L 0-2	
16	28	FL2	H	Brentford	1301	W 3-0	**Lowe** 25 60 Roberts 57
17	Nov 1	FL2	A	Exeter	4448	L 0-2	
18	**8**	**FAC 1**	**H**	**Millwall**	**1932**	**L 0-3**	
19	15	FL2	H	Morecambe	1647	L 1-2	Johnson 50
20	22	FL2	H	Aldershot	1653	L 0-1	
21	25	FL2	A	Darlington	2416	W 2-1	**Lowe** 37 Kelly 53
22	Dec 6	FL2	A	Bournemouth	4154	L 0-1	
23	13	FL2	H	Notts Co	1767	W 2-0	**Lowe** 12 Roberts 50
24	20	FL2	A	Bradford	12092	D 0-0	
25	26	FL2	H	Accrington	2223	W 2-0	**Lowe** 34 60 (p)
26	28	FL2	A	Macclesfield	2219	L 1-3	**Lowe** 56
27	Jan 13	FL2	H	Luton	1652	D 2-2	**Lowe** 37 (p) Ellison 52
28	17	FL2	H	Chesterfield	1806	L 1-3	Mozika 53
29	24	FL2	A	Lincoln	3760	D 1-1	Barry 31
30	27	FL2	A	Port Vale	4448	L 0-3	
31	31	FL2	H	Gillingham	1541	L 0-1	
32	Feb 3	FL2	H	Rochdale	1357	L 0-2	
33	7	FL2	A	Brentford	4719	L 0-3	
34	14	FL2	A	Morecambe	1795	L 1-3	Wilson 51
35	17	FL2	A	Shrewsbury	6133	L 0-1	
36	21	FL2	H	Exeter	1640	D 0-0	
37	28	FL2	H	Dagenham & Redbridge	1416	D 2-2	Mannix 86 Roberts 89
38	Mar 3	FL2	A	Wycombe	3713	L 0-2	
39	7	FL2	A	Barnet	2085	L 1-3	Ellison 58
40	10	FL2	H	Rotherham	1235	L 1-5	Ellison 14
41	14	FL2	H	Grimsby	2836	D 1-1	**Lowe** 56
42	21	FL2	A	Bury	3049	D 1-1	**Lowe** 90
43	28	FL2	H	Bradford	2735	D 0-0	
44	April 4	FL2	A	Notts Co	4025	W 2-1	Mannix 14 **Lowe** 49
45	04	FL2	H	Macclesfield	2248	L 0-2	
46	13	FL2	A	Accrington	1100	W 1-0	**Lowe** 41 (p)
47	18	FL2	H	Bournemouth	3349	L 0-2	
48	25	FL2	A	Aldershot	3100	D 2-2	**Lowe** 2 (p) Ellams 63
49	May 2	FL2	H	Darlington	1945	L 1-2	Miller 89 (og)

Ave. League Home Attendance: 1887

Goalscorers: Lowe 18, Ellison 9, Roberts 4, Linwood 2, Mannix 2, McManus 2, Mozika 2, Barry 1, Ellams 1, Johnson 1, Kelly 1, Wilson 1. Own Goals 2.

CURRENT SQUAD AS OF BEGINING OF 2009-10 SEASON

GOALKEEPERS		SQ NO.	HT	WT	D.O.B	AGE	P.O.B	CAREER	APPS	GOA
John	Danby		6'02"	14 07	20/9/83	25	Stoke	Kidderminster Rel 5/06, Stourport (2ML) 2/03, Chester 5/06		
DEFENDERS										
Neil	Ashton		5'08"	12 06	15/1/85	24	Liverpool	Tranmere, Shrewsbury (SL) 12/04, Shrewsbury 6/05 Rel c/s 09, Macclesfield (SL) 1/08, Chester 7/09		
Shaun	Kelly		6'01"	11 04	4/7/86	23	Liverpool	Chester, Vauxhall Motors (2ML) 9/07		
Michael	Lea		6'00"	12 00	4/11/87	21	Salford	Man Utd, Royal Antwerp (4ML) 8/07, Scunthorpe Undisc 7/08, Chester 7/09		
Rhys	Meynell		5'11"	12 03	17/8/88	20	Barnsley	Barnsley Rel c/s 08, Ossett A (L) 3/07, Gretna (SL) 1/08, Barnet (Trial) c/s 08, Stalybridge 8/08, AFC Telford (Trial) 6/09, Chester 7/09		
Kristian	Platt				15/12/91	17	Rock Ferry	Chester		
Conal	Rawlinson							Chester		
Kevin	Roberts		6'02"	14 00	10/3/87	22	Liverpool	Chester		
Tim	Ryan		6'00"	11 07	10/12/74	34	Stockport	Scunthorpe, Buxton 11/94, Doncaster 8/96 Rel c/s 97, Altrincham (2ML) 3/97, Southport 8/97, Doncaster 5/00 Rel 1/06, Peterborough 3/06 Rel c/s 06, Boston U 7/06, Darlington Undisc 1/07 Rel c/s 09, Harrogate T (L) 8/08, Chester 7/09		
MIDFIELDERS										
Anthony	Barry		5'07"	10 00	29/5/86	23	Liverpool	Everton (Trainee), Coventry, Accrington 4/05, Yeovil Undisc 1/06 Rel c/s 08, Chester 7/08		
Jay	Harris		5'07"	11 06	15/4/87	22	Liverpool	Everton Rel c/s 06, Accrington 8/06 Rel c/s 08, Chester 7/08		
David	Mannix		5'08"	11 06	24/9/85	23	Winsford	Liverpool, Accrington (L) 11/06, Ham Kam (Nor) 1/07, Accrington 1/08 Rel c/s 08, Chester 6/08		
Glenn	Rule		5'11"	11 07	30/11/89	19	Birkenhead	Chester		
Stephen	Vaughan		5'06"	11 11	22/1/85	24	Liverpool	Liverpool Rel c/s 04, Chester 6/04, Rochdale (L) 1/07, Boston U Undisc 1/07 Rel c/s 07, Chester 2/08, Droylsden (L) 2/08		
Ben	Wilkinson		5'11"	12 01	25/4/87	21	Sheffield	Sheff Wed (Yth), Sheff Utd (Yth), Derby (Scholar), Hull C, York C (Trial) 1/08, Gretna (SL) 1/08, York C 6/08 Rel 7/09, Altrincham (SL) 3/09, Chester 7/09		
Fabian	Yantorno		5'10"	11 04	4/9/82	26	Montevideo, Uru	C.A Bella Vista (Uru), Sambenedettese (Ita), Miramar Misiones (Uru) 7/06, Gretna 7/07 Rel 3/08, Hibernian 7/08 Rel c/s 09, Chester 7/09		
FORWARDS										
Lewis	Alessandra		5'09"	11 07	8/2/89	20	Bury	Oldham, Chester (L) 8/09		
Gregg	Blundell		5'11"	12 03	3/10/77	31	Liverpool	Tranmere 7/96, Knowsley U 11/96, Vauxhall Motors, Northwich £8,500 1/01, Doncaster £25,000 3/03, Chester £100,000 7/05, Darlington Undisc 1/07 Rel c/s 09, Accrington (2ML) 11/08, Chester 7/09		
Lloyd	Ellams				11/1/91	18	Chester	Chester, Droylsden (L) 9/08		

CHESTER CITY

Founded: 1885

Nickname: Blues

Club Colours: Blue & white shirts, white shorts, white socks.

Change Colours: Yellow shirts, yellow shorts, yellow socks.

Club Sponsor: Anderson & Co Solicitors

Previous League: Football League

Ground Address:	Deva Stadium, Bumpers Lane, Chester CH1 4LT
Telephone:	01244 371 376
Fax:	01244 390 265
email:	ccfctony@aol.co.uk
Official website:	www.chestercityfc.net

Directions: From Main Routes M6-M56. Go to the end of the M56 and follow signs for Chester (A540). Bear left on to A540 Chester and then turn left at the roundabout next to the garage. Follow this road for approx 3 miles to the next roundabout. Take the third exit signposted Queensferry and Sealand Road Industrial Estate and Retail Parks. Go straight on at the next traffic lights, straight on at the next roundabout. At the next traffic lights with Tesco's and Stokers Furniture in front of you, go straight ahead into Bumpers Lane. The ground is at the bottom of the road on the right. From the South (A483). Continue on A483 to roundabout at junction with A55. . Continue straight across, following signs to Chester A483 for 2.3 miles over three roundabouts and across River Dee. At next roundabout by statue, turn left (sign posted Queensferry A483, Ellesmere Port) into Nicholas St. Turn left at lights (sign posted Queensferry A548, Sealand Industrial Parks) into Watergate Street, which becomes Sealand Road. After approx one mile, turn left Bumpers Lane.Ground is on the right.

MATCH TICKETS:

Ticket office Telephone:	01244 371 376
Ticket Prices (08-09)	
Adults	£15.00
Concessions	£10.00
Under-16s	£5.00

Capacity:	6,012
Seats	3,284

Clubhouse:	The Blues Bar
Club Shop:	01244 390 269

PROGRAMME EDITOR
Terry Brunpton
Excel Print Ltd

CLUB STATISTICS

RECORDS

Attendance: 5,987 v Sacrborough 17.04.04 (Deva Stadium)
20,378 v Chelsea (FAC 3R replay) 16.01.52 (Sealand Road)

Victory: 12-0 v York City 01.02.36.

Career Goalscorer: Stuart Rimmer - 135

Career Appearances: Ray Gill - 406 (1951-62)

Transfer Fee Paid: £100,000 for Gregg Blundell from Rotherham.

Transfer Fee Received: £300,000 for Ian Rush from Liverpool

SENIOR HONOURS

Cheshire Senior Cup 1894-95, 96-97, 1903-04, 07-08, 08-09, 30-31, 31-32.
Welsh Cup 1907-08, 32-33, 46-47.
Herefordshire Senior Cup 1991-92 (shared).
Football Conference Champions 2003-04.

PREVIOUS

Leagues: Cheshire 1919-31. Football League 1931-2000, 2004-09. Conference 2000-04.

Name: Chester > 1983.

Grounds: Faulkner Street 1885-98. The Old Showground 98-99. Whipcord Lane 1901-06. 1906-90 Sealand Road. Moss Rose - Macclesfield F.C. (ground share) 1990-92.

CRAWLEY TOWN

Back Row (L-R): Mithun Nayee, Danny Forrest, Jamie Stevens, Brad Thomas, Nick Carter, Lewis Killeen, Jon Paul Pittman.
Middle: Denise McLean, Steven Trussell, Jake Wright, Adam Quinn, Simon Rayner, Steve Fletcher, Glenn Wilson, Richard Munn, Phil Jarman.
Front: Sam Pinault, Thomas We, Simon Stone, Chris Giles, Paul Raynor, Steve Evans (Manager), Dannie Bulman, Jamie Cook, Isaiah Rankin, Anton Rents Douglas.

CLUB PERSONNEL

Chairman: Victor Marley.

Vice-Chairman: Steve Mansell

Company Secretary: Alan Foot.

Additional Directors: John Duly, Thomas Scott, Susan Carter, Barry Munn.

Club Secretary: Barry Munn

Tel Nos: 01293 529 493

E-mail: barrymunn@hotmail.com

correspondence to Secretary at CLUB.

Commercial Manager: Victor Marley

Tel: 01293 410 000

Manager: Steve Evans.

Previous clubs as Manager:

Stamford AFC, Boston United.

Honours as Manager:

United Counties League 1996-97, 97-98.

Conference 2001-02.

Previous clubs as a Player: Bolton Wanderers, Clyde, Ayr United, St Johnstone.

Club therapist: Stephen Trussell.

Despite losing two of their first three games, Crawley Town were comfortably sitting on top of The Blue Square Premier table at the beginning of October with an impressive record of eight victories from their first twelve league matches. Goals appeared to be coming from all areas of their team with Jon-Paul Pittman on particularly good form.

A surprising home defeat by Havant & Waterlooville in the F.A.Cup was followed by a dip in League performances which took the Sussex club down to seventh place, but an excellent return to form for the Christmas and New Year fixtures gave their supporters hopes for a challenge leading to a serious promotion push.

It was Havant & Waterlooville who also eliminated their Premier League rivals in The Third Round of The F.A.Trophy. Crawley had beaten Chesham United 4-2 at home and a wonderful 5-0 result was achieved at Cambridge United placing them firmly amongst the favourites for the knock out competition and the play-offs.

Pittman had scored a glorious hat-trick in that memorable game but he was soon to be transferred, and with other squad changes the early season form couldn't be repeated and, although always within range of the play off places, Crawley could never find the necessary consistency. Three victories in the final twelve fixtures brought a sad end to a season of mixed fortunes.

CRAWLEY TOWN

BEST LGE ATT.: **3,207** v Kettering Town
LOWEST: **600** v Lewes

No.	Date	Comp	H/A	Opponents	Att:	Result	Goalscorers	Pos
1	Aug 9	BSP	H	York City	1372	L 0 - 1		
2	12		A	Lewes	1260	W 3 - 0	**Pittman** 41 Forrest 42 Weatherstone 74	
3	16		A	Forest Green Rovers	732	L 0 - 1		14
4	23		H	Torquay United	1154	W 3 - 1	**Pittman** 9 Pinault 32 (pen) Cook 7 (pen)	12
5	25		A	Stevenage Borough	1492	D 1 - 1	Wilson 74	
6	30		H	Northwich Victoria	776	W 5 - 2	Roberts 17 (og) Cook 24 58 Rents 27 Weatherstone 45	
7	Sept 2		H	Grays Athletic	1189	W 2 - 1	Killeen 21 Weatherstone 40	
8	6		A	Rushden & Diamonds	1376	W 1 - 0	Fletcher 90	3
9	13		H	Mansfield Town	2013	W 2 - 1	Quinn 16 Cook 46	1
10	20		A	Oxford United	3992	W 2 - 1	**Pittman** 36 Cook 41	1
11	23		A	Weymouth	1005	D 2 - 2	Weatherstone 1 Quinn 81	1
12	27		H	Kettering Town	3207	W 1 - 0	**Pittman** 12	1
13	Oct 4		A	Burton Albion	1915	L 1 - 2	Wilson 15	
14	7		H	Forest Green Rovers	876	D 2 - 2	Quinn 3 Cook 36	1
15	11		H	Barrow	1601	W 4 - 0	Wilson 36 Cook 43 58 (pen) **Pittman** 64	1
16	18		A	Histon	1256	L 0 - 1		2
17	**25**	**F.A.C. 4R**	**H**	**Havant & Waterlooville**	**1253**	**L 0 - 3**		
18	30		A	Salisbury City	884	L 0 - 2		5
19	**Nov 4**	**SS 3**	**H**	**Havant & Waterlooville**	**239**	**W 3 - 0**	**Pinault pen 44, Quinn 86, Rents 90**	
20	15		H	Cambridge United	1570	D 2 - 2	**Pittman** 30 Pinault 61 (pen)	6
21	20		H	Ebbsfleet United	922	L 1 - 2	**Pittman** 33	7
22	23		A	York City	1935	D 2 - 2	Quinn 54 Killeen 90	7
23	29		A	Northwich Victoria	610	W 1 - 0	Fletcher 84	6
24	Dec 6		H	Altrincham	978	W 4 - 0	Killeen 3 Cook 28 Pinault 43 **Pittman** 90	5
25	**16**	**F.A.T 1R**	**A**	**Chesham United**	**399**	**W 4 - 2**	**Pittman 5 Quinn 52 Fletcher 57 Giles 64**	
26	20		H	Kidderminster Harriers	1022	W 2 - 0	Malcolm 30 71	
27	26		A	Woking	1910	D 0 - 0		5
28	28		H	Eastbourne Borough	1479	W 1 - 0	**Pittman** 60	4
29	Jan 1		H	Woking	1525	D 2 - 2	Quinn 47 Malcolm 52	3
30	**14**	**F.A.T 2R**	**A**	**Cambridge United**	**1233**	**W 5 - 0**	**Weatherstone 10 PITTMAN 3 (56 85 88) Quinn 90**	
31	17		A	Mansfield Town	2414	L 0 - 1		3
32	**20**	**SS S4**	**H**	**Chelmsford City**	**304**	**W 2 - 1**	**Gill 10, Pittman 16**	
33	24		H	Oxford United	1603	L 0 - 1		4
34	27		A	Ebbsfleet United	795	D 4 - 4	Matthews 3 QUINN 3 (49 83 90)	
35	**Feb 16**	**F.A.T 3R**	**A**	**Havant & Waterlooville**	**413**	**L 0 - 2**		
36	21		H	Salisbury CIty	964	L 0 - 3		9
37	24		H	Lewes	600	W 5 - 1	Shaw 2 45 Rents 4 (pen) Weatherstone 36 Quinn 85	
38	28		A	Cambridge United	3231	D 1 - 1	Shaw 34	8
39	Mar 3		H	Wrexham	737	W 1 - 0	Weatherstone 74	
40	8		H	Weymouth	901	W 4 - 2	Gala 5 Bulman 25 Rents 28 Killeen 78	
41	10		A	Kidderminster Harriers	1280	L 0 - 2		6
42	14		H	Rushden & Diamonds	777	D 0 - 0		7
43	**17**	**SS QFS**	**H**	**Ebbsfleet United**	**844**	**L 1 - 2**	**Killeen 30**	
44	21		A	Wrexham	3303	W 2 - 0	Rankin 10 Matthews 25	7
45	28		A	Altrincham	960	D 2 - 2	Rankin 31 Wilson 88	9
46	31		A	Eastbourne Borough	1268	L 1 - 2	Jenkins 68 (og)	9
47	April 4		H	Burton Albion	1131	W 4 - 0	Giles 5 Cook 15 (pen) Forrest 68 Killeen 79	9
48	11		A	Torquay United	3031	W 2 - 0	Bulman 38 Matthews 90	8
49	13		H	Stevenage Borough	1161	L 0 - 2		8
50	15		A	Kettering Town	961	D 1 - 1	Bulman 20	
51	18		A	Barrow	1456	D 3 - 3	Cook 19 45 (pen) Rankin 76	9
52	21		A	Grays Athletic	630	L 0 - 1		
53	26		H	Histon	901	D 3 - 3	Cook 52 (pen) Malcolm 66 Shaw 82	9

Average Home Att: **1204 (961)** **Goals** **92 65**

Best Position: 1st **Worst:** 14th

Goalscorers: Pittman 14, Cook 13, Quinn 11, Weatherstone 7, Killeen 6, Malcolm 5, Pinault 4, Rents 4, Shaw 4, Wilson 4, Bulman 3, Fletcher 3, Matthews 3, Rankin 3, Forrest 2, Giles 2, Gala 1, Gill 1. Own Goals 2.

RAYNER 1	WRIGHT 6	GILES 5	WILSON 16	STEVENS 2	PINAULT 10	FORREST 7	BULMAN 8	PITTMAN 15	COOK 11	KILLEEN 14	THOMAS 12	WEATHERSTONE 4	DOUGLAS 18	MORGAN 22	RENTS 3	NAYEE 20	QUINN 21	RANKIN 17	CARTER 19	FLETCHER 9	DARK 23	JONES 22	DAYTON 24	MALCOLM 25	MILLS 18	RAYNOR 39	O'NEILL 26	CHALMERS 22	GILL 18	MATTHEWS 9	SHAW 24	NAPPER 15	GAIA 2	HURREN 12	LAKE-EDWARDS 27	
X	X	X	X	X	X	X	X	X	X	X	S	S	S	U	U																					1
X	X		X	U	X	X	X	X	U	X	X	X	S	U	X	U																				2
X	X		X	U	X	X	X	X	S	X	S	X		U	X		X	S																		3
X	X		S	U	X	X	X	X	S	X	X	X			X		X	S	U																	4
X	X		X	U	X	S	X	X	X	S	S	X	U		X		X	X																		5
X	X	S	X	U	X	X	X		X	X	U	X	S		X		X			S																6
X	X	U	X	U	X	X	X		X	X	S	X	S		X		X			S																7
X	X	U	X	U	X	X	X		X	X	U	X	S		X		X			S																8
X	X	U	X	U	X	X	X		X	X	S	X	S		X		X			S																9
X	X	S	X	S	X	X	X	X	X		U	X	U		X		X			S																10
X	X	U		X	X	X	X	X	X		U	X	S		X	U	X			S																11
X	X	S	X	U	X	X	X	X	X		U	X			X		X	S		S																12
X	X	S	X	U	X	X	X	X	X		S	X			X		X			S	U															13
X	X	X	X	U	X	X	X	X	X		U	X	U		S		X			S																14
X	X		X	U	X	X	X	X	X		U	X	S		X		X			S	S															15
X	X		X	U	X	X	X	X	X		X	X	S		X				U	S		U														16
X	X	S	X	U	X	S	X	X	X	U	S	X			X		X			X		U														17
X	X	X		X		X	X	S	X	X		X			S		X		U	S		U	X													18
X		X		X	X		X	X		X					X	S	X		S	X	S			X												19
X	X	X	X	S	X	X	X	X		U		S			X					X			U	X	S											20
X	X	X		X	X	U	X	X	S	X		S					X			X			S	X	U											21
X	X	X	X		X	S	X	X	X	S		X					X		U	S			U	X												22
X	X	X	X			X	X	X	X	S		X				U	X	U		S			S	X												23
X	X	X	X		X	U	X	S	X	X		X			U		X	S		S				X												24
X	X	X	X		X	S	X	X		X		X	U		U		X	X		S				S												25
X	X	X	X		X	S	X	S	X	X		X			S		X		U	U				X												26
X	X				X	X	X	X	X			X	U		X		X		U	S				X	S	U										27
X			X		X	X		X	X			X	S		X		X		U	X				X	U	S	U									28
X	X		X		X		X	X	X			X	U		X	U	X		U	S				X			U									29
X	X		X	U	S		X	X				X			X	S	X			X				X	S	U		X								30
X	X		X	U	U		X	X				X			X	U	X		U	X				X	U			X								31
X	X		X	U		X	S	X				S			X	U	X		S	X				X				X	X							32
X	X		X			S	X	X				X			X	U	X		U					X		U			X	X	S					33
X	X		X				X	X				X			X	S	X		U					X		U		X	U	X	S					34
X	X		X			X	X			X		X			X	U	X	S	U					U				X	U		X					35
X	X		X			S	X			X		S			X		X	X						X				X	U	S	X	U				36
X	X	S	S			X	X					X			X		X	U	U					X				X	S	X	X					37
X	X	S	X		U	X	X			S		X			X									X					U	X	X		X	S		38
X	X	S	X		U	X	X			U		X			X			S						X						X	X		X	U		39
X	X	U	X		X	X	X			S					X		U	S						X						X	X		X	S		40
X	X	X	X		S	U	X			S		X			X		U	S						X						X	X		X			41
X	X	S			X	X	X		U	X		X					X	S						X						S	X		X	U		42
X		X	X		X	X	X		S	X		S			X	U	X	X						X							U		U			43
X	X	X	X			S	X		U	S		X			X		X	X						X						X	S		U			44
X	X	X	X			S	X		S	U		X			X		X	X						X						X	U		U			45
X	X	X	X			X	X		X	X		X					X	S						S						X	U		U	U		46
X	X	X	X			X	X		X	S					X		X	S						X						X	S		U	U		47
X	X	X	X			X	X		X	X					X		X	S						U						S	X		S	U		48
X	X	X	X			X	X		X	S					X		X	X						X						S	S		U	U		49
X		X					X		S	X					X	U	X	X						S	U					X	X	S	X	X		50
X		X	S			U	X		X	S					X	U	X	S						X						X	X		X	X		51
X			S			X	S		U	X					X	S	U							X						X	X	X	X	X	X	52
X			X		S	X	X		X	X		S			X	U	X	U						S						X	X		X			53

Total League Appearances

46	41	18	36	4	26	31	44	22	27	19	3	34	0	0	36	0	37	6	0	4	0	0	1	25	0	0	0	4	1	15	12	1	9	3	1	X
0	0	8	4	2	2	7	1	3	5	10	6	5	10	0	3	2	0	12	0	17	1	0	2	3	2	1	0	0	1	4	5	1	1	2	0	S
0	0	5	0	14	3	4	0	0	4	3	7	0	5	3	2	9	3	3	12	1	1	2	2	1	4	3	2	0	3	0	2	1	5	6	0	U

Total Cup Appearances

7	5	3	6	1	4	3	6	5	1	4	0	4	0	0	6	0	7	2	0	4	0	0	0	4	0	0	0	3	1	0	1	0	0	0	0	X
0	0	1	0	0	1	2	1	0	1	0	1	2	0	0	0	2	0	1	2	1	1	0	0	1	1	0	0	0	0	0	0	0	0	0	0	S
0	0	0	0	3	0	0	0	0	0	1	0	0	1	0	1	3	0	0	1	0	0	1	0	1	0	1	0	0	1	0	1	0	1	0	0	U

CRAWLEY TOWN

CURRENT SQUAD AS OF BEGINING OF 2009-10 SEASON

GOALKEEPERS		SQ NO.	HT	WT	D.O.B	AGE	P.O.B	CAREER	APPS	GOA
Nick	Jordan	22	6'02"	13 01	13/11/89	19	Aldershot	Portsmouth (Scholar) Rel c/s 08, Exeter 8/08 Rel c/s 09, Crawley 8/09		
Simon	Rayner	1	6'04"	15 00	8/7/83	25	Vancouver, Can	Bournemouth, Bournemouth Poppies (6ML) 8/01, Barry T 2/02, Port Talbot 7/03, Newcastle (Trial) 5/04, Lincoln C 8/04 Rel 06/07, Alfreton (SL) 1/06, Torquay (SL) 3/07, Torquay 6/07, Boston U (SL) 1/08, Crawley 6/08	46	0
DEFENDERS										
Karl	Broadhurst	6	6'00"	11 07	18/3/80	29	Portsmouth	Bournemouth Rel c/s 07, Hereford 7/07 Rel c/s 09, Bournemouth (Trial) 7/08, Crawley 8/09		
Chris	Giles	5	6'02"	13 00	16/4/82	26	Milborne Port	Sherborne, Yeovil 7/99, Weston-S-Mare (2ML) 3/01, Weymouth (L) 8/02, Gravesend (L) 12/02, Woking (L) 2/04, Aldershot 3/04 Rel 5/05, Crawley 7/05, Forest Green 7/06 Rel 7/06 Injured, Forest Green 11/06 Rel 4/08, Crawley 5/08	26	1
Max	Lake-Edwards							Crawley	1	0
Adam	Quinn	21			2/6/83	25	Sheffield	Sheff Wed, Carlisle (Trial) 3/02, Halifax 8/02, Crawley 8/08	37	7
Sam	Rents	3	5'09"	11 03	22/6/87	21	Brighton	Brighton Rel 5/08, Worthing (L) 11/05, Crawley 5/08	39	3
Glenn	Wilson	16	6'01"	12 09	16/3/86	22	Lewisham	C.Palace Rel 5/06, AFC Wimbledon (L) 9/04, Bournemouth (Trial) 2/06, Rushden & D 6/06, Kidderminster (L) 3/07, Crawley 7/07	40	4
MIDFIELDERS										
Nick	Carter	19	5'10"	12 08	17/12/89	19	Eastbourne	Crawley	0	0
Barry	Cogan	17	5'09"	09 00	4/11/84	23	Sligo	Millwall, Barnet Undisc 8/06 Rel 5/07, Gillingham 7/07, Grays (SL) 3/08, Grays 7/08, Crawley 6/09		
Jamie	Cook	11	5'10"	10 09	2/9/79	28	Oxford	Oxford U Rel 1/01, Darlington (Trial) 1/01, Boston U 2/01, Stevenage 2/03, Bath C (L) 2/04, Maidenhead 7/04, Witney U 9/05, Rushden & D (NC) 1/07, Havant & W 3/07, Crawley 7/07	32	13
Eddie	Hutchinson	4	6'01"	13 00	23/2/82	26	Kingston	Sutton U, Brentford £75,000 8/00, Oxford U 7/06 Rel 4/09, Crawley 5/09		
Byron	Napper	18						Crawley	2	0
Thomas	Pinault	10	5'10"	11 01	4/12/81	26	Grasse, Fra	AS Cannes (Fra), Colchester 7/99 Rel c/s 04, Northampton (Trial) 7/04, Dundee U (Trial) 7/04, Grimsby 7/04 Rel 7/05, Year out, Brentford 7/06 Rel c/s 07, Crawley 7/07	28	3
Paul	Raynor		6'00"	12 11	29/4/66	42	Nottingham	Crawley Ass Man	1	0
Simon	Rusk	2	5'11"	12 08	17/12/81	26	Peterborough	Peterborough (Scholar), Cambridge C, Boston Utd 3/01 Rel c/s 07, Northwich 7/07 Rel 1/08, Rushden & D (L) 9/07, York C 1/08 Rel 5/09, Crawley 5/09		
Ben	Smith	23	5'08"	11 06	23/11/78	30	Chelmsford	Arsenal (Trainee), Reading 4/97, Yeovil 3/98, Southend 6/01 Rel c/s 02, Hereford 6/02, Shrewsbury 6/04, Weymouth 1/06, Hereford Undisc 1/07 Rel c/s 09, Crawley 8/09		
FORWARDS										
Charles	Ademeno	8	5'10"	11 13	12/12/88	20	Milton Keynes	Southend Rel 6/09, Bishops Stortford (2ML) 9/06, Cambridge U (L) 1/07, Welling (2ML) 11/07, Rushden & D (2ML) 2/08, Salisbury (5WL) 11/08, Salisbury (SL) 2/09, Crawley 7/09		
Danny	Forrest	7	5'10"	11 07	23/10/84	23	Keighley	Bradford C Rel 5/06, Halifax (SL) 8/05, Halifax 6/06, Hucknall (L) 1/08, Crawley 5/08	38	2
Lewis	Killeen	14	5'09"	10 07	23/9/82	25	Peterborough	Sheff Utd Rel c/s 03, Halifax (3ML), Halifax 6/03, Crawley 5/08	29	5
Jefferson	Louis	9	6'02"	13 02	22/2/79	29	Harrow	Chesham, Aylesbury 7/00, Thame U 3/01, Oxford U 3/02, Woking (L) 8/03, Gravesend (L) 8/04, Forest Green Free 9/04, Woking 12/04 Rel 5/05, Bristol R 5/05, Hemel Hempstead 11/05, Lewes 11/05, Worthing 11/05, Stevenage 12/05 Rel c/s 06, Eastleigh 7/06, Yeading 9/06 Rel 12/06, Havant & W 12/06, Weymouth 6/07 Rel 1/08, Maidenhead 1/08, Mansfield 1/08 Rel 5/08, Wrexham 6/08 Rel 5/09, Crawley 5/09		
Michael	Malcolm	15	5'10"	11 07	13/10/85	22	Harrow	Wycombe (Yth), Tottenham £10,000 Rel c/s 05, Stockport 7/05 Rel c/s 07, Kettering 8/07 Rel 9/07, Rushden & D 9/07, Thurrock 12/07, Weymouth 1/08, Crawley (2ML) 11/08 Perm 1/09	28	4
Mithan	Nayee	20	5'09"	11 02	3/3/90	19	Crawley	Crawley	2	0
Daniel	Powell	24	6'01"	13 03	12/3/91	18	Luton	MK Dons, Crawley (L) 8/09		

LOANEES		HT	WT	DOB	AGE	POB	From - To	APPS	GOA
(M)James	Dayton	5'08"	10 01	12/12/88	20	Enfield	C.Palace 10/08 - Rel 5/09	3	0
(F)Jon	Shaw	6'01"	12 09	10/11/83	24	Sheffield	Rochdale (SL) 1/09 -	17	5
(M)Lewis	Chalmers	6'00"	12 04	4/2/86	23	Manchester	Aldershot (2ML) 1/09 -	4	0
(F)Robbie	Matthews			2/3/82	26	Wiltshire	Salisbury (SL) 1/09 -	19	3

DEPARTURES		HT	WT	DOB	AGE	POB	From - To	APPS	GOA
(G)Nick	Morgan	6'07"					Braintree 7/08 - Rel 10/08, Braintree 2/09, Eastleigh (EL) 4/09	0	0
(G)Ashlee	Jones			4/8/87	21		Harrow 10/08 - Fisher 11/08, Wycombe NC 3/09	0	0
(M)Lewis	Dark	5'08"	11 06	10/4/89	20	Harlow	Wivenhoe NC 10/08 - Fisher 11/08, Grays NC 2/09	1	0
(M)Anton	Douglas						Kingstonian 8/08 - Rel 1/09, Welling 1/09	10	0
(F)Steve	Fletcher	6'02"	14 09	26/6/72	36	Hartlepool	Chesterfield 5/08 - Rel 1/09, Bournemouth 1/09	21	2
(D)Jamie	Stevens	5'11"		25/2/89	19	Holbeach	Boston U 6/07 - Northwich 1/09, Ebbsfleet (SL) 3/09 Rel 6/09	6	0
(F)Jon-Paul	Pittman	5'09"	11 00	24/10/86	21	Oklahoma City, USA	Doncaster 6/07 - Wycombe Undisc 2/09	25	10
(M)Ben	Gill	5'09"	10 11	9/10/87	21	Harrow	Cheltenham 1/09 - Weymouth 3/09	2	0
(M)Dannie	Bulman	5'09"	11 12	24/1/79	29	Ashford	Stevenage 1/07 - Oxford U 5/09	45	3
(D)Santos	Gaia	6'00"	12 04	8/9/78	29	Sao-Mateus-Es	Weymouth 2/09 - Rel 5/09, Truro C 6/09	10	1
(D)Gavin	Hurren	5'08"	13 07	22/10/85	22	Birmingham	Kings Lynn 2/09 - Rel 5/09, Tamworth 6/09	5	0
(F)Isaiah	Rankin	5'10"	11 00	22/5/78	30	London	Stevenage 7/08 - Rel 5/09	18	3
(M)Simon	Weatherstone	5'11"	11 00	26/1/80	28	Reading	Weymouth 5/08 - Rel 5/09, Eastbourne B 5/09	39	6
(F)Danny	Mills						Yth - Peterborough Undisc 7/09	2	0
(M)Romone	McCrae						Yth - Peterborough Undisc 7/09		
(D)Jake	Wright	5'11"	10 07	11/3/86	22	Keighley	Halifax 6/08 - Brighton 7/09	41	0
(D)Brannon	O'Neill						Yth -	0	0
(D)Bradley	Thomas	6'02"	13 00	29/3/84	24	Forest Gate	Yeovil 6/07 - Kings Lynn (SL) 10/08,	9	0

CRAWLEY TOWN

Formed: 1896

Nickname: Red Devils

Club Colours: Red shirts, shorts and socks.

Change Colours: Royal blue shirts, shorts and socks.

Club Sponsor: TBA

Previous League: Southern League.

Ground Address: Broadfield Stadium, Brighton Road, Crawley RH11 9RX
Tel No: 01293 410 000
Fax: 01293 410 002
General email address: info@crawley-town.fc.com
Official website: www.crawleytownfc.com

SIMPLE DIRECTIONS

By Road From M23 Jct. 11 take second exit off roundabout which is A23 towrds Crawley. Turn left at net roundabout to ground

Parking: Large Car Park at ground

MATCH TICKETS

Ticket office Telephone: 01293 410 000
Executive Area: Adult £35, concessions £26, Under 16's £17
West Stand: Adult £16, concessions £12, Under 16's £6
Terraces: Adult £13, concesions £9, under 16's £1

Capacity: 4,996
Seats: 1.080
Covered: 4,200
Clubhouse: Open matchdays and for private bookings plus evenings and weekend lunchtimes.
Refreshments: Available on matchdays.
Club Shop: Yes, fully stocked

PROGRAMME EDITORS
Leigh Edwards and Tony Pope.

CLUB STATISTICS

RECORDS

Attendance: 4,522 v Weymouth, Southern Premier 06.03.04

Victory: 10-0 v Chichester United, Sussex Lg 1955 and v Crowborough Sussex Fllodlit Cup 2001
Defeat: 0-10
Career Goalscorer: Phil Basey 108 (1968-72)
Career Appearances: John Maggs 652 (63-73 75-79)
Transfer Fee Paid:
Undisclosed to Wycombe for Ian Simpemba July 2004
Transfer Fee Received:
£75,000 from Brentford for Jay Lovett in 2000.

SENIOR HONOURS
Southern League Champions 2003-04
Southern League Southern Division R-Up 1983-84
Southern League Championship Match 2002-03, 2003-04
Sussex Senior Cup 88-89 90-91 02-03 R-Up (2)

PREVIOUS
Leagues: Sussex County 1951-56, Metroplitan 56-63 Southern 1964-2003
Grounds: Malthouse Farm 1896-1914,1938-40, Victory Hall & Rectory Field 1918-38,Yetmans Field 45-49, Town Mead 49-53 54-97 and Ifield Recreation Ground 53-54

EASTBOURNE BOROUGH

Back row: Dean Lightwood (*Goalkeeping Coach*), Matt Smart, Andy Ballard, Jay Lovett, Sam Crabb, Chris Winterton, Lee Hook, Ross Treleaven, Dominic Douglas, Evan Archibald, Jean-Michel Sigere, Simon Colbran (*Coach*), Ray Tuppen (*Physic*

Front row: Andy Atkin, Darren Baker, Neil Jenkins, Matt Crabb, Garry Wilson (*Team Manager*), Paul Armstrong (*Captain*), Allan Tait, Nick Greenwood (*Head Coach*), Simon Wormull, Pat Harding, Darren Budd, Mo Harkin, Nathan Crabb

CLUB PERSONNEL

Chairman: Len Smith.

Vice-Chairman: Mick Grimer.

Chief Executive: Mike Spooner.

Additional Directors: Angus Scott, Steve Carter.

Secretary

Myra Stephens

c/o Langney Sports Club, Priory Lane, Eastbourne

Sussex BN23 7QH

myra-ebfc@sky.com

Commercial Manager: Lorna Gosling

Tel: 01323 766 265 Ext 3

Press Officer: Colin Hutchinson

Tel: 01323 766 265 (Ext 223)

Manager: Garry Wilson.

Club therapist: Ray Tuppen.

Most tipsters had Borough as one of the favourites to be fighting in the relegation zone last season. So all credit to Garry Wilson's club, who, although they spent most of the first half of the season in the bottom ten, were never considered in danger of relegation.

Although they scored twenty nine goals home and away in the Blue Square Premier division they failed to find the net on fifteen occasions however, during the loan spell enjoyed by Ashley Barnes from Plymouth Argyle, the youngster scored five times and inspired his club to a change in form which included a fine 4-2 victory over Torquay United and a rise to a highest position of ninth.

The F.A. Cup didn't bring very much excitement last season as Borough lost after a long journey to replay their Fourth Qualifying Round tie at Barrow. In the F.A.Trophy they suffered an embarrassing defeat to Swindon Supermarine.

However, the first four fixtures of the New Year saw Borough produce maximum points which took them into the top ten, and the club never looked likely to be in any relegation trouble again. With an average attendance of over 1,500 Borough are steadily attracting more local supporters, and their excellent development last season augers well for the future.

EASTBOURNE BOROUGH

BEST LGE ATT.: 3,105 v Cambridge United
LOWEST: 919 v Ebbsfleet United

No.	Date	Comp	H/A	Opponents	Att:	Result	Goalscorers	Pos
1	Aug 9	BSP	H	Rushden & Diamonds	1605	L 0 - 1		
2	12		A	Stevenage Borough	1681	W 3 - 1	Harding 12 **Atkin** 14 55	
3	16		A	Oxford United	3969	L 3 - 6	Harding 11 Tait 17 **Armstrong** 68	17
4	23		H	Cambridge United	3105	L 0 - 3		
5	25		A	Grays Atheltic	641	W 1 - 0	Smart 90	15
6	30		H	Altrincham	1170	W 1 - 0	**Armstrong** 28	
7	Sept 2		H	Forest Green Rovers	1065	W 1 - 0	Crabb N 64	
8	6		A	Mansfield Town	2536	L 1 - 3	Crabb N 50	15
9	13		H	Histon	1045	D 1 - 1	Austin 44	14
10	20		A	Torquay United	1921	L 0 - 2		17
11	23		A	Ebbsfleet United	1120	D 1 - 1	**Atkin** 22	17
12	27		H	Kidderminster Harriers	1248	L 2 - 3	**Armstrong** 59 Crabb M 69	18
13	**30**	**SS S2**	**A**	**Fisher Athletic**	**58**	**W 3 - 2***	**Wormull 22, Sappleton 71, Atkin 99**	
14	Oct 4		A	Weymouth	931	L 2 - 3	Crabb M 8 Smart 58	
15	7		H	Kettering Town	1035	L 1 - 2	**Armstrong** 56	
16	12		H	Stevenage Borough	1618	W 2 - 1	Wormull 56 Taylor 90	18
17	18		A	Barrow	1206	L 1 - 3	Osborne 90	19
18	**25**	**F.A.C. 4Q**	**A**	**Oxford City**	**564**	**W 1 - 0**	**Baker 47**	
19	Nov 1		A	Northwich Victoria	564	W 2 - 1	**Armstrong** 27 Tait 83	18
20	**4**	**SS S3**	**H**	**Ebbsfleet United**	**300**	**L 1 - 3**	**Budd 57**	
21	**8**	**F.A.C. 1R**	**H**	**Barrow**	**1216**	**D 0 - 0**		
22	15		H	Woking	1105	D 0 - 0		18
23	**18**	**F.A.C. 1R r**	**A**	**Barrow**	**2031**	**L 0 - 4**		
24	22		A	Rushden & Diamonds	1037	L 0 - 2		18
25	29		A	Burton Albion	1870	L 0 - 2		19
26	Dec 6		H	Northwich Victoria	1088	W 4 - 1	Barnes 13 70 **Armstrong** 32 (pen) Wormull 67	18
27	9		H	Torquay United	1204	W 4 - 2	Barnes 8 M.Crabb 51 56 Smith 71	
28	**17**	**F.A.T. 1R**	**A**	**Swindon Supermarine**	**302**	**L 0 - 1**		
29	20		A	Wrexham	3483	L 0 - 5		16
30	26		H	Lewes	2216	W 1 - 0	**Armstrong** 30	15
31	28		A	Crawley Town	1479	L 0 - 1		15
32	Jan 1		A	Lewes	2232	W 2 - 0	Barnes 61 N.Crabb 90	13
33	17		A	Forest Green Rovers	854	W 2 - 1	Smith 63 Smart 88	12
34	24		H	York City	1668	W 2 - 1	Barnes 15 Austin 55	12
35	27		A	Woking	1101	W 4 - 0	**ATKIN** 3 (2 31 41) Smith 65	9
36	31		H	Mansfield Town	1420	L 1 - 2	**Atkin** 7	9
37	Feb 21		A	Histon	821	D 3 - 3	**Atkin** 34 Crabb M 45 Gargon 79	12
38	28		A	Kidderminster Harriers	1430	L 0 - 2		13
39	Mar 3		H	Oxford United	1168	L 0 - 3		
40	7		H	Wrexham	1428	W 1 - 0	Smart 85	13
41	14		A	Kettering Town	1415	W 1 - 0	Crabb N 78	13
42	17		H	Salisbury City	1047	D 0 - 0		
43	21		H	Burton Albion	1521	L 1 - 2	Brown 25	13
44	28		A	Salisbury City	1011	L 0 - 2		14
45	31		H	Crawley Town	1268	W 2 - 1	Pullan 47 N.Crabb 60	13
46	April 2		H	Ebbsfleet United	919	L 0 - 1		
47	4		H	Weymouth	1078	W 3 - 0	Crabb M 45 Jeffrey 83 90	12
48	7		A	Altrincham	605	D 2 - 2	Jeffery 8 Austin 40	11
49	11		A	Cambridge United	3391	L 1 - 2	**Armstrong** 59 (pen)	12
50	13		H	Grays Athletic	1305	W 2 - 1	Lovett 13 **Armstrong** 50 (pen)	
51	18		A	York City	2487	L 0 - 1		12
52	26		H	Barrow	1584	L 0 - 2		13

Average Home Att: 1387 (872) **Goals** 63 80

Best Position: 9th **Worst:** 19th

Goalscorers: Armstromg 9, Atkin 9, Crabb M 6, Barnes 5, Crabb N 5, Smart 4, Austin 3, Jeffrey 3, Smith 3, Wormull 3, Harding 2, Tait 2, Baker 1, Brown 1, Budd 1, Gargon 1, Lovett 1, Osbourne 1, Pullan 1, Sappleton 1, Taylor 1.

HOOK	BAKER	PULLAN	AUSTIN	JENKINS	M CRABB	HARDING	ARMSTRONG	SMART	ATKIN	SIGERE	WORMULL	N CRABB	TAIT	WINTERTON	LOVETT	HARKIN	BUDD	BALLARD	ILLUGASON	TAYLOR	OSBORNE	SAPPLETON	BROWN	SMITH	BARNES	GOULDING	LIGHTWOOD	JOHNSON	GARGAN	XANO	JORDAN	MINGLE	JEFFREY	
1	2	6	5	3	11	7	8	4	9	14	18	15	10	22	13	21	31	12	25	25	23	24	26	29	28	27	30	32	22	36	37	14	38	
X	X	X	X	X	X	X	X	X	X	X	S	S	S	U	U																			1
X	X	X	X	X		X	X	X	X	S	S	U	X	U	S	X																		2
X	X	X	X	X		X	X	X	X	U	S	S	X	U	S	X																		3
X	X	X	X	X	S	X	X	X	X	S			X	U	U	X	S																	4
X	X	X	X	X	S	X	X	X	X	X		S	S	U	X		U																	5
X	X	X	X	X		X	X	X		X		S	X	U	X	S	S	U																6
X	X	X	X	X	X	S	X	X				X	X	U	X	U	U		S															7
X	X	X	X	X	X	U	X	X				X	X	U	X	S	S		S															8
X	X	X	X	X	U	S	X	X				X	X	U	X	X	S		S															9
X	X	X	X	X	U	S	X	X	S		S	X	X		X	X	U																	10
X	X	X	X	X	X	S	X	X	X		S	S	X	U	X		U																	11
X	X	X	X	X	X	S	X	X	X		S	S	X	U	X		U																	12
	X		**S**	**U**	**U**	**X**	**S**		**S**		**X**	**X**	**X**	**X**	**X**	**X**	**X**	**X**				**X**												13
X	X	X	X	X	X	X	X	X	X		U	S	X	U	U		S																	14
X	X	X	X	X	X	U	X	X	X		X	X	S		S		U			S														15
X	X	U	X		X	S	X	X	X		X	S	X		X		U			S	X													16
X	U	X	X	X	X	S	X	X	X		X		S		U		S			X	X													17
X	**X**		**X**	**X**	**X**	**U**	**X**	**X**	**X**		**X**		**X**	**U**	**X**	**S**	**U**			**S**														18
X	X		X	X	X	X	X	X	X		S	X	S		U	S				U	X													19
		X	**U**	**U**		**X**		**S**	**S**		**X**	**S**	**X**	**X**	**X**	**X**	**X**	**X**		**X**	**X**													20
X	**X**	**X**		**X**	**X**	**X**		**X**	**X**		**U**	**S**	**X**	**U**	**X**	**S**	**U**			**U**			**X**											21
X	X	X	U	X	X	X		X	X		U	X			X	S	U			S			X											22
X	**X**	**X**	**S**	**X**	**X**	**X**		**X**	**X**		**U**	**X**		**U**	**X**	**S**	**U**			**S**			**X**											23
X	X	X	X	X	X	S		X	X		S		X		S	X	U			U			X											24
X	X	X	X	X	S	U	X	X	U		S				X	U							X	X	X									25
X	X	X	X	X	X	S	X	X	S		S	U			X	U								X	X									26
X	X	X	X	X	X	S	X		S		X	U			X	U	U							X	X									27
X	**X**	**X**	**X**	**X**	**X**	**U**	**X**	**S**	**U**		**X**				**X**	**U**								**X**	**X**	**S**								28
X	X	X	X	X	U	U	X	S	S		X				X	S								X	X	X								29
X		X	X	X	X	X	X	X	S		U	U			X	U								X	X	S								30
X		X	X	X	X	U	X	X	S		X	U			X	U								X	X	S								31
X		X		X	X	X		X	S		X	S			X								X	X	X	U	U	U						32
X	X	X	S	X	X	S		X	X		X	S		U	X								X	X				U						33
X	X	X	X	X	X	S		X	S		U	S			X								X	X	X			U						34
X	X	X	X	X	X	U		X	X		X	S			S								X	X			U	S						35
X	X	X	X		X	X		X	X		S	S			X								X	X					S	U	U			36
X	X	X	X		X	S	X	X	X		U	S			X								X	X					S			U		37
X	X	X	X	X	X	U	X	X	X		S	S			S								X	X							U			38
X	X	X	X	X	X	S	X	X	X		S	S			U								X									U	X	39
X	X	X	X	X	X	S	X	X			U	X			S								X								U	U	X	40
X	X	X	X	X	X	U	X	X			S	S			X								X						X			U	U	41
X	X	X	X	X	X	U	X	X	X		U	X			S								X						S				S	42
X	X	X	X	X	X	S	X	U	S		U	S			X								X						X				X	43
X	X	X	X	X	U	X	X				S		X		X								X						X		U	S	S	44
X	X	X	X	X	X	U	X	X			U	X	X		S								X									U	S	45
	X	X	S	X	X	X	U	U			X	S	X		X								S								X	X	X	46
X	X	X	X	X	X	U	X	X			S	X	X		S								X									U	S	47
X	X	X	X	X	X	S	X	U			X	X			S								X								U	S	X	48
X	X	X	X	X	X	U	X	X			U	X	X		S								X									U	S	49
	X	X	X	X	X	S	X	S			U	S	X		X								X								X	U	X	50
X	X	X	X	X	X	U	X	S			S	S	X		X								X									U	X	51
X	X	X	X	X	X	U	X	U	S		S	X	X		X								X										S	52
Total League Appearances																																		
44	42	44	42	43	36	14	38	37	21	3	11	14	21	0	28	6	0	0	0	1	3	0	23	13	8	1	0	0	3	0	2	1	7	X
0	0	0	2	0	3	18	0	3	10	2	18	21	5	0	12	5	6	0	3	3	0	0	1	0	0	2	0	1	3	0	0	2	6	S
0	1	1	1	0	4	14	1	4	1	1	11	5	0	13	6	6	10	1	0	2	0	0	0	0	0	1	2	3	0	1	5	9	1	U
Total Cup Appearances																																		
4	5	4	2	4	4	4	2	3	3	0	4	2	4	2	6	2	2	2	0	1	1	1	2	1	1	0	0	0	0	0	0	0	0	X
0	0	0	2	0	0	0	1	2	2	0	0	2	0	0	0	3	0	0	0	2	0	0	0	0	0	1	0	0	0	0	0	0	0	S
0	0	0	1	2	1	2	0	0	1	0	2	0	0	3	0	1	3	0	0	1	0	0	0	0	0	0	0	0	0	0	0	0	0	U

EASTBOURNE BOROUGH

CURRENT SQUAD AS OF BEGINING OF 2009-10 SEASON

GOALKEEPERS		SQ NO.	HT	WT	D.O.B	AGE	P.O.B	CAREER	APPS	GOA
Michael	Jordan	21	6'02"	13 02	7/4/86	23	Enfield	Arsenal Rel c/s 06, Yeovil (SL) 3/06, Chesterfield 7/06 Rel 3/08, Lewes 3/08, Stevenage 8/08, Eastbourne B 1/09	2	0
Danny	Knowles	1	6'00"	12 00	7/1/86	23	Sidcup	Gillingham Rel 4/06, Hastings U (L) 8/04, Welling (4ML) 1/05, East Thurrock (3ML) 11/05, Grays 8/06 Rel 5/08, AFC Wimbledon (6WL) 11/07, Crawley (7DL) 3/08, Fisher (SL) 3/08, Weymouth 7/08 Rel 2/09, Woking 2/09 Rel 5/09, Eastbourne B 5/09		
Dean	Lightwood							Newhaven, Ringmer, Saltdean, Shoreham, Lewes, Saltdean, Eastbourne B, Ringmer 8/03, Saltdean, Eastbourne B (Pl/Coach)	0	0

DEFENDERS										
Ben	Austin	5	5'09"	10 01	3/4/77	32	Hastings	Brighton (Jun), Eastbourne T, Eastbourne B 6/00	44	3
Darren	Baker	2	5'10"	09 06	23/11/74	34	Eastbourne	Brighton (Ass Sch), Littlehampton (Yth), Eastbourne B 6/92	42	0
Gary	Elphick	24	6'01"	13 02	17/10/85	23	Brighton	Brighton, Eastbourne B (L) 9/04, St Albans (SL) 12/04, Aldershot (2ML) 1/06, St Albans 3/06 Rel 12/07, Havant & W 12/07, Eastbourne B 5/09		
Matt	Hurley	20						Mile Oak, Burgess Hill 8/03, Shoreham, Eastbourne B 8/09		
Neil	Jenkins	3	5'06"	10 08	6/1/82	27	Carshalton	Wimbledon Rel c/s 02, Southend 8/02 Rel c/s 04, Crawley 6/04, Eastbourne B 7/06	43	0
Marc	Pullan	6	6'03"	14 06	28/2/74	35	Brighton	Peacehaven, Crawley 7/96 Rel c/s 98, Year Out, Wick 7/99, Crawley 1/00, Worthing 6/04, Eastbourne B 1/06	44	1

MIDFIELDERS										
Paul	Armstrong	8	5'08"	10 09	5/10/78	30	Dublin	Cherry Orchard (Ire) (Yth), Brighton Rel c/s 00, Airdrie 7/00, Airdrie U 7/02, Crawley 6/03, Eastbourne 6/06	38	9
Danny	Brown	26	6'00"	12 06	12/9/80	28	Bethnal Green	L.Orient, Barnet £40,000 5/99 Rel c/s 03, Oxford U 7/03 Rel c/s 05, Crawley 8/05 Rel 11/06, Cambridge U 11/06, Eastbourne B (2ML) 11/08, Perm 1/09	24	1
Matt	Crabb	11	5'10"	12 01	15/12/81	27	Eastbourne	Eastbourne U, Eastbourne B 7/00, Langney Sports (L) 8/00	39	6
Nathan	Crabb	15			26/6/85	24	Eastbourne	Eastbourne Utd Assoc, Eastbourne B 8/07	35	5
Simon	Johnson	12					Hailsham	Eastbourne B	1	0
Matt	Smart	4	5'10"	12 04	14/4/76	33	Crawley	Gillingham (Trainee, Crawley, Shoreham, Horsham, Wick, Horsham, Eastbourne B 7/01	40	4
Danny	Smith	7	5'10"	10 07	7/6/89	20	Plymouth	Plymouth Rel 5/09, Morecambe (L) 9/08, Eastbourne B (3ML) 11/08, Eastbourne B 5/09	13	3
Simon	Weatherstone	14	5'11"	11 00	26/1/80	29	Reading	Oxford U, Boston U 2/01, Yeovil £15,000 1/04, Hornchurch Undisc 9/04, Stevenage 11/04 Rel 5/06, Weymouth 6/06 Rel 5/08, Crawley 5/08 Rel 5/09, Eastbourne B 5/09		

FORWARDS										
Andy	Atkin	9	6'00"	11 11	19/1/81	28	Hastings	Sidley U, Little Common, Sidley U c/s 00, Hooe Sports, Little Common, Eastbourne Utd Assoc 3/01, Eastbourne B 3/05	31	8
Kane	Louis		5'11"	10 11	21/5/90	19		Brighton Rel c/s 09, Burgess Hill (L) 8/08, Luton (Trial) 7/09, Eastbourne B 8/09		
Liam	Marum	10	6'03"	12 00	17/11/87	21	London	Reading (Scholar) Rel c/s 06, Brighton (Trial) 7/06, Cambridge U 8/06, Woking 1/07 Rel 5/09, Eastbourne B 5/09		
Jamie	Taylor	18	5'07"	11 11	16/12/82	26	Crawley	Broadbridge H, Horsham c/s 01, Aldershot 8/02 Rel 2/04, Horsham (L) 2/03, Carshalton (L) 12/03, Oakwood 2/04, AFC Wimbledon 3/04, Horsham 10/04, Woking 12/06, Dag & Red 3/07, Grays (SL) 2/08, Grays 5/08, Eastbourne B 7/09		
Ross	Treleaven	19	5'09"	09 13	14/12/88	20	Brighton	Crowborough, Eastbourne B (Dual) 3/08 Perm c/s 08, Worthing (Dual) 8/08		

LOANEES		SN	HT	WT	DOB	AGE	POB	From - To	APPS	GOA
(F)Viktor Unnar	Illugason		6'01"	12 08	25/1/90	19	Reykjavik, Ice	Reading 9/08 -	3	0
(F)Lyle	Taylor							Millwall (2ML) 10/08 - Croydon Ath (L) 1/09 Rel 5/09	4	1
(D)Karleigh	Osborne		6'02"	12 04	19/3/88	21	Southall	Brentford 10/08	3	1
(F)Jeff	Goulding				13/5/84	25		Bournemouth 11/08 -	3	0
(F)Ashley	Barnes				31/10/89	19	Bath	Plymouth (2ML) 11/08 -	8	5
(F)Sam	Gargan		6'03"	11 12	24/6/88	21	Hurstpierrepoint	Brighton 1/09, 3/09 - Rel 5/09, Sutton U 8/09	6	1
(F)Jack	Jeffrey		5'08"	11 10	13/8/89	20	Gravesend	West Ham (SL) 3/09 - Rel c/s 09	13	3

DEPARTURES		SN	HT	WT	DOB	AGE	POB	From - To	APPS	GOA
(F)Evan	Archibald							Yth - Horsham 8/08		
(D)Dominic	Douglas							Bexhill U 9/06 - Worthing (Dual) 8/08 Perm		
(D)Pat	Sappleton				16/4/82	27	London	Margate 9/08 - Godalming T 11/08, Maidenhead 11/08	0	0
(D)Andy	Ballard						Oxford	Abingdon U 8/07 - Hastings U (Dual) 9/08, Oxford C 11/08	0	0
(F)Jean-Michel	Sigere		6'00"	12 08	26/1/77	32	Francois, Mart	Lewes 6/08 - Rel 1/09, Horsham (3ML) 10/08, Farnborough 1/09, Tonbridge 7/09	5	0
(G)Chris	Winterton		5'10"	12 06	18/11/88	20	Eastbourbe	Brighton 7/08 - Worthing (L) 12/08, Rel 1/09, Lewes 1/09 Rel 3/09, Finland		
(M)Mo	Harkin		5'09"	11 11	16/8/79	30	Derry	Havant & W 6/08 - Farnborough 1/09	11	0
(F)	Xano				20/4/83	26	San Jorge de Arrois, Port	Pampilhosa (Port) 11/08 - Rel	0	0
(G)Lee	Hook		5'09"	08 11	11/3/79	30	Margate	Sittingbourne 6/03 - Rel 5/09, Dover 5/09	44	0
(F)Allan	Tait				6/9/81	27	London	Canvey Island 6/06 - Rel 5/09, Basingstoke (3ML) 12/08, Dartford 5/09	26	2
(M)Jay	Lovett		6'01"	12 00	22/1/78	31	Plymouth	Lewes 6/06 - Rel 5/09, Whitehawk 8/09	40	1
(M)Jacob	Mingle							Horsham Undisc 2/09 - Rel 5/09, Braintree 6/09	3	0
(F)Pat	Harding				6/12/83	25		Hassocks 6/06 - Rel 5/09, Horsham 6/09	32	2
(M)Darren	Budd				9/9/84	24	Brighton	Bognor 10/07 - Horsham (Dual) 12/08 Perm	6	0
(M)Simon	Wormull		5'10"	12 03	12/12/76	32	Crawley	Lewes 6/08 - Rel 6/09, Farnborough 6/09	29	2
(M)Brett	Patton							Yth - Worthing 6/09		
(M)Sam	Crabb				25/10/87	21	Eastbourne	Eastbourne U c/s 08 - Eastbourne U (Dual) c/s 08, Lewes c/s 09		

EASTBOURNE BOROUGH

Formed: 1966

Nickname: Borough

Club Colours: Red shirts, black shorts, red socks.

Change Colours: All light blue.

Club Sponsor: Best Demolition Group.

Previous League: Southern League.

Ground Address: Langnet Sports Club, Priory Lane, Eastbourne BN23 7QH
Tel No: 01323 766 265
Fax: 01323 741 627
Official website: www.eastbourneboroughfc.co.uk

SIMPLE DIRECTIONS

By Road From M25 - take A27 or A23 to Polegate traffic lights at junction of A27/A22. Turn left, to large roundabout on A22 (0.5mile). Take A27 polegate bypass eastbound to next roundabout, you will pick up Crematorium signs. Follow the sign (2-3 miles) crematorium on your right. Proceed to mini roundabout, 500yds, turn right into Priory Rd, ground 500yds on left.

Parking: Approximately 400 spaces.

MATCH TICKETS

Ticket office Telephone: 01323 766 265
Adults: £13.00
Concessions: £9.00
U16's: £4.00
Seating Transfer: £2.00

Capacity: 4,151
Seats: 542
Covered: 2,500
Clubhouse: Open every evening and lunchtime
Club Shop: Yes

PROGRAMME EDITOR
Mike Spooner
Tel: 01323 471 071

CLUB STATISTICS

RECORDS

Attendance: 3,770 v Oxford United F.A. Cup 1st Rnd 05.11.05.

Victory: 10-1 v Haywards Heath Town Sussex Co. Div 1 91-92.

Defeat: 0-8 v Sheppey United (A) F.A. Vase 09.10.93.

0-8 v Peacehaven & Telscombe (A) Sussex Co Div 1 09.11.93.

Career Goalscorer: Nigel Hole - 146.

Career Appearances: Darren Baker - 689.

Transfer Fee Paid: £1,800 to Yeovil Town for Yemi Odoubade.

Received: £15,000 from Oxford United for Yemi Odoubade.

Senior Honours:

Sussex Co Champions 1999-00, 02-03.

Sussex Senior Cup 2001-2002.

Previous Leagues:

Eastbourne & Hastings, Sussex County, Southern.

Previous Name: Langney Sports.

EBBSFLEET UNITED

Back Row (L-R): Kwesi Appiah, Peter Hawkins, John Akinde, Gary MacDonald, Darius Charles, James Smith, Neil Barrett.
Middle: Ron Hillyard (goalkeeping coach), George Purcell, Ricky Shakes, Michael Gash, Rob French, Lance Cronin, Sam Mott, Kezie Ibe, Mark Ricketts, Luke Moore, Chris Domoney (fitness & conditioning).
Front: Ian Docker (youth coach), Craig Stone, Dean Pooley, Sacha Opinel, Alan Kimble, Liam Daish, Paul McCarthy, Danny Slatter, Stacy Long, Paul Wilson (sports therapist). Courtesy of EUFC.co.uk

CLUB PERSONNEL

Chairman: Duncan Holt.

Additional Directors: Brian Kilcullen.

Club Secretary: Peter Danzey.
c/o of the club.
Tel: 01474 533 796
e-mail: peter@eufc.co.uk

Commercial Manager: Barry Wickenden
(B) 01474 533 796
E-mail: wicks@eufc.co.uk

Press Officer: Charles Webster
(M) 07711 893 802
E-mail: media@eufc.co.uk

Manager: Liam Daish
Previous clubs as a manager: Havant & Water'ville, Welling United.
As a player: Portsmouth, Cambridge United, Barnet, Birmingham City, Coventry City & Eire
Assistant Manager: Paul McCarthy.
Club therapist: Paul Wilson.

After all the publicity sparked by thousands of "MyFootballClub" members being involved with the club, and the excellent F.A.Trophy success in front of 40,186 in May 2008, a bonus of £140,000 had been received for John Akinde and expectations were understandably high. Most supporters expected their club to be moving steadily upwards in the ever improving Blue Square Premier but at the end of the campaign manager Liam Daish and the supporters were disappointed.

The first half of the season saw the club battle to stay in the top half of the league and only two defeats in the first dozen games saw 'The Fleet' in fifth position. An F.A.Cup First Round tie saw the club lose 0-1 at Crewe Alexandra and league results deteriorated leaving them in fourteenth place at the New Year.

As holders, Ebbsfleet battled to retain the F.A.Trophy with much courage and determination. Bognor Regis Town (2-0 Away), Stalybridge Celtic (2-0 home) and Swindon Supermarine (2-0 home) were all beaten before being drawn away at Wrexham. A tight 0-0 draw brought the Welsh club back to Stonebridge Road and a 2-1 victory brought a place in the Semi-Finals once again.

Sadly for The Fleet they met a Stevenage Borough squad in top form and lost 2-4 on aggregate. The season finished for the Kent club and their supporters with the anti-climax of meaningless league fixtures and a finish to the season in fourteenth position.

EBBSFLEET UNITED

BEST LGE ATT.: 1,872 v Mansfield Town
LOWEST: 711 v Burton Albion

No.	Date	Comp	H/A	Opponents	Att:	Result	Goalscorers	Pos
1	Aug 9	BSP	H	Mansfield Town	1872	D 2 - 2	Moore 8 Long 28	
2	12		A	Rushden & Diamonds	1467	L 0 - 2		
3	18		A	Torquay United	1805	W 2 - 0	Moore 26 Akinde 78	15
4	23		H	Stevenage Borough	1420	W 4 - 0	Barrett 19 Akinde 45 Moore 69 (pen) Ibe 84	8
5	25		A	Lewes	851	D 0 - 0		9
6	30		H	Oxford United	1842	D 1 - 1	**Gash** 56	12
7	Sept 2		H	Cambridge United	1832	D 1 - 1	Moore 52	
8	6		A	Forest Green Rovers	1272	W 4 - 1	Barrett 3 Moore 42 **Gash** 66 Ibe 83	10
9	13		A	Wrexham	3132	L 2 - 3	Barrett 27 **Gash** 90	13
10	20		H	Woking	1498	W 2 - 0	Appiah 57 Barrett 58	8
11	23		H	Eastbourne Borough	1120	D 1 - 1	**Gash** 65	10
12	27		A	Barrow	1378	W 3 - 0	Moore 32 **Gash** 63 82	5
13	Oct 4		A	Altrincham	967	L 0 - 2		9
14	6		H	Histon	1226	L 0 - 1		
15	11		A	Kidderminster Harriers	1512	L 1 - 3	Shakes 15	11
16	18		H	Torquay United	1781	L 0 - 2		16
17	**25**	**F.A.C. 4Q**	**A**	**Woking**	**1462**	**D 2 - 2**	**Moore 68 (pen) 70 (pen)**	
18	**28**	**F.A.C. 4Q r**	**H**	**Woking**	**869**	**W 1 - 0**	**Ibe 19**	
19	Nov 1		A	Burton Albion	1584	L 1 - 3	Ibe 59	17
20	**4**	**SS 3**	**A**	**Eastbourne Borough**	**300**	**W 3 - 1**	**Ibe 2 (9, 42), Smith 22**	
21	**8**	**F.A.C. 1R**	**A**	**Crewe Alexandra**	**2593**	**L 0 - 1**		
22	15		H	Barrow	1187	W 1 - 0	Barrett 90	14
23	20		A	Crawley Town	922	W 2 - 1	**Gash** 83 Moore 90	13
24	23		H	Kettering Town	1018	D 0 - 0		13
25	29		A	Cambridge United	2807	L 0 - 1		13
26	**Dec 2**	**SS S4**	**H**	**Stevenage Borough**	**285**	**W 3 - 0**	**Purcell 14, Long 2 (24, 81)**	
27	6		H	Weymouth	1005	W 1 - 0	Purcell 24	12
28	9		H	Forest Green Rovers	728	L 0 - 1		
29	**16**	**F.A.T. 1R**	**A**	**Bognor Regis Town**	**299**	**W 2 - 0**	**Byrne (og)1 Long 45**	
30	20		A	York City	1997	L 1 - 3	**Gash** 26	
31	26		H	Grays Athletic	1143	L 0 - 1		13
32	28		A	Oxford United	5120	L 1 - 5	Long 77	14
33	Jan 1		A	Grays Athletic	748	L 1 - 3	Ibe 73	14
34	**13**	**F.A.T 2R**	**H**	**Stalybridge Celtic**	**467**	**W 2 - 1**	**Long 63 Hand 68**	
35	17		H	Rushden & Diamonds	1121	W 1 - 0	Barrett 41	15
36	24		A	Woking	1471	L 0 - 1		16
37	27		H	Crawley Town	795	D 4 - 4	Long 12 **Gash** 16 Sole 46 Shakes 64	
38	**31**	**F.A.T. 3R**	**H**	**Swindon Supermarine**	**3750**	**W 2 - 0**	**Gash 55 59**	
39	**Feb 21**	**F.A.T. 4R**	**A**	**Wrexham**	**3028**	**D 0 - 0**		
40	**24**	**F.A.T. 4R r**	**H**	**Wrexham**	**992**	**W 2 - 1**	**Sole 57 Moore 75**	
41	Mar 8		H	York City	1244	D 0 - 0		
42	11		H	Burton Albion	711	W 2 - 1	Sole 34 69 (pen)	
43	**14**	**F.A.T. SF 1**	**A**	**Stevenage Borough**	**2344**	**L 2 - 3**	**Barrett 61 Long 72**	
44	**17**	**SS QFS**	**A**	**Crawley Town**	**844**	**W 2 - 1**	**Smith 67, Slatter 85**	
45	**21**	**F.A.T. SF 2**	**H**	**Stevenage Borough**	**3008**	**L 0 - 1**		
46	24		A	Salisbury City	939	L 0 - 1		
47	**26**	**SS SFS**	**H**	**Forest Green Rovers**	**431**	**L 0 - 1**		
48	28		A	Kettering Town	1533	L 1 - 2	Sole 6	21
49	31		H	Altrincham	774	W 1 - 0	Shakes 6	19
50	April 2		A	Eastbourne Borough	919	W 1 - 0	**Gash** 56	
51	4		H	Northwhich Victoria	1003	W 1 - 0	Smith 69	15
52	7		A	Mansfield Town	1630	L 0 - 2		17
53	9		H	Kidderminster Harriers	979	D 1 - 1	Long 27 (pen)	
54	11		A	Stevenage Borough	1913	L 0 - 1		16
55	13		H	Lewes	1098	W 2 - 1	Yussuff 45 Sole 71 (pen)	
56	16		A	Histon	1015	L 2 - 5	Pooley 4 Sole 13	
57	18		A	Weymouth	1007	W 2 - 0	Shakes 5 Ibe 11	15
58	21		H	Wrexham	880	W 1 - 0	Ricketts 65	
59	23		A	Northwich Victoria	474	L 0 - 2		
60	26		H	Salisbury City	1390	D 2 2	McCarthy 52 Smith 90	

Average Home Att: 1203 (1088) **Goals 73 72**
Best Position: 5th **Worst:** 21st
Goalscorers: Gash 12, Moore 10, Long 9,Ibe 8, Barrett 7, Sole 7, Shakes 4, Smith 4, Akinde 2, Purcell 2, Appiah 1, Hand 1, McCarthy 1, Pooley 1, Ricketts 1, Slatter 1, Yussuff 1. Own Goals 1.

CRONIN 1	HAWKINS 2	SMITH 5	CHARLES 24	OPINEL 3	STONE 11	LONG 8	BARRETT 14	MOORE 18	SHAKES 16	GASH 9	AKINDE 19	MOTT 21	RICKETTS 15	APPIAH 22	PURCELL 17	McCARTHY 6	HAND 23	IBE 20	POOLEY 12	SLATTER 7	BOWES 25	FRENCH 30	MURRAY 26	DELICATE 27	SPRINGETT 28	CROOKS 4	DUNCAN 25	JUDGE 27	SOLE 26	MARTIN 10	HENRY 31	CUMBERS 22	WEST 29	COLE	CALLENDER	TURBINE	STEVENS 19	YUSSUF 23	
X	X	X	X	X	X	X	X	X	X	X	S	U	U	U	U																								1
X	X	X	X	X	X	X	X	X	X	X	S	U	U	S	S																								2
X	U		X	X	X	X	X	X	X	X	S	U	X		S	X	S																						3
X	U		X	X	X	X	X	X	X	X	S	U	X			X	S	S																					4
X	U		X	X	X	X	X	X		X	X	U	X		S	X	S	S																					5
X	S		X	X	X	X	X	X		X		U	X	U	X	X	S	S																					6
X			X	X	U	X	X	X	U	X		U	X		X	X	X	S	U																				7
X			X	X	S	X	X	X	S	X		U	X		X	X	X	S	U																				8
X		X	X	X	U	X	X	X	X	X		U	X				X	S	U	S																			9
X			X	X	S	X	X		X	X		U	X	S		X	X	X	U	S																			10
X			X	X	U	X	X	X		X		U	X	X		X	X	S	U	S																			11
X			X	X	S	X	X	X	S	X		U	X			X	X	U	S	X																			12
X	X	U	X		U	X	X	X	S	X		U	X				X	S	X	X																			13
X		U	X		S	X	X	X	X	X		U	X			X	X	S	X	S																			14
X	X	U			X		X	X	X	X		U	X		S	X	X	S	X	U																			15
X		U	X	X	S	X	X	X	X	X		U				X	X	U	X		S																		16
X	S	X	X		X	X	X	X	U	X		U	X		S	X	U	X	U		U																		17
X	U	X	X	X	X	X	X	X	S	X		U	X		S		U	X	U		U																		18
X		X	X	X	X	X	X		X	X			X		S		S	X	U		S	U																	19
U	X	X		U	X	S			X	S			X		X		X	X	X	X	S	X																	20
X	U	X	X	X	X	S	X		S	X		U	X		X		X	X	U	U	U																		21
X		X	X	X	X	S	X	X		X		U	X		X			S	U	S			X																22
X		X	X	X	X	X	X	X		X		U	X		S			U	U	S				X															23
X		X	X	X	X	X	X	X		X		U	X		S				U	S			S	X															24
X		X	X	X	X	X	X	X	S	X			X		S				U			U	S	X															25
X	U		X	X	S	X		X	S	U					X		X	X	X	X		U	X																26
X			X	X	S	X	X	X	U	X			S		X		X	U	X	X		U																	27
X	X			X	U	X	X	X		X			S		X		X	S	X	X		U	S																28
X	U	X		X	S	X		X	S	X					X		X	S	X	X		U	X																29
X	U	X		X	X	X		X	S	X			U		X			S	X	X		U	X																30
X	S	X		X		X	U	X	S	X		U			X		X	S	X	X			X																31
X	X	X		X	S	X	U	X	S				X		X		X	X				U	X		U														32
X	X			X	U	X	X	X	X	X			U		S		S	S	X	X			X																33
X	U	X		X	X	X	S	S	S	X		U	X		X		X	X	X																				34
X		X			X	X	X	X	S	X		U			X		X	U	U	U						X	X												35
X		X			X	X	X		S	X		U	U		X		X	S	U							X	X	X											36
X		X			X	X	X		X	X			U		U		X	U	S							X	X	U	X										37
X		X			X	X	X	S	X	X		U	S				X		U							X	X	S	X										38
X			X		X	X	X	S	X	X		U	S						U							X	X	S	X	X									39
X			X	S		X	X	X	S	X		U	X						U							X	X	U	X	X									40
X		U	X	X		X	X	X	S	X		U	X							U						X	S		X	X									41
X		U	X	X		X	X	X	U	X			X					U		S						X	S		X	X									42
X		S	X	X		X	X	X	S	X		U	X							X						X	S	U	X										43
		X							X			X			X	X			X	X		U			U			X			X	X	X	S	U	U			44
X		X	X	X		X		X	X	X		U	X		S					U						X			X			S					U		45
X		S	X			X		X	X			U	X		U					S						X	X		S	X		X					X		46
U	X	U		X					S			X			X	X			X	X							S	X			X	S	X	X					47
X		S	X	X		X		S	S	X		U														X	X		X	X		X					X	U	48
X			X	S		X		X	X	X		U	X		S	X				X						X				X			U					S	49
X		X	X	S		X		X	X	X		U	X		S	X				S						X				X			U						50
X		X	X	U		X			X	X		U	X		U	X				X						X			S	X			S						51
X		X	X	X		X			X	X		U	X		S					S						X			X		U		X				S		52
X			X	X		X			X	X		U	X		S				U	X						X			S		U		X				X		53
X			X	X		X			X	X		U	X		S			S	S							X			U				X				X	X	54
X			X	X		X			X	X		U	X		U			S	S							X			S				X				X	X	55
X	X		S			S						U	X		X			X	X							X		U	X		X		S				X	X	56
X	X		X			X		S	X			U	X		S	X		X	U							X			X				X					S	57
X			X			X		X		X		U	X		U	X		S	S								X		X				X				X	S	58
X						X		X	X			U	X		S	X		X	X						U				S		S		X				X	X	59
X		X	X	U		X		X	X			U	X		S	X		X	X										U				X					S	60
Total League Appearances																																							
46	9	18	35	31	16	43	29	34	23	40	1	0	34	1	12	19	17	7	12	10	0	0	5	3	0	16	6	1	8	7	1	2	8	0	0	0	8	4	X
0	2	2	1	2	7	2	0	2	11	0	4	0	2	2	17	0	6	19	5	11	2	0	3	0	0	0	2	0	5	0	1	0	2	0	0	0	1	4	S
0	4	6	0	2	6	0	2	0	3	0	0	37	6	2	6	0	0	7	14	3	0	6	0	0	2	0	0	2	2	0	2	0	2	0	0	0	0	1	U
Total Cup Appearances																																							
11	2	9	8	8	7	10	7	7	5	10	0	2	8	0	7	3	6	6	6	6	0	1	2	0	0	5	3	2	5	2	2	1	2	1	0	0	0	0	X
0	1	1	0	1	2	2	1	3	8	1	0	0	2	0	3	0	0	1	0	0	1	0	0	0	0	0	2	2	0	0	0	2	0	1	0	0	0	0	S
2	5	1	0	1	0	0	0	0	1	1	0	9	0	0	0	0	2	0	6	2	3	3	0	0	1	0	0	2	0	0	0	0	0	0	1	1	1	0	U

EBBSFLEET UNITED

CURRENT SQUAD AS OF BEGINING OF 2009-10 SEASON

GOALKEEPERS		SQ NO.	HT	WT	D.O.B	AGE	P.O.B	CAREER	APPS	GOA
Lance	Cronin	1	6'01"	13 02	11/9/85	23	Brighton	Brighton (Jun), C.Palace, Wycombe (L) 3/05, Oldham 11/05 Rel 2/06, Shrewsbury 2/06, MK Dons (Trial) 4/06, Gravesend/Ebbsfleet 8/06	46	0
Matthew	Lamprell	21						Millwall, Ebbsfleet 8/09		
DEFENDERS										
Darius	Charles	24	5'11"	11 10	10/12/87	21	Ealing	Brentford, Thurrock (L) 2/06, Yeading (L) 3/06, Staines (L) 10/06, Crawley (2ML) 2/07, Sutton U (L) 8/07, Ebbsfleet (SL) 3/08, Ebbsfleet (SL) 6/08 £15,000+ 1/09, York C Undisc 6/09	36	0
Jordan	Collins	3			7/12/88	20		Cambridge U Rel 5/09, Billericay (L) 11/07, Heybridge (SL) 3/08, Weymouth (SL) 11/08, Ebbsfleet 7/09		
Paul	McCarthy	6	5'10"	13 10	4/8/71	38	Cork	Brighton, Wycombe £100,000 7/96 Rel c/s 03, Oxford U (SL) 3/03, Oxford U 7/03, Rel c/s 04, Hornchurch 6/04, Gravesend/Ebbsfleet 11/04	19	1
Dean	Pooley	5	6'01"	11 02	10/9/86	22	Sidcup	Millwall Rel 12/06, Crawley (L) 3/06, Beckenham (L) 9/06, Bohemians 3/07 Rel 1/08, Ballymena 1/08 Rel 2/08, Ebbsfleet 8/08	17	1
Charlie	Read		6'00"	11 00	26/9/90	18		Millwall (Scholar), Ebbsfleet 8/09		
Will	Salmon	2			25/11/86	22	Basingstoke	Aldershot Rel c/s 07, Fleet T (SL) c/s 05, Fleet T (SL) 8/06, AFC Wimbledon 6/07 Rel 5/08, Fleet T (L) 2/08, Fleet T c/s 08, Ebbsfleet 8/09		
Steve	Springett							Ebbsfleet		
MIDFIELDERS										
Leon	Crooks	22	6'00"	11 12	21/11/85	23	Greenwich	Wimbledon/MK Dons, Wycombe Undisc 1/07 Rel 5/09, Ebbsfleet (3ML) 1/09, Ebbsfleet 8/09	16	0
Jamie	Forshaw	10	5'08"	11 00	21/11/90	18		Norwich (Sch), Southend Rel 5/09, Bishops Stortford (L) 11/08, Ebbsfleet 7/09		
Gavin	Heeroo	4	5'11"	11 07	2/9/84	24	Harringey	C.Palace Rel c/s 04, L.Orient (Trial) 4/04, Billericay c/s 04, Grays 10/04, Farnborough 3/05, Histon (Trial) 9/05, Cambridge U (SL) 11/05, Chelmsford 8/06 Rel 1/07, Fisher 1/07, Sutton U 7/08, Eastleigh 3/09 Rel 5/09, Ebbsfleet 7/09		
Ricky	Shakes	16	5'10"	12 00	26/1/85	24	Brixton	Bolton Rel c/s 05, Bristol R (L) 2/05, Bury (SL) 3/05, Swindon 8/05 Rel c/s 07, Brentford (Trial) 7/07, Brentford 8/07 Rel 5/08, Ebbsfleet 7/08	34	4
Scott	Shulton	15			31/1/90	19		Watford (Yth), Wycombe Rel 5/09, Hendon (WE) 11/07, Basingstoke (L) 9/08, Hendon (L) 12/08, Ebbsfleet 8/09		
Ishmael	Welsh	11	5'07"	10 10	4/9/87	21	Deptford	West Ham Rel c/s 06, Yeovil 7/06 Rel 5/08, Weymouth (L) 3/07, Torquay (5ML) 8/07, Forest Green (SL) 2/08, Grays 5/08, Ebbsfleet 7/09		
Michael	West	7						Ebbsfleet 10/08	10	0
Kane	Wills	14	5'09"	10 02	27/2/90	19	Shoreham	Brighton Rel 5/09, Bognor (L) 10/08, Bognor (SL) 1/09, Ebbsfleet 8/09		
FORWARDS										
Scott	Ginty		5'08"	11 11	17/5/91	18		Peterborough (Scholar) Rel c/s 09, Stamford (WE) 3/09, Ebbsfleet 8/09		
James	Lindie	9						Southend, Harlow (3ML) 1/08, CD Javea (Spa) (5ML) 7/08, Grays (L) 2/09, Bishops Stortford (SL) 3/09, Ebbsfleet 7/09		
Magno	Vieira	8	5'09"	11 07	13/2/85	24	Bahia, Bra	Wigan Rel c/s 05, Northampton (2ML) 1/04, Carlisle (SL) 8/04, Year out, Barnet 7/06 Rel c/s 07, Crawley 6/07 Rel 5/08, Cambridge U (SL) 3/08, Wycombe 6/08 Rel c/s 09, Ebbsfleet 8/09		
Ryan	Cole							Ebbsfleet	0	0
Sam	Callender							Ebbsfleet, Whitstable, Ramsgate 3/09	0	0
Myron	Turbine							Ebbsfleet	0	0

LOANEES		HT	WT	DOB	AGE	POB	From - To	APPS	GOA
(D)Gary	Bowes	5'11"	12 00	14/2/90	19	Ilford	Millwall 10/08 - Croydon Ath (L) 12/08, Rel 5/09	2	0
(M)Karl	Murray	5'11"	12 06	26/8/82	27	London	Bromley (2ML) 11/08 - Northwich (L) 1/09, Croydon Ath 2/09	8	0
(F)Giuseppe	Sole			8/1/88	21		Woking (SL) 1/09 -	13	5
(M)John	Martin	5'05"	10 00	15/7/81	28	Bethnal Green	Stevenage (2ML) 2/09 - Rel 5/09, Chelmsford 8/09	7	0
(F)Luis	Cumbers	6'00"	11 10	6/9/88	20	Chelmsford	Gillingham 3/09 -	2	1
(D)Jamie	Stevens	5'11"	11 04	25/2/89	20	Holbeach	Northwich (SL) 3/09 - Rel 6/09	9	0
(M)Rashid	Yussuf	6'01"	11 07	23/9/89	19	Poplar	Charlton (SL) 3/09 - Rel c/s 09, Gillingham 8/09	8	1

DEPARTURES		HT	WT	DOB	AGE	POB	From - To	APPS	GOA
(D)Gary	MacDonald	6'01"	12 12	25/10/79	29	Iselone, Ger	Woking 6/07 - Rel 8/08, Bognor 8/08 Rel 11/08, Hayes & Yeading 12/08		
(F)John	Akinde	6'02"	10 01	8/7/89	20	Gravesend	Yth - Bristol C £140,000 9/08, Wycombe (L) 3/09	5	2
(F)Kwesi	Appiah	5'11"	12 08	12/8/90	19	Peterborough	Yth - Peterborough NC 10/08, Weymouth (L) 2/09	3	1
(F)Matthew	Delicate	6'03"	13 08	7/2/82	27		Rochester Rhinos (USA) 11/08 - Rel 1/09	3	0
(M)Jamie	Hand	6'00"	11 08	7/2/84	25	Uxbridge	Lincoln C 8/08 - Rel 2/09, Chelmsford 2/09	23	0
(M)Danny	Slatter	5'08"	10 02	15/11/80	28	Cardiff	Welling 6/05, Farnborough 6/09	21	0
(D)Peter	Hawkins	6'00"	11 04	19/9/78	30	Maidstone	Rushden & D 3/06 - Maidstone (3ML) 1/09, Maidstone 5/09	11	0
(M)George	Purcell	5'11"	11 09	8/4/88	21	Gravesend	Gillingham 8/06 - Ramsgate (L) 2/09, Braintree 5/09	29	1
(M)Stacy	Long	5'08"	10 00	11/1/85	24	Bromley	Notts County 7/06 - Rel 5/09, Stevenage 6/09	45	4
(G)Rob	French	6'03"	13 09	15/7/90	19	Cambridge	Yth - Sittingbourne (L) 8/08, Bognor (L) 1/09, Faversham 6/09	0	0
(D)Sasha	Opinel	5'09"	12 00	9/4/77	32	Saint Maurice	Crawley 7/06 - Farnborough 6/09	33	0
(D)James	Smith	6'01"	13 12	30/8/86	23	London	Welling £3,000 + 6/05 - Farnborough 6/09	20	2
(M)Mark	Ricketts	6'00"	11 02	7/10/84	24	Sidcup	Charlton 8/06 - Woking 6/09	36	1
(F)Luke	Moore	5'11"	11 07	27/4/88	21	Gravesend	Yth - AFC Wimbledon 6/09	36	6
(M)Derek	Duncan	5'10"	10 11	23/4/87	22	Newham	Wycombe 1/09 - AFC Wimbledon 6/09	8	0
(M)Neil	Barrett	5'10"	11 00	24/12/81	27	Tooting	Woking 6/07 - York C Undisc 6/09	29	6
(F)Michael	Gash	5'09"	12 01	3/9/86	22	Cambridge	Cambridge C £20,000 7/08 - York C £55,000 7/09	40	11
(F)Kezie	Ibe	5'10"	12 00	6/12/82	26	London	Chelmsford 8/08 - AFC Wimbledon (L) 3/09, Farnborough 6/09	26	5
(G)Sam	Mott	6'01"	10 01	1/8/88	21	Gravesend	Yth - Croydon A (L) 12/08	0	0
(D)Chris	Henry						Yth -	2	0
(M)Craig	Stone	6'00"	10 05	19/12/88	19	Gravesend	Gillingham 6/08 -	23	0
(F)Matthew	Judge	6'00"	11 07	18/1/85	24	Barking	Sligo R 1/09 -	1	0

EBBSFLEET UNITED

Re-Formed: 1946

Nickname: The Fleet

Club Colours: Red shirts, white shorts, red socks.

Change Colours: White shirts, red shorts and white socks.

Club Sponsor: Eurostar Group Ltd

Previous League: Isthmian League

Ground Address: Stonebridge Road, Northfleet, Kent DA11 9GN
Tel No: 01474 533 796
Fax: 01474 324 754
General email address: info@eufc.co.uk
Official website: www.eufc.co.uk

SIMPLE DIRECTIONS

By Road From A2 take Northfleet/Southfleet exit (B262) follow to Northfleet then B2175 (Springflet Road) to junction A226. Turn left (The H~Ill, Northfleet) and road becomes Stonebridge Road. Ground is at the bottom of a steep hill on the right after a mile.

Parking: Room for about 500 cars.
By Rail: Ground is eight minutes from Northfleet (BR) station.

MATCH TICKETS

Ticket office Telephone: 01474 533 796
Ticket Prices: Terrace - £15/£7.
U16s - £23 for the season.
Capacity: 4,184
Seats: 500
Covered: 3,000
Clubhouse: Fleet Social Centre
Refreshments: Hot and cold food available on matchdays
Club Shop: Sells all types of club products

PROGRAMME EDITOR
Rachel Willett
Tel: 01474 533 796
rachel@eufc.co.uk

CLUB STATISTICS

RECORDS

Attendance: 12,036 v Sunderland F.A. Cup 4th Rd.12.02.63.
Victory: 8-1 v Clacton Town Southern League1962-63.
Defeat: 0-9 v Trowbridge Town Southern League Premeir 1991-92.
Career Goalscorer: Steve Portway 152 (92-94 97-01).
Career Appearances: Ken Burrett 537.
Transfer Fee Paid: £8,000 to Wokingham Town for Richard Newbery 1996, and to Tonbridge for Craig Williams '97.
Transfer Fee Received:
£35,000 from West Ham United for Jimmy Bullard 1998.

SENIOR HONOURS

F.A. Trophy 2007-08
Isthmian League Champions 2001-2002
Southern League Champions 1956-1957
Southern Division 1994-95
Division One South1974-75
Kent Senior Cup 1948-49, 52-53, 80-81, 99-00, 00-01, 01-02.

PREVIOUS

Leagues: Kent (as Gravesend Utd). Southern 1946-79 80-96.
Alliance Premier 1979-80. Isthmian 1997-2002.
Names: Gravesend United & Northfleet United merged in 1946 to form Gravesend & Northfleet.
Grounds: Central Avenue (Gravesend Utd).
(Northfleet always played at Stonebridge Road)

FOREST GREEN ROVERS

CLUB PERSONNEL

Chairman: Trevor Horsley.

Company Secretary: Tim Brown.

Directors: Jenny Anns, Martin Anns, Ken Boulton, Mike Bullingham, Mark Coles, Paul Dowdeswell, Colin Peake & Robert Savage (Supporters Trust Director)

Secretary
Colin Peake
Correspondence c/o club.
Mobile (B): 01453 834 860
E-mail: cpfgrfc@fsmail.net

Commercial Manager
Natalie Ward
Tel: (B): 01453 834 860
(M): 07795 313 100
E-mail: Natalie.wood@ forestgreenroversfc.com
Press Officer
Colin Peake

Manager: Jim Harvey
Assistant Manager: Jamie Pitman
Coach: Mick Byrne
Club therapist: Ian Rodgerson

The club with a lovely stadium at the top of a hill in a tiny Gloucestershire village is never expected to beat the big clubs from the industrial areas of the country, but managers like Jim Harvey know the non-league world and what is really possible. A brilliant start to the season saw Rovers top of the Blue Square Premier league at the end of August, but it was to be a topsy turvey season for all at The New Lawn and by November Rovers had dropped into the relegation zone.

It wasn't all bad news however, as F.A. Cup victories over Ashford Town (Middlesex), Team Bath and Rochdale brought a home tie against Derby County and the thrill of leading the Championship club by 2-0 and 3-2 before two late goals prevented a lucrative replay in the Midlands. As one knock out competition closed another got under way and Rovers enjoyed an F.A.Trophy run to the last sixteen, eliminating Hemel Hempstead Town, Redditch United and Hednesford Town before losing to eventual winners Stevenage Borough.

Apart from their nine national cup ties Rovers also reached the final of the Setanta Shield where they lost to AFC Telford United, so perhaps it wasn't surprising that their League form suffered. Once the Trophy run finished, five consecutive drawn games confirmed that Harvey's men were becoming difficult to beat and Andy Mangan was fast becoming the ace marksman of the Blue Square Premier. He scored six in the five draws including the first of three hat tricks that enabled him to finish the campaign with 27 goals and help Rovers to a safe league position of eighteenth.

In a season when they finished with a goal tally of 91-86 in the major competitions, and twenty one different players featuring as goalscorers, Rovers were always entertaining to watch. But maybe their supporters will be hoping for a little more consistency in the league next season.

FOREST GREEN ROVERS

BEST LGE ATT.: **2,027** v Oxford United
LOWEST: **464** v Histon

No.	Date	Comp	H/A	Opponents	Att:	Result	Goalscorers	Pos
1	Aug 9	BSP	A	Kettering Town	1348	D 1 - 1	Lawless 78	
2	12		H	Salisbury City	927	L 1 - 2	**Mangan** 57	
3	16		H	Crawley Town	732	W 1 - 0	**Mangan** 82	11
4	23		A	Woking	1617	W 1 - 0	Mohamed 48	11
5	25		H	Weymouth	1132	W 4 - 2	Smith 35 Rigoglioso 75 82 Fowler 90	4
6	30		A	Histon	740	W 1 - 0	Hardiker 20	1
7	Sept 2		A	Eastbourne Borough	1065	L 0 - 1		
8	6		H	Ebbsfleet United	1272	L 1 - 4	Rigoglioso 5	11
9	13		A	Northwich Victoria	603	D 0 - 0		12
10	20		H	Stevenage Borough	751	L 0 - 3		16
11	23		H	Torquay United	1022	L 1 - 2	Smith 45	16
12	27		A	Burton Albion	1545	L 2 - 4	Jones 7 **Mangan** 90	17
13	Oct 4		H	Wrexham	1218	L 2 - 3	**Mangan** 4 52	
14	7		A	Crawley Town	876	D 2 - 2	Smith 48 Mohamed 88	
15	11		A	Lewes	666	L 2 - 3	Platt 64 Smith 67	20
16	16		H	Cambridge United	789	D 2 - 2	Symons 19 Preece 72	
17	**25**	**F.A.C. 4Q**	**A**	**Ashford Town (Middx)**	**337**	**D 0 - 0**		
18	**28**	**F.A.C. 4Q r**	**H**	**Ashford Town (Middx)**	**425**	**W 4 - 0**	**Afful 18 90 Mohamed 46 75**	
19	Nov 1		A	Barrow	1440	L 1 - 3	**Mangan** 68	21
20	**4**	**SS 3**	**H**	**Oxford United**	**383**	**W 2 - 1***	**Mangan 7, Mohamed 118**	
21	**9**	**F.A.C 1R**	**A**	**Team Bath**	**906**	**W 1 - 0**	**Mohamed 75**	
22	15		H	Altrincham	851	L 1 - 3	**Mangan** 39	21
23	22		H	Mansfield Town	872	W 1 - 0	Lawless 11	
24	**29**	**F.A.C. 2R**	**H**	**Rochdale**	**1715**	**W 2 - 0**	**Smith 57 Low 56**	
25	**Dec 2**	**SS S4**	**H**	**Torquay United**	**421**	**W 1 - 0**	**Symons 87**	
26	6		H	Burton Albion	812	L 2 - 3	**Mangan** 7 Smith 69	21
27	9		A	Ebbsfleet United	728	W 1 - 0	Smith 42	
28	**13**	**F.A.T 1R**	**H**	**Hemel Hempstead Town**	**509**	**W 5 - 1**	**McDonald 5 45 Mangan 29 (pen) Clist 81 Fowler 86**	
29	20		H	Kettering Town	923	L 0 - 3		22
30	26		A	Kidderminster Harriers	2102	D 1 - 1	Bartlett 44	22
31	28		H	Barrow	747	W 2 - 1	Rigoglioso 19 **Mangan** 34	20
32	**Jan 3**	**F.A.C. 3R**	**H**	**Derby County**	**4836**	**L 3 - 4**	**Smith 14 Lawless 20 Stonehouse 72**	
33	**11**	**F.A.T. 2R**	**H**	**Redditch United**	**441**	**W 5 - 0**	**Rigoglioso 2 62 Clarke 24 (og) Symons 78 Platt 80**	
34	**14**	**SS QFS**	**A**	**Woking**	**499**	**D 2 - 2***	**Mangan 2 (81, 105) (won 5-4 on pens)**	
35	17		H	Eastboune Borough	854	W 1 - 0	Preece 45	22
36	20		A	Oxford United	3728	L 1 - 2	Brown 89	
37	23		A	Rushden & Diamonds	1066	D 2 - 2	Lawless 11 Ayres 67	22
38	27		A	Salisbury City	771	D 2 - 2	Clist 21 41	
39	**31**	**F.A.T. 3R**	**H**	**Hednesford Town**	**768**	**W 1 - 0**	**Rigoglioso 37**	
40	Feb 3		H	Histon	464	L 2 - 3	**Mangan** 45 Platt 56 (pen)	
41	18		H	Northwich Victoria	744	W 3 - 0	Hardiker 12 16 Lawless 87	19
42	**21**	**F.A.T 4R**	**A**	**Stevenage Borough**	**1348**	**L 0 - 4**		
43	24		A	Torquay United	1554	D 3 - 3	MANGAN 3 (28 pen 36 42)	
44	28		H	Grays Athletic	992	D 1 - 1	**Mangan** 28	19
45	Mar 3		A	Stevenage Borough	1242	D 1 - 1	**Mangan** 26	
46	7		H	Oxford United	2027	D 3 - 3	Jones 28 Platt 33 70	
47	10		A	Wrexham	2405	D 1 - 1	**Mangan** 76	18
48	14		A	Mansfield Town	2174	L 0 - 3		20
49	17		H	York City	681	D 1 - 1	Mohamad 41	
50	21		A	Altrincham	852	W 5 - 2	Lloyd 48 Palmer 50 Brown 54 Lawless 72 Platt 76 (pen)	17
51	**26**	**SS SFS**	**A**	**Ebbsfleet United**	**431**	**W 1 - 0**	**Mohamed 85**	
52	28		H	Lewes	898	W 4 - 1	MANGAN 3 (31 pen 64 86) Ayres 36	16
53	April 4		A	Cambridge United	3245	W 1 - 0	**Mangan** 14	16
54	7		H	Kidderminster Harriers	970	D 2 - 2	Platt 40 **Mangan** 77	15
55	**9**	**SS Final**	**H**	**AFC Telford**	**2323**	**D 0 - 0***	**(lost 0-3 on pens)**	
56	11		H	Woking	1109	L 0 - 2		17
57	13		A	Weymouth	1183	D 1 - 1	**Mangan** 51	
58	18		H	Rushden & Diamonds	1185	W 4 - 0	MANGAN 3 (6 71 85 pen) McNulty 65	17
59	21		A	York City	2164	L 1 - 2	Palmer 89	
60	26		A	Grays Athletic	1246	L 1 - 2	**Mangan** 26 (pen)	18

Average Home Att: 955 (1178) **Goals** 97 89

Best Position: 1st **Worst:** 21st

Goalscorers: Mangan 30, Mohamed 8, Smith 8, Platt 7, Rigoglioso 7, Lawless 6, Clist 3, Hardiker 3, Symons 3, Afful 2, Ayres 2, Brown 2, Fowler 2, Jones 2, McDonald 2, Palmer 2, Preece 2, Bartlett 1, Lloyd 1, Low 1, McNulty 1, Stonehouse 1. Own Goals 1.

ROBINSON 1	STONEHOUSE 3	LAWLESS 2	HARDIKER 5	CLIST 8	JONES 4	PITMAN 6	AFFUL 12	FOWLER 16	MOHAMED 17	MANGAN 9	MCDONALD 18	PLATT 10	SMITH 11	BURTON 25	PREECE 15	RIGOGLIOSO 7	THOMAS 22	MOLYNEUX 20	SIMPSON 24	SYMONS 21	GILL 6	KEMPSON 40	PASS 31	LOW 26	AYRES 24	ASHFORD 14	BROWN 26	LLOYD 27	BALDWIN 28	PALMER 29	CASEY 8	ELSE 20	PUGH 22	COURTNEY 23	
X	X	X	X	X	X	X	X	X	X	X	S	S	S	U	U																				1
X	S	X	X	X	X	X	S	X	X	X	X		S	U	X	U																			2
X	S	X	X	X	X		S	X	X	X	X		X	U	U	U	X																		3
X	S	X	X	X	X		X	X	X	S	X	S	X	U			X	U																	4
X	X	X	X	X	X		S	X	S	X		X	X	U		S	X	U																	5
X	X	X	X		X		S	X	X	X		X	X	U	U	S	X	U																	6
X	X	X	X		X		S	X	X	X		X	S	U	S	X	X	U																	7
X	X	X	X	X	X		S	X	X	X		S	X	U	S	X		U																	8
X	X			X	X		X	X	X			X	X	U	X	X	S	S	S																9
X	X	X		X	X		S		X	S	U	S	X	U	X	X		X		X															10
X	X	X			X		X		X	X	X	S	X	U	X	X		U	U	S															11
X	X	U			X		X			X	X	X	X	U	X	X		U	S	X															12
X	X			X	X		S	X	X	X	S	S	X	U	X			U		X	X														13
X	X				X		X	X	S	X	X	X	X	U	X			U	S	S	X														14
X	X				X		S	X	X	X	X	S	X	U	X			S	U	X	X														15
X	X	X		X	X		S	X	S	X	S		X	U	X			U		X	X														16
X	**X**	**X**	**U**	**X**			**X**	**X**	**S**	**X**	**X**		**X**	**U**	**X**		**U**	**X**	**S**																17
X	**X**	**X**	**U**	**X**	**X**		**X**	**X**	**X**	**S**			**X**	**U**		**S**	**S**	**X**	**U**		**X**														18
X			X	X	X		X	X	X	S		S	X	U		X	U	X		S	X														19
			X	**X**	**X**			**X**	**X**	**X**		**X**	**X**	**X**		**S**	**X**	**U**	**S**	**S**		**X**	**U**												20
U	**X**		**X**	**X**	**X**		**S**	**X**	**X**	**X**		**S**	**X**	**X**		**S**	**U**	**U**	**U**		**X**	**X**													21
	X			X	X		S		X	X		S	X	X			S	U		X	X	X	U	X											22
U	X	X		X	X		S	S	S	U		X	X	X						X	X	X		X											23
U	**X**			**X**	**X**		**U**	**X**	**S**	**X**	**U**	**X**	**X**	**X**	**U**	**S**	**S**				**X**	**X**		**X**											24
X	**X**						**X**	**X**	**X**		**X**	**X**	**X**	**U**	**X**	**S**	**X**	**U**		**S**		**X**		**U**											25
U	X			X	X		S	X		X	U	X	X	X		S				S	X	X		X											26
U	X			X	X			X		X	X		X	X	U	S	X			S	X	X		S											27
U	**X**			**X**	**X**			**X**	**S**	**X**	**X**	**S**	**X**	**X**	**X**		**X**			**S**	**X**														28
U	X			X	X			X	S	X	X	X		X	S		X			S	X	X			U										29
U	X	X		X	X		S	X	S	X	X		X	X	X	U					X				U										30
	X	X		X	X		U	X	U	X		S	X	X	X	X				S	X				S										31
U	**X**	**X**		**X**	**X**		**S**	**X**	**S**	**X**	**U**	**U**	**X**	**X**	**U**	**X**	**U**				**X**	**X**													32
U	**X**			**X**			**X**	**X**		**X**		**S**	**X**	**X**	**X**	**X**	**X**			**S**	**X**					**U**									33
X	**X**	**U**		**X**	**X**		**X**	**X**		**S**	**S**	**X**	**X**	**U**	**X**	**X**				**S**	**X**														34
U	X	X		X			S	X		X	S		X	X	X	X				U	X				X		S								35
U	X	X		X			X	X		U	X	S	X	X	X					S	X				X		S								36
U	X	X					U	X		X	U	X	X	X	X	U				U	X				X		X								37
U	X	X		X			U	X		X	X	U	X	X	X					U	X					U	X								38
X	**X**	**X**					**X**	**X**		**X**	**S**	**X**	**X**	**U**	**X**	**X**				**S**	**X**					**U**									39
X	X						S	X		X	S	X	X	U	X	X				S	X				X	U	X								40
X	X	X	X					X		X	S	X	S	U	X	X					U				X		X	S							41
X	**X**	**X**	**X**		**U**			**X**		**X**	**U**	**X**	**X**	**U**	**X**	**X**				**S**	**X**					**S**									42
U	X	X	X		X					X	X	S	X	X	X					S	U				X		X	S							43
U	X	X			X			S	S	X	X	X		X		S					X				X	U	X	X							44
U	X	X			X			X	U	X		X		X	X	U					X				X	U	X	U							45
S	X	X			X			X		X		X	U	X	X	S					X				X	U	X	S							46
U	X	X			X			X	S	X		X	S	X	X	U									X	U	X	X							47
U	X	X			X			X	U	X		X	S	X	X	S									X	S	X	X							48
U	X	X			X			X	X			X	S	X	X	S									X	U	X	X							49
U	X	X						X	X			X	X	X	X	S									X	U	X	X	S	S					50
U	**X**	**X**						**X**	**X**	**X**		**X**	**X**	**X**	**X**	**X**										**X**		**S**	**S**		**U**	**U**			51
U	X	X			X			X	X	X		X	S	X	X	U									X	S	X	S							52
U	X				X			X	S	X	S	X	X	X	X	S									X	U	X	X							53
	X				X			X	S	X	U	X	X	X	X	S							U		X	U	X	X							54
	X	**X**			**X**			**X**	**X**	**X**	**S**	**X**	**X**	**X**	**X**	**X**							**U**			**U**		**S**	**S**						55
		X			X			X		X	X	X	X	X	X								U		X		X	S		S	U	S			56
		X			X			X		X	X	X	X	X	X								U		X			X		U	U	U			57
U		X			X			X		X	X	X	S	X	X	X									X			X	S	U		S			58
U		X			X			X		X		X	X	X	X	X									U			X	S	S	X	S			59
U					X			U		X		X	X	X	X	X												X	X	S	S	X	X	S	60
Total League Appearances																																			
19	37	32	11	21	39	2	8	38	17	38	17	27	33	27	32	14	7	2	0	7	20	5	0	3	19	0	16	11	1	0	1	1	1	0	X
1	3	0	0	0	0	0	16	2	10	3	7	12	9	0	3	11	2	2	3	10	0	0	0	1	1	2	2	5	3	4	1	3	0	1	S
21	0	1	0	0	0	0	3	1	3	2	4	1	1	19	4	7	1	11	2	3	2	0	4	0	3	10	0	1	0	2	2	1	0	0	U
Total Cup Appearances																																			
6	13	7	3	9	8	0	6	14	6	11	3	8	14	8	9	7	4	2	0	0	9	5	0	1	0	1	0	0	0	0	0	0	0	0	X
0	0	0	0	0	0	0	2	0	4	2	3	3	0	0	0	5	2	0	2	7	0	0	0	0	0	1	0	2	2	0	0	0	0	0	S
6	0	1	2	0	1	0	1	0	0	0	3	1	0	6	2	0	3	3	2	0	0	0	2	1	0	3	0	0	0	0	1	1	0	0	U

FOREST GREEN ROVERS

CURRENT SQUAD AS OF BEGINING OF 2009-10 SEASON

GOALKEEPERS		SQ NO.	HT	WT	D.O.B	AGE	P.O.B	CAREER	APPS	GOA
Terry	Burton	1	6'02"	12 09	10/2/81	28	Hull	Hull C, Army, Wantage, Forest Green 8/07	27	0
Thomas	Pass	17			21/12/91	17	Gloucester	Forest Green Rovers	0	0
DEFENDERS										
Lee	Ayres	4	6'02"	12 06	28/8/82	5	Birmingham	Walsall (Yth), Evesham, Kidderminster 6/01, Stourport (L) 02, Tamworth (L) 9/03, Tamworth 11/03, Notts County (Trial) 7/04, Burton £10,000 8/04 Rel 4/06, Bristol R (Trial) c/s 06, Moor Green/Solihull Moors c/s 06, Bristol R (Trial) 10/06, Redditch 7/08, Forest Green 12/08	20	2
James	Baldwin	16						Forest Green	4	0
John	Else	12			8/6/89	20	Blackpool	Swindon (Yth), Reading (Yth), Bristol R (Yth), New College Academy, L.Orient (Res), Cirencester 8/07 Rel 2/08, Chippenham 3/08, Clevedon T 10/08, Forest Green, Stourport (L) 3/09	4	0
Mark	Preece	5	6'02"	13 07	3/6/87	22	Bristol	Bristol R Rel c/s 06, Gloucester (SL) 1/06, Kidderminster (Trial) 7/06, Forest Green 7/06, Weston-super-Mare (L) 1/07	35	2
Andy	Taylor	2	6'00"		28/12/85	23	Liverpool	Austin Aztex (USA), Forest Green 6/09		
MIDFIELDERS										
Steve	Davies	18			27/4/89	20		Afan Lido, Cirencester 7/08, Forest Green 7/09		
Michael	Fowler	20	5'11"	11 13	22/8/81	28	Cardiff	C.Palace Rel c/s 01, Woking 8/01, Newport C 3/02, Welling 7/03, Cwmbran 10/03, Merthyr T 7/05, Gloucester 6/06, Salisbury 1/07 Rel 7/09, Forest Green 7/09		
Paul	Lloyd	8	5'09"	10 11	26/3/87	22	Preston	Morecambe Rel 1/09, Burscough (2ML) 3/06, Fleetwood (L) 8/06, Bamber Bridge (L) 1/07, Workington 1/09, Forest Green 2/09	16	1
Curtis	McDonald	3	5'10"	10 08	24/3/88	21	Cardiff	Cardiff Rel c/s 07, Accrington (L) 11/06, Hereford (Trial) 7/07, Carmarthen 8/07, MKS Swit (Pol) 10/07, Forest Green (Reserves) 11/07, Forest Green 8/08	24	0
Sam	Mensah	23						Forest Green		
Ben	Pugh	15						Forest Green	1	0
Isaac	Shaze	22			25/6/89	20		Forest Green		
Jonathan	Smith	11			17/10/86	22	Preston	Morecambe Rel 5/07, Fleetwood (3ML) 1/06, Bamber Bridge (L) 1/07, Forest Green 7/07	42	6
Paul	Stonehouse	6	5'07"	11 03	13/7/87	22	Wegburg	Forest Green, Gloucester (L) 1/07	40	0
FORWARDS										
David	Brown	7	5'10"	12 06	2/10/78	31	Bolton	Man Utd, Hull (L) 3/98, Hull 7/98, Halifax (Trial) 8/01,Torquay 11/01, Chester 12/01, Telford 8/02, Hereford 6/03, Accrington 3/05 Rel 5/08, Burton (2ML) 11/06, Rushden & D (L) 1/08, Northwich (SL) 3/08, Barrow 10/08 Rel 1/09, Forest Green 1/09 Pl/Ass Man	18	3
Jon	Challinor	24	5'11"	11 11	2/12/80	28	Northampton	Rushden & D, Stamford 4/99, Cambridge C 2/01 , Kalamazoo Kingdom (USA), St Albans 5/02, Aldershot 8/03 Rel 5/05, Exeter 5/05, Rushden & D 5/07, Cambridge U £15,000 8/08, Forest Green (L) 8/09		
Andrew	Mangan	9	5'09"	10 03	30/8/86	23	Liverpool	Blackpool Rel c/s 05, Hyde U (SL) 3/05, Accrington 8/05 Rel c/s 07, Bury 7/07 Rel c/s 08, Accrington (L) 2/08, Forest Green 5/08	41	26
Marcus	Palmer	19	6'00"	11 07	22/12/88	20	Gloucester	Cheltenham (Scholar), Hereford 8/06, Gloucester (L) 2/08, Gloucester 8/08, Solihull Moors 8/08 Rel 11/08, Forest Green 11/08, Chippenham (L) 3/09	4	2
Conal	Platt	10	5'09"	10 10	14/10/86	22	Preston	Liverpool, Bournemouth 5/06 Rel c/s 07, Morecambe (L) 11/06, Weymouth (SL) 2/07, Weymouth 8/07, Rushden & D (SL) 2/08, Forest Green 5/08	39	6
Ross	Stearn	14	5'06"	10 07	17/9/71	17	Bristol	Bristol C (Scholar) Rel c/s 09, Cheltenham (Trial) 3/09, Yeovil (Trial) 7/09, Forest Green NC 8/09		
Paul	Casey							Forest Green	2	0
Russell	Courtney							Forest Green	1	0

LOANEES		HT	WT	DOB	AGE	POB	From - To	APPS	GOA
(D)Darran	Kempson	6'02"	12 13	6/12/84	24	Blackpool	Wrexham (2ML) 11/08 - Rel 7/09, Accrington 7/09	5	0
(M)Josh	Low	6'02"	14 03	15/2/79	30	Bristol	Cheltenham 11/08 -	4	0

DEPARTURES		HT	WT	DOB	AGE	POB	From - To	APPS	GOA
(M)Jamie	Pitman	5'09"	10 09	6/1/76	33	Trowbridge	Hereford 5/06 - Hereford (Physio) 9/08	2	0
(M)James	Simpson						ex Newport C 9/08 - Rel 12/08	3	0
(D)Lee	Molyneux	6'00"	11 05	16/1/83	26	Portsmouth	Cirencester 8/08 - Rel 12/08, Gloucester 12/08, Clevedon T 1/09	4	0
(D)Chris	Thomas			16/1/83	26		Carmarthen 8/08 - Rel 1/09, Carmarthen 1/09	9	0
(M)Simon	Clist	5'10"	11 05	13/6/81	28	Bournemouth	Barnet 5/06 - Oxford U Undisc 2/09	21	1
(D)John	Hardiker	5'11"	11 01	7/7/82	27	Preston	Fleetwood 12/06 - Rel 3/09, Stalybridge 3/09	11	3
(M)Lee	Fowler	5'07"	10 00	10/6/83	26	Cardiff	Newport C 6/08 - Rel 5/09, Kettering 6/09	40	1
(G)Ryan	Robinson	6'02"	13 02	13/10/82	26	Tebay	Morecambe 1/07 - Bath C 5/09	20	0
(D)Darren	Jones	6'01"	14 00	28/8/83	26	Newport	ex Newport C 3/06 - Rel 5/09, Hereford 6/09	39	2
(F)Kaid	Mohamed	5'11"		23/7/84	25	Cardiff	Swindon 7/08 - Rel c/s 09, Newport C (L) 1/09	27	3
(F)Michael	Symons			22/7/86	23	Gloucester	Clevedon T 8/08 - Gloucester (L) 8/08, Gloucester (SL) 2/09, Gloucester 5/09	17	1
(M)Les	Afful	5'06"	10 00	4/2/84	25	Liverpool	Exeter 5/06 - Truro C 6/09	24	0
(D)Alex	Lawless	5'11"	10 08	5/2/83	26	Llwynupion	Torquay 8/06 - York C 6/09	32	5
(D)Jerry	Gill	5'11"	12 00	8/9/70	38	Clevedon	Cheltenham (Pl/Ass Man) 10/08 - Rel 6/09	20	0
(M)Adriano	Rigoglioso	6'01"	12 07	28/5/79	30	Liverpool	Morecambe 1/07 - Grays 8/09	25	5
(D)Ben	Ashford	6'02"		1/4/89	20		Gloucester 2/08 -	2	0

FOREST GREEN ROVERS

Founded: 1890

Nickname: Rovers

Club Colours: Black & white striped shirts/black shorts/black socks.

Change Colours: Green shirts, shorts and socks.

Club Sponsor: Sheffield Insulation.

Previous League: Southern League

Ground Address: The New Lawn, Smiths Way, Nailsworth, Gloucestershire GL6 0FG
Telephone: 01453 834 860
Fax: 01453 835 291
General email address: admin@forestgreenroversfc.com
Official website: www.forestgreenroversfc.com

SIMPLE DIRECTIONS:
By Road: Nailsworth is on the A46 between Stroud and Bath. At mini roundabout in centre of town, turm up Spring Hill towards Forest Green and the stadium is half a mile up the hill on the left after the second roundabout. Ground is clearly signposted. Parking for 250+ in three separate car parks at the ground.

MATCH TICKETS:
Ticket office Telephone: 01453 834 860
Ticket Prices: Stand - £15, Concessions £10, Juniors (U16) £7.
Ground - £13, Concessions £8, Juniors (U16) £5.
Midweek Home Matchday: Tuesday
Capacity: 5,141
Seats: 2,000
Covered Terracing: 1,000
Green Man Public House Tel No: 01453 833 295 Open normal pub hours.
Restaurant Five Valley's Leisure (01453 832268) Available for bookings daily and open for meals on matchdays.

Club Shop: Open on matchdays only with souvenirs, programmes and memorabilia.

PROGRAMME EDITOR
Terry Brumpton
Tel: 01543 458 719

CLUB STATISTICS

RECORDS

Attendance:
4,836 v Derby County, F.A. Cup 3rd Rnd 03/01/2009.
Victory:
8-0 v Fareham Town, Southern League Southern Div. 96-97.
Defeat:
0-7 v Moor Green, Southern League, Midland Div. 85-86.
Career Goalscorer: Karl Bayliss.
Career Appearances: Alex Sykes.
Transfer Fee Paid:
£20,000 to Salisbury City for Adrian Randall.
Transfer Fee Received:
£35,000 from Nuneaton Borough for Marc McGregor from Oxford United for Wayne Hatswell.

SENIOR HONOURS
F.A. Vase Winners 1981-82
Southern League Premier Division Champions 1996-97
Hellenic League Champions 1981-82
Gloucestershire Senior Cup Winners 1984-5 85-6 86-7
Gloucestershire Senior Professional Cup 1984-5 85-6 86-7

PREVIOUS
Leagues: Stroud & Dist 1890-192, Glos Northern Sen.22-67 Glos.Co. 67-73, Hrellenic 73-82, Southern League 82-89.

GATESHEAD

Back Row (L-R): Carl Jones, Jamie Harwood, James Curtis, Paul Farman, Darren Forsyth, Stephane Pelonde, Craig Baxter. **Middle Row:** Graham, Wood (Chairman), Wayne Phillips, Michael Mackay (long term loan Hartlepool United), Phil Turnbull, Chris Swailes, Jim Provett, Alex Francis, Graemem Armstrong, Neale McDermott, Steven Baptist, Brian Waites (Vice Chairman). **Front Row:** Martin Brittain, Phil Cave, Christoph Ascherl, Jeff Wrightson (Assistant Manager), Ian Bogie (Manager), Paul Thompson (Coach), Kris Gate, Mark Robinson, Steven Richardson.

CLUB PERSONNEL

Chairman: Graham Wood

Vice-Chairman & Company Secretary: Brian Waites

Secretary: Mike Coulson.

2 Thropton Crescent, Gosforth, Newcastle Upon Tyne,

NE3 3HT

Tel: (H) 0191 285 6896 (M) 07912 869 943

Email: mike.coulson@gateshead-fc.com

Correspondence to Home

Commercial Manager: Brian Waites.

(M) 07990 508 057

Email: brian.waites@nbgroup.co.uk

Press Officer: Jeff Bowron.

(M) 07801 847 004

Email: jeffbowron@blueyonder.co.uk

Manager: Ian Bogie.

Assistant Manager: Jeff Wrightson.

Player/coach: Paul Thompson.

Club therapist: Mark Gibbons.

Following a season when they scored 114 senior goals and only failed to find the net three times, Gateshead supporters could hardly have expected an improvement. But although they only scored 90 and failed to score on nine occasions, Gateshead won promotion back to the Blue Square Premier through the play-offs.

'The Tynesiders' had lost their Conference place in 1998 and their return, with Whitley Bay's F.A. Vase success, at least gave the North Eastern football enthusiasts something to celebrate. The season hadn't started as well as expected for Gateshead and it wasn't until the New Year that a serious challenge for a top four position became consistent.

The two national knock-out cups brought little excitement as Droylsden knocked them out of the F.A. Cup after Gateshead had enjoyed a replayed victory over Witton Albion. The F.A.Trophy there was an immediate elimination at home to Harrogate Town.

By the end of March, automatic promotion as Champions was a definite possibility but end of season nerves produced just four victories in their last nine league games and Gateshead had to face the play-offs. The goalscoring of Novak (27) and Armstrong (17) had been inspirational during the season and a goal each put paid to Southport in the semi-finals and Wayne Phillips scored the all important promotion winner against AFC Telford United. Gateshead were back in the top flight and hopefully the goals will continue to flow for 'The Tynesiders'.

GATESHEAD

BEST LGE ATT.: **1,388** v Blyth Spartans
LOWEST: **264** v King's Lynn

No.	Date	Comp	H/A	Opponents	Att:	Result	Goalscorers	Pos
1	Aug 9	BSN	A	Redditch United	392	W 2 - 0	Armstrong 28 Blackstone 87 (pen)	
2	13		H	Droylsden	360	D 1 - 1	Armstrong 56	
3	17		H	Alfreton Town	361	W 3 - 0	Armstrong 2 77 Rae 85	
4	23		A	Gainsborough Trinity	365	D 0 - 0		3
5	25		H	Harrogate Town	509	L 1 - 3	Jones 2	
6	30		A	Hinckley United	479	L 0 - 2		10
7	Sept 2		A	Fleetwood Town	684	W 2 - 0	Armstrong 4 48	
8	**8**	**SS N1**	**A**	**Droylsden**	**190**	**W 2 - 1***	**Harwood 67, Armstrong 119**	
9	13		A	Tamworth	831	L 1 - 2	Gate 17	13
10	20		H	AFC Telford United	413	D 1 - 1	Armstrong 78	11
11	24		H	Stafford Rangers	265	L 0 - 1		
12	**27**	**F.A.C. 2Q**	**H**	**Witton Albion**	**212**	**D 1 - 1**	**Harwood 71**	
13	**30**	**F.A.C. 2Q r**	**A**	**Witton Albion**	**27**	**W 3 - 1**	**Armstrong 9 Southern 73 Turnbull 87**	
14	Oct 4		A	Vauxhall Motors	149	W 2 - 1	Southern 24 **Novak** 64	11
15	**11**	**F.A.C. 3Q**	**A**	**Droylsden**	**470**	**L 2 - 3**	**Francis 24 Harwood 53**	
16	14		H	Workington	350	L 2 - 4	Southern 60 Nelthorpe 88	
17	18		H	Southport	422	D 1 - 1	Armstrong 73	11
18	**21**	**SS N2**	**A**	**Blyth Spartans**	**632**	**W 2 - 1**	**Armstrong 70 90**	
19	Nov 1		A	Hyde United	301	W 5 - 2	**NOVAK** 4 (12 13 15 (pen) 50) Harwood 55	
20	**4**	**SS N3**	**A**	**Barrow**	**551**	**L 1 - 3***	**Novak 45**	
21	8		H	Burscough	334	W 4 - 1	**Novak** 23 Francis 52 Harwood 62 Armstrong 90	9
22	15		A	AFC Telford United	2086	L 0 - 1		10
23	19		H	King's Lynn	264	W 3 - 2	**NOVAK** 3 (26 32 49)	7
24	**22**	**F.A.T. 3Q**	**H**	**Harrogate Town**	**217**	**L 0 - 2**		
25	29		H	Hyde United	273	W 6 - 3	Novak 9 PHILLIPS 3 (26 37 75) Harwood 29 Southern 85	7
26	Dec 20		H	Redditch United	293	W 2 - 0	Phillips 45 **Novak** 54	6
27	26		A	Blyth Spartans	1292	W 1 - 0	Leeson 51 (og)	5
28	Jan 1		H	Blyth Spartans	1388	W 3 - 0	**Novak** 10 31 Jones 71	
29	3		A	Alfreton Town	448	W 3 - 1	Turnbull 20 **Novak** 45 83	4
30	11		H	Tamworth	331	W 5 - 1	**Novak** 35 (pen) 81 Francis 51 Phillips 84 Turnbull 86	2
31	17		A	Droylsden	295	D 0 - 0		
32	24		H	Solihull Moors	484	W 3 - 0	Armstrong 33 Harwood 45 Gate 90	2
33	27		H	Workington	463	W 2 - 1	Armstrong 9 Gate 55	
34	31		A	King's Lynn	966	L 0 - 2		2
35	Feb 14		A	Burscough	343	W 4 - 2	Phillips 4 65 Harwood 9 **Novak** 11	1
36	21		H	Hucknall Town	605	W 1 - 0	Harwood 73	1
37	24		A	Stalybridge Celtic	315	W 2 - 1	Harwood 15 80 (pen)	
38	28		H	Vauxhall Motors	602	D 2 - 2	**Novak** 18 Harwood 58	1
39	Mar 3		A	Farsley Celtic	198	W 1 - 0	Baxter 53	
40	7		A	Southport	1301	W 3 - 2	**Novak** 66 81Phillips 86	1
41	14		A	Solihull Moors	253	L 0 - 2		
42	18		H	Fleetwood Town	467	D 2 - 2	**Novak** 4 Armstrong 33	
43	21		H	Stalybridge Celtic	329	W 1 - 0	Jones 32	1
44	28		H	Hinckley United	601	W 5 - 1	**Novak** 15 59 Phillips 31 Stamp 71 Turnbull 83	1
45	April 4		A	Stafford Rangers	448	L 1 - 4	Armstrong 65	2
46	11		H	Gainsborough Trinity	486	W 1 - 0	**Novak** 90	2
47	13		A	Harrogate Town	447	L 0 - 1		
48	18		H	Farsley Celtic	568	W 3 - 0	**Novak** 54 Stamp 62 Armstrong 85	2
48	25		A	Hucknall Town	347	D 2 - 2	Smedley 34 (og) Armstrong 48	2
49	**29**	**Play-Off SF1**	**A**	**Southport**	**2346**	**W 1 - 0**	**Armstrong 15**	
50	**May 3**	**Play-Off SF2**	**H**	**Southport**	**1409**	**D 1 - 1**	**Novak 23**	
51	**8**	**Play-Off F**	**H**	**AFC Telford United**	**4121**	**W 1 - 0**	**Phillips 82**	

Average Home Att: 459 (303) **Goals** 95 62

Best Position: 1st **Worst:** 13th

Goalscorers: Novak 28, Armstrong 20, Harwood 12, Phillips 10, Southern 4, Turnbull 4, Francis 3, Gate 3, Jones 3, Baxter 1, Blackstone 1, Nelthorpe 1, Rae 1, Stamp 2. Own Goals 2.

MUSSELWHITE	BAXTER	BRACKSTONE	GATE	CURTIS	JONES	SOUTHERN	P TURNBULL	ARMSTRONG	HARWOOD	S TURNBULL	PHILLIPS	RAE	FRANCIS	THOMPSON	NORTON	SALVIN	HOCKING	NELTHORPE	NOBLE	NOVAK	MCCALLUM	SEED	NELLIS	MCNALL	HOLLOWAY	SMITH	CAVE	PROVETT	BROADBENT	BAPTISTE	PELONDE	STAMP	DINNING	
X	X	X	X	X	X	X	X	X	X	X	S	S	S	U	U																			1
X	X	X	X	X	X	X	X	X	X	X	S	U	S		U	S																		2
X	X		X	X	X	X	X	X	X	X	X	S	U		U	S	S																	3
X	X		X	X	X	X	X	X	S	X	X	S	U		U		U	X																4
X	X		X	X	X	X	X	X	S	X	X	S			U	S	U	X																5
X	X		X	X	X	S	X	X	S	X	X	U			U	S	X	X																6
X	X	U	X		X	X	X	X	S	X	X	S	S		U		X	X																7
U	X	X	S		X	S	S	X	X	X	X	X	X		X		X		U															8
X	X	X	X		X	X	X	X	S	X	X	U	S		U	S	X																	9
X	X	X	X	X	X	X	X	X	S	X	X	U	U		U		U																	10
X	X	X	X	X	X	U	X	X	S	U	X				U		S	X		X														11
X	X	X	X	X		X	X	X	X	S	X		S	U	U		X				U	U	U											12
X	X	X	X	X		X	S	X	X	X	X		S	S	U		X																	13
X	X	S	X	X		X	S		X	X	X		X	U	U		U	X		X														14
X	X	X	X	X		X	X	U	X	X			X	S	U		X				U	U		U										15
X	X	S	X	X		X	X		U	X	X		X	U	U		U	X		X														16
X	X	X	X	X		X	U	S	X	X	S		S		U		X	X		X														17
	X	U	X	X		S	U	X	X	X	X		S	U	X		X	X		X														18
X	X	U	X	X		S	S	X	X		X		X		U		X	X		X					S									19
	X		X	X	X	S	S	X	X	U	X		X	U	X		U	X		X														20
X	X		X	X	X	S	S	X	X	S	X		X		U			X		X					U									21
X	X		X	X	X	U	S	X	X	X	X		U		U			X		X					U									22
X	X		X	X	X	S	U	X	X	X	X		S		U			X		X					S									23
X	X		X	X	X	S	S	X	X	X			U		U			X		X					S	X								24
X	X		X		X	S	S	X	X	X	X		S		U		U			X					X	X								25
X	X	X	X	U	X		X	X	X	U	X		S		U		U			X					X									26
X	X		X	S	X	U	X	X	X	S	X		S		U					X					X	X								27
X	X	S	X	X	X	U	X	X	X	S	X		S		U					X						X								28
X	X	S	U	X	X	S	X		X	X	X		X		U		S			X						X								29
X	X	S		X	X	S	X	S	X	X	X		X		U		U			X						X								30
X	X	S	S	X	X		X	S	X	X	X		X		U		U			X						X								31
X	X	S	X	X	X		X	X	X	S	X		S		U		U			X						X								32
X	X	X	X	X	X		X	X	X	S	X		S		U		U			X						U								33
X	X	U	X	X			X	X	X	S	X		S		U		X			X					S	X								34
X	X		X	X			X	X	X	S	X		S				S			X					X	U	X	U						35
U	X		X		X		X		S	X	X						S			X					X	U	X	X	X	S				36
U	X		X	X	X		X		X	X	X		U				U			X						U	X	X	S					37
U	X		X	X	X		X		X	S	X		S							X						U	X	X	X		S			38
U	X		X	X	X		X	S	X	S	X									X					U	S	X	X	X					39
U	X		X	X	X		X	S	X	S	X		U							X					X		X	X	U					40
U	X		X	X			X	X	X	S	X		U							X					X		X	X	S		U			41
U	X		X	X			S	X	X	S	X		X				X			X						U	X	X	U					42
X	X		X	X	X		S	X	X	S	X		X				U			X						U	X	U						43
X	X		X	X	X		S	S	X	S	X		X				U			X							X	U				X		44
X	X		X	X	X		S	X	X	U	X		S				S			X							X	U					X	45
X	X		X	X	X		S	X	X	S	X		X				U			X							X	U				S		46
X	X		X	X	X		X	S	S	X	X						U			X						X	U	U				X		47
X	X		X	X			S	S	X		X		S							X						U	X	U			X	X	X	48
X	X			X			X	X	X	S	X		S				X			U						S	X	U				X	X	49
X	X		X	X	X		X	X	X	S	X						S			X							X	U				U	S	50
X	X		X	X	X		X	X	X	S	X						U			X							X	U				S	S	51
X	X		X	X	X		X	X	X	S	X						U			X							X	U				S	U	52
Total League Appearances																																		
35	42	8	38	36	32	11	29	28	32	21	39	0	11	0	0	0	8	12	0	32	0	0	0	0	7	9	14	7	3	0	1	4	3	X
0	0	7	1	1	0	7	11	8	9	16	3	5	18	0	0	5	6	0	0	0	0	0	0	0	3	2	0	0	2	1	1	1	0	S
7	0	3	1	1	0	4	2	0	1	3	0	4	7	3	27	0	16	0	0	1	0	0	0	0	3	8	1	8	2	0	1	0	0	U
Total Cup Appearances																																		
7	10	4	9	9	6	3	5	9	10	5	8	1	3	0	3	0	5	3	0	6	0	0	0	0	0	1	3	0	0	0	0	0	0	X
0	0	0	1	0	0	4	4	0	0	4	0	0	3	2	0	0	1	0	0	0	0	0	0	0	1	0	0	0	0	0	0	2	2	S
1	0	1	0	0	0	0	1	1	0	1	0	0	1	3	4	0	3	0	1	0	2	2	1	1	0	0	0	3	0	0	0	1	1	U

GATESHEAD

CURRENT SQUAD AS OF BEGINING OF 2009-10 SEASON

GOALKEEPERS		SQ NO.	HT	WT	D.O.B	AGE	P.O.B	CAREER	APPS	GOA
Paul	Farman	13			2/11/89	19	North Shields	Newcastle (Scholar). Blyth c/s 08, Mansfield (Trial) 1/09, Newcastle Blue Star (Dual) 1/09, Gateshead 6/09		
Jim	Provett	1	6'00"	13 04	22/12/82	26	Stockton	Hartlepool Rel c/s 07, Spennymoor (L) 12/01, Bury 7/07 Rel c/s 08, Harrogate T 7/08, Gateshead 2/09	7	0
Defenders										
Craig	Baxter	2	5'10"	09 10	27/9/86	22	Newcastle	Newcastle Rel c/s 06, Gateshead c/s 06	42	1
Phil	Cave	19			12/5/87	22	Newcastle	Newcastle (Scholar), Gateshead 8/07, Livingston 7/08, Gateshead (SL) 2/09, Gateshead 8/09	14	0
James	Curtis	5			13/4/82	27		Kenneck Ryhope CA, Washington, Gateshead 6/03	37	0
Carl	Jones	6	6'01"	12 02	3/9/86	22	Sunderland	Chester-le-Street, Hartlepool 9/04 Rel c/s 07, York C 8/07 Rel 1/08, Gateshead (L) 11/07, Gateshead (L) 1/08 Perm 1/08	32	3
Stephane	Pelonde	20			21/3/87	22		Le Havre (Fra), Mondeville (Fra), Gateshead 2/09	2	0
Mark	Robinson	3	5'09"	11 00	24/7/81	28	Guisborough	Hartlepool Rel 5/04, Spennymoor (L) 12/03, Scarborough (L) 2/04, Hereford 8/04, Stockport 5/05, Torquay 1/07 Rel c/s 07, York C 6/07 Rel 5/09, Gateshead 6/09		
Chris	Swailes	15	6'02"	12 11	19/10/70	38	Gateshead	Ipswich, Peterborough £10,000 3/91 Rel c/s 91, Boston U 7/91, Birmingham (L) 3/92, Kettering £5,000 c/s 92, Bridlington T, Guisborough (L), Doncaster 10/93, Ipswich £150,000 3/95, Bury £200,000 11/97, Rotherham 7/01, Oldham 7/05 Rel 12/06, Hamilton 3/07 Rel c/s 09, Gateshead 6/09		
MIDFIELDERS										
Christophe	Ascherl	22			17/6/86	23		Pen State University (USA), Mechterscheim (Ger), Gateshead 8/09		
Martin	Brittain	7	5'08"	10 07	29/12/84	24	Newcastle	Newcastle Rel c/s 06, Hull C (Trial) 7/06, Brighton (Trial) 7/06, Kilmarnock (Trial) 8/06, Ipswich 8/06 Rel c/s 07, Yeovil (2ML) 10/06, Yeovil (SL) 1/07, Carlisle 8/07 Rel 8/07, Scunthorpe 12/07 Rel 12/07, Walsall 1/08 Rel c/s 08, Toronto FC (Trial) 3/08,		
Alex	Francis	14	6'02"	12 08	7/1/90	19	Gateshead	Newcastle (Scholar) Rel 5/08, Gateshead 6/08	29	2
Kris	Gate	4	5'07"	10 03	1/1/85	24	Newcastle	Newcastle Rel c/s 07, Grimsby (Trial) 11/05, Gateshead 9/07	39	4
Jamie	Harwood	12			27/9/84	24		West Auckland, Crook T (2004), Worksop 7/06, Gateshead 12/06	41	8
Dean	McCallum				24/1/91	18	Gateshead	Gateshead	0	0
Neale	McDermott	17	5'11"	11 02	8/3/85	24	Newcastle	Newcastle, Fulham Undisc 1/03 Rel 5/06, Swindon (4ML) 8/05, Darlington (L) 2/06, Carlisle 8/06 Rel 4/08, Hartlepool (Trial) 3/08, Dundee (Trial) 6/08, Grimsby (Trial) 11/08, Wrexham (Trial) 12/08, R.A.A. Louviéroise (Bel), Gateshead 7/09		
Wayne	Phillips	11			29/8/85	24	South Shields	Newcastle (Yth), Sunderland (Yth), Peterlee Newtown, Blyth 3/03 Rel 1/05, Whitley Bay 1/05, Gateshead 7/07	42	9
Phil	Turnbull	8	5'11"	11 08	7/1/87	22	South Shields	Hartlepool Rel c/s 07, Gateshead (L) 12/05, Blyth (L) 3/07, York 7/07, Gateshead 2/08	40	1
FORWARDS										
Graeme	Armstrong	9	6'00"	12 08	28/6/83	26	Hexham	Haltwhistle U, Queen of the South 7/00, Annan Ath, Dunston Fed c/s 04, Gateshead £5,000 6/07	36	14
Steve	Baptiste	16						Birtley T. Gateshead 2/09	1	0
Darren	Forsyth	18	6'02"		21/2/88	21	Dublin	St Josephs Boys, Cherry Orchard, UCD 8/06, Shelbourne 7/08, Bray W 2/09, Gateshead 7/09		
Michael	Mackay	21	6'00"	11 07	11/10/82	26	Durham	Birtley, Durham, Consett 10/05, Hartlepool 2/07, Gateshead (5ML) 8/09		
Liam	McNall				29/10/91	17	Gateshead	Gateshead	0	0
Jordan	Nellis				5/4/92	17	Bedlington	Gateshead	0	0
Steven	Richardson	10					Gateshead	Chester-le-Street, Gateshead 10/04, Durham C 10/05, Gateshead 6/09		
Paul	Thompson		5'11"	11 13	17/4/73	36	Newcastle	Hartlepool Rel c/s 95, Gateshead, Stevenage £15,000 c/s 97, Kettering (L) 12/98, Gateshead (L) 3/99, Gateshead 6/99, Bishop Auckland 8/04, Blyth 9/04, Whitley Bay 10/04, Gateshead (Pl/Coach) 2/05	0	0

LOANEES		SN	HT	WT	DOB	AGE	POB	From - To	APPS	GOA
(M)Craig	Nelthorpe		5'10"	11 00	10/6/87	22	Doncaster	Doncaster (3ML) 8/08 - Rel 1/09, Oxford U 1/09 Rel 4/09, York C 5/09	12	1
(F)Daniel	Broadbent		5'10"	12 00	2/3/90	19	Leeds	Huddersfield 2/09 - Harrogate T (SL) 3/09, Rel 5/09	5	0
(F)Darryn	Stamp		6'01"	11 10	21/9/78	30	Beverley	Northwich (SL) 3/09 - Gainsborough 6/09	5	2
(M)Tony	Dinning		6'00"	13 05	12/4/75	34	Wallsend	Chester 3/09 - Hednesford 7/09	3	0

DEPARTURES		SN	HT	WT	DOB	AGE	POB	From - To	APPS	GOA
(M)Steve	Salvin				23/2/80	29	Newcastle	Newcastle Blue Star 8/06 - Newcastle Blue Star 9/08, Bishop Auckland 12/08	5	0
(F)Michael	Rae		5'10"	12 04	23/10/87	21	North Cleveland	Hartlepool c/s 08 - Whitby 10/08	5	1
(F)David	Southern				18/9/82	26	Gateshead	Newcastle Blue Star 7/06 - Newcastle Blue Star 4 fig 1/09	18	3
(G)Jack	Norton		6'00"		27/3/87	22		Tow Law (Dual) c/s 08 - Consett 2/09, Newcastle Blue Star 3/09	0	0
(F)Lee	Novak		6'00"	12 04	28/9/88	20	Newcastle	Newcastle Blue Star 9/08 - Huddersfield Undisc 2/09, Gateshead (SL) 2/09	32	27
(D)John	Brackstone		5'11"	10 08	9/2/85	24	Hartlepool	Darlington 5/08 - Blyth 2/09	15	1
(D)Ryan	Seed						Gateshead	Yth - Rel	0	0
(G)Paul	Musselwhite		6'02"	14 02	22/12/68	40	Portsmouth	Harrogate T 1/08 - Retired c/s 09, Lincoln C c/s 09	35	0
(D)Dan	Smith		5'10"	10 07	5/10/86	22	Sunderland	Aberdeen 11/08 - Rel 5/09	11	0
(M)Stephen	Turnbull		5'10"	11 00	7/1/87	22	South Shields	Hartlepool 7/08 - Rel 5/09, Blyth 6/09	37	2
(D)Matt	Hocking		6'01"	12 02	30/1/78	31	Boston	Southport 8/08 - Rel 5/09	14	0
(D)Darren	Holloway							Darlington 10/08 - Rel 5/09	10	0
(D)Mark	Bertram				2/4/90	19		Newcastle (Scholar) 6/08 -		
(D)Mattie	Noble		5'10"	11 00	23/11/88	20	Newcastle	Doncaster c/s 08 -	0	0

GATESHEAD

Formed: 1930

Nickname: Tynesiders.

Club Colours: White shirts, black shorts, black socks.

Change Colours: Blue shirts, white shorts, white socks.

Club Sponsor: Tech/Ops SEVCON.

Previous League: Northern Premier League

Ground address: International Stadium, Neilson Road, Gateshead NE10 0EF

Telephone No: 0191 478 3883

Mobile: 07912 869 943

Fax: 0191 478 3883

Email: info@gateshead-fc.com

Website: www.gateshead-fc.com

Simple Directions: From South follow A1(M) to Granada services (Birtley) take right hand fork marked A194(M)(Tyne Tunnel,South Shields) follow A194 to first roundabout, turn left into A184 -then three miles to Stadium.

Capacity: 11,795 **Seats**: 11,795 **Covered**: 3,300 **Floodlights**: Yes

MATCH TICKETS:

Ticket office Telephone: 0191 478 3883

Ticket Prices: Adult- £12. Concessions £7, Juniors (U16) £2 (accompanied by a full price adult).

Clubhouse: Bar inside Tyne & Wear stand open on matchdays.

Club Shop: Full range of souvenirs etc.

PROGRAMME EDITOR

Jeff Bowron

Tel: (M) 07801 847 004

Email: jeffbowron@blueyonder.co.uk

CLUB STATISTICS

RECORD

Attendance: 11,750 v Newcastle United Friendly 7th August 1995

Victory: 8-0 v Netherfield, N.P.L.

Defeat: 0-9 v Sutton United Conference 22.09.90

Goalscorer: Bob Topping 120

Career Appearances: Simon Smith 501 1985-94

Record Transfer Fee Paid:
£9,000 to Dagenham & Redbridge for Paul Cavell

Received:
Undisclosed from Rushden & Diamonds for Kenny Cramman

SENIOR HONOURS

Northern Premier League Champions 1982-83, 85-86.
Conference North Play-off Winners 2008-09.

PREVIOUS

Leagues: Football League 1930-60. N.Co E 1960-62.
North Regional 1962-68. NPL 1968-70, 73-83, 85-86, 87-90.
Wearside 1970-71. Midland 1971-72.
Alliance/Conference 1983-85, 86-87, 90-98

Ground: Redheugh Park 1930-1971

GRAYS ATHLETIC

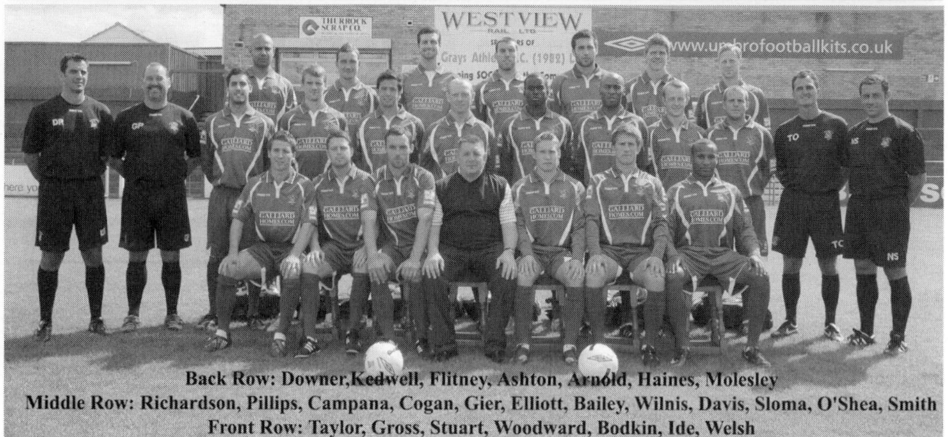

Back Row: Downer, Kedwell, Flitney, Ashton, Arnold, Haines, Molesley
Middle Row: Richardson, Pillips, Campana, Cogan, Gier, Elliott, Bailey, Wilnis, Davis, Sloma, O'Shea, Smith
Front Row: Taylor, Gross, Stuart, Woodward, Bodkin, Ide, Welsh

CLUB PERSONNEL

Chairman: John Moncur.

Vice Chairman: K Lamb.

Chief Executive: Mick Woodward.

Company Secretary: P O'Reilly.

Additional Directors

I Keen, P Spinks, J Spinks, J Woodward, N Gordon.

Secretary: Phil O'Reilly

Correspondenc c/o club.

Telephone: (B): 01375 377 753 (M): 07980 643 832

E-mail: graysathletic@btconnect.com

Commercial Manager: Keith Burns.

(M) 07752 161 633.

Press Officer

Kevin Lamb. (M): 07810 898 572

E-mail: press@graysathletic.co.uk

Manager: Alan Lewer.

Club therapist: Rebbeca Nutt.

Starting a league season as one of the favourites for relegation doesn't encourage confidence on or off the field, and when five of the first seven games are lost, supporters understandably fear the worst. Owner and Chairman Mick Woodward had acted as manager but he handed over to Tim O'Shea who was followed by Wayne Burnett who stayed a little longer before Gary Phillips took control. With the chairman also resigning and putting the club up for sale during the season and then changing his mind, continuity on and off the field was obviously missing.

An exciting F.A. Cup trip to Carlisle produced a splendid 1-1 draw but United won the replay 2-0 and the ever improving Hayes & Yeading club knocked ' The Blues' out of the F.A. Trophy at the end of the year when they were also dangerously placed in the relegation zone.

Scoring goals proved a problem all season with 31 scored at home and just 13 on their travels, and no marksman reached double figures for the season. So with relegation looking a probability, all credit to the fighting qualities of everyone involved in the very testing last six weeks of the season. Of the final ten matches, with Grays constantly in and out of the relegation zone, only two games were lost. Twelve points were gained in the last six fixtures, including victories over York City and Crawley Town.

The managerial team that inspired this excellent climax to a very ordinary season included the chairman and the dressing room influence of Craig Edwards and Phillips.

GRAYS ATHLETIC

BEST LGE ATT.: 1,246 v Forest Green Rovers
LOWEST: 415 v Weymouth

No.	Date	Comp	H/A	Opponents	Att:	Result	Goalscorers	Pos
1	Aug 9	BSP	A	Weymouth	1059	L 1 - 3	Molesley 6	
2	12		H	Kettering Town	696	D 1 - 1	Branston 72 (og)	
3	16		H	Northwich Victoria	523	W 2 - 1	Elliott 44 Sloma 67	12
4	23		A	Salisbury City	987	L 0 - 1		16
5	25		H	Eastbourne Borough	641	L 0 - 1		19
6	30		A	Mansfield Town	2378	L 0 - 1		21
7	Sept 2		A	Crawley Town	1189	L 1 - 2	Taylor 9	
8	7		H	Kidderminster Harriers	525	W 3 - 2	Thurgood 53 Sloma 67 **Cogan** 71	
9	13		A	Woking	3132	L 1 - 3	Molesley 10	20
10	20		H	Wrexham	746	W 2 - 1	St Amie 40 45	
11	26		H	Stevenage Borough	791	L 1 - 2	Stuart 49	
12	28		A	Cambridge United	1917	L 0 - 1		22
13	Oct 4		H	Lewes	729	D 0 - 0		22
14	7		A	Rushden & Diamonds	1124	L 0 - 1		
15	11		A	Northwich Victoria	579	L 0 - 2		22
16	18		H	Woking	581	D 1 - 1	**Cogan** 47	
17	**25**	**F.A.C. 4Q**	**H**	**AFC Totton**	**480**	**W 2 - 0**	**Elliott 51 Cogan 85 (pen)**	
18	Nov 1		A	Kidderminster Harriers	1400	L 0 - 2		23
19	**8**	**F.A.C. 1R**	**A**	**Carlisle United**	**3921**	**D 1 - 1**	**Stuart 52**	
20	15		H	Oxford United	892	W 2 - 0	Forrester 43 Sloma 87	22
21	22		A	Lewes	519	L 0 - 2		23
22	**25**	**SS S3**	**H**	**Chelmsford City**	**262**	**L 2 - 4**	**Sloma 28, McDonald 90**	
23	**29**	**F.A.C. 1R r**	**H**	**Carlisle United**	**1217**	**L 0 - 2**		
24	Dec 6		A	York City	2154	W 1 - 0	Thomas 26	22
25	9		A	Stevenage Borough	1289	D 0 - 0		
26	**16**	**F.A.T 1R**	**A**	**Hayes & Yeading**	**158**	**L 0 - 2**		
27	20		H	Barrow	502	W 2 - 1	**Cogan** 41 56	21
28	26		A	Ebbsfleet United	1143	W 1 - 0	Slabber 78	20
29	28		H	Histon	525	L 1 - 4	Welsh 37	22
30	Jan 1		H	Ebbsfleet United	748	W 3 - 1	Thurgood 31 Welsh 50 Stuart 79	16
31	17		H	Burton Albion	651	L 0 - 1		18
32	27		H	Weymouth	415	D 1 - 1		
33	Feb 14		A	Wrexham	3419	L 2 - 3	**Cogan** 30 **Pugh** 90	21
34	21		A	Barrow	1515	D 1 - 1	**Pugh** 65	
35	24		H	Cambridge United	754	L 0 - 1		
36	28		A	Forest Green Rovers	992	D 1 - 1	Welsh 70	22
37	Mar 3		H	Torquay United	510	L 1 - 2	Dinning 26	
38	7		H	Altrincham	710	W 2 - 1	**Cogan** 45 Slabber 52	21
39	10		A	Kettering Town	1117	D 0 - 0		22
40	14		A	Oxford United	4764	L 1 - 4	Dinning 62	22
41	17		A	Histon	641	L 1 - 4	**Pugh** 42	
42	21		H	Mansfield Town	802	W 2 - 1	Slabber 82 **Pugh** 90	21
43	24		A	Torquay United	1996	D 1 - 1	Taylor 38	
44	28		A	Burton Albion	2388	L 0 - 4		20
45	31		H	Rushden & Diamonds	695	D 0 - 0		21
46	April 4		H	York City	720	W 1 - 0	**Pugh** 39	19
47	11		H	Salisbury City	761	W 3 - 1	**Pugh** 12 43 Taylor 52	18
48	13		A	Eastbourne Borough	1305	L 1 - 2	Black 45	
49	18		A	Altrincham	1148	L 0 - 2		19
50	21		H	Crawley Town	630	W 1 - 0	Beavan 32	
51	26		H	Forest Green Rovers	1246	W 2 - 1	Thurgood 69 Berry 69	19

Average Home Att: 687 (919) **Goals** 49 73

Best Position: 12th **Worst:** 23rd

Goalscorers: Pugh 7, Cogan 7, Sloma 4, Slabber 3, Stuart 3, Taylor 3, Thurgood 3, Welsh 3, Dinning 2, Elliott 2, Molesley 2, St Amie 2, Beavan 1, Berry 1, Black 1, Forrester 1, McDonald 90, Thomas 1. Own Goals 1.

ARNOLD 12	STUART 4	ASHTON 5	GIER 2	WELSH 11	MOLESLEY 20	GROSS 3	ELLIOTT 7	KEDWELL 10	TAYLOR 9	COGAN 17	IDE 19	CAMPANA 21	SLOMA 8	BAILEY 14	FLITNEY 1	WILNIS 15,5	THURGOOD 24,6	BUTTON 26	ST AIMIE 27	RIGG 10	DAVIS 22,15	DIXON 28	DAYES 6	HICKIE 19	BATT 3	FORRESTER 21	MCCOLLIN 25	SLABBER 20,16	W THOMAS 23	BUTCHER 26	BEAVAN 19,3	PUGH 10	BERRY 6,18	LINDIE 16	BECKWITH 26,1	DINNING 5	HUDSON-ODOI 28,19	QUISTIN 25	BLACK 16,8	LONG 3,2	JONES 5,14	
X	X	X	X	X	X	X	X	X	X	S	S	S	U																													1
X	X	X	X	X	S	X	X	S	X	X	X	X	U	U																												2
X	X	X	X	S		X	X	X	X	X	S		X	S	U																											3
U	X	X	X	S		X	X	X		X	X	X	X	U	X	S	S																									4
U	X		X	X	S	X	U	X	X	X		U		X	X	X	X																									5
U	X	X	U	X	S		X	X	X	X		S	X	X	X	X																										6
U	X	X	S	X	S	X	X	X	X	X		U		X	X	X	S																									7
U	X	X	U	S	X		X	X	S	S	X	X	X		X	X	X																									8
U	X	X	U	S	X				X	X	X	S	X	X	X	X	X																									9
U	X		X	X	X		X			S	S		X	S		X	X	X	X	X																						10
U	X		X	X	X		X			S			X	S		X	X	X	X	X	S	U																				11
U	X			X	X		X			S			X	S			X	X	X	X	X	S	X	U																		12
U	X			X			S			X		S	X	X		U	X	X	X		X	X	X	S																		13
U	X			X			X			U			X	X		X		X	S	X	X	S		X																		14
U	X			S			U						X	X		X	X	X	S	X	X		X	X																		15
U	X		X	X			S			X			X			S	X	X		X	X	S		X																		16
U	**X**		**X**	**S**			**X**		**U**	**X**			**X**	**U**		**S**	**X**	**X**			**X**	**X**	**U**	**X**																		**17**
U	X		X	X			X			X			U			U	X	X			X		U		X	X																18
U	**X**	**X**	**X**	**X**			**S**		**U**	**X**			**X**	**U**		**X**	**X**	**X**			**S**		**X**	**S**			**X**															**19**
U	X	S	X	X			S			X			X	X				X			U		X		X	X	X	S														20
U	X	S	X	X			U			X			X			X	X	X					X		S	X	X	S														21
X		**U**	**X**	**X**			**X**			**S**			**X**	**X**		**X**	**U**	**U**			**X**					**X**																**22**
U	**X**	**X**	**X**	**X**			**U**			**X**			**X**			**X**	**X**	**X**			**U**		**X**	**U**			**X**															**23**
U	X	X								X			X			X	X	X			S		U	U	X	S	X	X	X													24
U	X	X	S	X						X			X				X	X			X		U	S	X	S		X	X													25
U	**X**	**X**	**U**	**X**						**X**			**X**				**X**	**X**			**X**		**U**	**S**	**X**			**X**	**X**													**26**
U	X	X	U	X						X			S			X	X	X					U	X	X	X		X														27
X	X	X		X									S	U		X	X						U	X	X	X		S	X													28
X	X	X	U	X						X			S			X	X						U	X	X	X		S	X													29
X	X	X	U	X						X			X			X	X				U		U	S	X			X	X													30
X	X		U	X						X			X	U		X	X				X			S	X			X	X	U												31
X	X	X	U	X			U			X			X	S			X				X								X	U	X	X	S									32
X	X		X	X						X				S		X	X				S							X			X	X	U	S	U							33
X	X		X	X						X				X		X					S							X			X	X	S	S	U							34
X	X		X	X						X						U	X				S							X			X	X	U	S	U	X						35
X	X		X	X			U			X						X	X				X							U				X	X	U	U	X						36
X	X		U	X			U			X						X	X				X							U			X	X	X	S	U	X						37
U	X		U	X			S			X						X	X				S							X			X	X	S		X	X	X					38
U	X		U				X			X						X	X				U							X			X	S		X	X	X	X	U				39
S	X		X				X			X						U	X				S							X			X	X		U	X	X	X	S				40
U	X		U						S	X						X	X				X							X			X	X			X	X	S	X				41
	X						X		X	X						X	X				S							S			X	X			X	S	X	U	X			42
	X						X		X	X						X					X							S			S	X	U		X	X	X	U	X			43
	X			S			X		X	X						X					X							S			X	X	U		X		X		X	S	U	44
X	X			X			X		S	X						U	X											X			X	X	S						X	S	X	45
X	X			X			X		X	X						X	X											S			X	X	U				U		U	X	U	46
X	X			X					X	X						X	X											S			X	X	S		U		X		S	X	U	47
X	X			X					X	X						X	X				U							S			X	X			S		X		S	X	U	48
	X			S			X		X	X						U	X				X							X		X	X						S		X	U	X	49
	X			X			X		X	X						X	X				X							S		X	X		S						X	U	U	50
	X			X			X			X						X	X				X							X		X	X		S				S		X	S	U	51

Total League Appearances

17	46	15	16	33	6	6	22	7	15	38	4	3	19	9	6	31	35	13	4	6	17	1	5	6	9	6	3	15	7	3	18	16	2	1	7	8	8	1	7	3	2	**X**
1	0	2	2	7	4	0	4	1	3	5	3	4	3	6	0	2	2	0	2	0	8	3	0	4	1	2	0	11	0	0	1	1	7	4	1	1	3	1	2	3	0	**S**
22	0	0	12	0	0	0	6	0	0	1	0	2	3	4	1	6	0	0	0	0	4	1	7	2	0	0	0	2	0	2	0	0	5	2	6	0	1	3	1	2	6	**U**

Total Cup Appearances

1	4	3	4	4	0	0	2	0	0	4	0	0	5	1	0	3	4	4	0	0	3	1	2	1	1	1	2	1	1	0	0	0	0	0	0	0	0	0	0	0	0	**X**
0	0	0	0	1	0	0	1	0	0	1	0	0	0	0	0	1	0	0	0	0	1	0	0	2	0	0	0	0	0	0	0	0	0	0	0	0	0	0	0	0	0	**S**
4	0	1	1	0	0	0	1	0	2	0	0	0	0	2	0	0	1	1	0	0	1	0	2	1	0	0	0	0	0	0	0	0	0	0	0	0	0	0	0	0	0	**U**

Also played: WOOLEY U(1,2).BODKIN X(1,3).MUNDAY U(3).REID S(5,6,9)U(10).HAINES S(14,15,16)X(22).S THOMAS X(14,15,16).GRAY X(17)S(18)U(19).LODGE S(17).BEANEY X(18).MCDONALD X(22,26)S(27). OLIMA S(23)U(30,31). TOWNSEND U(24). MCKENZIE X(28). OVERLAND U(29,30). TABIRI X(33,34,35)U(36). HOGARTH U(34). QUISTIN U(39,42,43)S(40)X(41). BATCHELOR S(41)U(42,43). SWEENEY U(45,50,51)S(49).

GRAYS ATHLETIC

CURRENT SQUAD AS OF BEGINING OF 2009-10 SEASON

GOALKEEPERS		SQ NO.	HT	WT	D.O.B	AGE	P.O.B	CAREER	APPS	GOA
Billy	Lumley							Wolves (Scholar), Glen Hoddle Soccer School 11/08, Brentford (Trial) 7/09, Grays 8/09		
DEFENDERS										
Craig	Braham-Barrett							Charlton (Yth), Sheff Wed (Yth), Aveley, Dulwich H 7/07, Potters Bar 10/07, Eastleigh, East Thurrock 2/08, Welling 5/08, Peterborough £10,000 + 10/08 Rel 7/09, Kettering (L) 1/09, Grays 8/09		
Ronnie	Bull	4	5'07"	10 11	27/12/80	28	Hackney	Millwall, Yeovil (2ML) 9/03, Barnet (Trial) 12/03, Brentford (3ML) 1/04 Undisc 4/04 Rel c/s 04, Grimsby 7/04 Rel c/s 05, New Zealand Knights 7/05, Rushden & D 1/06 Rel c/s 06, Basingstoke 10/06, Grays 11/06 Rel 1/07, Crawley 1/07, Ebbsfleet 1/08 Rel 5/08,		
Kenny	Davis	2	5'07"	11 02	17/4/88	21	London	Chelsea (Yth), Redbridge 3/05, Harlow c/s 05, Grays 8/08	25	0
Michael	Haswell				23/8/83	26	London	Wimbledon (Junior), Southend (Yth), Grays c/s 01, Romford 1/02, Grays 3/02, Wingate & F c/s 02, Harlow 7/04, Chelmsford 1/05, AFC Wimbledon 6/06 Rel 5/09, Grays 6/09		
Gavin	Hoyte	6	6'04"	12 06	24/6/86	23	Bedford	Wooton Blue Cross, Bedford T 12/05, Cambridge U 5/07 Rel 2/09, Hinckley U (L) 1/08, Halesowen T (3ML) 10/08, Weymouth 2/09, Grays 7/09		
Dave	McSweeney		5'11"	11 07	28/12/81	27	Basildon	Southend Rel c/s 04, Welling (L) 3/04, Billericay 8/04, Grays 6/09		
Fred	Murray	3	5'10"	11 12	22/5/82	27	Clonmel	Blackburn, Cambridge (3ML) 12/01 Perm 3/02, Northampton 7/04 Rel c/s 07, L.Orient (Trial) 7/07, Stafford R 8/07, Stevenage 1/08 Rel c/s 08, Exeter 9/08 Rel c/s 09, Grays 8/09		
MIDFIELDERS										
Tommy	Black		5'07"	11 10	26/11/79	29	Chigwell	Arsenal, Carlisle (L) 8/99, Bristol C (L) 12/99, C.Palace £250,000 7/00 Rel c/s 07, Sheff U (L) 9/04, Gillingham (SL) 1/06, Bradford C (L) 11/06, Southend 7/07 Rel c/s 08, Stevenage 10/08 Rel 1/09, Barnet 1/09 Rel 2/09, Grays NC 3/09 Rel c/s 09, Grays 8/0	9	1
Sam	Cutler	7			11/2/90	19	Sidcup	Cambridge U, Weymouth 5/08, Grays 8/09		
Richard	Graham	11	5'10"	11 10	5/8/79	30	Newry	QPR Rel c/s 01, Barnet 7/01, Chesham 9/01, Billericay 7/02 Rel c/s 03, Kettering 8/03, Barnet 7/04 Rel c/s 07, Dag & Red 7/07 Rel c/s 09, Kettering (SL) 1/09, Grays 7/09		
Sam	Long	8	6'00"	11 02	4/9/90	18	Bexley	Charlton Rel c/s 09, Grays (L) 3/09, Grays 7/09	6	0
Cameron	Mawer	5	5'10"	11 06	21/2/86	23	Stevenage	Watford (Scholar), Wealdstone 1/05, Stoke, Stockport (Trial) c/s 05, Grays 7/05 Rel 5/08, Weymouth 7/08, Grays 8/09		
Marcel	McKie		5'11"	11 09	22/9/84	24	Edmonton	Tottenham Rel 8/06, West Ham (Trial), Wycombe (Trial) 4/06, Dag & Red (Trial), Kettering 9/06 Rel 3/07, Crewe (Trial) 10/06, Lewes 3/07, St Albans 8/07 Rel 5/08, Potters Bar 9/08, Enfield T 12/08, Grays 6/09		
Nick	McKoy		6'00"	12 04	3/9/86	22	Newham	Wimbledon/MK Dons, Cardiff 7/06 Rel c/s 07, Torquay (SL) 1/07, Darlington (Trial) 1/07, Shrewsbury (Trial) 12/07, Potters Bar 8/08, St Johnstone 8/08 Rel 12/08, Enfield T 1/09, Grays 6/09		
Adriano	Rigoglioso	17	6'01"	12 07	28/5/79	30	Liverpool	Liverpool (Trainee), Marine 7/98, Morecambe 7/00, Doncaster £30,000 11/03 Rel 2/06, Southport (L) 11/05, Chester (Trial) 1/06, Morecambe 3/06 Rel 1/07, Forest Green (L) 9/06, Forest Green 1/07, Grays 8/09		
FORWARDS										
Billy	Crowther	18			31/10/88	20		L.Orient (Yth), AFC Hornchurch, Potters Bar, Brentwood, Grays 8/09		
Jerson	Dos Santos	15						Sutton U, C.Palace (Scholar) 8/08, Grays 6/09		
Serge	Makofo	20	5'11"	12 06	3/9/86	22	Kinshasa, DR Congo	Wimbledon/MK Dons, Kettering Undisc 3/06 Rel 5/07, Maidenhead 8/07, Halesowen T 3/08, Dorchester (Trial) 3/08, Potters Bar 3/08, Croydon Ath 12/08, Grays 6/09		
Lee	McEvilly	10	6'00"	13 00	15/4/82	27	Liverpool	Burscough, Rochdale £20,000 12/01 Rel c/s 04, Accrington (2ML) 1/04, Accrington 5/04, Wrexham 7/05 Rel 6/07, Accrington 7/07 Rel 5/08, Rochdale (2ML) 11/07, Cambridge U (SL) 1/08, Cambridge U 6/08, Rochdale (6WL) 11/08 Undisc 1/09 Rel 5/09, Barrow (L) 3/0		
Jamie	Slabber	9	6'02"	11 10	31/12/84	24	Enfield	Tottenham, AB Copenhagen (L) 3/04, Swindon (L) 12/04, Aldershot 3/05 Rel 5/05, Grays 7/05, Oxford U (L) 11/06, Stevenage 12/06 Rel 5/07, Rushden & D (Trial) 7/07, Havant & W 8/07 Rel 10/08, Grays NC 10/08	26	3
Charlie	Taylor	14			28/12/85	23	Lewisham	C.Palace Rel, Notts Forest, Welling 1/04, Hornchurch 5/04, Fisher 10/04, Margate 11/05, Fisher 1/06 Rel 7/06, Dulwich H c/s 07, Grays 7/09		

LOANEES		HT	WT	DOB	AGE	POB	From - To	APPS	GOA
(M)Kieron	St Aimie	6'01"	13 00	4/5/89	20	Brent	Barnet 9/08 - Stevenage (L) 11/08, Lewes (L) 1/09, Rel 2/09, Thurrock 3/09, Hitchin 3/09, Maidenhead 8/09	6	2
(F)Sean	Rigg	5'09"	12 01	1/10/88	20	Bristol	Bristol R 9/08 -	6	0
(G)David	Button	6'03"	13 00	27/2/89	20	Stevenage	Tottenham (3ML) 9/08 - Bournemouth (L) 1/09, Luton (L) 3/09, Dag & Red (L) 4/09	13	0
(F)Jonny	Dixon	5'09"	11 01	16/1/84	25	Murcia, Spa	Brighton 9/08 - Eastleigh (2ML) 1/09, Rel c/s 09, Retired 7/09	4	0
(F)Simon	Thomas			21/7/84	25	London	Crystal Palace 10/08 - Rotherham (L) 2/09	3	0
(F)Bradley	Gray	5'11"	11 07	5/7/90	19	Swindon	L.Orient 10/08 - St Albans (L) 11/08, AFC Hornchurch (L) 1/09, Dulwich Hamlet (L) 2/09, St Albans (L) 3/09, Rel 5/09, Salisbury 7/09	1	0

LOANEES cont.		HT	WT	DOB	AGE	POB	From - To	APPS	GOA
(F)Andre	McCollin	5'06"	10 06	8/7/87	22		Yeovil 11/08 -	3	0
(F)Wes	Thomas			23/1/87	22		Dag & Red (2ML) 12/08 -	7	2
(G)Lee	Butcher			11/10/88	20	Waltham Forest	Tottenham 1/09 - St Albans (L) 3/09, Grays (L) 4/09	3	0
(F)Andrew	Pugh	5'09"	12 05	28/1/89	20	Gravesend	Gillingham (SL) 1/09 -	17	7
(F)Harry	Hogarth			2/10/88	20		Luton 1/09 - Rel 7/09	0	0
(D)George	Beavan	5'09"	12 02	12/1/90	19	Luton	Luton 1/09, (SL) 3/09 -	19	1
(M)Joe	Tabiri	5'10"	11 07	16/10/89	19	London	Barnet 1/09 -	3	0
(F)James	Lindie						Southend 2/09 - Bishops Stortford (SL) 3/09, Ebbsfleet 7/09	5	0
(M)Tony	Dinning	6'00"	13 05	12/4/75	34	Wallsend	Chester 2/09 - Gateshead (L) 3/09, Hednesford 7/09	9	2
(F)Bradley	Hudson-Odoi	5'08"		29/11/88	20	Ghana	Hereford (SL) 3/09 - Rel 5/09, Histon 8/09	11	0
(D)Ronnie	Jones						Southend 3/09 -	2	0

DEPARTURES		**HT**	**WT**	**DOB**	**AGE**	**POB**	**From - To**	**APPS**	**GOA**
(M)Jamie	Day	5'10"	11 04	13/9/79	29	Bexley	Welling 5/07 - Rel 8/08, Dartford 8/08		
(G)Joe	Wooley			20/9/89	19		Charlton (Yth) c/s 08 - Rel 8/08, Thurrock 10/08	0	0
(D)Jonathan	Munday			13/4/88	20		Kidderminster 8/08 - Rel 8/08, Lewes (Trial) 9/08, St Albans 11/08, Sutton U 1/09, Hitchin 2/09	0	0
(F)Danny	Kedwell			22/10/85	23	Kent	Welling 5/07 - AFC Wimbledon 9/08	8	0
(F)Charlie	Ide	5'09"	11 00	10/5/88	21	Sunbury	Brentford 5/08 - Rel 9/08, Wivenhoe 9/08, Croydon Ath 1/09, Carshalton 2/09	7	0
(D)Simon	Downer	5'11"	12 08	19/10/81	27	Romford	Weymouth 1/07 - Rel 10/08, Wivenhoe 10/08, Sutton U 11/08, Rushden & D 1/09		
(D)Lee	Canoville	6'01"	12 00	14/3/81	28	Ealing	Notts County 9/08 - Rel 10/08, Halesowen T 10/08, Gainsborough (SL) 2/09, Boston U 7/09		
(M)Alex	Campana	5'11"	12 01	11/10/88	20	Harrow	Watford 8/08 - Wivenhoe 10/08, Thurrock 11/08 Rel 2/09, Enfield T 2/09	7	0
(M)Kenny	Beaney			27/7/86	23		Fisher NC 10/08 - Beckenham 12/08, Thurrock 12/08, Bromley 2/09	1	0
(F)Craig	Reid	5'10"	11 10	17/12/88	20	Coventry	Cheltenham NC 8/08 - Newport C (3ML) 9/08 Perm 12/08	3	0
(M)Mark	Molesley			11/3/81	28	Hillingdon	Stevenage 5/08 - Bournemouth (10WL) 10/08 Perm 1/09	10	2
(F)Dean	McDonald	5'07"	10 12	19/2/86	23	Lambeth	Rushden & D 11/08 - Rel 1/09, Northwich 1/09 Rel 2/09, Tooting & M 3/09, Farnborough 5/09		
(G)Simon	Overland	6'04"	10 01	28/12/85	24	London	Carshalton (Dual) 12/08 - Boreham Wood 3/09, Hayes & Yeading c/s 09		
(D)Gavin	Dayes	6'01"	13 03	8/6/84	25	London	Fisher 9/08 - Rel 1/09, Welling 1/09	5	0
(F)Scott	Forrester			7/5/82	27		Metropolitain Police NC 10/08 - Rel 1/09, Metropolitan Police 1/09, Croydon Ath 7/09	8	1
(F)Leon	McKenzie			18/10/84	24		Thurrock 12/08 - Rel 1/09, Bishops Stortford 6/09	1	0
(M)Luke	Hickie	5'11"	11 07	17/8/88	21	Croydon	Fisher 9/08 - Rel 1/09	10	0
(D)Adam	Gross	5'10"	10 09	16/2/86	23	Greenwich	Barnet 5/07 - Rel 1/09, Welling (L) 10/08, Dartford (L) 11/08, Dartford 1/09	6	0
(D)Damien	Batt	5'10"	11 06	16/9/84	24	Hoddesdon	Fisher NC 10/08 - Oxford U 1/09	10	0
(G)Ross	Flitney	6'01"	11 11	1/6/84	25	Hitchin	Barnet 5/07 - Rel 1/09, Croydon Ath (2ML) 12/08, Croydon Ath 1/09	6	0
(M)Sam	Sloma	5'08"	11 06	29/10/82	26	London	Dag & Red 6/08 - Rel 1/09, Chelmsford 2/09 Rel 5/09, Woking 6/09	22	3
(D)Jon	Ashton	6'02"	13 12	4/10/82	26	Nuneaton	Rushden & D 5/07 - Stevenage 1/09	17	0
(M)Matt	Bodkin	5'06"	10 11	16/9/86	22	Chatham	Welling 12/06 - Rel 2/09, Eastleigh (6ML) 8/08, Dover 2/09 Rel 5/09, Thurrock 5/09	2	0
(G)Darren	Behcet	6'00"	11 07	8/10/86	22	London	Sutton U NC 1/09 - AFC Hornchurch 2/09		
(F)Paul	Olima			6/8/86	23	Dublin	Walton Casuals 11/08 - Walton Casuals (L) 12/08 Perm, Croydon Ath 1/09, Hitchin 2/09		
(D)Ludovic	Quistin	5'10"		24/5/84	25	Gualaloup, WI	Fisher NC 2/09 - AFC Hornchurch 2/09, Hednesford 3/09	2	0
(F)Fabian	Batchelor			16/11/89	19	London	Colchester NC 3/09 - Rel 3/09, Concord R 4/09	1	0
(M)Stuart	Thurgood	5'08"	11 10	4/11/81	27	Enfield	Gillingham (SL) 8/08 Perm 1/09 - Dag & Red 5/09	37	3
(M)Barry	Cogan	5'09"	09 00	4/11/84	24	Sligo	Gillingham 7/08 - Crawley 6/09	43	6
(D)Jamie	Stuart	5'10"	11 00	15/10/76	32	Southwark	Hornchurch 11/04 - Rushden & D 6/09	46	2
(F)Jamie	Taylor			16/12/82	26	Crawley	Dag & Red 5/08 - Eastbourne B 7/09	18	3
(D)Mark	Haines	6'03"		28/9/89	19		Northampton 5/08 - East Thurrock (L) 9/08, Chelmsford 7/09	0	0
(D)Allan	McLeod			19/4/80	29	Islington	Tooting & M 6/09 - Tooting & M 7/09		
(M)Ishmael	Welsh	5'07"	10 10	4/9/87	21	Deptford	Yeovil 5/08 - Ebbsfleet 7/09	40	3
(D)Shayne	Mangodza						Dulwich H 7/09 - Rel 8/09		
(G)Steve	Arnold	6'01"		22/8/89	20	Welham Green	Norwich (Yth) 6/08 - Rel c/s 09	18	0
(G)Rob	Beckwith	6'01"	13 12	12/9/84	24	Hackney	Barnet NC 2/09 - Rel c/s 09	8	0
(D)Rob	Gier	5'09"	11 07	6/1/80	29	Ascot	Aldershot 5/08 - Rel c/s 09	18	0
(D)Fabian	Wilnis	5'08"	12 06	23/8/70	39	Paramaribo, Surinam	Ipswich 8/08 - Rel c/s 09	33	0
(M)Stefan	Bailey	5'11"	12 08	10/11/87	21	Brent	QPR 6/08 - Farnborough (L) 2/09, Rel c/s 09	15	0
(M)Tyrone	Berry	5'08"	10 02	20/2/87	22	London	ex Gillingham 1/09 - Rel c/s 09	9	1
(M)Lewis	Dark	5'08"	11 06	10/4/89	20	Harlow	Fisher NC 2/09 - Rel		
(M)Stuart	Elliott	5'08"	11 05	27/8/77	32	Willesden	York C 5/08 - Durham C 6/09	26	1
(F)Efe	Echanomi			27/9/86	22		Tiptree 11/08 - Rel		
(F)Danny	Lodge			31/3/86	23		Thurrock 10/08 - Rel	0	0
(F)Joe	Sweeney			13/1/90	19		AFC Hornchurch NC 3/09 -	1	0
(F)Ashley	Townsend						Yth -	0	0

GRAYS ATHLETIC

Founded: 1890

Nickname: The Blues

Club Colours: Sky blue shirts, shorts and socks.

Change Colours: White shirts, shorts and socks.

Club Sponsor: Galliard Homes.

Previous League: Isthmian League.

Ground Address: The Recreation Ground, Bridge Road, Grays, Essex RM17 6BZ
Telephone: 01375 377 753
Facsimile: 01375 391 649
E-mail: graysathletic@btconnect.com
Website: www.graysathletic.co.uk

SIMPLE DIRECTIONS: Seven minutes walk from Grays BR station. Turn right round one way system then right into Clarence Road and at end into Bridge Road. Or from A13 towards Southend from London, take Grays exit towards town centre, keep left on one way sytem, continue up hill for about half a mile, turn right into Bridge Street and ground is half a mile on left. Bus No 370 passes Bridge Road..

MATCH TICKETS:
Ticket office Telephone: 01375 377 753
Ticket Prices: Adults - £13. Senor Citizens - £8. Students - £10. Children (11-16) - £8, (8-11) - £4.

Midweek Home Matchday: Tuesday 7.45 pm

Capacity: 4,000 **Seats:** 950 **Covered:**1,500
Clubhouse: Open Daily (01375 377 753).
Club Shop: On ground and open on matchdays

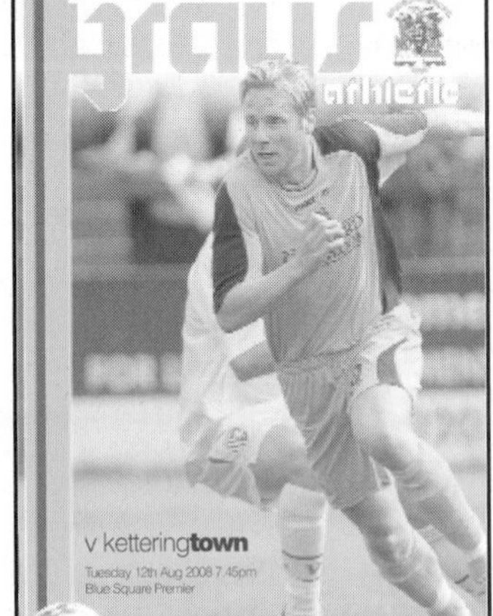

CLUB STATISTICS

RECORDS

Attendance:
9,500 v Chelmsford City, F.A. Cup 4th Qualifying Round 1959

Victory: 12-0 v Tooting & Mitcham United, London League 24.02.23

Defeat: 0-12 v Enfield (A) Athenian League 20.04.63

Career Goalscorer: Harry Brand 269 (1944-520)

Career Appearances: Phil Sammons 673 (1982-97)

Transfer Fee Paid: To Canvey Island for Ian Durant.

Transfer Fee Received: From Crystal Palace for Tony Witter, Plymouth for Dwight Marshall and Wycombe for Matt Lawrence

SENIOR HONOURS

Conference South Champions 2004-05
F.A. Trophy 2004-05 2005-06
Essex Senior Cup (x8)

PREVIOUS LEAGUES:

Athenian 1912-14, 1958-83.
London 1914-1924 1926-1939.
Kent 1924-1926 Corinthian 1945-1958 Isthmian 1958-2004.

PROGRAMME EDITOR

Kevin Lamb
Tel: 07810 898 572
E-mail: press@graysathletic.co.uk

HAYES & YEADING UNITED

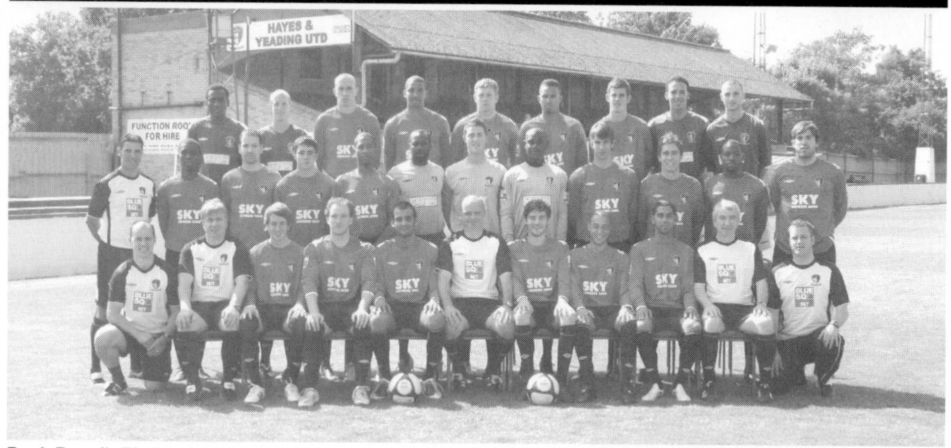

Back Row (L-R): Aga Briandt, Ray Curtis, Matt Ruby, Josh Scott, Will Hendry, Staforde Palmer, Neil Martin, Malakai Bulley, Ollie Fayed. **Middle Row:** Darron Wilkinson (Reserve Team Asst. Manager), Esmond James, Scott Fitzgerald, Billy Hughes, James Mulley, Delroy Preddie, Aaron Howe, Simon Grant, Steven Gregory, Peter Collins, Leon Solomon, Steve Perkins. **Front Row:** Colin Davies (Reserve Team Manager), Gareth Hall (Asst. Manager), Toby Little, Kieran Knight, Nevin Saroya, Garry Haylock (Manager), Tom Cadmore, Danny Allen-Page, Ram Marwa, Tony O'Driscoll (Coach), Ewen Fairgrieve (Therapist).

CLUB PERSONNEL

Chairman: Derek Goodall.
Vice Chairman: Trevor Griffith.
Company Secretary: John Bond.
Managing Director: Derrick Matthews.
Additional Directors: N Griffith T Griffith, T Gorman, C Hanland, J Bond, A Radford, S East, D Matthews, E Stevens, Dean Goodall.

Secretary: Bill Gritt
Pantiles, 17 Willow Chase, Hazelmere,
Bucks, HP15 7QP
(H): 01494 527 333
(M): 07710 102 004 B: 020 8573 8388
Email: juneguk@aol.com

Commercial Manager: Bill Perryman.
(B) 020 8756 1200 (M) 07780 870 920
Email: yfcperryman@hotmail.com

Press Officer: Nick Bell & Tim Fuell
Nick (M) 07906 303 696
nicholas.bell@talk21.com
Tim (M) 07782 284 164
tim.fuell@journalist.co.uk

Manager: Garry Haylock.
Assistant Manager: Gareth Hall.
Club therapist: Ewan Fairgrieve.

The relatively 'new' club after amalgamation probably surprised a few non-league pundits last season in the way they were never out of the top ten and, as the campaign developed so did their consistency, and a peak was reached just at the right time with a run of ten consecutive victories that took the Middlesex club into a very safe fourth position which ensured a play-off place.

The knock out cups also brought some excitement with victories over Staines Town and Kingstonian before Oxford United ended the F.A. Cup run at the Kassam Stadium. A.F.C Telford United also proved a stumbling block after F.A. Trophy victories over Chelmsford City and Grays Athletic.

Josh Scott (24 goals) and Will Hendry (14) enjoyed a great season in front of goal, and in the last thirteen league games a very well-marshalled defence achieved nine clean sheets. So a well balanced and talented squad looked forward to the end of season challenge.

The play-offs produced two thrilling games as far as Hayes & Yeading were concerned. A 2-4 home first leg defeat by Eastleigh was overturned with an amazing 4-0 victory after extra-time in the second leg. This was followed by another recovery at Hampton & Richmond in the final, which saw them promoted with a 3-2 victory having trailed 1-2 with twenty minutes to go. The club is definitely on a 'high' and a good start will be important in the Premier Division.

HAYES & YEADING UNITED

BEST LGE ATT.: **1,526** v AFC Wimbledon
LOWEST: **184** v Dorchester Town

No.	Date	Comp	H/A	Opponents	Att:	Result	Goalscorers	Pos
1	Aug 9	BSS	H	Chelmsford City	456	L 0 - 1		
2	12		A	Team Bath	161	L 1 - 4	Marwa 45	
3	16		A	Worcester City	824	W 3 - 0	Hendry 6 **Scott** 21 (pen) Fitzgerald 70	
4	23		H	Bishop's Stortford	229	W 1 - 0	Knight 90	10
5	25		A	Hampton & Richmond B	654	W 3 - 2	Marwa 29 80 **Scott** 66 (pen)	
6	30		H	Welling United	239	W 2 - 1	**Scott** 68 (pen) Palmer 76	6
7	Sept 2		A	Bath City	437	W 1 - 0	Fitzgerald 65	
8	6		H	Thurrock	238	W 2 - 1	Mulley 20 Gregory 29	3
9	**9**	**SS S1**	**A**	**St Albans City**	**165**	**W 1 - 0**	**Palmer 15**	
10	13		A	Dorchester Town	506	W 2 - 1	Hendry 19 Cadmore 24	2
11	20		H	AFC Wimbledon	1526	W 2 - 1	**Scott** 24 Fitzgerald 39	1
12	**27**	**F.A.C. 2Q**	**A**	**Staines Town**	**561**	**D 0 - 0**		
13	**30**	**F.A.C. 2Q r**	**H**	**Staines Town**	**348**	**W 5 - 3***	**Hendry16 43 Ruby 26 Knight 99 James 119**	
14	Oct 4		H	Braintree Town	264	L 0 - 1		3
15	**7**	**SS S2**	**A**	**Thurrock**	**68**	**D 3 - 3***	**Scott 34 pen 90 + 8 Fitzgerald 87 (Lost 4-5 on pens)**	
16	**11**	**F.A.C. 3Q**	**A**	**Kingstonian**	**578**	**W 3 - 1**	**Hendry 46 87(pen) Scott 7 (pen)**	
17	18		A	Eastleigh	512	D 3 - 3	**Scott** 13 32 Knight 47	5
18	21		H	Fisher Athletic	228	L 3 - 4	Marwa 50 Knight 79 90	
19	**25**	**F.A.C. 4Q**	**A**	**Oxford United**	**2521**	**L 0 - 2**		
20	Nov 1		H	Havant & Waterlooville	273	W 2 - 1	Hendry 85 Fitzgerald 90	
21	8		A	Newport County	679	W 5 - 1	Perkins 8 Mulley 50 Fitzgerald 62 64 **Scott** 71	3
22	15		A	St Albans City	587	D 1 - 1	Hendry 85	2
23	18		A	Bromley	317	L 0 - 1		
24	**22**	**F.A.T 3Q**	**H**	**Chelmsford Town**	**347**	**W 4 - 1**	**KNIGHT 4 (12 47 72 88)**	
25	29		H	Team Bath	272	D 1 - 1	**Scott** 6	2
26	Dec 6		H	Eastleigh	285	L 0 - 1		5
27	**16**	**F.A.T 1R**	**H**	**Grays Athletic**	**158**	**W 2 - 0**	**Caddy 10 Mulley 12**	
28	20		A	Chelmsford City	1502	L 1 - 2	Ruby 14	8
29	26		H	Maidenhead United	331	W 2 - 0	**Scott** 73 75	7
30	Jan 1		A	Maidenhead United	564	L 0 - 2		
31	**13**	**F.A.T 2R**	**A**	**AFC Telford United**	**986**	**L 0 - 4**		
32	17		H	Bath City	276	D 2 - 2	**Scott** 13 S.Jones 31 (og)	
33	24		A	Bognor Regis Town	333	D 1 - 1	**Scott** 85	9
34	27		H	Dorchester Town	184	W 2 - 1	Coleman 15 Marwa 18	
35	31		A	Basingstoke Town	338	D 1 - 1	Mulley 47	7
36	Feb 10		A	AFC Wimbledon	2621	L 0 - 2		
37	14		A	Havant & Waterlooville	626	D 2 - 2	Palmer 47 Marwa 87	7
38	21		H	St Albans City	258	W 2 - 1	Marwa 43 Ruby 48	6
39	24		A	Welling United	389	W 2 - 0	**Scott** 10 80	
40	28		H	Newport County	311	W 2 - 0	Marwa 11 **Scott** 52	6
41	Mar 7		H	Basingstoke Town	256	W 5 - 0	**Scott** 27 71 Aimable 36 (og) Binns 65 Palmer 83	5
42	10		H	Worcester City	219	W 3 - 1	**Scott** 11 Binns 14 Hendry 83	5
43	14		A	Thurrock	286	W 1 - 0	Hendry 77 (pen)	5
44	17		A	Braintree town	485	W 1 - 0		
45	28		A	Weston-s-Mare	281	W 2 - 1	Palmer 48 50	
46	April 4		H	Bromley	301	W 2 - 1	Hendry 32 66	4
47	7		H	Weston-s-mare	255	W 3 - 0	**Scott** 39 50 Palmer 40	
48	11		A	Bishop's Stortford	444	D 0 - 0		4
49	13		H	Hampton & Richmond	565	D 0 - 0		
50	18		A	Fisher Athletic	215	W 5 - 0	**Scott** 6 Little 11 53 Gregory 48 Perkins 66	4
51	25		H	Bognor Regis Town	325	W 3 - 1	Ruby 36 **Scott** 77 Palmer 90	4
52	**28**	**Play-off SF1**	**H**	**Eastleigh**	**517**	**L 2 - 4**	**Hendry 72 (pen) Ruby 89**	
53	**May 2**	**Play-off SF2**	**A**	**Eastleigh**	**1445**	**W 4 - 0**	**Perkins 45 Hendry 81 (pen) Fitzgerald 93 97 aet**	
54	**7**	**Play-off F**	**A**	**Hampton & Richmond**	**3111**	**W 3 - 2**	**Fitzgerald 17 Gregory 72 74**	

Average Home Att: 347 (279) **Goals** 101 63

Best Position: 1st **Worst:** 10th

Golascorers: Scott 25, Hendry 14, Fitzgerald 10, Knight 9, Marwa 8, Palmer 8, Ruby 5, Gregory 4, Mulley 4, Perkins 3, Binns 2, Little 2, Caddy 1, Cadmore 1, Coleman 1, James 1. Own Goals 2.

PREDDIE	ALLEN-PAGE	MULLEY	CADMORE	SAROYA	GREGORY	HUGHES	MARWA	FITZGERALD	PALMER	MEHMET	JAMES	KNIGHT	SCOTT	FAYED	HOWE	DIKUIZA	HENDRY	MARTIN	RUBY	COLLINS	PERKINS	GRANT	SOLOMAN	LOVELL	BULL	LITTLE	COSTA	MACDONALD	COLEMAN	BOTHAM	BINNS	WILLIAMS	
X	X	X	X	X	X	X	X	X	X	X	S	S	S	U	U																		1
X	X	X	X	X	X	U	X	X	S		S	X	S		U	X	X																2
X	X	S	X	U	X		X	X	S		X	S	X		U		X	X	X														3
X	X	S	X				X	X	S		X	S	X		U		X	X	X	U													4
X	X	S	X		X		X	S	U		X	X	X		S		X	X	X	U													5
	X	X	X		X		X	S	S			X	X		X		X	X	X	U	U	U											6
	X	X	X		X		X	X	U		U	S	X		X		X	X	X	U		U											7
U	X	X	X		X		X	X	S		S	S	X		X		X	X	X	U													8
X	X	X	X	X	X		X	S	X		S	X	X		U		S		U	X													9
U	X	X	X		X		X	X	S		S	S	X		X		X	X	X	U													10
U	X	X	X	U	X			X	S		X	S	X		X		X	X	X	U													11
U	X	X	X	U	X			X	X		S	U	X	U	X		X	X	X	U	U												12
U	X	X	X	S	X		X	X	U		S	S	X		X		X	X	X	U	U												13
U	X	X	X	U	X		X	X			S	S	X		X		X	X	X	U													14
X	X	X	X	X			X	S			X	X	X		U		S		S	X	X												15
X	X	X	U	X	X		X	X			S	S	X		U		X	X	X	U	S		U										16
X	X	X		X	X		X	S			U	X	X		U		X		X	U	X			U									17
X	X	X		X	X		X	S			X	X			U		X		X	X	U		U	S									18
X	X	X	X	S	X		X	S			S	X	X		U		X		X	X	U		U	U									19
X	X	X	X	S			X	S			S	X	X		U		X		X	U	X				X								20
X	X	X	X		U		X	X			X	U	X		U				X	S	X			S	X								21
X	X	X	X		U		X	X			X	S			U		X		X	U	X				X	S							22
X	X	X	X		X		X	X			S	S	X		U		X		X		U				X	S							23
U	S	X	X		X		X	X			X	X			X		U		X	S	S				X	X							24
U	X	X	X		X		S				X	X	X		X		X		X	U	U			U	X								25
U	X	X	X		X		S	X			X	X			X		X			X			U		X		S	U					26
U	X	X	X		X		X		U		X		X		X				X	X	U		S	U				X					27
U	X	X	X		X		X		S		X		X		X				X	X	S		S	U				X					28
U	X	X	X		X		X				S		X		X				X	U	S		U					X	X	X			29
U	X	X	X		X		X				S	S	X		X				X	U	U							X	X	X			30
U	X	X			S		X				S	X	S		X		X		X	X	X			U				X		X			31
U		X	X		X		X				X	S	X		X		X		X	U	U							X	U	X			32
U	S	X	X				X		X			X	X		X		X		X	U	X							X	S	S			33
U	X	X	X				X		S		U	S	X		X		X		X	X	X			U					X				34
U	X	X	X		X		X		S		S	U	X		X		X		X		S							X	X				35
U	X	X	X		X		X	X	X		S	S	X		X					U	X							X	S				36
X	X	X	X		X		X	X	S		S		X						X	U		U						X	S		X		37
X	X	S	X		X		X				X		X		U		X		X	U	U							X	U		X		38
X	X	S	X		X		X		S		X		X		U		X		X	U	U							X			X		39
X		X	X		X		X		S		X		X		U		X		X	U	U			U				X			X		40
X	X	S			X		X		S		X		X		U		X		X	X	X			U		S					X		41
X	X	X			X		X		S		U		X		U		X		X		X			S		S		X			X		42
X	X	X	X		X		X	S	X						U		X		X	S	U					U		X			X		43
X		X	X		X		X	S	X				X		U		X		X	U	S					U		X			X		44
X		X	X		X		X	X	X		S				U		X		X		S			U		U		X			X		45
X		X	X		X		X	X	X		S				U		X		X	U	S					U		X			X		46
X		X	X		X		X	U	X		U		X		U		X		X	U	S							X			X		47
X		X	X		X		X	S	X		S		X		U		X			U	X					U		X			X		48
X	X	X	S		X		X	X	X				S		U				X	U	X					X		X			S		49
X	X	X	X		X		S	S	U				X		U		X		X		X					X		X			S		50
	X	X	X		X		X	S	S				X		X		X		X	S	U					X					X	U	51
	X	X	X		X		X	S	S				X		X		X		X		U					U		X			X	U	52
X		X	X		X		X	X	X		S				U		S		X	S	X					U		X			X		53
X		X	X		X		X	X	U		S				U		X		X	U	X					U		X			X		54
Total League Appearances																																	
25	34	36	37	4	36	1	38	18	10	1	15	9	33	0	17	1	34	9	37	5	12	0	0	0	6	3	0	20	4	3	13	0	X
0	1	6	1	1	0	0	3	10	16	0	15	14	3	0	1	0	0	0	0	3	7	0	1	3	0	4	1	0	3	1	2	0	S
14	0	0	0	3	2	1	0	1	3	0	5	2	0	1	23	0	0	0	0	26	11	3	3	7	0	5	0	1	2	0	0	1	U
Total Cup Appearances																																	
6	9	12	10	3	10	0	11	6	3	0	3	5	8	0	6	0	7	3	10	5	4	0	0	0	1	1	0	5	0	1	3	0	X
0	1	0	0	2	1	0	0	4	1	0	8	2	1	0	0	0	3	0	1	2	2	0	1	0	0	0	0	0	0	0	0	0	S
5	0	0	1	1	0	0	0	0	3	0	0	1	0	1	6	0	1	0	1	4	5	0	2	3	0	3	0	0	0	0	0	1	U

HAYES & YEADING UNITED

CURRENT SQUAD AS OF BEGINING OF 2009-10 SEASON

GOALKEEPERS		SQ NO.	HT	WT	D.O.B	AGE	P.O.B	CAREER	APPS	GOA
Chris	Baker	25						Ash U, Hayes & Yeading 7/09		
Simon	Overland	1	6'05"	10 01	28/12/85	23	London	Millwall Rel 2/04, Kettering (L) 3/00, Kettering NC 2/04, Gravesend 3/04, Grays 8/04, Dag & Red 1/05, Redbridge (L) 2/05, Maldon T 3/05, Dag & Red 6/05, Fisher (Dual) 11/05, Ashford T (L) 3/06, Ashford T (Dual) 8/06, Dulwich H (L) 12/06 Perm 1/07, Fisher 6/07 Rel 11/08, Cashalton 12/08, Grays (Dual) 12/08, Boreham Wood 3/09, Hayes & Yeading c/s 09		
Delroy	Preddie	21			14/7/76	33	Berkshire	Northampton (Trainee), Slough c/s 94, Walton & H (L) 3/96, Walton & H 8/96, Chesham 7/99, Yeading 5/03, Maidenhead 11/06, Staines 8/07, Hayes & Yeading 8/07	25	0
DEFENDERS										
Danny	Allen-Page	2	5'08"	10 13	30/10/83	25	London	C.Palace (AS), Brentford, Farnborough 3/04, Yeading/Hayes & Yeading 7/06	35	0
Tom	Cadmore	4	6'00"	13 01	26/1/88	21	Rickmansworth	Watford (Yth), Wycombe Rel 5/08, Yeading (3ML) 8/07, Hayes & Yeading 7/08	38	1
Sami	El-Abd	14			1/1/88	21	Brighton	Crawley, Burgess Hill (2ML) 9/05, Team Bath 8/06, Hayes & Yeading 7/09		
Adam	Green	3	5'11"	10 11	12/1/84	25	Hillingdon	Fulham Rel 5/06, Sheff Wed (L) 1/05, Bournemouth (L) 3/05, Bristol C (SL) 1/06, Grays 7/06 Rel 1/07, Woking 1/07 Rel c/s 08, Grimsby (Trial) 12/08, Hayes & Yeading 7/09		
Esmond	James	17			4/2/90	19		Hayes & Yeading	30	0
Matt	Ruby	5			18/3/86	23	Chertsey	Woking Rel 8/08, Northwood (L) 10/05, Fleet T (L) 1/06, Basingstoke (L) 3/06, Bognor Regis (L) 3/07, Hayes & Yeading 8/08	37	3
Charlie	Wassmer	22			21/3/91	18		Hayes & Yeading		
MIDFIELDERS										
Dale	Binns	11			8/7/81	28	London	Hendon, Cambridge C 8/04, Stevenage 6/06 Rel 5/07, Lewes 7/07, Maidenhead 5/08, Hayes & Yeading 2/09	15	2
Marc	Canham	8	5'11"	12 03	11/9/82	26	Wegburg, Ger	Colchester Rel 6/03, Bournemouth (Trial) c/s 03, Team Bath 8/03, Yeovil (Trial) 2/05, Hayes & Yeading 7/09		
Justin	Cochrane	15	5'11"	11 07	26/1/82	27	Hackney	QPR Rel c/s 02, Reading (Trial) 1/02, Bournemouth (Trial) 3/02, Cambridge U (Trial) 7/02, Hayes 8/02, Crewe £50,000 7/03 Rel c/s 06, Gillingham (L) 2/06, Luton (Trial) 4/06, Rotherham 7/06 Rel c/s 07, Yeovil 8/07 Rel 1/08, Millwall 3/08 Rel c/s 08, L.Orient (Trial), Rushden & D 12/08 Rel 1/09, Aldershot T 2/09 Rel 5/09		
Toby	Little	19			19/2/89	20		Hayes/Hayes & Yeading	7	2
Rambir	Marwa	6			10/1/80	29	Barkingside	L.Orient (Trainee), Erith & B 2/00, Ilford 7/00, Erith & B 1/01, Australia, L.Orient (Trial) 6/03, Grays 8/03, St Albans 8/04, Dag & Red 5/05, St Albans (L) 1/06 (Perm) 3/06, Hayes & Yeading (L) 11/07 Perm 12/07	41	8
James	Mulley	7			30/9/88	20		Yeading/Hayes & Yeading	42	3
FORWARDS										
Scott	Fitzgerald	10	5'11"	12 00	18/11/79	29	Hillingdon	Northwood, Watford 3/03, Swansea (L) 9/04, L.Orient (L) 1/05, Oldham (Trial) 2/05, Brentford (L) 3/05, Brentford Undisc 3/05 Rel 1/07, Oxford U (6WL) 11/05, Walsall (2ML) 2/06, AFC Wimbledon (L) 8/06, AFC Wimbledon (2ML) 11/06, Basingstoke 1/07, Hayes & Yeading 8/08	28	6
Rob	Gradwell	9	6'02"	13 07	16/12/90	18	Hillingdon	Birmingham (Scholar) Rel c/s 09, Luton (Trial) 4/09, Lincoln C (Trial) 7/09, Hayes & Yeading c/s 09		
Jake	Lovell	20			20/9/90	18		Hayes & Yeading	3	0
Stafforde	Palmer	12			23/4/88	21		Hayes/Hayes & Yeading, Northwood (L) 12/08, Maidenhead (3ML) 6/09	26	7

LOANEES		SN	HT	WT	DOB	AGE	POB	From - To	APPS	GOA
(M)Calum	Botham				28/12/89	19		Wycombe 12/08 - Rel 5/09	4	0
(D)Jack	Pattison							Exeter 3/09 -		

DEPARTURES		SN	HT	WT	DOB	AGE	POB	From - To	APPS	GOA
(D)Neil	Martin							Exeter (L) 8/08 Perm 9/08 - Rel 10/08, Salisbury 1/09, Dorchester 8/09	9	0
(D)Nevin	Saroya		6'03"	13 01	15/9/80	28	Hillingdon	Hampton & R 8/01 - Rel 12/08, Maidenhead 12/08	5	0
(D)Ronnie	Bull		5'07"	10 11	27/12/80	28	Hackney	Fisher 10/08 - Exeter (Dual) 10/08 Perm 1/09 Rel c/s 09, Grays 8/09	6	0
(F)Kieran	Knight						Middlesex	Northwood 7/04 - Hampton & R 2/09	23	4
(F)Omari	Coleman		5'11"	11 13	23/11/80	28	Birmingham	Fisher 12/08 - Rel 2/09, Kingstonian 3/09	7	1
(M)Dan	Mehmet							Yth - Rel 4/09	1	0
(M)Steven	Gregory		6'01"	12 04	19/3/87	22	Aylesbury	Wycombe 7/08 - AFC Wimbledon Undisc 5/09	36	2
(D)Gary	MacDonald		6'01"	12 12	25/10/79	29	Iselone, Ger	Bognor 12/08 - Havant & W 6/09	20	1
(F)Josh	Scott							Hayes/Hayes & Yeading, Dag & Red 6/09	36	22
(G)Aaron	Howe							Carshalton 8/08 - Havant & W 7/09	18	0
(M)Steve	Perkins				5/11/75	33	Southport	Welling 8/07 - Rel 8/09	19	2
(G)Simon	Grant							Yth -	0	0
(G)Steve	Williams		6'06"	13 10	21/4/83	26	Oxford	ex Lewes 3/09 - Rel	0	0
(D)Peter	Collins						Hillingdon	Yth -	8	0
(D)Bobby	Hughes							Yth -	1	0
(D)Leon	Soloman							Welling 8/08 - Walton Casuals (L) 12/08, Rel	1	0
(M)Andre	Costa							Yth -	1	0
(M)Mohammed	Dikuiza							Brentford 4/08 -	1	0
(M)Ollie	Fayed							Yth -	0	0
(M)Will	Hendry		5'11"	12 10	10/11/86	22	Slough	Grays 1/07 -	34	8

HAYES & YEADING UNITED

Formed: 2007 (After the amalgamation of Hayes and Yeading)

Club Colours: Red shirts, black shorts, black socks.

Change Colours: Blue shirts, white shorts, white socks.

Club Sponsor: Barratts

Previous League: Isthmian League

Ground address: Townfield House, Church Road, Hayes, Middlesex UB3 2LE.
Telephone: 0208 573 2075
Mobile: 07816 123 418
Fax: 0208 573 0933
Email: hayesandyeadingunited@fsmail.com
Website: www.hyufc.net
Simple Directions: M25, M4 A312 (Hayes by-pass) Take A4020 (Uxbridge Rd) and Church Road is on the left.
Car Parking: At ground - £1.
Capacity: 6,500 **Seats**: 450 **Covered** 2,450 **Floodlights**: Yes

MATCH TICKETS:
Ticket office Telephone: 0208 573 2075
Ticket Prices: Adults - £12. Senor Citizens - £7. Students - £7. Under 16s - £7. Under 7s - Free. Transfer to seating - £2.

Clubhouse: Open from lunchtime at weekends and mid week evenings.
Club Shop: Yes.
Local Press: Hayes Gazette.
Local Radio: Capital Radio.

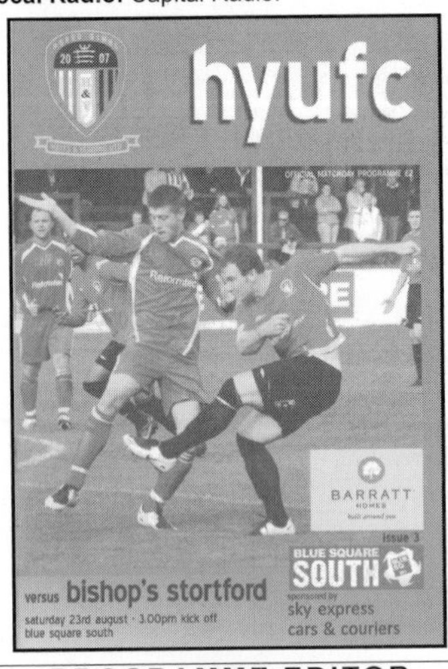

PROGRAMME EDITOR

Ray Peploe

(H) 01296 632615 (M) 07739 988247

Email: hyufc@btinternet.com

CLUB STATISTICS

RECORDS

Attendance: 1,526 v AFC Wimbledon, Conf. South, 20.09.08.

Victory: 6-1 v Bromley, Conf. South, 09.02.08.

5-0 v Basingstoke Town, Conf. South, 07.03.09.

Defeat: 0-5 v Aldershot Town, F.A. Trophy 1st Round, 15.12.07.

Career Goalscorer: Josh Scott - 40 (2007-09).

Career Appearances: Danny Allen-Page - 81 (2007-09).

Transfer Fee Paid: Unknown.

Received: Unkown.

SENIOR HONOURS

Conference South Play-off Winners 2008-09.

PREVIOUS

Names: Botwell Mission. Hayes. Yeading.

HISTON

CLUB PERSONNEL

Chairman: Gareth Baldwin.

Vice Chairman: John Webster.

Company Secretary: Lisa Baldwin.

Additional Directors: Angelo Dama, Allen Soraff, Colin Pettit.

Secretary: Lisa Baldwin
Telephone: (B): 01223 237 373 (M): 07810 525 256
E-mail: lisa@histonfc.co.uk
correspondence to Secretary at club.

Commercial Manager: Paul Shadrack
Telephone: (M): 07967 471 292
E-mail: paulshadrack@ntlworld.com

Press Officer: Graham Eales
Telephone: (B): 01223 237 373 (M): 07977 471 023
E-mail: graham@histonfc.co.uk

Manager: Steve Fallon

Previous clubs: Kettering Town, Cambridge United, Cambridge City.

Coach: John Beck

Sports therapists: Roy Johnson.

Once again the club representing a little village on the outskirts of Cambridge made progress and finished in their highest ever position of third, qualifying for the play-offs for the first time. The ground is now up to Football League standard and is also 'home' to the Cambridgeshire County F.A.

If their annual improvement is to continue, a Wembley appearance or promotion to Division Two will be achieved in the 2009-2010 campaign. The managerial team of Steve Fallon and John Beck has been together all the way up the non-league pyramid and equally loyal and long serving administrators are led by Gareth and Lisa Baldwin.

Last season didn't start well with two points out of the first nine leaving 'The Stutes' in eighteenth position, but the managerial team's experience proved invaluable as one or two new signings settled in with the long serving majority of the squad. By early October Histon were in second place and stayed within the top six for the rest of the season, earning a place in the play-offs where they were beaten by Torquay United. Only thirteen players scored during the campaign but six of these recorded eight or more with Jack Midson finishing with an impressive twenty-one.

The highlight of the season was a wonderful 1-0 F.A. Cup victory over Leeds United which followed a success against Swindon Town. This cup run was brought to an end by Swansea City and another disappointment was an early exit from the F.A. Trophy at the hands of local rivals Cambridge Untied. However it was Histon's best season ever - what's next?

HISTON

BEST LGE ATT.: 2,716 v Kettering Town
LOWEST: 541 v Barrow

No.	Date	Comp	H/A	Opponents	Att:	Result	Goalscorers	Pos
1	Aug 9	BSP	H	Torquay United	928	D 1 - 1	Knight-Percival 89	
2	12		A	Mansfield Town	2703	L 0 - 1		
3	16		A	York City	2125	D 1 - 1	Wright 38 (pen)	18
4	23		H	Burton Albion	910	W 4 - 3	WRIGHT 3 (18 pen 27 31 pen) **Midson** 87	13
5	25		A	Rushden & Diamonds	1613	W 2 - 1	Murray 16 **Midson** 54	12
6	30		H	Forest Green Rovers	740	L 0 - 1		16
7	Sept 2		H	Altrincham	692	W 1 - 0	Gwillm 74	
8	6		A	Weymouth	1003	W 5 - 2	**Midson** 31 Bygrave 33 (og) Reeves 63 72 Wright 90	6
9	13		A	Eastbourne Borough	1045	D 1 - 1	**Midson** 58	6
10	20		H	Northwich Victoria	829	W 2 - 1	Reeves 6 Barker 77	5
11	23		H	Lewes	592	D 1 - 1	**Midson** 90	5
12	27		A	Woking	1797	L 0 - 1		8
13	Oct 4		H	Salisbury City	961	W 2 - 0	Simpson 53 Bass 76 (og)	5
14	6		A	Ebbsfleet United	1226	W 1 - 0	Reeves 45	2
15	18		H	Crawley Town	1256	W 1 - 0	Murray 75	
16	**25**	**F.A.C. 4Q**	**A**	**Durham City**	**257**	**D 2 - 2**	**Simpson 35 84**	
17	**28**	**F.A.C. 4Q r**	**H**	**Durham City**	**411**	**W 5 - 2**	**Midson 6, 90 Wright 57 59 Simpson 68**	
18	Nov 1		A	Altrincham	953	W 1 - 0	**Midson** 72	3
19	**3**	**SS N3**	**A**	**Hinckley United**	**202**	**L 1 - 2**	**Reeves pen 5**	
20	**8**	**F.A.C 1R**	**H**	**Swindon Town**	**1541**	**W 1 - 0**	**Wright 66**	
21	15		H	Kettering Town	2716	W 1 - 0	**Midson** 52	3
22	18		A	Stevenage Borough	1623	W 3 - 1	Mitchell-King 1 Knight-Percival 34 Gwillm 71	
23	22		H	Oxford United	1242	W 5 - 2	Knight-Percival 5 31 **Midson** 18 Wright 72 Mitchell-King 74	1
24	**30**	**F.A.C 2R**	**H**	**Leeds United**	**4500**	**W 1 - 0**	**Langston 39**	
25	Dec 6		H	Woking	1249	W 1 - 0	Oyebanjo 90	2
26	9		H	York City	901	D 1 - 1	Parslow 59 (og)	
27	**13**	**F.A.T 1R**	**H**	**Cambridge United**	**1332**	**L 2 - 3**	**Midson 5 Knight-Percival 60**	
28	20		A	Torquay United	2201	L 1 - 4	Wright 49	
29	26		A	Cambridge United	6488	D 2 - 2	**Midson** 49 Murray 59	3
30	28		A	Grays Athletic	525	W 4 - 1	Langston 69 **Midson** 71 Knight-Percival 74 Reeves 89	2
31	**Jan 13**	**F.A.C 2R**	**H**	**Swansea City**	**2821**	**L 1 - 2**	**Simpson 84**	
32	17		A	Northwich Victoria	438	W 2 - 1	Knight-Percival 90 Simpson 90	2
33	27		A	Kidderminster Harriers	1277	L 0 - 2		
34	Feb 3		A	Forest Green Rovers	464	D 2 - 2	Knight-Percival 77 Simpson 86	2
35	14		A	Salisbury City	906	W 4 - 0	**Midson** 30 76 Wright 54 (pen) Murray 77	2
36	21		H	Eastbourne Borough	821	D 3 - 3	**Midson** 8 Murray 24 90	2
37	24		H	Barrow	541	W 2 - 0	Murray 84 Wright 86	2
38	28		A	Lewes	345	W 3 - 0	Simpson 25 Barker 53 71	2
39	March 2		H	Cambridge United	2 579	D 1 - 1	**Midson** 85	3
40	7		A	Kettering Town	1870	L 0 - 1		
41	10		A	Barrow	965	L 0 - 1		3
42	17		H	Grays Athletic	641	W 4 - 1	BARKER 3 (11 24 30) Murray 18	3
43	24		H	Stevenage Borough	1133	D 0 - 0		
44	28		H	Wrexham	1106	W 1 - 0	Simpson 30	4
45	31		H	Mansfield Town	914	W 3 - 0	Murray 41 Knight-Percival 45 86	3
46	April 4		A	Oxford United	6231	L 1 - 2	**Midson** 17	4
47	7		A	Wrexham	2234	D 0 - 0		4
48	11		A	Burton Albion	3311	L 1 - 3	Andrews 90	5
49	13		H	Rushden & Diamonds	1263	D 0 - 0		6
50	16		H	Ebbsfleet United	1015	W 5 - 2	**Midson** 14 72 Barker 42 Langston 60 Wright 90	3
51	18		H	Kidderminster Harriers	1718	D 1 - 1	**Midson** 4	3
52	21		H	Weymouth	1016	W 1 - 0	Langston 5	
53	26		A	Crawley Town	901	D 3 - 3	**Midson** 11 39 Barker 35	3
54	**May 1**	**Play Off SF1**	**A**	**Torquay United**	**3737**	**L 0 - 2**		
55	**4**	**Play Off SF2**	**H**	**Torquay United**	**2481**	**W 1 - 0**	**Andrews 16**	

Average Home Att: 1402 (1063) **Goals 92 61**

Best Position: 1st **Worst:** 18th

Goalscorers: Midson 23, Wright 13, Knight-Percival 10, Murray 9, Simpson 9, Barker 8, Reeves 7, Langston 4, Gwillm 2, Mitchell-King 2, Andrews 2, Oyebanjo 1. Own Goals 3.

NAISBITT 1	LANGSTON 5	GWILLIM 25	KENNEDY 7	POPE 2	MURRAY 10	KNIGHT-PERCIVAL 18	MITCHELL-KING 4	MIDSON 12	WRIGHT 23	REEVES 9	OKAY 3	ANDREWS 8	NIGHTINGALE 17	OYEBANJO 21	ADA 37	BARKER 11	KEY 13	COKER 22	CAMPBELL 15	SIMPSON 24	DALBY 19	WELCH 13	ROSE 26	SPARKES 14	BRENNAN 20	PATTERSON 22	BYGRAVE 6	ROACHE 9	PACQUETTE 17	STEWART 16	
X	X	X	X	X	X	X	X	X	X	X	S	S	S	U	U																1
X	X		X	X	X	X	X	X	X	X	X	S	U	S	U	U															2
X	X		X		X	X	X	X	X	S	X	S	U	X	X	S	U														3
X	X		S		X	X	X	X	X	U	X	X	S	X	X	U	U														4
X	X		U		X		X	X	X	S		X	X	X	X	X	U	S	S												5
X	X	X	S		X	X	X	X	X	S		X	S	X	X	U	U														6
X	X	X	U	U	X	S	X	X	X	S		X	U	X	X	X															7
X	X	X	U		X	X	X	X	X	X		S	U	X	X		U			U											8
X	X	X	U	S	X	X		X	X	X	S	U		X	X		U			X											9
X	X	X		S	X	X		X		X	X	U		X	X	S	U			X	U										10
X	X	X		U	X	X	S	X		X	X	S	U	X	X	S				X											11
X	X	X		U	X	X	X	X		X	U	S	S	X	X	S				X											12
X	X	X		X	X	S	X	X	S	X	U	U	U	X		X				X											13
X	X	X		U	X	S	X	X	S	X		U		X	X	X				X		U									14
X	X	X		U	X	S	X	X	S	X		S		X	X	X				X		U									15
X	**X**	**X**	**U**	**U**		**X**	**X**	**X**	**S**	**X**	**S**	**S**	**U**	**X**	**X**	**X**				**X**		**U**									16
X	**X**		**U**	**X**		**S**	**X**	**X**	**X**	**S**	**X**	**S**		**X**	**X**	**X**				**X**		**U**									17
X	X	X		U	X	S	X	X	X	U		U		X	X	X				X		U									18
U	**X**	**U**	**X**	**X**		**X**			**U**	**X**	**X**	**X**	**X**	**X**	**U**	**X**				**U**		**X**									19
X	**X**	**X**	**U**	**U**	**X**	**S**	**X**	**X**	**X**	**S**	**U**	**U**		**X**	**X**	**X**				**X**		**U**									20
X	X	X		U		X	X	X	X	S		S		X	X	X				X		U	U								21
X	X	X		X		X	X	X	X	U	U	U			X	X				X		U	S								22
X	X	X		X		X	X	X	X	S	U	S			X	X				X		U	U								23
X	**X**	**X**	**U**	**U**	**S**	**X**	**X**	**X**	**X**	**U**	**U**	**U**		**X**	**X**	**X**				**X**		**U**									24
X	X	X		U	X	X	X	X	X	S		U		X	X	U				X		U									25
X	X	X		U	X	X	X	X	X	S		U		X	X	U				X		U									26
X	**X**	**X**	**U**	**S**	**X**	**X**	**X**	**X**	**X**	**U**	**U**	**X**		**X**						**X**				**U**							27
X		X	S	X	X	X		X	X	U	U	X		X	X					X		U		U							28
U	X	X	U	U	X	X		X	X	X	U	S		X	X					X		X									29
U	X	X	X		X	X		X	X	X	S	S		X	X							X		U	U						30
X	**X**		**U**	**U**	**X**	**X**	**X**		**X**	**X**		**S**		**X**	**X**	**U**				**X**		**U**				**X**	**S**				31
X	X		U	S	X	X	X	X	X			S		X	X					X		U				X	U				32
X	X	X	U	U	X	X	X	X	X			U		X		U				X		U					X				33
X	X	X		U	X	X	X	X	X			U		X		U				X		U					X	S			34
X	X	X	U	X	X		X	X	X			S			X	X				X		U					U	S			35
X	X	X		X	X	X		X	X			S		S	X	X				X		U					U		S		36
X	X	X	U	U	X			X	X			S		X	X	X				X		U						S	X		37
X	X	X		U	X		X	X	X			S		X	X	X				X		U						S	S		38
X	X	X		U	X		X	X	X			U		X	X	X				X		U						S	U		39
X	X	X		U	X	X	X	X	X			S		X	X	U				X								S	U		40
X	X	X		U	X	X	X	X				U		X	X	X				X		U						U	U		41
X	X	X		U	X	X	X	X				S		X	X	X				X		U						S	U		42
X	X	X	U	U	X	X	X	X				U		X	X	X				X		U						S			43
X	X	X		U	X	X	X	X				S		X	X	X				X		U					U	U			44
X	X	X		U	X	X	X	X				S		X	X	X				X		U					U	S			45
X	X	X		S		X	X	X	X			S		X	X	X				X		U					U	S			46
X	X	X		U	X	X	X	X	X					X	X	U				X		U					U	U			47
X	X	X		U	X	X	X	X	X			S		X	X	X						U					U	S			48
X	X	X		U	X	X	X	X	X			S		X	X	S				X		U						U			49
X	X	X		X	U	X	X	X	X			X		U	X	X						U					U	S			50
U	X	X		X	S	X	X	X	X			X		U	X	X						X					U	U			51
X	X	X		X	S	X	X	X	X			X		S	X	X						U						U		U	52
X	X	X		X	X	X	X	X				S		X	X	X				U		S					U	U			53
	X	**X**		**X**	**X**	**X**	**X**	**X**				**S**		**X**	**X**	**X**	**U**			**U**		**X**					**U**	**U**			54
X	**X**	**X**		**U**	**X**	**X**	**X**	**X**				**X**		**X**	**X**	**X**				**S**		**U**					**U**	**U**			55
Total League Appearances																															
43	45	41	4	12	39	36	38	46	34	12	5	8	1	37	41	25	0	0	0	32	0	3	0	0	0	1	2	0	1	0	**X**
0	0	0	3	4	2	5	1	0	3	8	3	24	4	3	0	5	0	1	1	0	0	1	1	0	0	0	0	12	2	0	**S**
3	0	0	10	24	1	0	0	0	0	4	6	13	6	3	2	9	7	0	0	2	1	28	2	2	1	0	11	7	4	1	**U**
Total Cup Appearances																															
7	9	6	1	3	5	7	8	7	5	3	2	3	1	9	7	7	0	0	0	6	0	2	0	0	0	1	0	0	0	0	**X**
0	0	0	0	1	1	2	0	0	1	2	1	4	0	0	0	0	0	0	0	1	0	0	0	0	0	0	1	0	0	0	**S**
1	0	1	6	5	0	0	0	0	1	2	3	2	1	0	1	1	1	0	0	2	0	6	0	1	0	0	2	2	0	0	**U**

HISTON

CURRENT SQUAD AS OF BEGINING OF 2009-10 SEASON

GOALKEEPERS		SQ NO.	HT	WT	D.O.B	AGE	P.O.B	CAREER	APPS	GOA
Danny	Naisbitt	1	6'01"	11 12	25/11/78	30	Bishop Auckland	Middlesbrough (Trainee), Walsall, Bromsgrove (Trial) c/s 99, Barnet 8/99 Rel 9/03, Carlisle (L) 8/02, Southend (Trial), Harlow 9/03, Brentford 10/03, Cambridge C 11/03, Dag & Red 12/03 Rel 2/04, Peterborough 3/04, Hendon 3/04, Welling 3/04, AFC Wimbledon 6/04, Grimsby (Trial) 3/05, Lewes (L) 3/05, Cambridge C 9/05, Histon 5/07	43	0
Joe	Welch	27	6'02"	12 12	29/11/88	20	Welwyn Garden	Southend Rel c/s 07, Diss T (L) 3/07, Bishops Stortford c/s 07 Rel 8/08, Cheshunt 8/08, Histon 10/08	4	0
DEFENDERS										
Seb	Baxter	36						Histon		
Nathan	Bowden-Haase	4			26/4/84	25		Chesham, Yeading 8/06 small fee, Hemel Hempstead (SL) 2/07, Hemel Hempstead c/s 07, Histon 6/09		
Adam	Bygrave	6	5'09"	12 02	24/2/89	20	Walthamstow	Reading Rel c/s 08, Gillingham (SL) 11/07, Weymouth 5/08, Histon £5,000 1/09	2	0
Gareth	Gwillim	3	6'00"	12 06	9/2/83	26	Farnborough	Welling (Yth), C.Palace, Ashford T 3/02, Farnborough 9/02 (02/03 1,0), B.Stortford (SL) 11/02, B.Stortford 6/03, Histon 6/07	41	2
Matt	Langston	5	6'02"	12 04	2/4/81	28	Brighton	Watford Rel c/s 03, Aldershot (L) 12/02, Barnet (SL) 3/03, Stevenage 8/03, Cambridge C 11/03, Histon 6/06	45	3
Lanre	Oyebanjo	21	6'01"	11 04	24/4/90	19	London	Brentford Rel c/s 08, Histon 7/08	40	1
Craig	Pope	16	5'10"	11 07	17/9/82	26	Islington	Barnet Rel 5/03, Cambridge C 8/03, Histon 5/07	16	0
Lee	Smith							Bury T, Histon 8/09		
Joe	Stroud	33						Histon		
Adam	Tann	2	6'00"	12 08	12/5/82	27	Fakenham	Norwich (Yth), Cambridge U Rel c/s 05, Cambridge C (SL) 3/01, Reading (Trial) 7/05, Ipswich (Trial) 8/05, Rushden & D (Trial), Gravesend 10/05, Notts County 11/05, L.Orient 1/06 Rel c/s 07, Notts County 8/07 Rel c/s 09, Histon 7/09		
MIDFIELDERS										
Neil	Andrews	8	5'11"	11 11	20/4/79	30	Cambridge	Cambridge C, Histon 7/97	32	1
Jamie	Barker	11	6'01"	12 01	26/10/79	29	Cambridge	Histon	30	8
Lee	Brennan	20	5'10"	12 02	11/11/91	17	Peterborough	Histon, Man Utd (Trial) 8/08	0	0
Jay	Dowie	31						Histon		
John	Kennedy	7	5'08"	10 07	19/8/78	31	Cambridge	Ipswich Rel c/s 00, Canvey Island 7/00, Histon 5/06	7	0
Nathaniel	Knight-Percival	18	6'00"	11 07	31/3/87	22	Cambridge	Histon	41	9
Josh	Simpson	24	5'10"	12 02	6/3/87	22	Cambridge	Cambridge C, Cambridge U 6/06 Rel 6/07, Cambridge C 6/07, Histon Undisc 9/08	32	5
James	Stevenson	32						Histon		
Callum	Stewart	15	5'09"	12 06	1/10/90	18	Cambridge	Histon	0	0
FORWARDS										
Tyler	Campbell	19	6'00"	12 12	17/5/91	18	London	Histon, Harlow (SL) 6/09	1	0
Michael	Frew	9			8/8/84	25	Peterborough	Peterborough (Scholar), Yaxley 1/03, Lincoln C (Trial) 3/04 Nuneaton 8/04, Hucknall 3/06 (SL), Kings Lynn 6/06, Cambridge C 3/09, Histon 5/09		
Craig	Hammond							Histon (Yth), Mildenhall (L) 10/06 Perm, Royston 4 fig 12/07, Histon 8/09		
Bradley	Hudson-Odoi	10	5'08"		29/11/88	20	Ghana	Fulham (Scholar) Rel 1/08, C.Palace (Trial) 2/08, Hereford 7/08 Rel c/s 09, Grays (SL) 3/09, Histon 8/09		
Kieran	Leabon	22	5'11"	12 01	24/9/88	20	Chelmsford	Ipswich (Scholar) Rel c/s 07, Boston U 8/07, Histon 7/09		
Sam	Mason-Smith	34						Histon		
Lee	Roache		5'09"	11 00	30/4/84	25	Leytonstone	Protec Youth, Barnet Rel 5/06, B.Stortford (L) 12/03, Windsor & E (L) 1/04, Yeading (2ML) 1/06, Cambridge C 7/06, Eastleigh (L) 12/08, Histon Undisc 1/09	12	0
Daniel	Sparkes	14	6'04"	14 09	20/7/91	18	Peterborough	Histon	0	0
Lewis	Taffe	35						Histon		
Andrew	Tidswell	12						Histon		
Danny	Wright	23	6'02"	13 08	10/9/84	24	Southampton	Attleborough, Dereham c/s 05, Grimsby (Trial) 12/05, Histon 3/07	37	10

PLAYING SQUAD

LOANEES		SN	HT	WT	DOB	AGE	POB	From - To	APPS	GOA
(F)Romone	Rose		5'09"	11 05	19/1/90	19	Reading	QPR 11/08 - Northampton (L) 8/09	1	0
(F)Richard	Pacquette		6'00"	12 06	23/1/83	26	Paddington	Maidenhead 2/09 - Rel 5/09, York C 5/09	3	0

DEPARTURES		SN	HT	WT	DOB	AGE	POB	From - To	APPS	GOA
(D)Ben	Coker							Northampton (Scholar) 8/08 - Barton R (L) 9/08, Bury T 10/08	1	0
(M)Adrian	Cambridge		6'01"		17/7/74	35	Cambridge	Cambridge C 1/00 - Cambridge C (L) 9/08 Perm		
(D)Erkan	Okay		5'08"		29/1/85	24	Cambridge	Aylesbury 7/04 - Rel 1/09, Kettering (Trial) 1/09, Nuneaton T NC 1/09, Chelmsford 1/09	8	0
(F)Damien	Reeves		5'09"	11 10	18/12/85	23	Doncaster	Farsley Celtic 6/08 - Northwich 1/09, Farsley Celtic 3/09, Alfreton 7/09	20	5
(M)Robbie	Nightingale		5'11"		18/10/80	28	Cambridge	Cambridge C (3ML) 8/04 Perm 11/04 - Cambridge C (2ML) 11/08 Perm 1/09	5	0
(G)Lance	Key		6'03"	15 00	13/5/68	41	Kettering	Kingstonian 9/04 - Wivenhoe (Dual) 9/08	0	0
(F)Jack	Midson		5'08"	11 07	21/7/83	26	Stevenage	Bishops Stortford Undisc 1/08 - Oxford U 5/09	46	20
(D)Patrick	Ada		6'00"		14/1/85	24	Yaounde, Cam	Exeter 5/07 - Crewe 5/09	41	0
(M)Antonio	Murray		5'08"	11 00	15/9/84	24	Cambridge	Hibernian 8/06 - Rel 5/09	41	9
(D)Marlon	Patterson		5'09"	11 10	24/6/83	26	London	Dag & Red 1/09 - Rel 5/09, Bishops Stortford (SL) 2/09, Staines 7/09	1	0
(D)Matt	Mitchell-King		6'04"		12/9/83	25	Cambridge	Mildenhall 12/05 - Crewe 6/09	39	2
(M)Adam	Dalby		5'11"		10/2/90	19	Coventry	Yth - Ely C 7/09	0	0
(G)Luke	Howard							Hitchin 1/09 -		

HISTON

Founded: 1904

Nickname: The Stutes.

Club Colours: Red and black striped shirts, black, black.

Change Colours: Sky blue and white shrts, navy blue shorts, sky blue socks.

Club Sponsor: Hill Partnership Ltd.

Previous League: Southern League

Ground Address: The Glassworld Stadium, Bridge Road, Impington Cambridge CB4 9PH

Telephone: 01223 237 373

Facsimile: 01223 237 373

E-mail: info@histonfc.co.uk

Website: www.histonfc.co.uk

SIMPLE DIRECTIONS: From M11 Junction 14, take the A14 Eastbound signed Newmarket, take the first exit off A14 onto B1049, signed Histon/Impington. Take the first exit left off roundabout, go straight over traffic lights (Holiday Inn hotel on right). Turn right into ground just before pedestrian crossing.

MATCH TICKETS

Ticket Prices: Grandstand - Adult £15, Consessions £10, Under 16 & Junior Stutes £4.
Terrace - Adult £14, Consessions £9, Under 16 & Junior Stutes £3.
Junior Stutes (Under 14) £1.

Capacity 3,250 Seats: 450 Covered: 1,800

Clubhouse: Open daily hot & cold food. Tel: 01223 237 373

Club Shop: Yes

PROGRAMME EDITOR
Stuart Hamilton
Telephone: Mobile: 07917 340 601
E-mail: stuart.hamilton10@tesco.net

CLUB STATISTICS

RECORDS

Attendance : 6,400 v Kings Lynn F.A. Cup 1956

Recent best: 2,6 54 v Yeovil Town F.A. Cup 2nd Rd. Nov. 2004.

Victory: 11-0 v March Town Cambs Invitation Cup 15.02.2001.

Defeat: 1-8 v Ely City Eastern Counties Div.1 1994.

Career Goalscorer: Neil Kennedy (292)

Career Appearances: Neil Andrews and Neil Kennedy

Record Transfer Fee Paid:

£6000 to Chelmsford City for Ian Cambridge, 2000.

Received: £30,000 from Manchester United for Guiliano Maiorana.

SENIOR HONOURS:

Eastern Counties League Cup 1990-91.

Eastern Counties Champions 1999-2000.

Southern Premier Champions 2004-05.

Conference South Champions 2006-07.

PREVIOUS

Names: Histon Institute.

Leagues: Cambs 1904-1948. Spartan 1948-60. Delphian 1960-63. Eastern Counties 1966-2000. Southern 2000-05.

KETTERING TOWN

CLUB PERSONNEL

Chairman: Imraan Ladak.

Company Secretary: David Harris.

Additional Directors: Amanda de Choisy,

Tony Reeves, Ken Samuel, Lee Thorn.

Secretary: Bob Brown

Tel: (M): 07989 175167

Email: info@ketteringtownfc.co.uk

Correspondence to: Club

Commercial Manager: Lee Thorn

Tel: (M): 07958 102 344

Email: ktfcsales@tiscali.co.uk

Press Officer: Simon de Choisy

Tel: (M): 07979 646 863

Manager: Mark Cooper

Assistant Manager: Nicky Eaden.

Youth Development Office: Justin Boyd-Navazo.

Club therapists: James Davidson.

Any senior club that qualifies for eleven national cup ties must have given their supporters some wonderful memories of a lively season. Kettering Town reached the Fourth Round of the F.A. Cup and, having beaten Burton Albion (H 3-0), Lincoln City (A 2-1), Notts County (A 1-1, H 2-1) and Eastwood Town (H 2-1), they put up a battling performance live on television losing 2-4 after two late Fulham goals.

This cup run came after a very solid start in 'The Poppies' first season back at non-league's highest level. Four draws were followed by three victories and, in their first sixteen games, Mark Cooper's side only suffered three defeats and found themselves top of the Blue Square Premier Division.

It was not surprising that Kettering found themselves amongst the favourites for The F.A. Trophy and they certainly started well with a 4-1 victory over Cambridge City before equalising in injury time at Tiverton and then winning the home replay on penalties. This brought a visit from AFC Telford United and a defeat by the only goal of the match.

At this stage, goals had been flowing and a half way position of tenth gave a realistic chance of a play-off place. Having only failed to score in six of the first thirty five games, the pressure was now on, and with points valuable, their strikers drew a blank in ten of their last twenty fixtures. This was strange as Gareth Seddon, Craig Westcarr and Jean-Paul Marna are all highly rated in front of goal Although the rest of the league may have worked out the Kettering way of playing, the Rockingham Road lads will be amongst the favourites in the 2009-2010 campaign.

KETTERING TOWN

BEST LGE ATT.: **2,897** v Rushden & Diamonds
LOWEST: **867** v Lewes

No.	Date	Comp	H/A	Opponents	Att:	Result	Goalscorers	Pos
1	Aug 9	BSP	H	Forest Green Rovers	1346	D 1 - 1	Dempster 14	
2	12		A	Grays Athletic	696	D 1 - 1	Dempster 78	
3	16		A	Altrincham	1045	D 1 - 1	**Seddon** 5 (pen)	
4	23		H	Rushden & Diamonds	2897	D 1 - 1	**Seddon** 9	15
5	25		A	Cambridge United	3489	W 2 - 1	Westcarr 51 Beardsley 82	14
6	30		H	Woking	1493	W 1 - 0	Marna 81	9
7	Sept 2		H	Stevenage Borough	1592	W 1 - 0	Beardsley 15	
8	6		A	Oxford United	4499	D 1 - 1	**Seddon** 90	
9	13		H	York City	2017	W 4 - 0	Christie 20 65 **Seddon** 43 54 (pen)	3
10	20		A	Barrow	1596	W 4 - 2	Westcarr 12 **Seddon** 56 63 Marna 86	2
11	22		H	Burton Albion	1616	L 0 - 1		2
12	27		A	Crawley Town	3207	L 0 - 1		6
13	Oct 4		H	Northwich Victoria	1401	W 2 - 1	Beardsley 72 Westcarr 81	3
14	7		A	Eastbourne Borough	1035	W 2 - 1	Beardsley 39 Westcarr 50	2
15	11		A	Salisbury City	1191	W 2 - 1	Dempster 76 Christie 90	2
16	18		H	Kidderminster Harriers	2010	W 1 - 0	Dempster 83	1
17	**21**	**SS S2**	**H**	**Bishops Stortford**	**450**	**W 4 - 2**	**Marna 4, Seddon 2 (5, 36), A Potter 48**	
18	**25**	**F.A.C. 4Q**	**H**	**Burton Albion**	**1728**	**W 3 - 0**	**Seddon 57 Dempster 71 Potter 90**	
19	Nov 1		H	Weymouth	1607	L 0 - 1		1
20	**4**	**SS 3**	**H**	**Thurrock**	**438**	**W 4 - 1**	**Westcarr 34, Solkhon 2 (62, 86), Beardsley 75**	
21	**8**	**F.A.C. 1R**	**H**	**Lincoln City**	**3314**	**D 1 - 1**	**Geohaghan 85**	
22	15		A	Histon	2718	L 0 - 1		5
23	**18**	**F.A.C 1R r**	**A**	**Lincoln City**	**3953**	**W 2 - 1**	**Westcarr 68 Christie 90**	
24	23		A	Ebbsfleet United	1018	D 0 - 0		6
25	**30**	**F.A.C. 2R**	**A**	**Notts County**	**4451**	**D 1 - 1**	**Solkhorn 18**	
26	**Dec 2**	**SS N4**	**A**	**Hinckley United**	**270**	**W 3 - 2***	**A Potter 12, Solkhon 90, Seddon 120**	
27	6		A	Wrexham	3687	L 1 - 2	Christie 42	9
28	**10**	**F.A.C. 2R r**	**H**	**Notts County**	**3019**	**W 2 - 1**	**Solkhon 53 Seddon 54**	
29	**13**	**F.A.T 1R**	**A**	**Cambridge City**	**432**	**W 4 - 1**	**Dempster 26 Arthur 65 Solkhon 72 Westcarr 74**	
30	20		A	Forest Green Rovers	923	W 2 - 0	Potter 29 **Seddon** 32 (pen)	9
31	26		H	Mansfield Town	2433	L 1 - 3	Christie 33 (pen)	9
32	**Jan 3**	**F.A.C. 3R**	**H**	**Eastwood Town**	**5090**	**W 2 - 1**	**Westcarr 22 Seddon 58**	
33	**11**	**F.A.T 2R**	**A**	**Tiverton Town**	**604**	**D 1 - 1**	**Graham 90**	
34	**14**	**F.A.T 2R r**	**H**	**Tiverton Town**	**816**	**D 1 - 1***	**Westcarr 87 (won 4-1 on pens)**	
35	17		H	Salisbury City	1541	W 1 - 0	Dempster 90	9
36	**20**	**SS QFN**	**A**	**AFC Telford**	**874**	**L 2 - 3***	**A Potter 46, Marna 76**	
37	**24**	**F.A.C 4R**	**H**	**Fulham**	**5406**	**L 2 - 4**	**Westcarr 38 83 (pen)**	
38	27		A	Stevenage Borough	1880	L 1 - 2	Lee 44	
39	**31**	**F.A.T 3R**	**H**	**AFC Telford United**	**1692**	**L 0 - 1**		
40	Feb 14		A	Woking	1414	W 1 - 0	Marna 20	10
41	17		A	Mansfield Town	2355	D 0 - 0		
42	21		H	Torquay United	1869	W 2 - 1	Marna 9 **Seddon** 12 (pen)	10
43	24		A	Northwich Victoria	479	D 0 - 0		10
44	Mar 3		H	Altrincham	1036	W 3 - 1	Marna 9 74 Solkhon 90	
45	7		H	Histon	1870	W 1 - 0	**Seddon** 54	
46	10		H	Grays Athletic	1117	D 0 - 0		9
47	14		H	Eastbourne Borough	1415	L 0 - 1		10
48	17		H	Lewes	867	W 1 - 0	Marna 24	
49	19		H	Oxford United	1716	L 1 - 2	Marna 77	
50	21		A	Weymouth	3711	W 2 - 0	**Seddon** 53 Loroughon 81	9
51	24		A	York City	1714	D 0 - 0		
52	28		H	Ebbsfleet United	1533	W 2 - 1	Wright 22 55	8
53	31		A	Burton Albion	2624	D 1 - 1	**Seddon** 20	7
54	April 4		A	Torquay United	2503	L 0 - 2		8
55	7		H	Barrow	976	D 0 - 0		8
56	11		A	Rushden & Diamonds	3406	L 0 - 1		9
57	13		H	Cambridge United	2340	L 1 - 2	**Seddon** 90	
58	15		H	Crawley Town	961	D 1 - 1	Marna 64	
59	18		H	Wrexham	1497	W 1 - 0	Charles 3	8
60	21		A	Lewes	343	W 2 1	**Seddon** 6 64	
61	26		A	Kidderminster Harriers	2896	W 1 0	Wright 90	8

Average Home Att: **1615 (1497)** **Goals** **79 55**

Best Position: 1st **Worst:** 15th

Goalscorers: Seddon 21, Marna 11, Westcarr 11, Dempster 7, Solkhon 7, Christie 6, Beardsley 5, Potter 5, Wright 3, Arthur 1, Charles 1, Geohaghan 1, Graham 1, Lee 1, Loroughan 1.

HARPER	DEMPSTER	GEOHAGHAN	SOLKHON	JASZCZUN	A POTTER	WARLOW	BRANSTON	WRACK	BEARDSLEY	SEDDON	TAYLOR	MARNA	BOUCAUD	DORRILL	L GRAHAM	EADEN	WESTCARR	CHRISTIE	GALBRAITH	D LEE	POWER	ARTHUR	WILLIAMS	SMITH	RAWLE	BENNETT	CARRILLO	R GRAHAM	BRAHAM-BARRETT	J LEE	ROBINSON	ARTUS	L POTTER	WHATSIZE	LOROUGNON	WRIGHT	COOPER	CHARLES	
1	6	23	8	3	7	18	5	4	9	19	14	10	17	13	16	2	32	28	11	25		14	12	22	20	34	38	16	33	24	27	15	14	31	18	29	25	20	
X	X	X	X	X	X	X	X	X	X	X	S	S	S	U	U																								1
X	X	X	X	X	X	X	X	X	U	X	S	X	S	U	U																								2
X	X	X	X	X	X	S	X	X	S	X		X	X	U	S	U																							3
X	S	X	X	X	X	U	X	X	X	X		S	X	U		X	S																						4
X	X	X		X	X	X	X	X	S	X		S	X	U	S	U	X																						5
X	S	X	S	X	X		X	X	X	X		S	X	U	U	X	X																						6
X	S	X	S	X	X		X	X	X	X		S	X	U	U	X	X																						7
X	U	X	S	X	X		X	X	S	X		S	X	U		X	X	X																					8
X	S	X	S	X	X		X	X	S	X		U	X	U		X	X	X																					9
X	S	X	X	X	U		X	X	S	X		S	X	U		X	X	X																					10
X	U	X	X	X	S		X	X	S	X		S	X	U		X	X	X																					11
X	S	X	X	X	S		X	X	S	X		X	X	U		X	X		U																				12
X	X		S	X	X		X	X	X	X		S	X		U	X	X		U	S																			13
X	X	X	S	X	U		X	X	X	X		S	X			X	X		U	S																			14
X	X	X	U	X	S		X	X	X	S		S	X			X	X	X		U																			15
X	X	X	S	X	X		X	X	X	S		S	X			U	X	X		U																			16
X	**X**	**X**	**X**		**X**			**U**	**U**	**X**		**X**	**S**	**U**		**X**	**X**		**X**	**X**	**S**																		17
X	**X**	**X**	**U**	**X**	**X**		**X**	**X**	**U**	**X**		**X**	**X**	**U**		**S**	**S**	**X**																					18
X	X	X	U	X	X		X	X	U	X		X	X			U	U	X		U																			19
X	**X**	**X**	**X**	**X**	**U**			**S**	**X**	**S**		**S**	**U**			**X**	**X**	**X**		**X**		**X**																	20
X	**X**	**X**	**S**	**X**	**X**			**X**	**S**	**X**		**S**	**X**	**U**		**X**	**U**	**X**				**X**	**U**																21
X	X	X	S	X	X			X	U	X		S	X			X	S	X				X	U																22
X	**X**	**X**	**X**	**X**	**X**		**X**	**S**	**X**	**S**		**X**	**X**				**X**	**S**	**U**			**U**	**U**	**U**															23
X	X	X	X	X	X		X	X	X	S						U	X	X	U			S		S															24
X	**X**	**X**	**X**	**X**	**X**		**X**	**U**		**S**		**S**	**X**				**X**	**X**	**U**			**S**	**U**		**X**	**U**													25
X		**X**	**S**	**S**	**X**			**X**		**X**			**U**			**X**	**S**	**X**	**X**			**X**	**X**		**U**	**X**													26
X	X	X	X	X	X		X	S		S			X			U	X	X				U			X	S													27
X	**X**	**X**	**X**	**X**	**X**		**X**	**X**		**X**		**S**	**X**	**U**		**U**	**X**	**S**				**U**			**U**	**U**													28
X	**X**	**X**	**X**	**X**	**S**			**X**				**X**	**X**	**U**		**U**	**X**	**S**				**X**				**X**	**S**												29
X		X	X	X	X		X	X		X		S		U		X	X	S				S			U	X													30
X	S	X	X	X	X		X	X				S	X			U	X	X				S				X													31
X	**S**	**X**	**S**	**X**	**U**		**X**	**X**	**U**	**X**		**U**	**X**	**U**		**U**	**X**	**X**								**X**		**X**											32
X	**X**	**X**	**S**		**U**			**X**	**S**			**X**	**X**	**U**		**U**	**X**	**X**								**X**		**X**	**X**										33
X	**X**		**X**		**X**			**S**	**X**			**S**	**X**	**U**		**X**	**S**	**X**								**X**		**X**	**X**										34
X	X		X		S		X	X	U			U	X	U		X	X	S										X	X	X									35
X	**X**				**X**		**X**	**X**	**X**	**S**		**X**	**S**	**U**		**X**	**X**		**X**								**U**	**S**			**X**								36
X	**X**	**X**	**X**	**X**	**S**			**U**	**S**	**X**		**S**	**X**			**X**	**X**		**U**							**X**		**X**											37
X	X	X	S		S			U	S	X			X			U	X									X		X	X	X		X							38
X	**X**	**X**			**S**		**X**	**S**	**U**	**X**		**S**	**X**			**U**	**X**									**X**		**X**		**X**		**X**							39
X	U	X	S		X		X	S	S			X	X				X									X		X		U		X	X						40
X	U	X	S		X		X	S	S			X	X			U	X									X		X				X	X						41
X	S	X	S				X	S	U	X		X	X				X									X		X		U		X	X						42
X	X	X	X		X		X	X	U	X		S	U				X											S		S		X	X						43
X	X	X	X		S		X	S	S	X		X	X			U	X											X		U			X						44
X	X	X	X		S		X	X	S	X		X	X				X											U		S			X	U					45
X	X	X	X		U			X	S	X		X	X				X									X		S		S			X	U					46
X	X	X	X		S			U	X	X			X				X									X		X		S			X	U	S				47
X	X	X	U		X			X	S	X		X	X				S									X		X		U			X		S				48
X	X	X	X		X			X	S	S		X	X				X									X		U					X	U	U				49
X	X	X	X		X			X	S	X		U														X		X					X	U	S	X	U		50
X	S	X	U		X		X	X	S			X	X													X		X					X	U	S	X			51
X	U	X	S		X		X	X	S	X		X	X													X							X		U	X		S	52
X	U	X	S		X		X	X	S	X		S	X													X							X		U	X		X	53
X	X	X	X		U		X		S	X		S	X			U	S									X							X			X		X	54
X	X	X	U		X		X		S	X		X	X			X	X											U					X			S		S	55
X	X	X	U		X		X		X	S		X	X			X	X									U							X			S		S	56
X	U	X	X				X		S	X		S	X				S									X		X					X	U		X		X	57
X	X	X	S		X		X		S	X		X	X			X	X											U					X			U		U	58
X	X	X					X		X			X	X			X	X									U		S					X	U		S		X	59
X		X			S		X		X	X		X	X			X	X									U							X	U		S	U	X	60
X		X			S		X		X	X		X	X			X	X											S					X	U		S	U	X	61
Total League Appearances																																							
46	27	44	21	22	29	3	39	31	14	34	0	20	40	0	0	20	33	11	0	0	0	1	0	0	1	16	0	11	2	2	0	5	22	0	0	6	0	6	**X**
0	9	0	15	0	10	1	0	5	23	6	2	19	2	0	2	0	5	2	0	2	0	3	0	1	0	1	0	4	0	4	0	0	0	0	4	5	0	3	**S**
0	7	0	6	0	4	1	0	2	6	0	0	3	1	14	5	11	1	0	4	3	0	1	1	0	1	3	0	4	0	4	0	0	0	10	3	1	3	1	**U**
Total Cup Appearances																																							
15	13	13	8	9	9	0	7	8	4	8	0	6	11	0	0	7	11	8	3	2	0	4	1	0	1	7	0	5	2	1	1	1	0	0	0	0	0	0	**X**
0	1	0	4	1	3	0	0	4	3	4	0	7	2	0	0	1	3	3	0	0	1	1	0	0	0	0	1	1	0	0	0	0	0	0	0	0	0	0	**S**
0	0	0	1	0	3	0	0	3	4	0	0	1	2	9	0	5	1	0	3	0	0	2	3	1	2	2	1	0	0	0	0	0	0	0	0	0	0	0	**U**

KETTERING TOWN

CURRENT SQUAD AS OF BEGINING OF 2009-10 SEASON

GOALKEEPERS		SQ NO.	HT	WT	D.O.B	AGE	P.O.B	CAREER	APPS	GOA
Niall	Cooper	13						Sileby R, Kettering 7/09		
Lee	Harper	1	6'01"	14 06	30/9/71	37	Chelsea	Sittingbourne, Arsenal £150,000 6/94, QPR £125,000 7/97 Rel c/s 01, Walsall 7/01, Northampton 7/02, MK Dons (3ML) 10/06 Perm 1/07 Rel c/s 07, Kettering 8/07	46	0
DEFENDERS										
John	Dempster	6	6'00"	11 07	1/4/83	26	Kettering	Rushden & D, Oxford U 1/06 Rel 2/07, Kettering (L) 1/07 Kettering 3/07	36	5
Nicky	Eaden	2	5'10"	12 08	12/12/72	36	Sheffield	Barnsley, Birmingham 7/00, Wigan (L) 9/02 Perm 10/02, Notts Forest 8/05 Rel c/s 07, Lincoln C (2ML) 8/06, Lincoln C (2ML) 11/06, Lincoln C (SL) 1/07, Halesowen T 8/07, Solihull Moors 9/07, Kettering 10/07	20	0
Exodus	Geohaghan	23	6'07"	11 11	27/2/85	24	London	West Brom (Scholar), Sutton Coldfield, Bromsgrove Undisc 8/05, Redditch U 7/06, Kettering (L) 7/08 Undisc 8/08	44	0
James	Jennings	3	5'10"	11 02	2/9/87	21	Manchester	Macclesfield, Altrincham (2ML) 1/08, Kettering 7/09		
Ian	Roper	5	6'03"	13 04	20/6/77	32	Nuneaton	Walsall Rel c/s 08, Luton 8/08, Kettering 7/09		
Greg	Taylor	12			15/1/90	19	Bedford	Rushden & D (Yth), Northampton Rel c/s 09, Kettering 6/09		
MIDFIELDERS										
Ryan	Beswick	11			12/1/88	21	Walton-on-Thames	Leicester, Redditch (SL) 1/09, Kettering 5/09		
Andre	Boucaud	17	5'10"	10 02	9/10/84	24	Enfield	Reading Rel c/s 04, Peterborough (SL) 3/03, Peterborough (2ML) 8/03, Walsall (Trial) 2/04, Peterborough 7/04, Aldershot (3ML) 9/05, Kettering 5/06, Wycombe 8/07 Rel c/s 08, Kettering 8/08	42	0
Mark	Cooper	25	5'08"	11 04	18/12/68	40	Wakefield	Bristol C Rel c/s 89, Exeter 10/89, Southend (L) 3/90, Birmingham P/E 9/91, Fulham £40,000 11/92, Huddersfield (L) 3/93, Wycombe 1/94, Exeter 2/94 Rel c/s 96, Hartlepool 7/96, Macclesfield (2ML) 9/97, L.Orient 12/97, Rushden & D 1/98, Telford (L) 10/99, Hednesford 6/00, Forest Green 2/01, Tamworth 5/02 Pl/Man 5/04 Rel 1/07, Hinckley U 1/07, Kettering (Man) 5/07	0	0
Lee	Fowler	8	5'07"	10 00	10/6/83	26	Cardiff	Coventry, Cardiff (L) 3/03, Huddersfield (3ML) 8/03 (Perm) 11/03, Grimsby (Trial) 7/05, Scarboough (2ML) 11/05 (Perm) 1/06 Rel c/s 06, Burton 5/06, Newport C (SL) 3/07, Newport C 5/07, Forest Green 6/08 Rel 5/09, Kettering 6/09		
Patrick	Noubissie		5'10"	11 04	25/6/83	26	Bois-Colombes (Fra)	CS Brétigny-sur-Orge (Fra), Le Mée-sur-Seine SF (Fra), CS Sedan Ardennes (Fra), US Roye Foot Picardie 80 (Fra), Sporting Toulon (Fra) 7/05, Crewe 11/06 Rel 1/07, Swindon 1/07 Rel c/s 07, Hibernian 8/07 Rel c/s 08, Livingston (3ML) 8/07, Dundee (L) 3/08, Ayia Napa (Cyp) 7/08, Kettering 8/09		
Danny	Thomas	20	5'07"	11 05	1/5/81	28	Leamington Spa	Notts Forest (Trainee), Leicester 5/98, Bournemouth (L) 2/02 Undisc 2/02, Notts County (Trial) 3/04, Boston U 3/04 Rel c/s 06, Grimsby (Trial) 8/06, Cheltenham (Trial) 9/06, Shrewsbury 11/06, Hereford 1/07 Rel c/s 07, Macclesfield 7/07 Rel c/s 09, Kettering 8/09		
Darren	Wrack	4	5'09"	12 10	5/5/76	33	Cleethorpes	Derby, Grimsby £100,000 7/96 Rel c/s 98, Shrewsbury (L) 2/97, Walsall 8/98 Rel c/s 08, Kettering 7/08	36	0
FORWARDS										
Francis	Green	7	5'09"	11 04	25/4/80	29	Derby	Ilkeston, Peterborough £25,000 3/98, Lincoln C (L) 9/03 £7,500 9/03 Rel c/s 06, Boston U (2ML) 11/05, Boston U 8/06, Macclesfield 8/07 Rel c/s 09, Kettering 7/09		
Jean-Paul	Marna	10			21/2/81	28		Paris St Germain (Fra), Berkhamstead, Kettering 3/06	39	9
James	McPike	18	5'10"	11 02	4/10/88	20	Birmingham	Birmingham, Solihull Moors (3ML) 1/09, Kettering 5/09		
Gareth	Seddon	19	5'11"	12 00	23/5/80	29	Burnley	Accrington, Atherstone, RAF Codsall, Everton (Trial), Bury 8/01 Rel c/s 04, Northwich (L) 1/03, Rushden & D 5/04 Retired 1/05, Padiham 8/05, Worcester 3/06, Hyde 6/06, Kettering Undisc 7/08	40	16
Damian	Spencer	9	6'01"	14 05	19/9/81	27	Ascot	Bristol C Rel c/s 02, Exeter (2ML) 3/01, Cheltenham 8/02 Rel c/s 09, Brentford (L) 3/09, Kettering 7/09		
Jamie	Yates	16	5'07"	10 11	24/12/88	20	Sheffield	Rotherham Rel 5/09, Burton (3ML) 1/09, Kettering 7/09		
Joe	Power							Kettering	0	0

PLAYING SQUAD

LOANEES		SN	HT	WT	DOB	AGE	POB	From - To	APPS	GOA
(M)Alfie	Potter		5'07"	09 06	9/1/89	20	London	Peterborough (SL) 8/08 - Oxford U (SL) 7/09	39	1
(M)Owain	Warlow		6'00"	12 00	3/7/88	21	Pontypridd	Lincoln C 8/08 - Rel 5/09, Llanelli 6/09	4	0
(F)lyseden	Christie		5'10"	12 02	14/11/76	32	Coventry	Stevenage (4ML) 9/08 - Torquay 2/09 Rel 5/09	13	5
(M)Chris	Arthur				25/1/90	19		QPR (3ML) 11/08 - Rushden & D (L) 2/09, Rel 6/09	4	0
(D)Peter	Williams						Coventry	Wolves 11/08 -	0	0
(D)Dale	Bennett				6/1/90	19		Watford (SL) 11/08 -	17	0
(M)Richard	Graham		5'10"	11 10	5/8/79	30	Newry	Dag & Red (SL) 1/09 - Rel c/s 09, Grays 7/09	15	0
(D)Craig	Braham-Barrett							Peterborough 1/09 - Grays 8/09	2	0
(M)Frankie	Artus		6'00"	11 02	27/9/88	20	Bristol	Bristol C 1/09 - Cheltenham (L) 3/09	5	0
(D)Luke	Potter		6'04"	14 09	17/7/89	20	Stafford	Barnsley (SL) 2/09 -	22	0
(F)Ben	Wright				10/8/88	21	Basingstoke	Peterborough (6WL) 3/09 -	11	3
(F)Ryan	Charles		6'00"	11 13	30/9/89	19	Enfield	Luton 3/09 -	9	1

DEPARTURES		SN	HT	WT	DOB	AGE	POB	From - To	APPS	GOA
(M)Daryl	Taylor		5'10"	11 03	14/11/84	24	Birmingham	Halifax 8/08 - Halesowen T 8/08, Hinckley U 10/08, Halesowen T 3/09	2	0
(D)Kevin	Spencer							Tamworth 6/07 - Rel 8/08, Solihull Moors 8/08 Rel 10/08, Stratford T, Worcester 3/09		
(D)Tom	Kemp		6'03"		16/1/87	22	Ashby	Grays 6/07 - Halesowen T (L) 8/08 Perm, Worcester 11/08		
(M)Dwane	Lee		6'03"	13 09	26/11/79	29	Hillingdon	Maidenhead 5/08 - Halesowen T (L) 8/08, Rel 11/08, AFC Wimbledon 12/08	2	0
(F)Mark	Rawle		5'11"	12 02	27/4/79	30	Leicester	Alfreton 6/07 - Redditch 10/08, Kettering 11/08 Rel 1/09, Redditch 1/09, Tamworth 2/09, Brackley 3/09	1	0
(M)Jon	Brady		5'10"	11 02	14/1/75	34	Newcastle (Aus)	Cambridge U 6/07 - Rel 12/08, Brackley 1/09 Man 4/09		
(F)Marvin	Robinson		5'11"	12 09	11/4/80	29	Crewe	ex Oxford U, Kettering 1/09, Redditch 1/09	0	0
(D)Ryan	Collis							Yth - Atherstone (L) 8/08, Stamford (L) 9/08 Perm, Loughborough D 1/09		
(D)Tommy	Jaszczun		5'11"	11 02	16/9/77	31	Kettering	Cambridge U 5/07 - Rel 3/09, Corby T 3/09	22	0
(F)Nathan	Smith				26/3/85	24	Birmingham	Stafford R 6/08 - Rel 3/09	1	0
(M)David	Galbraith		5'08"	11 00	20/12/83	25	Luton	Boston U 1/08 - Rel 3/09, Kings Lynn 6/09 Rel 7/09	0	0
(M)Brett	Solkhon		5'11"	12 06	12/9/82	26	Canvey Island	Rushden & D 2/03 - Rel 4/09, Corby 5/09	36	0
(F)Craig	Westcarr		5'11"	11 04	29/1/85	24	Nottingham	Stevenage 8/08 - Rel 4/09, Noots County 5/09	38	4
(F)Chris	Beardsley		6'00"	12 02	28/2/84	25	Derby	York C (L) 12/07 Perm 1/08 - Rel 4/09, Kidderminster (L) 11/08, Stevenage 5/09	37	4
(D)Luke	Graham		6'03"	12 07	27/4/86	23	Kettering	Northampton 5/06 - Kings Lynn (SL) 10/08, Mansfield 5/09	2	0
(F)Jason	Lee		6'03"	13 08	9/5/71	38	Forest Gate	Mansfield 1/09 - Corby 3/09	6	1
(G)Dan	Whatsize		6'02"		14/8/90	19	Leicester	Mansfield 3/09 - Kings Lynn 6/09	0	0
(D)Guy	Branston				9/1/79	30	Leicester	Notts County 2/08 - Burton 7/09	39	0
(F)Andre	Lorougnon				20/12/88	20		Barwell 3/09 - Barwell, Hinckley U 7/09	4	1
(G)Stuart	Dorrill				16/11/90	18	Kettering	Newport Pagnell -	0	0
(M)Enzo	Carrillo							Buckingham T -	0	0
(D)Ashley	Lawrence							Yth - Atherstone (L) 8/08		

KETTERING TOWN

Founded: 1872
Nickname: The Poppies.
Club Colours: Red shirts, black shorts and black socks.
Change Colours: Royal blue shirts, royal blue shorts and royal blue socks.
Club Sponsor: DRC Locums.
Previous League: Southern League

Ground Address: Rockingham Road, Kettering NN16 9AW.
Telephone: 01536 483 028
Facsimile: 01536 412 273
E-mail: info@ketteringtownfc.co.uk
Website: www.ketteringtownfc.co.uk

SIMPLE DIRECTIONS: A43 to Kettering from M1 jct 15. Use A14 to jct 7 follow A43 to Corby/Stamford to 1st roundabout, turn right onto A6003 and ground is half a mile. From North M1 or M6 use jct 19 then to A 14 jct 7 as above.

MATCH TICKETS

Ticket Prices: Main stand - Adult £10-£18. Consessions £8-£14. Under 16 £4-£7.
Terrace - Adult £9-£16. Consessions £6-£12. Under 16 £3-6.

Capacity 6,170 Seats: 1,800 Covered: 4,000

Club Shop: Open before and after matches. Also Alex Elmore's in town centre.

No image available

PROGRAMME EDITOR
Paul Cooke
07825 558 442
E:companioncooke@btinternet.com

CLUB STATISTICS

RECORDS

Attendance:
11,536 v Peterborough, F.A. Cup 1st Round Replay 1958-1959
Victory: 16-0 v Higham YMCI (F.A. Cup 1909)
Defeat: 0-13 v Mardy, Southern Lg Div 2 1911-12
Career Goalscorer: Roy Clayton 171 (1972-810
Career Appearances: Roger Ashby
Record Transfer Fee Paid:
£25,000 to Macclesfield for Carl Alford. in1994
Received: £150,000 from Newcastle United for Andy Hunt

SENIOR HONOURS

Blue Square North 2007-08
Southern League Champions (x4)

PREVIOUS

Leagues: Northants League, Midland League, Birmingham League, Central Alliance. United Counties, Southern League, Conference 79-01 02-03
Grounds: North Park and Green Lane

KIDDERMINSTER HARRIERS

CLUB PERSONNEL

Chairman: Barry Norgrove.

Vice Chairman: Neil Savery.

Company Secretary: Oliver Hunt.

Additional Directors: Wayne Allen, John Baldwin, Robert Dignam, Gordon Howard, Keith Chandler.

Secretary: Roger Barlow

Club: 01562 513 954

(M): 07973 237 626

E-mail: roger.barlow@harriers.co.uk

correspondence to Secretary at club.

Commercial Manager: Helen MacDonald

Telephone: (M): 07740 816 888

Email: helen.macdonald@harriers.co.uk

Press Officer: Matt Wall.

Telephone: (B): 01562 513 955. (M): 07725 536 272.

Manager: Mark Yates.

Assistant Manager: Neil Howarth.

Club therapist: Gavin Crowe.

Although only winning one of their first five games, a wonderful run of seven victories in the next nine matches took them up to second place and a top ten place was held for the rest of the season. Indeed for the last two months Mark Yates' squad were never out of the top six and were considered a very safe bet for the play-offs.

Matthew Barnes-Homer (21 Goals) and Justin Richards (20 goals) developed into a well respected strike partnership and an F.A.Cup run brought 'Kiddy' a glorious pairing at Coventry City in the 3rd Round in front of 13,652. The F.A.Trophy also provided three rounds of knock out football but a replay defeat at York brought the run to an end in the Fourth Round.

March fixtures brought the Harriers the wonderful goal tally of 7-0 in six undefeated games, the defence was superb and Kiddy looked certainties for at least the play-offs as nine goals were scored in victories over Woking and Stevenage Borough and fourth place seemed very comfortable.

Sadly, there were only two home fixtures in the last seven games and just one victory left Kidderminster in sixth place and the realisation that the club's powerful squad would have to be dismantled as a realistic budget would have to be adhered to in the season ahead.

KIDDERMINSTER HARRIERS

BEST LGE ATT.: **3,025** v Burton Albion
LOWEST: **1,211** v Crawley Town

No.	Date	Comp	H/A	Opponents	Att:	Result	Goalscorers	Pos
1	Aug 9	BSP	H	Lewes	1503	D 1 - 1	Richards 22	
2	12		A	Cambridge United	3008	L 1 - 3	Richards 90	
3	16		A	Mansfield Town	2479	L 2 - 4	**Barnes-Homer** 69 Richards 80	21
4	23		H	Altrincham	1335	W 4 - 0	Creighton 6 Richards 34 (pen) Brittain 70 Smikle 84	14
5	25		A	Burton Albion	1798	D 2 - 2	**Barnes-Homer** 76 Jones 81	
6	30		H	Rushden & Diamonds	1524	W 2 - 1	Penn 14 79	14
7	Sept 4		H	Torquay United	1345	W 1 - 0	**Barnes-Homer** 44	
8	7		A	Grays Athletic	525	L 2 - 3	Richards 58 **Barnes-Homer** 88	
9	13		H	Oxford United	2065	W 1 - 0	**Barnes-Homer** 22	9
10	20		A	Weymouth	1014	W 2 - 1	Richards 22 Knights 90	7
11	23		H	York City	1481	W 2 - 0	Smikle 63 Richards 90	3
12	27		A	Eastbourne Borough	1248	W 3 - 2	Richards 14 Simkin 37 Ferrell 62	2
13	Oct 4		H	Barrow	1686	L 0 - 1		4
14	7		A	Northwich Victoria	725	D 1 - 1	Smikle 47	6
15	11		H	Ebbsfleet United	1512	W 3 - 1	MacKenzie 63 Smikle 68 **Barnes-Homer** 74	4
16	18		A	Kettering Town	2010	L 0 - 1		7
17	**25**	**F.A.C. 4Q**	**A**	**King's Lynn**	**1460**	**W 5 - 1**	**Barnes-Homer 26 Penn 30 Brittain 40 Smikle 48 Richards 62**	
18	Nov 1		H	Grays Athletic	1400	W 2 - 0	Richards 40 **Barnes-Homer** 59	6
2	**4**	**SS N3**	**A**	**Burton Albion**	**554**	**L 2 - 3**	**McDermott 26, Knights 43**	
19	**8**	**F.A.C. 1R**	**H**	**Cambridge United**	**1717**	**W 1 - 0**	**Richards 17 (pen)**	
20	15		A	Rushden & Diamonds	1391	W 1 - 0	Richards 42 (pen)	4
21	22		H	Wrexham	2403	W 1 - 0	Smikle 26	4
22	25		A	Oxford United	3690	L 0 - 1		4
23	**29**	**F.A.C 2R**	**H**	**Curzon Ashton**	**2070**	**W 2 - 0**	**Moore 38 Creighton 65**	
24	Dec 6		H	Salisbury City	1325	W 3 - 2	Bass 10 (og) **Barnes-Homer** 30 Bartlett 54 (og)	4
25	9		H	Mansfield Town	1266	W 2 - 0	Lowe 73 Richards 85	
26	**16**	**F.A.T. 1R**	**H**	**Burscough**	**685**	**W 3 - 1**	**Brittain 45 Jones 50 Moore 65**	**4**
27	20		A	Crawley Town	1022	L 0 - 2		4
28	26		H	Forest Green Rovers	2102	D 1 - 1	Riley 45	4
29	28		A	Torquay United	2749	W 1 - 0	Riley 73	3
30	**Jan 3**	**F.A.C. 3R**	**A**	**Coventry City**	**13652**	**L 0 - 2**		
31	**13**	**F.A.T. 2R**	**A**	**Ilkeston Town**	**401**	**W 5 - 3**	**Richards 18 Smikle 20 Brittain 52 Penn 68 Moore 83**	
32	17		H	Weymouth	1569	L 0 - 2		6
33	24		A	Barrow	1532	L 0 - 1		7
34	27		H	Histon	1277	W 2 - 0	**Barnes-Homer** 17 90	
35	**31**	**F.A.T 3R**	**H**	**York City**	**1113**	**D 1 - 1**	**Brittain 35**	
36	**Feb 12**	**F.A.T. 3R r**	**A**	**York City**	**683**	**D 1 - 1***	**Richards 79 (Lost 13-12 on pens)**	
37	15		H	Northwich Victoria	14 10	L 1 - 2	**Barnes-Homer** 10	8
38	17		H	Cambridge United	1361	L 1 - 3	**Barnes-Homer** 38	
39	28		H	Eastbourne Borough	1430	W 2 - 0	**Barnes-Homer** 21 24	7
40	Mar 7		A	Salisbury City	1105	D 0 - 0		10
41	10		H	Crawley Town	1211	W 2 - 0	Lowe 28 Richards 63	7
42	14		A	Lewes	385	W 1 - 0	Richards 19	6
43	21		H	Woking	1594	W 3 - 0	Riley 40 Richards 68 McPhee 90	
44	23		A	Wrexham	2674	W 1 - 0	McPhee 90	
45	28		A	York City	2384	D 0 - 0		6
46	April 1		A	Woking	751	W 5 - 1	Lowe 18 **Barnes-Homer** 28 39 McPhee 45 Smikle 72	6
47	4		H	Stevenage Borough	2115	W 4 - 2	**Barnes-Homer** 44 Penn 49 Richards 58 Brittain 61	5
48	7		A	Forest Green Rovers	970	D 2 - 2	Brittain 30 Moore 88	5
49	9		A	Ebbsfleet United	979	D 1 - 1	**Barnes-Homer** 83	
50	11		A	Altrincham	1142	D 2 - 2	Brittain 49 **Barnes-Homer** 73	4
51	13		H	Burton Albion	3025	W 2 - 1	**Barnes-Homer** 68 Smikle 80	4
52	18		A	Histon	1718	D 1 - 1	Lowe 29	5
53	21		A	Stevenage Borough	2530	L 1 - 3	Richards 45	
54	26		H	Kettering Town	2896	L 0 - 1		6

Average Home Att: **1688 (1556)** **Goals** **89 61**

Best Position: 2nd **Worst:** 21st

Goalscorers: Barnes-Homer 21, Richards 20, Smikle 9, Brittain 8, Penn 5, Moore 4, Lowe 3, McPhee 3, Riley 3, Creighton 2, Jones 2, Knights 2, Ferrell 1, Lowe 1, MacKenzie 1, McDermott 1, Simkin 1. Own Goals 2.

BARTLETT 1	CREIGHTON 5	JONES 6	BOWLER 23	BAKER 3	BENNETT 20	FERRELL 4	RUSSELL 7	PENN 10	RICHARDS 11	KNIGHTS 8	BRITTAIN 16	BARNES-HOMER 9	MCDERMOTT 17	COLEMAN 12	RILEY 18	BIGNOT 2	LOWE 21	SMIKLE 14	MCGRATH 15	FOLEY 19	MACKENZIE 22	MOORE 7	HAYWARD 24	BEARDSLEY 25	ARMSTRONG 15	CARR 25	MCPHEE 26	
X	X	X	X	X	X	X	X	X	X	X	S	S	S	U	U													1
X	X	X	X		S	X	X	X	X	X	S	X	S	U	U	X												2
X	X	X	X		X	X	X	X	X	X	S	S	S	U	U	X												3
X	X	X		X	U	X		X	X	S	X	X	X	U			X	S	S									4
X	X	X		X	S	X		X	X	S	X	X	X	U			X	S	U									5
X	X	X		X	S	X		X	X	U	X	X	S	U			X	X	U									6
X	X	X		X	S	X		X	X	U	X	X	S	U			X	X	U									7
X	X	X		X	S	X		X	X	S	X	X	U	U			X	X	U									8
X	X	X		X	S	X		X	X	S	X	X	U	U			X	X		U								9
X	X	X	U	X		X		X	X	S	X	X	S	U			X	X		U								10
X	X	X	U	X		X		X	X	U	X	X	S	U			X	X		U								11
X	X	X		X	S	X		X	X	S	X	X	U	U			X	X			S							12
X	X	X		X	U	X		X	X	S	X	X	S	U			X	X			S							13
X	X	X		X	S	X		X	X	S	X	X	U	U			X	X			U							14
X	X	X		X	S	S		X		X	X	X	U	U			X	X			X	S						15
X	X	X		X	U	S		X		S	X	X	S	U			X	X			X	X						16
X	**X**	**X**	**U**	**X**	**S**	**X**		**X**	**X**	**U**	**X**	**X**	**U**	**U**	**S**		**X**	**X**				**S**						17
X	X			X	S	X		X	X	S	X	X	U	U	X		X	X				S						18
	U		**X**		**X**	**X**		**S**	**U**	**X**	**X**	**S**	**X**	**X**	**X**		**X**	**X**				**X**	**S**					19
X	**X**		**U**	**X**	**S**	**X**		**X**	**X**	**U**	**X**	**X**	**U**	**U**	**X**		**X**	**X**				**S**	**U**					20
X	X	S		X	S	X		X	X	S	X	X		U	X		X	X				U						21
X	X	S		X	U	X		X	X	S	X	X		U	X		X	X				U						22
X	X	U	U	X		X		X		X	X	S	S	U	X		X	X				X						23
X	**X**	**S**	**U**	**X**	**U**	**X**		**X**		**S**	**X**	**X**	**S**	**U**	**X**		**X**	**X**				**X**	**U**					24
X	X	S		X	X			X	X	U	X	X	S		X		X	X				U		S				25
X	X	U		X	X	S		X	X		X	X	S		X		X	X				U		S				26
X		**X**	**S**	**X**		**X**		**X**	**X**	**U**	**X**	**X**	**X**		**X**		**X**	**S**		**U**		**S**						27
X	X	S			X	X		X	X	U	X	X	S	U	X		X	X				S						28
X		X		X	X	X			X	S	X	X	S	U	X		X	X				S		U				29
X	X	S		X	X	X		X	X		X	X		U	X		X	S				U		S				30
X	**X**	**U**		**X**	**X**	**X**		**X**	**X**	**S**	**X**	**X**	**U**	**U**	**X**		**X**	**S**		**U**		**S**						31
X	**X**	**S**		**X**		**X**		**X**	**X**	**U**	**X**	**S**	**S**	**U**	**X**		**X**	**X**				**X**						32
X	X	U		X	U	X		X	X	S	X	S	S		X		X	X				X						33
X	X	U			X	X		X	X	X	S	X	S		X		X	U				U			X			34
X		X		U	X	X			X	X	U	X	X		X	S	X	S				U			X			35
X	**U**	**X**		**X**	**X**	**X**			**X**	**X**	**S**	**X**	**X**	**U**	**X**		**X**	**S**				**U**						36
X	**X**	**U**		**X**	**X**	**X**			**X**	**S**	**X**	**X**	**X**	**U**	**X**		**X**	**S**				**S**						37
X	X	X		U	S	X			X	X	X	X	U				X	S				S			X	X		38
X	X	X		S	X	X			X	S	X	X	S				X	X				U			X	U		39
X	X	U			X	U		S		X	X	X	X		X		X	S							X	S	X	40
X	X	U		X	X			S	S	X	X	X	X		X		X	S								U	X	41
X	X	U		X	X			X	X	X	U	X			X		X	S				S				S	X	42
X	X	U		X	X			X	X	X	S	X			X		X	S				S				U	X	43
X	X	U		X	X			X	X	X	S	X			X		X	S				S				U	X	44
X	X	U		X	X			X	X	X	S	X			X		X	S				U				S	X	45
X	X	U			X			X	X	X	S	X			X		X	S				U			X	U	X	46
X	X	X		X	X			X	X	X	U	X					X	S				S			U	S	X	47
X	X	U		X	X			X	X	X	S	X			X		X	U				S				S	X	48
X	X	S		X	X			X	X	U	X	X			X		X	S				S				U	X	49
X	X	X		X	X	U		S		X	S	X					X	S				X			U	X	X	50
X	S	X				X		X		U	X	S	U		X		X	X				X			X	S	X	51
X	X	S		X	X	X		X		X	S	X			X		X	S				U				U	X	52
X	X	S		X	X	U		X	X	X	U	X			X		X	S				U					X	53
X	X	U		X	X	U		X	X	S	X	X			X		X	S				S					X	54
X	X			X	X	U		S	X	X	S	X	X		X		X	S				U					X	55
Total League Appearances																												
46	43	23	3	36	25	28	3	38	38	21	30	41	6	0	26	2	43	22	0	0	2	5	0	0	7	2	16	X
0	1	8	0	1	12	3	0	4	1	16	12	5	17	0	0	1	0	19	1	0	2	12	0	3	0	6	0	S
0	0	13	3	2	5	5	0	0	0	7	4	0	8	23	3	0	0	2	4	3	1	13	0	1	2	7	0	U
Total Cup Appearances																												
8	6	3	1	8	4	9	0	6	7	2	8	7	4	1	8	0	9	5	0	0	0	3	0	0	0	0	0	X
0	0	2	1	0	2	0	0	1	0	3	1	2	2	0	1	0	0	4	0	0	0	5	1	0	0	0	0	S
0	2	2	3	0	1	0	0	0	1	4	0	0	3	7	0	0	0	0	0	2	0	1	2	0	0	0	0	U

KIDDERMINSTER HARRIERS

CURRANT SQUAD AS OF BEGINING OF 2009-10 SEASON

GOALKEEPERS		SQ NO.	HT	WT	D.O.B	AGE	P.O.B	CAREER	APPS	GOA
Dean	Coleman	1	6'01"	12 10	18/9/85	23	Dudley	Walsall Rel 5/06, Redditch (L) 12/04, Halesowen T (SL) 8/05, Bromsgrove 6/06, Willenhall 10/06, Kidderminster 7/07	0	0
Jasbir	Singh	12	6'02"	13 05	12/3/90	19		Shrewsbury Rel s/09, Bridgnorth (L) 8/08, Hinckley U (L) 10/08, Sutton Coldfield (L) 1/09, Kidderminster 8/09		
DEFENDERS										
Lee	Baker	3	5'10"	12 01	20/1/89	20	Redditch	West Brom, Kidderminster (5ML) 8/08, Kidderminster 1/09	37	0
Gavin	Caines	5	6'01"	12 00	20/9/83	25	Birmingham	Walsall Rel c/s 04, Stafford R (2ML) 12/03, Cheltenham 7/04 Rel c/s 09, Kidderminster 8/09		
Zac	Costello	20						Notts Forest (Yth), Cambridge U (Yth), Kidderminster 8/09		
Duane	Courtney	2	5'11"	11 03	7/1/85	24	Oldbury	Derby (Yth), Birmingham (Scholar) Rel c/s 04, AFC Telford 9/04, Burnley £25,000 8/05 Rel 8/06, The New Saints 9/06 Rel c/s 09, Kidderminster 7/09		
Liam	Dolman	15	6'01"	12 07	26/9/87	21	Brixworth	Northampton Rel c/s 09, Aylesbury (L) 8/05, Bishops Stortford (L) 1/06, Kettering (L) 2/06, Bishops Stortford (L) 3/06, Kidderminster 8/09		
Neil	Howarth		6'03"	13 07	15/11/71	37	Bolton	Burnley, Macclesfield (L) 9/93, Macclesfield (SL) 2/94), Macclesfield c/s 94, Cheltenham £7,000 £7,500 2/99 Rel c/s 03, Telford 6/03, AFC Telford 5/04, Kidderminster 1/06		
Martin	Riley	6	6'00"	12 01	5/12/86	22	Wolverhampton	Wolves, Shrewsbury 3/08 Rel c/s 08, Kidderminster 8/08	26	3
Tom	Sharpe	17	6'02"	13 04	12/10/88	20	Nottingham	Notts Forest Rel 5/09, Bury (6WL) 11/07, Halifax (L) 1/08, Stalybridge (3ML) 9/08, Kidderminster 7/09		
MIDFIELDERS										
Dean	Bennett	8	5'10"	11 00	13/12/77	31	Wolverhampton	Aston Villa (Jun), WBA 12/96, Bromsgrove 9/98, Kidderminster £30,000 1/99, Wrexham Bosman 7/04 Rel c/s 06, Chester 7/06 Rel 5/08, Kidderminster (3ML) 8/07 (SL) 1/08, Kidderminster c/s 08	37	0
John	Finnigan	4	5'08"	10 11	29/3/76	33	Wakefield	Notts Forest, Lincoln C (SL) 3/98, Lincoln C £50,000 6/98, Cheltenham 3/02, Kidderminster 7/09		
Nathan	Hayward	19	5'08"	12 01	8/11/91	17	Kidderminster	Birmingham (Yth), Kidderminster, Wolves (Trial) 11/08	0	0
David	McDermott	11	5'05"	10 00	6/2/88	21	Stourbridge	Walsall Rel c/s 08, Halesowen T (L) 1/07, Kidderminster 8/08	23	0
Brian	Smikle	14	5'11"	11 09	3/11/85	23	Tipton	WBA Rel 6/06, Hereford (SL) 2/05, Halifax (SL) 2/06, Kidderminster 7/06	41	8
FORWARDS										
Matthew	Barnes-Homer	9	5'11"	12 05	25/1/86	23	Dudley	Wolves (Sch) Rel c/s 04, Aldershot 9/04 Rel 11/04, Hednesford 2/05, Bromsgrove 3/05, Sracuse (USA), Virginia Beach Mariners (USA), Tividale 7/06, Willenhall 8/06, Wycombe 3/07 Rel 5/07, Kidderminster 7/07	46	20
Aaron	Farrell	18	6'00"	12 06	24/4/86	23		Kidderminster (Yth), Solihull B 8/04, Evesham 12/04, Bedworth 2/05, Sutton Coldfield 2/06, Solihull B 8/06, Halesowen T 3/07, Rushall O 11/07, Stratford T 12/07, Sutton Coldfield 8/08, Kidderminster 7/09		
Kyle	Hadley	16	5'08"	11 07	27/11/86	22		Oldhill T, Lye T, Stourbridge 6/07, Kidderminster 7/09		
Darryl	Knights	10	5'07"	10 01	1/5/88	21	Ipswich	Ipswich Rel c/s 07, L.Orient (Trial) 1/07, Yeovil (SL) 2/07, Yeovil 7/07 Rel 5/08, Cambridge U (2ML) 10/07, Kidderminster (SL) 1/08, Kidderminster 5/08	37	1
Chris	McPhee	7	5'11"	11 09	20/3/83	26	Eastbourne	Brighton Rel 5/06, Aldershot (3ML) 8/05, Swindon (SL) 3/06, Torquay 7/06, Ebbsfleet 8/07 Rel 6/08, Weymouth 7/08 Rel 2/09, Kidderminster 2/09	16	3

LOANEES		HT	WT	DOB	AGE	POB	From - To	APPS	GOA
(M)Neil	Mackenzie	6'02"	12 05	15/4/76	33	Birmingham	Notts County 9/08 - Port Vale (L) 11/08, Rel 1/09, Burton (Trial) 1/09, Mansfield 1/09 Rel 4/09, Tamworth 6/09	4	1
(F)Chris	Beardsley	6'00"	12 02	28/2/84	25	Derby	Kettering 11/08 - Rel 4/09, Stevenage 5/09	3	0

DEPARTURES		HT	WT	DOB	AGE	POB	From - To	APPS	GOA
(M)Simon	Russell	5'07"	10 06	19/3/85	24	Hull	Hull C 7/04 - York C 8/08	3	0
(M)Michael	McGrath			4/9/85	23		Yth - Rel 1/09, Worcester (3ML) 9/08, Oxford U (Trial) 1/09, Galway Utd 2/09	1	0
(D)Michael	Bowler	5'11"	12 00	8/9/87	21	Glossop	Northwich 8/08 - Rel 2/09, Stalybridge 2/09	3	0
(D)Paul	Bignot	6'01"	12 03	14/2/86	23	Birmingham	Crewe 6/07 - Rel 2/09, Newport C (3ML) 9/08, Newport C 2/09	3	0
(M)Sam	Foley	6'00"	10 08	17/10/86	22	Upton	Cheltenham 8/08 - Redditch (2ML) 10/08, Newport C (SL) 2/09 Perm 4/09		0
0									
(D)Luke	Jones	5'09"	11 09	10/4/87	22	Blackburn	Shrewsbury 5/08 - Rel 5/09, Mansfield 5/09	31	1
(G)Adam	Bartlett	6'00"	11 10	27/2/86	23	Newcastle	Blyth 5/08 - Rel 5/09, Cambridge U (L) 5/09, Hereford 6/09	46	0
(F)Justin	Richards	6'00"	11 10	16/10/80	28	Sandwell	Peterborough 6/07 - Rel 5/09, Oxford U (SL) 1/08, Cheltenham 6/0939		16
(D)Keith	Lowe	6'02"	13 03	13/9/85	24	Wolverhampton	Wolves 8/08 - Rel 5/09, Hereford 5/09	43	4
(M)Michael	Carr	5'08"	10 07	6/12/83	25	Crewe	Morecambe 2/09 - Rel 5/09, Stalybridge 7/09	8	0
(M)Martin	Brittain	5'08"	10 07	29/12/84	24	Newcastle	Walsall 8/08 - Rel 5/09, Gateshead 6/09	42	4
(M)Craig	Armstrong	5'11"	12 09	23/5/75	34	South Shields	Cheltenham 1/09 - Rel 5/09, Mansfield 6/09	7	0
(D)Mark	Creighton	6'04"		8/10/81	27	Birmingham	Redditch 6/06 - Oxford U Small Fee 5/09	44	1
(M)Andy	Ferrell	5'08"	11 05	9/1/84	25	Newcastle	Hereford 6/07 - York C 5/09	31	1
(F)Stefan	Moore	5'10"	11 00	28/9/83	25	Birmingham	Walsall 10/08 - Sillhill (Dual) 4/09	17	1
(M)Russell	Penn	5'11"	11 05	8/11/85	23	Wordsley	Scunthorpe 7/05 - Burton Undisc 7/09	42	3

KIDDERMINSTER HARRIERS

Founded: 1886

Nickname: Harriers

Club Colours: Red and white halved shirts, white shorts, white socks.

Change Colours: Royal blue shirts, royal blue shorts, royal blue socks.

Club Sponsor: Tim Rose Electrical.

Previous League: Football League.

Ground Address:	Aggborough Stadium, Hoo Road, Kidderminster, DY10 1NB
Telephone:	01562 823 931
Facsimile:	01562 827 329
Website:	www.harriers.co.uk

SIMPLE DIRECTIONS:

By Road: From North - M5 Junction 3, A456 to Kidderminster. From south - M5 Junction 6, A449 to Kidderminster Alt M40/M42 Junction 1 A38 to Bromsgrove, A448 to Kidderminster (All routes follow SVR (steam Railway) signs) - Ground is 400 yards from station. Hoo Road signed both ends.

MATCH TICKETS:

Ticket Prices: Seats -Adults £16, Concessions £11, Under 16 £8, Under 8 Free.
Terraces - Adults £13, Concessions £8, Under 16 £5, Under 8 Free.

Ticket office Telephone: 01562 823 931

Capacity:	6,419
Seats:	3,175
Covered:	3,062
Social facilities	Harriers Arms (Public House)
Refreshments at the ground:	Hot and Cold food in all areas.
Club Shop:	Souvenirs & leisurewear (01562 63341)

PROGRAMME EDITOR
Matt Wall
Telephone: (B) 01562 513 955
(M) 07725 536 272
matt.wall@harriers.co.uk

CLUB STATISTICS

RECORDS

Attendance: 9,155 v Hereford United 27 Nov. 1948

Victory: 25-0 v Hereford (H) Birmingham Senior Cup 12.10.1889

Defeat: 0-13 v Darwen (A) F.A.Cup1st 24.01.1891

Career Goalscorer: Peter Wassell 432 1963-1974

Career Appearances: Brendan Wassall 686 1962-1974

Transfer Fee Paid:

£80,000 to Nuneaton B for Andy Ducross July 2000.

Transfer Fee Received:

£380,000 from W.B.A. for Lee Hughes July 1997.

SENIOR HONOURS

F.A.Trophy 1986-87.

Conference Champions 1993-94, 1999-2000.

PREVIOUS

Leagues: Birmingham1889-90,1891-1939, 47-48, 60-62.

Midland 1890-1891. Southern 1939-45, 48-60, 72-83.

Birmingham Combination 1945-47. West Midlands 1962-72.

Football League 2000-05.

LUTON TOWN

CLUB PERSONNEL

Chairman: Nick Owen.

Chief Executive & Managing Director: Gary Sweet.

Additional Directors: Antony Brown, Stephen Browne, Andrew Cook, Bob Curson, David Wilkinson, Mick Pattinson, Joe Patinson, Paul Ballantyne, Ginny Bradwell.

Secretary: Adam Cockfield
Tel: (B): 01582 411622 (M): 07838 608789
Correspondence to: Club
Email: adam.cockfield@2020mission.com

Commerical Manager: Dave Hoskins
Tel: (B): 01582 411622
Email: David.hoskins@2020mission.com

Press Officer: Andrew Barringer
Tel: (B): 01582 411622 (M): 07853 116201
Email: andrew.barringer@2020mission.com

Manager: Mick Harford.

Coaches: Alan Neilson & Kevin Watson.

Club therapist: Harry Scott-Stockman.

Youth Development Officer: Gregg Broughton.

The most prestigious club to join The Football Conference will obviously need to show great character to compete in the Blue Square Premier (as it is now called) and take the season seriously with a positive attitude to their supporters, opponents and the media.

So far, manager Harford has been a wonderful example creating a good impression having visited some of his future opponents and watched a number of their end of season games. It appears 'The Hatters' supporters are determined to see their club back to The Football League, and just as they did at Wembley in their wonderful Johnstone's Paint Trophy Final, they plan to roar their heroes on and return to The Football League at the first attempt as Champions, just as Lincoln City and Darlington did in the early Alliance days.

Every true football fan feels sorry for the loyal supporters and indeed players who suffer for some silly legal and financial mistakes often made by egotistical money men with no real love of the game or the club in question. The majority of true football people will have admired Mick Harford's attitude and Chairman Nick Owen's determination to keep their dignity and to work hard to achieve results in their new surroundings.

Luton Town will attract big crowds and much publicity, they will bring attention to the Blue Square Premier and if their supporters and their management continue to show dignity and good honest football principles they will become a popular senior member of their new Non-League Family.

LUTON TOWN

BEST LGE ATT.: 7,149 v Port Vale
LOWEST: 5,248 v Brentford

No.	Date	Comp	H/A	Opponents	Att:	Result	Goalscorers
1	Aug 9	FL2	H	Port Vale	7149	L 1-3	Parkin 35
2	**12**	**LGC 1**	**H**	**Plymouth**	**2682**	**W 2-0**	**Jarvis 15 Plummer 77**
3	16	FL2	A	Gillingham	5339	W 1-0	Parkin 3
4	23	FL2	H	Notts County	6085	D 1-1	**Martin** 49
5	**26**	**LGC 2**	**A**	**Reading**	**7498**	**L 1-5**	**Charles 80**
6	30	FL2	A	Exeter City	5328	W 1-0	Parkin 47
7	Sept 6	FL2	A	Macclesfield	2349	L 1-2	Charles 90
8	13	FL2	H	Aldershot Town	6462	W 3-1	Spillane 17 Hall 89 **Martin** 90
9	20	FL2	A	Rotherham	4095	L 0-1	
10	27	FL2	H	Chester City	5731	D 1-1	Hall 41
11	Oct 4	FL2	A	Bradford City	13083	D 1-1	Spillane 86
12	**7**	**JPT (S) R2**	**H**	**Brentford**	**2029**	**W 2-2***	**Hall 39 Martin 55 (aet 4-3 on pens)**
13	11	FL2	H	Darlington	5560	L 1-2	Gnakpa 31
14	18	FL2	H	Accrington	5492	L 1-2	Hall 34
15	21	FL2	A	Grimsby Town	4021	D 2-2	Craddock 24 (p) 90
16	25	FL2	A	Bury	3052	W 2-1	Craddock 35 Roper 44
17	Nov 1	FL2	A	Shrewsbury	6188	L 0-3	
18	**4**	**JPT (S) QF**	**A**	**Walsall**	**1844**	**W 1-0**	**Jarvis 90**
19	**8**	**FAC 1**	**H**	**Altrincham**	**3200**	**D 0-0**	
20	15	FL2	H	Dagenham & R	5402	W 2-1	Davis 7 McVeigh 41
21	**18**	**FAC 1r**	**A**	**Altrincham**	**2397**	**D 0-0***	**(won 4-2 on pens)**
22	22	FL2	A	Rochdale	2901	L 0-2	
23	25	FL2	H	Brentford	5248	L 0-1	
24	**29**	**FAC 2**	**A**	**Southend**	**4111**	**L 1-3**	**Spillane 80**
25	Dec 2	FL2	H	Bournemouth	6773	D 3-3	Garry 18 (og) Gallen 56 McVeigh 85 (p)
26	6	FL2	H	Barnet	5536	W 3-1	McVeigh 11 **Martin** 15 Townsend 88 (og)
27	13	FL2	A	Wycombe	5567	D 0-0	
28	**16**	**JPT (S) SF**	**H**	**Colchester**	**2638**	**W 1-0**	**Gnakpa 29**
29	20	FL2	H	Morecambe	5664	D 1-1	Spillane 51
30	26	FL2	A	Chesterfield	4243	D 2-2	Craddock 56 Roper 90
31	28	FL2	H	Lincoln City	6643	W 3-2	**Martin** 31 33 Roper 60
32	Jan 13	FL2	A	Chester City	1652	D 2-2	**Martin** 22 Emanuel 27
33	17	FL2	A	Darlington	3319	L 1-5	**Martin** 30
34	**20**	**JPT (S) (F1)**	**A**	**Brighton**	**6127**	**D 0-0**	
35	24	FL2	H	Bradford City	6053	D 3-3	Hall 4 90 Wasiu 37
36	27	FL2	A	Bournemouth	5230	D 1-1	Hollands 11 (og)
37	31	FL2	H	Bury	5545	L 1-2	Hall 36
38	Feb 14	FL2	A	Dagenham & R	2310	L 1-2	Henderson 58
39	**17**	**JPT (S) (F2)**	**H**	**Brighton**	**8711**	**D 1-1***	**Craddock 2 (won 4-3 on pens)**
40	21	FL2	H	Shrewsbury	5661	W 3-1	Craddock 15 Parkin 35 Hall 73
41	24	FL2	A	Accrington	1033	D 0-0	
42	28	FL2	A	Port Vale	5689	W 3-1	Hall 43 Gallen 52 **Martin** 63
43	Mar 3	FL2	H	Gillingham	5739	D 0-0	
44	7	FL2	H	Exeter City	6460	L 1-2	Craddock 39
45	10	FL2	A	Notts County	2886	W 2-0	**Martin** 25 Craddock 45 (p)
46	14	FL2	A	Aldershot Town	3098	L 1-2	Craddock 35
47	17	FL2	H	Grimsby Town	5830	W 2'-1	Bower 45 Hall 89
48	21	FL2	H	Macclesfield	5363	W 1-0	Craddock 69 (p)
49	28	FL2	A	Morecambe	2599	W 2-1	**Martin** 43 Gallen 59
50	31	FL2	H	Rotherham	5975	L 2-4	**Martin** 42 Hall 70
51	**April 5**	**JPT Final**	**N**	**Scunthorpe**	**55378**	**W 3-2***	**Martin 32 Craddock 70 Gnakpa 95**
52	11	FL2	A	Lincoln City	4664	D 0-0	
53	13	FL2	H	Chesterfield	6494	D 0-0	
54	18	FL2	A	Barnet	2808	D 1-1	Jarvis 49
55	21	FL2	H	Wycombe	6553	L 0-1	
56	25	FL2	H	Rochdale	7025	D 1-1	Craddock 33 (p)
57	May 1	FL2	A	Brentford	10223	L 0-2	

Average Home Att: 6,019

Goalscorers: Martin 13, Craddock 12, Hall 11, Parkin 4, Spillane 4, Gallen 3, Gnakpa 3, Jarvis 3, McVeigh 3, Roper 3, Charles 2, Bower 1, Davis 1, Emanuel 1, Henderson 1, Plummer 1, Wasiu 1. Own Goals 3.

CURRENT SQUAD AS OF BEGINING OF 2009-10 SEASON

GOALKEEPERS		SQ NO.	HT	WT	D.O.B	AGE	P.O.B	CAREER	APPS	GOA
Mark	Tyler	1	6'00"	12 09	2/4/77	32	Norwich	Peterborough, Billericay (3ML) 1/96, Yeovil (L) 11/96, Hull C (L) 1/08, Watford (2ML) 9/08, Bury (2ML) 1/09, Luton 6/09		
Shane	Gore	13	6'01"	12 00	28/10/81	27	Ashford	Wimbledon, Peterborough (L) 9/03, St Albans (L) 10/03, Barnet 10/03 Rel 5/05, Stevenage 6/05 Rel 5/06 Havant & W 6/06 Rel 6/07, Thurrock 8/07, East Thurrock 9/07, Maidenhead 5/08, Luton 8/09		
DEFENDERS										
Ed	Asafu-Adjaye	2	5'11"	12 04	22/12/88	20	Southwark	Luton, Walton & H (L) 3/07, Salisbury (3ML) 1/08		
George	Beavan	25	5'09"	12 02	12/1/90	19	Luton	Luton, Salisbury (L) 9/08, Grays (L) 1/09, Grays (SL) 3/09		
Shane	Blackett	12	6'00"	12 11	3/10/82	26	Luton	Dunstable, Arlesey 8/03, Dag & Red 5/04, Peterborough Undisc 1/07, Luton 7/09		
Lewis	Emanuel	3	5'08"	11 12	14/10/83	25	Bradford	Bradford C Rel c/s 06, Luton 7/06, Brentford (2ML) 10/07, Birmingham (Trial) 7/08, Southend (Trial) 8/08		
Claude	Gnapka	18	6'02"	13 05	9/6/83	26	Marseille, Fra	Montpellier (Fra) (Yth), Marignane (Fra) 7/01, Beaucaire (Fra) 7/02, Racing Santander B (Spa) 7/03, Alaves B (Spa) 7/05, FC Vaduz (Lie) 7/06 Rel 12/06, Swindon 3/07, Peterborough 7/07 Rel c/s 08, Luton 8/08		
George	Pilkington	6	5'11"	11 06	7/11/81	27	Rugeley	Everton Rel c/s 03, Exeter (2ML) 11/02, Port Vale 7/03 Rel c/s 08, Luton 8/08		
Callum	Reynolds	21			10/11/89	19	Luton	Rushden & D, Rugby T (WE) 3/07, Portsmouth 7/07, Basingstoke (L) 3/09, Luton (6ML) 7/09		
Alan	White	5	6'01"	13 02	22/3/76	33	Darlington	Derby (Sch), Middlesbrough, Luton £40,000 9/97 Rel c/s 00, Colchester (6WL) 11/99, Colchester 7/00 Rel c/s 04, L.Orient 7/04, Boston U 3/05, Notts County 7/06, Peterborough (SL) 3/07, Darlington 7/07, Luton 7/09		
MIDFIELDERS										
Andy	Burgess	11	6'02"	11 11	10/8/81	28	Bedford	Luton (Jun), Rushden & D, Oxford U 1/06, Rushden & D 8/07, Luton 5/09		
Asa	Hall	14	6'02"	11 09	29/11/86	22	Sandwell	Wolves (Yth), Birmingham Rel c/s 08, Boston U (3ML) 1/06, Ashford T (L) 3/07, Shrewsbury (SL) 1/08, Luton 8/08		
Jake	Howells	15	5'09"	11 08	18/4/91	18	St Albans	Luton		
Rossi	Jarvis	16	5'11"	11 03	11/3/88	21	Fakenham	Norwich Rel c/s 08, Torquay (L) 1/07, Rotherham (SL) 3/07, Luton 8/08		
Keith	Keane	4	5'09"	11 01	20/11/86	22	Luton	Luton		
Adam	Newton	7	5'10"	11 06	4/12/80	28	Grays	West Ham Rel c/s 02, Portsmouth (2ML) 7/99, Notts County (SL) 11/00, L.Orient (6WL) 3/02, Peterborough 7/02, Brentford 6/08 Rel c/s 09, Luton 7/09		
Kevin	Nicholls	8	6'00"	11 00	2/1/79	30	Newham	Charlton, Brighton (L) 2/99, Wigan £250,000 6/99, Luton £25,000 8/01, Leeds £700,000 7/06, Preston £700,000 7/07, Luton 8/08		
Adam	Watkins	30			8/9/91			Luton		
FORWARDS										
Steve	Basham	19	6'00"	12 00	2/12/77	31	Southampton	Southampton, Wrexham (L) 2/98, Preston (SL) 2/99, Preston £200,000 7/99 Rel c/s 02, Oxford U 8/02 Rel 5/07, Exeter 7/07 Rel c/s 09, Luton 8/09		
Ryan	Charles	17	6'00"	11 13	30/9/89	19	Enfield	Luton, Hitchin (SL) 3/07, Hinckley U (WE) 12/07, Kettering (L) 3/09 (08/09		
Tom	Craddock	10	5'11"	11 10	14/10/86	22	Darlington	Middlesbrough, Wrexham (L) 10/06, Hartlepool (L) 2/08, Luton (3ML) 10/08, Luton £80,000 1/09		
Kevin	Gallen	20	5'11"	12 10	21/9/75	33	Chiswick	QPR Rel c/s 07, Huddersfield 8/00 Rel c/s 01, Barnsley 7/01, QPR 11/01 Rel c/s 07, Plymouth (SL) 1/07, MK Dons 8/07, Luton (2ML) 11/08 Perm 1/09		
Liam	Hatch	9	6'02"	12 03	3/4/82	27	Hitchin	Herne Bay, Gravesend 6/01, Ashford T (L) 2/02, Barnet £23,000 7/03, Peterborough £150,000 1/08, Darlington (SL) 8/08, Luton (SL) 6/09		

LUTON TOWN

Founded: 1885

Nickname: The Hatters

Club Colours: Orange shirts, white shorts, white socks.

Change Colours: White shirts, navy blue shorts, navy blue socks.

Club Sponsor: easyJet.

Previous League: Football League.

Ground Address:	Kenilworth Stadium, 1 Maple Road, Luton, LU4 8AW.
Telephone:	01582 411 622
Facsimile:	01582 405 070
E-mail:	lubsec@lutontown.co.uk
Website:	www.lutontown.co.uk

SIMPLE DIRECTIONS:

By Road: From the North: Exit the M1 at Junction 11, and join the A505 towards Luton. Follow the A505 for approximately 1.5 miles and Kenilworth Road is on your right as you leave the one-way system along Dunstable Road. To park, follow the one-way around, turning left, right and right again all in about 100 yards so that you do a complete U-turn and then take the second left into Ash Road. Continue down to the bottom, turn left at the end and the club is in front of you. Continue straight past the club and the road bends immediately over a dual carriageway bridge. Beyond this is plenty of street parking (and a great fish shop) if you are early. From the South: You can join the M1 from the M25 at Junction 21A, which is Junction 6 of the M1. Exit at Junction 11 and follow directions above in From the North. From the East: If you are on the A1, leave at Junction 8 of the A1(M) and take the A602 towards Hitchin, then follow the signs to Luton along the A505. When you come into Luton, head for the City Centre and once you reach the one-way system, follow signs to Dunstable and you will see Kenilworth Road on your left. From the West: Come in on the A505 and follow the directions above in From the North.

MATCH TICKETS:

Ticket Prices:	**Stands (All areas)** Adults £18. Senior (Age 65-75) £13, (Over 75) £10. Young Adult (Age 17-21) £13. Youth (Age 10-16) £8. Juniors (Under 10) £5.
Ticket Office Tel:	01582 416 976
Capacity:	10,226

PROGRAMME EDITOR
Andrew Barringer
Tel: (B): 01582 411622 (M): 07853 116201
Email: andrew.barringer@2020mission.com

CLUB STATISTICS

RECORDS

Attendance: 30,069 v Blackpool, FA Cup 6th Rnd replay, 04.03.59.

Victory: 12-0 v Bristol Rovers, Division 3 South 13.04.1936.

Defeat: 0-9 v Small Heath, Division 2 12.11.1898.

Career Goalscorer (Lge): Gordon Turner - 243 (1949-64).

Career Appearances (Lge): Bob Morton - 495 (1948-64).

Transfer Fee Paid: £850,000 for Lars Elstrup from Odense.

Transfer Fee Received: £2,500,000 from Arsenal for John Hartson.

SENIOR HONOURS

Football League Division 3 South Champions 1936-37.

Football League Division 4 Champions 1967-68.

Football League Division 2 Champions 1981-82.

Football League Cup Winners 1988.

Football League Trophy 2008-09.

PREVIOUS

Leagues: Football League 1897-1900, 1920-2009.

Southern 1900-1920.

Grounds: Excelsior, Dallow Lane 1885-97.

Dunstable Road 1897-1905.

MANSFIELD TOWN

CLUB PERSONNEL

Chairman: Andrew Perry.

Chief Executive: Stewart Rickersey.

Additional Directors: Andrew Saunders,

Steve Middleton.

Secretary: Laura Atherton

Tel: (B): 01623 482482 (M): 07871 826863

Correspondence to: Club

Email: info@mansfieldtown.net

or laura.atherton@mansfieldtown.net

Press Officer: Mark Stevenson.

Tel: (B): 01623 482 482 (M): 07733 889 424.

Email: mark.stevenson@mansfieldtown.net

Manager: David Holdsworth.

Club therapist: Jason Truscott.

Head of Youth Development: David Jervis.

Relegation from The Football League comes as a terrible shock for supporters, especially as financial restraints often necessitate the club releasing most of their players and building a brand new squad. However, Mansfield Town's first experience of Conference football was encouraging as seven points from the first nine saw them comfortably placed in second position.

Although top spot was achieved at the beginning of August, all ideas of a promotion challenge gradually slipped away as four points were deducted for playing ineligible players and a run of five consecutive league defeats brought about manager Billy McEwan's departure.

No encouragement was salvaged from cup runs, as a replay victory over York City in The F.A.Cup was followed by a defeat at local rivals Chesterfield and in The F.A.Trophy Wrexham won their First Round tie 2-1in Wales. By this time, Mansfield had sunk to 19th position in the Blue Square Premier and the new manager David Holdsworth had the job of re-building the squad.

The second half of the season saw improved consistency with only one defeat in the first two months of 2009 and a comfortable mid table position was retained until the end of the campaign giving supporters hope for an improved performance.

MANSFIELD TOWN

BEST LGE ATT.: **3,634** v Stevenage Borough
LOWEST: **1,553** v Oxford United

No.	Date	Comp	H/A	Opponents	Att:	Result	Goalscorers	Pos
1	Aug 9	BSP	A	Ebbsfleet United	1872	D 2 - 2	Blackwood 63 **Stallard** 90	
2	12		H	Histon	2703	W 1 - 0	Lee 16	
3	16		H	Kidderminster Harriers	2479	W 4 - 2	**Stallard** 20 (pen) 45 Blackwood 32, **O'Connor** 90	2
4	23		A	Barrow	2063	L 1 - 2	Lee 41	9
5	25		H	Northwich Victoria	2741	W 3 - 2	**O'Connor** 25 28 **Stallard** 90	5
6	30		H	Grays Athletic	2378	W 1 - 0	**Stallard** 25 (pen)	2
7	Sept 2		A	York City	2520	D 1 - 1	Blackwood 52	
8	6		H	Eastbourne United	2536	W 3 - 1	**Stallard** 13 Arnold 41 Somner 88	1
9	13		A	Crawley Town	2013	L 1 - 2	Silk 79	4
10	20		H	Cambridge United	3171	D 1 - 1	O'Hare 51	4
11	23		A	Altrincham	1005	L 0 - 1		7
12	27		A	Salisbury City	1494	W 3 - 2	Bass 60 (og) **Stallard** 63 **O'Connor** 70	3
13	Oct 4		H	Woking	2563	L 0 - 1		7
14	7		A	Stevenage Borough	1517	L 2 - 3	Hurren 56 **O'Connor** 59	
15	13		A	Burton Albion	2871	L 0 - 1		
16	18		H	Wrexham	2757	L 1 - 2	Sinclair 29	14
17	**25**	**F.A.C 4Q**	**A**	**York City**	**1976**	**D 0 - 0**		
18	**28**	**F.A.C. 4Q r**	**H**	**York City**	**2004**	**W 1 - 0**	**Somner 50**	
19	Nov 1		A	Torquay United	2267	L 0 - 2		19
20	**4**	**SS N3**	**A**	**York City**	**608**	**D 1 - 1***	**Sinclair 46 (lost 2-4 on pens)**	
21	**8**	**F.A.C. 1R**	**A**	**Chesterfield**	**6612**	**L 1 - 3**	**Arnold 78**	**19**
22	15		H	Salisbury City	1921	W 3 - 0	Sinclair 19 Ahmed 36 (pen) **Stallard** 89	
23	22		A	Forest Green Rovers	872	L 0 - 1		19
24	29		A	Weymouth	931	D 1 - 1	Sinclair 42	
25	Dec 4		H	Oxford United	1553	L 1 - 3	Arnold 21	19
26	9		A	Kidderminster Harriers	1266	L 0 - 2		
27	**13**	**F.A.T. 1R**	**A**	**Wrexham**	**1559**	**L 1 - 2**	**O'Connor 69**	
28	20		H	Weymouth	1841	W 2 - 1	Ahmed 58 D'Laryea 90	
29	26		A	Kettering Town	2433	W 3 - 1	Sinclair 26 **O'Connor** 80 Arnold 86	18
30	29		H	Burton Albion	3612	L 0 - 2		18
31	Jan 17		H	Crawley Town	2414	W 1 - 0	**Duffy** 29	17
32	24		A	Lewes	598	W 1 - 0	Mayo 22	
33	27		H	Rushden & Diamonds	2028	D 0 - 0		
34	31		A	Eastbourne Borough	1420	W 2 - 1	D'Laryea 45 Garner 79	14
35	Feb 7		H	York City	2576	W 1 - 0	**Duffy** 42 (pen)	12
36	17		H	Kettering Town	2355	D 0 - 0		
37	21		A	Oxford United	4618	L 0 - 1		15
38	28		A	Rushden & Diamonds	1774	W 1 - 0	**Duffy** 90 (pen)	12
39	Mar 7		H	Lewes	2434	W 1 - 0	Arnold 70	
40	10		A	Cambridge United	2781	L 1 - 2	**Duffy** 34	12
41	14		H	Forest Green Rovers	2174	W 3 - 0	**Stallard** 10 **Duffy** 53 (pen) Garner 80	
42	21		A	Grays Athletic	802	L 1 - 2	Clare 73	12
43	28		H	Torquay United	2437	D 1 - 1	**Duffy** 36	13
44	31		A	Histon	914	L 0 - 3		15
45	April 4		A	Wrexham	2401	L 0 - 2		14
46	7		H	Ebbsfleet United	1630	W 2 - 0	Briscoe 22 **Duffy** 47	13
47	11		H	Barrow	2122	D 2 - 2	Williams 47 **O'Connor** 79	13
48	13		A	Northwich Victoria	858	L 0 - 2		
49	18		A	Woking	2096	D 2 - 2	**Duffy** 41 80	13
50	21		H	Altrincham	1682	W 2 - 0	Garner 29 Arnold 52	
51	26		H	Stevenage Borough	3634	W 2 - 1	Garner 71 **O'Connor** 88	12

Average Home Att: **2424 (2821)** **Goals** **61 61**

Best Position: 1st **Worst:** 19th

Goalscorers: Duffy 9, O'Connor 9, Stallard 9, Arnold 6, Sinclair 5, Garner 4, Blackwood 3, Ahmed 2, D'Laryea 2, Lee 2, Somner 2, Briscoe 1, Clare 1, Hurren 1, Mayo 1, O'Hara 1, Silk 1, Williams 1. Own Goal 1.

GAMBLE 1	O'HARE 6	SILK 2	MOSES 5	ARNOLD 7	BLACKWOOD 11	SOMNER 8	D'LARYEA 4	O'CONNOR 21	STALLARD 9	JEANNIN 20	LEE 10	HERRIOTT 25	HURREN 18	ROBINSON 31	SHAW 14	WOOD 12	TRIMMER 23	MCGHEE 17	CHANOT 15	KNIGHT 30	SINCLAIR 28	AHMED 14	KAY 3	KITCHEN 32	MARRIOTT 1	GARNER 19	BRISCOE 15	DUFFY 28	AMEOBI 24	WHATSIZE 26	MAYO 30	WOODHOUSE 14	HOWELL 10	SHAW 16	MACKENZIE 33	GARDNER 29	WHITE 13	HAVERN 32	WILLIAMS 3	CLARE 24	HOTCHKISS 26	
X	X	X	X	X	X	X	X	X	X	X	S	U	U	U	U																											1
X	X	X	X	X	X	X	X	S	X	X	X	U	U	U	U																											2
X	X	X	X	X	X	X	X	S	X	X	X	U	U	S	U																											3
X	X	X	X	X	X	X	X	S	X	X	X	U	S	S	U																											4
X	X	X	X	X		X	X	X	X	X		U	X	S	U	U	U																									5
X	X	X	X	X	X	X	X		X	X	X	U	U	S	U		U																									6
X	X	X	X	X	X	X	X	X	X	X		U	U	S	U		U																									7
X	X	X	X	X	X	X	X	X	X	X		U	S	S	U		U																									8
X	X	X	X	X	X	X	X	S	X	X		U	U	X	U			U																								9
X	X	X	X	X	X	X	X		X	X	X	U	U	U	U			U																								10
X	X	X	X	X	X	X	X		X	X	X	U	S	S	U			U																								11
X	X	X	X	X	X	X	S	X	X	X	S	U	X	S		U																										12
X	X	X		X	X	X	S	X	X	X	S	U	X	S		U			X																							13
X	X	X		X	X	S	X	X	X	X	S	U	X	S		U			X																							14
X	X	X	X	X	X	X	X	X	S	S	X		X	S		U				U																						15
X		X	X	X	X	U	X		X	X	S		S	S					X	U	X																					16
X	**X**	**X**	**X**	**X**	**X**	**X**	**X**	**S**	**U**	**X**	**X**		**S**	**U**		**U**			**U**	**U**	**X**																					17
X		**X**	**X**	**X**		**X**	**X**	**S**	**S**	**X**	**X**		**X**	**U**		**U**			**X**	**U**	**X**																					18
X	U	X	X	X		X	X	X	S	X	X	U	U						X		S	X																				19
X	**X**			**X**			**S**	**X**	**X**	**X**		**U**	**X**			**X**	**U**	**S**	**X**		**X**	**X**																				20
X	**X**	**X**	**X**	**X**		**X**	**X**	**S**	**S**	**X**	**X**	**U**	**U**			**U**			**U**		**X**	**X**	**U**																			21
X	X	X	X	X		X	X	S	S	X	X	U	S						U		X	X																				22
X	X	X	X	X		X	X	S	S	X	X	U	U						U		X	X																				23
X	X	X	X	S		X	X	S	U	X	X		U			U			X		X	X																				24
X	X	X	X	X		X	X	S	S	X	X		U			U					X	X	U																			25
	X	X	X	X		S	X	S		X	X		X			U		U			X	X	U																			26
U	**X**	**X**		**X**	**S**	**X**	**X**	**X**		**X**			**X**				**S**				**X**	**S**	**X**	**U**																		27
X	X	X		X	S	U	X	X		X	S	U	X								X	X	X	U																		28
X		X	X	X	U	U	X	X		X	S	U	X								X	X	X	U																		29
X		X	X	X	S	U	X	X		X	S	U	X								X	X	X	U																		30
		X	X	X		X	X	X	S	X													S		X	X	X	X	S	U												31
		X	X		S	X	X	X																	X	X	X	X	S	U	X	X	U	U								32
		X	X		X	X	X	X																	X	X	X	X	S	U	X		S	U	S							33
		X	X		X	X	X	S															X		X	X	S	X	X	U		X	S		U							34
			X		X	X	X	X	U																X	X	S	X	S		X	X			S	X	U					35
	X	S	X	X	S	X	X		S																X		X	X			X	X			U	X	U					36
		X	X	X	S	X	X	S																	X	X	X	X			X	X			S		U	U				37
		X	X	X	X	X	X	X	S																X	X		X			X				S		U	U	S			38
		X	X	X	X		X	X																	X	X	S	X			X	U			X		U	U	S			39
		X	X	X		X	X	S	X																X	X	S	X			X				U	S	U		X			40
		X	X	X		X	X	S	X																X	X	S	X			X	S				U	U		X			41
		X	X	X			X		X																X	X	S	X			X	X			S		U	U	X	S		42
	U	X	X	X			X		S																X	X	X	X			X				X		U		X	S	U	43
	X	X	X	X			X	X																	X	X	S	X				U			X		U	U	X	S		44
	U		X	X		X	X	S																	X	X	S	X			X	X					U	X	X	S		45
	U		X	S		X		S																	X	X	X	X				X			U		U	X	X	X	X	46
	U		X	S		X		S																	X	X	X	X				X					S	X	X	X	X	47
	U		X	S		X		X				U														X	X	S				X					X	X	X	X	X	48
	S	X	X	X			U	S																		X	X	X				X		X		S	X		X		X	49
	X	X	U	X			U	X																		X		X						X		S	X		X	S	X	50
		X	X	X			X	S	S																X	X		X						S		X	U		X	X	X	51
Total League Appearances																																										
24	24	40	42	38	20	33	39	21	18	25	13	0	9	1	0	0	0	0	5	0	9	9	4	0	18	20	10	20	1	0	12	11	0	2	3	3	3	4	12	4	6	**X**
0	1	1	0	4	5	2	2	18	10	1	8	0	5	12	0	0	0	0	0	0	1	0	1	0	0	0	8	1	4	0	0	1	2	1	5	3	1	0	2	5	0	**S**
0	6	0	1	0	1	4	2	0	2	0	0	21	11	3	11	8	4	4	2	2	0	0	2	3	0	0	0	0	0	4	0	2	1	2	4	1	13	5	0	0	1	**U**
Total Cup Appearances																																										
4	4	4	3	5	1	4	4	2	1	5	3	0	3	0	0	1	0	0	2	0	5	2	1	0	0	0	0	0	0	0	0	0	0	0	0	0	0	0	0	0	0	**X**
0	0	0	0	0	1	0	1	3	2	0	0	0	1	0	0	0	1	1	0	0	0	1	0	0	0	0	0	0	0	0	0	0	0	0	0	0	0	0	0	0	0	**S**
1	0	0	0	0	0	0	0	0	1	0	0	2	1	2	0	3	1	0	2	2	0	0	1	1	0	0	0	0	0	0	0	0	0	0	0	0	0	0	0	0	0	**U**

Also Played: WEDGBURY X(16). GOWARD U (18). BURRELL U(18,31). LANGFORD S(20). ANNERSON X(26,27). HIGGINSON U(47) S(48). NAYLOR U(49,51) X(50). RYAN S(50).

MANSFIELD TOWN

CURRENT SQUAD AS OF BEGINING OF 2009-10 SEASON

GOALKEEPERS		SQ NO.	HT	WT	D.O.B	AGE	P.O.B	CAREER	APPS	GOA
Alan	Marriott	1	6'01"	12 05	3/9/78	30	Bedford	Tottenham Rel c/s 99, Lincoln C 8/99 Rel c/s 08, Rushden & D 7/08, Mansfield 1/09	18	0
Timothy	Sandercombe	20	6'04"	13 12	15/6/89	20	Plymouth	QPR (Yth), Plymouth (Scholar) Rel c/s 07, Tiverton (L) 11/06, Notts County 7/07 Rel c/s 08, Torquay (Trial), Stafford R 9/08, Mansfield 5/09		
DEFENDERS										
Scott	Garner	6	6'02"		20/9/89	19	Coventry	Leicester, Ilkeston (L) 10/08, Mansfield 1/09	20	4
Luke	Graham	15	6'03"	12 07	27/4/86	23	Kettering	Northampton, Aylesbury (L) 12/04, Kettering (2ML) 2/05, Forest Green (SL) 8/05, Kettering 5/06, Kings Lynn (SL) 10/08, Mansfield 5/09		
Paul	Heckingbottom	3	6'00"	12 05	17/7/77	32	Barnsley	Man Utd (Trainee), Sunderland 7/95, Scarborough (SL) 10/97, Hartlepool (L) 9/98, Sheff Utd (Trial), Bolton (Trial), Stockport (Trial), Darlington 3/99 Rel c/s 02, Norwich 7/02, Bradford C 7/03, Sheff Wed 7/04, Barnsley Undisc 1/06, Bradford C (6ML) 7/07, Bradford C 1/08 Rel c/s 09, Mansfield 6/09		
Luke	Jones	5	5'09"	11 09	10/4/87	22	Blackburn	Blackburn Rel c/s 06, Shrewsbury 11/06 Rel 4/08, Kidderminster (2ML) 1/08, Kidderminster 5/08 Rel 5/09, Mansfield 5/09		
Gary	Silk	16	5'09"	13 07	13/9/84	24	Newport, IOW	Portsmouth Rel c/s 06, Barnet (L) 12/03, Wycombe (8ML) 7/04, Boston U (SL) 1/06, Notts County 7/06 Rel c/s 08, Mansfield 7/08	41	1
Ben	Turner	22			22/9/91	17		Mansfield		
Jason	Ventrella							Mansfield		
MIDFIELDERS										
Craig	Armstrong	12	5'11"	12 09	23/5/75	34	South Shields	Notts Forest, Burnley (3ML) 12/94, Bristol R (L) 1/96, Bristol R (SL) 3/96, Gillingham (2ML) 10/96, Watford (L) 1/97, Watford (6WL) 3/97, Huddersfield £750,000 2/99, Sheff Wed £100,000 2/02, Grimsby (2ML) 2/04, Bradford C 1/05 Rel c/s 05, Cheltenham 7/05		
Jonathan	D'Laryea	18	5'10"	12 02	3/9/85	23	Manchester	Man City, Mansfield (3ML) 10/05, Mansfield 1/06	41	2
Scott	Gardner	2	5'09"	11 04	1/4/88	21	Luxembourg	Leeds Rel 1/09, Farsley Celtic (L) 1/08, Farsley Celtic (L) 9/08, Mansfield 2/09	6	0
Conor	Higginson	23			27/1/92	17	Ollerton	Mansfield	1	0
Steven	Istead	14	5'08"	11 04	23/4/86	23	South Shields	Newcastle (Yth), Hartlepool Rel c/s 06. Gateshead 7/06, Consett 1/07, Peterhead c/s 07, Ilkeston 6/08, Mansfield 6/09		
Gary	Mills	4	5'09"	11 06	20/5/81	28	Sheppey	Rushden & D, Yeovil (Trial) 6/06, Crawley 8/06, Rushden & D 1/07 Rel 5/07, Tamworth 6/07, Kettering 10/07, Stevenage 5/08, Mansfield 6/09		
Tom	Naylor	21			28/6/91	18	Sutton-in-Ashfield	Mansfield	1	0
Matt	Somner	8	6'00"	13 02	8/12/82	26	Isleworth	Brentford, Cambridge (2ML) 12/04 Perm 2/05, Bristol R NC 8/05, Aldershot 8/05, Notts County 6/06 Rel 6/08, Mansfield 7/08	35	1
Ryan	Williams	11	5'04"	11 02	31/8/78	31	Chesterfield	Mansfield, Tranmere £70,000 + 8/97, Chesterfield (3ML) 11/99 £80,000 2/00, Hull C £150,000 7/01, Bristol R (2ML) 10/03 Perm 12/03, Forest Green (2ML) 12/04, Aldershot (L) 8/05, Aldershot 1/06 Rel 4/08, Weymouth 5/08 Rel 2/09, Mansfield 2/09	14	1
FORWARDS										
Jason	Bradley	27	6'03"	13 00	16/3/89	20	Sheffield	Sheff Wed Rel c/s 08, Buxton (L) 10/07, Darlington 7/08, Buxton (L) 9/08, Blyth (L) 11/08, Gainsborough (SL) 2/09, Mansfield 7/09		
Louis	Briscoe	7	6'00"	11 13	2/4/88	21	Burton	Port Vale Rel 1/07, Stafford R (Trial), Moor Green 3/07, Leek T 7/07, Huston Dynamoes (USA) (Trial) 3/08, Hednesford 6/08, Gresley R 9/08, Stafford R 11/08, Ilkeston 12/08, Mansfield 1/09	18	1
Daryl	Clare	10	5'09"	11 00	1/8/78	31	Jersey	Grimsby Rel c/s 01, Northampton (3ML) 11/99, Northampton (L) 11/00, Cheltenham (L) 12/00, Boston U 7/01, Chester £25,000 10/02, Boston U Undisc 11/04, Crawley 8/05 £60,000, Burton 3/06, Rushden & D 5/08, Mansfield (SL) 3/09, Mansfield 5/09	9	1
Robert	Duffy	9	6'01"	12 04	2/12/82	26	Swansea	Rushden & D Rel c/s 05, Stamford (L) 1/05, Peterborough (Trial) 7/05, Cambridge U 8/05, Kettering 9/05, Gainsborough 1/06, Stevenage 3/06 Rel 5/06, Oxford U 8/06 Rel 4/08, Wrexham (SL) 1/08, Mansfield (Trial) c/s 07, Newport C 7/08, Mansfield 1/09	21	9
Kyle	Nix	26	5'06"	09 10	21/1/86	23	Sydney, Aust	Man Utd (Trainee), Aston Villa 7/02 Rel c/s 05, Sheff Utd 7/05 Rel c/s 06, Barnsley (SL) 2/06, Scunthorpe (Trial) 7/06, Buxton 11/06, Parkgate Rel c/s 07, Bradford C 7/07 Rel c/s 09, Mansfield 7/09		

Kyle	Perry	19	6'04"	14 05	5/3/86	23	Birmingham	Walsall Rel c/s 05, Moor Green (L) 8/04, AFC Telford (SL) 9/04, AFC Telford c/s 05 Rel 7/06, Hednesford c/s 06, Willenhall 9/06, Chasetown 6/07, Port Vale (Nominal) 1/08 Rel c/s 09, Northwich (L) 3/09, Mansfield 7/09		
Grant	Ryan	24			5/2/91	18	Nottingham	Mansfield	1	0
Jake	Speight	17	5'07"	11 02	28/9/85	23	Sheffield	Sheff Utd, Leigh RMI (L) 3/05, Bury (Trial) c/s 05, Scarborough (L) 8/05 Perm 9/05, Bury (6WL) 12/05 Nominal 1/06 Rel 4/07, Northwich 6/07 Rel 5/08, Farsley Celtic 9/08, Droylsden 2/09, Mansfield 5/09		

LOANEES		SN	HT	WT	DOB	AGE	POB	From - To	APPS	GOA
(G)Paddy	Gamble		5'10"	10 12	1/9/88	20	Bulwell	Notts Forest (5ML) 7/08 - Rel 5/09, Alfreton 8/09	24	0
(D)Maxime	Chanot		6'00"	12 07	21/11/89	19	Nancy, Fra	Sheff Utd (2ML) 10/08 -	5	0
(F)Emile	Sinclair		6'00"	11 04	20/12/87	21	Leeds	Notts Forest (3ML) 10/08 - Rel 5/09	10	4
(M)Samuel	Wedgbury				26/2/89	20	Oldbury	Sheff Utd 10/08 -	1	0
(M)Adnan	Ahmed		5'10"	11 02	7/6/84	25	Burnley	Tranmere (2ML) 10/08 - Port Vale (L) 1/09	9	2
(G)Jamie	Annerson		6'02"	13 02	10/11/88	20	Sheffield	Sheff Utd 12/08 -	1	0
(F)Tomi	Ameobi		6'03"	12 10	16/8/88	21	Newcastle	Doncaster 1/09 - Rel 5/09	5	0
(M)Ollie	Hotchkiss				27/9/89	19	Houghton-le-Spring	Leeds (SL) 3/09 -	6	0

DEPARTURES		SN	HT	WT	DOB	AGE	POB	From - To	APPS	GOA
(M)Tom	Shaw		6'00"	12 00	1/12/86	22	Nottingham	Rushden & D 8/08 - Rel 10/08, Tamworth 10/08	0	0
(F)Anthony	Robinson				31/12/80	28	Birmingham	Worcester 8/08 - Rel 10/08, Studley 10/08, Redditch 11/08 Rel 11/08, Halesowen T 11/08, Stratford T 11/08, Hednesford 11/08, Oxford C 12/08, Evesham 2/09, Atherstone T 3/09, Kings Lynn 7/09	13	0
(G)David	Knight		6'00"	11 07	15/1/87	22	Sunderland	Swansea 10/08 - Rel c/s 09, Darlington 7/09	0	0
(F)Jason	Lee		6'03"	13 08	9/5/71	38	Forest Gate	Notts County 7/08 - Kettering 1/09, Corby 3/09	21	2
(D)Gavin	Hurren		5'08"	13 07	22/10/85	23	Birmingham	Kidderminster 7/08 - Rel 1/09, Kings Lynn 1/09, Crawley 2/09 Rel 5/09, Tamworth 6/09	14	1
(D)Ashley	Kitchen		5'11"	11 00	10/10/88	20	Edwinstowe	Yth - Rel 1/09, Glapwell 2/09	0	0
(D)James	Kay		5'09"	11 07	9/2/89	20	Rotherham	Sheff Wed 9/08 - Rel 2/09, Belper 3/09	5	0
(G)Dan	Whatsize		6'02"		14/8/90	19	Leicester	Worksop 1/09 - Rel 2/09, Kettering 3/09, Kings Lynn 6/09	0	0
(M)Alexandre	Jeannin		6'00"	11 06	30/12/77	31	Troyes	Oxford U 8/08 - Rel c/s 09	26	0
(M)Neil	Mackenzie		6'02"	12 05	15/4/76	33	Birmingham	Notts County 1/09 - Rel 4/09, Tamworth 6/09	8	0
(D)Gianluca	Havern		6'01"	13 00	24/9/88	20	Manchester	Stockport 2/09 - Rel 5/09	4	0
(D)Paul	Mayo		5'11"	11 09	13/10/81	27	Lincoln	Notts County 1/09 - Rel 5/09, Corby T 6/09	12	1
(D)Chris	Wood		6'00"	10 11	24/1/87	22	Worksop	Yth - Rel 7/09, Ilkeston (L) 1/09, Boston U 7/09	0	0
(M)Warren	Burrell		5'10"	10 06	3/6/90	19	Sheffield	Yth - Rel 7/09	0	0
(M)Ryan	Goward		5'09"	10 08	1/11/89	19		Yth - Rel 7/09, Glapwell (SL) 1/09	0	0
(F)Lewis	Trimmer		5'07"	10 00	30/10/89	19	Norwich	Yth - Rel 7/09, Glapwell (SL) 1/09	0	0
(M)Jamie	McGhee		5'08"	10 07	28/9/89	19	Grantham	Yth - Rel 7/09, Corby T 7/09	0	0
(F)Michael	Blackwood		5'10"	11 04	30/9/79	29	Birmingham	Kidderminster 7/08 - Rel 5/09, Tamworth (SL) 3/09, Tamworth 5/09	25	3
(F)Anthony	Howell				27/5/86	23		Ilkeston 1/09 - Rel 5/09, Alfreton (SL) 3/09, Alfreton 5/09	2	0
(D)Adie	Moses		5'10"	12 08	4/5/75	34	Doncaster	Lincoln C 7/08 - Rel c/s 09, Gainsborough 6/09	42	0
(D)Alan	O'Hare		6'02"	12 02	31/7/82	27	Drogheda. Ire	Chesterfield 7/08 - Rel 6/09, York C 6/09	25	1
(F)Aaron	O'Connor		5'10"	12 00	9/8/83	26	Nottingham	Grays 8/08 - Rushden & D 6/09	39	8
(M)Curtis	Woodhouse		5'08"	11 00	17/4/80	29	Driffield	Rushden & D 1/09 - Harrogate T 6/09	12	0
(M)Curtis	Shaw	25			24/6/87	22	Nottingham	Ilkeston 1/09 - Rel 7/09	3	0
(F)Mark	Stallard		6'00"	13 06	21/10/74	34	Derby	Lincoln C 7/08 - Corby T 7/09	28	9
(G)Jason	White		6'03"	12 07	28/1/83	26	Sutton-in-Ashfield	Notts Forest (Yth) - Kings Lynn 8/09	4	0
(M)Nathan	Arnold		5'08"	10 07	26/7/87	22	Mansfield	Yth - Rel c/s 09, Hyde U 8/09	42	5
(G)Luke	Herriott							Yth - Gainsborough c/s 09	0	0
(F)Nick	Langford				23/4/92	17	Sutton-in-Ashfield	Yth -	0	0

MANSFIELD TOWN

Founded: 1897

Nickname: The Stags

Club Colours: Amber shirts, blue shorts, blue socks.

Change Colours: Blue & white striped shirts, black shorts, black socks.

Club Sponsor: Hymas Holmes.

Previous League: Football League.

Ground Address: Field Mill Stadium, Quarry Lane, Mansfield, NG18 5DA

Telephone: 01623 482 482

Facsimile: 01623 482 495

E-mail: info@mansfieldtown.net

Website: www.mansfieldtown.net

SIMPLE DIRECTIONS:

By Road: From North: Take M1, exiting at J29, then join A617 to Mansfield, after around 6miles turn right into Rosemary St, then proceed to Quarry Lane where you should turn right to the ground. From South: Take M1, exiting at J28, then take the A38 to Mansfield, after around 6 miles turn right into Belvedere Street (at Crossroads), then after a quarter of a mile turn right into Quarry Lane.

MATCH TICKETS:

Ticket Prices:
Quarry Lane End - Adult £16, Concessions £8.
North Stand (away end) - Adult £16, Concessions £8.
West Stand upper tier - Adult £16, Concessions £8.
West Stand lower tier - Adult £16, Concessions £8.

Refreshments: Food and drink bars around the ground.

PROGRAMME EDITOR
Mark Stevenson
Tel: (M) 07733 889 424
Email: mark.stevenson@mansfieldtown.net

CLUB STATISTICS

RECORDS

Attendance: 24,467 v Nottingham Forest, FA Cup 3rd Rnd 10.01.53.
Victory: 9-2 v Rotherham United, Div.3 South 29.08.31.
Defeat: 1-8 v Walsall, Div.3 North 19.01.33.
Career Goalscorer (Lge): Harry Johnson - 104 (1931-36).
Career Appearances (Lge): Rod Arnold - 440 (1970-83).
Transfer Fee Paid: £150,000 for Lee Peacock from Carlisle United.
Transfer Fee Received: £655,000 from Tottenham for Colin Calderwood.

SENIOR HONOURS

Football League Division 4 Champions 1974-75.
Football League Division 3 Champions 1976-77.
Football League Trophy 1987.

PREVIOUS

Names: Mansfield Wesleyans 1897-1906.
Mansfield Wesley 1906-10.
Leagues: Mansfield & District Amateur 1902-06.
Notts & District 06-11. Central Alliance 1911-14, 1915-21
Notts & Derbyshire 1914-15. Midland League 1921-26.
Midland Combination 1926-31. Football League 1931-2008.
Grounds: Newgate Lane 1902-12. Radcliffe Gate 1912-19.

OXFORD UNITED

CLUB PERSONNEL

Chairman: Kelvin Thomas.

Directors: Nick Merry.

General Manager/Secretary

Mick Brown

Telephone: 01865 337 504

(M): 07833 148 883.

Email: gm@oufc.co.uk

correspondence to Secretary at club.

Commercial Manager

David Jackson

Tel: (B): 01865 337517 (M): 07825 511911

Press Officer

Chris Williams

Tel: (B) 01865 337 523. (M) 07941 607 842

E-mail: cwilliams@oufc.co.uk

Manager: Chris Wilder.

Coach: Mickey Lewis.

Goalkeeping Coach: Alan Hodgkinson MBE.

Club therapist: Charlie Greig.

Clubs who drop out of The Football League often need a few seasons to reorganise administratively, rebuild the playing squad and sort out financial matters. Oxford United have now worked their way through two difficult campaigns in which early hopes for promotion had been dashed.

However, the second half of last season saw the club re-emerge as a real force in the Blue Square Premier division and there are now hopes that the splendid Kassam Stadium will see a very serious promotion challenge under the guidance of manager Chris Wilder, who had taken over from Darren Patterson last November.

United had beaten Hayes & Yeading and Dorchester Town to reach the F.A.Cup Second Round but lost at Torquay and another ex Football league club York City beat them 2-1 in the F.A.Trophy 2nd Round.

During the season twenty two players registered goals for United but only ace marksman James Constable reached double figures with an impressive total of 26, which earned him a place in the successful England C squad.

Chasing a play off place in a wonderful end of season challenge, United attracted 10,298 for their home game against a relegated Northwich Victoria who were enjoying their best form of the season. Sadly it resulted in United's first defeat in twelve matches but the future looks great and there will be great optimism for the next campaign.

OXFORD UNITED

BEST LGE ATT.: **10,298** v Northwich Victoria
LOWEST: **3,690** v Kidderminster Harriers

No.	Date	Comp	H/A	Opponents	Att:	Result	Goalscorers	Pos
1	Aug 9	BSP	A	Barrow	2790	L 0 - 3		
2	12		H	Weymouth	4547	L 0 - 1		
3	16		H	Eastbourne Borough	3969	W 6 - 3	**Constable** 5 79 Reid 7 Pullan 41 (og) Hutchinson 69 Quinn 88	
4	21		A	Wrexham	3515	L 0 - 2		19
5	25		H	Woking	4314	D 0 - 0		18
6	30		A	Ebbsfleet Town	1842	D 1 - 1	Reid 90	17
7	Sept 2		A	Northwich Victoria	973	W 2 - 1	**Constable** 54 68	
8	6		H	Kettering Town	4499	D 1 - 1	Odubade 72	17
9	13		A	Kidderminster Harriers	2065	L 0 - 1		19
10	20		H	Crawley Town	3992	L 1 - 2	Odubade 17 (pen)	20
11	23		H	Cambridge United	4170	W 3 - 1	Guy 4 Murray 72 Haldane 90	19
12	27		A	Lewes	1156	L 1 - 2	Burnell 63	19
13	Oct 4		H	Rushden & Diamonds	4645	W 2 - 1	Quinn 42 Trainer 45	18
14	9		A	Torquay United	1955	D 1 - 1	Trainer 89	18
15	12		A	Altrincham	1806	L 0 - 1		19
16	18		H	Burton Albion	4494	W 2 - 1	Trainer 8 **Constable** 50 (pen)	18
17	**25**	**F.A.C. 4Q**	**H**	**Hayes & Yeading**	**2521**	**W 2 - 0**	**Guy 57 Constable 72**	
18	Nov 1		H	York City	4449	W 1 - 0	Odubade 87 (pen)	15
19	**4**	**SS S3**	**A**	**Forest Green Rovers**	**383**	**L 1 - 2***	**Hutchinson 52**	
20	**8**	**F.A.C. 1R**	**H**	**Dorchester Town**	**3196**	**D 0 - 0**		
21	15		A	Grays Athletic	892	L 0 - 2		17
22	**18**	**F.A.C. 1R r**	**A**	**Dorchester Town**	**1474**	**W 3 - 1***	**Constable 78 Trainer 110 Odubade 120**	
23	22		A	Histon	1242	L 2 - 5	Willmott 27 Hutchinson 80	17
24	25		H	Kidderminster Harriers	3690	W 1 - 0	**Constable** 25 (pen)	14
25	**29**	**F.A.C.2R**	**A**	**Torquay United**	**2647**	**L 0 - 2**		
26	Dec 4		A	Mansfield Town	1553	W 3 - 1	**Constable** 9 Guy 58 Deering 72	13
27	9		A	Weymouth	822	D 2 - 2	Day 42 Guy 82	
28	**13**	**F.A.T 1R**	**A**	**AFC Sudbury**	**434**	**W 2 - 0**	**Guy 30 85**	
29	20		H	Stevenage Borough	4343	D 1 - 1	**Constable** 43	13
30	26		A	Salisbury City	2418	L 1 - 2	Deering 55	14
31	28		H	Ebbsfleet United	5120	W 5 - 1	Haldane 16 **Constable** 20 Odubade 51 Trainer 81 Fisher 85	12
32	Jan 1		H	Salisbury City	5312	W 2 - 0	**Constable** 71 Sappleton 84	11
33	**13**	**F.A.T 2R**	**H**	**York City**	**1958**	**L 1 - 2**	**Constable 61**	
34	17		H	Altincham	4249	W 1 - 0	**Constable** 68	10
35	20		H	Forest Green Rovers	3728	W 2 - 1	Odubade 70 **Constable** 73	
36	23		A	Crawley Town	1603	W 1 - 0	Murray 61	9
37	29		A	Cambridge United	3774	D 1 - 1	Murray 9	
38	Feb 1		H	Lewes	4595	W 2 - 1	Murray 17 Foster 82	
39	14		H	Barrow	4532	W 3 - 0	Farrell 62 Haldene 79 Odubade 86	9
40	21		H	Mansfield Town	4618	W 1 - 0	Nelthorpe 60	7
41	28		H	Torquay United	5837	L 0 - 2		9
42	Mar 3		A	Eastbourne Borough	1168	W 3 - 0	Murray 43 Clist 70 Farrell 90	
43	7		A	Forest Green Rovers	2027	D 3 - 3	**Constable** 21 (pen) 27 (pen) Murray 65	6
44	14		H	Grays Atheltic	4764	W 4 - 1	Sandwith 8 **Constable** 26 45 Chapman 69	8
45	19		A	Kettering United	1716	W 2 - 1	Nelthorpe 6 Willmott 8	8
46	24		A	Rushden & Diamonds	2085	W 3 - 1	**Constable** 36 61(pen) Clist 87	
47	28		A	Stevenage Borough	3700	D 1 - 1	**Constable** 69 (pen)	7
48	April 4		H	Histon	6231	W 2 - 1	**Constable** 66 84	7
49	7		A	York City	2268	D 0 - 0		7
50	11		H	Wrexham	5832	W 1 - 0	**Constable** 90	7
51	13		A	Woking	3791	W 2 - 0	Murray 5 Clist 18	
52	17		A	Burton Albion	6192	W 1 - 0	Chapman 70	7
53	26		H	Northwich Victoria	10 298	L 1 - 2	**Constable** 84	7

Average Home Att: **4985 (4472)** **Goals** **81 58**

Best Position: 6th **Worst:** 20th

Goalscorers: Constable 26, Murray 7, Odubade 7, Guy 6, Trainer 5, Clist 3, Haldane 3, Hutchinson 3, Chapman 2, Deering 2, Farrell 2, Nelthorpe 2, Quinn 2, Willmott 2, Burnell 1, Day 1, Fisher 1, Foster 1, Pullan 1, Reid 1, Sandwith 1, Sappleton 1. Own Goals 1.

HINCHLIFFE 25	CLARKE 16	CARRUTHERS 3	FOSTER 5	DAVIES 20	QUINN 6	MURRAY 8	BURNELL 4	HALDANE 11	ODUBADE 7	CONSTABLE 9	WILLMOTT 14	HUSBANDS 24	REID 23	COLE 15	FISHER 17	DAY 2	DEERING 19	HUTCHINSON 26	TAYLOR 20	GUY 10	OSBORNE 28	GROVES 27	EVANS 29	TURLEY 1	TRAINER 12	DOBSON 30	SAMPSON 31	SAPPLETON 32	KILLOCK 35	CHAPMAN 33	NELTHORPE 34	BATT 12	FARRELL 10	CLIST 15	SANDWITH 21	
X	X	X	X	X	X	X	X	X	X	X	S	S	S	U	U																					1
U		X	X		X	X	X	X	X	X		X	S	X	S	X	S	U																		2
U		X	X		X	X	X	X	X	X			X	X	U	X	S	S	U																	3
U		X	X	U	X	X		X	X	X	S		X	X	S	X	S	X																		4
U	S	X			X	X		X	X	X	X		S	X	U	X	S	X		X																5
U	X	X	X		X	X	X	S	X	S	X		S	X		U		X		X																6
X	U	X			X	X	X	S	U	X	X		X			U	U	X		X	X															7
X	U	X			X	X	X	X	S	X	X		X			U	S			X	X	U														8
X	U	S			X	X	X	X	S	X	X		X				S			X	X		X	U												9
S	X	U			X	X	X	X	X	U	X						S			S	X		X	X	X											10
U	X	X	X		U	X	X	S	X	X			S				U			X	X			X	X											11
U	X	X	X		U	X	X	S	X	X							S	S		X	X			X	X											12
U	X	X	X		X	X	X	X	X		S						U	U	U	X				X	X											13
U	X	X	X		X	X	X	X	S	X	U						S	U		X				X	X											14
U	X	X	X		X	X	X	X	X							U	S	S	S	X				X	X											15
U	X	X	X		X	X		X	S	X						U	X	U	S	X				X	X											16
U	X	X	X			X		X	S	X	X					U	X	U	S	X		U		X	X	S										17
U		X	X			X	U	X	S	X	X					X	X	S	U	X				X	X											18
U	U	X					X	X	X	X	X					X		X	S	S		X	S	X	X											19
U	U	X				X	X	X	S	X	X					X	X	X	U	S		U		X	X	S										20
U	U	X			X	X	X	X	S	X	X					X	X	S		S				X	X											21
U	X	X	X			X	U	X	S	X	U				U	X	X	X	U	X				X	S											22
S	U	X	X			X	U	U	S	X	X					X	X	X		X				X	X											23
U	X	X	X			X	U	X	X	X	U					X	X	X		S				X	S											24
U	X	X	X			X	U	X	X	X	U				U	X	X	X	S			S		X			U									25
U		X	X			X	X	U	S	X	X				U	X	S	X		X				X	X											26
U			X			X	X	S	S	X	X				U	X	X	X		X			U	X	X											27
U		X	X			X	X	S	S	X	X					X	X	X		X			U	X	S											28
U	U	U	X			X	X	X	S	X	X					X	X	S		X				X	X											29
U	S		X			X	X	X	S	X	X				S	X	X			X			U	X	X											30
U	X		X			X		X	X	X	X				S	X		X	S			S	U	X	X											31
U	X		X			X		X		X	X				U	X		X	S	X			S	X	X			S								32
U	X	S	X				S	X	X	X						X		X	U					X	U			X	X	X						33
U		S	X			X	X	X	X	X	X					S		U						X				S	X	X	X					34
U			X			X	X	X	S	X	X					S		S	U					X				X	X	X	X					35
U		X	X			X	U	S	X	X	X							S						X				S	X	X	X	X				36
U		X	X			X	X	X	S	X	X					U		S						X				U		X	X	X				37
U	U	X	X			X		X	S		X					S		X	U					X						X	X	X	X			38
U		X	X			X		X	S	X	X					U		U						X						X	X	X	S	X		39
U	U	X	X			X	U		S	X	X							U						X						X	X	X	X	X		40
U		X	X			X		S	S	X	X							U						X						X	X	X	X	X	S	41
U		X	X			X		X	X	X	X					U		S						X						X		X	S	X	S	42
U		X				X	U	X	S	X	X					X		X				U		X			U			X			X		X	43
U		S	X			X		X	X	X	X					U		U						X						X		X	S	X	X	44
U		S	X			S		X	U	X	X							S						X						X	X	X	X	X	X	45
U		X	X			X		S	X	X	X					U		S						X						X	X	X	S	X		46
U		X	X			X		X	S	X	X							U						X						X	X	X	S	X	S	47
U		U	X			X		X	S	X	X					U		S						X						X	X		X	X	X	48
U		U	X			X		X	S	X	X					U		S						X						X	X	X		X	X	49
U		U	X			X		X	X	X	X							U						X						X	S	X	S	X	X	50
U		X	X			X		S	S	X	X							S						X						X	U	X	X	X	X	51
U		U	X			X		X	S	X	X							S						X						X	X	X	S	X	X	52
U		X	X			X		X	X	X						U		U						X						X	S	X	S	X	X	53
Total League Appearances																																				
4	12	31	39	1	15	45	21	34	20	41	34	1	5	5	0	15	8	12	0	18	6	0	2	37	16	0	0	1	3	20	14	16	7	14	9	X
2	2	4	0	0	0	1	0	9	23	1	3	1	5	0	4	3	11	16	4	3	0	1	1	0	1	0	0	3	0	0	2	0	8	0	3	S
40	8	6	0	1	2	0	6	2	2	1	2	0	0	1	6	13	3	12	5	0	0	2	3	1	0	0	1	1	0	0	1	0	0	0	0	U
Total Cup Appearances																																				
0	4	6	5	0	0	5	3	6	3	7	4	0	0	0	0	6	5	6	0	3	0	1	0	7	3	0	0	1	1	1	0	0	0	0	0	X
0	0	1	0	0	0	0	1	1	4	0	0	0	0	0	0	0	0	0	3	2	0	1	1	0	2	2	0	0	0	0	0	0	0	0	0	S
7	2	0	0	0	0	0	2	0	0	0	2	0	0	0	2	1	0	1	3	0	0	2	1	0	1	0	1	0	0	0	0	0	0	0	0	U

OXFORD UNITED

CURRENT SQUAD AS OF BEGINING OF 2009-10 SEASON

GOALKEEPERS		SQ NO.	HT	WT	D.O.B	AGE	P.O.B	CAREER	APPS	GOA
Ryan	Clarke	21	6'01"	12 00	30/4/82	27	Bristol	Bristol R Rel 5/06, Southend (L) 10/04, Kidderminster (L) 11/04, Forest Green (SL) 7/05, Torquay (Trial) 7/06, Salisbury 8/06, Northwich (5WL) 11/08 Perm 1/09, Oxford U 5/09		
Billy	Turley	1	6'04"	15 07	15/7/72	37	Wolverhampton	Evesham U, Northampton 7/95, Kettering (SL) 1/97, L.Orient (3ML) 2/98, Rushden & D £130,000 6/99 Rel 2/05, Oxford U 7/05	37	0
DEFENDERS										
Damien	Batt	2	5'10"	11 06	16/9/84	24	Hoddesdon	Norwich (Sch), Wycombe (Trial) 2/04, Cheltenham (Trial) 2/04, Wycombe (Trial) 3/04, Bournemouth (Trial) Redbridge 8/04, Barnet 9/04 Rel 5/06, St Albans 8/06, Stevenage 1/07 Rel 5/08, St Albans (3ML) 9/07, Woking (SL) 2/08, Fisher 8/08 Rel 10/08, Grays NC 10/08, Oxford U 1/09	16	0
Chris	Carruthers	23	5'10"	12 03	19/8/83	26	Kettering	Northampton, Hornchurch (L) 11/04, Kettering (L) 1/05, Bristol R (SL) 3/05, Bristol R Undisc 7/05 Rel c/s 08, Oxford U 7/08	35	0
Adam	Chapman	7			29/11/89	19	Doncaster	Sheff Utd, Oxford U (SL) 1/09, Oxford U £15,000 5/09	20	2
Mark	Creighton	6	6'04"	12 01	8/10/81	27	Birmingham	Kidderminster (Yth), Moor Green, Paget R, Halesowen T, Redditch, Bromsgrove, Willenhall 1/02, Redditch 8/05, Kidderminster 6/06, Oxford U Small Fee 5/09		
Rhys	Day	16	6'02"	13 06	31/8/82	27	Bridgend	Man City, Blackpool (3ML) 12/01, Cambridge U (L) 9/02, Mansfield (2ML) 11/02 Perm 1/03 Rel c/s 05, Aldershot 7/06 Rel c/s 09, Oxford U 7/09		
Luke	Foster	5	6'02"	12 08	8/9/85	23	Mexborough	Sheff Wed, Scarborough (4ML) 9/04, Alfreton (L) 2/05, Lincoln C 8/05 Rel 1/07, York C (2ML) 10/06, Stalybridge 1/07, Oxford U 2/07	39	1
Shane	Killock	19	6'00"	12 04	12/3/89	20	Huddersfield	Ossett A (Yth), Huddersfield, Hyde U (SL) 2/08, Harrogate T (L) 9/08, Oxford U (L) 1/09 Perm 2/09	3	0
Ian	Sampson	28						Oxford U, Didcot T (WE) 10/08, Didcot T (7ML) 5/09	0	0
Kevin	Sandwith	3	5'11"	13 06	30/4/78	31	Workington	Carlisle, Barrow 9/98, Telford 2/99, Doncaster 5/01 Rel 9/02, Halifax 11/02, Lincoln C 3/04, Macclesfield 7/05, Swansea (Trial) 11/05, Chester 6/06 Rel c/s 08, Weymouth 7/08 Rel 2/09, Oxford U 2/09	12	1
MIDFIELDERS										
Declan	Benjamin	29	6'00"	11 04	4/2/91	18		Oxford U, Abingdon U (L), Banbury U (L) 8/09		
Dannie	Bulman	4	5'09"	11 12	24/1/79	30	Ashford	Ashford T, Wycombe (Trial) 97/98, Wycombe £5,000 + 6/98 Rel c/s 04, Stevenage 6/04 Rel 12/06, Crawley (4ML) 8/06, Crawley 1/07, Oxford U 5/09		
Simon	Clist	11	5'10"	11 05	13/6/81	28	Bournemouth	Tottenham (Trainee) Rel c/s 99, Bristol C 7/99, Torquay (2ML) 2/03, Barnet AL 1/04 Rel 5/06, Forest Green 5/06, Oxford U Undisc 2/09	14	3
Sam	Deering	20	5'05"	11 00	26/2/91	18	London	Oxford U	19	2
Richard	Groves	27	5'10"	11 00	4/1/91	18		Oxford U, Banbury U (WE) 10/08	1	0
Marcus	Kelly	14	5'07"	10 00	16/3/86	23	Kettering	Rushden & D, Oxford U 5/09		
Adam	Murray	8	5'09"	10 00	30/9/81	27	Birmingham	Derby, Mansfield (SL) 2/02, Kidderminster (L) 8/03, Solihull 11/03, Burton 11/03, Notts County 11/03, Kidderminster 1/04, Mansfield 6/04, Carlisle Nominal 3/05, Torquay £10,000 8/06, Macclesfield £17,500 1/07, Oxford U Undisc 1/08	46	7
Alfie	Potter	15	5'07"	09 06	9/1/89	20	London	Wimbledon (Yth), Millwall (Scholar), Peterborough, Kvinisdel (Nor) (L) (07), Grays (L) 9/07, Havant & W (3ML) 11/07, AFC Wimbledon (SL) 2/08, Kettering (SL) 8/08, Oxford U (SL) 7/09		
Alex	Rhodes	18	5'09"	10 04	23/1/82	27	Cambridge	Newmarket T, Norwich (Trial) 9/03, Yeovil (Trial) 10/03, Ipswich (Trial) 10/03, Brentford £7,500 11/03, Swindon (L) 10/06, Grays (7WL) 3/07, Bradford C 8/07, Rotherham 7/08 Rel 5/09, Woking (SL) 3/09, Oxford U 7/09		
FORWARDS										
James	Constable	9	6'02"	12 02	4/10/84	24	Malmesbury	Cirencester, Chippenham, Swansea (Trial) 11/05, Walsall (6WL) 11/05 £4,000 1/06, Kidderminster (2ML) 11/06 Perm 1/07, Shrewsbury Undisc 1/08, Oxford U (SL) 7/08 Undisc 6/09	42	23
Matthew	Green	24	5'08"	10 06	13/5/87	22	Bath	Bristol C (Yth), Cirencester (Yth), Newport C c/s 05, Cardiff C £10,000 1/07 Rel 5/08, Darlington (L) 10/07, Oxford U (L) 11/07, Oxford U (SL) 1/08, Torquay 5/08, Oxford U (SL) 6/09		
Jack	Midson	10	5'08"	11 07	21/7/83	26	Stevenage	Stevenage, Arlesey 8/03, Dag & Red 8/04, Hemel Hempstead (L) 12/04, Bishops Stortford 7/05, Histon Undisc 1/08, Oxford U 5/09		

LOANEES		HT	WT	DOB	AGE	POB	From - To	APPS	GOA
(G)Jake	Cole	6'02"	13 00	11/9/85	23	Hammersmith	QPR (3ML) 7/08 - Barnet (L) 3/09, Rel 5/09, Barnet 7/09	5	0
(F)Jamie	Guy	6'01"	13 00	1/8/87	22	Barking	Colchester (5ML) 7/08 - Dag & Red (L) 3/09	21	2
(F)Lewis	Haldane	6'00"	11 13	13/3/85	24	Trowbridge	Bristol R (SL) 7/08 -	43	3
(D)Karleigh	Osborne	6'02"	12 04	19/3/88	21	Southall	Brentford 9/08 - Eastbourne B (L) 10/08	6	0
(M)Ricky	Sappleton	5'10"	11 13	8/12/89	19	Kingston, Jam	Leicester 1/09 - AFC Telford (SL) 3/09	4	1
(F)Craig	Farrell	6'00"	12 11	5/12/82	26	Middlesbrough	York C (SL) 1/09 - Rushden & D (PE) 6/09	15	2

DEPARTURES			HT	WT	DOB	AGE	POB	From - To	APPS	GOA
(M)Rob	Davies		5'09"	11 03	24/3/87	22	Tywyn	Barakaldo CF (Spa) 7/08 Rel 8/08 - Worcester 9/08	1	0
(F)Michael	Husbands		5'08"	10 10	13/11/83	25	Birmingham	AFC Telford 8/08 - Rel 8/08	2	0
(M)Levi	Reid		5'05"	11 04	19/1/83	26	Stafford	Macclesfield 8/08 - Rel 9/08, Mansfield (Trial) 1/09	10	2
(M)Paul	Evans		5'08"	12 06	1/9/74	34	Oswestry	Bradford C 9/08 - Rel 1/09, FC Halifax 1/09, Rhyl 6/09	3	0
(D)James	Clarke							Yth - Oxford C 2/09	14	0
(F)Alex	Fisher		6'02"	12 00	30/6/90	19		Yth - Rel 3/09, Bognor (L) 9/08, Oxford C (L) 1/09, Oxford C 6/09	4	1
(D)Matthew	Day		5'11"	13 07	24/3/87	22	Newbury	Portsmouth 8/06 - Rel 4/09	18	1
(D)Chris	Willmott		6'02"	11 13	30/9/77	31	Bedford	Northampton 7/05 - Rel 4/09	37	2
(M)Eddie	Hutchinson		6'01"	13 00	23/2/82	27	Kingston	Brentford 7/06 - Rel 4/09, Crawley 5/09	28	2
(M)Craig	Nelthorpe		5'10"	11 00	10/6/87	22	Doncaster	Doncaster 1/09 - Rel 4/09, York C 5/09	16	2
(M)Barry	Quinn		6'00"	12 02	9/5/79	30	Dublin	Coventry 5/04 - Rel 4/09	15	2
(M)Phil	Trainer		6'00"	12 00	3/7/81	28	Wolverhampton	Moor Green/Solihull Moors 7/07 - Rel 4/09, AFC Telford (SL) 1/09, AFC Telford 5/09	17	4
(F)Yemi	Odubade		5'07"	11 07	4/7/84	25	Lagos	Eastbourne B 1/06 - Rel 4/09, Stevenage 5/09	43	6
(F)Matt	Taylor							Yth - Rel 4/09, Banbury U (L) 9/08, Brackley (L) 2/09, Didcot T 5/09	4	0
(M)Joe	Burnell	26	5'10"	11 01	10/10/80	28	Bristol	Northampton 7/08 - Rel 7/09, Exeter (Trial) 4/09, Exeter 7/09	21	1
(G)Ben	Hinchliffe		5'10"	11 07	9/10/88	20	Preston	Derby 7/08 -	6	0
(M)James	Dobson		6'00"	12 02	13/10/91	17		Yth -	0	0
(D)Luke	Bennett		6'02"	12 00				Yth - Banbury (WE) 7/08		

OXFORD UNITED

Re-formed: 1893

Nickname: U's

Club Colours: Yellow shirts, navy blue shorts, navy blue socks.

Change Colours: White shirts, white shorts, white socks.

Club Sponsor: Buildbase

Previous League: Football League

Ground Address: The Kassam Stadium, Grenoble Road, Oxford OX4 4XP
Telephone: 01865 337 500
Facsimile: 01865 337 501
Mobile: 07833 148 883
E-mail: admin@oufc.co.uk
Web address: www.oufc.co.uk

SIMPLE DIRECTIONS
By road: The Kassam Stadium is clearly signposted on all major approach roads to Oxford.
By Rail: Nearest Railway Station is Oxford (five miles from ground)

MATCH TICKETS
Match day prices: Adult: £16.00-£19.50, Student: £12.50-£14.50, Under 16 or over 65: £8.50-£13.00, 4-under 11: £5.50-£13.00.

Capacity: 12,500

Clubhouse: 'Priory & Question Mark' public house and nearby restaurants for pre match meets.

Refreshments: Bars around the ground.

Club Shop: Fully stocked.

No image available

PROGRAMME EDITOR
Chris Williams
Tel: (M) 07941 607842 (B) 01865 337 523
Email: cwilliams@oufc.co.uk

CLUB STATISTICS

RECORDS

Attendance: 22,730 v P.N.E. 6th Rd F.A.Cup 1963-1964.

Victory: 9-1 F.A.Cup First Round 1994-95 v Dorchester Town.

Defeat: 0-7 Division One v Sunderland 1998-1999.

Career Goalscorer: Graham Atkinson 771962-73.

Career Appearances: John Shuker 478 1962-1977.

Transfer Fee Paid: £475,000 to Aberdeen for Dean Windass August 1998.

Transfer Fee Received: £1,600,000 from Leicester City for Matt Elliott Jan 1997.

SENIOR HONOURS

Football League Division 3 Champions 1967-68, 83-84.

Football League Division 2 Champions1984-85.

Football League Cup Winners 1985-1986.

PREVIOUS

Names: 1893 Headington, 1894 -1960 Headington United.

Recent Ground: Manor Ground 1925-2001.

RUSHDEN & DIAMONDS

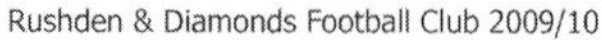

Rushden & Diamonds Football Club 2009/10

Back Row: Rob Wolleaston - Max Porter - Cliff Akurang - Sam Smith - Curtis Osano - Michael Corcoran

Middle Row: 1st Team Coach Michael Stone - Aaron O'Connor - Jamie McGuinness - Joe Day - Dale Roberts - Craig Farrell - Jake Beecroft - Physio Simon Parsell

Front Row: James Reid - Neil Cousins - Nicky McNamara - Team Captain Jamie Stuart - Manager Justin Edinburgh - Lee Tomlin - Matt Pattison - Kurt Robinson - Mark Byrne

CLUB PERSONNEL

Chairman: Keith Cousins.

Company Secretary: Matt Wild.

Managing Director: Helen Thompson.

Additional Directors: Bob Scott, Steve Parker.

Secretary: Matt Wild

Telephone: (H) 01223 830 253

(M) 07813 019 090 (B) 01933 654 180

E-mail: club.secretary@rd-fc.co.uk

correspondence to Secretary at CLUB

Commercial Manager

Rachel Roberts

Tel: (M): 07912 480 055

E-mail: Rachel-roberts@rd-fc.co.uk

Press Officer: Matthew Banyard

Tel: (B): 01933 652 000 (M): 07891 173 846

Email: matthew.banyard@rd-fc.co.uk

Manager: Justin Edinburgh.

Assistant Manager: Michael Stone.

Youth Development Manager: Paul Driver.

Club therapist: Simon Parsell.

Local supporters of Rushden and Diamonds had been used to changing fortunes. From two struggling clubs playing as Rushden Town and Irthlingborough Diamonds, their amalgamation brought two small followings together but when a wonderful stadium emerged and money became available for the club to soar through the ranks to the top of non-league football and into the Football League. A small and bewildered band of supporters enjoyed their seasons of glamour but weren't really surprised when the dream died and their new club returned to settle down in the Conference.

Last season with Gary Hill, an experienced and successful non-league manager in charge, hopes were high. But by half way through the season Diamonds had lost to Evesham United in the F.A.Cup and although holding a comfortable place just outside the play off positions at Christmas early new year form collapsed and Justin Edinburgh was brought in to take over as manager.

Form did improve a little but never to the extent that promotion could be considered. The F.A.Trophy brought a success against Newport County and a loss to Torquay United but the luckiest break for the club was a fixture at Weymouth the week after all the Dorset club's senior players contracts had been cancelled. A freak 9-0 victory over a youth team was only followed by five more victories and the club stayed in eleventh place for the last two months of the campaign.

With sensible team building and a well structured pre-season, the manager has shown he can produce a winning squad so supporters will be hoping that the only way is up and the impressive Nene Park will again be a happy place.

RUSHDEN & DIAMONDS

BEST LGE ATT.: **3,406** v Kettering Town
LOWEST: **928** v Lewes

No.	Date	Comp	H/A	Opponents	Att:	Result	Goalscorers	Pos
1	Aug 9	BSP	A	Eastbourne Borough	1605	W 1 - 0	Woodhouse 26 (pen)	
2	12		H	Ebbsfleet United	1467	W 2 - 0	**Smith** 64 Phillips 77	8
3	17		H	Wrexham	1445	D 1 - 1	**Smith** 61	3
4	23		A	Kettering Town	2897	D 1 - 1	**Smith** 83	5
5	25		H	Histon	1613	L 1 - 2	Corcoran 64	
6	30		A	KIdderminster Harriers	1524	L 1 - 2	McDonald 11	15
7	Sept 2		A	Barrow	1663	D 1 - 1	Knight 27	
8	6		H	Crawley Town	1376	L 0 - 1		16
9	11		A	Lewes		W 4 - 0	Clare 54 Knight 67 73 Hope 69	15
10	20		H	Burton Albion	1448	W 2 - 1	Clare 45 Wolleaston 83	9
11	23		A	Wrexham	2805	W 3 - 0	Clare 11 Hope 32 83	6
12	29		H	Altrincham	1341	D 1 - 1	Knight 77	8
13	Oct 4		A	Oxford United	4645	L 1 - 2	Clare 57	11
14	7		H	Grays Athletic	1124	W 1 - 0	Kelly 24	7
15	12		H	Torquay United	1649	L 1 - 3	**Smith** 68	
16	18		A	York City	2313	L 0 - 2		12
17	**25**	**F.A.C. 4Q**	**A**	**Evesham United**	**609**	**L 0 - 2**		
18	Nov 1		A	Cambridge United	3547	D 0 - 0		12
19	**4**	**SS S3**	**H**	**Stevenage Borough**	**430**	**L 0 - 3**		
20	8		H	Weymouth	1002	W 1 - 0	Clare 54	10
21	15		H	Kiderminster Harriers	1391	L 0 - 1		10
22	22		H	Eastbourne United	1037	W 2 - 0	Tomlin 34 Rankine 56	10
23	29		A	Altrincham	924	W 4 - 0	Burgess 30 88 Tomlin 41 Osano 65	
24	Dec 6		H	Barrow	1120	D 1 - 1	Phillips 72	8
25	9		A	Woking	1119	D 1 - 1	Rankine 41	
26	**13**	**F.A.T 1R**	**A**	**Newport County**	**603**	**D 1 - 1**	**Rankine 56**	
27	**16**	**F.A.T R r**	**H**	**Newport County**	**421**	**D 1 - 1**	**Smith 90 (won 4-2 on pens)**	
28	20		H	Northwich Victoria	1134	W 2 - 1	**Smith** 67 Tomlin 70	8
29	26		A	Stevenage Borough	2012	L 1 - 3	Tomlin 77	8
30	Jan 1		H	Stevenage Borough	1853	D 1 - 1	**Smith** 90	8
31	**10**	**F.A.T 2nd Rd**	**A**	**Torquay United**	**1728**	**L 0 - 1**		
32	17		A	Ebbsfleet United	1121	L 0 - 1		11
33	23		H	Forest Green Rovers	1066	D 2 - 2	Tomlin 12 Corcoran 29	10
34	27		A	Mansfield Town	2028	D 0 - 0		
35	Feb 1		H	Cambridge United	2058	L 1 - 2	**Smith** 41	
36	9		A	Burton Albion	1291	L 0 - 3		12
37	21		A	Weymouth	967	W 9 - 0	Rankine 8 49 Tomlin 12 18 Hope 33 Wolleaston 59 Kelly 66 75 Robinson 88	
38	24		H	York City	1020	W 2 - 0	Burgess 58 Wolleaston 72	11
39	28		H	Mansfield Town	1774	L 0 - 1		11
40	Mar 7		A	Torquay United	2161	D 1 - 1	Tomlin 65	11
41	10		H	Lewes	928	W 2 - 1	Wolleaston 2 Rankine 51 (pen)	11
42	14		A	Crawley Town	777	D 0 - 0		
43	21		A	Salisbury City	924	D 1 - 1	Wolleaston 18	11
44	24		H	Oxford United	2085	L 1 - 3	Wolleaston 59	
45	28		A	Northwich Victoria	687	L 2 - 4	Rankine 61 (pen) Wolleaston 62	11
46	31		A	Grays Athletic	695	D 0 - 0		11
47	April 4		H	Salisbury City	1352	W 2 - 1	Hope 31 Cousins 42	11
48	11		H	Kettering Town	3406	W 1 - 0	**Smith** 82	11
49	13		A	Histon	1263	D 0 - 0		
50	18		A	Forest Green Rovers	1185	L 0 - 4		11
51	26		H	Woking	1676	W 3 - 1	Wolleaston 6 Rankine 35 Beecroft 50	11

Average Home Att: **1494 (1737)** **Goals** **63 58**

Best Position: 6th **Worst:** 16th

Goalscorers: Smith 9, Tomlin 8, Rankine 8, Wolleaston 8, Clare 5, Hope 5, Knight 4, Burgess 3, Kelly 3, Corcoran 2, Phillips 2, Beecroft 1, Cousins 1, McDonald 1, Osano 1, Robinson 1, Woodhouse 1.

MARRIOTT 1	BURTON 18	HOPE 5	OSANO 2	JELLEYMAN 3	WOODHOUSE 8	BURGESS 11	D MCDONALD 6	KELLY 23	TOMLIN 15	PHILLIPS 9	CORCORAN 24	WOLLEASTON 17	GULLIVER 4	MITCHELL 12	SMITH 25	BEECROFT 21	J ROBERTS 22	RANKINE 14	KNIGHT 7	MCGUINESS 20	CLARE 10	DAY 26	PANTHER 16	D ROBERTS 19	MOLONEY 16	A MCDONALD 29	HILLIARD 27	FORTUNE 12	BODEN 22	BOLASIE 32	BROWN 33	ROGET 16	COCHRANE 22	COUSINS 12	DOWNER 6	ROBINSON 8	COX 28	BROADBENT 9	ARTHUR 16	MCNAMARA 4	FORD 16	
X	X	X	X	X	X	X	X	X	X	X	S	S	S	U	U																											1
X	S	X	X	X	X	X	X	X	X	X	S	U	X		S	U																										2
X	X	X	X	X	X	X	U	U	X	X	X	X			S	S	U																									3
X	X	X	X	X	X	X	U	S	X	X	X	S			S		U	X																								4
X	X	X	X	X	X	X		S	X	X	S	X			S		U	U	X																							5
X	S	X	X	X		X	X			X		X	U		S	X	X	S	X	U																						6
X	S	X	X	X	X	X		U		X	X	X			S	S	X	U	X																							7
X	X	X	X		X	X		S		X	X	X	U		U	S	X	S	X																							8
X	X	X	X	X	X	X			X	U	S	X	S					S	X		X	U																				9
X	X	X	X			X		U	X	S	X	X	U			S		S	X		X		X																			10
X		X	X	S	X	X		U	X	S	X	X	X			U		S	X		X																					11
X		X	X	U	X	X		S	X	S	X	X	X					S	X		X	U																				12
	X	X	X	X	X	S		X	X	S	U	X	U					S	X		X			X																		13
	U	X	X		X	X		X	S	X	X	S	X		U				S		X		X	X																		14
		X	X	U	X	X		X	S	X	X	U	X		S				S		X		X	X																		15
		X	X	X	X	X		U	X	X	X	S	X		S	U			X		S			X																		16
U		**X**	**X**	**X**	**X**	**X**		**S**	**X**	**X**	**X**	**U**	**U**		**S**	**U**			**S**		**X**			**X**	**X**																	17
		X	X		X	X		X			X	X			X	S				U	X	U		X	X	U	U															18
			X		**S**	**X**		**X**		**S**	**X**	**X**			**X**	**X**				**S**	**X**	**U**		**X**	**X**	**X**	**U**															19
		X	X		X			X	S	S	S	X			U			X			X	U		X	X			X	X													20
		X	X		X	S		X	S	S	X	X						X			X	U		X	X			U	X													21
		X	X	X				S	X	X	X	X			S			X			U			X	X			U	S	X												22
		X	X	X		X		S	X		X	X			U			X			S			X				U	S	X	X											23
		X	X	X	U	X		S	X	S	X	X			S			X						X				U		X	X											24
U		X	X		X	X		S	X	X	X	X			S			X						X						X	U	U										25
U		**X**	**X**	**S**	**X**	**X**		**S**	**X**	**X**	**X**	**X**			**S**			**X**						**X**						**X**	**U**											26
U		**X**	**X**	**X**	**X**			**X**	**X**	**S**	**X**	**X**			**S**			**X**		**U**				**X**						**S**	**X**											27
U		X	X	S	X			X	X		X	X			X			X						X						S	S	U	X									28
U		X	X	X	X			X	X			X			X	S		X						X						S		X	U	S								29
U		X	X	U				S	X		X	S			S	X		X						X						X			X	X	X							30
		X	**X**					**X**	**X**		**X**	**X**			**S**			**X**		**U**		**U**		**X**			**S**			**X**			**X**			**X**	**U**					31
		X	X			X		X	X		S				S	X		X				U		X									U	S	X	X		X				32
		X	X			X		X	X		X	U			S			X		S		U		X									X	S		X		X				33
		X	X	U		X		X			X	X			S	X		X		S		U		X										X		X		U				34
		X	X					X	X		X	X			X	X				S		U		X			U							X		X	U	S				35
		X	X			X		X	X		X	X			X	S		S		U		U		X										S	X	X						36
		X	X			X		X	X		X	X			S	U		X		S		U		X										S	X	X						37
		X	X			X		X	X		X	X			S	S		S		U		U		X										X	X	X						38
		X	X			X		X	X		X	X			S	S		U				U		X										X	X	X			S			39
		X	X	S		X		S	X			X			S	X		X		U				X			U								X	X			X			40
		X	X	U		X		X	X			X			S	X		X		U				X			U								X	X			U			41
		X	X			X		X	X		S	X			S	X		X		U				X										S	X	X			U			42
		X	X	U		X		X	X		X	X			U	X		X		U				X										S		X			U			43
		X	X			X		X	X		X	X			S	X		X						X										S	S	X			U	U		44
		X				X		X	X		X	X			S	X		S		U				X			U							X	X	X				U		45
		X				X		X	X			X			S	X		X		U				X			U							X	X	X			U	S		46
		X				X		X	X			X			S	X		X		U				X			U							X	X	X				S	U	47
		X				X		X	X			X			S	X		X		U				X			S							X	X	X				S	U	48
		X				X		S	X		X	U			X			X		U				X			U							X	X	X				X	U	49
		X				X		X	S		X	X			X	S		S		U				X			U							X	X	X				X		50
		X				X		X	X		X	X			S	X		X		S		U		X										S	X	X				U		51
Total League Appearances																																										
12	8	46	39	14	20	38	3	28	36	13	31	36	6	0	7	15	3	24	10	0	10	0	3	34	4	0	0	1	2	5	2	1	3	11	16	20	0	2	1	2	0	**X**
0	3	0	0	3	0	2	0	11	5	7	7	5	2	0	27	10	0	11	2	5	2	0	0	0	0	0	1	0	2	2	1	0	0	9	1	0	0	1	1	3	0	**S**
4	1	0	0	6	1	0	2	5	0	1	1	4	4	1	6	4	3	3	0	14	1	14	0	0	0	1	9	4	0	0	1	2	2	0	0	0	1	1	5	3	3	**U**
Total Cup Appearances																																										
0	0	4	5	2	3	3	0	3	4	2	5	4	0	0	1	1	0	3	0	0	2	0	0	5	2	1	0	0	0	2	1	0	1	0	0	1	0	0	0	0	0	**X**
0	0	0	0	1	1	0	0	2	0	2	0	0	0	0	4	0	0	0	1	1	0	0	0	0	0	0	1	0	0	1	0	0	0	0	0	0	0	0	0	0	0	**S**
3	0	0	0	0	0	0	0	0	0	0	0	1	1	0	0	1	0	0	0	2	0	2	0	0	0	0	1	0	0	0	1	0	0	0	0	0	1	0	0	0	0	**U**

RUSHDEN & DIAMONDS

CURRENT SQUAD AS OF BEGINING OF 2009-10 SEASON

GOALKEEPERS		SQ NO.	HT	WT	D.O.B	AGE	P.O.B	CAREER	APPS	GOA
Joe	Day	13					Brighton	C.Palace (Sch), Rushden & D 1/07, Brackley T (L) 3/09	0	0
Dale	Roberts	1	6'03"	11 06	22/10/86	22	Horden	Middlesbrough (Scholar), Sunderland (Scholar), Notts Forest, Eastwood T (SL) 3/06, Alfreton (SL) 7/06, Rushden & D (3ML) 1/08, Rushden & D (3ML) 10/08 Perm 1/09	34	0
DEFENDERS										
Simon	Downer	6	5'11"	12 08	19/10/81	27	Romford	L.Orient Rel 5/04, Newcastle (Trial) 2/01, Aldershot (SL) 3/04 (03/04 8,0), Retired, Hornchurch 11/04 Rel c/s 05, Weymouth 7/05, Grays 1/07 Rel 10/08, Wivenhoe 10/08, Sutton U 11/08, Rushden & D 1/09	17	0
Jack	Higgins	22			30/7/91	18	Burnley	Crewe (Yth), Boston U (Yth), Rushden & D 7/07, Daventry T (WE) 2/09, Billericay (L) 3/09, Hemel Hempstead (3ML) 8/09		
Curtis	Osano	2	5'11"	11 04	8/3/87	22	Nakuru, Kenya	Reading Rel c/s 08, Aldershot T (3ML) 10/06, Woking (SL) 1/07, Rushden & D (SL) 7/07, Rushden & D 7/08	39	1
Kurt	Robinson	3	5'08"	11 00	21/10/89	19	Basildon	West Ham (Yth), Southend (Yth), Ipswich Rel 5/09, Northampton (6WL) 11/08, Rushden & D (SL) 1/09, Rushden & D 7/09	20	1
Jamie	Stuart	5	5'10"	11 00	15/10/76	32	Southwark	Charlton cc 12/97, Millwall 9/98 Rel c/s 01, Cambridge U (Trial) 7/01, Bury 10/01, Southend 6/03 Rel c/s 04, Hornchurch 7/04, Grays 11/04, Rushden & D 6/09		
MIDFIELDERS										
Jake	Beecroft	15			4/9/89	19		Rushden & D, Solihull Moors (6WL) 11/08	25	1
Mark	Byrne	20	5'08"	11 00	9/11/88	20	Dublin	Crumlin U, Notts Forest 7/07, Burton (SL) 3/09, Rushden & D (6ML) 7/09		
Michael	Corcoran	16	5'10"	11 04	28/12/87	21	Coalisland	Cardiff, Oxford U (3ML) 1/07, Oxford U 7/07 Rel 1/08, Rushden & D 1/08	38	2
Lewis	Hilliard	21			2/10/90	18	March	Rushden & D, Ware (WE) 2/09, Hemel Hempstead (WE) 3/09, Hemel Hempstead (3ML) 8/09	1	0
Jamie	McGuinness	17			4/5/90	19		Luton (Scholar) Rel c/s 08, Rushden & D 7/08	5	0
Nicky	McNamara	14			11/12/89	19		Hull Rel 1/09, Boston U (Trial), Spalding U 1/09, Rushden & D 3/09	5	0
Matt	Pattison	18			24/3/84	25	Surrey	Camberley, Farnborough 7/03, Woking 6/07 Rel 5/09, Rushden & D 6/09		
Max	Porter	4	5'11"	13 00	29/6/87	22	Hornchurch	Brighton (Yth), Gillingham (Yth), Southend (Sch), Cambridge U (6WL) 11/05 Perm 1/06, Bishops Stortford 6/06, Barnet Undisc 5/07 Rel c/s 09, Rushden & D 7/09		
James	Reid	11	5'10"	11 04	28/2/90	19	Nottingham	Notts Forest, Rushden & D (6ML) 7/09		
Robert	Wolleaston	8	5'11"	11 07	21/12/79	29	Perivale	Chelsea Rel c/s 03, Bristol R (L) 3/00, Portsmouth (SL) 3/01, Northampton (3ML) 7/01, Luton (Trial) 3/03, Bradford C 7/03, Wimbledon (Trial) 3/04, Oxford U 7/04 Rel 10/05, USA, Cambridge U 2/06, Rushden & D 6/08	41	8
FORWARDS										
Cliff	Akurang	25	6'02"	12 03	27/2/81	28	Ghana	Chelsea (Jun), Luton (Trainee), Chesham, Hitchin 8/00 Rel 12/01, Purfleet/Thurrock 12/01, Heybridge Swifts 2/05, Dag & Red (L) 11/05, Dag & Red 1/06, Thurrock (SL) 1/07, Histon 5/07, Barnet Undisc 1/08, Weymouth (SL) 3/09, Rushden & D (SL) 7/09		
Neil	Cousins	12			23/4/82	27	Essex	Burnham R, Maldon T c/s 01, Braintree 7/02, Heybridge 12/02, Billericay c/s 04, Heybridge 11/05, Rushden & D 12/08	20	1
Craig	Farrell	9	6'00"	12 11	5/12/82	26	Middlesbrough	Leeds, Carlisle (2ML) 10/02 (Undisc) 12/02 Rel 5/05, Exeter c/s 05 Rel 5/06, York C 6/06, Oxford U (SL) 1/09, Rushden & D P/E 6/09		
Aaron	O'Connor	7	5'10"	12 00	9/8/83	26	Nottingham	Ilkeston, Scunthorpe 12/02 Rel 2/03, Ilkeston 3/03, Nuneaton c/s 03, Ilkeston, Gresley R 7/04, Rushden & D (Trial) 6/06 Grays 1/07, Mansfield 8/08, Rushden & D 6/09		
Sam	Smith	19			20/5/90	19	Corby	Corby (Yth), Rushden & D 2/07	34	8
Lee	Tomlin	10	5'11"	10 09	12/1/89	20	Leicester	Leicester (Jun), Rushden & D 1/05, Liverpool (Trial) 4/06, Brackley (L) 10/07	41	8
Others										
Sean	Calcutt							Rushden & D, Ware (WE) 3/09		
George	Cox						Bedford	Rushden & D	0	0
Aynsley	McDonald						Earls Barton	Rushden & D	0	0

LOANEES		HT	WT	DOB	AGE	POB	From - To	APPS	GOA
(M)Emmanuel	Panther	5'11"	13 08	11/5/84	25	Glasgow	Exeter 9/08 -	3	0
(D)Brendan	Moloney	6'01"	11 12	18/1/89	20	Enfield	Notts Forest (2ML) 10/08 -	4	0
(D)Clayton	Fortune	6'03"	13 10	10/11/82	26	Forest Gate	Darlington 11/08 - Rel c/s 09, Weston-Super-Mare 7/09	1	0
(F)Luke	Boden	6'01"	12 00	26/11/88	20	Sheffield	Sheff Wed 11/08 -	4	0
(D)Joe	Wilcox	6'01"	11 05	18/4/89	20	Northampton	Scunthorpe 11/08 -		
(M)Yannick	Bolasie			24/5/89	20		Plymouth (2ML) 11/08 - Barnet (L) 1/09, Barnet (SL) 7/09	7	0
(F)Simon	Brown	5'10"	11 00	18/9/83	25	West Bromwich	Wrexham (5WL) 11/08 - York C (SL) 1/09	3	0
(F)Daniel	Broadbent	5'10"	12 00	2/3/90	19	Leeds	Huddersfield 1/09 - Gateshead (L) 2/09, Harrogate T (SL) 3/09, Rel 5/09	3	0
(M)Chris	Arthur			25/1/90	19		QPR 2/09 - Rel 6/09	2	0

DEPARTURES		HT	WT	DOB	AGE	POB	From - To	APPS	GOA
(G)Martyn	Margarson	6'03"	13 08	7/6/88	21		Yth - Boston U (L) 9/08 Perm 9/08, Radcliffe B (L) 2/09		
(D)Justyn	Roberts	6'00"	10 04	12/2/86	23	Lewisham	Weymouth 8/08 - Newport C (L) 9/08 Perm 9/08 Rel 10/08, Tooting & M Rel 5/09, Sutton U 7/09	3	0
(M)Scott	Mitchell	5'11"	12 00	2/9/85	23	Ely	Peterborough 6/08 - Kings Lynn (4ML) 9/08, Perm 10/08	0	0
(D)Sagi	Burton	6'02"	13 06	25/11/77	31	Birmingham	Barnet 7/08 - Rel 10/08	11	0
(D)Philip	Gulliver	6'02"	13 05	12/9/82	26	Bishop Auckland	Hereford 5/07 - Rel 10/08, Oxford C 11/08, Corby 11/08	8	0
(F)Dean	McDonald	5'07"	10 12	19/2/86	23	Lambeth	Inverness Caledonian 7/08 - Rel 11/08, Grays 11/08 Rel 1/09, Northwich 1/09 Rel 2/09, Tooting & M 3/09, Farnborough 5/09	3	1
(F)Leon	Knight	5'05"	09 06	16/9/82	26	Hackney	Wycombe 8/08 - Sacked 12/08, Thrasivoulos Athens (Gree) 1/09	12	4
(D)Leo	Roget	6'01"	12 02	1/8/77	32	Ilford	Braintree 11/08 - Rel 1/09	1	0
(M)Curtis	Woodhouse	5'08"	11 00	17/4/80	29	Driffield	ex Grimsby 11/06 - Mansfield 1/09, Harrogate T 6/09	20	1
(F)Lee	Phillips	5'10"	12 00	16/9/80	28	Penzance	Torquay Undisc 5/08 - Weymouth 1/09 Rel 2/09, Cambridge U 3/09	20	2
(G)Alan	Marriott	6'01"	12 05	3/9/78	30	Bedford	Lincoln C 7/08 - Mansfield 1/09	12	0
(M)Justin	Cochrane	5'11"	11 07	26/1/82	27	Hackney	Millwall 12/08 - Rel 1/09, Aldershot T 2/09 Rel 5/09, Hayes & Yeading c/s 09	3	0
(F)Daryl	Clare	5'09"	11 00	1/8/78	31	Jersey	Burton 5/08 - Mansfield (SL) 3/09, Mansfield 5/09	12	5
(M)Marcus	Kelly	5'07"	10 00	16/3/86	23	Kettering	Yth - Oxford U 5/09	39	3
(M)Andy	Burgess	6'02"	11 11	10/8/81	28	Bedford	Oxford U 8/07 - Luton 5/09	40	3
(D)Gareth	Jelleyman	5'10"	10 06	14/11/80	28	Holywell	Mansfield 7/08 - Rel 5/09, Barrow (SL) 3/09, AFC Telford 6/09	17	0
(D)Chris	Hope	6'01"	13 01	14/11/72	36	Sheffield	Gillingham 7/06 - Corby T 6/09	46	5
(F)Michael	Rankine	6'01"	14 12	15/1/85	24	Doncaster	Alfreton 7/06 - Bournemouth (L) 10/08, York C £10,000 + P/E 6/09	35	7
(D)Josh	Ford			28/6/90	19	Bristol	Mangotsfield 3/09 -	0	0

RUSHDEN & DIAMONDS

Founded: 1992

Nickname: Diamonds

Club Colours: White with blue sleeved shirts, blue shorts, white socks.

Change Colours: Yellow shirts, yellow shorts, yellow socks.

Club Sponsor: Haart Estate Agents.

Previous League: Football League

Ground Address: Nene Park, Irthlingborough, Northants NN9 5QF
Telephone: 01933 652 000
Facsimile: 01933 654 190
Mobile: 07813 019 090
E-mail: club.secretary@rd-fc.co.uk
Web address: www.thediamondsfc.com

Office Opening Hours: 9.00am-5.0pm
SIMPLE DIRECTIONS:
By Road: Nene Park is situated three quarters of a mile north of the A45/A6 junction.
By Rail: Nearest Railway stationis Wellingborough (six miles)

MATCH TICKETS:
Ticket office Telephone: 01933 652 936.

CAPACITY: 6,635

Clubhouse & Refreshments: Social facilities open all day every day with full restaurant facilities

Club Shop: Sells all types of memorabillia. Manager: Matthew Banyard.

PROGRAMME EDITOR
Gill Wignall
Tel: (B) 01933 652 000
gill.wignall@rdst.co.uk

CLUB STATISTICS

RECORDS

Attendance: 6,431 v Leeds United F.A.Cup 3rd Rd1998-99

Record Victory: 8-0 v Desborough T County Cup 94-95

Career Goalscorer: Darren Collins 153

Career Appearances: Gary Butterworth 290

Transfer Fee Paid: Undisclosed to Morecambe for Justin Jackson

Transfer Fee Received: Undisclosed from Doncaster Rovers for Justin Jackson.

SENIOR HONOURS

Football League Division Three Champions 2002-2003
Conference Champions 2000-2001
Conference Championship Shield 2000-2001
Southern League Premier Champions 1995-1996
Southern League Midland Division Champions 1993-1994
Northants Huillier Senior Cup 1993-94 & 1998-99

PREVIOUS

Names: Irthlingborough Diamonds and Rushden Town merged in 1992.

Leagues: Southern League1992-1996. Conference 1996-2001. Football League 2001-06.

SALISBURY CITY

Back Row (L-R): Toby Osman, Jamie Turley, Jonathan Davies, Robbie Matthews, Patrick Cox, James Bittner, Bradley Gray, Stuart Anderson, Dan Webb, Ben Osman, Luke Ruddick, Dan Spence.

Front row: Darrell Clarke, Matt Tubbs, Robbie Sinclair, Kev Bushby, Conrad Parrott, Nick Holmes, Tommy Widdrington, Micky Western, Sean Clohessy, Chris Flood, Ryan O'Hara.

CLUB PERSONNEL

Chairman: Neville Beal.

Secretary: Alec Hayter.

37 Lackford Avenue, Totton,

Southampton, Hants SO40 9BS

Telephone: (H): 02380 867 195

(B): 02380 867 195

(M): 07844 477 168

E-mail: alechayter@onetel.com

or alechayter@googlemail.com

Press Officer: See secretary.

Manager: Tommy Widdrington.

Assistant Manager: Barry Blankley.

Goalkeeping Coach: Ian Harris.

Physios: Conrad Parrott.

Constant financial worries and off field problems took the edge off the season for City supporters but, having lost at home to champions to be Burton Albion in the first game of the season, four victories took Salisbury to the top of The Blue Square Premier before the end of August - so was it going to be their year?

Sadly, a disastrous run of results from mid September to mid October took 'The Whites' down to eighteenth place and out of the F.A.Cup at the hands of Team Bath. Luckily for the club, reliable striker Charlie Griffin scored consistently throughout the campaign and finished with a magnificent total of twenty two out of a club total of fifty four with the next highest scorer totalling six!

An F.A.Trophy run could have lifted morale but a 2-1 victory over Woking was followed by a 0-3 defeat at Burton. With off field problems featured in the press it was a difficult time for all concerned and the directors all offered to resign at the end of the season to allow someone with more financial backing to take the club forward.

All credit to the management led by Nick Holmes for keeping his club out of the danger zone all season, a fine run of form in March ensured safety and although results weren't so impressive as the campaign closed, City scored in all nine of the last fixtures and their supporters stood by them with an average home league 'gate' of almost 1,200.

SALISBURY CITY

BEST LGE ATT.: **2,418** v Oxford United
LOWEST: **579** v Lewes

No.	Date	Comp	H/A	Opponents	Att:	Result	Goalscorers	Pos
1	Aug 9	BSP	H	Burton Albion	1122	L 0 - 1		
2	12		A	Forest Green Rovers	927	W 2 - 1	Clarke 18 47	
3	16		A	Lewes	564	W 4 - 1	Sandell 19 30 **Griffin** 87 90	7
4	23		H	Grays Athletic	987	W 1 - 1	Tubbs 55 (pen)	4
5	25		A	Torquay United	2001	W 1 - 0	**Griffin** 90	1
6	30		H	Wrexham	1532	L 1 - 4	Sandell 10	4
7	Sept 2		H	Weymouth	1382	W 1 - 0	Feeney 55	
8	6		A	Altrincham	1002	D 0 - 0		4
9	13		H	Barrow	1116	W 3 - 0	Fowler 44 Sandell 68 (pen) **Griffin** 83	2
10	20		A	York City	2280	D 1 - 1	Clohessy 72	3
11	23		A	Woking	1369	L 0 - 1		4
12	27		H	Mansfield Town	1494	L 2 - 3	Sandell 11 Feeney 61	7
13	Oct 4		A	Histon	961	L 0 - 2		10
14	7		H	Altrincham	950	L 1 - 3	**Griffin** 90	
15	11		H	Kettering Town	1191	L 1 - 2	**Griffin** 5	13
16	18		A	Stevenage Borough	1712	L 0 - 2		17
17	**25**	**F.A.C. 4Q**	**A**	**Team Bath**	**649**	**L 0 - 1**		
18	30		H	Crawley Town	884	W 2 - 0	Rayner 50 (og) Clohessy 75	14
19	**Nov 4**	**SS 3**	**A**	**Bath City**	**230**	**W 1 - 0**	**Matthews 7**	
20	15		A	Mansfield Town	1921	L 0 - 3		16
21	22		H	Northwich Victoria	999	D 1 - 1	Robinson 2	14
22	29		H	York City	986	D 1 - 1	**Griffin** 40	
23	**Dec 2**	**SS S4**	**H**	**Woking**	**297**	**L 0 - 3**		
24	6		A	Kidderminster Harriers	1325	L 2 - 3	**Griffin** 45 Duffon 65	17
25	9		H	Lewes	579	L 1 - 2	**Griffin** 55 (pen)	
26	**16**	**F.A.T. 1R**	**A**	**Woking**	**506**	**W 2 - 1**	**Fowler 43 Griffin 89**	
27	20		A	Cambridge United	3340	L 0 - 4		18
28	26		H	Oxford United	2418	W 2 - 1	**Griffin** 4 Ademeno 17	17
29	Jan 1		A	Oxford United	5312	L 0 - 2		17
30	**10**	**F.A.T. 2R**	**A**	**Burton Albion**	**1472**	**L 0 - 3**		
31	17		A	Kettering Town	1541	L 0 - 1		19
32	24		H	Stevenage Borough	1015	L 2 - 4	**Griffin** 70 83	21
33	27		H	Forest Green Rovers	771	D 2 - 2	**Griffin** 6 80	
34	31		A	Barrow	1613	D 0 - 0		
35	Feb 14		H	Histon	908	L 0 - 4		20
36	17		H	Woking	923	W 1 - 0	**Griffin** 4	
37	21		A	Crawley Town	964	W 3 - 0	Clarke 43 **Griffin** 48 Webb 90	16
38	28		A	Wrexham	3206	D 1 - 1	Ademeno 73	16
39	Mar 7		H	Kidderminster Harriers	1105	D 0 - 0		16
40	10		A	Weymouth	1005	W 4 - 0	Todd 31 Tubbs 55 **Griffin** 68 Clarke 72	16
41	14		A	Burton Albion	2274	W 2 - 1	**Griffin** 34 Ademeno 45	15
42	17		A	Eastbourne Borough	1047	D 0 - 0		
43	21		H	Rushden & Diamonds	924	D 1 - 1	Sangari 78	14
44	24		H	Ebbsfleet United	939	W 1 - 0	Clohessy 4	
45	28		H	Eastbourne Borough	1011	W 2 - 0	Duffon 70 Ademano 82	12
46	31		A	Northwich Victoria	532	D 1 - 1	**Griffin** 56	12
47	April 4		A	Rushden & Diamonds	1352	L 1 - 2	Sangare 86	13
48	11		A	Grays Athletic	761	L 1 - 3	Ademeno 70	14
49	13		H	Torquay United	2039	D 2 - 2	**Griffin** 45 Ademeno 81	
50	18		H	Cambridge United	1031	L 1 - 2	**Griffin** 32	16
51	26		A	Ebbsfleet United	1390	D 2 - 2	Sinclair 32 Tubbs 84	16

Average Home Att: **1144 (1690)** **Goals** **57 73**

Best Position: 1st **Worst:** 21st

Goalscorers: Griffin 22, Ademeno 6, Sandell 5, Clarke 4, Clohessy 3, Tubbs 3, Duffon 2, Feeney 2, Fowler 2, Sangari 2, Matthews 1, Robinson 1, Sinclair 1, Todd 1, Webb 1. Own Goals 1.

BITTNER 23	BASS 2	COOK 4	BARTLETT 8	BOND 5	TURK 7	ROBINSON 3	D CLARKE 15	FEENEY 19	SANDELL 11	TUBBS 10	MATTHEWS 9	HERRING 12	DUTTON 16	DAVIES 14	WIDDRINGTON 13	GRIFFIN 18	SANGARE 17	FOWLER 6	CLOHESSY 20	BEAVAN 22	SINCLAIR 33	MAHER 24	HARRIS	COX 21	RUDDICK 26	HILL 22	ADEMENO 27	WEBB 28	WINFIELD 18	SPENCE 31	MARTIN 29	TODD 4	BROUGH 5	PORTER 1	PEARCE 7	T OSMAN 24	B OSMAN 22	
X	X	X	X	X	X	X	X	X	X	X	S	S	U	U	U																							1
X	X	X	X	X	X		X	X	X	X	S	X		U	U	S	U																					2
X	X	X	X	X	X		X	X	X	X	S	X		U		S	U	S																				3
X	X	X	X	X	X	U	X	X	X	X	S	X				S	U	S																				4
X	U	S	X	X	S	X	X	X	X	U	X	X				S	X	X																				5
X	X	X	S	X	X	X	X	X	X	X	S		U			S	U	X																				6
X	X	X	X	X	X	X		X	X	X	U		U	U		S	U	X																				7
X	X	X	X		X		S	X	X	X	S	X	U	U		S	X	X																				8
X	X	X			X	X	S	X	X	U	U	X	S	S		X	X	X																				9
X	X	X			X		S	X	X	S	S	X	U	U		X	X	X	X																			10
X	X	X	U		X		X	X	X	X	S	X	S	U		S			X	X																		11
X	X	X	X		X		S	X	X	X	S	X		U	U	S			X	X																		12
X	X	X	X		X	X	S	S	X	X	U	X	U			S	X		X																			13
X	X	X	X		X	X		X	X	X	S	X	S	U		S			X	U																		14
X		X	U		X	X	X	X		X	U	S	X	S		X	X		X	S																		15
X	X	X	X		X	X	S	X	X	S	S	U		U		X			X		X																	16
X	**X**	**X**	**U**		**X**	**X**	**X**	**S**	**X**	**X**	**U**	**S**	**S**			**X**			**X**		**X**	**U**	**U**															**17**
X	X	X	X		S	S	U	S	X	X	U	X	X			X			X		X																	18
X	**X**	**X**	**X**		**X**			**X**	**X**		**X**		**X**	**S**		**S**			**X**		**X**	**U**		**U**	**U**													**19**
X	X	S	X		U	U	X					X	X	X		X	X		X		X	S			S													20
X	X	X			S	X	U	S				X	X	X		X			X		X	S			U	X												21
X	X			U		X	S					X	X			X	X		X		X	U			U	X	X	S										22
X			**X**	**X**		**U**	**X**					**U**		**X**		**X**	**X**		**S**		**X**	**X**		**S**	**S**	**S**	**X**											**23**
X	X		S	S		X	U					X	X			X	X		X		X				S	U	X	X										24
X	X		X	U		U	S					X	X			X	X		X		X				S	S	X	X										25
X	**X**		**S**	**X**			**X**					**X**				**S**	**X**	**X**	**X**		**X**	**U**		**U**	**X**	**U**	**X**											**26**
X	X		U	X								X	U			S		X	X		X	X		U	X	S	X	X										27
X	X		X	X		U	X	X				X	S	U		X		X							X	U	X	S										28
X	X			X			X	X		S		X	U			X	S	X	X						X	S	X	U										29
X	**X**		**X**				**U**	**X**		**X**		**X**	**S**			**X**	**X**	**X**	**U**					**U**	**X**			**S**	**X**									**30**
X	U		S				X	U		X	X	U	X			S	X	X	X						X			X	X									31
X	X		X	S		U		X		X		U	X			X		X	X									S	X	X	U							32
X	X		X	U			S	X		X		U	X			X		X	X						U			U	X	X								33
X	X		X				S	X		X		U	X		U	X		X	X						U			S	X	X								34
X	X		X				S			X			X			X	U	X	S						S		X	U		X		X	X					35
X	U						X			X		X	S			X	U	X	X						X		X	S		U		X	X					36
X	U						X			X		X	S			X	U	X	X						X		X	S		U		X	X					37
X	S						X			X			U			X	X	X	X		S				X		X	U				X	X	U				38
X	U						X			X		X	U			X	U	X	X		S				X		X	S				X	X					39
X	U						X			X		X	S			X	U	X	X		S				X		X	S				X	X					40
X	U						X					X	S			X	U	X	X		X				X		X	U			U	X	X					41
X	S						X					X	X			X	U	X	X					U	X		X	U			U	X	X					42
X	S						X					X	X	X	U	X	X		X					U	X			X			S		X	U				43
X	X						X					X	X	S	U	X			X					U	X			X			U		X	U	X			44
X	X						X					X	X	S		X			X					U	X		S	X			U		X	U	X			45
X	X						X			S		X	X		U	X			X					U	X		S	X			U		X		X			46
X	X						X			S		X	X			X	X	S	X					U	X		S	X			U		X					47
X	X						X			X		X	U			X	X	X	X						X		X	S			U				S	S		48
X	U						X			X		X	S			X	X	X	X					U	X		X	X			U					U		49
X							X			X		X	U			X		X	X		S			S	X		X				X				X	U	U	50
X	S						X			X		X				X		X	X		X			U	X			X			U				X	S	U	51
Total League Appearances																																						
46	32	17	19	10	15	12	28	20	16	27	2	35	18	3	0	32	16	25	35	2	10	1	0	0	20	2	17	11	4	4	1	8	13	0	5	0	0	**X**
0	4	2	3	2	3	1	11	3	0	5	11	2	9	4	0	13	1	3	1	1	4	2	0	1	4	3	3	9	0	0	1	0	0	0	1	2	0	**S**
0	8	0	3	3	1	5	3	1	0	2	5	5	12	11	7	0	12	0	0	1	0	1	0	9	4	2	0	6	0	2	10	0	0	4	0	2	2	**U**
Total Cup Appearances																																						
5	4	2	3	2	2	1	3	2	2	2	1	2	1	1	0	3	3	2	3	0	4	1	0	0	2	0	2	0	1	0	0	0	0	0	0	0	0	**X**
0	0	0	1	0	0	0	0	1	0	0	0	1	2	1	0	2	0	0	1	0	0	0	0	1	1	1	0	1	0	0	0	0	0	0	0	0	0	**S**
0	0	0	1	0	0	1	1	0	0	0	1	1	0	0	0	0	0	0	1	0	0	3	1	3	1	1	0	0	0	0	0	0	0	0	0	0	0	**U**

SALISBURY CITY

CURRENT SQUAD AS OF BEGINING OF 2009-10 SEASON

GOALKEEPERS		SQ NO.	HT	WT	D.O.B	AGE	P.O.B	CAREER	Apps	Gls
James	Bittner	1	6'02"	13 01	2/2/82	27	Devizes	Swindon (Trainee), Fulham 7/00, Salisbury 11/01, Bournemouth 3/02, Torquay (Trial) 7/02, Cheltenham (Trial) 7/02, Chippenham 8/02, Southend (Trial) 7/03, Exeter 8/03 Rel 4/05, Torquay 6/05 Rel 5/06, Woking 12/06 Rel 5/07, Salisbury 6/07, Chippenham (L) 11	46	0
DEFENDERS										
Sean	Clohessy	2	5'11"	12 07	12/12/86	22	Croydon	Arsenal (Scholar), Gillingham c/s 05 Rel c/s 09, Salisbury (SL) 9/08, Salisbury 7/09	36	3
Ryan	O'Hara	11	5'08"	08 13	24/7/89	20		Swindon (Yth), Dundee (Yth), Gretna Rel 3/08, Forest Green (Trial) 3/09, Swindon Supermarine 9/08, Salisbury 7/09		
Luke	Ruddick	15			3/3/90	19		Brentford, Ashford T (Middx), Walton Casuals 9/08, Hampton & R 10/08 Harrow 11/08, Salisbury 11/08	24	0
Daniel	Spence	12	5'10"	12 06	22/10/89	19		Reading, Woking (2ML) 10/08, Salisbury (L) 1/09, Salisbury 7/09	4	0
Jamie	Turley	5	6'01"	14 00	7/4/90	19		Wycombe Rel c/s 09, Hitchin (L) 2/08, Hendon (2ML) 11/08, Salisbury 7/09		
MIDFIELDERS										
Stuart	Anderson	4	6'0"	11 09	22/4/86	23	Banff	Southampton, Blackpool 12/04 Rel c/s 06, Ross C (SL) 1/06, Ross C c/s 06, Livingston 3/07, Peterhead c/s 07, Salisbury 7/09		
Darrell	Clarke	8	5'10"	10 11	16/12/77	31	Mansfield	Mansfield, Hartlepool Undisc 7/01 Rel c/s 07, Stockport (L) 1/05, Port Vale (L) 9/05, Rochdale (5ML) 7/06, Salisbury 7/07	39	4
Patrick	Cox	16			10/10/89	19		Reading, Salisbury 10/08, Bognor (2ML) 1/09	1	0
Chris	Flood	17						Andover (Yth), Winchester (Yth), Farnborough 6/07, Brentford, Thatcham (WE) 12/07, QPR 8/08 Rel 1/09, Salisbury 8/09		
Ben	Osman	18	5'10"	10 13	24/9/90	18		Exeter Rel c/s 09, Salisbury (L) 3/09, Salisbury 8/09	0	0
Rob	Sinclair	7			29/8/89	19	Bedford	Luton Rel 5/08, Salisbury (SL) 1/08, Salisbury 5/08	14	1
Tommy	Widdrington		5'10"	12 02	1/10/71	37	Newcastle	Southampton, Wigan (L) 9/91, Grimsby £300,000 7/96 Rel c/s 99, Port Vale (SL) 3/99, Port Vale 6/99 Rel c/s 01 Hartlepool 7/01 Rel c/s 03, Macclesfield 8/03 Rel 1/05, Port Vale 1/05, Salisbury (Pl/Coach) 2/05		
FORWARDS										
Bradley	Gray	14	5'11"	11 07	5/7/90	19	Swindon	L.Orient Rel 5/09, St Albans (WE) 1/08, Grays (WE) 10/08, St Albans (L) 11/08, AFC Hornchurch (L) 1/09, Dulwich Hamlet (L) 2/09, St Albans (L) 3/09, Salisbury 7/09		
Toby	Osman	19	5'10"	10 10	24/9/90	18		Exeter Rel c/s 09, Salisbury (L) 3/09, Salisbury 8/09	2	0
Matt	Tubbs	10			15/7/84	25	Bournemouth	AFC Bournemouth (Yth), Bolton Wanderers (Trainee), Dorchester, Salisbury 10/03, Bournemouth (6WL) 11/08	32	3
Danny	Webb	6	6'01"	11 08	2/7/83	26	Poole	Southampton (Scholar), Southend 12/00, Brighton (SL) 12/01, Brighton (L) 11/02, Hull C 12/02, Lincoln C (L) 3/03, Cambridge U (2ML) 12/03 Perm 2/04 Rel c/s 05, Weymouth 6/05, Yeovil 12/05, Rushden & D (L) 1/07, Woking (L) 3/07, Marsaxlokk (Mal) 7/07, AFC Wimbledon 7/07 Rel 5/08, Chelmsford 7/08 Rel 9/08, Havant & W 10/08, Salisbury 11/08	20	1

LOANEES		SN	HT	WT	DOB	AGE	POB	From - To	APPS	GOA
(D)George	Beavan		5'09"	12 02	12/1/90	19	Luton	Luton 9/08 - Grays (L) 1/09, Grays (L) 3/09	3	0
(M)Rory	Hill				28/3/90	19	Lewisham	Gillingham 11/08 - Bishops Stortford 3/09	5	0
(F)Charles	Ademeno		5'10"	11 13	12/12/88	20	Milton Keynes	Southend (5WL) 11/08 (SL) 2/09 - Rel 5/09, Crawley 5/09	20	6
(D)Dave	Winfield		6'03"	13 08	24/3/88	21	Aldershot	Aldershot 1/09 -	4	0
(M)Michael	Brough		6'00"	11 07	1/8/81	28	Nottingham	Torquay (SL) 2/09 -	13	0
(D)Chris	Todd		6'01"	12 01	22/8/81	28	Swansea	Torquay 2/09 -	8	1

DEPARTURES		SN	HT	WT	DOB	AGE	POB	From - To	APPS	GOA
Robbie	Matthews	9			2/3/82	27	Wiltshire	Bournemouth (Yth), Swindon (Yth), Salisbury, Bemerton Heath Harlequins 11/01, Eastleigh c/s 02, Southampton (Trial), Bristol R (Trial) 2/03, Salisbury 9/04, Havant & W (6WL) 11/08, Crawley (SL) 1/09, Kidderminster 8/09	13	0
(M)Andy	Sandell		5'11"	11 09	8/9/83	25	Calne	Bristol R (L) 8/07 Undisc 8/07 - Aldershot (6WL) 11/08 Undisc 1/09	16	5
(G)Ryan	Clarke		6'01"	12 00	30/4/82	27	Bristol	Bristol R 8/06 - Northwich (5WL) 11/08 Perm 1/09, Oxford U 5/09		
(M)Stephen	Maher		5'10"	11 01	3/3/88	21	Dublin	Yeovil 11/08 - Weymouth (Trial) 1/09, St Patricks 1/09	3	0
(D)Tim	Bond				29/11/84	24	Carshalton	Bournemouth 2/04 - Rel 1/09, Sutton U 2/09, Bognor 7/09	12	0
(M)Liam	Feeney				28/4/86	23		Hayes/Hayes & Yeading 6/07 - Southend (5WL) 11/08, Bournemouth Undisc 2/09	23	2
(D)Matt	Robinson		5'11"	11 04	23/12/74	34	Exeter	Forest Green 12/06 - AFC Totton 2/09	13	1
(D)Scott	Bartlett				30/5/79	30	Salisbury	Cirencester 2/00 - Rel 2/09, Weston-Super-Mare 2/09	22	0
(M)Wayne	Turk				21/1/81	28	Gloucestershire	Cirencester 7/00 - Newport C (SL) 11/08 Perm 4/09	18	0
(D)Aaron	Cook		6'01"	11 05	6/12/79	29	Caerphilly	Bashley 3/04 - Newport C (SL) 11/08 Perm 4/09	19	0
(F)Charlie	Griffin		6'00"	12 07	25/6/79	30	Bath	Newport C 8/08 - Stevenage 5/09	45	21
(D)Sam	Pearce				11/2/87	22	Portsmouth	Bognor Regis 3/09 - Havant & W 6/09	6	0
(D)Jon	Bass		6'00"	12 02	1/1/76	33	Weston-S-Mare	Bristol R 6/06 - Retired 6/09	36	0
(M)Ian	Herring		6'01"	11 12	14/2/84	25	Swindon	Chippenham 9/07- Northwich 7/09	37	0
(M)Michael	Fowler		5'11"	11 13	22/8/81	28	Cardiff	Gloucester 1/07 - Rel 7/09, Forest Green 7/09	28	1
(D)Djoumin	Sangare				16/12/83	25	Dunkerque	Stafford R 7/08 - York C 7/09	17	2
(M)Brian	Dutton		5'11"	12 00	12/4/85	24	Malton	Pickering T 8/08 - Harrogate T 7/09	27	2
(D)Neil	Martin							ex Hayes & Yeading 1/09 - Dorchester 8/09	2	0
(M)Jonathan	Davies							Yth - AFC Totton (SL) 1/09	7	0
(G)Grant	Porter							Yth -	0	0
	Harris								0	0

SALISBURY CITY

Founded: 1947

Nickname: The Whites.

Club Colours: White shirts, black shorts, white socks.

Change Colours: Orange shirts, black shorts, orange socks.

Club Sponsor: InExcess.

Previous League: Southern League

Ground Address:	Raymond McEnhill Stadium, Partridge Way, Old Sarum, Salisbury, Wilts SP4 6PU
Telephone:	01722 776 655
Facsimile:	01722 323 100
Mobile:	07884 477 168
E-mail:	info@salisburycity-fc.co.uk
Website:	www.salisburycity-fc.co.uk

SIMPLE DIRECTIONS:

By Road: The ground is on northern edge of the city and is well signposted off the A345 main Salisbury to Amesbury road.
Matchday car parking £2.

MATCH TICKETS: Adults £13. Concessions (senior citizens/students/unemployed) £9
16-21-year-olds £7. Children (under 16) £3.
Transfer to Stand £2.

Ticket office Telephone: 01722 326 454 (Club)

Capacity: 5,000 **Seats:** 500 **Covered:** 2,247

Clubhouse: On ground with hot and cold snacks.

Refreshments: Two tea huts plus public bar.

Club Shop: Open all week and matchdays.

PROGRAMME EDITOR
Paul Orsborn
Tel: (B) 01722 324 733
Email: info@sarumgraphics.co.uk

CLUB STATISTICS

RECORDS

Attendance: At present ground: 3,100 v Nottingham Forest, FA Cup 2nd Rnd 2006.

Victory: 11-1 v RAF Colerne (H) Western Lg Div 2 1948

Defeat: 0-7 v Minehead (A) Southern League 1975

Career Goalscorer: Royston Watts 180 (1959-1965)

Career Appearances: Barry Fitch 713 (1963-1975)

Transfer Fees: Paid: £15,000 for Craig Davis (Bashley)

Received: £20,000 Adrian Randall (Forest Green Rovers)

SENIOR HONOURS

Southern Champions 1994-5, 2005-06.

Western League Champions 1957-58, 60-61.

PREVIOUS

Names: Salisbury F.C.

Leagues: Western League 1947-68. Southern 1968-2004. Isthmian 2004-205.

STEVENAGE BOROUGH

no up-to-date image available

CLUB PERSONNEL

Chairman: Phillip Wallace.

Vice-Chairman: Michael Shortland.

Company Secretary: Phillip Wallace.

Chief Executive: Bob Makin.

Additional Directors: Paul Wallace, Marcus Taverner.

Secretary: Roger Austin
Telephone: (H): 01462 625 043
(B): 01438 218 072. (M): 07814 575 914.
E-mail: rogera@stevenageborofc.com
correspondence to Secretary at club.

Commercial Manager: Clive Abrey
Telephone: (B): 01438 218 083
(M): 07960 619 314
E-mail: clivea@stevenageborofc.com

Press Officer: Mark Venables
(M): 07841 645 331
Email: Marksvenables@hotmail.com

Manager: Graham Westley.

Assistant Manager: John Dreyer.

Club therapist: Paul Dando.

It's difficult to understand why Stevenage Borough haven't yet joined The Football League. The wonderful burst up the non-league pyramid and the Conference championship in 1995-96 without qualifying for promotion, has been followed by regular impressive competitive seasons at the top of the non-league world without making that final step up.

The return of Graham Westley saw a quick strengthening of the squad, a period of getting used to each other and a final third of the campaign, in which Borough were the 'form' team in the Blue Square Conference.

Earlier in the season an exciting F.A.Cup visit to Leicester CIty was an excellent experience but it was good to see a top club obviously benefiting from their F.A.Trophy run. Their path to Wembley produces some tough opposition but from the beginning of December the national knock out competition seemed to break up the pressure of the league chase for points and a play-off position.

A run of twenty-four unbeaten games including ten consecutive victories created a wonderful spirit in the club and no one enjoyed it more than the lively twin strike force of Steve Morison (32 goals) and Lee Boylan (14). The promotion run finished sadly after a great Cambridge United comeback in the play-offs, but the club received its reward with a very well deserved F.A.Trophy success against York City at Wembley.

STEVENAGE BOROUGH

BEST LGE ATT.: 3,700 v Oxford United
LOWEST: 1,242 v Forest Green Rovers

No.	Date	Comp	H/A	Opponents	Att:	Result	Goalscorers	Pos
1	Aug 9	BSP	A	Wrexham	4901	L 0 - 5		
2	12		H	Eastbourne Borough	1681	L 1 - 3	Drury 44	
3	16		H	Weymouth	1357	D 1 - 1	Willock 26	23
4	23		A	Ebbsfleet United	1420	L 0 - 4		23
5	25		H	Crawley Town	1492	D 1 - 1	Cole16	
6	30		A	Barrow	1764	W 3 - 1	Willock 30 Laird 45 Wilson 76	20
7	Sept 2		A	Kettering Town	1592	L 0 - 1		
8	6		H	Burton Albion	1717	W 4 - 1	Boylan 3 **MORISON** 3 (19 55 56)	18
9	13		H	Altrincham	1804	W 3 - 0	**Morison** 16 74 (pen) Cole M 36	18
10	20		A	Forest Green Rovers	751	W 3 - 0	Boylan 2 **Morison** 23 Willock 90	14
11	26		A	Grays Athletic	791	W 2 - 1	Cole 47 52	
12	28		H	York City	1917	D 3 - 3	Robinson 2 (og) **Morison** 18 56	12
13	Oct 4		A	Torquay United	2066	L 0 - 3		14
14	7		H	Mansfield Town	1517	W 3 - 2	**Morison** 45 (pen) Cole 64 Bostwick 80	
15	12		A	Eastbourne Borough	1618	L 1 - 2	Anaclet 66	12
16	18		H	Salisbury City	1712	W 2 - 0	Albrighton 56 **Morison** 86	
17	**25**	**F.A.C. 4Q**	**H**	**Horsham**	**1051**	**D 2 - 2**	**Cole 32 Laird 81**	
18	**29**	**F.A.C. 4Q r**	**A**	**Horsham**	**640**	**W 4 - 1**	**McMahon 73 Willock 75 90 Morison 89**	
19	Nov 1		A	Woking	1955	W 1 - 0	Vincenti 11	9
20	**4**	**SS 3**	**A**	**Rushden & Diamonds**	**430**	**W 3 - 0**	**Drury 84, Wilson 86, Thomas 88**	
21	**8**	**F.A.C. 1R**	**A**	**Leicester City**	**7586**	**L 0 - 3**		
22	15		H	Northwich Victoria	2536	D 1 - 1	Drury 64	9
23	18		H	Histon	1623	L 1 - 3	**Morison** 21	
24	22		A	Burton Albion	1944	L 0 - 2		12
25	29		H	Wrexham	1673	L 1 - 2	Willock 64	11
26	**Dec 2**	**SS S4**	**A**	**Ebbsfleet United**	**285**	**L 0 - 3**		
27	6		A	Lewes	486	W 2 - 0	**Morison** 74 (pen) Vincenti 90	11
28	9		H	Grays Athletic	1289	D 0 - 0		
29	**13**	**F.A.T. 1R**	**H**	**St Albans City**	**737**	**W 4 - 1**	**Drury 43 Morison 84 90 Boylan 87**	
30	20		A	Oxford United	4343	D 1 - 1	Bridges 27	10
31	26		H	Rushden & Diamonds	2012	W 3 - 1	**Morison** 41 59 Boylan 47	10
32	28		A	Cambridge United	3351	D 1 - 1	Cole 90 (pen)	
33	Jan 1		A	Rushden & Diamonds	1853	D 1 - 1	**Morison** 32	9
34	3		H	Lewes	1764	W 3 - 0	Boylan 33 **Morison** 36 87	8
35	**13**	**F.A.T. 2R**	**A**	**Farnborough**	**705**	**W 2 - 0**	**Roberts 17 Boylan 34**	
36	17		H	Barrow	2205	W 3 - 0	Bridges 39 **Morison** 50 53	7
37	24		A	Salisbury City	1015	W 4 - 2	COLE 3 (38 87 90) Drury 66	3
38	27		H	Kettering Town	1880	W 2 - 1	Murphy 49 Vincenti 83	
39	**31**	**F.A.T. 3R**	**H**	**Burton Albion**	**1296**	**W 4 - 0**	**Morison 31 59 Cole 51 Bridges 88**	
40	Feb 14		A	Weymouth	1226	W 3 - 0	Drury 43 **Morison** 86 Bostwick 88	3
41	**21**	**F.A.T. 4R**	**H**	**Forest Green Rovers**	**1348**	**W 4 - 0**	**Drury 23 Bridges 58 Roberts 69 Morison 72**	
42	24		H	Woking	1965	W 1 - 0	Boylan 59	
43	28		A	Altrincham	958	W 2 - 1	Drury 72 Roberts 90	3
44	Mar 3		H	Forest Green Rovers	1242	D 1 - 1	Cole 32 (pen)	
45	7		A	Northwich Victoria	801	W 1 - 0	Roberts 55	5
46	**14**	**F.A.T. SF1**	**H**	**Ebbsfleet United**	**2344**	**W 3 - 2**	**Morison 7 Boylan 32 Bridges 81**	
47	**21**	**F.A.T. SF2**	**A**	**Ebbsfleet United**	**3008**	**W 1 - 0**	**Vincenti 90**	
48	24		A	Histon	1133	D 0 - 0		
49	28		H	Oxford United	3700	D 1 - 1	Bridges 51	6
50	31		A	York City	1924	W 2 - 0	Boylan 48 **Morison** 67	5
51	April 4		A	Kidderminster Harriers	2115	L 2 - 4	Boylan 7 Cole 22	
52	7		H	Cambridge United	3408	W 2 - 1	Mendes 4 Boylan 31	
53	11		H	Ebbsfleet United	1913	W 1 - 0	Cole M 32	
54	13		A	Crawley Town	1161	W 2 - 0	Bostwick 40 Willock 88	5
55	18		H	Torquay United	2819	D 0 - 0		6
56	21		H	Kidderminster Harriers	2530	W 3 - 1	**Morison** 3 Boylan 47 64	
57	26		A	Mansfield Town	3634	L 1 - 2	Laird 85	
58	**30**	**Play Off SF1**	**H**	**Cambridge United**	**4446**	**W 3 - 1**	**Roberts 47 Morison 61 64**	
59	**May 4**	**Play Off SF 2**	**A**	**Cambridge United**	**6507**	**L 0 - 3**		
60	**9**	**F.A.T Final**	**N**	**York City**	**27102**	**W 2 - 0**	**Morison 69 Boylan 90**	

Average Home Att: 1989 (2132) **Goals 105 67**
Best Position: 3rd **Worst:** 23rd
Goalscorers: Morison 32, Boylan 14, Cole 14, Drury 8, Willock 7, Bridges 6, Roberts 5, Vincenti 4, Bostwick 3, Laird 3, Wilson 2, Albrighton 1, Anaclet 1, McMahon 1, Mendes 1, Murphy 1, Thomas 1. Own Goals 1.

BAYES 1	ALBRIGHTON 6	HENRY 25	ANACLET 4	MILLS 8	LAIRD 3	BOSTWICK 24	MORISON 20	DRURY 23	MCMAHON 13	COLE 21	BOYLAN 10	THOMAS 7	WILSON 2	JORDAN 31	OLIVER 5	CHRISTIE 9	WILLOCK 19	NURSE 32	ANDERSON 27	VINCENTI 30	JUNAID 33	DAY 16	UPSON 11	MARTIN 15	SMITH	MCDEVITT 26	BLACK 11	BURKE 22	CAZAUBON	GIBSON 35	BRINKMAN 17	BRADSHAW 28	ROBERTS 14	ST AIMIE 28	PARKES 33	BUCHANAN 14	BRIDGES 18	MURPHY 7	ASHTON 5	MENDES 11	MAAMRIA 9	
X	X	X	X	X	X	X	X	X	X	X	S	S	S	U	U																											1
X	X	X	X	X	X	X		X	S		X	X	U	U	S	X	S																									2
X	U	X	X	X	X	X		X	X		S	X	S	U	X	S	X																									3
X	X	X		X	X	X				X		X	X	U	X	X		S	S	U	U																					4
U	X	X	U	X	X	U	X			X		S	X		X	U	X			X		X																				5
U			X	X	X	X	X		X		S	S	X		X	U	X	S		X		X																				6
-	X		X	X	X	X		X		S	S	X	U	X		X	U		X		X	S																				7
-X	X	S		X	X	X		X	S	X	U	X	U	X					U		X		X																			8
-X	X	S		X	X	X		X	S	X	S	X	U	X					U		X		X																			9
-X	X	S		X	X	X			X	X	U	X		X		S			S		X		X	U																		10
U	X	X	S	S	X	X	X			X	X	S	X		X		U					X		X																		11
U	X	X	S		X	X	X			X		X	X				S			X		X	U	X		U																12
U	X	X	S	S	X	X	X			X			X		X		U		S	X		X		X																		13
U	U	X	S	X	X	X	X		X	X		U	X		X					U		X					X															14
U	U	X	X	X	X	X	X		X	X			S		X		S					X		X			S															15
U	X	S	X			X	X	X	X	S			X		X		S			U		X		X			X															16
U	X	U	X	U	S	X	X	X	X	X		S	X		X		S			U		X		X																		17
U	X	X	X	X	X	X	X	X	X			X			S		S			S		X		U		U																18
U	X	X	X	X	U	X	X		X	S		U	X		S		X			X		X																				19
X					X	X		X				X	X		X		X							X		X		X	S	U	U											20
U	X	X	X	X	U	X	X	X	X	S		U	X		S		S			X		X		U																		21
U	X	X	X	X	U		X	X	S	X	X		X		S					X		X					S															22
U	X	X		U	X	X	X		X	S	X		X		X		S					X		X			S															23
U		X		X	X	X	S	X		S	X	U			X		X			X		X					X					U										24
U		X		X	X	U		X		X	S	X			X		X			X		X					U						X	S								25
X	X				U	X					X	X	X		X					X		U		U			X							X	X	S	S					26
U		X		X	X		X	X		X	S		X		X		X			S		X								U			X	U								27
U	U	X		X	X		X	X		X	U		X		X		X			S		X											X		U							28
U	X			X	X	U	X	X		S	X		X				X		S	X		X					S						X									29
U	X	X			X	X	X	S		X	X		X		U		S			S		X											X				X					30
U	X	X		S	X	X	X	X		X	X				U		S		S			X											X				X					31
U	X	X	X	U	X	X		X		X					U		X		S	S		X											X				X					32
U	X	X		S	X	X	X	X		X	X				U		S		U			X											X				X					33
U	X	X			X	X	X	X		X	X						S		S	U		X											X				X	S				34
U	X	X			X	X	X	X		X	X				U		S		S			X											X				X					35
S	X	X			X	X	X	X		X	X				U		S		S			X											X				X	U				36
U	X	X		S	X	X	X	X		X			S		S					U		X											X				X	X				37
U		X	U	S	X	X	X	X		X			X				U			S		X											X				X	X				38
U		X		S	X	X	X	X		X	X		S				U			S		X											X				X	X				39
U	S	X			X	X	X	X		X	X		S				U			S		X											X				X	X				40
X	S	X			X	X	X	X		X	X		S				S		U	U													X				X	X				41
X	U	X			X	X	X	X		X	X		S				U			S													X				X	X	S			42
U	X			U	X	X	X	X		X	X		S				S			S		X											X				X		X			43
U	U	X		S	X	X	X	X		X			S						S	X		X											X				X		X			44
U		X		U	X	X	X	X		X	X		S				U			S		X											X				X		X			45
U	S			S	X	X	X	X		X	X		X				U			S		X											X				X	X				46
U	S			S	X	X	X	X		X	X		X				U			S		X											X				X	X				47
U	U			S	X	X	X			X	S		X				X			U		X											X				X	X	X			48
U		X		S	X	X	X			X	X		U							S		X											X				X	S	X	X		49
U	S	X		X	X	X	X			X	X						U			S		X											X					X	X	S		50
U	S	X		X	X	X	X			X	X						S			S		X											X					X	X	U		51
U	S		U	X	X		X			X	X		X				U			S		X		X									X						X	X		52
U	X		S	X	X		X			X			X				X			S		X		X		U													X	X	S	53
U	U	X		X	X	X	X			X	X		X				S			S		X											X						X	U		54
U	U	X		X	X	X	X	S		X	X		X				S					X											X					X		U		55
U	X	X			X	X	X	X		X	X		S				S			U		X											X					X		S		56
U	X	X		U	X	X	X	X		X	X		S				S					X											X					X		S		57
U		X		S	X	X	X	X			X		S				S			U		X											X					X	X	X		58
U		X		X	X	X	X	X			X		S				S			U		X											X					X	X	S		59
U	U	X	S	X		X	X	X			X		X				U			X		X											X					X			U	60
Total League Appearances																																										
5	25	40	9	21	43	39	40	23	11	36	25	5	24	0	18	2	12	0	0	10	0	41	0	11	0	0	3	0	0	0	0	0	25	0	0	0	15	10	10	3	0	X
1	4	1	8	9	0	0	1	2	2	6	7	6	11	0	4	1	17	2	7	16	0	0	1	0	0	0	3	0	0	0	0	0	0	1	0	0	0	2	1	3	1	S
36	9	0	3	5	2	2	0	0	0	0	1	5	2	7	6	2	8	1	1	9	1	0	1	0	1	2	1	0	0	1	0	1	0	1	1	0	0	1	0	3	0	U
Total Cup Appearances																																										
3	6	8	3	5	10	13	12	13	3	6	10	3	8	0	3	0	2	0	0	4	0	11	0	2	0	1	1	1	0	0	0	0	9	1	1	0	5	7	2	1	0	X
0	3	0	1	4	1	0	0	0	0	2	0	1	4	0	2	0	7	0	2	4	0	0	0	0	0	0	1	0	1	0	0	0	0	0	0	1	1	0	0	1	0	S
11	1	1	0	1	2	1	0	0	0	0	0	1	0	0	1	0	4	0	1	4	0	1	0	3	0	1	0	0	0	1	1	0	0	0	0	0	0	0	0	0	1	U

Also Played: ATKINS U(20). SWAINE U(20).

STEVENAGE BOROUGH

CURRENT SQUAD AS OF BEGINING OF 2009-10 SEASON

GOALKEEPERS		SQ NO.	HT	WT	D.O.B	AGE	P.O.B	CAREER	APPS	GOA
Ashley	Bayes	1	6'01"	13 05	19/4/72	37	Lincoln	Brentford Rel c/s 93, Torquay 8/93 Rel c/s 96, Exeter 7/96 Rel c/s 99, L.Orient 7/99 Rel c/s 02, Bohemians (Ire) c/s 02, Woking 3/03, Hornchurch 5/04, Grays 11/04 Rel 5/07, Crawley 6/07 Rel 5/08, Stevenage 5/08	6	0
Chris	Day	16	6'02"	13 07	28/7/75	34	Walthamstow	Tottenham, C.Palace £225,000 8/96, Watford P/E 7/97, Lincoln C (3ML) 12/00, QPR 7/01 Rel c/s 05, Aylesbury (2ML) 10/02, Preston (L) 2/05, Oldham 8/05, Millwall Undisc 7/06 Rel c/s 08, Stevenage 8/08	41	0
Jordan	Gibson							Stevenage	0	0

DEFENDERS		SQ NO.	HT	WT	D.O.B	AGE	P.O.B	CAREER	APPS	GOA
Mark	Albrighton	6	6'01"	12 07	6/3/76	33	Nuneaton	Nuneaton, Atherstone 8/95, Telford £15,000 10/99, Doncaster 5/02, Chester (2ML) 2/06, Boston U 5/06, Darlington (L) 11/06, Rushden & D (L) 1/07, Cambridge U 6/07, Stevenage 5/08	29	1
Jon	Ashton	5	6'02"	13 12	4/10/82	26	Nuneaton	Leicester, Notts County (L) 11/02, Notts County (Trial) 7/03, Oxford U (L) 8/03 (Perm) 9/03 Rel 5/06, Bristol C (Trial) 5/06, Rushden & D 6/06, Grays 5/07, Stevenage 1/09	11	0
Danny	Blanchett				12/3/88	21	Wembley	QPR (Trainee), Northwood (Yth), Hendon 12/04, Harrow 8/05, Cambridge C 3/06, Liverpool (Trial) 2/07, Peterborough Undisc 3/07, Port Vale (Trial) 7/09, Stevenage (L) 8/09		
Michael	Bostwick	24			17/5/88	21		Millwall, Crawley (SL) 3/06, Crawley (5ML) 8/06, Rushden & D 1/07 Rel c/s 07, Ebbsfleet 8/07, Stevenage 5/08	39	3
Ron	Henry	25	5'11"	11 10	2/1/84	25	Hemel Hempstead	Tottenham Rel 11/03, Southend (L) 3/03, Fisher 2/04, Dublin C, Stevenage 1/05	41	0
Scott	Laird	3	5'09"	11 08	15/5/88	21	Taunton	Plymouth, Tiverton (L) 3/07, Torquay (3ML) 9/07, Stevenage (L) 1/08 Perm 1/08	43	2
Mark	Roberts	14	6'01"	12 00	16/10/83	25	Northwich	Crewe, Southport (2ML) 11/05, Chester (L) 1/06, Southport (SL) 3/06, Halifax (5ML) 8/06, Northwich (L) 1/07 Perm 1/07, Accrington 7/07, Northwich (L) 3/08, Northwich 5/08, Stevenage (6WL) 11/08 £5,000 1/09	25	2
Lawrie	Wilson	2	5'11"	11 06	11/9/87	21	London	Charlton (Scholar), Colchester Rel c/s 07, Welling (L) 12/06, Stevenage 8/07	35	1

MIDFIELDERS		SQ NO.	HT	WT	D.O.B	AGE	P.O.B	CAREER	APPS	GOA
Jerome	Anderson				8/12/88	20		Oxford U, Stevenage 7/07, St Albans (L) 8/07, Brackley (L) 1/08, Welling (L) 10/08, Brackley (L) 8/09	7	0
Harry	Atkins							Stevenage	0	0
Joel	Byrom	13	6'00"	12 04	14/9/86	22	Oswaldtwistle	Blackburn Rel c/s 06, Accrington 8/06, Clitheroe 1/07, Southport (L) 8/07, Northwich 1/08, Stevenage £15,000 5/09		
Tyrone	Cazaubon							Stevenage	0	0
David	Bridges	18	6'00"	12 00	22/9/82	26	Huntingdon	Cambridge U, New England Rev (USA) (Trial) c/s 04, Chesterfield (Trial) 7/04, Northampton (Trial) 8/04, Latvia c/s 04, Braintree 1/05, Rushden & D 2/05, Histon 3/05, Cambridge U 8/05 Rel 5/07, Kettering 7/07, Stevenage 5/08	15	3
Mitchell	Cole	21	5'11"	11 05	6/10/85	23	London	West Ham, Grays 8/04, Southend £45,000 7/05, Northampton (2ML) 9/06, Stevenage Undisc 1/07	42	12
Andy	Drury	23	5'11"	12 08	28/11/83	25	Kent	Sittingbourne, Gravesend £1,700 7/03 Rel 5/06, Lewes 6/06 Rel 5/08, Stevenage 5/08	25	5
Stacy	Long	8	5'08"	10 00	11/1/85	24	Bromley	Charlton Rel 5/05, Luton (Trial) 3/05, Bristol C (Trial) 3/05, Notts County (Trial) 4/05, Notts County 8/05 Rel 5/06, Gravesend/Ebbsfleet 7/06 Rel 5/09, Stevenage 6/09		
Darren	Murphy	7	6'00"	11 10	28/7/85	24	Cork	Cobh Ramlers, Cork C 1/07, Stevenage 12/08	12	1
Eddie	Odhiambo (Was Anaclet)	4	5'09"	10 00	31/8/85	24	Arusha, Tanzania	Southampton Rel 5/06, Chester (L) 12/04, Tamworth (3ML) 11/05, Oxford U 7/06, Stevenage 7/08	17	1
Theo	Swaine							Stevenage	0	0
Peter	Vincenti	30	6'02"		7/7/86	23		St Peter (Jer), Millwall 8/07 Rel 12/07, Stevenage 1/08	26	3

FORWARDS										
Chris	Beardsley	20	6'00"	12 02	28/2/84	25	Derby	Mansfield Rel c/s 04, Worksop (L) 1/04, Doncaster 8/04, Kidderminster 12/04, Mansfield 8/05, Rushden & D (L) 1/07 Perm 1/07 Rel 5/07, York C 6/07, Kettering (L) 12/07 Perm 1/08 Rel 4/09, Kidderminster (L) 11/08, Stevenage 5/09		
Lee	Boylan	10	5'06"	11 06	2/9/78	30	Witham	West Ham Rel c/s 99, Kingstonian (L) 12/98, Trelleborgs (Swe) c/s 99, Exeter (2ML) 11/99, Kingstonian 2/00 Rel c/s 00, Southend (Trial), Hayes 10/00, Stevenage, Heybridge S, Canvey Island 8/01, Grays 7/06, Chelmsford (L) 2/07, Cambridge U 5/07, Stevenage Undisc 6/08	32	10
Charlie	Griffin	9	6'00"	12 07	25/6/79	30	Bath	Bristol R (Ass Sch), Melksham, Chippenham T 7/98, Swindon £10,000 1/99, Yeovil (L) 10/99, Woking (L) 10/00 £15,000 11/00, Havant (L) 11/01, Chippenham T (L) 2/02, Chippenham 9/02, Forest Green 5/04, Wycombe 5/05, Forest Green (5ML) 7/06, Newport C 2/07 Rel 6/08, Salisbury NC 8/08, Stevenage 5/09		
Dino	Maamria		6'00"	12 02	18/2/74	35	Burnley	Glentoran, Ayr, Doncaster, Southport 7/00, Leigh RMI 7/01, Stevenage 5-fig AL 2/03, Charleston Batt 5/03 (USA), Stevenage 9/03, Charleston Battery (L) c/s 04, Southport 7/06 Temp Man 1/07, Rushden & D 1/07, Southport (SL) 3/07, Northwich 8/07 Temp Man 9/07 Perm Man Rel 10/08, Hyde U 11/08, Stevenage Ass Man 11/08	1	0
Yemi	Odubade	11	5'07"	11 07	4/7/84	25	Lagos	Eastbourne T, Yeovil 7/04, Eastbourne B 2/05, Oxford U 1/06 Rel 4/09, Stevenage 5/09		

LOANEES		HT	WT	DOB	AGE	POB	From - To	APPS	GOA
(M)Edward	Upson	5'10"	11 07	21/11/89	19	Bury-St-Edmunds	Ipswich (3ML) 9/08 -	1	0
(D)Jordan	Parkes	6'00"	12 00	27/7/89	20	Watford	Watford 11/08 -	0	0
(M)Kieron	St Aimie	6'01"	13 00	4/5/89	20	Brent	Barnet 11/08 - Lewes (L) 1/09, Rel 2/09, Thurrock 3/09, Hitchin 3/09, Maidenhead 8/09	1	0
(F)Junior	Mendes	5'10"	11 04	15/9/76	32	Balham	Aldershot (SL) 3/09 - Rel c/s 09	6	1

DEPARTURES		HT	WT	DOB	AGE	POB	From - To	APPS	GOA
(F)Craig	Westcarr	5'11"	11 04	29/1/85	24	Nottingham	Kettering 5/08 - Kettering 8/08 Rel 4/09, Notts County 5/09		
(M)Chris	Nurse			7/5/84	25	Croydon	Tamworth 8/08 - Welling 9/08 Rel 10/08, Tamworth 1/09, Rochester Rhinos (USA) 3/09	2	0
(G)Steve	Smith			3/6/79	30		Oxford C 9/08 - Aylesbury, Maidenhead 11/08	0	0
(F)Dayo	Junaid						Tooting & Mitcham 8/08 - Rel	0	0
(F)Anthony	Thomas			30/8/82	27	London	Barnet 5/08 - Hemel Hempstead 12/08, Farnborough 6/09	11	0
(M)Tommy	Black	5'07"	11 10	26/11/79	29	Chigwell	Southend 10/08 - Rel 1/09, Barnet 1/09 Rel 2/09, Grays 3/09 Rel c/s 09, Grays 8/09	6	0
(M)Luke	Cole						Exeter (Yth) 6/08 - Rel 12/08, Taunton 12/08		
(G)James	Russell	6'00"		19/9/87	21	Welwyn	Chelsea 8/07 - Halesowen T (L) 8/08, Arlesey (SL) 11/08, Canvey Island 7/09		
(M)Daryl	McMahon	5'11"	12 02	10/10/83	25	Dublin	L.Orient 1/07 - Cambridge U 1/09	13	0
(M)Scott	Balderson					Australia	Yth - Bognor Regis (L) 8/08, Hitchin (2ML) 11/08, Australia 1/09		
(G)Michael	Jordan	6'02"	13 02	7/4/86	23	Enfield	Lewes 8/08 - Eastbourne B 1/09	0	0
(F)Iyseden	Christie	5'10"	12 02	14/11/76	32	Coventry	Kidderminster 7/08 - Rel 1/09, Kettering (4ML) 9/08, Torquay 2/09 Rel 5/09	3	0
(D)Luke	Oliver	6'07"	14 05	1/5/84	25	Hammersmith	Yeovil £15,000 1/06 - Wycombe Undisc 1/09	22	0
(F)Steve	Morison	6'02"	12 00	28/8/83	26	London	Bishops Stortford 5 fig 8/06 - Millwall £130,000 5/09	41	22
(M)John	Martin	5'05"	10 00	15/7/81	28	Bethnal Green	Grays 5/07 - Rel 5/09, Ebbsfleet (2ML) 2/09, Chelmsford 8/09	11	0
(F)Callum	Willock	6'01"	12 08	29/10/81	27	Waterloo	Port Vale 1/08 - Rel 5/09	29	5
(M)Gary	Mills	5'09"	11 06	20/5/81	28	Sheppey	Kettering 5/08 - Mansfield 6/09	30	0
(D)Liam	McDevitt						Yth -Rel 5/09, Dartford (L) 11/08, Hitchin (3ML) 12/08	0	0
(F)George	Brinkman						Yth - Rel 5/09, Arlesey T (L) 8/08, Ware (L) 12/08	0	0
(F)Elliott	Buchanan						Northwood 1/08 - Rel 5/09, Boreham Wood (L) 8/08, Concord R (L) 2/09		
(F)Zak	Burke						Yth - Rel 5/09, Bognor Regis (L) 8/08, Tooting & M (2ML) 11/08, Ware (L) 12/08, Hitchin 7/09	0	0
(D)Jack	Bradshaw						Yth - Rel 5/09, Maidenhead (L) 8/08, Ware (L) 2/09, Maidenhead (L) 3/09, Maidenhead 8/09	0	0

STEVENAGE BOROUGH

Formed: 1976 after the demise of former club Stevenage Athletic.

Nickname: Boro.

Club Colours: Red & white shirts, red shorts, red socks.

Change Colours: Blue shirts, blue shorts, blue socks..

Club Sponsor: Megaman.

Previous League: Isthmian League.

Ground Address: Stevenage Stadium, Broadhall Way, Stevenage, Herts SG2 8RH
Tel No: 01438 223 223
Fax: 01438 743 666
General email address: rogera@stevenageborofc.com
Official website: http://www.stevenageborofc.com

SIMPLE DIRECTIONS
By Road: Stevenage South exit off A1(M) - ground on right at second roundabout.Spectators are however advised to go straight on at this roundabout and park inthe Showground opposite the stadium. The stadium is one mile from Stevenage BRstation. Buses SB4 and SB5.

MATCH TICKETS
Ticket office Telephone: 01438 223223
Ticket Prices: West and South Stands - Adults £16/£15. Concessions £13/£12.
Children (U11) £8/£7.
North and East Stands - Adults £13/£12. Concessions £11/£10. Juniors (U16) £5.
Children (U11) £3/£2.
Access for visiting supporters is via the South Stand only.
Capacity: 7,107
Seats: 3,404
Covered: 3,703
Clubhouse: Tel.: 01438 218 079. Clubhouse at ground open Monday to Friday 7 - 11pm,
Saturday noon - 2.00 & 4.30 - 11pm, Sunday: All day from noon.
Club Shop: Mon - Sat 9-5.30. Broadhall Way, Stevenage. 01438 218061. Sells a complete range of club merchandise including a customising service. Mail Order, credit cards accepted.

No image available

MATCHDAY PROGRAMME
Clive Abrey
B: 01438 218 083 M: 07960 619 314
Email: clivea@stevenageborofc.com

CLUB STATISTICS

RECORDS

Attendance: 6,489 v Kidderminster H .Conf.25.01.97

Victory: 11-1 v British Timken Ath (H) UCL Div 1 1980-81

Defeat 0-7 v Southwick (h) Isthmian Div 1 1987-88

Career Goalscorer: Barry Hayles

Career Appearances: Martin Gittings

Transfer Fee Paid:

£20,000 to Hereford United for Richard Leadbetter 1999.

Transfer Fee Received:

£300,000 from Bristol Rovers for Barry Hayles 1999.

SENIOR HONOURS

FA Trophy 2006-07, 08-09.

GM Vauxhall Conference 1995-96.

Isthmian Premier Divison 1993-94.

Isthmian Division One 1991-92.

Herts Senior Cup R-up 1985-86, 93-94.

PREVIOUS LEAGUES

Chiltern Youth 76-79, South Combination ,Utd Co 80-84 and Isthmian League 1984-1994

Grounds: King George V Playing Field 1976-80

TAMWORTH

CLUB PERSONNEL

Chairman: Bob Andrews.

Vice Chairman: Stephen Lathbury.

Company Secertary: Brian Whitehouse.

Additional Directors: Steve Greaves, John Holcroft, Paul Keeton, Martin Newbold.

Secretary: Rod Hadley
Tel: (H): 01827 66786
(B): 01827 65798 Option 2
(M): 07811 267 304
Correspondence to: Club
Email: clubsec@thelambs.co.uk

Commercial Manager: Nick Lunn
(M): 07795 841106
Email: commercial@thelambs.co.uk

Press Officer: Dave Clayton
(H): 01827 706538 (M): 07967 756918
Email: davec.tfc@hotmail.co.uk.

Manager: Gary Mills.

Assistant Manager: Darron Gee.

Club therapist: Chris Leary.

A quiet start to the campaign gave Gary Mills' squad a chance to settle down in their best formation and after two months their supporters realised that a special season could be theirs to enjoy. A 4-1 victory at Workington took 'The Lambs ' to the top of the table in October and apart from a dip of form in March their consistency ensured that automatic promotion would be confirmed before the vital away fixture with AFC Telford United on the last day of the season.

At the end of a superb run of eight successive victories that had taken 'The Lambs' to the top, a 0-4 defeat at Barrow in the 4th Qualifying Round of the F.A.Cup was a shock and was followed by elimination from the F.A.Trophy, when Workington gained some revenge with a 1-0 victory at The Lamb Ground.

Gareth Sheldon enjoying his best ever season with 24 goals supported by Nick Wright (13) and Alex Rodwell (10) and only four defeats in the rest of season with one club, AFC Telford United, preventing The Lambs from scoring in their two fixtures, provided a consistency that proved too much for their rivals and top place was retained for the last month of the season.

Manager Mills and his helpers will be keen to hold on to Wright who was selected for England C and will hope that Sheldon can retain his goalscoring form but to consolidate back in the Premier division the squad will no doubt be strengthened.

TAMWORTH

BEST LGE ATT.: **1,410** v Hinckley United
LOWEST: **468** v Alfreton Town

No.	Date	Comp	H/A	Opponents	Att:	Result	Goalscorers	Pos
1	Aug 9	BSN	A	Droylsden	414	D 1 - 1	Wright 26	
2	12		H	Stalybridge Celtic	615	L 0 - 3		
3	16		H	Burscough	609	W 6 - 2	Rodman 7 66 **Sheldon** 25 Wright 46 73 Pritchard 50	8
4	23		A	Stafford Rangers	958	W 1 - 0	Lyttle 58	
5	25		H	Redditch United	708	D 1 - 1	**Sheldon** 20	
6	30		A	Fleetwood Town	1051	W 2 - 1	Wright 24 **Sheldon** 90	6
7	Sept 2		A	Alfreton Town	413	D 1 - 1	Foster 14	
8	6		H	Harrogate Town	533	W 3 - 1	**Sheldon** 9 Rodman 55 Wright 62	4
9	**9**	**SS N1**	**A**	**Kings Lynn**	**510**	**W 2 - 1**	**Sheridan 2 Pritchard 25**	
10	13		H	Gateshead	831	W 2 - 1	Wright 83 89 (pen)	3
11	20		A	Blyth Spartans	550	W 4 - 0	**Sheldon** 25 83 (pen) Wright 65 Lea 85	3
12	**27**	**F.A.C. 2Q**	**A**	**Worcester City**	**898**	**W 1 - 0**	**Wylde 65**	
13	Oct 4		H	Hyde United	859	W 2 - 0	**Sheldon** 42 Pritchard 47	2
14	**6**	**SS N2**	**A**	**Hinckley United**	**267**	**L 1 - 2**	**Pritchard 76**	
15	**11**	**F.A.C. 3Q**	**H**	**East Thurrock**	**608**	**W 3 - 1**	**Shaw 17 Pritchard 19 Sheldon 63**	
16	18		A	Workington	403	W 4 - 1	Wright 42 Pritchard 56 Rodman 59 **Sheldon** 67	1
17	21		A	King's Lynn	742	W 2 - 1	Smith 12 Rodman 33	
18	**25**	**F.A.C 4Q**	**H**	**Barrow**	**1012**	**L 0 - 4**		
19	Nov 1		H	Gainsborough Trinity	838	D 0 - 0		1
20	8		A	Stalybridge Celtic	611	D 2 - 2	Smith 31 Pritchard 68	1
21	15		A	Farsley Celtic	377	W 3 - 1	**Sheldon** 11 42 Rodman 52	1
22	**22**	**F.A.T. 3Q**	**H**	**Workington**	**433**	**L 0 - 1**		
23	Dec 6		H	Solihull Moors	621	W 1 - 0	**Sheldon** 66 (pen)	1
24	9		H	Alfreton Town	468	L 1 - 2	Shaw 38	
25	20		H	Droylsden	690	W 2 - 0	Rodman 7 Pritchard 76	1
26	26		A	Hinckley United	1366	W 3 - 1	McAughtrie 72 **Sheldon** 74 85	1
27	11		A	Gateshead	331	L 1 - 5	**Sheldon** 64	
28	Jan 17		H	Hucknall Town	1132	D 1 - 1	**Sheldon** 34	1
29	24		A	Hyde United	541	W 2 - 1	Birley 40 Rodman 87 (pen)	1
30	27		H	King's Lynn	617	W 2 - 0	**Sheldon** 9 Nicholson 90	
31	Feb 7		H	AFC Telford United	1352	L 0 - 1		1
32	14		A	Vauxhal Motors	254	D 2 - 2	Rodman 38 McAughtrie 80	
33	21		H	Workington	707	W 1 - 0	**Sheldon** 75	2
34	24		A	Gainsborough Trinity	321	W 1 - 0	Pritchard 71	
35	28		A	Solihull Moors	546	D 1 - 1	Birley 27	
36	Mar 3		H	Southport	703	D 1 - 1	Sheridan 34	2
37	7		H	Farsley Celtic	723	W 2 - 1	Rodman 28 **Sheldon** 55 (pen)	
38	14		H	Blyth Spartans	671	D 1 - 1	**Sheldon** 66	
39	21		A	Hucknall Town	356	W 3 - 2	Pritchard 24 **Sheldon** 45 64	2
40	24		A	Burscough	309	W 1 - 0	**Sheldon** 10	
41	28		H	Fleetwood Town	784	W 2 - 1	Blackwood 6 **Sheldon** 9	2
42	31		A	Southport	1353	W 1 - 0	Wright 34	
43	April 4		A	Harrogate Town	531	D 2 - 2	Wright 44 Wylde 63	1
44	11		H	Stafford Rangers	1214	L 1 - 2	Wylde 70	1
45	13		A	Redditch United	615	D 1 - 1	Tait 58	
46	18		H	Vauxhall Motors	1012	W 2 - 0	Lyttle 27 Wright 36	1
47	21		H	Hinckley United	1410	W 1 - 0	Wright 55	CH
48	25		A	AFC Telford United	2423	D 0 - 0		1

Average Home Att: **814 (910)** **Goals** **77 50**

Best Position: 1st **Worst:** 8th

Goalscorers: Sheldon 24, Wright 13, Pritchard 10, Rodman 10, Wylde 3, Birley 2, Lyttle 2, McAughtrie 2, Sheridan 2, Smith 2, Blackwood 1, Foster 1, Lea 1, Nicholson 1, Shaw 2, Tait 1.

CH - Became Champions.

No.	PUDDY	SMITH	MCAUGHTRIE	LANGDON	FOSTER	WRIGHT	WYLDE	HILDRETH	RODMAN	PRITCHARD	SHELDON	SHERIDAN	LYTTLE	LEA	WARBURTON	LAW	BURGESS	JONES	BEVAN	SHAW	MURPHY	BIRLEY	WHATSIZE	MELBOURNE	ALCOCK	MORRISON	NURSE	REID	NICHOLSON	RAWLE	REDFEARN	BLACKWOOD	DUDLEY	RICKETTS	TAIT	MILLS
	X	X	X	X	X	X	X	X	X	X	X	S	U	U	U	U																				
1	X	X	X	X	X	X	X	X	X	X	X	S	S	U	U	U																				
2	X		X	X	X	X	X	X	X	X	X	U	X	S	S	U	S																			
3	X	X	X	X	X	X	X		X	X	X	S	X	S	U	U	U																			
4	X	X	X	X	X	X	X		X	X	X	S	X	U	U	U	U																			
5	X	X	X	X	X	X	X	S	X	X	X	S	X	S	U	U																				
6	X	X	X	X	X	X	X	U	X	X	X	U	X	U	U	U																				
7	X	X	X	X	X	X	X	U	X	X	X	S	X	S	U	U																				
8	**X**	**S**	**X**	**S**		**U**	**X**	**X**	**U**	**X**	**S**	**X**		**X**	**X**	**X**	**X**	**X**																		
9	X	X	X	X	X	X	X	S	X	X	X	S	X	S	U	U																				
10	X	X		X	X	X	X	X	X	X	X	S	X	S	U	S	U																			
11		**X**	**U**	**X**	**X**	**X**	**X**	**X**	**X**	**X**	**X**	**S**	**X**	**S**	**U**	**U**	**U**	**U**	**X**																	
12		X		X	X	X	X	X	X	X	X	S	X	S	U	U	U		X																	
13	**X**	**U**	**X**	**X**		**X**	**U**	**X**	**S**	**S**	**S**	**X**		**X**	**X**	**X**	**X**	**X**																		
14		**X**	**U**	**X**	**X**	**X**	**X**		**X**	**X**	**X**	**S**	**X**	**U**		**U**	**U**	**U**	**X**	**X**	**S**															
15		X		X	X	X	X		X	X	X	S	X	S		U	U		X	X		S														
16		X	U	X	X	X	X		X	X	X	S	X	U			U		X	X		S														
17		**X**	**S**	**X**	**X**	**X**	**X**		**X**	**X**	**X**	**S**	**X**	**U**		**U**	**U**		**X**	**X**	**U**	**S**														
18		X		X	X	X	X		X	X	X	S	X	S		U	U		X	X		S														
19	X	X		X	X	X	X		X	X	X	S	X	U		U	S			X		U														
20		X	U	X	X	X	X		X	X	X	S		U		U	X		X	X		S														
21		**X**	**S**	**X**	**X**	**X**	**X**		**X**	**X**	**X**	**S**		**U**		**U**	**X**		**X**	**X**		**S**														
22		X	X		X	X	X		X	X	X	U	X	S		U	S			X		S	X													
23		X	X		X	S	X		X	X	X	S		U		U	S		X	X		X		X												
24		X	S		X	X	X		X	X	X	U		S		X	X			X		U		U	X											
25			X		X	X	X		X	X	X	U	U			X	X			X		S		U	X	S										
26		X	S		X	X	X		X	X	X	S	X	U		X				X		U			X		S									
27			X		X		X		X	X	X	X	X	U		U	U			X		S			X		U	X								
28		X	U	X	X		X		X	X	X	S	X				U			X		X			X	U		S								
29		X	X	X	X				X	X	X	S	X			U	U			X		X			X			U	S							
30		X	X	X	X	S	S		X	X		S	X				U			X		U			X				X	X						
31		X	S	X	X		X		X	X	X	U	X							X		S			X			S	X	U						
32		X	X		X	X	X			S	X	S	X	U			U			X		X			X			X	U							
33			X		X	X	X		X	X	X	S	X	U			U			X		U			X			X	U							
34		U	X			X	X		X	X	X	S	X	U			U			X		X			X			X	U							
35		X	X		X		X		X	X	X	X	X	U			U			X		S			X		U		S							
36		X	X		X		X		X		X	X	X	U			U			X		X			X		U		S		U					
37		X	X	U	X	S	X			X	X	X	X	U			U			X		X			X				S							
38		X	X		X	X	X		U	X	X	X	X	U			U			S					X				U			X				
39		X	X		X	X	X			X	X	X	X	U			U			S		S			X				U			X				
40		X			X	X	X			X	X	X	X							S		U			X				U			X	X	S	U	
41		X			X	X	X			X	X	X	X							U		U			X				U			X	X	S	U	
42		X			X	X	X			X	X	X	X							U		U			X				U			X	X	S	U	
43		X			X	X	X		S	X	X	X	X							U					X				S			X	X	S	U	
44		X	U		X	X	X		S	U	X	U	X							X					X				S			X	X		X	
45		X	U		X	X	X		X	U	X	S	X												X				S			X	X	S	X	
46		X	U		X	X	X		X	X	X	S	X												X				U			U	X	S	X	
47		X	U		X	U	X		X		S		X							S					X				X			X	X	X	X	S
48																																				
49																																				
50																																				
51																																				
52																																				
53																																				

Total League Appearances

	PUDDY	SMITH	MCAUGHTRIE	LANGDON	FOSTER	WRIGHT	WYLDE	HILDRETH	RODMAN	PRITCHARD	SHELDON	SHERIDAN	LYTTLE	LEA	WARBURTON	LAW	BURGESS	JONES	BEVAN	SHAW	MURPHY	BIRLEY	WHATSIZE	MELBOURNE	ALCOCK	MORRISON	NURSE	REID	NICHOLSON	RAWLE	REDFEARN	BLACKWOOD	DUDLEY	RICKETTS	TAIT	MILLS
X	11	37	23	20	41	32	40	5	33	37	40	10	36	0	0	3	3	0	6	22	0	7	1	1	24	0	0	4	3	1	0	9	8	1	4	0
S	0	0	3	0	0	3	1	2	2	1	1	24	1	11	1	1	4	0	0	4	0	10	0	0	0	1	1	2	7	0	0	0	0	6	0	1
U	0	1	7	1	0	1	0	2	1	2	0	7	2	18	10	18	19	0	0	3	0	8	0	2	0	1	3	1	9	1	1	1	0	0	4	0

Total Cup Appearances

	PUDDY	SMITH	MCAUGHTRIE	LANGDON	FOSTER	WRIGHT	WYLDE	HILDRETH	RODMAN	PRITCHARD	SHELDON	SHERIDAN	LYTTLE	LEA	WARBURTON	LAW	BURGESS	JONES	BEVAN	SHAW	MURPHY	BIRLEY	WHATSIZE	MELBOURNE	ALCOCK	MORRISON	NURSE	REID	NICHOLSON	RAWLE	REDFEARN	BLACKWOOD	DUDLEY	RICKETTS	TAIT	MILLS
X	2	4	2	5	4	5	5	3	4	5	4	2	3	2	2	2	3	2	4	3	0	0	0	0	0	0	0	0	0	0	0	0	0	0	0	0
S	0	1	2	1	0	0	0	0	1	1	2	4	0	1	0	0	0	0	0	0	1	2	0	0	0	0	0	0	0	0	0	0	0	0	0	0
U	0	1	2	0	0	1	1	0	1	0	0	0	0	3	1	4	3	2	0	0	1	0	0	0	0	0	0	0	0	0	0	0	0	0	0	0

TAMWORTH

CURRANT SQUAD AS OF BEGINING OF 2008-09 SEASON

GOALKEEPERS		SQ NO.	HT	WT	D.O.B	AGE	P.O.B	CAREER	APPS	GOA
Danny	Alcock	1	5'11"	11 03	15/2/84	25	Salford	Stoke, Barnsley 10/03 Rel c/s 04, Accrington 8/04 Rel 5/06, Stafford R 8/06, Tamworth 12/08	24	0
Dale	Belford	19	5'10"	13 01	11/7/67	42	Tamworth	Aston Villa Rel c/s 86, Sutton Coldfield, Notts County 3/87 Rel c/s 88, VS Rugby, Nuneaton, Tamworth, Sutton Coldfield, Nuneaton, Tamworth, Hinckley T 1/96, Sutton Coldfield 6/97, Hinckley U, Atherstone, Sutton Coldfield 1/00, Atherstone 7/00, Gresley 9/0		
Elliot	Jones							Tamworth		
DEFENDERS										
Michael	Briscoe	16	5'11"	12 00	4/7/83	26	Northampton	Harpole, Coventry 4/03 Rel c/s 04, Macclesfield 7/04 Rel 5/06, Burton (SL) 3/05, Kettering (Trial) c/s 06, Hucknall 9/06, Tamworth (L) 2/07, Tamworth 5/07, Halesowen T 8/08, Redditch 2/09, Tamworth 6/09		
Gavin	Hurren	8	5'08"	13 07	22/10/85	23	Birmingham	N.Forest Rel c/s 05, Kidderminster 7/05 Rel 4/08, Bromsgrove (L) 1/06, Mansfield 7/08 Rel 1/09, Kings Lynn 1/09, Crawley 2/09 Rel 5/09, Tamworth 6/09		
Dominic	Langdon	17	6'02"	11 00	14/9/88	20	Kettering	Rushden & D, Tamworth 7/07	20	0
Des	Lyttle	15	5'09"	12 13	24/9/71	37	Wolverhampton	Leicester, Worcester 8/91, Swansea £12,500 7/92, Notts Forest £375,000 7/93 Rel c/s 99, Port Vale (6WL) 11/98, Watford 7/99, WBA (SL) 3/00, WBA 6/00 Rel c/s 03, Stourport 10/03, Northampton 11/03 Rel c/s 04, Boston U (Trial) 7/04, Forest Green 9/04 Rel 4/	37	2
Craig	Reid							Tamworth	6	0
Chris	Smith	4	5'11"	11 06	30/6/81	28	Derby	Leeds (Yth), Reading Rel c/s 01, Hayes (L) 12/99, York (Trial) 3/01, Kidderminster (Trial) 4/01, York C 5/01 Rel c/s 04, Stafford R 8/04 Rel c/s 05, Worcester 7/05, Tamworth 5/08	37	2
Richard	Tait	2	5'11"		2/12/89	19	Galashiels	Curzon Ashton, Notts Forest 12/07 Rel 5/09, Tamworth (L) 3/09 Tamworth 5/09	4	1
Michael	Wylde	5	6'02"	13 02	6/1/87	22	Birmingham	Cheltenham Rel c/s 08, Cirencester (WE) 12/05, Kidderminster (SL) 3/08, Tamworth 7/08	41	2
MIDFIELDERS										
Michael	Blackwood	3	5'10"	11 04	30/9/79	29	Birmingham	Aston Villa Rel c/s 00, Chester (2ML) 9/99, Wrexham 6/00 Rel c/s 02, Worcester 8/02, Stevenage 9/02, Halesowen 3/03, Telford 8/03, Lincoln C 7/04 Rel c/s 05, Kidderminster 7/05 Rel c/s 08, Oxford U (SL) 1/08, Mansfield 7/08 Rel 5/09, Tamworth (SL) 3/09, Tamworth 5/09	9	1
Anthony	Bruce	20	5'10"	11 00	12/2/90	19	Birmingham	West Brom (Scholar) Rel 3/09, Mansfield (Trial) 3/08, Bridgnorth 3/09, Tamworth 8/09		
Seb	Lake-Gaskin		5'09"	12 01	24/2/91	18		West Brom (Scholar) Rel c/s 09, Tamworth 8/09		
Neil	Mackenzie	6	6'02"	12 05	15/4/76	33	Birmingham	West Brom (Trainee), Stoke 11/95, Cambridge U (L) 3/99, Cambridge U £45,000 10/99 Rel 11/00, Kidderminster 11/00, Blackpool 7/01, Mansfield 8/02, Macclesfield (3ML) 11/04 Undisc 2/05, Scunthorpe (5WL) 11/05 Perm 1/06 Rel c/s 07, Hereford (L) 10/06, Notts County 7/07 Rel 1/09, Kidderminster (L) 9/08, Port Vale (L) 11/08 Burton (Trial) 1/09, Mansfield 1/09 Rel 4/09, Tamworth 6/09		
Gary	Mills	18	5'11"	11 09	11/11/61	48	Northampton	Notts Forest cc 3/82, Seattle S (USA) 3/82, Derby Undisc 10/82, Seattle S (USA) 3/83, Notts Forest Undisc 7/83, Notts County Undisc 8/87, Leicester Undisc 3/89, Notts County £50,000 9/94 Rel c/s 96, Grantham (Pl/Man) c/s 96, Gresley R 7/98, Kings Lynn (P/Man) 11/98 Boston U 12/00, Tamworth (Pl/Man) 1/01, Coventry (Coach) 5/02, Notts County (Man) 1/04 left 11/04, Glapwell 4/05, Alfreton (Pl/Man) 5/05, Tamworth (Pl/Man) 1/07	1	0
Bradley	Pritchard	11			19/12/85	23	Zimbabwe	C.Palace, Carshalton 12/04, Nuneaton B, Tamworth 6/08	38	7
Tom	Shaw	14	6'00"	12 00	1/12/86	22	Nottingham	Notts Forest (Jun), Rushden & D (7/04) Rel 7/08, Mansfield 8/08 Rel 10/08, Tamworth 10/08	26	1
Jake	Sheridan	12	5'09"	11 06	8/7/86	23	Nottingham	Notts County (Yth), Dunkirk, Notts County 8/05 Rel c/s 07, Tamworth 7/07	34	1
Dale	Warburton							Tamworth	1	0

FORWARDS

Trevor	Benjamin		6'02"	13 07	8/2/79	30	Kettering	Cambridge U, Leicester £1 million 7/00, C,Palace (L) 12/01, Norwich (L) 2/02, West Brom (L) 3/02, Gillingham (L) 9/03, Rushden & D (2ML) 11/03, Brighton (2ML) 1/04, Northampton (L) 12/04 Perm 1/05, Coventry Undisc 2/05 Rel c/s 05, Peterborough 7/05, Watford (L) 9/05, Swindon (SL) 1/06, Boston U (L) 2/07, Walsall (SL) 3/07, Hereford 8/07 Rel c/s 08, Chester (Trial) 7/08, Gainsborough 8/08 Rel 8/08, Stevenage (Trial) 9/08, Gillingham (Trial) 9/08, Northwich 10/08 (08/09 2,0) Rel 10/08, Hednesford 11/08, Wellingborough 12/08, Kidsgrove 2/09, Rushden & D (Trial) 7/09, Tamworth 8/09		
Stuart	Nicholson	9	5'10"	11 07	3/2/87	22	Newcastle	West Brom Rel c/s 08, Bristol R (2ML) 11/06, Bristol R (3ML) 1/07, Shrewsbury (4ML) 8/07, Wrexham (3ML) 1/08, Newcastle Blue Star 8/08, Tamworth 1/09	10	1
Alex	Rodman	10	6'00"		15/12/87	21	Sutton Coldfield	Aston Villa (Trainee), Leamington 8/05, Alfreton (Trial) c/s 06, Grantham 8/06, Lincoln U 6/07 Rel 11/07, Gainsborough 11/07, Nuneaton 1/08, Tamworth 5/08	35	10
Nick	Wright	7	6'02"	12 00	25/11/87	21	Birmingham	Birmingham, Tamworth (L) 1/06, Bristol C (L) 10/06, Northampton (6WL) 11/06, Ashford T (L) 3/07, Halesowen T 8/07, Tamworth 10/07	35	13

LOANEES		HT	WT	DOB	AGE	POB	From - To	APPS	GOA
(G)Willem	Puddy	5'10"	11 07	4/10/87	21	Salisbury	Cheltenham (4ML) 7/08 - Bath C (3ML) 7/09	11	0
(G)David	Bevan	6'02"	13 00	24/6/89	20	Cork	Aston Villa 9/08 -	6	0
(D)James	Hancox						West Brom 12/08 - Rel 1/09 Bromsgrove 2/09		
(G)Dan	Whatsize	6'02"		14/8/90	19	Leicester	Chesterfield 12/08 - Worksop (L) 12/08, Mansfield 1/09 Rel 2/09, Kettering 3/09, Kings Lynn 6/09	1	0
(D)Alex	Melbourne						Wolves 12/08 -	1	0
Mark	Dudley						Derby 3/09 -	8	0

DEPARTURES			HT	WT	DOB	AGE	POB	From - To	APPS	GOA
(M)Lee	Hildreth	M	6'00"	11 02	22/11/88	20	Nuneaton	Coventry 7/08 - Corby 10/08, Brackley T 7/09	7	0
(F)Harry	Hambleton							Hednesford c/s 08 - Stourbridge 10/08, Dudley Sports (L) 11/08		
(F)Luke	Edwards				5/7/89	20	Burton	ex Shrewsbury 7/07 - Atherstone (L) 9/08, Gresley R 10/08, Atherstone 11/08, Hednesford 1/09, Kings Lynn 7/09 Rel 7/09		
Levi	Chambers							Yth - Willenhall 10/08		
(M)Cameron	Jones		5'08"		23/11/89	19	Australia	ex Walsall 5/08 - Bromsgrove 10/08	0	0
(M)Chris	Nurse				7/5/84	25	Croydon	Halesowen T 1/09 - Rochester Rhinos (USA) 3/09	1	0
(F)Mark	Rawle		5'11"	12 02	27/4/79	30	Leicester	Redditch 2/09 - Brackley 3/09	1	0
(D)Craig	McAughtrie		6'04"	13 10	3/3/81	28	Burton	Stafford R Undisc 9/07 - Rel 5/09, Kings Lynn 6/09	26	2
(M)Dean	Lea							Yth - Rel 5/09, Solihull Moors 6/09	11	1
(D)Callum	Burgess				13/2/90	19		Coventry c/s 08 - Rel 5/09	7	0
Shawn	Boothe							Yth - Bromsgrove 5/09, Atherstone T 6/09		
(F)Gareth	Sheldon		5'11"	11 10	21/1/80	29	Birmingham	Halesowen T 5/07 - Kings Lynn 6/09	41	23
(F)Gary	Ricketts				13/7/75	34	Nottingham	Hucknall 3/09 - Ilkeston 6/09	7	0
(M)Matt	Birley							Bromsgrove 10/08 - Kings Lynn 6/09	17	2
(M)Martin	Foster		5'05"	9 10	29/10/77	31	Sheffield	Rushden & D 1/08 - Eastwood T 6/09	41	1
(D)Brendan	Murphy							Yth - Atherstone 6/09	0	0
(D)Graeme	Law		5'10"	10 10	6/10/84	24	Kirkcaldy	Farsley Celtic (L) 10/07 Perm 11/07 - Rel c/s 09, Stalybridge 8/09	4	0
(F)Stefan	Morrison							Port Talbot 12/08 - Worcester (Trial) 2/09	1	0
	Redfearn								0	0
(G)Simon	Lynn							Romulus (L) 10/08		

TAMWORTH

Formed: 1933

Nickname: The Lambs.

Club Colours: Red shirts, red shorts, red socks.

Change Colours: Royal blue shirts, royal blue shorts, royal blue socks.

Club Sponsor: Snowdome - Tamworth

Previous League: Southern League

Ground address: The Lamb Ground, Kettlebrook, Tamworth, Staffordshire, B77 1AA

Telephone: 01827 65798.

Mobile: 07811 267 304.

Fax: 01827 62236.

E-mail: clubsec@thelambs.co.uk.

Website: www.thelambs.co.uk

Simple Directions: Follow the signs for Town Centre/Snowdrome, then for Kettlebrook. Parking: The entrance to the ground and car park is in Kettlebrook Road, 50 yards from the traffic island by the railway viaduct.

Car Parkng: £1 per car.

MATCH TICKETS

Ticket office Telephone: 01827 65798

Ticket Prices: Terraces - Adults £12. Concessions £7.

Maind Stand Seats - Adults £14. Concessions £9.

Capacity: 4,100 Seats: 518 Covered: 1,191 Floodlights: Yes

Clubhouse: Open matchdays.

Club Shop: Yes.

No image available

PROGRAMME EDITOR

Dave Clayton

(H): 01827 706538 (M): 07967 756918

Email: davec.tfc@hotmail.co.uk

CLUB STATISTICS

RECORDS

Attendance: 5,500 v Torquay United, F.A. Cup Round 1, 15.11.1969.

Victory: 14-4 v Holbrook Institute (H) Bass Vase 1934.

Defeat: 0-11 v Solihull (A) B'ham Comb. 1940.

Career Goalscorer: Graham Jessop - 195.

Career Appearances: Dave Seedhouse - 869.

Transfer Fee Paid:

£7,500 To Ilkeston Town for David Hemmings Dec.2000.

Transfer Fee Received:

£7,500 from Telford United for Martin Myers 1990.

SENIOR HONOURS

Birmingham Senior Cup 1960-61, 65-66, 68-69.

West Midlands League Champions 1964-64, 65-66, 71-72, 87-88.

Southern Midland Division Champions 1996-97.

F.A.Vase 1988-89.

Southern League Premier Division Champions 2002-03.

Conference North Champions 2008-09.

PREVIOUS

Leagues: Birmingham Combination 33-54,

West Midlands (originally B'ham League) 54-72 84-88,

Southern 72-79 83-84.89-03 Northern Premier 1979-83.

Ground: Jolly Sailor Ground 1933-34.

WREXHAM

Back Row (L-R): Simon Brown, Silvio Spann, Hedi Taboubi, Wes Baynes, Andy Fleming, Luke Carding, Neil Taylor, Lamine Sakho, Jamie McCluskey. **Middle Row:** Alan Jones (Kit Manager), Matty Wolfenden, Marc Williams, Gareth Taylor, Sam Russell, Mansour Assoumani, Chris Maxwell, Christian Smith, Mike Williams, Kai Edwards, Mal Purchase (Fitness & Conditioning Coach), Mel Pejic (Physio). **Front Row:** Adrian Ceislewicz, Nathan Fairhhurst, Mark Jones, Curtis Obeng, Dean Saunders (Manager), Brian Carey (Assistant Manager), Matty Hurdman, Sam Williamson, Johnny Hunt, Obi Anoruo.

CLUB PERSONNEL

Chairman: Geoffrey Moss.

Company Secretary: Paul Atkinson.

Chief Executive: Paul Retout.

Additional Directors: Paul Atkinson and Ian Roberts.

Secretary: Geraint Parry.

Telephone: (B): 01978 296 393.

(M): 07801 749 021.

Email: garaint.parry@wrexhamfc.tv

correspondence to Secretary at club.

Commercial Manager: Phil Sadler.

Tel: (M) 07876 565 398 (B) 01978 296 398

Email: phill.sadler@wrexhamfc.tv

Press Officer: See secretary.

Manager: Dean Saunders.

Assistant Manager: Terry Darracott & Brian Carey.

Coach: Joey Jones.

Club therapist: Mel Pejic.

Here was a new name for the Blue Square Premier, one that wasn't expected to be leaving The Football League, and after their first match as a non-league club, Wrexham's 5-0 thrashing of Stevenage Borough made them most experts' certainty for promotion. However, by the end of September The Robins had dropped to 14th position and the well respected manager Brian Little was asked to hand over to Dean Saunders.

Strikers Jefferson Louis and Marc Williams were potentially the best strike force in the competition but after a bright start Louis faded and Williams missed the last third of the season through injury. A surprise defeat by Eastwood Town in the F.A.Cup was disappointing, but victories over Mansfield Town, Basingstoke Town and Workington created expectations of a possible F.A.Trophy Final appearance at Wembley but they were shattered by Ebbsfleet United in a Fourth Round replay.

Dean Saunders brought a number of new names in to join the squad and over the whole campaign forty seven different players represented 'The Reds' but results didn't improve and in the last seventeen league games only two victories were achieved with no goals scored in eight of the last eleven games.

Clubs dropping out of the Football League often take two or thee seasons to sort out their problems, re-group and challenge for promotion. So the examples of Doncaster Rovers, Exeter City and Torquay United should act as encouragingly good examples for clubs like Wrexham, Mansfield Town, York City and Oxford United in the coming season.

WREXHAM

BEST LGE ATT.: 5,173 v York City
LOWEST: 2,234 v Histon

No.	Date	Comp	H/A	Opponents	Att:	Result	Goalscorers	Pos
1	Aug 9	BSP	H	Stevenage Borough	4901	W 5 - 0	Kearney 18 **Louis** 6 Whalley 71 Smith 85 Williams Marc 87	
2	14		A	York City	2603	L 0 - 1		13
3	17		A	Rushden & Diamonds	1445	D 1 - 1	Whalley 75	6
4	21		H	Oxford United	3515	W 2 - 0	Evans 20 **Louis** 90	
5	25		A	Altrincham	2619	D 1 - 1	**Louis** 39	
6	30		A	Salisbury City	1532	W 4 - 1	Whalley 43 90 **Louis** 54 76	5
7	Sept 2		H	Burton Albion	4104	L 0 - 1		
8	6		A	Cambridge United	3076	L 0 - 2		13
9	13		H	Ebbsfleet United	3132	W 3 - 2	**Louis** 37 51 Brown S 77 (pen)	8
10	20		A	Grays Athletic	746	L 1 - 2	Mackin 51	12
11	23		H	Rushden & Diamonds	2805	L 0 - 3		13
12	27		H	Torquay United	2897	D 1 - 1	Brown S 88	14
13	Oct 4		A	Forest Green Rovers	1216	W 3 - 2	Williams Marc 29 65 **Louis** 90	
14	7		H	York City	5173	W 3 - 1	Allen 65 Taylor 85 Williams 90	8
15	18		A	Mansfield United	2757	W 2 - 1	Williams Mike 32 Williams Marc 57	
16	**25**	**F.A.C. 4Q**	**H**	**Eastwood Town**	**3115**	**D 0 - 0**		
17	**28**	**F.A.C. 4Q r**	**A**	**Eastwood Town**	**860**	**L 0 - 2**		
18	Nov 1		H	Lewes	3201	W 2 - 0	Westwood 18 Mike Williams 69	8
19	**4**	**SS 3**	**A**	**Altrincham**	**537**	**W 2 - 1***	**Marc Williams 48, Louis 112**	
20	15		A	Weymouth	1207	W 3 - 1	Wolfe 15 **Louis** 83 Williams Marc 84	8
21	22		A	Kidderminster Harriers	2403	L 0 - 1		8
22	29		A	Stevenage Borough	1673	W 2 - 1	**Louis** 56 Williams Marc 81	7
23	Dec 6		H	Kettering Town	3687	W 2 - 1	Suffo 88 (pen) Brown 90	9
24	**9**	**SS N4**	**H**	**Southport**	**1123**	**L 1 - 2***	**Marc Williams 41**	
25	**13**	**F.A.T 1R**	**H**	**Mansfield Town**	**1559**	**W 2 - 1**	**Brown 2 Westwood 9**	
26	20		H	Eastbourne Borough	3463	W 5 - 0	WILLIAMS Marc 3 (44 66 90) **Louis** 47 Taylor 90	
27	26		A	Barrow	1250	D 1 - 1	**Louis** 90	7
28	28		H	Woking	4803	D 1 - 1	Williams M 34	7
29	**Jan 13**	**F.A.T 2R**	**A**	**Basingstoke Town**	**597**	**W 2 - 1**	**Aimable 14 (og) Louis 57**	
30	16		A	Torquay United	1642	D 1 - 1	Flynn 31	8
31	23		H	Cambridge United	3103	W 2 - 0	Brown 25 **Louis** 59	8
32	27		H	Northwich Victoria	3722	D 3 - 3	Evans 64 Williams Marc 79 Suffo 90 (pen)	
33	**31**	**F.A.T. 3R**	**A**	**Workington**	**1029**	**W 3 - 1**	**Fairhurst 78 (pen) Williams 83 85**	
34	Feb 7		A	Lewes	689	W 2 - 0	Williams Marc 68 Baynes 83	5
35	14		H	Grays Athletic	3419	W 3 - 2	Fairhurst 6 Brown 55 Flynn 57	4
36	17		A	Burton Albion	3262	L 1 - 2	**Louis** 23	4
37	**21**	**F.A.T. 4R**	**H**	**Ebbsfleet United**	**3028**	**D 0 - 0**		
38	**24**	**F.A.T 4R r**	**A**	**Ebbsfleet United**	**992**	**L 1 - 2**	**Louis 51**	
39	28		H	Salisbury City	3206	D 1 - 1	Flynn 6	6
40	Mar 4		A	Crawley Town	737	L 0 - 1		
41	7		A	Eastbourne Borough	1428	L 0 - 1		
42	10		H	Forest Green Rovers	2405	D 1 - 1	**Louis** 86	8
43	14		A	Woking	2792	D 1 - 1	Baynes 12	9
44	17		A	Northwich Victoria	1709	W 2 - 1	Janson 15 Fairhurst 74	
45	21		H	Crawley Town	3303	L 0 - 2		10
46	23		H	Kidderminster Harriers	2674	L 0 - 1		
47	28		A	Histon	1106	L 0 - 1		10
48	April 2		H	Barrow	2272	D 1 - 1	Anoruo 76	
49	4		H	Mansfield Town	2401	W 2 - 0	Anoruo 10 (pen) Crofts 25	
50	7		H	Histon	2234	D 0 - 0		10
51	11		A	Oxford United	5832	L 0 - 1		10
52	13		H	Altrincham	2564	L 0 - 1		
53	18		A	Kettering Town	1497	L 0 - 1		10
54	21		A	Ebbsfleet United	880	L 0 - 1		
55	26		H	Weymouth	2756	W 2 - 0	Proctor 30 Flynn 33	10

Average Home Att: 3367 (4234) **Goals** 75 58

Best Position: 4th **Worst:** 14th

Goalscorers: Louis 18, Marc Williams 17, Brown S 6, Flynn 4, Whalley 4, Fairhurst 3, Anoruo 2, Baynes 2, Evans 2, Suffo 2, Taylor 2, Westwood 2, Mike Williams 2, Allen 1, Crofts 1, Janson 1, Kearney 1, Mackin 1, Proctor 1, Smith 1, Wolfe 1. Own Goals 1.

WARD 1	KEMPSON 4	SPENDER 17	N BROWN 6	TREMARCO 3	WHALLEY 10	KEARNEY 14	AISTON 23	MACKIN 12	S BROWN 8	LOUIS 9	SMITH 25	S EVANS 5	MARC WILLIAMS 21	A WILLIAMS 26	BAYNES 7	N TAYLOR 11	G EVANS 24	PROCTOR 18	MIKE WILLIAMS 15	FLEMING 19	MURTAGH 22	SPANN 16	WESTWOOD 29	ANORUO 31	DE LAET 32	TSIAKLIS 33	WOOLFE 35	FAIRHURST 36	SUFFO 34	WILLIAMSON 38	J BROWN 40	ABBOTT 41	FLYNN 39	GYAN 22	MCCLUSKEY 20	COLLIN 5	CROFTS 25	CURTIS 24	JANSEN 10	NIELSEN 32	MAXWELL 27	
X	X	X	X	X	X	X	X	X	X	X	S	S	S	U	U																										1
X	X	X	X	X	X	X	X		X	X	X	S	S	U	S	U																									2
X	X	X		X	X	X	X	X	X	X		X	U	U	S	S																									3
X	X	X		X	X	X	X	X	S	X		X		U	S	S	U																								4
X	X	X		X	X	X	X	X	S	X		X		U	S	S	U																								5
X	X	X	X	X	X	X	S	S	X	X	U	X		U			S																								6
X	X	X		X	X	X	S	X	X	X	S	X		U	X		U	S																							7
X	X	X		X	X	X	S	X	X	X	U			U	X		U	S																							8
X	X	X		X	X	X		X	X	X	S	X		U	S	X		S	U																						9
X	X	X	S	X	X	X		X	X	X		X		U	S	X		S	U																						10
X	X	U	X	X	X	X	X	X	S	X	S	X	S	U				X																							11
X	X	X	X	X	X			X	X	S	X	U	X		S	S			X	U																					12
X			X		X			X	U	X		X	X	U	X	X		S	X	X	U																				13
X	U			X	U			S		X		X	X	U	X	X		U	X	X		X																			14
X				X		U	S	X	X			S	X	U	X	X		X	X			S	X																		15
X	U		U	X	X	S	S	X	S			X	X	U	X	X		X			U	X	X																		16
X	U			X	S	X		X			S	X	X	U	X	X		S	U		U	X	X	X																	17
X					X			X		X	U	U	X	U	X	X		U	X			S	X		X	X															18
X					X	S		X	S	X	X	U	X	U		X			X			S	X		X	X															19
X				X	S					X	S	U	X	U	X				X			S	X		X	X	X	X													20
X				X				S		X		U	X		X	S			X				X		X	X	X	X	S												21
X					S					X	S	U	X		X	S			X				X			X	X	X	U	X	X										22
X						S	S			X	U	U	X			X			X				X			X	X	X	S	X	X										23
						X	U	X		X	X	X	X	X		X			S	S							X		S	X	X										24
X						U	S				S		X			X			X	X			X			U	X	X	X	X	X	S									25
X						U				X	U		X			X			X	X			X			X	X	S	S	X	X	S									26
X		S								X	U		X			X			X	X			X				X	X	S	X	X	U	S								27
X							S			X			X		X		U		X	X			X				X	S	S	X	X	U	X								28
X		S				U	S			X		X				X			X	X		U					X	X	S	X	X		X								29
X		X					S			X		U	X						X	X		U	X				U	X	U	X	X		X								30
X							S			X		U	X			X			X	X		S	X				S	X	U	X	X		X								31
X	U									X		X	X			X			X	X		U					X	X	S	X	X		S	U							32
X	U									S		X	S			X			X	U		X					X	X	X	S	X		X	X							33
X	U									X			X		S	X			X	X			X				S	X	S	X	X		X	U							34
X										X			X		S	X			X	X			X					X	S	X	X		X	U	S	U					35
X										X			X		S	X			X	X			X					U	S	X	X		X		S	U	X					36
X	S						X			X					X				X	X		S						S	U	X	X			X	U	X	X					37
X	U									X			X		U	X			X	X			X					S	S	X	X		X		S		X					38
X										X			X		U				X	X			X					U	S	X	X		X		S	U	X	X				39
X										X					U			S	X	X			X					S	S	X	X		X		X	U	X	X				40
X							X			X					S			X	U	U			X					X	S	X	S		X			X	X	X				41
										X				X				X	U	X		S	X	S				U	U	X	X		X			X	X	X				42
										X				X	X			S		X		S	X	S				U	U	X			X			X	X	X	X			43
				X										X	X			X	S			U	X	S				X	U		S		X			X	X	X	X			44
										S				X		U		X	S				X	U				X	S	X	X		X			X	X	X	X			45
							X			X				X		X		S	U	X			X	X				U	U	X	S		X			X	X					46
	X					U	X			S					U				X	X			X	S				X		S		X	X			X	X			X		47
						U				S					X			X	X	X		X	X	S					X	X			S			U	X	X		X		48
										X					S	X			X	X		X	X	X				S		S	U		X			U	X	X		X		49
										X					S	X			X	X		X	X					U	U	S	X		S			X	X			X		50
										X					U	S			X	X		X	X	S				U		X			X			S	X	X		X		51
															X	S		S		X		X	X	X				U		X	U		X		S	X	X				X	52
						S				X						X		U				X	X	S				X		U	S		X		X	X	X	X			X	53
	X					X	X			X								S		X			X	X				U		X	U		X		S	S		X			X	54
	X					X	X									U		X		X			X	U				S		X	S		X		X			X			X	55

Total League Appearances

WARD 1	KEMPSON 4	SPENDER 17	N BROWN 6	TREMARCO 3	WHALLEY 10	KEARNEY 14	AISTON 23	MACKIN 12	S BROWN 8	LOUIS 9	SMITH 25	S EVANS 5	MARC WILLIAMS 21	A WILLIAMS 26	BAYNES 7	N TAYLOR 11	G EVANS 24	PROCTOR 18	MIKE WILLIAMS 15	FLEMING 19	MURTAGH 22	SPANN 16	WESTWOOD 29	ANORUO 31	DE LAET 32	TSIAKLIS 33	WOOLFE 35	FAIRHURST 36	SUFFO 34	WILLIAMSON 38	J BROWN 40	ABBOTT 41	FLYNN 39	GYAN 22	MCCLUSKEY 20	COLLIN 5	CROFTS 25	CURTIS 24	JANSEN 10	NIELSEN 32	MAXWELL 27	
32	15	12	6	17	14	13	11	13	10	38	2	11	19	5	14	18	0	8	25	24	0	7	31	4	3	6	8	15	1	23	16	1	21	0	3	10	16	13	3	5	4	X
0	0	1	1	0	2	2	8	3	3	4	6	3	3	0	13	8	1	10	2	0	0	6	0	7	0	0	2	5	13	3	5	1	4	0	5	2	0	0	0	0	0	S
0	3	1	0	0	1	4	0	0	1	0	6	8	1	16	5	3	5	3	5	2	1	3	0	2	0	0	1	9	8	1	3	2	0	3	0	6	0	0	0	0	0	U

Total Cup Appearances

WARD 1	KEMPSON 4	SPENDER 17	N BROWN 6	TREMARCO 3	WHALLEY 10	KEARNEY 14	AISTON 23	MACKIN 12	S BROWN 8	LOUIS 9	SMITH 25	S EVANS 5	MARC WILLIAMS 21	A WILLIAMS 26	BAYNES 7	N TAYLOR 11	G EVANS 24	PROCTOR 18	MIKE WILLIAMS 15	FLEMING 19	MURTAGH 22	SPANN 16	WESTWOOD 29	ANORUO 31	DE LAET 32	TSIAKLIS 33	WOOLFE 35	FAIRHURST 36	SUFFO 34	WILLIAMSON 38	J BROWN 40	ABBOTT 41	FLYNN 39	GYAN 22	MCCLUSKEY 20	COLLIN 5	CROFTS 25	CURTIS 24	JANSEN 10	NIELSEN 32	MAXWELL 27	
8	0	0	0	2	2	2	1	4	0	5	2	5	6	1	3	8	0	1	6	4	0	3	5	1	1	1	4	3	2	5	6	0	3	2	0	1	2	0	0	0	0	X
0	1	1	0	0	1	2	3	0	2	1	2	0	1	0	0	0	0	1	1	1	0	2	0	0	0	0	0	2	3	1	0	1	0	0	1	0	0	0	0	0	0	S
0	4	0	1	0	0	2	1	0	0	0	0	1	0	3	1	0	0	0	1	1	2	1	0	0	0	1	0	0	1	0	0	0	0	0	1	0	0	0	0	0	0	U

Also Played: PEJIC U(3,13), X(8). CRITCHELL X(4,5) U24). ALLEN X(14,15). EDWARDS U(21) S(55). ASSOUMANI X(50,51,52).

WREXHAM

CURRENT SQUAD AS OF BEGINING OF 2009-10 SEASON

GOALKEEPERS		SQ NO.	HT	WT	D.O.B	AGE	P.O.B	CAREER	APPS	GOA
Chris	Maxwell	27			30/7/90	19	Wrexham	Wrexham, Connahs Quay (6ML) 8/08	4	0
Sam	Russell	1	6'00"	10 13	4/10/82	26	Middlesbrough	Middlesbrough Rel c/s 04, Gateshead (SL) 2/02, Darlington (L) 12/02, Scunthorpe (3ML) 8/03, Darlington 8/04 Rel c/s 07, MK Dons (Trial) 7/07, Rochdale 8/07 Rel c/s 09, Wrexham 8/09		

DEFENDERS										
Mansour	Assoumani	4	6'02"	12 00	30/1/83	26	Nice, Fra	Montpellier (Fra), FC Saarbrucken (Ger) 7/06, Sportfreunde Siegen (Ger) 7/07 Rel 6/08, Leeds 12/08 Rel 1/09, Crewe (Trial) 1/09, Wrexham 3/09	3	0
Wes	Baynes	18	5'11"	10 10	12/10/88	20	Chester	Wrexham	27	2
Kai	Edwards	21	6'00"	12 02	29/1/91	18		Wrexham	1	0
Curtis	Obeng	2	5'09"	11 00	14/2/89	20	Manchester	Man City Rel c/s 09, Wigan (Trial) 7/09, Wrexham 8/09		
Neil	Taylor	11	5'09"	10 01	7/2/89	20	St Asaph	Wrexham	26	2
Ashley	Westwood	5	5'11"	11 02	31/8/76	33	Bridgnorth	Man Utd, Crewe £40,000 7/95, Bradford C £150,000 7/98, Sheff Wed (L) 8/00 £150,000 9/00 Rel c/s 03, Northampton 7/03 Rel c/s 06, Chester 8/06 Rel 12/07, Swindon (SL) 3/07, Port Vale (4ML) 8/07, Stevenage 1/08 Rel 7/08, Lincoln C (Trial) 10/08, Wrexham 10/08	31	1
Mike	Williams	15	5'11"	12 00	27/10/86	22	Rhos-on-Sea	Wrexham	27	2
Sam	Williamson	3	5'08"	11 09	15/10/87	21	Macclesfield	Man City, Wrexham (2ML) 11/08 Perm 1/09	26	0

MIDFIELDERS										
Steve	Abbott				31/7/82	26	Whiston	Congleton, St Helens, Leigh RMI, Team Bath 7/06, Wrexham 12/08, The New Saints (L) 7/09	2	0
Adrian	Cielslewicz	17	5'10"		16/11/90	18		Man City, Wrexham 6/09		
Nathan	Fairhurst	14	5'10"	10 05	16/10/89	19	Preston	Preston, Wrexham (SL) 11/08, Wrexham 7/09	20	2
Andrew	Fleming	19	6'01"	12 00	5/10/87	21	Liverpool	Wrexham	24	0
Mark	Jones	7	5'11"	10 12	15/8/83	26	Wrexham	Wrexham Rel c/s 08, Rochdale 8/08 Rel c/s 09, Wrexham 7/09		
Jamie	McCluskey	20	5'06"	08 09	6/11/87	21	Bellshill	Hibernian, St Johnstone 7/07 Rel c/s 08, Wrexham 2/09	8	0
Christian	Smith	25	6'02"	13 02	10/12/87	21	Crewe	Port Vale Rel c/s 07, Cambridge U (L) 1/07, Northwich (L) 3/07, Bury (Trial) 7/07, Clyde c/s 07 Rel 6/08, Wrexham 8/08 Rel 1/09, Macclesfield (Trial) 1/09, York C 1/09 Rel 5/09, Wrexham 8/09	8	1
Silvio	Spann	16	5'11"	10 12	21/8/81	28	Couva, Trin	Docs Khelwalaas (Trin), West Connection (Trin), Perugia (Ita) 7/01, SS Sambenedettese (Ita) (SL) 1/02, West Connection (Trin) 9/02, Dinamo Zagreb (Cro) (SL) 3/04, Yokahama FC (Jap) 1/05, West Connection (Trin) 11/06, Sheff Utd (Trial) 7/07, Wrexham 8/07	13	0
Heidi	Taboubi	8	5'10"	11 04	24/2/83	26	Cavaillon, Fra	Montpellier (Fra), Lunel GC (Fra), Avignon (Fra), Vergèze Entente Perrier (Fra), RCO Agde (Fra), Raon L Etape (Fra), AC Arles (Fra) c/s 07, Wrexham 7/09		

FORWARDS										
Obi	Anoruo	23	5'10"	11 06	28/8/91	18	Nigeria	Wrexham	11	2
Simon	Brown	25	5'10"	11 00	18/9/83	25	West Bromwich	West Brom, Kidderminster (SL) 3/04, Kidderminster (3ML) 7/04, Mansfield £50,000 12/04 Rel c/s 08, Wrexham 6/08, Rushden & D (5WL) 11/08, York C (SL) 1/09	13	2
Lamine	Sakho	22	5'10"	11 02	28/9/77	31	Louga, Sen	Nimes (Fra), Lens (Fra) 7/99, Marseille (Fra) 1/02, Leeds (SL) 8/03, Saint Etienne (Fra) 1/05, Montpellier (Fra) 1/07, Alki Larnaca (Cyp) 7/08, Wrexham 8/09		
Gareth	Taylor	9	6'02"	13 08	25/2/73	36	Weston-S-Mare	Southampton (Trainee), Bristol R 7/91, C.Palace £750,000 9/95, Sheff Utd P/E 3/96, Man City £400,000 11/98 Rel c/s 01, Port Vale (L) 1/00, QPR (2ML) 3/00, Burnley (SL) 2/01, Burnley 6/01, Notts Forest £500,000 8/03 Rel c/s 06, Crewe (SL) 1/06, Tranmere 7/06, Doncaster (L) 1/08 Undisc 2/08 Rel c/s 09, Carlisle (L) 3/09, Wrexham 6/09		
Marc	Williams	10	5'09"	11 02	27/7/88	21	Colwyn Bay	Wrexham	22	13
Matthew	Wolfenden	24	5'09"	11 08	23/1/87	22	Oldham	Oldham Rel 7/09, Wrexham 7/09		

LOANEES		SN	HT	WT	DOB	AGE	POB	From - To	APPS	GOA
(M)Joe	Allen		5'06"	09 10	14/3/90	19	Carmarthen	Swansea 10/08 -	2	1
(D)Ritchie	De Laet		6'01"	12 02	28/11/88	20	Belgium	Stoke 10/08 - Man Utd 1/09	3	0
(M)Angelos	Tsiaklis		5'10"	10 12	2/10/89	19		Man City (3ML) 10/08 -	6	0
(M)Nathan	Woolfe		5'11"	12 05	6/10/88	20	Manchester	Bolton (3ML) 11/08 -	10	1
(F)Jonathan	Brown		5'11"	11 04	17/4/90	19	Bridgend	Cardiff (SL) 11/08 -	21	3
(M)Ryan	Flynn		5'08"	10 00	4/9/88	20	Scotland	Liverpool (SL) 11/08 -	25	4
(M)Andrew	Crofts		5'10"	12 09	29/5/84	25	Chatham	Gillingham (SL) 2/09 -	16	1
(G)Gunnar	Nielsen		6'03"	14 00	7/10/86	22		Man City 3/09 -	5	0

DEPARTURES		SN	HT	WT	DOB	AGE	POB	From - To	APPS	GOA
(M)Conall	Murtagh		6'00"	11 11	29/6/85	24	Belfast	Southport 6/07 - TNS 1/09	0	0
(D)Steve	Evans		6'05"	13 05	26/2/79	30	Wrexham	TNS 6/06 - TNS 1/09	14	2
(D)Shaun	Pejic		6'01"	12 03	16/11/82	26	Hereford	Yth - Rel 2/09, York C 2/09 Rel c/s 09	1	0
(D)Gareth	Evans		6'01"	12 12	10/1/87	22	Wrexham	Newi Cefn Druids (Yth c/s 04) (Pro) 8/06 - Rel 1/09	1	0
(G)Gavin	Ward		6'03"	14 12	30/6/70	39	Sutton Coldfield	Chester 1/08 - Rel 4/09, Hednesford 7/09	32	0
(G)Anthony	Williams		6'01"	13 05	20/9/77	31	Ogwr	Carlisle 7/07 - Rel 4/09, Neath Ath 6/09	5	0
(D)Chris	Marriott				24/9/89	20		Tranmere (Yth) - Rel 4/09, Newi Cefn Druids (SL) 8/08, The New Saints 5/09		
(M)Christian	Gyan		5'09"	11 11	2/11/78	30	Terna	TPS Turku (Fin) 1/09 - Rel 4/09	0	0
(D)Simon	Spender		5'11"	11 00	15/11/85	23	Mold	Yth - Rel 4/09, Barrow (SL) 3/09, Barrow 5/09	13	0
(M)Sam	Aiston		6'01"	14 00	21/11/76	32	Newcastle	Northampton (2ML) 11/07 - Perm 1/08 Rel 4/09, Hednesford 7/09	19	0
(F)Jefferson	Louis		6'02"	13 02	22/2/79	30	Harrow	Mansfield 6/08 - Rel 5/09, Crawley 5/09	42	15
(F)Patrick	Suffo		5'09"	12 12	17/1/78	31	Ebolowa, Cam	Puertollano 11/08 - Rel 5/09	14	2
(M)Levi	Mackin		6'01"	12 00	4/4/86	23	Chester	Yth - Rel 5/09, York C (SL) 1/09, York C 5/09	16	1
(M)Shaun	Whalley		5'09"	10 07	7/8/87	22	Prescot	Accrington 6/08 - Rel 5/09, Southport (SL) 2/09	16	4
(D)Carl	Tremarco		5'08"	11 11	11/10/85	23	Liverpool	Tranmere 1/08 - Darlington (2ML) 1/09, Macclesfield 6/09	17	0
(D)Kyle	Critchell		6'00"	12 02	18/1/87	22	Dorchester	Weymouth 6/08 - Rel 6/09, York C (2ML) 1/09, Weymouth (L) 3/09, Weymouth 6/09	2	0
(F)Matt	Jansen		5'11"	10 12	20/10/77	31	Carlisle	ex Carlisle 3/09 - Leigh Genesis 6/09	3	1
(D)Nat	Brown		6'02"	12 06	15/6/81	28	Sheffield	Lincoln C 6/08 - Rel 6/09, Macclesfield (SL) 11/08	7	0
(F)Michael	Proctor		5'11"	12 07	3/10/80	28	Sunderland	Hartlepool 7/07 - Rel 7/09	18	1
(D)Darran	Kempson		6'02"	12 13	6/12/84	24	Blackpool	Shrewsbury 7/08 - Rel 7/09, Forest Green (2ML) 11/08, Accrington 7/09	15	0
(M)Tom	Kearney		5'09"	10 12	7/10/81	27	Liverpool	Halifax 6/08 - Rel 7/09, Altrincham 7/09	15	1
(D)John	Curtis		5'10"	11 07	3/9/78	30	Nuneaton	Worcester 2/09 - Northampton 7/09	13	0
(D)Aurelien	Collin		6'00"	12 01	8/3/86	23	Enghien-les-Bains	Panserraikos (Gre) 2/09 - Vitoria Setubal (Por) 8/09	12	0

WREXHAM

Founded: 1872.

Nickname: The Robins.

Club Colours: Red shirts, white shorts, white socks.

Change Colours: White shirts, red shorts, red socks.

Club Sponsor: Lease Direct

Previous League: Football League

Ground Address: Racecourse Ground, Mold Road, Wrexham, LL11 2AH
Tel No: 01978 262 129
Fax: 01978 357 821
Mobile: 07801 749 021
General email address: info@wrexhamfc.tv
Official website: www.wrexhamfc.tv

SIMPLE DIRECTIONS

By Road From Wrexham by-pass (A483) exit at Mold Junction (A451). Follow signs for Town Centre and football ground is half mile on left hand side.

MATCH TICKETS

Ticket office Telephone: 01978 262 129

Ticket Prices (Pre-booked): Yale Stand - Adults £17 (£14). Concessions £12 (£10). Juniors £5.
Mold Road Stand - Adults £18 (£16). Concessions £12 (£10).
Eric Roberts Stand - Adults £17 (£14). Concessions £12 (£10). Juniors £5 (Pre-booked)

Capacity: 15,500 **Seats:** 10,100 **Covered:** 15,500

Refreshments: Food and drink bars around the ground.
Club Shop: Yes.

PROGRAMME EDITOR
David Roberts
Tel: (H): 01978 362244 (M): 07525 649362
Email: david.e.rob@btinternet.com

CLUB STATISTICS

RECORDS

Victory: 10-1 v Hartlepool United, Division Four, 03.03.1962.

Career Goalscorer: Tommy Bamford - 201.

SENIOR HONOURS

Football League Third Division 1977-78.

The Combination x4 during 1896-1905.

LDV Vans Trophy 2004-05.

Welsh League 1894-95, 1895-96.

Welsh F.A. Cup x23.

FAW Premier Cup 1997-98, 99-00, 00-01, 02-03, 03-04.

PREVIOUS

Names: Wrexham Athletic for the 1882-83 season only.

League: The Combination 1890-94, 1896-1906.

Welsh League 1894-1896. Birmingham & District 1906-21.

Football League 1921-2008.

Grounds: Rhosddu Recreation Ground during the 1881-82 & 1882-83 seasons.

YORK CITY

Back Row (L-R): Andrew McWilliams, Michael Gash, Jimmy Sangare, Richard Brodie, Ben Purkiss, Michaeal Rankine, Alan O'Hare, Richard Pacquette, Michael Emmerson. **Middle Row:** Simon Russell, Adam Smith, Jeff Miller, Josh Mimms, Alex Lawless, Michael Ingham, Steve Torpey, Levi Mackin, Craig Nelthorpe. **Front Row:** Andrew Ferrell, Neil Barrett, Andrew Porter, Daniel Parslow, Martin Foyle, David McGurk, James Meredith.

CLUB PERSONNEL

Managing Director: Jason McGill.

Company Secretary: Nick Bassett.

Additional Directors: Terry Doyle, Sophie Hicks,

Ian McAndrew, Rob McGill.

Secretary: Nick Bassett

Telephone: (B): 01904 624 447. (M): 07885 539 956

E-mail: nick.bassett@ycfc.net

correspondence to Secretary at club.

Commercial Manager: Ross Potter

Tel: (M): 07949 966686

Email: ross.potter@ycfc.net

Press Officer: Sophie Hicks

Telephone: (B): 01653 691 500. (M): 07734 172 625

E-mail: sophie@jmpackaging.com

Manager: Martin Foyle.

Assistant Manager: Andy Porter.

Club therapist: Jeff Miller.

Clubs dropping down from the Football League often have to rebuild their playing staff and appear to misjudge the standard needed if a serious promotion challenge is to be kept going through a long season. York City, under the guidance of Colin Walker kicked off with an eight match unbeaten run, but a closer look at their results shows that although they scored in each game the sequence included five consecutive draws and in no game had City players scored two goals, on the two occasions the opponents net had been found twice, own goals had helped.

This statistic could be considered to be nit picking but a glance at the rest of the season's results shows that on only three occasions did York score three times and they failed to find the net on seventeen occasions. Without Richard Brodie's twenty goals relegation might have been a realistic threat.

As it was, poor results took 'The Minstermen' into the bottom half of the table and the manager was replaced by Martin Foyle. A quick exit from the F.A.Cup had been disappointing but having reached the semi-final of The F.A.Trophy in their first season in the competition, City once again made exciting progress by eliminating Northwich Victoria, Oxford United, Kidderminster Harriers and Havant & Waterlooville before winning both semi-final legs against A.F.C.Telford United.

A Wembley appearance was a big thrill for players and supporters alike, although the performance provided a disappointing defeat by Stevenage Borough who had suffered a play off defeat themselves. York City supporters will consider the last two seasons quite long enough to prepare a squad capable of a serious promotion challenge but they know they will have to improve a great deal.

YORK CITY

BEST LGE ATT.: **2,703** v Burton Albion
LOWEST: **1,122** v Weymouth

No.	Date	Comp	H/A	Opponents	Att:	Result	Goalscorers	Pos
1	Aug 9	BSP	A	Crawley Town	1372	W 1 - 0	Farrell 71	
2	14		H	Wrexham	2603	W 1 - 0	Greaves 74	
3	16		H	Histon	2125	D 1 - 1	McBreen 69	5
4	23		A	Northwich Victoria	1065	D 2 - 2	**Brodie** 26 Crowett 57 (og)	6
5	25		H	Barrow	2664	D 1 - 1	**Brodie** 3	7
6	28		A	Torquay United	1598	D 1 - 1	Sodje 87	11
7	Sept 2		H	Mansfield Town	2520	D 1 - 1	Sodje 35	
8	6		H	Woking	2307	W 2 - 0	McBreen 38 Bunce 49 (og)	7
9	13		A	Kettering Town	2017	L 2 - 4	**Brodie** 23 Purkiss 49	11
10	20		H	Salisbury City	2280	D 1 - 1	McBreen 86	10
11	23		A	Kidderminster Harriers	1481	L 0 - 2		12
12	28		A	Stevenage Borough	2971	D 3 - 3	Sodje 24 45 Farrell 48	15
13	Oct 4		H	Cambridge United	2608	D 0 - 0		15
14	7		A	Wrexham	5173	L 1 - 3	Wilkinson 90	
15	11		A	Woking	2341	W 2 - 0	Wilkinson 66 McBreen 72	12
16	18		H	Rushden & Diamonds	2313	W 2 - 0	Robinson 18 Farrell 50	
17	**25**	**F.A.C. 4Q**	**H**	**Mansfield Town**	**1976**	**D 0 - 0**		
18	**28**	**F.A.C. 4Q r**	**A**	**Mansfield Town**	**2004**	**L 0 - 1**		
19	Nov 1		A	Oxford United	4449	L 0 - 1		13
20	**4**	**SS 3**	**H**	**Mansfield Town**	**608**	**D 1 - 1***	**Greaves 90 (Won 4-2 on pens)**	
21	15		H	Torquay United	2412	L 1 - 2	Greaves 85	15
22	18		A	Cambridge United	2914	L 0 - 1		
23	23		H	Crawley Town	1935	D 2 - 2	Sodje 7 48	14
24	29		A	Salisbury City	986	D 1 - 1	**Brodie** 83	
25	Dec 6		H	Grays Ahletic	2154	L 0 - 1		15
26	9		A	Histon	901	D 1 - 1	**Brodie** 14	
27	**16**	**F.A.T 1R**	**A**	**Northwich Victoria**	**393**	**W 2 - 0**	**Brodie 20 50**	
28	20		H	Ebbsfleet United	1997	W 3 - 1	Smith 60 **Brodie** 67 Sodje 77	14
29	26		A	Burton Albion	3578	L 1 - 2	Smith 53	
30	28		H	Altrincham	2389	L 1 - 2	**Brodie** 32	16
31	Jan 1		H	Burton Albion	2703	L 1 - 2	**Brodie** 39	
32	**13**	**F.A.T 2R**	**A**	**Oxford United**	**1958**	**W 2 - 1**	**Brodie 48 82**	
33	17		H	Lewes	2073	W 3 - 0	**Brodie** 56 78 Smith 68	16
34	**20**	**SS N4**	**A**	**Barrow**	**596**	**L 1 - 3**	**Russell 78**	
35	24		A	Eastbourne Borough	1668	L 1 - 2	Smith 63	
36	27		A	Altrincham	1027	D 1 - 1	**Brodie** 46	
37	**31**	**F.A.T 3R**	**A**	**Kidderminster Harriers**	**1113**	**W 1 - 0**	**Boyes 25**	
38	Feb 7		A	Mansfield Town	2576	L 0 - 1		17
39	**12**	**F.A.T. 3R**	**H**	**Kidderminster Harriers**	**683**	**D 1 - 1***	**McBreen 74 (Won 13-12 on pens)**	
40	**21**	**F.A.T 4R**	**H**	**Havant & Waterlooville**	**1679**	**W 2 - 0**	**McBreen 45 82**	
41	24		A	Rushden & Diamonds	1020	L 0 - 2		
42	28		H	Weymouth	2349	W 2 - 0	**Brodie** 23 90	17
43	Mar 8		A	Ebbsfleet United	1244	D 0 - 0		
44	**14**	**F.A.T SF1**	**A**	**A.F.C. Telford United**	**2792**	**W 2 - 0**	**Rusk 10 Purkiss 68**	
45	17		A	Forest Green Rovers	681	D 1 - 1	Sodje 86	16
46	**21**	**F.A.T. SF2**	**H**	**A.F.C. Telford United**	**3512**	**W 2 - 1**	**Brodie 20 McBreen 60**	
47	24		H	Kettering Town	1714	D 0 - 0		
48	28		H	Kidderminter Harriers	2384	D 0 - 0		18
49	31		H	Stevenage Borough	1924	L 0 - 2		20
50	April 4		A	Grays Athletic	720	L 0 - 1		21
51	7		H	Oxford United	2268	D 0 - 0		21
52	11		H	Northwich Victoria	2421	L 1 - 2	Robinson 68 (pen)	22
53	13		A	Barrow	2168	D 0 - 0		
54	18		H	Eastbourne United	2487	W 1 - 0	McBreen 35	20
55	21		H	Forest Green Rovers	2530	W 2 - 1	Boyes 59 **Brodie** 63	
56	23		H	Weymouth	1122	W 2 - 1	**Brodie** 14 Boyes 77	
57	26		A	Lewes	802	D 1 - 1	Greaves 80	17
58	**May 9**	**F.A.T. Final**	**N**	**Stevenage Borough**	**27102**	**L 0 2**		

Average Home Att: 2360 (2258) **Goals** 61 60

Best Position: 5th **Worst:** 21st

Goalscorers: Brodie 20, McBreen 9, Sodje 8, Greaves 4, Smith 4, Boyes 3, Farrell 3, Purkiss 2, Robinson 2, Wilkinson 2, Rusk 1, Russell 1. Own Goals 2.

KRYSIAK 1	GREAVES 8	MCGURK 5	ROBINSON 3	PARSLOW 6	PURKISS 2	WILKINSON 12	RUSK 15	FARRELL 10	BRODIE 16	MCBREEN 9	MIMMS 13	KELLY 4	HENDERSON 17	MCWILLIAMS 20	SODJE 7	SHEPHERD 19	MCDONALD 1	RUSSELL 11	INGHAM 24	BEADLE 21	BORE 23	BOYES 18	HOLMES 26	ROTHERY 21	HOGG 14	DYER 28	A SMITH 23	CRITCHELL 21	BROWN 26	MACKIN 17	C SMITH 27	RADCLIFFE 22	PEJIC 25	TORPEY 28	
X	X	X	X	X	X	X	X	X	X	X	U	U	U	U	U																				1
X	X	X	X	X	X	X	X	X	X	X	S	U	S		S	U																			2
	X	X	X	X	X	X	X	X	S	X	X	U	X		S	S	U																		3
		X	X	X	X	X	X	X	X	X	X	S	X		S			S	U	U															4
	X	X	X	X	X	S	X	X	X		U	U	X		S	S		X	X																5
	X	X	X	X	X	X	X	X	X	X	U	U	S		S			S	X																6
	X	X	X	X	X	X		S	X	X	U	U			X	U		X	X		S														7
	X	X	X	X	X	X		S	X	X	U	U				S		X	X		X	S													8
	X	X	X	X	X	S		S	X	X	U		X	U	S			X	X		X														9
	X	X	X	X	X	S	X	X	X	S	U	U			X			X	X		S														10
		X	X	X	X	X	X	S	X	X	U	U	U		S			X	X				X												11
	X	X	X	X	X	S	X	X	S	S	U			U	X			X	X				X												12
	X	X	X	X	X	S	X	X	S	X	U			U				X	X			S	X												13
	X	X	X	X	X	X	X	X	S	X	U	S	U			S		X	X																14
	S	X	X	X	X	X	X	X		X	U	X				U		U	X			S	X												15
	S	X	X	X	X	X	X	X	S	X	U	X						S	X			U	X												16
	X	**X**	**X**	**X**	**X**	**X**	**X**	**X**		**X**	**U**	**X**		**U**	**S**	**U**		**S**	**X**			**S**		**U**											17
	X	**X**	**X**	**X**	**X**	**X**	**X**			**X**	**U**	**U**	**U**	**U**	**S**	**S**		**X**	**X**			**S**		**X**											18
	X	X	X	X	X	U	X	S		X	U	X			X			X	X			S		S											19
	X	**X**		**X**	**X**	**U**	**X**	**S**			**U**			**X**	**X**			**X**	**X**			**S**		**S**	**X**	**X**									20
	X	X	X	X	X		X	S		S	U	X			X			S	X			U			X	X									21
	X	X	X	X	X	S	X	X		X	U	X			S			S	X					U	X										22
	X	X	U	X	X		X	S	S		U	U		X	X	X			X						X	X									23
	X	X	X	X	X	S	X	X	S	X	U	U		X	X				X								S								24
	X	X	X	X	X	S	X	X		X	U	U		X				X	X			S					S								25
	X	X		X	X	U	X	S	X	S	S	U		X	X				X						X		X								26
	X	**X**	**X**	**X**	**X**		**X**	**S**	**X**	**U**	**U**			**X**	**X**			**S**	**X**			**S**			**X**										27
	X	X	X	X	X		X		X	U	U			X	X			S	X			U			X		S								28
	X	X		X	X		X		X	S	U	U		X	X			S	X			S			X		X								29
	X	X		X	X	S	X		X	S	U	U		X	X			X	X			S					X								30
		X	X	X		S	X	S	X	X	U	X		U	S			X	X						X		X								31
	X	**X**	**X**	**X**		**X**		**S**	**X**	**X**	**U**	**S**		**X**	**U**	**S**		**X**	**X**									**X**							32
	X		X	X			S		X	X	U	X		X	S	S		U	X								X	X	X						33
	X		**X**	**X**		**X**	**U**	**S**		**X**	**U**	**X**		**X**	**X**	**S**		**X**	**X**			**S**						**X**							34
	X		X	X			X	S	X			U		X		S		U	X			S						X	X	X	X				35
			X	X	X		X		X	U	U			S	U				X			X					S	X	X	X	X				36
			X	**X**	**X**	**U**	**X**		**X**	**X**	**U**			**X**	**U**			**U**	**X**			**X**						**X**		**X**		**U**			37
	U		X	X			X		X	X				U	U	S			X			X					S	X	X	X	X				38
	X		**X**	**X**			**X**		**X**	**X**	**U**			**X**	**S**	**U**		**S**	**X**			**X**						**X**		**X**		**S**			39
	S		**X**	**X**			**X**		**X**	**X**	**U**			**X**	**S**	**U**		**S**	**X**			**X**						**X**		**X**			**X**		40
	U			X			X		X	X				X	S			U	X			S					S	X	X	X	X		X		41
	S		X	X			S		X	X	X				S			X				U					X	X	U	X	X		X		42
		S	X	X	X		X			X				U	S			X	X			X					U		S	X	X		X		43
	S	**S**	**X**	**X**	**X**		**X**		**X**	**X**	**U**			**X**	**S**			**U**	**X**			**X**								**X**			**X**		44
	U	X	X	X	X		X		X					S	S			U	X			S							X	X	X		X		45
	S	**S**	**X**	**X**	**X**		**X**		**X**	**X**	**U**			**X**	**S**			**U**	**X**			**X**								**X**			**X**		46
	S	U	X	X	X		X		X	X				X	S				X			X					U		S	X			X		47
	S	S	X	X	X		X		X	X				X	X			U	X			U							S	X			X		48
	U	U	X	X	X		X		X	X				X	X			U	X			S							S	X			X		49
	S	X	X	X	X		X			U				X	X			S	X			S							X	X	U		X		50
	X	X	X	X	U					X				U	X			U	X			X			S		S		X		X		X		51
	X	X	X	X	S				S	X					X				X			X			U		S		X	U	X		X		52
	S	X	U	X	X				X	S	U				S				X			X					X		X	X	X		X		53
	U	X	U	X	X				X	X					S				X			X					X		S	X	X		X	S	54
	U	X	U	X	X				X	X					S				X			X					X		S	X	X		X	U	55
	S	X	U	X	X				X	X					S				X			X					X		U	X	X		X	U	56
	X		X		X		X		S		X				X			X	U			S			X		U		X		S		X	X	57
	X	**X**	**U**	**X**	**X**		**X**		**X**	**X**	**U**			**S**	**S**			**S**	**X**			**X**								**X**			**X**		58
Total League Appearances																																			
2	27	35	37	45	38	11	35	15	29	31	4	7	4	14	17	1	0	16	40	0	2	10	5	0	8	2	10	6	11	15	13	0	15	1	X
0	8	2	0	0	1	10	2	10	9	7	2	2	2	2	19	7	0	8	0	0	2	13	0	1	1	0	8	0	6	0	1	0	0	1	S
0	6	2	5	0	1	2	0	0	0	3	26	16	3	8	3	3	1	8	2	1	0	5	0	1	1	0	3	0	2	1	1	0	0	2	U
Total Cup Appearances																																			
0	8	6	10	12	8	4	10	1	8	10	0	2	0	9	3	0	0	4	12	0	0	6	0	1	2	1	0	5	0	6	0	0	4	0	X
0	3	2	0	0	0	0	0	4	0	0	0	1	0	1	7	3	0	5	0	0	0	5	0	1	0	0	0	0	0	0	0	1	0	0	S
0	0	0	1	0	0	2	1	0	0	1	12	1	1	2	2	3	0	3	0	0	0	0	0	1	0	0	0	0	0	0	0	1	0	0	U

YORK CITY

CURRENT SQUAD AS OF BEGINING OF 2009-10 SEASON

GOALKEEPERS		SQ NO.	HT	WT	D.O.B	AGE	P.O.B	CAREER	APPS	GOA
Michael	Ingham	24	6'04"	13 12	7/9/80	28	Preston	Malachians, Cliftonville 7/98, Sunderland £30,000 7/99, Carlisle (2ML) 10/99, Coleraine (SL) 8/00, Stoke (L) 12/01, Stockport (2ML) 8/02, Darlington (L) 11/02, York C (SL) 1/03, Wrexham (SL) 3/04, Doncaster (L) 11/04, Coleraine (L),Wrexham 7/05 Rel c/s 07, Hereford 8/07 Rel c/s 08, York C 5/08	40	0
Josh	Mimms	13	6'02"	12 12	5/8/89	20	Rotherham	Liverpool (Scholar), Wolves (Trial) 7/07, Bohemians (Trial) 7/07, York C 10/07	6	0
DEFENDERS										
Alex	Lawless	12	5'11"	10 08	5/2/83	26	Llwynupion	Fulham, Torquay 7/05 Rel 5/06, Forest Green 8/06, York C 6/09		
David	McGurk	5	6'00"	11 10	30/9/82	26	Middlesbrough	Darlington, Bishop Auckland (L) 8/04, York (L) 9/04, York 6ML 8/05, York (SL) 1/06, York 6/06	37	0
Andy	McWilliams	20	5'08"		5/11/89	19	Stockton	York C	16	0
James	Meredith	3	6'00"	11 09	4/4/88	21	Albury, Aust	Derby Rel c/s 07, Cambridge U (L) 10/06, Chesterfield (L) 2/07, Sligo R 8/07 Rel 12/07, Shrewsbury 1/08 Rel 6/09, AFC Telford (SL) 10/08, York C 7/09		
Alan	O'Hare	4	6'02"	12 02	31/7/82	27	Drogheda. Ire	Bolton, Chesterfield (SL) 1/02, Chesterfield (L) 10/02 Perm 11/02 Rel c/s 08, Mansfield 7/08 Rel 6/09, York C 6/09		
Daniel	Parslow	6	5'11"	12 05	11/9/85	23	Rhymney Valley	Cardiff Rel c/s 06, York C 8/06	45	0
Ben	Purkiss	2	6'02"	12 12	1/4/84	25	Sheffield	Sheff Utd Rel c/s 03, Gainsborough 8/03, York C (SL) 3/07, York C 8/07	39	1
Djoumin	Sangare	21			16/12/83	25	Dunkerque	Wasquehal (Fra), Redbridge 9/04, Chelmsford 1/05, Redbridge 1/05, Lewes, St Albans (L) 8/05, Grays 8/06 Rel 5/07, St Albans (SL) 1/07, Stafford R 7/07, Salisbury 7/08, York C 7/09		
MIDFIELDERS										
Neil	Barrett	14	5'10"	11 00	24/12/81	27	Tooting	Chelsea (Jun), Portsmouth (Trial) 3/01, Portsmouth 7/01, Dundee (3ML) 1/04, Dundee 7/04 Rel 9/05, Livingston 9/05 Rel 1/06, Exeter 9/06 Rel 12/06, Woking 1/07, Ebbsfleet 6/07, York C Undisc 6/09		
Andy	Ferrell	8	5'08"	11 05	9/1/84	25	Newcastle	Newcastle Rel c/s 04, Watford 7/04 Rel c/s 05, Hereford 8/05 Rel 5/07, Kidderminster (L) 3/07, Kidderminster 6/07, York C 5/09		
Levi	Mackin	17	6'01"	12 00	4/4/86	23	Chester	Wrexham Rel 5/09, Droylsden (3ML) 1/08, York C (SL) 1/09, York C 5/09	15	0
Craig	Nelthorpe	11	5'10"	11 00	10/6/87	22	Doncaster	Doncaster Rel 1/09, Hucknall (L) 12/05, Kidderminster (L) 10/06, Gateshead (2ML/Dual) 11/06, Halifax (L) 1/08, Darlington (SL) 3/08, Gateshead (3ML) 8/08, Oxford U 1/09, York C 5/09		
Simon	Russell	19	5'07"	10 06	19/3/85	24	Hull	Hull C, Kidderminster 7/04, York C 8/08	24	0
FORWARDS										
Richard	Brodie	16	6'02"	12 13	8/7/87	22	Gateshead	Whickham, Bolton (Trial), Newcastle Benfield c/s 06, York C 2/07, Barrow (L) 10/08	38	15
Michael	Emmerson	18			29/11/90	18	Middlesbrough	York C		
Michael	Gash	9	5'09"	12 01	3/9/86	22	Cambridge	Cambridge C, Cambridge U 6/06, Cambridge C (L) 1/07, Cambridge C 5/07, Ebbsfleet £20,000 7/08, York C £55,000 7/09		
Richard	Pacquette	10	6'00"	12 06	23/1/83	26	Paddington	QPR Rel 6/04, Stevenage (L) 10/02, Dag & Red (L) 12/03, Mansfield (L) 2/04, MK Dons 9/04 Rel 11/04, Fisher 11/04, Brentford 11/04, Farnborough 12/04 Rel 1/05, Stevenage 1/05 Rel 1/05, Grimsby (Trial) 1/05, St Albans 2/05, Hemel Hempstead 3/05, Hampton & R 3/05, Worthing 7/05, Thurrock (L) 2/06, Havant & W 3/06, Maidenhead 3/08, Histon (L) 2/09, York C 7/09		
Michael	Rankine	15	6'01"	14 12	15/1/85	24	Doncaster	Armthorpe Welfare, Barrow 8/03, Scunthorpe 9/04, Barrow (L) 8/05, Lincoln C (Trial) 12/05, Alfreton 1/06, Rushden & D 7/06, Bournemouth (L) 10/08, York C £10,000 + P/E 6/09		
Adam	Smith	7	5'11"	12 00	20/2/85	24	Huddersfield	Chesterfield Rel 6/08, Lincoln C (L) 1/08, Gainsborough 8/08, York C (2ML) 11/08, York C Undisc 1/09	18	3
Steve	Torpey		6'03"	13 06	8/12/70	38	Islington	Millwall, Bradford C 11/90, Swansea 8/93, Bristol C 8/97, Notts County (L) 8/98, Scunthorpe 2/00 Rel c/s 07, Lincoln C 7/07 Rel 1/08, Farsley Celtic (2ML) 11/07 Perm 1/08, North Ferriby (L) 9/08 Perm, York (Yth Coach) 12/08	2	0

LOANEES		HT	WT	DOB	AGE	POB	From - To	APPS	GOA
(G)Artur	Krysiak	6'01"	12 00	11/8/89	20	Lodz, Pol	Birmingham 8/08 - Swansea C (3ML) 9/08, Motherwell (SL) 1/09	2	0
(F)Peter	Bore	5'11"	11 04	4/11/87	21	Grimsby	Grimsby 9/08 -	4	0
(M)Peter	Holmes	5'11"	11 13	18/11/80	28	Bishop Auckland	Rotherham 9/08 -	5	1
(D)Kyle	Critchell	6'00"	12 02	18/1/87	22	Dorchester	Wrexham (2ML) 1/09 - Weymouth (L) 3/09, Rel 6/09, Weymouth 6/09	6	0
(F)Simon	Brown	5'10"	11 00	18/9/83	25	West Bromwich	Wrexham (SL) 1/09 -	17	0

DEPARTURES		HT	WT	DOB	AGE	POB	From - To	APPS	GOA
(D)Jimmy	Beadle			23/6/88	21	Scarborough	Steinkjer FK (Nor) 1/08 - Whitby (L) 8/08 Perm 9/08	0	0
(M)Gavin	Rothery			22/9/87	21	Morley	Leeds 10/08 - Rel 12/08, Harrogate T 12/08, Carlisle 3/09	1	0
(F)Bruce	Dyer	6'00"	11 03	13/4/75	34	Ilford	Chesterfield 11/08 - Rel 12/08	2	0
(D)Tom	Hirst					Skipton	Hull C 9/08 - Rel 1/09, Harrogate T 1/09		
(M)Niall	Henderson	5'09"		7/2/88	21	Craigavon, NI	Raith 6/08 - Rel 1/09, Newry T	6	0
(D)Darren	Kelly	6'01"	12 10	30/6/79	30	Derry	Derry 8/07 - Rel c/s 09	9	0
(F)Daniel	McBreen	6'01"	13 01	23/4/77	32	Burnley	St Johnstone 6/08 - North Queensland Fury (Aus) 7/09	38	5
(D)Mark	Robinson	5'09"	11 00	24/7/81	28	Guisborough	Torquay 6/07 - Rel 5/09, Gateshead 6/09	37	2
(M)Steven	Hogg	6'03"	11 11	1/10/85	23	Bury	Gretna 6/08 - Rel 5/09	9	0
(M)Simon	Rusk	5'11"	12 08	17/12/81	27	Peterborough	Northwich 1/08 - Rel 5/09, Crawley 5/09	37	0
(M)Liam	Shepherd						Yth - Rel 5/09, Farsley Celtic 6/09	8	0
(D)Josh	Radcliffe						Yth - Rel 5/09, Harrogate RA (L) 10/08, Farsley Celtic 7/09	0	0
(M)Christian	Smith	6'02"	13 02	10/12/87	21	Crewe	Wrexham 1/09 - Rel 5/09, Wrexham 8/09	14	1
(G)Jonathan	McDonald			6/2/91	18	Stockton	Yth - Rel 5/09	0	0
(D)Mark	Greaves	6'01"	13 00	22/1/75	34	Hull	Burton 5/08 - Rel 6/09, Gainsborough 7/09	35	3
(F)Craig	Farrell	6'00"	12 11	5/12/82	26	Middlesbrough	Exeter 6/06 - Oxford U (SL) 1/09, Rushden & D P/E 6/09	25	3
(F)Onome	Sodje	5'09"	12 06	17/7/88	21	Nigeria	Gravesend/Ebbsfleet 6/07 - Barnsley 6/09	36	7
(M)Ben	Wilkinson	5'11"	12 01	25/4/87	22	Sheffield	Hull C 6/08 - Rel 7/09, Altrincham (SL) 3/09, Chester 7/09	21	2
(F)Adam	Boyes						Yth - Scunthorpe £80,000 7/09	23	2
(D)Shaun	Pejic	6'01"	12 03	16/11/82	26	Hereford	Wrexham 2/09 - Rel c/s 09	15	0

YORK CITY

Formed: 1922.

Nickname: Minstermen.

Club Colours: Red and blue halved shirts, blue shorts, blue socks.

Change Colours: Sky blue shirts, sky blue shorts, sky blue socks.

Club Sponsor: CLP Industries.

Previous League: Football League

Ground Address: Bootham Crescent , York YO30 7AQ
Tel No: 01904 624 447
Fax: 01904 631 457
Mobile: 07885 539 956
General email address: nick.bassett@ycfc.net
Official website: www.ycfc.net

SIMPLE DIRECTIONS
By Road
From Tadcaster (A64) take left turning onto A1232 (outer ring road), continue for approx 5 miles to A19 then turn right into York and continue for justover a mile. Bootham Crescent is a turning on the left opposite the Crane Hotel

MATCH TICKETS
Ticket office Telephone: 01904 624 447
Ticket Prices:
Main Stand & Enclosure - Adults £17. Over 65's/Under 16's/Students £11.
Family Stand - Adults/Over 65's £15. Under 16's/Students £6.
David Longhurst Stand - Adults £14. Over 65's/Under 16's/Students £9.
Popular Stand - Adults £15, Over 65's/Under 16's/Students £10.
Away Terracing - Adults £14. Concessions £9. Transfer to seating £1.

Capacity: 9,496 **Seats:** 1,844. **Covered:** 7,000.
Clubhouse: Open for supporters of both sides.
Refreshments: Bars around the ground.
Club Shop: Fully equipped with club merchandise.

PROGRAMME EDITOR
Terry Doyle
Telephone: (B): 01904 784 400
(M): 07712 660 359
E-mail: terry.doyle@cliveowen.com

CLUB STATISTICS

RECORDS

Attendance: 28,123 v Huddersfield Town F.A.Cup 6th Rd 1938

Victory: 9-1 v Southport Div 3 (N) 1957.

Defeat: 0-12 v Chester City Div 3 (N) 1936.

Career Goalscorer: Norman Wilkinson

Career Appearances: Barry Jackson

Transfer Fee Paid:

£140,000 to Burnley for Adrian Randall Dec. 1995

Transfer Fee Received: £1,000,000 from Manchester United for Jonathan Greening March 1998.

SENIOR HONOURS

Football League Div 3 Champions 1983-84.

F.A.Cup Semi-Final 1955 when in Division Three.

PREVIOUS

Grounds: Fulfordgate 1922 -1932.

SETANTA SHIELD 2008-09

FIRST ROUND

AFC Telford Utd 3 Gainsborough 2 *aet (Sept 9)* Att: 652
Alfreton Town 2 **Stafford Rangers** 3 *(Sept 17)*
Basingstoke Town 1 **Fisher Athletic** 3 *(Sept 9)* Att: 139
Bishop's Stortford 2 Bromley 1 *(Sept 9)* Att: 201
Bognor Regis Town 2 Worcester City 0 *(Sept 9)* Att: 168
Braintree Town 3 Hampton/Richmond 0 *(Sept 9)* Att: 127
Burscough 1 **Blyth Spartans** 4 *(Sept 9)* Att: 160
Chelmsford City 1 AFC Wimbledon 0 *(Sept 8)* Att: 575
Dorchester Town 4 **Newport Co.** 5 *aet (Sept 9)* Att: 178
Droylsden 1 **Gateshead** 2 *(Sept 8)* Att: 190
Eastleigh 4 Weston-sr-Mare 4 *aet* (5-4p) *(Sept 9)* Att: 173
Farsley Celtic 3 Workington 1 *(Sept 9)* Att: 101
Harrogate T. 1 **Fleetwood** 1 *aet* (4-5p) *(Sept 9)* Att: 174
Hucknall Town 1 **Hinckley United** 3 *(Sept 9)* Att: 192
Hyde United 1 **Vauxhall Motors** 2 *(Sept 8)* Att: 97
King's Lynn 1 **Tamworth** 2 *(Sept 9)* Att: 510
Maidenhead 1 **Havant/Waterlooville** 2 *(Sept 9)* Att: 171
Redditch United 0 **Solihull Moors** 1 *(Sept 23)* Att: 157
St Albans City 0 **Hayes & Yeading** 1 *(Sept 9)* Att: 165
Stalybridge Celtic 1 **Southport** 4 *(Sept 9)* Att: 231
Team Bath 1 **Bath City** 2 *aet (Sept 9)*
Thurrock 2 Welling United 0 *(Sept 9)*

SECOND ROUND

AFC Telford Utd 2 Redditch Utd 1 *aet (Oct 7)* Att: 692
Altrincham 1 Farsley Celtic 1 *aet* (4-2p) *(Oct 14)* Att: 259
Barrow 3 Fleetwood Town 2 *(Oct 14)* Att: 618
Bath City 4 Newport County 1 *(Oct 28)* Att: 241
Blyth Spartans 1 **Gateshead** 2 *(Oct 21)* Att: 632
Chelmsford City 3 Braintree Town 1 *(Oct 6)* Att: 474
Eastleigh 2 **Havant & Waterlooville** 3 *(Oct 7)* Att: 489
Fisher Athletic 2 **Eastbourne Boro.** 3 *(Sept 30)* Att: 58
Hinckley United 2 Tamworth 1 *(Oct 6)* Att: 267
Kettering Town 4 Bishop's Stortford 2 *(Oct 21)* Att: 420
Lewes 0 **Bognor Regis Town** 2 *(Oct 14)* Att: 222
Stafford Rangers 3 Northwich Vics 1 *(Oct 14)* Att: 327
Thurrock 3 Hayes & Yeading 3 *aet* (5-4p) *(Oct 7)*
Vauxhall Motors 0 **Southport** 3 *(Oct 7)* Att: 163

THIRD ROUND

AFC Telford United 4 Cambridge Utd 3 *(Nov 4)* Att: 941
Altrincham 1 **Wrexham** 2 *aet (Nov 4)* Att: 534
Barrow 3 Gateshead 1 *(Nov 4)* Att: 551
Bath City 0 **Salisbury City** 1 *(Nov 4)* Att: 230
Burton Albion 3 Kidderminster H. 2 *(Nov 4)* Att: 554
Crawley T. 3 Havant & Waterlooville 0 *(Nov 4)* Att: 239
Eastbourne Borough 1 **Ebbsfleet Utd** 3 *(Nov 4)* Att: 300
Forest Green Rovers 2 Oxford United 1 *(Nov 4)* Att: 383
Grays Athletic 2 **Chelmsford City** 4 *(Nov 25)* Att: 262
Hinckley United 2 Histon 1 *(Nov 3)* Att: 202
Kettering Town 4 Thurrock 1 *(Nov 4)* Att: 435
Rushden & Diamonds 0 **Stevenage B.** 3 *(Nov 4)* Att: 430
Stafford Rangers 1 **Southport** 2 *(Nov 4)* Att: 261
Weymouth 0 **Torquay United** 3 *(Nov 4)* Att: 621
Woking 3 Bognor Regis Town 0 *(Nov 8)* Att: 460
York City 1 Mansfield Town 1 *aet* (4-2p) *(Nov 4)*

FOURTH ROUND

AFC Telford United 3 Burton Albion 0 *(Dec 2)* Att: 875
Barrow 3 York City 1 *(Jan 20)* Att: 596
Crawley Town 2 Chelmsford City 1 *(Dec 16)* Att: 304
Ebbsfleet Utd 3 Stevenage Borough 0 *(Dec 2)* Att: 285
Forest Green Rovers 1 Torquay Utd 0 *(Dec 2)* Att: 421
Hinckley United 2 **Kettering Town** 3 *aet (Dec 1)* Att: 270
Salisbury City 0 **Woking** 3 *(Dec 2)* Att: 297
Wrexham 1 **Southport** 3 *aet (Dec 9)* Att: 1123

QUARTER-FINALS

AFC Telford Utd 3 Kettering T. 2 *aet (Jan 20)* Att: 874
Barrow 3 Southport 1 *(Feb 3)* Att: 678
Crawley Town 1 Ebbsfleet United 2 *(Mar 17)* Att: 844
Woking 2 **Forest Green R.** 2 *aet* (4-5p) *(Jan 13)* Att: 499

SEMI-FINAL

Barrow 0 **AFC Telford United** 1 *(Mar 26)* Att: 2,109
Ebbsfleet United 0 **Forest Green Rovers 1** *(Mar 26)* Att: 431

FINAL

(April 9th at Forest Green Rovers)

Forest Green Rovers 0 **AFC Telford United** 0 (0-3p) ***Att:*** 2,323

BURTON ALBION

BEST LGE ATT.: **6,192** v Oxford United
LOWEST: **1,291** v Rushden & Diamonds

No.	Date	Comp	H/A	Opponents	Att:	Result	Goalscorers	Pos
1	Aug 9	BSP	A	Salisbury City	1122	W 1 - 0	**Pearson** 2	
2	12		H	Northwich Victoria	1701	D 1 - 1	Webster 83	
3	16		H	Woking	1456	W 3 - 2	Goodfellow 58 84 **Pearson** 65 (pen)	4
4	23		A	Histon	910	L 3 - 4	Stride 40 **Pearson** 45 (pen) McGrath 85	10
5	25		H	Kidderminster Harriers	1798	D 2 - 2	**Pearson** 31 Brayford 78	11
6	30		H	Lewes	1432	W 5 - 2	**Pearson** 10 Gilroy 23 Webster 60 89 Harrod 71	6
7	Sept 2		A	Wrexham	4104	W 1 - 0	Harrad15	1
8	6		A	Stevenage Borough	1717	L 1 - 4	Corbett 75	9
9	13		H	Weymouth	1435	D 1 - 1	**Pearson** 38	7
10	20		A	Rushden & Diamonds	1448	L 1 - 2	Harrad 66 (pen)	11
11	22		A	Kettering Town	1616	W 1 - 0	**Pearson** 79	7
12	27		H	Forest Green Rovers	1545	W 4 - 2	Gilroy 58 Goodfellow 71 Harrad 75 (pen) 90	4
13	Oct 4		H	Crawley Town	1915	W 2 - 1	**Pearson** 37 90 (pen)	2
14	7		A	Barrow	1466	D 0 - 0		4
15	13		H	Mansfield Town	2871	W 1 - 0	McGrath 43	3
16	18		A	Oxford United	4494	L 1 - 2	Webster 89	6
17	**25**	**F.A.C. 4Q**	**A**	**Kettering Town**	**1726**	**L 0 - 3**		
18	Nov 1		H	Ebbsfleet United	1584	W 3 - 1	Webster 3 81 Gilroy 55	4
19	**4**	**SS 3**	**H**	**Kidderminster Harriers**	**554**	**W 3 - 2**	**Harrad 6, Austin 50, Banim 85**	
20	8		A	Northwich Victoria	932	W 1 - 0	Harrad 19	1
21	15		A	Lewes	630	W 1 - 0	**Pearson** 45 (Pen)	1
22	22		H	Stevenage Borough	1944	W 2 - 0	Simpson 32 70	2
23	29		H	Eastbourne Borough	1870	W 2 - 0	**Pearson** 56 (pen) Armstrong 81	1
24	**Dec 2**	**SS N4**	**A**	**AFC Telford**	**875**	**L 0 - 3**		
25	6		A	Forest Green Rovers	812	W 3 - 2	Harrod 21 27 **Pearson** 58 (pen)	1
26	9		H	Cambridge United	1804	W 3 - 1	McGrath 5 Harrad 42 (pen) **Pearson** 84	1
27	**16**	**F.A.T 1R**	**H**	**Farsley Celtic**	**923**	**D 1 - 1**	**Pearson 28**	
28	20		A	Altrincham	931	W 3 - 1	**Pearson** 40 65 (pen) McGrath 86	1
29	**23**	**F.A.T. 1R r**	**A**	**Farsley Celtic**	**262**	**D 2 - 2**	**Banim 15 51 (won 3-2 after pens)**	
30	26		H	York City	3578	W 2 - 1	Harrad 62 Greaves 70 (og)	1
31	29		A	Mansfield Town	3612	W 2 - 0	**Pearson** 26 Goodfellow 38	1
32	Jan 1		A	York City	2703	W 3 - 1	Simpson 34 Harrad 62 Godfellow 83	1
33	**10**	**F.A.T. 2R**	**H**	**Salisbury City**	**1472**	**W 3 - 0**	**Webster 13 73 Goodfellow 24**	
34	17		A	Grays Athletic	651	W 1 - 0	Yates 31	1
35	24		H	Altrincham	2124	D 1 - 1	Harrad 52	1
36	26		H	Barrow	1939	W 2 - 1	Harrad 52 Buxton 59	
37	**31**	**F.A.T 3R**	**A**	**Stevenage Borough**	**1296**	**L 0 - 4**		
38	Feb 9		H	Rushden & Diamonds	1291	W 3 - 0	McGrath 40 Austin 45 Harrad 64	1
39	17		H	Wrexham	3262	W 2 - 1	Butler 57 Morris 79	
40	28		A	Woking	1813	D 0 - 0		1
41	Mar 7		A	Cambridge United	4377	L 0 - 2		
42	11		A	Ebbsfleet United	711	L 1 - 2	**Pearson** 49	1
43	14		H	Salisbury City	2274	L 1 - 2	Morris 82	1
44	17		A	Weymouth	848	W 5 - 0	Morris 24 52 Harrad 37 Gilroy 44 Hoyte 86 (og)	
45	21		A	Eastbourne Borough	1521	W 2 - 1	Butler 63 **Pearson** 90	1
46	28		H	Grays Athletic	2388	W 4 - 0	Morris 2 22 McGrath16 Gilroy 84	1
47	31		H	Kettering Town	2624	D 1 - 1	Stride 8	1
48	April 4		A	Crawley Town	1131	L 0 - 4		1
49	6		H	Torquay United	4891	L 0 - 1		1
50	11		H	Histon	3311	W 3 - 1	Webster 13 Corbett 53 Austin 84	1
51	13		A	Kidderminster Harriers	3025	L 1 - 2	Morris 45	1
52	17		H	Oxford United	6192	L 0 - 1		1
53	26		A	Torquay United	4528	L 1 - 2	Goodfellow 8 Became Champions	

Average Home Att: 2465 (1595) **Goals** 90 64

Best Position: 1st **Worst:** 11th

Goalscorers: Pearson 19, Harrad 16, Webster 9, Goodfellow 7, Morris 7, McGrath 6, Gilroy 5, Austin 3, Banim 3, Simpson 3, Butler 2, Corbett 2, Stride 2, Armstrong 1, Brayford 1, Buxton 1, Yates 1. Own Goals 2.

POOLE 1	JAMES 5	AUSTIN 15	HOLMES 12	BAILEY 19	WEBSTER 3	MCGRATH 6	BRAYFORD 2	BANIM 10	CORBETT 8	PEARSON 18	HARRAD 9	STRIDE 7	DEENEY 13	GOODFELLOW 14	GILROY 11	SIMPSON 4	BUXTON 16	MORRIS 17	A YATES 21	NEWBY 22	CLOUGH 20	SIMMONS 23	ARMSTRONG 24	MCCUBBIN 26	J YATES 21	BUTLER 25	BYRNE 27	MARTIN 31	
X	X	X	X	X	X	X	X	X	X	X	S	S	U	U	U														1
X	X	X	X	X	S	X	X	X	X	X	S	S	U	U	X														2
X	X	X	U		X	X	X	X	X	X	S	S	U	S	X	X													3
X		U	U	X	X	X	X	S	X	X	X	X	U	S		X	X												4
X		X	U	X	X	X	X	X	X	X	S	S	U	X		X		S											5
X		S	U		X	X	X	X	X	X	S	X	U	S	X	X			X										6
X		X	U		X	X		X	X		X	S	U	S	X	X	X		X	S									7
X		X	S			X		S	X	X	X	X	U	U	X	X	X		X	S									8
X		X	U			X		X	X	X	S	X	U	S	X	X	X		X	S									9
X		X	U			X		S	X	X	S	X	U	S	X	X	X		X	X									10
		X	X	S		X		S	X	X	U	S	X	X	X		X	U	X	X									11
			X	U	X	X		X	X	X	S	X	X	X	X		X	S	U	S									12
U			X	S	X	X			X	X	X	X	X	X	X		X	S	U	S									13
U		U	X	X	X	X			X	X	X		X	X	X	S	X	S		S									14
X			S	S	X	X		U	X	X	S	X		X	X	X	X	X		U									15
X		S	U	X	X	X			X	X	S		U	X	X	X	X	X		S									16
X	**U**	**X**	**X**	**S**	**X**	**X**		**X**	**X**	**X**	**X**		**U**	**S**	**U**	**X**	**X**			**S**	**U**								17
X	X	S		S	X	X			X	X	S		U	U	X	X	X			X		X							18
U	**X**	**X**	**X**	**X**	**X**	**S**		**X**	**X**	**X**	**X**		**X**			**U**		**S**				**X**							19
X	X	S		U	X	X		U	X	X	X		U		X	X	X	S		X									20
X	X	S		U	X	X		S	X	X	S		U		X	X	X	X		X									21
X	X	S			X	X			X	X	X		U	U	X	X	X			X		S	S						22
X	X	S	U			X		S	X	X	X		U		X	X	X	S		X			X						23
U		**X**	**X**	**X**	**X**			**X**		**S**	**S**		**X**	**X**				**X**		**S**	**U**	**X**	**X**	**X**					24
X	X	S	S		X	X			X	X	X		U		X	X	X	S		X			U						25
X	X	S	S		X	X			X	S	X		U		X	X	X	X		X			U						26
U		**X**	**X**	**U**	**X**				**X**	**X**	**X**		**X**		**X**	**X**		**S**		**S**		**X**	**X**	**S**					27
X	X	S	S		X	X			X	X	X		U		X	X	X	X		S			U						28
U		**X**	**X**	**X**	**S**	**S**		**X**	**X**		**X**		**X**	**X**		**X**	**S**				**U**		**X**	**X**					29
X		X	S	U	X	X		U	X	X	X		U	S	X	X	X	X											30
X		X	S		X	X		S	X	X	X		U	S	X	X	X	X					U						31
X	U	X	S		X	X			X	X	X		U	X		X	X	S		X			S						32
X	**X**	**S**	**U**		**X**	**X**			**X**	**X**	**X**		**U**	**X**		**X**	**X**	**S**		**S**					**X**				33
X	X	X	U		X	X				X	X	U	U	X		X	X	S		S					X				34
X	X	S			X	X			X	X	X	S	U	X	S	X	X	U							X				35
X	X	X	U			X			X	X	X	S	U	X	X	X	X	S							U				36
X	**S**	**X**	**U**			**X**			**X**	**S**	**X**	**X**	**U**	**X**		**X**	**X**	**X**		**S**					**X**				37
X	X	X	S			X			X	X	X	U	U	X	X	X	X	S							U				38
X	X	X			U	X			X	X	X	S	U	X	X	X	X	S								S			39
X	X	X	U		S	X			X	X	X	S	U	X	X	X	X									S			40
X	X	X	U		X	X			X	S	X	U	U	S	X	X	X									X			41
X	X	U	S		X	X			X	X	X	S	U	X		X	X			S					X				42
X	X	S			X	X			X	X	X	S	U	X	X	X	X	S							U				43
X	X	U			X	X			X	S	X	X	U		X	X	X	X							S		S		44
X	X	U			X	X			X	S	X	X	U		X	X	X	X								S	S		45
X	X	U			X	X			X	S	X	X	U		X	X	X	X								S	S		46
X	X	U			X	X			X	U		X	U	S	X	X	X	X								S	X		47
X		X	U		X	X			X	S		X	U	S	X	X	X	X								S	X		48
X	X	S	U		X	X			X	X			U	S	X	X	X			U						X	X		49
	X	S			X	X			X		X	X	X	U	X	X	X	X		S						S	U		50
	X	S			X	X			X		X	X	X	U	X	X	X	X		S						S	U		51
	X	U			X	X			X		S	X	X	X	X	X	X	X								S	U	U	52
	X	U			X	X			X	U		X	X	X		X	X	X		U						X	S	U	53
Total League Appearances																													
38	29	19	6	6	36	46	6	8	45	34	28	17	8	18	38	40	41	16	6	10	0	1	1	0	3	3	3	0	X
0	0	15	10	4	2	0	0	7	0	6	13	12	0	12	1	1	0	13	0	12	0	1	2	0	1	9	4	0	S
2	1	9	15	4	1	0	0	3	0	2	1	3	37	7	1	0	0	2	2	3	0	0	4	0	3	0	3	2	U
Total Cup Appearances																													
3	2	6	5	3	5	3	0	4	6	4	6	1	4	4	1	5	3	2	0	0	0	3	3	2	2	0	0	0	X
0	1	1	0	1	1	2	0	0	0	2	1	0	0	1	0	0	1	3	0	5	0	0	0	1	0	0	0	0	S
4	1	0	2	1	0	0	0	0	0	0	0	0	3	0	1	1	0	0	0	0	3	0	0	0	0	0	0	0	U

TORQUAY UNITED

BEST LGE ATT.: **4,528** v Burton Albion
LOWEST: **1,554** v Forest Green Rovers

No.	Date	Comp	H/A	Opponents	Att:	Result		
1	Aug 9	BSP	A	Histon	S928	D 1 - 1	**Sills** 55 (pen)	
2	12		H	Woking	2881	W 2 - 1	Benyon 60 Carlisle 82	
3	18		H	Ebbsfleet United	1805	L 0 - 2		11
4	23		A	Crawley Town	1154	L 1 - 3	Dsane 49	17
5	25		H	Salisbury City	2001	L 0 - 1		20
6	28		H	York City	1598	D 1 - 1	Stevens 65	18
7	Sept 4		A	Kidderminster Harriers	1345	L 0 - 1		20
8	7		H	Northwich Victoria	1752	W 2 - 1	Carlisle 9 **Sills** (pen) 90	
9	13		A	Cambridge United	4041	W 1 - 0	Carlisle 90	17
10	20		H	Eastbourne Borough	1921	W 2 - 0	Thompson 23 Hargreaves 73	
11	23		A	Forest Green Rovers	1022	W 2 - 1	Benyon 69 Green 90	11
12	27		A	Wrexham	2897	D 1 - 1	**Sills** 35	11
13	Oct 4		H	Stevenage Borough	2066	W 3 - 0	Robertson 67 **Sills** 71 Wroe 87	8
14	9		H	Oxford United	1955	D 1 - 1	Robertson 21	8
15	13		A	Rushden & Diamonds	1649	W 3 - 1	Carlisle 7 **Sills** 15 Wroe 51	7
16	18		A	Ebbsfleet United	1781	W 2 - 0	Wroe 42 Carlisle 55	5
17	**25**	**F.A.C. 4Q**	**H**	**Chipstead**	**1800**	**W 4 - 1**	**Thompson 9 40 Sills 67 88**	
18	Nov 1		H	Mansfield Town	2267	W 2 - 0	Dsane 54 Woods 69	2
19	**4**	**SS 3**	**A**	**Weymouth**	**621**	**W 3 - 0**	**Sills 2 16 Benyon 78**	
20	**8**	**F.A.C. 1R**	**H**	**Evesham United**	**2275**	**W 2 - 0**	**Sills 28 75**	
21	15		A	York City	2412	W 2 - 1	Dsane 68 Ellis 90	2
22	18		H	Lewes	2118	W 4 - 1	**Sills** 1 44 Stevens 27 47	
23	22		A	Woking	2452	D 2 - 2	Benyon 55 Stevens 65	
24	**29**	**F.A.C 2R**	**H**	**Oxford United**	**2647**	**W 2 - 0**	**Benyon 41 83**	
25	**Dec 2**	**SS S4**	**A**	**Forest Green Rovers**	**421**	**L 0-1**		
26	6		H	Cambridge United	2310	D 0 - 0		3
27	9		A	Eastbourne Borough	1204	L 2 - 4	Benyon 34 **Sills** 90	
28	**13**	**F.A.T 1R**	**H**	**Bath City**	**1176**	**W 2 - 0**	**Mansell 52** Dsane **69**	
29	20		H	Histon	2201	W 4 - 1	Dsane 7 22 Wroe 62 **Sills** 85	3
30	26		A	Weymouth	2323	W 1 - 0	Green 24	2
31	28		H	Kidderminster Harriers	2749	L 0 - 1		5
32	**Jan 3**	**F.A.C. 3R**	**H**	**Blackpool**	**3654**	**W 1 - 0**	**Green 32**	
33	**10**	**F.A.T. 2R**	**H**	**Rushden & Diamonds**	**1728**	**W 1 - 0**	**Hargreaves 69**	
34	16		H	Wrexham	1842	D 1 - 1	Dsane 61	4
35	**24**	**F.A.C. 4R**	**H**	**Coventry City**	**6018**	**L 0 - 1**		
36	27		A	Lewes	558	W 2 - 0	Nicholson 43 Dsane 83	
37	**31**	**F.A.T 3R**	**A**	**Southport**	**980**	**L 0 - 3**		
38	Feb 10		H	Weymouth	1743	L 0 - 2		
39	14		H	Altrincham	1760	W 3 - 1	**Sills** 19 55 (pen) Benyon 76	5
40	21		A	Kettering Town	1869	L 1 - 2	Nicholson 45	6
41	24		H	Forest Green Rovers	1554	D 3 - 3	Green 18 Hargreaves 45 Christie 80	6
42	28		A	Oxford United	5837	W 2 - 0	Benyon 64 70	5
43	Mar 3		A	Grays Athletic	310	W 2 - 1	Nicholson 12 Carlisle 86	
44	7		H	Rushden & Diamonds	2161	D 1 - 1	**Sills** 41	
45	10		A	Altrincham	735	W 1 - 0	Carlisle 90	4
46	14		H	Barrow	2269	W 4 - 1	Wroe 4 Benyon 39 **Sills** 68 Green 90	
47	21		A	Northwich Victoria	705	W 3 - 2	Todd 49 **Sills** 68 Dsane 76	3
48	24		H	Grays Athletic	1996	D 1 - 1	Dsane 47	
49	28		A	Mansfield Town	2437	D 1 - 1	Sturrock 64	3
50	April 4		H	Kettering Town	2503	W 2 - 0	Robertson 20 Sturrock 65	3
51	6		A	Burton Albion	4891	W 1 - 0	Stevens 10	2
52	11		H	Crawley Town	3031	L 0 - 2		3
53	13		A	Salisbury City	2039	D 2 - 2	Carlisle 20 (pen) Wroe 90	3
54	18		A	Stevenage Borough	2819	D 0 - 0		4
55	21		A	Barrow	1918	D 1 - 1	Hargreaves 49	
56	26		H	Burton Albion	4528	W 2 - 1	Hargreaves 13 Benyon 46	4
57	**May 1**	**Play-Off SF1**	**H**	**Histon**	**3737**	**W 2 - 0**	**Wroe 36 Sills 74**	
58	**4**	**Play Off SF2**	**A**	**Histon**	**2482**	**L 0 - 1**		
59	**17**	**Play-off F**	**N**	**Cambridge United**	**35089**	**W 2 - 0**	**Hargreaves 35, Sills 75**	

Average Home Att: 2218 (3126) **Goals** 91 53
Best Position: 2nd **Worst:** 20th
Goalscorers: Sills 22, Benyon 12, Dsane 10, Carlisle 8, Wroe 7, Hargreaves 6, Green 5, Stevens 5, Nicholson 3, Robertson 3, Thompson 3, Sturrock 2, Mansell 1, Christie 1, Ellis 1, Todd 1, Woods 1.

POKE 1	TODD 6	STEVENS 19	MANSELL 7	HARGREAVES 14	THOMPSON 12	WROE 11	CARLISLE 15	HODGES 16	SILLS 8	BENYON 9	CARAYOL 18	D'SANE 10	NICHOLSON 3	BROUGH 2	GREEN 17	ROBERTSON 5	ADAMS 24	ELLIS 25	WOODS 4	YEOMAN 22	BEVAN 20	CHARRAN 28	WESTCOTT 27	PLUMMER 32	CHRISTIE 21	STURROCK 33	RICE 23	
X	X	X	X	X	X	X	X	X	X	X	S	S	U	U	U													1
X	X	X	X	X	X	X	X	X	X	X	S	U	S	U	S													2
X	X	X	X	X	X	X	X		X	X	S	U	X	U	S	S												3
X		U	X	X	X		X	X	S	S	X	X	X	X	X		S	U										4
X		S	X	X			X	X	X	U	X	X		U	S	X	U	X	X									5
X		S	X	X		U	X	X	X	U	X	X		U	S	X		X	X									6
X		U	X	X		U	X	X	X	S	S	X	X		S	X		X	X									7
X		S	X	X	S	U	X	X	S	X	X				X	X		X	X	U								8
X	X	S	X	X	X	X	X	X	X	U	X				S	S	U	X										9
X	X	S	X	X	X	X	X	X	X	S	X		U		S		U		X									10
X	X	U	X	X	X	X		X	X	S	X	X	S		S		U		X									11
		U	X	X	S	X		X	X	X	U	S	X		X	X	U		X		X							12
		U	X	X	S	X	X	U	X		S	X	X		X	X	U		X		X							13
		X	X	X	U	X	X	S	X		S		X		X	X	U		X	S	X							14
		X	X	X	S	X	X	S	X	U	S		X		X	X	U		X		X							15
		U	X	X	X	X	X	U	X	S	U	X	X			X	U		X		X							16
		U	**X**	**X**	**X**	**X**		**X**	**X**	**S**	**X**	**X**	**X**	**U**			**U**	**U**	**X**		**X**	**S**	**U**					**17**
		S	X	X	X	X		X	X	U	X	X	X				U	U	X		X	S						18
		S	**X**	**X**	**X**	**X**		**X**	**X**	**S**	**X**	**X**	**X**	**U**	**S**		**U**		**X**		**X**							**19**
		S	**X**	**X**	**X**	**X**		**X**	**X**	**S**	**X**	**X**	**X**	**U**	**U**		**U**	**U**	**X**		**X**	**U**						**20**
		U	X	X	X	X		X	X	U		X	X	U	S		U	X	X		X							21
		X	X	X	X	X		X	X	S	S	X	X		U		U	U	X		X							22
		X	X	X	X	X		X	X	S	X		X	U	U		U	U	X		X							23
		U	**X**	**X**	**X**	**X**		**X**	**X**	**S**	**X**	**X**	**X**	**U**	**S**	**U**	**U**	**U**	**X**		**X**							**24**
X		**X**	**X**		**S**	**S**		**U**	**U**	**X**	**X**		**X**	**X**	**X**	**X**	**X**	**X**				**S**						**25**
		X	X	X	U	X	X	X	X	X	S		X		S	U	U		X		X							26
		X	X	X	U	X	X	X	X	X	S		X	S	U	U			X		X							27
		S	**X**	**X**	**U**	**X**	**X**	**X**	**X**		**U**	**X**	**X**		**X**	**U**	**U**		**X**		**X**							**28**
		U	X	X	U	X	X	X	X	S	S	X	X		X	U			X		X							29
		S	X	X	U	X	X	X	X	S	X		X		X	U	U		X		X							30
		X	X	X	S	X	X	X	X	S			X	U	X	U	U		X		X							31
		U	**X**	**X**	**S**	**X**	**X**	**X**	**X**	**S**		**X**	**X**		**X**	**U**	**U**	**U**	**X**		**X**			**U**				**32**
		S	**X**	**X**	**S**	**X**	**X**	**X**		**S**		**X**	**X**		**X**	**U**	**U**		**X**		**X**			**X**				**33**
		U	X	X	U	X	X	X	X	S		X	X		X	U			X		X			U				34
U		**S**	**X**	**X**	**U**	**X**	**X**	**X**	**X**	**S**	**S**	**X**	**X**		**X**	**U**	**U**		**X**		**X**							**35**
U		U	X	X	X		X		X	S	U	X	X		U	X	X		X		X							36
U			**X**	**X**	**X**	**X**		**X**	**X**	**S**	**S**	**X**	**X**		**S**	**U**	**X**		**X**		**X**							**37**
		S	X	X	U	X	X	X	X	U	S	X	X		U	X					X				X			38
		U	X	X	U	X	X	U	X	X	U	X	X			X			X		X				S			39
		U	X		X	X	X	X	X	X	S	X	X		S	X		U			X				S			40
		S	X	X	U	X		X	X	X	X	U	X		X	U			X		X				S			41
		U	X	X	U	X		X	X	S	X	S	X		X	S			X		X				X			42
		U	X	X	S	X	S		X	X	X		X		X	X	S	U	X		X							43
		S	X	X	U	X	U	U	X	X	X		X		X	X		U	X		X							44
		U	X	X	X	X	S	X		X	U		X		X	X	U	X		U	X							45
		X	U	X	X	X	S	X	X	X	U		X		S	X		X			X				U			46
	X	X	S	X	X	X	X	X	X	S	U	S	X			X					X				U			47
	X	S		X		X	X	X	X	X	U	X	X		S	X		U			X				U			48
	X	S		X		X	X	X	X	U		X	X			X	U	U			X				U	X		49
	X	S	X	X		X	X	U	X	S	U	X	X			X					X				U	X		50
	X		X	X		X	X	S		S	U		X		U	X	U				X							51
	X	X	X	X		X	X	U	X	S	S	S	X	U		X					X					X		52
	X	U	X			X	X	U	X	X	S	X	X	X	S	X					X				S			53
	X	U	X	X		X	X	S	X	U	S	X	X			X					X				U	X		54
S	X	S		X	U	X	X	X	X	U		X	X			X		S			X					X		55
X	X	X	X	X		X	X	U	X	X	U		X			X									U	S	U	56
X	**X**	**X**	**X**	**X**		**X**	**X**	**U**	**X**		**U**		**X**		**U**	**X**									**S**	**X**	**U**	**57**
X	**X**	**X**	**X**	**X**		**X**	**X**	**S**	**X**	**S**	**U**		**X**			**X**		**U**								**X**	**U**	**58**
X	**X**	**X**	**X**	**X**	**S**	**X**	**X**	**S**	**X**	**X**	**S**		**X**		**U**	**X**											**U**	**59**
Total League Appearances																												
12	16	14	41	44	17	40	34	31	42	17	14	22	38	2	15	27	1	8	27	0	34	0	0	0	2	5	0	**X**
1	0	14	1	0	6	0	3	4	2	17	16	5	2	1	14	3	2	1	0	1	0	1	0	0	4	1	0	**S**
1	0	17	1	0	12	3	1	8	0	10	11	3	2	9	7	7	19	9	0	2	0	0	0	1	7	0	1	**U**
Total Cup Appearances																												
4	3	4	13	12	5	12	7	9	11	2	5	9	13	1	5	4	2	1	9	0	9	0	0	1	0	2	0	**X**
0	0	5	0	0	4	1	0	2	0	9	3	0	0	0	3	0	0	0	0	0	0	2	0	0	1	0	0	**S**
2	0	3	0	0	2	0	0	2	1	0	3	0	0	4	3	6	8	5	0	0	0	1	1	1	0	0	3	**U**

Top left: Farsley's Curtis Aspden gets up above his defence to punch clear, whilst in the same match Stephen Downes keeps his body between the ball and Alfreton's Tom Curtis (above).

Above: Tom Field scores the first of two penalties for Vauxhall Motors against Tamworth. Left: Chris Noone prepares to get past Tamworth's Tom Shaw during the same game.

Photos: Bill Wheatcroft.

A.F.C.TELFORD UNITED

Back row, (L-R): Ruddy Farquharson, Scott Embrey, Tom Field, Matt Nolan, Phil Trainer, Jamie Vermiglio, Stephen Clark.
Middle row: Derek Wellings, Steve Torpey, Danny Carey-Bertram, Jimmy Turner, Ryan Young, Jon Adams, Lee Vaughan, Steve Jagielka, Dean Williams
Front row: Liam Blakeman, Carl Rodgers, Andy Brown, Rob Smith, Stuart Whitehead, Steve Wynn, Gavin Cowan, Danny Edwards, Gareth Jelleyman.

CLUB PERSONNEL

Chairman: Lee Carter.

Vice-Chairman: Win Pryce.

Company Secretary: Ian Tyrer.

Additional Directors: David Topping, Ian Dosser.

Secretary: Stuart Massey.

Tel: (B): 01952 640064 (M): 07877 804926

Correspondence to: Club

Email: stuart.massey@afctu.co.uk

Commercial Manager: Anton Gunter.

(M): 07500 888 739

Manager: Rob Smith.

Club therapist: Rudy Farqharson.

One of the favourites for promotion last season, 'The Bucks' did just about everything expected of them except win the play off final!. Wonderful home league support averaged just under 2,000, and every cup competition was taken seriously. The Setanta Shield was won on penalties against Forest Green Rovers and thirteen cup ties were fought out in The F.A.Cup and F.A.Trophy.

Corby Town, Hendon and Northwich Victoria were beaten in the F.A Cup before going out to Southend United after a replay and The Trophy Semi -Final elimination by York City was a bitter blow after an impressive list of successes against Gainsborough Trinity, Boston United, Hayes & Yeading, Kettering Town and Southport!

Local supporters must be confident for the season ahead, especially if Danny Carey-Bertram (20 goals) and Andy Brown (17) are retained. Last season's Blue Square North form was certainly consistent despite the massive number of cup ties and all credit to Rob Smith and his managerial team for keeping the pressure on all season.

Even the play-offs were fought out bravely at the end of the season after a senior campaign featuring fifty eight quality matches plus the Sertanta Shield games. The play-offs produced five goals against Alfreton Town but a trip to Gateshead for the final proved just one challenge too much. A terrific season had finished with a disappointment, but expectations are high for the season ahead.

AFC TELFORD UNITED

BEST LGE ATT.: **3,558** v Southport
LOWEST: **1,482** v Harrogate Town

No.	Date	Comp	H/A	Opponents	Att:	Result	Goalscorers	Pos
1	Aug 9	BSN	A	Stalybridge Celtic	762	D 2 - 2	Adams 44 Brown 61	
2	12		H	Hinckley United	1792	W 4 - 2	Brown 4 FEARNS 3 (43 47 81)	
3	16		H	Blyth Spartans	1750	W 2 - 1	Naylor 29 Fearns 51	3
4	23		A	Redditch United	669	W 1 - 0	Brown 28	
5	25		H	Alfreton Town	2026	D 0 - 0		
6	30		A	Droylsden	544	L 0 - 1		4
7	Sept 2		A	Harrogate Town	443	L 0 - 2		
8	6		H	Gainsborough Trinity	1860	W 2 - 1	Vermiglio 32 Cowan 88	5
9	**8**	**SS N1**	**H**	**Gainsborough Trinity**	**652**	**W 3 - 2***	**Stevens 62, Adams 80, Vermiglio 104**	
10	13		H	Fleetwood Town	1805	D 0 - 0		6
11	20		A	Gateshead	413	D 1 - 1	Moore 63	7
12	**27**	**F.A.C. 2Q**	**H**	**Corby Town**	**1262**	**W 3 - 2**	**FEARNS 3 (10 26 43)**	
13	Oct 4		H	Workington	1753	D 0 - 0		6
14	**7**	**SS N2**	**H**	**Solihull Moors**	**692**	**W 2 - 1***	**Naylor pen 11, Jagielka 95**	
15	**11**	**F.A.C. 3Q**	**A**	**Hendon**	**377**	**W 2 - 1**	**Fearns 11 Moore 44**	
16	18		A	Burscough	495	W 2 - 0	Brown 61 Carey-Bertram 90	5
17	21		H	Solihull Moors	1510	W 3 - 0	Brown 33 Carey Bertram 48 Moore 72	
18	**28**	**F.A.C. 4Q**	**A**	**Northwich Victoria**	**1003**	**W 3 - 0**	**Moore 16 68 Brown 45 (pen)**	
19	Nov 1		H	Hucknall Town	1803	W 3 - 1	BROWN 3 (82 83 89)	4
20	**4**	**SS 3**	**H**	**Cambridge United**	**941**	**W 4 - 3**	**Carey-Bertram 9, Rodgers 21, Fearns 53, 73**	
21	**8**	**F.A.C 1R**	**H**	**Southend United**	**3631**	**D 2 - 2**	**Adams 70 83**	
22	15		H	Gateshead	2086	W 1 - 0	Meredith 66	5
23	**18**	**F.A.C. 1R r**	**A**	**Southend United**	**4415**	**L 0 - 2**		
24	**22**	**F.A.T. 3Q**	**A**	**Gainsborough Trinity**	**441**	**W 2 - 0**	**Carey-Bertram 75 Fearns 90**	
25	29		A	Hucknall Town	365	W 5 - 0	Khela 6 Rodgers 38 Fearns 42 Moore 60 Carey-Bertram 85	4
26	**Dec 2**	**SS N4**	**H**	**Burton Albion**	**875**	**W 3 - 0**	**Carey-Bertram 5, 60 Brown pen 38**	
27	6		H	Southport	3558	W 1 - 0	Brown 73	
28	**13**	**F.A.T 1R**	**A**	**Boston United**	**895**	**W 2 - 1**	**Carey-Bertram 34 Jagielka 42**	
29	20		H	Stalybridge Celtic	1890	W 1 - 0	Turner 82	3
30	26		A	Stafford Rangers	1815	W 3 - 1	Pierpoint 61 (og) Brown 78 (pen) 83	3
31	Jan 1		H	Stafford Rangers	3140	L 0 - 1		3
32	3		A	King's Lynn	932	D 1 - 1	Brown 79	3
33	**13**	**F.A.T 2R**	**H**	**Hayes & Yeading**	**986**	**W 4 - 0**	**Brown 8 11 Rodgers 50 Carey-Bertram 69**	
34	**20**	**SS QFN**	**H**	**Kettering Town**	**874**	**W 3 - 2***	**Fearns 16, Vermiglio 53, 95**	
35	17		H	Hyde United	1888	L 2 - 3	Carey-Bertram 32 Fearns 84	4
36	24		A	Fleetwood Town	1078	L 0 - 1		4
37	27		A	Solihull Moors	324	W 3 - 1	Cowan 28 Carey-Bertram 33 Blakeman 59	
38	**31**	**F.A.T 3R**	**A**	**Kettering Town**	**1692**	**W 1 - 0**	**Carey-Bertram 23**	
39	Feb 7		A	Tamworth	1352	W 1 - 0	Carey-Bertram 43 (pen)	4
40	14		A	Workington	405	L 0 - 1		4
41	17		H	Vauxhall Motors	1667	W 5 - 1	Danks 35 FEARNS 3 (58 73 80) Blakeman 87	
42	**21**	**F.A.T. 4R**	**H**	**Southport**	**2059**	**D 2 - 2**	**Adams 20 Carey-Bertram 33 (pen)**	
43	**24**	**F.A.T. 4R r**	**A**	**Southport**	**895**	**W 1 - 0**	**Rodgers 9**	**4**
44	28		A	Hyde United	502	W 4 - 0	Rodgers 39 Carey-Bertram 55 Danks 74 85	
45	Mar 7		H	King's Lynn	1990	D 1 - 1	Carey-Bertram 90	
46	10		A	Vauxhall Motors	256	D 0 - 0		4
47	**14**	**F.A.T. SF1**	**H**	**York City**	**2792**	**L 0 - 2**		
48	17		A	Blyth Spartans	501	L 0 - 2		4
49	**21**	**F.A.T. SF2**	**A**	**York City**	**3512**	**L 1 - 2**	**Brown 86**	
50	23		A	Hinckley United	815	W 2 - 0	Trainer 40 90	
51	**26**	**SS SFN**	**A**	**Barrow**	**2109**	**W 1 - 0**	**Sappleton 60**	
52	28		H	Droylsden	1819	W 2 - 0	Brown 29 49	4
53	31		A	Farsley Celtic	230	L 0 - 1		
54	April 4		A	Gainsborough Trinity	292	W 2 - 1	Rodgers 27 Blakeman 78	4
55	7		H	Harrogate Town	1482	W 3 - 1	Sappleton 16 Brown 61 84	
56	**9**	**SS Final**	**A**	**Forest Green Rovers**	**2323**	**D 0 - 0***	**(Won 3-0 on pens)**	
57	11		H	Redditch United	2028	D 1 - 1	Adams 21	5
58	13		A	Alfreton Town	904	L 1 - 3	Vaughn 71	
59	15		H	Farsley Celtic	1520	W 2 - 1	Rodgers 74 89	
60	18		A	Southport	1305	D 1 - 1	Trainer 67	5
61	21		H	Burscough	1642	W 3 - 0	Carey-Bertram 6 52 Trainer 52	
62	26		H	Tamworth	2423	D 0 - 0		4
63	**29**	**Play-Off SF1**	**H**	**Alfreton Town**	**2346**	**W 2 0**	**Nwadike 48 Carey-Bertram 78**	
64	**May 3**	**Play-Off SF2**	**A**	**Alfreton Town**	**2244**	**L 3 4**	**Edwards 18 Carey-Bertram 42 Rodgers 51**	
65	**8**	**Play-Off F**	**A**	**Gateshead**	**4121**	**L 0 1**		

Average Home Att: 1973 (2108) **Goals 109 60**
Best Position: 3rd **Worst:** 7th
Goalscorers: Brown 21, Carey-Bertram 20, Fearns 17, Rodgers 9, Adams 6, Moore 5, Trainer 4, Vermiglio 4, Blakeman 3, Danks 3, Cowan 3, Jagielka 2, Naylor 2, Sappleton 2, Edwards 1, Khela 1, Meredith 1, Nwadike 1, Stevens 1, Turner 1, Vaughn 1, Own Goals 1.

YOUNG	NAYLOR	JAGIELKA	COWAN	WHITEHEAD	KHELA	ADAMS	NWADIKE	FEARNS	BROWN	BLAKEMAN	VERMIGLIO	MOORE	STEVENS	FITZPATRICK	RODGERS	EMBREY	VAUGHAN	FORSDICK	CHARLTON	TURNER	MEREDITH	CAREY-	BERTRAM	TAYLOR	WORTHING-	TON	EDWARDS	WILLIAMS	TRAINER	LEWIS	DANKS	SAPPLETON	
X	X	X	X	X	X	X	X	X	X	X	S	S	U	U																			1
X	X	X	X	X		X	X	X	X	X	X	S	S	S	U	U																	2
X	X	X	X	X		X	X	X	X	X	S	U	S	S	X		U															3
X	X	U	X	X		X	X	X	X	S	S	X	S	U	X		X															4
X	X	U	X	X		X	X	X	X	X	S	S	S	U	X		X															5
X	X	X	X	X		X	U	X	X	U	S	S	S	X	X		X															6
X	X	U	X	X	X	X	X	X	X	U	X	U		U	U			X														7
X	X	S	X	X	X	X	X	X	X		X	S	S	U	U			X														8
X	S	X	S	U	X	S	U	X			X	X	X	X	X		X		X													9
X	X	S	X	X	X	X	U	X	X		X	X	S	U	U		X															10
X	U	U	X	X	X	X	X	U	X	S	X	X	X		U		X															11
X	S	U	X	X	X	X	S	X	X	X	X	X	S		U		X															12
X	S	S	X		X	X	U	X	X	X	X	X	S		U		X		X													13
X	X	X	X		X	S	X	X	S	X	X	S	X		X		U			U												14
X	S	S	X	X	X	X	U	X	X	X	X	X	U				X			S												15
X	X	S	X	X	X	U	X	X	X	X	X	U					S				X	S											16
X	U	S	X	X	S	X	U	S	X	X	X	X					X				X	X											17
X	X	X	X	X	U		S	S	X	X	X	X	U		S		X				X												18
X	S	X	X	X	U		S	X	X	X	X	X			U		X				X	S											19
X	X	S	X	X	X	X	U	S	X	X		S			X		U				X	X											20
X	X	S	X	X	U	X		S	X	X	X	X			S		X				X		U										21
X	X	S	X	X	U	X		S	X	X		S			X		X				X	X		U									22
X	X	S	X	X	U	X		S	X	X	U	X			X		X				X		U										23
X		X	X	X	X	S		X	S	X	U	U			X		X			S	X	X											24
X		S	X		X	X		X	X	X	U	X			X		X			U	X	S			S								25
X		X	X		X	S		S	X	X	S	X			X		U			X	X	X											26
X		S	X		X	X		S	X	X	U	X			X		X			U	X	X			S								27
X	U	X	X		X	S		X		X	S	X			X		S			X	X	X											28
X	U	S	X		X	X		X	X	X	S	X			X		X			S	X				U								29
X		U	X		X	S		X	X	X	X	S			X		X			U	X	S			X								30
X	X	S	X		X	X		X	X	X	U	X			X						U	X	S			S								31
X	S		X		X	X		U	X	X	X	X			S						X	X	X			S								32
X			X			S		S	X	X	X	X			X	U	X			X	X	X		U		S						33
X	X		X	X	U	X		X		X	X	X									S	X	X				U		S				34
X	U		X	U		X		S	X	X	X	X									X	X	X			S		X	S				35
X	U		X	X	U	X		X		X	X	S									X	X	S			X		X	S				36
X	S		X	X	U	X		X		X		S					X			U	X	X			X		X	S				37
X	X		X	X	U	X				X	X	X					X	U		S	X	X				U		S				38
X			X	X	U	X	S	S		X	X	X					X			U		X			X		S		X			39
X				X	X	X		S		S	X				S						X	X	X			X	U	X	U	X			40
X			X	X	U	X	S	S		X						X		X			U	X	X			X		S		X			41
X		S	X	X	S	X		X	U	X	X				X		X	U		S	X	X										42
X		U	X	X	S	X		X	S	X	X		S		X		X			U	X	X										43
X			X	X	X		U	S	X	X					X		X			U	X	X			S		X		S			44
X			X	X	U	X	U			X		S			X		X			U	X	X			S		X		X			45
X	U		X	X	U	S	X			X		S			S						X	X	X			X		X		X			46
X	S	U	X	X	X	X			X	X		X			X	U		S		X	X				U						47
X	S	S	X	X	U	X	X			U		X			X						X	X				U		X		X			48
X		S	X	X	U	X			X	X		X			X		X	S		S	X	X				U						49
X		S	X	X	U	X	X		X						X		X	U			X	U					X		U	X			50
X		X	S	X	X	S	X			X		U			S		U			X	X						X	X	X			51
X		S	X	X	U	X			X	X					X		X				X	S			U		X		S	X			52
X		S		X	X	X	X		X	U							X			U	X	X			S		X		S	X			53
X		U	X		X	X	S		X	X		U			X		X			S	X				X			S		X			54
X		S	X	X		X			X	X		S			X		X			U	X				X			U	S	X			55
X		X	X	X	X	S	X		X	S		X			X		X			U								S	X	U			56
X	U	X	X	X	U	X	U			X		S			X		X			S		X			X				X				57
X		S	X	X	X	X	X			U		S			X		X			U	X	X			S					X			58
X	X	U	X		X		U			X		X			X						S	X	X			S		X		S	X			59
X	X	S	X		X		S			X		U			X						X	X	S			X		X	U	X				60
X	X	S	X		X		X			X		S					X			S	X	X			X		X	U	U				61
X	X	X		X		S	X				S	X			U	X	S			X		X			X		U	X					62
X		U	X	X			X		X	X		U			X		X			U	X	X			S		X	S					63
X	U	S	X	X			X		X	X	S				X		X			S	X	X			X				U				64
X		S	X	X			X		X	X	U	S			X		X			U	X	X			X				S				65
Total League Appearances																																		
42	16	7	39	30	21	33	16	18	28	30	15	16	1	1	22	1	26	2	1	8	28	18	0	0	13	0	14	1	8	7			X
0	5	18	0	0	1	3	5	8	0	3	7	15	8	2	3	0	2	0	0	5	0	8	0	0	10	0	2	4	5	0			S
0	7	7	0	1	12	1	8	2	0	5	3	5	1	6	8	1	1	1	0	12	0	1	0	1	3	1	1	4	2	0			U
Total Cup Appearances																																		
23	7	8	21	18	11	11	6	9	14	21	11	14	2	1	16	0	16	0	1	5	18	13	0	0	2	0	1	1	2	1			X
0	4	8	2	0	2	8	2	6	3	1	3	3	2	0	3	0	1	2	0	7	0	0	0	0	1	1	0	4	1	0			S
0	2	4	0	1	6	0	3	0	1	0	3	3	2	0	1	2	4	2	0	5	0	0	2	1	0	4	0	0	1	1			U

AFC TELFORD

CURRENT SQUAD AS OF BEGINING OF 2009-10 SEASON

GOALKEEPERS	HT	WT	D.O.B	AGE	P.O.B	CAREER	APPS	GOA
Ryan Young			25/12/79	29	Birmingham	Plymouth (Trainee), Chasetown, Nuneaton, Halesowen T (L) 10/01, Hucknall T 2/02, Hednesford 5/03, Redditch 6/05, AFC Telford 9/05, Kettering 2/06, Willenhall 3/06, Hednesford 6/06, AFC Telford 5/07	42	0
DEFENDERS								
Gavin Cowan	6'04"	14 04	24/5/81	28	Hanover(Ger)	Exeter (Trainee), Braintree 7/99, Canvey Island 12/02, Nuneaton (L) 12/04, Nuneaton (L) 2/05, Shrewsbury £5,000 + 3/05, Kidderminster (L) 8/06, Grays 1/07 Rel 6/07, Nuneaton (L) 3/07, Nuneaton 6/07, AFC Telford 5/08	39	2
Gareth Jelleyman	5'10"	10 06	14/11/80	28	Holywell	Norwich (Yth), Peterborough, Boston U (L) 12/98, Boston U (L) 8/04, Mansfield (L) 1/05 Perm 1/05, Rushden & D 7/08 Rel 5/09, Barrow (SL) 3/09, AFC Telford 6/09		
Jimmy Turner	5'11"	11 04	4/10/83	25	Derby	Derby Rel c/s 04, Forest Green 8/04, Gresley R, Runcorn 11/04, Farnborough 1/05 Rel 5/05, Tamworth 6/05, AFC Telford (L) 2/06 Perm 3/06, Bromsgrove (L) 10/08	13	1
Lee Vaughan	5'07"	11 00	15/7/86	23	Birmingham	Birmingham C (Yth), Portsmouth (Yth), Walsall 2/05, Willenhall (L) 8/05, AFC Telford 2/0628		1
Stuart Whitehead	6'00"	12 02	17/7/76	33	Bromsgrove	Bromsgrove, Bolton 9/95 Rel c/s 98, Carlisle 7/98, Darlington 10/02, Telford 6/03, Shrewsbury 6/04, Kidderminster 5/06, AFC Telford 1/08	30	0
MIDFIELDERS								
Jon Adams			8/1/85	24		Leamington, AFC Telford	36	2
Liam Blakeman			6/9/82	26	Southport	Blackburn Rel c/s 02, Southport 7/02, Leigh RMI 11/02, St Helens 1/03, Burscough 7/03, Southport 1/06, AFC Telford 5/08	33	3
Danny Edwards			27/10/83	25	Shrewsbury	Shrewsbury, Stafford R (SL) 3/03, Stafford R 8/03, Redditch 6/07, AFC Telford 11/08	23	1
Scott Embrey						AFC Telford	1	0
Tom Field			2/8/85	24	Liverpool	Everton (Trainee), Leigh RMI, TNS c/s 05, Stalybridge 8/05, Southport 10/05, Witton 11/05, Vauxhall Motors 12/05, Leigh RMI/Leigh Genesis 5/08, Vauxhall Motors 11/08, AFC Telford 6/09		
Steve Jagielka	5'08"	11 03	10/3/78	31	Manchester	Stoke Rel c/s 97, Shrewsbury 7/97, Sheff Utd 11/03 Rel c/s 5/04, Scarborough (L) 3/04, Accrington 5/04 Rel 5/06, Droylsden 7/06, AFC Telford 6/07, Bridgnorth (L) 3/09	25	0
Carl Rodgers			26/3/83	26	Chester	Chester (Yth), Caernarfon c/s 02, TNS 3/04, Colwyn Bay 5/04, AFC Telford 5/06	25	4
Phil Trainer	6'00"	12 00	3/7/81	28	Wolverhampton	Crewe Rel c/s 02, Hyde (3ML) 12/00, Hednesford (3ML) 11/01, Stalybridge (L) 3/02, Northwich 8/02, Kidsgrove 9/02, Halesowen 12/02, Tamworth 8/03, Stourport S (L) 9/03, Moor Green/Solihull Moors (L) 10/03 Perm 11/03, Oxford U 7/07 Rel 4/09, AFC Telford (SL) 1/09, AFC Telford 5/07	16	6
Jamie Vermiglio			10/6/82	27		Chorley 7/03, Scarborough 7/06, AFC Telford 5/07	22	1
FORWARDS								
Andy Brown			3/3/86	23	Lincoln	Scunthorpe (Scholar), Harrogate T (L) 3/05, Hinckley 5/05, Nuneaton 7/07, AFC Telford 6/08	28	15
Danny Carey-Bertram	5'11"	13 00	14/6/84	25	Birmingham	WBA, Hereford 9/03 Rel 6/06, Cambridge U 6/06 Rel 1/07, Forest Green Rovers 1/07 Rel 4/08, Bath C 8/08, AFC Telford 10/08	26	11
Matt Nolan	6'00"	12 00	25/2/82	27	Hitchin	Hitchin, Peterborough 9/03, Cambridge C (2ML) 1/04, St Albans (L) 11/04, Kettering (L) 12/04, Ballymena (L) 2/05, Cambridge U 8/05 Rel 12/05, Kings Lynn 12/05, Corby 6/08, AFC Telford 6/09		
Steve Torpey	5'09"	10 08	16/9/81	27	Kirkby	Liverpool Rel c/s 01, Chesterfield (Trial) 7/01, Port Vale 8/01 Rel 9/01, Scarborough 10/01 Rel 12/01, Prescot Cables 8/02, Altrincham 10/04, Prescot Cables 2/05, FCUM 7/05, Halifax 8/06, Stalybridge (SL) 2/08, Stalybridge 6/08, AFC Telford 6/09		

LOANEES	HT	WT	DOB	AGE	POB	From - To	APPS	GOA
(D)James Meredith	6'00"	11 09	4/4/88	21	Albury	Shrewsbury (SL) 10/08 - York C 5/09	28	1
(M)Ricky Sappleton	5'10"	11 13	8/12/89	19	Kingston, Jam	Leicester (SL) 3/09 -	7	1

DEPARTURES	HT	WT	DOB	AGE	POB	From - To	APPS	GOA
(D)Elliot Durrell						Yth - Hednesford 7/08		
(M)Gary Fitzpatrick	5'10"	10 06	5/8/71	38	Birmingham	Nuneaton 3/07 - Rushall O 9/08	3	0
(D)Asa Charlton	5'11"	12 00	7/12/77	31	Cosford	Mansfield 5/07 - Hednesford (L) 9/08, Redditch 10/08	1	0
(F)Terry Fearns	5'11"	10 12	24/10/77	31	Liverpool	Droylsden 3/08 - Rel 4/09, Chorley 7/09	26	7
(F)Mark Danks	5'09"	10 08	8/2/84	25	Worley	Halesowen T 2/09 - Rel 5/09, Northwich 7/09	13	3
(F)Matty Lewis	6'02"	12 02	20/3/84	25	Coventry	Halesowen T 5/07 - Rel 5/09, Atherstone (L) 12/08, Hednesford (L) 2/09, Solihull Moors 6/09	5	0
(D)Indy Khela	6'00"	12 06	6/10/83	25	Birmingham	Willenhall 2/06 - Rel 5/09, Solihull Moors 6/09	22	1
(M)Martin Naylor	5'09"	10 02	2/8/77	32	Walsall	TNS 7/08 - Rel 5/09, Rhyl 6/09	21	1
(M)Simon Forsdick			1/7/83	26	Cambridge	Hednesford T 9/07 - Nuneaton T (L) 8/08, Bloxwich U (L) 8/08, Rushall O (Dual) 2/09, Stratford T (Dual) 3/09, Nuneaton T (L) 3/09 Perm 6/09	2	0
(M)Emeka Nwadike	6'00"	12 07	9/8/78	31	Camberwell	Worcester 3/08 - Hinckley U (2ML) 11/08, Eastwood T 6/09	21	0
(F)Lee Moore			9/11/85	23	Bathgate	Tamworth (3ML) 9/06 £5,000 12/06 - Nuneaton T 6/09	31	3
(M)Justin Worthington						Yth -	0	0
(F)Jarred Stevens			25/10/89	19		Birmingham C 8/08 - Rushall O (L) 10/08	9	0
(G)Stephen Taylor						Bridgnorth 11/08 -	0	0
(G)Dean Williams							0	0

A.F.C. TELFORD UNITED

Founded: 2004

Nickname: The Bucks.

Club Colours: White shirts, black shorts, black socks..

Change Colours: Red shirts, red shorts, red socks.

Club Sponsor: Cap Gemini

Previous League: Northern Premier

Ground address: The New Bucks Head Stadium, Watling Street, Wellington Telford TF1 2TU

Telephone: 01952 640 064

Mobile: 07811 358 330

Fax: 01952 640 021

Email: office@telfordutd.co.uk

Capacity: 6,380 **Seats**: 2,004 **Covered**: 5,000 **Floodlights**:Yes

Simple Directions: Leave M54 at Jct6 take A 5223 signposted Wellington.Take second exit at second roundabout and left at third. First right after railway bridge. Car park entrance on left. Officials make way to hotel car park by ground.

Clubhouse: Hotel

Club Shop: Yes

Local Radio: BBC Radio Shropshire, Beacon Radio,Telford FM and WABC

Local Press: Shropshire Star and Wellington News

PROGRAMME EDITOR

James Baylis

Tel: (M) 07977 481 186

(B) 01952 415 534

Email: james.baylis@ppmedia.co.uk

CLUB STATISTICS

RECORDS

Attendance: 4,215 v Kendal Town N.P.L. Play off Final

Victory: 7-0 v Runcorn (a) N.P.L. Div 1 2005-2006

Defeat: 3-6 v Bradford (P.A.) (H) N.P.L. 2005-2006

Career Goalscorer: Kyle Perry 32 - September 2004 - July 2006

Career Appearances: Stuart Brock 132 - July 2004 - present day

Record Transfer Fee Paid:

£5,000 for Lee Moore from Tamworth - 08.12.06

Received: £33,000 from Burnley for Duane Courtney - 31.08.05

Senior Honours:

N.P.L. Div 1 Play Off Winners 2004-05.

N.P.L. Prem Play Off Winners 2006-07.

Conference League Cup Winners 2008-09.

Previous Leagues: Predecessors: Birmingham, Cheshire, Southern and Conference. As AFC: Northern Premier League.

Previous Name: Telford United

ALFRETON TOWN

Back row (L-R): Dougie Woodhouse-Roe (fitness instructor), Leo Fortune-West, Tony Butler, Paul Ellender, Danny Davidson, Brian Cusworth, Tom Evans, Joe McCormack, Matt wilson, Martin McIntosh, Josh Law, Danny Reet, Nicky Law (manager), Russ O'Neill (assistant manager).
Front row: Paul Winter (physiotherapist), Anton Brown, Tom Curtis, Simon Marples, Jordan Hall, Marc Grocott (now back with Stoke City), Danny Mayman, Jimmy Phillips (now back with Stoke City), Ben Muirhead, Kris Bowler, Kyle McFadzean, Paul Clayton and Paul Smith (physiotherapist).

CLUB PERSONNEL

Chairman: Wayne Bradley.
Company Secretary: Wayne Bradley.
Additional Directors: Steve Taylor, Sean Egan, Dave Gregory.

Secretary: Bryan Rudkin.
12 Crown Terrace, Bridge Street, Belper,
Derbyshire DE56 1BD
Tel Nos: (H/B) 01773 825 468
(M) 07710 444 195
Email: waynebradley@healthcaremedia.co.uk

Commercial Manager: Roger Thompson.
(M) 07984 192 745
Email: r.k.thompson@sky.com
Press Officer: Kev Miles
Tel (H): 01773 769519 (B): 01773 514165
(M): 07855 516873
Email: atfcwebmanager@aol.com

Manager: Nicky Law.
Assistant Manager: Russ O'Neill.
Club therapist: Paul Madin.

Even the most ardent Alfreton Town supporter might have been wary of forecasting involvement with the play-offs when, just one victory in the first seven league games last season left them in thirteenth position. But there had also only been one defeat and as the season developed 'The Reds' proved they certainly were a very hard club to beat.

An F.A.Cup run included victories over Shepshed Dynamo, Ilkeston Town, Retford Town and Bury Town before they found Scunthorpe United just too strong for them in the First Round Proper. In the F.A.Trophy, cup heroes Blyth Spartans were beaten, but a disappointing performance against Redditch Unlted saw them knocked out in the First Round Proper.

The goalscoring reputations of Paul Clayton and Liam Hearn brought England C caps to both strikers and this underlined just how far the Alfreton club had come in recent seasons. They only failed to score in two games in the new year and their consistency took then into the Play-Offs where they met hot favourites Telford. One victory each wasn't enough as The Reds lost 3-4 on aggregate.

Experienced and well respected manager Nicky Law has already helped 'The Reds to their best ever season and there is no reason why they cannot improve again if they keep their international strikers and make one or two additions to the squad.

ALFRETON TOWN

BEST LGE ATT.: 904 v AFC Telford United
LOWEST: 307 v Burscough

No.	Date	Comp	H/A	Opponents	Att:	Result	Goalscorers	Pos
1	Aug 9	BSN	H	Hyde United	390	W 3 - 2	**Clayton** 34 Davidson 35 Law 90	
2	12		A	Solihull Moors	191	D 2 - 2	Fortune-West 81 82	9
3	16		A	Gateshead	361	L 0 - 3		
4	23		H	King's Lynn	501	D 1 - 1	Cusworth 50	12
5	25		A	AFC Telford United	2126	D 0 - 0		
6	30		H	Workington	316	D 0 - 0		13
7	Sept 2		H	Tamworth	413	D 1 - 1	Fortune-West 37	
8	6		A	Southport	1012	W 1 - 0	Fortune-West 34	10
9	13		H	Burscough	307	W 2 - 0	Bowler 22 Fortune-West 37	7
10	**16**	**SS N1**	**H**	**Stafford Rangers**	**201**	**L 2 - 3**	**Clayton 10 Loukes 40 (og)**	
11	20		A	Fleetwood Town	812	D 1 - 1	**Clayton** 28	8
12	**27**	**F.A.C. 2Q**	**A**	**Shepshed Dynamo**	**374**	**W 2 - 1**	**Fortune-West 15 Cusworth 90**	
13	Oct 4		H	Droylsden	318	L 2 - 3	Hearn 15 Davidson 68	12
14	**11**	**F.A.C. 3Q**	**H**	**Ilkeston Town**	**277**	**D 0 - 0**		
15	**14**	**F.A.C. 3Q r**	**A**	**Ilkeston Town**	**848**	**W 3 - 1**	**Davidson 1 Law 3 (pen) Clayton 36**	
16	18		A	Harrogate Town	423	D 2 - 2	**Clayton** 58 87	12
17	21		H	Gainsborough Trinity	307	L 1 - 4	McIntosh 24	
18	**25**	**F.A.C. 4Q**	**A**	**Retford Town**	**922**	**W 3 - 1**	**Fortune -West 41 Clayton 44 78**	
19	Nov 1		H	Stalybridge Celtic	371	W 2 - 1	**Clayton** 35 Law 62 (pen)	14
20	4		A	Redditch United	166	D 2 - 2	McIntosh 37 90	
21	**8**	**F.A.C. 1R**	**H**	**Bury Town**	**1060**	**W 4 - 1**	**McIntosh 4 Fortune-West 61 Law 65 (pen) Clayton 90**	
22	15		H	Solihull Moors	409	W 4 - 1	Davidson 3 74 Collins 23 (og) Cusworth 39	9
23	**22**	**F.A.T 3Q**	**A**	**Blyth Spartans**	**446**	**W 4 - 3**	**Law 36 (pen) Clayton 38 78 Hearn 90**	
24	**29**	**F.A.C 2R**	**A**	**Scunthorpe United**	**4249**	**L 0 - 4**		
25	Dec 6		H	Fleetwood Town	321	D 3 - 3	Hearn 10 75 McIntosh 82	12
26	9		A	Tamworth	468	W 2 - 1	Hearn 16 40	8
27	**16**	**F.A.T. 1R**	**H**	**Redditch United**	**192**	**L 0 - 1**		
28	20		A	Hyde United	220	D 1 - 1	Hearn 37	8
29	26		H	Hucknall Town	571	W 5 - 0	**Clayton** 16 MUIRHEAD 4 (26 45 62 72)	8
30	Jan 3		H	Gateshead	448	L 1 - 3	**Clayton** 90	8
31	13		A	Hucknall Town	365	D 1 - 1	Hearn 45	
32	17		H	Harrogate Town	383	W 4 - 1	Hall 50 HEARN 3 (53 78 81)	7
33	24		A	Gainsborough Trinity	369	W 2 - 0	Hearn 39 **Clayton** 80	5
34	31		H	Farsley Celtic	421	W 3 - 1	**Clayton** 27 Hearn 80 Brown 87	5
35	Feb 21		H	Vauxhall Motors	392	W 3 - 1	Bowler 14 Hearn 67 **Clayton** 90	5
36	4		A	Burscough	233	W 3 - 1	HEARNE 3 (4 42 70)	
37	28		H	Blyth Spartans	480	D 1 - 1	McIntosh 28 (pen)	5
38	Mar 7		A	Droylsden	354	L 0 - 2		
39	10		A	Blyth Spartans	549	D 2 - 2	Mcintosh 36 **Clayton** 85	
40	14		H	Hinckley United	444	D 1 - 1	Hall 49	
41	21		A	Vauxhall Motors	168	D 1 - 1	Howell 45	6
42	24		A	Stafford Rangers	377	W 2 - 0	McFadzean 2 Ross 66 (pen)	
43	28		A	Workington	307	W 3 - 0	Brown 40 Hearn 56 **Clayton** 76	5
44	31		H	Stafford Rangers	415	W 2 - 0	Brown 14 76	
45	April 4		H	Southport	589	W 2 - 0	Ross 4 **Clayton** 58	5
46	7		A	Stalybridge Celtic	445	W 2 - 0	Howell 36 Brown 85	
47	11		A	King's Lynn	1007	W 4 - 0	McFadzean 30 Ross 63 Curtis 70 **Clayton** 80	4
48	13		H	AFC Telford United	904	W 3 - 1	Howell 54 78 **Clayton** 79	
49	18		A	Hinckley United	607	D 1 - 1	**Clayton** 69	4
50	21		A	Farsley Celtic	227	D 3 - 3	Brown 8 **Clayton** 12 Law 45	
51	25		H	Redditch United	522	W 2 - 0	Hall 45 Hearn 86	3
52	**29**	**Play-Off SF1**	**A**	**AFC Telford United**	**2346**	**L 0 - 2**		
53	**May 3**	**Play-Off SF2**	**H**	**AFC Telford United**	**2244**	**W 4 - 3**	**Butler 9 Brown 15 Clayton 49 Howell 73 (pen)**	

Average Home Att: 439 (375) **Goals** 103 68

Best Position: 3rd **Worst:** 14th

Goalscorers: Clayton 25, Hearn 19, Fortune -West 8, McIntosh 7, Brown 7, Law 6, Davidson 5, Howell 5, Muirhead 4, Cusworth 3, Hall 3, Ross 3, Bowler 2, McFadzean 2, Butler 1, Curtis 1. Own Goals 2.

EVANS	MARPLES	BOWLER	ELLENDER	MCINTOSH	CURTIS	LAW	HALL	CLAYTON	DAVIDSON	FORTUNE-WEST	MUIRHEAD	BUTLER	PHILLIPS	MCCORMACK	MCFADZEAN	CUSWORTH	MAYMAN	BROWN	OLIVER	HEARN	SUTCLIFFE	FLINT	WILSON	SMITH	DICKINSON	HOWELL	ROSS	
X	X	X	X	X	X	X	X	X	X	X	S	U	U	U	U													1
X	X	X	X	X	X	X	X	X	X	X	S	U		U	S	S												2
X	X		X	X	X	X		S	X	X	X	X		U	X	S	S											3
X	X	S	X	X	X	X	S	X	X		X	U		U	X	X		U										4
X	X	X	X	X	X	X	X	X	U	S	X	U				U	S	X										5
X	X	X	X	X	X	X	X	X		S	X	U				S	S	X	U									6
X	X	X	X	X	X	S	X	X		X	X	U				U	U	X	U									7
X	X	X	X	X	X	S	X	X		X	X	S				S	U	X	U									8
X	X	X		X	X	S	X	X		X	X	X		U		S	U	X	U									9
X	X	S		X		X	X	X	S	S	X	X		U		X	X	X	U									10
X	X	X			X	X	X	X	U	X	X	X				S	S	X		S	U							11
X	X	X		X	X	X		X	S	X	X	X				S	S	X			U							12
X		X		X	X	X		S	X	X	S					X	X	X		X	U	U						13
X		X		X	X	X		S	X	X	X	X				X	U	X			U		S					14
X		X		X	X	X	S	X	X	U	X	X				U	U	X			U		X					15
X		X			X	X	U	X	X	X	X	X				S	S	X		S	U		X					16
X		X		X	X	X		X	X	U	X	X				S	S	X		S	U		X					17
X		X		X	U	X	S	X	U	X	X	X				U	X	X			U		X					18
X				X	S	X	X	X	U	X	X	X				S	X	X		S	U		X					19
X			X	X		U	X	U	X	S	X	U				X	X	X		X	U	X						20
X	S	S	U	X	X	X	X	X	U	X	X	X				U	X	X			U	U						21
X	X	X	U	X	X		X		X			X			S	X	X	X		S	U	U						22
X		X		X	X	X	X	X	X	U	X	X			S	U	X			S	U							23
X	S	X	U	X	X	X	X	X	S	U	X	X			X	S	U	X			U							24
U	X	X		X	X	X	X	X	S		U	X			X		S			X	X		S					25
U	X	S	U		X	X	X	X	U		X	X			X		U			X	X		X					26
U		X	U	U	X	X	X		X	S	X	X			X	S				X	X		X					27
U	X		U		X	X	X		X	S	X	X				S		X		X	X		X					28
U	X		X		X	X	X	X	S		X				X	S		U		X	X		X	S				29
U	X		X		X	X	X	X	S		X	U			X			S		X	X		X	S				30
U	X			U	X	X	X	X	S		U	X			X	S		X		X	X		X					31
U	X			X	X	S	X	X		S	S	U			X	X		X		X	X		X					32
U	X			X	X	X	X	X	U		U	U			X	U		X		X	X		X					33
U	X			X	X	X	X	X	S		U	U			X	S		X		X	X		X					34
U		X	U	X	X	X	X	X	U			U			X			X		X	X		X					35
U		X	U	X	X	X	X	X	U		U	U			X			X		X	X		X					36
U	U	X		X	X	X	X	X	U		S				X			X		X	X	U	X					37
U	X	X		X	X	X	X	X	S		S				X	S		X			X	X						38
U	X	X		X	X	U	S	X			U				X	S		X				X	X		X	X		39
	X	U			X	S	X				X	U			X	X		X			U	X	X		X	X		40
	X	U			X	S	X	X							X	U		X		X	U	X	X		X	X	S	41
	X	U				X	S	X				U			X	S		X		X	U	X	X		X	X	X	42
	X	U				X	U	X				U			X	U		X		X	U	X	X		X	X	X	43
	X	S			U	X	S	X				X			X	U		X		X	U	X			X	X	X	44
	X	X			S	X	U	X				X			X	U		X			U	U	X		X	X	X	45
	X				X	X	U	X			U	X			X	U		X			U	U	X		X	X	X	46
	X				X	X	S	X				X			X	S		X		S	U	U	X		X	X	X	47
					X	X	U	X			U	X			X	U		X		U	U	X	X		X	X	X	48
	X				X	X	U	X				X			X	U		X		S	U	S	X		X	X	X	49
					X	X	X	X			U	S			X	U		X		X	U	X	X		X	X	U	50
					X	S	X	S			X	X			X	X		X		X	U	X	U		X	X	S	51
				U		X	S	X			U	X			X	S		X		X	U	X	X		X	X	X	52
					S	S	X	X			U	X			X	U		X		X	U	X	X		X	X	X	53
Total League Appearances																												
16	31	19	11	23	36	32	28	35	10	10	18	18	0	0	27	7	4	34	0	20	13	11	25	0	13	13	8	X
0	0	3	0	0	2	7	5	3	6	5	6	2	0	0	2	17	7	1	0	7	0	1	1	2	0	0	2	S
14	1	4	5	1	1	2	6	1	8	1	9	16	1	5	1	11	4	2	4	1	19	6	1	0	0	0	1	U
Total Cup Appearances																												
8	2	7	0	8	7	10	6	9	4	4	9	11	0	0	4	2	4	9	0	3	1	2	5	0	2	2	2	X
0	2	2	0	0	1	1	3	1	3	2	0	0	0	0	1	4	1	0	0	1	0	0	1	0	0	0	0	S
1	0	0	3	2	1	0	0	0	2	3	2	0	0	1	0	5	3	0	1	0	9	1	0	0	0	0	0	U

ALFRETON TOWN

CURRENT SQUAD AS OF BEGINING OF 2009-10 SEASON

GOALKEEPERS	HT	WT	D.O.B	AGE	P.O.B	CAREER	APPS	GOA
Craig Dootson	6'04"	14 02	23/5/79	28	Preston	Preston (Yth), Morecambe, Bamber Bridge, Leigh RMI £4,000 7/00, Bradford PA (2ML) 10/01, Stalybridge 5/02, Bury 7/05 Rel 5/06, Hinckley (L) 1/06, Hyde 6/06, Alfreton 5/09		
Paddy Gamble	5'10"	10 12	1/9/88	19	Bulwell	Notts Forest Rel 5/09, York C (2ML) 3/07, Stalybridge (SL) 7/07, Mansfield (5ML) 8/08, Alfreton 8/09		
DEFENDERS								
Aden Flint	6'06"		11/7/89	20		Pinxton FC, Alfreton (L) 10/08 Undisc 11/08, Matlock (L) 12/08	12	0
Kyle McFadzean	6'01"	13 04	20/2/87	21	Sheffield	Sheff Utd Rel c/s 07, Alfreton 6/07	29	2
Richard Pell			17/11/82	24	Boston	Notts Forest (Jun), York C (Ass Sch), Lincoln, USA, Boston T 7/99, Chesterfield (Trial), Gainsborough 8/04, Blyth 5/08 Rel 5/09, Alfreton 5/09		
Dominic Roma	5'10"	11 11	29/11/85	22	Sheffield	Sheff Utd Rel c/s 07, Boston U (L) 2/05, Notts County (Trial) 7/05, Tamworth (SL) 2/06, Hinckley U 7/07, Alfreton 5/09		
MIDFIELDERS								
Kris Bowler			26/10/83	24		Rotherham (Scholar), Wakefield & Emley 7/03, Matlock 2/04, Alfreton Undisc 7/07, Worksop (L) 8/09	22	2
Anton Brown			3/7/87	21		Mansfield (Scholar), Greenwood Meadows, Alfreton c/s 06	35	6
Matty Burke			14/12/85	23		Blackpool (Scholar), Salford C, Barrow, Vauxhall Motors c/s 08, Alfreton 6/09		
Tom Curtis	5'08"	11 12	1/3/73	35	Exeter	Derby Rel c/s 93, Chesterfield 8/93, Portsmouth £150,000 8/00, Walsall (L) 9/01, Tranmere (2ML) 8/02, Mansfield 12/02, Chester 7/05 Rel c/s 06, Notts County 7/06, Nuneaton (L) 12/06 Perm 2/07, Alfreton 6/08	38	1
Jordan Hall			7/5/84	24		Chesterfield (Scholar), Hucknall, Buxton c/s 05, Hucknall (2ML) 1/08, Alfreton 3/08	33	3
Josh Law			20/7/89	19		Chesterfield Rel c/s 08, Alfreton (SL) 10/07, Alfreton 5/08	39	3
Ian Ross	5'10"	11 00	23/1/86	22	Sheffield	Sheff Utd, Boston U (3ML) 8/05, Bury (SL) 3/06, Notts County (SL) 7/06, Rotherham (2ML) 11/07 Perm 1/08 Rel c/s 08, Gainsborough 8/08, Alfreton 3/09 Rel 5/09	10	3
Andy Todd	6'00"	11 03	22/2/79	30	Nottingham	Eastwood T, N.Forest 2/96, Scarborough 2/99, Eastwood T 5/99, Ilkeston 3/00, Eastwood T 7/01, Worksop 10/01, Hucknall 12/03, Burton 7/05, Accrington (SL) 1/06, Accrington Undisc 6/06, Rotherham 8/07 Rel c/s 09, Accrington (SL) 1/08, Eastwood T (3ML) 10/08		
Matt Wilson			10/3/87	21		Darlington, Mackinlay Park, Sheffield Hallam Univ, Diddington T, Grantham, Alfreton 8/07, Worksop (3ML) 8/08	26	0
FORWARDS								
Paul Clayton						Barnsley (Scholar), Parkgate, Gainsborough 7/07, Alfreton 12/07	38	17
Liam Hearn			27/8/85	24		Santos, Hucknall c/s 06, Eastwood T 10/07, Chasetown 1/08, Quorn 1/08, Alfreton 9/08	27	20
Anthony Howell			27/5/86	23		Carlton T, Shepshed D 9/05, Carlton T 11/06, Grantham 3/07, Notts County (Trial) c/s 07, Eastwood T 6/07, Worksop 9/07, Eastwood (L) 1/08 Perm, Ilkeston 8/08, Mansfield 1/09 Rel 5/09, Alfreton (SL) 3/09, Alfreton 5/09	13	4
Damien Reeves	5'09"	11 10	18/12/85	22	Doncaster	Leeds Rel c/s 05, Scarborough (Trial) c/s 05, Barnsley (Trial) 9/05, Wakefield & Emley 10/05, Farsley Celtic 1/06, Histon 6/08, Northwich 1/09, Farsley Celtic 3/09, Alfreton 7/09		

LOANEES	HT	WT	DOB	AGE	POB	From - To	APPS	GOA
(M)Marc Grocott			11/11/89	18		Stoke, Alfreton (L) 7/08, Solihull Moors (L) 9/08, Stafford R (L) 10/08, Rel 6/09		
(M)Jimmy Phillips			20/9/89	18		Stoke, Alfreton (L) 7/08, Stafford R (L) 9/08, Rel 6/09	0	0

DEPARTURES	HT	WT	DOB	AGE	POB	From - To	APPS	GOA
(F)Dean Oliver	6'00"	12 05	4/12/87	21	Derby	Sheff Utd 8/08 - Eastwood T 10/08, Buxton 11/08, Belper 11/08	0	0
(F)Danny Reet	6'01"	14 02	31/1/87	22	Sheffield	Mansfield (6ML) 9/07, Perm 3/08 - Glapwell (L) 8/08 Perm, Dinnington T 10/08, Buxton 10/08		
(F)Leo Fortune-West	6'04"	13 10	9/4/71	37	Stratford	Cambridge U 6/08 - Rel 1/09, North Ferriby 2/09, Goole AFC 7/09	15	5
(F)Danny Davidson	6/05"		23/10/79	28	Derby	Moor Green/Solihull Moors 5/08 - Rel 5/09, Matlock (L) 3/09, Boston U 8/09	16	4
(D)Paul Ellender	6'01"	12 07	21/10/74	33	Scunthorpe	Boston U 5/08 - Rel 5/09, Boston U (SL) 3/09, Retford U 7/09	11	0
(D)Martin McIntosh	6'03"	13 07	19/3/71	37	East Kilbride	Mansfield 5/08 - Rel 5/09, Guiseley 8/09	23	6
(M)Danny Mayman			8/5/79	29	Nottingham	Hucknall 5/08 - Rel 5/09	11	0
(M)Ben Muirhead	5'09"	11 02	5/1/83	25	Doncaster	Rochdale 8/08 - Rel 5/09	24	2
(G)Tommy Evans	6'00"	13 02	31/12/76	31	Doncaster	York C 7/08 - Rel 5/09, Gainsborough (L) 3/09, Boston U 7/09	16	0
(G)Kyle Sutcliffe						Farsley Celtic 9/08 - Rel 5/09	13	0
(G)Steve Dickinson			1/12/73	35		Burscough 3/09 - Bradford PA 6/09	13	0
(F)Brian Cusworth			25/7/79	29	Sheffield	Parkgate 5/07 - Stocksbridge PS 8/09	24	2
(G)Joe McCormack	6'01"		3/5/89	19		Shirebrook 8/08 - Rel	0	0
(D)Tony Butler	6'02"	12 00	28/9/72	35	Stockport	Hinckley U 11/07 - Wakefield (L) 2/09	20	0
(D)Simon Marples	5'10"	11 00	30/7/75	33	Sheffield	Chester 6/08 - Rel c/s 09	31	0
(M)Marquin Smith						Carlton T 12/08 - Rel	2	0

ALFRETON TOWN

Founded: 1959

Nickname: The Reds.

Club Colours: Red shirts, shorts and socks.

Change Colours: Yellow shirts, shorts and socks.

Club Sponsor: Impact Marketing & Publicity Ltd.

Previous League: Northern Premier

Ground address: Impact Arena, North Street, Alfreton, Derbyshire DE55 7FZ.

Telephone: 01773 830 277

Fax: 01773 836 164

Email: bryanrudkin@hotmail.com

Club Website: www.alfretontownfc.com

Capacity: 3,600 **Seats**: 1,500 **Covered**: 2,600 **Floodlights**: Yes

Simple Directions: M1 jct 28 and A38 towards Derby for a mile then left onto B600. Right at main road to town centre and left after half a mile down North Street. Ground on right. Alfreton BR 1/2 mile. Buses 91,92,93 from Derby and Mansfield.

Clubhouse: Ground bar open matchdays. Supporters bar outside ground open daily.

Club Shop: Yes.

Local Press: Derbyshire Times, Derby Evening Telegraph

Local Radio: Radio Derby

no image available

PROGRAMME EDITOR
Chris Tacey
Tel: (H) 01302 725 944
(M) 07815 852 531 (B) 0113 296 3227
Email: ctacey5087@aol.com

CLUB STATISTICS

RECORDS

Attendance: 5,023 v Matlock Town Central Alliance 1960

Victory: 15-0 v Loughborough, Midland League 1969-70

Defeat: 1-9 v Solihull F.A.T. 1997, 0-8 v Bridlington 1992

Career Goalscorer: J.Harrison 303

Career Appearances: J.Harrison 560 + 1

Transfer Fee Paid: £2,000 to Worksop Town for Mick Goddard

Received: £7,000 from Ilkeston Town for Paul Eshelby

SENIOR HONOURS:

N.Co.E Champions 84-85 2001-02 Derbyshire Senior Cup (7)

N.P.L.Division 1 Champions 2002-03.

PREVIOUS

Leagues: Central Alliance (pre re-formation 21-25) 59-61 Midland Co: 25-27 61-82 N.Co. East 82-87 NPL 87-99

BLYTH SPARTANS

Back Row (L-R): Mick Tait (Manager), Adam Sadler (Assistant Manager), Michael Tait, Simon Todd, Robert Dale, Mark Bell, Jack Norton, Kenny Boyle, John Alexander, Darren Craddock, Gary Neasham (Physiotherapist), Tony Kennedy (Kit Manager).
Front Row: Shaun Reay, Adrian Webster, John Brackstone, Andrew Leeson, Chris McCabe, Gareth Williams, Josh Gillies, Stephen Harrison, Ian Graham, Stephen Turnbull.

CLUB PERSONNEL

Chairman: Mr A R Platten.

Vice-Chairman: Mr K Scott.

Company Secretary: Mr C Baxter.

Additional Directors: Ian Evans, Gordon Young, Steve Ord and Robert Harding.

Secretary: Ian Evans
5 Bath Terrace, Blyth,
Northumberland NE24 3AX
Tel: (H) 01670 369 308 (B) 01670 352 373
(M) 07905 984 308
Email: generalmanager@blythspartans.com

Commercial Manager: Robert Harding.
Tel: (M) 07747 619 775 (B) 01670 352 373

Press Officer: Brian Grey.
Tel: (H) 0191 265 6244 (B) 0191 549 2842

Manager: Mick Tait.

Assistant Manager: Adam Sadler.

Club therapist: Gray Neasham.

A north eastern club already famous for its F.A.Cup run into The 6th Round draw in 1978, hit the headlines again when beating Shrewsbury Town and Bournemouth before conceding just one goal to Blackburn Rovers in their Third Round tie.

Experienced manager Harry Dunn had a tough season in the league however, and never managed a run of the sufficient consistency to provide results to take them away from the relegation zone. The worry of this situation seemed to prove too much for the board who did not renew the manager's contract at the end of the campaign and he returned to Whitby Town.

Spartans only consistent spell in the League had come after the euphoria of the televised Blackburn cup tie when three consecutive victories were gained to help the club into nineteenth place. Patchy form however, kept the pressure on all involved, and it wasn't until the very last league games that real consistency was achieved, and in the last five fixtures four wins provided a final table finish of fifteenth place that looked deceivingly safe.

Gateshead's promotion will be a fine example to the clubs whose travelling from the North East can sometimes be a problem for local players, but hopefully for Spartans, their fine tradition at the top of the non-league pyramid will stand them in good stead for the future.

BLYTH SPARTANS

BEST LGE ATT.: 1,292 v Gateshead
LOWEST: 404 v Hucknall Town

No.	Date	Comp	H/A	Opponents	Att:	Result	Goalscorers	Pos
1	Aug 9	BSN	H	Solihull Moors	412	W 3 - 0	G.Williams 54 Todd 73 **Dale** 83 (pen)	
2	12		A	Southport	827	L 1 - 2	Leeson 45	
3	16		A	AFC Telford United	1750	L 1 - 2	G.Williams 68	12
4	23		H	Workington	451	W 3 - 1	Bell 15 Hume 37 G Williams 45	9
5	25		A	Farsley Celtic	375	L 0 - 3		
6	30		H	Hucknall Town	404	W 3 - 0	**Dale** 57 (pen) 64 Wiliams 68	
7	Sept 2		H	Hyde United	405	W 3 - 0	Dalton 25 35 Pell 64	
8	**9**	**SS N1**	**A**	**Burscough**	**160**	**W 4 - 1**	**Dale 42, 60 Poole 52 Hume 74**	
9	13		A	Stafford Rangers	545	L 0 - 1		10
10	20		H	Tamworth	550	L 0 - 4		12
11	**27**	**F.A.C. 2Q**	**A**	**Whitby Town**	**403**	**D 2 - 2**	**McCabe 81 Dalton 84**	
12	**30**	**F.A.C. 2Q r**	**H**	**Whitby Town**	**408**	**W 5 - 2**	**Williams 17 McCabe 36 DALE 3 (36 70 pen 85)**	
13	Oct 4		H	King's Lynn	433	L 2 - 4	McCabe 14 Williams 19	15
14	**11**	**F.A.C. 3Q**	**A**	**Buxton**	**556**	**W 1 - 0**	**Williams 11**	
15	18		A	Redditch United	179	L 0 - 2		16
16	**21**	**SS N2**	**H**	**Gateshead**	**632**	**L 1 - 2**	**Rowntree 19**	
17	**25**	**F.A.C. 4Q**	**H**	**Sheffield**	**880**	**W 3 - 1**	**Brown 58 Reay 65 Dale 76**	
18	28		A	Vauxhall Motors	126	L 1 - 2	Reay 35	
19	Nov 1		A	Droylsden	337	L 0 - 2		18
20	**8**	**F.A.C. 1R**	**H**	**Shrewsbury Town**	**2742**	**W 3 - 1**	**Reay 1 29 Todd 53**	
21	11		A	Harrogate Town	328	L 1 - 3	Gildea 14	
22	15		A	Gainsborough Trinity	347	D 0 - 0		20
23	**22**	**F.A.T 3Q**	**H**	**Alfreton Town**	**446**	**L 3 - 4**	**McCabe 20 63 Gildea 75**	
24	**29**	**F.A.C 2R**	**A**	**Bournemouth**	**4165**	**D 0 - 0**		
25	**Dec 16**	**F.A.C 2R r**	**H**	**Bournemouth**	**4040**	**W 1 - 0**	**Dalton 89**	
26	20		A	Solihull Moors	182	L 0 - 2		21
27	26		H	Gateshead	1292	L 0 - 1		21
28	Jan 1		A	Gateshead	1388	L 0 - 3		
29	**5**	**F.A.C 3R**	**H**	**Blackburn Rovers**	**3445**	**L 0 - 1**		**21**
30	17		H	Fleetwood Town	651	W 3 - 0	Reay 47 90 Wiliams 56	21
31	20		H	Hinckley United	466	W 1 - 0	Reay 16	
32	24		A	King's Lynn	1041	W 3 - 2	Pell 16 Walton 44 53	19
33	27		H	Harrogate Town	825	L 3 - 4	**Dale** 33 Reay 45 61	
34	31		A	Hinckley United	420	L 1 - 2	Banks 45	19
35	Feb 21		H	Burscough	495	L 0 - 2		21
36	24		A	Fleetwood Town	587	L 0 - 1		
37	28		A	Alfreton Town	480	D 1 - 1	McCabe 29	21
38	Mar 7		H	Stalybridge Celtic	559	D 0 - 0		
39	10		H	Alfreton Town	549	D 2 - 2	Bown 2 29	
40	14		A	Tamworth	671	D 1 - 1	McCabe 55	21
41	17		H	AFC Telford United	501	W 2 - 0	Walton 14 **Dale** 26 (pen)	
42	21		H	Stafford Rangers	502	W 2 - 1	Brown 2 Pierpoint 79 (og)	19
43	24		A	Stalybridge Celtic	351	L 0 - 2		
44	28		A	Hucknall Town	239	D 1 - 1	McCabe 15	19
45	31		H	Redditch United	586	W 1 - 0	**Dale** (pen) 45	
46	April 4		H	Vauxhall Motors	519	L 0 - 1		19
47	6		A	Hyde United	338	L 0 - 1		
48	9		H	Droylsden	502	L 0 - 1		
49	11		A	Workington	366	W 1 - 0	Shandron 53	19
50	13		H	Farsley Celtic	628	W 5 - 0	Aspden 3 Shandray 48 Reay 62 Pell 69 **Dale** 90	
51	18		H	Gainsborough Trinity	583	D 1 - 1	Reay 23	18
52	21		H	Southport	563	W 1 - 0	Walton 77	
53	25		A	Burscough	402	W 3 - 2	McCabe 49 Dalton 50 Reay 85	

Average Home Att: **566 (487)** **Goals** **73 71**

Best Position: 9th **Worst:** 21st

Goalscorers: Dale 13, Reay 12, McCabe 9, Williams G 8, Brown 4, Dalton 5, Pell 3, Walton 4, Shandray 3, Aspden 2, Hume 2, Banks 1, Bell 1, Gildea 1, Leeson 1, Poole, Rowntree 1, Todd 1. Own Goals 1.

M BELL	WILLIAMS	BOYLE	PELL	TODD	LEESON	DALTON	MCCABE	DALE	HUME	WRIGHT	P BELL	POOLE	SNOWDEN	FENTON	BROWN	SMITH	GLADWIN	HINDMARSH	POWELL	A GILDEA	FARMAN	WATSON	ROWNTREE	LAIDLAW	REAY	BRADLEY	EVANS	RICHARDS	WALTON	WHITE	WEBSTER	BANKS	BRACKSTONE	SHAW	SHANDRAN	
X	X	X	X	X	X	X	X	X	X	X	S	S	U	U	U																					1
X	X	X	X	X	X	X	X	X	X	X	S	S	U	U	S																					2
X	X	X	X	X	X	X		X	X	X	S	S	U	U	X																					3
X	X		X	X	X	X	S	X	X	X	X	S	S	U	X																					4
X	X	S	X	X	X	X	X	X	X	X		S	U	U	X																					5
X	X	U	X	X	X	X	X	X	X	X	U	S	U		X	S																				6
X	X	S	X	X	X	X	X	X	X	X	U	S	U		X	S																				7
X	X	U	X	X	X	X	X	X	X	X	S	S	S	U	X																					8
X	X	S	X	X	X		X	X		X	X	X	S	S	X																					9
X	X	S	X	X	X		X	X	X		X	X	U	U	X		S	S																		10
	X	U	X	X	X	X	X	X	S	X	X	S	U	U	X				X	S																11
	X	S	X	X	X	X	X	X	X	X	U	S	U	U	X				X	S																12
	X	X	X	X	U	X	X	X	X	X	S	S		U	X				X	S																13
	X	X	X	X	X	X		X	X	S	S	U		U			S			X	X	X														14
U	X	X	X	X	X	S		X	X	U				U	X					X	X	X	S													15
	X	X	S	X	U	X		S	X	X				U	X					X	X	S	X	X												16
U	X	X	X	X	X	X		X		U		S		U	X					X	X	X			S											17
U		X	X	X	X	X		X		X		S		U	X		S				X	X			X											18
X		X		X	X	X		S		X		S		U	X		X			X	U	X			X											19
X	X	X	X	X	X	S	X	X	U	X		S		U			U			X	U	S			X											20
X	X	X	X	X	X	S		X	U	S		X			X					X	U	S			X											21
X	X	X	X		X	S	U	X		X		X		U	U						U	X			X	X										22
X	X	X	X		X		X	X	S	U		S			X					X	U	U			X	X										23
X	X	X	X		X	S	X	X	X	U		S		U	X					X	U	S			X											24
X	X	X	X		X	S		X	X	S		X		U			U			X	U	X			X		U									25
X	X	X			X	X	X	X	S			U		U	X					X	U	S			X			X								26
X	X	X	X		X	X	X		X	X		S		U	U						U	X			X			S								27
U	U	X	U		X	X			X	U		X			X						X	X		X	S			X	X							28
X	X	X	X	S	X	X	X	X	U	S		U			U					X	U	U			X					X						29
X	X	X	X	X	X	U	X	X							S					X	U				X				S	X	S					30
X	X	X	X	X	X	U		X		S					S						U				X				X	X	X	S				31
X	X	X	X	X	X	U		X		S					X						U				X				X	S	X	S				32
X	X	X	X	X	X	U		X		S					X						U				X				X	S	X	S				33
X	X	X	X	X	X	S		X		S				U	X						U				X					U	X	X				34
	X	X		X	X	S	U	X		S					X					U	X			U	X						X	X	X			35
	X	X	X	X	X	U	S	X		X					X					S	X				X						X	S	U			36
	X	X	X		X	U	X	X		U					X					S	X			S	X				X		X	U				37
	X	X	X	U	X	X	X	X							X					X	X			U	X						S	S	S			38
	X	X	X	S	X	X	X	X						U	X					U	X			U					X		X	U				39
	X	X	X	X	X	U	X	X							S						X			U	U				X		X	S	X			40
	X	X	X	X	X	U	X	X							S						X			U	S				X		X	S	X			41
	X	X	X	X	X	U		X							X					S	X			S	S				X		X	U	X			42
X	X	X	X	U	X	S		S							X					X				U	X				X		X	X		S		43
X	X	X	X	U	X		X	X							X					X	U				S				X		X	S	S			44
X	X	X	X	S				X							X					X	U			U	S				X		X	U	X		X	45
X		X	X	X	S	S		X							X					X	U			U	S				X			X	X		X	46
X	X	X	U	X	X		S	X							X						U				S				X		X	S	X		X	47
X	X	U	X	S	X		X	S							S					X	U				X				X		X		X		X	48
X	X	X	S	U	X		X	X							X						U				X				S		X	S	X		X	49
X	X	X	S	S	X	S	X	X							X						U				X				U		X		X		X	50
X	X	X	X	U	X	S	X	X												S	U				X				S		X		X		X	51
X	X	X	X	X	X		X	X																S	X				X		X					52
X	X		X	X	X	S	X	X						U							S			X	X				X		X		S			53
Total League Apperances																																				
30	38	34	35	28	39	15	23	37	12	14	3	5	0	0	30	0	1	0	1	11	11	6	0	2	22	1	0	2	17	2	21	4	11	0	7	X
0	0	4	2	4	1	10	3	3	1	6	4	11	2	1	6	2	2	1	0	5	1	2	1	3	7	0	0	1	3	2	2	10	3	1	0	S
3	1	2	2	5	1	9	2	0	1	3	2	1	7	16	3	0	0	0	0	2	18	0	0	8	1	0	0	0	1	1	0	4	1	0	0	U
Total Cup Apperances																																				
6	11	8	10	7	10	7	7	10	6	5	1	1	0	0	7	0	0	0	2	8	3	3	1	1	5	1	0	0	0	1	0	0	0	0	0	X
0	0	1	1	1	0	3	0	1	2	3	2	7	1	0	0	0	1	0	0	2	0	3	0	0	1	0	0	0	0	0	0	0	0	0	0	S
1	0	2	0	0	1	0	0	0	2	3	1	2	2	9	1	0	2	0	0	0	5	2	0	0	0	0	1	0	0	0	0	0	0	0	0	U

BLYTH SPARTANS

CURRENT SQUAD AS OF BEGINING OF 2009-10 SEASON

GOALKEEPERS	HT	WT	D.O.B	AGE	P.O.B	CAREER	APPS	GOA
Marc Bell			9/10/82	26		West Auckland, Gateshead, Whitby, Blyth 6/08	30	0
Jack Norton	6'00"		27/3/87	22		Darlington, Whitby 7/06, Darlington (L) 12/06, Guisborough, South Shields, Northallerton, Tow Law 1/08, Gateshead (Dual) c/s 08, Consett 2/09, Newcastle Blue Star 3/09, Blyth 8/09		
DEFENDERS								
Kenny Boyle			27/6/85	24		Whickham, Blyth 8/07	38	0
John Brackstone	5'11"	10 08	9/2/85	24	Hartlepool	Hartlepool Rel c/s 07, Darlington 7/07 Rel 5/08, Gateshead 5/08, Blyth 2/09	14	0
Darren Craddock	5'11"	12 02	23/2/85	24	Bishop Auckland	Hartlepool Rel 5/06, Whitby (L) 1/04, York (L) 1/06, York 5/06 Rel 4/08, Newcastle Blue Star 6/08, Blyth 6/09		
Stephen Harrison			3/2/82	27	Hexham	Sunderland Rel c/s 02, Carlisle (Trial) 3/02, Bristol R (Trial) 4/02, Gateshead 7/02, Blyth 8/04, Gateshead 1/05, Durham C 6/06, Blyth 7/09		
Andrew Leeson	5'10"	11 00	27/9/83	25	Cape Town, SA	Burnley Rel 8/03, Blyth, Newcastle Blue Star 11/05, Blyth 12/05	40	1
Chris McCabe			13/11/80	28		Jarrow Roofing, Sunderland Nissan, Blyth 12/04	26	5
MIDFIELDERS								
Josh Gilles			12/6/90	19		Sunderland Nissan, Newcastle Blue Star 1/09, Blyth 7/09		
Michael Tait			24/6/88	21		Darlington (Yth), Gretna Rel c/s 08, Newcastle Blue Star (SL) 1/08, Blyth 8/08, Newcastle Blue Star 9/08, Workington 11/08, Newcastle Blue Star 1/09, Blyth 6/09		
Simon Todd			3/12/89	19		Darlington, Blyth (3ML) 8/08 (SL) 1/09 Perm 2/09, Ostavalls (Swe) 5/09, Blyth 8/09	32	1
Stephen Turnbull	5'10"	11 00	7/1/87	22	South Shields	Hartlepool Rel 5/08, Gateshead (L) 12/05, Bury (2ML) 11/06, Rochdale (L) 3/07, Gateshead 7/08 Rel 5/09, Blyth 6/09		
Adrian Webster	5'08"	10 09	11/10/80	28	Hawkes Bay, NZ	Charlton (Trainee), Faversham, Colchester 5/99, Ashford T 2/00, Folkestone I 10/00, Ashford T 11/00, Welling 3/01, Maidstone 7/01, Torquay (Trial) 3/02, Margate 8/02, Maidstone 8/02, St George (Aust) c/s 03, Darlington 10/04 Rel c/s 06, Perth Glory (Aust)	23	0
Gareth Williams			1/4/80	29	Co Durham	Whickham, Whitley Bay, Blyth 8/00	38	6
FORWARDS								
John Alexander	5'11"	12 00	24/9/85	23	Middlesbrough	Darlington Rel c/s 04, Bishop Auckland (L) 12/02, Marske U, Billingham T, Blyth 7/09		
Robert Dale			11/6/84	25		Ryton, West Allotmment, Blyth, Oxford U (Trial) c/s 06	40	7
Ian Graham			4/2/87	22		Sunderland (Scholar), Newcastle Benfield, Blyth 6/09		
Sean Reay	6'01"	12 00	20/5/89	20	Jarrow	Darlington, Harrogate T (2ML) 8/08, Blyth Spartans 10/08	29	9

LOANEES	HT	WT	DOB	AGE	POB	From - To	APPS	GOA
(F)Jason Bradley	6'03"	13 00	16/3/89	20	Sheffield	Darlington 11/08 - Gainsborough (SL) 2/09, Mansfield 7/09	1	0

DEPARTURES	HT	WT	DOB	AGE	POB	From - To	APPS	GOA
(F)Martin Smith			13/11/74	34		Darlington 8/08 - Retired 9/08	2	0
(F)Daniel Hindmarsh			1/3/91	18		Monkseaton (Yth) - Rel	1	0
(M)Adam Gladwin			9/9/89	19		ex Darlington - Morpeth, Bedlington T 1/09	3	0
(D)Peter Snowden			26/6/81	28	Blyth	Newcastle Blue Star 11/04 - Newcastle Blue Star 10/08, Bedlington 6/09	2	0
(F)Adam Rowntree			18/4/89	20		Washington - Newcastle Benfield	1	0
(F)Phil Bell			3/9/83	25		Newcastle Blue Star 4 Fig 10/07 - Whitley Bay 11/08	7	1
(M)Karl Richards			8/3/76	33		Spennymoor 11/08 - Newcastle Blue Star 1/09	3	0
(D)Jamie Poole			10/10/87	21		Stokesley SC 8/08 - Seaham Red Star 1/09, Bedlington 5/09	16	0
(F)Anthony Hume			21/3/89	20		Northallerton 8/08 - Seaham Red Star 1/09, Spennymoor 1/09	13	1
(F)Bradley Smith			14/4/88	21		Newcastle C 10/08 -		
(M)Paul Watson			31/3/83	26		North Shields c/s 08 - Dunston Fed 1/09	8	0
(D)Alex White			28/8/88	21		Stranraer 12/08 - Tow Law 2/09, Ilkeston 6/09	4	0
(M)Andy Wright	5'06"	10 06	21/10/78	30	Leeds	Leigh RMI 8/08 - Newcastle Blue Star 3/09	20	0
(M)Steven Shaw			11/10/85	23		Ryton 3/09 - Rel, Ryton, Bedlington 5/09	1	0
(D)Richard Pell			17/11/82	26	Boston	Gainsborough 5/08 - Rel 5/09, Alfreton 5/09	37	3
(F)Graham Fenton	5'10"	12 10	22/5/74	25	Wallsend	Blackpool (Pl/Ass Man) 7/03 - Rel 5/09	1	0
(F)Anthony Shandran	5'11"	12 00	17/9/81	27	North Shields	Bedlington 3/09 - Bedlington 6/09	7	3
(F)Stuart Banks						Sunderland Nissan 1/09 - Rel 6/09	14	1
(G)Paul Farman			2/11/89	19	North Shields	Newcastle (Scholar) c/s 08 - Mansfield (Trial) 1/09, Gateshead 6/09	12	0
(F)Ged Dalton	5'08"	10 04	30/3/90	19	Beverley	Carlisle 3/08 - Whitby T 7/09	25	3
(M)Alex Gildea			15/9/80	28	Scarborough	USA Coaching 9/08 - Whitby T 7/09	16	1
(G)Gareth Powell			23/3/80	29		Bedlington 9/08 - Bedlington	1	0
(D)Gary Brown			19/7/87	22		Jarrow Roofing 1/08 - Durham C c/s 09	36	2
(D)Adam Laidlaw	6'05"	15 00	22/8/87	22		Brandon U - Tow Law (L), Whitby	5	0
(M)Mark Evans			1/8/85	24		Ryton -	0	0
(F)Marc Walton			24/2/86	23		Ryton 12/08 - Durham C c/s 09	20	5

BLYTH SPARTANS

Founded: 1899

Nickname: Spartans.

Club Colours: Green & white striped shirts, black shorts, green socks.

Change Colours: Yellow shirts, red shorts, red socks.

Club Sponsor: Carlsberg

Previous League: Northern Premier

Ground address: Croft Park, Blyth, Northumberland NE24 3JE.

Telephone: 01670 352 373

Fax: 01670 545 592

Mobile: 07905 984 308

Email: generalmanager@blythspartans.com

Website: www.blythspartansafc.co.uk

Capacity: 6,000 **Seats:** 300 **Covered:** 1,000 **Floodlights:** Yes

Simple Directions: From Tyne Tunnel heading North on A19 take Cramlington turning A1061 follow signs for Newsham/Blyth. Right fork at railway gates in Newsham go down Plessey Rd. Ground is on left.

Clubhouse:. Open every night plus lunchtimes at week ends.(01670 352 373)

Club Shop: Fully stocked.

PROGRAMME EDITOR

Scott Dewhurst

Tel: (M) 07755 8212213

(B) 01670 360115

Email: scottdewhurst@blythspartansafc.co.uk

CLUB STATISTICS

RECORDS

Attendance: (at Croft Park)10,186 v Hartlepools Utd.F.A.C. 8.12.56
Victory: 18-0 v Gateshead Town N..Alliance 28.12.07
Defeat: 0-10 v Darlington N E Lg,12.12.14.
v Newcastle Res. Northumberland Cup 26.03.27
v Middlesbrough Res.N.E.Lg.27.08 55
Goalscorer: Not known.
Career Appearances: Eddie Alder 605 (1965-1968)
Goals in a Season: Tommy Orrick 54
Goals in a Career: Brian Slane 294 19969-1977
Record Transfer Fee Paid: Not known.
Received: £30,000 from Hull City for Les Mutrie

SENIOR HONOURS

Northern League (10) R-up (5) Northumberland Senior Cup (19)

PREVIOUS

Leagues: Northumberland 01-07, Northern All 07-13 46-47 North Eastern (4) Northern Comb.: 45-46, Midland 58-60, Northern Co 60-62 and Northern 62-94 Northern Premier 1994-06.

CORBY TOWN

Back Row (L-R): Paul Tocco, Ian Jackson (coach), Chris Hope, Gavin Strachan, Lawrie Dudfield, John Turner, Mark Osborn, Phil Gulliver, Ayden Duffy, Jason Lee, Mark Stallard, Paul Mayo, Brett Solkhon, Steve Towers.
Front Row: Jamie McGhee, Phil Watt, Dean West, Steve Diggin, Danny Nicholls (assistant manager), Graham Drury (manager), Kevin Grundy (physio), Leon Mettam, Tommy Jaszczun, David Deeney.
(photograph by David Tilley)

CLUB PERSONNEL

Chairman: Peter Mallinger.

Vice-Chairman: Michael Leech.

Company Secretary: Michael Leech.

Additional Directors: David Dunham, Les Manning, Ian Hopewell.

Secretary: Gerry Lucas.
8 Richmond Avenue, Kettering, Northants.
NN15 5JG
Tel: (H): 01536 513 507 (M): 07932 633 343
Email: gerry21@googlemail.com

Commercial Manager: Peter Mallinger.
Tel: (M): 07702 640 148
Email: mallingerp@yahoo.co.uk

Press Officer: See secretary.

Manager: Graham Drury

Assistant Manager: Danny Nichols.

Club therapist: Kevin Grundy.

One of the best promotion battles in non-league football was witnessed in The Southern Premier Division last season. Corby Town who had chased Farnborough for most of the campaign finished strongest, clinching the title and promotion by winning their last six fixtures.

A reasonable start had taken 'The Steelmen' into second place by the end of September, but a lapse of form in which a run of four defeats with fifteen goals conceded, took them down to eighth position by the new year. A drastic change in fortunes was needed and a timely run of five games without a goal conceded saw the club safely back to second place and the promotion chase was on once again.

Two matches in the F.A.Cup and F.A.Trophy neither inspired the fans, nor affected the team's concentration on the championship. The Metropolitan Police were beaten in the Cup before A.F.C.Telford United won their Second Qualifying Round tie and in the Trophy, Corby had beaten Bedford but were eliminated by Chesham United.

Only two defeats for Corby in the second half of the season put so much pressure on leaders Farnborough that the Hampshire club eventually cracked. The ambitious Corby administrative team will be planning for further progress in the coming season although they only failed to score in six of their forty six senior fixtures last season. Strikers Steve Diggin (22 goals) and Leon Mettam (17) enjoyed a prolific campaign but the squad will be strengthened and Corby supporters will be looking forward to their football in The Blue Square North.

CORBY TOWN

BEST LGE ATT.: 1,969 v Banbury United
LOWEST: 179 v Hitchin Town

No.	Date	Comp	H/A	Opponents	Att:	Result	Goalscorers	Pos
1	Aug 16	Southern P.	H	Yate Town	308	D 1 - 1	O'Halloran 65	
2	18		A	Cambridge City	295	L 2 - 3	**Diggin** 5 (pen) 28	
3	23		A	Stourbridge	165	W 2 - 0	Hibbert 16 Nolan 37	12
4	25		H	Brackley Town	320	W 2 - 0	Hibbert 8 33	
5	30		A	Swindon Supermarine	165	W 4 - 1	Nolan 26 29 Towers 55 **Diggin** 66	2
6	Sept 3		H	Hemel Hempstead T	305	D 0 - 0		
7	6		H	Merthyr Tydfil	262	W 2 - 1	Nolan 6 39	2
8	**13**	**F.A.C. 1Q**	**A**	**Metropolitan Police**	**139**	**W 3 - 0**	**Nolan 10 Warren 13 Mettam 89**	
9	20		A	Mangotsfield United	164	W 3 - 0	Ball 20 (og) Mettam 83 Nolan 90	
10	**27**	**F.A.C. 2Q**	**A**	**AFC Telford United**	**1262**	**L 2 - 3**	**Burgess 5 Towers 47**	
11	Oct 4		A	Bashley	291	W 3 - 0	Towers 14 **Diggin** 59 61	2
12	8		H	Oxford City	314	L 0 - 1		3
13	**18**	**F.A.T. 1Q**	**A**	**Bedford Town**	**374**	**W 2 - 1**	**Diggin 25 63 (pen)**	
14	25		A	Bedford Town	453	W 5 - 1	**Diggin** 21 Burgess 30 Brennan 37 O'Halloran 66 Battersby 88	2
15	**Nov 1**	**F.A.T. 2Q**	**H**	**Chesham United**	**279**	**L 2 - 3**	**Burgess 14 Diggin 37**	
16	8		H	Clevedon Town	262	W 4 - 0	**DIGGIN** 3 (22 24 40 pen) Mettam 82	1
17	15		A	Gloucester CIty	291	W 3 - 1	Brennan 34 Burgess 70 Mettam 78	
18	22		H	Evesham United	349	D 0 - 0		2
19	29		H	Halesowen Town	417	L 1 - 2	Hildreth 26	5
20	Dec 6		A	Chippenham Town	395	L 1 - 3	**Diggin** 77	5
21	20		H	Tiverton Town	240	L 1 - 4	Brennan 90	6
22	27		A	Brackley Town	328	L 0 - 5		8
23	Jan 1		H	Rugby Town	369	W 2 - 0	**Diggin** 45 84	
24	13		A	Hemel Hempstead T	311	W 1 - 0	Hildrith 13	8
25	20		A	Banbury United	151	W 4 - 0	**DIGGIN** 3 (2 26 32) Turner 64	
26	24		H	Cambridge CIty	325	D 0 - 0		4
27	27		A	Oxford City	206	W 1 - 0	Gulliver 19	
28	31		H	Bashley	251	W 3 - 1	Nurse 65 Burgess 69 89	2
29	Feb 17		A	Hitchin Town	273	D 2 - 2	**Diggin** 33 Hibbert 83	
30	21		A	MerthyrTydfil	686	W 2 - 0	Burgess 4 **Diggin** 87	2
31	25		H	Bedford Town	240	L 1 - 2	Warren 51	
32	28		H	Mangotsfield United	248	D 1 - 1	Mettam 86 (pen)	2
33	Mar 4		H	Stourbridge	180	D 0 - 0		
34	7		A	Clevedon Town	148	W 3 - 1	**Diggin** 8 (pen) Brennan 30 Francis 44	2
35	11		H	Hitchin Town	179	W 2 - 0	Mettam 41 O'Halloran 45	
36	14		H	Gloucester City	265	L 1 - 2	Towers 90	2
37	17		A	Yate Town	155	W 2 - 0	Mettam 42 Towers 86	
38	21		A	Farnborough	2230	D 3 - 3	Lee 33 Turner 49 Towers 60	2
39	28		H	Chippenham Town	232	W 3 - 0	Mettam 2 (pen) Francis 12 54	3
40	31		A	Evesham Unit	140	D 1 - 1	Lee 35	
41	April 4		A	Halesowen Town	294	W 5 - 0	METTAM 3 (9 34 57) Lee 24 Towers 83	2
42	8		H	Farnborough	668	W 3 - 1	Lee 13 Mettam 25 Francis 30	
43	11		H	Swindon Supermarine	361	W 2 - 1	Mettam 44 (pen) **Diggin** 51	2
44	13		A	Rugby Town	410	W 2 - 0	Towers 61 Turner 89	
45	18		A	Tiverton Town	372	W 2 - 0	Mettam 28 (pen) Warren 80 (pen)	1
46	25		H	Banbury United	1969	W 5 - 0	Mattam 44 70 Towers 60 Francis 77 88	1

Average Home Att: 384 (235) **Goals** 94 45

Best Position: 1st **Worst:** 12th

Goalscorers: Diggin 22, Mettam 17, Towers 9, Burgess 7, Nolan 7, Francis 6, Brennan 4, Hibbert 4, Lee 4, O'Halloran 3, Turner 3, Warren 3, Battersby 1, Gulliver 1, Hildrith 1, Nurse 1. Own Goals 1.

CURRENT SQUAD AS OF BEGINING OF 2009-10 SEASON

GOALKEEPERS	HT	WT	D.O.B	AGE	P.O.B	CAREER	APPS	GOA
Ayden Duffy	6'05"	15 00	16/11/86	22	Kettering	Lincoln C Rel c/s 09, Bourne T (L), Grantham (WE) 11/04, Bourne T (L) 1/05, Buxton (L) 8/05, Lincoln Moorlands (L) 11/05, Stamford (2ML) 1/06, Cambridge U (L) 3/06, Stamford (L) 4/06, Stamford (L) 8/06, Worksop (3ML) 9/06, Stamford (L) 1/08, Corby T 7/09		
Steven Norris	6'01"		3/10/90	18		Norwich (Yth), Ipswich (Yth), Kings Lynn (Scholar), Swaffham (L) (07/08), Corby T 6/09		
Mark Osborn	6'02"	14 01	18/6/81	28	Bletchley	Wycombe Rel c/s 03, Carshalton (3ML) 12/00, Farnborough (L) 4/02, Farnborough (SL) 8/02, Farnborough 5/03, Kettering 3/05, Histon 5/07, Halesowen T (3ML) 10/07 Perm 1/08, Corby T 7/08		

DEFENDERS	HT	WT	D.O.B	AGE	P.O.B	CAREER	APPS	GOA
David Deeney	5'09"	10 06	12/1/87	22	Bulawayo, Zim	Luton, Hitchin 3/06, Hemel Hempstead 6/08, Corby T 5/09		
Philip Gulliver	6'02"	13 05	12/9/82	26	Bishop Auckland	Middlesbrough Rel c/s 04, Blackpool (L) 11/02, Carlisle (L) 12/02, Bournemouth (SL) 3/03, Bury (2ML) 10/03, Scunthorpe (L) 1/04, Rushden & D 8/04, Hereford 7/06, Rushden & D 5/07 Rel 10/08, Oxford C 11/08, Corby 11/08		
Chris Hope	6'01"	13 01	14/11/72	36	Sheffield	Darlington (Jun), Notts Forest 8/90, Kettering (SL) 1/93, Scunthorpe £50,000 7/93, Gillingham 7/00 £250,000 Rel 5/06, Rushden & D 7/06, Corby T 6/09		
Tommy Jaszczun	5'11"	11 02	16/9/77	31	Kettering	Aston Villa, Blackpool £30,000 1/00 Rel c/s 04, Northampton 7/04, Rochdale 7/05, Cambridge U (SL) 1/06, Cambridge U 7/06 Ret 3/07, Kettering 5/07 Rel 3/09, Corby T 3/09		
Paul Mayo	5'11"	11 09	13/10/81	27	Lincoln	Notts Forest (Scholar), Lincoln C (Sch) 10/99 Pro 4/00, Dag & Red (L) 10/02, Watford £65,000 3/04, Lincoln C 8/05, Notts County 7/07, Darlington (L) 1/08, Mansfield 1/09 Rel 5/09, Corby T 6/09		
Philip Watt	5'11"	11 05	10/1/88	21	Rotherham	Rotherham (Yth), Lincoln C Rel 2/08, Grantham (WE) 2/06, Grantham (L) 9/06, Corby (L) 1/08, Corby 2/08		
Dean West	5'10"	12 02	5/12/72	36	Morley	Leeds (Yth), Lincoln C, Bury P/E 9/95, Burnley 7/99, Lincoln C 7/04, Boston U P/E 9/04 Rel c/s 05, Kings Lynn 7/05, Corby T 7/08		

MIDFIELDERS	HT	WT	D.O.B	AGE	P.O.B	CAREER	APPS	GOA
Jack Defty			7/9/81	27		Kings Lynn, Corby T 6/09		
Jamie McGhee	5'08"	10 07	28/9/89	19	Grantham	Mansfield Rel 7/09, Corby T 7/09		
Scott Mitchell	5'11"	12 00	2/9/85	23	Ely	Ipswich Rel 5/06, Livingston 7/06, Peterborough 1/08, Stevenage (L) 3/08, Rushden & D 6/08, Kings Lynn (4ML) 9/08, Perm 10/08, Corby T 6/09		
Brett Solkhon	5'11"	12 06	12/9/82	26	Canvey Island	Ipswich (Yth), Arsenal (Yth), Rushden & D 7/00 Rel 1/03, Kettering 2/03 Rel 4/09, Corby 5/09		
Gavin Strachan	5'11"	11 07	23/12/78	30	Aberdeen	Coventry Yth, Dundee (3ML) 1/99, Motherwell (L) 2/02, Blackpool (Trial) 2/03, Peterborough 3/03, Southend 3/03 Rel c/s 03, Sheff Wed (Trial) 7/03, Hartlepool 8/03, Stockport (L) 10/05, Peterborough (L) 1/07, Peterborough 1/07 Rel 1/08, Notts County 1/08 Rel c/s 09, Corby T 7/09		
Steve Towers			17/8/85	24		Oadby, Rothwell c/s 04, Corby 6/06 Rel 10/07, Stamford 10/07, Corby T 5/08		

FORWARDS	HT	WT	D.O.B	AGE	P.O.B	CAREER	APPS	GOA
Steve Diggin			2/11/87	21		Aston Villa (Yth), Wycombe (Yth), Cogenhoe, Kings Lynn 2/07, Cogenhoe 3/07, Corby 6/07		
Jason Lee	6'03"	13 08	9/5/71	38	Forest Gate	Charlton, Fisher (L) 8/89, Stockport (L) 2/91, Lincoln C £35,000 3/91, Southend (L) 8/93 £150,000 9/93, N.Forest £200,000 3/94, Charlton (2ML) 2/97, Grimsby (L) 3/97, Watford £200,000 6/97, Chesterfield £250,000 8/98, Peterborough (2ML) 1/00 £50,000 3/00		
Leon Mettam	5'09"	11 01	9/12/86	22	Lincoln	Lincoln C Rel c/s 07, Stamford 6/07, Corby T Undisc 2/08		
Mark Stallard	6'00"	13 06	21/10/74	34	Derby	Deby, Fulham (L) 9/94, Bradford C £110,000 1/96, Preston (L) 2/97, Wycombe £100,000 3/97, Notts County £10,000 3/99, Barnsley 1/04 Rel c/s 05, Chesterfield (2ML) 10/04, Notts County (SL) 2/05, Shrewsbury 7/05 Rel c/s 06, Lincoln C 7/06 Rel c/s 08, Mansfield 7/08, Corby T 7/09		
John Turner	5'10"	11 00	12/2/86	23	Harrow	Aston Villa (Yth), Cambridge U (Yth c/s02), Rushden & D (Trial) 10/05, Scunthorpe (Trial) 11/05, Aldershot (L) 11/05, Rushden & D 1/06, Grays 8/06 Rel 5/07 , Braintree (L) 10/06, Bishops Stortford (L) 1/07, Kings Lynn 5/07 Rel 1/09 Corby T 1/09		

Departures	HT	WT	DOB	AGE	POB	From - To	APPS	GOA
(F)Lawrie Dudfield	6'01"	13 09	7/5/80	29	Southwark	Chelmsford 5/09 - Rel 7/09		
(D)Tom Bonner	6'00"	11 06	6/2/88	21	Camden	Solihull Moors 6/09 - Ilkeston 8/09		

CORBY TOWN

Founded: 1948

Nickname: The Steelmen.

Club Colours: Black & white shirts, black shorts, black socks.

Change Colours: Yellow shirts, royal blue shorts, yellow socks.

Club Sponsor: Tresham College

Previous League: Southern League

Ground address: Rockingham Triangle Stadium, Rockingham Road, Corby NN17 2AE

Telephone: 01536 406 640

Fax: 01536 513 507

Mobile: 07932 633 343

Email: gerry21@googlemail.com

Website: www.corbytown.net

Capacity: 6,000 **Seats:** 300 **Covered:** 1,000 **Floodlights:** Yes

Simple Directions: On Northern outskirts of town at junction of A6003 and A6116 opposite entrance to Rockingham Castle grounds.

Clubhouse: Trackside bar open on matchdays and during week for hot snacks. **Club Shop:** Yes.

Local Radio: BBC Radio Northampton,Northants 96, Connect FM and Corby Radio.

Local Press: Northampton Evening Telegraph, Herald & Post and The Citizen

no image available

PROGRAMME EDITOR

David Tilley

Tel: (H) 01536 403 667

Email: david.tilley59@tiscali.co.uk

CLUB STATISTICS

RECORDS

Attendance: 2,240 v Watford (friendly) 1986-1987

Career Goalscorer:David Holbauer 159 1984-1995

Career Appearances: Derek Walker 601 1979-1920

Transfer Fee Paid: £2,700 to Barnet for Elwun Edwards 1981

Received: £20,000 from Oxford United for Matt Murphy 1993

SENIOR HONOURS

United Counties League Champions 1950-51, 51-52.

Southern League Premier Division Champions 2008-09.

Northants Senior Cup (6)

PREVIOUS

Leagues: United Counties League 1935-1952.

Midland League 1952-1958. Southern League 1958-2009.

DROYLSDEN

CLUB PERSONNEL

Chairman: David Pace.

Company Secretary: Bryan Pace.

Secretary: Alan Slater.

83 King Edward Road, Hyde,

Cheshire, SK14 5JJ

Telephone: (H) 0161 368 3687

(B) 0161 370 1426

(M) 07989 024 777

E-mail: alan583@btinternet.com

Commercial Manager: Stella Quimm

Tel: (M) 07887 933 095

Press Officer: David Pace.

Tel: (B) 0161 335 0129

(M) 07850 369 588

Manager: David Pace.

Club therapist: Danny Gabrielson MCSP DIP

Supporters of 'The Bloods' will probably remember the 2008-2009 season for their club's extraordinary F.A.Cup exploits.

An excellent victory over Darlington in a home replay, having previously disposed of Bradford P.A.,Gateshead and Belper Town earned a home tie with Chesterfield. Two abandoned games were then followed by a fine 2-2 away draw and what appeared to be entry into the 3rd Round after a 2-1 home replay victory. But after all that, their match winning goalscorer Sean Newton was adjudged to have been ineligible so the tie was forfeited!

The league season had started with an unbeaten run of eight games but only two of these were victories and Dave Pace's club spent most of the season trying to produce the necessary consistency to push them into play-off contention.

The F.A.Cup excitement had overshadowed the club's quick departure from the F.A.Trophy at Farsley Celtic and it wasn't until the last six weeks of the season that a place in the top ten was held consistently.

Only three defeats were suffered in the last fourteen fixtures and five victories in six games placed Droylsden in sixth position with just three vital games to play. Away draws at Harrogate and Stalybridge were followed by a sad end to a strange campaign, as 'The Bloods' lost 1-3 to Farsley Celtic at The Burcher's Arms. Perhaps a less dramatic but more consistent season will be welcomed in August.

DROYLSDEN

BEST LGE ATT.: **772** v Stalybridge Celtic
LOWEST: **278** v King's Lynn

No.	Date	Comp	H/A	Opponents	Att:	Result	Goalscorers	Pos
1	Aug 9	BSN	H	Tamworth	414	D 1 - 1	Halford 60	
2	13		A	Gateshead	360	D 1 - 1	**Newton** 70	
3	16		A	King's Lynn	1035	D 2 - 2	Townson 70 Lamb 77	
4	23		H	Hyde United	467	W 2 - 1	Burns 74 **Newton** 89	10
5	25		A	Hucknall Town	374	D 1 - 1	Prince 37	
6	31		H	AFC Telford United	544	W 1 - 0	Prince 48	6
7	Sept 1		H	Workington	386	D 1 - 1	Prince 84	
8	**8**	**SS N1**	**H**	**Gateshead**	**190**	**L 1 - 2***	**Townson 46**	
9	13		A	Farsley Celtic	259	D 1 - 1	Townson 87	11
10	20		H	Stafford Rangers	420	L 0 - 1		13
11	**27**	**F.A.C. 2Q**	**H**	**Bradford P.A.**	**425**	**W 2 - 1**	**Cryam 18 Newton 70 (pen)**	
12	Oct 4		A	Alfreton Town	318	W 3 - 2	Lamb 3 Rouse 79 Townson 83	10
13	**11**	**F.A.C. 3Q**	**H**	**Gateshead**	**470**	**W 3 - 2**	**Townson 20 Byron 43 Lamb 82**	
14	18		H	Gainsborough Trinity	377	W 3 - 2	Beck 33 36 **Newton** 89 (pen)	9
15	**25**	**F.A.C. 4Q**	**H**	**Belper Town**	**557**	**D 0 - 0**		
16	**28**	**F.A.C. 4Q r**	**A**	**Belper Town**	**568**	**W 2 - 1**	**Maguire 15 Townson 27**	
17	Nov 1		H	Blyth Spartans	337	W 2 - 0	Rouse 65 Brown 90	
18	**8**	**F.A.C. 1R**	**A**	**Darlington**	**2479**	**D 0 - 0**		
19	11		A	Solihull Moors	148	L 1 - 2	Maguire 68	
20	**18**	**F.A.C. 1R r**	**H**	**Darlington**	**1672**	**W 1 - 0**	**Tipton 26**	
21	15		H	Redditch United	339	D 2 - 2	Byron 50 Rouse 73	11
22	**22**	**F.A.T 3Q**	**A**	**Farsley Celtic**	**202**	**L 0 - 2**		
23	Dec 6		H	Harrogate Town	324	W 2 - 1	**Gray** 34 Beck 65	9
24	**9**	**F.A.C 2R**	**A**	**Chesterfield**	**5698**	**D 2 - 2**	**Brown 49 Halford 81**	
25	20		A	Tamworth	690	L 0 - 2		11
26	**23**	**F.A.C. 2R r**	**H**	**Chesterfield**	**2824**	**W 2 - 1**	**Newton 31 55 (pen)** Droylsden expelled for playing an ineligible player	
27	26		H	Vauxhall Motors	306	L 1 - 2	Brown 33	11
28	Jan 17		H	Gateshead	295	D 0 - 0		14
29	20		A	Burscough	270	W 1 - 0	Tipton 90	
30	24		A	Redditch United	205	W 4 - 0	Maguire 8 **Gray** 12 18 Townson 46	10
31	27		A	Gainsborough Trinity	244	L 0 - 1		
32	31		H	Burscough	295	W 3 - 1	Cryan 57 Townson 83 Fitzpatrick 90	10
33	Feb 21		H	Farsley Celtic	326	W 2 - 0	**Newton** 43 Brown 77	9
34	24		A	Workington	281	D 1 - 1	Halford 30	
35	28		A	Fleetwood Town	1407	L 1 - 2	McGuire 79	10
36	Mar 3		A	Vauxhall Motors	149	W 4 - 1	**NEWTON** 3 (10 39 44) Townson 71	
37	7		H	Alfreton Town	354	W 2 - 0	**Gray** 65 Soruel 84	
38	9		A	Hinckley United	351	L 0 - 1		
39	14		A	Stafford Rangers	474	D 0 - 0		9
40	16		H	Stalybridge Celtic	772	D 1 - 1	**Gray** 51	
41	21		H	Southport	489	D 0 - 0		9
42	26		H	Hinckley United	450	W 3 - 0	Speight 50 79 Hacker 65	
43	28		A	AFC Telford United	1819	L 0 - 2		8
44	30		H	King's Lynn	278	W 1 - 0	Brown 35	7
45	April 4		H	Solihull Moors	280	W 2 - 1	McGuire 58 Speight 88	7
46	7		A	Southport	619	L 1 - 3	Banim 61	
47	9		A	Blyth Spartans	403	W 2 - 0	**Gray** 30 81	
48	11		A	Hyde United	557	W 3 - 1	**Gray** 22 57 Patterson 89	6
49	13		H	Hucknall Town	307	W 5 - 1	Hacker 15 **Gray** 53 Speight 18 Patterson 35 Fitzpatrick 68	
50	18		A	Harrowgate Town	362	D 1 - 1	Speight 70	6
51	21		A	Stalybridge Celtic	614	D 2 - 2	Byron 50 90	
52	25		H	Fleetwood Town	632	L 1 - 3	Byron 40	7

Average Home Att: 400 (643) **Goals** 77 55

Best Position: 6th **Worst:** 13th

Goalscorers: Gray 10, Newton 10, Townson 9, Byron 5, Brown 5, Maguire 5, Speight 5, Beck 3, Halford 3, Lamb 3, Prince 3, Rouse 3, Cryam 2, Fitzpatrick 2, Hacker 2, Patterson 2, Tipton 2, Banim 1, Burns 1, Soruel 1.

KENNEDY	COO	BROWNHILL	DUGDALE	HALFORD	SORVEL	BROWN	PICKFORD	GEDMAN	TOWNSON	PRINCE	LAMB	BURBEARY	NEWTON	CRYAN	ELLIS	ROCHE	MCGUIRE	BYRON	BURNS	MEADOWCROFT	CLANCY	MAWSON	ALLEN	ROUSE	TANDY	BECK	TIPTON	RUFFER	GRAY	HUNT	FITZPATRICK	MORRIS	SPEIGHT	BANIM	PATTERSON	
X	X	X	X	X	X	X	X	X	X	X	S	S	S	U	U																					1
X		U	X	X	X	U		X	S	X	X	X	X	S	S	X	X																			2
X		S		X	X	S		X	S		X	X	X			X	X	X	X	U	U															3
		S		X	X	S		X	X		S	X	X		U	X	X	X	X	U		X														4
		X			X	S		S	S	X	X	X	X	U	U		X	X	X	X		X														5
	S	X			X				X	X	X	X	X	X	S	U	X	X	U	S		X														6
	U	X			X	X		X	S	X	S	X	X	X				X	X	U		X	S													7
	X	U	X		X	S	X		X	X	X		X	U	S					X		X	X	S												8
		X	U		X	U	X		X	X	X		X	X		S		X	S			X	X	S												9
		S	U		X	S	U		X		S	X	X	X		X	X	X	X			X		X												10
		X	S	U	X	S	X		X		X	X	X	X		U	X	X			U	X		S	U											11
		X	X		X	S	X		X		X	X	X	X		U	X					X		S	U	S										12
		X		X	X	S	X		X		X	X	X	U		U	U	X			U	X		S		X	S									13
		X		X	X	X			X		X	X	X	U		U		X				X		S	S	X	S									14
		X	U	X	X	S	X		X		X	X	X	U		U		X			U	X		S	U	X	S									15
		X	U		X	S			X	U	X		X	X		U	X	X			U	X		U		X	X									16
		X	U		X	S				X	X		X	X		U	X	X				X		S	S	X	X									17
		X	U		X	S	X		X	S	X	U	X	X		U	X	X			S	X		U			X									18
		X	X	U	X	S	X		X	S	X		X	X		U	X				X			S			X									19
		X	U	S		X	U		U	X	X	S	X	X		U	X	X			X			S		X	X									20
		U		U		X			X	X	S	S	X			X	X	X			X			S		X	X	X								21
		U	X	X			X		X	X	X	X	X	U		X	X				X			S		S	S									22
		S	U		X	S	X		X	X		U				X		X				X		S	X	X		X	X							23
		X		X	X	X	S		S	X	X	U	X	X		U		S			U	X			U	X	X									24
		S		U	X	U	X		X		S		X			X		X				X			S	X	X	X	X							25
		X		U	U	X	X		S	U	X	U	X	X			X	X			U	X			U	X	X									26
		X		U	U	X	X		S		S	S		X			X	X				X			X	X	X		X							27
		S		U	X	S	U			X	X		X	X		X	X	X				X				X	S		X							28
		X		U		S	X		S	X			X	X			X	X				X				X	S	U	X	X						29
		U		X	X		X		X	S	X		X	U		X	X					X				S	S	X	X							30
		U		X	X	S	X		X	S	X		X	U		X	X					X				S		X		X						31
		X		U	X	X			S	X	S		X	X		U	X	X				X				X			X		S					32
		U		U	X	X			X	S	X		X	X		X	X	X				X				S	S		X							33
		X		X			X			S	X		X			U	X	X				X				X	X	U	X		S	S				34
		U			X		S		S		X		X	X		X	X	X				X				X	X	U	X		S					35
		X		X	X		X		X	S	S		X	U			X					X				U		X	X			S	X			36
		X		X	X		X		X	S	S		X	U			X					X				U		X	X			S	X			37
		X		U		S	X		U	S	X		X	X			X	X				X				X			X			S	X			38
		X		X	X	X				S	X		X				X	U				X				S	X	X			S	U	X			39
		X		X	X	X	S				S		X			S	X	U				X				X	U	X	X				X			40
		X		X	X	X	U				S		X			U	X	U				X				X	U	X					X	X		41
		X		X		X	S						X				X					X				X		X	X				X	X	S	42
		X		X	X	S	X				X		X			U	X	U				X					S	X				S		X	X	43
		X		U	U	X	S				X					X	X	X				X				X	S	X			S		X	X		44
		X			U	X	U						X	U			X	X				X				X		X	X		S		X	X	S	45
		X			U	X	S				X		X	U			X	X				X				X		X			S		X	X	S	46
		X		X	X		X				S		X	U			X					X				U	X	X	X		S	U	X			47
		X		X	X	S					U		X				X	U				X				X	X	X	X		S		X		S	48
		X		X		X	U				S					X	X	U				X				X		X	X		S	S	X		X	49
		X		X	U	X					S		S			X	X	U				X				X		X	X		S		X		X	50
		X		X	X	S					U		X			U	X	S				X				X		X	X		S		X		X	51
		X		X	X	X					S		X	U		U	X	X				X					S		X			U	X		X	52
Total League Appearances																																				
3	1	30	4	21	31	17	16	5	16	12	20	9	36	14	0	15	36	24	5	1	2	37	1	1	2	22	10	20	22	2	0	0	16	6	5	X
0	1	6	0	0	0	15	5	1	8	9	16	3	2	1	2	2	0	1	1	1	0	0	1	7	3	5	8	0	0	0	12	6	0	0	4	S
0	1	6	4	10	5	3	5	0	1	0	2	1	0	11	3	11	0	7	1	3	1	0	0	0	1	3	2	3	0	0	0	3	0	0	0	U
Total Cup Appearances																																				
0	1	8	2	4	7	3	7	0	7	4	10	4	10	6	0	1	6	7	0	1	2	8	1	0	0	6	5	0	0	0	0	0	0	0	0	X
0	0	0	1	1	0	6	1	0	2	1	0	1	0	0	1	0	0	1	0	0	1	0	0	6	0	1	3	0	0	0	0	0	0	0	0	S
0	0	2	4	2	1	0	1	0	1	2	0	3	0	4	0	7	1	0	0	0	6	0	0	2	4	0	0	0	0	0	0	0	0	0	0	U

DROYLSDEN

CURRENT SQUAD AS OF BEGINING OF 2009-10 SEASON

GOALKEEPERS	HT	WT	D.O.B	AGE	P.O.B	CAREER	APPS	GOA
Chris Howarth	6'02"	12 10	23/5/86	23	Bolton	Bolton Rel c/s 07, Stockport (L) 1/06, St Johnstone (Trial) c/s 06, Oldham (L) 8/06, Carlisle (SL) 3/07, Carlisle 7/07 Rel c/s 09, Droylsden 8/09		
Craig Mawson	6'02"	13 04	16/5/79	30	Keighley	Burnley, Lincoln (2ML) 9/00, Halifax 2/01 Rel c/s 01, Morecambe 8/01 Rel c/s 04, Oldham 8/04 Rel 10/04, Hereford 10/04, Halifax 6/06, FC Halifax 7/08, Droylsden 8/08	37	0
DEFENDERS								
Liam Brownhill			28/11/86	22	Altrincham	Stockport Rel c/s 05, Altrincham (Trial) c/s 05, Bangor C 8/05, Connahs Quay 10/05, Witton 12/05, Droylsden 6/08	36	0
Michael Byron	6'02"	11 03	16/8/87	22	Liverpool	Hull C Rel c/s 07, Scarborough (L) 8/06, Hinckley U (2ML) 10/06, Notts County (SL) 3/07, Notts County 9/07 Rel 1/08, Hinckley U (3ML) 11/07 Perm 2/08, Droylsden c/s 08	25	3
Lewis Craig						Burnley (Scholar), Barnoldswick T, Droylsden 7/09		
Colin Cryan	5'10"	13 00	23/3/81	28	Dublin	Sheff Utd Rel c/s 04, Scarborough (L) 10/02, Scarborough (L) 10/03, Scarborough 7/04 Rel 6/05, Lincoln C 8/05, Boston U 1/07 Rel c/s 07, Droylsden 7/07	15	1
Steve Halford	5'10"	12 10	21/9/80	28	Bury	Bury Rel 9/01, Chester 10/01, Accrington 1/02, Radcliffe B (L) 11/04, Droylsden (L) 2/05, Droylsden 7/05, Flixton (Dual) 10/08	21	4
Lee Roche	5'10"	10 11	28/10/80	28	Bolton	Man Utd Rel c/s 03, Wrexham (SL) 7/00, Burnley 7/03 Rel c/s 05, Wrexham 7/05 Rel c/s 07, Droylsden 10/07	17	0
Lee Woodyatt			16/7/83	26	Chester	Chester, Leigh RMI (L) 1/03, Northwich 7/03 Rel c/s 04, Vauxhall Motors 10/04, Barrow 6/07 Rel 5/09, Droylsden 7/09		
MIDFIELDERS								
Steven Beck			4/6/84	25	Liverpool	Everton Rel 6/03, Wigan (Trial) c/s 03, TNS/The New Saints 7/03, Droylsden 10/08	27	3
Alex Brown						Crewe (Scholar), Witton 7/06, Droylsden 6/08	32	4
Paul Brown	5'11"	12 00	10/9/84	24	Liverpool	Tranmere Rel c/s 06, Accrington (L) 8/05, Barrow 7/06, Kingston City (Aus) 2/07, Barrow 8/07 Rel 5/09, Droylsden 6/09		
Stuart Graves	5'11"	11 07	4/6/80	29	Bebbington	Tranmere (Trainee), Stockport, Southport 8/98, Poulton V, Heswall, TNS c/s 00, Rhyl 12/00, TNS 7/01, Newtown, Rhyl 8/02, Bradford PA 6/08, Droylsden 7/09		
Rob Lloyd	6'00"	11 10	13/8/86	23	Chester	Crewe, Witton (2ML) 11/05, Witton (4ML) 10/06 Perm 2/07, FC Halifax 9/08, Droylsden 7/09		
Steve Pickford			24/12/77	31	Ashton	Glossop NE, Leigh RMI 3/99, Glossop NE, Stalybridge 7/99, Southport 5/02, Hyde U 6/06, Droylsden 7/08	21	0
Carl Ruffer	5'08"	10 04	20/12/74	34	Chester	Everton Rel c/s 94, Runcorn c/s 94, Blackpool (Trial) c/s 00, Chester 8/00, Droylsden (L) 3/04, Morecambe 5/04 Rel 11/05, Droylsden 11/05, Rhyl 6/07, Bradford PA 7/08 (Pl/Ass Man) 7/08, Droylsden 11/08	20	1
Neil Sorvel	6'00"	12 09	2/3/73	36	Whiston	Crewe, Macclesfield 8/92, Crewe 6/99, Shrewsbury 7/05 Rel 1/07, Morecambe 1/07 Rel c/s 08, Southport (L) 1/08, Droylsden 7/08	31	1
Danny Williams	6'01"	13 00	12/7/79	30	Wrexham	Liverpool, Wrexham 3/99 Rel c/s 01, Doncaster (L) 1/01, Kidderminster 7/01, Chester (L) 2/04, Bristol R 3/04 Rel c/s 04, Wrexham 8/04 Rel c/s 08, Rhyl c/s 08, Droylsden 7/09		
FORWARDS								
Jody Banim	5'08"	13 01	1/4/78	31	Manchester	Man Utd (Trainee), Trafford, Altrincham, Flixton, Hyde, Rossendale, Radcliffe B c/s 01, Shrewsbury £20,000 + 12/03, Accrington (L) 8/04, Droylsden Undisc 9/04, Stalybridge 9/05, Droylsden Undisc 5/06, Torquay (SL) 2/08, Burton 5/08 Rel 4/09, Altrincham (L) 1/09, Droylsden (SL) 3/09, Real Marylands Monarchs (USA) 4/09, Salford C 7/09, Droylsden 8/09	6	1
Tony Gray		6/4/84	25		Newton, Bangor C 9/04, Burscough 7/05, Southport 6/06, Droylsden 12/08		22	11
Alex Meechan	5'08"	10 10	29/1/80	29	Plymouth	Swindon, Bristol C 7/98, Forest Green (2ML) 8/00, Yeovil (L) 11/00, Forest Green NC 12/00, Dag & Red 6/03, Forest Green (3ML) 11/03 Perm 2/04 Rel 6/04, Luton (Trial) 7/04, Leigh RMI 8/04 Rel 11/04, Halifax 11/04 Rel 4/05, Forest Green 7/05 Rel 1/07, Chester 1/07 Rel c/s 07, York C 7/07, Stalybridge 11/07, Altrincham 6/08 Rel 3/09, Stalybridge (L) 1/09, Stalybridge 3/09, Droylsden 7/09		
Simon Yeo	5'10"	11 08	20/10/73	35	Stockport	Army, Fivemiletown (NI), Ards (NI) 9/97, Curzon Ashton 10/97, Coleraine (NI) 11/97, Hyde U c/s 98, Atherton Coll (L) 9/98, Lincoln C 5/02, New Zealand Knights c/s 05, Lincoln C 1/06, Peterborough 8/06, Chester Undisc 1/07 Rel c/s 08, Bury (SL) 1/08, Macclesfield 7/08 Rel c/s 09, Droylsden 7/09		

LOANEES	HT	WT	DOB	AGE	POB	From - To	APPS	GOA
(F)Aaron Burns	5'10"		8/11/87	21	Manchester	Northwich (3ML) 8/08 -	6	1
(F)Lloyd Ellams			11/1/91	18	Chester	Chester 9/08 -		
(F)Domaine Rouse	5'06"	10 10	4/7/89	20	Stretford	Bury 9/08 - Fleetwood (SL) 3/09	8	3
(F)Lee Hunt	6'01"	13 01	5/6/81	28	Chester	Barrow 1/09 - Rel 5/09, Rhyl 6/09	2	0

DEPARTURES	HT	WT	DOB	AGE	POB	From - To	APPS	GOA
(F)Matthew Berkeley	5'11"	10 10	3/8/87	22	Manchester	Workington 6/08 - Leigh Genesis 8/08, Mossley 11/08, Hyde U 11/08, TNS 1/09		
(G)John Kennedy	6'01"	14 10	30/11/80	28	Rotherham	Witton 6/08 - FC Halifax 8/08, Worksop 6/09	3	0
(M)Danny Ellis	5'10"	12 07	18/11/88	20	Stockport	Stockport 7/08 - FC Halifax 9/08, Salford C, Rossendale 2/09	2	0
(D)Danny Meadowcroft	6'04"	12 05	22/5/85	24	Macclesfield	Northwich c/s 08 - FC Halifax 10/08, Northwich 3/09	2	0
(M)Damien Allen	5'11"	11 04	1/8/86	23	Cheadle	Morecambe 9/08 - Flixton (Dual) 10/08, FC Halifax 10/08	2	0
(D)Cavell Coo	5'09"	11 03	7/8/87	22	Manchester	Witton 6/08 - FC Halifax (L) 9/08 Perm	2	0
(F)Paul Gedman			14/6/81	27		Bradford PA 7/08 - FC Halifax (L) 9/08 Perm 10/08, Hyde U 7/09	6	0
(M)Jamie Tandy			1/9/84	25	Manchester	Hyde U 9/08 - Flixton (Dual) 10/08, Salford C 1/09	5	0
(M)Ashley Burbeary			29/11/86	22		Stalybridge 11/07 - Mansfield (Trial) 1/09, Gainsborough 1/09	12	0
(G)Kyle Clancy						Blackpool 7/08 - Salford C 2/09, Burscough 3/09, Northwich 7/09	2	0
(M)Neil Prince	5'11"	10 07	17/3/83	26	Liverpool	Southport 7/08 - Southport 3/09, Marine 7/09	21	3
(F)Jake Speight						Farsley Celtic 2/09 - Mansfield 5/09	16	5
(M)Jamie McGuire	5'07"	11 01	13/11/83	25	Birkenhead	Cammell Laird 7/07 - Fleetwood 5/09	36	4
(F)Rory Patterson						Bradford PA 3/09 - Coleraine 6/09	9	3
(D)Sean Newton	6'02"	13 00	23/9/88	20	Liverpool	Chester 8/08 - Barrow 7/09	38	5
(D)Adam Dugdale	6'03"	12 07	12/9/87	21	Liverpool	Southport 1/08 - Royal Racing Football Club Montegnee (Bel) 2/09, Barrow 7/09	4	0
(F)Matthew Tipton	5'11"	13 05	29/6/80	29	Conwy	Hyde U Undisc 10/08 - Macclesfield 4 fig 7/09	18	1
(M)Gareth Morris					Ashton	Hyde U 2/09 - Rel	6	0
(F)Kevin Townson	5'08"	10 03	19/4/83	26	Liverpool	The New Saints 7/08 - Rel	24	6
Ian Fitzpatrick						Ashton U 1/09 - Rel	12	2
(F)Carl Lamb			10/11/84	24		The New Saints 7/08 - Rel 8/09	36	2

DROYLSDEN

Formed: 1892.

Nickname: The Bloods.

Club Colours: Red shirts, red shorts, red socks.

Change Colours: Silver shirts, navy shorts, navy socks.

Club Sponsor: Boulting PLC.

Previous League: Northern Premier League.

Ground Address:	The Butchers Arms Ground, Market Street, Droylsden, Manchester M43 7AY.
Telephone No:	0161 370 1426
Mobile:	07989 024 777
Fax:	0161 370 8341
Email:	alans83@btinternet.com
Website:	www.droylsdenfc.co.uk

SIMPLE DIRECTIONS

By Road Jct 23 M60 signed to Manchester. Join A635 (towards Manchester). Right at lights onto A662 to Droylsden. Turn right into Market Street after half a mile, then over lights and ground is on left.

Capacity: 3,500 **Seats:** 500 **Covered:** 2,000

Clubhouse:	Pub hours except matchdays.
Club Shop:	Yes.

Local Press:	Tameside Reporter, Tameside Advertiser.
Local Radio:	BBC Manchester.

PROGRAMME EDITOR
Steven Jarvis
Tel: (M) 07792 906 929
Email: stevenjarvis@googlemail.com

CLUB STATISTICS

RECORDS

Attendance: 4,250 v Grimsby

Victory: 13-2 v Lucas Sports Club.

Defeat: Not known.

Career Goalscorer: E.Gillibrand - 275 (1931-35)

Career Appearances: Paul Phillips - 326

Record Transfer Fee Paid: For Terry Fearns 2005 (undisclosed).

Received: £11,000 from Crewe Alexandra for Tony Naylor 1990

SENIOR HONOURS

Conference North Champions 2006-07.

Northern Premier League Division 1 Champions 1998-99.

Manchester Premier Cup: (3) Manchester Senior Cup (3)

PREVIOUS

Leagues: Manchester. Lancs Combination 1936-39, 50-68.

Cheshire County: 1939-50 68-82. North West Counties 1982-87.

Northern Premier 1986-2004.

EASTWOOD TOWN

Back L/R Wayne Diuk, Anton Foster, Kris Mathews, Chris Shaw, Ian Holmes
Middle Steve Hutchinson, Matt Rhead, Marc Smith, Ian Deakin, Paul Robinson, Simon Sturdy, Russell Cooke, Nick Taylor (physio)
Front Ross Gardner, Craig Swinscoe, Lindon Meikle, Paul Cox, Richard Cooper, Tristram Whitman, Richard Dunning

CLUB PERSONNEL

Chairman: Robert Young.

Company Secretary: Anthony Minnis.

General Manager: Rachel Thornton.

Secretary: Paddy Farrell.

7 Primrose Rise, Newthorpe, Notts. NG16 2BB

Tel: (H) 01773 786 186 (M) 07742 596 567

Email: patrick.farrell2@ntlworld.com

Commercial Manager: Ms Alex Ottewell.

Tel: (M) 07815 529 370.

Email: aottewell@dtdpoker.com

Press Officer: Andy Cope.

Tel: (M) 07843 493 825

Email: lydias.dad@googlemail.com

Manager: Paul Cox.

Club therapist: Nick Taylor.

In their best ever season, Eastwood Town celebrated promotion to The Blue Square North as Unibond Champions, having lost only five league games and only failed to score in seven matches in all senior competitions. A five point advantage over second placed Ilkeston Town and a league goal tally of 82 all added up to a tremendous success.

The F.A.Cup also brought great excitement for the Badgers' supporters as the whole club enjoyed their first ever appearance in the Third Round Proper. Victories over Kidsgrove Athletic (H) 4-0, Lincoln United (A) 1-0, Harrogate Town 2-2 (H) 2-0 (A), Wrexham (A) 0-0, (H) 2-0, Brackley Town (H) 2-1, Wycombe Wanderers (H) 2-0 all added up to an historic cup run, before the luck of the draw failed to give 'The Badgers' a glamourous Third round tie and they lost 1-2 at Kettering.

Town used their cup experiences to boost the clubs' confidence in a serious challenge for the Unibond title and a quick exit from the F.A.Trophy at home to Ilkeston Town left the second half of the campaign free to concentrate on accumulating valuable points.

By the end of January, Eastwood were top of the table and they never looked like being overtaken. Four goalscorers achieved double figures with Ian Holmes leading the way with twenty-three, but the management have worked hard to strengthen their excellent squad, everyone at Eastwood is looking forward to the coming season with great excitement.

EASTWOOD TOWN

BEST LGE ATT.: **2,000** v Ossett Town
LOWEST: **314** v Ashton United

No.	Date	Comp	H/A	Opponents	Att:	Result	Goalscorers	Pos
1	Aug 16	Unibond P.	H	Leigh Genesis	384	W 2 - 0	**Holmes** 23 Meikle L 89	
2	20		A	Worksop Town	342	D 1 - 1	Meikle L 77	
3	23		A	Kendal Town	196	L 0 - 2		11
4	25		H	North Ferriby United	330	W 5 - 0	**HOLMES** 4 (36 40 pen 48 75) Whitman 87	
5	30		H	Bradford P.A.	420	D 1 - 1	**Holmes** 45	8
6	Sept 2		A	Matlock Town	410	D 1 - 1	Smith M 89	
7	9		H	Hednesford Town	387	W 2 - 1	Shaw 37 **Holmes** 53	9
8	**13**	**F.A.C. 1Q**	**H**	**Kidsgrove Athletic**	**230**	**W 4 - 0**	**Smith 58 70 Gardner 65 85**	
9	20		A	Guiseley	366	L 1 - 2	Sturdy 31	10
10	23		A	Frickley Athletic	295	D 0 - 0		
11	**27**	**F.A.C. 2Q**	**A**	**Lincoln United**	**115**	**W 1 - 0**	**Shaw 82**	
12	Oct 4		H	Nantwich Town	345	W 3 - 1	Dunning 51 Todd 53 **Holmes** 59	9
13	7		H	Ashton United	314	W 2 - 1	Robinson 62 **Holmes** 78	
14	**11**	**F.A.C. 3Q**	**H**	**Harrogate Town**	**4501**	**D 2 - 2**	**Hume 66 Robinson 78**	
15	**14**	**F.A.C. 3Qr**	**A**	**Harrogate Town**	**285**	**W 2 - 0**	**Dunning 26 Holmes 32**	
16	**18**	**F.A.T 1Q**	**H**	**Ilkeston Town**	**504**	**L 0 - 2**		
17	**25**	**F.A.C. 4Q**	**A**	**Wrexham**	**3115**	**D 0 - 0**		
18	**28**	**F.A.C. 4Qr**	**H**	**Wrexham**	**860**	**W 2 - 0**	**Todd 22 Holmes 82**	
19	Nov 1		A	Witton Albion	232	W 2 - 1	Hume 15 Dunning 59	9
20	**8**	**F.A.C 1R**	**H**	**Brackley Town**	**960**	**W 2 - 1**	**Cooke 54 Meikle 65**	
21	11		A	Ossett Town	155	W 3 - 0	**Holmes** 6 Meikle 40 Rhead 79	
22	15		H	Ilkeston Town	640	D 2 - 2	**Holmes** 83 Todd 90	10
23	19		A	F.C.United	1636	W 1 - 0	**Holmes** 44 (pen)	
24	22		H	Worksop Town	427	W 4 - 0	Knox 21 Dunning 40 Rhead 63 Meikle 64	
25	**29**	**F.A.Cup 2R**	**H**	**Wycombe Wanderers**	**1955**	**W 2 - 0**	**Meikle 34 Knox 90**	
26	Dec 6		H	FC United	820	W 4 - 2	**Holmes** 13 (pen) 74 Todd 20 80	4
27	13		H	Buxton	530	W 2 - 1	Dunning 12 Gardner 87	
28	20		A	Nantwich Town	692	D 2 - 2	Rhead 55 Robinson 90	2
29	26		A	Boston United	1270	W 1 - 0	**Holmes** 60	
30	Jan 3	F.A.C. 3R	A	Kettering Town	5090	L 1 - 2	Robinson 60	
31	17		A	Leigh Genesis		W 4 - 0	**Holmes** 70 77 Meikle 71 Knox 86	
32	20		H	Boston United	485	W 1 - 0	**Holmes** 43	
33	24		A	Bradford P.A.	620	W 2 - 0	Gardner 21 Meikle 37	1
34	31		H	Witton Albion	540	W 2 - 1	**Holmes** 30 80	1
35	Feb 7		A	Cammel Laird	129	L 0 - 1		1
36	21		A	Hednesford Town	860	W 1 - 0	Todd 61	
37	24		H	Prescot Cables	462	D 1 - 1	Foster 10	
38	28		H	Whitby Town	602	D 1 - 1	Dunning 76	1
39	Mar 4		A	Whitby Town	229	W 3 - 1	Todd 76 Smith 78 Hume 83	
40	7		A	North Ferriby United	340	D 2 - 2	Smith 5 **Holmes** 15 (pen)	1
41	9		H	Marine	438	W 4 - 0	Hume 27 Smith 47 Meikle 54 Holland 87	
42	14		H	Cammell Laird	516	W 4 - 1	SMITH 3 (44 76 89) Meikle 55	1
43	17		A	Marine	210	W 2 - 1	Holland 29 Smith 50	
44	21		A	Buxton	472	D 0 - 0		1
45	23		H	Guiseley	577	L 1 - 3	Todd 90	
46	28		H	Kendall Town	518	D 1 - 1	Todd 5	1
47	April 4		A	Prescot Cables	203	W 5 - 1	Knox 2 Meikle 19 Cooper 60 Hume 85 88	1
48	7		H	Matlock Town	648	W 1 - 0	Robinson 31	
49	10		A	Ilkeston Town	2288	L 0 - 1		
50	13		H	Frickley Athletic	940	W 4 - 2	Holland 3 Dunning 9 Meikle 30 Knox 60	1
51	18		A	Ashton United	273	D 2 - 2	Todd 69 Knox78	1
52	25		H	Ossett Town	2000	W 2 - 0	Holland 38 (pen) Knox 82	1

Average Home Att: **587 (264)** **Goals** **98 44**

Best Position: 1st **Worst:** 11th

Goalscorers: Holmes 23, Meikle L 12, Smith M 10, Todd 10, Dunning 7, Knox 7, Hume 6, Robinson 5, Gardner 4, Holland 4, Rhead 3, Shaw 2, Cooke 1, Cooper 1, Foster 1, Sturdy 1, Whitman 1.

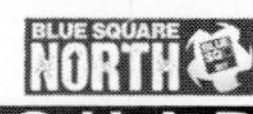

CURRENT SQUAD AS OF BEGINING OF 2009-10 SEASON

GOALKEEPERS	HT	WT	D.O.B	AGE	P.O.B	CAREER	APPS	GOA
Ian Deakin	6'00"	14 03	5/2/87	22	Birmingham	Notts Forest, Eastwood c/s 06		
Alex Goddard						Notts County, Eastwood T 9/07		
DEFENDERS								
Ben Chapman	5'06"	11 05	2/3/79	30	Scunthorpe	Grimsby Rel c/s 02, Boston U 8/02 Rel c/s 04, Grimsby (Trial) 7/04, Alfreton 8/04, Northwich 7/05, Nuneaton 7/06 Rel 5/07, Kings Lynn 6/07, Eastwood T 3/09		
Richard Cooper	5'08"	11 06	27/9/79	29	Nottingham	Notts Forest, York C (6WL) 3/01 Undisc 4/01 Rel c/s 04, Alfreton 7/04, Eastwood 8/05		
Mark Hume	6'02"	13 04	21/5/78	31	Barnsley	Barnsley Rel c/s 98, Doncaster 8/98, Gainsborough (L) 10/99, Barrow (L) 11/99, Barrow 1/00, Scunthorpe (Trial) 10/01, Alfreton £4,000 2/04, Stalybridge 7/06, Harrogate T 6/07, Buxton 6/08, Eastwood T 9/08		
Tom Marshall	6'04"		16/11/87	21		Hednesford, Eastwood T 5/09		
Robert McCormick						Mansfield (Jun), Dunkirk, Eastwood 7/09		
Robert Paling						Staveley MW, Eastwood T 12/07		
Paul Robinson			26/9/82	26		Notts Forest, Fleetwood, Hucknall 9/05, Bradford PA 3/06, Ilkeston 5/06, Hednesford 6/07, Eastwood 6/08		
MIDFIELDERS								
Dion Chambers			16/12/89	19	Nottingham	Swansea, Neath A (SL) Eastwood T 7/09		
Russell Cooke			18/5/81	28		Notts County (Trainee), Hucknall c/s 99, Leigh RMI 8/03, Ilkeston 9/03, Hucknall c/s 04, Eastwood 6/08		
Anton Foster			25/6/82	27		Ilkeston, Alfreton (L) (00/01), Eastwood (L) 1/03, Gedling T c/s 03, Belper c/s 04, Sheffield FC 8/05, Buxton 10/05, Eastwood T £10,000 7/08		
Martin Foster	5'05"	9 10	29/10/77	31	Sheffield	Leeds Rel c/s 98, Blackpool (L) 12/97, Morton 7/98, Doncaster 4/99, Ilkeston (L) 9/00, Forest Green AL 1/01, Halifax 7/04, Oxford U (SL) 1/07, Rushden & D 5/07, Tamworth 1/08, Eastwood T 6/09		
Ross Gardner	5'08"	10 06	15/12/85	23	South Shields	Newcastle, Notts Forest 8/03, Port Vale (2ML) 11/06 Perm 1/07 Rel 6/07, Ilkeston 7/07, Eastwood 7/08		
Emeka Nwadike	6'00"	12 07	9/8/78	31	Camberwell	Wolves, Shrewsbury 12/96 Rel c/s 98, Grantham 6/98, Kings Lynn 11/99, Ilkeston 1/01, Alfreton 6/03, Worcester 6/07, AFC Telford NC 3/08, Hinckley U (2ML) 11/08, Eastwood T 6/09		
Rory Prendergast	5'08"	12 00	6/4/78	31	Pontefract	Rochdale (Trainee), Barnsley Rel c/s 98, York 8/98, Oldham 3/99, Gainsborough, Northwich 7/99 Rel 12/99, Nuneaton 2/00, Emley c/s 00, Frickley 12/01, Bradford PA 7/02, Accrington £7,500 12/02, Blackpool Undisc 7/05, Halifax (2ML) 11/05, Rochdale 1/07 Rel		
FORWARDS								
David Brown	5'11"	11 09	29/5/89	20	York	Leeds (Trainee), Notts Forest 7/07, Eastwood T (2ML) 11/07, Bradford C 1/08 Rel c/s 08, York C (Trial) 7/08, Guiseley 7/08, AFC Halifax 1/09, Eastwood T 6/09		
Danny Holland			18/2/83	26	Mansfield	Sheff Utd (Yth), Chesterfield (Yth), Staveley MW, Matlock 8/02, Grimsby (Trial) 7/04, Hucknall 8/04, Harrogate T (L) 11/04 Perm 12/04, Eastwood T Undisc 2/09		
Ian Holmes	6'00"	12 05	29/6/85	24	Ellesmere Port	University Football, Matlock c/s 06, Mansfield Undisc 8/07 Rel 5/08, AFC Telford (SL) 3/08, Eastwood T 7/08		
Peter Knox			30/9/79	29	Yorkshire	Gainsborough T, Weymouth 8/99, Bridport 1/00, Dorchester (Cover) 10/00, Bridgwater T 2/01, Merthyr 10/01, Taunton, Ossett T 11/02, Armthorpe Welfare (L), Stocksbridge PS 8/03, Eastwood 12/03, Hednesford 5/07 Rel 9/07, Alfreton 9/07, Hucknall 4 fig 2/08 Rel 9/08, Eastwood 9/08, Frickley (L) 3/09		
Lindon Meikle			21/3/88	21	Nottingham	Vernon Colts, Eastwood T 7/04		
Marc Smith			7/4/74	35	Doncaster	Armthorpe Welfare, Eastwood T 8/00, Harrogate T (L) 2/03 £2,000 3/03, Guiseley £5,000 7/06, Eastwood T (Undisc) 1/08		
Ryan Whitehurst			6/9/89	19		Notts Forest, Eastwood T 7/09		
DEPARTURES								
(M)Ross Gardner	5'08"	10 06	15/12/85	23	South Shields	Newcastle, Notts Forest 8/03, Port Vale (2ML) 11/06 Perm 1/07 Rel 6/07, Ilkeston 7/07, Eastwood 7/08 Rel 7/09		

EASTWOOD TOWN

Formed: 1953.

Nickname: The Badgers.

Club Colours: White with black trimmed shirts, black shorts, black socks.

Change Colours: Red with white trimmed shirts, white shorts, red socks.

Club Sponsor: DTD Poker.com.

Previous League: Northern Premier League.

Ground Address: Coronation Park, Eastwood, Notts NG16 3GL.

Telephone No: 01773 712 301

Fax: 01773 712 301 (Match days only)

Website: www.eastwoodtownfc.co.uk

SIMPLE DIRECTIONS

From North: M1 jct 27 follow Heanor signs via Brinsley to lights in Eastwood. Turn left then first right after fire station- ground on Chewton Street.

From South: M1 jct 26. Take A610 to Ripley, leave at first exit (B60100) towards Eastwood. Left at lights and first left at 'Man in Space', ground entrance on Chewton Street.

Capacity: 5,500 **Seats:** 650 **Covered:** 1,150

Clubhouse: Social club open normal licensing hours (Sat 11am-11pm, midweek matches 6.30-11pm). Hot & cold food available.

Club Shop: Programmes, mugs, scarves, badges etc.

Local Radio: BBC Nottingham and Radio Trent

Local Press: Eastwood & Kimberly Advertiser

PROGRAMME EDITOR
Andy Cope
Tel: (M) 07843 493 825
Email: lydias.dad@googlemail.com

CLUB STATISTICS

RECORDS

Attendance: 2,723 v Enfield F.A.Amateur Cup Frbruary 1965

Career Goalscorer: Martin Wright 147

Career Appearances: Arthur Rowley over 800 games (no bookings) 1955-76

Victory: 21-0 v Rufford Colliery 1954-55

Defeat: 0-8 v Hucknall Town (a) 2000-01

Transfer Fee Paid: £500 to Gainsborough Trinity for Jamie Kay

Transfer Fee Received: £72,500 from Middlesbrough for Richard Liburd.

SENIOR HONOURS

Midland League Champions 1975-76.

Northern Premier League Premier Division Champions 2008-09.

Notts Senior Cup (x10).

PREVIOUS

Leagues:Notts Alliance 1953-61. Central Alliance 1961-67.
East Mids 1967-71. Midland Counties 1971-82.
Northern Counties East 1982-87, 2003-04.
Northern Premier 1987-2003, 04-09.

FARSLEY CELTIC

Back Row (L-R): Stephen Downes, Ryan Serrant, Neil Stevens, Chris Stabb, Dominic Krief, Simeon Bambrook, Craig Bentham, Jamie Price.
Middle: Steve Torpey, Rory Prendergast, Andy Campbell, Matthew James, Tom Penford, Georges Santos, Curtis Aspden, Mark Jackson, James Knowles, Roy Stamer, James Grayson (Press Officer).
Front: Gareth Liversedge (Physio), Gary Stokes (Goalkeeping Coach), Neil Parsley (Assistant Manager), Alan Hirst (Assistant Secretary), Andy Firbank (Chairman), John Deacey (Manager), John Palmer (President), Amjad Iqbal (Captain), Paul Glover (Director), Josh Greaves (Secretary).

CLUB PERSONNEL

Chairman: TBC.

Vice Chairman: John Palmer.

Company Secretary: Martin Carrington.

Managing Director: Paul Glover.

Additional Directors: Paul Grayson and Terry Deighton.

Secretary: Joshua Greaves
Telephone: (B): 0113 255 7292
(M): 07725 999 758
Email: farsleyceltic1908@supanet.com
correspondence to Secretary at club.

Commercial Manager: Michael Binns.
Tel: (M) 07976 185 882
Email: farsleyceltic1908@supanet.com

Press Officer: James Grayson.
Tel: (M) 07912 934 417
Email: jamesgrayson@yahoo.com

Manager: Neil Parsley.

Club therapist: Gareth Liversedge.

Feeling a little bruised from their experiences in the Premier Division, manager John Deacey found it difficult to settle his new squad into a successful rhythm, and after a poor start with two victories in the first eleven games including an F.A.Cup loss at Stalybridge, he was replaced by coach Neil Parsley.

Improved results took Celtic up to seventh position and an encouraging F.A.Trophy victory over Droylsden and an exciting penalty shoot out loss to Premier leaders Burton Albion, lifted spirits before the club was surprised by the resignation of successful chairman Andy Firbank in the New Year.

Sadly, worse was to come, as results deteriorated and eight consecutive defeats took the club down to a dangerous eighteenth position. Scoring became a real problem and with the last two games to play, Celtic had only managed to score two on three occasions in the New Year.

Luckily the form of the clubs below Farsley was also desperate as Celtic had to face two clubs already certain of play-off places. A thrilling 3-3 draw with Alfreton Town was followed by an extraordinary 5-1 defeat of Southport and the final table shows a five point lead over relegated Hyde United.

FARSLEY CELTIC

BEST LGE ATT.: **647** v Harrogate Town
LOWEST: **168** v Workington

No.	Date	Comp	H/A	Opponents	Att:	Result	Goalscorers	Pos
1	Aug 9	BSN	A	Stafford Rangers	678	L 0 - 1		
2	12		H	Fleetwood Town	241	W 4 - 1	Campbell 47 72 **Walshaw** 79 James 90	
3	16		H	Hinckley United	287	L 2 - 3	Campbell 23 Downes 63 (pen)	4
4	23		A	Burscough	250	D 0 - 0		14
5	25		H	Blyth Spartans	375	W 3 - 0	**Walshaw** 36 57 Campbell 87	
6	30		A	Redditch United	248	L 1 - 3	Campbell 34	12
7	Sept 2		A	Gainsborough Trinity	314	D 0 - 0		
8	6		H	Stalybridge Celtic	250	L 2 - 3	Campbell 18 **Walshaw** 52	15
9	**9**	**SS N1**	**H**	**Workington**	**101**	**W 3 - 1**	**James (2) Bett 82**	
10	13		H	Droylsden	259	D 1 - 1	Bett 61	16
11	20		A	Solihull Moors	184	L 1 - 2	**Walshaw** 31	
12	**27**	**F.A.C. 2Q**	**A**	**Stalybridge Celtic**	**500**	**L 0 - 4**		
13	Oct 4		H	Hucknall Town	300	W 4 - 0	Timons 55 (og) Banford 81 Speight 85 **Walshaw** 89	13
14	11		H	Hyde United	222	W 2 - 1	**Walshaw** 54 80	
15	**14**	**SS N2**	**A**	**Altrincham**	**259**	**D 1 - 1***	**Penford 120 (Lost 2-4 on pens)**	
16	18		A	King's Lynn	1121	W 4 - 1	**Walshaw** 24 26 Knowles 59 Speight 90	
17	25		H	Gainsborough Trinity	251	W 2 - 1	Campbell 65 Krief 76	7
18	Nov 1		H	Vauxhall Motors	289	L 0 - 1		7
19	8		A	Workington	307	W 2 - 0	Tuck 16 Campbell 50 (pen)	7
20	15		H	Tamworth	377	L 1 - 3	Penford 90	11
21	**22**	**F.A.T 3Q**	**H**	**Droylsden**	**202**	**W 2 - 0**	**Iqbal 59 James 86**	
22	**Dec 16**	**F.A.T 1R**	**A**	**Burton Albion**	**923**	**D 1 - 1**	**Speight 1**	
23	20		H	Stafford Rangers	257	W 4 - 0	Speight 26 70 Tuck 57 81	9
24	**23**	**F.A.T. 1R r**	**H**	**Burton Albion**	**262**	**D 2 - 2**	**Campbell 16 Bentham 60 (Lost 2-3 on pens)**	
25	26		A	Harrogate Town	646	L 0 - 1		10
26	Jan 1		H	Harrogate Town	647	W 1 - 0	Jackson 54	
27	17		H	King's Lynn	309	D 1 - 1	Broughton 90	9
28	24		A	Vauxhall Motors	146	L 0 - 2		11
29	26		A	Hyde United	264	L 1 - 3	Speight 72	
30	31		A	Alfreton Town	421	L 1 - 3	Forrest 21	13
31	Feb 21		A	Droylsden	326	L 0 - 2		15
32	Mar 3		H	Gateshead	198	L 0 - 1		
33	7		A	Tamworth	723	L 1 - 2	Grant 58	17
34	10		H	Workington	168	L 0 - 5		
35	14		A	Southport	702	L 0 - 1		18
36	17		A	Hinckley United	524	W 2 - 1	Malcher 73 Reeves 74	
37	21		H	Solihull Moors	250	L 0 - 1		17
38	24		A	Hucknall Town	139	W 2 - 1	Tuck 14 Bentham 38	
39	28		H	Redditch United	241	L 1 - 2	Jackson 35	17
40	31		H	AFC Telford United	230	W 1 - 0	Reeves 30	
41	April 4		A	Stalybridge Celtic	516	L 0 - 1		17
42	7		A	Fleetwood Town	671	L 1 - 2	Penford 66	
43	11		H	Burscough	235	W 5 - 1	Prendergast 43 Tuck 56 85 Reeves 59 Grant 79	16
44	13		A	Blyth Spartans	628	L 0 - 5		
45	15		A	AFC Telford United	1520	L 0 - 2		19
46	18		A	Gateshead	568	L 0 - 3		19
47	21		H	Alfreton Town	227	D 3 - 3	Tuck 20 Krief 57 Reeves 90	
48	25		H	Southport	407	W 5 - 1	Reeves 4 Krief 24 71 Forrest 61 Aspin 83	

Average Home Att: 287 (704) **Goals** 67 74

Best Position: 4th **Worst:** 19th

Goalscorers: Walshaw 10, Campbell 9, Tuck 7, Speight 6, Reeves 5, James 4, Krief 4, Penford 3, Bentham 2, Bett 2, Forrest 2, Grant 2, Jackson 2, Aspin 1, Banford 1, Broughton 1, Downes 1, Knowles 1, Iqbal 1, Malcher 1, Prendergast 1. Own Goals 1.

ASPDEN	PRICE	BAMBROOK	KRIEF	M JACKSON	SANTOS	DOWNES	BENTHAM	WALSHAW	CAMPBELL	PRENDERGAST	WATSON	JAMES	STEVENS	PENFORD	BACKHOUSE	KNOWLES	TORPEY	STABB	SERRANT	A IQBAL	BETT	SPEIGHT	GARDNER	TUCK	SAYNOR	BROUGHTON	DRISCOLL	T JACKSON	HOPE	FORREST	D'LARYEA	HOTCHKISS	MALCHER	OVINGTON	GRANT	REEVES	S IQBAL	STRICKLAND	GREEN	ASPIN	WALTON	
X	X	X	X	X	X	X	X	X	X	X	S	S	S	U	U																											**1**
X	X	U	X	X	X	X	X	S	X	X	X	X	S	S		U																										**2**
X	X	U	X	X	X	X		S	X	X	X	X	U	S		X	S																									**3**
X	X	X	X	X	X	X		X	X	X		S		X	U	S	U	U																								**4**
X	X	S	X	X	X	X		X	X			X	U	U		X	S	X	U																							**5**
X	X	X	X	X	X	X	S	X	X	S			S			X	U	X	U																							**6**
X	X		X	U	S	X	X	X	X	X		S	U			X		X		X	S																					**7**
X				S	X	X	X	X	X	X		X	U	X	U			X	U	X	S																					**8**
X				**X**	**X**	**U**	**X**	**S**		**X**		**X**	**S**	**X**	**U**	**X**		**U**	**X**		**X**	**X**																				**9**
X			S	S	U	X	X	X	X	X		X		X		X		X		X	S	U																				**10**
X			X	X		X		X		X		X	S	X	U	X		X	U		S	S	X																			**11**
X			**X**	**X**	**X**	**X**		**X**		**X**		**S**		**S**	**U**	**X**		**X**	**S**	**X**		**U**	**X**																			**12**
X			X	X		X		X		X		X	U	S	U	S		X	X	X		S	X																			**13**
X	U					X		X	S	X		X	U	X	U	X		X	X	X		X		S																		**14**
X	**S**		**X**			**U**		**S**	**X**	**S**		**X**		**X**	**U**	**X**		**X**	**X**	**X**		**X**		**X**																		**15**
X	S		X	U				X	X	S		X		X	U	X		X	X	X		S		X																		**16**
X	S		X	U				X	X	S		X		X	U	X		X	X	X		S		X																		**17**
X	U		X				U	X	X	S		X		X	U	X		X	X	X		S		X																		**18**
X	X		X				X	X	X	U		U		X		S		X	X	X		S		X	U																	**19**
X	X		X	U		U	X		X			S		X		X		X	U	X		X		X	U																	**20**
X	**X**		**X**	**U**		**S**	**X**		**X**			**X**				**X**			**X**	**X**		**X**		**X**	**U**	**S**	**S**															**21**
X	**X**			**S**		**U**	**X**		**X**	**X**				**X**		**X**		**S**	**X**	**X**		**X**		**X**	**U**		**S**															**22**
X	X		X	U		S	X		X	X				U		X		U	X	X		X		X	U																	**23**
X	**X**		**X**	**U**		**S**	**X**		**X**	**X**				**S**		**X**		**S**	**X**	**X**		**X**		**X**	**U**																	**24**
X	X		X	U		X	X		X					U		X		U	X	X		X		X	U		S															**25**
X	X		X	S		X			X	S				X		X			X	X		X		X	U	U	U															**26**
X	X		X	U		X	X		X					S		X			X	X		X		X	U	S	U															**27**
X	X		X	X		X	X							X					X	X		X		X	U	S	S	U														**28**
X	X		X	X			X						X	U					X	X		X		X	U	S	X		U													**29**
X	X		X	X		X	X							X					X			X		X	U		S	S	U	X												**30**
X				S		X	X							U					X	X		X		X	U		U			S	X	X	X	X								**31**
X				X			X			X				X					X					X	U		U	U		S	X	X	X	X								**32**
X				X			X			X				X					X					X	U		U	U		S	X	X	U	X	X							**33**
X			X	X			X			X				U					X					X	U			S		S	X	X	U	X		X						**34**
X			X	X			X			X				X										X	U		U	U		U	X	X	U		X	X						**35**
X			X	X			X			X				X										X	U		S	U	U		X	X	S		X	X						**36**
X			X	X			X			X									X					S	U		U	U		S	X	X	X		X	X						**37**
X			X	X			X			X									X					X	U		U	U		U	X		U		X	X	X					**38**
X			X	X			X			X									X					X	U			U			X		S		X	X	X	S	S			**39**
X			X	X			X			X				U										X	U						X		U		X	X	U	U	X	X		**40**
X			X	X						X				U										X	S						X		S		X	X	U	U	X	X	X	**41**
X				X						X				X					S					X	U						X		S		X	X	S	U	X	X	X	**42**
X				X						X				X					X					X	U		S			U	X		S		X	X	S			X	X	**43**
X				X						X				X					U					X	U		X				X		X		S	S	X		X	X	S	**44**
X			X	X						X				X					X					X	U		U	U		S	X				X	X			S		X	**45**
			X	X						X				S	U				X					X	X		U			S	X				X	X	X		S		X	**46**
X			X	X						X				X					U					X	U		S	X		S			S		X	X				X	X	**47**
X			X	X			X			X				S					X						U		S	X		X			S		X	X				X	U	**48**

Total League Appearances

ASPDEN	PRICE	BAMBROOK	KRIEF	M JACKSON	SANTOS	DOWNES	BENTHAM	WALSHAW	CAMPBELL	PRENDERGAST	WATSON	JAMES	STEVENS	PENFORD	BACKHOUSE	KNOWLES	TORPEY	STABB	SERRANT	A IQBAL	BETT	SPEIGHT	GARDNER	TUCK	SAYNOR	BROUGHTON	DRISCOLL	T JACKSON	HOPE	FORREST	D'LARYEA	HOTCHKISS	MALCHER	OVINGTON	GRANT	REEVES	S IQBAL	STRICKLAND	GREEN	ASPIN	WALTON	
41	16	3	33	28	7	18	24	14	18	28	2	11	1	22	0	15	0	13	24	17	0	10	2	28	1	0	2	2	0	2	16	7	4	4	14	14	4	0	4	7	6	**X**
0	2	1	1	4	1	1	1	2	1	5	1	4	4	6	0	3	2	0	1	0	4	6	0	2	1	3	7	2	0	8	0	0	7	0	1	1	2	1	3	0	1	**S**
0	2	2	0	7	1	1	1	0	0	1	0	1	6	9	10	1	2	3	7	0	0	1	0	0	25	1	10	9	3	3	0	0	5	0	0	0	2	3	0	0	1	**U**

Total Cup Appearances

ASPDEN	PRICE	BAMBROOK	KRIEF	M JACKSON	SANTOS	DOWNES	BENTHAM	WALSHAW	CAMPBELL	PRENDERGAST	WATSON	JAMES	STEVENS	PENFORD	BACKHOUSE	KNOWLES	TORPEY	STABB	SERRANT	A IQBAL	BETT	SPEIGHT	GARDNER	TUCK	SAYNOR	BROUGHTON	DRISCOLL	T JACKSON	HOPE	FORREST	D'LARYEA	HOTCHKISS	MALCHER	OVINGTON	GRANT	REEVES	S IQBAL	STRICKLAND	GREEN	ASPIN	WALTON	
6	3	0	4	2	2	1	4	1	4	4	0	3	0	3	0	6	0	2	5	5	1	5	1	4	0	0	0	0	0	0	0	0	0	0	0	0	0	0	0	0	0	**X**
0	1	0	0	1	0	2	0	2	0	1	0	1	1	2	0	0	0	2	1	0	0	0	0	0	0	1	2	0	0	0	0	0	0	0	0	0	0	0	0	0	0	**S**
0	0	0	0	2	0	3	0	0	0	0	0	0	0	0	3	0	0	1	0	0	0	1	0	0	3	0	0	0	0	0	0	0	0	0	0	0	0	0	0	0	0	**U**

Also played: WATERFIELD U(29,30).

FARSLEY CELTIC

CURRENT SQUAD AS OF BEGINING OF 2009-10 SEASON

GOALKEEPERS	HT	WT	D.O.B	AGE	P.O.B	CAREER	APPS	GOA
Josh Bell	6'01"	13 02	22/1/90	19		Farsley Celtic (Yth), Oldham Rel c/s 09, Farsley Celtic 8/09		
Piotr Skiba						Poland, Bradford PA c/s 06, Ossett T (L) 3/07 Perm, Guiseley 2/08 Rel c/s 09, Farsley Celtic 8/09		
DEFENDERS								
Josh Hope						Farsley Celtic, Garforth (L) 1/09	0	0
Mark Jackson	6'00"	12 10	30/9/77	31	Barnsley	Leeds, Huddersfield (L) 10/98, Barnsley (L) 1/00, Scunthorpe 3/00, Kidderminster 2/05, Rochdale £17,500 1/06 Rel c/s 07, Farsley Celtic 6/07	32	2
Tom Jackson						Farsley Celtic, Harrogate RA (L) 11/08	4	0
Patrece Liburd			1/3/88	21	Leeds	Bradford C (Yth), Notts Forest (Yth), Cardiff C (Trial) c/s 07, Guiseley 8/07, Worcester 8/07 Rel 11/07, Garforth 2/08, Dorchester 2/08 Rel 1/09, Macclesfield 3/09 Rel c/s 09, Farsley Celtic 7/09		
Dave Pickering	5'08"	11 00	14/9/90	18		Huddersfield (Scholar) Rel c/s 09, Farsley Celtic 7/09		
Josh Radcliffe						York C Rel 5/09, Harrogate RA (L) 10/08, Farsley Celtic 7/09		
Ryan Serrant	5'09"	10 03	3/1/88	21	London	Leeds Rel c/s 07, Guiseley (L) 12/06, Guiseley (L) 2/07, Farsley Celtic (L) 3/07, Farsley Celtic c/s 07	25	0
Dave Syers						Ossett A, Harrogate T 3/09, Farsley Celtic 6/09		
MIDFIELDERS								
Tom Claisse						Bradford C (Scholar), Whitby, AFC Goole 3/07, Whitby 10/07 Rel 7/08, Ossett T, Bradford PA 11/08		
Scott Driscoll						Farsley Celtic	9	0
Shazad Iqbal						Farsley Celtic	6	0
Dominic Krief	5'09"	10 06	15/9/83	25	Leeds	Leeds, Frickley 1/04, Harrogate Town 7/04, Southport 6/05, Farsley Celtic 12/05, Stalybridge 12/06, Bradford PA 3/07, Guiseley 8/07, Farsley Celtic 1/08	34	4
Liam Shepherd						York C Rel 5/09, Farsley Celtic 6/09		
Ben Waterfield						Farsley Celtic	0	0
Matty Young	5'08"	11 03	25/10/85	23	Leeds	Huddersfield Rel c/s 08, Harrogate T 7/08 Rel c/s 09, Farsley Celtic c/s 09		
FORWARDS								
Simeon Bambrook			27/3/72	37	Leeds	Garforth, Emley, Garforth, Emley/Wakefield & Emley 2/00, Worksop 9/03, Farsley Celtic 6/05, Guiseley 9/08, Farsley Celtic (Pl/Ass Man) 6/09	4	0
Lee Ellington	5'10"	11 07	3/7/80	29	Bradford	Eccleshill Utd, Hull C, Altrincham (Trial), Exeter 3/00, Walton & H 4/00, Gainsborough 10/00, Stalybridge 7/05, Farsley Celtic 6/09		
Gareth Grant	5'10"	10 04	6/9/80	28	Leeds	Bradford C Rel c/s 02, Halifax (L) 2/99, Bolton (SL) 3/00, Lincoln C (L) 2/01, Darlington (Trial) 10/01, Halifax (Trial) 7/02, Chester (Trial) 8/02, Lincoln C (Trial) 1/03, Gainsborough T 2/03, Scarborough (L) 1/05, Harrogate T 6/05, Farsley Celtic 7/06,	15	2
Tom Woolard						USA, Farsley Celtic 8/09		

LOANEES	HT	WT	DOB	AGE	POB	From - To	APPS	GOA
(M)Scott Gardner	5'09"	11 04	1/4/88	21	Luxembourg	Leeds 9/08 - Rel 1/09, Mansfield 2/09	2	0
Mark Bett						Bradford PA 9/08 -	4	1
(M)Chris Ovington						Leeds 2/09 - Rel 5/09	4	0
(M)Ollie Hotchkiss			27/9/89	19	Houghton-le-Spring	Leeds 2/09 - Mansfield (SL) 3/09	7	0
(D)Nathan D'Laryea	5'10"	12 02	3/9/85	23	Manchester	Rochdale (2ML) 2/09 - Rel 5/09, Hyde U 7/09	16	0
(D)Kenny Strickland	5'10"	11 05	10/10/90	18	Ormskirk	Man Utd (Scholar) 3/09 - Rel c/s 09	1	0
(F)Darren Green	6'00"	11 00	15/5/89	20	Preston	Stockport 3/09 - Rel c/s 09, Barrow 8/09	7	0

DEPARTURES	HT	WT	DOB	AGE	POB	From - To	APPS	GOA
(M)Roy Stamer			14/5/78	31	Germany	Guiseley 10/05 - Bradford PA 9/08		
(F)Steve Torpey	6'03"	13 06	8/12/70	38	Islington	Lincoln C (2ML) 11/07 Perm 1/08 - North Ferriby (L) 9/08 Perm, York (Yth Coach) 12/08	2	0
(D)Georges Santos	6'03"	14 08	15/8/70	39	Marseille, Fr	Alfreton 1/08 - Fleetwood 9/08	8	0
(M)Neil Stevens						Yth - Buxton 11/08	5	0
(F)James Walshaw			12/2/84	25		Leek T 7/08 - Wakefield 11/08, Guiseley 3/09	16	8
(M)Matthew James						Local 8/08 - Bradford PA 12/08	15	1
(M)James Knowles			21/5/83	26	Leeds	Harrogate RA 12/03 - Bradford PA 1/09	18	1
(F)Andy Campbell	5'11"	11 07	18/4/79	30	Stockton	Halifax 7/08 - Bradford PA 1/09	19	8
(M)Stephen Downes	5'06"	09 12	22/11/81	27	Leeds	Glasshoughton W 3/07 - Bradford PA Undisc 2/09	19	1
(D)Jamie Price	5'09"	11 00	27/10/81	27	Normanton	Harrogate T 6/08 - Bradford PA 2/09	18	0
(F)Jake Speight						ex Northwich 9/08 - Rel 3/09, Droylsden 3/09, Mansfield 5/09	16	6
(M)Amjad Iqbal					Bradford	Thackley 7/01 - Bradford PA Undisc 3/09	17	0
(D)Mike Aspin			20/10/89	19	Blackburn	Northwich 3/09 - Nahon Pathom (Tha), Northwich 7/09	7	1
(D)Craig Bentham	5'09"	11 06	7/3/85	24	Bradford	Bradford C 6/08 - Rel 7/09	25	1
(F)Damien Reeves	5'09"	11 10	18/12/85	23	Doncaster	Northwich 3/09 - Alfreton 7/09	15	5
(G)Curtis Aspden	6'01"	11 12	16/11/87	21	Blackburn	Hull C (L) 1/08 Perm 1/08 - Northwich 8/09	41	0
(G)Chris Backhouse	5'10"		13/12/88	20	Leeds	Sunderland 11/07 - Buxton (L) 11/08	0	0
(G)Ben Saynor	6'03"	12 04	6/3/89	21	Leeds	ex Bradford C 11/08 -	2	0
(D)Chris Stabb	5'09"	11 12	12/10/76	32	Bradford	Ossett T 7/02 -	13	0
(M)Luke Malcher	5'08"		14/11/88	20	Halifax	Harrogate T 2/09 -	11	1
(M)Tom Penford	5'10"	11 03	5/1/85	24	Leeds	Bradford C 6/08 -	28	3
(M)Rory Prendergast	5'08"	12 00	6/4/78	31	Pontefract	Rochdale 2/08 -	33	1
(M)Chris Walton						ex Alfreton 3/09 -	7	0
(M)Andy Watson	5'10"	11 00	13/11/78	30	Leeds	Chester 7/05 -	3	0
(F)Danny Forrest						Guiseley 1/09 -	10	2
(F)Lee Tuck						Yth - FC Halifax c/s 09	30	8
(F)Scott Broughton						Liversedge -	3	1

FARSLEY CELTIC

Formed: 1908

Nickname: Villagers.

Club Colours: Royal blue shirts, royal blue shorts, white Socks.

Change Colours: White shirts, white shorts, blue socks.

Club Sponsor: TBC.

Previous League: Northern Premier League

Ground Address: Throstle Nest, Newlands, Farsley LS28 5BE

Telephone: 0113 255 7292

Mobile: 07725 999 758

Facsimile: 0113 256 1517

Email: farsleyceltic1908@supanet.com

Website: www.farsleyceltic.net

SIMPLE DIRECTIONS From B6157 pass Police and Fire stations on the left, turn down New Street at Tradex warehouse before turning right into Newlands. Ground at bottom of road. One mile from Pudsey (BR).

Capacity: 4,000 **Seats:** 300 **Covered:** 1,500

Clubhouse: Open every evening and lunchtimes at weekends.

Club Shop: Yes.

no image available

CLUB STATISTICS

RECORD

Attendance:

11,000 (at Elland Rd) v Tranmere Rovers F.A.Cup 1st Rd. 1974

Victory: Not known.

Defeat: Not known.

Goalscorer: Not known.

Career Appearances: Not known.

Record Transfer Fee Received: Not known.

Received Paid: Not known.

SENIOR HONOURS

West Riding Co. Cup (9) N.P.L. Cup

PREVIOUS

Leagues: West Riding Co Amateur, Leeds Red Triangle, Yorkshire 1949-82. Northern Counties East 1982-87. Northern Premier League 1987-06.

Grounds: Red Lane Farsley, Calverley Lane Farsley prior to 1948.

PROGRAMME EDITOR

James Grayson

Tel: (M) 07912 934417

(B) 0113 255 7292

E: jamesagrayson@yahoo.com

FLEETWOOD TOWN

Back Row (L-R): Mark Peers, Andy Bell, Steve Foster, Phil Robinson, Rory Winters, Ricky Mercer, Ashley Dunn. Colin Potts.
Middle row: Danny Moore Physio, Russell Hitchin Physio, Paul Haddow, Adam Warlow, Nathan Pond, Mike Hale, Danny Hurst, Phil Doughty, Phil Denney,Simon Garner, Barry McCloughlin Kit Manager,
Front row: Kevin Leadbetter, Shaun Beeley, Kieran Walmsley, Andy Whittaker Coach, Tony Greenwood Manager, Nigel Greenwood Asst Manager, Jamie Milligan Captain, Warren Beattie, Lennie Reid.

CLUB PERSONNEL

Chairman: Andrew Pilley.

Vice-Chairman: Phil Brown.

Company Secretary: Phil Brown.

Chief Executive: Steve Curwood.

Additional Director: Paul Cambridge.

Secretary: Steve Edwards.

20 Ullswater Avenue, Thurnton Cleveleys FY5 4AW.

Tel: (M) 07894 526 810

Email: stephen@stephen89.wanadoo.co.uk

Commercial Manager: Steve Curwood

Tel: (M) 07773 027 706

Email: steve.curwood@fleetwoodtownfc.com

Press Officer: Derick Thomas.

Tel: (M) 07917 055 433

Email: press@fleetwoodtownfc.com

Manager: Mickey Mellon.

Club therapist: Russell Hitchen.

Another year of progress for Fleetwood started with some controversy, as manager Tony Greenwood, who had led the club to three promotions in four years, lost his job after 'Town' had suffered a poor start to the campaign having invested in some experienced players. One victory in ten matches was not considered good enough and ex Burnley player Mickey Mellon took over.

With the new players settling in and fresh leadership, 'The Fishermen' certainly improved and were inspired by an exciting F.A.Cup run, enjoying victories over Wakefield, Frickley Athletic, Nantwich Town and Leiston before losing a thriller, 2-3 at home to Hartlepool United.

This run wasn't matched by their disappointing F.A.Trophy defeat away to Ossett Town, but league results were improving by the week helped by the prolific goalscoring of Adam Warlow (23 goals) and Andy Bell (13). Only in the first match did Fleetwood fail to score in 2009, and this consistency saw them steadily move up the table.

With an average attendance of just below a thousand, the Fleetwood fans showed how they appreciated their little club's improvement but, hopefully for the manager's sake, the club will be challenging for at least a play off position next season. They certainly finished the campaign in fine form with an unbeaten run of six games with a goal difference of 13-5 and hat tricks from Sean Clancy and Michael Wilde!

FLEETWOOD TOWN

BEST LGE ATT.: **1,511** v Southport
LOWEST: **502** v Gainsborough Trinity

No.	Date	Comp	H/A	Opponents	Att:	Result	Goalscorers	Pos
1	Aug 12	BSN	A	Farsley Celtic	241	L 1 - 4	Potts 83	
2	16		A	Hyde United	316	L 3 - 5	Milligan 30 (pen) Beattie 48 Peers 67	22
3	23		H	Vauxhall Motors	941	W 2 - 0	**Warlow** 20 31	17
4	25		A	Southport	1304	D 1 - 1	**Warlow** 8	
5	30		H	Tamworth	1051	L 1 - 2	Bell 90	
6	Sept 2		H	Gateshead	684	L 0 - 2		
7	6		A	King's Lynn	1143	L 0 - 1		21
8	**9**	**SS N1**	**A**	**Harrogate Town**	**174**	**D 1 - 1***	**Denney 24 (Won 5-4 pn pens)**	
9	13		A	AFC Telford United	1805	D 0 - 0		19
10	16		H	Hucknall Town	702	L 1 - 3	Walmesley 11	
11	20		H	Alfreton Town	812	D 1 - 1	Bell 83	21
12	**27**	**F.A.C. 2Q**	**A**	**Wakefield**	**161**	**W 3 - 0**	**Warlow 3 Milligan 72 Potts 78**	
13	Oct 4		A	Gainsborough Trinity	200	W 4 - 3	Bell 23 LEADBETTER 3 (73 76 83)	18
14	**11**	**F.A.C. 3Q**	**H**	**Frickley Athletic**	**874**	**W 2 - 0**	**Bell 7 Mercer 12**	
15	**14**	**SS N2**	**A**	**Barrow**	**618**	**L 2 - 3**	**Walmesley 8 Warlow 53**	
16	18		H	Stalybridge Celtic	1315	L 1 - 2	**Warlow** 44	19
17	21		H	Burscough	515	W 3 - 1	**Warlow** 22 Bell 36 Dunn 90	
18	**25**	**F.A.C. 4Q**	**H**	**Nantwich Town**	**874**	**W 4 - 3**	**BELL 3 (38 70 89) Pond 50**	
19	Nov 1		H	Hinckley United	894	W 1 - 0	Bell 85	17
20	**8**	**F.A.C. 1R**	**A**	**Leiston**	**1250**	**D 0 - 0**		
21	15		A	Stafford Rangers	420	W 2 - 1	Wilson 8 (og) Foster 89	15
22	**18**	**F.A.C. 1R r**	**H**	**Leiston**	**2010**	**W 2 - 0**	**Bell 48 Warlow 79**	
23	**2 2**	**F.A.T 3Q**	**A**	**Ossett Town**	**151**	**L 1 - 3**	**Warlow 85**	
24	25		A	Harrogate Town	261	L 2 - 5	**Warlow** 60 Milligan 90	16
25	**29**	**F.A.C. 2R**	**H**	**Hartlepool United**	**3280**	**L 2 - 3**	**Bell 14 Warlow 66**	
26	Dec 6		A	Alfreton Town	321	D 3 - 3	**Warlow** 27 Milligan 41 (pen) Leadbetter 90	16
27	20		A	Hucknall Town	271	L 2 - 3	**Warlow** 10 Milligan 80	13
28	26		H	Workington	1269	W 1 - 0	Pond 77	16
29	Jan 17		A	Blyth Spartans	651	L 0 - 3		18
30	24		H	AFC Telford United	1078	W 1 - 0	Milligan 45	16
31	27		A	Burscough	365	D 1 - 1	Foster 71	
32	31		H	Solihull Moors	811	W 2 - 1	Pond 16 Mercer 19	15
33	Feb 14		H	Redditch United	1042	W 3 - 1	Wilde 42 77 Mercer 65	13
34	21		A	Solihull Moors	197	D 2 - 2	Mercer 58 Williams 68	13
35	24		H	Blyth Spartans	587	W 1 - 0	Wilde 29	
36	28		H	Droylsden	1407	W 2 - 1	Connors 8 **Warlow** 28	11
37	Mar 3		H	Hyde United	611	L 1 - 3	**Warlow** 32	
38	7		A	Hinckley United	427	L 1 - 2	Milligan 66 (pen)	11
39	10		H	Gainsborough Trinity	502	D 2 - 2	**Warlow** 14 63	
40	14		A	Stalybridge Celtic	573	W 5 - 0	Connors 33 **Warlow** 49 58 Mercer 53 Bell 75	11
41	18		A	Gateshead	467	D 2 - 2	Milligan 72 Mercer 81	
42	21		H	Harrogate Town	1051	W 1 - 0	**Warlow** 54	10
43	24		A	Redditch United	221	D 1 - 1	Pond 85	
44	28		A	Tamworth	784	L 1 - 2	Connors 68	10
45	30		A	Workington	331	L 2 - 3	Clancy 65 **Warlow** 87	
46	April 4		H	King's Lynn	909	W 3 - 0	CLANCY 3 (22 31 47)	10
47	7		H	Farsley Celtic	671	W 2 - 1	Wilde 2 Miligan 90 (pen)	
48	11		A	Vauxhall Motors	239	W 2 - 0	Bell 30 **Warlow** 78	9
49	13		H	Southport	1511	D 1 - 1	Mercer 67	
50	18		H	Stafford Rangers	1190	D 2 - 2	**Warlow** 38 86	9
51	25		A	Droylsden	632	W 3 - 1	WILDE 3 (16 48 85)	8

Average Home Att: **931 (698)** **Goals** **87 79**

Best Position: 8th **Worst:** 22nd

Goalscorers: Warlow 24, Bell 13, Milligan 9, Mercer 7, Wilde 7, Clancy 4, Leadbetter 4, Pond 4, Connors 3, Foster 2, Potts 2, Walmesley 2, Beattie 1, Denney 1, Dunn 1, Peers 1, Williams 1. Own Goals 1.

HURST	BEELEY	GARNER	DOUGHTY	MERCER	POND	POTTS	MILLIGAN	WARLOW	FOSTER	PEERS	WALMSLEY	HILLS	DENNEY	BEATTIE	HALE	KILBANE	DUNN	BAYLISS	BELL	THOMPSON	PENSWICK	LEADBETTER	ROBINSON	SANTOS	MORAN	KAY	WEBB	HOLLAND	HUNT	MAYLETT	S WILLIAMS	KELLY	ELDERTON	TAYLOR	BARRATT	WILDE	C WILLIAMS	CONNORS	CLANCY	ADAMS	ROUSE	
X	X	X	X	X	X	X	X	X	X	X	S	S	S	U	U																											**1**
X	U	U	X	X	X	U	X	X	S	X		X	X	X	U	X																										**2**
X		S	X		X	U	X	X	S	X	X	X	X	X		X	S	U																								**3**
X		U	X		X	U	X	X	S	X	X	X	S	X		X	X	U																								**4**
X		X	X		U	S	X	X	S	X	X		X	X		X	X	U	S																							**5**
X		U	X		X	S	X	X	X		X	X	S	X		X	U	X	S																							**6**
X			X		X	S	X	X		X	X	X	S	X		X	U	U	S	X																						**7**
	X		**U**	**X**	**X**	**X**	**X**				**S**	**S**	**S**	**X**	**X**	**U**	**X**	**X**	**X**	**X**																						**8**
U	X		S	X	X	U	X	S			S	X	X	X	X		X	X	X																							**9**
U	X		U	X		X	X		S		X	X	X	X	X	U		X	X		U																					**10**
	X		X	X		S	X		X	S	X	X		X	X	S			X		U	X																				**11**
	U		**X**	**U**		**X**	**X**	**X**	**S**	**S**	**X**	**X**	**U**	**X**	**X**	**X**	**S**		**X**			**X**	**U**																			**12**
U			X			X	X	X	S		X	X		X	X	X	S		X			X		S	U																	**13**
X	**S**		**U**	**X**		**X**	**X**	**X**	**S**		**X**	**X**		**X**	**U**	**X**	**U**		**X**		**U**	**X**	**U**																			**14**
X			**U**	**X**	**X**	**S**	**X**	**X**	**X**		**X**	**X**		**X**	**U**	**X**	**U**						**X**		**S**																	**15**
X				U	X	X	S	X	S		X	X		X	U				X			X		X	S	X																**16**
X				U	X	X	X	X	U		X	X		X	U		S		X					X	S	X																**17**
X				**X**	**X**		**X**	**X**	**U**		**X**	**X**		**X**	**U**	**U**	**X**		**X**		**U**	**U**	**U**			**X**	**S**															**18**
X	X				X	S	X	X	U		X						U		X		X	X		X	S	X	U															**19**
X	**U**			**X**	**X**	**X**	**X**	**X**	**S**		**X**	**X**		**S**			**U**		**X**			**X**	**S**			**X**	**U**															**20**
X				X	X			X	S		X	X		U					X		X	X		U		X		X	S	S												**21**
X				**X**	**X**	**U**	**X**	**S**	**X**		**X**	**X**		**X**	**U**	**S**	**U**		**X**		**X**	**U**	**S**			**X**																**22**
X	**S**						**X**	**X**	**S**		**X**	**X**		**X**		**U**			**X**		**X**	**U**	**X**	**X**		**X**			**S**													**23**
X	U						X	X	U		X				U	U					U	X	X	X		X		X	X	X												**24**
X	**U**			**X**			**X**	**X**	**U**		**X**	**X**		**X**	**U**				**X**		**U**	**U**	**X**			**X**			**S**	**X**	**U**											**25**
X				X	X		X	X			X	X		X					U			X	U			S		X	S	X	U											**26**
X	X			U	X		X	X		S		X		S					X			X	S			X		U		X	X											**27**
X	S			X	X		X	X	U	X	X			X			X		X		X					S				S	U											**28**
X				X	X		X	X	S	S	X	X		X	U				S											X		X	X	U								**29**
X				X	X		X	X	S		X	X		U								U								U		X	S	X	X	X						**30**
X				X	X		X	X	S	U	X			S								S						X		U			X	X	X	X						**31**
X				X	X		X		X	S	X			S	U							S								U		X	X	X	X	X						**32**
X				X			X	X			X			U	U		X					U								U		X	X	X	X	X	S					**33**
X				X	S		X	X			X						X		S									U		S			X	X	X	X	X					**34**
X	X			X	X		X	X			U						U		S									U		U		X	X	X		X	X					**35**
X	X			X	X		X	X			U				U		S		U											S			X	X		X	X	X				**36**
X	X			X			X	X			U				U				S											S		S	X	X		X	X	X	X			**37**
X	X			X	S		S	X			X	U			U				S													X	X	X		X		X	X			**38**
X	X			X	X		S	X			U								X		U											S	X	X		S	X	X	X			**39**
X	X			X	S		X	X							U				S		S												X	X		X	X	X	X	U		**40**
X	X			X	X		X	X				S			U				X		S												X	X		U	X		X	U		**41**
X	X			X	X		X	X				U			U				U		U												X	X		X	X		X	U		**42**
X	X			X	X		X	X				U			U				S			S											X	X		X	X		X	U		**43**
	X			X	S		X	X				U		U	X							U											X	X		X		X	X		S	**44**
	X				X		X	X				X		X	X						U												U	X		X		X	S	U	X	**45**
X	X			X	S		X	X				X		X					S														S	X		X		X	X	U	U	**46**
X	X			X	S		X	X				X		X					U			U											U	X		X		X	X		S	**47**
X	X			X	X		X	X				U		X					X			X											X	X		S	S		S		U	**48**
X	X			X	X		X	X				X		X	U				U			U											U	X		X	U		X			**49**
X	X			X	X		X	X				U							U			X											X	X		X	S	S	S	X		**50**
X	X			X	X		X	X				X			U				S		U	S											U	X		X	X		X			**51**

Total League Appearances

HURST	BEELEY	GARNER	DOUGHTY	MERCER	POND	POTTS	MILLIGAN	WARLOW	FOSTER	PEERS	WALMSLEY	HILLS	DENNEY	BEATTIE	HALE	KILBANE	DUNN	BAYLISS	BELL	THOMPSON	PENSWICK	LEADBETTER	ROBINSON	SANTOS	MORAN	KAY	WEBB	HOLLAND	HUNT	MAYLETT	S WILLIAMS	KELLY	ELDERTON	TAYLOR	BARRATT	WILDE	C WILLIAMS	CONNORS	CLANCY	ADAMS	ROUSE	
36	23	2	9	30	29	5	38	38	4	7	22	21	5	20	6	7	6	3	13	1	3	10	1	4	0	6	0	4	1	4	1	6	17	22	5	19	10	9	12	1	1	**X**
0	1	1	1	0	6	5	3	1	11	4	2	2	4	3	0	1	4	0	12	0	2	4	1	1	3	2	0	0	2	5	0	2	2	0	0	2	3	1	3	0	2	**S**
3	2	3	1	3	1	4	0	0	4	1	4	6	0	5	17	2	4	4	6	0	7	5	1	1	1	0	1	3	0	5	2	0	4	1	0	1	1	0	0	6	2	**U**

Total Cup Appearances

HURST	BEELEY	GARNER	DOUGHTY	MERCER	POND	POTTS	MILLIGAN	WARLOW	FOSTER	PEERS	WALMSLEY	HILLS	DENNEY	BEATTIE	HALE	KILBANE	DUNN	BAYLISS	BELL	THOMPSON	PENSWICK	LEADBETTER	ROBINSON	SANTOS	MORAN	KAY	WEBB	HOLLAND	HUNT	MAYLETT	S WILLIAMS	KELLY	ELDERTON	TAYLOR	BARRATT	WILDE	C WILLIAMS	CONNORS	CLANCY	ADAMS	ROUSE	
7	1	0	1	7	5	4	9	7	2	0	8	8	0	8	2	3	2	1	8	1	2	3	3	1	0	5	0	0	0	1	0	0	0	0	0	0	0	0	0	0	0	**X**
0	2	0	0	0	0	1	0	1	4	1	1	1	1	1	0	1	1	0	0	0	0	0	2	0	1	0	1	0	2	0	0	0	0	0	0	0	0	0	0	0	0	**S**
0	3	0	3	1	0	1	0	0	2	0	0	0	1	0	5	3	4	0	0	0	3	4	3	0	0	0	1	0	0	0	1	0	0	0	0	0	0	0	0	0	0	**U**

Also played: RAWCLIFFE U(11). BRADLEY U(34). ANANE X(44) U(45).

FLEETWOOD TOWN

CURRENT SQUAD AS OF BEGINING OF 2009-10 SEASON

GOALKEEPERS	HT	WT	D.O.B	AGE	P.O.B	CAREER	APPS	GOA
Aaron Grundy	6'01"	12 07	21/1/88	21	Bolton	Bury Rel c/s 08, FCUM (L) 2/08, Oxford U (Trial) 7/08, Burscough 8/08, Warrington 1/09, Cambridge U NC 3/09, Fleetwood 8/09		
Danny Hurst						Cheadle, Radcliffe 7/00, Sheff Wed (Trial) 2/03, Fleetwood 5 fig 1/07	36	0
DEFENDERS								
Shaun Beeley	5'10"	11 04	21/11/88	20		Oldham (Scholar) Rel c/s 07, Southport 8/07, Fleetwood 11/07, Salford C (L) 1/09	24	0
Sean Clancy	5'08"	09 12	16/9/87	21	Liverpool	Blackpool, Southport 8/06, Burscough (L) 3/07, USA, Shrewsbury NC 8/07, Altrincham 8/07 Rel 9/07, Burscough 9/07, Fleetwood Undisc 3/09	15	4
Phil Doughty	6'02"	13 02	6/9/86	22	Kirkham	Blackpool Rel c/s 08, Leigh RMI (L) 1/05, Barrow (SL) 3/07, Macclesfield (2ML) 11/07, Accrington (L) 1/08, Fleetwood 8/08, Welshpool (SL) 1/09, AFC Fylde (SL) 6/09	10	0
John Hills	5'09"	12 08	21/4/78	31	St Annes-on-Sea	Blackpool, Everon £90,000 11/95, Swansea (2ML) 1/97, Swansea (L) 8/97, Blackpool (L) 1/98 £75,000 2/98, Gillingham 8/03 Rel c/s 05, Sheff Wed 7/05 Rel c/s 07, Blackpool 7/07 Rel c/s 08, Fleetwood 8/08	23	0
Steve McNulty			26/9/83	25	Liverpool	Liverpool Rel 6/03, Chester (Trial) 3/03, Blackpool (Trial) 7/03, Burscough c/s 03, Vauxhall Motors £3,500 2/05, Barrow 6/07, Fleetwood £17,000 6/09		
Ricky Mercer					Preston	Preston (Scholar), Lancaster 11/02, Kendal 6/04, Fleetwood 12/06	30	6
Michael Taylor	6'02"	13 10	21/11/82	26	Liverpool	Blackburn Rel c/s 04, Carlisle (3ML) 9/02, Rochdale (L) 3/03, Reading (Trial) 12/03, Wycombe (Trial) 3/04, Cheltenham 7/04, Forest Green (2ML) 3/06, Halifax 7/06 Rel 7/06, Lancaster 7/06 Rel 10/06, Barrow 10/06, Hyde U 10/06, TNS Undisc 8/07, Fleetwood 1/09	22	0
Ashley Wooliscroft	5'10"	11 02	28/12/79	29	Stoke	Stoke Rel c/s 01, Telford 9/01, Newtown 8/03, Leek T 9/03, Kidsgrove A 10/06, Hednesford 10/07, Stalybridge 10/07, Newcastle T 3/09, Fleetwood 5/09		
Alan Wright	5'05"	10 02	28/9/71	37	Ashton-under-Lyne	Blackpool, Blackburn 10/91, Aston Villa 3/95, Middlesbrough 8/03, Sheff Utd (3ML) 10/03 Perm 1/04 Rel c/s 07, Derby (SL) 2/06, Leeds (L) 10/06, Cardiff (6WL) 11/06, Doncaster (L) 2/07, Notts Forest (SL) 3/07, Oldham (Trial) 7/07, Cheltenham 10/07 Rel c/s 09, Fleetwood 7/09		
MIDFIELDERS								
Steve Connors			5/1/86	23	Liverpool	Witton, Bradford PA 5/07, Fleetwood 2/09	10	3
Lee Dodgson			24/3/84	25	Lancaster	Morecambe, Leek T (2ML) 1/06, Fleetwood 7/06, Lancaster 8/06, Kendal T 11/06, Forest Green 1/07 Rel 4/08, Lancaster 8/08, Fleetwood 5/09		
Kevin Leadbetter			10/9/79	29	Liverpool	Skelmersdale, Southport Undisc 8/01, Runcorn (L) 9/01, Hyde (L) 12/01, Runcorn £5,000 1/02, Southport Undisc 1/04, Burscough 6/06, Skelmersdale 10/07, Fleetwood 5/08, Southport (L) 2/09	14	4
Jamie McGuire	5'07"	11 01	13/11/83	25	Birkenhead	Tranmere Rel c/s 04, Northwich (L) 3/03, Northwich (2ML) 11/03, Cammell Laird c/s 04, Stockport (Trial) c/s 06, Droylsden 7/07, Fleetwood 5/09		
Jamie Milligan	5'06"	09 12	3/1/80	29	Blackpool	Everton, Blackpool 3/01 cc c/s 03, Macclesfield 8/03 Rel 9/03, Leigh RMI 9/03, Droylsden 9/03, Hyde 12/03, Fleetwood 12/05	41	8
Jamie Mullan			10/2/88	21	Nottingham	Notts County (Yth), Man Utd Rel c/s 07, Leeds (Trial) 5/07, Huddersfield (Trial) 8/07, Carlisle (Trial) 9/07, Rochdale 11/07, Northwich 1/08, Fleetwood 5/09		
Nathan Pond						Lancaster, Fleetwood, Bamber Bridge (Trial) 7/05	35	3

FORWARDS								
Andy Bell	5'10"	12 06	4/2/84	25	Blackburn	Blackburn Rel c/s 03, Wycombe (Trial) 4/03, Bournemouth (Trial) 4/03, Wycombe 10/03 Rel 2/04, York C 3/04 Rel c/s 04, Hednesford 8/04, Fleetwood 2/06	25	7
Tom Cahill	5'10"	12 08	21/11/86	22	Derby	Euxton Villa, Matlock 9/06, Rotherham 5/07 Rel c/s 09, Altrincham (3ML) 1/08, Ilkeston (3ML) 10/08, Fleetwood 8/09		
Nick Rogan			15/10/83	25	Blackpool	Kendal T, Morecambe 7/02 Rel 5/05, Workington (L) 3/05, Leigh RMI (Trial) 5/05, Lancaster 7/05, Southport 10/05, Barrow 2/06 Rel 5/09, Vauxhall Motors (L) 10/08, Fleetwood 6/09		
Adam Warlow			3/2/87	22	Southport	Crewe Rel c/s 07, Witton (SL) 8/06, Witton 5/07, Fleetwood 6/08	39	19
Michael Wilde			27/8/83	26	Birkenhead	West Kirby, Poulton Victoria, TNS/The New Saints 8/02, Fleetwood 1/09	21	7
Chris Williams	5'08"	9 00	2/2/85	24	Manchester	Stockport, Grimsby (L) 9/04, Leigh RMI (L) 12/05, Northwich (L) 2/06 (Perm) 3/06, Bradford PA 1/08, Stalybridge 7/08, Fleetwood 2/09	13	1

LOANEES	HT	WT	DOB	AGE	POB	From - To	APPS	GOA
(M)Ashton Bayliss						Blackpool 8/08 - Burscough (SL) 3/09	3	0
(F)Chris Thompson	5'10"	11 12	7/2/82	27	Warrington	Barrow 9/08 - Hyde U (L) 10/08, Leigh Genesis (SL) 1/09 Perm 3/09	1	0
(M)Matty Kay	5'09"	11 00	12/10/89	19	Blackpool	Blackpool 10/08 -	8	0
(F)Lee Hunt	6'01"	13 01	5/6/81	28	Chester	Barrow 11/08 - Droylsden (L) 1/09, Rel 5/09, Rhyl 6/09	3	0
(D)Paul Barratt			15/9/87	21	Manchester	Northwich 1/09 - Rel 3/09	5	0
(F)Domaine Rouse	5'06"	10 10	4/7/89	20	Stretford	Bury (SL) 3/09 -	3	0
(D)Ricky Anane	5'08"	11 02	18/2/89	20	Manchester	Bury (SL) 3/09 - Rel c/s 09, Woking 7/09	1	0

DEPARTURES	HT	WT	DOB	AGE	POB	From - To	APPS	GOA
(D)Simon Garner						Stalybridge 6/08 - Rel 9/08, FCUM 9/08	3	0
(F)Phil Denney	6'02"	13 04	6/1/79	30	Bury	Mossley 10/05 - Guiseley 10/08 Rel 2/09, Rossendale 2/09, Bamber Bridge 6/09	9	0
(D)Sean Webb	6'03"		4/1/83	26		ThorSport (Ice) 10/08 - Rel 11/08, Shamrock R 2/09	0	0
(D)Farrell Kilbane	6'00"	13 00	21/10/74	34	Preston	Burscough 5/08 - Hyde U 11/08, Burscough 7/09	8	0
(D)Phil Robinson	5'09"	11 00	28/9/80	28	Manchester	Bamber Bridge - AFC Fylde 1/09, Bamber Bridge 6/09	2	0
(F)Andy Moran	5'11"	11 03	7/10/79	29	Wigan	Rhyl 1/08 - Rel 1/09, Colwyn Bay (L) 8/08, Colwyn Bay (L) 11/08, Caernarfon 1/09, Prestatyn 5/09	3	0
(D)Steve Williams						Hyde U 11/08 - Rel 1/09, Bamber Bridge 2/09, Bradford C Undisc c/s 09	1	0
(M)Colin Potts			26/2/78	31	Lancashire	Altrincham 3/08 - Rel 1/09	10	1
(F)Steve Foster	5'09"	13 01	30/12/81	27	Urmston	AFC Telford 5/07 - Salford C 2/09, Witton 8/09	15	2
(M)Mark Peers			14/5/84	25	St Helens	Witton Undisc 6/08 - Rel 2/09, FC Halifax 2/09	11	1
(M)Chris Holland	5'09"	11 05	11/9/76	32	Whalley	Leigh Genesis 11/08 - Burscough 3/09, Guiseley 7/09	4	0
(M)Brad Maylett	5'08"	10 07	24/12/80	28	Manchester	Leigh RMI/Leigh Genesis 11/08 - Rel 3/09, Witton 3/09	9	0
(D)Ashley Dunn						Morecambe 1/08 - Witton (L) 11/08, Witton (L) 1/09, Witton (L) 3/09 Undisc 3/09, Bamber Bridge 6/09	10	1
(M)Warren Beattie			18/10/86	22	Preston	Porthmadog 1/08 - Rel 5/09, Kendal T (L) 2/09, Kendal T 6/09	23	1
(D)Dylan Adams	5'08"	11 12	29/7/89	20	Liverpool	Preston 3/09 - Rel 5/09	1	0
(D)Kieran Walmsley			11/12/83	25	Preston	Morecambe 8/07 - Rel 5/09, Kendal T (SL) 3/09, Kendal T 6/09	24	1
(F)Danny Penswick						Blackpool c/s 08 - Rel 5/09, Witton (L) 2/09, AFC Fylde 8/09	5	0
(G)Mike Hale						Burnley (Scholar) - Bamber Bridge 6/09	6	0
(M)Jimmy Kelly	5'07"	11 09	14/2/73	36	Liverpool	Rhyl 1/09 - Colwyn Bay 7/09	8	0
(D)Georges Santos	6'03"	14 08	15/8/70	39	Marseille, Fr	Farsley Celtic 9/08 -	5	0
(D)Ryan Elderton	5'10"	12 06	3/11/83	25	Morecambe	Lancaster 1/09 -	19	0
Bradley							0	0
Jason Rawcliffe							0	0

FLEETWOOD TOWN

Formed: 1908

Nickname: The Fishermen.

Club Colours: Red and white shirts, white shorts, red socks.

Change Colours: Royal blue shirts, shorts and socks.

Club Sponsor: Commercial Power

Previous League: Northern Premier League

Ground address: Highbury Stadium, Park Avenue, Fleetwood, Lancashire FY7 6TX.

Telephone: 01253 770 702

Mobile: 07773 027 706

Fax: 0871 789 0957

Email: info@fleetwoodtownfc.com

Club Website: www.fleetwoodtownfc.co.uk

Simple Directions: from M55 junction 3 follow signs to Fleetwood on A585 for about eleven miles then turn left at Nautical College traffic island (campus on left) at second island take sixth exit into into Hatfield Avenue. Ground is 3/4 mile on left.

Capacity: 3,000 **Seats**: 250 **Covered**:1,200 **Floodlights**: Yes

Clubhouse: Smart refurbished club room with bar, dance floor and Sky TV can be booked.

Club Shop: Full range of products

Local Radio: Radio Lancashire

Local Press: Fleetwood Weekly News & Chronicle and Blackpool Evening Gazette

no image available

PROGRAMME EDITOR

Derick Thomas.
Tel: (M) 07917 055 433
Email: press@fleetwoodtownfc.com

CLUB STATISTICS

RECORD

Attendance: 7,900 v Liverpool F.C. 12 August 2003.

SENIOR HONOURS

North West Counties Division Two Champions 1998-1999.

North West Counties Division One Champions 2004-2005.

Northern Premier League Cup 2006-07.

PREVIOUS

Names: Fleetwood 1908.

Fleetwood Wanderers 1997 then in the same year reverted to

Fleetwood Freeport and Fleetwood Town in 2002.

GAINSBOROUGH TRINITY

Supplied by The Gainsborough Standard.

CLUB PERSONNEL

Chairman: Peter Swann.

Company Secretary: Richard Coleman.

Additional Directors: P Lobley, A Lobley, GT Holmes, T Bland, G Lyner.

Secretaryr: Grahame Lyner
2 Claremont Road, Gainsborough, Lincs. DN21 1QW
Tel No: (H) 01427 612 791
(M) 07789 950 552
(B) 01427 614 134
Email: grahamelyner@btconnect.com

Commercial Manager: Geoff Holmes
Tel: (M) 07970 414 513
Email: geoffholmes@live.com

Press Officer: Peter Swann.
Tel: (M) 07977 410 703.

Manager: TBA.

Club therapist: Doug Kyle.

Only suffering your second defeat after eight games at the beginning of the season might suggest you would be higher than thirteenth in the table, but Trinity only actually won two and failed to scored in four. However, a patchy season included some great results and showed what was possible, but a lack of consistency always prevented a serious challenge.

First game defeats in the F.A.Cup and F.A.Trophy to Halesowen Town and A.F.C. Telford United respectively, provided no financial bonus or indeed a confidence booster.

Four games without scoring or winning in November, underlined the need for an experienced striker and Luke Beckett was signed from Huddersfield Town. He provided 15 goals before the end of season, and in the next seven games only one defeat and a goal tally of 17-12 provided entertainment and seven goals for Beckett.

Sadly the season drifted away with only one victory (on the last day of the season) in the last dozen matches, leaving 'The Blues' to finish in mid table and hoping for more consistent campaigns in the future.

GAINSBOROUGH TRINITY

BEST LGE ATT.: **526** v King's Lynn
LOWEST: **200** v Fleetwood

No.	Date	Comp	H/A	Opponents	Att:	Result	Goalscorers	Pos
1	Aug 9	BSN	H	Southport	460	L 0 - 1		
2	12		A	Hucknall Town	329	W 2 - 1	Marrison 8 Mallon 68	
3	16		A	Solihull Moors	172	W 3 - 2	Austin 12 McMahon 20 Lukic 71	5
4	23		H	Gateshead	365	D 0 - 0		7
5	25		A	Hyde United	251	D 0 - 0		
6	30		H	Vauxhall Motors	310	D 1 - 1	Smith 59	
7	Sept 2		H	Farsley Celtic	314	D 0 - 0		
8	6		A	AFC Telford United	1860	L 1 - 2	Bird 56	13
9	**9**	**SS N1**	**A**	**AFC Telford**	**652**	**L 2 - 3***	**Smith 8 McMahon 50**	
10	13		H	Redditch United	287	W 4 - 1	Bird 30 Spafford 49 McMahon 67 (pen) Hall 89	
11	20		A	Burscough	310	W 2 - 0	McMahon 14 (pen) 63 (pen)	6
12	**27**	**F.A.C. 2Q**	**A**	**Halesowen Town**	**502**	**L 0 - 3**		
13	Oct 4		H	Fleetwood Town	200	L 3 - 4	Bird 51 McMahon 58 Davies 82	7
14	18		A	Droylsden	377	L 2 - 3	Bird 23 50	
15	21		A	Alfreton Town	307	W 4 - 1	BIRD 3 (60 63 70) Smith 76	
16	25		A	Farsley Celtic	251	L 1 - 2	Mallon 14	9
17	Nov 1		A	Tamworth	838	D 0 - 0		10
18	8		H	Stafford Rangers	390	L 0 - 3		13
19	15		H	Blyth Spartans	347	D 0 - 0		14
20	**22**	**F.A.T 3Q**	**H**	**AFC Telford United**	**441**	**L 0 - 2**		
21	29		A	Harrogate Town	458	W 3 - 0	McMahon 6 Austin 76 Beckett 89	10
22	Dec 6		H	Stalybridge Celtic	384	D 3 - 3	Beckett 4 90 McMahon 62 (pen)	8
23	20		A	Southport	785	L 3 - 5	Beckett 33 Ross 41 Wilson 48	10
24	26		H	King's Lynn	526	W 2 - 0	Beckett 35 55	9
25	Jan 1		A	King's Lynn	1051	D 2 - 2	Marrison 62 McMahon 83	
26	3		H	Solihull Moors	343	D 1 - 1	McMahon 64 (pen)	10
27	13		H	Hinckley United	269	W 3 - 1	McMahon 11 Ross 32 Beckett 65	
28	17		A	Workington	381	L 0 - 5		8
29	24		H	Alfreton Town	369	L 0 - 2		8
30	27		H	Droylsden	244	W 1 - 0	Beckett 7	
31	31		A	Stafford Rangers	446	L 0 - 2		8
32	Feb 14		A	Hinckley United	414	W 2 - 0	Burbeary 23 McMahon 65	8
33	21		A	Stalybridge Celtic	552	W 2 - 1	Beckett 6 McMahon 34	8
34	24		H	Tamworth	321	L 0 - 1		
35	Mar 3		H	Burscough	211	L 0 - 4		
36	7		H	Workington	294	L 1 - 2	Beckett 25	10
37	10		A	Fleetwood Town	502	D 2 - 2	Burbeary 42 77 (pen)	
38	14		H	Hucknall Town	319	D 2 - 2	Beckett 20 50	
39	21		A	Redditch United	280	D 1 - 1	Hall 2	11
40	28		A	Vauxhall Motors	167	D 1 - 1	Beckett 7	12
41	April 4		H	AFC Telford United	292	L 1 - 2	Bird 70	12
42	11		A	Gateshead	486	L 0 - 1		13
43	13		H	Hyde United	290	L 0 - 1		
44	18		A	Blyth Spartans	583	D 1 - 1	Beckett 48	14
45	25		H	Harrogate Town	332	W 3 - 2	Mallon 34 Hall 52 Beckett 72 (pen)	13

Average Home Att: 327 (408) **Goals** 59 71

Best Position: 5th **Worst:** 14th

Goalscorers: Beckett 15, McMahon 13, Bird 9, Burbeary 3, Hall 3, Mallon 3, Smith 3, Austin 2, Marrison 2, Ross 2, Davies 1, Lukic 1, Spafford 1, Wilson 1.

SOLLITT	GREENWOOD	DRURY	ELLIS	LUKIC	ANSON	AUSTIN	MCMAHON	MARRISON	MALLON	HALL	BIRD	BURLEY	SPAFFORD	REEVES	ROSS	BENJAMIN	BUCKLEY	SMITH	DAVIS	DAVIES	DUDGEON	NEWSHAM	JAMESON	BECKETT	WILSON	CULLINGWORTH	BURBEARY	BRADLEY	NEEDHAM	CANOVILLE	PEAT	EVANS	BARNES	
X	X	X	X	X	X	X	X	X	X	X	S	U	U	U																				**1**
X	X	X	X	X	X	X	X	X	X	X	U	U	U	U	U																			**2**
X	X	X	X	X	X	X	X	X	X	X	U	U	U		U	S																		**3**
X	X	X	X	X	X	X	X	X	X	X	U	S	U		S	S																		**4**
X	X	X	X	X	X	S	X	X	X	X	S		U		U	X	U																	**5**
X	X	X	X	X	X	U	X	X	X	S	S	U	U		X			X																**6**
X	X	X	X	X	X		S	S	X	X	X	S	U	U	X			X																**7**
X	X		X	X	X	S	X	X	X		S	X	U	U	X			X	U															**8**
X	**S**	**U**	**X**	**X**	**X**	**X**	**X**	**U**	**S**		**X**	**X**	**X**		**X**			**X**	**S**															**9**
X	U	X	X	X	X	X	X	S	S	X	X	U	X		U			X																**10**
X		X	X	X	X		X	X	S	X	S	S	X		U			X	U	X														**11**
X	**U**	**X**	**X**	**X**		**U**	**X**	**X**	**X**	**X**	**S**	**S**	**X**		**S**			**X**	**U**	**X**	**U**													**12**
X	X	X		X			X	S	U	X	X	U	U		X			X	U	X	X													**13**
X	X	X	X	X	X		X	U	U	X	X		U		U			X		S		X												**14**
X	X	X	X	X	X	U	X		X	X	X		U		S			X		S		S												**15**
X		X	X	X	X	U	X	S	X	X	X		U		U			X		X		S												**16**
X		X		X	X	U	X	S	X	X	X		X		U			X	U	X		S												**17**
X		X	U	X	X	U	X	S		X	X		X		S			X	U	X		X												**18**
X	X	X	U	X	X	X	X	X		X	X		X					S	S	U		S												**19**
X	**X**	**X**	**U**	**X**	**X**	**X**		**X**		**X**	**X**		**X**	**S**	**U**			**X**	**S**	**U**														**20**
	X	X	U	X	X	S	X	U	S	X	U		X		X					X			X	X										**21**
	X	X	U	X	X	U	X	U	S	X	S		X		X					X			X	X										**22**
	X	X	S		X	U	X	U	S	X			X		X					X			X	X	X	U								**23**
X	X	X	X		X	U	X	U	S	X			U		X					X				X	X	U								**24**
X		X	X		X	U	X	S	X	X	S		U		X					X				X	X	U								**25**
X	U	X		X		X	X	X	S	S	X		U		X				U					X	X	X								**26**
X	X	X	X	X	X		X		S	X					X				X					X										**27**
X	X	X		X	X		X	S	S	X	S		U		X				X	U				X	X									**28**
X		X		X		U	X	S	X	X	X		X		X			S	U	X				X	S									**29**
X		X		X	X		X	S	S	X	U		X						X	X				X	U	U	X							**30**
X		X	U	X	X	X		S	X	X			X						U	X				X	S	S	X							**31**
X	X	X		X	X		X	U	X	X			X							U				X	U	U	X							**32**
X	X	X		X	X	S	X		X	X			X											X	U	U	X	S	U					**33**
X	X	X		X	X	X		U	X	X			X											X	U	U	X	S	S					**34**
X	X	X			X	X		S	X	X			X		S									X	U	U	X		S	X				**35**
X	U			X		U			X	X			X		X				U					X	U	X	X	S	X	X				**36**
X	X					S		U	X	X			X		X				U					X	U	X	X	U	X	X				**37**
X		S		X		S		U	X	X			X		U									X		X	X	U	X	X	X			**38**
	U	X		X	X	S		U	X	X			U											X			X	U	X	X	X	X		**39**
U	X	X			X	U	X		X	S			U											X			X	U	X	X	X	X		**40**
X	X	U		X		U	X		X	X	X		X						U					X		U	X				X	U		**41**
U	S	S		X			X		X	X	X		X						U					X			S		X	X	X	X		**42**
S	S	X		X		U	X		X	X									S					X		U	X		X	X	X	X		**43**
X	S	X		X	X		X		X	X	U								S					X		X	U		X	U	X			**44**
	S	X		X		U	X		X	X	S								X					X		U	X		S	X	X		X	**45**
Total League Appearances																																		
34	25	36	16	36	32	10	34	10	28	38	13	1	20	0	15	1	0	11	4	13	1	2	3	25	5	5	14	0	8	9	8	4	1	**X**
1	4	2	1	0	0	7	1	12	10	3	9	3	0	0	4	2	0	2	3	2	0	4	0	0	2	1	1	3	3	0	0	0	0	**S**
2	4	1	5	0	0	15	0	10	2	0	6	6	18	4	9	0	1	0	12	3	0	0	0	0	7	11	1	4	1	1	0	1	0	**U**
Total Cup Appearances																																		
3	1	2	2	3	2	2	2	2	1	2	2	1	3	0	1	0	0	3	0	1	0	0	0	0	0	0	0	0	0	0	0	0	0	**X**
0	1	0	0	0	0	0	0	0	1	0	1	1	0	1	1	0	0	0	2	0	0	0	0	0	0	0	0	0	0	0	0	0	0	**S**
0	1	1	1	0	0	1	0	1	0	0	0	0	0	0	1	0	0	0	1	1	1	0	0	0	0	0	0	0	0	0	0	0	0	**U**

GAINSBOROUGH TRINITY

CURRENT SQUAD AS OF BEGINING OF 2009-10 SEASON

GOALKEEPERS	HT	WT	D.O.B	AGE	P.O.B	CAREER	APPS	GOA
Phil Barnes	6'01"	11 01	2/3/79	30	Sheffield	Rotherham, Blackpool £100,000 7/97 Rel c/s 04, Sheff Utd 7/04, Torquay (L) 2/05, QPR (L) 2/06, Grimsby Undisc 6/06 Rel 3/09, Gainsborough 4/09	1	0
Luke Herriott						Mansfield, Gainsborough c/s 09		

DEFENDERS	HT	WT	D.O.B	AGE	P.O.B	CAREER	APPS	GOA
Mark Greaves	6'01"	13 00	22/1/75	34	Hull	Gainsborough, Brigg T, Hull C 6/96, Boston U 8/02, Burton 7/07 Rel 5/08, York C 5/08 Rel 6/09, Gainsborough 7/09		
Adie Moses	5'10"	12 08	4/5/75	34	Doncaster	Barnsley, Huddersfield £225,000 12/00, Crewe 7/03 Rel c/s 06, Lincoln C 7/06 Rel c/s 08, Mansfield 7/08, Gainsborough 6/09		
Wes Parker	5'08"	10 05	7/12/83	25	Boston	Grimsby Rel c/s 04, Scarborough (Trial) c/s 04, Brigg T, Gainsborough 9/04, Boston U 5/08 Rel c/s 09, Gainsborough 5/09		
Nathan Peat	5'09"	10 09	19/9/82	26	Hull	Hull C, Cambridge U (2ML) 12/03, Lincoln C (SL) 7/04, York 8/05 Rel 5/07, Harrogate T 6/07, Gainsborough 3/09	8	0
Jake Picton	6'00"	11 00	6/1/91	18	Pontefract	Scunthorpe, Gainsborough (3ML) 8/09		
Neil Spafford						Boston T, Gainsborough 7/07	20	1

MIDFIELDERS	HT	WT	D.O.B	AGE	P.O.B	CAREER	APPS	GOA
Matt Austin						Notts County Rel c/s 08, Gainsborough (L) 1/07, Gainsborough (SL) 12/07, Gainsborough c/s 08	17	2
Ashley Burbeary			29/11/86	22		Mansfield (Scholar), Gainsborough (SL) 1/06, Alfreton 8/06, Stalybridge 7/07, Droylsden 11/07, Mansfield (Trial) 1/09, Gainsborough 1/09	15	2
Josh Davies						Gainsborough	7	0
Darren Dunning	5'06"	11 12	8/1/81	28	Scarborough	Blackburn Rel c/s 03, Bristol C (2ML) 8/00, Rochdale (L) 11/01, Blackpool (L) 3/02, Torquay (2ML) 11/02, Macclesfield (3ML) 1/03, York 7/03, Harrogate T 7/06, Gainsborough 5/09		
Chris Hall			3/3/83	26	Lincoln	Lincoln U, Burton 5/04, Gainsborough 6/07, York C (SL) 3/08	41	3
James Hunt	5'08"	10 03	17/12/76	32	Derby	Notts County Rel c/s 97, Northampton 8/97, Oxford U 7/02 Rel c/s 04, Bristol R 7/04 Rel c/s 07, Grimsby (3ML) 1/07, Grimsby 7/07 Rel c/s 09, Gainsborough 7/09		
Lewis McMahon	5'09"	10 10	2/5/85	24	Doncaster	Sheff Wed, Notts County 7/05 Rel c/s 06, York C 8/06 Rel 5/07, Gainsborough 7/07	35	11
Ryan Semple	5'11"	10 11	4/7/85	24	Belfast	Peterborough, Man Utd (Trial) 2/03, Farnborough (3ML) 11/03, Lincoln C 7/06 Rel 1/08, Chester (6WL) 11/06, Rushden & D (L) 8/07, Oxford U NC 2/08, Brackley T 3/08, Boston U (Trial) c/s 08, Deeping R 8/08, Haverhill R (Dual) 3/09, Gainsborough 6/09		
Ryan Toulson			18/11/85	23		Halifax, Stocksbridge (L) 9/05, Altrincham (SL) 1/08, Harrogate T 6/08, Gainsborough 5/09		

FORWARDS	HT	WT	D.O.B	AGE	P.O.B	CAREER	APPS	GOA
Luke Beckett	5'11"	11 02	25/11/76	32	Sheffield	Barnsley, Chester 6/98, Chesterfield £75,000 7/00, Stockport £100,000 12/01, Sheff Utd £50,000 11/04, Huddersfield (6WL) 1/05, Oldham (SL) 3/05, Oldham (SL) 7/05, Huddersfield £85,000 7/06 Rel 11/08, Gainsborough 11/08	25	17
Ryan Mallon	5'09"	11 08	22/3/83	26	Sheffield	Sheff Utd Rel c/s 03, Halifax (3ML) 8/02, Scarborough (2ML) 11/02, Halifax 6/03 Rel 4/05, Alfreton (L) 12/04, Gainsborough (SL) 1/05, York C 8/05, Gainsborough (L) 12/05 Perm 1/06	38	3
David Reeves	6'01"	13 08	19/11/67	41	Birkenhead	Heswall, Sheff Wed 8/86, Scunthorpe (L) 12/86, Scunthorpe (L) 10/87, Burnley (4ML) 11/87, Bolton 8/89, Notts County 3/93, Carlisle 10/93, Preston 10/96, Chesterfield 11/97, Oldham (L) 12/01 Perm 1/02 Rel 11/02, Chesterfield (3ML) 8/02, Chesterfield 12/02	0	0
Darryn Stamp	6'01"	11 10	21/9/78	30	Beverley	Hessle, Scunthorpe 7/97 Rel c/s 01, Halifax (L) 2/00, Scarborough (L) 3/01, Scarborough 5/01, Northampton £30,000 5/02, Chester 8/03, Kidderminster (L) 11/04, Stevenage 1/05, York C (3ML) 10/06, Halifax 1/07, Northwich (SL) 3/08, Northwich 8/08, Gateshead (SL) 3/09, Gainsborough 6/09		

LOANEES	HT	WT	DOB	AGE	POB	From - To	APPS	GOA
(F)Marc Newsham	5'10"	9 11	24/3/87	22	Hatfield	Rotherham 10/08 - Sheffield FC (L) 12/08, Ilkeston (L) 1/09, Rel 5/09, Boston U 6/09	6	0
(G)Aaron Jameson						Sheff Wed 11/08 - Ilkeston (SL) 2/09	3	0
(F)Jason Bradley	6'03"	13 00	16/3/89	20	Sheffield	Darlington (SL) 2/09 - Mansfield 7/09	3	0
(D)Lee Canoville	6'01"	12 00	14/3/81	28	Ealing	Halesowen T (SL) 2/09 - Boston U 7/09	9	0
(G)Tommy Evans	6'00"	13 02	31/12/76	32	Doncaster	Alfreton 3/09 - Rel 5/09, Boston U 7/09	4	0

DEPARTURES	HT	WT	DOB	AGE	POB	From - To	APPS	GOA
(F)Liam Nimmo	6'00"	11 05	28/12/84	24	Boston	Holbeach U 1/08 - Holbeach U 7/08		
(F)Trevor Benjamin	6'02"	13 07	8/2/79	30	Kettering	Hereford 8/08 - Rel 8/08, Stevenage (Trial) 9/08, Northwich 10/08 Rel 10/08, Hednesford 11/08, Wellingborough 12/08, Kidsgrove 2/09, Tamworth 8/09	3	0
(M)Adam Burley	5'10"	12 06	27/11/80	28	Sheffield	Worcester 12/07 - Hednesford 10/08, Chasetown 2/09, Belper T 3/09	4	0
(D)James Dudgeon	6'02"	12 04	19/3/81	28	Newcastle	Stalybridge 1/08 - Worksop (L) 10/08, Newcastle Blue Star 11/08, Wakefield 2/09, Ilkeston 6/09	1	0
(F)Adam Smith			20/2/85	24	Huddersfield	Chesterfield 8/08 - York C (2ML) 11/08, York C Undisc 1/09	13	2
(D)Bobby Wilson			11/8/88	21	Harlow	Stafford R 12/08 - Stafford R NC 3/09	7	1
(M)Ian Ross	5'10"	11 00	23/1/86	23	Sheffield	Rotherham 8/08 - Alfreton 3/09 Rel 5/09	19	2
(F)Colin Marrison	6'01"	12 05	23/9/85	23	Sheffield	Tamworth 5/08 - Rel c/s 09, Retford U (L) 3/09, Retford U 5/09	22	2
(D)Nick Ellis						Sheff Utd (Scholar) 7/05 - Rel c/s 09, Retford U 6/09	17	0
(M)Gareth Davies	6'01"	12 00	4/2/83	26	Chesterfield	Halifax 7/08 - Rel c/s 09	15	1
(F)Liam Needham	5'11"	12 02	19/10/85	23	Sheffield	Notts County 12/06 - Rel 5/09, Guiseley c/s 09	11	0
(D)Danny Anson					Sheffield	Stocksbridge PS 6/06 - Worksop 6/09	32	0
(D)James Cullingworth			18/9/87	21	Nottingham	Stafford R 12/08 - Rel 5/09, Boston U 6/09	6	0
(D)James Lukic					Sheffield	Matlock 6/08 - Matlock 6/09	36	1
(M)Martin Drury						Belper T 7/07 - Bradford PA 6/09	38	0
(F)Simon Bird	5'11"		24/7/83	26	Lincoln	Notts Forest (Jun), Lincoln C, Lincoln U, Louisville Cardinals (USA) 8/04 - North Ferriby (L) 2/09, North Ferriby c/s 09	22	9
(G)Adam Sollitt	6'00"	13 06	22/6/77	32	Sheffield	Worksop 6/06 - Matlock 8/09	35	0
(D)Ross Greenwood	5'11"	11 05	1/11/85	23	York	York C 4/08 -	29	0
Buckley							0	0

GAINSBOROUGH TRINITY

Formed: 1873

Nickname: The Blues.

Club Colours: Royal blue shirts, royal blue shorts, royal blue socks.

Change Colours: Yellow shirts, shorts and socks.

Club Sponsor: Marshalls Yard

Previous League: Northern Premier League

Ground address: The Northolme, Gainsborough, Lincolnshire DN21 2QW

Telephone: 01427 613 295 (office) 613 688 (social club)

Mobile: 07789 850 552

Fax: 01427 613 295

Website: www.gainsboroughtrinity.com

Simple Directions: The Northolme is situated on the A159 Gainsborough to Scunthorpe road. Two miles from Lea Road.

Capacity: 4,340 **Seats**: 504 **Covered**: 2,500 **Floodlights**:Yes

Clubhouse: Open on matchdays. Blues club open every evening

Club Shop: Yes.

Local Radio: BBC Radio Lincs and Linc FM

Local Press: Gainsborough Standard and Lincolnshire Echo

no image available

PROGRAMME EDITOR

David Tinsley

Tel: (M) 07950 420 185

Email: dgt.1@virgin.net

CLUB STATISTICS

RECORD

Attendance: 9,760 v Scunthorpe United Midland League 1948

Victory: 7-0 v Fleetwood Town and Great Harwood Town

Defeat: 1-7 V Stalybridge Celtic (N.P.L.) 2000-2001

1-7 V Brentford F.A.Cup 03-04 & Stalybridge C NPL 00-01

Career Goalscorer: Not known.

Career Appearances: Not Known.

Record Transfer Fee Paid: £3,000 to Buxton for Stuart Lowe

Received: £30,000 from Lincoln City for Tony James

SENIOR HONOURS

Midland League Champions 1890-91, 1927-28, 48-49, 66-67,

Lincs Senior Cup (12)

PREVIOUS

Leagues: Midland Counties 1889-96, 1912-60, 61-68.

Football League 1896-1912. Central Alliance 1960-61.

Northern Premier League 1968-2004.

GLOUCESTER CITY

Back row, Ken Blackburn (Youth Coach), Matt Sysum, Jack Pitcher, Jack Harris, Sam Ellis, Tom Hamblin, Kev Sawyer, Ollie Hall, Ash Thomas, Mike Symons, Alex Allard, Matt Rose, Lee Marshall, Lee Randall (Kit Manager).
Middle Row : Doug Foxwell (Chief Scout), Kevin Allard (Exec), Mike Dunstan (Exec), Phil Warren (Supporters Trust), Adie Tandy (Physio), Dave Mehew (Manager), David Phillips (Chairman), Tim Harris (General Manager), Adrian Harris (Assistant Manager), Nigel Hughes (Exec), Dave Hatton (Youth Secretary), John Davis (Exec), Stewart Martyn (Goalkeeping Coach).
Front Row : Dr Bob Byrne (Club Doctor), Jack Twyman, Lee Smith, Tom Webb, Luke Ballinger, Neil Mustoe (Captain), Alex Sykes, James Upcott, Karl Nash, Jamie Reid, Shaun Wetson (Secretary).

CLUB PERSONNEL

Chairman: Dave Phillips.

Company Secretary: Nigel Hughes.

Secretaryr: Shaun Wetson.

30 Horsebere Road, Hucclecote GL3 3PT.

(H): 01452 530 409

(B): 01452 530 409

(M): 07813 931 781

Email: swgcfc@gmail.com

Press Officer: Mike Dunstan.

Tel: (M) 07899 74951

Email: mikedunstan@blueyonder.co.uk

Manager: David Mehew.

Club therapist: Neil Light.

Most of the publicity after their play-off success, featuring Gloucester City, had surrounded their geographical position within the Blue Square 'family'. This was unfortunate as their success was a fine achievement for a club without a true home. To register 93 senior goals in the season and only fail to score in four of their forty seven matches indicates a very positive attitude and with twenty individual scorers, goals were scored from all positions. City were also probably awarded more penalties than any other senior non-league club, as Alex Sykes scored eleven with Mike Symons and Lee Smith two a piece. These included seven in a run of nine games and how many others were missed?

A very disappointing 3-5 F.A.Cup defeat at Chalfont St Peter immediately put paid to any extra funds being collected from a cup run. The F.A.Trophy was little better as Bromsgrove Rovers were beaten 4-2 away and then a poor performance at East Thurrock United saw them knocked out of the competition by the same score.

With no cup ties to think about, concentration was focused on the league and wonderful mid season consistency produced an unbeaten run of eighteen games from December to March which left them in second position. With serious thoughts of a play off place, maybe the pressure suddenly affected results and one point from three games shook the supporters' confidence.

However, City certainly showed their character at 'the death' and three victories in the last four fixtures saw them qualify to play Cambridge City at home in the Play-Off Semi-Final and a fine 3-1 victory took them to favourites Farnborough in the Final, where a Matt Rose first half goal took them into a division that they were not too keen to join. Hopefully it won't be as bad as they have imagined and it will certainly be important for the players and management to show the positive attitude of last season.

GLOUCESTER CITY

BEST LGE ATT.: 431 v Farnborough
LOWEST: 160 v Hemel Hempstead

No.	Date	Comp	H/A	Opponents	Att:	Result	Goalscorers	Pos
1	Aug 16	Southern P.	H	Stourbridge	245	W 4 - 0	Symons 8 60 Ballinger 12 Marshall 79	
2	19		A	Tiverton Town	446	D 2 - 2	Mustoe 34 (pen) 61 (pen)	
3	23		A	Evesham United	207	D 2 - 2	Ballinger 10 Symons 59	
4	25		H	Oxford City	302	D 2 - 2	Harris J 23 Symons 69	
5	30		A	Yate Town	403	W 2 - 0	Pitcher 25 Ballinger 70	5
6	Sept 2		H	Bashley	236	W 3 - 0	Ballinger 39 Symons 42 56	
7	6		A	Farnborough	700	L 1 - 2	**Sykes** 69 (pen)	5
8	**13**	**F.A.C. 1Q**	**A**	**Chalfont St Peter**	**145**	**L 3 - 5**	**Pitcher 62 Sysom 76 Sykes 83 (pen)**	
9	20		H	Bedford Town	270	L 0 - 1		7
10	Oct 4		H	Chippenham Town	380	W 2 - 0	Pitcher 25 Belle 71 (og)	6
11	7		A	Banbury United	235	W 5 - 1	Webb 8 **Sykes** 24 (pen) Pitcher 35 Smith 51 Hamblin 55	
12	**18**	**F.A.T.1Q**	**A**	**Bromsgrove Rovers**	**362**	**W 4 - 2**	**Sykes 10 (pen) 83 Morford 66 85**	
13	25		H	Halesowen Town	366	L 1 - 2	Smith 45 (pen)	6
14	**Nov 1**	**F.A.T. 2Q**	**A**	**East Thurrock United**	**134**	**L 2 - 4**	**Harris 8 Sykes 83**	
15	8		A	Merthyr Tydfil	328	L 1 - 2	**Sykes** 58 (pen)	9
16	11		H	Mangotsfield United	201	W 5 - 2	**SYKES** 3 1(pen) 24 65) Morford 39 Webb76	
17	15		H	Corby Town	291	L 1 - 3	**Sykes** 52	6
18	22		A	Rugby Town	193	W 3 - 1	Smith 28 **Sykes** 30 (pen) Pitcher 73	6
19	29		A	Clevedon Town	93	W 4 - 1	Marshall 15 Welch 40 Smith 70 (pen) Pitcher 77	
20	Dec 6		H	Brackley Town	225	L 0 - 1		6
21	20		A	Hitchin Town	288	D 1 - 1	Thomas 44	8
22	27		A	Oxford City	265	D 1 - 1	Smith 67	9
23	Jan 1		H	Swindon Supermarine	382	W 3 - 1	**Sykes** 37 40 Pitcher 56	
24	17		A	Bashley	300	D 1 - 1	Smith 9	9
25	20		H	Hemel Hempstead	160	W 2 - 1	**Sykes** 45 57 (pen)	
26	24		H	Tiverton Town	285	W 2 - 1	Pitcher 31 **Sykes** 52 (pen)	6
27	27		H	Banbury United	215	D 1 - 1	Pitcher 53	
28	31		A	Chippenham Town	468	D 2 - 2	Kite 47 (og) Keverew 90	5
29	Feb 14		A	Halesowen Town	434	W 2 - 1	**Sykes** 24 (pen) 39	4
30	21		H	Farnborough	431	D 0 - 0		6
31	28		A	Bedford Town	379	D 1 - 1	**Sykes** 61	
32	Mar 7		H	Merthyr Tydfil	315	D 1 - 1	Pitcher 43	
33	10		A	Mangotsfield Town	185	W 1 - 0	Morford 2	
34	14		A	Corby Town	265	W 2 - 1	Symons 52 **Sykes** 71	4
35	17		H	Evesham United	210	W 2 - 0	Smith 39 45	
36	21		H	Cambridge City	275	W 2 - 1	Richards 47 Morford 70	3
37	25		H	Rugby Town	265	W 3 - 1	**Sykes** 42 (pen) Morford 82 Smith 90	
38	28		A	Brackley Town	307	W 3 - 2	Symons 3 Perpetuni 24 (og) Smith 73	2
39	30		A	Cambrdge City	301	L 1 - 2	**Sykes** 73	
40	April 4		H	Clevedon Town	300	L 0 - 1		3
41	7		A	Stourbridge	236	D 1 - 1	Webb 55	
42	11		H	Yate Town	303	W 4 - 0	Symons 25 83 Harris 28 Grubb 78	3
43	13		A	Swindon Supermarine	301	W 1 - 0	Ballinger 49	
44	18		H	Hitchin Town	295	W 4 - 1	Symons 31 Smith 40 **Sykes** 53 58	3
45	25		A	Hemel Hempstead	684	L 1 - 2	Pitcher 9	3
46	**28**	**Play-Off SF**	**H**	**Cambridge City**	**745**	**W 3 - 1**	**Harris 21 Smith 33 Symons 90**	
47	**May 3**	**Play-Off F**	**A**	**Farnborough**	**1715**	**W 1 - 0**	**Rose 29**	

Average Home Att: **283 (302)** **Goals** **93 58**

Best Position: 2nd **Worst:** 9th

Goalscorers: Sykes 25, Smith 12, Symons 12, Pitcher 11, Morford 6, Ballinger 5, Harris J 4, Webb 3, Marshall 2, Mustoe 2, Grubb 1, Hamblin 1, Keverew 1, Richards 1, Rose 1, Sysom 1, Thomas 1, Welch 1. Own Goals 3.

PLAYING SQUAD

CURRENT SQUAD AS OF BEGINING OF 2009-10 SEASON

GOALKEEPERS	HT	WT	D.O.B	AGE	P.O.B	CAREER	APPS	GOA
Mike Green	6'01"	13 01	23/7/89	20	Bristol	Bristol R, Mangotsfield (L) 9/06, Clevedon T (L) 3/09, Gloucester (SL) 7/09		
Danny Holdcroft			22/5/78	31	Chester	Flexsys Cefn Druids, Buckley T, Caernarfon 3/02, Almondsbury, Hungerford 9/08, Larkhall, Gloucester 7/09		
DEFENDERS								
Tom Hamblin	6'01"					Mangotsfield (Yth), Bristol Manor Farm, Gloucester 5/06		
Alex Kite	6'00"	12 05	7/3/89	20	Kent	Bristol R, Oxford C (L) 9/08, Chippenham (3ML) 11/08, Weston-Super-Mare (L) 2/09, Gloucester (L) 7/09		
Lee Marshall						Bristol Manor Farm, Paulton 1/07, Gloucester 6/08		
Neil Mustoe	5'09"	12 10	5/11/76	32	Gloucester	Man Utd, Wigan Undisc 1/98 Cambridge U 7/98 Rel c/s 02, Hartlepool (Trial) 7/01, Cambridge C (L) 9/01, Gloucester 8/02, Stevenage 1/03, Yeovil 2/03 Rel c/s 03, Gloucester 8/03 Temp Man 1/06		
Matt Sysum						Gloucester, Cirencester (L) 12/08		
MIDFIELDERS								
Sam Ellis						Gloucester		
Adie Harris						Gloucester (Ass Man)		
Jack Harris			7/6/89	20	Bristol	Avonmouth, Hallen, Gloucester c/s 08		
Brett James						Gloucester		
Eddie Jones						Gloucester		
James Palmer	5'07"	11 04	30/3/88	21	Bristol	Bristol R, Weston-Super-Mare 1/08, Gloucester (L) 1/09, Gloucester 6/09		
Marc Richards						Cheltenham (Yth), Cinderford, Weston-Super-Mare, Swindon Supermarine 2/02, Cinderford 10/02, Cirencester 7/03, Gloucester 3/07, Chippenham 8/08, Gloucester 10/08		
Sam Robinson						Met Police, Leatherhead 10/08, Corinthian Casuals 11/08, Woking, Gloucester 8/09		
Matt Rose			3/5/76	33	Cheltenham	Cheltenham, St Marks, Moreton T, Cirencester, Gloucester 8/99, Newport C 3/00, Weston-Super-Mare 4 fig 10/03, Gloucester 6/07		
Lee Smith			8/9/83	25	Coney Hill	Gloucester, Cirencester 6/05, Weston-Super-Mare 6/07, Gloucester 9/07		
Alex Sykes			2/4/74	35	Newcastle under Lyme	Westfields, Mansfield 6/92 Rel c/s 94, Cheltenham, Endsleigh, Forest Green 3/96, Nuneaton 6/00, Forest Green (L) 3/01, Forest Green P/E 1/02, Bath C (L) 10/03, Bath C 9/04, Gloucester (L) 12/05, Gloucester 6/06		
Dan Wallington						Swindon, Gloucester c/s 09		
Tom Webb						Luton (Yth), Gloucester 7/00, Viney St Swithens (L), Highworth T (L)		
Dan Wixey						Gloucester		
FORWARDS								
Luke Ballinger			26/2/88	21	Bath	Bristol C (Scholar), Melksham, Mangotsfield 6/07, Gloucester 6/08		
Will Morford						Staunton & Corse, Tuffley Rovers, Slimbridge, Gloucester 10/07		
Jack Pitcher			13/6/83	26	Bristol	Winterbourne U, Mangotsfield 9/02, Bristol R (Trial) 10/02, Clevedon T 7/04, Gloucester 5/07		
Curtis Russell						Viney Hill, Gloucester 8/09		
Michael Symons			22/7/86	23	Gloucester	Ilfracombe, Barnstaple 7/04, Slimbridge (Dual) 12/04, Bideford 9/05, Cirencester 1/06, Clevedon T 3/07, Forest Green 8/08, Gloucester (L) 8/08, Gloucester (SL) 2/09, Gloucester 5/09		

GLOUCESTER CITY

Formed: 1889

Nickname: The Tigers.

Club Colours: Yellow and black shirts, black shorts, black socks.

Change Colours: Sky blue shirts, navy shorts, sky blue socks.

Club Sponsor: SsangYong

Previous League: Southern League

Ground address: The Corinium Stadium, Kingshill Lane, Circencester, Glos. GL7 1HS.
(Ground share with Cirencester Town)

Telephone: 01285 654 543 (Cirencester Town Ground number)

Mobile: 07813 931 781

Fax: 01452 530 409 (Secretary)

Email: swgfc@gmail.com

Website: www.gloucestercityafc.com

Simple Directions: Leave bypass (A417) at Burford Road roundabout. Aim for Stow, turn right at junction, first left into Kingshill Lane. Ground 500 yards on right.

Capacity: 4,500 **Seats**: 550 **Covered**: 1,250 **Floodlights**:Yes

Clubhouse: Yes.

Club Shop: Yes

Local Radio: Severn Sound and BBC Radio Gloucestershire.

Local Press: Gloucester Citizen and Western Daily Press.

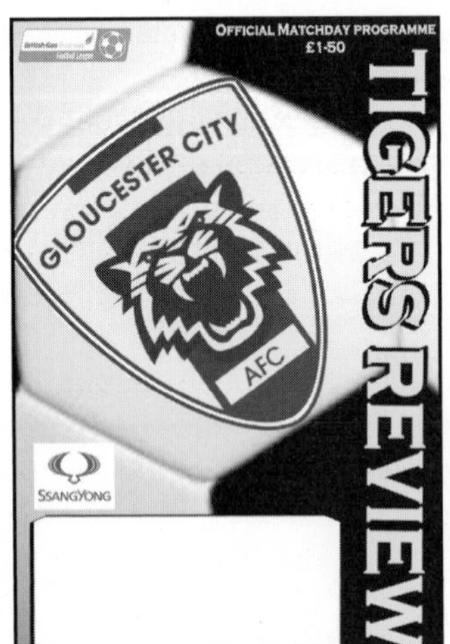

PROGRAMME EDITOR

Mike Dunstan.

Tel: (M) 07899 74951

Email: mikedunstan@blueyonder.co.uk

CLUB STATISTICS

RECORD
Attendance: 10,500 v Tottenham, Friendly 1952 (at Longlevens)
4,000 v Dagenham & Redbridge F.A.Trophy Semi-Final12.04.97 (at Meadow Park)
Victory: 10-1 v Sudbury Town (H) F.A.Cup 3rd Q. Rd 17.10 98
Defeat: 1-12 v Gillingham 09.11.46
Career Goalscorer: Reg Weaver - 250 (1930s)
Career Appearances: Stan Myers & Frank Tredgett (1950s)
Record Transfer Fee Paid:£ 25,000 to Worcester City for Steve Ferguson 1990-91
Received: £25,000 from AFC Bournemouth for Ian Hedges 1990.

SENIOR HONOURS
Southern League Cup Winners 1955-56
Southern League Midland Division 1988-89
Gloucestershire Senior Cup (x19)

PREVIOUS
Name: Gloucester Y.M.C.A.
Leagues: Bristol & District (now Western) 1893-96.
Gloucester & District 1897-1907
North Gloucestershire 1907-10.
Gloucestershire North Senior 1920-34
Birmingham Combination 1935-39
Southern League 1939-2009.
Grounds: Longlevens 1935-65. Horton Road 1965-86.
Meadow Park 1986-2007.

HARROGATE TOWN

CLUB PERSONNEL

Chairman: Bill Fotherby.

Vice-Chairman: Andrew Thurkill.

Company Secretary: Brian Russell.

Chief Executive: Bernard Fotherby.

Additional Directors: Howard Matthews, George Dunnington.

Secretary: Alan Williams.

Correspondence C/o Club

Tel: (H) 01423 524780

(M) 07879 281 207

(B) 01423 883 671

Email: harrogatetown@unicombox.co.uk

Commercial Manager & Press Officer: As secretary.

Manager: Simon Weaver.

Club therapist: Matt Unwin.

It was a sad end to four seasons of exciting progress at Harrogate's Town club where they had always been considered amongst the favourites for at least the play offs. Neil Aspin had built a strong squad and once again they started last season in fine form featuring in the top three until mid November.

Replays against Workington and then Eastwood Town didn't take the club further than the 3rd Qualifying Round in The F.A.Cup and neither did the F.A.Trophy bring any financial help as they lost in The First Round Proper to Durham City having beaten Gateshead 2-0 in the North East.

Jamie Smith scored a glorious four goals in an excellent defeat of Fleetwood Town on 25th November, but this seemed to signal a dip in their fortunes as goals seemed to dry up and the next seven league games brought just one win and three goals. It was announced early in the new year that there were financial troubles and all the squad were made available on the transfer list.

Not surprisingly the drive towards the play-offs was all over, and the poor manager lost his enthusiasm and faith in the club and the supporters were shattered as they watched their club battling, with little consistency, to finish in the top ten.

HARROGATE TOWN

BEST LGE ATT.: 646 v Farsley Celtic
LOWEST: 220 v Solihull Moors

No.	Date	Comp	H/A	Opponents	Att:	Result	Goalscorers	Pos
1	Aug 9	BSN	H	Vauxhall Motors	308	W 2 - 0	Dunning 33 (pen) 75	
2	12		A	Workington	446	D 0 - 0		
3	16		A	Southport	818	L 0 - 1		13
4	23		H	Hitchin Town	351	W 2 - 0	Marshall 51 Holland 65	
5	25		A	Gateshead	509	W 3 - 1	Marshall 36 Whittle 79 **Smith** 90	
6	30		H	Hyde United	362	W 2 - 1	**Smith** 69 Marshall 70	2
7	Sept 2		H	AFC Telford United	443	W 2 - 0	Holland 37 Dunning 88	
8	6		A	Tamworth	533	L 1 - 3	Ingram 60	2
9	**9**	**SS N1**	**H**	**Fleetwood Town**	**174**	**D 1 - 1***	**Holland 42 (Lost 4-5 on pens)**	
10	13		A	Stalybridge Celtic	515	W 3 - 1	Young 10 Holland 27 Dean 31	2
11	20		H	King's Lynn	548	W 4 - 0	Dean 13 Dunning 22 Young 81 90	
12	**27**	**F.A.C. 2Q**	**A**	**Workington**	**413**	**D 0 - 0**		
13	**30**	**F.A.C. 2Q r**	**H**	**Workington**	**305**	**D 0 - 0**	**Workington won 5-4 after penalties**	
14	Oct 4		A	Stafford Rangers	576	D 0 - 0		3
15	**11**	**F.A.C. 3Q**	**A**	**Eastwood Town**	**401**	**D 2 - 2**	**Dunning 45 Dean 57 (pen)**	
16	**14**	**F.A.C. 3Q r**	**H**	**Eastwood Town**	**285**	**L 0 - 2**		
17	18		H	Alfreton Town	423	D 2 - 2	Fortune-West 42 (og) Dunning 76 (pen)	3
18	25		A	Solihull Borough	150	D 1 - 1	Peat 30	3
19	Nov 1		A	Burscough	350	W 2 - 0	Lowe 81 Marshall 85	3
20	11		H	Blyth Spartans	328	W 3 - 1	Dunning 6 Gray 48 **Smith** 70	
21	15		A	Hinckley United	521	L 0 - 2		3
22	**22**	**F.A.T 3Q**	**A**	**Gateshead**	**217**	**W 2 - 0**	**Marshall 9 51**	**3**
23	25		H	Fleetwood Town	261	W 5 - 2	**SMITH** 4 (29 31 68 75) Dean 67	2
24	29		H	Gainsborough Trinity	458	L 0 - 3		3
25	Dec 6		A	Droylsden	324	L 1 - 2	Dean 14	4
26	**13**	**F.A.T. 1R**	**A**	**Durham City**	**232**	**L 0 - 2**		
27	20		A	Vauxhall Motors	156	L 0 - 1		4
28	26		H	Farsley Celtic	646	W 1 - 0	Marshall 34	4
29	Jan 1		A	Farsley Celtic	647	L 0 - 1		
30	17		A	Alfreton Town	383	L 1 - 4	Marshall 9	5
31	24		H	Stafford Rangers	338	D 3 - 3	Holland 27 Dean 40 Peat 70	6
32	27		A	Byth Spartans	825	W 4 - 3	Peat 26 Leeson 70 (og) Hardy 79 Marshall 87	
33	31		H	Stalybridge Celtic	467	L 0 - 1		6
34	Feb 17		H	Burscough	272	W 2 - 0	Marshall 6 **Smith** 57	6
35	24		A	King's Lynn	656	W 3 - 2	Dean 74 Peat 75 Marshall 85	
36	28		H	Hinckley United	334	D 2 - 2	Dean 50 Gray 73	6
37	Mar 7		H	Redditch United	342	D 1 - 1	Dean 76	
38	10		H	Southport	286	L 0 - 3		
39	21		A	Fleetwood Town	1051	L 0 - 1		8
40	24		H	Workington	258	L 0 - 1		
41	28		A	Hyde United	301	W 3 - 2	Marshall 6 65 Dunning 9 (pen)	7
42	31		H	Solihull Moors	220	W 4 - 0	**SMITH** 3 (31 80 85) Dunning 49	8
43	April 4		H	Tamworth	431	D 2 - 2	**Smith** 42 Dean 69	8
44	7		A	AFC Telford United	1482	L 1 - 3	Dean 30	
45	11		A	Hucknall Town	222	D 1 - 1	**Smith** 19	8
46	13		H	Gateshead	447	W 1 - 0	Gray 39	
47	18		H	Droylsden	362	D 1 - 1	Gray 5	8
48	21		A	Redditch United	244	L 1 - 2	Broadbent 31	
49	25		A	Gainsborough Trinity	332	L 2 - 3	**Smith** 40 Gray 68	9

Average Home Att: 375 (542) **Goals** 71 64

Best Position: 2nd **Worst:** 13th

Goalscorers: Smith 14, Marshall 13, Dean 11, Dunning 9, Gray 5, Holland 5, Peat 4, Young 3, Broadbent 1, Hardy 1, Ingram 1, Lowe 1, Whittle 1. Own Goals 2.

PROVETT	HARDY	LOWE	TOULSON	WHITTLE	PEAT	YOUNG	DUNNING	SMITH	HOLLAND	RODDY	MARSHALL	GRAY	REAY	ORMSBY	HEDGE	INGRAM	RYAN	KILLOCK	DEAN	IBRAHIM	DELANEY	MALCHER	CARTMAN	ROTHERY	HIRST	MASON	CHARNLEY	BROADBENT	SYERS	WIACEK	
X	X	X	X	X	X	X	X	X	X	X	S	S	S	U	U																1
X	X	X	X	X	X	X	X	X	X	X			S	U	U																2
X	X	X	X	X	X	X	X	X	S	X	S		X	S	U																3
X		X	X	X	X	X	X	X	X	X	S	U	S	S	U	X															4
X		X	X	X	X	X	X	S	X	X	X	U	U	U	U	X															5
X		X	X	X	X	X	X	S	X	X	X	U	S	S		X															6
X		X	X			X	X		X	X	X	U	U	U	U	X	X	X													7
X		X	X			X	X		X	X	X	S	S	U	U	X	X	X													8
X		X	X		U	X	X		X	X	X	X	S	S	U	X		X													9
X		X	X		X	X	X		X	X	S	U	U	U	U	X		X	X												10
X		U	X		X	X	X	X	X	X	S	U	S		U	X		X	X												11
X		U	X	X	X	X	X	X	X	X	U	S			U	X			X												12
X		X	X	X	X	X	X	S	X	X	S	S			U	X			X												13
X	S		X	X	X	X	X	U	X	X	S	S			U	X		X	X												14
X	X	U	X	X	X	X	X	S	X	X	U	U			U	X			X												15
X	X	S	X	X	X	X	X	S		X	X	S			U	X			X												16
X	X	S	X	X	X	X	X	S		X	X	U		U	U	X			X												17
X	U	X	X	X	X	X	X	S		X	X	S		U	U	X			X												18
X	X	X	X	U	X		X	X		X	X	X		S	U	X				U											19
X	X	X	X	S	X		X	X		X	X	X		S	U	X				S											20
X	X	X	X	U	X		X	X		X	X	X		S	U	X															21
X	U	X	X	X	X		X	X		X	X	S		U	U	X			X	U											22
X	X	X	X	X	X		X	X			X	S			U	X			X	S	U										23
X	X	X	X	X			X	X		X	X				U	X			X	U	U										24
X	X	X	X	X	X	S	X	X			X				U	X			X	U	U										25
X	X	X	X		X	X	X	X		X	X			U	U	X				U		S									26
X	X	X	X	X	X			X		X	X			U	U	X						X	S								27
X	X	X	X	X	X		X	X		X	X			S	U							X	U								28
X	X		X	X	X		X	X	S	X	X			U	U							X	S	X							29
X		X	X	X	X	X	X	X	X		X	S		S					X			S									30
X	X	X	X	X	X	X	X	S	X		X	U		U					X			U									31
X	X		X	X	X	X	X	X	X		X	S							X												32
X	X	X		X	X	X		X	X		X	X		U					X		U				U						33
	X	S	X	X	X	X	X	X			X	X		U	X				X						U						34
	X	S	X	X	X	X	X	X			X	X		U	X				X												35
	X	X	X	X	X	X	X	S			X	X		U	X				X		U				U						36
	X	X	X	X		X	X	X			X	X		U	X				X						S	S	U				37
	X	X	X	X		S	X	X			X	X		U	X										X	X	S				38
	X	X	X	X		X	X	X			X			S	X	X									S	X	U				39
		X	X	U		X	X	X			X			U	X	X									X	S	X	X			40
		X	X			X	X	X			X			S	X	X									X	U	X	X			41
	X	X	X			X	X	X			X	X		S	X	X									U	S		X			42
	X	X	X			X	X	X			X	X		U	X	X			S						U		U	X			43
	X	X	X			X	X	X			X	X		U	X	X			X						U		U	S	U		44
	X	X	X			X	X	X			X	X		U	X	X			X						U		U	S	S		45
	X	X	X			X	X	X			X	X		U	X	X			X						U		S	U		U	46
	X		X			X	X	U			X	X		U	X	X			X						U		X	X		U	47
	X		X			U	X	U			X	X				X			X						U		X	X	X	X	48
	X	X	X			S	X	X			X	X		U	X	X			X								U	S	X	U	49

Total League Appearances

PROVETT	HARDY	LOWE	TOULSON	WHITTLE	PEAT	YOUNG	DUNNING	SMITH	HOLLAND	RODDY	MARSHALL	GRAY	REAY	ORMSBY	HEDGE	INGRAM	RYAN	KILLOCK	DEAN	IBRAHIM	DELANEY	MALCHER	CARTMAN	ROTHERY	HIRST	MASON	CHARNLEY	BROADBENT	SYERS	WIACEK	
26	30	33	41	25	26	30	40	30	14	20	35	17	1	0	15	28	2	5	22	0	0	3	0	1	3	2	4	6	2	1	X
0	1	3	0	1	0	3	0	6	2	0	6	7	6	11	0	0	0	0	1	2	0	1	2	0	2	3	2	3	1	0	S
0	1	1	0	3	0	1	0	3	0	0	0	8	3	24	21	0	0	0	0	3	5	1	1	0	10	1	6	1	1	3	U

Total Cup Appearances

PROVETT	HARDY	LOWE	TOULSON	WHITTLE	PEAT	YOUNG	DUNNING	SMITH	HOLLAND	RODDY	MARSHALL	GRAY	REAY	ORMSBY	HEDGE	INGRAM	RYAN	KILLOCK	DEAN	IBRAHIM	DELANEY	MALCHER	CARTMAN	ROTHERY	HIRST	MASON	CHARNLEY	BROADBENT	SYERS	WIACEK	
7	3	4	7	5	6	6	7	3	4	7	4	1	0	0	0	7	0	1	5	0	0	0	0	0	0	0	0	0	0	0	X
0	0	1	0	0	0	0	0	3	0	0	1	4	1	1	0	0	0	0	0	0	0	1	0	0	0	0	0	0	0	0	S
0	1	2	0	0	1	0	0	0	0	0	2	1	0	2	7	0	0	0	0	2	0	0	0	0	0	0	0	0	0	0	U

HARROGATE TOWN

CURRENT SQUAD AS OF BEGINING OF 2009-10 SEASON

GOALKEEPERS	HT	WT	D.O.B	AGE	P.O.B	CAREER	APPS	GOA
Stephen Hernandez			17/8/89	20	Doncaster	Sheff Wed (Scholar), Sheff Utd Rel 7/09, Worksop (L) 9/07, Worksop (SL) 1/08, Harrogate T 8/09		
John Lamb						Halifax, Guiseley, Leigh RMI c/s 05, Eccleshill Utd, Bradford PA 3/08, Ossett T, Harrogate T 6/09		
DEFENDERS								
Matt Bloomer	6'00"	13 00	3/11/78	30	Grimsby	Grimsby Rel c/s 01, Hull C (Trial) 4/01, Hull C 7/01, Lincoln C (L) 3/02, Telford (3ML) 8/02, Lincoln C 12/02 Rel 5/06, Grimsby (L) 1/06, Cambridge U (2ML) 3/06, Cambridge U 7/06 Rel 1/07, Grimsby 1/07 Rel c/s 07, Boston U 7/07, Harrogate T 6/09		
Simon Harrison	5'09"	10 08	24/12/88	20	Nether Edge	Rotherham, Matlock 8/08, Ilkeston 1/09, Harrogate T 6/09		
Kevin Sharp	5'09"	11 11	19/9/74	34	Ontario, Can	Auxerre (Fr), Leeds £60,000 10/92, Wigan £100,000 11/95 Rel 11/01, Wrexham NC 11/01, Huddersfield 8/02, Scunthorpe 7/03 Rel c/s 05, Shrewsbury 7/05 Rel 4/06, Guiseley 10/06, Hamilton Ac 11/06 Rel 1/07, Northwich (Pl/Coach) 6/07, Guiseley 10/07, Wigan (Coach), Harrogate T (Pl/Ass Man) 6/09		
Simon Sturdy					Yorkshire	Glasshoughton, Rowntrees, Tadcaster, Pickering T c/s 99, Harrogate T 7/02 Rel c/s 05, Droylsden 7/05, Guiseley 7/06, Eastwood 6/08, Harrogate T 6/09		
Simon Weaver	6'01"	10 08	20/12/77	31	Doncaster	Sheff Wed Rel c/s 98, Doncaster (L) 2/97, Ilkeston, Grimsby (Trial) c/s 99, Nuneaton 2/00, Lincoln C 8/02, Macclesfield (2ML) 10/04, Kidderminster 12/04 Rel c/s 05, Scarborough 6/05 Rel 5/06, York C 8/06 Rel 8/06, Tamworth 8/06 Rel c/s 07, Salisbury (Trial) c/s 07, Boston U 12/07 Rel 5/08, Kings Lynn 5/08 Rel 1/09, Redditch 1/09, Ilkeston 2/09, Harrogate T (Pl/Man) 5/09		
Michael Wood			13/1/90	19		Boston U, Harrogate T 8/09		
MIDFIELDERS								
Warren Burrell	5'10"	10 06	3/6/90	19	Sheffield	Mansfield Rel 7/09, Harrogate T 8/09		
Mario Campagna						Gretna (Yth) Rel 3/08, Harrogate Railway, Harrogate CSC., Knaresborough, Workington (Trial) 7/09, Harrogate T 8/09		
Luke Durham	5'10"	11 00	6/9/90	18		Huddersfield (Scholar) Rel c/s 09, Harrogate T 7/09		
Brian Dutton	5'11"	12 00	12/4/85	24	Malton	Pickering T, Scarborough (Trial), Swindon (Trial), Cambridge U 11/03 Rel c/s 04, Pickering T 6/04, Weymouth 3/05, Eastleigh 5/06 Rel 10/06, Weymouth 1/07 Rel c/s 07, York C (Trial) c/s 07, Mangotsfield (Trial), Dorchester 9/07 Rel 10/07, Pickering T 3/08,		
Chris Emms			23/7/84	25		Middlesbrough (Scholar), Peterlee, Gateshead 11/04, Peterlee, Billingham T 6/05, Durham, Newcastle Blue Star, ECU Joondaloop (Aust) 4/09, Harrogate T 7/09		
Dean Gent						Carlton, Harrogate T 6/09		
Dave McTiernan			13/7/84	25		Peterlee Newtown, Whitby 7/03, Newcastle Blue Star 8/07, Harrogate T 6/09		
Leon Scott						Peterlee, Dunston Fed, Newcastle Blue Star 8/07, Whitby 9/08, Harrogate 6/09		
Curtis Woodhouse	5'08"	11 00	17/4/80	29	Driffield	Sheff Utd, Birmingham £1 million 2/01, Rotherham (3ML) 2/03, Peterborough 10/03, Hull C £25,000 5/05, Grimsby 1/06 Retired c/s 06, Pro Boxer, Rushden & D 11/06 Rel 1/07, Rushden & D 3/07, Mansfield 1/09, Harrogate T 6/09		
FORWARDS								
Daniel Broadbent	5'10"	12 00	2/3/90	19	Leeds	Huddersfield Rel 5/09, Rushden & D (L) 1/09, Gateshead (L) 2/09, Harrogate T (SL) 3/09, Harrogate T 8/09	9	0
Jon Maloney	6'00"	11 12	3/3/85	24	Leeds	Doncaster Rel c/s 05, York (3ML) 12/04, University of Montevallo (USA) c/s 05, Harrogate T 7/09		
Ollie Ryan	5'09"	11 00	26/9/85	23	Boston	Lincoln C Rel 3/08, Spalding (L) 9/04, Ilkeston (L) 11/05, Hucknall 3/08 Rel 5/08, Bourne T (Dual) 4/09, Boston U 7/08, Harrogate T 6/09		
Zeph Thomas						Rotherham (Scholar), Ilkeston 12/08, AFC Emley 3/09, Harrogate 8/09		

LOANEES	HT	WT	DOB	AGE	POB	From - To	APPS	GOA
(F)Sean Reay	6'01"	12 00	20/5/89	20	Jarrow	Darlington (2ML) 8/08 - Blyth Spartans 10/08	7	0
(D)Tim Ryan	6'00"	11 07	10/12/74	34	Stockport	Darlington 8/08 - Rel c/s 09, Chester 7/09	2	0
(D)Shane Killock	6'00"	12 04	12/3/89	20	Huddersfield	Huddersfield 8/08 - Oxford U (L) 1/09	5	0
(M)Nathan Cartman	5'06"	11 00	4/11/89	19		Leeds 12/08 - Curzon Ashton (L) 2/09, Rel 5/09	2	0
(D)Luke Charnley	6'00"	12 00	19/12/90	18		Bury 3/09 - Rel c/s 09	6	0
(F)Chris Mason	5'11"	11 03	28/11/90	18	Blackburn	Bury 3/09 - Rel c/s 09	5	0

DEPARTURES	HT	WT	DOB	AGE	POB	From - To	APPS	GOA
(G)Jim Provett	6'00"	13 04	22/12/82	26	Stockton	Bury 7/08 - Gateshead 2/09	26	0
(F)Danny Holland			18/2/83	26	Mansfield	Hucknall (L) 11/04 Perm 12/04 - Eastwood T Undisc 2/09	16	4
(M)Luke Malcher	5'08"		14/11/88	20	Halifax	Huddersfield 12/08 - Rel 2/09, Farsley Celtic 2/09	4	0
(D)Nathan Peat	5'09"	10 09	19/9/82	26	Hull	York 6/07 - Gainsborough 3/09	26	4
(M)Michael Roddy			22/9/88	20	Stockton	Stalybridge 7/08 - Guiseley 1/09, Witton 3/09	20	0
(M)Gavin Rothery			22/9/87	21	Morley	York C 12/08 - Carlisle U 3/09	1	0
(M)Ryan Toulson			18/11/85	23		Halifax 6/08 - Gainsborough 5/09	41	0
(M)Darren Dunning	5'06"	11 12	8/1/81	28	Scarborough	York 7/06 - Gainsborough 5/09	40	8
(M)Matty Young	5'08"	11 03	25/10/85	23	Leeds	Huddersfield 7/08 - Rel c/s 09, Farsley Celtic c/s 09	33	3
(D)Dave Syers						Ossett A 3/09 - Farsley Celtic 6/09	3	0
(G)Jonathan Hedge	6'02"	13 02	19/7/88	21	Rotherham	Halifax - FC Halifax 7/09	15	0
(F)James Dean	5'11"	11 07	15/5/85	24	Blackburn	Hyde U 9/08 - FC Halifax 7/09	23	10
(D)Denny Ingram	5'11"	11 13	27/6/76	33	Sunderland	Scarborough 6/07 - Whitby T 7/09	28	1
(G)Lukasz Wiacek						Yth -	1	0
(D)Jake Delaney						Yth -	0	0
(D)Aaron Hardy	5'08"	11 04	26/5/86	23	Pontefract	Huddersfield 7/08 - FC Halifax c/s 09	31	1
(D)Tom Hirst					Skipton	York C 1/09 -	5	0
(D)Danny Lowe	5'07"	10 05	12/1/84	25	Barnsley	Harrogate RA 3/08 - Rel c/s 09, FC Halifax c/s 09	36	1
(D)Liam Ormsby						Barnsley (Scholar) 7/08 - Ossett T (L) 9/08	11	0
(D)Justin Whittle	6'01"	12 12	18/3/71	38	Derby	Grimsby 6/08 - North Ferriby (L) 3/09 Perm 3/09	26	1
(M)Nick Gray	6'01"	10 06	17/10/85	23	Harrogate	Halifax 6/08 - FC Halifax c/s 09	24	5
(F)Jadey Ibrahim						Yth -	2	0
(F)Richard Marshall						Harrogate RA 7/08 - Rel c/s 09, FC Halifax c/s 09	41	10
(F)Jamie Smith						Sheffield FC 6/08 - Rel c/s 09	36	12

HARROGATE TOWN

Formed: 1919

Nickname: Town.

Club Colours: Yellow and black shirts, black shorts, black socks.

Change Colours: Royal blue and gold shirts, royal blue shorts, royal blue socks.

Club Sponsor: CNG (Contract Natural Gas).

Previous League: Northern Premier League

Ground address: The CNG Stadium, Wetherby Road, Harrogate, HG2 7SA.

Telephone: 01423 883 671.

Fax: 01423 883 675

Mobile: 07879 281 207

Email: harrogatetown@unicombox.co.uk

Website: www.harrogatetown.com

Simple Directions: From A1 to towards Wetherby take A661 to Harrogate. On entering town go straight over roundabout and lights (Woodlands Pub). Gound is 500 yards on right.

Capacity: 3,291 **Seats**: 502 **Covered**:1,300 **Floodlights**: Yes

Clubhouse: Open every matchday (Tel No: 01423 883 671)

Club Shop: Yes.

Local Press: Yorkshire Post Group and Harrogate Advertiser Series

Local Radio: BBC Radio Yorkshire and Stray FM.

PROGRAMME EDITOR

Peter Arnett

Tel: (M) 07894 401 110

Email: harrogatetownprog@btinternet.com

CLUB STATISTICS

RECORD

Attendance: 4,280 v Railway Athletic , Whitworth Cup Final 1950
Victory: 13-0 v Micklefield.
Defeat: 1-10 v Methley United 1956
Career Goalscorer: Jimmy Hague 135 (1956-7 to 1957-8, 1961-2 to 193-74 & 1973-74 to 1975-76)
Career Appearances: Paul Williamson 428 (1980-81 1982-83 to 1984-85 and 1986-87 to 1992-93)
Record Transfer Fee Paid: for Mark Haran from Worksop T. and Lee Morris from Frickley A .2004-05
Received: from York City for Dave Merris 2003-2004

SENIOR HONOURS

Northern Premier League Division 1 Champions 2001-02.
West Riding County Cup 1962-63, 72-73, 85-86.
West Riding Challenge Cup (2)

PREVIOUS

Leagues: West Riding 1919-20. Yorkshire 1920-21, 22-31, 57-82.
Midland 1921-22. Northern 1931- 32.
Harrogate & Dist. 1935-37, 40-46. W. Riding Co. Amateur 1937-40.
West Yorkshire 1946-57. Northern Counties East 1982-87.
Northern Premier League 1987-2004.

HINCKLEY UNITED

HINCKLEY UNITED 2009/10

Back row (left to right): Leigh Platnauer, Adam Webster, Lee Collins, Stuart Giddings, Jack Roberts.
Middle row (left to right): Andy Keeling (physio), Nobby (kitman), Andy Gooding, Daniel Barker, Paul Lister, Chris Mackenzie, Chukki Eribenne, Matt West, James Mace, Chima Dozie, Nicky Platnauer (assistant manager), Steve Cook (youth team manager.)
Front row (left to right): Neil Cartwright, Connor Franklin, Alex Taylor, Stuart Storer (player/coach), Dean Thomas (manager), Andy Hall, Richard Lavery, Louis Hamilton.

CLUB PERSONNEL

Chairman: Kevin Downes.

Vice-Chairman: Robert Mayne.

Company Secretary: Ray Baggott.

Additional Directors: A Dyer, Mrs E Dyer, G Farmer, S Millidge, D Newman, M Sutton, M Tansey, P Taylor, D Radburn.

Secretary: Ray Baggott
Correspondence C/o Club
Tel: H: 01455 447 277
(M) 07802 355 249
(B) 01455 840 088
Email: raybaggott@yahoo.co.uk

Commercial Manager: Dave Riche.
(M) 07809 113 088
(B) 01455 840 088
Email: daveriche@greenekingstadium.co.uk

Press Officer: Andy Gibbs.
Tel: (M) 07977 516 703
Email: andy.gibbs57@ntlworld.com

Manager: Dean Thomas.

Club therapist: Julie Hayton.

Having enjoyed some consistent challenges at the top of the table and having settled into their smart new ground, the 2007-08 season had been a disappointment so the last campaign, although eventually achieving very little, was at least an improvement, as for most of the season United had been challenging in the top half of the table.

Perhaps the fact that twenty one different players had scored for United suggested that long serving manager Dean Thomas couldn't find a settled attack.The club's best scoring spell coincided with their F.A.Cup run to the Fourth Qualifying Round in which Solihull Moors and Hitchin Town were beaten before United lost to Curzon Ashton on penalties after a replay. A defeat in their first F.A.Trophy tie against Burscough was especially disappointing as it was in front of their home fans.

A poor spell of results in the new year, when four matches brought no points and a goal ratio of 0-11, saw United drift away from the play off zone and took them down to eleventh place, nine points below the vital fifth placed club. Two very heavy away defeats against Stalybridge Celtic (1-7) and Gateshead (0-5), were also upsetting to the fans, for whom the end of season couldn't come quick enough.

However, for the last home game an excellent crowd of 607, probably influenced by Alfreton Town's play off challenge, turned up to watch a gritty 1-1 draw and the Hinckley management will know that if they can get a winning squad in place the potential support is there for them. An attendance of 1336 came for the visit of Tamworth, 850 for AFC Telford United and 639 for Southport, so Marstons Stadium hosting a championship chasing Hinckley United could be an exciting place to be watching football!

HINCKLEY UNITED

BEST LGE ATT.: **1,366** v Tamworth
LOWEST: **343** v Hyde United

No.	Date	Comp	H/A	Opponents	Att:	Result	Goalscorers	Pos
1	Aug 9	BSN	H	Workington	541	W 1 - 0	McIlwain 24	
2	12		A	AFC Telford United	1792	L 2 - 4	Hall 43 Taylor 76	
3	16		A	Farsley Celtic	287	W 3 - 2	Lavery 40 Hall 58 Taylor 64	6
4	23		H	Solihull Moors	484	D 0 - 0		8
5	25		A	King's Lynn	1326	D 1 - 1	Murphy 35	
6	30		H	Gateshead	479	W 2 - 0	Gooding 15 Platnauer 29	5
7	Sept 1		H	Southport	639	D 1 - 1	Hall 13	
8	6		A	Hyde United	285	D 0 - 0		6
9	**9**	**SS N1**	**A**	**Hucknall Town**	**192**	**W 3 - 1**	**Webster 7 Platnauer 32 Kelly 87**	
10	13		A	Vauxhall Motors	139	W 4 - 0	Bonner 18 Hall 56 **Webster** 67 Murphy 80	4
11	20		H	Stalybridge Celtic	559	L 0 - 1		5
12	**27**	**F.A.C. 2Q**	**H**	**Solihull Moors**	**510**	**W 4 - 0**	**Platnauer 25 Bonner 33 Webster 50 52**	
13	Oct 4		H	Burscough	470	L 0 - 1		8
14	**6**	**SS N2**	**H**	**Tamworth**	**267**	**W 2 - 1**	**Platnauer 2 (40, 47)**	
15	**11**	**F.A.C. 3Q**	**A**	**Hitchin Town**	**503**	**W 2 - 1**	**Poole 54 90**	
16	18		A	Hucknall Town	303	W 2 - 1	Gooding 1 **Webster** 14	7
17	20		H	Redditch United	459	W 4 - 2	**Webster** 45 (pen) Hall 51 90 Kelly 88	
18	**25**	**F.A.C. 4Q**	**H**	**Curzon Ashton**	**555**	**D 1 - 1**	**Webster 88**	
19	**27**	**F.A.C. 4Q r**	**A**	**Curzon Ashton**	**519**	**D 1 - 1***	**Barker 24 (Lost 2-3 on pen)**	
20	Nov 1		A	Fleetwood Town	894	L 0 - 1		6
21	**3**	**SS 3**	**H**	**Histon**	**202**	**W 2 - 1**	**Webster 25 Hall 81**	
22	8		A	Redditch United	286	W 2 - 0	Hall 50 Nwadake 64	6
23	15		H	Harrogate Town	521	W 2 - 0	**Webster** 24 (pen) Moses-Garvey 55	6
24	**22**	**F.A.T. 3Q**	**H**	**Burscough**	**251**	**L 1 - 2**	**Webster 19 (pen)**	
25	**Dec 2**	**SS N4**	**H**	**Kettering Town**	**270**	**L 2 - 3***	**Lavery 30, Webster 84**	
26	6		H	Hucknall Town	417	W 4 - 0	Bailey 42 Taylor 62 86 Hall 80	5
27	26		H	Tamworth	1366	L 1 - 3	Hall 40	7
28	Jan 13		A	Gainsborough Trinity	269	L 1 - 3		
29	17		H	Vauxhall Motors	433	L 2 - 3	Gooding 28 Cartwright 82	10
30	20		A	Blyth Spartans	466	L 0 - 1		
31	24		A	Burscough	331	D 1 - 1	Gooding 63	9
32	31		H	Blyth Spartans	420	W 2 - 1	Lavery 18 Roma 35	9
33	Feb 14		H	Gainsborough Trinity	414	L 0 - 2		10
34	17		A	Southport	717	D 0 - 0		
35	23		H	Stafford Rangers	428	W 4 - 0	**Webster** 15 (pen) Hall 21 Lloyd 72 80	
36	28		A	Harrogate Town	334	D 2 - 2	**Webster** 66 Gooding 67	9
37	Mar 3		A	Stalybridge Celtic	332	L 1 - 7	**Webster** 75	
38	7		H	Fleetwood Town	427	W 2 - 1	Hall 45 52	
39	9		H	Droylsden	351	W 1 - 0	Roma 31	8
40	14		A	Alfreton Town	444	D 1 - 1	Pollard 74	8
41	16		H	Farsley Celtic	524	L 1 - 2	Roma 18	
42	21		A	Workington	331	W 3 - 1	**Webster** 12 (pen) Dozie 26 76	7
43	23		H	AFC Telford United	850	L 0 - 2		
44	26		A	Droylsden	450	L 0 - 3		
45	28		A	Gateshead	601	L 0 - 5		9
46	April 4		H	Hyde United	343	L 0 - 1		11
47	11		A	Solihull Moors	200	W 3 - 1	Lavery 48 64 **Webster** 59	10
48	13		H	King's Lynn	397	W 1 - 0	**Webster** 23	
49	18		H	Alfreton Town	607	D 1 - 1	McIlwain 90	10
50	21		A	Tamworth	1410	L 0 - 1		
51	25		A	Stafford Rangers	511	L 1 - 3	Taylor 12	10

Average Home Att: 530 (603) **Goals** 74 69

Best Position: 5th **Worst:** 11th

Goalscorers: Webster 17, Hall 13, Gooding 5, Lavery 5, Platnauer 5, Taylor 5, Roma 3, Bonner 2, Dozie 2, Kelly 2, Lloyd 2, Murphy 2, Poole 2, McIlwain 2, Bailey 1, Barker 1, Cartwright 1, Moses-Garvey 1, Murphy 1, Nwadake 1, Pollard 1.

MCKENZIE	ROMA	FRANKLIN	LAVERY	MCILWAIN	BIRCH	HALL	GOODING	MURPHY	MCPHEE	CHILTON	A TAYLOR	LLOYD	BONNER	PLATNAUER	BUTCHER	STEWART	WEBSTER	KELLY	SMITH	STORER	GIDDINGS	D TAYLOR	BANCROFT	DOZIE	GUNDELACH	SINGH	HINDS	CARTWRIGHT	MOSES-GARVEY	NWADIKE	POLLARD	BAILEY	BRADSHAW	SUTTON	HAMILTON	WARRINGTON	
X	X	X	X	X	X	X	X	X	X	X	S	S	U	U																							**1**
X	X	X	X	X	X	X	X	X	X	X	S	S	S	U	U																						**2**
X		X	X	X	X	X	X	X		S	X	X	X	S	U	U																					**3**
X		X	X		X	X	X	X	S	X	X	S	X	X	U																						**4**
X		X	X		X	X	X	X	U	U	X	X	X	X	U		S																				**5**
X		X	X	S	X	X	X	X		U	X	X	X	X	U		S	S																			**6**
X	U	X	X	X	U	X	X	X		U		X	X	X	U		X	S																			**7**
X	U	X	X	X	U	X	X	X				X	X	X	U		X	S																			**8**
X	**S**	**X**	**X**	**X**		**X**		**U**			**U**	**X**	**X**	**X**	**X**		**X**	**X**	**S**																		**9**
X	X	X	X			X	X	S			S	X	X	X			X	X		S																	**10**
X	X	X	X		U	X	X	S			S	X	X	X			X	X		U	U																**11**
X	**X**	**X**			**S**	**X**	**X**	**S**			**X**	**X**	**X**	**X**			**X**	**S**		**U**	**X**																**12**
X	X	X			S	X	X	U			X	X	X	X			X	S				X															**13**
X	**X**	**X**				**X**	**X**				**U**	**X**	**X**	**X**			**X**	**X**	**U**			**X**	**S**	**S**	**U**												**14**
X	**X**	**X**			**U**	**X**	**X**	**U**			**S**	**X**	**X**	**X**			**X**	**X**		**U**	**X**			**S**			**U**										**15**
X	X	X	U		X	X	X	U			X	X	X				X	S		U		X		U													**16**
	X	X	U		U	X	X				X	X	X	X			X	S		U		X		S		X											**17**
X	**X**	**X**	**X**		**U**	**X**	**X**				**X**		**X**	**X**			**X**	**X**		**U**	**U**			**S**			**U**	**S**									**18**
X	**X**	**X**	**X**		**U**	**X**	**X**				**S**		**X**	**X**			**X**	**X**		**U**	**X**						**U**	**S**									**19**
	X	X	X		X	X	X				U			X			X	S		U	U	X				X		X	U								**20**
U	**X**	**X**			**X**	**X**	**X**				**U**			**X**			**X**	**U**		**U**	**X**	**X**	**U**			**X**		**X**									**21**
X	X	X	U	U	X	X	X				S			X			X				U	X				U		X		X							**22**
X	X	X	U	X	S	X	X				U			X			X				S	X						X	S	X							**23**
X	**X**	**X**	**S**		**X**	**X**	**X**				**S**		**U**	**X**			**X**			**U**	**U**							**X**	**X**	**X**							**24**
X	**X**	**X**	**X**		**X**	**X**	**X**				**X**	**U**	**S**	**X**			**X**			**U**	**S**							**X**			**S**						**25**
X	X	X			X	X	X				X	U	U	X							S							X		X	S	X					**26**
X	X	X		U	X	X	X				X		S	X			S				X							S		X	U	X					**27**
X	X	X	X	X	U	X	X				X	S	U	X			X			U								X		S							**28**
X	X	X	X	X	U	X	X				X	S	U	X			X				U							X		U							**29**
X	X	X	X	X	X	X	X				S	U		X			X				U							S		X							**30**
X	X	X	X	X	X	X	X				S	U	S	X			X			U								S		X							**31**
X	X	X	X	X		X	U				X	U		X			X			U		U						X		X	S						**32**
X	X	X		X		X					X	X		X			X		U	U	X	X									S						**33**
X	X	X	X	X		X	X				X	X		X			X		U	U	U							U			S						**34**
X	X	X	X	X		X	X				X	X		X			X				S	U						S			S		U				**35**
X	X	X	X	X		X	X				X	X					X		U	U	X							S			S						**36**
X	X					X	X				U	X		X			X		S	U	X							X			X		X				**37**
X	X	X	X	X		X	X				S	X					X		U	S								X			X		U				**38**
X	X	X		X		X	X				U	X					X		U	X				U				X			X		U				**39**
X	X	X		X		X	X				X	X					X		U	S	X			U				X			S		U				**40**
X	X	X		X							X	X					X		U	X	X			S				X			X		S	U			**41**
X	X	X	X	X			X				X						X		S		U			X				X			X		U				**42**
X	X	X	X	X			X				X	X					X		U					X				X			U		U				**43**
X	X	X	X	X			X				X	X				U	X		U					X				X			S						**44**
X	X	X		X			X				X	X		X		U	X		S	U				X				X							S	S	**45**
X	X	X	X	X			X				S	X		X			X		U	U				X				X			U				S		**46**
X	X	X	X	X		U	X				X	X		X			X		U	U				S				X							U		**47**
X	X	X	X	X		S	X				X	X		X			X		U					S				X			U				U		**48**
X	X	X	X	X		X	X				X	S		X			X			U	S			U				X							U		**49**
X	X	X	X	X		X	X				X	U					X			U	X							X							U	U	**50**
X	X		X	X		X	X				X	X					X			U	X			S				X			S				S	U	**51**
Total League Appearances																																					
40	36	40	29	29	13	34	39	8	2	3	27	26	11	28	0	0	34	2	0	2	8	7	0	5	0	2	0	22	0	7	5	2	1	0	0	0	**X**
0	0	0	0	1	2	1	0	2	1	1	9	6	3	1	0	0	3	7	3	3	4	0	0	5	0	0	0	5	1	1	9	0	1	0	3	1	**S**
0	2	0	4	2	6	1	1	2	1	3	4	5	4	2	7	3	0	0	12	17	7	2	0	4	0	1	0	1	1	1	4	0	6	1	4	2	**U**
Total Cup Appearances																																					
8	8	9	4	1	3	9	8	0	0	0	3	4	6	9	1	0	9	5	0	0	4	2	0	0	0	1	0	3	1	1	0	0	0	0	0	0	**X**
0	1	0	1	0	1	0	0	1	0	0	3	0	1	0	0	0	0	1	1	0	1	0	1	3	0	0	0	2	0	0	1	0	0	0	0	0	**S**
1	0	0	0	0	3	0	0	2	0	0	3	1	1	0	0	0	0	1	1	7	2	0	1	0	1	0	3	0	0	0	0	0	0	0	0	0	**U**

HINCKLEY UNITED

CURRENT SQUAD AS OF BEGINING OF 2009-10 SEASON

GOALKEEPERS	HT	WT	D.O.B	AGE	P.O.B	CAREER	APPS	GOA
Nick Jupp					Ashford	Hinckley U, Coalville (Dual) 8/09		
Chris Mackenzie	6'00"	12 09	14/5/72	37	Northampton	Corby, Hereford £15,000 7/94 (97/98 7,0), L.Orient 10/97 Rel c/s 99, Nuneaton (L) 3/99, Nuneaton 8/99, Telford 6/03, Hereford (L) 4/04, Chester 5/04, Shrewsbury 5/06, Kidderminster (2ML) 9/07, Kidderminster Undisc 1/08 Rel 5/08, Hinckley U 6/08	40	0
DEFENDERS								
Lee Collins	6'01"	12 06	10/9/77	31	Birmingham	Aston Villa, Stoke 2/99, Cambridge U (L) 8/00, Moor Green (SL) 3/01, Halesowen T 6/01, Moor Green/Solihull Moors 5/03, Hinckley U 7/09		
Connor Franklin			1/9/87	21	Leicester	Nuneaton, Hinckley U 6/08	40	0
Paul Lister					Sheffield	Burton, Grantham (SL) 11/08, Hinckley U 7/09		
James Mace						Coleshill, Bedworth 1/07, Atherstone, Hinckley U 7/09		
Leigh Platnauer						Hinckley U, Gresley R (Dual) 12/07	29	1
Stuart Storer	5'11"	12 12	16/1/67	42	Harborough	Mansfield Rel 3/84, VS Rugby, Birmingham 7/84, Everton 3/87, Wigan (2ML) 7/87, Bolton (L) 12/87 £25,000 1/88, Exeter £25,000 3/93, Brighton £15,000 3/95 Rel c/s 99, Atherstone 9/99, Kettering 10/99 Rel 2/00, Chesham 2/00, Hinckley U 3/01	5	0
MIDFIELDERS								
Daniel Barker						South America, Hinckley U c/s 09		
Neil Cartwright			25/6/82	27	Wrexham	Hinckley U	27	1
Dan Dillon	5'09"	10 07	6/9/86	22	Huntingdon	Carlisle Rel 3/06, Workington (4ML) 8/05, Workington 3/06, Team Bath 7/06, Worcester (Trial) 5/09, Hinckley U 6/09		
Stuart Giddings	6'00"	11 08	27/3/86	23	Coventry	Coventry Rel c/s 08, Oldham (L) 8/07, Lincoln C (Trial) 7/08, Hinckley U 9/08	12	0
Andy Gooding	5'07"	10 05	30/4/88	21	Coventry	Coventry Rel 1/08, Burton (2ML) 8/07, Rushden & D 1/08 Rel 5/08, Hinckley U 7/08	39	5
Andy Hall			25/1/86	23	Northampton	Coventry (Scholar), Kettering 7/05 Rel c/s 08, Halesowen T (SL) 3/08, Hinckley U 7/08	35	12
Lewis Hamilton						Hinckley U	3	0
Richard Lavery			28/5/77	32	Coventry	Bedworth, Hinckley A, Nuneaton, Stratford T, Massey Ferguson, Sutton Coldfield, Atherstone 11/99, Tamworth 2/00, Hinckley U 7/00, Nuneaton 7/01 (01/02 35,0, 02/03 28,1), Telford 7/03 (03/04 28,1), Hinckley U 6/04, Leamington 10/08	29	5
Jack Roberts	6'02"	10 00	10/11/90	18		Lincoln C (Scholar) Rel c/s 09, Hinckley U c/s 09, Coalville (Dual) 8/09		
FORWARDS								
Chima Dozie			6/5/82	27		Naxaar Lions (Mal), Hinckley U 8/08, Bedworth (L) 10/08	10	2
Chukki Eribenne	5'10"	11 12	2/11/80	28	Westminster	Coventry Yth Rel c/s 00, Bournemouth 7/00 Rel c/s 03, Hereford (L) 10/02, Northampton (Trial) 5/03, Havant & W 8/03, Weymouth 7/04, Aldershot (L) 12/04, Farnborough (L) 1/05, Grays 1/07 Rel 5/07, Gravesend (SL) 3/07, Ebbsfleet 5/07 Rel 5/08, Sutton U 8/08, Hinckley U 8/09		
Andre Lorougnon			20/12/88	20		Sporting Toulon (Fra), Coventry (Scholar), Stafford R (SL) 3/07, Barwell, Kettering 3/09, Barwell, Hinckley U 7/09		
Nicholas Pollard						Hinckley Downes, Hinckley U 12/08, Oadby T (Dual) 8/09	14	1
Alex Taylor			11/11/85	23	Wolverhampton	Kidderminster, Stafford R, Hinckley U 8/08	36	5
Adam Webster	6'01"	12 05	3/7/80	29	Thurmarston	Thurmarston, Notts County 2/99 Rel c/s 00, Grantham (L) 9/99, Bedworth (L) 12/99, Bedworth 7/00, Worcester £8,000 12/01, Hinckley U 2/08	37	10
Matt West						Coventry (Scholar), Hinckley U 7/09		

LOANEES	HT	WT	DOB	AGE	POB	From - To	APPS	GOA
(G)Jasbir Singh	6'02"	13 05	12/3/90	19		Shrewsbury 10/08 - Sutton Coldfield (L) 1/09, Rel 5/09, Kidderminster 8/09	2	0
(F)Aaron Moses-Garvey	5'08"	11 13	6/9/89	19	Birmingham	Birmingham 10/08 - Worcester 7/09	1	1
(M)Emeka Nwadike	6'00"	12 07	9/8/78	31	Camberwell	AFC Telford (2ML) 11/08 - Eastwood T 6/09	8	1
(D)Matt Bailey	6'05"	11 06	12/3/86	23	Nantwich	Northwich 12/08 -	2	1

DEPARTURES	HT	WT	DOB	AGE	POB	From - To	APPS	GOA
(F)Lee Chilton						Alvechurch 6/08 - Rel 9/08, Willenhall 9/08, Stourbridge 6/09	4	0
(D)Aaron Butcher						Oadby T 8/08 - Rel 9/08, Swaffham, Wisbech 12/08	0	0
(D)Jamie Lenton			6/1/77	32	Nuneaton	Nuneaton (2ML) 1/03 Perm 3/03 - Leamington 10/08, Bedworth 6/09		
(F)Leon Kelly	6'01"	12 04	26/6/78	31	Coventry	Worcester 3/06 - Rel 11/08, Solihull Moors 11/08 Rel 12/08, Bromsgrove 12/08, Hyde U 4/09	9	1
(D)Tom Bonner	6'00"	11 06	6/2/88	21	Camden	Corby 1/08 - Solihull Moors 2/09, Corby T 5/09	14	1
(D)Tom Birch						Cheltenham c/s 06 - Rel 2/09, Hednesford (L) 1/08, Bradford PA 2/09	15	0
(M)Daryl Taylor	5'10"	11 03	14/11/84	24	Birmingham	Halesowen T 10/08 - Halesowen T 3/09	7	0
(D)Dominic Roma	5'10"	11 11	29/11/85	23	Sheffield	Sheff Utd U 7/07 - Alfreton 5/09	36	3
(D)Craig McIlwain			1/1/80	29	Burton Latimer	Nuneaton 6/08 - Brackley T 6/09	30	2
(M)Callum Lloyd	5'09"	11 04	1/1/86	23	Nottingham	Kettering (L) 10/07, Perm 11/07 - Rel c/s 09	32	2
(G)Denham Hinds						Yth -	0	0
(D)Andy Gundelach						Yth -	0	0
(F)Gary McPhee	6'00"	12 00	18/4/80	29	Glasgow	Bromsgrove 8/08 -	3	0
(F)Gez Murphy					Leicester	Nuneaton 6/07 - Nuneaton T (L) 10/08	10	2
(F)Luke Bradshaw						Yth -	2	0
(F)Phil Warrington						Yth -	1	0
Sutton						Yth -	0	0
Nathan Bancroft						Yth -	0	0
Curtis Smith						Yth -	3	0
Lewis Stewart			18/5/92	17		Yth -	0	0

HINCKLEY UNITED

Formed: 1997

Nickname: United.

Club Colours: Red, navy and white shirts, navy and white shorts, Red, navy and white socks.

Change Colours: White with black trimmed shirts, black with white trimmed shorts and socks.

Club Sponsor: Greene King Brewery.

Previous League: Southern League

Ground address: The Greene King Stadium, Leicester Road, Hinckley LE10 3DR

Telephone No: 01455 840 088

Mobile: 07802 355 249

Fax: 01455 840 099

Email: admin@hinckleyunited.com

Website: www.hinckleyunited.com

Simple Directions: M6 Jct 2 then from M69 Jct 2 take A5 north (Tamworth/Nuneaton) and at 3rd roundabout (Dodwells) take 2nd exit (A47 to Earl Shilton). Marston Stadium just under two miles on right.

Capacity: 4,329 **Seats**: 630 **Covered**: 2,695 **Floodlights**:Yes

Clubhouse: Entrance outside the ground and open pub hours.

Club Shop: Yes, off reception.

Local Radio: BBC Radio Leicester, Fosseway Radio.

Local Press: Heartland Evening News, Hinckley Times, Leicester Mercury, Coventry Evening Telegraph.

PROGRAMME EDITOR
c/o the club

CLUB STATISTICS

RECORD

Attendance: 2,278 v Nuneaton Borough 10.12.05

Victory: 9-1 v Rocester (A) 28.08 2000

Defeat: 0-6 v Redditch United (a) 07.11.1988

Career Goalscorer: Jamie Lenton 74

Career Appearances: Jamie Lenton 280

Record Transfer Fee Paid:

£5,000 to Kidderminster Harriers for Matt Lewis .

Received: £1,000 from Ilkeston Town for Justin Jenkins.

SENIOR HONOURS

Southern League Western Division Champions 2000-01.

PREVIOUS

Names: Today's club formed after Hinckley Athletic and Hinckley Town merged in 1997.

Leagues (as United): Southern 1997-2004.

HYDE UNITED

Back Row (L-R): Tolson (manager), Liversedge(physio), Mooney, Eastham, Jones, Burns, Lynch, Smith, D'Laryea, Lees, Harrison (coach).
Front Row: Manship, Armstrong, Scott McNiven, Rick, Stott, David McNiven, Barrie, Arnold, Rowbotham, Bryan.

CLUB PERSONNEL

Chairman: Stephen Hartley.

Additional Directors: A M Beard, E Kirsch,

D Farrington, M I Knowles, A A Fruhwirth, S K Howard,

J Whitehead, J Jackson.

Secretary: Tony Beard,

30 Fishermans Close, Winterley,

Sandbach, CW11 4SW

Tel: (H) & (F): 01270 212 473

(M): 07778 792 502

E-mail: aliandtony@ukonline.co.uk

Commercial Manager & Press Officer: As secretary.

Manager: Neil Tolson.

Club therapist: Ian Liversedge.

A campaign that never got off the ground as far as Hyde United were concerned has left their supporters just grateful that they still have a club, and it will carry on competing in The Blue Square North! At no time last season did 'The Tigers' look comfortable and it was no surprise when the long serving, and previously successful Steve Waywell, left the club after a poor start.

By the beginning of October, United had sunk to nineteenth place and new manager Neil Tolson found it difficult to bring about any improvement. Whitley Bay knocked them out of the F.A.Cup and Hednesford Town also prevented progress in the F.A.Trophy after a replay.

Only once did Hyde manage two consecutive victories and sadly they were too late to save the club from a relegation place. Without Chris Simm's twenty goals, their final position of twentieth, five points behind Farsley Celtic could have been worse.

As it turned out, the demotion of King's Lynn to the Northern Premier League gave the twentieth club in the Blue Square North a reprieve, so hopefully, Hyde United have learnt from their frightening experience and will protect their supporters from ever again having to cope with such an unpleasant experience.

HYDE UNITED

BEST LGE ATT.: 871 v Stalybridge Celtic
LOWEST: 220 v Alfreton Town

No.	Date	Comp	H/A	Opponents	Att:	Result	Goalscorers	Pos
1	Aug 9	BSN	A	Alfreton Town	390	L 2 - 3	**Simm** 32 Moden 87	
2	11		H	Burscough	303	L 0 - 1		
3	16		H	Fleetwood Town	316	W 5 - 3	**SIMM** 3 (27 71 83) Innes 47 Tipton 79 (pen)	13
4	23		A	Droylsden	467	L 1 - 2	Dean 17	
5	25		H	Gainsborough Trinity	251	D 0 - 0		
6	30		A	Harrogate Town	362	L 1 - 3	Dean 90	
7	Sept 2		A	Blyth Spartans	405	L 0 - 3		
8	6		H	Hinckley United	285	D 0 - 0		19
9	**8**	**SS N1**	**H**	**Vauxhall Motors**	**97**	**L 1 - 2**	**Tipton 24 (pen)**	
10	13		A	King's Lynn	1098	L 1 - 4	Tipton	20
11	20		H	Vauxhall Motors	264	W 3 - 1	Owens 27 **Simm** 37 Clee 76	17
12	**27**	**F.A.C. 2Q**	**A**	**Whitley Bay**	**364**	**L 1 - 3**	**Lynch 65**	
13	Oct 4		A	Tamworth	859	L 0 - 2		19
14	11		A	Farsley Celtic	222	L 1 - 2	Wharton 51	
15	18		H	Stafford Rangers	375	D 1 - 1	**Simm** 90	20
16	25		A	Hucknall Town	214	W 1 - 0	**Simm** 66 (pen)	18
17	Nov 1		H	Gateshead	301	L 2 - 5	**Simm** 26 Cartwright 65	19
18	8		A	Solihull Moors	180	D 2 - 2	Daly 2 (og) Clee 70	18
19	15		H	Workington	303	D 4 - 4	**Simm** 18 Maamria 28 Tolson 62 90	19
20	**22**	**F.A.T 3Q**	**H**	**Hednesford Town**	**275**	**D 1 - 1**	**Simm 36**	
21	**25**	**F.A.T 3Q r**	**A**	**Hednesford Town**	**263**	**L 0 - 5**		
22	29		A	Gateshead	273	L 3 - 6	**Simm** 48 (pen) Tolson 53 Kilbane 73	19
23	Dec 6		A	Burscough	362	D 2 - 2	Douglas-Pringle 21 **Simm** 32	19
24	20		H	Alfreton Town	220	D 1 - 1	Douglas-Pringle 17 (pen)	
25	26		H	Stalybridge Celtic	871	L 0 - 2		
26	Jan 17		A	AFC Telford United	1888	W 3 - 2	Douglas-Pringle 48 **Simm** 53 Clee 87	19
27	24		H	Tamworth	541	L 1 - 2	**Simm** 22 (pen)	19
28	26		H	Farsley Celtic	264	W 3 - 1	Douglas-Pringle 32 Clee 69 **Simm** 83	
29	31		H	Redditch United	271	L 1 - 2	Douglas-Pringle 14	
30	Feb 7		A	Southport	851	L 0 - 2		20
31	14		H	Hucknall Town	301	W 2 - 0	**Simm** 45 (pen) Morley 45	
32	21		A	Stafford Rangers	500	L 0 - 2		19
33	28		H	AFC Telford United	502	L 0 - 4		20
34	Mar 3		A	Fleetwood Town	611	W 3 - 1	Fitzhenry 60 68 Douglas-Pringle76	
35	10		A	Stalybridge Celtic	604	L 1 - 4	Lynch 58	
36	14		A	Workington	328	D 2 - 2	Douglas-Pringle 44 Clee 60	20
37	21		H	King's Lynn	305	L 0 - 1		21
38	24		A	Vauxhall Motors	201	L 1 - 2	**Simm** 12	
39	28		H	Harrogate Town	301	L 2 - 3	Douglas-Pringle 35 Tolson 84	21
40	April 4		A	Hinckley United	343	W 1 - 0	Douglas-Pringle 68	
41	6		H	Blyth Spartans	338	W 1 - 0	Owens 78	
42	11		H	Droylsden	557	L 1 - 3	Newton 77 (og)	20
43	13		A	Gainsborough Trinity	290	W 1 - 0	**Simm** 70	
44	15		H	Southport	438	D 1 - 1	Tolson 70	20
45	18		A	Redditch United	337	L 0 - 1		
46	25		H	Solihull Moors	251	W 3 - 1	**Simm** 43 47 Lynch 58	20

Average Home Att: 360 (445) **Goals 59 90**

Best Position: 13th **Worst:** 21st

Goalscorers: Simm 20, Douglas-Pringle 9, Clee 5, Tolson 5, Lynch 3, Tipton 3, Dean 2, Fitzhenry 2, Owens 2, Cartwright 1, Innes 1, Kilbane 1, Maamria 1, Moden 1, Morley 1, Wharton 1. Own Goals 2.

DOOTSON	MADEN	LYNCH	MORLEY	MUNROE	BAILEY	CARTWRIGHT	INNES	TIPTON	DEAN	SIMM	HARRISON	RICK	BRASS	SHELMERDINE	BUNTING	BERNSTEIN	TANDY	CLEE	COWARD	COOKE	A OAKES	GEE	TOLSON	WILLIAMS	OWENS	WHARTON	IGENOZA	THOMPSON	MARSH	MAAMRIA	KILBANE	BERKELEY	MANSHIP	DOUGLAS-PRINGLE	HOWARTH	FITZHENRY	LOMAX	THOMPSON	KIRKBRIDE	KELLY	BOCKERIE	
X	X	X	X	X	X	X	X	X	X	X	S	U	U	U	U																											1
X	X	X	X	X	X	X	X	X	X	X	S	S	S		U	U																										2
X	X	X			X	X	X	X	X	X	S	S	X	S	U	U	X																									3
X	X	X	X	X	X	X	X		X	X	U	S		U		U	X	S																								4
X	X	X		X	U	X		U	X	X	X	X				U	X	X	U																							5
X	X	X		X	S	X		X	X	X	X	S	X			U		X	U																							6
	X	X		X	X	X		X	X			X	X		U	X		X	U	U	U	U																				7
X	X	X	X	X		X	X	X	X	S	X	U	X			U		S		U																						8
X	**X**	**X**	**X**	**X**	**X**	**X**	**X**	**X**				**S**	**X**			**U**		**X**		**S**		**U**	**S**																			**9**
X		X		X	U	X	X	X		X	X	S	X			U		X		S				X	S																	10
X		X		X		X		X		X		S	X			U	S	X	U	X					X	X	S															11
X	**X**	**X**	**U**	**X**		**X**				**X**		**S**	**X**			**U**		**X**	**U**		**S**		**S**		**X**	**X**	**X**															**12**
X		X				X	X	X		X	X	U	X			U		X	S		X			U	X		U															13
X		X	X			X	X				S	U	X			U		X	S		X			U	X	X		X														14
X		X	S			X	X			S		U	X			U		X			X			X	U	X		X	X													15
X		X	S	U		X	X			X		U	X			U		X			X			X	U			X	X													16
X		X	S	S		X	X			X			X			U		X			X			X	U	S		X	X													17
X	X	U	X	S		X	U			X			X					X			X			X		S		U	X	X												18
X	X		X	X		X	U			X	U	U	X					X			X		S			X			S	X												19
X	**X**		**X**	**U**		**X**	**X**			**X**			**X**			**U**		**X**			**X**		**S**	**X**	**U**	**X**			**S**													**20**
X	**X**			**X**		**X**	**X**			**X**	**U**	**U**	**X**			**U**		**X**			**X**		**U**	**X**		**X**			**U**													**21**
X		X		X			X			X	U	U	X			U		X			X		S		X						X	X	S									22
X		X	U	X			X			X		S	X			U		X			X				X						X		U	X	S							23
X		X	U	X			S					X	X			U		X			X										X		U	X	U	X	X					24
X		X		X			U			S		X	X			U		X			X										X		S	X	U	X	X					25
X		X					S			X		X	X			U		X		S	X										X		X	S	U	X	X					26
		X	U	X			U			X		X				X		X		U	X						S				X		X	X	U	X						27
		X	U				S			X		X				X		X		X	X	U					S				X		X	X		X						28
		X		U			S			X		X				X		X		X	X						U				X		X	X	S	X	S					29
X		X	X	U			X					S				U		X		X	X		S				S				X		X	X		X						30
X		X	X	U			X			X		X				U		X		U	X						S				X		X		S	X						31
X		X	X	X			X			X		S				U		X		U	X						S				X		X	X	S							32
X			X	X			X			X		X				U		X		U	X						S				X		X	S	S	X						33
X		X	X	X			S			S		U				U				U	X		X								X		X	X	X	X						34
		X	X	X			U			S	U	S				X		X			X		X				S				X		X	X	X							35
		X	X	X			U			X		S				X		X			X		S				U				X		X	X	X							36
U		X		X			U			X		U				X		X			X		S		S						X		X	X	X	X						37
U		X	X				X			X		S				X		X		X	X		S		S		U				X		X	X								38
U		X	X				X					S				X		X		X	S		S		X		U				X		X	X		X						39
X		X	X				U					U						X					S		U						X		X	X		X		X	X	X	U	40
X		X	X	U			U			X		U						X							S						X		X			X		X	X	X	U	41
X		X	X	S						S		S				U		X							U						X		X	X		X		X	X	X		42
X		X		X						X		U						X					S		U						X		X	X		X		X	X	S	U	43
X				X			S			X		X						X		U	U		S		X						X		X					X	X	X	U	44
X		X		X			U			X		X						X					S								X		X	S		S		X	X	X	U	45
X		X	X	X						X		X						X		S	S		U		U						X			X				X	X		S	46
Total League Appearances																																										
33	10	38	20	25	5	17	19	9	8	30	5	13	18	0	0	9	3	36	0	6	24	0	2	5	7	4	0	4	4	2	25	1	20	18	4	16	3	7	7	5	0	**X**
0	0	0	3	3	1	0	6	0	0	6	4	14	1	1	0	0	1	2	2	3	2	0	11	0	4	2	8	0	1	0	0	0	2	3	5	1	1	0	0	1	1	**S**
3	0	1	4	5	2	0	10	1	0	0	4	13	1	2	4	24	0	0	4	8	2	2	1	2	7	0	5	1	0	0	0	0	2	0	4	0	0	0	0	0	5	**U**
Total Cup Appearances																																										
4	4	2	2	3	1	4	3	1	0	3	0	0	4	0	0	0	0	4	0	0	2	0	0	2	1	3	1	0	0	0	0	0	0	0	0	0	0	0	0	0	0	**X**
0	0	0	0	0	0	0	0	0	0	0	0	2	0	0	0	0	0	0	0	1	1	0	3	0	0	0	0	0	1	0	0	0	0	0	0	0	0	0	0	0	0	**S**
0	0	0	1	1	0	0	0	0	0	0	1	1	0	0	0	4	0	0	1	0	0	1	1	0	1	0	0	0	1	0	0	0	0	0	0	0	0	0	0	0	0	**U**

Also played: TURNER U(5), S(6). O'BRIEN U(12). SHEVLIN U(28,36).

HYDE UNITED

CURRENT SQUAD AS OF BEGINING OF 2009-10 SEASON

GOALKEEPERS	HT	WT	D.O.B	AGE	P.O.B	CAREER	APPS	GOA
Will Burns						Hyde U		
Michael Jones	6'04"	12 05	3/12/87	21	Liverpool	Wrexham Rel 5/08, Hinckley U (L) 3/08, Northwich 5/08, Rhyl (SL) 1/09, Hyde U 7/09		
DEFENDERS								
Lincoln Adams			17/9/79	29	Huddersfield	Halifax, Wakefield & Emley, Ashton U 8/03, Stalybridge 12/04, Hyde U 2/05 Rel c/s 07, Bradford PA c/s 07, Leek T 3/08 Rel 3/08, Bay Ath, FC Halifax 8/08, Hyde U 7/09		
Nathan D'Laryea	5'10"	12 02	3/9/85	23	Manchester	Man City Rel c/s 07, Macclesfield (L) 1/07, Rochdale 7/07 Rel c/s 09, Farsley Celtic (2ML) 2/09		
Ashley Eastham			22/3/91	18		Blackpool, Hyde U (L) 8/09		
Mark Lees						Mossley, Curzon Ashton, Stalybridge, New Mills, Buxton 1/08, Ashton U 2/09, Hyde U 7/09		
Chris Lynch	5'10"		29/12/84	24	Manchester	Wigan (Scholar) Rel c/s 04, Hyde U c/s 04	38	2
Scott McNiven	5'10"	10 08	27/5/78	31	Leeds	Oldham Rel c/s 02, Oxford U 7/02, Mansfield 7/04 Rel c/s 05, Chester Rel 5/06, Morecambe 8/06 Rel 8/06, Fleetwood 9/06, Guiseley 2/07, Farsley Celtic 6/07, AFC Fylde 7/08, Hyde U 8/09		
Ben Rowbotham						Hyde U		
Dean Stott						Burnley (Trainee) Rel c/s 08, Preston 5/08 Rel c/s 09, Hyde U 8/09		
MIDFIELDERS								
Paul Armstrong			3/4/86	23	Manchester	Oldham (Scholar), Mossley (WE) 12/04, Barrow (WE) 3/05, Hyde U c/s 05, Ashton U 12/06 Rel c/s 07, Flixton, Connahs Quay 1/08, Hyde U 7/09		
Nathan Arnold	5'08"	10 07	26/7/87	22	Mansfield	Mansfield Rel c/s 09, Grimsby (Trial) c/s 09, Hyde U 8/09		
Daniel Barrie	5'10"	11 07	1/10/90	18	Ormskirk	Bolton (Yth), Wigan (Scholar) Rel c/s 09, Hyde U 7/09		
Gerry Harrison	5'10"	12 12	15/4/72	37	Lambeth	Watford Rel c/s 91, Bristol C 7/91, Cardiff (2ML) 1/92, Hereford (L) 11/93, Huddersfield Undisc 3/94 Rel c/s 94, Burnley 8/94, Sunderland 7/98 Rel c/s 00, Luton (3ML) 12/98, Hull (SL) 3/99, Hull (L) 10/99, Burnley (SL) 3/00, Halifax 8/00 Rel 10/00, Prestwich Heys, Leigh RMI 11/01 Rel c/s 04, York 9/04 Rel 9/04, Northwich 10/04 Rel 11/04, Hyde U 2/05	9	0
Aiden Kirkbride	6'00"	10 07	26/11/90	18	Ormskirk	Liverpool (Yth), Wigan c/s 07, Hyde U (L) 3/09, Hyde U 7/09	7	0
Tom Manship	5'08"	11 02	27/3/87	22	Melton Mowbray	West Brom (Yth), Mansfield (Scholar), Hinckley c/s 05, Rugby (L) 9/06, Grantham 10/06, Cheltenham NC 8/07, Hucknall (L) 11/07, Hucknall (L) 3/08, Hyde U 11/08	22	0
Robbie Smith						Padiham, Hyde U 7/09		
Greg Traynor	5'10"	11 00	17/10/84	24	Salford	Wigan, Bradford PA (L) 10/04, Hyde U (L) 3/05, Hyde U 12/05, Ashton U c/s 06, Chorley 3/07, Flixton, Radcliffe B, Flixton, Hyde U 7/09		
FORWARDS								
Daniel Douglas-Pringle	5'10"	11 07	8/12/84	24	Manchester	Man City (Scholar), Bury (Scholar), Chorley (L) 10/04 Perm 11/04, Leigh RMI 1/05 (04/05 1,0) Rel 2/05, Woodley Sports 2/05, Alfreton 7/07, Curzon Ashton Undisc 9/07, Chorley 2/08, Woodley Sports 8/08, Hyde U 11/08	21	9
Paul Gedman			14/6/81	28		Bradford C (Trial), Halifax (02/03 2,0), Wrexham (Trial), Flexsys CD, TNS, Bangor C 8/03, Burscough 7/04, Hyde U 10/06, Bradford PA (L) 9/07 Perm 9/07, Droylsden 7/08, FC Halifax (L) 9/08 Perm 10/08, Hyde U 7/09		
David McNiven	5'10"	12 00	27/5/78	31	Leeds	Oldham Rel c/s 00, Linfield (L) 3/97, Scarborough (L) 2/00, Southport (L) 3/00, York 8/00 Rel c/s 01, Chester 7/01, Hamilton 10/01, Northwich 7/02, Kidsgrove (L) 11/02, Leigh RMI 8/03, Q.O.South 7/04, Scarborough 1/06, Morecambe 6/06, Stafford R (L) 1/07,		
Scott Mooney						Asfordby Amateurs, Holwell Sports, Hyde U 7/09		
Lee Rick						Macclesfield (Yth), Hyde U	27	0
Neil Tolson	6'02"	12 04	25/10/73	35	Wordsley	Walsall, Oldham £150,000 3/92, Bradford C £50,000 12/93, Chester (L) 1/95, York £60,000 7/96 Rel c/s 99, Southend 7/99 Rel c/s 01, Retired, Leigh RMI 10/02, Kettering 1/03 Rel 1/03, Halifax 3/03, Hyde 7/03 Pl/Ass Man c/s 07, Radcliffe B (L) 2/06	13	5

LOANEES	HT	WT	DOB	AGE	POB	From - To	APPS	GOA
(F)Chris Thompson	5'10"	11 12	7/2/82	27	Warrington	Barrow 10/08 - Leigh Genesis (SL) 1/09 Perm 3/09	4	0
(D)David Thompson						Bury 3/09 -	7	0

DEPARTURES	HT	WT	DOB	AGE	POB	From - To	APPS	GOA
(F)James Dean	5'11"	11 07	15/5/85	24	Blackburn	Stalybridge 6/08 - Harrogate T 9/08	8	2
(M)Mitchell Bailey	5'09"	12 04	31/12/88	20	Manchester	Huddersfield 8/08 - Mossley 9/08, Rossendale 11/08	6	0
(D)Matty Bunting						Hyde U, New Mills 10/08	0	0
(F)Matthew Tipton	5'11"	13 05	29/6/80	29	Conwy	Bury 8/07 - Droylsden Undisc 10/08	9	2
(M)Jamie Tandy			1/9/84	24	Manchester	Bradford PA 8/08 - Droylsden 9/08, Flixton (Dual) 10/08, Salford C 1/09	4	0
(F)Dino Maamria	6'00"	12 02	18/2/74	35	Burnley	Northwich 11/08 - Stevenage Ass Man 11/08	2	1
(F)Phil Marsh	5'10"	11 13	15/11/86	22	St Helens	Blackpool 8/08 - Rel 9/08, Hyde U 10/08 Rel 11/08, Leigh Genesis 12/08, FCUM 3/09	5	0
(M)Nathan Wharton			2/11/80	28	Oldham	Ashton U 9/08 - Rel 11/08	6	1
(M)Lee Cartwright	5'09"	11 07	19/9/72	36	Rawtenstall	Scarborough 5/07 - Rel 11/08	17	1
(D)Wayne Maden			24/3/83	26	Blackpool	Rio Grande Ohio (USA) 7/08 - Rel 11/08, Squires Gate, Chorley 6/09	10	1
(M)Steve Bushell	5'09"	11 06	28/12/72	36	Manchester	Halifax 1/08 - Bradford PA 11/08		
(D)Steve Williams						Bamber Bridge 8/08 - Fleetwood 11/08 Rel 1/09, Bamber Bridge 2/09, Bradford Undisc 7/09	5	0
(F)Matthew Berkeley	5'11"	10 10	3/8/87	22	Manchester	Mossley 11/08 - TNS 1/09	1	0
(M)Chris Brass	5'09"	12 06	24/7/75	34	Easington	Bury 7/07 - Bury (Caretaker Man) 1/08, Bury Ass Man 2/09	19	0
(F)Carl Lomax	6'00"					Clitheroe 12/08 - FCUM 2/09	4	0
(M)Gareth Morris					Ashton	Droylsden 3/08 - Droylsden 2/09		
(D)Paul Howarth			6/7/81	28		ex Accrington 12/08 - Leigh Genesis 3/09	9	0
(M)Chris Cooke						Mossley c/s 07 - Mossley (L) 3/09 Perm 3/09	9	0
(F)Chris Simm	6'00"	12 08	10/4/84	25	Wigan	Leigh RMI 7/07 - Southport 5/09	36	19
(G)Craig Dootson	6'04"	14 02	23/5/79	30	Preston	Bury 6/06 - Alfreton 5/09	33	0
(D)Dave Morley			25/9/77	31		Macclesfied 10/07 - Bangor C 6/09	23	1
(D)Farrell Kilbane	6'00"	13 00	21/10/74	34	Preston	Fleetwood 11/08 - Burscough 7/09	25	1
(M)Nicky Clee					Huddersfield	Ashton U 6/05 - Altrincham 7/09	38	5
(D)Mark Innes	5'09"	12 10	27/9/78	30	Bellshill	ex Port Vale 8/07 - New Mills 7/09	25	1
(G)Elliot Bernstein						Hanwell T 8/08 -	9	0
(D)Neil Fitzhenry	6'00"	12 03	24/9/78	30	Billinge	Burscough 12/08 -	17	2
(D)Adam Oakes						8/08 -	26	0
(M)Karl Munroe	6'00"	10 08	23/9/79	29	Manchester	Altrincham 1/08 - Rel 7/08, Hyde U 8/08	28	0
(M)Joe Shelmerdine						Local 8/08 -	1	0
(F)Chris Coward	6'01"	11 07	23/7/89	20	Manchester	Stockport 8/08 -	2	0
(F)Bobby Gee						Yth -	0	0
(F)Leon Kelly	6'01"	12 04	26/6/78	31	Coventry	Bromsgrove 3/09 -	6	0
Harry Bockerie						Yth -	1	0
Andrew Shevlin						Yth -	0	0
Ken O'Brien						Yth -	0	0
Joel Igenoza						Yth -	8	0
David Owens						9/08 -	11	2
Milton Turner						8/08 -	1	0

HYDE UNITED

Formed: 1919

Nickname: The Tigers.

Club Colours: Red shirts, white shorts, red socks.

Change Colours: Orange shirts, black shorts, orange socks.

Club Sponsor: TBC

Previous League: Northern Premier League

Ground address: Tameside Stadium, Ewen Fields,Walker Lane, Hyde SK14 2SB

Telephone: 0871 200 2116

Mobile: 07778 792 502

Fax: 0871 200 2118

Email: aliandtony@ukonline.co.uk

Official website: www.hydeunited.com

Simple Directions: On entering Hyde follow signs for Tameside Leisure Park. In Walker Lane take second car park entrance near Leisure Pool and follow road around pool. Quarter of a mile from Newton(BR).

Train from Manchester (15min).

Capacity: 4,250 **Seats:** 660 **Covered:** 2,000 **Floodlights**: Yes

Club Shop: Full range of club accessories.

Local Radio: Key 103 and BBC Radio Manchester

Local Press: Tameside Advertiser and Hyde Reporter

no image available

PROGRAMME EDITOR
Mark Dring
(M) 07960 868 946
Email: mark@dring16.fsnet.co.uk

CLUB STATISTICS

RECORD

Attendance: 9,500 v Nelson F.A.Cup 1952

Victory: 9-1 v South Liverpool

Defeat: 0-26 v P.N.E. F.A..Cup as Hyde F.C.

Career Goalscorer: David Nolan - 117 in 404 apps. (1992-2003)

Ged Kimmins - 117 in 274 apps. (1993-98)

Career Appearances: David Nolan - 404 (1992-2003)

Record Transfer Fee Paid:

£8,000 to Mossley for Jim McCluskie 1989

Received: £ 50,000 from Crewe Alexandra for Colin Little 1995

SENIOR HONOURS

Northern Premier Champions 2004-05, Lge Cup (3).

Northern Premier Div. 1 Champions 2003-04.

Cheshire Senior Cup (7), Manchester Premier Cup (5).

PREVIOUS

Leagues: Lancs & Cheshire 1919-21 Manchester 1921-30.

Cheshire County 1930-68 1970-82.

Northern Premier League 1968-70, 1983-2004.

ILKESTON TOWN

Back Row (L to R): Kevin Wilson (Manager), Jon Douglas, Luke Waterfall, Dan Holmes, Dan Lowson, Gary Ricketts,David Bevan, Tom Bonner, Keiran Murphy,(Capt.), David Graham, Steve Huntington (Coach)
Front row; Paul Winter (Physio), Alex White, Josh Burge, Liam Green, Sam Duncum, Paul Dempsey, Dan Holmes, Amari Morgan-Smith, Darren Caskey (Coach)

CLUB PERSONNEL

Chairman: Denis Harris.

Vice Chairman: Jim Cheetham.

Company Secretary: Denis Harris.

Additional Directors: David Murphy, Giovanni Sansone.

Secretary: Keith Burnand.
2 Woodland Grove, Clowne, Chesterfield, Derbyshire S43 4AT.
Tel: (M) 07887 832 125
Email: kfootball@tiscali.co.uk

Commercial Manager: Paul Winter.
Tel: (M) 07517 449 112.

Press Officer: Denis Harris.
Tel: (M) 07794 049 057
Email: denis@propertyinvestmentportfolio.com

Manager: Kevin Wilson.

Club therapist: Paul Winter.

A wonderful season finished off with a story book ending as 'The Robins' beat Kendal Town 4-3 and Nantwich Town 2-1 in the Play-Offs, both after extra time. It had all started with a home draw against Kendal in front of 393 fans but, nine victories in the next ten games changed the whole perception of the season and Ilkeston Town were enjoying life on top of The Northern Premier League table.

Two F.A.Cup victories also helped, but after beating Matlock Town and Stewarts & Lloyds, Alfreton Town won a replay at The New Manor Ground and it was on to the F.A.Trophy which really did bring supporters some excitement. An away trip to Eastwood Town and a fine 2-0 success against a club who were hitting the headlines in the F.A.Cup, brought another trip to another N.P.L. club and another victory by the same score.

A third away tie was won 2-1 at Chasetown, who had also enjoyed recent Cup success, and Ilkeston were rewarded with a home tie against Ossett Town and a 3-2 victory gave 'The Robins' the draw they were looking forward to - a visit from the well respected Kidderminster Harriers. Supporters were not disappointed with eight goals but Harriers won 5-3.

Once the cup games were over, Ilkeston settled down to concentrate on their league position and achieved a tremendous run of eighteen unbeaten games which only included six draws. They were always favourites for second place but of course this meant the play-offs and the storybook ending!

ILKESTON TOWN

BEST LGE ATT.: 2,288 v Eastwood Town
LOWEST: 270 v Boston United

No.	Date	Comp	H/A	Opponents	Att:	Result	Goalscorers	Pos
1	Aug 16	Unibond P.	H	Kendal Town	393	D 1 - 1	Morgan-Smith 84	
2	19		A	Buxton	372	W 2 - 0	Morgan-Smith 28 67	
3	23		A	Leigh Genesis	150	W 2 - 1	Douglas 85 Adam 87	5
4	25		H	Frickley Athletic	495	W 1 - 0	Howell 10 (pen)	
5	30		H	North Ferriby United	421	W 1 - 0	Morgan-Smith 22	2
6	Sept 2		A	Southport	271	L 0 - 2		
7	6		A	Marine	293	W 2 - 0	Morgan-Smith 24 47	1
8	**13**	**F.A.C. 1Q**	**H**	**Matlock Town**	**495**	**W 4 - 1**	**Howell 4 Duncan 31 Istead 56 Douglas 90**	
9	20		A	Bradford PA	425	W 1 - 0	Mitchell 8	1
10	24		A	Worksop Town	332	W 1 - 0	Douglas 77	
11	**27**	**F.A.C. 2Q**	**H**	**Stewarts & Lloyds**	**177**	**W 3 - 2**	**Douglas 42 Adam 50 Morgan-Smith 52**	
12	Oct 4		H	Guiseley	603	L 0 - 1		1
13	7		H	Ossett Town	374	W 2 - 1	Duncan 28 Hay (og) 43	
14	**11**	**F.A.C. 3Q**	**A**	**Alfreton Town**	**449**	**D 0 - 0**		
15	**14**	**F.A.C.3Qr**	**H**	**Alfreton Town**	**848**	**L 1 - 3**	**Green 90**	
16	**18**	**F.A.T. 1Q**	**A**	**Eastwood Town**	**504**	**W 2 - 0**	**Howell 18 Istead 66**	
17	21		H	Bradford PA	289	D 0 - 0		
18	25		H	Hednesford Town	541	L 0 - 1		3
19	29		A	F.C.United	1550	L 1 - 3	Garner 41	
20	**Nov 1**	**F.A.T. 2Q**	**A**	**Ashton United**	**142**	**W 2 - 0**	**Cahill 48 Douglas 60**	
21	8		A	Frickley Athletic	226	D 1 - 1	Pringle 71	5
22	15		A	Eastwood Town	640	D 2 - 2	Cooke 1 (og) **Cahill** 22	
23	**22**	**F.A.T 3Q**	**A**	**Chasetown**	**471**	**W 2 - 1**	**Morgan-Smith 25 Cahill 37**	
24	29		H	Witton Albion	361	W 3 - 1	**Cahill** 18 Garner 42 Murphy 69	8
25	Dec 6		A	Prescott Cables	175	W 2 - 0	Douglas 16 **Cahill** 58	
26	9		H	Boston United	270	D 1 - 1	Douglas 10	6
27	**16**	**F.A.T. 1R**	**H**	**Ossett Town**	**205**	**W 3 - 2**	**Douglas 67 Istead 83 Howell 87**	
28	20		A	Ashton United	130	D 1 - 1	Douglas 59	5
29	26		H	Matlock Town	779	D 2 - 2	Briscoe 11 Douglas 90	
30	**Jan 13**	**F.A.T. 2R**	**H**	**Kidderminster Harriers**	**401**	**L 3 - 5**	**Cahill 27 75 Newsham 60**	
31	17		H	Nantwich Town	386	W 3 - 2	**Cahill** 43 (pen) 66 Newsham 76	5
32	31		H	Ashton United	341	W 2 - 1	Pringle 18 **Cahill** 24	6
33	Feb 14		A	Matlock Town	415	D 1 - 1	Thompson 37	5
34	21		H	Worksop Town	510	D 3 - 3	Weaver 34 Newsham 56 Douglas 80	8
35	24		A	Hednesford Town	351	W 1 - 0	**Cahill** 51	
36	28		H	Leigh Genesis	399	W 3 - 1	Duncan 41 **Cahill** 42 Newsham 65	
37	Mar 7		A	Cammell Laird	124	W 1 - 0	Douglas 76	
38	14		H	Buxton	554	W 1 - 0	Weaver 41	3
39	17		H	Whitby Town	368	W 1 - 0	Newsham 15	
40	21		A	Ossett Town	154	W 3 - 1	Douglas 13 Morgan-Smith 21 42	3
41	24		H	Cammel Laird	364	W 2 - 1	**Cahill** 35 Sleath 53	
42	26		A	Guiseley	240	D 1 - 1	Hurst 40	2
43	28		H	Prescott Cables	465	W 3 - 0	McIntosh 27 (og) Istead 76 Douglas 89	
44	31		A	North Ferriby United	198	D 0 - 0		
45	April 4		A	Kendal Town	262	D 1 - 1	Newsham 15	2
46	10		H	Eastwood Town	2288	W 1 - 0	Newsham 28	2
47	13		A	Boston United	1100	D 0 - 0		
48	15		A	Nantwich Town	537	W 1 - 1	Pringle 15	
49	18		H	F.C.United	1313	L 0 - 1		2
50	21		H	Marine	341	W 5 - 0	Douglas 21 Wilde 24 **CAHILL** 3 (45pen 58 66)	
51	25		A	Whitby Town	504	L 0 - 3		2
52	**28**	**Play-Off SF**	**H**	**Kendal Town**	**653**	**W 4 - 3***	**Sleath 32 Cahill 59 (pen) Newsham 61 Murphy 108**	
53	**May 2**	**Play-Off F**	**H**	**Nantwich Town**	**1784**	**W 2 - 1***	**Pringle 10 Weaver 94 aet**	

Average Home Att: 565 (307) **Goals** 85 53

Best Position: 1st **Worst:** 8th

Goalscorers: Cahill 17, Douglas 15, Morgan-Smith 10, Newsham 8, Howell 4, Istead 4, Pringle 4, Duncan 3, Weaver 3, Adam 2, Garner 2, Murphy 2, Sleath 2, Green 1, Briscoe 1, Hurst 1, Mitchell 1, Thompson 1, Wilde 1. Own Goals 3.

CURRENT SQUAD AS OF BEGINING OF 2009-10 SEASON

GOALKEEPERS	HT	WT	D.O.B	AGE	P.O.B	CAREER	APPS	GOA
(F)Rory Boulding	5'10"	11 03	4/3/87	21	Sheffield	Mansfield 9/07 -	4	0
David Bevan	6'02"	13 00	24/6/89	20	Cork	Aston Villa, Tamworth (L) 9/08, Ilkeston (L) 8/09		
Dan Lowson			4/2/88	21		Gretna, Newcastle Blue Star, Ilkeston 7/09		
DEFENDERS								
Tom Bonner	6'00"	11 06	6/2/88	21	Camden	Northampton Rel 1/07, Bedford (SL) 2/06, Nuneaton (L) 8/06, Rushden & D 1/07 Rel 8/07, Bedford (L) 2/07, Heybridge (L) 3/07, Corby T 8/07, Hinckley U 1/08, Solihull Moors 2/09, Corby T 6/09, Ilkeston 8/09		
Paul Dempsey	5'11"	12 00	3/12/81	27	Birkenhead	Sheff Utd, Northampton 3/01 Rel c/s 02, Aukland Kingz (NZ) 4/02, Scarborough 1/03 Rel c/s 03, RKSV Leonidas Rotterdam (Holl) 5/03, Worksop 8/04, Hucknall 6/06, Worksop 6/08, Wakefield 2/09, Ilkeston 6/09		
James Dudgeon	6'02"	12 04	19/3/81	28	Newcastle	Barnsley Rel c/s 03,Lincoln C (SL) 11/00, Scarborough 5/03, Halifax 9/03 Rel 4/04, Worksop 7/04, York 6/05 Rel 5/07, Stalybridge 6/07, Gateshead (L) 11/07, Gainsborough 1/08, Worksop (L) 10/08, Newcastle Blue Star 11/08, Wakefield 2/09, Ilkeston 6/09		
Richie Holmes	6'01"	13 00	1/10/90	18		Chesterfield Rel c/s 09, Ilkeston 6/09		
Kieran Murphy	5'11"	11 00	21/12/87	21	Kingston	MK Dons Rel 5/08, Aylesbury (L) 8/06, Maidenhead (L) 11/06, Hendon (L) 12/06, Walton & H (L) 3/07, Crawley (SL) 11/07 (07/08 23,1), Ilkeston c/s 08		
Charlie O'Loughlin	6'01"	13 02	17/3/89	20	Birmingham	Port Vale Rel 4/08, Nantwich (L) 11/07, Hinckley U (L) 1/08, Nantwich 6/08, Ilkeston 6/09		
Luke Waterfall	6'02"	12 11	30/7/90	19	Sheffield	Barnsley (Scholar), Tranmere 7/08 Rel c/s 09, Altrincham (L) 10/08, Oxford U (Trial) 7/09, York C (Trial) 7/09, Ilkeston 8/09		
Alex White			28/8/88	21		Middlesbrough (Yth), Hartlepool (Yth), Gretna, Stranraer 8/07 Rel 12/08, Blyth 12/08, Tow Law 2/09, Mansfield (Trial) 4/09, Ilkeston 6/09		
MIDFIELDERS								
Josh Burge						Grimsby (Scholar) Rel c/s 08, Aston Villa (Trial) 1/07, Appalachian State University (USA) c/s 08, Ilkeston 6/09		
Chris Davies	5'10"	11 10	8/4/84	25	Rotherham	Barnsley (Yth), Leeds U (Yth), Rotherham (Yth), Lincoln C, Spalding (L) 2/03, Stamford (L) 9/03, Hucknall 1/04, Worksop 8/04, Stocksbridge 9/04, Belper 9/04, Lincoln U 12/04, Spalding U c/s 07, Frickley 1/08, Ilkeston 6/09		
Sam Duncum	5'09"	11 02	18/2/87	22	Sheffield	Rotherham Rel 5/08, York C (2ML) 2/08, Ilkeston 5/08		
Liam Green	5'09"	10 00	17/3/88	21	Grimsby	Doncaster Rel c/s 07, Guiseley (L) 12/06, Boston U 7/07, Ilkeston 7/09		
Mitchell Griffiths			22/10/90	18		Boston U, Ilkeston 7/09		
Dan Holmes	6'00"	12 00	17/11/86	22	Burton	Port Vale Rel c/s 06, Burton 7/06 Rel 5/09, Ilkeston 7/09		
FORWARDS								
Jon Douglas					Coventry	Rugby U, Kidderminster, Tamworth, Rugby U 1/04, Bedworth 7/05, Grantham 5/06, Hednesford 3/07, Lincoln U 6/07, Shepshed D 9/07, Lincoln U 11/07, Ilkeston 1/08		
David Graham	5'10"	11 05	6/10/78	30	Edinburgh	Rangers, Dunfermline 11/98, Inverness Caledonian (2ML) 1/01, Lincoln C, Sheffield FC 3/09, Torquay 3/01, Wigan 6/04, Sheff Wed 8/05, Huddersfield (SL) 1/06, Bradford C (5ML) 7/06, Torquay (SL) 3/07, Gillingham 8/07 Rel 1/08, Lincoln C 7/08 Rel 12/08, Sheffield FC 3/09, Ilkeston 8/09		
Joe Harris	6'03"	13 04	13/7/91	18		Swansea (Scholar) Rel c/s 09, Ilkeston 7/09		
Amari Morgan-Smith	6'00"	13 06	3/4/89	20	Wolverhampton	Wolves (Yth), Crewe (Scholar), Alsager T (WE) 3/07, Stockport 8/07 Rel c/s 08, Ilkeston 6/08		
Gary Ricketts			13/7/75	34	Nottingham	Notts Forest (Yth), Heanor, Arnold, Hinckley U c/s 99, Cambridge U (Trial) 1/00, Hucknall £1,500 3/01, Nuneaton 5/07, Hucknall 9/07, Tamworth 3/09, Ilkeston 6/09		

ILKESTON TOWN

Formed: 1945

Nickname: The Robins.

Club Colours: Red shirts, red shorts, red socks.

Change Colours: Blue and black striped shirts, black shorts, black socks.

Club Sponsor: Belfield Furnishings Ltd

Previous League: Northern Premier League

Ground address: New Manor Ground, Awsworth Road, Ilkeston, Derbyshire DE7 8JF.

Telephone. No: 0115 944 429496

Fax: 0115 944 42949

Mobile: 07887 832 125

Social Club: 0115 932 4094

Email: kfootball@tiscali.co.uk

Club Website: www.ilkeston-townfc.co.uk

Simple Directions: From M1 jct26. Exit onto A610 towards Ripley, take first exit (to Awsworth) and Ilkeston (A6906) follow bypass signed Ilkeston A6906. Turn right after half a mile (signed Cotmanhay). Ground 400 yards on left.

Capacity: 3,029 **Seats**: 550 **Covered**: 2,000 **Floodlights**:Yes

Clubhouse: Open Thursday to Sundays and Matchdays.

Club Shop: Wide range of souvenirs etc.

PROGRAMME EDITOR

Mic Capill

Tel: (M) 07887 788 727

Email: mic.capill@live.co.uk

CLUB STATISTICS

RECORD

Attendance: (Manor Ground) 9,592 v Peterborough Utd, FAC 4thQ, 1955-56.
(New Manor Ground) 2,538 v Rushden and Dia. FAC 1st Round 1999/00.
Victory: 14-2 v Codnor M.W. 1946-47
Defeat: 1-11 v Grantham Town 1947-48 0-10 v VS Rugby 1985-86
Goalscorer: Jackie Ward - 141
Career Appearances: Terry Swincoe - 377
Transfer Fee Paid: £ 7,500 to Southport for Justin O'Reilly 1998
Received: £25,000 from Peterborough United for Francis Green

SENIOR HONOURS
Midland Counties League Champions 1967/68.
West Midlands League Champions 1993/94
West Midlands Division One Champions 1991/92.
Central Alliance Champions 1951/52, 52/53, 53/54, 54/55.
Derbyshire Senior Cup 1948/49, 52/53, 55/56, 57/58, 62/63, 82/83, 92/93, 98/99, 99/00, 05/06, 06/07.
West Midlands League (Premier) Cup 1993/94.
West Midlands League (Div One) Cup 1991/92.
Central Alliance League Cup 1957/58
Central Midlands League Cup 1986/87.

PREVIOUS
Leagues: Notts & Derbyshire 1945-47. Central Alliance 1947-61.
Midlands Counties 1961-71, 73-82.
Southern League 1971-73, 95-04.
Northern Counties East 1982-86. Central Midlands 1986-90.
West Midlands Regional 1990-94.
Northern Premier 2004-09.
Previous Ground: Manor Ground 1945-1992.

NORTHWICH VICTORIA

no up-to-date image available

CLUB PERSONNEL

Chairman: James Rushe.

Additional Directors:

Martin Rushe, Howard Roberts.

Secretary: Derek Nuttall.

10 Cedar Close, Lostock Gralam,

Northwich, CW9 7XA

Tel: (H) 01606 43350 (M) 07787 345082

(B) 01606 815 200 Email: drnuttall@aol.com

Press Officer: David Thomas

Tel: (H): 01606 45144. (B): 01606 815 200

(M): 07798 564 596

E-Mail: dave.thomas@northwichvics.co.uk

Manager: Andy Preece.

Club therapist: Gary Thompson.

No supporter of a football club could possibly have imagined a worse nightmare for a season containing one disaster after another. The Vics had hung on for two years and many loyal and long standing followers had been lost despite the move to a fine new stadium. Day to day running of their 'new' club upset many supporters and relegation was the final disappointment.

The first victory wasn't achieved until the eleventh league game and by then the club were in the relegation zone. AFC Telford United beat Northwich in the F.A.Cup and the managerial merry go round took on the characteristics of a ridiculous farce. Dino Maamria, who had kept The Vics up in 2008, left in October and was replaced by Mike Marsh, who was soon to move on to be coach of Bradford City. Then Steve King, who had been a great success at Lewes, took up the reigns, but found the general running of the club so different from what he had expected and left when the owner locked the club officials out of Victoria Stadium forcing The Vics to play at Moss Lane, Altrincham.

There were no cup successes to lift morale around the club, as a First Round defeat at home to York City in the F.A.Trophy followed their F.A.Cup exit, but there was an extraordinary end to the season when, under the guidance of Andy Preece only one game was lost in the last nine with a final six consecutive victories.

What a glorious end to a terrible season. and now there must be hope, at least on the playing field.

NORTHWICH VICTORIA

BEST LGE ATT.: **1,709** v Wrexham
LOWEST: **428** v Histon

No.	Date	Comp	H/A	Opponents	Att:	Result	Goalscorers	Pos
1	Aug 9	BSP	H	Cambridge United	1445	L 0 - 1		
2	12		A	Burton Albion	1701	D 1 - 1	Stamp 29	
3	16		A	Grays Athletic	523	L 1 - 2	Flynn 85	
4	23		H	York City	1065	D 2 - 2	McGurk 15 (og) **Allan** 42	21
5	25		A	Mansfield Town	2741	L 2 - 3	Stamp 60 Steele 86	21
6	30		A	Crawley Town	776	L 2 - 5	Steele 50 Mullan 54	22
7	Sept 2		H	Oxford United	973	L 1 - 2	Stamp 50	
8	7		A	Torquay United	1752	L 1 - 2	Steele 52	22
9	13		H	Forest Green Rovers	603	D 0 - 0		23
10	20		A	Histon	829	L 1 - 2	Grand 19	23
11	23		H	Barrow	906	W 2 - 1	Welch 47 Burns 85	23
12	27		H	Weymouth	700	L 2 - 3	Roberts 60 Burns 74	24
13	Oct 4		A	Kettering Town	1401	L 1 - 2	Byrom 53	24
14	7		H	Kidderminster Harriers	725	D 1 - 1	Brown 89	
15	11		H	Grays Athletic	579	W 2 - 0	Crowell 70 Stamp 85	
16	**14**	**SS N2**	**A**	**Stafford Rangers**	**327**	**L 1 - 3**	**Allan 55**	
17	18		A	Lewes	669	W 3 - 2	**Allan** 8 Stamp 11 Williams 52 (pen)	
18	**28**	**F.A.Cup 4Q**	**H**	**AFC Telford United**	**1003**	**L 0 - 3**		
19	Nov 1		H	Eastbourne Borough	564	L 1 - 2	Burns 54	22
20	8		H	Burton Albion	932	L 0 - 1		22
21	15		A	Stevenage Borough	2536	D 1 - 1	Stamp 28	
22	22		A	Salisbury City	999	D 1 - 1	Winn 56	22
23	29		H	Crawley Town	610	L 0 - 1		22
24	Dec 6		A	Eastbourne Borough	1086	L 1 - 4	Wagstaff 26	23
25	**16**	**F.A.T 1R**	**H**	**York City**	**393**	**L 0 - 2**		
26	20		A	Rushden & Diamonds	1134	L 1 - 2	Crowell 15	24
27	26		H	Altrincham	1400	L 0 - 1		24
28	Jan 17		H	Histon	428	L 1 - 2	Crowell 14	24
29	24		A	Weymouth	1105	L 0 - 3		24
30	27		A	Wrexham	3722	L 3 - 4	Bailey 59 85 Robinson 82	
31	31		A	Woking	1092	L 1 - 4	Bailey 56	
32	Feb 3		A	Altrincham	1209	L 0 - 1		24
33	15		A	Kiddermister Harriers	1410	W 2 - 1	Reeves 30 McDonald 82	24
34	18		A	Forest Green Rovers	744	L 0 - 3		
35	24		H	Kettering Town	479	D 0 - 0		
36	28		A	Barrow	1437	D 0 - 0		23
37	Mar 7		H	Stevenage Borough	801	L 0 - 1		23
38	15		A	Cambridge United	2662	L 1 - 4	Joyce 35	23
39	17		H	Wrexham	1709	L 1 - 2	Perry 13	
40	21		H	Torquay United	705	L 2 - 3	Perry 34 **Allan** 56	23
41	28		H	Rushden & Diamonds	687	W 4 - 2	BYROM 3 (13 57 68) Joyce 71	23
42	31		H	Salisbury City	532	D 1 - 1	Grand 23	23
43	April 4		A	Ebbsfleet United	1003	L 0 - 1		23
44	7		H	Woking	450	W 2 - 0	Grand 25 Horrocks 78	23
45	11		A	York City	2421	W 2 - 1	**Allan** 26 90	23
46	13		H	Mansfield Town	858	W 2 - 0	Grand 31 Elam 76	
47	18		H	Lewes	487	W 3 - 0	Grand 32 **Allan** 78 83	Rel
48	23		H	Ebbsfleet United	474	W 2 - 0	Burns 61 **Allan** 83	23
49	26		A	Oxford United	10298	W 2 - 1	Mullan 45 Crowell 90	

Average Home Att: **787 (908)** **Goals** **56 81**

Best Position: 21st **Worst:** 24th

Goalscorers: Allan 9, Stamp 6, Grand 5, Crowell 4, Burns 4, Byrom 4, Bailey 3, Steele 3, Joyce 2, Mullan 2, Perry, 2, Brown 1, Elam 1, Flynn 1, Horrocks 1, McDonald 1, Reeves 1, Roberts 1, Robinson 1, Wagstaff 1, Welch 1, Williams 1, Winn 1. Own Goals 1.

Rel: Relegated.

TYNAN 1	SUTTON 2	ROBERTS 5	BROWN 3	WELCH 4	CROWELL 6	BARRATT 11	BYROM 8	MULLAN 7	STAMP 24	STEELE 9	FLYNN 13	BYRNE 16	ALLAN 10	JONES 12	BAILEY 15	WILLIAMS 23	ASPIN 17	P MARSH 21	GRAND 25	BURNS 20	WINN 19	RILEY 31	FARRAN 22	RICHARDS 32	HORROCKS 27	YUSSUF 33	WAGSTAFF 34	ANTWI 30	LODGE 22	STEVE ROBINSON 5	CLARKE 35	PRICE 18	ELAM 36	MURRAY 37	MCDONALD 38	STEVENS 19	CONROY 31	REEVES 26	PERRY 14	MEADOWCROFT 5	JOYCE 18	
X	X	X	X	X	X	X	X	X	X	X	S	S	S	U	U																											1
X	X	X	X	X	X		X	X	X	X		S	U	U	U	X																										2
X		X	X	X	X		X	X	X	X	S	S	U	U	S	X	X																									3
X	X	X	X	X	X		X	X	X	S	X	S	X	U	S	U																										4
X	X	X	X	X	X			S	X	S	X	X	X	U	U	X	S																									5
X	U	X	X		S			S	X	X	X	X	X	U	X		X	S																								6
X		X	X		S	U		X	X	X	X	S	X	U	X		X																									7
X		X		X	X	S		S	X	X	X		X	U	U		X	S	X																							8
X		X	X		X	S			X		X	S	X	U	U	X	X	S	X																							9
X		X	X	U	X	S			X		X		X	U	S	X	X	S	X																							10
X		X		X	X	U	S	X			X		X	U		X	X	S	X	X																						11
X		X	S	X	X		X	X	S		S	U	X			X	X		X	X																						12
X		X	U	X	X		X	X	S		U	X	X	U	U		X		X	X																						13
X		X	X	U	X		X	X	S		S	X	X	U	U		X		X	X																						14
X		X	X	U	X		X	X	S		S	X	X	U			X		X	X																						15
		X	X	X				S			X	X	X	X	S	U	X		X	U	X																					16
X		X	X	X					X				X	U		X	X		X	X	X	S	S																			17
X		X	X	X	X			S			U	S	X	U		X	X		X	X	X	U	U																			18
U		X		X	X			S			X		X	X			X		X	X	X	X		S	S																	19
U		X	U	X				S	S		X		X	X	S		X		X	X	X					X	X															20
		X	S		X			S	X		S			X	U		X		X	X	X					X	X	X														21
U		X	X	U	X			S			X			X	U		X			X	X					X	X	X	S													22
X			X	U	X		X		S	S	U						X		X	X	X					X	X		S	X												23
				S	X		S		X	X			U				X		X	S	X					X	X	X	U	X	X											24
U			U	X	X			X	X	X	X		S						X	S	X					X		X			X	U										25
X			X	U	X				X	U			S	U			X		X	U	X					X		X	X			X										26
X			X	U	X				X	S			S				X		X	S	X					X		X	X		U	X										27
X			X		X				U	X			X		S		X		X										X	X	S	U	X	X	U							28
					X					X			X		U		U		X										X	X	X	U	X	X		X	X	S				29
					X				S	X					S		X		X										X	X	X	U	X	X	U	X	U	X				30
				S	X		U			X					X		X												X	X	X	U	X	X	U	X	U	X				31
					X		X		S	X					X		X												U	X	X	U	X	X	U	X	S	X				32
					X		X	X	U	S					X		U		X										S	X	X		X		X	X	U	X				33
					X		X	X	S	S					X		U		X										S	X	X		X		X	X	U	X				34
			X		X	S	X	X					X		X		X		X	X					U						X		X			S		S				35
			X		X	X	X	S					X		X		X		X	S				U	U						X		X			U		X				36
			X		X	S		X							X		X		X	S				U	U						X		X			U		X	X			37
			X		X	U	S	S					X		X		X			U					S						X		X						X	X	X	38
			X		X		S	S	S				X		X		X			U					X						X		X						X	X	X	39
			X		X		S	U	S				X		X		X		X	U					X						X		X						X	U	X	40
			X		X		X	U					X		X		S		X	S					X						X		X						X	U	X	41
			X		X		X	X					X		X				X	U				U	X						X		S						X	U	X	42
			X		X		X	X					X		X				X	S		U		U	S						X		X						X	S	X	43
			X		X		X	S					X		X				X	X			U	S	S						X		X							X	X	44
			X		X		X	S					X		X				X	X		U		S	U						X		X							X	X	45
			X		X		X	S					X						X	X		S		S	X						X		X							X	X	46
			X				X	S					X		X				X	X		S	S	U	X						X		X							X	X	47
							X	X					X		X				X	X		S	U	U	X						X		X							X	X	48
					S		X	X					X		X				X	X		S	U	U	X						X		X							X	X	49

Total League Appearances

TYNAN	SUTTON	ROBERTS	BROWN	WELCH	CROWELL	BARRATT	BYROM	MULLAN	STAMP	STEELE	FLYNN	BYRNE	ALLAN	JONES	BAILEY	WILLIAMS	ASPIN	P MARSH	GRAND	BURNS	WINN	RILEY	FARRAN	RICHARDS	HORROCKS	YUSSUF	WAGSTAFF	ANTWI	LODGE	STEVE ROBINSON	CLARKE	PRICE	ELAM	MURRAY	MCDONALD	STEVENS	CONROY	REEVES	PERRY	MEADOWCROFT	JOYCE	
20	4	20	30	12	39	2	23	18	15	12	11	5	31	4	20	8	30	0	34	18	9	1	0	0	8	7	5	5	6	9	22	2	21	5	2	6	1	7	7	8	12	**X**
0	0	0	2	2	3	5	5	14	11	6	6	6	3	0	6	0	2	5	0	6	0	5	2	4	4	0	0	0	4	0	1	0	1	0	0	1	1	2	0	1	0	**S**
3	1	0	2	7	0	3	1	2	2	1	2	1	3	16	10	1	3	0	0	5	0	2	3	7	4	0	0	0	2	0	1	5	0	0	4	2	4	0	0	3	0	**U**

Total Cup Appearances

TYNAN	SUTTON	ROBERTS	BROWN	WELCH	CROWELL	BARRATT	BYROM	MULLAN	STAMP	STEELE	FLYNN	BYRNE	ALLAN	JONES	BAILEY	WILLIAMS	ASPIN	P MARSH	GRAND	BURNS	WINN	RILEY	FARRAN	RICHARDS	HORROCKS	YUSSUF	WAGSTAFF	ANTWI	LODGE	STEVE ROBINSON	CLARKE	PRICE	ELAM	MURRAY	MCDONALD	STEVENS	CONROY	REEVES	PERRY	MEADOWCROFT	JOYCE	
1	0	2	2	3	2	0	0	1	1	1	2	1	2	1	0	1	2	0	3	1	3	0	0	0	0	1	0	1	0	0	1	0	0	0	0	0	0	0	0	0	0	**X**
0	0	0	0	0	0	0	0	2	0	0	0	1	1	0	1	0	0	0	0	1	0	0	0	0	0	0	0	0	0	0	0	0	0	0	0	0	0	0	0	0	0	**S**
1	0	0	1	0	0	0	0	0	0	0	1	0	0	1	0	1	0	0	0	1	0	1	1	0	0	0	0	0	0	0	0	1	0	0	0	0	0	0	0	0	0	**U**

ALSO PLAYED: BARNES S(2). M MARSH X(6). ALMEIDA S(7) U(12). CARR X(7,9,10) S(11). KING X(8). BENJAMIN S(15,17,18) X(16). WHARTON S(16) U(17). MOORE U(19). STUART ROBINSON U(21,29). WESTHEAD U(35). WHITLEY X(37,38) U(39).

NORTHWICH VICTORIA

CURRENT SQUAD AS OF BEGINING OF 2009-10 SEASON

GOALKEEPERS	HT	WT	D.O.B	AGE	P.O.B	CAREER	APPS	GOA
Curtis Aspden	6'01"	11 12	16/11/87	21	Blackburn	Burnley (Yth), Bolton (Yth), Hull C, Scarborough (3ML) 8/06, Harrogate T (6ML) 6/07, Boston U (L) 12/07, Farsley Celtic (L) 1/08 Perm 1/08, Northwich 8/09		
Kyle Clancy						Blackpool, Droylsden 7/08, Salford C 2/09, Burscough 3/09, Northwich 7/09		
James Coates			22/2/85	24		Man City (Jun), Mansfield (Sch) Rel c/s 04, Worcester 10/04, Burton 3/05, Moor Green 7/05, Leigh RMI 2/06, Worcester c/s 06, Bromsgrove (L) 11/06, Hucknall 2/07, Kidsgrove A (L) 3/07, Kidsgrove A c/s 07, Altrincham (Trial) c/s 08, Vauxhall Motors 8/08, Northwich 7/09		
DEFENDERS								
Mike Aspin			20/10/89	19	Blackburn	Preston (Scholar), Northwich 8/08 Rel 3/09, Farsley Celtic 3/09, Nahon Pathom (Tha), Northwich 7/09	32	0
Matt Bailey	6'05"	11 06	12/3/86	23	Nantwich	Nantwich (Yth), Stockport 11/02, Altrincham (L) 3/04, Scunthorpe (L) 8/04, Northwich 3/05, Crewe Undisc 5/05 Rel 5/08, Hereford (L) 9/05, Southport (L) 1/06, Lancaster (L) 3/06, Barrow (2ML) 1/07, Weymouth (SL) 3/08, Northwich 5/08, Hinckley U (L) 12/08	26	3
Junior Brown	5'09"	10 12	7/5/89	20	Crewe	Crewe Rel c/s 08, Kidsgrove (L) 12/07, Witton (L) 3/08, FC Halifax c/s 08, Northwich 8/09		
Ryan Brown	5'10"	11 02	15/3/85	24	Stoke	Port Vale Rel c/s 05, Leek T 8/05, Northwich 6/06	32	1
Mark Cadwallader	6'00"	10 05	8/7/88	21		Chester (Yth), Lancaster (L) 11/06, Bangor C 3/07, Connahs Quay 6/07, Airbus UK 7/08, Northwich 6/09		
Simon Grand	6'00"	10 03	23/2/84	25	Chorley	Rochdale Rel c/s 04, Carlisle 8/04, Grimsby (L) 1/07 Undisc 1/07 Rel c/s 07, Morecambe 8/07 Rel c/s 08, Northwich 9/08, Chester (Trial) 9/08	34	5
Nat Kerr	6'00"	10 10	31/10/87	21	Manchester	Crewe, Rotherham 1/07 Rel c/s 08, Northwich (SL) 11/07, Woodley Sports 8/08 Rel 9/08, Barrow 10/08 Rel 5/09, Northwich 7/09		
DannyMeadowcroft	6'04"	12 05	22/5/85	24	Macclesfield	Stockport, Mossley (L) 10/04 Perm 11/04, Morecambe 7/06 Rel 5/07, Mossley (L) 11/06, Bradford PA 7/07, Ossett T 10/07, Northwich 1/08 Rel 5/08, Droylsden c/s 08, FC Halifax 10/08, Northwich 3/09	9	0
MIDFIELDERS								
Lee Elam	5'08"	10 12	24/9/76	32	Bradford	Guiseley, Southport 11/98, Morecambe 8/02, Halifax 5/03, Yeovil (L) 10/03 Perm 11/03, Chester (L) 3/04, Hornchurch 5/04, Burton 11/04, Morecambe 11/04 Rel 5/05, Crawley 7/05 Rel 9/05, Weymouth 9/05, Exeter 1/07 Rel 5/08, Altrincham 7/08 Rel 1/09, Northwich 1/09	22	1
Ross Farran						Northwich	2	0
Ian Herring	6'01"	11 12	14/2/84	25	Swindon	Swindon, Salisbury (L) 12/02, Chippenham (L) 3/03, Chippenham (L) 12/03 Perm 1/04, Salisbury 9/07, Weston-Super-Mare (SL) 3/08, Northwich 7/09		
Mike O'Connor						Woodley Sports, Northwich 7/09		
Wayne Riley						Northwich	6	0
Harry Winter						Trafford, Northwich 7/09		
FORWARDS								
Jonny Allan	6'00"	11 03	24/5/83	26	Penrith	Carlisle Rel c/s 02, Workington 8/02, Oxford U (Trial) 8/02 Northwich 8/02, Tranmere (Trial) 7/03, Lancaster 11/03, Halifax 12/03, Northwich 8/04	34	8
Aaron Burns	5'10"		8/11/87	21	Manchester	Man Utd (Scholar) Rel c/s 07, Leeds (Trial) 5/07, Afurelding (Ice) c/s 07, Cardiff C 7/07, FCUM 10/07, Northwich 1/08, Droylsden (3ML) 8/0824		4
Mark Danks	5'09"	10 08	8/2/84	25	Worley	Wolves (Scholar), Bradford City 7/02, Halesowen T (SL) 3/03, Hednesford 7/03. Aberystwyth 5/04, Forest Green 8/04, Stafford R (2ML) 9/04, Kettering (L) 3/05, Bromsgrove (L), Cirencester (L) 1/06, Worcester 1/06, Halesowen T 5/08, AFC Telford 2/09 Rel 5/09		
Cayne Hanley	5'10"		10/9/88	20	Manchester	Burnley Rel c/s 06, Kidderminster (L) 3/06, Hyde (L) 3/06, Yeovil (Trial) 4/06, Darlington (Trial) 7/06, York, Stalybridge 12/06, FCUM 9/07, Northwich 1/08 Rel 5/08, Leigh RMI (SL) 3/08, Woodley Sports 9/08, Northwich 8/09		
Luke Horrocks						Bury (Scholar), Chorley (WE) 9/04, Woodley Sports c/s 05, Northwich 11/07 Rel 5/08, Woodley Sports 8/08 Rel 9/08, Northwich 10/08	12	1
Jon Newby	6'00"	12 00	28/11/78	30	Warrington	Liverpool, Carlisle (L) 12/99, Crewe (2ML) 3/00, Sheff Utd (3ML) 8/00, Bury (2ML) 2/01 £100,000 3/01 Rel c/s 03, Huddersfield 8/03, York C (L) 3/04, Bury 8/04 Rel 5/06, Kidderminster (L) 3/06, Wrexham 8/06 Rel 12/06, Southport 1/07 Rel 5/07, Morecambe 8/07 Rel c/s 08, Morton c/s 08, Rel 5/09, Burton (SL) 9/08, Northwich 7/09		

LOANEES	HT	WT	DOB	AGE	POB	From - To	APPS	GOA
(M)Michael Carr	5'08"	10 07	6/12/83	25	Crewe	Morecambe 9/08 - Rel 1/09, Kidderminster 2/09 Rel 5/09, Stalybridge 7/09	4	0
(F)Peter Winn	6'00"	11 09	19/12/88	20	Cleethorpes	Scunthorpe (3ML) 10/08 - Barrow (L) 2/09	9	1
(M)Scott Wagstaff	5'10"	10 03	31/3/90	19	Maidstone	Charlton 11/08 -	5	1
(M)Rashid Yussuf	6'01"	11 07	23/9/89	19	Poplar	Charlton (2ML) 11/08 - Ebbsfleet (SL) 3/09, Rel c/s 09, Gillingham c/s 09	7	0
(D)Will Antwi	6'02"	12 08	19/10/82	26	Epsom	Wycombe (6WL) 11/08 - Rel 5/09	5	0
(M)Karl Murray	5'11"	12 06	26/8/82	27	London	Bromley 1/09 - Croydon Ath 2/09	5	0
(F)Kyle Perry	6'04"	14 05	5/3/86	23	Birmingham	Port Vale 3/09 - Mansfield 6/09	7	2
(M)Luke Joyce	5'11"	12 03	9/7/87	22	Bolton	Carlisle (SL) 3/09 - Rel 5/09, Accrington c/s 09	12	2

DEPARTURES	HT	WT	DOB	AGE	POB	From - To	APPS	GOA
(M)Michael Barnes	5'10"	11 05	24/6/88	21	Chorley	Man Utd 8/08 - Rel 8/08, Southport 10/08, FC Halifax 1/09, Lancaster (Trial) 6/09, AFC Fylde 8/09	1	0
(F)Martins Almeida							1	0
(M)Mark King	5'11"	12 04	6/6/88	21	Blackburn	Accrington 9/08 - Rel 9/08	1	0
(F)Phil Marsh	5'10"	11 13	15/11/86	22	St Helens	Blackpool 8/08 - Rel 9/08, Hyde U 10/08 Rel 11/08, Leigh Genesis 12/08, FCUM 3/09	5	0
(F)Dino Maamria	6'00"	12 02	18/2/74	35	Burnley	Rushden & D 11/08 - Stevenage Ass Man 11/08		
(F)Trevor Benjamin	6'02"	13 07	8/2/79	30	Kettering	Gainsborough 10/08 - Rel 10/08, Hednesford 11/08, Wellingborough 12/08, Kidsgrove 2/09, Tamworth 8/09	2	0
(F)Michael Byrne	5'10"	11 06	14/5/85	24	Ashton-u-Lyne	Stockport 2/05 - Rel 10/08, Forest Green, Stalybridge 12/08 Rel 1/09	11	0
(F)Ben Wharton	5'09"	11 00	17/6/90	19	Stockport	Padiham 10/08 - Rel 10/08, Atherton Coll 10/08, Radcliffe 11/08, Buxton 11/08	0	0
(M)Mike Marsh	5'08"	11 00	21/7/69	40	Liverpool	Preston as Ass Man 2/08 Caretaker man 10/08 - Resigned 11/08, Bradford PA (Ass Man) 11/08	1	0
(M)Peter Moore	5'08"	11 01	13/8/88	21	Liverpool	Wigan 10/08 - Rel 11/08, Warrington 1/09, Southport 3/09, Bala T 8/09	0	0
(D)Mark Roberts	6'01"	12 00	16/10/83	25	Northwich	Accrington 5/08 - Stevenage (6WL) 11/08 £5,000 1/09	20	1
(D)Ritchie Sutton	6'00"	11 05	29/4/86	23	Stoke	Stafford R 5/08 - Rel 1/09, FC Halifax (L) 12/08 Perm 1/09, Nantwich 6/09	4	0
(M)Christopher Flynn	5'11"	12 04	5/11/87	21	Market Drayton	Stafford R 5/08 - Rel 1/09, Stafford R 1/09, Eastwood T 3/09 Rel 5/09, Nantwich 6/09	17	1
(D)Jay Conroy	6'02"	12 02	2/3/86	23	Ryegate	Havant & W 1/09 - Rel 2/09, AFC Wimbledon 3/09	2	0
(F)Dean McDonald	5'07"	10 12	19/2/86	23	Lambeth	Grays 1/09 - Rel 2/09, Tooting & M 3/09, Farnborough 5/09	2	1
(D)Steve Robinson			31/1/76	33	Edmonton	Chelmsford (6WL) 11/08 Perm 1/09 - Chelmsford 2/09, Farnborough 8/09	9	1
(G)Stuart Robinson	6'08"					ex Lewes 11/08 - Fisher 2/09	0	0
(M)Dean Lodge			16/4/86	23		Kingstonian 11/08 - Kingstonian 3/09, Grays (Trial) 6/09	10	0
(F)Damien Reeves	5'09"	11 10	18/12/85	23	Doncaster	Histon 1/09 - Farsley Celtic 3/09, Alfreton 7/09	9	1
(D)Paul Barratt			15/9/87	21	Manchester	Southport 5/08 - Rel 3/09, Fleetwood (L) 1/09, Southport 5/09	7	0
(M)Owen Price	5'09"	11 13	20/10/86	22	London	TPS Turku (Fin) 12/08 - Rel 4/09, Sweden, Farnborough 7/09	2	0
(M)Jamie Mullan			10/2/88	21	Nottingham	Rochdale 1/08 - Fleetwood 5/09	32	2
(M)Joel Byrom	6'00"	12 04	14/9/86	22	Oswaldtwistle	Clitheroe 1/08 - Stevenage £15,000 5/09	28	4
(G)Ryan Clarke	6'01"	12 00	30/4/82	27	Bristol	Salisbury (5WL) 11/08 Perm 1/09 - Oxford U 5/09	23	0
(F)Lee Steele	5'09"	12 05	8/12/73	35	Liverpool	Chester 8/07 - Barrow (SL) 2/09, Oxford C 6/09	18	3
(F)Darryn Stamp	6'01"	11 10	21/9/78	30	Beverley	Halifax 8/08 - Gateshead (SL) 3/09, Gainsborough 6/09	26	6
(M)Matthew Crowell	5'09"	10 10	3/7/84	25	Bridgend	Wrexham 1/08 - Central Coast Mariners (Trial) 5/09, Altrincham 7/09	42	4
(G)Scott Tynan	6'02"	13 03	27/11/83	25	Knowsley	Ebbsfleet 10/07 - Rel c/s 09	20	0
(D)Michael Welch	6'03"	11 12	11/1/82	27	Crewe	Accrington 7/07 - Altrincham (2ML) 2/09, Altrincham c/s 09	14	1
(D)Jamie Stevens	5'11"		25/2/89	20	Holbeach	Crawley 1/09 - Rel 6/09, Ebbsfleet (SL) 3/09	7	0
(G)Michael Jones	6'04"	12 05	3/12/87	21	Liverpool	Wrexham 5/08 - Rhyl (SL) 1/09, Hyde U 7/09	4	0
(G)Mark Westhead	6'02"	13 12	19/7/75	34	Blackpool	ex Droylsden 2/09 -	0	0
(M)Jeff Whitley	5'08"	11 06	28/1/79	30	Zambia	Woodley Sports 3/09 -	2	0
(M)Danny Williams	5'09"	10 01	2/3/81	28	Sheffield	Rushden & D 10/07 -	8	1
(F)Leonard Richards						Woodley Sports 10/08 -	4	0

NORTHWICH VICTORIA

Founded: 1874

Nickname: Vics, Greens or Trickies.

Club Colours: Green & white shirts, white shorts, white socks.

Change Colours: Yellow shirts, royal blue shorts, royal blue socks.

Club Sponsor: TBC.

Previous League: Northern Premier League

Ground Address:	Victoria Stadium, Wincham Avenue, Northwich, Cheshire CW9 6GB
Telephone:	01606 815 200
Facsimile:	01606 815 242
E-mail:	drnuttall@aol.com
Website:	www.northwichvics.co.uk

SIMPLE DIRECTIONS: From Jct 19 M6 follow A556 towards Northwich for about three miles. Turn right onto the A559 towards Lostock (as the road becomes a dual carriageway).Turn right at the traffic lights immediately before the Slow & Easy pub. Turn left at the crossroads by the Black Greyhound public house (signposted). Follow the road until the Renault Garage on the left and turn left into Wincham Avenue. The ground is at the bottom of the road on the right.

By Rail: Nearest Railway Stations are Northwich (1mile) or Hartford (2 miles)

CAPACITY:	5,300
Seats:	1.180
Covered:	3,700

Social Facilities Six Entertainment Boxes. Two Executive Suites. Herriots Bar will be open to all fans Italian and Spanish sections in a large restaurant.

Club Shop: Programmes and souvenirs available

no image available

PROGRAMME EDITOR

David Thomas
Tel: (H) 01606 45144 (M) 07798 564596
(B) 01606 815 200
Email: david.thomas@northwichvics.co.uk

CLUB STATISTICS

RECORDS

Attendance:
11,290 v Witton Albion Cheshire League Good Friday 1949

Victory: 17-0 v Marple Association 1883

Defeat: 3-10 v Port Vale 1931

Career Goalscorer: Peter Burns 160 1955 -1965

Career Apperances: Ken Jones 970 1969 -1985

Transfer Fee Paid:
£12,000 to Hyde United for Malcolm O'Connor August 1988

Transfer Fee Received:
£50,000 from Leyton Orient for Gary Fletcher June 1921
from Chester City for Neil Morton October 1990

SENIOR HONOURS

F.A.Trophy Winners 1983-84
Cheshire Senior Cup (x15)
Staffordshire Senior Cup (x3)

PREVIOUS

Leagues: The Combination 1890-1892, Football League Div 2 1892-94, The Combination 1894 1898 The Cheshire League: 1898-1900, Manchester 1900-12, Lancashire 1912-1919, Cheshire County 1919-1968 and Northern Premier League 1968-79.

REDDITCH UNITED

CLUB PERSONNEL

Chairman: Ken Rae.

Company Secretary: Ken Rae.

Additional Directors: Gary Whild, Dave Chatwin.

Secretary: Tim Delaney.

Correspondence c/o the club.

Tel: (M) 07827 963 212.

Email: sec.rufc@yahoo.co.uk

Commercial Manager: Debbie Cox.

Tel: (M) 07921 998 069.

Press Officer: As secretary.

Manager: Gary Whild.

Club therapist: Peter James

When the season has hardly started and your club settles in the bottom four, supporters fear the worst. However, by the end of the season Redditch followers had become used to a constant stop start campaign in which poor form was improved with occasional good performances, but the lack of a consistent run meant that 'The Reds" never really settled in the top half of the table.

A disappointingly quick departure from The F.A.Cup at Belper United was followed by an encouraging run in The F.A.Trophy. Cammell Laird were beaten after a replay away from home and an excellent 1-0 victory gained at Alfreton Town, before Forest Green Rovers proved too strong in the Second Round at The New Lawn.

By this time, early in the new year, there was still the hope that a consistent run could possibly produce a late challenge for a play off place, but with only one victory a slump to twentieth position brought quite the opposite. Local talk about a merger with Bromsgrove Rovers didn't appeal to the Reds's supporters but neither did the idea of relegation.

The last eleven games brought the most consistent spell of the season with just two defeats and produced nineteen points that saw Redditch United finish in a very pleasing fourteenth position.

REDDITCH UNITED

BEST LGE ATT.: **669** v AFC Telford United
LOWEST: **164** v Burscough

No.	Date	Comp	H/A	Opponents	Att:	Result	Goalscorers	Pos
1	Aug 9	BSN	H	Gateshead	392	L 0 - 2		
2	12		A	Blyth Spartans	1168	D 1 - 1	Downes 67	
3	16		A	Vauxhall Motors	143	D 1 - 1	Rikards 9	18
4	23		H	AFC Telford United	669	L 0 - 1		19
5	25		A	Tamworth	708	D 1 - 1	Storey 78	
6	30		H	Farsley Celtic	248	W 3 - 1	Daly 7 60 (pen) Verma 45	16
7	Sept 2		H	Hucknall Town	214	D 2 - 2	Johnson 44 Daly 57 (pen)	
8	6		A	Workington	403	W 1 - 0	Storey 60	12
9	13		A	Gainsborough Trinity	287	L 1 - 4	Downes 90	15
10	20		H	Southport	391	L 0 - 2		15
11	**23**	**SS N1**	**H**	**Solihull Moors**	**157**	**L 0 - 1**		
12	**27**	**F.A.C. 2Q**	**A**	**Belper Town**	**301**	**L 1 - 4**	**Storey 80**	
13	Oct 4		A	Stalybridge Celtic	479	D 3 - 3	Rawle 12 25 Downes 80	16
14	18		H	Blyth Spartans	179	W 2 - 0	Murray 53 Foley 87	
15	20		A	Hinckley United		L 2 - 4	Downes 10 Murphy 62	
16	25		A	Southport	639	W 3 - 2	Edwards 40 Rawle 58 Ayres 80	11
17	Nov 1		A	Stafford Rangers	556	W 1 - 0	Foley 38	
18	4		H	Alfreton Town	166	D 2 - 2	Foley 20 Verma 75	
19	8		H	Hinckley United	286	L 0 - 2		12
20	15		A	Droylsden	339	D 2 - 2	Ayres 20 Verma 56	13
21	**22**	**F.A.T. 3Q**	**H**	**Cammell Laird**	**200**	**D 1 - 1**	**Ayres 36**	
22	**25**	**F.A.T. 3Q r**	**A**	**Cammell Laird**	**132**	**W 2 - 0**	**Murray 57 Rawle 86**	
23	29		H	Burscough	164	L 1 - 2	Softley 64	14
24	**Dec 16**	**F.A.T 1st Rd**	**A**	**Alfreton Town**	**192**	**W 1 - 0**	**Smith 44**	
25	20		A	Gateshead	293	L 0 - 2		14
26	26		H	Solihull Moors	390	D 0 - 0		15
27	Jan 1		A	Solihull Moors	360	L 1 - 2	Edwards 7 (og)	
28	**11**	**F.A.T 2nd Rd**	**A**	**Forest Green Rovers**	**441**	**L 0 - 5**		
29	24		H	Droyslden	205	L 0 - 4		18
30	31		A	Hyde United	271	W 2 - 1	Robinson 23 **Beswick** 30	17
31	Feb 14		A	Fleetwood Town	1042	L 1 - 3	**Beswick** 33	17
32	21		H	King's Lynn	332	L 1 - 2	**Beswick** 82 (pen)	
33	24		A	Hucknall Town	475	W 2 - 0	**Beswick** 47 Storey 70	
34	28		H	Stalybridge Celtic	211	L 0 - 1		18
35	Mar 7		A	Harrogate Town	342	D 1 - 1	Hay 40	
36	10		H	Stafford Rangers	217	D 2 - 2	Heggs 49 Storey 59	
37	14		A	Burscough	201	L 0 - 1		19
38	21		H	Gainsborough Trinity	280	D 1 - 1	**Beswick** 82 (pen)	20
39	24		H	Fleetwood Town	221	D 1 - 1	Spittle 77	
40	28		A	Farsley Celtic	241	W 2 - 1	Hay 32 Byrne 53	18
41	31		A	Blyth Spartans	586	L 0 - 1		
42	April 4		H	Workington	204	W 2 - 0	**Beswick** 15 Storey 71	18
43	7		H	Vauxhall Motors	216	W 2 - 1	Hay 13 Storey 71	
44	11		A	AFC Telford United	2028	D 1 - 1	**Beswick** 64	17
45	13		H	Tamworth	615	D 1 - 1	Byrne 13	
46	18		H	Hyde United	337	W 1 - 0	Byrne 90	15
47	21		H	Harrogate Town	244	W 2 - 1	Byrne 23 **Beswick** 66	
48	25		A	Alfreton Town	522	L 0 - 2		14

Average Home Att: **294 (406)** **Goals** **54 72**

Best Position: 11th **Worst:** 20th

Goalscorers: Beswick 8, Downes 5, Storey 5, Rawle 4, Byrne 4, Ayres 3, Foley 3, Storey 3, Verma 3, Daly 2, Hay 3, Murray 1, Edwards 1, Heggs 1, Johnson 1, Murphy 1, Robinson 1, Rikards 1, Softley 1, Smith 1, Spittle 1. Own Goals 1.

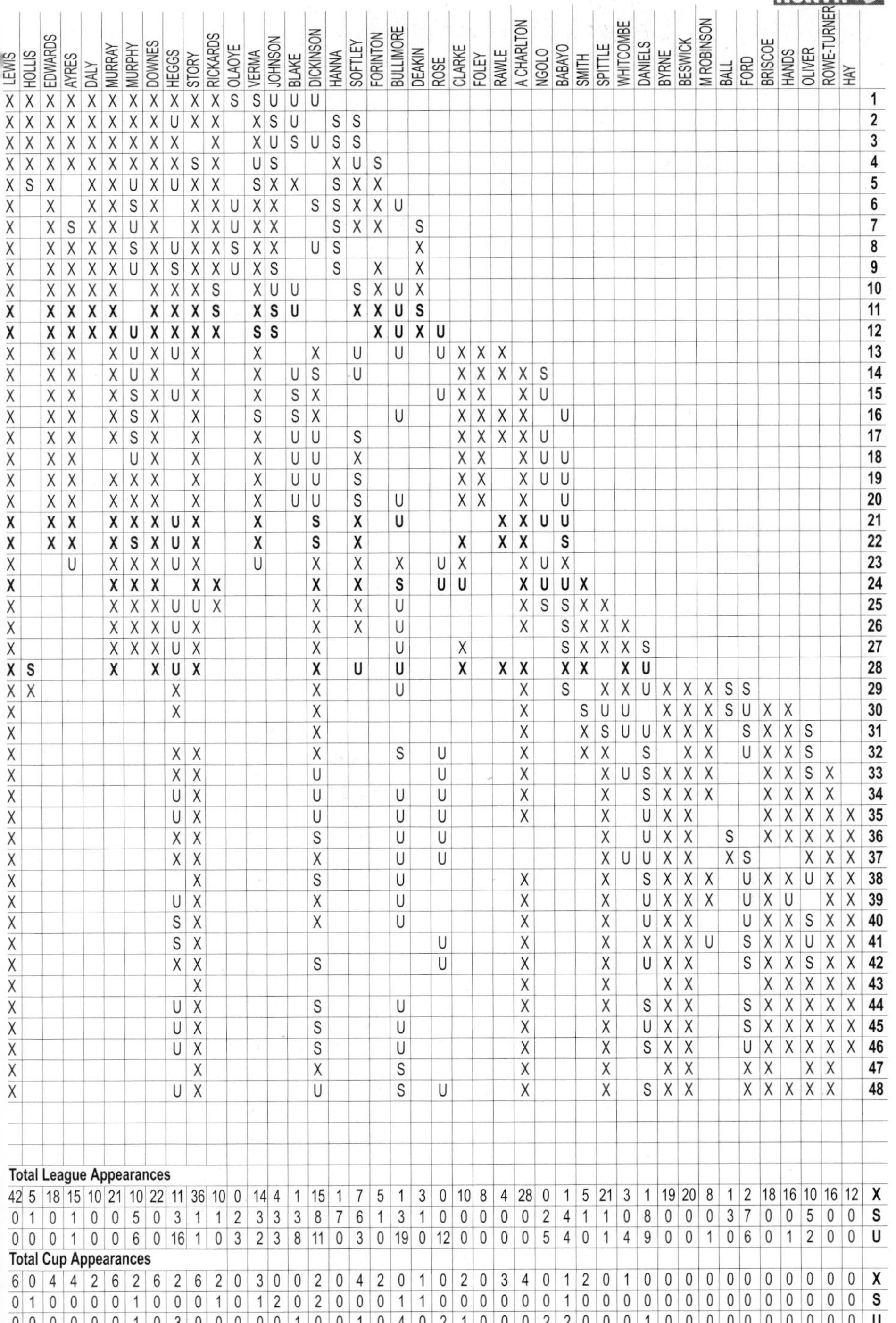

LEWIS	HOLLIS	EDWARDS	AYRES	DALY	MURRAY	MURPHY	DOWNES	HEGGS	STORY	RICKARDS	OLAOYE	VERMA	JOHNSON	BLAKE	DICKINSON	HANNA	SOFTLEY	FORINTON	BULLIMORE	DEAKIN	ROSE	CLARKE	FOLEY	RAWLE	A CHARLTON	NGOLO	BABAYO	SMITH	SPITTLE	WHITCOMBE	DANIELS	BYRNE	BESWICK	M ROBINSON	BALL	FORD	BRISCOE	HANDS	OLIVER	ROWE-TURNER	HAY	
X	X	X	X	X	X	X	X	X	X	X	S	S	U	U	U																											1
X	X	X	X	X	X	X	X	U	X	X		X	S	U		S	S																									2
X	X	X	X	X	X	X	X	X		X		X	U	S	U	S	S																									3
X	X	X	X	X	X	X	X	X	S	X		U	S			X	U	S																								4
X	S	X		X	X	U	X	U	X	X		S	X	X		S	X	X																								5
X		X		X	X	S	X		X	X	U	X	X		S	S	X	X	U																							6
X		X	S	X	X	U	X		X	X	U	X	X			S	X	X		S																						7
X		X	X	X	X	S	X	U	X	X	S	X	X		U	S				X																						8
X		X	X	X	X	U	X	S	X	X	U	X	S			S		X		X																						9
X		X	X	X	X		X	X	X	S		X	U	U			S	X	U	X																						10
X		**X**	**X**	**X**	**X**		**X**	**X**	**X**	**S**		**X**	**S**	**U**			**X**	**X**	**U**	**S**																						**11**
X		**X**	**X**	**X**	**X**	**U**	**X**	**X**	**X**	**X**		**S**	**S**					**X**	**U**	**X**	**U**																					**12**
X		X	X		X	U	X	U	X			X			X		U		U		U	X	X	X																		13
X		X	X		X	U	X		X			X		U	S		U					X	X	X	X	S																14
X		X	X		X	S	X	U	X			X		S	X						U	X	X		X	U																15
X		X	X		X	S	X		X			S		S	X				U			X	X	X	X		U															16
X		X	X		X	S	X		X			X		U	U		S					X	X	X	X	U																17
X		X	X			U	X		X			X		U	U		X					X	X		X	U	U															18
X		X	X		X	X	X		X			X		U	U		S					X	X		X	U	U															19
X		X	X		X	X	X		X			X		U	U		S		U			X	X		X		U															20
X		**X**	**X**		**X**	**X**	**X**	**U**	**X**			**X**			**S**		**X**		**U**					**X**	**X**	**U**	**U**															**21**
X		**X**	**X**		**X**	**S**	**X**	**U**	**X**			**X**			**S**		**X**					**X**		**X**	**X**		**S**															**22**
X			U		X	X	X	U	X			U			X		X		X		U	X			X	U	X															23
X					**X**	**X**	**X**		**X**	**X**					**X**		**X**		**S**		**U**	**U**			**X**	**U**	**U**	**X**														**24**
X					X	X	X	U	U	X					X		X		U						X	S	S	X	X													25
X					X	X	X	U	X						X		X		U						X		S	X	X	X												26
X					X	X	X	U	X						X				U			X					S	X	X	X	S											27
X	**S**				**X**		**X**	**U**	**X**						**X**		**U**		**U**			**X**		**X**	**X**		**X**	**X**		**X**	**U**											**28**
X	X							X							X				U						X		S		X	X	U	X	X	X	S	S						29
X								X							X										X			S	U	U		X	X	X	S	U	X	X				30
X															X										X			X	S	U	U	X	X	X		S	X	X	S			31
X								X	X						X				S		U				X			X	X		S		X	X		U	X	X	S			32
X								X	X						U						U				X				X	U	S	X	X	X			X	X	S	X		33
X								U	X						U				U		U				X				X		S	X	X	X			X	X	X	X		34
X								U	X						U				U		U				X				X		U	X	X				X	X	X	X	X	35
X								X	X						S				U		U								X		U	X	X		S		X	X	X	X	X	36
X								X	X						X				U		U								X	U	U	X	X		X	S			X	X	X	37
X									X						S				U						X				X		S	X	X	X		U	X	X	U	X	X	38
X								U	X						X				U						X				X		U	X	X	X		U	X	U		X	X	39
X								S	X						X				U						X				X		U	X	X			U	X	X	S	X	X	40
X								S	X												U				X				X		X	X	X	U		S	X	X	U	X	X	41
X								X	X						S						U				X				X		U	X	X			S	X	X	S	X	X	42
X									X																X				X			X	X				X	X	X	X	X	43
X								U	X						S				U						X				X		S	X	X			S	X	X	X	X	X	44
X								U	X						S				U						X				X		U	X	X			S	X	X	X	X	X	45
X								U	X						S				U						X				X		S	X	X			U	X	X	X	X	X	46
X									X						X				S						X				X			X	X			X	X		X	X		47
X								U	X						U				S		U				X				X		S	X	X			X	X	X	X	X		48
Total League Appearances																																										
42	5	18	15	10	21	10	22	11	36	10	0	14	4	1	15	1	7	5	1	3	0	10	8	4	28	0	1	5	21	3	1	19	20	8	1	2	18	16	10	16	12	**X**
0	1	0	1	0	0	5	0	3	1	1	2	3	3	3	8	7	6	1	3	1	0	0	0	0	0	2	4	1	1	0	8	0	0	0	3	7	0	0	5	0	0	**S**
0	0	0	1	0	0	6	0	16	1	0	3	2	3	8	11	0	3	0	19	0	12	0	0	0	0	5	4	0	1	4	9	0	0	1	0	6	0	1	2	0	0	**U**
Total Cup Appearances																																										
6	0	4	4	2	6	2	6	2	6	2	0	3	0	0	2	0	4	2	0	1	0	2	0	3	4	0	1	2	0	1	0	0	0	0	0	0	0	0	0	0	0	**X**
0	1	0	0	0	0	1	0	0	0	1	0	1	2	0	2	0	0	0	1	1	0	0	0	0	0	0	1	0	0	0	0	0	0	0	0	0	0	0	0	0	0	**S**
0	0	0	0	0	0	1	0	3	0	0	0	0	0	1	0	0	1	0	4	0	2	1	0	0	0	2	2	0	0	0	1	0	0	0	0	0	0	0	0	0	0	**U**

Also played: A ROBINSON X(18). JONES X(24,25,27) U(26). S CHARLTON S(26) U(27). MCKERR X(29,30,31). WEAVER X(30,31).

REDDITCH UNITED

CURRENT SQUAD AS OF BEGINING OF 2009-10 SEASON

GOALKEEPERS	HT	WT	D.O.B	AGE	P.O.B	CAREER	APPS	GOA
Danny Lewis	6'01"	14 00	18/6/82	27	Redditch	Alvechurch, Studley, Kidderminster 5/04, Moor Green 6/06, Redditch 6/07	42	0
DEFENDERS								
Bradley Bullimore						Redditch	4	0
Asa Charlton	5'11"	12 00	7/12/77	31	Cosford	Stoke, Kidderminster, Willenhall 8/96, Telford c/s 97, Willenhall, Sandwell B, Rushall O c/s 99, Stourport S 7/01, Worcester 8/02, Halesowen T 1/03 Rel 10/04, Redditch 10/04, Mansfield 11/06 Rel 5/07, AFC Telford 5/07, Hednesford (L) 9/08, Redditch 10/08	28	0
Chris Dickinson						Redditch	23	0
Liam Francis			27/9/89	19	Birmingham	Coventry Rel c/s 08, Stratford T, Redditch 8/09		
Lucan Spittle	6'03"					Sutton Coldfield, Willenhall 11/06, Bromsgrove 5/07, Redditch 12/07, Wilenhall 1/08, Chasetown 1/08, Redditch 12/08	22	1
MIDFIELDERS								
David Bridgwater	6'00"	12 07	27/9/80	28	Stourbridge	Aston Villa (Yth), Preston (Trainee), Telford Rel c/s 01, Halesowen H (L) 11/99, Bromsgrove (L) 3/01, TNS 8/01, Aberystwyth 5/04, Moor Green 11/04, Bromsgrove 5/07, Kings Lynn 5/08 Rel 9/08, Stourbridge, Redditch 8/09		
Jack Byrne						Stratford T, Redditch 1/09	19	4
Joe Clark						Redditch		
James Cooper	5'09"	11 02	4/1/90	19		Lincoln C (Scholar) Rel c/s 09, Redditch 8/09		
Andy Ducros	5'04"	9 08	16/8/77	31	Evesham	Coventry Yth Rel c/s 99, Nuneaton 8/99, Wigan (Trial) 11/99, Kidderminster £100,000 7/00, Nuneaton (L) 10/02 (L) 12/02, Burton 2/03 Rel c/s 07, Solihull Moors 10/07 Rel 1/09, Barwell 1/09, Redditch 8/09		
Jamie Shields						Birmingham, Redditch 8/09		
Mat Weyman						Wolverhampton U, Dudley T, Redditch c/s 09		
FORWARDS								
Graham Ashton						Rushall O, Dudley T, Redditch		
Richard Ball					Birmingham	West Brom (Yth), Weymouth, Bromsgrove, Paget R, Bromsgrove, Bloxwich, Oldbury, RC Warwick, Stourport, Halesowen T 12/03, Stourport 2/04, Sutton Coldfield Undisc 7/04, Evesham 12/04, Redditch 4 fig 2/07, Bromsgrove (L) 2/09, Sutton Coldfield (SL) 3/09	4	0
Shane Benjamin					Birmingham	Castle Vale, Grosvenor Park 8/03, Hednesford, Studley, Evesham 1/06, Shepshed D, Stourbridge 2/09, Redditch 6/09		
Francino Francis	6'02"	14 03	18/1/87	22	Jamaica	Stoke (Yth), Watford Rel c/s 06, Kidderminster (2M) 1/06 (05/06 6,0), Wealdstone (SL) 3/06, Redditch c/s 06, Quorn 3/07, Rushall O 11/07, Halesowen T 12/07, Willenhall 1/08, Coalville, Barwell 3/08, Redditch 8/09		
Gary Hay					Birmingham	Fairfield Villa, Paget R, Alvechurch, Willenhall 3/02, Halesowen T 6/05, Willenhall 8/05, AFC Telford 2/06, Bromsgrove 10/06, Kidderminster NC 2/07, Bromsgrove 5/07, Evesham 1/08, Hednesford 2/09, Redditch 3/09	12	3
Jamie Sheldon	5'11"	11 05	14/8/91	18		Birmingham (Scholar) Rel c/s 09, Redditch c/s 09		

LOANEES	HT	WT	DOB	AGE	POB	From - To	APPS	GOA
(M)Sam Foley	6'00"	10 08	17/10/86	22	Upton	Kidderminster (2ML) 10/08 - Newport C (SL) 2/09 Perm 4/09	8	3
(M)Craig Jones			12/12/89	19	Hereford	Hereford 12/08 -	2	0
(D)Michael McKerr						Birmingham 1/09 -	3	0
(M)Ryan Beswick			12/1/88	21	Walton-on-Thames	Leicester (SL) 1/09 - Kettering 5/09	20	8
(D)Lathaniel Rowe-Turner			12/11/89	19	Leicester	Leicester 2/09 -	16	0

DEPARTURES	HT	WT	DOB	AGE	POB	From - To	APPS	GOA
(D)Liam Daly						Corby T 12/07 - Rel 10/08, Solihull Moors 10/08	10	3
(M)Graham Deakin	5'10"	11 05	24/4/87	22	Birmingham	Walsall 1/07 - Rel 10/08, Bromsgrove 10/08, Halesowen T 3/09, Sutton Coldfield 6/09	4	0
(F)Howard Forinton	5'11"	12 04	18/9/75	33	Boston	Banbury U 6/07 - Rel 10/08, Banbury U 10/08	6	0
(F)Chris Hanna						Walsall 8/08 - Bromsgrove 10/08, Rushall O 3/09	8	0
(F)Anthony Robinson			31/12/80	28	Birmingham	Mansfield 11/08 - Rel 11/08, Halesowen T 11/08, Stratford T 11/08, Hednesford 11/08, Oxford C 12/08 Evesham 2/09, Atherstone T 3/09, Kings Lynn 7/09	1	0
(M)Danny Edwards			27/10/83	28	Shrewsbury	Stafford R 6/07 - AFC Telford 11/08	18	1
(D)Lee Ayres	6'02"	12 06	28/8/82	27	Birmingham	Moor Green/Solihull Moors 7/08 - Forest Green NC 12/08	16	2
(M)Lee Downes	6'00"	12 00	27/2/83	26	Dudley	Stafford R 10/06 Rel 1/09 - Solihull Moors 2/09	22	4
(D)Matty Clarke						ex Redditch 10/08 - Rel 1/09, Halesowen T 2/09	10	0
(M)Aman Verma						Bedworth c/s 08 - Leicester 12/08	17	3
(M)Richard Softley			28/6/76	33		Moor Green 6/02 - Leamington 1/09	13	1
(F)Scott Rickards	5'09"	12 00	3/11/81	27	Sutton Coldfield	Brackley 2/08 - Rel 10/08, Shepshed D 10/08, Redditch 12/08, Solihull Moors 12/08	11	1
(D)Simon Weaver	6'01"	10 08	20/12/77	31	Doncaster	Kings Lynn 1/09 - Ilkeston 2/09, Harrogate T (Pl/Man) 5/09	2	0
(F)Mark Rawle	5'11"	12 02	27/4/79	30	Leicester	Kettering 10/08 - Kettering 11/08 Rel 1/09, Redditch 1/09, Tamworth 2/09, Brackley 3/09	4	3
(M)Chris Murphy	5'05"	09 06	8/3/83	26	Leamington	Cheltenham 7/05 - Leamington 2/09	15	1
(D)Liam Murray	6'03"	11 00	1/8/85	24	Stafford	Droylsden 2/08 - Stafford R 2/09 Rel 5/09, Solihull Moors 6/09, Kings Lynn 7/09	21	1
(F)Carl Heggs	6'01"	12 10	11/10/70	38	Leicester	Tamworth (Pl/Coach) 10/07 - Kings Lynn (Man) 6/08	14	1
Jordan Smith						Thurnby Rangers 12/08 - Kings Lynn 6/09	6	0
(M)Owen Story	5'11"	10 10	3/8/84	25	Burton	Hinckley U 6/08 - Kings Lynn 6/09	37	6
(D)Michael Briscoe	5'11"	12 00	4/7/83	26	Northampton	Halesowen T 2/09 - Tamworth 6/09	18	0
(G)Steve Rose						Yth -	0	0
(D)Jamie Oliver						Dudley Town 1/09 -	15	0
(D)Damien Whitcombe						Chasetown 11/08, Stourbridge, Redditch 12/08	3	0
(M)Jamie Blake						Birmingham C 8/08 -	4	0
(M)Mark Hands						Evesham 1/09 -	16	0
(M)Simon Hollis			7/11/79	29	Birmingham	Solihull Moors 7/08 -	6	0
(M)Alex Johnson						Hinckley U 8/08 -	7	1
(F)Aaron Daniels						Highgate U 1/09 -	9	0
(F)Abdul Babayo							5	0
(F)Jonathan Ngolo	6'02"	11 02				Wolves (Yth) 10/08 -	2	0
(F)Dolapo Olaoye	5'10"	12 04	17/10/82	26	Lagos, Nig	Stafford R 8/08 - Rugby T (L) 8/08	2	0
(F)Marvin Robinson	5'11"	12 09	11/4/80	29	Crewe	Kettering 1/09 -	8	1
Danial Ford						Yth -	9	0
S Charlton						Yth -	1	0

REDDITCH UNITED

Formed: 1891

Nickname: The Reds.

Club Colours: Red shirts, shorts and socks.

Change Colours: White shirts, blue shorts, blue socks.

Club Sponsor: TBC

Previous League: Southern.

Ground address: Valley Stadium, Bromsgrove Road, Redditch B97 4RN

Telephone: 01527 67450

Mobile: 07748 300 407

Email: redditchunited@yahoo.co.uk

Website: www.redditchunitedfc.co.uk

Simple Directions: Access 7 on town ring road takes you into Bromsgrove Road (via Unicorn Hill).

Ground entrance is 400 yards past traffic lights on right.

Capacity: 5,000 **Seats**: 400 **Covered**: 2,000 **Floodlights**: Yes

Clubhouse: Open matchdays and private hire.

Club Shop: Yes

Local Press: Redditch Advertiser, Birmingham Evening Mail and Redditch Standard

Local Radio: BBC Hereford & Worcester.

PROGRAMME EDITOR
Tracey Rae
Email: traceydrae@yahoo.co.uk

CLUB STATISTICS

RECORD
Attendance: 5,500 v Bromsgrove Rovers. League 1954-55
Victory: Not known.
Defeat: Not known.
Career Goalscorer: Not known.
Career Appearances: Not known.
Record Transfer Fee Paid:
£3,000 to Halesowen Town for Paul Joinson
Received: £40,000 from Aston Villa for David Farrell

SENIOR HONOURS
Worcestershire Senior Cup Winners 1893-94, 1929-30, 1974-75, 1975-76, 2008.
Birmingham Senior Cup Winners 1924-25, 31-32, 38-39, 76-77, 2004-05.
Southern League Division 1 North Champions 1975-76.
Staffs Senior Cup 1990-91.
Southern League Western Division Champions 2003-04.

PREVIOUS
Name: Redditch Town.
Leagues: Birmingham Combination 1905-21, 29-39, 46-53.
West Midlands 1921-29, 53-72.
Southern 1972-79, 81-2004.
Alliance 1979-80.
Ground: HDA Sports Ground, Millsborough Road.

SOLIHULL MOORS

no up-to-date image available

CLUB PERSONNEL

Chairman: Nigel Collins.

Vice-Chairman: Graham Davison.

Company Secretary: Margaret Smith.

Additional Directors: John Bassford, Ray Bird, Ian Childs, Geoff Hood, Chris Hooper, Joe Murphy, Trevor Stevens, Danny Thomas.

Secretary: Robin Lamb.
14 Regal Close, Scimitar Park, Two Gates, Tamworth B77 1GT.
Tel: (M) 07976 752 493.
Email: robin5@btinternet.com

Commercial Manager: Chris Hooper.
(M): 07866 532 914.

Press Officer: Father Ronald Crane ssc.
Tel: 07742 588 685

Manager: Bob Faulkner.

Club therapist: Lindsay Davis.

A season that really didn't produce any highlights, at least saw 'The Moors' avoid any serious threat of relegation in the second half of the campaign. Home league attendances were understandably disappointing with a season's average of 234 but at least supporters were rewarded with a home record of only six defeats, which was a lot better than the form they produced on the road.

Only two cup ties in the main knock out competitions during a season really were a disappointment to club supporters. The F.A.Cup involvement was ended at Hinckley United with a 1-2 defeat whilst Durham City travelled to the Midlands to win 2-1.

The importance of consistency in scoring was shown as, by mid season, The Moors had failed to find the net in ten different matches. However, in the new year, after two blanks in January, they failed to score only once more and a run of nine unbeaten games took the club up to fourteenth place and ensured their safety for the season.

Nineteen different goalscorers in the season were an indication of many team changes and the club will be hoping for a far more settled campaign in the future and possibly a little more cup excitement could improve the home support.

SOLIHULL MOORS

BEST LGE ATT.: 546 v Tamworth
LOWEST: 148 v Droylsden

No.	Date	Comp	H/A	Opponents	Att:	Result	Goalscorers	Pos
1	Aug 9	BSN	A	Blyth Spartans	412	L 0 - 3		
2	12		H	Alfreton Town	191	D 2 - 2	Gould 26 Middleton 50	
3	16		H	Gainsborough Trinity	172	L 2 - 3	**Edwards** 36 79	20
4	23		A	Hinckley United	484	D 0 - 0		20
5	25		H	Stafford Rangers	314	L 0 - 1		
6	30		A	Burscough	255	W 2 - 1	**Edwards** 7 Spencer 20	
7	Sept 2		A	Stalybridge Celtic	377	L 0 - 5		
8	13		A	Workington	410	L 1 - 2	Palmer 60	21
9	20		H	Farsley Celtic	184	W 2 - 1	Middleton 43 (pen) Ducros 45	18
10	**23**	**SS N1**	**A**	**Redditch United**	**157**	**W 1 - 0**	**Edwards 87**	
11	**27**	**F.A.C. 2Q**	**A**	**Hinckley United**	**510**	**L 1 - 2**	**Middleton 54**	
12	Oct 4		A	Southport	851	L 0 - 3		20
13	**7**	**SS N2**	**A**	**AFC Telford**	**692**	**L 1 - 2***	**Edwards 53**	
14	18		H	Vauxhall Motors	200	W 3 - 2	Ducros 22 Palmer 67 Faulds 79	17
15	21		A	AFC Telford United	1510	L 0 - 3		
16	25		H	Harrogate Town	150	D 1 - 1	**Edwards** 18	
17	Nov 1		A	King's Lynn	970	L 0 - 3		20
18	8		H	Hyde United	180	D 2 - 2	Daly 12 Moore 36	19
19	11		H	Droylsden	148	W 2 - 1	Gardner 72 83	
20	15		A	Alfreton Town	409	L 1 - 4	Daly 84	18
21	**22**	**F.A.T. 3Q**	**H**	**Durham City**	**186**	**L 1 - 2**	**Edwards 5**	
22	29		H	Southport	150	L 0 - 2		18
23	Dec 6		A	Tamworth	621	L 0 - 1		18
24	20		H	Blyth Spartans	162	W 2 - 0	Motteram 15 Gardner 71	
25	26		A	Redditch United	390	D 0 - 0		15
26	Jan 1		H	Redditch United	360	W 2 - 1	Daly 18 **Edwards** 60	
27	3		A	Gainsborough Trinity	343	D 1 - 1	English 71	
28	17		H	Stalybridge Celtic	253	L 0 - 2		16
29	24		A	Gateshead	484	L 0 - 3		17
30	27		H	AFC Telford United	324	L 1 - 3	Streete 41	
31	Feb 1		A	Fleetwood Town	811	L 1 - 2	Sedgemoor 90	
32	17		H	Workington	183	W 2 - 0	McPike 45 Fairhurst 85	
33	21		H	Fleetwood Town	197	D 2 - 2	Fairhurst 20 Downes 87	17
34	24		A	Vauxhall Motors	144	D 2 - 2	Middleton 26 **Edwards** 48	
35	28		H	Tamworth	546	D 1 - 1	Sedgemore 89	17
36	Mar 7		A	Hucknall Town	268	W 2 - 0	Rickards 39 Sedgemore 45	16
37	10		H	KIng's Lynn	164	D 1 - 1	McPike 89	
38	14		H	Gateshead	253	W 2 - 0	McPike 72 Gardner 86	16
39	21		A	Farsley Celtic	250	W 1 - 0	**Edwards** 66	14
40	28		H	Burscough	196	W 3 - 2	**Edwards** 9 McPike 24 Sedgemore 41	14
41	31		A	Harrogate Town	220	L 0 - 4		
42	April 4		A	Droylsden	280	L 1 - 2	McPike 50	
43	11		H	Hinckley United	200	L 1 - 3	McPike 21	18
44	13		A	Stafford Rangers	588	W 2 - 0	Downes 43 McPike 85	
45	18		H	Hucknall Town	200	W 3 - 1	Rickards 32 English 53 Dempster 88	13
46	25		A	Hyde United	251	L 1 - 3	**Edwards** 55	16

Average Home Att: 234 (327) **Goals 53 79**

Best Position: 13th **Worst:** 21st

Goalscorers: Edwards 12, McPike 7, Gardner 4, Middleton 4, Sedgemore 4, Daly 3, Downes 2, Ducros 2, English 2, Fairhurst 2, Palmer 2, Rickards 2, Faulds 1, Gould 1, Moore 1, Motteram 1, Spencer 1, Streete 1, Dempster 1.

CRANE	STREETE	TRAVIS	MOTTERAM	SEDGEMORE	TUOHY	FAULDS	EDWARDS	DUCROS	MIDDLETON	ENGLISH	MOORE	SHILTON	RACHEL	O'TOOLE	COLLINS	GOULD	RITCHIE	SPENCER	ANDERSON	PALMER	GROCUTT	MIDWORTH L	DALY	STRACHAN	GARDNER	KELLY	BEECROFT	PRICE	RICKARDS	DEMPSTER	O'BRIEN	REECE	CHAMBERS	MCPIKE	A DALY	FAIRHURST	DOWNES	BONNER	BUSWELL	RECCI	JOHNSON	
X	X	X	X	X	X	X	X	X	X	X	S	S	U	U																												1
X	X	X	X	X	S	U	X	X	X	X	S		S	U	X	X																										2
	X		X	X	X	S	X	X	X	X	S	S	X	U	X	X	U																									3
X	X	X	X		U	S	X	X	S	X	X	X	U		X	X	U																									4
X	X	X	X		X	X	X		S		X	X	U	S	X	X	S																									5
X	X	X	S		X	S	X		X			X	U	U	X		X	X	X	S																						6
X	X	X	X		X	X	X		X	U		X	U		U			X		X																						7
X	X	X	S		U	X		U	X	S	X	X			X			X		X	X	U																				8
X	X	X	U			U	X	X	X	X	S	X	U		X					X	X	S																				9
X	**X**	**X**			**U**	**U**	**X**	**X**	**S**	**X**	**S**	**X**	**U**		**X**					**X**	**X**	**X**																				10
X	**X**	**X**	**U**		**U**	**S**	**X**	**X**	**S**	**X**	**S**	**X**	**U**		**X**					**X**	**X**	**X**		**U**																		11
X	X	X			U	S	X		X	X	S		U		X				X	S		X	X	X																		12
X	**X**	**X**	**S**		**S**	**X**	**X**	**U**	**X**	**X**	**X**		**U**		**X**				**X**	**S**		**X**																				13
X	U	X	X			X	X	X	S	S			U		X	X			S	X		X	X																			14
X	U	X	X			X	X	X	S	S			U		X	X			S	X		X	X																			15
X	U	X	X			X	X	U	X	X	S		U		X	U			X	X			X																			16
X	S	X	X		U	X	X	S	X	X	S		U		X				X	X			X																			17
X	U	X	X	X	U	X	X	X		X	X		U		X					S			X		S																	18
X	U	X	X	X	S	X	X	X		X	X		U		X					S			X		S																	19
X	S	X	X	X	U	X	X	X		X	X		U		X					S			X		S																	20
X	**X**	**X**	**X**	**X**	**U**	**S**	**X**	**S**	**X**	**X**	**U**												**X**		**S**	**X**	**X**															21
X	X	X	X	X	X	S	X	S		X			U		U								X		S	X	X															22
X	S		X	X	X	U	S	X	X	X			U		X								X		S	X	X															23
X	X	X	X	S	X		X	X		X			U						U				X		X	S	X															24
X	X	X	X	X			X	X	S	X			U		X				S				X		X			U														25
X	X	X	X	X	U		X	X		X			U		X				S				X		X			S	S													26
X	X	X	X	X	U		X			X			U		X				S				X					X	X	S												27
X	X	X		X									U		X				U									S	X	S	X	X	X	X	X							28
X	X	X		X	S	S			X	S			U		X								X						X		X	X	X		U							29
X	X	X	U	X	S	X			X	X			U		X								X						X		X	S			S							30
X	X	X	X	X	X	S			X	X			U										X						S			S		X	U	X						31
X	X	X	U	X	X	S	X		X	X			U																S					X		S	X	X				32
X	X	X	S	X	X	U	X			X			U		U														X					S		X	X	X				33
X	X	X	U	X		S	X		X	X			U		X														S					S		X	X	X				34
X	X	X	S	X	U	U	X		X	X													X						S					S		X	X	X				35
X	X	X	S	X			X		X	X			U		U								X					U	X					S			X	X				36
X	X	X	S	X			X		X	X			U		U								X					S	X					S			X	X				37
X	X	X	X	X			X		U	X			U		X										S				S					X			X	X	U			38
X	X		X	X			X		U	X			U		X										S				X	S				X			X	X	S			39
X	X	S	X	X		S	X		U	X			U		X										S				X					X			X	X				40
X	X		X	X		S	X		S	X			U		X										S				X					X			X	X				41
X	X	X	X	X		S	X		U	X			U		X										S				S					X			X	X				42
X	X	X	X	X		U	X		S	X			U		X										S					S				X			X	X				43
X	X		U	X		X	S		S	X			U		X										X				X	S				X			X	X				44
X	X	U	U	X		X	S		S	X					X										X				X	S				X			X	X				45
X	X	X	U	X		X	X		S				U												X				X	S							X	X		X	S	46
Total League Appearances																																										
41	34	35	26	30	11	15	34	14	19	33	6	6	1	0	31	6	1	3	4	7	2	3	20	1	6	2	3	1	13	0	3	2	2	11	1	4	15	15	0	1	0	X
0	3	1	6	1	4	12	3	2	10	4	7	2	1	1	0	0	1	0	5	5	0	1	0	0	11	1	0	3	7	7	0	2	0	5	1	1	0	0	1	0	1	S
0	5	1	7	0	9	6	0	2	4	1	0	0	37	4	5	1	2	0	2	0	0	1	0	0	0	0	0	2	0	0	0	0	0	0	2	0	0	0	1	0	0	U
Total Cup Appearances																																										
4	4	4	1	1	0	1	4	2	2	4	1	2	0	0	3	0	0	0	1	2	2	3	1	0	0	1	1	0	0	0	0	0	0	0	0	0	0	0	0	0	0	X
0	0	0	1	0	1	2	0	1	2	0	2	0	0	0	0	0	0	0	0	1	0	0	0	0	1	0	0	0	0	0	0	0	0	0	0	0	0	0	0	0	0	S
0	0	0	1	0	3	1	0	1	0	0	1	0	3	0	0	0	0	0	0	0	0	0	0	1	0	0	0	0	0	0	0	0	0	0	0	0	0	0	0	0	0	U

Also Played: DOYLE U(25).

SOLIHULL MOORS

CURRENT SQUAD AS OF BEGINING OF 2009-10 SEASON

GOALKEEPERS	HT	WT	D.O.B	AGE	P.O.B	CAREER	APPS	GOA
Daniel Crane	6'03"	14 11	27/5/84	25	Birmingham	WBA Rel c/s 04, Burton 8/04, Moor Green (L) 10/05, Rushden & D 1/06, Lewes (L) 10/06, Cambridge U 1/07, Kings Lynn 3/07, Bromsgrove 3/07, Corby 6/07, Solihull Moors 1/08	41	0
Adam Rachel	5'11"	12 08	10/12/76	31	Birmingham	Aston Villa, Blackpool 9/99, Northwich (L) 10/00, Moor Green 7/01	2	0
DEFENDERS								
Liam Daly						Evesham, Corby T 7/07, Redditch 12/07 Rel 10/08, Solihull Moors 10/08	20	3
Indy Khela	6'00"	12 06	6/10/83	24	Birmingham	Bedworth, Coventry Marconi, Kidderminster 8/02, Evesham (L) (02/03), Evesham 6/03, Willenhall, AFC Telford 2/06 Rel 5/09, Solihull Moors 6/09		
Phil Midworth			17/5/85	24		WBA (Sch), Burton 2/05, Moor Green/Solihull Moors 3/05. Bromsgrove (L) 3/09	4	0
Loyiso Recci						Solihull Moors	1	0
Darren Stapleton			19/3/87	22	Dublin	Cherry Orchard, Reading, Kildare County, Shamrock 11/07 Rel 2/09, Solihull Moors 8/09		
Theo Streete	6'01"	12 06	23/11/87	21	Birmingham	Derby, Doncaster (4ML) 9/06, Bristol R (Trial) 1/07, Grimsby (Trial) 1/07, Rotherham 1/07, Solihull Moors 1/07	37	1
MIDFIELDERS								
Charlton Davies			24/1/89	20	Coleshill	Walsall, Solihull Moors (L) 12/07, Solihull Moors 8/09		
Lee Downes	6'00"	12 00	27/2/83	26	Dudley	Wolves cc 00/01, Kidderminster, Stafford R 8/02 Rel 10/06, Redditch 10/06 Rel 1/09, Solihull Moors 2/09	15	2
Junior English						Moor Green/Solihull Moors	37	2
Peter Faulds	5'07"	10 00	26/8/82	27	Birmingham	Kidderminster Rel c/s 02, Moor Green/Solihull Moors 8/02, Stratford T (L)	27	1
Tim Gould						Boldmere St M, Solihull Moors 7/07	6	1
Dean Lea						Tamworth Rel 5/09, Solihull Moors 6/09		
Alex Price						Solihull Moors, Stratford T (L) 3/09	4	0
FORWARDS								
Junior Brown						Solihull Moors		
Jake Edwards	6'01"	12 08	11/5/76	33	Prestwich	James Maddison Univ (USA), Tranmere (Trial), Wrexham 8/98, Blackpool (L) 3/99, Telford (2ML) 11/99 £20,000 1/00, Charleston Batt (USA) 7/02, Yeovil 8/03 Rel c/s 04, Exeter 7/04, Tamworth (3ML) 10/05, Chester (SL) 3/06, Crawley 8/06, Tamworth 1/07, Burton 5/07 Rel 5/08, Solihull Moors 8/08	37	9
Ross Dempster						Solihull Moors	7	1
Mark Gardner						Birmingham, Highgate U, Stafford R (Trial) 10/08, Solihull Moors 11/08	17	4
Marvin Johnson						Solihull Moors	1	0
Matty Lewis	6'02"	12 02	20/3/84	25	Coventry	Coventry Marconi, Kidderminster 7/01, Aston Villa (Trial) 7/02, Evesham (L) 10/02, Bath C (L) 12/02, Solihull (2ML) 1/03, Hinckley U (L) 9/03, Hinckley U £5,000 12/03, Evesham 11/05, Kettering 12/05, Hinckley U 2/06, Halesowen T 5/06, AFC Telford 5/07 Rel 5/09, Atherstone (L) 12/08, Hednesford (L) 2/09, Solihull Moors 6/09		

LOANEES	HT	WT	DOB	AGE	POB	From - To	APPS	GOA
(F)Marc Grocutt			11/11/89	19		Stoke 9/08 - Stafford R (L) 10/08, Rel 6/09	2	0
(M)Jake Beecroft			4/9/89	19		Rushden & D (6WL) 11/08 -	3	0
(F)James McPike	5'10"	11 02	4/10/88	20	Birmingham	Birmingham (3ML) 1/09 - Kettering 5/09	16	7
(M)James O'Brien			8/6/90	19	Dublin	Birmingham 1/09 -	3	0
(M)Charlie Reece	5'11"	11 03	8/9/88	20	Birmingham	Bristol R 1/09 -	4	0
(F)Waide Fairhurst			7/5/89	20	Sheffield	Doncaster 1/09 -	5	2

DEPARTURES	HT	WT	DOB	AGE	POB	From - To	APPS	GOA
(M)Joe O'Toole			2/6/89	20		Stoke (Scholar) 8/08 - Highgate U, Rushall O 10/08	1	0
(D)Kevin Spencer						Kettering 8/08 - Rel 10/08, Stratford T, Worcester 3/09	3	1
(M)Sam Shilton	5'11"	11 06	21/7/78	31	Nottingham	Kettering 8/08 - Rel 10/08	8	0
(F)Craig Strachan			19/5/82	27		Halesowen T 10/08 - Rel	1	0
(F)Leon Kelly	6'01"	12 04	26/6/78	31	Coventry	Hinckley U 11/08 - Rel 12/08, Bromsgrove 12/08, Hyde U 4/09	3	0
(F)Jason Moore			20/1/83	26	Nuneaton	Bedworth c/s 06 - Rel 12/08, Bedworth 12/08	13	1
(M)Andy Ducros	5'04"	9 08	16/8/77	32	Evesham	Burton 10/07 - Rel 1/09, Barwell, Redditch 8/09	16	2
(F)Dale Anderson	5'11"	11 12	10/11/79	29	Birmingham	Burton 5/06 - Bromsgrove (L) 11/08 Rel 1/09, Hednesford 1/09	9	0
(M)Marcus Palmer	6'00"	11 07	22/12/88	20	Gloucester	Gloucester 8/08 - Rel, Forest Green 3/09	12	2
(F)Andy Ritchie			3/11/89	19		Coventry c/s 08 -	2	0
(M)James Chambers	5'10"	12 01	14/2/87	22	Dublin	Shelbourne 1/09 - Drogheda 3/09	2	0
(M)Michael Tuohy			6/6/87	20	Birmingham	Tamworth 6/08 - Leamington 5/09	15	0
(D)Tom Bonner	6'00"	11 06	6/2/88	21	Camden	Hinckley U 2/09 - Corby T 6/09, Ilkeston 8/09	15	0
(D)Simon Travis	5'10"	11 00	22/3/77	32	Preston	Nuneaton 7/08 - Leamington 6/09	36	0
(M)Jake Sedgemore	6'01"	12 10	20/10/78	30	Wolverhampton	Altrincham 6/08 - Nantwich 6/09	31	4
(M)Darren Middleton	6'00"	11 05	28/12/78	30	Lichfield	Worcester 7/04 - Chasetown 6/09	29	3
(D)Liam Murray	6'03"	11 00	1/8/85	24	Stafford	Droylsden 2/08 - Stafford R 2/09 Rel 5/09, Solihull Moors 6/09, Kings Lynn 7/09		
(D)Lee Collins	6'01"	12 06	10/9/77	31	Birmingham	Halesowen T 5/03 - Hinckley U 7/09	31	0
(M)Carl Motteram	5'05"	9 11	3/9/84	24	Birmingham	Torquay 2/07 -	32	1
(F)Scott Rickards	5'09"	12 00	3/11/81	27	Sutton Coldfield	Redditch 12/08 -	20	2
Ashley Buswell						Yth -	1	0
Adam Daly						Yth - Bromsgrove (L) 2/09	2	0
Liam Doyle						Yth -	0	0

SOLIHULL MOORS

Formed: 2007 (After the amalgamation of Solihull Borough and Moor Green).

Club Colours: White shirts, black shorts, white socks.

Change Colours: Yellow shirts, royal blue shorts, royal blue socks.

Club Sponsor: Apex Roofing & Cladding

Ground Address: Damson Park, Damson Parkway, Solihull, B91 2PP

Telephone: 0121 705 6770

Fax: 0121 711 4045

Email: smfc@blueyonder.co.uk

Website: www.solihullmoorsfc.co.uk

SIMPLE DIRECTIONS:

By Road: M42 Junction 6 and take A45 towards Birmingham. After about 1 1/2 miles turn left at traffic lights onto Damson Parkway. Ground is approximately 1 mile on the right.

Capacity: 3,050. **Seats:** 280. **Covered:** 1,000.

Clubhouse: Yes.

Club Shop: Merchandise in the clubhouse.

Local Press: Solihull Times, Solihull News, Sunday Mercury & Sports Argus.

Local Radio: Radio WM & BRMB.

no image available

PROGRAMME EDITOR

James Newbold

Tel: (B) 07919 255 491

Email: info@thedesignery.co.uk

CLUB STATISTICS

RECORDS

Attendance:

1,076 v Rushden & Diamonds, FA Cup 4th Q., 27.10.07.

Victory: 4-1 v Southport, Conference South, 05.04.08.

Defeat: 1-6 v Kettering Town, Conference South, 01.01.08.

Goalscorer: Darren Middleton -15 (2007-09)

Career Appearances: Carl Motteram - 71 (2007-09).

Record Transfer Fee Paid: Not known.

Received: Not known.

SENIOR HONOURS

None

PREVIOUS

Names: Solihull Borough 1953-2007. Moor Green 1901-2007.

SOUTHPORT

Back row (L-R): Chris Lever, Rob Marsh-Evans, Tony McMillan, Earl Davis, Sean Gray. **Middle Row:** Paul Barratt, Alan Moogan, Ciaran Kilheeney, Michael Powell, Simon Shaw, Kevin Lee, Steve Daly, Chris Simm Robbie Booth. **Front Row:** Mal Liptrot, Bradley Barnes, Mel Singleton, Ashley Winn, Chris Price, Adam Flynn, Liam Watson, Matty McGinn, Allan Smart, Zac Aley, Scott Macauley.

CLUB PERSONNEL

Chairman: Charles Clapham.

Vice-Chairman: Sam Shrouder.

Company Secretary: Ken Hilton.

Chief Executive: Haydn Preece.

Additional Directors: Andrew Pope, Tim Medcroft, Stephen Porter, Gordon Medcroft, Roy Holden.

Secretary: Ken Hilton
Correspondance c/o the club.
(H): 01704 894 504
(B): 01704 533 422
(M): 07802 661 906
secretary@southportfc.net

Commercial Manager & Press Officer:
Haydn Preece
(H): 01704 570 689
(M): 07976 555 782
commercial@southportfc.net

Manager: Liam Watson.

Assistant Manager: Chris Price.

Club therapist: John Bradshaw.

Southport were one of the favourites for promotion and showed consistently good form throughout the campaign until the final weeks when the pressure seemed to effect the goalscorers. With Liam Watson back as manager, a great start to the season took 'The Sandgrounders' to the top of the table, where they remained until October.

After an F.A.Cup victory over Vauxhall Motors it was disappointing to lose in the Third Qualifying Round to Boston United but The F.A.Trophy provided an enjoyable run until losing to A.F.C. Telford United in a Fourth Round replay. Victories had been achieved over Vauxhall Motors again, Altrincham, Durham City after a replay, and Torquay United with a fine 3-0 scoreline and despite ten cup ties, Southport stayed in the top four of the Blue Square North throughout the season.

Despite Steve Daly and Cairen Kilheeney scoring eighteen senior goals each, another sixteen players featured as scorers, giving the club a fine reputation for attacking from all areas of the field and finishing with a seasons' total of 82 goals. Although, sadly for Southport's loyal supporters, it was an end of season dearth of goals that eventually prevented one of the league's most consistent clubs from gaining promotion.

Just two victories and ten goals in the last eleven games saw Southport lose to Gateshead in their two legged play-off 0-1 (H) and 0-0 (A). So a long and basically successful season finished without promotion or a Wembley appearance, but who will bet against them next season?

SOUTHPORT

BEST LGE ATT.: **1,353** v Tamworth
LOWEST: **544** v Vauxhall Motors

No.	Date	Comp	H/A	Opponents	Att:	Result	Goalscorers	Pos
1	Aug 9	BSN	A	Gainsborough Trinity	460	W 1 - 0	Powell 57	
2	12		H	Blyth Spartans	827	W 2 - 1	Powell 27 Gray 87	
3	16		H	Harrogate Town	818	W 1 - 0	Kilheeney 22	
4	23		A	Stalybridge Celtic	747	W 1 - 0	Gray 17	1
5	25		H	Fleetwood Town	1304	D 1 - 1	Duffy 28	
6	30		A	Stafford Rangers	671	W 3 - 0	Powell 6 Duffy 11 Robinson 15	1
7	Sept 1		A	Hinckley United	639	D 1 - 1	Kilheeney 90 (pen)	
8	6		H	Alfreton Town	1012	L 0 - 1		1
9	**9**	**SS N1**	**A**	**Stalybridge Celtic**	**231**	**W 4 - 1**	**Daly 4 Booth 29 Robinson 79 T Gray 81**	
10	13		H	Hucknall Town	823	W 3 - 0	Kilheeney 22 32 McGinn 34	1
11	20		A	Redditch United	391	W 2 - 0	Duffy 31 Kilheeney 58	
12	**27**	**F.A.C. 2Q**	**H**	**Vauxhall Motors**	**593**	**W 3 - 2**	**Robinson 14 60 Connolly 77**	
13	Oct 4		H	Solihull Moors	851	W 3 - 0	Kilheeney 41 Moogan 62 **Daly** 71	1
14	**7**	**SS N2**	**A**	**Vauxhall Motors**	**163**	**W 3 - 0**	**McGinn 12 T Gray 78 Kilheeney 90**	
15	**11**	**F.A.C. 3Q**	**H**	**Boston United**	**792**	**L 0 - 2**		
16	18		A	Gateshead	422	D 1 - 1	Kilheeney 30	2
17	21		H	Vauxhall Motors	544	W 5 - 2	Kilheeney 2 Robinson 15 24 Gray 83 Lee 90	
18	25		H	Redditch United	639	L 2 - 3	Powell 19 Duffy 23	2
19	Nov 1		H	Workington	650	D 0 - 0		2
20	**4**	**SS 3**	**A**	**Stafford Rangers**	**261**	**W 2 - 1**	**Daly 27 T Gray 71**	
21	15		H	King's Lynn	853	W 2 - 1	**Daly** 19 Kilheeney 24	
22	**22**	**F.A.T. 3Q**	**A**	**Vauxhall Motors**	**278**	**D 0 - 0**		
23	**25**	**F.A.T.3Q r**	**H**	**Vauxhall Motors**	**224**	**W 2 - 1**	**Kilheeney 45 Gray 65**	
24	29		A	Solihull Borough	150	W 2 - 0	Kilheeney 21 **Daly** 57	
25	Dec 6		A	AFC Telford United	3558	L 0 - 1		2
26	**9**	**SS N4**	**A**	**Wrexham**	**1123**	**W 2 - 1***	**Daly 56 96 (pens)**	
27	**13**	**F.A.T. 1R**	**A**	**Altrincham**	**609**	**W 4 - 1**	**Daly 67 80 Duffy 71 Kilheeney 77 (pen)**	
28	20		H	Gainsborough Trinity	785	W 5 - 3	Winn 1 84 Kilheeney 4 Moogan 15 **Daly** 15	
29	26		A	Burscough	1133	W 3 - 2	**Daly** 36 Kilheeny 81 McGinn 89	2
30	**Jan 10**	**F.A.T. 2R**	**A**	**Durham City**	**387**	**D 1 - 1**	**Winn 49**	
31	**13**	**F.A.T. 2R r**	**H**	**Durham City**	**533**	**W 3 - 1**	**Bailey 46 72 Duffy 74**	
32	24		A	Hucknall Town	354	D 0 - 0		3
33	27		A	Vauxhall Motors	317	D 0 - 0		
34	**31**	**F.A.T. 3R**	**H**	**Torquay United**	**980**	**W 3 - 0**	**Daly 13 75 Lee 81**	
35	**Feb 3**	**SS QFN**	**A**	**Barrow**	**678**	**L 1 - 3**	**McGinn 7**	
36	Feb 7		H	Hyde United	851	W 2 - 0	**Daly** 36 89	3
37	14		A	King's Lynn	972	D 0 - 0		3
38	17		H	Hinckley United	717	D 0 - 0		4
39	**21**	**F.A.T.4Q**	**A**	**AFC Telford United**	**2059**	**D 2 - 2**	**Lee 7 Leadbetter 87**	
40	**24**	**F.A.T 4R r**	**H**	**AFC Telford United**	**895**	**L 0 - 1**		
41	28		A	Workington	441	W 1 - 0	Kilheeney 14	4
42	Mar 3		A	Tamworth	703	D 1 - 1	Powell 10	
43	7		H	Gateshead	1301	L 2 - 3	Powell 38 **Daly** 72	
44	10		A	Harrogate Town	286	W 3 - 0	Gray 39 Kilheeney 59 73	
45	14		H	Farsley Celtic	702	W 1 - 0	Booth 81	3
46	17		H	Burscough	978	W 3 - 0	Flynn 38 McGinn 46 Smart 78	
47	21		A	Droylsden	489	D 0 - 0		3
48	28		H	Stafford Rangers	873	W 3 - 2	Prince 37 **Daly** 39 40	3
49	31		H	Tamworth	1353	L 0 - 1		
50	April 4		A	Alfreton Town	589	L 0 - 2		
51	7		H	Droylsden	619	W 3 - 1	**Daly** 43 47 Lee 66	
52	11		H	Stalybridge Celtic	951	W 2 - 0	**Daly** 34 79 (pen)	3
53	13		A	Fleetwood Town	1511	D 1 - 1	Kilheeney 90	
54	15		A	Hyde United	438	D 1 - 1	Powell 20	
55	18		H	AFC Telford United	1305	D 1 - 1	Booth 34	3
56	21		A	Blyth Spartans	563	L 0 - 1		
57	25		A	Farsley Celtic	407	L 1 - 5	Aley 3	
58	**29**	**Play-Off SF1**	**H**	**Gateshead**	**2346**	**L 0 - 1**		
59	**May 3**	**Play-Off SF2**	**A**	**Gateshead**	**1408**	**D 1 - 1**	**Booth 52**	

Average Home Att: 929 (1014) **Goals** 94 55

Best Position: 1st **Worst:** 4th

Goalscorers: Daly 22, Kilheeney 19, Gray 7, Powell 7, Duffy 6, McGinn 6, Robinson 6, Booth 4, Lee 4, Winn 3, Bailey 2, Moogan 2, Aley 1, Connolly 1, Flynn 1, Leadbetter 1, Prince 1, Smart 1.

MCMILLAN	LEE	LEVER	DAVIS	CONNOLLY	DOOLAN	DUFFY	POWELL	T GRAY	KILHEENEY	NOONE	ROBINSON	DALY	MCGINN	S GRAY	BOOTH	PRICE	FLYNN	MOOGAN	BARNES	ATKINS	WINN	HIBBERT	DRENCH	SMART	ALEY	HOLDEN	WHALLEY	MILLINGTON	LEADBETTER	MOORE	PRINCE	MITCHLEY	GRISEDALE	HEDGES	
X	X	X	X	X	X	X	X	X	X	X	S	S	S	U	U																				1
X	X	X	X	X	X	X	X	X	X		S	U	X	S	S	U																			2
X	X	X	X	X	X	X	X	X	X		S	S	X	U	S	U																			3
X	X	X	X	X	X	X	X	X	X		S	S	X	S	U		U																		4
X	X	X	X	X	X	X	X	X	X		U	S	S	U	X		S																		5
X	X	X		X	X	X	X	U	X		X	S	X	S	S		X	U																	6
X		U	X		S	X	X	X	S		S	X	X	X	X	U	X	X																	7
X		S	X	X	X	X	X	X	X		S	U	X	U	X		X	S																	8
X		X	U	X	X	S	S	X	U		S	X	X	X	X	X	X																		9
X	U	X	X	X	U	X	X	S	X			X	X	S	S		X	X																	10
X	X	X	U	X	X	X	S	S	X			X	X	U	S		X	X																	11
X	X	X	X	S	U	U	X	X	S		X		X	U	X	S	X	X																	12
X	X	X		X	U	X	X	S	X		X	S	X	S	U		X	X																	13
X	X	U	X	X	X	S	X	X	S			X	X	X	X		U	U																	14
X	U	X	X	X	X	X	U	S	X		X	S	X	S	U	U	X	X																	15
X	X	X	S	X	X	X	X	X	X		U	S		U	S		X	X																	16
X	X	X	X	U		X	X	S	X		X	S		U	S		X	X	X																17
X	X	X	X	X		X	X	S	X		X	U		U	U		S	X	X																18
	X	X	U	X	S	X	X	X			X	S		U	S		X	X	X	X															19
U	X	S	X	X		S	X	X				X	X	X	X		S	X	U	X															20
X	X	X	U	X		X	X	S	X		S	X	X	U			X	X	S																21
X	X	X	S	X	U	X	X	X	X				X	U	U		X	X	U																22
X	X	X	U	X		X	X	X	X		S		X	S	U		X	X	S																23
X	X		U	X	U		X	U	X		U	X	X	X		U	X	X	X																24
X	X		S	X	U	X	X		X		S	X	X	S	U		X	X			X														25
X	S	X	X		X	X					X	S	S	X	X	U	X	X	X			U													26
X	X		X		S	X	X		X			X	X	U	S	U	X	X	S		X														27
X	X		X		U	X	S		X		U	X	X	X	S		X	X	S		X														28
X	X		X			X	X		X		S	X	X	X	S	U	X		S		X	U													29
X	X	X	X	U		X	X		X		U	X		X	U	U	X				X		U												30
X	X	S	X	U		S	X		X		S	X		X	X		X	X			X		U												31
X	X	X	X	U		S	X		X		S	X	S		X		X	X			X		U												32
X	X	X	X	X		X	S		X		X	S	X		U		U	X			X		U												33
X	X	X	X	U		X	X		U		S	X	X	S	X		X				X		U												34
X	X	X	U	X	X		X				X		X	X	X		X					U		S	S	S									35
X	X	X	X	U		S	X		S			X	X	S	X		X				X		U				X								36
X		X	X	U		S	X				S	X	X	X	X		X				X		U				X	U							37
X	X	X	X	U		X	X				S	X	X		S		X				X		U				X	U							38
X	X	X	X				X					X	X		X	S	X				X			S			X		S						39
X	X		X	U			X		X			X	X	S	X	S	X				X		U				S		X						40
X	X	X	X	U			X		X			X	X	X	S	U	X						U				X		S						41
X	X	X	X	S			X		X				X	X	S	U	X						U	S			X		X						42
X	X	X	X	U			X		S			X	S	U	X		X	X			X		U				X								43
X	X		U	X			S		X			X	X	X	S		X	X			X		U				S		X						44
X	X	X		X					X			X	X	S	S		X	X			X		U				S		X	U					45
X		X	U	X					X				X	X	X		X	X			X		U	S			X		S	S					46
X	X	X		X					X			X	X	S	S		X	X			X		U	S					X	U					47
X	X		X	X					X			X	X	X	X			X		U	X						U			S	S	S			48
X	X	X	X				U		X			X	X	S	X		X	X		U	X										S	S			49
X	X	X	X				X		X				S	U	X		X	X		U	X									S	X	S			50
X	X	U	X				X		X			X	X	X	S		X	X		U	X									S		S			51
X	X	X	X				X		X			X	X	X	S		X			U	X									S	S	U			52
X	X	S	X				X		X				X	X	X		X	X		S	X						S			U		U			53
U		X	X				X		X				X	S	X		X	X		X	X						S			U	X	U			54
X		X	X				X		X			X	X	X	X		X	X		U							S			U	S	S			55
X		X	X						X			X	X	X	X	U	X			U	X			S			S			X	S				56
													U	U		X		U		X	U			X	X	X	X	X		X	X	X	X	S	57
X		X	X				U					X	X	X	X		X	X		U	X						X			U	U	S			58
X		X	X				X		X			X	X	U	X		X	X		U	X				U		S			U					59
Total League Appearances																																			
39	33	31	29	22	9	21	31	9	35	1	6	23	32	15	15	1	33	26	4	3	21	0	0	1	1	1	8	1	4	2	3	1	1	0	X
0	0	2	2	1	2	3	4	6	3	0	12	10	5	11	18	0	2	1	3	1	0	0	0	4	0	0	6	0	2	5	5	5	0	1	S
1	1	2	6	7	5	0	1	2	0	0	4	3	1	13	6	8	2	2	0	7	1	1	12	0	0	0	1	2	0	5	0	3	0	0	U
Total Cup Appearances																																			
16	12	12	13	7	5	7	13	6	8	0	4	11	14	8	12	1	15	10	1	1	8	0	0	0	0	0	2	0	1	0	0	0	0	0	X
0	1	2	1	1	1	4	1	1	2	0	4	2	1	4	1	3	1	0	2	0	0	0	0	2	1	1	2	0	1	0	0	1	0	0	S
1	1	1	3	4	2	1	2	0	2	0	1	0	0	4	4	4	1	1	2	2	0	2	4	0	1	0	0	0	0	2	1	0	0	0	U

SOUTHPORT

CURRENT SQUAD AS OF BEGINING OF 2009-10 SEASON

GOALKEEPERS	HT	WT	D.O.B	AGE	P.O.B	CAREER	Apps	Gls
Anthony McMillan			19/2/82	27	Wigan	Preston (Scholar), Wigan, Runcorn, Lancaster 3/05, Burscough 6/06, Lancaster (2ML) 11/06, Ashton U (L) 2/07, Colwyn Bay (L) 3/07, Southport 7/08	39	0
DEFENDERS								
Paul Barratt			15/9/87	21	Manchester	Liverpool (Yth) Rel c/s 07, Worcester 8/07, Southport 11/07, Northwich 5/08 Rel 3/09, Fleetwood (L) 1/09, Southport 5/09		
Earl Davis	6'01"	13 02	17/5/83	26	Manchester	Burnley, Southport (SL) 3/03, Southport 12/03, Swansea NC 1/04 Rel 2/04, Southport 2/04, Hyde U c/s 06, Burscough (3ML) 11/07 Perm 2/08, Southport 7/08	31	0
Adam Flynn			12/10/84	24		Liverpool (Scholar), Prescot Cables 8/04, Burscough 6/07, Southport 7/08	35	1
Shaun Gray			28/1/87	22	Ormskirk	Morecambe, Fleetwood (L) 1/06, Clitheroe (L) 8/06, Fleetwood 12/06, Prescot Cables (L) 1/08, Burscough 5/08, Southport 7/08	26	1
Kevin Lee	6'00"	11 10	4/11/85	23	Liverpool	Wigan, Accrington (L) 10/05, Blackpool (L) 3/06, Southport 7/06	33	2
Chris Lever			13/2/87	22	Oldham	Oldham Rel c/s 07, Stalybridge (SL) 3/07, Southport c/s 07	33	0
Robert Marsh-Evans	6'03"	12 08	13/10/86	22	Abergele	Chester Rel 1/08, Droylsden (L) 8/07, Vauxhall Motors (3ML) 9/07, Leigh RMI/Leigh Genesis 1/08 Rel 11/08, Vauxhall Motors 11/08, Southport 5/09		
MIDFIELDERS								
Bradley Barnes			12/12/88	20		Bolton (Yth), Flixton, Morecambe (Trial) 7/08, Barrow (Trial) 7/08, Trafford 9/08, Southport 8/09		
Robbie Booth	5'07"	11 08	30/12/85	23	Liverpool	Everton (Scholar), Chester (Sch) (Pro) 3/05 Rel c/s 05, Southport 7/05, Burscough (L) 1/06, Burscough 9/06, Southport 7/08	33	2
Matty McGinn			27/6/83	26	Fazackerley	Southport, Runcorn 8/02, Southport 7/05 Rel 9/06, Burscough 9/06, Southport 7/08	37	3
Alan Moogan			22/2/84	25	Liverpool	Everton Rel c/s 04, Injured, Burscough c/s 06, Southport 7/08	27	2
Mike Powell			11/9/85	23	Ormskirk	Southport	35	7
Ashley Winn	5'11"	11 02	1/12/85	23	Stockton	Middlesbrough (Yth), Oldham Rel 5/05, York C 8/05 Rel 5/06, Stalybridge (L) 3/06, Stalybridge 7/06, Barrow 7/08, Southport (L) 12/08, Southport 1/09	21	2
FORWARDS								
Zac Aley			17/8/91	18	Fazackerley	Southport	1	1
Steve Daly			10/12/81	27	Fazackerley	Wigan (Yth), Local, Runcorn 6/03, Southport 10/03, Droylsden 8/06, Burscough 5/08, Southport 7/08	33	14
Ciaren Kilheeney	5'11"	11 09	9/1/84	25	Stockport	Man City (Trainee), Mossley 1/03, Exeter 3/03, Droylsden 5/03, Radcliffe B 11/04, Ashton U 9/05, Burscough 9/06, Southport 6/08	38	16
Chris Simm	6'00"	12 08	10/4/84	25	Wigan	Congleton, Leigh RMI c/s 04, Wrexham (Trial) 7/07, Hyde 7/07, Southport 5/09		
OTHERS								
Shaun Holden			12/12/91	17	Fazackerley	Southport	1	0
Connor Millington			21/3/92	17	Liverpool	Southport	1	0
Alex Grisedale			8/10/90	18	Liverpool	Southport	1	0
John Hedges			8/2/92	17	Fazackerley	Southport	1	0

LOANEES	HT	WT	DOB	AGE	POB	From - To	APPS	GOA
(G)Ross Atkins			3/11/89	19	Derby	Derby 10/08, 3/09 -	4	0
(M)Shaun Whalley	5'09"	10 07	7/8/87	22	Prescot	Wrexham (SL) 2/09 - Rel 5/09	14	0
(M)Kevin Leadbetter			10/9/79	29	Liverpool	Fleetwood 2/09 -	6	0
(M)Danny Mitchley			7/10/89	19	Liverpool	Blackpool (SL) 3/09 -	6	0

DEPARTURES	HT	WT	DOB	AGE	POB	From - To	APPS	GOA
(F)Craig Noone			17/11/87	21		Burscough 7/08 - Plymouth Undisc 8/08	1	0
(M)Steven Morrison	6'00"	10 13	10/9/88	20	Southport	Everton 9/08 - Skelmersdale 10/08		
(F)Tony Gray			6/4/84	25		Burscough 6/06 - Droylsden 12/08	15	3
(M)Michael Barnes	5'10"	11 05	24/6/88	21	Chorley	Northwich 10/08 - FC Halifax 1/09, Lancaster (Trial) 6/09, AFC Fylde 8/09	7	0
(M)John Doolan	6'01"	13 00	7/2/74	35	Liverpool	Rochdale (Pl/Coach) 6/08 - Rel 2/09	11	0
(F)Neil Robinson	5'10"	13 07	18/11/79	29	Liverpool	Burscough Undisc 10/07 - Rel 2/09, Skelmersdale 2/09	18	3
(F)Josh Hine			4/3/91	18		Yth - Burscough 3/09		
(G)Steven Drench	6'01"	12 09	11/9/85	23	Salford	Morecambe 6/08 - Stevenage (Trial) 8/08, Cambridge U (4ML) 8/08, Leigh Genesis 3/09	0	0
(G)Zak Hibbert			28/6/88	21	Whangeria (NZ)	Burscough 12/08 - Accrington 3/09, Chorley 7/09	0	0
(M)Mark Duffy			7/10/85	23		Prescot Cables 1/07 - Morecambe (SL) 2/09, £20,000 5/09	24	4
(D)James Connolly			7/3/81	28		Burscough 7/08 - Burscough 7/09	23	0
(M)Neil Prince	5'11"	10 07	17/3/83	26	Liverpool	Droylsden 3/09 - Marine 7/09	8	1
(M)Peter Moore	5'08"	11 01	13/8/88	21	Liverpool	Warrington 3/09 - Bala T 8/09	7	0
(D)Chris Price	5'09"	11 09	24/10/75	23	Liverpool	Burscough 7/08 -	1	0
(F)Allan Smart	6'02"	12 10	8/7/74	35	Perth	Burcough (Coach) 10/08 (Reg as player) 2/09 -	5	1

SOUTHPORT

Formed: 1881

Nickname: The Sandgrounders.

Club Colours: Yellow shirts, shorts and socks.

Change Colours: White shirts, shorts and socks.

Club Sponsor: Palace Chemicals.

Previous League: Northern Premier League

Ground Address: Haig Avenue,Southport, Merseyside. PR8 6JZ

Telephone: 01704 533 422.

Mobile: 07802 661 906.

Fax: 01704 533 455.

Email: secretary@southportfc.net.

Social Club: 01704 530 182.

Website: www.southportfc.net

SIMPLE DIRECTIONS:

By Road: Leave M6 at junction 26, join M58 to junction 3, join A570 signposted Southport and follow A570 through Ormskirk town centre following signs for Southport. At the big roundabout(McDonalds on left) take fourth exit and proceed with playing fields on your left. Retail Park on right and turn left before main traffic lights into Haig Avenue. Ground is on the left.

Capacity: 6,008 **Seats:** 1,660 **Covered:** 2,760 **Floodlights:** Yes

Clubhouse: Open every evening and match days.

Club Shop: Fully stocked

Local Press: Southport Visitor, The Champion

Local Radio: Dune FM, Radio Merseyside, Radio Lancashire

PROGRAMME EDITOR

Rob Urwin

(M) 07790 04 1514 (B) 01704 533 422

Email: rob@southportfcstats.co.uk

CLUB STATISTICS

Record Attendance: 20,010 v Newcastle United F.A.Cup 1932.
Victory: 8-1 v Nelson 01.01.31.
Defeat: 0-11 v Oldham Athletic 26.12.62
Career Goalscorer: Alan Spence - 98
Career Appearances: Arthur Peat - 401 (1962-1972)
Transfer Fee Paid:
£20,000 to Macclesfield Town for Martin McDonald.
Transfer Fee Received:
Undisclosed from Morecambe for Carl Baker 2007.

SENIOR HONOURS

Lancashire League Champions 1902-03.
Lancashire Combination Division 2 Champions 1903-04.
Lancashire Senior Cup Winners 1904-05.
Liverpool Senior Cup Winners 1930-31, 31-32, 43-44, 62-63, 74-75, 90-91, 92-93, 98-99. Shared 1957-58, 63-64.
Football League Division Four Champions 1972-73.
Northern Premier League Challenge Cup Winners 1990-91.
Northern Premier League Champions 1992-93.
Conference North Champions 2004-05.

PREVIOUS

Names: Southport Central and Southport Vulcan.
Leagues: Preston & District. Lancashire 1889-1903.
Lancashire Combination 1903-11. Central 1911-21
Football League 1921-78. Northern Premier League 1978-93, 03-04.
Conference 1993-2003.
Grounds: Sussex Road Sports Ground. Scarisbrick New Road.
Ash Lane (later named Haig Avenue).

STAFFORD RANGERS

Back row (L-R): Bobby Wilson, Wayne Daniel (Capt) Stuart Pierpoint, Nick Wellecomme.
Centre row: Simon Davies(Kit Manager) Tom Ingram, Danny Allen, Alex Gibson (no longer at the club) Danny Alcock, Ishmale Reid, Nick Amos, Steve Bateman (Physio)
Front row: Jonathan Loukes, David MacPherson, Carl Palmer, Chris Brindley (Asst Manager) Steve Bull M.B.E.(Manager) Darren Read (Coach) David McNiven, Andre Francis, Paul McMahon.

CLUB PERSONNEL

Chairman: Jon Downing.

Company Secretary: Mike Hughes.

Additional Directors: Roly Tonge, Cliff Went, Reg Bates, Rod Woodward, Ian Seddon.

Secretary: Mike Hughes

(H): 01785 254 879.

(B): 01785 602 430

(M): 07850 996 386

E-mail: mike.hughes@staffordrangersfc.o.uk

correspondence to Secretary at club.

Commercial Manager: David Taylor.

Tel: (M) 07515 379 573.

Email: david.taylor@staffordrangersfc.co.uk

Manager: Chris Brindley.

Club therapist: Steve Bateman.

Stafford Rangers have featured as one of non-league football's most successful clubs since the introduction of the Football Conference, but their supporters have had to watch their favourites rebuilding in the Blue Square North and they have not looked like challenging for a return to the top level recently.

With Midland hero Steve Bull in charge, Rangers still failed to get off to a confident start but three consecutive victories in September took them to fifth place, their best position of the season. However, at no other time did the club manage two or more consecutive wins until their desperate end of season battle for survival.

Defeat in their first game in both F.A.Cup, away to Coalville Town, and F.A. Trophy away to King's Lynn, didn't help confidence, and a change of manager saw Chris Brindley take responsibility. League results didn't improve however and by April, Rangers were in danger of being dragged into the relegation zone, as they had failed to score in seven of eleven games in February and March.

However, after four straight losses, an impressive 4-1 home victory against promotion challengers Gateshead inspired everyone connected with the club to a lively end of season, at the end of which, Stafford Rangers had survived and finished in eighteenth position six points clear of danger.

STAFFORD RANGERS

BEST LGE ATT.: **1,815** v AFC Telford United
LOWEST: **377** v Workington

No.	Date	Comp	H/A	Opponents	Att:	Result	Goalscorers	Pos
1	Aug 9	BSN	H	Farsley Celtic	678	W 1 - 0	Thorley 71	
2	12		A	Vauxhall Motors	187	D 1 - 1	Wright 79	
3	16		A	Workington	452	D 2 - 2	**McNiven** 4 11	6
4	23		H	Tamworth	958	L 0 - 1		11
5	25		A	Solihull Moors	314	W 1 - 0	**McNiven** 17	
6	30		H	Southport	671	L 0 - 3		11
7	Sept 2		H	King's Lynn	476	D 0 - 0		
8	13		H	Blyth Spartans	545	W 1 - 0	Thorley 66	12
1	**16**	**SS N1**	**A**	**Alfreton Town**	**201**	**W 3 - 2**	**McNiven 32 Wellecomme 42 73**	
9	20		A	Droylsden	420	W 1 - 0	Phillips 82	9
10	24		A	Gateshead	265	W 1 - 0	Macpherson 31	
11	**27**	**F.A.C. 2Q**	**A**	**Coalvlle Town**	**410**	**L 1 - 2**	**Wellcombe 43**	
12	Oct 4		H	Harrogate Town	576	D 0 - 0		5
3	**14**	**SS N2**	**H**	**Northwich Victoria**	**327**	**W 3 - 1**	**McNiven 31 37 Phillips 80**	
13	18		A	Hyde United	375	D 1 - 1	**McNiven** 67	6
14	21		H	Hucknall Town	403	D 0 - 0		
15	25		A	Stalybridge Celtic	505	L 0 - 2		9
16	Nov 1		H	Redditch United	556	L 0 - 1		9
4	**4**	**SS N3**	**H**	**Southport**	**261**	**L 1 - 2**	**Phillips 26**	
17	8		A	Gainsborough Trinity	390	W 3 - 0	Wilson 45 **McNiven** 50 Ingram 84	8
18	15		H	Fleetwood Town	420	L 1 - 2	Kay 12 (og)	8
19	**22**	**F.A.T. 3Q**	**A**	**King's Lynn**	**749**	**L 2 - 3**	**Palmer 45 Magee 47**	
20	29		A	King's Lynn	924	D 2 - 2	Phillips 19 **McNiven** 84 (pen)	8
21	Dec 6		H	Vauxhall Motors	514	L 0 - 1		10
22	20		A	Farsley Celtic	257	L 0 - 4		13
23	26		H	AFC Telford United	1815	L 1 - 3	Miller 23	13
24	Jan 1		A	AFC Telford United	3140	W 1 - 0	Craven 32	
25	17		H	Burscough	494	L 0 - 2		
26	24		A	Harrogate Town	338	D 3 - 3	Flynn 56 85 Proffitt 86	13
27	27		A	Hucknall Town	241	L 1 - 3	**McNiven** 22	
28	31		H	Gainsborough Trinity	446	W 2 - 0	Miller 23 **McNiven** 86	12
29	Feb 14		H	Stalybridge Celtic	721	L 0 - 1		14
30	17		H	Hyde United	500	W 2 - 0	Daniel 78 **McNiven** 90	12
31	23		A	Hinckley United	428	L 0 - 4		
32	28		A	Burscough	348	L 0 - 2		14
33	Mar 10		A	Redditch United	217	D 2 - 2	**McNiven** 65 (pen) 90	
34	14		H	Droylsden	474	D 0 - 0		15
35	17		H	Workington	377	D 0 - 0		
36	21		A	Blyth Spartans	502	L 1 - 2	**McNiven** 25	16
37	24		H	Alfreton Town	377	L 0 - 2		
38	28		A	Southport	873	L 2 - 3	Thorley 1 Wellecombe 23	16
39	30		A	Alfreton Town	415	L 0 - 2		
40	April 4		H	Gateshead	448	W 4 - 1	Clements 6 23 Murray 50 Wellecmbe 62	16
41	11		A	Tamworth	1214	W 2 - 1	Moult 33 Thorley 56	
42	13		H	Solihull Moors	588	L 0 - 2		
43	18		A	Fleetwood Town	1190	D 2 - 2	Moult 8 Amos 64	17
44	25		H	Hinckley United	511	W 3 - 1	**McNiven** 50 Moult 58 Thorley 87	18

Average Home Att: 598 (852) **Goals** 51 66

Best Position: 5th **Worst:** 18th

Goalscorers: McNiven 16, Wellecombe 5, Phillips 4, Thorley 4, Moult 3, Clements 2, Flynn 2, Miller 2, Amos 1, Craven 1, Daniel 1, Ingram 1, Macpherson 1, Magee 1, Murray 1, Palmer 1, Proffitt 1, Thorley 1, Wilson 1, Wright 1.Own Goals 1.

ALCOCK	THORLEY	REID	WILSON	DANIEL	AMOS	PALMER	MACPHERSON	MCNIVEN	WELLECOMME	LOUKES	DOVEY	INGRAM	MCMAHON	MORRIS	ALLEN	FRANCIS	PIERPOINT	DACRES	MCDONALD	SPALDING	SANDERCOMBE	PHILLIPS	CULLINGWORTH	PROFFITT	ROGERS	GROCUTT	MOULT	MAGEE	JONES	BRISCOE	MILLAR	CRAVEN	BRANNAN	BRINDLEY	FLYNN	BUCKHAM	DODD	MURRAY	CLEMENTS	ONOKAH	PATRICK	
X	X	X	X	X	X	X	X	X	X	X	S	S	U	U	U																											
X	X	X	X	X	X	X	X	X	X	X	S	S	S	U	U																											**1**
X	X		X	X	X	X	X	X	X	U	S	U		S	U	X	X																									**2**
X	X	X	X	X	X	X	X	X	X	S		U	S	S	U		X																									**3**
X	X		S	X	X	X	X	X	X	X		S	S	X	U	U	X																									**4**
X	X		X	X	X		X	X	X			S	S		U	X	X	X	S	U																						**5**
X	X		X	X	X	X	X	X		X		S	U	U	S	X	X			U																						**6**
	X		X	X	X	X	X	X	S	X		U	U		U	X	X				X	S																				**7**
	X		**X**	**X**	**X**	**X**	**U**	**X**	**X**	**X**		**U**	**S**		**U**	**U**	**X**				**X**	**X**																				**8**
	X		X	X	X	X	X	S	X	X			U	S	U	U	X				X	X																				**9**
	X		X	X		X	X	S	X	X		S	U	X	U	S	X				X	X																				**10**
		U	**X**	**X**		**X**	**X**	**X**	**X**	**X**		**S**			**U**	**X**	**X**	**S**		**U**	**X**	**X**																				**11**
	X		X			X	X	U	X	X		U	U		U	X	X			U	X	X	X																			**12**
	X		**X**	**U**		**X**	**X**	**X**		**X**		**X**	**S**	**U**	**U**	**X**	**X**				**X**	**X**		**S**																		**13**
	X		X			X	X	X		X		X	S	U	U		X				X	X	X	S	U																	**14**
	X		X			X	X	X		X		X	U	U	U		X				X	X	X	S	U																	**15**
			X			X	S	X		X		X	S		U		X				X	X	X	U	U	X	X															**16**
U			X	S		X	S	X		X		U	X				X				X	X	X	S		X	X															**17**
X			**X**	**X**		**X**	**X**	**X**		**X**		**X**	**U**				**X**				**U**	**X**		**S**	**U**		**X**															**18**
X			X	X	S	X	X	X		X		S	U				X				U	X	S			X	X															**19**
X			X	X		X	X	X				S	U			U	X				U	X	X	S		X	X															**20**
X			**X**	**X**	**U**	**X**	**X**	**X**				**X**			**U**	**X**						**X**	**X**	**S**		**X**		**S**	**U**													**21**
X			X	X		X	X	S				U			U	X	X					X	S	S			X	X		X												**22**
X			X	X		X	X	X				U			U	X	X					X	U	U			X	S		X												**23**
		X		X	X			X							U	X	X			S	X			X				X	S		X	X	S	U								**24**
		X		X	X			X	S						U	X	X			S	X			U			X	X			X	X	S									**25**
		X		X	U			X	S						U	X	X				X			U			X	X	U		X	X	X									**26**
		X		X	U			X	S	S					U	X	X				X			S			X	X			X	X	X									**27**
		S		X	X			X		X					U	X	X				X			S			X	X			X		S	U	X							**28**
		S		X				X		X					U	X	X				X			X			X	X	U		X		S	U	X							**29**
	X	U		X				X	X	X					U	X	X				X			U			X	S			X		S		X							**30**
	X	S		X				X	X	X				U	U	X					X				U		X	S			X		X		X							**31**
	X			X				X	X	X					U	X	X				X						X	S			X		U		X	S	U					**32**
	X			X				X	S	X					U	X	X				X				U		X	X			X				X	S	S					**33**
	X			X				X	X	U					U	X	X				X						X	S			X				X	S	U	X				**34**
	X			X				X						U	U	X	X				X						X	X			X			U		S	U	X	X			**35**
	X		X	X				X	S					U		X	X				X						X	X			S					U	U	X	X			**36**
	X		X	X				X	X						U	X	X				X						X	U			S					U	U	X	X			**37**
	X		X	X	U			X	X						U	X	X				X						X	S								S	U	X	X			**38**
	X		X	X	S			X	X						U	X	X				X						X	S								S	U	X	X			**39**
	X		X	X	S			X	X						U	X	X				X						X	U								U	U	X	X			**40**
			X	X	X				X						U	X	X				X				U			X						U		S		X	X	X	S	**41**
			X	X	X			X	X						U	X	X				X						X	S								U		X	X	S	S	**42**
	X		X	X	X			X	X						U	X					X				U		X	U						U			U	X			X	**43**
	X		X	X	X			X	X						U	X					X				U		X	S	U							S		X			X	**44**
	X		X	X	X			X	X						U	X									U		X	U						U		U		X			X	**45**
	X		X	X	X			X	X						U	X	X				X				S		X	S	U							U					X	**46**
Total League Appearances																																										
11	28	7	29	37	18	18	17	37	23	19	0	3	1	2	0	30	36	1	0	0	30	11	6	2	0	4	27	11	0	2	12	4	3	0	7	0	0	12	8	1	4	**X**
0	0	3	1	1	3	0	2	3	6	2	3	8	6	3	1	1	0	0	1	2	0	1	2	7	1	0	0	10	1	0	2	0	5	0	0	8	1	0	0	1	2	**S**
1	0	1	0	0	3	0	0	1	0	2	0	7	9	8	37	3	0	0	0	3	2	0	1	5	9	0	0	4	4	0	0	0	1	7	0	6	9	0	0	0	0	**U**
Total Cup Appearances																																										
2	2	0	5	4	1	5	4	5	2	4	0	3	0	0	0	3	4	0	0	0	3	5	1	0	0	1	1	0	0	0	0	0	0	0	0	0	0	0	0	0	0	**X**
0	0	0	0	0	0	0	0	0	0	0	0	1	2	0	0	0	0	1	0	0	0	0	0	3	0	0	0	1	0	0	0	0	0	0	0	0	0	0	0	0	0	**S**
0	0	1	0	1	1	0	1	0	0	0	0	1	1	1	4	1	0	0	0	1	1	0	0	0	1	0	0	0	1	0	0	0	0	0	0	0	0	0	0	0	0	**U**

Also Played: RANSOME X(45)

STAFFORD RANGERS

CURRENT SQUAD AS OF BEGINING OF 2009-10 SEASON

GOALKEEPERS	HT	WT	D.O.B	AGE	P.O.B	CAREER	Apps	Gls
Danny Allen			13/9/90	18	Stafford	Stafford R	1	0
Lee Evans			24/5/83	26	Sutton Coldfield	Ilkeston, Stourport 6/03, Willenhall, Bedworth 8/04, Bromsgrove c/s 05, Chasetown 5/06, Gresley R (L) 10/08, Stafford R 6/09		
Tom Harrison	6'00"	13 07	11/11/90	18		Stoke (Scholar) Rel c/s 09, Stafford R 8/09		
DEFENDERS								
Nick Amos			23/7/75	34	Ilford	Rainham T, Hornchurch, Rushall O, Bromsgrove 7/95, Hednesford 1/99, Gresley (L) 4/99, Rushall O (L) 1/00, Solihull 7/00, Halesowen T 10/04, Stafford R 6/08	21	1
Andy Owens	6'03"	13 05	15/10/89	19		Liverpool (Yth), Stoke, Leek T (WE) 2/08, Glen Hoddle Soccer Academy, Stafford R 8/09		
Jonathan Patrick			24/5/91	18	Wolverhampton	Walsall Rel 3/09, Stafford R 3/09	6	0
Joe Rogers			20/2/92	17	Stafford	Stafford R	1	0
Richard Vauls	5'11"	11 08	23/9/90	18		Stoke (Scholar) Rel c/s 09, Stafford R 7/09		
Bobby Wilson			11/8/88	21	Harlow	Notts Forest (Yth), Notts County, Hucknall (SL) 3/07, Hucknall 8/07, Stafford R 7/08, Gainsborough 12/08, Stafford R NC 3/09	30	1
MIDFIELDERS								
Ross Davidson	6'02"	11 05	6/9/89	19	Burton	Port Vale, Stafford R (L) 8/09		
Andre Francis			25/4/85	24	Birmingham	Stafford R, Rushall O, Halesowen T 6/07, Romulus 1/08, Stafford R 7/08	31	0
Craig Hulme			8/5/89	20	Stafford	Stafford T, Stafford R 7/09		
Fabrice Kasiama						Wolves (Scholar), Gillingham (Trial) 4/09, Stafford R 8/09		
Luke Morgan	5'08"	10 02	26/10/88	20	Leeds	Bradford C Rel c/s 08, Ossett A (L) 11/07, Droylsden (L) 1/08, Glen Hoddle Soccer Academy (Spa), Stafford R 7/09		
Jake Moult	5'10"	10 05	10/2/89	20	Stoke	Port Vale (Scholar), Plymouth 7/07 Rel c/s 08, Kidderminster (SL) 3/08, Leek T 8/08, Stafford R 10/08	27	3
Tom Thorley	5'10"	11 08	5/4/90	19	Stafford	Stoke Rel 6/09, Stafford R (3ML) 7/08, Burscough (L) 10/08, Stafford R (SL) 1/09, Stafford R 7/09	28	6
FORWARDS								
Ben Mills			29/3/89	20	Stoke	Leek T, Newcastle T 7/07, Leek T 9/08, Stafford R 7/09		
Dorryl Proffitt			2/5/85	24	Stafford	Man City, Leek T 11/04, Preston (Trial) 11/04, Burnley (Trial) 12/04, Oldham (Trial) 1/05, Crawley 11/05 Rel 2/06, Hinckley U 2/06, Millwall (Trial) c/s 06, Leek T 9/06 Rel 2/07, Witton 2/07, Newcastle T (L) 3/07, Alsager 10/07, FC Halifax 7/08 Rel 8/08, Witton 8/08 Rel 10/08, Stafford R 10/8, Newcastle T 2/09, Safford R 8/09	9	1
Nick Wellecomme			31/5/84	25	Stafford	Brocton, Newcastle T, Stafford R 3/08	29	2
Chris Brindley						Stafford R (Man) 12/08	0	0

LOANEES	HT	WT	DOB	AGE	POB	FROM - TO	APPS	GOA
(M)Jimmy Phillips	5'06"		20/9/89	19	Stoke	Stoke 9/08 - Rel 6/09	12	2
(F)Marc Grocutt			11/11/89	19	Stoke	Stoke 10/08 - Rel 6/09	4	0
(M)Christian Millar	5'11"	11 00	23/11/89	19	Stoke	Macclesfield (2ML) 12/08 - Rel 5/09	14	2
(M)Dean Craven			17/2/79	30		Bromsgrove 12/08 - Hednesford 2/09	4	1
(M)Chris Clements			6/2/90	19		Crewe 3/09 -	8	2
(G)Lloyd Ransome						Port Vale (EL) 4/09 -	1	0

DEPARTURES	HT	WT	DOB	AGE	POB	From - To	APPS	GOA
(M)Christian Dacres						Alsager T 8/08 - Rel 10/08, Stone Dominoes 10/08, Rocester 12/08	1	0
(F)Paul McMahon						Newcastle T c/s 08 - Leek T (Dual) 10/08 Perm 12/08	7	0
(M)Carl Palmer			2/11/78	29	Wolverhampton	Nuneaton 6/08 - Rushall O 12/08	18	0
(M)Dave MacPherson			27/7/79	30	Stoke	Witton 6/08 - Rel 12/08, Leek 12/08, Nantwich 1/09	19	1
(F)Louis Briscoe						Gresley 11/08 - Ilkeston 12/08, Mansfield 1/09	2	0
(D)James Cullingworth			18/9/87	21	Nottingham	Hucknall 10/08 - Gainsborough 12/08, Rel 5/09, Boston U 6/09	8	0
(M)Tom Ingram					Leicester	Notts County 8/07 - Hinckley U 12/08	11	1
(G)Danny Alcock	5'11"	11 03	15/2/84	25	Salford	Accrington 8/06 - Tamworth 12/08	11	0
(M)Steve Brannan			7/9/86	22	Stoke	Leek T 12/08 - Leek T 2/09	8	0
(M)Christopher Flynn	5'11"	12 04	5/11/87	21	Market Drayton	Northwich 1/09 - Eastwood T 3/09 Rel 5/09, Nantwich 6/09	7	2
(M)Jonathan Loukes			12/6/88	21	Sheffield	USA 3/08 - USA 3/09	21	0
(M)Ishmael Reid			13/5/86	23	Stafford	Rocester 2/08 - Rel 10/08, Stafford R 12/08, Leek T 3/09	10	0
(G)Timothy Sandercombe	6'04"	13 12	15/6/89	20	Plymouth	ex Notts County 9/08 - Mansfield 5/09	30	0
(D)Wayne Daniel			12/12/76	32	Birmingham	Boldmere St Michaels 6/02 - Worcester 6/09	38	1
(D)Liam Murray	6'03"	11 00	1/8/85	24	Stafford	Redditch 2/09 - Rel 5/09, Solihull Moors 6/09, Kings Lynn 7/09	12	1
(D)Stuart Pierpoint						Halesowen T 7/08 - Nuneaton T 6/09	36	0
(D)Alan Dodd					Stoke	Leek CSOB 2/09 - Leek CSOB 7/09	1	0
(F)David McNiven	5'10"	12 00	27/5/78	31	Leeds	Morecambe 8/07 - Hyde U 7/09	40	13
(M)Charlie Jones						Yth - Brocton (L) 12/08	1	0
(M)Alex Morris	6'00"	11 08	5/10/82	26	Stoke	Nantwich 8/08 -	5	0
(M)Tom Spalding			3/11/89	19	Sutton Coldfield	Wolves -	2	0
(F)Matt Buckham			27/4/83	26	Durham	Stafford T 1/09 -	8	0
(F)Lyndon Dovey						Stourbridge 7/08 - Stourbridge (L) 9/08	3	0
(F)Mark Magee			3/10/89	19	Cheltenham	Bristol C 11/08 -	21	0
(F)Tony Onokah						Chasetown 3/09 -	2	0
Nathan McDonald						Yth -	1	0

STAFFORD RANGERS

Founded: 1876.

Nickname: Rangers

Club Colours: Black & white striped shirts, black shorts, black socks.

Change Colours: Red shirts, shorts and socks.

Club Sponsor: Stan Robinson (Stafford) Ltd. Express Pallets Nationwide.

Previous League: Northern Premier League.

Ground Address: Marston Road, Stafford ST16 3BX
Telephone: 01785 602 430
Facsimile: 01785 602 431
Mobile: 07850 996 386
E-mail: srfcmarstonroad@tiscali.co.uk
Website: www.staffordrangers.co.uk

SIMPLE DIRECTIONS: M6 Jct 14 A34 (Stone) to roundabout, straight over to Beaconside, then take third right into Common Road. Ground one mile ahead. From Town centre follow signs for B5066 (Sandon) turn left by new housing estate.
By Rail: Nearest Railway Station is Stafford (Two miles from ground)

MATCH TICKETS:
Ticket office Telephone: 01785 602 430

CAPACITY: 6,000 **Seats:** 4264 **Covered:** 3,500

Clubhouse: Open matchdays and every evening.
Social Club No.: 01785 602432
Refreshments: Available on matchdays
Club Shop: Programmes and souvenirs available
Local radio: Express & Star & Staffordshire Newsletter

no image available

PROGRAMME EDITOR

David Taylor.

Tel: (M) 07515 379 573.

Email: david.taylor@staffordrangersfc.co.uk

CLUB STATISTICS

RECORDS

Attendance: 8,536 v Rotherham Utd F.A. Cup 3rd Rd 1975

Victory: 14-0 v Kidsgrove Athletic Staffs.Senior Cup 2003

Defeat: 0-12 v Burton Town Birmingham League 1930

Career Goalscorer: M.Cullerton 176

Career Apperances: Jim Sargent

Transfer Fee Paid: £13,000 to VS Rugby for S.Butterworth

Transfer Fee Received: £100,000 from Crystal Palace for Stan Collymore.

SENIOR HONOURS

Northern Premier League Champions 1971-72 1984-85

F.A.Trophy Winners 1971-72 1978-79

Staffordshire Senior Cup Winners (7)

PREVIOUS

Leagues: Shropshire 1891-93 B'ham 1893-96 N.Staffs 1896-1900, Cheshire 1900-01, B'ham Comb. 1900-12 46-52, Cheshire Co 52-69 N.P.L. 69-79 83-85 Alliance 79-83 Conf: 85-95.

STALYBRIDGE CELTIC

Back row (L-R): Michael O'Connor, Rhys Meynell, Greg Wilkinson, Barrie Keeling, Ben Richardson, Ryan Campbell, Chris Spooner. **Middle Row:** Rebecca Webb (Sports Therapist), David Pover (Sports Therapist), Nicky Platt, Garry Burke, Matty Barlow, Paul Phillips, Paul Sykes, Lee Ellington, Nathan Joynes, Wayne Richardson (Fitness Coach), Mark Storah (Kit man). **Front Row:** Paul Mitchell (Assistant manager), Danny Wood, Chris Williams, Terry Barwick, Steve Burr (Manager), Keith Briggs (Captain), Steve Torpey, Ashley Wooliscroft, Andy Fearn (Chief Scout).

CLUB PERSONNEL

Chairman: Rob Gorski.

Vice-Chairman: Syd White.

Company Secretary: Gerald Crossley.

Additional Directors: Dorothy Norton,

Gordon Greenwood, Bill McCallum, Colin Fielding,

John Dillon, Les Taylor.

Secretary: Martyn Torr

(B): 0161 633 1117

(M): 07860 841 765

office@stalybridgeceltic.co.uk

correspondence to Secretary at club.

Commercial Manager: John Hall.

Tel: (M) 07813 864 492

Managers: Steve Burr.

Assistant Manager: Benny Phillips.

Club therapist: David Pover.

Although hovering around the play off zone for most of the season, Celtic just couldn't find the consistency for long enough to stay in the top five at the vital time. Steve Burr, one of non-league football's most respected managers, is hoping to strengthen his squad to enable them to go the extra step in the coming campaign, and for a club which was never out of the top seven, he may not have too many gaps to fill.

There was no real cup excitement with an F.A.Cup 2nd Qualifying Round home victory over Fleetwood Town being followed by a staggering 1-6 home defeat against Durham City. The F.A.Trophy provided away wins against Whitby Town and Stourbridge which were followed by another away trip to holders Ebbsfleet United and a 1-2 defeat.

Celtic recorded a tremendous 7-1 victory over Hinckley United on the first Saturday of March, and at that time, Burr's boys had only failed to score on two occasions. So it was particularly frustrating that as the battle for the play off places developed Celtic failed to score in six of their next ten games .

This proved to be the deciding period of the season as an excellent run-in to the campaign brought ten points from twelve but only provided a final position of sixth, one place and six points behind fifth club Southport.

STALYBRIDGE CELTIC

BEST LGE ATT.: **762** v AFC Telford United
LOWEST: **315** v Gateshead

No.	Date	Comp	H/A	Opponents	Att:	Result	Goalscorers	Pos
1	Aug 9	BSN	H	AFC Telford United	762	D 2 - 2	**Torpey** 7 Williams 71	
2	12		A	Tamworth	615	W 3 - 0	Joynes 41 Barwick 62 Ellington 81	
3	16		A	Hucknall Town	337	W 3 - 2	Barwick 43 Ellington 62 **Torpey** 66	2
4	23		H	Southport	747	L 0 - 1		4
5	25		A	Vauxhall Motors	271	D 1 - 1	Joynes 40	
6	30		H	King's Lynn	489	D 1 - 1	Williams 3	
7	Sept 2		H	Solihull Moors	377	W 5 - 0	Joynes 44 **Barlow** 49 65 Briggs 55 **Torpey** 58	
8	6		A	Farsley Celtic	250	W 3 - 2	Williams 9 Santos 75 (og) Smart 88	3
9	**9**	**SS N1**	**H**	**Southport**	**231**	**L 1 - 4**	**Smart 42**	
10	13		H	Harrogate Town	515	L 1 - 3	**Barlow** 77	5
11	20		A	Hinckley United	559	W 1 - 0	Ellington 35	4
12	**27**	**F.A.C. 2Q**	**H**	**Farsley Celtic**	**500**	**W 4 - 0**	**Ellington 26 Barwick 35 Torpey 41 Barlow 59**	
13	Oct 4		H	Redditch United	479	D 3 - 3	Smart 46 **Torpey** 57 66	4
14	**11**	**F.A.C. 3Q**	**H**	**Durham City**	**525**	**L 1 - 6**	**Williams 5**	
15	18		A	Fleetwood Town	1315	W 2 - 1	**Torpey** 53 Ellington 65	4
16	25		H	Stafford Rangers	505	W 2 - 0	Sharpe 31 Briggs 41	
17	Nov 1		A	Alfreton Town	371	L 1 - 2	Platt 21	5
18	8		H	Tamworth	611	D 2 - 2	Smart 18 75	4
19	15		A	Burscough	358	W 2 - 0	Battersby 7 Williams 57	4
20	**26**	**F.A.T 3Q**	**A**	**Whitby Town**	**176**	**W 3 - 0**	**Wood 27 Woliscroft 47 Joynes 79**	
21	Dec 6		A	Gainsborough Trinity	384	D 3 - 3	Smart 28 Joynes 49 **Barlow** 89	6
22	**16**	**F.A.T 1R**	**A**	**Stourbridge**	**148**	**W 6 - 1**	**Ellington 22 Barwick 27 Barlow 60 81 Torpey 67 Platt 88**	
23	20		A	AFC Telford United	1890	L 0 - 1		7
24	26		A	Hyde United	871	W 2 - 0	**Barlow** 54 Keeling 58	
25	**Jan 13**	**F.A.T 2R**	**A**	**Ebbsfleet United**	**467**	**L 1 - 2**	**Joynes 52**	
26	17		A	Solihull Moors	253	W 2 - 0	Platt 22 **Barlow** 31	6
27	20		H	Hucknall Town	336	D 2 - 2	Briggs 33 Smart 78	
28	24		H	Workington	659	L 1 - 4	Joynes 77	
29	31		A	Harrogate Town	467	W 1 - 0	Joynes 12	7
30	Feb 14		A	Stafford Rangers	721	W 1 - 0	Briggs 19	
31	21		H	Gainsborough Trinity	552	L 1 - 2	Smart 22	7
32	24		H	Gateshead	315	L 1 - 2	Meechan 33	
33	28		A	Redditch United	211	W 1 - 0	Bowler 44	7
34	Mar 3		H	Hinckley United	332	W 7 - 1	Denham 5 Ellington 68 **Torpey** 71 **Barlow** 78 Barwick 82 Joynes 84 89	
35	7		A	Blyth Spartans	559	D 0 - 0		
36	10		H	Hyde United	604	W 4 - 1	**Barlow** 32 **Torpey** 68 87 Briggs 72	
37	14		H	Fleetwood Town	573	L 0 - 5		5
38	16		A	Droylsden	772	D 1 - 1	**Barlow** 90	
39	21		A	Gateshead	529	L 0 - 1		5
40	24		H	Blyth Spartans	351	W 2 - 0	Leeso 65 (og) Ellington 72	
41	28		A	King's Lynn	962	L 0 - 1		
42	April 4		H	Farsley Celtic	516	W 1 - 0	Hardiker 55	6
43	7		H	Alfreton Town	445	L 0 - 2		
44	11		A	Southport	951	L 0 - 2		7
45	13		H	Vauxhall Motors	401	W 1 - 0	Holmes 44 (og)	
46	18		H	Burscough	381	W 4 - 0	Briggs 38 Smart 44 Jennings 80 (pen) 88	7
47	21		H	Droylsden	614	D 2 - 2	Ellington 48 (pen) 80	
48	25		A	Workington	389	W 2 - 0	Barwick 30 **Torpey** 46	6

Average Home Att: **503 (538)** **Goals** **87 63**

Best Position: 2nd **Worst:** 7th

Goalscorers: Barlow 12, Torpey 12, Joynes 10, Ellington 10, Smart 9, Barwick 6, Briggs 6, Williams 5, Jennings 2, Platt 3, Battersby 1, Bowler 1, Denham 1, Hardiker 1, Keeling 1, Meechan 1, Sharpe 1, Wood 1, Wooliscroft 1. Own Goals 3.

PHILLIPS	WOOLISCROFT	WOOD	KEELING	BARWICK	SYKES	TORPEY	BRIGGS	ELLINGTON	JOYNES	WILLIAMS	BARLOW	PLATT	WILKINSON	BURKE	MEYNELL	O'CONNER	SMART	RICHARDSON	SHARPE	SAUNDERS	WRIGLEY	BATTERSBY	EVANS	COCKS	BYRNE	JENNINGS	MEECHAN	BOWLER	DENHAM	CONNOR	JACKSON	HARDIKER	NEWBOLD	
X	X	X	X	X	X	X	X	X	X	X	S	S	U	U	U																			1
X	X	X	X	X	X	X	X	X	X	X	S	S	U	U	S																			2
X	X	X	X	X	X	X	X	X	X	X	S	S	U		S	U																		3
X	X	X	X	X	X	X	X	X	X	X	S	S	U		S	U																		4
X	X	X	X	X	X	X	X	X	X	X	S	S	U		S	U																		5
X	X	U	X	X	X	X	X	X	X	X	S	S	U		X		S																	6
X	X	S	X	X	X	X	X	X	X	X	S	S	U		X		U																	7
X	X	S	X	X	X	X	X	X		X	X	S	U		X	U	S																	8
X	X	X	X	X	X	S	U	S		S	X	X			X	X	X	U																9
X	X	S	X		X	X	X	X	U	X	X	U	U		X	U	X																	10
X	X	S	U		X	X	X	X	S	X	X	S	U		X		X		X															11
X	X	S	U	X	X	X	X	X		X	X	U	S		X	U	S		X	U														12
X	X	U	U	X	X	X	X	X		X	X	U	U		X		S		X															13
X	X	U	S	X	X	X	X	X	S	X	S	U	U		X		X		X		U													14
X	X		U	X	S	X	X	X	S	X	X	S	U		X		X		X															15
X		S	S	X		X	X	X	U	U	X	X	S		X		X		X			X												16
X			X	X		X	X	X	U		X	X	U		X		X					X	U	U										17
X		U	U	X		X	X	X	X	S	S	X	S		X		X		X			X												18
X	X	S		X				X	X	X	S	X	S		X		X		X			X	U	U										19
X	X	X	X	X		U		S	X	X	S	X	S		X		X		X				U											20
X	X		X	X				U	X	X			U		X		X		X			X			X									21
X	X		X	X		X		X		X	S	S	S		X		X		X						X									22
X	X		X	X		X	X	X	S	U	X	U	U		X		X		X						S									23
X	X		X	X		X	X	X	U	U	X	U	U		X		X					X	U											24
X	X		X	X	U	X	X	X	X	S	X	S	U		X		X				U													25
X	X		X	S	S	X	X	U	X		X	X	S		X		X					X												26
X	X		X	S	S	X	X	S	X		X	X	U		X		X					X												27
X	X		X	S	S	X	X	S	X		X	X			X		X					X				U								28
X	X		X	X	X	X		S	X		S	S	U		X		X					X				U	X							29
X	X		X	X	X	X	X	S	X		S	U	U		X		X					S					X							30
X	X		X	X	X	X	X		U		S		U		X		X					X				S	X	U						31
X	X		X	X	X	X	X		S		X		U		S		X					X				U	X	S						32
X	X		X		X	X	X	S	S		X	U			X							X				U	X	X						33
X	X		X	S	X	X	X	X	S		X	U			X							U				S		X	X					34
X	X		X	U	X	X	X	X	S		X	U			X											S		X	X	U				35
X	X		X	U	X	X	X	X	S		X	S			X											S		X	X	U				36
X	X			X	X	X		X	U		X	S	U		X											S		X	X		X			37
X	X		X	S	X	X	X	S	X		X		U		X											S		X	X		U			38
X	X		X	X	X	X	X	S			X		S		U											S		X	X			X		39
X	X		X	X	X	X	X	X			X		U		S											S		X				X		40
X	X		X	S	S	X	X	X			S		U		X											U	X	X				X	X	41
X			X	X	S	X	X	S			X		U		X		S					X				U	X					X	X	42
X			X	X	U	X	X	S			X		U		S		X					X					X	U				X	X	43
X			X	X	X	S	X	X			X		U		U		X					X					X	S				X	S	44
X			X	X	X	U	X	X			U		X		X		X					X				S	X	S					S	45
X			X	X	X	S	X	X			U		X		X		X					X				S	U	S					X	46
X			X	U	X	S	X	X			S		X		X		X					X					X	S				X		47
X			U	X	X	X	X	X			X		X		S		X					X					S	S				X		48
Total League Appearances																																		
42	32	5	34	30	28	36	38	29	16	14	25	7	4	0	31	0	23	0	8	0	0	20	0	0	1	0	11	9	6	0	1	8	4	X
0	0	6	1	6	6	3	0	9	8	1	14	13	5	0	8	0	4	0	0	0	0	1	0	0	1	10	1	6	0	0	0	0	2	S
0	0	3	5	3	1	1	0	2	6	3	2	8	28	2	3	5	1	0	0	0	0	1	3	2	0	6	1	2	0	2	1	0	0	U
Total Cup Appearances																																		
6	6	2	4	6	3	4	3	4	2	4	3	2	0	0	6	1	5	0	4	0	0	0	0	0	1	0	0	0	0	0	0	0	0	X
0	0	1	1	0	0	1	0	2	1	2	3	2	3	0	0	0	1	0	0	0	0	0	0	0	0	0	0	0	0	0	0	0	0	S
0	0	1	1	0	1	1	1	0	0	0	0	2	2	0	0	1	0	1	0	1	2	0	1	0	0	0	0	0	0	0	0	0	0	U

STALYBRIDGE CELTIC

CURRENT SQUAD AS OF BEGINING OF 2009-10 SEASON

GOALKEEPERS	HT	WT	D.O.B	AGE	P.O.B	CAREER	Apps	Gls
Ryan Moss	6'00"	12 06	5/3/91	18		Macclesfield (Scholar) Rel c/s 09, Stalybridge 8/09		
Paul Phillips			15/11/78	30	Manchester	Man Utd, Bury, Buxton, Curzon Ashton, Droylsden 12/99, Stalybridge 5/08	42	0
DEFENDERS								
Richard Battersby	5'08"	10 03	13/6/79	30	York	Oldham Rel c/s 99, Radcliffe B 11/99, Northwich £5,000 7/05, Altrincham 1/08 Rel 9/08, Radcliffe B 10/08, Stalybridge 10/08, Salford C (Dual) 3/09, New Mills (L) 3/09	21	1
John Hardiker	5'11"	11 01	7/7/82	27	Preston	Morecambe, Stockport £150,000 1/02 Rel c/s 05, Bury 7/05, Morecambe (3ML) 10/05 Perm 1/06, Fleetwood 7/06, Forest Green (L) 11/06 Perm 12/06 Rel 3/09, Stalybridge 3/09	8	1
Graeme Law	5'10"	10 10	6/10/84	24	Kirkcaldy	York, Dundee 2/06, Tamworth 7/06, Farsley Celtic 7/07, Tamworth (L) 10/07 Perm 11/07 Rel c/s 09, Stalybridge 8/09		
Andrew Smart	6'01"	14 00	17/3/86	23	Wythenshawe	Altrincham (Yth), Macclesfield, Northwich (SL) 1/07, Stalybridge 6/07	27	8
Steve Woods	5'11"	11 13	15/12/76	32	Davenham	Stoke, Plymouth (SL) 3/98, Chesterfield 7/99 Rel c/s 01, Darlington (Trial) 11/00, Darlington (Trial) 7/01,Torquay 8/01 Rel 4/09, Stalybridge 8/09		
MIDFIELDERS								
Osebi Abadaki						Blackburn (Yth), Baguley, Altrincham (Yth), Stalybridge 8/09		
Keith Briggs			11/12/81	27	Glossop	Stalybridge (Yth), Stockport 8/99, Norwich £65,000 1/03, Crewe (L) 8/04, Stockport 1/05 Rel 1/08, Shrewsbury 1/08 Rel 1/08, Mansfield 2/08, Stalybridge 7/08	38	6
Michael Carr	5'08"	10 07	6/12/83	25	Crewe	Macclesfield, Northwich 1/05, Morecambe 5/08 Rel 1/09, Northwich (L) 9/08, Kidderminster 2/09 Rel 5/09, Stalybridge 7/09		
Dave Hankin	6'03"		25/3/85	24		Preston (Yth), Bamber Bridge, Squires Gate, Clitheroe 2/08, Stalybridge 6/09		
Barrie Keeling			19/8/78	31	Oldham	Man City (Yth), Morecambe 8/98, Bamber Bridge (L) 9/00, Marine Castle (Sin), Radcliffe B 1/02, Stalybridge 6/03, Radcliffe (L) 8/07	35	1
Michael O'Conner						Stalybridge	0	0
Warren Peyton	5'09"	11 03	13/12/79	29	Manchester	Bolton, Rochdale 10/99 Rel c/s 00, Bury 9/00, Nuneaton 7/01, Doncaster 12/02, Leigh RMI 7/03 Rel c/s 05, Altrincham 11/05 Rel 5/09, Stalybridge 6/09		
Greg Wilkinson						East Manchester, Stalybridge 2/08	9	0
FORWARDS								
Matty Barlow	5'11"	10 02	25/6/87	22	Oldham	Oldham Rel c/s 07, Stafford R (L) 11/06, Stalybridge (L) 1/07, Stalybridge 7/07	39	9
Conner Jennings						Stalybridge	10	3
Joe O'Neill	6'00"	10 05	28/10/82	26	Blackburn	Preston, Bury (SL) 7/03, Mansfield (3ML) 8/04, Chester (3ML) 1/05, York 7/05 Rel 5/06, Altrincham 6/06 Rel 5/09, Stalybridge 6/09		
OTHERS								
Mark Connor						Stalybridge	0	0
Jonathan Jackson						Stalybridge	1	0
Daniel Cocks						Stalybridge	0	0
Darren Evans						Stalybridge	0	0

LOANEES	HT	WT	DOB	AGE	POB	From - To	APPS	GOA
(D)Tom Sharpe	6'02"	13 04	12/10/88	20	Nottingham	Notts Forest (3ML) 9/08 - Rel 5/09, Kidderminster 7/09	8	1
(F)Chris Denham	6'00"	12 11	14/9/82	26		Altrincham 3/09 -	6	1
(F)Adam Newbold			16/11/89	19	Nottingham	Notts Forest (SL) 3/09 - Rel 5/09	6	0

DEPARTURES	HT	WT	DOB	AGE	POB	From - To	APPS	GOA
(D)Gary Burke			1/1/82	27	Ashton	Droylsden 1/08 - Curzon Ashton 8/08, Witton 9/08	0	0
(M)Ryan Campbell						Yth - Buxton 10/08		
(F)Michael Byrne	5'10"	11 06	14/5/85	24	Ashton-u-Lyne	Forest Green 12/08 - Rel 1/09	2	0
(F)Ben Richardson						Curzon Ashton (Jun) - Mossley 1/09	0	0
(F)Chris Williams	5'08"	9 00	2/2/85	24	Manchester	Bradford PA 7/08 - Fleetwood 2/09	15	4
(F)Nathan Joynes	6'01"	12 00	7/8/85	24	Hoyland	Halifax 7/08 - FC Halifax 3/09, Guiseley 8/09	24	7
(M)Nicky Platt			5/12/87	21		FCUM 7/08 - Rel 3/09, FCUM 3/09, Mandurah City (Aust) 6/09	20	2
(D)Ashley Wooliscroft	5'10"	11 02	28/12/79	29	Stoke	Hednesford 10/07 - Newcastle T 3/09, Fleetwood 5/09	32	0
(G)Matt Wrigley						Yth - Bamber Bridge 2/09	0	0
(F)Steve Torpey	5'09"	10 08	16/9/81	27	Kirkby	Halifax 6/08 - AFC Telford 6/09	39	10
(F)Lee Ellington	5'10"	11 07	3/7/80	29	Bradford	Gainsborough 7/05 - Farsley Celtic 6/09	38	8
(D)Rhys Meynell	5'11"	12 03	17/8/88	21	Barnsley	Barnsley 8/08 - AFC Telford (Trial) 6/09, Chester 7/09	39	0
(M)Paul Sykes	6'00"		13/1/77	32	Pontefract	Worksop £5,000 5/04 - FC Halifax 7/09	34	0
(F)Alex Meechan	5'08"	10 10	29/1/80	29	Plymouth	Altrincham 3/09 - Droylsden 7/09	12	1
(M)Chris Spooner						Yth - Belper 7/09		
(G)Russell Saunders	6'02"	12 06	3/1/89	20	Bury	Wigan 9/08 - Ashton U 1/09, Altrincham 7/09	0	0
(D)Michael Bowler	5'11"	12 00	8/9/87	21	Glossop	Kidderminster 2/09 -	15	1
(M)Terry Barwick	5'11"	10 12	11/1/83	26	Sheffield	Northwich 6/07 -	36	4
(M)Daniel Wood	5'08"	10 12	17/2/84	25	Sheffield	Gainsborough 5/08 - Guiseley (L) 12/08, Matlock (L) 1/09	11	0

STALYBRIDGE CELTIC

Formed: 1909

Nickname: Celtic.

Club Colours: Royal blue shirts, white shorts, royal blue socks.

Change Colours: Yellow shirts, yellow shorts, yellow socks.

Club Sponsor: Pavillion Group of Companies

Previous League: Northern Premier League

Ground address: Bower Fold, Mottram Road, Stalybridge, Cheshire SK15 2RT

Telephone: 0161 338 2828

Mobile: 07813 864 492

Fax: 0161 338 8256

Email: office@stalybridgeceltic

Website: www.stalybridgeceltic.co.uk

Capacity: 6,108 **Seats**: 1,200 **Cover** 2,400: **Floodlights**: Yes

Simple Directions: From Stockport and South M60, M67 to end of motorway through large roundabout to traffic lights. Then left to mini roundabout and left again into Mottram Road. Follow signs to Stalybridge, down hill and ground is on left by Hare & Hounds pub and F.X.Leisure Gym.

Clubhouse: Open Matchdays Club Shop: Contact Bob Rhodes Tel: 01457 76044

Local Radio: G.M.R. (BBC Manchester) 96.2 The Revolution

Local Press: Manchester Evening News, Saturday News Pink, Ashton Reporter Ashton Advertiser.

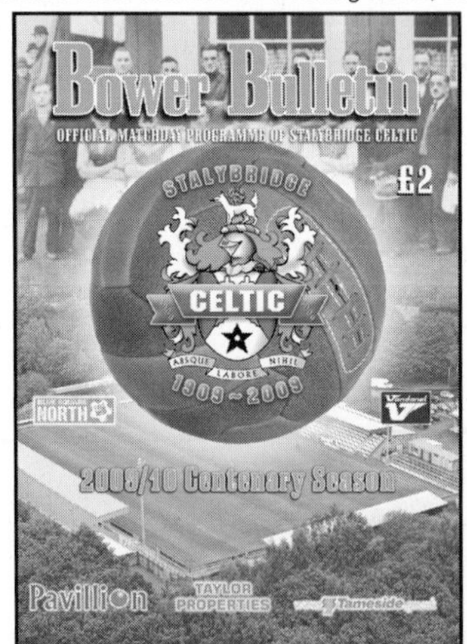

PROGRAMME EDITOR

Nick Shaw

(M) 07973 424 975

(B) 0161 633 1117

Email: nick@newimage.co.uk

CLUB STATISTICS

RECORDS

Attendance : 9,753 v W.B.A. F.A.Cup Replay 1922-23

Victory: 16-2 v Manchester NE 1.5.26 & Nantwich 22.10.32

Defeat: 1-10 v Wellington Town 9.3.46.

Career Goalscorer In Career: Harry Dennison 215

In a Season: Cecil Smith - 77 1931-32

Career Appearances: **In Career**: Kevan Keelan 395

Record Transfer Fee Paid:

£15,000 to Kettering Town for Ian Arnold 1995

Received: £16,000 from Southport for Lee Trundle

SENIOR HONOURS

Northern Premier 1991-92, 2000-01

Cheshire Senior Cup (2)

Manchester Senior Cup 1922-23

PREVIOUS

Leagues: Lancs Comb. 11-12, Central Lge 1912-21, Southern 1914-15, Football Lg 21-23, Cheshire Co., 23-82 N.W.Co 82-87 NPL 87-92 Conference: 92-98 01-02

VAUXHALL MOTORS

Back Row (L-R): Chris Noone, Chris Lane (capt), Danzelle St Louis-Hamilton, Alan Griffiths, Josh Wilson, Lee Dames.
Front: James Holden, Jordan Holmes, Karl Noon, Josh Hine, Craig Davies.

CLUB PERSONNEL

Chairman: Alan Bartlam.
Vice-Chairman: Stephen McInerney.
Company Secretary: Carole Paisey.
Additional Directors: Mr AJ Woodley, Mr L Jones, Mr D Mathers, Mrs L Bartlam, Mr M Harper, Mr N Kelly, Mrs C Mathers, Mr A Wilson, Mr P Jarvis, Mrs L Edmunds, Mrs F Wilson.

Secretary: Carole Paisey
31 South Road, West Kirby
Wirral CH48 3HG
(H): 0151 625 6936
(M): 07789 235 647
Email: alan.vauxhall@tiscali.co.uk

Commercial Manager: Mike Harper.
(H): 0151 645 4561
(M): 07817 400 202
Email: mike.harper@sky.com
Press Officer: Phil Jarvis.
Tel: (M) 07825 544 706
Email: pjarvis14@yahoo.co.uk

Manager: Carl Macauley.
Club therapist: TBC.

A season that started in disastrous fashion and had everyone involved with the club fearing the worst, finished as the best in the club's history, with a final position of eleventh in The Blue Square North. The club had only retained its place in the division through the demotion of Nuneaton Borough at the end of the 2007-08 campaign so manger Carl Macauley's achievement in turning their fortunes around, despite a lack of available funds, must rank among the best of the year.

Clubs cannot budget for extra finances from Cup runs but they are very welcome when they come. Unfortunately for the Merseyside club an F.A.Cup local 'derby' with Southport attracted nearly 600 to Haig Avenue but after a thrilling cup tie the home club won 3-2. The F.A.Trophy brought another clash with Southport and it took'The Sandgrounders' a home replay to win through to the First Round Proper.

The season took off for Macauley's squad in December, although they showed tremendous spirit throughout the campaign. Five successive victories and two draws took them up to eleventh position, and despite a lapse in form, they came back to achieve ninth place for a week after another inspired run of five wins and three draws in March.

Having enjoyed these successful bursts, perhaps it was surprising and disappointing to sign off in their most successful season with five consecutive defeats in which they only scored twice. Hopefully, the next campaign will see Vauxhall Motors find their impressive best form more consistently.

VAUXHALL MOTORS

BEST LGE ATT.: **511** v King's Lynn
LOWEST: **125** v Blyth Spartans

No.	Date	Comp	H/A	Opponents	Att:	Result	Goalscorers	Pos
1	Aug 9	BSN	A	Harrogate Town	308	L 0 - 2		
2	12		H	Stafford Rangers	187	D 1 - 1	Wright 79	
3	16		H	Redditch United	143	D 1 - 1	Nelson 66	
4	23		A	Fleetwood Town	941	L 0 - 2		21
5	25		H	Stalybridge Celtic	271	D 1 - 1	Griffiths 60	
6	30		A	Gainsborough Trinity	310	D 1 - 1	Rooney 89	
7	Sept 2		A	Burscough	242	W 1 - 0	Wright 69	
8	**8**	**SS N1**	**A**	**Hyde United**	**97**	**W 2 - 1**	**McFadden 16 Noone 28**	
9	13		H	Hinckley United	139	L 0 - 4		18
10	20		A	Hyde United	264	L 1 - 3	**Noone** 42	
11	**27**	**F.A.C. 2Q**	**A**	**Southport**	**593**	**L 2 - 3**	**Rooney 44 52 (pen)**	
12	Oct 4		H	Gateshead	149	L 1 - 2	**Noone** 9	21
13	**7**	**SS N2**	**H**	**Southport**	**163**	**L 0 - 3**		
14	18		A	Solihull Moors	200	L 2 - 3	Travis 18 (og) Wright 90	21
15	21		A	Southport	54	L 2 - 5	Holmes 16 85	
16	25		H	Workington	143	W 3 - 0	**Noone** 7 70 Holden 30	
17	28		H	Blyth Spartans	125	W 2 - 1	**Noone** 22 Rooney 57	
18	Nov 1		A	Farsley Celtic	289	W 1 - 0	Iqbal 86 (og)	16
19	15		H	Hucknall Town	174	L 2 - 3	Wright 72 85 (pen)	17
20	**22**	**F.A.T 3Q**	**H**	**Southport**	**278**	**D 0 - 0**		
21	**25**	**F.A.T.3Q r**	**A**	**Southport**	**224**	**L 1 - 2**	**Noone 26**	
22	29		A	Workington	294	L 1 - 2	**Noone** 6	17
23	Dec 6		A	Stafford Rangers	514	W 1 - 0	Marsh-Evans 72	17
24	20		H	Harrogate Town	156	W 1 - 0	Field 19	15
25	27		A	Droylsden	306	W 2 - 1	Ofobo 27 Griffiths 52	
26	Jan 17		A	Hinckley United	433	W 3 - 2	Marsh-Evans 44 **Noone** 72 Egerton 79	
27	24		H	Farsley Celtic	146	W 2 - 0	**Noone** 36 Griffiths 50	12
28	27		H	Southport	317	D 0 - 0		11
29	Feb 14		H	Tamworth	254	D 2 - 2	Field 24 (pen) 30 (pen)	11
30	17		A	AFC Telford United	1667	L 1 - 5	**Noone** 26	
31	21		A	Alfreton Town	392	L 1 - 3	Field 58 (pen)	14
32	24		H	Solihull Moors	144	D 2 - 2	Griffiths 57 85	
33	28		A	Gateshead	602	D 2 - 2	Field 71 (pen) C.**Noone** 72	
34	Mar 3		H	Droylsden	149	L 1 - 4	Field 63	
35	7		H	Burscough	225	W 2 - 0	Furlong 3 Field 79	
36	10		H	AFC Telford United	256	W 2 - 0	**Noone** 3 6	
37	14		A	King's Lynn	939	D 1 - 1	Hannigan 90	12
38	21		H	Alfreton Town	168	D 1 - 1	Furlong 22	12
39	24		H	Hyde United	201	W 2 - 1	Furlong 36 Hannigan 88	
40	28		H	Gainsborough Trinity	167	D 1 - 1	Field 77 (pen)	11
41	31		A	Hucknall Town	132	W 1 - 0	Hannigan	
42	April 4		A	Blyth Spartans	519	W 1 - 0	Furlong 1	9
43	7		A	Redditch United	216	L 1 - 2	Wright 77	
44	11		H	Fleetwood Town	239	L 0 - 2		11
45	13		A	Stalybridge Celtic	401	L 0 - 1		
46	18		A	Tamworth	1012	L 0 - 2		11
47	25		H	King's Lynn	511	L 1 - 3	**Noone** 35	11

Average Home Att: 203 (211) **Goals** 56 75

Best Position: 9th **Worst:** 21st

Goalscorers: Noone 15, Field 8, Wright 6, Griffiths 5, Rooney 4, Hannigan 3, Furlong 4, Holmes 2, Marsh- Evans 2, Egerton 1, Holden 1, McFadden 1, Nelson 1, Ofobo 1. Own Goals 2.

COATES	OWENS	DAMES	GRIFFITHS	BRANNAN	HOLMES	HOLDEN	BURKE	MCFADDEN	ROONEY	K SMITH	NOON	NELSON	WRIGHT	HANNIGAN	DICKINSON	NOONE	EGERTON	ROBINSON	MCDOWELL	ROGAN	J SMITH	FIELD	MARSH-EVANS	MCCUBBIN	OTOBO	RITCHIE	FURLONG	MUSTAFFA	MACAULEY	MCAULEY	
X	X	X	X	X	X	X	X	X	X	X	S	S	U	U	U																1
X	X	X	X	X	X	X	X	X	U	X	X		S	U	U	S															2
X	X	X	X	X	X	X	X	X		U	X	S	S	U	U	X															3
X	X	X	X	X	X		X	S	X	S	X	X	U	U		X															4
X	X		X	X	X	U	X	S	X	U	X	X	S	U		X	X														5
X	X	U	X	X	X	U	X	S	X	U	X	X	S			X	X														6
X	X	S	X	X	X	U	X	S	X	U	X	X	S			X	X														7
X	X		X	S	X	X	X	X			X	X	U	U		X	X														8
X	X	S	X	X	X	S	X	X	S		X	X	U	U		X	X														9
X	X	X	X	X	U	X	X		X		X	S	U	X		X	U	S													10
X	X	X	X	X	X	X	X		X		X	S	S	U			X		U												11
X	X	X	X	X	X	X	X		X		X	S	S	S			X		U												12
X	X		X	X		S	X		X		X	X	U	X		X	X		S												13
X	X	U	X	X	X	U			X		X	S	S	X		X	X		S	X											14
X	X		X	X	X	X	X	S	U		X			X		X	S		S	X											15
X	X	X		X	X	X	X	S	S		X		U			X	U		S	X	X										16
X	X	X		X	X	X	X	U	X		X		U			X	U		U		X										17
X	X	X			X	X	X	U	X		X		U			X	U		U		X	X									18
X	X	X			X	X	X				X		S	U		X	U					X	X	X							19
X	X	X			X	X	X	U	X		X		X	X		X	U							U							20
X	X	X			X	X	X	S			X		X	X		X	X							S							21
X		X			X	X	X	S			X		X			X	X					X	X	S	S	U					22
X		X	X		X	X	X	U					U			X	X					X	X	S	X	U					23
X		X	X		X	X	X	S			X		S			X						X	X		X	U					24
X		X	X		X	X	X	S			X		U			X	S					X	X		X	U					25
X	S	X	X		X	X		S			X		U			X	X					X	X		X	U					26
X	S	X	X		X	X	X	S			X		U			X	X					X	X		U						27
X	S	X	X		X	X	X	U			X		U			X	X					X	X								28
X	S	X	X		X	X	X				X		U	U		X	X					X	X		U		S				29
X	X		X		X	X	X				X		U	U		X	X					X	X		S		S				30
X	X		X		X	X	X				X		S	S		S	X					X	X		U		X				31
X	X		X		X	X	X				X		S	U		X	S					X	X		U		X				32
X	X		X		X	X	X				S		U	S		X	X					X	X		S		X	U			33
X	X		X		X	S	X				X			U		X	X					X	X		U		X	U			34
X	X		X		X	X	X				X		U	S		X	S					X	X		S		X	U			35
X	X		X		X	X	X				X		U	X		X	S					X			S		X	U			36
X	X		X		X	X	X				X		S	X			S					X	X		X			U			37
X		S	X		X	X	X				X		U	X		X	S					X	X		U		X	U			38
X		X	X		X	X	X				X		S	X			S					X	X				X	U			39
X	U	X	X			X	X				X		S	X		U	X					X	X				X	U			40
X		X	X			X	X				X		X	X		S	X					X	X					U	U	U	41
X		X	X			X	X				X		S	X		X	X					U	X				X	U	U		42
X		X	X			X	X				U		S	X		X	X					X	X				X	U	U		43
X		X	X		S	S	X						X	X		X	X					X	X				X		U		44
X		X	X		X	X	X							X		X	X					X	X					U	U	U	45
X		X	X		X	X	X				X			X		X	U					X					X		U	U	46
X		X	X		X	X	X				X			X		X	S					X					X		S		47

Total League Appearances

COATES	OWENS	DAMES	GRIFFITHS	BRANNAN	HOLMES	HOLDEN	BURKE	MCFADDEN	ROONEY	K SMITH	NOON	NELSON	WRIGHT	HANNIGAN	DICKINSON	NOONE	EGERTON	ROBINSON	MCDOWELL	ROGAN	J SMITH	FIELD	MARSH-EVANS	MCCUBBIN	OTOBO	RITCHIE	FURLONG	MUSTAFFA	MACAULEY	MCAULEY	
42	24	27	37	14	36	34	40	4	10	2	36	5	3	15	0	34	22	0	0	3	3	27	24	1	5	0	14	0	0	0	X
0	4	3	0	0	1	3	0	11	2	1	2	5	16	4	0	3	9	1	3	0	0	0	0	2	5	0	2	0	1	0	S
0	1	2	0	0	1	4	0	4	2	4	1	0	18	11	3	1	6	0	3	0	0	1	0	0	6	5	0	12	6	3	U

Total Cup Appearances

COATES	OWENS	DAMES	GRIFFITHS	BRANNAN	HOLMES	HOLDEN	BURKE	MCFADDEN	ROONEY	K SMITH	NOON	NELSON	WRIGHT	HANNIGAN	DICKINSON	NOONE	EGERTON	ROBINSON	MCDOWELL	ROGAN	J SMITH	FIELD	MARSH-EVANS	MCCUBBIN	OTOBO	RITCHIE	FURLONG	MUSTAFFA	MACAULEY	MCAULEY	
5	5	3	3	2	4	4	5	1	3	0	5	2	2	3	0	4	4	0	0	0	0	0	0	0	0	0	0	0	0	0	X
0	0	0	0	1	0	1	0	1	0	0	0	1	1	0	0	0	0	0	1	0	0	0	0	1	0	0	0	0	0	0	S
0	0	0	0	0	0	0	0	1	0	0	0	0	2	2	0	0	1	0	1	0	0	0	0	1	0	0	0	0	0	0	U

Also Played: O'HARE: U(2) HADZIK: S(8,10) X(9) DICKENSON : U(30) GRESTY: S(31) U(37) X(49) LANGTON: X(49)

VAUXHALL MOTORS

CURRENT SQUAD AS OF BEGINING OF 2009-10 SEASON

GOALKEEPERS	HT	WT	D.O.B	AGE	P.O.B	CAREER	Apps	Gls
Zharir Mustaffa						Vauxhall Motors	0	0
Danzelle St Louis-Hamilton	6'04"	12 13	7/5/90	19	Stevenage	Watford (Yth), Stoke, Bristol R (3ML) 2/09, Vauxhall Motors (5ML) 7/09		

DEFENDERS	HT	WT	D.O.B	AGE	P.O.B	CAREER	Apps	Gls
Lee Dames			21/1/86	23	Liverpool	Tranmere (Yth), Burscough, Vauxhall Motors 6/06	30	0
Jonathan Egerton						Vauxhall Motors	31	1
Chris Lane	6'00"	12 10	24/5/79	30	Liverpool	Everton Rel c/s 98, Hereford 6/98, Southport 1/01, Morecambe 5/03, Leigh RMI 1/04, Chester 2/04, Leigh RMI 6/04, Southport 5/05 Rel 5/07, Altrincham 6/07 Rel 5/09, Vauxhall Motors 7/09		
Brian Moogan			4/9/84	24		Everton Rel c/s 04, Macclesfield (Trial), Lancaster 11/04, Vauxhall Motors 3/05, Burscough 10/07, Vauxhall Motors 6/09		

MIDFIELDERS	HT	WT	D.O.B	AGE	P.O.B	CAREER	Apps	Gls
Craig Davies			21/12/88	20		Morecambe, Lancaster, Gap Connahs Quay 7/08, Burscough 11/08, Vauxhall Motors c/s 09		
Alan Griffiths			24/2/85	24		Tranmere, Vauxhall Motors c/s 03	37	4
Tom Hannigan						Vauxhall Motors	19	3
James Holden						Bury, Ashton U, Chorley 6/07, FCUM 12/07, Barrow (Trial) c/s 08, Vauxhall Motors 7/08, Bala T 6/09, Vauxhall Motors 7/09	37	1
Jordan Holmes						ex Liverpool (Sch), Skelmersdale, Lancaster 12/06, Vauxhall Motors 8/07	37	1
Keith Smith			21/8/81	28		Vauxhall Motors, Caernarfon 9/08, Burscough 2/09, Vauxhall Motors 8/09	3	0
Josh Wilson			5/7/88	21	Liverpool	Stoke (Scholar) Rel 6/06, Abroad, Northwich 7/07 Rel 5/08, Leigh RMI/Leigh Genesis 5/08, Burscough 11/08, Vauxhall Motors 8/09		

FORWARDS	HT	WT	D.O.B	AGE	P.O.B	CAREER	Apps	Gls
Lee Furlong			9/8/79	30		Southport, Burscough 6/01, Marine 1/03, Witton 9/03, Newton, Runcorn 8/05, Vauxhall Motors 3/06, Caernarfon 7/08, Vauxhall Motors 1/09	16	6
Josh Hine			4/3/91	18		Southport, Burscough 3/09, Vauxhall Motors 7/09		
Karl Noon			15/9/86	22		Tranmere (Yth), Liverpool (Scholar) Rel c/s 05, Chester (Reserves), Prescot Cables, Bamber Bridge, Marine 12/06, Southport c/s 07, Bangor C (L) 1/08 Perm, Vauxhall Motors 8/08	38	9
Chris Noone	6'02"	12 00	25/10/84	24	Liverpool	Everton, Vauxhall Motors, La Nucia (Spa), Caernarfon c/s 07 Rel 9/07, Banned, Vauxhall Motors c/s 08	37	3

FORWARDS	HT	WT	D.O.B	AGE	P.O.B	CAREER	Apps	Gls
Fran Smith						Vauxhall Motors		
Scott McAuley						Vauxhall Motors (Physio)	0	0
Carl Macauley						Vauxhall Motors Man	1	0

LOANEES	HT	WT	DOB	AGE	POB	From - To	APPS	GOA
(F)Nick Rogan			15/10/83	25	Blackpool	Barrow 10/08 - Rel 5/09, Fleetwood 6/09	3	1
(F)Martin McCubbin						Blackburn 11/08 - Welshpool T (L) 1/09	3	0

DEPARTURES	HT	WT	DOB	AGE	POB	From - To	APPS	GOA
(M)Mike Garrity			6/5/80	29	Liverpool	Runcorn (Pl/Yth Man) 3/05 - Rel c/s 08, Caernarfon 9/08		
(D)Richard Gresty						ex Altrincham 1/08 - Trafford 9/08		
(M)Ged Brannan	6'00"	12 05	15/1/72	37	Liverpool	ex Morecambe 11/07 - Burscough (Pl/Coach) 10/08	14	0
(F)Rio Nelson						Barrow 7/08 - Flixton 10/08	10	1
(F)Nick Robinson						FCUM 9/08 - FCUM 10/08 Rel 1/09, Australia	1	0
(D)James Smith	5'10"	11 08	17/10/85	23	Liverpool	Stockport - Altrincham 11/08	3	0
(D)James Glendenning						Colwyn Bay 11/08 - Caernarfon 1/09		
(F)Thomas Rooney	6'00"	12 05	30/12/84	24	Liverpool	Cammell Laird 7/08 - Witton 12/08	12	2
(F)Pat McFadden			4/4/87	22		Altrincham 7/08 - Rel 2/09, Abbey Hey 2/09, Ashton U 2/09, Altrincham (Dual) 3/09	15	0
(F)Saul Otobo						Maldon T 12/08 - Witton 3/09	10	1
(F)Paul Taylor						ex Man City c/s 07 - Rel 4/09, Chester (3ML) 7/08		
(D)Robert Marsh-Evans	6'03"	12 08	13/10/86	22	Abergele	Leigh RMI/Leigh Genesis 11/08 - Southport 5/09	24	2
(M)Matty Burke						Salford C c/s 08 - Alfreton 6/09	40	0
(M)Tom Field			2/8/85	23	Liverpool	Leigh Genesis 11/08 - AFC Telford 6/09	27	8
(G)James Coates			22/2/85	24		Kidsgrove A 8/08 - Northwich 7/09	42	0
Ritchie						Yth -	0	0
(F)Anthony Wright	5'11"	11 00	6/3/78	31	Liverpool	Colwyn Bay 5/08 -	19	6
(M)Anthony McDowell						ex Shrewsbury (Yth) 9/08 -	3	0
(G)Aidan Dickinson						Yth -	0	0
(D)Lee Owens						ex Wigan -	28	0

VAUXHALL MOTORS

Formed: 1963

Nickname: The Motormen.

Club Colours: White shirts, navy blue shorts, white shorts.

Change Colours: Sky blue shirts, shorts and socks.

Club Sponsor: Lookers (Wirral)

Previous League: Northern Premier League

Ground address: Rivacre Park, Rivacre Road, Ellesmere Port, South Wirrall CH66 1NJ

Telephone & Fax: 0151 328 1114

Mobile: 07789 235 647

Social Club: 0151 327 2294

Email: alan.vauxhall@tiscali.co.uk

Website: www.vmfc.com

Simple Directions: M53 Jct 5 take A41 to Chester. First lights left to Hooton Green. Left at T junction to the end, turn right at T junction into Rivacre Road. Ground on right.

Capacity: 3,500 **Seats:** 266 **Covered:** 1,000 **Floodlights:** Yes

Clubhouse: Yes

Club Shop: Yes

PROGRAMME EDITOR

Mike Harper

(H) 0151 645 4561 (M) 07817 400202

Email: mike.harper@sky.com

CLUB STATISTICS

RECORDS

Attendance : 1,500 F.A.X1 Fixture, opening of Rivacre Park, 1987

Career Goalscorer: Terry Fearrns - 111

Career Apearances: Carl Jesbitt - 509

Transfer Fee Paid: Undisclosed

Transfer Fee Received: Undisclosed

Senior Honours

Wirral Senior Cup 1987

PREVIOUS

Leagues: Ellesmere Port, Wirral Combination,

West Cheshire 66-87, 92-95. North West Counties 87-92 95-2000.

Northern Premier.

Names: Vauxhall Motors 1963-87 Vauxhall GM 1995-99.

WORKINGTON

Back Row (L-R): Jim Rowland (kitman), Stephen Hindmarch, Phil McLuckie, Lee Andrews, Gari Rowntree, Jonny Wright, Tony Caig, Aaran Taylor, Gareth Arnison, Kyle May, Dan Shannon, Andy Langford, Sue Pollock (physiotherapist), Alan Clark (kitman).
Front row: Tony Hopper (captain), Darren Casson, Callum Ruttledge, Adam Main, Darren Edmondson, Viv Busby, Andy Hardman, Dan Robinson, Anthony Wright, Mathew Henney.

CLUB PERSONNEL

Chairman: Humphrey Dobie.

Vice-Chairman: Jos Taylor.

Company Secretary: Humphrey Dobie.

Additional Directors: Thex Johnston, Colin Doorbar, Alec Graham, Dave Wilson.

Secretary: Steve Durham

10, Grant Drive, Whitehaven, Cumbria CA28 6JS

(H): 01946 61380

(M): 07899 938 156

sbj.durham@btinternet.com

Commercial Manager: Clare McAleavey

(B): 01900 602 871

Email: workington.reds@tiscali.co.uk

Manager: Darren Edmondson.

Club therapist: Sue Pollock.

After a mixed season it was difficult to decide whether Workington should be pleased with the campaign overall, but certainly a finish in twelfth position was a lot better than could have been expected when in seventeenth place at Christmas.

Only two victories in the first thirteen fixtures was a worry and included a replay defeat in the F.A.Cup away at Harrogate. The F.A.Trophy brought more success however, with three brilliant victories against good opposition - Tamworth (A) 1-0, King's Lynn (H) 4-3 and Barrow (A) 3-0 before Wrexham travelled to Borough Park and won 3-1.

By the time the cup run was all over, 'The Reds' had dropped down to sixteenth place in the league and the end of season battle for points appeared to be more likely to help avoiding the relegation zone rather than the play-off places. Graham Arnison and the Wright brothers (Johnny and Tony) scored 42 senior goals between them and it was their form that could decide how Workington finished the season.

Although never really building a consistent run of results, Workington achieved seven victories despite failing to score in eight games before the season ended, with manager Darren Edmondson's given a three year contract and promising to strengthen his squad with the future play-offs in mind.

WORKINGTON

BEST LGE ATT.: 452 v Stafford Rangers
LOWEST: 255 v Hucknall Town

No.	Date	Comp	H/A	Opponents	Att:	Result	Goalscorers	Pos
1	Aug 9	BSN	A	Hinckley United	541	L 0 - 1		
2	12		H	Harrogate Town	446	D 0 - 0		
3	16		H	Stafford Rangers	452	D 2 - 2	K.May 15 Hopper 73	17
4	23		A	Blyth Spartans	451	L 1 - 3	Wright J 23	18
5	25		H	Burscough	377	W 4 - 1	Wright J 7 27 Hopper 14 Wright A 81	
6	30		A	Alfreton Town	316	D 0 - 0		15
7	Sept 2		A	Droylsden	386	D 1 - 1	Wright J 2	
8	6		H	Redditch United	403	L 0 - 1		17
9	**9**	**SS N1**	**A**	**Farsley Celtic**	**101**	**L 1 - 3**	**Anthony 10**	
10	13		H	Solihull Moors	410	W 2 - 1	**Arnison** 25 46	
11	20		A	Hucknall Town	291	D 0 - 0		14
12	**27**	**F.A.C. 2Q**	**H**	**Harrogate Town**	**413**	**D 0 - 0**		
13	**30**	**F.A.C. 2Q r**	**A**	**Harrogate Town**	**305**	**D 0 - 0***	**(Lost 4-5 on pens)**	
14	Oct 4		A	AFC Telford United	1753	D 0 - 0		14
15	14		A	Gateshead	340	W 4 - 2	May 36 Anthony 49 Vipond 60 82	
16	18		H	Tamworth	403	L 1 - 4	**Arnison** 42	
17	25		A	Vauxhall Motors	143	L 0 - 3		
18	Nov 1		A	Southport	650	D 0 - 0		
19	8		H	Farsley Celtic	307	L 0 - 2		15
20	15		A	Hyde United	303	D 4 - 4	Wright A 12 Wright J 54 65 Vipond 67	
21	**22**	**F.A.T 3Q**	**A**	**Tamworth**	**433**	**W 1 - 0**	**Wright J. 78**	
22	29		H	Vauxhall Motors	294	W 3 - 1	Wright J 50 **Arnison** 68 71	15
23	Dec 6		H	King's Lynn	325	D 1 - 1	Wright J 19	15
24	**13**	**F.A.T. 1R**	**H**	**King's Lynn**	**240**	**W 4 - 3**	**McLuckie 4 Arnison 11 63 (pen) Compton 71**	
25	26		A	Fleetwood Town	1269	L 0 - 1		17
26	**Jan 13**	**F.A.T 2R**	**A**	**Barrow**	**1614**	**W 3 - 0**	**Arnison 26 (pen) 87 McLuckie 34**	
27	17		H	Gainsborough Trinity	381	W 5 - 0	Wright J 6 85 **Arnison** 6 Hopper 30 Wright A 65	15
28	24		A	Stalybridge Celtic	659	W 4 - 1	Wright J 13 Wright A 21 **Arnison** 68 Hardman 89	
29	28		A	Gateshead	463	L 1 - 2	McLuckie 49	
30	**31**	**F.A.T 3R**	**H**	**Wrexham**	**1029**	**L 1 - 3**	**Wright J 72**	
31	Feb 14		H	AFC Teford United	405	W 1 - 9	**Arnison** 69	16
32	17		A	Solihull Moors	183	L 0 - 2		
33	21		A	Tamworth	707	L 0 - 1		16
34	24		H	Droylsden	281	D 1 - 1	**Arnison** 61 (pen)	
35	28		H	Southport	441	L 0 - 1		16
36	Mar 7		A	Gainsboroough Trinity	294	W 2 - 1	A.Wright 24 82	
37	10		A	Farsley Celtic	168	W 5 - 0	**Arnison** 11 23 Wright J 54 62 Cook 74	
38	14		H	Hyde United	328	D 2 - 2	Cook 32 **Arnison** 58	14
39	17		A	Stafford Rangers	377	D 0 - 0		
40	21		H	Hinckley United	331	L 1 - 3	**Arnison** 34	15
41	24		A	Harrogate Town	258	W 1 - 0	Wright A 2	
42	28		H	Alfreton Town	307	L 0 - 3		15
43	30		H	Fleetwood Town	331	W 3 - 2	**Arnison** 12 22 Wright A. 83	
44	April 4		A	Redditch United	204	L 0 - 2		13
45	6		H	Hucknall Town	255	W 1 - 0	Cook 90	
46	11		H	Blyth Spartans	366	L 0 - 1		12
47	13		A	Burscough	274	L 1 - 2	Hardman 42	
48	18		A	King's Lynn	884	W 3 - 1	Cook 35 55 Ruttledge 70	12
49	25		H	Stalybridge Celtic	389	L 0 - 2		12

Average Home Att: 344 (388) **Goals** 64 73

Best Position: 12th **Worst:** 18th

Goalscorers: Arnison 19, Wright J 15, Wright A 8, Cook 5, Hopper 3, McLuckie 3, Vipond 3, Anthony 2, Hardman 2, May K 2, Compton 1, Ruttledge 1.

COLLIN	HOPPER	ANDREWS	MAY	KIRKUP	HEWSON	ANTHONY	ROBINSON	J WRIGHT	ROWNTREE	A WRIGHT	JOHNSTON	HARDMAN	MCLUCKIE	RUDD	GULLEN	ARNISON	EARL	VIPOND	EDMONDSON	COLEMAN	TAIT	CAMPION	LANGFORD	DORNEY	ANANE	LLOYD	COOK	GORDON	RUTTLEDGE	MAIN	
X	X	X	X	X	X	X	X	X	X	X	S	S	U	U	U																1
X		X	X	X	X	X	X	X		X	X	S	X	U	S	S	U														2
X	X	X	X	X		X	X	X	U	X	X	S	X		U	S		S													3
X	X	X	X	X	U	X	X	X	U	X	X	S	X			S		S													4
X	X	X	X	S	X	X	S	X	X	X			U		S	X		X	U												5
X		X		X	X		X	X	X	X	X	S	U		U	X	U	X	U												6
X		X		X	X	U	X	X	X	X	X	X	S			S		X	U												7
X	U	X		X	X	S	X	X	X	X	X	X	U			S		X	U												8
X	**X**	**X**	**S**	**X**	**X**	**X**	**U**	**X**	**X**	**X**			**U**			**X**		**X**	**U**												**9**
X	X		X	X	X	X	S	X	X	X	S	U	U			X		X	U												10
X	X	X	X	U	X	X	S	X	X	X	S		U			X		X	U												11
X	**X**	**X**	**X**	**U**	**X**		**S**	**X**	**X**	**X**	**X**	**U**	**S**			**X**		**X**	**U**												**12**
X		**X**	**X**	**S**	**X**		**X**		**X**	**X**	**X**	**S**	**X**			**X**		**X**	**U**												**13**
X	X	X	X	S	X		X	U	X	X		S	X			X		X	U												14
X	X	X	X	U	X	X	X		X	X	S	U	S			X		X	U												15
X	X	X	X	U	X	X	X		X	X	S	S	S			X		X	U												16
X	X	X	X	U	X	X	X		X	X	X	S	S					X	U	S											17
X	X	X	X		X	X			X	X	S	U	X			X		X	U	S											18
X	X		X		X		X	S	X	X	X	S	X			X		X	U	U											19
X	X	X	X		X		U	X	X	X	S	S	X			X		X	U	S											20
X	**X**	**X**	**X**		**X**		**U**	**X**	**X**	**X**		**U**	**X**			**X**		**X**	**U**	**U**											**21**
X	X	X	X		X		U	X	X	X		S	X			X		X	U	S	U										22
X	X	X	X		X		U	X	X	X	S	S	X			X		X		S	U										23
X			**X**		**X**		**U**	**X**	**X**	**X**		**U**	**X**			**X**		**X**	**U**	**U**		**X**	**X**								**24**
X	X		X		X		S	X	X	X			X			X		X	U		U	X	U								25
X	**X**	**X**	**X**		**X**		**U**	**X**	**X**	**X**		**S**	**X**			**X**		**X**	**U**				**S**								**26**
X	X	X	X		X		S	X	X	X		S	X			X		X	U		S		U								27
X	X	X	X		X		S	X	X	X		S	X			X		X	U				S								28
X	X	X	X		X		S	X	X	X		S	X			X		X	U				S								29
X	**X**	**X**	**X**				**U**	**X**	**X**	**X**		**S**	**X**			**X**		**X**					**X**	**S**	**U**	**U**					**30**
X	X	X	X				X		X	X			X			X		X	U				X	S	S						31
X	X	X	X				X		X	X			X			X		X	U				X	S	U		S				32
X	X	X	X				U		X	X		S	X			X		X	U				X	S	S		X				33
X	X	X	X				U	X	X	S		U	X			X		X					X	X	U		S				34
X	X	X	X				U	X	X	X		S	X			X		X					X	S	U		S				35
X	X	X	X				S	X	X	X		U	X			X		X	U				X				S				36
X		X	X				S	X	X	X		S	X			X		X	U				X				X				37
X		X	X				S	X	X	X		S	X			X		X	U				X				X	U			38
X		X	X				U	X	X	X		S	X			X		X	U				X				X	U			39
X	U	X	X				U	X	X	X		S	X			X		X	U				X				X	U			40
X	X	X	X				S	X	X	X		S	X			X			U				X				X	S			41
X	X	X	X				S	X	X	X		S	X			X			U				X				X				42
X	X	X	X				S	X	X	X		X	X			X			U				X				S		U	U	43
X	X	X	X				S	X	X	X		X	X			X			U				X					S		S	44
X	X	X	X				S	X	X	X		X	X			X			U				X				S	U		U	45
X	X	X	X				S	X	X	X		X	X			X							X				S	U	S	U	46
X	X		X				X	X		X		X	X			X			S				X				X		S	U	47
X	X						X	X	U	X		X	X			S			X				X				X	X	S	S	48
X	X	X					X		U	X		X	X			X			U				X					X	X	S	49
Total League Appearances																															
42	34	37	37	8	21	11	17	32	36	41	8	9	32	0	0	34	0	29	1	0	0	1	19	1	0	0	9	2	1	0	**X**
0	0	0	0	2	0	1	16	1	0	1	8	23	4	0	2	6	0	2	1	5	1	0	2	4	2	0	7	2	3	3	**S**
0	2	0	0	4	1	1	8	1	4	0	0	5	6	2	3	0	2	0	32	1	3	0	2	0	3	0	0	5	1	4	**U**
Total Cup Appearances																															
7	5	6	6	1	6	1	1	6	7	7	2	0	5	0	0	7	0	7	0	0	0	1	2	0	0	0	0	0	0	0	**X**
0	0	0	1	1	0	0	1	0	0	0	0	3	1	0	0	0	0	0	0	0	0	0	1	1	0	0	0	0	0	0	**S**
0	0	0	0	1	0	0	5	0	0	0	0	3	1	0	0	0	0	0	6	2	0	0	0	0	1	1	0	0	0	0	**U**

WORKINGTON

CURRENT SQUAD AS OF BEGINING OF 2009-10 SEASON

GOALKEEPERS	HT	WT	D.O.B	AGE	P.O.B	CAREER	Apps	Gls
Tony Caig	6'01"	13 04	11/4/74	35	Cleaton Moor	Carlisle, Blackpool £40,000 3/99, Charlton (2ML) 11/00 Perm 1/01 Rel c/s 01, Hibernian 7/01, Newcastle 1/03, Barnsley (L) 1/04, Vancouver Whitecaps (Can) 4/06 Rel 9/07, Gretna 10/07 Rel 1/08, Houston Dynamos (USA) 4/08 Rel 12/08, Chesterfield 3/09 Rel c/s		
Aaron Taylor						Annan Ath, Penrith, Workington c/s 07, Barrow 7/08 Rel 9/08, Penrith, Workington (Trial) 2/09, Workington 3/09		
DEFENDERS								
Lee Andrews	6'00"	11 06	23/4/83	26	Carlisle	Carlisle Rel 5/06, Rochdale (L) 2/03, York (2ML) 11/05, Torquay (L) 3/06, Torquay 5/06 Rel c/s 07, Newcastle Blue Star 9/07, Workington 1/08	37	0
Darren Casson						Gretna, Newcastle Blue Star 8/07, South Shields 8/08, Workington 8/09		
Darren Edmondson	6'00"	12 12	4/11/71	37	Coniston	Carlisle, Huddersfield 3/97, Plymouth (L) 9/98, York C 3/00 Rel c/s 04, Chester 8/04 Rel c/s 05, Barrow 8/05, Workington 1/06	2	0
Kevin Gray	6'00"	14 00	7/1/72	37	Sheffield	Mansfield, Huddersfield 7/94 Rel c/s 02, Stockport, (L) 8/00, Tranmere 7/02, Carlisle 11/03 Rel c/s 07, Chesterfield 7/07 Rel c/s 08, Workington 7/08		
Andrew Langford	5'11"	12 05	3/7/88	21	Manchester	Morecambe Rel c/s 08, Leek T (L) 11/07, Workington 12/08	21	0
Kyle May			7/9/82	26	Doncaster	Carlisle Rel c/s 02, Gretna 8/02, Workington (5ML) 8/04, Workington 1/05	37	2
Gari Rowntree						Carlisle (Yth), Blackburn, Workington 3/07	36	0
MIDFIELDERS								
Matt Henney	6'00"	11 08	9/8/76	33	Carlisle	Windscales, Workington, Gretna 7/02 Rel 8/03, Workington 8/03, Barrow 6/07 Rel 5/09, Workington 5/09		
David Hewson			5/5/83	26		Gretna, Workington	21	0
Tony Hopper	5'11"	12 08	31/5/76	33	Carlisle	Carlisle Rel c/s 00, Barrow (L) 3/93, Bohemians 8/00, Workington 1/01, Carlisle 2/01 Rel c/s 02, Barrow 8/02, Workington 10/02	34	3
Shaun Vipond	5'11"	11 04	25/12/88	20	Hexham	Carlisle, Workington (3ML) 8/08 Perm 11/08, Hamilton (Trial) 1/09, Sweden 3/09 Rel 5/09, Workington 8/09	31	3
Anthony Wright						Penrith, Workington 6/06	42	7
FORWARDS								
Gareth Arnison						Morecambe, Workington 8/05, Kendal (L) 12/06 Perm 1/07, Workington 8/08	40	15
Andrew Hardman						Carlisle, Workington 2/08	32	2
Stephen Hindmarch	5'10"	11 11	16/11/89	19	Penrith	Carlisle Rel c/s 08, Shrewsbury 7/08 Rel c/s 09, Workington 6/09		
Dan Robinson	5'10"	10 10	21/5/89	20	Penrith	Gretna, Workington 6/08	33	0
Callum Ruttledge						Morecambe (Yth), Workington 3/09	4	1
Dan Shannon						Workington 8/09		
Johnny Wright						Whitehaven Amateurs, Workington 8/07	33	14

LOANEES	HT	WT	DOB	AGE	POB	From - To	APPS	GOA
(D)Darren Campion	5'11"	12 00	17/10/88	20	Birmingham	Carlisle 12/08 -	1	0
(D)Ricky Anane	5'08"	11 02	18/2/89	20	Manchester	Bury 2/09 - Fleetwood (SL) 3/09, Rel c/s 09, Woking 7/09	2	0
(M)Jack Dorney	5'08"	11 00	9/1/90	19	Ashton-under-Lyne	Bury 2/09 - Leigh Genesis (SL) 3/09	5	0
(F)Andy Cook	6'01"		18/10/90	18	Bishop Auckland	Carlisle 2/09, 3/09 -	16	5

DEPARTURES	HT	WT	DOB	AGE	POB	From - To	APPS	GOA
(D)Dan Gullen						Yth - Whitehaven Amateurs (Dual) 9/08	2	0
(D)Dan Kirkup	6'03"	12 07	19/5/88	21	Hexham	Carlisle c/s 08 - Hawkes Bay United (NZ) 10/08	10	0
(M)Graham Anthony	5'08"	10 08	9/8/75	34	Jarrow	Barrow £2,000 7/06 - Penrith 11/08	12	1
(M)Michael Tait			24/6/88	21		Newcastle Blue Star 11/08 - Newcastle Blue Star, Blyth 6/09	1	0
(M)Paul Lloyd	5'09"	10 11	26/3/87	22	Preston	Morecambe 1/09 - Forest Green 2/09	0	0
(G)Adam Collin	6'03"	12 04	9/12/84	24	Penrith	Newcastle 8/04 - Carlisle 5/09	42	0
(D)Dean Gordon	6'00"	13 04	10/2/73	36	Croydon	Ilkeston 3/09 -	4	0
(D)Phil McLuckie						Morecambe (3ML) 12/07 Perm 3/08 -	36	1
(M)James Earl						Yth -	0	0
(M)Steven Rudd						Yth -	0	0
(F)Craig Johnston			22/10/82	26	Carlisle	Carlisle 3/01 -	16	0
Adam Main						Yth -	3	0
Martyn Coleman						Yth -	5	0

WORKINGTON

Formed: 1884

Nickname: Reds.

Club Colours: Red shirts, red shorts, red socks.

Change Colours: Blue shirts, blue shorts, blue socks.

Club Sponsor: Romar Innovate

Previous League: Northern Premier League

Ground address: Borough Park, Workington, Cumbria CA14 2DT

Telephone: 01900 602 871

Fax: 01900 67432

Email: workington.reds@tiscali.co.uk

Website: www.workingtonafc.com

Simple Directions: A66 into town. Right at T junction, follow A596 for 3/4 mile. Ground is signposted and visible.

Capacity: 2,500 Seats: 500 Covered: 1,000 Floodlights: Yes

Clubhouse: Open matchdays and for private functions

Club Shop: Yes.

Local Radio: BBC Radio Cumbria , C.F.M.

Local Press: Evening News & Star, Times & Star

PROGRAMME EDITOR

Paul Armstrong

(H) 01900 64899 (M) 07951 243717

Email: paul@workingtonafc.com

CLUB STATISTICS

RECORDS

Attendance: 21,000 v Manchester United F.A.Cup 3rd Rd 04.01.58

Victory: 17-1 v Cockermouth Crusaders, Cumberland Sen.Lg. 19.01.01

Defeat: 0-9 v Chorley (A) NPL Premier 10.11.87

Career Goalscorer: Billy Charlton 193

Career Appearances: Bobby Brown 419

Record Transfer Fee Paid:

£6,000 for Ken Chisolm from Sunderland 1956

Received £33,000 from Liverpool for Ian McDonald 1974

SENIOR HONOURS:

Cumberland County Cup (23)

PREVIOUS

Leagues: Cumberland Assoc. 1890-94,

Cumberland Senior League 1894-1901, 03-04.

Lancashire 1901-03, Lancashire Combination 1904-10.

North Eastern 1910-11, 21-51. Football League 1951-77.

Grounds: Various 1884-1921. Lonsdale Park 1921-37

BASINGSTOKE TOWN

Basingstoke Town Football Club 2009-2010 Season
Blue Square South

Back row (left to right): Adam Aimiable, Phil Ruggles, Matt Finlay, Joe Dolan (Captain), Ross Kitteridge (GK), Lewis Christon, Craig Smith, Rob Watkins, Jide Ogunbote

Front row (left to right): Robbie Rice, Matt Warner, Tom Williamson, Sean Hankin, David Pratt, Ryan Stevens, Jahson Downes, Tom Walsh, Ian Jones

CLUB PERSONNEL

Chairman: Rafi Razzak.

Vice-Chairman: Ian Halloway.

Company Secretary: David Knight.

Additional Directors: Sarah Parsons, Paul Carney, David Partridge, Margaret Dimbleby.

Secretary: Richard Trodd
5 Lehar Close, Brighton Hill, Basingstoke RG22 4HT
(H) 01256 413 076
(B): 01276 856 642
(M): 07887 507 447
richard.trodd@ntlworld.com

Commercial Manager: Ian Halloway
(M) 07595 588 811
Email: ian.halloway@ntlworld.com

Press Officer: David Partridge.
Tel: (M) 07979 845 479
Email: dave.partridge_btfc@tiscali.co.uk

Manager: Frank Gray.

Assistant Manager: Gerry Murphy.

Club therapist: TBC.

When your first victory isn't achieved until the eleventh fixture of the season, the chance of a successful season could be considered unlikely. Goals were hard to get and by October Basingstoke had slipped into bottom place.

A lively F.A.Cup run threatened to lift the gloom but after victories over Hamworthy United and Bashley in a replay, a 1-4 scoreline at Bury Town limited their interest in the competition. The F.A.Trophy also brought two victories, at home to Thurrock and Brackley Town but another tie at Camrose Road wasn't so productive as Wrexham won 2-1.

Confidence was not high in the New Year as 'The Dragons' were still in the relegation zone, but a second 2-0 scoreline against Bromley, which gave them a double over the Kent club, signalled a mini fight back and although it wasn't spectacular, at least the Basingstoke fans could now see their club outside the bottom three places.

Although goals were obviously still not coming easily, the team were battling and only four defeats in the last two months of the season brought a steady accumulation of vital points, and a final position two places and six points ahead of the relegation zone.

BASINGSTOKE TOWN

BEST LGE ATT.: **1,509** v AFC Wimbledon
LOWEST: **223** v Welling United

No.	Date	Comp	H/A	Opponents	Att:	Result	Goalscorers	Pos
1	Aug 9	BSS	H	Hampton & Richmond B	440	D 1 - 1	Faulkner 24 (pen)	
2	12		A	Dorchester Town	518	D 0 - 0		
3	16		A	Welling United	531	D 1 - 1	Faulkner 35	13
4	23		H	AFC Wimbledon	1509	L 0 - 1		14
5	25		A	Havant & Waterlooville	759	L 1 - 5	**Ruggles** 90	
6	30		H	Chelmsford City	282	L 1 - 2	Faulkner 37	20
7	Sept 2		H	Worcester City	312	D 0 - 0		
8	6		A	Bishop's Stortford	364	L 2 - 3	Dolan 9 Gibbs 44	19
9	**9**	**SS S1**	**H**	**Fisher Athletic**	**139**	**L 1 - 3**	**Tarpey 29**	
10	13		A	Fisher Athletc	213	L 0 - 1		21
11	20		H	Team Bath	290	L 1 - 3	Tucknott 87	22
12	**27**	**F.A.C. 2Q**	**H**	**Hamworthy United**	**329**	**W 3 - 1**	**BEAUMONT 3 (31 46pen 68)**	
13	Oct 4		H	St Albans City	280	L 1 - 2	**Ruggles** 44	22
14	**11**	**F.A.C. 3Q**	**H**	**Bashley**	**356**	**D 2 - 2**	**Bryant 2 Ruggles15**	
15	**14**	**F.A.C. 3Q r**	**A**	**Bashley**	**349**	**W 3 - 0**	**Williamson 39 Bryant 88 90**	
16	18		A	Bromley	467	W 2 - 0	Bryant 26 Montague 29	21
17	**25**	**F.A.C. 4Q**	**A**	**Bury Town**	**1121**	**L 1 - 4**	**Warner 25**	
18	Nov 1		H	Newport County	350	D 0 - 0		21
19	8		A	Thurrock	443	L 0 - 6		
20	11		H	Weston-s-Mare	320	L 0 - 1		
21	15		H	Braintree Town	250	D 2 - 2	Watkins 34 Montague 38	21
22	**22**	**F.A.T 3Q**	**H**	**Thurrock**	**280**	**W 1 - 0**	**Ruggles 82**	
23	29		A	Weston-s-Mare	267	W 3 - 0	**Ruggles** 15 40 Maledon 61	21
24	Dec 6		H	Bishop's Stortford	300	D 1 - 1	Dolan 90	21
25	**16**	**F.A.T. 1R**	**H**	**Brackley Town**	**221**	**W 3 - 1**	**Watkins 66 Hankin 74 Jombarti 77**	
26	20		A	Hampton & Richmond B	644	D 0 - 0		20
27	26		H	Eastleigh	474	W 1 - 0	Hankin 70	20
28	Jan 1		A	Eastleigh	1015	L 0 - 1		20
29	**13**	**F.A.T 2R**	**H**	**Wrexham**	**597**	**L 1 - 2**	**Jombarti**	
30	17		H	Bognor Regis Town	371	D 0 - 0		20
31	24		A	Newport County	844	L 0 - 3		20
32	27		H	Bromley	245	W 2 - 0	Dolan 47 Jombarti 89	
33	Feb 1		H	Hayes & Yeading	338	D 1 - 1	Bossman 15	
34	7		A	Bognor Regis Town	352	W 3 - 2	Tarpey 85 90 **Ruggles** 87	20
35	14		A	Team Bath	200	W 2 - 1	**Ruggles** 30 Stephens 86	19
36	21		H	Dorchester Town	732	D 0 - 0		18
37	24		A	St Albans City	222	L 0 - 3		
38	28		H	Bath City	447	W 1 - 0	**Ruggles** 56	18
39	Mar 7		A	Hayes & Yeaing	258	L 0 - 5		
40	10		H	Welling United	223	D 0 - 0		
41	14		A	Maidenhead United	293	W 2 - 1	Stephens 6 Warner 67	17
42	16		A	Chelmsford City	1054	D 2 - 2	Aimable 9 57	
43	21		H	Fisher Athletic	496	D 2 - 2	Stephens 36 Warner 59	17
44	24		A	Bath City	430	L 0 - 1		
45	28		A	Braintree Town	483	W 1 - 0	Hankin 87	17
46	April 4		H	Thurrock	354	W 1 - 0	Hankin 63	16
47	10		A	AFC Wimbledon	4136	L 0 - 1		
48	13		H	Havant & Waterlooville	507	D 2 - 2	**Ruggles** 40 Tarpey 75	
49	18		H	Maidenhead United	409	L 0 - 1		18
50	25		A	Worceser City	608	D 0 - 0		18

Average Home Att: 425 (500) **Goals** 51 68

Best Position: 13th **Worst:** 22nd

Goalscorers: Ruggles 10, Bryant 4, Hankin 4, Tarpey 4, Beaumont 3, Dolan 3, Faulkner 3, Jombarti 3, Stephens 3, Warner 3, Aimable 2, Montague 2, Watkins 2, Bossman 1, Gibbs 1, Maledon 1, Tucknott 1, Wiliamson 1.

KITTERIDGE	LEWIS	HANKIN	BRISTOW	DOLAN	WATKINS	TUCKNOTT	WILLIAMSON	FAULKNER	JOMBARTI	WARNER	RUGGLES	OGUNBOTE	TARPEY	PERKINS	GIBBS	LOVEGROVE	WALLER	AIMABLE	BOTHAM	SHULTON	BRYANT	JONES	SMITH	MALEDON	MONTAGUE	HATELEY	MITCHELL-COOP	ATKINSON	TAIT	BOSSMAN	STEPHENS	VOCKINS	REYNOLDS	CHRISTON	
X	X	X	X	X	X	X	X	X	X	X	S	S	U	U	U																				1
X	X	X	X	X	X	X	X	X	X	X	S	U	S		S	U																			2
X	X		X	X	X	X	X	X	X	X	X	U	S		S	U	U																		3
X	X		X	X	X	X	X	X	X		X	U	X	U	S	S	U																		4
X	X	X	X		X	X	X	X	X		S	U	S		X	X	U	U																	5
X	X	X	X	X	X	X	X	X	X		X	U	S		S	U	U																		6
X	X	X	X	X	X	X	X	X	X		X	U	U		S	U		U																	7
X	U	X	X	X	X	X	X	X	X		U	U	S		X	X		U																	8
X	S	X		X	X	X	X		X		X	S	X	U	S	X	U	X																	9
X		X	X	X	U		X	X	X		S	U	X		S	X		U	X	X															10
X	X	X	X		X	X	X		X		U	U	U		S			S	X	X	X														11
X	X	X			X	X	X		X		X	S	S	U	S	X	U		X		X	U	U												12
X		X			X	X	X		X		X	U	S		U	X	S	X	X	S	X														13
X		X	U		X		X		X	X	X	U	U		S	U	U	X	X	S	X			X											14
X	U	X	X		X		X		X	X	X	S	S		U	U	U	X			X	U		X											15
X			X	U	X		X		X	X	U	U	S		U			X			X			X	X	X									16
X		U	X	S	X		X		X	X	X	U	S		U		S	X			X	U		X		X									17
X		X	X	X	X				X	X		U	S		U		U	S			X			X	X	X									18
				X	X				X	X	X		S			U	X	X			X	U		X	X	X	S	U							19
X				X	X				X	X	X	U	S			U	U	X			X	U			X	X	X								20
X		X		X	X				X	X	X	U	S			S	U	X						X	X	X	U								21
X		X	X	X	X		U		X	X	X	U	S					U			X			X		X	U								22
X		U	X	X	X				X	X	X	S	S				U	X			X			X		X	U								23
X		U		X	X		X		X	X	X	U	S				U	X			X			X		X	U								24
X		X		S	X		X		X	X	X	U	S					X			X	U		X		X	U								25
X	U	X		X	X		X		X	X		X	U				U	X			X	S					U		X						26
X		X		X	X		X		X	X			S				U	X				U				X	U		X	X	U				27
X		X		X	X		X		X	X	S		S					X				U		U		X	U		X	X					28
X				X	X		X		X	X	S	U	S				U	X						X		X	U		X	X					29
X		X		X	X		X		X	X	S	U	S					X						U		X	U		X	X					30
X		X		X	X		X		X	X	X	X	S					X				U		U			S		X	S					31
X		X		X	X		X		X	X	S	U	U					X				U		X			U		X	X					32
X		X		X	X		X		X	X	U	S	S					X				S		X			U		X	X					33
X		X			X				X	X	S	X	S				U	X				X		X			S		X	X	U				34
X		X		X	X	U	X		X	X	X	U	X									U		S			X		X		S				35
X				X	X	S	X		X	X	X	S	X				U					U		X					X		S	X			36
X		X		X	X	S	X		X	X	X	S	U					X				U		X					X		S				37
X		U		X	X	U	X			X	X	S	S					X				U		X			X		X		X				38
X		S		X	X	S	X		X	X	X	U	X					X						X			U		X		S				39
X				X	X	S	X		X	X	X	X	S				U					U		X			X		X		S				40
X						U	X		X	X	X	X	S				U	X				U		X			X		U		X		X		41
X						S	X		X	X	X	X	S				U	X				U		X			X		U		X		X		42
X		U				U	X		X	X	X	X	S				U	X				U		X			X				X		X		43
X		X				X	X		X	X	X	U	S				U	X				U		X			U				X		X		44
X		X				X	X		X	X	X	S	S					X				S		X			U				X		X	U	45
X		X			U	X			X	X	X	X	S					U				S		X			U				X		X	X	46
X		X		S	U	S			X	X	X	X	S					U				X		X							X		X	X	47
X		X		X	S	U			X	X	X	U	S					S				X		X			X				X		X		48
X		X		X		S	X		X		X	X	S				U	X				S		X			X				X			U	49
X		X		X	S	S	X		X	X	X	X	S					U				U		X							X			X	50
Total League Appearances																																			
41	8	28	13	30	31	13	33	9	41	33	27	11	5	0	2	4	1	24	3	2	9	3	0	24	5	10	9	0	14	6	11	1	8	3	X
0	0	1	0	1	2	8	0	0	0	0	8	7	31	0	7	2	1	3	0	1	0	5	0	1	0	0	3	0	0	1	5	0	0	0	S
0	2	4	0	1	3	5	0	0	0	0	4	21	6	2	4	6	19	7	0	0	0	16	0	3	0	0	13	1	2	0	2	0	0	2	U
Total Cup Appearances																																			
8	1	6	3	3	8	2	7	0	8	6	7	0	1	0	0	2	0	6	2	0	6	0	0	6	0	4	0	0	1	1	0	0	0	0	X
0	1	0	0	2	0	0	0	0	0	0	1	3	6	0	3	0	1	0	0	1	0	0	0	0	0	0	0	0	0	0	0	0	0	0	S
0	1	1	1	0	0	1	0	0	0	0	0	5	1	2	2	2	5	1	0	0	0	4	1	0	0	0	3	0	0	0	0	0	0	0	U

BASINGSTOKE TOWN

CURRENT SQUAD AS OF BEGINING OF 2009-10 SEASON

GOALKEEPERS	HT	WT	D.O.B	AGE	P.O.B	CAREER	Apps	Gls
Craig Atkinson						Whitchurch U, Basingstoke 8/08	0	0
Ross Kitteridge			28/12/89	19	Reading	Arsenal (Yth), Reading (Scholar) Rel c/s 09, Basingstoke (Trial) c/s 07, Eastleigh (L) 11/07, Basingstoke (SL) 7/08, Basingstoke 7/09	41	0

DEFENDERS	HT	WT	D.O.B	AGE	P.O.B	CAREER	Apps	Gls
Adam Aimable					Basingstoke	Basingstoke	27	2
Lewis Christon	6'00"	12 02	24/1/89	20	Milton Keynes	Wycombe Rel 1/09, Woking (L) 1/08, AFC Wimbledon (SL) 3/08, Oxford C (L) 11/08, Basingstoke NC 3/09	3	0
Joe Dolan	6'03"	13 05	27/5/80	29	Harrow	Chelsea (Trainee), Millwall 4/98, Walton & H (L) 9/04, Crawley (3ML) 10/04, Stockport (2ML) 1/05, Brighton (L) 3/05, L.Orient 7/05, Stockport (L) 10/05, Fisher (2ML) 11/05, Canvey Island 1/06, Basingstoke 7/06	31	3
Scott Perkins						Basingstoke	0	0
Robert Rice	5'08"	11 11	23/2/89	20	Hendon	Fulham (Yth), Wycombe Rel c/s 09, Wealdstone (L) 1/08, Basingstoke 6/09		
Craig Smith						Basingstoke	0	0
Mark Vockins			8/12/86	22	Basingstoke	Basingstoke	1	0
Robbie Watkins	5'10"		14/10/85	23	Carshalton	Fulham Rel 5/06, Crawley (L) 1/05, Gravesend (3ML) 1/06, Basingstoke 11/06 Rel 3/08, Baingstoke 5/08	33	1

MIDFIELDERS	HT	WT	D.O.B	AGE	P.O.B	CAREER	Apps	Gls
Matt Finlay	6'02"	12 00	25/1/90	19	Salisbury	Bournemouth (Trainee) Rel c/s 08, Salisbury (Trial) c/s 08, Bashley 8/08, Basingstoke NC 6/09		
Gary Frewen			21/11/90	18		Reading Rel c/s 09, Basingstoke 8/09		
Sean Hankin	5'11"	12 04	28/2/81	28	Camberley	C.Palace, Torquay (2ML) 10/01 £20,000 12/01, Margate 10/03, Northwich 11/03, Crawley 1/04 Rel 5/05, Lewes 7/05, St Albans 10/05, Farnborough 12/05, Basingstoke 5/07	29	2
Ian Jones			13/9/89	19	Basingstoke	Southampton (Scholar) Rel c/s 08, Basingstoke c/s 08	8	0
Jordan Lumsden	5'10"	10 02	3/2/91	18		Wycombe (Scholar) Rel c/s 09, Basingstoke 8/09		
Jide Ogunbote						Woking, Corinthian C (L) 9/07, Basingstoke 8/08	18	0
David Pratt			1/8/87	22		Swindon Supermarine, Chippenham 6/07, Basingstoke 5/09		
Tom Walsh						Basingstoke	Basingstoke	
Matt Warner			12/5/85	24	Farnham	Wycombe, Baingstoke (2ML) 10/03, Team Bath, Farnborough, Basingstoke 7/06	33	2
Tom Williamson	5'09"	10 02	24/12/84	24	Leicester	Leicester Rel c/s 04, Canvey Island 10/04 Rel 4/05, Grays 7/05, Bishops Stortford 8/07 Rel 5/08, Basingstoke 7/08	33	0

FORWARDS	HT	WT	D.O.B	AGE	P.O.B	CAREER	Apps	Gls
Jahson Downes			3/11/90	18		Reading Rel c/s 09, Bognor Regis (SL) 1/09, Basingstoke 6/09		
Phil Ruggles			26/10/82	26	Surrey	Woking Rel c/s 02, Leatherhead (L) 8/01, Hendon (L) 9/01, Carshalton (L) 1/02, Molesey (L) 3/02, Leatherhead 7/02, Worthing 6/04, Kingstonian 10/04, Molesey 8/05, Carshalton 5/07, Walton & H 12/07, Basingstoke 7/08	35	8
Ryan Stephens					Basingstoke	Basingstoke Rel 5/06, Basingstoke 12/08	16	3

LOANEES	HT	WT	DOB	AGE	POB	From - To	APPS	GOA
(M)Calum Botham			28/12/89	19		MK Dons (Yth), Wycombe 9/08 - Hayes & Yeading (L) 12/08, Rel 5/09	3	0
(M)Scott Shulton			31/1/90	19		Watford (Yth), Wycombe 9/08 - Hendon (L) 12/08, Rel 5/09, Ebbsfleet 8/09	3	0
(M)Mitchell Bryant						Reading 9/08 -	9	1
(F)Ross Montague	6'00"	12 11	1/11/88	20	Twickenham	Brentford 10/08 -	5	2
(M)Tom Hateley			12/9/89	19		Reading 10/08 -	10	0
(F)Allan Tait			6/9/81	27	London	Eastbourne (3ML) 12/08 - Rel 5/09, Dartford 5/09	14	0
(F)Kelvin Bossman	6'00"					Reading 12/08 - Woking (SL) 2/09	7	1
(D)Callum Reynolds			10/11/89	19	Luton	Portsmouth 3/09 -	8	1

DEPARTURES	HT	WT	DOB	AGE	POB	From - To	APPS	GOA
(F)James Faulkner			22/11/87	21	Aylesbury	Aylesbury 7/08 - Rel 9/08, Oxford C 9/08, Aylesbury FC 8/09	9	3
(F)Carl Gibbs			12/3/84	25	Walton-on-Thames	Kingstonian 8/08 - Fisher 10/08	9	1
(D)Jamie Lovegrove			2/12/89	19		College Football USA 8/08 - Rel 11/08, Fisher 12/08	6	0
(D)Jason Bristow	6'02"	11 00	23/4/80	29	Basingstoke	Reading 7/99 - Retired 3/09	13	0
(F)David Tarpay			14/11/88	20		C.Palace (Yth) - Rel 5/09, Hampton & R c/s 09	36	3
(F)Sam Tucknott						Welling 8/08 - Rel 5/09	21	1
(M)Sido Jombarti			20/8/87	22	Portugal	Weymouth 7/08 - Bath C 5/09	41	1
(M)Jerome Maledon			24/2/88	21		Woking 10/08 - Woking 6/09	25	1
(G)Chris Waller						Yth -	2	0
(D)Miles Mitchell-Coop						Wivenhoe 11/08 - Rel 5/09	12	0
(D)Aiden Lewis						Thatcham 7/08 - Rel 11/08	8	0

BASINGSTOKE TOWN

Formed: 1896

Nickname: Dragons.

Club Colours: Royal blue & yellow shirts, royal blue shorts, royal blue socks.

Change Colours: Red shirts, red shorts, red socks.

Club Sponsor: Centreprise International.

Previous League: Isthmian League

Ground address: Camrose Road, Western Way, Basingstoke RG22 6EZ

Telephone: 01256 327 575

Mobile: 07887 507 447

Fax: 01256 869 997

Social Club: 01256 464 353

Email: richard.trodd@ntlworld.com

Website: www.basingstoketown.net

Simple Directions: Exit 6 off M3 and follow A30 west. Ground off Winchester Road.

Two miles from bus and rail stations

Capacity: 6,000 **Seats:** 651 **Covered:** 2,000 **Floodlights:**Yes

Clubhouse: Open daily including lunchtimes.

Club Shop: Open Daily

Local Radio: Radio 210 and Kestral Radio

Local Press: Basingstoke Gazette

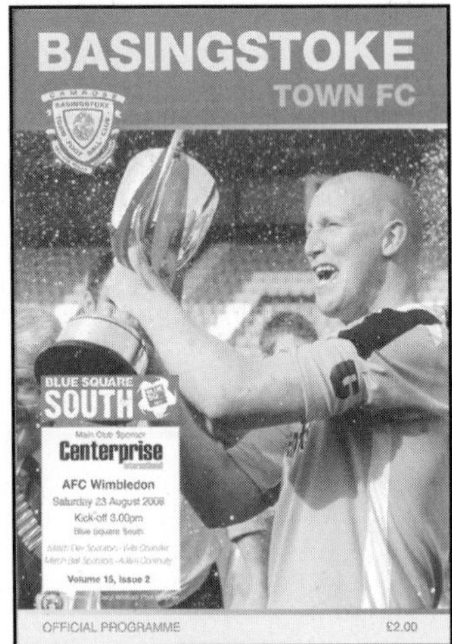

PROGRAMME EDITOR

David Partridge

(H) 01256 464606 (M) 07979 845479

Email: dave.partridge_btfc@tiscali.co.uk

CLUB STATISTICS

RECORDS

Attendance: 5,085 v Wycombe Wanderers FAC 1st Rd replay 97-98

Victory: 10-1 v Chichester City (H) F.A. Cup 1st Qual 1976

Defeat: 0-8 v Aylesbury United Southern League April 1979

Career Goalscorer: Paul Coombs - 159 (91-99)

Career Appearances: Billy Coomb

Record Transfer Fee Paid:

£4,750 to Gosport Borough for Steve Ingham

Received: Undisclosed from Wycombe Wanderers for Sergio Torres

SENIOR HONOURS

Hampshire League Champions 1967-68, 69-70, 70-71.

Southern League Southern Division Champions 1984-85.

Hampshire Senior Cup Winners 1970-71, 89-90, 95-96, 07-08.

PREVIOUS

Leagues: Hampshire 1900-40, 45-71. Southern 1971-87.

Isthmian 1987-2004.

Grounds: Castle Field 1896-1947

BATH CITY

CLUB PERSONNEL

Chairman: Geoff Todd.

Vice-Chairman: John Reynolds.

Company Secretary & Manging Director:

Paul Williams.

Additional Directors: Phil Weaver, Andrew Pierce.

Secretary: Quentin Edwards

18 Highland Road, Twerton, Bath BA2 1DY

(H): 01225 359 087

(B&M): 07785 795 532

qcath@blueyonder.co.uk

Commercial Manager: David Gane.

Tel: (M) 07855 390 217.

Email: mail@bathcityfootballclub.co.uk

Press Officer: Paul Williams

(B): 01225 423 087

(M): 07764 656 179

mail@bathcityfootballclub.co.uk

Manager: Adie Britton.

Assistant Manager: Lee Howells.

Club therapist: Dave Lukins.

Considered by many as a non-league 'sleeping giant' in the West of England, City are expected to challenge for honours every season but the last campaign never really saw Bath at their best and after a quiet start, some good patches of form were unable to lift the club into a serious challenge for a play-off place.

Two home games in the F.A.Cup brought a victory over neighbours Clevedon Town followed by a disappointing defeat by Aylesbury United and it was in October that John Relish decided to hand the managerial responsibilities over to Adie Britton. The F.A.Trophy was equally frustrating with East Thurrock United beaten at home followed by a defeat at Torquay United, but there was always a chance that a good run could bring a play-off place.

The Christmas fixtures brought some hope to Twerton Park as an unbeaten run of four games moved City into seventh place but consistency was missing and a run of three defeats took them back a couple of places.

Supporters were tearing their hair as another good run followed with three wins again taking them back to seventh position but despite steady goalscoring by Dave Gilroy (16 goals), Stewart Douglas (10) and Darren Edwards (10), City never managed to force their way into the top five.

Bath City are a well respected club with an impressive ground and tradition. They will need to replace striker Gilroy but the Relish Youth Acadamy will hope to supply young talent. With just a little more consistency a challenge at the top of the table will soon attract lively support and it could then be 'The Romans' turn next season.

BATH CITY

BEST LGE ATT.: 1,675 v AFC Wimbledon
LOWEST: 310 v Bishop's Stortford

No.	Date	Comp	H/A	Opponents	Att:	Result	Goalscorers	Pos
1	Aug 9	BSS	H	Welling United	628	L 0 - 4		
2	12		A	Maidenhead United	369	D 0 - 0		
3	16		A	Bishop's Stortford	335	W 2 - 0	Hogg 21 D.Edwards 60	12
4	23		H	Team Bath	820	D 1 - 1	Douglas 15 (pen)	
5	25		A	Worcester City	915	W 1 - 0	Douglas 45 (pen)	
6	30		H	AFC Wimbledon	1675	D 2 - 2	Paul 49 Jones 70	10
7	Sept 2		H	Hayes & Yeading	437	L 0 - 1		
8	6		A	Havant &Waterlooville	703	D 0 - 0		13
9	**9**	**SS S1**	**A**	**Team Bath**	**280**	**W 2 - 1***	**Gilroy pen 90 Edwards 110**	
10	13		A	Hampton & Richmond B	301	L 1 - 3	Cochin 52	14
11	20		H	Eastleigh	675	D 1 - 1	Carey-Bertram 59	15
12	**27**	**F.A.C. 2Q**	**H**	**Clevedon Town**	**486**	**W 2 - 0**	**Gilroy 48 Cochlin 73**	
13	Oct 4		A	Bognor Regis Town	302	W 2 - 0	Carey-Bertram 39 Douglas 87	13
14	**11**	**F.A.C. 3Q**	**H**	**Aylesbury United**	**577**	**L 0 - 1**		
15	18		H	Fisher Athletic	509	W 1 - 0	Paul 72	11
16	25		A	St Albans City	472	L 1 - 2	Simpson 13	
17	**28**	**SS S2**	**H**	**Newport County**	**241**	**W 4 - 1**	**Gilroy 42 45 54 62**	
18	Nov 1		A	Weston-s-Mare	428	W 1 - 0	**Gilroy** 49	11
19	**4**	**SS S3**	**H**	**Salisbury City**	**230**	**L 0 - 1**		
20	8		H	Bromley	520	L 1 - 3	**Gilroy** 89	11
21	15		A	Chelmsford City	1265	W 3 - 2	Evans 39 Douglas 46 Jones 60	11
22	**22**	**F.A.T 3Q**	**H**	**East Thurrock United**	**359**	**W 5 - 1**	**Simpson 46 GILROY 3 (58 73 89) Jones 70**	
23	29		H	Maidenhead United	500	W 1 - 0	Holland 8	11
24	Dec 6		A	Braintree Town	507	W 4 - 0	Jones 62 EDWARDS 3 (53 65 82)	
25	**13**	**F.A.T. 1R**	**A**	**Torquay United**	**1176**	**L 0 - 2**		
26	20		A	Welling United	621	L 1 - 2	Coupe 64	10
27	26		H	Dorchester Town	695	W 2 - 0	**Gilroy** 25 39	9
28	Jan 1		A	Dorchester Town	750	W 2 - 0	Holland 58 Edwards 88 (pen)	9
29	15		A	Hayes & Yeading	276	D 2 - 2	Edwards 5 **Gilroy** 87	9
30	24		H	St Albans City	676	D 1 - 1	Everitt 1 (og)	7
31	27		A	Eastleigh	507	L 0 - 2		
32	31		H	Newport County	1137	W 2 - 1	Edwards 6 Holland 90	8
33	Feb 14		A	AFC Wimbledon	3043	L 2 - 3	**Gilroy** 82 Edwards 89	
34	21		H	Hampton & Richmond B	552	L 0 - 1		9
35	24		H	Weston -s-Mare	466	W 3 - 0	**Gilroy** 56 Holland 69 Coupe 76	
36	28		A	Basingstoke Town	447	L 0 - 1		8
37	Mar 7		H	Bognor Regis Town	497	L 0 - 1		
38	9		A	Fisher Atletic	177	L 0 - 1		
39	14		H	Havant & Waterlooville	467	W 2 - 1	Douglas 12 71 (pen)	9
40	18		A	Newport County	734	W 4 - 0	DOUGLAS 3 (14 18 52) Edwards 56	
41	24		H	Basingstoke Town	430	W 1 - 0	Edwards 7	
42	28		A	Bromley	505	D 1 - 1	Badman 54	7
43	31		H	Thurrock	409	D 2 - 2	Douglas 46 Hogg 55	
44	April 4		H	Braintree Town	486	W 3 - 2	**GILROY** 3 (21pen 35 39)	7
45	7		H	Bishop's Stortford	310	L 2 - 3	Hogg 31 Jones 42	
46	11		A	Team Bath	496	W 1 - 0	Hogg 6	
47	13		H	Worcester City	484	W 1 - 0	Holland 22	
48	18		H	Chelmsford City	604	W 2 - 1	**Gilroy** 51 69 (pen)	7
49	25		A	Thurrock	288	L 0 - 2		

Average Home Att: 618 (784) **Goals** 69 53

Best Position: 7th **Worst:** 15th

Goalscorers: Gilroy 21, Edwards D 11, Douglas 10, Holland 5, Jones 5, Hogg 4, Carey-Bertram 2, Cochin 2, Coupe 2, Paul 2. Simpson 2, Badman 1, Evans 1. Own Goals 1.

P EVANS	SIMPSON	ROLLO	COUPE	HOLLAND	BADMAN	HOGG	ROGERS	EDWARDS	DOUGLAS	GOSLING	SLOCOMBE	PAUL	S JONES	COCHLIN	G JONES	CALDWELL	CAREY-BERTRAM	PERRIN	WOOD	CONNOLLY	GILROY	R EVANS	COLLIER	GIBB	KLEIN-DAVIES	MARSH-BROWN	
X	X	X	X	X	X	X	X	X	X	X	S	S	S	U	U												1
X	X	X	X	X	U	X	X	X	X		S	S	X	U	X	U											2
X	X	X	X	X	U	X	X	X	X		S	S	X	U	X		S										3
X	X	X	X	X	S	X	X	X	X		U	S	X	U	X		S										4
	X	X	X	X	S	X	X		X		U	S	X	S	X		X	X	U								5
	X	X	X	X	S	X	X		X		U	S	X	U	X		X	X	S								6
	X	X	X	X	S	X	X		X	S	S	X	X	U	X			X	U								7
X		X	X	X	X	X	X	S	X		X	X	S	S	X	U			U								8
		X	X	X	X	X	S	X			X		S	X		U		X	X	X	S						9
X	S	X	X	X	X	X	S	X			X		S	X		U	U			X	X						10
X	X	X	X		X			X	S	S	X	U	X	X		U	S			X	X						11
X	X	X		X	X	X	U	X	S	X	S	U	X	X			S				X						12
X	X	X		X	X	X		U	S	X	S		S	X	U		X			X	X						13
X	X	X	U	X	X	X		S	S	X	S	U	U	X	U		X			X	X						14
X	X	X	X	X	U	X	U	S	X	U	X	S			X					X	X						15
X	X	X	X	X	X	X	U	S	X	U		S	U		X					X	X						16
X	X		X	X			X	X	S		X				X					X	X	X	S				17
X	X	X	X	X	X	X		X	S	U	S	U			X					X	X	S					18
X	X	U	X	X	X	X		S	X		X	X	U		X						S	X	S				19
X	X	X	X	X		X		X	S		X	U	U		X					X	X	S					20
X	X	X	X	X		X		S	X		X	U	X		X					U	U	X					21
X	X	X	X	X	X		S	S	X		X	U	X		X					U	S	X					22
	X	X	X	X	X		S	S	X			S	U		X			X		X	X	X					23
	X	X	X	X	X	U	S	S	X		U		U		X			X		X	X	X					24
	X	X	X	X	U	X	S	S	X		X		U		X			X		X	S	X					25
		X	X	X		X	X	X	S		X		U					X		X	X	X	U	U			26
		X	X	X	X	X	X	S	X		S		U		X			X		X	X	S		U			27
		X	X	X	X	X	S	S	X		U		S		X			X		X	X	X		U			28
	S	X	X	X		X		X	S		U		X		X			X		X	X	X		S			29
	X	X	X	X		X		X	S		S		S		X			X		X	X	X		U			30
	S	X	X	X	X	X		X	S		U		U		X			X		X	X	X					31
	X	X	X	X	U	X		X	S		X		S		U			X		X	X	X		S			32
	S	X	X	X	X	X		X	X		U		X		X	U		X		X	S	S					33
	X	X	S	X		X	S	X	U		S		X		X	U		X		X	X	X					34
X	X	X	X	X		X	X	X	U		S		S		X	U				X	X	S					35
X	X	X	X	X	X	X	S	X	S		U		X		X	U					X	S					36
X	S	X	X	X	U	X	X	X	S				U		X	U				X	X	X					37
X	X	X	X	X		X	S	X	X		X				U	U				X	S	X					38
X	U	X	X	X	X	X	X	X	X		X									X	S	U		S	S		39
X	S	X	X	X	X	X	X	X	X		X									X	U	U		S	S		40
X	X	X	X	X	X		X	X	X						X	U				X	S			S	S		41
X	S	X	X	X	X		X	X	X		U		U		X					X	S			X	S		42
X	X	X	X	X		X	X	X	X		X				S					X	S			U	U	S	43
X	X	X	X	X	X	X	X	X			U		S		X	U					X			S	S		44
X	X	X	X	X	X	X	X	X	S				U		X					S	X			S	U		45
X	X	X	X	X	X	X	S	X	X				S		X					X	S			U	U		
X	X	X	X	X	X	X	U		X		U		X		S					S	X			X	S		
X	X	X	X	X	X	X	U		X		U		S		X					X	X			U		U	
X	X	X	X	X	X	X	S				S		X		X	U				X	X			U		U	
Total League Appearances																											
28	30	42	40	41	24	37	19	27	25	2	12	2	14	3	31	0	3	14	0	29	25	12	0	2	0	0	X
0	7	0	1	0	4	0	9	8	12	2	11	9	11	2	2	0	3	0	1	2	7	6	0	7	6	1	S
0	1	0	0	0	5	1	4	1	2	3	13	4	10	6	4	13	1	0	3	1	2	2	1	8	3	2	U
Total Cup Appearances																											
5	6	5	5	7	5	5	1	3	3	2	5	1	2	3	4	0	1	2	1	4	3	4	0	0	0	0	X
0	0	0	0	0	0	0	3	4	3	0	2	0	1	0	0	0	1	0	0	0	4	0	2	0	0	0	S
0	0	1	1	0	1	0	1	0	0	0	0	3	3	0	1	1	0	0	0	1	0	0	0	0	0	0	U

BATH CITY

CURRENT SQUAD AS OF BEGINING OF 2009-10 SEASON

GOALKEEPERS	HT	WT	D.O.B	AGE	P.O.B	CAREER	Apps	Gls
Steve Perrin	5'11"		27/10/70	38	Melksham	Trowbridge T, Chippenham, Melksham, Weston-s-Mare (Cover), Forest Green 3/99 Rel 4/05, Bath C (L) 10/04, Chippenham 7/05, Bath C 2/07	14	0
Willem Puddy	5'10"	11 07	4/10/87	21	Salisbury	Bristol C (Yth), Cheltenham, Mangotsfield (L) 10/06, Yate (L) 2/07, Stafford R (L) 10/07, Tamworth (4ML) 7/08, Bath C (3ML) 7/09		
Ryan Robinson	6'02"	13 02	13/10/82	26	Tebay	Blackburn, Wigan (Trial) 9/02, Southend 7/03 Rel c/s 04, Wivenhoe (L) 10/03, Morecambe 9/04 , Kendal T (L) 9/04, Southport (L) 8/06, Southport (L) 9/06, Forest Green 1/07, Bath C 5/09		
DEFENDERS								
Matt Coupe			7/10/78	30	St Asaph	Bristol C, Forest Green, Gloucester c/s 99, Clevedon T 9/99, Bath C c/s 01, Aberystwyth, Forest Green 1/02, Chippenham (L) 1/03, Bath C 2/03	41	2
Raiff Gwinnett			9/11/90	18		Exeter (Yth), Torquay (Yth) (Pro c/s 08), Weymouth 4/09, Bath C 8/09		
Chris Holland	6'00"	10 06	29/8/80	29	Taunton	Bournemouth (Trainee), Bristol C Rel c/s 00, Exeter (L), Team Bath 9/00, Bath C (L) 3/05, Bath C 8/05, Weston-Super-Mare (2ML) 11/05, Gloucester (L) 2/06	41	6
Lee Howells	5'11"	11 12	14/10/68	40	Fremantle, Aust	Bristol R, Brisbane Lions (Aust), Rochedale Rovers (Aust), Cheltenham 11/91 Rel c/s 04, Merthyr (L) 2/04, Merthyr 7/04, Mangotsfield 7/05, Clevedon 12/05, Mangotsfield (Man) 3/06, Bath C (Pl/Coach) c/s 07		
Gethin Jones	5'11"	12 04	8/9/81	27	Carmarthen	Carmarthen, Cardiff 8/00 Rel c/s 03, Weymouth (L) 9/02, Merthyr 8/03, Bath C 6/05	33	4
Jim Rollo	6'00"	11 00	22/5/76	33	Wisbech	Walsall, Yate 9/95, Cardiff C 3/97 Rel c/s 98, Forest Green 7/98 Rel c/s 99, Cirencester (L) 10/98, Bath C (L) 1/99, Clevedon c/s 99, Merthyr, Bath C 5/02	42	0
Sekani Simpson	5'10"	11 10	11/3/84	25	Bristol	Bristol C (Sch) Rel c/s 05, Forest Green (L) 3/04, Tamworth (L) 9/04, Forest Green 7/05 Rel 5/06, Weston-Super-Mare 8/06 Rel 9/06 Bath C 10/06	37	1
MIDFIELDERS								
Mark Badman			21/12/79	29	Bath	Bristol C Rel c/s 99, Clevedon 7/99, Bath C 10/01, Chippenham 5/02, Bath C 8/08	28	1
Marcus Browning	6'00"	12 10	22/4/71	38	Bristol	Bristol R, Hereford (L) 9/92, Huddersfield £500,000 2/97, Gillingham (L) 11/98, Gillingham £175,000 3/99 Rel c/s 02, Bournemouth 8/02 Rel c/s 07, Weymouth (Pl/Coach) 8/07 Rel c/s 08 Re-signed 1/09, Bath C 7/09		
Ashley Caldwell						Forest Green, Bath C 8/08, Paulton R (3ML) 7/09	0	0
Adam Connolly	5'09"	12 04	10/4/86	23	Manchester	Cheltenham Rel c/s 08, Newport C (Trial) 7/08, Hednesford 8/08, Bath C 9/08	31	0
Aaron Cornwall			28/2/87	22	Bristol	Bristol Manor Farm, Mangotsfield 7/06 Rel 7/07, Chippenham c/s 07, Bournemouth (Trial) 2/08, Halesowen T 6/08, Bath C NC 8/09		
Richard Evans	5'09"	11 08	19/6/83	26	Cardiff	Birmingham, Sheffield Wed 3/03 Rel 1/06, Colchester (Trial) 7/05, Shrewsbury 1/06 Rel c/s 06, Grimsby (Trial) 7/06, Newport C 8/06 Rel 10/08, Bath C 10/08	18	1
Lewis Hogg	5'09"	11 11	13/9/82	26	Bristol	Bristol R Rel c/s 03, Barnet 8/03, Weston-s-Mare 12/03, Bath C 5/06	37	4
Sido Jombarti			20/8/87	22	Portugal	Weymouth 7/07 Rel 4/08, Cambridge U (Trial) 4/08, Basingstoke 7/08, Bath C 5/09		
Mike Perrott			24/3/89	20		Melksham T, Team Bath 8/07, Bath C 7/09		

FORWARDS

Stuart Douglas	5'09"	12 05	9/4/78	31	Enfield	Luton Rel c/s 02, Oxford U (L) 10/01, Rushden & D (2ML) 1/02, Boston U 8/02 Rel c/s 04, RoPS Rovaniemi (Fin), Dag & Red 11/04 Rel 1/05, Crawley 8/05 Rel 11/05, Eastleigh 12/05 Pl/Comm Man 4/06, Lymington & New Milton (L) 12/06, Weston-Super-Mare 3/07, Weymouth 7/07 Rel 5/08, Bath C 6/08	37	10
Darren Edwards			4/8/80	29	Bristol	Bristol Manor Farm, Mangotsfield 98, Bristol R (Trial) 4/02,, Tiverton 1/04, Mangotsfield 9/04, Yate T 1/05, Bath C 12/06	35	9
Kaid Mohamed	5'11"		23/7/84	25	Cardiff	Ely Rangers, Cwmbran c/s 03, Llanelli 1/05, Cwmbran 7/05, Llanelli 12/05, Carmarthen 2/06, Wrexham (Trial) c/s 07, Swindon 8/07, Torquay (2ML) 1/08, Forest Green 7/08 Rel c/s 09, Newport C (L) 1/09, Bath C 8/09		
Jamie Taylor	5'11"	11 00	4/4/91	18		Swindon (Scholar) Rel c/s 09, Bath C 7/09, Paulton R (3ML) 7/09		

LOANEES	HT	WT	DOB	AGE	POB	From - To	APPS	GOA
(F)Josh Klein-Davies	5'11"	13 09	6/7/89	20	Bristol	Bristol R 3/09 - Rel 4/09, Weymouth (Trial) 7/09, Weston-Super-Mare 8/09	6	0

DEPARTURES	HT	WT	DOB	AGE	POB	From - To	APPS	GOA
(F)Danny Carey-Bertram	5'11"	13 00	14/6/84	25	Birmingham	Forest Green Rovers 8/08 - AFC Telford 10/08	6	2
(D)Paul Cochlin			23/8/83	26	Cardiff	Newport C 6/08 - Newport C 10/08	5	1
(M)Jason Wood					Bristol	Yate T 5/07 - Rel 10/08, Chippenham (L) 9/08	1	0
(M)Jamie Gosling	6'00"	10 06	21/3/82	27	Bath	Hungerford 6/08 - Rel 11/08, Hungerford 11/08	4	0
(G)Paul Evans	6'04"	15 00	28/12/73	35	Newcastle, SA	Rushden & D 1/04 - Rel c/s 09, Emigrating to Australia	28	0
(M)Scott Rogers	5'11"	11 00	23/5/79	30	Bristol	Forest Green 3/06 - Newport C (L) 1/09, Newport C 4/09	28	0
(F)Dave Gilroy	5'11"	11 05	23/12/82	26	Yeovil	Chippenham 5/07 - Newport C 4/09	32	12
(M)Steve Jones			25/12/70	38	Bristol	Forest Green 10/03 - Rel 4/09, Bishops Cleeve 7/09	25	0
(F)Martin Paul			2/11/75	33	Whalley	Chippenham 3/07 - Paulton (Dual) 8/08, Mangotsfield 6/09	11	2
(M)Martin Slocombe			8/11/88	20	Weston-Super-Mare	Bristol C 8/08 - Weymouth 7/09	23	0
(M)Lee Collier						Larkhall Ath 10/08 - Larkhall Ath, Mangotsfield 7/09	0	0
(M)Ali Gibb	5'09"	11 07	17/2/76	33	Salisbury	Hartlepool 6/08 - Yate T (L) 2/09, Newport C (Trial) 6/09	9	0
(M)Ronayne Marsh-Brown (ex Benjamin)	5'10"	12 00	13/11/84	24	Chiswick	Winchester 3/09 -	1	0

BATH CITY

Formed: 1889

Nickname: The Romans.

Club Colours: Black & white shirts, black shorts, black socks.

Change Colours: Red shirts, red shorts, red socks.

Club Sponsor: SN Scaffolds.

Previous League: Southern League

Ground address: Twerton Park, Twerton, Bath, North East Somerset BA2 1DB

Telephone 01225 423 087

Fax: 01225 481 391

Email: mail@bathcityfootballclub.co.uk

Website: www.bathcityfc.com

Simple Directions: Twerton Park is situated off the A4/A36 Lower Bristol Road on the Bristol side of Bath.

Capacity: 8,840 **Seats:** 1,017 **Covered:** 4,800 **Floodlights:** Yes

Clubhouse: Several Bars open all week

Club Shop: Yes

PROGRAMME EDITOR

Mark Stillman

Tel: (M) 07929 110 109

Email: mark@chrisstillman.co.uk

CLUB STATISTICS

RECORDS

Attendance:18,020 v Brighton & Hove Albion F.A.Cup.
Victory: 8-0 v Boston United 1998-99.
Defeat: 0-9 v Yeovil Town 1946-47.
Career Goalscorer: Paul Randall - 106.
Career Appearance: David Mogg - 530.
Transfer Fee Paid: £15,000 to Bristol City for Micky Tanner.
Received: £80,000 from Southampton for Jason Dodd.

SENIOR HONOURS

Southern League Western Division 2 Champions 1928-29.
Southern League Western Division Champions 1933-34.
Southern League Champions 1959-60, 77-78, 2006-07.
Southern League Cup Winners 1978-79.
Somerset Premier Cup Winners 1951-52, 52-53, 57-58, 59-60, 65-66, 67-68. 69-70, 77-78, 80-81, 81-82, 83-84, 84-85, 85-86, 88-89, 89-90, 93-94, 94-95, 2007-08.

PREVIOUS

Names: Bath AFC 1889-92. Bath Railway FC 1902-05.
Bath Amateurs 1913-23 (Reserve side)
Leagues: Western 1908-21. Southern 1921-79, 88-90, 97-2007.
Alliance/Conference 1979-88, 90-97.
Grounds: The Belvoir Ground 1889-92 & 1902-15.
Lambridge Show Ground 1919-32.

BISHOP'S STORTFORD

Back row – left to right idemudia okijie - richard howell - precious koko - peter dean - danny harris - nicky eyre - steve king tom champion - kyri kyprianou - craig edwards.
front row - dave jude (physio) - piers wixon - danny green - liam hopkins - paul goodacre - martin hayes (manager) - matt jones - michael hyem - george jermy - colin talor (physio).

CLUB PERSONNEL

Chairman: Luigu Del Basso.

Company Secretary: Franco Del Basso.

Operations Manager: John Turner.

Secretary: Ian Kettridge

25 Cox Ley, Hatfield Heath

Bishop's Stortford, Herts CM22 7ER

(H): 01279 730 533

(M): 07904 169 017

ianket@aol.com

Commercial Manager: John Turner.

Tel: (M) 07710 079 158

Email: j.turner@bsfc.co.uk

Press Officer: As secretary.

Manager: Mark Simpson.

Club therapist: David Jude.

A club representing a town with supporters who react well to a successful side and are geographically well placed to attract senior players from the home counties, Bishop's Stortford have enjoyed some special seasons in the not too distant past, but have recently been battling to make an impact in The Blue Square South.

The 2008-2009 season was no different as a poor start saw The Blues sink down to twentieth position by November having also been dumped out of the F.A.Cup at Dorchester Town after victories over Wingate & Finchley and Rugby Town. The F.A.Trophy didn't bring any encouragement either as Tiverton Town drew 0-0 at Woodside Park and won the replay in Devon 1-0. Longest serving manager Martin Hayes was replaced by his assistant Mark Simpson.

The New Year saw 'The Bishops' difficult to beat, and steady but unspectacular progress edged them back up the table. Only five games were lost and an unbeaten run of five matches brought eleven points and a final place in the top ten of the League.

Management will obviously be hoping to build around the squad who lifted the club up the table in the second half of the season and who only failed to score in five games in the New Year. Danny Harris and Lewis Smith were steady goalscorers with the experienced Roy Essandoh in support, but Charlie Sheringham from Welling United should add extra firepower and 'The Bishops' could be a club to challenge for honours next season.

BISHOP'S STORTFORD

BEST LGE ATT.: **1,004** v Braintree Town
LOWEST: **231** v Hampton & Richmond B.

No.	Date	Comp	H/A	Opponents	Att:	Result	Goalscorers	Pos
1	Aug 9	BSS	A	Weston-S-Mare	185	L 1 - 2	Wixon 62 (pen)	
2	12		H	Bromley	404	D 1 - 1	Edwards 86	
3	16		H	Bath City	335	L 0 - 2		17
4	23		A	Hayes & Yeading	229	L 0 - 1		19
5	25		H	Thurrock	323	W 2 - 1	**Harris** 28 Wixon 62	
6	30		A	Bognor Regis Town	319	W 2 - 0	Champion 7 Webster 52	14
7	Sept 2		A	St Albans City	448	L 0 - 2		
8	6		H	Basingstoke Town	364	W 3 - 2	Edwards 46 Okijie 76 **Harris** 79	12
9	**9**	**SS S1**	**H**	**Bromley**	**201**	**W 2 - 1**	**Wixon 54 P Dean 73**	
10	13		H	Newport County	414	D 1 - 1	Essandoh 40	13
11	20		A	Maidenhead United	361	L 2 - 3	**Harris** 17 Dean 51	
12	**27**	**F.A.C. 2Q**	**H**	**Wingate & Finchley**	**303**	**W 3 - 2**	**HARRIS 3 (16pen 54 pen 67)**	
13	Oct 4		H	Welling United	372	L 0 - 1		16
14	**11**	**F.A.C 3Q**	**H**	**Rugby Town**	**411**	**W 2 - 1**	**Harris 59 Wixon 90 (pen)**	
15	18		A	AFC Wimbledon	3072	L 1 - 4	Wixon 3	16
16	**21**	**SS S2**	**A**	**Kettering Town**	**450**	**L 2 - 4**	**Chick 75 Okojie 90**	
17	**25**	**F.A.C. 4Q**	**A**	**Dorchester Town**	**433**	**L 0 - 1**		
18	27		A	Chelmsford City	1279	D 3 - 3	Wixon 16 (pen) **Harris** 20 53	
19	Nov 1		H	Dorchester Town	331	L 0 - 2		19
20	15		H	Fisher Athletic	323	L 0 - 1		20
21	18		H	Hampton & Richmond B	231	L 1 - 3	Jackman 15	
22	**22**	**F.A.T 2Q**	**H**	**Tiverton Town**	**271**	**D 0 - 0**		
23	**26**	**F.A.T.2Q r**	**A**	**Tiverton Town**	**280**	**L 0 - 1**		
24	29		A	Newport County	654	W 1 - 0	Mason 69	19
25	Dec 6		A	Basingstoke Town	300	D 1 - 1	Jackman 82	19
26	20		H	Weston-s-Mare	281	W 2 - 1	Smith 27 Green 82	18
27	26		A	Braintree Town	1003	L 0 - 2		19
28	Jan 1		H	Braintree Town	1004	L 0 - 3		
29	17		A	Welling United	529	W 3 - 1	Green 53 (pen) Higgins 75 **Harris** 90	19
30	24		H	Maidenhead United	342	W 2 - 0	Dean 42 Smith 49	18
31	27		H	AFC Wimbledon	1003	L 0 - 1		
32	31		A	Worcester City	644	W 3 - 1	Smith 12 31 Dean 75	17
33	Feb 14		H	St Albans City	602	D 1 - 1	Smith 33	17
34	17		H	Team Bath	259	W 4 - 3	Jackman 42 90 **Harris** 73 Essandoh 83	
35	21		A	Eastleigh	588	D 1 - 1	Essandoh 75	15
36	24		A	Hampton & Richmond B	278	L 1 - 2	**Harris** 20	
37	28		H	Chelmsford City	801	W 2 - 1	Jackman 2 Dean 22	14
38	Mar 7		A	Dorchester Town	378	W 2 - 0	Goodacre 40 Prestedge 59	15
39	9		A	Havant & Waterlooville	572	L 0 - 3		
40	14		H	Worcester City	403	W 3 - 0	Essandoh 2 Smith 35 Patterson 40	14
41	21		H	Bognor Regis	492	W 2 - 0	Wright 41 **Harris** 45	13
42	24		A	Bromley	259	L 0 - 1		
43	28		A	Fisher Athletic	159	W 3 - 0	SMITH 3 (14 45 81)	12
44	April 4		H	Eastleigh	381	L 3 - 4	Prestedge 61 Lindie 76 Smith 89	13
45	7		A	Bath City	310	W 3 - 2	Lindie 51 66 Green 75	
46	11		H	Hayes & Yeading	444	D 0 - 0		11
47	13		A	Thurrock	334	W 3 - 1	Green 10 Champion 38 Smith 50	
48	18		H	Havant & Waterlooville	421	W 1 - 0	**Harris** 49	
49	25		A	Team Bath	212	D 2 - 2	Smith 81 Essandoh 90	9

Average Home Att: 454 (457) **Goals** 69 70

Best Position: 9th **Worst:** 20th

Goalscorers: Harris 14, Smith 12, Wixon 6, Dean 5, Essandoh 5, Jackman 5, Green 4, Lindie 3, Champion 2, Edwards 2, Prestedge 2, Okijie 2, Chick 1, Goodacre 1, Higgins 1, Mason 1, Patterson 1, Webster 1, Wright 1.

EYRE	M JONES	KOKO	CHAMPION	GOODACRE	KING	WIXON	EDWARDS	P DEAN	HARRIS	JERMY	OKOJIE	KYPRIANOU	HOPKINS	WEBSTER	HASLER	TAYLOR	HYEM	MASON	ESSANDOH	HOWELL	CHICK	GREEN	ALAILIE	MILLER	JACKMAN	FORSHAW	PATTERSON	H DEAN	SMITH	COOPER	HIGGINS	BERNARD	LETTEJALLOW	PRESTEDGE	WRIGHT	ANGUS	WEBB	HILL	DJ GREEN	LINDIE	R JONES	
X	X	X	X	X	X	X	X	X	X	X	S	S	U	U	U																											1
X	X	X	X	X	X	X	X	X	S		S	X	U	X	U	U																										2
X		X	X	X	U	X	X	X	X	S	X	S	X		U	X	S																									3
X	X	X	X	X	X	S	X	X	X	X	S	X			U	U	U																									4
X	X	U	X	X	X	X	X	S	X	S	X			X	U	X		S																								5
X	X	U	X		X	X	X	S	X		X			X	U	X	X	S	S																							6
X	X	U		X	X	X	X	S	X		S			X	U	X	X	X	S																							7
X	X			X	X	U	X	S	X	X	X		S	X	U			X	X	S																						8
		X	**X**	**X**	**X**	**S**	**S**	**X**	**S**	**X**	**X**		**X**		**X**	**U**		**X**	**X**	**U**																						**9**
X	U	X	X	X		S	X	X	X		X		X		S			X	X	S																						10
	X	X	S	X	X	X		X	X		X		X		X	U	S	X	U	S																						11
X	**X**		**X**	**U**	**X**	**S**	**X**	**X**	**X**	**S**	**X**		**U**			**X**		**X**	**X**																							**12**
X	X	U	X	X	X	X	X	X	X		S				U	X		S	S	X																						13
X	**X**	**X**	**X**		**X**	**S**	**X**	**X**	**X**	**U**	**X**		**U**		**U**		**U**	**X**	**X**	**S**	**U**																					**14**
X	X		X			X	X	X	X		S		X	X	U		X	S	X		S	U																				15
	X	**S**	**X**			**X**	**X**	**X**	**U**		**X**		**X**	**X**	**X**		**X**	**U**			**S**	**S**	**X**																			**16**
X	**X**	**X**	**X**			**S**	**X**	**X**	**X**		**X**		**U**		**U**		**S**	**X**	**X**		**U**	**S**		**X**																		**17**
X	X	X	X			X	U	S	X		X		X		U		U	U				X	X	X																		18
X	U	X	X			X	X	S	X		X		X		U		S	S				X	X	X																		19
X	U		X	X		S	X		X		X		X		U			S		S			X	X	X	X																20
X	X	X		X		S	X		X		S				U		S	X				X	X	U	X	X																21
X	**X**	**U**	**X**	**X**		**U**	**X**	**U**	**X**						**U**			**X**	**X**	**S**		**X**		**X**		**X**																**22**
X	**X**			**X**		**U**	**X**	**S**	**X**				**X**		**U**		**X**	**X**	**X**			**X**				**S**																**23**
X	X		X	X		S		X	X				X					S	S			X				X	X	X														24
X	X		X	X		X		S					X				S	X	S			X			X		X	X														25
X	X		X	X		U		S					X				U	S	S			X			X	X	X	X	X													26
X	X		X	X				S	S									U	S			X			X	X	X	X	X	X	U											27
X	X		X	X	S			X	S						U		U	X	X			X						X	X	X	S											28
X	X		X	X					X						U		U	S	S			X			X				X	X	S	X	X									29
X	X		X	X					X						U		U	S	S			X			X			X	X		S		X									30
X	X			X					X						U			S	S			X			X			X	X	X	S	X	X									31
X	X		S	X					X								U	U	S			X						X	X	X	X	X	X	S								32
X	X		U	X					X									U	S	S		X			S			X	X	X		X	X		X							33
X	X		X	U					X									S	S	S		X			X			X		X		X	X	U	X							34
X	X		X	S					X									S	S	U		X			X			X		X		X	X	U	X							35
	X			X					X									S	S			X			X		X	X	S			U	X		X	X	U					36
X	X		X	X					X										U			X			X		S	X	X			X	X	S	S	U						37
X	X		X	X					X										S			X					X		X			X	X	X	U	U	U	S				38
X	X			X					S										X			X					X		X	X		S	X	X	X		U	S				39
X	X		S	X					X										X						U		X		X	X			X	X	X	U	S	S				40
X	X		X	X					X													X			U		X			X		S	X	X	X	U	S	S				41
X	X			X					X													X					X			X		S	X	X	X	U	S	X	S			42
X	U		S	X															U			X					X		X	X		X		X	S	U		X		X	X	43
X	X		X	X					X										X			X					S		X			X	X	X		S		U		S	U	44
X	X			X					X										S			X					X			X			X		X	S	U	X	S	X		45
X	X		X						X													X					X		X	X			X	S	U	X		S	U	X	S	46
X	U		X						X										S			X					S		X			U		X	X	X	S	X	X	X		47
X			X	X					X										S			X					X		X			X		X	U	U		X	S	S	X	48
X	X		X	U					X										S		S	X							X			X		X	X			X	U	S	X	49
Total League Appearances																																										
40	35	9	29	33	9	12	14	10	35	3	9	2	10	6	1	5	3	7	7	1	0	28	4	3	12	5	14	13	18	15	1	12	17	10	11	3	0	6	1	4	3	**X**
0	0	0	4	1	1	5	0	9	4	2	7	2	1	0	1	0	5	14	20	6	2	0	0	0	1	0	3	0	1	0	4	3	0	3	2	2	4	5	3	3	1	**S**
0	5	4	1	2	1	2	1	0	0	0	0	0	2	1	18	3	7	4	3	1	0	1	0	1	2	0	0	0	0	0	1	2	0	2	3	7	4	1	2	0	1	**U**
Total Cup Appearances																																										
5	6	3	6	3	3	1	6	5	5	1	5	0	3	1	2	1	2	6	6	0	0	2	1	2	0	1	0	0	0	0	0	0	0	0	0	0	0	0	0	0	0	**X**
0	0	1	0	0	0	4	1	1	1	1	0	0	0	0	0	0	1	0	0	2	1	2	0	0	0	1	0	0	0	0	0	0	0	0	0	0	0	0	0	0	0	**S**
0	0	1	0	1	0	2	0	1	1	1	0	0	3	0	4	1	1	1	0	1	2	0	0	0	0	0	0	0	0	0	0	0	0	0	0	0	0	0	0	0	0	**U**

Also Played: PACK U(12,25). BARKER X(23). BRISTOW S(23). CHAPMAN U(25). PETTIGREW X(30) U(31). THOMPSON X(36). CURLEY U(39).

BISHOP'S STORTFORD

CURRENT SQUAD AS OF BEGINING OF 2009-10 SEASON

GOALKEEPERS	HT	WT	D.O.B	AGE	P.O.B	CAREER	Apps	Gls
Nick Eyre	5'10"	10 10	7/9/85	23	Braintree	Tottenham Rel c/s 05, Grays (L) 10/04, Grays 7/05 Rel 7/06, Rushden & D 8/06 Rel 12/06, Histon (Trial), Dag & Red 2/07, St Albans 7/07, Grays (L) 3/08, Bishops Stortford 7/08	40	0
Nedjet Hussain						QPR, Southend, Accrington, Margate, Thurrock c/s 07, Hillingdon B (L), Cheshunt (L) 2/08, Bishops Stortford c/s 09		
DEFENDERS								
Stevland Angus	6'00"	12 00	16/9/80	28	Westminster	West Ham, Bournemouth (2ML) 8/00, Cambridge U 7/01 Rel c/s 05, Hull C (6WL) 12/04, Scunthorpe (SL) 1/05, Shrewsbury (Trial) 7/05, Southend (Trial) 8/05, Grays 8/05 Rel 5/06, Barnet (SL) 1/06, Torquay 7/06, Grimsby (Trial) 7/07,Barnet 8/07, Fisher 10/07 Rel, Braintree 8/08, Concord R 9/08, Bishops Stortford 2/09	5	0
Narada Bernard	5'02"	10 05	30/1/81	28	Bristol	Tottenham (Trainee), Arsenal 7/99 Rel c/s 00, Bournemouth 7/00 Rel c/s 03, Kidderminster (Trial) 7/03, Woking 8/03 Rel 11/03, Torquay 11/03 Rel 1/04, Welling 9/04, Barnet, Farnborough 1/05 Rel 3/05, Rushden & D (Trial) 2/05, Dover 3/05, Yeading (Trial) 8/05, Hemel Hempstead 8/05, Fisher 8/06, Rushden & D (NC) 1/07, Weymouth 1/07 Rel 2/08, Maidenhead 2/08, Bishops Stortford (L) 1/09 Perm 2/09	15	0
Tom Champion			15/5/86	23	London	Watford (Yth), Barnet 8/04 (04/05 2,0) Rel c/s 05, Wealdstone (L) 3/05, Bishops Stortford 7/05	33	2
David Chick			27/2/85	24	Norwich	Norwich (Sch), Kings Lynn 1/04, Boston U (Trial) 2/04, Cheltenham (Trial) 2/04, Cambridge U 7/05 Rel 2/06, Peterborough (Trial) 10/06, Cambridge C 3/07 Rel 5/07, Boston U 9/07, Cambridge C 10/07 Rel 11/07, Bishops Stortford 10/08, AFC Sudbury (L) 12/08	2	0
Grant Cooper	6'02"		16/9/77	31	London	Enfield, Chesham 5/02, Bishops Stortford, Dag & Red, Dublin C (Ire), Hemel Hempstead 1/05, Hornchurch 3/05, Kings Lynn 7/05, Maidenhead 3/07 Rel 1/09, Bishops Stortford (L) 12/08 Bishops Stortford 1/09	15	0
Craig Edwards	5'10"	11 03	8/7/82	27	London	Tottenham (Yth), Southend, Grays 7/01, Ford U 3/03, Redbridge, Chelmsford 1/05, Bishops Stortford 6/06	14	2
Paul Goodacre						Burnham Ramblers, Maldon T 8/02, Bishops Stortford 6/06	34	1
Matt Jones			19/11/76	32		Havant T, Waterlooville, BAT, Havant & W, Eastleigh, Bashley, St Albans, Bashley, Salisbury, Bishops Stortford	35	0
Ritchie Jones						Northampton Rel 11/08, Cheshunt 12/08, Gillingham (Trial) 3/09, Dag & Red (Trial), Bishops Stortford 3/09	4	0
Ben Nunn			24/9/80	18		Boston U, Rushden & D Rel 7/08, Cambridge C 8/08 Rel 6/09, Bishops Stortford c/s 09		
Mark Wright			20/1/87	22	London	Norwich (Jun), Tottenham (Scholar), Charlton (Scholar), Southend, Lewes (L) 12/05, Grays 8/06, Crawley (2ML) 11/06, St Albans (L) 2/07, Rushden & D (L) 3/07, Bishops Stortford 7/07 Rel 12/07, Fisher 12/07, Thurrock 9/08, Bishops Stortford 2/09	13	1
MIDFIELDERS								
Ben Bowditch	5'10"	12 00	19/2/84	25	Bishops Stortford	Tottenham, AB Copenhagen (Den) (3ML) 3/04, Colchester 8/04, Barnet 8/05, Yeading (L) 3/06, Cambridge C 7/06, St Albans 8/08 Rel 10/08, Bishops Stortford 7/09		
Danny Harris			7/7/86	23	Newnham	Tilbury, East Thurrock, Bishops Stortford 12/07	39	10
Rory Hill			28/3/90	19	Lewisham	Gillingham Rel 1/09, Salisbury (L) 11/08, Bishops Stortford 3/09	11	0
Richard Howell			29/8/82	27	Hitchin	C.Palace, Stevenage 3/02, B.Stortford (L) 3/03, B.Stortford 5/03, AFC Sudbury (L) 12/08	7	0
Baimass Lettejallow	5'09"	10 12	16/4/84	25	London	Barnet, Braintree 10/03, Harlow 1/04, Dag & Red 1/05, Aveley (L) 2/07, Thurrock (SL) 9/07, Thurrock (3ML) 8/08, Bishops Stortford (SL) 1/09, Bishops Stortford c/s 09	17	0
Ashley Nicholls	5'11"	11 11	30/10/81	27	Ipswich	Ipswich Wan, Ipswich 7/00 Rel c/s 02, Canvey Island (L) 2/02, Hereford (Trial) 7/02, Darlington 8/02, Cambridge U (SL) 2/04, Cambridge U 7/04, Rushden & D (3ML) 8/05, Rushden & D 1/06, Grays 8/06, Boston U 7/07, Maidenhead 4/08 Rel 5/09, Bishops Stortford		
Ola Okinawo						Bishops Stortford		
Reece Prestedge						Bishops Stortford, Dag & Red, Brimsdown, Cheshunt 6/08, Bishops Stortford 2/09	13	2
Charlie Simpson						Bishops Stortford, Aveley (L) 11/07, Cheshunt (L) 2/09		
FORWARDS								
Adam Bolle			17/9/90	18		L.Orient, Brentwood (WE) 12/08, Bishops Stortford c/s 09		
Roy Essandoh	6'00"	12 04	17/2/76	33	Belfast	Cumbernauld Jun, Motherwell 12/94, St Polten (Aus) 6/97, East Fife 2/98, VPS Vassa (Fin) 5/98, Rushden & D 1/01, Wycombe 2/01 Rel c/s 01, Carlisle (Trial) 7/01, Barnet 9/01 (01/02 6,1), Cambridge C 12/01, Bishops Stortford 8/02, Billericay 9/02, Grays 12/02, Bishos Stortford 5/03, Gravesend (L) 1/04 £4,000 3/04 Rel 5/05, Kettering 8/05, Bishops Stortford 9/05 Rel c/s 08, Cambridge C c/s 08, Bishops Stortford 11/08	27	5
Duane Jackman						St Albans (Jun), Bishops Stortford, Brimsdown 8/06, St Albans 9/06 (06/07 6,1), Rel 10/06, Brimsdown 11/06, Aveley 12/06, Potters Bar c/s 07, Cheshunt 8/08, Bishops Stortford 11/08	13	5

	HT	WT	DOB	AGE	POB	From - To		
Leon McKenzie			18/10/84	24		L.Orient, Waltham Forest, Thurrock 6/06 Rel 12/08, Luton (Trial) 12/08, Grays 12/08 Rel 1/09, Bishops Stortford 6/09		
Louis Riddle	5'11"	12 00	29/8/82	27	Harlow	West Ham, Stevenage (L) 2/02, Stevenage 10/02, Braintree (L) 2/03, Braintree 5/03, Cambridge C 8/03, Braintree 6/04 Rel 5/09, Bishop Stortford 5/09		
Charlie Sheringham	6'01"	11 06	17/4/88	21	Chingford	Millwall (Yth), Tottenham (Yth), Bournemouth (Trial), Ipswich (Scholar) Rel c/s 05, Charlton, C.Palace Rel 1/08, Crystal Palace Blatimore (USA) (L) 4/07 Cambridge C 3/08, Welling 6/08, Bishops Stortford 5/09		
Ashley Taylor-Forbes						Arsenal (Yth), Goldsdown Road, Bishops Stortford, Dag & Red, Brimsdown, Cheshunt 6/08, Bishops Stortford 3/09		

LOANEES	HT	WT	DOB	AGE	POB	From - To	APPS	GOA
(D)Michael Alailie						Dag & Red 10/08 - Witham T (L) 12/08, Billericay (L) 2/09	4	0
(D)Ashley Miller						West Ham 10/08 -	3	0
(M)Jamie Forshaw						Southend 11/08 - Rel 5/09, Ebbsfleet 7/09	5	0
(D)Marlon Patterson	5'09"	11 10	24/6/83	26	London	Dag & Red 11/08 - Histon 1/09, Bishops Stortford (SL) 2/09, Rel 5/09, Staines 7/09	17	1
(M)Harley Dean	6'03"	12 12	26/7/91	18		Dag & Red (3ML) 11/08 - Thurrock (SL) 3/09	13	3
(F)James Lindie						Southend (SL) 3/09 - Ebbsfleet 7/09	7	3

DEPARTURES	HT	WT	DOB	AGE	POB	From - To	APPS	GOA
(F)Kyrie Kyprianou						Enfield T 8/08 - Rel 8/08	4	0
(M)George Jermy						Wivenhoe 7/08 - AFC Sudbury (3ML) 9/08 Perm	5	0
(D)Precious Koko						Potters Bar 7/08 - Rel 12/08	9	0
(M)Dee Okojie						Leyton 8/08 - Rel 12/08, Harlow, Billericay 3/09, Boreham Wood 6/09	16	1
(D)Adam Pettigrew	6'00"	13 01	12/11/86	22	Hackney	Cheshunt 1/09 - AFC Sudbury 2/09	1	0
(M)Michael Hyem			18/11/88	20	Brampton	Cambridge U 7/08 - St Neots 3/09	8	0
(F)Danny Green			9/7/88	21		Cambridge C 7/08 - Dag & Red 5/09	28	4
(M)Danny Lunan	6'00"	13 00	14/3/84	25	Farnborough	Thurrock c/s 07 - Tiptree 6/09		
(D)Steve King						Brentwood 7/08 - Brentwood (L) 1/09, Brentwood (Trial) 6/09, Welling 7/09	10	0
(M)Danny (DJ) Green						Harlow 3/09 - St Albans 8/09	4	0
(G)Charlie Hasler			19/12/85	23	Leyton	Enfield T 7/08 - Maldon T (Dual) 12/08, Redbridge 2/09	2	0
(G)Stuart Pack							0	0
(G)Ed Thompson	5'10"	12 12	8/1/83	26	Finchley	Dag & Red 2/09 -	1	0
(D)Luke Webster			12/10/88	20	Harlow	Burnham Ramblers 8/08 -	6	1
(M)Danny Chapman							0	0
(M)Scott Curley						AFC Hornchurch 1/09 -	0	0
(M)Liam Hopkins					Essex	Braintree 7/08 - Concord R (L) 2/09	11	0
(M)Jason Mason						USA - Wingate & F (L) 3/09	21	1
(M)Sam Taylor						Barking & East Ham c/s 06 - Concord R (L) 2/09	5	0
(M)Jimmy Webb						Great Wakering 2/09 -	4	0
(F)Peter Dean						Wealdstone 8/08 - Hendon (L) 1/09	19	1
(F)Sam Higgins						Fisher 12/08 - Brentwood (L) 2/09	5	1
(F)Lewis Smith			27/10/89	19		Fulham (SL) 12/08 Perm 3/09 - Gillingham (Trial) 3/09, Bournemouth (Trial) 4/09	19	12
(F)Piers Wixon			14/2/90	19		Cambridge U c/s 08 - AFC Sudbury (2ML) 1/09, Concord R (L) 3/09	17	4
Scott Barker						Yth -	0	0
Ross Bristow						Yth -	0	0

BISHOP'S STORTFORD

Formed: 1874

Nickname: Blues or Bishops.

Club Colours: Blue with white sleeved shirts, blue shorts, blue socks.

Change Colours: Red shirts, red shorts, red socks.

Club Sponsor: Servebase

Previous League: Isthmian League

Ground address: Woodside Park, Dunmow Road, Bishop's Stortford, Herts CM23 5RG.

Telephone: 08700 339 930

Mobile: 07904 169 017

Fax: 08700 339 931

Email: ianket@aol.com

Website: www.bsfc.co.uk

Simple Directions: M11 Jct 8 A1250 towards town centre. Left at first roundabout. Woodside is first on right opposite Golf Club.

Capacity: 4,000 **Seats**: 298 **Covered**: 700 **Floodlights**: Yes

Clubhouse: Extensive bars and function rooms. Open lunchtimes, evening and matchdays Mick Wheeler c/o club

Shop: Full stock.

Local Radio: Essex FM Breeze AM Mercury FM Three Counties.

Local Press: Bishop's Stortford Citizen, Herts & Essex Observer and The Herald.

PROGRAMME EDITOR

Ben Dellow

Tel: (M) 07531 138 560

Email: b.dellow@bsfc.co.uk

CLUB STATISTICS

RECORDS

Attendance: 6,000 F.A.Cup 2nd Rd 1972 and 2 nd Rd replay 1983

Victory: 11-0 v Nettleswell & Buntwill, Herts Jun Cup 1911

Defeat: 0-13 v Cheshunt (H) Herts Sen. Cup 1926

Career Goalscorer: Since 1929. Jimmy Badcock 123

Career Appearances: Phil Hopkins 543

Record Transfer Fee Paid: Undisclosed to Grays Athletic for Vinnie John 1999.

Received: Undisclosed from Dagenham & Redbridge for Glen Southam.

SENIOR HONOURS

F.A.Trophy 1980-81
F.A.Amateur Cup 1973-74
Premier Inter League Cup 1989-90
Isthmian Division 1 1980-81
Athenian 1969-70
London Senior Cup 1973-4
Herts Senior Cup (9)

PREVIOUS

Leagues: Stansted & Dist 1906-19.
Saffron Walden & District. East Herts 1896-97, 1902-06, 19-21.
Herts County 1921-25, 27-29.
Herts & Essex Border 1925-27. Spartan 1929-51.
Delphian 1951-63. Athenian 1963-73. Isthmian 1974-2004.

BRAINTREE TOWN

Back Row (L-R): Joe Bruce, Lee Patterson (manager), Sean Marks, Craig Holloway, Ben Chenery, Gareth Williams, Ryan Moran (part hidden), Louis Riddle, Ian Wiles, Derek Parnham (coach), Billy Burgess, James Hawes, Adrian Deane. **Front Row -** Samuel Mason & Toby Eldred (mascots), Bradley Quinton, Chris Piper, Mark Jones, Andy Porter, Dave Bryant, Micky Shinn, Lee Burns.

CLUB PERSONNEL

Chairman: Lee Harding.

Company Secretary: Bird Luckin.

Additional Directors: Kim Cowell, Vic Dixon,

Barry Shepherd, Alan Stuckey, Terry Thorogood.

Secretary: Tom Woodley

19A Bailey Bridge Road, Braintree, Essex CM7 5TT

(H): 01376 326 234

(M): 07950 537 179

tawoodley@btinternet.com

Commercial Manager: Alan Stuckey

Tel: (M) 07800 886 849

Press Officer: Lee Harding

(M): 07771 810 440

braintreetfc@aol.com

Manager: Robbie Garvey.

Club therapist: Steve Gracie.

Possibly taking their lead from some of the senior professional clubs, the Braintree Board shared managerial responsibilities with three leaders during the last campaign. The Blue Square South programme started with Lee Patterson in charge but a poor start to the season saw 'The Iron' in the bottom four after nine games with just one victory.

Kingstonian delivered a 4-0 F.A.Cup knockout blow, and just a few weeks later, Farnborough repeated the four goal deficit with a 6-2 F.A.Trophy drubbing. Bradley Quinton, a player/assistant manager took over and the league position certainly improved with a relatively safe mid-table position secured by January.

However, despite the reasonably consistent goalscoring of the experienced striker Danny Hockton, victories were still hard to achieve and obviously they weren't coming quickly enough for the chairman who brought in Robbie Garvey from the Dagenham & Redbridge back room staff to take over in April.

Safety was secured without too much trouble, although in the new year they could never achieve two successive victories. Many players have left the club giving the new manager a chance to build his own squad and no doubt he will be judged fairly quickly on their quality, probably after a couple of months next season. There is no doubt that a successful team at The Cressing Road Stadium will be well supported as an average crowd of over 500 a match supported 'The Iron' at home last season.

BRAINTREE

BEST LGE ATT.: 1,278 v Chelmsford City
LOWEST: 350 v Newport County

No.	Date	Comp	H/A	Opponents	Att:	Result	Goalscorers	Pos
1	Aug 9	BSS	H	Dorchester Town	515	L 0 - 1		
2	12		A	Welling United	519	L 0 - 1		
3	16		A	Maidenhead United	322	L 1 - 2	Riddle 16	
4	23		H	Hampton & Richmond B	451	L 1 - 2	Marks 25	21
5	25		A	Chelmsford City	1711	D 1 - 1	Burns 34	
6	30		H	TeamBath	497	W 4 - 1	Burns 1 Riddle 8 Marks 11 31	18
7	Sept 2		H	AFC Wimbledon	1123	L 0 - 1		
8	6		A	Eastleigh	525	L 1 - 2	Marks 9	18
9	**9**	**SS S1**	**H**	**Hampton & Richmond B**	**127**	**W 3 - 0**	**Williams 2, Burgess 32, Jeffrey 60 (og)**	
10	13		A	Worcester City	703	D 2 - 2	Marks 17 Williams 27	19
11	20		H	Bromley	482	W 2 - 0	Williams 36 67	16
12	**27**	**F.A.C. 2Q**	**A**	**Kingstonian**	**356**	**L 0 - 4**		
13	Oct 4		A	Hayes & Yeading	264	W 1 - 0	Marks 55	15
14	**6**	**SS S2**	**A**	**Chelmsford City**	**474**	**L 1 - 3**	**Williams 90**	
15	18		H	Newport County	350	W 3 - 2	Hockton 24 79 Burgess 45	15
16	21		H	Thurrock	449	L 1 - 2	Moran 32	
17	Nov 1		A	Bognor Regis Town	200	W 2 - 0	Williams 55 Burgess 66	12
18	8		H	Weston-s-Mare	423	D 1 - 1	Hockton 81	13
19	15		A	Basingstoke Town	250	D 2 - 2	Quinton 86 Riddle 83	15
20	**22**	**F.A.T 3Q**	**H**	**Farnborough**	**212**	**D 1 - 1**	**Hawes 16**	
21	**25**	**F.A.T.3Q r**	**A**	**Farnborough**	**321**	**L 2 - 6**	**Marks 37 Hawes 65**	
22	29		H	St Albans City	400	W 1 - 0	Marks 75	13
23	Dec 1		A	Havant & Waterlooville	453	D 1 - 1	Hawes 38	
24	6		H	Bath City	507	L 0 - 4		13
25	20		A	Dorchester Town	461	D 2 - 2	Williams 19 25	14
26	26		H	Bishop's Stortford	1003	W 2 - 0	Riddle 28 (pen) 71	13
27	Jan 1		A	Bishop's Stortford	1004	W 3 - 0	Piper 4 Williams 36 Burns 49	
28	17		H	Eastleigh	479	D 1 - 1	Hockton 57	12
29	24		A	AFC Wimbledon	3229	L 1 - 5	Hockton 41	12
30	26		A	Fisher Athletic	173	W 2 - 0	Hawes 5 Quinton 62 (pen)	
31	31		H	Bognor Regis Town	459	D 1 - 1	Marks 87	11
32	Feb 17		H	Maidenhead United	600	L 0 - 2		
33	21		A	Weston-super-Mare	254	L 1 - 3	Shinn 76	13
34	24		H	Havant & Waterlooville	414	W 1 - 0	Marks 64	
35	28		H	Welling United	556	D 1 - 1	Hockton 62	13
36	Mar 7		A	Newport County	714	L 1 - 2	Hockton 52	14
37	14		A	Bromley	449	W 4 - 1	Hockton 11 33 Porter 15 Riddle 84	13
38	17		H	Hayes & Yeading	465	L 0 - 1		
39	21		A	Team Bath	87	W 3 - 0	Hockton 39 45 Quinton 36 (pen))	12
40	24		H	Worcester City	425	D 1 - 1	Quinton 15 (pen)	
41	28		H	Basingstoke town	483	L 0 - 1		13
42	April 4		A	Bath City	486	L 2 - 3	Hockton 33 O'Sullivan 37	
43	7		H	Fisher Athletic	399	W 2 - 0	Riddle 29 (pen) Williams 40	
44	11		A	Hampton & Richmond B	650	L 1 - 2	Shinn 80	14
45	13		H	Chelmsford City	1278	L 1 - 2	Hockton 58	
46	18		A	St Albans City	385	W 3 - 0	Hawes 16 Hockton 64 Williams 74	14
47	21		A	Thurrock	255	L 0 - 1		14

Average Home Att: 560 (582) **Goals** 64 68

Best Position: 11th **Worst:** 21st

Goalscorers: Hockton 14, Williams 11, Marks 10, Riddle 7, Hawes 5, Quinton 4, Burgess 3, Burns 3, Shinn 2, Moran 1, O'Sullivan 1, Piper 1, Porter 1. Own Goals 1.

HOLLOWAY	BURGESS	HAWES	BRUCE	CHENERY	B QUINTON	SHINN	PIPER	BURNS	BRYANT	RIDDLE	GRAZIOLI	O'SULLIVAN	MARKS	DEANE	MORAN	WILES	PORTER	JONES	WILLIAMS	ANGUS	OVERALL	TEK	HOCKTON	PALMER	ROGET	HAVERSON	MCLAREN	LASKOWSKI	J JONES	MORGAN	SHIPTON	COOK	BUNAMI	D QUINTON	FINCH	
X	X	X	X	X	X	X	X	X	X	X	S	S	S	U	U																					1
X	X	U	X	X		U	X	X	S	X	X	X	S	U		X	X																			2
X	X	U	U			X	X	X	S	X	X	S	X		X	X		X	S																	3
X	X	X	X			X	X	X		X	S	S	X	U	X	U			X	U																4
X	X	X	X		U	X	X	X		X	S	X	X		X	U	U		S																	5
X		X	X		S	X	X	X		X	S	X	X		X		U	S	U	X																6
X	X	X	X		U	X	X	X		X	S	X	X		X		S	U	S																	7
X	X	X	X		X	X	X	X			S	X	X		X	U	S	S	U																	8
X	**X**	**X**	**X**		**X**		**X**	**X**			**S**	**X**	**X**	**U**	**X**	**U**	**S**	**S**	**X**																	**9**
X	X	X	X		X		X	X		S		X	X	U	X		S	U	X	S																10
X		X	X		X	U	X	X		X		X	X	S			X		X	U	U	U														11
X		**X**	**X**		**X**	**U**	**X**	**X**		**X**		**X**	**X**	**S**	**U**		**X**	**U**	**X**				**S**	**S**												**12**
X	X	X	X		X	S	X			X		U	X	S	X		X	U	U				X													13
X	**X**	**X**	**X**		**X**	**U**	**X**			**X**		**X**	**X**	**U**	**X**		**X**	**U**	**S**		**U**															**14**
X	X	X	X		U	X	X	X		S			X	U	X		U	X	S				X													15
X	X	X	X		S	X	X	X		S			X		X			X	S				X													16
X	X	X	X		S	X	X	X		X		S	S		X		U	U	X				X													17
X	X	U	X		S	X	X	X		X		S	U		X			X	X				X		S											18
X	X				X	X	X	U		X		U	U		X		U	X	X				X		X											19
X	**X**	**X**	**X**		**X**	**X**	**X**	**U**				**S**	**S**		**S**		**U**	**X**	**X**				**X**		**X**											**20**
X	**X**	**X**	**X**		**X**	**U**	**X**	**X**		**X**		**U**	**X**		**S**			**X**	**U**				**U**		**X**											**21**
X	X	X	U		X	X	S	X		X		X	X				U	X	S				X	U												22
X	X	X	S		X	X	S	X		X		X	X		U		S	X	U				X													23
X	X	X			X	X	S	X		X		X	X				S	X	S				X													24
X	X		X		X		X	X				X	X		X		U	U	X				X			S	U	U								25
X	X	S	X		X		X	X		X		X	X		X		U	S	X				U			U										26
X	X	S	X		X		X	X		X		U	X		X		U	U	X				X			U										27
X	X	S	X		X	S	X	X		X			X		X		U	U	X				X			U										28
X	X	S	X		X	S	X	X		X			X		X		U	S	X				X			U										29
X	X	X	U		X	X	X	U				X	X		X		S	X	S				X			U										30
X	X	X	S		X	X	X			S		X	X		X		U	S	X				X			U										31
X	X	X	X					X				S	X				X	X	X				X			X	U		S	U						32
X	X	X	S			X	S	X				U	X		X		X	X	S				X			X				U						33
X	X	X	X		X	X	S	X				U	X		X		X	X	U				S							U						34
X	X	X	X		X	X	S	X				S	X		X		X	X	U				S							U						35
X	X				X	X		X		U		S	X		X		X		X				X							U	X	S	U			36
X	X		X		X		X			X		S	S		X		X		X				X							U	X	U	S			37
X	X		X		X		X	S		X		U	S		X		X		X				X							U	X		U			38
X	X		X		X	S	X	X		X		S	X		X		X		S				X							U	U					39
X	X		X		X	S	X	X		X		U	X		X		X	S	S				X							U						40
X	X	U	X		X	X	X	X		X		U	X		X			S	S				X											S		41
X	X	X	X		U	S	X	X		X		S	S		X			X	X				X							U						42
X	X	S	X		X	S	U	X		X		X	X		X			X	X											U				U		43
X	X	X	X		X	X	S			X		X			X			S	X				X				U			U				S		44
X	X	X	X		U	X	X						U		X		U	X	X				X				S			U				X		45
U	X	X			X	X	X	X							X		U	X	X				X				S			X				S	S	46
U	X	X	X		X	X	S					X			X		U	X	X				X				U			X					U	47

Total League Appearances

40	40	26	32	2	28	26	31	33	1	27	2	17	30	0	35	2	12	18	22	1	0	0	28	0	1	2	0	0	0	2	3	0	0	1	0	**X**
0	0	5	3	0	4	7	8	1	2	4	6	11	6	2	0	0	6	8	12	1	0	0	2	0	1	1	2	0	1	0	0	1	1	3	1	**S**
2	0	4	3	0	5	2	1	2	0	1	0	8	3	5	2	3	15	7	6	2	1	1	1	1	0	6	4	1	0	13	1	1	2	1	1	**U**

Total Cup Appearances

5	4	5	5	0	5	1	5	3	0	3	0	3	4	0	2	0	2	2	3	0	0	0	1	0	2	0	0	0	0	0	0	0	0	0	0	**X**
0	0	0	0	0	0	0	0	0	0	0	1	1	1	1	2	0	1	1	1	0	0	0	1	1	0	0	0	0	0	0	0	0	0	0	0	**S**
0	0	0	0	0	0	3	0	1	0	0	0	1	0	2	1	1	1	2	1	0	1	0	1	0	0	0	0	0	0	0	0	0	0	0	0	**U**

BRAINTREE TOWN

CURRENT SQUAD AS OF BEGINING OF 2009-10 SEASON

GOALKEEPERS	HT	WT	D.O.B	AGE	P.O.B	CAREER	Apps	Gls
Nathan McDonald						Braintree		
Nick Morgan	6'07"					West Ham (Yth), Southend (Scholar) Rel c/s 05, Braintree 7/05 Rel 5/08, Crawley 7/08 Rel 10/08, Braintree 2/09, Eastleigh (EL) 4/09	2	0
DEFENDERS								
Adam Bailey-Dennis						Colchester, Felixstowe & W (WE) 1/09, Braintree 5/09		
Joe Bruce	6'00"	12 00	5/7/83	26	London	Luton Rel c/s 02, Wingate & Finchley (SL) 1/02, Molesey, Hitchin 3/03, Grays 8/03 Rel 5/06, Maidenhead (2ML) 1/06, Basingstoke 6/06, Welling 3/07, Cambridge C 6/07, Braintree 7/08	35	0
Lynvall Duncan						Clapton, Ashford T (Kent), Leatherhead 12/05, Billericay 9/08, Braintree 5/09		
Andrew Howell	5'11"	12 01	18/3/89	20	Great Yarmouth	Norwich (Yth), QPR Rel c/s 08, Wealdstone (SL) 2/08, Tooting & M c/s 08, Braintree 6/09		
Mark Jones						Burnham Ramblers, Billericay, Romford, Braintree 2/00		
Ryan Moran			31/3/82	27		Luton, St Albans 3/00, Boreham Wood 8/03, Braintree 2/08	35	1
Ryan Peters			21/8/87	22		Brentford (Sch), Windsor & E (2ML) 9/04, Gravesend (L) 12/04, Crawley (L) 11/06, AFC Wimbledon (L) 3/07, Margate 1/08, Braintree 5/09		
MIDFIELDERS								
Matt Game			24/3/85	24	Upney	L.Orient (Scholar) Rel c/s 04, Braintree (2ML) 11/03, Billericay 7/04, Braintree 5/09		
Jacob Mingle						Charlton (Yth), C.Palace (Yth), Kingston Youth Academy, Staines c/s 04, Ashford T (Middx) (2ML) 12/04 Perm 2/05 Rel 10/06, Horsham 11/06, Eastbourne B Undisc 2/09 Rel 5/09, Braintree 6/09		
George Purcell	5'11"	11 09	8/4/88	21	Gravesend	Gillingham, Gravesend/Ebbsfleet 8/06, Heybridge (L) 9/07, Ramsgate (L) 2/09, Braintree 5/09		
Phil Starkey	6'00"	12 06	10/9/87	21	Dartford	C.Palace Rel c/s 07, Ebbsfleet 8/07, Tonbridge A (L) 1/08 Perm, Ebbsfleet (Trial) 7/09, Braintree 8/09		
Tommy Tejan-Sie	5'06"	11 08	23/11/88	20	London	Arsenal (Yth), Leicester (Yth), Dag & Red, Wingate & F (L) 8/07, Billericay (L) 3/08, Braintree (L) 7/09		
FORWARDS								
Leon Antoine						Maldon T, Aveley 12/06, Tilbury 3/07, Boreham Wood, Redbridge, Canvey Island 7/08, Braintree c/s 09		
Sean Marks					Essex	Heybridge, Braintree £1,000 5/08	36	9
Bradley Quinton						Hornchurch, Aveley, Romford, Bishops Stortford, Braintree 1/00 Temp Man 10/07	32	4

DEPARTURES	HT	WT	DOB	AGE	POB	From - To	APPS	GOA
(D)Ben Chenery	6'01"	12 03	28/1/77	32	Ipswich	Chelmsford 3/08 - Rel 8/08, Needham Market 8/08	2	0
(F)David Bryant			9/6/82	27		Thurrock 5/08 - Rel 8/08, Thurrock 8/08	3	0
(D)Stevland Angus	6'00"	12 00	16/9/80	28	Westminster	ex Fisher 8/08 - Concord R 9/08, Bishops Stortford 2/09	2	0
(F)Giuliano Grazioli	5'10"	12 00	23/3/75	34	Marylebone	Barnet 8/08 - Dover 9/08 Rel 5/09	8	0
(G)Paul Rutherford			12/11/84	24	Bury St Edmonds	Halstead T 6/08 - Wivenhoe 9/08		
(M)Robbie Martin			29/12/84	24		Watford 5/04 - Havant & W 10/08		
(D)Leo Roget						Harlow 11/08 - Rel 11/08, Rushden & D 11/08	2	0
(D)Ian Wiles	6'00"	11 09	28/4/80	29	Woodford	Heybridge 5/08 - AFC Hornchurch, Heybridge 12/08 Rel 2/09	2	0
(M)Adrian Deane			24/2/83	26		Erith & B 1/08 - Billericay (L) 10/08, Erith & B 1/09, Billericay 3/09	2	0
(D)Jack Haverson	6'02"	10 12	12/9/87	21	Sidcup	Sittingbourne 12/08 - Margate 3/09	3	0
(F)Danny Hockton	5'11"	11 11	7/2/79	30	Barking	Bromley Undisc 9/08 - Rel 5/09, Chelmsford 6/09	30	14
(F)Wayne O'Sullivan			12/12/84	24	Brent	Stevenage 6/08 - Rel 5/09, Hendon 6/09	28	1
(M)Chris Piper			20/10/81	27	London	Eastleigh 7/08 - Rel 5/09	39	1
(F)Gareth Williams	5'10"	11 13	10/9/82	26	Germiston	Bromley 5/08 - Rel 5/09, Bromley 6/09	34	9
(M)Mickey Shinn						Heybridge £1,500 9/07 - Rel 5/09, Billericay 5/09	33	2
(M)Billy Burgess						Welling, Braintree 6/04 Rel 5/09, Dartford 6/09	40	2
(F)Louis Riddle	5'11"	12 00	29/8/82	27	Harlow	Cambridge C 6/04 - Rel 5/09, Bishop Stortford 5/09	31	7
(M)James Hawes			7/8/85	24	London	Leyton 10/05 - Sutton U 5/09	31	3
(M)Lee Burns						East Thurrock 10/07 - Dartford 6/09	34	3
(D)Danny Shipton						Yth - Haverhill 7/09	3	0
(D)Anthony Cook	5'07"	11 02	10/8/89	20	London	Concord R 3/09 - Chelmsford 7/09	1	0
(G)Craig Holloway			10/8/84	25	Blackheath	Bromley 5/08 - Chelmsford 7/09	40	0
(M)Darren Quinton	5'08"	9 11	28/4/86	23	Romford	Cambridge U 3/09 - St Albans 8/09	4	0
(G)Harry Laskowsi						Yth -	0	0
(G)Ricky Palmer						Yth -	0	0
(D)Luke Overall						Yth -	0	0
(M)Frank Bunami						Yth -	1	0
(M)Andy Porter					Essex	St Margaretsbury 2/03 -	18	1
(F)Jack Jones						Yth -	1	0
Finch						Yth -	1	0
Ross Mclaren						Yth -	2	0
Tekan Tek						Yth -	0	0

BRAINTREE TOWN

Formed: 1898
Nickname: The Iron.
Club Colours: Yellow shirts, yellow shorts, yellow socks.
Change Colours: Blue shirts,blue shorts, blue socks.
Club Sponsor: WestDrive
Previous League: Isthmian League

Ground address: The Cressing Road Stadium, Clockhouse Way, Braintree, Essex CM7 3RD.

Telephone: 01376 345 617

Fax: 01376 330 976

Email: braintreetfc@aol.com

Website: www.braintreetownfc.org.uk

Simple Directions: From Braintree by-pass, turn into Braintree at the Galleys Corner roundabout. Ground is sign-posted and three quarters of a mile on left. Entrance in Clockhouse Way.

Capacity: 4,000 **Seats:** 550 **Covered:** 1,769 Floodlights: Yes

Clubhouse: Open evenings and mid day at weekends

Club Shop: Yes.

Local Radio: BBC Essex and Essex Radio

PROGRAMME EDITOR

Lee Harding
Email: braintreetfc@aol.com

CLUB STATISTICS

RECORDS
Attendance: 4,000 v Spurs Testimonial May 1952
Victory: 12-0 v Thetford (Eastern League) 1935-3
Defeat :0-14 v Chelmsford City (A) N. Essex Lg.1923
Goalscorer: **Career:** Chris Guy 211 1963-90
Season Gary Bennett 57 97-98
Career Appearances: Paul Young 524 (1966-77)
Transfer Fee Paid: to Hornchurch for Danny Gay.
Received: £10,000 from Brentford for Matt Metcalf and from Colchester United for John Cheesewright

SENIOR HONOURS
Isthmian Champions 2005-06,
Eastern Counties (3)
East Anglian Cup (3)
Essex Senior Cup 95-96

PREVIOUS
Leagues: N.Essex 1898-1925, Essex & Suffolk Border,25-29 55-64, Spartan 28-35, Eastern Co. 35-37 38-39 52-55 70-91 Essex Co: 37-38 London 45-52 Gt London 64-66 Metropolitan 66-70 and Southern 91-96 Isthmian 1996-06.
Grounds: The Fair Field 1898-1903, Spaldings Meadow & Panfield Lane

BROMLEY

Photo: edboydenphotos.co.uk

CLUB PERSONNEL

CLUB PERSONNEL

Chairman: Paul Greenwood.

Company Secretary: Mike Coles.

Secretary: Colin Russell

2A New Road,South Darenth Dartford, Kent, DA4 9AR

(H): 01322 865 936

(M): 07970 031 511

Email: colin.russell@thefa.com

Commercial Manager: Jeremy Dolke.

Tel: (B) 020 8460 5291.

Email: jerry@bromleyfc.co.uk

Press Officer: Jeff Hutton.

Tel: (M) 07702 162 240

Wmail: info@bromleyfc.com

Manager: Mark Goldberg.

Club therapist: Sam Paterson.

One of the most attractive Blue Square sides in recent seasons, Bromley's off field administrative situation and budget cuts threatened to affect the clubs' progress, but with Mark Goldberg in charge for the 2008-2009 campaign, supporters had high hopes for an exciting challenge for honours.

An unspectacular start saw 'The Lillywhites' in mid-table and out of the F.A.Cup by the beginning of October, having lost at home to A.F.C.Hornchurch. Consistency seemed to be lacking, but by the time Bromley had been knocked out of the F.A.Trophy, in their first tie at Swindon Supermarine, they had managed to move up to tenth position in the table and hopes were high for the second half of the campaign.

The signing of Warren McBean proved a great success and the speedy striker finished the season with 21 goals with back up from Ryan Hall with eleven. Although the second half of the season saw more goals and more points, consistency was never a strength and there were only seven well spaced out victories.

Their average home attendance was over 500 in a relatively unspectacular season, and a Bromley side fighting for honours could probably attract twice that each week. The financial situation at the club will probably dictate.

BROMLEY

BEST LGE ATT.: **2,177** v AFC Wimbledon
LOWEST: **206** v Bognor Regis Town

No.	Date	Comp	H/A	Opponents	Att:	Result	Goalscorers	Pos
1	Aug 9	BSS	H	Maidenhead United	438	L 1 - 2	Fazackerley 5	
2	12		A	Bishop's Stortford	404	D 1 - 1	Toppin 41	
3	16		A	Havant & Waterlooville	622	W 1 - 0	Fazackerley 16	11
4	23		H	Eastleigh	466	W 5 - 1	Corneille 29 43 **McBean** 51 Hockton 66 77	8
5	25		A	AFC Wimbledon	3149	L 1 - 3	Hockton 62	
6	30		H	Worcester City	505	L 0 - 2		13
7	Sept 2		H	Chelmsford City	527	D 2 - 2	Fazackerlay 5 Hall 45	
8	6		A	Hampton & Richmond B	517	D 1 - 1	Harper 38 (og)	14
9	**9**	**SS S1**	**A**	**Bishops Stortford**	**201**	**L 1 - 2**	**Fazackerley 60**	
10	13		H	Weston-s-Mare	345	W 3 - 0	Obaze 47 Hockton 55 83	11
11	20		A	Braintree Town	482	L 0 - 2		12
12	**27**	**F.A.C. 2Q**	**H**	**AFC Hornchurch**	**581**	**L 0 - 1**		
13	Oct 4		A	Newport County	746	L 0 - 3		14
14	11		A	Chelmsford City	1102	W 1 - 0	Fazackerley 68	12
15	18		H	Basingstoke Town	467	L 0 - 2		14
16	21		A	Bognor Regis Town	255	D 1 - 1	**McBean** 9	
17	Nov 1		H	St Albans City	373	L 2 - 3	McDonnell 60 90	14
18	8		A	Bath City	520	W 3 - 1	**McBean** 2 67 L'Anson 36	12
19	15		A	Team Bath	130	W 3 - 0	McDonnell 42 **McBean** 57 87	12
20	18		H	Hayes & Yeading	317	L 0 - 1	**McBean** 21	
21	**22**	**F.A.T 3Q**	**A**	**Swindon Supermarine**	**229**	**L 0 - 1**		
22	29		H	Thurrock	427	D 3 - 3	Hall 24 **McBean** 37 90	10
23	Dec 6		A	Fisher Athletic	330	W 2 - 0	McDonnell 22 Hall 89	10
24	20		A	Maidenhead United	364	L 0 - 4		11
25	26		H	Welling United	739	L 1 - 3	**McBean** 37	11
26	Jan 1		A	Welling United	1255	D 2 - 2	Hall 63 Sheringham 70 (og)	
27	3		H	Havant & Waterlooville	447	D 2 - 2	Hall 29 **McBean** 90	12
28	17		A	St Albans City	514	W 5 - 4	Hall 22 **McBean** 29 74 Stone 31 L'Anson 85	10
29	24		H	Dorchester Town	423	W 1 - 0	**McBean** 38	10
30	27		A	Basingstoke Town	245	L 0 - 2		
31	31		H	Hampton & Richmond B	382	L 0 - 2		10
32	Feb 14		A	Worcester City	635	L 0 - 1		12
33	21		H	Newport County	561	W 2 - 1	Gillman 7 Hall 89	11
34	24		H	Bognor Regis Town	206	W 1 - 0	**McBean** 43 (pen)	
35	28		A	Thurrock	320	D 1 - 1	Hall 13	10
36	Mar 7		H	Fisher Athletc	471	W 3 - 1	**McBean** 39 73 Chabban 56	9
37	14		H	Braintree Town	449	L 1 - 4	Robinson 90	10
38	21		A	Weston-s-Mare	305	L 1 - 2	L'Anson 36	11
39	24		H	Bishop's Stortford	259	W 1 - 0	**McBean** 60	
40	28		H	Bath City	505	D 1 - 1	Harding 47	11
41	April 4		A	Hayes & Yeading	301	L 1 - 2	Hall 89	11
42	10		A	Eastleigh	937	L 0 - 1		13
43	13		H	AFC Wimbledon	2177	D 2 - 2	Hall 56 90	
44	18		H	Team Bath	410	W 4 - 0	Beaney 16 **McBean** 46 62 Stone 68	13
45	25		A	Dorchester Town	558	L 1 - 2	**McBean** 2 (pen)	13

Average Home Att: 519 (632) **Goals** 61 69

Best Position: 9th **Worst:** 14th

Goalscorers: McBean 21, Hall 11, Fazackerley 5, Hockton 5, McDonnell 4, L'Anson 3, Cornielle 2, Stone 2, Beaney 1, Chabban 1, Gillman 1, Harding 1, Obaze 1, Robinson 1, Toppin 1. Own Goals 1.

WILLIAMS	I'ANSON	HAVERSON	TOPPIN	CLARK	GILLMAN	JOSEPH	MURRAY	HOCKTON	MCDONNELL	FAZACKERLEY	OBAZE	MCBEAN	DAVIS	MANNING	MAY	CORNEILLE	EVERITT	NORVAL	O'SULLIVAN	ANDERSON	SWAIBU	HALL	JOHN	SOBERS	MANN	HARDING	MANUELLA	LAYIWOLA	ROBINSON	DOLBY	STONE	CROOK	WATTS	LEDGISTER	MYERS	CHAABAN	DALHOUSE	ZANZI	BEANEY	FRAY	PAKASA	
X	X	X	X	X	X	X	X	X	X	X	S	S	U	U	U																											**1**
X	X	X	X	X	X	S	S	X	X	X	X	S	U		U	X																										**2**
X	X	U	X	X	X	X	U	U	X	X	X	X	U		S	X																										**3**
X	X	U	X	X	X	X	S	S	X		X	X	S			X	X	U																								**4**
X	X	U	X	X	X	X	S	S	X		X	X	S			X	X	U																								**5**
X	X	X	X	X	X		X	X				X				X	X		S	U																						**6**
X	X	U	X	X		S				X		X	U		X	X	X		S	U	X	X																				**7**
X	X	U	X	X	X			S		X		X	U		X	X	X		S		S	X																				**8**
X		**U**		**X**	**X**			**X**		**X**	**X**	**X**	**U**		**X**	**X**		**U**		**U**	**X**	**X**	**S**																			**9**
X	S				X	U		X	U	X	X	X	U			X			X	X	X	X	S																			**10**
X	X		U		X	S		X	S	X	X	X					U	U		X	X	X																				**11**
X	**X**		**X**		**X**	**S**			**X**	**X**	**X**	**X**				**U**	**X**	**U**	**X**		**X**	**S**		**S**	**U**																	**12**
X	X			U	X	X			X	X		X		U		X	X		S	U	X			X		S																**13**
X	X			X	X	S			X	X	U					X	X	U	X		S			X			X	U														**14**
X	X			X	X	S				X		S				X		U	X	X	X			X			X	U	S													**15**
X	X			X	X	U	X			X		X			X	S	X		S		S			X			U		X													**16**
X	X				X	S	X		X		U	X				X		U			X	X		X			X		S	U												**17**
X	X				X	S			X			X	U					X			X	X		X	U		U		X	X	S											**18**
X	X				X				X			X	X					X			X			X			S		X	X	S											**19**
X	X				X	U			X			X	U			S		X			X	X		X			S		X	X	S											**20**
X					**X**	**S**			**X**			**X**	**U**			**X**					**X**	**X**		**X**		**S**	**X**	**S**	**X**	**X**	**U**											**21**
X	X				X				X		U	X				S		X			X	X		X		S	U		X	X	S											**22**
X	X				X				X		U	X	U					X			X	X		X		S			X	X	S	S										**23**
X	X				X				X		U	X	U					X				X	S	X					X	X	U	X	S									**24**
X	X				X				X		U	X	X					X				X		X		S			X	X	U	U	S									**25**
X									X		X		U	U		X		X				X		X		X			X	X	S	X	S									**26**
X											X	X	U	U		X		X			X	X		X		X			X	U	S	U	X									**27**
X	X				X							X	S	U		X		X				X		X		S		S	X	X	X			U								**28**
X	X				X							X	U			X		X				X	U			S			X	X	X			U	X	S						**29**
X	X				X						U	X	U			X		X				X	U			X			X	X	U				X	U						**30**
X	X				X						X	X	U			X						X	U			S			X	X	X			U	X	S						**31**
X					X						U	X	S			X						X	U			U				X	X					S	X	X	X			**32**
X	X				X						U	X	U									X		X				U	X	S	U					X	X		X	X		**33**
X	X				X							X				X		S				X		X		U			S	S						X	X	U	X	X		**34**
X	X				X						U	X	U			X		X				X				U			S	X	S					X	X		X			**35**
X	X				X							X	U					S				X		X					X	S	S					X	X	U	X		X	**36**
X	X				X							X	U					X				X		X		S			S	X	S					X		X	X		U	**37**
X	X				X							X	S	U		U		X				X		X		X			X	X	S					X					U	**38**
X	X				X							X	S	U		S		X				X		X		X			U	X	X					X					U	**39**
X	X				X							X	S			S		X				X		X		X			S	X	X					X						**40**
X	X				X							X				X		U				X		X		S			S	U	X					X	S		X	X		**41**
X					X						S	S	U	U		X						X		X					X	X	X					X	X		S	X		**42**
X	S				X							S		U				S				X		X					X	X	X					X	X		X	X	U	**43**
X					X						U	X	X	U				X				X				S				S	X					X	X		X	X	S	**44**
X					X							X	U			X		U				X		X		X			S	S	X					X	X		X		S	**45**
Total League Appearances																																										
42	34	3	8	11	39	5	4	5	16	11	9	35	3	0	3	24	8	18	3	3	12	31	0	26	0	7	3	0	19	20	11	2	1	0	3	13	9	2	10	6	1	**X**
0	2	0	0	0	0	7	3	3	1	0	2	5	7	0	1	5	0	3	5	0	3	0	2	0	0	10	2	1	8	5	11	1	3	0	0	3	1	0	1	0	2	**S**
0	0	5	1	1	0	3	1	1	1	0	11	0	21	10	2	1	1	8	0	3	0	0	4	0	1	3	3	3	1	3	4	2	0	3	0	1	0	2	0	0	4	**U**
Total Cup Appearances																																										
3	1	0	1	1	3	0	0	1	2	2	2	3	0	0	1	2	1	0	1	0	3	2	0	1	0	0	1	0	1	1	0	0	0	0	0	0	0	0	0	0	0	**X**
0	0	0	0	0	0	2	0	0	0	0	0	0	0	0	0	0	0	0	0	0	0	1	1	1	0	1	0	1	0	0	0	0	0	0	0	0	0	0	0	0	0	**S**
0	0	1	0	0	0	0	0	0	0	0	0	0	2	0	0	1	0	2	0	1	0	0	0	0	1	0	0	0	0	0	1	0	0	0	0	0	0	0	0	0	0	**U**

Also Played: SIMPSON S(6). SHAW S(6). BELL U(6). KUDJODJI X(11). HART S(19).

BROMLEY

CURRENT SQUAD AS OF BEGINING OF 2009-10 SEASON

GOALKEEPERS	HT	WT	D.O.B	AGE	P.O.B	CAREER	Apps	Gls
Gareth Williams						Corinthian C, Horsham 8/06, Sutton U 8/07, Croydon A 1/08, Bromley 2/08	42	0

DEFENDERS	HT	WT	D.O.B	AGE	P.O.B	CAREER	Apps	Gls
Mark Corneille	5'07"	10 05	31/5/86	23	London	Gillingham Rel c/s 06, Eastbourne B (2ML) 12/05, Folkestone I (L) 2/06, Bromley c/s 06	29	2
Aaron Dalhouse			22/9/89	19		C.Palace Rel 2/09, Bournemouth (Trial) 12/08, Bromley 2/09	10	0
Harrison Dunk						Bromley		
Arron Fray						Bromley	6	0
Rob Gillman	6'02"	13 08	26/4/84	25	London	Luton, Enfield (L) 3/03, Ashford T (Middx) 8/03, Bishops Stortford 7/04, Ashford T (Middx) 7/07, Bishops Stortford 12/07, Bromley 5/08	39	1
Tutu Henriques					Zimbabwe	University of Luton, Carshalton c/s 02, Bromley 7/04		
Liam Norval			7/10/87	21	Cardiff	West Ham (Jun), Newcastle (Trial) 2/04, Leicester (Jun) Rel c/s 06, Cambridge U 10/06 Rel 10/06, Thurrock 1/07 Rel 9/07, Bromley 8/08	21	0
Donal O'Sullivan						Welling, Southall, Ashford T, Southall, Dartford 1/05, Southall, Bromley 2/06, Out Injured, Bromley 7/08 Rel 10/08, Bromley 8/09	8	0
Jerome Sobers	6'02"	13 05	18/4/86	23	London	Ford U, Ipswich 2/04 Rel c/s 05, Brentford (L) 3/05, Chelmsford 7/05, Bromley 10/06, Braintree 7/07 Rel 10/07, Bromley 10/07	26	0

MIDFIELDERS	HT	WT	D.O.B	AGE	P.O.B	CAREER	Apps	Gls
Ashley Carew	6'00"	11 00	17/12/85	23	Lambeth	Gillingham (Jun), Welling (L) 9/04, Maidstone (L) 10/04, Worthing (L) 11/04, Aveley (L) 8/05 Bromley 12/05 Rel 1/06, Sutton U 2/06, Beckenham 7/06, Fisher 1/07, Beckenham (Dual) 2/07, Barnet 5/07 Rel 3/09, Eastleigh (2ML) 1/09, Eastleigh 3/09, Bromley 6/0		
Ryan Dolby						Bromley	25	0
Nicky Greene						Yeading, Walton & H (L) 10/06, Sutton U 7/07 Rel 6/08, Thurrock 8/08 Rel 9/08, Fisher 10/08, Bromley 8/09		
Ryan Hall	5'10"	10 04	4/1/88	21	Dulwich	C.Palace Rel 5/08, Lewes (L) 12/06, Dag & Red (2ML) 1/08, Crawley (SL) 3/08, Bromley 9/08	31	11
Salifou Ibrahima						Bromley 8/09		
Luke I'Anson			2/8/88	21		Athletico De Coin (Sp) Rel c/s 07, Bromley 11/07	36	3

FORWARDS	HT	WT	D.O.B	AGE	P.O.B	CAREER	Apps	Gls
Marcus Cassius						Erith T, Bromley 8/09		
Warren McBean			13/2/86	23	London	Watford (Jun), Broxbourne B, Barnet 7/04, Waltham Forest (L) 3/05, Farnborough 8/05 Rel 8/06, Braintree 8/06 Rel 10,06, St Albans 10/06 Rel 10/06, Sutton U 10/06, Eastleigh (2ML) 2/08, Bromley 6/08	40	21
Gareth Williams	5'10"	11 13	10/9/82	26	Germiston	C.Palace, Colchester (2ML) 1/03, Cambridge U (L) 10/03, Bournemouth (L) 2/04, Colchester (SL) 3/04, Colchester P/E 9/04 Rel 5/06, Blackpool (SL) 3/06, Yeovil (Trial) 8/06, Bromley 9/06, Weymouth 9/06, Basingstoke 10/06, Bromley 10/06, Braintree 5/08 Rel 5/09, Bromley 6/09		

DEPARTURES	HT	WT	DOB	AGE	POB	From - To	APPS	GOA
(F)Omari Coleman	5'11"	11 13	23/11/80	28	Birmingham	Welling 3/08 - Croydon Ath Rel 9/08, Fisher 10/08, Hayes & Yeading 12/08 Rel 2/09, Kingstonian 3/09		
Nathan Simpson						Potters Bar, Dulwich H 1/09, Met Police 3/09	1	0
(F)Danny Hockton	5'11"	11 11	7/2/79	30	Barking	Margate 6/07 - Braintree Undisc 9/08 Rel 5/09, Chelmsford 6/09	8	5
(D)Jack Haverson	6'02"	10 12	12/9/87	21	Sidcup	Sittingbourne 12/08 - Margate 3/09	3	0
(M)Adrian Toppin						Staines 5/08 - Carshalton	8	1
(M)Louis Bell						Lewes 10/08 Rel 12/08, Croydon Ath 12/08	0	0
(F)Ben Kudjodji	6'00"	11 11	23/4/89	20	Luton	C.Palace 9/08 - Croydon A 9/08 Rel 9/08, Cheltenham (Reserves)	1	0
(F)Jay May						Dartford Tribunal 6/08 - Ramsgate (L) 9/08, Ramsgate 10/08, Dartford 3/09	4	0
(M)Steve Clark	6'01"	12 05	10/2/82	27	London	Weymouth 8/07 - Rel 10/08, Eastleigh 10/08	11	0
Ijah Anderson							3	0
(M)Louis Fazackerley			24/7/84	25	Winchester	Bishops Stortford 5/08 - Welling 10/08	11	4
(D)Adam Everitt			28/6/82	27	Hemel Hempstead	AFC Hornchurch 8/08 - St Albans 11/08	8	0
(M)Anthony Joseph						Ashford T (Middx) 5/08 - Rel 12/08, Kingstonian 12/08, Ashford Town (Middx) 3/09	12	0
Fiston Manuella						AFC Hornchurch 10/08 - Rel 12/08	5	0
Patric Layiwola						Rel 12/08	1	0
(F)Nic McDonnell			2/5/81	28	Surrey	AFC Wimbledon 5/08 - Break from playing 1/09	17	4
(D)Moses Swaibu	6'02"	11 11	9/5/89	20	Croydon	C.Palace 9/08 - Lincoln C 1/09	15	0
(M)Kirk Watts			9/2/79	30		Croydon A 12/08 - Tooting 1/09, Tonbridge A 6/09	4	0
(M)Karl Murray	5'11"	12 06	26/8/82	27	London	Eastleigh 6/08 - Sutton U (L) 9/08, Ebbsfleet (2ML) 11/08, Northwich (L) 1/09, Croydon Ath 2/09	7	0
(D)David Obaze						Southend 8/08 - Rel 5/09	11	1
(F)Jacob Erskine	6'01"	13 06	13/1/89	20	London	Dag & Red 6/09 - Gillingham 8/09		
(G)Neale Manning						Ashford T c/s 08 -	0	0
(D)Theo Davis			30/4/88	21		Aldershot T (Reserves) 11/07 -	10	0
(D)Daniel Pakasa						Royal White Stars Woluwe (Bel) 3/09 -	3	0
(D)Vincenzo Zanzi						Virtus Castelfranco (Ita) 2/09 - Ramsgate (Dual) 3/09	2	0
(M)Kenny Beaney			27/7/86	23		Thurrock 2/09 -	11	1
(M)Harry Harding						Yth -	17	1
(M)Alistair John	6'00"	14 00	23/11/87	21		Stevenage 9/08 -	2	0
(F)Ali Chaaban			16/3/82	27	Lebanon	Break from Football 1/09 - Staines (Dual) 4/09	16	0
(F)Ashley-Paul Robinson	5'09"	14 01	5/12/89	19	Croydon	C.Palace 10/08 -	27	1
Ryan Myers						Yth -	3	0
Marvin Ledgister						Yth -	0	0
Billy Crook						Yth -	3	0
Joe Hart						Yth -	1	0
Adrian Stone						Walton & H 10/08 -	22	2
Matthew Mann							0	0
Jamie Shaw							1	0

BROMLEY

Formed: 1892

Nickname: The Lillywhites.

Club Colours: White shirts, black shorts, black socks.

Change Colours: Red shirts, shorts and socks.

Club Sponsor: Networkers MSB

Previous League: Isthmian League

Ground address: The Stadium, Hayes Lane, Bromley, Kent BR2 9EF

Telephone: 020 8460 5291

Mobile: 07970 031 511

Fax: 020 8313 3992

Email: info@bromleyfc.net

Website: www.bromleyfc.net

Simple Directions: M25 Jct4 then A21 towards London.

Capacity: 5,000 **Seats**: 1,300 **Covered:** 2,500 **Floodlights**: Yes

Clubhouse: Open Matchdays

Club Shop: Yes.

Local Radio: Radio Kent, Bromley Local Radio

Local Press: Bromley Times, South London Press.

no image available

PROGRAMME EDITOR

Jeff Hutton

(M) 07702 162 240

Email: info@bromleyfc.net

CLUB STATISTICS

RECORDS

Attendance : 10,798 v Nigeria 1950.

Victory: 13-1 v Redhill Athenian Lg. 1945-46

Defeat: 1-11 v Barking Athenian Lg. 1933-34

Career Goalscorer: George Brown 570 (1938-61)

Career Appearances: George Brown

Record Transfer Fee Paid: Unknown

Record Transfer Fee Received: £ 50,000 from Millwall for John Goodman.

SENIOR HONOURS

Isthmian Champions 1908-10, 53-54, 60-61.

Athenian League Champions 1922-23, 48-49, 50-51.

Kent Senior Cup (x5) Kent Am.Cup (x12) London Senior Cup (x4).

PREVIOUS

Leagues: S.London, Southern, London, W.Kent, S.Suburban, Kent, Spartan1907-08. Isthmian 1908-11, 52-2007 Athenian 1919-1952.

CHELMSFORD CITY

Back Row (L-R) -Chris Moore, Ian Cousins, Andy Duncan, Spencer Knight, James Lawson, Danny Gay, Ashley Harrison,Chris Duffy, Dave Rainford, Steve Robinson, Danny Webb, Steve Ward.
Front Row: Jason Hallett, Ollie Berquez, Bertie Brayley, Kevin James, Ricky Holmes, Stuart Ainsley, Justin Miller, Jeff Minton, Jon Keeling Greg Oates.

CLUB PERSONNEL

Chairman: Mansell Wallace.

Vice-Chairman: Paul Hopkins.

Company Secretary: Trevor Smith.

Additional Director: Martyn Gard,

Martin Bissett (non executive).

Secretary: Alan Brown.

10, Sandpiper Walk, Chelmsford, Essex CN2 8XJ.

Tel: (B) 01245 290 959

(M) 07963 626 381

Email: algbrown@blueyonder.co.uk

Commercial Manager: Aaron Desmond.

Tel: (M) 07802 807 197

Email: aaron.desmond@chelmsfordcityfc.com

Press Officer: Chris Evans

(M) 07799 030 669

Email: chris.evans@brookevillemedia.co.uk

Director of Football: Jeff King.

Head Coach: Glenn Pennyfather.

Club therapist: Ken Steggles.

One of the favourites for promotion last season certainly appeared to be living up to expectations, when, after three months of the campaign Chelmsford City were comfortably perched on the top of the table. An F.A.Cup defeat at Bury Town hadn't worried them and it appeared as if their priorities were firmly concentrated on promotion.

By the new year the situation was the same. A one match F.A.Trophy involvement at Hayes & Yeading had been brushed off and a run of five consecutive league victories leading up to the New Year established 'The Clarets' exactly where they wanted to be, top by nine points with two extra games played over the second placed club.

It was the New Year that signalled the beginning of the Chelmsford wobble and only once more did Jeff King's squad manage two consecutive league victories. Whether it was nerves, injuries or just poor form, the clubs chasing were given a boost and the pressure got worse as the weeks went by.

A play-off place seemed a certainty but incredible form from AFC Wimbledon swept the championship away from all other contenders including the stuttering Chelmsford. An in form Hampton & Richmond Borough snuffed out City's hopes in the two legged play-off semi-final, and with Manager King's decision to move 'upstairs' and give responsibility to his long term right hand man Glenn Pennyfather, Chelmsford City will be even more determined to gain promotion next season.

CHELMSFORD CITY

BEST LGE ATT.: 2,318 v AFC Wimbledon
LOWEST: 851 v Team Bath

No.	Date	Comp	H/A	Opponents	Att:	Result	Goalscorers	Pos
1	Aug 9	BSS	A	Hayes & Yeading	456	W 1 - 0	Brayley 27	
2	11		H	Fisher Athletic	1232	W 3 - 0	**Rainford** 5 68 James 90	
3	16		H	Newport County	1093	D 0 - 0		
4	23		A	St Albans City	623	W 2 - 1	Brayley 10 Holmes 38	4
5	25		H	Braintree Town	1711	D 1 - 1	James 90	
6	30		A	Basingstoke Town	282	W 2 - 1	Brayley 35 Holmes 20	2
7	Sept 2		A	Bromley	527	D 2 - 2	Keeling 53 Holmes 83	
8	6		H	Bognor Regis Town	1215	W 2 - 1	Duncan 36 Brayley 58	2
9	**8**	**SS S1**	**H**	**AFC Wimbledon**	**575**	**W 1 - 0**	**Brayley 14**	
10	13		H	Havant & Waterlooville	1104	L 1 - 2	Duncan 52	5
11	20		A	Weston-s-Mare	308	W 4 - 1	Robinson 22 Brayley 49 58 Keeling 80	4
12	**27**	**F.A.C. 2Q**	**A**	**Bury Town**	**698**	**L 1 - 2**	**Minton 87**	
13	Oct 4		H	Eastleigh	1128	W 3 - 0	**RAINFORD** 3 (11pen 56 90)	2
14	**6**	**SS S2**	**H**	**Braintree Town**	**474**	**W 3 - 1**	**Berquez 16 31, Brayley 61**	
15	11		H	Bromley	1102	L 0 - 1		
16	18		A	Dorchester Town	508	W 1 - 0	**Rainford** 2	1
17	25		A	Fisher Athletic	200	W 1 - 0	**Rainford** 67	1
18	27		H	Bishop's Stortford	1279	D 3 - 3	Keeling 10 Berquez 33 Duncan 36	
19	Nov 1		H	AFC Wimbledon	2318	W 3 - 2	Berquez 3 Moore 53 56	1
20	8		A	Maidenhead United	782	W 2 - 0	Minton 68 Moore 89	1
21	15		H	Bath City	1265	L 2 - 3	**Rainford** 20 72 (pen)	1
22	**22**	**F.A.T 3Q**	**A**	**Hayes & Yeading**	**347**	**L 1 - 4**	**Rainford 86 (pen)**	
23	**25**	**SS 3**	**A**	**Grays Athletic**	**262**	**W 4 - 2**	**Brayley 21 Hallett 37 73 Minton 88**	
24	29		A	Worcester City	647	W 1 - 0	Berquez 35	1
25	Dec 6		A	Welling United	780	W 3 - 1	Keeling 60 **Rainford** 80 (pen) Holmes 84	1
26	20		H	Hayes & Yeading	1502	W 2 - 1	Hallett 71 **Rainford** 82 (pen)	1
27	27		A	Thurrock	812	W 1 - 0	James 90	1
28	Jan 1		H	Thurrock	2014	W 3 - 2	Berquez 39 Hallett 88 Duncan 90	1
29	3		A	Newport County	902	L 1 - 3	James 86	
30	17		A	Havant & Waterlooville	921	D 1 - 1	Knight 14	1
31	**20**	**SS S4**	**A**	**Crawley Town**	**304**	**L 1 - 2**	**Brayley 24**	
32	24		H	Welling United	1408	W 2 - 0	Berquez 24 Knight 62	1
33	31		A	AFC Wimbledon	4690	L 1 - 3	James 64	
34	Feb 7		A	Eastleigh	828	L 1 - 2	Hallett 78	2
35	14		H	Dorchester City	1035	W 2 - 1	Sloma 64 85	2
36	21		A	Bognor Regis Town	451	L 1 - 2	Berquez 36	3
37	22		H	Team Bath	851	D 1 - 1	Hallett 19	
38	28		A	Bishop's Stortford	801	L 1 - 2	Hand 56	4
39	Mar 7		H	Maidenhead United	1203	W 2 - 1	**Rainford** 6 Berquez 64	3
40	16		H	Basingstoke Town	1054	D 2 - 2	James 20 Holmes 52	
41	21		A	Hampton & Richmond B	816	L 1 - 4	Moore 65	5
42	28		A	Team Bath	159	L 0 - 2		5
43	April 4		H	Worcester City	1055	W 2 - 0	Berquez 42 **Rainford** 59	5
44	6		H	Hampton & Richmond B	1114	W 3 - 2	Berquez 4 Hallett 35 Duncan 57	
45	10		H	St Albans City	1459	D 1 - 1	Duncan 20	5
46	13		A	Braintree Town	1278	W 2 - 1	Lawson 86 Berquez 87	
47	18		A	Bath City	604	L 1 - 2	**Rainford** 38	5
48	25		H	Weston-s-Mare	1665	W 4 - 1	Knight 22 **Rainford** 26 Dudfield 87 Rand 90 (og)	5
49	**28**	**Play-off SF1**	**H**	**Hampton & Richmond B**	**1708**	**L 1 - 3**	**Rainford 59**	
50	**May 2**	**Play-off SF2**	**A**	**Hampton & Richmond B**	**1235**	**D 0 - 0**		

Average Home Att: 1474 (1356) **Goals 84 67**

Best Position: 1st **Worst:** 5th

Goalscorers: Rainford 17, Berquez 12, Brayley 10, Hallett 7, Duncan 6, James 6, Holmes 5, Keeling 4, Moore 4, Knight 3, Minton 3, Sloma 2, Dudfield 1, Lawson 1, Waterman 1, Watson 1. Own Goals 1.

GAY	MILLER	COUSINS	DUNCAN	WARD	JAMES	BERQUEZ	MINTON	KEELING	BRAYLEY	HOLMES	AINSLEY	LAWSON	MOORE	RAINFORD	HARRISON	KNIGHT	HALLETT	ROBINSON	DUFFY	CARLILE	BROWN	HUNTER	BAKER	OATES	OKAY	DUDFIELD	SLOMA	HAND	MODESTE	
X	X	X	X	X	X	X	X	X	X	X	S	S	S	U	U															1
X	X	X	X	X	X		X	X	X	X		S	S	X	U	S	U													2
X	X	X	X	X	X		X	X	X	X		S	S	X	U	S		U												3
X	X	X	X	X	X	X	X	U	X	X		S	S	X	U			U												4
X	X	X	X	X	X	X		X	X	X		S	S	X	U		U	U												5
X	X	X	S	X	X	X		U	X	X		S	X	X	U		S	X												6
X	X	X	X	U	X	X		S	X	X		U	X	X	U	U		X												7
X	X	X	X	U	X	X	X	S	X	X				X	U		S	X	S											8
U		**X**		**X**	**U**	**X**	**U**	**X**	**X**	**S**	**U**	**X**		**X**	**X**	**X**	**X**		**X**											9
X		X	X	X	X	X	X	S	X	X				X	U	U	S	S	X											10
X		X	U	X	X	X	X	S	X	X				X	U	S	S	X	X											11
X	**S**		**X**	**U**	**X**	**X**	**X**	**S**	**X**	**X**		**U**	**S**	**X**	**U**	**X**		**X**	**X**											12
X	X		U	X	X	X	X	S	X	X		S	S	X	U	X		X												13
U	**X**		**S**	**X**	**X**	**X**	**U**	**X**	**X**			**S**	**X**	**X**	**X**	**X**		**X**		**S**										14
X	X		U	X	X	X	S	X	X	S			X	X	U	X	S	X												15
X	X		X	X	X	X	X	S	X	X			S	X	U	X	U	S												16
X	X		X		X	X	X	S	S	X		U	X	X	U	X	S	X												17
X	X		X		S	X	X	X	U	X			X	X	U	X	S	X	S											18
X	X	X	X		S	X	X	X	X	X		U	S	X	U		U	X												19
X	X	S	X		S	X	X	X	U	X		U	X	X	U	X		X												20
X	X	X	X		X	X	X	X	S	X		U	X	X	U		S				U									21
X	**X**	**X**	**X**	**X**	**X**	**S**	**X**	**X**	**S**	**X**			**X**	**X**	**U**		**S**		**U**											22
U	**X**	**X**		**X**	**X**	**X**	**S**	**X**	**X**	**X**		**U**	**S**	**X**	**X**		**X**					**U**								23
X	X	U	X	X	X	X	X		X	X		U	U	X	U	X	S													24
X	X	S	X	X	X		X	X	X	X		S		X	U	X	U						U							25
X			X	X	X	X		X	X	X		U	U	X	U	X	S						X	U						26
X	X	S	X	X	X	X	X	X	S	X			U	X	U		S						X							27
X	X	U	X	X	X	X	X	X	S	X				X	U	S	S						X							28
X	X	X	X		X		X	X	X	X			U	X	U	U	S						X	U						29
X		X	X	X	S	X			X	X		X	S	X	U	X	X						S	U						30
X		**U**	**X**	**X**	**S**	**X**	**X**	**X**	**X**	**X**		**X**	**U**	**X**	**U**	**X**	**S**													31
X			X	X	S	X	X	X		X		X	X	X	U	X	S								S	U				32
X		U	X	X	X	X	X		X			X	X	X	U		S							U	X	S				33
X		U	X	X	X	X				X		X	S	X	U		S		U						X	X	X			34
X		X	X		X	X	X	S		X			S	X	U		S		U						X	X	X			35
U		U	X	X	X	X	X	X				X	S	X	X		S									X	X	S		36
X		X	X	X	X	X	X	X				X	S	X	U		X									S	U	U		37
X		X	S	X	X	X	X	X				X		S	U		X	X								S	U	X		38
X		X			U	X		S		X			X	X	U	X	U	X							X	U	X	X		39
X		X	S		X	X		S		X			X	X	U	X	S	X								U	X	X		40
X			X		X	X	U			X		X	X	X	U	X	S	X								S	U	X		41
X		X	X		X	X	S	S	X	X			S	X	U	X		X									U	X		42
U			X	X	X	X	X	X	X	X				X	X		S	S								U	X	S		43
U			X	X	X	X	X		X	X				X	X		X	U								U	X	S	U	44
U		S	X	X	X	X	X	S	X	X				X	X		X	S									X	U		45
X		X		X	X	X			X	X		S		X	U			X			U					S	X	X	S	46
U		X		X			X		S			X	X	X	X		S	X			U					X	X	X	S	47
X		X	X	U			X		X			X	S	X	U	X	X	X								S		X	S	48
X		**X**	**X**	**X**		**X**	**X**			**X**		**X**	**S**	**X**	**U**	**U**	**X**	**U**								**S**		**X**		49
U		**U**	**U**	**X**		**X**	**X**		**S**	**X**		**X**	**S**		**X**	**X**	**X**	**X**								**X**		**X**		50
Total League Appearances																														
37	21	23	33	28	34	36	30	19	26	35	0	10	13	40	5	16	6	18	2	0	0	0	4	0	4	4	10	8	0	**X**
0	0	4	3	0	5	0	2	12	5	1	1	9	15	1	0	4	22	4	2	0	0	0	1	0	1	6	0	3	3	**S**
5	0	5	3	3	1	0	1	2	2	0	0	7	4	1	37	3	6	4	2	0	3	0	1	4	0	5	4	2	1	**U**
Total Cup Appearances																														
4	3	4	4	7	4	7	5	5	5	6	0	4	2	7	4	5	4	3	2	0	0	0	0	0	0	1	0	2	0	**X**
0	1	0	1	0	1	1	1	1	2	1	0	1	4	0	0	0	2	0	0	1	0	0	0	0	0	1	0	0	0	**S**
4	0	2	1	1	1	0	2	0	0	0	1	2	1	0	4	1	0	1	1	0	0	1	0	0	0	0	0	0	0	**U**

CHELMSFORD CITY

CURRENT SQUAD AS OF BEGINING OF 2009-10 SEASON

GOALKEEPERS	HT	WT	D.O.B	AGE	P.O.B	CAREER	Apps	Gls
Ashley Harrison					Southend	Basildon, Southend Manor, Canvey Island, Dover c/s 98, Canvey Island 7/99, Redbridge (L) 9/04, Great Wakering (3ML) 11/05, Great Wakering 5/06, Chelmsford 10/06	5	0
Craig Holloway			10/8/84	25	Blackheath	Arsenal Rel c/s 04, Farnborough 6/04, Southend (2ML) 1/05, Gravesend 8/05, Injured, Bromley 3/08, Braintree 5/08, Chelmsford 7/09		
DEFENDERS								
Josh Brown						Chelmsford	0	0
Danny Bunce			30/4/86	23		West Ham Rel c/s 05, Cambridge U NC 11/05 Rel 5/06, Woking 7/06 Rel 6/09, Chelmsford 7/09		
Anthony Cook	5'07"	11 02	10/8/89	20	London	Cardiff (Yth), Croydon Ath, Dag & Red 8/07, Carshalton (L) 10/08, Concord R (L) 12/08 Perm, Braintree (Dual) 3/09, Chelmsford 7/09		
Mark Haines	6'03"		28/9/89	19		Northampton, Cheshunt (WE) 2/08, Grays (WE) 3/08, Grays 5/08, East Thurrock (L) 9/08, Chelmsford 7/09		
Matt Lock	5'11"	11 04	10/3/84	25	Barnstaple	Exeter Rel c/s 03, Team Bath 8/03, Tiverton 7/04, Mangotsfield (SL) 12/04 Perm 6/05 Rel 9/06, Team Bath 10/06, Newport C (Trial) 6/09, Chelmsford 7/09		
Ben Martin	6'07"	13 08	25/11/82	26	Harpenden	Harpenden, Aylesbury 3/03, Swindon 8/03 Rel c/s 04, Lincoln C (L) 10/03, Farnborough (L) 1/04, St Albans 8/04, Staines (L) 11/06, Leighton (L) 1/07, Wealdstone (L) 1/07, Chelmsford 7/09		
Erkan Okay	5'08"		29/1/85	24	Cambridge	Ipswich (Scholar), Aylesbury 3/04, Histon 7/04 Rel 1/09, Kettering (Trial) 1/09, Nuneaton T NC 1/09, Chelmsford 1/09	5	0
Steve Ward			17/4/71	38		Grays, Canvey Island £3,000 10/96, Chelmsford 7/06	28	0
MIDFIELDERS								
Ollie Berquez					Essex	Ipswich (Jun), Heybridge S, Chelmsford, St Albans 7/01, Chelmsford, Dag & Red, Braintree 9/02, Canvey Island 12/02, Stevenage 6/05 Rel 5/06, Woking 6/06, Maldon (Pl/Coach) 5/07, Chelmsford Undisc 11/07	36	10
Ryan Carolan			19/9/89	19	Romford	C.Palace Rel c/s 09, Chelmsford 8/09		
Jamie Hand	6'00"	11 08	7/2/84	25	Uxbridge	Watford, Oxford U (2ML) 8/04, Livingston (3ML) 1/05, Peterborough (3ML) 9/05, Fisher 1/06, Northampton (SL) 2/06, Chester 7/06, Lincoln C 8/07 Rel 5/08, Oxford U (SL) 2/08, Ebbsfleet 8/08 Rel 2/09, Chelmsford 2/09	11	1
John Martin	5'05"	10 00	15/7/81	28	Bethnal Green	L.Orient Rel c/s 03, Woking (Trial) 7/03, Farnborough 8/03, Hornchurch 9/03, Grays 11/04, Stevenage 5/07 Rel 5/09, Ebbsfleet (2ML) 2/09, Chelmsford 8/09		
Ricky Modeste						Chelmsford	3	0
Dave Rainford	6'00"	11 11	21/4/79	30	Stepney	Colchester Rel c/s 99, Scarborough (L) 12/98, Slough 6/99, Grays c/s 01, Heybridge S 7/02, Slough 11/02, Ford U 1/03, Bishops Stortford 3/03, Dag & Red 5/06, Chelmsford 6/08	41	15
FORWARDS								
Bert Brayley	5'09"	12 07	5/9/81	27	Basildon	West Ham (Sch), QPR 8/00 Rel c/s 01, Swindon 8/01 Rel c/s 02, Southend (Trial), Canvey Island 8/02, Heybridge (L) 9/03, Hornchurch £17,500 1/04, Braintree (2ML) 7/04, Billericay (L) 9/04, Heybridge 11/04, Farnborough 2/05, Thurrock 3/05, Aldershot (NC) 8/05, Margate 9/05, Grays 9/05, Margate (L) 10/05, Margate 12/05, Eastleigh 9/06, Braintree 11/06, Chelmsford c/s 07 Rel 2/09, Eastleigh 2/09, Chelmsford 3/09 Rel 7/09, Re-signed 8/09	31	6
Rob Edmans						Witham T, Chelmsford 8/09		
Simon Glover						Wycombe (Yth), Faversham, Ashford T 2/00, Welling c/s 00, Ashford T (L) 10/01, Fisher 1/02, Dover 3/02, Ashford T (2ML) 1/04, Folkestone I 5/04, Heybridge 10/05, Ashford T c/s 06, Bromley 6/07 Rel 3/08, Tonbridge A 3/08, Chelmsford 7/09		
Jason Hallett					Essex	Waltham Abbey, Canvey Island 11/03, Chelmsford 7/06	28	5
Danny Hockton	5'11"	11 11	7/2/79	30	Barking	Millwall, L.Orient (L) 9/99, Stevenage 1/00, Barry T (L) 9/00, Dover £7,500 12/00, Chelmsford 8/01 Rel 5/02, Crawley 5/02, Billericay 7/03, Margate 1/06, Bromley 6/07, Braintree Undisc 9/08 Rel 5/09, Chelmsford 6/09		
Ricky Holmes						Millwall (Yth), Southend (Yth), Southend Manor, Chelmsford 11/05	36	5

DEPARTURES	HT	WT	DOB	AGE	POB	From - To	APPS	GOA
(F)Danny Webb	6'01"	11 08	2/7/83	26	Poole	AFC Wimbledon 7/08 - Rel 9/08, Havant & W 10/08, Salisbury 11/08		
(D)Stuart Ainsley						Ipswich (Scholar) 7/06 - Rel 9/08, Needham Market, Canvey Island 10/08, AFC Sudbury 7/09	1	0
(D)Justin Miller	6'01"	12 12	16/12/80	28	Johannesburg, SA	Port Vale 7/08 - Rel 1/09	21	0
(D)Greg Oates	6'00"	12 04	3/10/81	27	Maldon	Maldon T 1/08 - Rel 2/09	0	0
(M)James Baker						Welling 12/08 - Rel 2/09, Welling 2/09, Billericay 5/09	5	0
(G)Danny Gay	6'00"	13 00	5/8/82	27	Kings Lynn	Heybridge c/s 07 - Rel 5/09	37	0
(D)Ian Cousins						Heybridge c/s 08 - Rel 5/09, Billericay (Pl/Coach) 5/09	27	0
(D)Andy Duncan	5'11"	13 04	20/10/77	31	Hexham	Cambridge U 6/07 - Rel 5/09	36	6
(M)Spencer Knight					Herts	Leyton 7/06 - Rel 5/09, Welling 6/09 Rel 7/09	20	3
(M)Sam Sloma	5'08"	11 06	29/10/82	26	London	Grays 2/09 - Rel 5/09, Woking 6/09	10	2
(F)Lawrie Dudfield	6'01"	13 09	7/5/80	29	Southwark	Cork C 1/09 - Rel 5/09, Corby T 5/09 Rel 7/09	10	1
(F)Chris Moore	5'09"	11 05	13/1/80	29	Middlesex	Dag & Red 7/08 - Rel 5/09	28	4
(F)James Lawson	5'09"	10 03	21/1/87	28	Basildon	Grays (3ML) 10/07 Perm 1/08 - Welling 6/09	19	1
(M)Jeff Minton	5'06"	11 10	28/12/73	35	Hackney	Canvey Island 7/06 - Rel 6/09, Welling 7/09	32	1
(F)Kevin James	5'07"	11 12	3/1/80	29	Southwark	Eastleigh 7/08 - Rel 6/09	39	6
(M)Chris Duffy	5'10"	11 07	31/10/73	35	Eccles	Canvey Island 7/06 - East Thurrock (Pl/Physio) 7/09	4	0
(D)Steve Robinson			31/1/76	33	Edmonton	Lewes 7/08 - Northwich (6WL) 11/08 Perm 1/09, Chelmsford 2/09, Farnborough 8/09	22	1
(M)Jon Keeling			6/6/76	33	Essex	Gravesend/Ebbsfleet 6/07 - Rel 8/09	31	4
(D)Jack Carlile						Yth -	0	0
Brad Hunter						Yth - Witham T (L) 1/09, Great Wakering (L) 2/09	0	0

CHELMSFORD CITY

Formed: 1938

Nickname: City or Clarets.

Club Colours: White & claret shirts, white shorts, white socks.

Change Colours: Claret & white hooped shirts, claret shorts, claret socks.

Club Sponsor: Unicorn Asset Management.

Previous League: Southern League

Ground address: Chelmsford Sport and Athletic Centre, Salerno Way, Chelmsford, Essex CM1 2EH

Telephone: 01245 290 959

Email: enquiries@chelmsfordcityfc.com

Website: www.chelmsfordcityfc.com

Simple Directions: From A120 Gt.Dunmow, take A130 to Chelmsford and turn right into one way system at end of Essex Regiment Way. At third lights turn right A1061 for Sawbridgeworth. After one mile at second lights right into Chignal Road and then after another mile right into Melbourne Avenue and left into Salerno Way before flats.

Capacity: 3,000 **Seats:** 1,300 **Covered:** 1,300 **Floodlights:** Yes.

Clubhouse: Open every evening and available for hire.

Club Shop: Fully stocked. Contact: Mark Fleming via the club.

Local Radio: Essex Radio, Breeze AM , BBC Essex & Chelner FM

Local Press: Essex Chronicle,Chelmsford Weekly News, E.Anglian Daily Times and Evening Gazette

PROGRAMME EDITOR

Mandy Smith

H: 01473 824 782

Email: mandysmith41@hotmail.com

CLUB STATISTICS

RECORDS

Attendance: 16,807 v Colchester United, Southern League 10.09.49
at Salerno Way 2,998 v Billericay Town Ryman Lge January 2006

Victory: 10-1 v Bashley (H) Southern League 26.04.2000

Defeat: 2-10 v Barking (A) F.A.Trophy 11.11.78

Career Goalscorer: Tony Butcher - 287 (1957-71)

Career Appearances: Derek Tiffin - 550 (1950-63)

Record Transfer Fee Paid:
£10,000 to Dover Athletic for Tony Rogers 1992

Received: £50,000 from Peterborough United for David Morrison

SENIOR HONOURS

Southern League.Champions 1945-46, 67-68 ,71-72.
Southern Division 1988-89.
Southern League Cup 1945-46, 59-60, 90-91.
Non-League Champions Cup 1971-72
Essex Professional Cup 1957-58, 69-70, 70-71, 73-74, 74-75.
Essex Senior Cup 1985-86, 88-89, 92-93, 02-03.

PREVIOUS

Grounds: New Writtle Street 1938-97 Maldon Town 97-98
Billericay Town 1998-2005

DORCHESTER TOWN

Back row, left to right: Michael MacEntaggert Ryan Moss , Mark Jermyn, Nathan Peprah-Annan, Leon Osei, Tom Mitchell, Gary Bowles, Regan Coward,Bill Puckett, Patrece Liburd , Micky Walker, Ivan Forbes , Jamie Mudge Geoff Dine (physio).
Front row: Darren Watts, Jamie Gleeson, Mitch Nicholson,Danny Clay, Jake Smeeton,RoyO'Brien, Ronayne Benjamin Marsh-Brown , Nick Crittenden, Kevin Hill

CLUB PERSONNEL

CLUB PERSONNEL

Chairman: David Roberts.

Company Secretary: David Martin.

Additional Directors: Neill Blake, Darin Courtney.

Secretary: David Martin

21 Diggory Crescent, Dorchester Dorset DT1 2SP

(H): 01305 262 345

(M): 07971 172 795

dave27@talktalk.net

Commerical Manager: Brian Benjafield.

Tel: (M) 07811 087 417

Press Officer: As secretary.

Manager: Roy O'Brien.

Club therapist: Geoff Dine.

With a change of ownership now with a season's experience, Dorchester Town supporters were hoping for an improved challenge for at least a top half finish and perhaps a cup run. In reality the challenge didn't materialise, the management changed , form dropped and supporters rebelled against the board, especially after a rumour had linked the club with a merger with big rivals Weymouth.

The lovely Avenue Stadium was not a happy place to be although the bright spot of the campaign was a cup run that saw Newport County defeated after a replay, plus victories over Gosport Borough and Bishop's Stortford, also after a replay. Then a First Round Proper trip to Oxford United where over 3,000 watched a 0-0 draw and 1,474 saw the replay won by United 3-1 after extra time.

In January wages were cut and morale was low all round as results deteriorated. Uxbridge had knocked 'The Magpies' out of the F.A.Trophy in London and League form saw them sinking fast. Manager Shaun Brooks resigned and his place was taken by Roy O'Brien a centre back who had recently left the club in a cost cutting excercise.

By this time, Dorchester fans were getting desperate and the atmosphere was generally agressive, and not one conducive to point winning team performances. Town were heading for relegation and with one game to go, against Bromley at home, Dorchester had to win to stay up and did so with a desperate 2-1 victory in front of 558 supporters all of whom deserve a happier campaign next season.

DORCHESTER TOWN

BEST LGE ATT.: **759** v Bath City
LOWEST: **253** v Fisher Athletic

No.	Date	Comp	H/A	Opponents	Att:	Result	Goalscorers	Pos
1	Aug 9	BSS	A	Braintree Town	515	W 1 - 0	Crittenden 81	
2	12		H	Basingstoke Town	518	D 0 - 0		
3	16		H	St Albans City	490	D 1 - 1	**Mudge** 13	
4	23		A	Newport County	852	D 4 - 4	K.Hill 18 90 **Moss** 58 Osei 82	11
5	25		H	Weston-s-Mare	482	L 1 - 2	**Mudge** 34	
6	30		A	Fisher Athletic	179	L 0 - 4		15
7	Sept 2		H	Team Bath	357	D 2 - 2	**Moss** 18 **Mudge** 38	
8	6		A	Welling United	560	D 0 - 0		16
1	**9**	**SS S1**	**H**	**Newport County**	**178**	**L 4 - 5***	**Nicholson 18 Osei 69 Fogden 72 Bowles 109**	
9	13		H	Hayes & Yeading	506	L 1 - 2	**Mudge** 75	16
10	20		A	Thurrock	196	L 0 - 1		17
11	**27**	**F.A.C. 2Q**	**H**	**Newport County**	**242**	**D 2 - 2**	**Moss 17 51 (pen)**	
12	**Oct 1**	**F.A.C. 2Q r**	**A**	**Newport County**	**653**	**W 2 - 1**	**Crittenden 60 83**	
13	4		A	Maidenhead United	343	L 1 - 2	Crittenden 47	18
14	**11**	**F.A.C 3Q**	**H**	**Gosport Borough**	**436**	**W 1 - 0**	**Moss 65**	
15	18		H	Chelmsford City	508	L 0 - 1		18
16	21		A	Eastleigh	392	W 1 - 0	Clay 59	
17	**25**	**F.A.C. 4Q**	**H**	**Bishop's Stortford**	**433**	**L 0 - 1**		
18	Nov 1		A	Bishop's Stortford	331	W 2 - 0	**Moss** 17 50	17
19	**8**	**F.A.C. 1R**	**A**	**Oxford United**	**3196**	**D 0 - 0**		
20	15		A	Hampton & Richmond B	458	L 0 - 2		17
21	**18**	**F.A.C. 1R r**	**H**	**Oxford United**	**1474**	**L 1 - 3**	**Mudge 22**	
22	**22**	**F.A.T 3Q**	**A**	**Uxbridge**	**110**	**L 1 - 2**	**Mudge 6 (pen)**	
23	29		H	Welling United	366	D 1 - 1	**Mudge** 58	18
24	Dec 6		A	Havant & Waterlooville	484	W 2 - 1	Gleeson 6 **Mudge** 41	16
25	9		H	Bognor Regis Town	344	W 1 - 0	**Moss** 27	
26	13		H	Thurrock	357	W 4 - 3	Fogden 34 **MUDGE** 3 (37 50 70)	13
27	20		H	Braintree Town	461	D 2 - 2	O'Brien 63 Fogdon 90	13
28	26		A	Bath City	695	L 0 - 2		14
29	Jan 1		H	Bath City	759	L 0 - 2		15
30	13		H	AFC Wimbledon	736	D 1 - 1	**Moss** 58	
31	17		H	Worcester City	433	W 3 - 1	Fogdon 21 33 **Moss** 89	14
32	24		A	Bromley	423	L 0 - 1		15
33	27		A	Hayes & Yeading	184	L 1 - 2	**Moss** 13	
34	31		H	Eastleigh	543	L 0 - 4		16
35	Feb 10		H	Fisher Athletic	253	W 3 - 0	Crittenden 15 (pen) Nicholson 68 Clarke 76	
36	14		A	Chelmsford City	1035	L 1 - 2	Hutchings 59	15
37	21		A	Basingstoke Town	732	D 0 - 0		16
38	28		A	Team Bath	107	L 1 - 4	Nicholson 79	17
39	Mar 7		H	Bishop's Stortford	378	L 0 - 2		17
40	14		A	AFC Wimbledon	3354	L 0 - 2		19
41	17		H	Havant & Waterlooville	322	W 1 - 0	Gleeson 33	
42	21		H	Maidenhead United	361	L 0 - 3		19
43	24		A	St Albans City	311	L 0 - 2		
44	28		A	Worcester City	493	D 0 - 0		19
45	April 4		H	Hampton & Richmond	411	L 0 - 1		19
46	11		H	Newport County	519	L 0 - 1		19
47	13		A	Weston-s-Mare	275	D 2 - 2	Erskine 40 Walsh 62	
48	18		A	BognorRegis Town	400	D 0 - 0		19
49	25		H	Bromley	558	W 2 - 1	Gleeson 19 Mitchell 27	19

Average Home Att: 460 (436) **Goals** 50 75

Best Position: 11th **Worst:** 19th

Goalscorers: Moss 11, Mudge 11, Crittendon 5, Fogden 5, Gleeson 3, Nicholson 3, Hill K 2, Osei 2, Bowles 1, Clarke 1, Clay 1, Erskine 1, Hutchings 1, Mitchell 1, O'Brien 1, Walsh 1.

STEWART	BOWLES	SMEATON	O'BRIEN	LIBURD	CLAY	CRITTENDEN	HILL	MOSS	MUDGE	FORBES	OSEI	WALKER	PEPRAH	NICHOLSON	COWARD	MARSH-BROWN	MITCHELL	BROWNE	WATTS	GLEESON	FOGDEN	JERMYN	CRITCHEL	TAYLOR	RODRIGUES	CLARKE	KELLAWAY	JOHNSON	HUTCHINGS	REEVE	WHITTINGHAM	WEBB	VICKERS	ERSKINE	WALSH	
X	X	X	X	X	X	X	X	X	X	X	S	U	U	U	U																					1
X	X	X	X	X	X	X	X	X	X		X	S	U		U	U	U																			2
X	X	X		X	X	X	X	X	X		X		X	S	U	S		U	U																	3
X		X		X	X	X	X	X	X		S	S	X	X		S	U	X	U																	4
X	X	X		X	X	X	X	X	X		S	S		X	U	X			U	S																5
X		X		X	X	X	X	X	X		S	X	U	X	U	S	S				X															6
X	X			X		X	X	X	X		S		U	U	U	X	X		S	X	X															7
X	X			X		X	X	X	X		S	U	U	S	U	X	X			X	X															8
X	**S**	**X**		**U**		**S**			**X**		**X**	**X**	**X**	**X**	**U**	**S**	**X**		**X**	**X**	**X**															**9**
X	X	X		X	X	X	X	X	X		S		U			X	U		U	S	X															10
X	X	X		U	X	X	X	X	X		S		U			X	S		S	X	X															11
X		**X**		**X**	**X**	**X**	**X**	**X**	**X**		**S**		**U**	**S**	**U**	**S**	**U**		**U**	**X**	**X**	**X**														**12**
X		**X**		**X**	**X**	**X**	**X**	**X**	**S**				**U**	**S**	**U**	**X**	**X**	**S**	**U**	**U**	**X**	**X**														**13**
X	S	X		X	X	X	X	X	S					X	U	U	X			U	X	X														14
X	**X**	**X**		**U**	**S**	**X**	**X**	**X**	**X**					**U**	**U**		**X**	**U**	**U**	**X**	**X**	**X**	**U**													**15**
	X	X		U	X	X	X	X	X				U		X	U		U	S	X	X	X														16
X	X	X		U	X	X	X	X					U		U	S		U	X	X	X	X														17
X	**X**			**U**	**X**	**X**	**X**	**X**	**X**				**U**	**S**	**U**	**X**	**U**	**U**	**U**	**X**	**X**	**X**														**18**
X				X	X	X	X	X	X				U	S	U	X		U	U	X	X	X														19
X	**X**			**U**	**X**	**X**	**X**	**X**	**X**				**U**	**S**	**U**	**X**	**U**	**U**	**U**	**X**	**X**	**X**														**20**
X	X			S	X		X	X	X				U	X		X	S		U	X	X	X														21
X				**X**	**X**	**X**	**X**	**X**	**X**				**U**	**X**	**U**	**X**	**S**		**S**	**X**		**X**	**U**	**U**												**22**
X				**X**	**X**	**X**	**X**	**X**	**X**				**X**	**S**	**U**	**S**	**X**		**S**	**X**		**X**	**U**													**23**
X				X	X	X	X	X	X				U	X	U	X	U		U	X		X														24
X	X		U	X	X	X	X		X				X	X	U		U			X	S	X			U											25
X	X			X	X	X	X	X	X				U	S	U	S	U			X	X	X														26
X	X		S	X	X	X	X	X	X				U	S	U		U			X	X	X														27
X			X	X	X	X	X	X	X					S	U	S	U			X	X	X			U											28
X		S	X		X	X	X	X	X						U	X	S			X	X	X			U											29
X			X	S	X	X	X	X	X				U	S	U	X				X	X	X			U											30
X	U		X	U	X	X	X	X	X					S	U	X			U	X	X	X														31
X			X	U	X	X	X	X	X					S	U	X	S		S	X	X	X														32
X	S	U	X	U	X		X	X	X				U	S		X			X	X	X	X														33
X	S	S	X	U	X	X	X	X	X				U	S		X			X		X	X														34
X	X	X				X	X						X	X	U	X			X	X	S	X	U		S	S										35
X	X	X	X			X	X	X						X	U				X	U		X	U			X	S	U								36
X	X	X	X			X	X							X	U				S	X		X	U	U		X		U	X							37
X	X	X	S		U	X	X							X	U				U	X		X				S			X	X	X					38
X	X	X	X				X							S	U		U		X	U						X			X	X	X	X				39
X	X	X	X			X	X							X	U	X	S		U	X		X				S			X			U				40
X		U	U			X	X							S	U	X	X		X	X		X				U			X	X			X			41
X		U	X			X	X							X	U	X	U		U	X		X				U				X			X	X		42
X			X			X	X							S	U	X	X		S	X		X				U				S			X	X	X	43
X	X	X				X	X							S	U	X	U		U	X		X								U			X	X	X	44
X	X	X				X	X							X	U		U		U	X		X				U				U			X	X	X	45
X	X	X				X	X							U	U		X		S	X		X				S				U			X	X	X	47
X		X	X			X	X			S				X	U		X		S	X		X				U				U				X	X	48
X		X				X	X			S				X	U		X		U	X		X				U							X	X	X	49
X		X				X	X			U				X	U		X		S	X		X				U				U			X	X	X	50
X	X	X								X					U		X		X	X		X	U	U		U	U						X	X	X	51
																																				52
Total League Appearances																																				
41	24	24	16	16	24	38	41	26	24	2	2	1	4	17	1	20	10	1	8	31	19	31	0	0	0	3	0	0	5	4	2	1	9	9	8	**X**
0	3	2	2	2	0	0	0	0	1	2	8	3	0	15	0	6	6	0	9	2	2	0	0	0	1	4	1	0	0	1	0	0	0	0	0	**S**
0	1	3	2	7	1	0	0	0	0	1	0	2	17	3	35	3	12	4	14	3	0	0	4	2	4	8	1	2	0	5	0	1	0	0	0	**U**
Total Cup Appearances																																				
8	3	4	0	4	6	7	7	7	7	0	1	1	2	2	0	4	4	0	1	7	6	7	0	0	0	0	0	0	0	0	0	0	0	0	0	**X**
0	1	0	0	0	1	1	0	0	1	0	1	0	0	5	0	3	1	1	2	0	0	0	0	0	0	0	0	0	0	0	0	0	0	0	0	**S**
0	0	0	0	4	0	0	0	0	0	0	0	0	5	1	8	0	3	3	5	1	0	0	3	1	0	0	0	0	0	0	0	0	0	0	0	**U**

DORCHESTER TOWN

CURRENT SQUAD AS OF BEGINING OF 2009-10 SEASON

GOALKEEPERS	HT	WT	D.O.B	AGE	P.O.B	CAREER	Apps	Gls
Regan Coward						Dorchester	1	0
Ryan Northmore	6'01"	13 01	5/9/80	28	Plymouth	Torquay, Team Bath 9/02, Woking 7/03, Bath C (L) 12/03, Yeovil (SL) 3/04, Team Bath 7/04, Weston-Super-Mare (3ML) 9/04, Weston-Super-Mare (SL) 12/04, Weston-Super-Mare 6/05 Weston (Yth Man) 5/09, Dorchester 8/09		
DEFENDERS								
Gary Bowles			30/12/88	20		Cardiff (Yth), Yeovil, Dorchester 8/07	27	0
Neil Martin						Exeter, Hayes & Yeading (L) 8/08 Perm 9/08 Rel 10/08, Salisbury 1/09, Dorchester 8/09		
Roy O'Brien	6'01"	12 00	27/11/74	34	Cork	Arsenal Rel c/s 96, Wigan 8/96, Bournemouth 8/96 Rel 12/96, Dorchester T, Yeovil 8/00, Weymouth (2ML) 12/04, Weymouth (Pl/Coach) 2/05, Dorchester 6/07 Rel 1/09, Dorchester 2/09 (Pl/Man) 3/09	18	1
Jake Smeaton	5'08"	11	9/8/88	20	Yeovil	Yeovil Rel c/s 07, Dorchester 8/07	26	0
Ashley Vickers	6'03"	13 10	14/6/72	37	Sheffield	Sheff Utd, Worcester, Malvern T, 61 Club, Heybridge Swifts, Peterborough £5,000 12/97, St Albans 8/98, Dag & Red 3/00, Weymouth 5/06, Eastleigh 3/08, Newport C (L) 8/08 Perm 9/08, Dorchester (Pl/Coach) 3/09	9	0
MIDFIELDERS								
Nick Crittenden	5'08"	10 11	11/11/78	30	Ascot	Chelsea Rel 6/00, Plymouth (L) 11/98, Yeovil 8/00 Rel c/s 03 Re-signed, Rel c/s 04, Aldershot 6/04, Weymouth 5/06 Rel 5/08, Dorchester 6/08	38	3
Steve Devlin						Holt U, Wincanton, Dorchester c/s 09		
Jamie Gleeson	6'00"	12 03	15/1/85	24	Poole	Southampton Rel c/s 04, Kidderminster 7/04 Rel c/s 05, Eastleigh (L) 10/04, Dorchester 8/05	33	3
Kevin Hill	5'08"	10 03	6/3/76	33	Exeter	Torrington, Torquay 8/97, Rel 6/08, Dorchester 6/08	41	2
Mark Jermyn	6'00"	11 05	16/4/81	28	Germany	Torquay Rel 2/00, Dorchester 8/00	31	0
Tom Mitchell			21/9/87	21	Poole	Portsmouth, Dorchester 7/07, Gosport (L) 1/09	16	1
Harry Montacute						Yeovil (Yth), Dorchester c/s 09		
FORWARDS								
Jules Emati						Dawlish, Dorchester 8/09		
Ivan Forbes			1/12/86	22	Portimao, Port	Kingsbury London Tigers, Yeovil (Trial) c/s 07, Dorchester 8/07	4	0
Matt Groves			17/4/80	29	Poole	Portsmouth, Dorchester 11/98, Lewes 9/07, Eastleigh 5/08 Rel 5/09, Dorchester 6/09		
Ryan Moss	5'11"	12 04	14/11/86	22	Dorchester	Bournemouth Rel c/s 05, Dorchester 8/05, Bashley 7/06, Dorchester Undisc 6/08 Rel 2/09, Bashley 2/09, Dorchester c/s 09	26	8
Phil Walsh					Bristol	Almondsbury T, Clevedon 1/03, Taunton 9/03, Clevedon 11/03, Almondsbury T 7/04, Bath C 8/05, Tiverton (L) 2/08, Newport C 6/08, Tiverton (3ML) 9/08 Undisc 12/08, Dorchester 3/09	8	1
OTHERS								
Connor Flood						Dorchester		
Adam Taylor						Dorchester	0	0

LOANEES	HT	WT	DOB	AGE	POB	From - To	APPS	GOA
(M)Steve Hutchings	6'00"	12 00	13/12/90	18	Portsmouth	Bournemouth 2/09 - Havant & W 8/09	5	1
(D)Daniel Reeve			3/1/90	19	Newport, IOW	Brading T (Trial) 2/09 -	5	0
(M)George Webb						Bournemouth 2/09 -	1	0
(F)Jacob Erskine	6'01"	13 06	13/1/89	20	London	Dag & Red (6WL) 3/09 - Bromley 6/09, Gillingham 8/09	9	1

DEPARTURES	HT	WT	DOB	AGE	POB	From - To	APPS	GOA
(M)Leon Osei						Wingate & F 7/08 - Rel 10/08, Newport C 10/08	10	1
(D)Alex Browne			5/5/73	36	Weymouth	Weymouth 6/03 - Wimborne (Pl/Man) 11/08	1	0
(F)Jamie Mudge			25/3/83	26	Exeter	Dawlish 6/08 - Tiverton 1/09	25	9
(D)Patrece Liburd			1/3/88	21	Leeds	Garforth 2/08 - Rel 1/09, Macclesfield 3/09 Rel c/s 09, Farsley Celtic 7/09	18	0
Helder Rodrigues					Portugal	?? 12/08 - Rel 1/09	1	0
(F)Wesley Fogden	5'08"	10 04	12/4/88	21	Brighton	Brighton 9/08 - Havant & W 2/09	21	4
(D)Nathan Peprah			12/1/88	21	Accra, Ghana	Havant & W 3/08 - Rel 2/09, Halesowen T 2/09, Winchester 3/09	4	0
(M)Daniel Clay			15/12/85	23	Doncaster	Salisbury 6/08 Rel 1/09, Dorchester 2/09 - Truro C (L) 3/09, Truro C 6/09	24	1
(M)Ronayne Marsh-Brown (ex Benjamin)	5'10"	12 00	13/11/84	24	Chiswick	Welling 7/08 - Southampton (Trial) 3/09, Winchester 3/09, Bath C 3/09	26	0
(M)Darren Watts						Yeovil (Yth) 7/07 - Rel 7/09	17	0
(G)Gareth Stewart	6'00"	12 08	3/2/80	29	Preston	Bournemouth 8/08 -	41	0
(D)Danny Critchel			10/7/91	18	Dorchester	Yth -	0	0
(D)Michael Walker			27/9/83	25	Weymouth	Portland United 8/08 -	4	0
(M)Mitchell Nicholson			13/4/90	19	Adelaide, Aust	Croydon Kings (Aust) 7/07 -	32	2
(F)Tom Clarke	5'08"	09 13	2/1/89	20	Worthing	Bognor 1/09 -	7	1
(F)Richard Whittingham						Bournemouth NC 2/09 -	2	0
Neil Kellaway						Yth -	1	0
Mat Johnson						Yth -	0	0

DORCHESTER TOWN

Formed: 1880

Nickname: The Magpies.

Club Colours: White shirts, black shorts, black socks.

Change Colours: Sky blue shirts, navy blue shorts, sky blue socks.

Club Sponsor: Wessex Royale Hotel.

Previous League: Southern League

Ground address: The Jewson Stadium, Weymouth Avenue, Dorchester DT1 2SP

Telephone: 01305 262 451

Mobile: 07971 172 795

Fax: 01305 267 623

Email: dave72@talktalk.net

Website: www.dorchestertownfc.co.uk

Simple Directions: Situated at the junction of the town by-pass(A35) and the Weymouth road (A354)

Capacity: 5,009 **Seats:** 710 **Covered:** 2,846 **Floodlights:**Yes

Clubhouse: Dorchester Lounge Club- access via main entrance to stadium.

Club Shop: Fully Stocked.

Local Radio: Radio Solent and Wessex FM.

Local Press: Dorset Evening Echo, Western Gazette and Western Daily Press.

PROGRAMME EDITOR

Annie Greenslade

(M) 07748 842000 (B) 01305 262451

Email: anniegreenslade@aol.com

CLUB STATISTICS

RECORDS

Attendance: 4,159 v Weymouth, Southern Premier 1999

Career Goalscorer: Denis Cheney 61 (in one season)

Career Appearances: Derek 'Dinkie' Curtis 458 1950-66

Record Transfer Fee Paid: £12,000 to Gloucester City for Chris Townsend 1990

Received: £35,000 from Portsmouth for Trevor Senior

Victory: 7-0 v Canterbury (A)Southern Lg.Southern Div 86-87

Defeat: 0-13 v Welton Rovers (A) Western League 1966

SENIOR HONOURS

Southern League 1985-86.

Western League 1954-55.

Dorset Senior Cup (7)

PREVIOUS

Leagues:Dorset, Western 1947-72

Grounds: Council recreation Ground,

Weymouth Avenue 1908-1929,The Avenue Ground,

Weymouth Avenue 1929--1990

DOVER ATHLETIC

Back row (L-R): Matt Fish, Nicky Southall, Craig Cloke, Shaun Welford, Olly Schulz.
Middle: Robin Hastie (Kit manager), Darren Beale (1st team coach), Dean Hill, Frannie Collin, Lee Hook, John Whitehouse, Jake Leberl, Sam Gore, Tim Dixon (1st team coach).
Front: Jerahl Hughes, John Keister, Lee Browning, Jon Wallis, Andy Hessenthaler (Manager), Darren Hare (Assistant Manager), James Rogers, Sammy Moore, Tom Davis, Adam Birchall.

CLUB PERSONNEL

CLUB PERSONNEL

Chairman: Jim Parmenter.

Company Secretary: Frank Clarke.

Additional Directors: Chris Oakley, Scott Ruthford, Roger Knight.

Secretary: Frank Clarke.

14 Marine Avenue, Dymchurch, Kent TN29 0TR

Tel: (B) 1304 822 373

(M) 07794 102 664

Email: frank.clarke@doverathletic.com

Commerical Manager: Andrew Findley.

Tel: (M) 07970 522 199

Email: andrew.findley@doverathletic.com

Press Officer: Steve Parmenter.

Tel: (B) 01227 833 525

Email: steve.parmenter@doverathletic.com

Manager: Andy Hessenthaler.

Assistant Manager: Darren Hare.

Club therapist: Andy Hyland.

The 2008-2009 season will be remembered by Dover supporters for years to come as a wonderful campaign in which The Ryman championship was won and 100 senior goals scored in 48 games. Andy Hessenthaler's squad only suffered six defeats and there were only seven matches in which 'The Whites' failed to score.

Two of those six losses were of course in the cups, and it was A.F.C. Wimbledon who knocked Dover out of the F.A.Cup in a replay at Kingston, after Tonbridge Angels (A) 2-1 and Needham Market (H) 3-1 had been eliminated. In the F.A.Trophy 'The Whites' won at Staines Town by 2-0 but then surprisingly lost 2-3 at home to Cambridge City.

Hessenthaler's squad hit the top of the table after eight league games and were never caught before winning the championship with five games to go. The worst defeat was inflicted by Harrow Borough who won 3-0 in the first week of December, but Dover lost only one more game, and that was 21 matches later, and in a glorious season, won 37 games.

In a season when a century of goals were shared out between seventeen players, Fran Collin (24) and Shaun Welford (17) were the most reliable goalscorers. The Dover fans enjoyed a wonderful campaign and it was no surprise that the average home league attendance was over 1,200. Obviously they will be looking forward to competition at a higher level, but they will be hoping for another exciting campaign fought out at the top of the Blue Square South.

DOVER ATHLETIC

BEST LGE ATT.: 2,760 v Tooting & Mitcham Utd
LOWEST: 751 v Harlow Town

No.	Date	Comp	H/A	Opponents	Att:	Result	Goalscorers	Pos
1	Aug 16	Ryman P.	H	Harrow Borough	906	W 4 - 0	Rogers 47 59 Moore 66 69	
2	20		A	Dartford	1781	W 2 - 0	Wallis 51 Moore 87	
3	23		A	AFC Hornchurch	487	L 0 - 1		5
4	25		H	Margate	1512	W 1 - 0	Welford 82	
5	30		A	Boreham Wood	218	W 3 - 2	Welford 2 **Collin** 26 (pen) 52	2
6	Sept 2		H	Horsham	948	W 2 - 1	Wallis 74 86	
7	6		H	Ashford Town (Middx)	1009	W 3 - 2	**Collin** 3 Browning 26 Rogers 69	2
8	9		A	Hendon	279	W 2 - 0	Welford 44 **Collin** 50	1
9	**13**	**F.A.C. 1Q**	**A**	**Tonbridge Angels**	**797**	**W 2 - 1**	**Wallis 39 Welford 67**	
10	20		A	Hastings United	645	W 1 - 0	**Collin** 42 (pen)	1
11	23		H	Ramsgate	1417	W 4 - 1	**Collin** 3 54 Browning 49 Pouton 81 (pen)	
12	**27**	**F.A.C. 2Q**	**H**	**Needham Market**	**860**	**W 3 - 1**	**Browning 4 Collin 36 Hughes 90**	
13	Oct 4		A	Carshalton Athletic	528	W 1 - 0	**Collin** 13	1
14	**11**	**F.A.C. 3Q**	**H**	**AFC Wimbledon**	**2710**	**D 0 - 0**		
15	**15**	**F.A.C. 3Qr**	**A**	**AFC Wimbledon**		**L 0 - 2**		
16	**18**	**F.A.T. 1Q**	**A**	**Staines Town**	**320**	**W 2 - 0**	**Collin 6 Hughes 87**	
17	25		A	Canvey Island	573	W 3 - 0	**Collin** 36 Welford 65 Moore 85	1
18	**Nov 4**	**F.A.T. 2Q**	**H**	**Cambridge City**	**509**	**L 2 - 3**	**Welford 15 Collin 44**	
19	8		A	Staines Town	491	W 3 - 2	**Collin** 4 (pen) Welford 29 90	1
20	15		H	Heybridge Swifts	1009	W 2 - 1	Pouton 76 Hughes 79	
21	18		A	Sutton United	569	L 0 - 1		
22	22		A	Wealdstone	448	W 2 - 1	Keister 27 Pouton 64	1
23	29		H	Tonbridge Angels	1105	W 3 - 0	**Collin** 47 Moore 56 Ball 58	1
24	Dec 6		A	Harrow Borough	246	L 0 - 3		1
25	9		H	Harlow Town	751	W 2 - 0	**Collin** 3 Grazioli 61	
26	13		H	Dartford	1208	W 4 - 2	Wallis 40 Ball 55 Rogers 72 Schulz 85	1
27	16		H	Tooting & Mitcham U	2760	W 3 - 0	Grazioli 14 Moore 34 44	
28	20		A	Horsham	362	W 2 - 1	Browning 35 Welford 73	
29	27		H	Maidstone United	2545	W 3 - 0	**Collin** 19 pen 50 Welford 81	1
30	Jan 3		A	Margate	1339	W 2 - 0	Welford 19 33	1
31	13		H	Billericay Town	922	W 2 - 1	Rogers 48 Ball 78	
32	17		A	Ashford Town (Middx)	283	W 2 - 1	Hughes 69 Browning 75	1
33	24		H	Hastings United	1205	W 3 - 2	Ball 28 Grazioli 57 Schulz 59	
34	31		A	Ramsgate	1002	D 0 - 0		1
35	Feb 7		H	Hendon	976	W 3 - 0	Moore 37 Welford 41 **Collin** 79	1
36	14		H	Carshalton Athletic	1095	D 2 - 2	**Collin** 59 (pen) Hughes 90	
37	21		A	Harlow Town	601	W 4 - 1	Browning 14 32 **Collin** 61 82	1
38	28		H	Canvey Island	1083	W 2 - 1	Browning 6 Hughes 77	1
39	Mar 3		H	AFC Hornchurch	907	W 2 - 1	Moore 42 Pouton 85	
40	7		A	Tooting & Mitcham U	488	D 1 - 1	**Collin** 85 (pen)	
41	14		H	Staines Town	2019	D 0 - 0		1
42	21		A	Billericay Town	502	W 3 - 2	Hill 28 Welford 43 Browning 56	1
43	28		H	Sutton United	1404	W 6 - 0	Rogers 37 **Collin** 54 Welford 60 84 Bodkin 78 Hill 88	CH
44	April 4		A	Heybridge Swifts	282	D 1 - 1	Welford 70	
45	11		H	Boreham Wood	1346	L 1 - 2	Sidebe 56	1
46	13		A	Maidstone United	689	W 2 - 0	Wallis 56(pen) Rogers 78	
47	18		H	Wealdstone	1024	W 3 - 1	Fish 4 Gore 55 **Collin** 70	1
48	25		A	Tonbridge Angels	856	W 2 - 0	Sidebe 17 Wallis 32 (pen)	1

Average Home Att: 1293 **Goals 100 41**

Best Position: 1st **Worst:** 5th

Goalscorers: Collin 24, Welford 17, Browning 9, Moore 9, Rogers 7, Wallis 7, Hughes 6, Ball 4, Pouton 4, Grazioli 3, Hill 2, Schulz 2, Sidebi 2, Bodkin 1, Fish 1, Gore 1, Kiester 1.

CH - Became Champions.

CURRENT SQUAD AS OF BEGINING OF 2009-10 SEASON

GOALKEEPERS	HT	WT	D.O.B	AGE	P.O.B	CAREER	Apps	Gls
Lee Hook	5'09"	08 11	11/3/79	30	Margate	Wolves (Yth), Exeter, Ramsgate, Whitstable, Sittingbourne 9/02, Eastbourne B 6/03 Rel 5/09, Dover 5/09		
John Whitehouse						Charlton (Jun), Corinthian, Erith & B, Fisher, Greenwich B, Fisher, Greenwich B, Ashford T 8/01, Dartford c/s 05, Tunbridge Wells c/s 05, Chatham T 7/06, Dover 1/08		
DEFENDERS								
Craig Cloke						Dover		
Matt Fish	6'01"	11 00	5/1/89	20		C.Palace (Scholar) Rel c/s 07, AFC Wimbledon (SL) 3/07, Dover 7/07		
Samuel Gore	5'11"	11 02	29/11/88	20	Dover	Chelsea (Yth), Dover (Yth), Gillingham (Scholar) Rel c/s 07, Dover 6/07		
Dean Hill						Dover (Yth), Ashford T, Sittingbourne 2/04, Ramsgate 6/05, Dover 5/08		
Ollie Schulz						Ramsgate, Dover 5/08		
Danny Walder			3/9/89	19		Gillingham Rel 1/09, Ramsgate (3ML) 10/08 Perm 1/09, Dover 8/09		
MIDFIELDERS								
Tom Davis	5'10"	11 07	17/2/84	25	Bromley	Fulham Rel c/s 04, Gravesend 9/04, St Albans (L) 11/04, St Albans 2/05, Lewes 4 fig 7/07, AFC Wimbledon 5/08 Rel 5/09, Dover 6/09		
Jerahl Hughes	5'07"	11 09	10/8/89	20	Brighton	C.Palace (Scholar) Rel c/s 07, Yeovil 7/07 Rel c/s 08, Worthing (L) 2/08, Dover 7/08		
John Keister	5'08"	11 00	11/11/70	38	Manchester	Tigres (Sierra Leone), Faweh FC, Walsall 9/93, Chester 1/00 Rel c/s 00, Shrewsbury 10/00, Stevenage 2/01, Margate 3/01 Rel 5/06, Dover 5/06		
Jake Leberl			2/4/77	32	Morden	Crewe, Dover 8/97 Rel c/s 02, Margate 8/02, Dag & Red 6/04, AFC Wimbledon 7/07 Rel 5/09, Dover 6/09		
Sammy Moore	5'08"	9 00	7/9/87	21	Deal	Chelsea (Yth), Ipswich, Brentford (6ML) 7/07, Stevenage 1/08 Rel 5/08, Dover 6/08		
James Rogers						Dover		
Nicky Southall	5'10"	12 12	28/1/72	37	Stockton	Darlington (Jun), Hartlepool 2/91, Grimsby 7/95, Gillingham 12/97, Bolton 6/01, Norwich (2ML) 9/02, Gillingham (L) 12/02 Perm 12/02 Rel c/s 05, Notts Forest 8/05, Gillingham 1/07 Rel c/s 09 Dover (L) 9/08, Dover 7/09		
Jon Wallis	5'07"	10 08	4/4/86	23	Gravesend	Chelsea (Jun), Gilingham Rel 5/06, Hastings U (3ML) 8/04, Hastings U (L) 9/05 Hereford 6/06 Rel 3/07, Dover (2ML) 11/06, Dag & Red (L) 2/07, Dover 3/07		
FORWARDS								
Adam Birchall	5'07"	11 03	2/12/84	24	Maidstone	Arsenal Rel c/s 05, Wycombe (3ML) 8/04, Mansfield 8/05, Barnet (6WL) 11/06, Barnet Undisc 1/07 Rel c/s 09, Dover 7/09		
Lee Browning						Gillingham (Jun), Aston Villa (Trial), Derby (Trial), Sittingbourne 7/03, Dover 9/07		
Francis Collin	5'11"	11 11	20/4/87	22	Chatham	Chatham, Gillingham c/s 05 Rel c/s 07, Dover 6/07		
Shaun Welford					Ashington	Corinthian, Dover, Ramsgate 12/04, Dover 10/07		

DOVER ATHLETIC

Formed: 1983
Nickname: The Whites.
Club Colours: White shirts, black shorts, black socks.
Change Colours: Light blue shirts, light blue shorts, light blue socks.
Club Sponsor: Perrys Vauxhall
Previous League: Southern League

Ground address: Crabble Athletic Ground, Lewisham, Dover, Kent CT17 0PA

Telephone: 01304 822 373

Fax: 01304 821 383

Email: enquiries@doverathletic.com

Website: www.doverathletic.com

Simple Directions: Follow A2 from Canterbury until you pass the Forte Post House on left and approach a roundabout with MacDonalds and petrol station on the left. Turn right to 'town centre' and follow down hill.

Capacity: 6,500 **Seats:** 1,000 **Covered:** 4,900 **Floodlights:**Yes

Clubhouse: Open seven days a week. Meals available.

Club Shop: Yes.

Local Radio: Radio Kent, Invicta amd FM KFM Radio

Local Press: Dover Express and Dover Mercury

PROGRAMME EDITOR

Chris Collins

Tel: (H) 01304 822 704

Email: chriscollins@doverathletic.com

CLUB STATISTICS

RECORDS
Attendance: 4,186 v Oxford United FAC 1st Round November 2002
Victory: :7-0 v Weymouth 03.04.90
Defeat: 1-7 v Poole Town
Career Goalscorer: Lennie Lee - 160
Career Appearances: Jason Bartlett - 359
Record Transfer Fee Paid: £50,000 to Farnborough Town for David Leworthy August 1993
Received: £50,000 from Brentford for Ricky Reina 1997

SENIOR HONOURS
Southern Premier Champions 1989-90, 92-93.
Southern Division 1987-88.
Premier Inter League Cup 1990-91.
Kent Senior Cup 1990-91.
Isthmian League Champions 2008-09.

PREVIOUS
Name: Dover F.C.
Leagues: Kent, Southern, Conference, Southern

EASTLEIGH

Back Row (L-R): Tony Taggart, Shaun McAuley, Peter Adeniyi, Brett Williams, Aaron Martin, Jason Matthews, Dan Loader, Tom Jordan, Michael Green, Sam Doswell, Brett Poate, Warren Goodhind.
Front Row: Danny Smith, Ian Oliver, Anthony Riviere, Jamie Brown, Phil Pearpoint, Gareth Howells, Ian Baird, Matt Gray, Andy Cook, Steve Clark, Andy Forbes, Richard Gillespie, Trevor Challis

CLUB PERSONNEL

Chairman: Paul Murray.

Vice-Chairman: Mike Geddes.

Company Secretary: Alan Williams.

Managing Director: David Malone.

Additional Directors: John Dunn, Chris Evans, Darren Ridge, Derek Brooks (President), Alan Prebbie, Alan Harding, Peter Vickery, Andrew White, Stephen Brookwell.

Secretary: Ray Murphy.
21 Villette Close, Christchurch, Dorset BH23 2NR.
Tel: (B) 07801 638 158
Email: raymurphy@ntlworld.com

Commercial Manager: Denis Bundy.
Tel: (M) 07775 514 333.
Email: info@denisbundy.co.uk

Press Officer: Malcolm Clarke
(H): 02380 615 903
(B): 02380 911 160
mclarke@eastleigh.ac.uk

Manager: Ian Baird.

Club therapist: Danielle Ray.

Most clubs who successfully challenge for league championships or promotion improve as the campaign develops. They reach some sort of a peak when it is needed at the climax when pressure, injuries and general nerves can ruin the most composed of clubs.

Eastleigh did just about everything right. A steady but unspectacular start saw them very rarely outside the top ten. Then as the turn of the year was approached, four consecutive victories took 'The Spitfires' into second place.

The second half to the season and the run in was faced with confidence. Another four consecutive victories in early February including the defeat of Chelmsford City, developed into a run of fourteen games with twelve victories and only one defeat, but the competition in the Division was so strong Eastleigh were still only in third position.

A quite unbelievable defeat to Bognor with just two games to go looked desperate, but really didn't make much difference as they had safely gained a play-off place five points behind the Champions and twelve points ahead of the sixth placed club. Sadly for Eastleigh, a bang on form Hayes & Yeading came back from 2-4 in the first leg to win the second game 4-0 after extra time. This was a heartbreaking end to a terrific season for Eastleigh, effected by some vital injuries but suggesting an exciting future which can't come quickly enough.

EASTLEIGH

BEST LGE ATT.: 2,283 v AFC Wimbledon
LOWEST: 392 v Dorchester Town

No.	Date	Comp	H/A	Opponents	Att:	Result	Goalscorers	Pos
1	Aug 9	BSS	A	Thurrock	231	W 1 - 0	Byles 82	
2	12		H	Newport County	787	D 3 - 3	Riviere 40 45 Groves 64	
3	16		H	Fisher Athletic	494	W 3 - 0	Baker 30 Adeniyl 49 Riviere 79	3
4	23		A	Bromley	466	L 1 - 4	Groves 90	
5	25		H	Bognor Regis Town	907	W 2 - 1	Baker 24 **Taggart** 67	
6	30		A	St Albans City	408	L 0 - 5		7
7	Sept 1		A	Weston-s-Mere	254	D 1 - 1	Baker 86	
8	6		H	Braintree Town	525	W 2 - 1	Brown 79 Riviere 90	
9	**9**	**SS S1**	**H**	**Weston-Super-Mare**	**173**	**D 4 - 4***	**Groves 74 Roberts 90 101 Taggart 105 (Won 5-4 on pens)**	
10	13		H	Welling United	612	W 4 - 2	Bodkin 11 40 Groves 32 52	4
11	20		A	Bath City	675	D 1 - 1	Brown 22	6
12	**27**	**F.A.C. 2Q**	**H**	**Farnborough**	**687**	**W 1 - 0**	**Riviere 84**	
13	Oct 4		A	Chelmsford City	1128	L 0 - 3		6
14	**7**	**SS S2**	**H**	**Havant & Waterlooville**	**489**	**L 2 - 3**	**Baker 40 Bodkin 48**	
15	**11**	**F.A.C. 3Q**	**A**	**Burgess Hill Town**	**336**	**L 0 - 1**		
16	18		H	Hayes & Yeading	512	D 3 - 3	Riviere 2 Brown 8 53	9
17	21		H	Dorchester Town	392	L 0 - 1		
18	Nov 1		H	Hampton & Richmond B	551	W 2 - 1	Jordan 64 **Taggart** 81	9
19	8		A	Welling United	501	L 2 - 3	Forbes 65 90	10
20	15		A	Maidenhead United	401	W 4 - 1	Adeniyl 13 **Taggart** 50 Forbes 51 58	9
21	**22**	**F.A.T 3Q**	**H**	**Bashley**	**424**	**L 0 - 2**		
22	25		A	Team Bath	104	W 3 - 1	Groves 4 **Taggart** 47 Adeniyl 75	
23	29		H	Havant & Waterlooville	913	W 2 - 0	Riviere 38 Bodkin 83	3
24	Dec 2		A	AFC Wimbledon	2358	W 2 - 0	Harris 28 **Taggart** 85 (pen)	
25	6		A	Hayes & Yeading	285	W 1 - 0	Jordan 86	2
27	20		H	Thurrock	509	D 1 - 1	Groves 46	2
28	26		A	Basingstoke Town	474	L 0 - 1		3
29	Jan 1		H	Basingstoke Town	1015	W 1 - 0	Forbes 44	3
30	17		A	Braintree Town	479	D 1 - 1	Jordan 90	
31	24		H	Team Bath	544	L 1 - 3	Dixon 89	4
32	27		H	Bath City	507	W 2 - 0	Jordan 63 Martin 68	
33	31		A	Dorchester Town	543	W 4 - 0	Riviere 32 Martin 44 Jordan 48 Groves 77	4
34	Feb 7		H	Chelmsford City	828	W 2 - 1	Riviere 14 Brown 68	3
35	18		A	Fisher Athletic	287	W 2 - 1	Dixon10 **Taggart** 42	3
36	21		H	Bishop's Stortford	588	D 1 - 1	Williams 6	4
37	25		A	Newport Cunty	540	W 1 - 0	Carew 52	
38	28		H	Maidenhead United	552	D 0 - 0		3
39	Mar 7		A	Hampton & Richmond B	704	L 1 - 2	R.Lake 32 (og)	4
40	14		H	Weston-s-Mare	502	W 1 - 0	**Taggart** 68	3
41	21		A	Worcester City	577	W 1 - 0	**Taggart** 87 (pen)	3
42	28		H	AFC Wimbledon	2283	W 2 - 1	Jordan 61 Dixon 77	3
43	31		H	St Albans City	567	W 3 - 0	Dixon 13 Brown 22 **Taggart** 29	
44	April 4		A	Bishop's Stortford	381	W 4 - 3	Dixon 6 **Taggart** 51 Martin 53 Williams 86	3
45	10		H	Bromley	937	W 1 - 0	**Taggart** 9 (pen)	3
46	13		A	Bognor Regis Town	442	L 0 - 1		
47	18		H	Worcester City	648	W 1 - 0	Carew 18	3
48	25		A	Havant & Waterlooville	1239	D 2 - 2	Carew 38 Groves 85	3
49	**28**	**Play-off SF1**	**A**	**Hayes & Yeading**	**517**	**W 4 - 2**	**Taggart 5 Williams 26 Riviere 45 Mulley 50 (og)**	
50	**May 2**	**Play-off SF2**	**H**	**Hayes & Yeading**	**1445**	**L 0 - 4***		

Average Home Att: 723 (710) **Goals** 80 65

Best Position: 2nd **Worst:** 10th

Goalscorers: Taggart 13, Riviere 10, Groves 9, Brown 6, Jordan 6, Dixon 5, Forbes 5, Baker 4, Bodkin 4, Adeniyl 3, Carew 3, Martin 3, Williams 3, Roberts 2, Byles 1, Harris 1. Own Goals 2.

MATTHEWS	HARRIS	CHALLIS	BYLES	JORDAN	VICKERS	MASON	TAGGART	GROVES	BAKER	MARSHALL	BROWN	MARTIN	SHEPHERD	MILBURN	HOWELLS	RIVIERE	ADENIYI	GRIFFITHS	CLARKE	BODKIN	HUGHES	MAXWELL	GOODHIND	ROBERTS	DUTTON-BLACK	FORBES	DAVIES	CLARK	GRAY	WILLIAMS	BAIRD	SHARP	ROACHE	DIXON	CAREW	BRAYLEY	HEEROO	THOMAS	FLOOD	MORGAN	
X	X	X	X	X	X	X	X	X	X	X	S	U	U	U	U																										1
X	X	X	X	X	S	U	X	X	X	X	S	U			U	X	X																								2
X	X	X	X	X	U	S	X	X	X		S				U	X	X	X	S																						3
X	X	X	X	X	S	U	X	X	X		S				U	X	X		S	X																					4
X		X	X	X	U	U	X	X	X		X	X			U	X	X		S		S																				5
X		X	X	X		U	X	X	X		X	X			U	X	X		S		S	U																			6
X	X	X	X	X			X	X	S		X	U			U	X	X		U		X		U																		7
X	X	X	X	X			X	S	X		S				U	X	X			X	X		U	S																	8
U	**X**		**X**	**X**			**S**	**X**	**S**			**U**			**X**	**X**	**X**			**X**	**X**		**X**	**S**	**X**																9
X	X	X	X	X			X	X	S		X				U	X	X			X	S		U	S																	10
X	X	X	X				X	X	S		X	U			U	X	X			X	S		X	S																	11
X	**X**	**X**	**X**	**U**			**X**	**X**	**X**		**S**	**U**			**U**	**X**	**X**			**X**	**U**		**X**	**S**		**S**															12
X	X	X	X	U			X	X	S		X				U	X	X			S	X		X			S															13
X	**X**	**X**	**X**	**X**			**X**	**X**	**X**						**U**	**X**	**X**			**X**	**S**			**U**		**S**	**S**														14
X	**X**	**X**	**X**	**X**			**X**	**X**	**X**		**S**				**U**	**X**	**X**			**X**	**U**		**U**	**U**		**S**															15
X	X		X	X			X	X			X	U			U	X	X			X			X	S		S	S														16
X		X	X	X			X	X			X	U			U	X	X			X			X	S		S	U														17
X			X	X		U	X	X			S	U			U	X	X			X			X			X		X	U												18
X	X	U	X	X			X	S			X	U			U	X	X			S			X			X		X													19
X	X	U	X	X			X	X			S	U			U	X	X			S			X			X		X													20
X	**X**	**S**		**X**			**X**	**X**			**S**	**S**			**U**	**X**	**X**			**X**			**X**			**X**		**X**	**U**												21
X	X		X	X			X	X			X	S			U	X	X			S			U			X		X		S											22
X	X		X	X			X	X			X	S			U	X	X			S			U			X		X		U											23
X	X		X	X			X	X			X	X			U	X	X			S								X	U	S	U										24
X	X		X	X			X	X			X	U			U	X	X			S		U				X		X		U											25
X	X	U	X				X	X				X			U	X	X						U			X		X		U		X	S								26
X		X	X	X			X	X			S	X			U	X	X						U			X		X		S			S								27
X	X		X	X			X	S			X	U			U	X	X						U			X		X				X	S								28
X	X	X		X			X	S			X	U			U	X	X					U	X							S		X		X							29
X	X		X	X			X	S			X	U			U	X	X						S							S		X		X	X						30
X		U	X	X			X	X			X	X			U	X	X					S	X							S		U			X						31
X			X	X			X	X			X	X			U	X	X					S	X							S		S		U	X						32
X			X	X			X	S			X	X			U	X	X						X					S		S		U		X	X						33
X		S	X	X			X	S			X	X			U	X	X											X		S		U		X	X						34
X		S	X	X			X	S			X	X			U	X	X					U						X		X		S			X						35
X		U	X	X			X	S			X	X			U	X	X											X		X		S			X	S					36
X		U	X	X							X	X			U	X	X					S	X					X		X		U			X	S					37
X			X			U		X				X			U		X					U	X							X		X			X	X	X	S	U		38
X		U	X	X			S	S			X	X					X						X					X		X		U			X	S	X				39
X		U	X	X			X	S			X	X			U		X						X					X		X		U		S	X						40
X		U	X	X			X	U			X	X					X						X					S		S		U		X	X		X				41
X		U	X	X			X	S			X	X					X						X					S		S		U		X	X		X				42
X		U	X	X			X	S			X	X			U		X											X		S		U		X	X		X				43
X		U	X	X			X	S			X	X				U	X											X		S		U		X	X		X				44
X		S	X	X			S	X				X				U	X						X					X		S		U		X	X		X				45
X		S	X	X			X	S				X			U	X	X						X					U		X		U		X	X						46
		S	X	X		U	X	S			X	X					X					U	S					X		X				X	X					X	47
X		**U**	**X**	**X**			**X**	**S**			**X**	**X**			**U**	**X**	**X**						**X**					**S**		**X**					**X**		**S**				48
X		**S**	**X**	**X**			**X**	**S**			**X**	**X**			**U**	**X**	**X**											**X**		**X**		**U**			**X**		**S**				49
Total League Appearances																																									
41	20	14	41	38	1	1	38	24	7	2	30	22	0	0	0	32	41	1	0	7	3	0	19	0	0	9	0	20	0	8	0	5	0	11	18	1	7	0	0	1	X
0	0	5	0	0	2	1	2	16	4	0	8	2	0	0	0	0	0	0	4	7	4	3	2	5	0	3	1	3	0	14	0	3	3	1	0	3	0	1	0	0	S
0	0	12	0	1	2	7	0	1	0	0	0	13	1	1	36	2	0	0	1	0	0	6	8	0	0	0	1	1	2	3	1	12	0	1	0	0	0	0	1	0	U
Total Cup Appearances																																									
6	5	3	6	6	0	0	6	5	3	0	2	2	0	0	1	7	7	0	0	5	1	0	4	0	1	1	0	2	0	2	0	0	0	0	2	0	0	0	0	0	X
0	0	2	0	0	0	0	1	2	1	0	3	1	0	0	0	0	0	0	0	0	1	0	0	2	0	3	1	1	0	0	0	0	0	0	0	0	2	0	0	0	S
1	0	1	0	1	0	0	0	0	0	0	0	2	0	0	6	0	0	0	0	0	2	0	1	2	0	0	0	0	1	0	0	1	0	0	0	0	0	0	0	0	U

EASTLEIGH

CURRENT SQUAD AS OF BEGINING OF 2009-10 SEASON

GOALKEEPERS	HT	WT	D.O.B	AGE	P.O.B	CAREER	Apps	Gls
Gareth Howells			13/6/70	39	Guildford	Tottenham, Torquay, Farnborough, Hellenic (SA), Dorking, St Albans, Sutton U, Aldershot 5/01, Havant & W 7/03, Eastleigh (Pl/Coach) 10/07	0	0
Dan Loader						Christchurch, Eastleigh c/s 09		
Jason Matthews	6'00"	12 02	15/3/75	34	Paulton	Mangotsfield, Welton R, Westbury, Bath C, Paulton, Nuneaton, Taunton 8/98, Exeter 8/99 Rel c/s 00, Aberystwyth c/s 00, Cleveden 6/01, Weymouth 8/02, Eastleigh 3/08	41	0
DEFENDERS								
Trevor Challis	5'08"	11 06	23/10/75	33	Paddington	QPR, Bristol R 7/98 Rel c/s 03, Exeter (Trial) 7/03, Telford 8/03, Shrewsbury 3/04 Rel c/s 05, Weymouth 7/05, Eastleigh 6/08	19	0
Sam Doswell						Eastleigh		
Warren Goodhind	5'11"	11 06	16/8/77	32	Johannesburg, SA	Barnet, Millwall (Trial) 7/01, Cambridge U £80,000 9/01 Rel c/s 05, Rochdale 9/05, Oxford U (SL) 2/06, Bishops Stortford 3/07, Dag & Red (Trial) c/s 07, Ebbsfleet 8/07, Eastleigh (L) 11/07 Perm Rel 5/08, Harrow c/s 08, Eastleigh 8/08	21	0
Michael Green			12/5/89	20		Christchurch, New Milton T 10/07, Christchurch, Eastleigh 5/09		
Tom Jordan	6'04"	12 04	24/5/81	28	Manchester	Bristol C Rel c/s 02, Huddersfield (Trial) 3/02, Carlisle (Trial) 7/02, Exeter (Trial) 7/02, Southend 8/02 Rel c/s 03, Tamworth 8/03, Forest Green 3/04, Havant & W 8/04, Eastleigh 6/08	38	6
Arron Martin						Eastleigh	24	3
Ian Oliver			9/10/85	23	Southampton	Reading (Yth), Bournemouth (Yth), Swindon (Scholar), Eastleigh 7/05, Farnborough (3ML) 10/07 Perm 1/08, Eastleigh 6/09		
MIDFIELDERS								
Peter Adeniyi					London	Erith T, Dulwich H, Lewes 7/03, Beckenham 6/05, Bromley 7/06, Eastleigh 12/07	41	3
Jamie Brown					Bournemouth	BAT Sports, Dorchester 7/01, Eastleigh 4 fig 9/06	38	6
Steve Clark	6'01"	12 05	10/2/82	27	London	West Ham, Southend (2ML) 11/01, Southend 1/02 Rel c/s 04, Macclesfield (L) 9/03, Hornchurch c/s 04, Weymouth 12/04, Dag & Red 12/04, Weymouth 3/05, Fisher 5/06 Rel 5/07, Bromley 8/07 Rel 10/08, Eastleigh 10/08	23	0
Shaun McAuley						Hayes & Yeading, Hampton & R c/s 07, Walton Casuals (Dual) 10/07, Eastleigh 7/09		
Brett Poate			30/9/83	25	Southampton	Southampton Rel 2/03, Havant & W (2ML) 8/02, QPR (Trial) 2/03, Havant & W 2/03 Rel 4/09, Bognor Regis (L) 1/04, Eastleigh 4/09		
Anthony Riviere			9/11/78	30	Kent	Faversham, Welling 11/98, Fisher 6/04 Rel 5/07, Eastleigh 7/07	32	7
Danny Smith	5'11"	11 04	17/8/82	27	Southampton	Bashley (Yth), Bournemouth Rel c/s 02, Winchester 7/02, Eastleigh 7/04, Bashley (3ML) 12/07, Bashley 3/08, Bognor Regis 7/08, Eastleigh 5/09		
Tony Taggart			7/10/81	27	London	Brentford Rel c/s 00, Farnborough c/s 00, Barnet 6/03, Farnborough 8/04, Weymouth 6/05, Havant & W 12/05, Eastleigh 7/08	40	11
FORWARDS								
Andy Forbes			28/5/79	30	Reading	Reading, Basingstoke, Andover, Winchester 8/02, Eastleigh 8/04	12	5
Richard Gillespie						Southampton (Yth), Bashley, Salisbury (SL) 3/05, Eastleigh Undisc 6/09		
Brett Williams			1/12/87	21	Southampton	Eastleigh (Yth), Winchester, Eastleigh 11/08	22	2
Matt Gray			18/9/81	27		Eastleigh (Coach)	0	0
Ian Baird						Eastleigh (Manager)	0	0

LOANEES	HT	WT	DOB	AGE	POB	From - To	APPS	GOA
(M)Matt Bodkin	5'06"	10 11	16/9/86	22	Chatham	Grays (6ML) 8/08 - Dover 2/09, Rel 5/09, Thurrock 5/09	14	3
(M)Adam Roberts			8/11/87	21	Southampton	Sutton U (Dual) 9/08 - VT FC 10/08	5	0
(F)Lee Roache	5'09"	11 00	30/4/84	25	Leytonstone	Cambridge C 12/08 - Histon Undisc 1/09	3	0
(F)Jonny Dixon	5'09"	11 01	16/1/84	25	Murcia, Spa	Brighton (2ML) 1/09 - Rel c/s 09, Retired 7/09	12	5
(G)Nick Morgan	6'07"					Braintree (EL) 4/09 -	1	0

DEPARTURES	HT	WT	DOB	AGE	POB	From - To	APPS	GOA
(M)Mark Marshall			9/5/86	23		Grays (L) 12/07 Perm_ Bournemouth (Trial) 8/08, Swindon Undisc 8/08	2	0
(F)Leroy Griffiths	5'11"	13 05	30/12/76	32	London	Gillingham 8/08 - Staines 8/08	1	0
(F)Tom Clarke	5'08"	09 13	2/1/89	20	Worthing	Bridgwater 8/08 - Bognor 9/08	4	0
(D)Ashley Vickers	6'03"	13 10	14/6/72	27	Sheffield	Weymouth 3/08 - Newport C (L) 8/08 Perm 9/08, Dorchester (Pl/Coach) 3/09	3	0
(M)Josh Dutton-Black			29/12/87	21	Oxford	Bognor 9/08 - AFC Totton, Didcot T 1/09	0	0
(M)David Hughes			30/12/72	36	St Albans	Southampton (Pl/Ass Man) 7/01 (Pl/Man 7/07) - Rel 10/08, Sutton U 10/08, AFC Totton 6/09	7	0
(M)James Baker						Braintree 6/08 - Welling 10/08, Chelmsford 12/08 Rel 2/09, Welling 2/09, Billericay 5/09	11	3
(D)Neil Davies			28/11/75	33	Batley	Westfield c/s 08 - Uxbridge 10/08	1	0
(F)Bert Brayley	5'09"	12 07	5/9/81	27	Basildon	Chelmsford 2/09 - Chelmsford 3/09 Rel 7/09 Re-signed 8/09	4	0
(D)Luke Byles	5'11"	12 00	8/1/84	25	Southampton	Havant & W 8/07 - Rel c/s 09, Travelling	41	1
(M)Andy Harris	5'10"	12 05	26/2/77	32	Springs, SA	Weymouth (L) 9/06 Perm 10/06 - Rel 5/09, Weymouth 5/09	20	1
(M)Gavin Heeroo	5'11"	11 07	2/9/84	24	Harringey	Sutton U 3/09 - Rel 5/09, Ebbsfleet 7/09	7	0
(F)Matt Groves			17/4/80	29	Poole	Lewes 5/08 - Rel 5/09, Dorchester 6/09	40	8
(M)Ashley Carew	6'00"	11 00	17/12/85	23	Lambeth	Barnet 3/09 - Bromley 6/09	18	3
(D)Adam Gatcum						Corinthian Casuals 3/09 -		
(D)Adam Shepherd						Newport IOW (Yth) c/s 07 -	0	0
(M)Chris Mason			11/1/91	18	Southampton	Bournemouth (Yth) -	2	0
(M)Neil Sharp	6'01"	12 05	19/1/78	31	Hemel Hempstead	Cambridge C 12/08 -	8	0
(M)Martin Thomas	5'08"	12 06	12/9/73	35	Lyndhurst	ex AFC Totton 3/09 -	1	0
(F)Joe Maxwell						Yth -	3	0
(F)Arron Milburn						Portsmouth (Yth) -	0	0
(M)Chris Flood						QPR 3/09 - Salisbury 8/09	0	0

EASTLEIGH

Formed: 1946

Nickname: The Spitfires.

Club Colours: White shirts, blue shorts, white socks.

Change Colours: Red shirts, shorts and socks.

Club Sponsor: Silverlake Garage.

Previous League: Isthmian League

Gound address: Silverlake Stadium 'Ten Acres', Stoneham Lane, North Stoneham, Eastleigh SO50 9HT

Telephone: 02380 613 361

Mobile: 07801 638 158

Fax: 02380 612 379

Email: admin@eastleigh-fc.co.uk

Website: www.eastleigh-fc.co.uk

Simple Directions: M27 Jct 5 to roundabout exit marked Stoneham Lane. Carry on to next roundabout and drive down Stoneham Lane, turning right opposite Concord Club. Ground 400 yards on left.

Capacity: 2,300 **Seats**: 175 **Covered**: 385 **Floodlights**: Yes

Clubhouse: 11-11 Mon-Sat plus mid day Sundays.

Club Shop: Yes

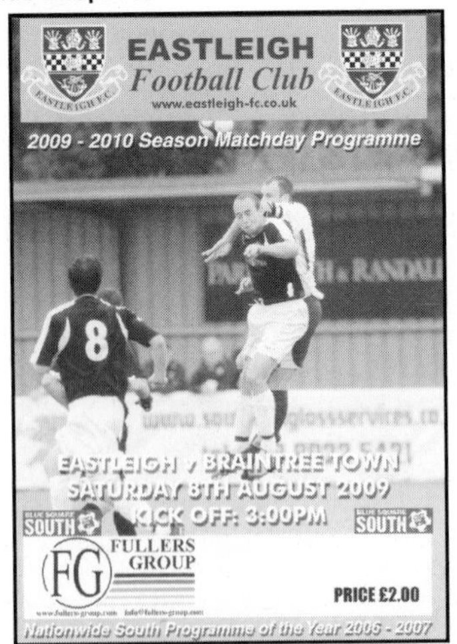

PROGRAMME EDITOR

Mike Denning

(M) 07941 338 216

Email: mike.denning@talk21.com

CLUB STATISTICS

RECORDS

Attendance: 2,589 V Southampton July 2005

Victory: 12-1 v Hythe & Dibden (H) 11.12.48

Defeat: 0-11 v Austin Sports (A) 01.01.47

Career Goalscorer: Johnnie Williams 177

Career Appearances: Ian Knight 611

Record Transfer Fee Paid:

£10,000 to Newport (I.O.W.) for Colin Matthews

Received: Undisclosed

SENIOR HONOURS

Wessex Division One 2002-03.

Wessex League Cup 1992, 2003.

Southampton Senior League (West) 1950.

PREVIOUS

Leagues: Southampton Jnr & Snr 46-59 Hampshire 50-86

Wessex 86-2003. Isthmian Premier 2004-2005

Names: Swaythling Athletic 1946-59. Swaythling 1973-80.

HAMPTON & RICHMOND BOROUGH

Back Row (left to right) Alan Devonshire (Manager), Stuart Lake, Ian Hodges, Orlando Jeffrey, Graham Harper, Matt Lovett, Chico Ramos, Jamie Collins, Craig Tanner, John Scarborough. Steve Tyson, Dean Inman, Keiron Knight, Steve McPherson (Chairman)
Front Row; Dean Wells, Ashley Smith, Dudley Gardner, Leon Yarnie, Francis Quarm, Jon McDonald, Lawrence Yaku, Robbie Kember, Marcello Fernandes, David Tarpey

Hampton & Richmond Borough are sponsored by

1st Express Maintenance

CLUB PERSONNEL

Chairman: Steve McPherson.

Company Secretary: Gerry Jones.

President: Alan Simpson.

Managing Director: Steve O'Neill.

Additional Directors: Nick Hornsey, Nick Lyons,

Chas Milner, Brian Barwick, Marc Cranfield-Adams.

Secretary: Nick Hornsey

8 The Avenue, Hampton, Middlesex TW12 7RS

(M): 07768 861 446

nickhornsey@btinternet.com

Press Officer: Les Rance

(M): 07732 122 850

lesrance1949@virginmedia.com

Manager: Alan Devonshire.

Club therapist: TBA.

After play-off disappointment in 2008 an excellent league campaign saw 'The Beavers' back in the play-offs and the big match pressure was on again. The top five in the division really enjoyed consistent results and it had been very difficult for any club outside that group to break in.

After a steady start, third place was reached at the beginning of September and Borough were never out of the top five for the rest of the season. Brackley Town had ended any hopes of an F.A.Cup run after earlier victories against Dartford and Whyteleafe, and one game at home to Bury Town was enough to end their involvement with the F.A.Trophy.

The New Year signalled Hampton & Richmond really turning on the power and until the end of the season only three more league games were lost and a run of nine victories could still only secure them second place. Attendances were good especially for the end of season local 'derby' against A.F.C.Wimbledon when a thrilling 1-1 draw was watched by 3,225.

The play-offs brought success against a Chelmsford City club who had strangely lost their confidence in the second half of the season but 'The Beavers' then faced Hayes & Yeading, who must have thought they were unbeatable having come back from four down in the first leg to beat Eastleigh in the semi-final 6-4 on aggregate after extra time. Their confidence was understandable, and they won at The Beveree 3-2 after conceding the first and third goals to a desperate home side who saw a great season finally come to a close with nothing but pride to show for it.

HAMPTON & RICHMOND BORO'

BEST LGE ATT.: 3,225 v AFC Wimbledon
LOWEST: 278 v Bishop's Stortford

No.	Date	Comp	H/A	Opponents	Att:	Result	Goalscorers	Pos
1	Aug 9	BSS	A	Basingstoke Town	440	D 1 - 1	**Yaku** 75	
2	12		H	Bognor Regis Town	430	D 0 - 0		
3	16		H	Weston-s-Mare	365	W 4 - 1	S.Lake 11 17 R Kember 19 57	9
4	23		A	Braintree Town	451	W 2 - 1	Hodges 15 73 (pen)	7
5	25		H	Hayes & Yeading	654	L 2 - 3	Scarborough 18 Wright 83	
6	30		A	Newport County	931	L 0 - 1		
7	Sept 2		A	Thurrock	243	D 3 - 3	Scarborough 56 Jeffrey 68 **Yaku** 76	
8	6		H	Bromley	517	D 1 - 1	R.Lake 40 (pen)	11
9	**9**	**SS S1**	**A**	**Braintree Town**	**127**	**L 0 - 3**		
10	13		H	Bath City	501	W 3 - 1	Tanner 23 **Yaku** 29 Holland 86 (og)	9
11	20		A	Havant & Waterlooville	732	W 4 - 1	Wright 15 Matthews 47 Scarborough 75 R Lake 81	7
12	**27**	**F.A.C. 2Q**	**A**	**Dartford**	**1057**	**W 1 - 0**	**Matthews 43**	
13	Oct 4		A	Fisher Athletic	128	W 2 - 0	**Yaku** 20 43	7
14	**11**	**F.A.C 3Q**	**H**	**Whyteleafe**	**501**	**W 2 - 0**	**Yaku 18 Matthews 77**	
15	18		H	Team Bath	615	W 3 - 0	Scarborough 45 McAuley 50 Wright 54	6
16	21		H	Maidenhead United	390	W 1 - 0	Wright 23	
17	**25**	**F.A.C. 4Q**	**H**	**Brackley Town**	**582**	**L 0 - 1**		
18	Nov 1		A	Eastleigh	551	L 1 - 2	Wright 5	7
19	8		H	Worcester City	549	L 1 - 2	Wright 11	8
20	15		H	Dorchester Town	458	H 2 - 0	Tanner 10 Wright 69	8
21	18		A	Bishop's Stortford	231	W 3 - 1	Tyson 32 Wright 81 **Yaku** 87	
22	**22**	**F.A.T 3Q**	**H**	**Bury Town**	**334**	**L 1 - 2**	**Matthews 24**	
23	29		A	AFC Wimbledon	3366	D 1 - 1	Wells 69	4
24	Dec 6		A	Bognor Regis T	328	W 1 - 0	Wright 57	3
25	20		H	Basingstoke Town	644	D 0 - 0		4
26	26		A	St Albans City	609	D 2 - 2	**Yaku** 53 Hodges 78	4
27	Jan 1		H	St Albans City	687	D 0 - 0		
28	3		A	Weston-s-Mare	311	W 3 - 0	WRIGHT 3 (16 58 75 (pen)	4
29	17		A	Team Bath	171	W 2 - 0	**Yaku** 59 Wright 89	3
30	24		H	Thurrock	786	W 3 - 1	Hughes 12 (og) Quam 53 McAuley 75	3
31	31		A	Bromley	382	W 2 - 0	**Yaku** 3 Hodges 48	3
32	Feb 14		H	Fisher Athletic	401	W 3 - 0	Quarm 10 Hodges 11 Lake R 78	3
33	17		H	Welling United	475	W 2 - 0	**Yaku** 73 Badu 82	
34	21		A	Bath City	552	W 1 - 0	Quarm 77	2
35	24		H	Bishop's Stortford	278	W 2 - 1	Quarm 68 pen 75 pen	
36	28		A	Worcester City	667	W 2 - 1	Knight 50 Hodges 90	2
37	Mar 3		H	Newport County	409	L 0 - 1		
38	7		H	Eastleigh	704	W 2 - 1	Quarm 81 Knight 90	2
39	14		A	Welling United	605	L 0 - 4		2
40	21		H	Chelmsford City	816	W 4 - 1	Scarborough 16 Hodges 68 **Yaku** 81 85	2
41	28		H	Havant & Waterlooville	622	W 2 - 1	Knight 47 Hodges 85	2
42	April 4		A	Dorchester Town	411	W 1 - 0	**Yaku** 49	2
43	6		A	Chelmsford City	1114	L 2 - 3	Scarborough 48 Wells 77	
44	11		H	Braintree Town	650	W 2 - 1	Wells 34 Badu 40	2
45	13		A	Hayes & Yeading	565	D 0 - 0		
46	18		H	AFC Wimbledon	3225	D 1 - 1	Quarm 52	2
47	25		A	Maidenhead United	436	W 3 - 0	Fernandas 44 **Yaku** 54 57	2
47	**28**	**Play-off SF1**	**A**	**Chelmsford City**	**1708**	**W 3 - 1**	**Yaku 44 50 Hodges 83**	
48	**May 2**	**Play-off SF2**	**H**	**Chelmsford City**	**1235**	**D 0 - 0**		
50	**7**	**Play-off F**	**H**	**Hayes & Yeading**	**3111**	**L 2 - 3**	**McCauley 50 Hodges 70**	

Average Home Att: 675 (514) **Goals** 83 47

Best Position: 2nd **Worst:** 11th

Goalscorers: Yaku 18, Wright 13, Hodges 10, Quarm 7, Scarborough 6, Matthews 4, Knight 3, Lake R 3, Wells 3, Badu 2, Kember 2, Lake S 2, McAuley 3, Tanner 2, Fernandas 1, Jeffrey 1, Tyson 1. Own Goals 2.

LOVETT	HARPER	R LAKE	JEFFREY	SCARBOROUGH	WELLS	S LAKE	MCAULEY	YAKU	HODGES	KEMBER	WRIGHT	HARRIS	TYSON	BRAITHWAITE	FERNANDES	COOKE	MATTHEWS	BOXALL	BADU	QUARM	DRAKE	TANNER	ROBINSON	RUDDICK	ROFFEY	BROWN	BLACKSHAW	FRANCIS	KNIGHT	TALBOT	INMAN	MCDONALD	HUGGINS	ATIASE	
X	X	X	X	X	X	X	X	X	X	X	S	S	U	U	U																				1
X	X	X	X	X	X	X	X	X	X	X	S	S	U	U	U																				2
X	X	X		X	X	X	X	X	X	X		U	S	X	S	S																			3
X	X	X	X	X	X	X		X	X	X		U	U	U	S	S	X																		4
X	X	X		X	X	X		X	X	X	S	U	U	X	S	X	S																		5
X		U	X	X	X	U		S	X	X	X		X	U	X	S	X	X																	6
X	X	X	X	X	X	X		X	X		S		U	U	X	S	X		U																7
X	X	X	X	X	X	X		X	X		S			U	X		X		S	U															8
	X	**U**	**X**	**U**	**X**	**S**		**X**						**X**	**X**		**X**		**X**	**X**	**X**	**X**	**S**												9
X	X	U	X	X	X	X		X	X		S			U	S		X			X		X													10
X		S	X	X	X			U	X	X	X			S	X		X			X		X	U												11
X		**U**	**X**	**X**	**X**	**S**	**U**	**S**	**X**	**X**	**X**			**S**	**X**		**X**			**X**		**X**													12
X		U		X	X	X	S	X			X		S	X	X		X			X		X		S											13
X		**S**		**X**		**X**	**X**	**X**	**U**	**S**	**X**		**S**	**X**	**X**		**X**			**X**		**X**		**U**	**U**										14
X		S		X	X	X	S	X		X	X		S	X	X		X					X		U											15
X		S	X	X	X		X	X	S		X		X	U	X		X					X	U	U											16
X	**S**	**U**	**X**	**X**	**X**		**X**	**X**	**S**		**X**		**S**	**U**	**X**		**X**			**X**		**X**	**U**		**U**										17
X	S		X	X	X		S	X			X		X	U	X		X			X		X				U									18
X	S		X		X		S	X			X		X	X	X		X		S	X		X				U	U								19
X	X	U	X	X	X		X	S			X		S	U	X		X		S	X		X													20
X	X	S	X	X	X		X	S			X		X	U	X		X		S			X													21
X	**X**	**X**	**X**	**X**	**X**		**X**	**S**	**S**	**X**	**X**		**X**		**U**		**X**		**S**								**U**								22
X	X	U	X	X	X		S	X	S	X	X		S	U	X		X					X													23
X	X	U	X	X	X	U	X	S	X	X	X				X		X		S	S															24
X	X	X	X	X	X	X	S	S	X	X	X						X			U															25
X		X	X	X	X	X	S	X	S	U	X		U		X		X		U	X															26
X	X	U	X	X	X	S	X	X	X	U	S		U		X		X			X															27
X	U	X	X	X	X	X	S	X		X	X		S		X		X		S	U															28
X		X	X	X	X	X	U	X	X	S	S		U		X		X		S	X															29
X	X	X	X	X	X	X	S	X	X	S			U		S		X		U	X															30
X	X	S	X		X	X	X	X	X	S					X		X		S	X								U							31
X	X	U	X	X	X	X	X	X	X	S			S		U		X			X									S						32
X	S	U	X	X	X	X	X	X	X				U		X		X		S	X									S						33
X	X	U	X	X	X	X	S	X	X	U			U		X		X			X									S						34
X	X	S	X		X	X	X	X	X	S			U		X		X			X									S	U					35
X	X	S	X	X	X	X	S	X	S						X		X			X									X		U				36
X	X	S	X	X	X	X	X	X	S	X			S				X												X		U				37
X	U	X	X	X	X	X	X	X	X	S			U		X					X					U				S						38
X	X	S	X	X	X	X	S	X	U				S		X		X			X									X						39
X	X		X	X	X	X	X	S	X				S		X		X		U										X			S	U		40
X	X		X	X	X	X	X	S	X				S		X				U	X									X			S	U		41
X	X	U	X	X	X	X	U	X	X				U		X		X			X									S			S			42
X	X	U	X	X	X		X	S	X				U		S		X		U	X									X			X			43
X	X		X	X	X	X	S	U	X				U		S		X		S	X									X			X			44
X		U	X	X	X	X	X	S	S				S		X		X			X									X			X			45
X		S	X	X	X	X	X	S	X				S		X					X					U				X		U	X			46
X	S	X			S		U	X					X	X	X		U		X								X	X	S		X			X	47
X	**X**	**S**	**X**		**X**	**X**	**X**	**X**	**X**				**U**	**U**	**X**		**X**		**U**	**X**									**S**						48
X	**X**	**S**	**X**		**X**	**X**	**X**	**X**					**U**	**U**	**X**		**X**		**S**	**X**								**S**	**X**						49
X	**X**	**U**	**X**	**U**	**X**	**X**	**X**	**S**	**X**				**S**		**X**		**X**		**S**	**X**									**X**						50
Total League Appearances																																			
42	27	14	37	38	41	30	19	30	27	13	14	0	6	6	30	1	34	1	1	24	0	10	0	0	0	0	1	1	9	0	1	4	0	1	**X**
0	4	10	0	0	1	1	13	10	6	6	8	2	13	1	7	4	1	0	10	1	0	0	0	1	0	0	0	0	7	0	0	3	0	0	**S**
0	2	13	0	0	0	2	3	2	1	3	0	3	16	12	3	0	1	0	6	3	0	0	2	2	2	2	1	1	0	1	3	0	2	0	**U**
Total Cup Appearances																																			
7	5	1	7	4	7	4	6	5	3	2	4	0	1	2	7	0	8	0	1	7	1	4	0	0	0	0	0	0	2	0	0	0	0	0	**X**
0	1	3	0	0	0	2	0	3	2	1	0	0	3	1	0	0	0	0	3	0	0	0	1	0	0	0	0	1	1	0	0	0	0	0	**S**
0	0	4	0	2	0	0	1	0	1	0	0	0	2	3	1	0	0	0	1	0	0	0	1	1	2	0	1	0	0	0	0	0	0	0	**U**

HAMTPON & RICHMOND

CURRENT SQUAD AS OF BEGINING OF 2009-10 SEASON

GOALKEEPERS	HT	WT	D.O.B	AGE	P.O.B	CAREER	Apps	Gls
Kevin Davies						Wits Univ (SA), Spartak (SA), Sutton U, Kingstonian, Aylesbury 4/03, Hayes/Hayes & Yeading 8/04, Sutton U 1/08, Hampton & R 8/09		
Matt Lovett			5/9/79	29	Middlesex	Staines, Hampton & R 6/05	42	0
Trevor Roffey						Hampton & R (Gk Coach)	0	0
Joe Talbot						Hampton & R	0	0
DEFENDERS								
Elliot Braithwaite						Wycombe (Yth) Rel c/s 08 QPR (Trial) 3/09, Didcot T, Hampton & R 8/08, Walton Casuals (L) 11/08, Ashford T (L) 12/08	7	0
Jack Francis						Hampton & R	1	0
Graham Harper					London	Portsmouth (Scholar), Carshalton, Croydon Ath, Croydon c/s 99, Lewes 8/02, Whyteleafe 8/03, Hampton & R 8/04	31	0
Romario Henry						Kingstonian, Hampton & R 11/08		
Dean Inman						Hampton & R	1	0
Orlando Jeffrey	6'02"		23/9/77	31	Berkshire	Burnham, Thatcham, Maidenhead, Hampton & R c/s 03, Hayes 5/05, Hampton & R 8/07	37	1
Jon McDonald			18/5/85	24	Kingston	Staines, Hampton & R 3/09	7	0
John Scarborough	6'01"		13/3/79	30	Gravesend	Gravesend, Ashford T, Herne Bay, Eastbourne B, Tilbury, Billericay c/s 03, Tilbury 2/04, Chelmsford (Trial) c/s 04, Dover 9/04, Sutton U 9/04, Hampton & R 6/08	38	6
Craig Tanner			13/2/86	23	Surrey	Tooting & Mitcham, Sutton U 10/06, Hampton & R 2/08, Leatherhead (L) 9/08	10	2
Dean Wells	6'01"	13 02	25/3/85	24	Isleworth	Brentford Rel c/s 04, Hampton & R 6/04	42	3
MIDFIELDERS								
Jesse Atiase						Hampton & R	1	0
James Blackshaw						Hampton & R	1	0
Jamie Collins	6'03"	12 00	28/9/84	24	Barking	Watford, Havant & W 2/05, Hampton & R 7/09		
Marcello Fernandes			23/7/76	33	Cape Town, SA	Hellenic (SA), Maidenhead, Staines (99/00), Feltham, Hampton & R 8/03, Wealdstone (Dual) 3/07	37	1
Stuart Lake			17/11/79	29	London	Wimbledon, Walton & Hersham, Farnborough 10/98, Northwood 3/99, Yeading, Northwood, Marlow 2/03, Uxbridge 7/04, Ashford T (Middx), Hampton & R 2/07	31	3
Barrie Matthews	5'09"	10 10	1/2/83	26	Cinderford	Cirencester (Yth), Watford Rel c/s 03, Swindon S (SL) 3/03, Swindon S 8/03, Hornchurch 1/04, Maidenhead 8/04, Hampton & R 9/05	35	1
Francis Quarm			1/8/83	26		Dulwich H (Yth), Tooting & M (Yth), Dulwich H 7/01, Hampton & R 7/05, Windsor & E (Dual) 9/07	25	7
Ashley Smith			22/12/83	25		Flackwell Heath, Burnham, Flackwell Heath 11/04, Maidenhead c/s 06, Hampton & R 8/09		
Steve Tyson			20/4/88	21		AFC Wimbledon Rel 6/08, Walton Casuals, Hampton & R 8/08, Walton Casuals (Dual), Burnham (L) 1/09	19	1
FORWARDS								
Craig Dundas						Local, Croydon, Dulwich H 1/04, Cyprus, Dulwich H c/s 05, Carshalton 11/05, Sutton U 11/07 Rel c/s 09, Carshalton (Trial) 7/09, Tooting & M (Trial) 8/09, Hampton & R 8/09		
Ian Hodges			18/10/82	26	Cornwall	Porthleven, St Ives, Hayes 8/01, Slough 2/03, Hampton & R 6/06	33	8
Levi King						Hampton & R		
Kieran Knight					Middlesex	Southall, Chertsey, Southall, Northwood, Aylesbury, Enfield, Northwood 8/02, Hayes/Hayes & Yeading 7/04, Hampton & R 2/09	16	3
David Tarpay			14/11/88	20		C.Palace (Yth), Basingstoke Rel 5/09, Hampton & R c/s 09		
Lawrence Yaku					Nigeria	Wealdstone, Ruislip Manor, Wokingham 7/99, Maidenhead 5/02, Hampton & R 8/05	40	15

DEPARTURES	HT	WT	DOB	AGE	POB	From - To	APPS	GOA
(M)Stephen Cooke	5'08"	09 08	15/2/83	26	Walsall	ex Halesowen T 8/08 - Rel 9/08, Stourport 2/09, Weymouth 3/09	5	0
(D)Danny Boxall			24/8/77	32	Croydon	Retired 8/08 - Whyteleafe, Croydon A Retired 12/08	1	0
(M)Glen Harris						Slough - Burnham 9/08, Slough 10/08	2	0
(D)Luke Ruddick			3/3/90	19		Walton Casuals 10/08 - Harrow 11/08, Salisbury 11/08	1	0
(F)Ben Wright			10/8/88	21		Carshalton 8/08 - Peterborough Undisc 1/09, Kettering (6WL) 3/09	22	13
(D)Chris Robinson						Staines - Walton Casuals (L), Uxbridge 2/09	0	0
(D)Ryan Lake						Ashford T (Middx) 2/06 - Kingstonian 7/09	24	2
(M)Shaun McAuley						Hayes & Yeading c/s 07 - Eastleigh 7/09	32	2
(G)Kieran Drake						??? -Hampton & R	0	0
(M)Josh Huggins			3/11/90	18		Aldershot T 3/09 -	0	0
(M)Robert Kember			21/8/81	28	Wimbledon	Eastbourne B 7/08 -	19	2
(F)Nana Badu						Walton Casuals 6/08 - Walton Casuals (L) 10/08	11	2
Jermaine Brown						Yth -	0	0

HAMPTON & RICHMOND BOROUGH

Formed: 1921

Nickname: Beavers or Borough.

Club Colours: Red shirts, shorts and socks.

Change Colours: Light blue shirts, shorts and socks.

Club Sponsor: African Revival

Previous League: Isthmian League

Ground address: MEM Beveree Stadium, Beavor Close, off Station Road, Hampton TW12 2BX

Telephone: 0208 8979 2456

Email: info@hamptonfc.com

Website: www.hamptonfc.net

Simple Directions: From Hampton Court Bridge onto A 308, after a mile right into Church St (A3110) and left after White Hart pub into High St. Station Road is on right.

Capacity: 3,000 **Seats:** 300 Covered: 800 **Floodlights:**Yes

Clubhouse: Matchdays & training nights. Function hall for hire.

Club Shop: Yes.

Local Press: Middlesex Chronicle, Surrey Comet, Richmond & Twickenham Times and The Informer.

The Beveree Review 2009/10
Hampton & Richmond Borough FC
Main Sponsor
1st Express Maintenance
Kit Supplier
Vandanel
Club Charity
African Revival
Carling
A&A
League Sponsors
Blue Square South
The Beavers v Thurrock FC
Saturday 29th August
Kick off 3pm
£2.50

PROGRAMME EDITOR

Stefan Rance

(M) 07968 778 761

Email: Stefan.rance@taagl.com

CLUB STATISTICS

RECORDS

Attendance : 2,520 v AFC Wimbledon - 11.10.05

Victory: 11-1 v Eastbourne United, Isthmian Div 2 (S) 91--92

Defeat: 0-13 v Hounslow Town Middx Sen Cup 62-3

Career Goalscorer: Peter Allen - 176 1964-73

Career Appearances: Tim Hollands - 750 1977-95

Record Transfer Fee Paid:£3,000 to Chesham United for Matt Flitter June 2000

Received: £40,000 from Q.P.R. for Leroy Phillips

SENIOR HONOURS

Champions Isthmian League 2006-07

London Senior Cup (2)

Spartan League (4)

PREVIOUS

Leagues: Kingston & Dist., S.W. Middx, Surrey Senior 1959-64. Spartan 1964-71. Athenian. Isthmian.

HAVANT & WATERLOOVILLE

Back row (L-R): Martin Matthews (Kit Manager), Ryan Woodford, Gary MacDonald, Gary Norgate, Nathan Ashmore, Aaron Howe, Jay Gasson, Sam Pearce, Paul Hinshelwood, Stuart Page (Academy Manager). **Centre Row:** Sarah Taylor (Assistant Physio), Robbie Martin, Luke Nightingale, Mustafa Tyriaki, Jake Newton, Ian Simpemba (Club Captain), Shaun Wilkinson, Stephen Hutchings, Conor Geoghegan, Manny Williams, Wes Fogden, Claire Alexandra (Assistant Physio), Ollie Jones (Goalkeeper Coach). **Front Row:** Phil Ashwell (Therapist), John Dyer (Director), John Carter (Director), Adrian Aymes (Fitness Coach), Shaun Gale (Manager), Steve Johnson (Assistant Manager), Kevin Moore (Director), Pat Walsh (Director), Trevor Brock (Secretary/Director).

CLUB PERSONNEL

Chairman: Derek Pope.

Company Secretary: Ray Jones.

Additional Directors: Trevor Brock, John Carter, John Dyer, Kevin Moore, Pat Walsh, Adrian Hewett.

Secretary: Trevor Brock

2 Betula Close, Waterlooville, Hants PO7 8EJ

(H): 02392 267 276

(M): 07768 271 143

trevor.brock52@yahoo.com

Commercial Manager: Adrian Aymes.

Tel: (B) 02392 787 822

Email: adi@thehawksfc.com

Press Officer: As secretary.

Manager: Shaun Gale.

Assistant Manager: Steve Johnson.

Club therapist: Phil Ashwell.

With their F.A.Cup heroics from the previous season still fresh in most supporters minds, 'The Hawks' were expected to enjoy a season near the top of The Blue Square South and at least challenge for promotion. But despite the extra cash from the cup run, they probably suffered from the fact that every club attempted to raise their game to put them back in their place after their national burst of publicity.

Cup ties however still brought the best out of the Hampshire club and five F.A.Cup matches brought victories over Shortwood United after a replay, Godalming Town and Crawley Town, before a First Round tie against high flying Division Two club Brentford was lost 2-3 at Westleigh Park.

The F.A.Trophy brought one more cup tie as The Hawks played six matches against Fisher Athletic (A) 2-0, Bury Town (H) 3-1, Lewes (A) 3-3 (H) 4-3, Crawley Town (H) 2-0 and finally, in the Fourth Round they lost to York City by the only two goals of the game. These cup runs lit up the season as their league position was deteriorating.

Only five victories in the new year took Havant & Waterlooville very close to the danger zone and in the last two months of the season it was the goalscoring of Luke Nightingale (6 including 4 penalties) and Craig Watkins (7) who produced their best form in the last third of the campaign and enabled a safe finish in fifteenth position, eight points clear of the drop.

HAVANT & WATERLOOVILLE

BEST LGE ATT.: 1,756 v AFC Wimbledon
LOWEST: 453 v Braintree Town

No.	Date	Comp	H/A	Opponents	Att:	Result	Goalscorers	Pos
1	Aug 9	BSS	A	St Albans City	522	D 1 - 1	Simpemba 72	
2	11		H	Weston-s-Mare	620	L 2 - 3	Holloway 85 Henry 90	
3	16		H	Bromley	622	L 0 - 1		
4	23		A	Fisher Athletic	173	D 1 - 1	Elphick 78	15
5	25		H	Basinstoke Town	759	W 5 - 1	Gray 24 Poate 51 Nightingale 53 (pen) Collins 59 Henry 84	
6	30		A	Thurrock	261	W 3 - 2	Gray 13 **Watkins** 31 Henry 76	11
7	Sept 3		A	Newport County	859	W 2 - 0	Gargan 32 Henry 83	
8	6		H	Bath City	703	D 0 - 0		9
9	**9**	**SS S1**	**A**	**Maidenhead United**	**171**	**W 2 - 1**	**Cooper 14 (og) Elphick 74**	
10	13		A	Chelmsford City	1104	W 2 - 1	Elphick 25 **Watkins** 68	7
11	20		H	Hampton & Richmond B	732	L 1 - 4	**Watkins** 61	
12	**27**	**F.A.C. 2Q**	**H**	**Shortwood United**	**422**	**D 2 - 2**	**Elphick 21 Simpemba 58**	
13		**F.A.C 2Q r**	**A**	**Shortwood United**	**310**	**W 1 - 0**	**Holloway 70**	
14	Oct 4		A	Team Bath	200	L 0 - 1		11
15	**7**	**SS S2**	**A**	**Eastleigh**	**489**	**W 3 - 2**	**Gasson 38, Elphick 90, Collins pen 90**	
16	**11**	**F.A.C. 3Q**	**H**	**Godalming Town**	**462**	**W 2 - 1**	**Holloway 9 Booth 16**	
17	18		H	Worcester City	651	L 0 - 2		13
18	21		A	AFC Wimbledon	2711	L 0 - 3		
19	**25**	**F.A.C. 4Q**	**A**	**Crawley Town**	**1253**	**W 3 - 0**	**Simpemba 41 86 Watkins 72**	
20	Nov 1		A	Hayes & Yeading	273	L 1 - 2	Webb 80	15
21	**4**	**SS S3**	**A**	**Crawley Town**	**239**	**L 0 - 3**		
22	**9**	**F.A.Cup 1R**	**H**	**Brentford**	**1631**	**L 1 - 3**	**Simpemba 73**	
23	15		H	Newport County	601	D 1 - 1	Booth 86	16
24	**23**	**F.A.T 3Q**	**A**	**Fisher Athletic**	**170**	**W 2 - 0**	**Bussens 55 Heath 74**	
25	29		A	Eastleigh	913	L 0 - 2		16
26	Dec 1		H	Braintree Town	453	D 1 - 1	Collins 90	
27	6		H	Dorchester Town	484	L 1 - 2	Poate 81	17
28	**15**	**F.A.T. 1R**	**H**	**Bury Town**	**232**	**W 3 - 1**	**WATKINS 3 (26 48 56)**	
29	20		H	St Albans City	541	W 2 - 0	**Watkins** 34 Holloway 40	17
30	26		A	Bognor Regis Town	458	W 5 - 1	Collins 18 (pen) Henry 33 Matthews 70 Simpemba 73 Nightingale 90	
31	Jan 1		H	Bognor Regis Town	971	D 2 - 2	Elphick 52 Collins 75 (pen)	
32	3		A	Bromley	447	D 2 - 2	Henry 8 Collins 71 (pen)	14
33	**13**	**F.A.T 2R**	**A**	**Lewes**	**258**	**D 3 - 3**	**Nightingale 45 (pen) Simpemba 66 Booth 87**	
34	17		H	Chelmsford City	921	D 1 - 1		
35	**19**	**F.A.T 2R r**	**H**	**Lewes**	**258**	**W 4 - 3**	**Gray 5 Walker 34 Simpemba 45 Booth 77**	
36	24		A	Worcester City	714	D 2 - 2	Holloway 40 Compton 90	
37	27		A	Maidenhead Unted	213	L 0 - 1		19
38	Feb 14		H	Hayes & Yeading	626	D 2 - 2	Hinshelwood 50 **Watkins** 88	18
39	**16**	**F.A.T. 3R**	**H**	**Crawley Town**	**413**	**W 2 - 0**	**Watkins 35 Nightingale 83 (pen)**	
40	**21**	**F.A.T. 4R**	**A**	**York City**	**1679**	**L 0 - 2**		
41	24		A	Braintree Town	414	L 0 - 1		
42	28		H	AFC Wimbledon	1756	D 0 - 0		
43	Mar 2		H	Team Bath	545	W 2 - 1	Nightingale 84 (pen) **Watkins** 89	
44	7		A	Welling United	485	L 1 - 2	**Watkins** 21	18
45	9		H	Bshop's Stortford	572	W 3 - 0	**Watkins** 67 Gray 73 82	
46	14		A	Bath City	487	L 1 - 2	Nightingale 31 (pen)	18
47	17		A	Dorchester Town	322	L 0 - 1		
48	21		H	Thurrock	574	D 2 - 2	Gasson 21 Nightingale 37 (pen)	
49	23		A	Weston-s-Mare	263	W 1 - 0	**Watkins** 62	19
50	28		A	Hampton & Richmond	622	L 1 - 2	Nightingale 67	
51	April 4		H	Maidenhead United	626	D 3 - 3	**Watkins** 19 Nightingale 23 (pen) Medley 60	
52	6		H	Welling United	557	W 1 - 0	Wilkinson 36	
53	11		H	Fisher Athletic	616	W 3 - 0	Medley 2 Nightingale 41 **Watkins** 72	15
54	13		A	Basingstoke Town	507	D 2 - 2	Fogden 46 Butters 81	
55	18		A	Bishop's Stortford	421	L 0 - 1		
56	21		H	Eastleigh	1239	D 2 - 2	**Watkins** 21 Walker 77	15

Average Home Att: 722 (752) **Goals** 87 79

Best Position: 7th **Worst:** 19th

Golascorers: Watkins 18, Nightingale 10, Simpemba 8, Collins 6, Elphick 6, Henry 6, Booth 5, Holloway 5, Gray 4, Medley 2, Poate 2, Walker 2, Bussens 2, Butters 1, Fogden 2, Gasson 2, Heath 1, Hinshelwod 1, Matthews 1, Webb 1, Wilkinson 1. Own goals 1.

SCRIVEN	WILKINSON	GASSON	COLLINS	BUTTERS	SMITH	SIMPEMBA	HOLLOWAY	NIGHTINGALE	WATKINS	POATE	BAPTISTE	GARGAN	GRAY	ELPHICK	CONROY	HENRY	SLABBER	BOOTH	ASHMORE	WALKER	FARRUGIA	BALDACCHINO	WEBB	ROYCE	JAMES	BROOKER	ROGERS	FORD	MATTHEWS	MARTIN	COMPTON	COOK	HINSHELWOOD	CASTLES	FOGDEN	MEDLEY	THOMPSON	THORNE	
X	X	X	X	X	X	X	X	X	X	X	S	S	S	U	U																								1
X	U	X	X		X	X	X	U	S		X	X	X	X	U	X	U																						2
X	X	X	X	X	X	X	X	U	S		X	X	S	S	X	U																							3
X	U	X	X	U	X	X	X	X	X	X	S		X	X		S	U																						4
X	S	X	X	U	X	X	X	X	X	X	U		X	X		S	S																						5
X	S	X	X			X	X	X	X	X		S	X	X	X	S	U	U																					6
X	S	X	X			X	X	U	X	X		X	X	X	X	S	S		U																				7
X	U	X	X			X	X	X	X	X			X	X	X	S	S	S	U																				8
	S	X	X			X	X	S	U	X			X	X	X	X	X	S	X	U																			9
X	S	X	X			X	X	X	X	X	S		X	X	X		U	S	U																				10
X	X	X				X	X	X	X	X	S		X		X	X	U	S	U	S																			11
U	U	X			S	X	X	S	X	X			X	X	X		X	X	X	U	U	U																	12
X	U	X			X	X	X	X	X	X			X	X	X		U	S	U	U	U	U																	13
X	U	X	X		X	X	X	X		X			X	X			S	X	U	U		U																	14
X	S	X	X		X	X	X	X		X			X	X			S	X	U	U			S																15
X	X	X	X	U	X	X	X	X					X	X			S	X	U	S		U		S	U														16
X	U	X	X	U	X	X	X	X	X					X	X			X		U			S	S															17
X	X	X	X		X	X	X	X	S				X	X	U			X	U				S	S															18
X	X	S	X		X	X	X	X	X				X	X	X			S	U	S	U			U															19
X	X	S	X		X	X	X	X	X				X	X	X					U			S	U		S													20
U	X	X				S		U		X				X		S		X	X	X			X	X		X	X												21
X	X	X	X			X	X	X	X	S			X	X	X	S		S	U			U						U											22
X		X	X	U		X		S	X	X			S	X	X	X		S	U	X									X										23
X		X	X	U		X	X	X	S	S				X	X	S		X	U	X									X										24
X		X	X	U		X	X	X	S	S				X	X	S		X	U	X									X										25
X	S	X	X	U		X	X	S	S	X				X	X	X		X		U									X										26
X	X		X	U		X	X	U	S	X				X	X	X		X		U									X	S									27
X			X	X			X	S	X	X			U	X	X	X		S	U	X									X	S									28
X			X	X		S	X	S	X	X				X	X	X		S		X									X	U	U								29
X			X			X	X	S	X	X			U	X	X	X		S		X									X	U	S								30
X	U		X			X	X	S	X	X			S	X	X	X		S											X	U	X								31
X	S		X			X	X	X	X	X			X	X		X		S	U	U										S	X								32
X	S					X	X	X	X				X	X		X		S	U	X								U		S	X	X							33
		U				X	X	X	X	X			S	X		X		S	X	U										U	X	X	X						34
		S	U			X	X	S	X	X			X	X		X		X	X	X										S	U	X							35
		U	S			X	X	S		X			X	X		X		X	X	X										U	S	X	X						36
U		S	X			X	X	X		X			S	X		X		X	X											S	X	X	U						37
U		S				X	X		X	X			S	X		S		X	X	U												X	X	X	X				38
X		X				X		X	X	X			X	X		X		X	U	X		U					S	U		S									39
X		X	S			X		X	X	X			U	X				X	U	X							U			S		X			X				40
X		X	X			X		X	X	X			S	X				S	U	U										S		X	X	X					41
X		X	X			X		S	X	X			X	X				X	U	S							U	U		X			X						42
X		X	X			X	S	X	X	X			U	X				S		U										S			X	X	X				43
X		X				X	X	X	X	X			S	X				S	U	U												X	X	U	X				44
X		X				X		S	X	X			X	X				X	U	S								U		X			X	S	X				45
X		X			U	X		X	X	X			X	X				S	U	S										X			X	U	X				46
X		X			U	X		X	X	X			X	X		S		S		X										S			X	U	X				47
X	S	X	X		S	X		X	X	U			X	X		X				S										U			X		X				48
X	X	X	X	U	U	X		X	X				U	X		S				U													X		X	X			49
X	X	X	X	U	U	X		X	X				U	X		U				U													X		X	X			50
X	X	X	X	U	U	X		X	X				S	X						S										U			X		X	X			51
X	X	X	X	U	U	X		X	X				S	X						U										U			X		X	X			52
X	X	X	X	U	S	X		X	X					X						S										S			X		X	X	U		53
X	X	X	X	X	X	X		X	X										U											S			U		X	X	U	U	54
	X	X	X	X	X	X		X	X					U					X	S										S			U		X	X	U		55
U	X	X	X	X				X	X					X					X	S							U			S			X		X	X	S		56
Total League Appearances																																							
36	14	32	34	6	11	40	26	29	33	27	2	3	18	37	15	13	0	11	6	6	0	0	0	0	0	0	0	0	7	3	4	6	17	3	15	8	0	0	X
0	7	3	1	0	2	1	1	8	6	1	4	2	11	1	0	9	4	14	0	9	0	0	3	2	0	1	0	0	0	10	2	0	0	1	0	0	1	0	S
3	6	2	0	12	6	0	0	4	0	1	1	0	4	2	3	2	5	1	15	14	0	1	0	1	0	0	2	2	0	8	1	0	3	3	0	0	3	1	U
Total Cup Appearances																																							
10	4	10	7	1	4	12	11	9	9	9	0	0	10	14	7	5	2	8	4	7	0	0	1	1	0	1	1	0	2	0	1	3	0	0	1	0	0	0	X
0	3	2	1	0	1	1	0	4	1	2	0	0	0	0	0	3	2	6	0	2	0	0	1	1	0	0	1	0	0	5	0	0	0	0	0	0	0	0	S
2	2	0	1	2	0	0	0	1	1	0	0	0	2	0	0	0	1	0	10	4	3	5	0	1	1	0	1	3	0	0	1	0	0	0	0	0	0	0	U

HAVANT & WATERLOOVILLE

CURRENT SQUAD AS OF BEGINING OF 2009-10 SEASON

GOALKEEPERS	HT	WT	D.O.B	AGE	P.O.B	CAREER	Apps	Gls
Nathan Ashmore						Havant & W	6	0
Aaron Howe						Woking Rel 5/07, Carshalton (L) 2/07, Carshalton c/s 07, Hayes & Yeading 8/08, Havant & W 7/09		
DEFENDERS								
Jay Gasson			29/12/84	24		Fulham (Yth), Croydon A, Whyteleafe 10/03, Croydon A 2/04, Corinthian Casuals 7/04, Farnborough 6/05, Woking 6/07 Rel 5/08, Havant & W 5/08	35	1
Paul Hinshelwood	6'02"	14 00	11/10/87	21	Chatham	Brighton Rel c/s 07, Torquay 6/07 Rel 5/08, Tiverton (L) 11/07, Bognor 8/08, Havant & W 1/09	17	1
Gary MacDonald	6'01"	12 12	25/10/79	29	Iselone, Ger	Portsmouth Rel c/s 99, Havant & W 7/99, Peterborough Undisc 2/01, Stevenage (L) 11/02, £10,000 12/02, Woking 7/03 Rel 5/07, Ebbsfleet 6/07 Rel 8/08, Bognor 8/08 Rel 11/08, Hayes & Yeading 12/08, Havant & W 6/09		
Jake Newton			9/6/84	25	Hammersmith	Hampton & R (Yth), Kingston Academy, Staines c/s 03, Chalfont St Peter (L) 2/04, Bashley 2/05, Staines 7/05, Havant & W 7/09		
Sam Pearce			11/2/87	22	Portsmouth	Havant & W, Fleet T 3/06, South Africa, Bognor Regis 8/08, Salisbury 3/09, Havant & W 6/09		
Ian Simpemba	6'02"	12 08	28/3/83	26	Dublin	Wycombe, Woking (3ML) 10/02, Woking (L) 9/03, Crawley Undisc 7/04, Aldershot (SL) 3/06, Lewes 6/06, Havant & W 5/08	41	2
Ryan Woodford	5'11"	11 08	14/8/91	18		Portsmouth (Scholar) Rel c/s 09, Havant & W 7/09		
MIDFIELDERS								
Steve Hutchings	6'00"	12 00	13/12/90	18	Portsmouth	Bournemouth Rel c/s 09, Dorchester (L) 2/09, Havant & W 8/09		
Robbie Martin			29/12/84	24		Watford, Hornchurch (L) 3/04, Braintree 5/04, Havant & W 10/08	13	0
Steven Walker						Portsmouth (Scholar), Rel c/s 08 Havant & W 5/08	15	1
Shaun Wilkinson	5'07"	11 00	12/9/81	27	Portsmouth	Brighton, Havant & W (L) 12/01, Chesterfield (L) 11/02, Havant & W (2ML) 9/03 Perm 11/03, Weymouth £5,000 2/04, Havant & W 12/04, Weymouth, Havant & W 1/07, Lewes (2ML) 1/09	21	1
FORWARDS								
Wesley Fogden	5'08"	10 04	12/4/88	21	Brighton	Brighton Rel 9/08, Dorchester (L) 8/08, Dorchester 9/08, Havant & W 2/09	15	2
Luke Nightingale	5'11"	12 03	22/12/80	28	Portsmouth	Portsmouth Rel c/s 03, Swindon (L) 12/02, Southend 8/03, Weymouth 9/03 Rel c/s 04, Bognor 7/04, Havant & W 3/08	37	9
Gary Norgate			23/5/83	26		Chichester, Arundel, Midhurst, Arundel 7/08, Havant & W NC 8/09		
Mustafa Tiryaki						Turkey, Maidenhead c/s 08, Potters Bar (L) 10/08, Godalming (L) 12/08, Cheltenham (Trial) 5/09, Havant & W 7/09		
Manny Williams			13/11/81	27	London	Notts County (Yth), Millwall (Yth), Concord R, Bowers Utd, Leyton 7/01, Yeading 9/05, Leyton 7/06, Maidenhead 8/07, Woking 5/08 Rel 5/09, Maidenhead (2ML) 11/08, Weston-Super-Mare (3ML) 1/09, Havant & W 6/09		

LOANEES	HT	WT	DOB	AGE	POB	From - To	APPS	GOA
(F)Sam Gargan	6'03"	11 12	24/6/88	21	Hurstpierrepoint	Brighton 8/08 - Lewes (L) 9/08, Eastbourne B (L) 1/09, Eastbourne B (L) 3/09, Rel 5/09, Sutton U 8/09	5	1
(M)Dan Royce	5'09"	11 13	26/11/89	19	Chichester	Brighton 10/08 - Rel 5/09	2	0
(F)Robbie Matthews			2/3/82	27	Wiltshire	Salisbury (6WL) 11/08 - Crawley 1/09	7	1
(D)Steve Cook	6'01"	12 12	19/4/91	18	Hastings	Brighton 12/08 -	6	0
(M)Louis Castles	5'09"	10 06	20/9/90	18		Portsmouth 2/09 - Bognor Regis (SL) 3/09 Rel c/s 09	4	0
(F)Luke Medley	6'01"	13 03	21/6/89	20	Greenwich	Barnet (SL) 3/09 - Woking (6ML) 7/09	8	2

DEPARTURES	HT	WT	DOB	AGE	POB	From - To	APPS	GOA
(F)Rocky Baptiste	6'02"	11 11	7/7/72	37	Clapham	Margate 7/05 - Maidenhead 9/08 Rel 3/09, AFC Wimbledon 3/09	6	0
(F)Jamie Slabber	6'02"	11 10	31/12/84	24	Enfield	Stevenage 8/07 - Rel 10/08, Grays NC 10/08	4	0
(F)Danny Webb	6'01"	11 08	2/7/83	26	Poole	Chelmsford 10/08 - Salisbury 11/08	3	1
(D)Jay Conroy	6'02"	12 02	2/3/86	23	Ryegate	Lewes 5/08 - Rel 1/09, Northwich 1/09 Rel 2/09, AFC Wimbledon 3/09	15	0
(M)Jack Compton	5'08"	10 07	2/9/88	20	Portsmouth	Brighton 12/08 - Weston-Super-Mare 2/09	6	1
(F)Paul Booth			8/1/77	32	Gillingham	Lewes 5/08 - Rel 3/09, Tonbridge A 3/09	25	1
(M)Brett Poate			30/9/83	25	Southampton	Southampton c/s 03 - Rel 4/09, Eastleigh 4/09	28	2
(D)Gary Elphick	6'01"	13 02	17/10/85	23	Brighton	St Albans 12/07 - Eastbourne B 5/09	38	3
(G)Kevin Scriven					Bournemouth	Farnborough 6/07 - Sutton U 6/09	36	0
(F)Charlie Henry			1/7/87	22	Stevenage	Dorchester 11/07 - Newport C 6/09	22	6
(M)Charlie Oatway	5'07"	10 10	28/11/73	35	Hammersmith	Brighton 9/07 (Pl/Ass Man) 10/07 - Rel 6/09		
(M)Matt Gray			7/1/84	25	Slough	Woking 8/08 - Carshalton 6/09	29	3
(M)Gary Holloway			19/3/79	30	Kingston	Lewes 5/08 - Farnborough 7/09	27	2
(M)Jamie Collins	6'03"	12 00	28/9/84	24	Barking	Watford 2/05 - Hampton & R 7/09	35	5
(D)Guy Butters	6'03"	14 02	30/10/69	39	Hillingdon	Brighton 5/08 - Lewes (2ML) 1/09	6	1
(D)Jack Farrugia						Yth -	0	0
(D)Jamie Ford						Yth -	0	0
(D)Oliver Thorne						Slough 3/09 -	0	0
(M)Paul Brooker	5'08"	10 00	25/11/76	32	Hammersmith	Chertsey 10/08 -	1	0
(M)Jay Smith	5'11"	11 07	29/12/81	27	Hammersmith	Grays 7/07 -	13	0
(M)Leslie Thompson	5'10"	11 02	3/10/88	20	Newham	ex Bolton 4/09	1	0
(F)Alex Baldacchino						Yth -	0	0
(F)Jack James						Yth -	0	0
(F)Craig Watkins			4/5/86	23	Croydon	Sutton U 10/07 -	39	12
Andy Rogers						Yth -	0	0

HAVANT & WATERLOOVILLE

Formed: 1998

Nickname: Hawks.

Club Colours: White shirts, white shorts, white socks.

Change Colours: Yellow shirts, royal blue shorts, yellow socks.

Club Sponsor: Carlsberg UK Ltd

Previous League: Southern League

Ground address: Westleigh Park, Martin Road, West Leigh, Havant PO9 5TH

Telephone: 02392 787 822

Mobile: 07768 271 143

Fax: 02392 262 367

Email: trevor.brock52@yahoo.com

Social Club: 02392 787 822

Website: www.havantandwaterlooville.net

Simple Directions: Take B2149 to Havant off the A27 (or B2149 to Petersfield if leaving Havant) second turning off dual carriageway into Bartons Road then first right into Martins Road.

Capacity: 4,800 **Seats**: 562 **Covered**:3,500 **Floodlights**: Yes

Clubhouse: Open every day with function rooms for hire.

Club Shop: Yes, fully stocked.

Local Press: The News (Portsmouth)

Local Radio: BBC Radio Solent, Power FM and The Quay

PROGRAMME EDITOR

Adrian Aymes

(M) 07984 150 032

Email: adi@thehawksfc.com

CLUB STATISTICS

RECORDS

Attendance: 4,400 v Swansea City, FA Cup 3rd Rnd 05.01.2008.

Victory: 9-0 v Moneyfields, Hants. 23.10.01 Senior Cup

Defeat: 0-5 v Worcester City Southern Premier 20.03.04

Career Goalscorer: James Taylor -138

Career Appearances: James Taylor 256 + 41 as sub

Transfer Fee Paid: £5,000 to Bashley for John Wilson

Received: £15,000 from Peterborough United for Gary McDonald

SENIOR HONOURS

Southern League Southern Division Champions 1998-99.

Russell Coates Cup 2003-04.

PREVIOUS

Leagues: Portsmouth 1958-71. Hampshire 1971-86.

Wessex 1986-91 Southern 1998-2004

Names: Havant Town & Waterlooville merged in1998.

LEWES

Back row, (L-R): Justin Skinner (Coach), Steve King (Manager), Paul Booth, Andrew Drury, Paul Kennett, Ian Simpemba, Steven Williams, Aaron France, Leon Legge, Jay Conroy, Lewis Hamilton, Stephen Robinson, Jean-Michel Sigere, Ray Bugg (Kit man), Bob Childs (physio).
Front: Steven Elliott, Tom Davis, Ross Trevellin, Craig O'Connor, Simon Wormull, Dale Binns, Ian Selley, Gary Holloway, Kirk Watts

CLUB PERSONNEL

Chairman: Martin Elliott.

Company Secretary: David Arnold.

Additional Directors: Kevin Fingerneissl.

Secretary: Carole Bailey

Castleworks, Westgate Street, Lewes, East Sussex

BN7 1YR.

Tel: (B) 01273 472 100. (M) 07793 404 140.

Email: carole.bailey@lewesfc.com

Commercial Manager: John Brownbridge.

Tel: (M) 07973 865 862.

Email: johnbrownbridge@hotmail.com

Press Officer: James Boyes.

Tel: (M) 07962 113 550.

Email: james-boyes@lineone.net

Manager: Steve Ibbotson.

Assistant Manager: Jason Hopkinson.

Club therapist: TBA.

It is difficult to imagine what the long standing Lewes supporters must have thought when one of their directors was quoted as saying 'at no time had their manager Steve King been asked to get the club promotion'! Surely every manager, supporter and presumably player, should want their club to be successful and win football matches.

The fact that successful manager Steve King was sacked before he could take up the challenge of competing at a higher level last season, more or less ensured that the club would struggle in the Blue Square Premier. Kevin Keehan never really had a chance to save the club from an embarrassing campaign and when 'The Rooks' failed to achieve a victory until Forest Green Rovers were beaten 3-2 on 11th October, the writing was on the wall.

Early exits from the F.A.Cup against Leiston of The Eastern Counties League, and then The F.A.Trophy at the hands of Havant & Waterlooville, didn't lift the gloom, although a replay against 'The Hawks' did break the depressing possibility of twenty consecutive defeats.

This disastrous form brought another managerial change and Steve Ibbotson helped out on a caretaker basis, but a very sad period in the club's history came to end with a depressing relegation and very few positive vibes within a club that had appeared to be out of their depth at the Premier level.

LEWES

BEST LGE ATT.: 2,434 v Mansfield Town
LOWEST: 337 v Altrincham

No.	Date	Comp	H/A	Opponents	Att:	Result	Goalscorers	Pos
1	Aug 9	BSP	A	Kidderminster Harriers	1503	D 1 - 1	Bennett 43 (o.g)	
2	12		H	Crawley Town	1260	L 0 - 3		
3	16		H	Salisbury City	564	L 1 - 4	Fenelon 24	22
4	23		A	Weymouth	1172	L 0 - 2		22
5	25		H	Ebbsfleet United	851	D 0 - 0		22
6	30		A	Burton Albion	1432	L 2 - 5	Taylor 15 Standing 19 (pen)	23
7	Sept 2		A	Woking	1604	D 1 - 1	Taylor 23	
8	6		H	Barrow	679	L 0 - 3		22
9	11		H	Rushden & Diamonds	636	L 0 - 4		24
10	20		A	Altrincham	827	L 0 - 1		24
11	23		A	Histon	592	D 1 - 1	Gargan 2	24
12	27		H	Oxford United	1158	W 2 - 1	Standing 79 Gargan 88	23
13	Oct 4		A	Grays Athletic	729	D 0 - 0		23
14	7		A	Cambridge United	3194	L 0 - 1		
15	11		H	Forest Green Rovers	666	W 3 - 2	**Keehan** 35 38 Gargan 43	23
16	**14**	**SS S2**	**H**	**Bognor Regis Town**	**222**	**L 0 - 2**		
17	18		H	Northwich Victoria	669	L 2 - 3	Taylor 36 Roberts 90 (og)	24
18	**25**	**F.A.C. 4Q**	**A**	**Leiston**	**847**	**D 1 - 1**	**Cox 23**	
19	**28**	**F.A.C. 4Q r**	**H**	**Leiston**	**363**	**L 1 - 3**	**Wheeler 73**	
20	Nov 2		A	Wrexham	3201	L 0 - 2		24
21	15		H	Burton Albion	630	L 0 - 1		24
22	18		A	Torquay United	2118	L 1 - 4	Taylor 51	
23	22		H	Grays Athletic	519	W 2 - 0	Taylor 5 Standing 35 (pen)	24
24	Dec 6		H	Stevenage Borough	486	L 0 - 2		24
25	9		A	Salisbury City	579	W 2 - 1	Fenelon 32 Tabiri 42	
26	**13**	**F.A.T. 1R**	**A**	**Team Bath**	**206**	**W 2 - 1**	**Cullip 24 Standing 76 (pen)**	
27	20		H	Woking	694	L 0 - 2		23
28	26		A	Eastbourne Borough	2216	L 0 - 1		23
29	Jan 1		H	Eastbourne Borough	2232	L 0 - 2		23
30	3		A	Stevenage Borough	1764	L 0 - 3		23
31	**13**	**F.A.T 2R**	**H**	**Havant & Waterlooville**	**258**	**D 3 - 3**	**Keehan 4 Standing 57 (pen) Charles 60**	
32	17		A	York City	2073	L 0 - 3		23
33	**19**	**F.A.T. 2R r**	**A**	**Havant & Waterlooville**	**302**	**L 3 - 4**	**St Aimie 30 Foreman 60 Simpemba 65 (og)**	
34	24		H	Mansfield Town	598	L 0 - 1		
35	27		H	Torquay United	558	L 0 - 2		
36	Feb 1		A	Oxford United	4595	L 1 - 2	**Keehan** 11	
37	7		H	Wrexham	689	L 0 - 2		23
38	21		H	Cambridge United	962	L 0 - 2		24
39	24		A	Crawley Town	600	L 1 - 5	**Keehan** 51	
40	28		H	Lewes	345	L 0 - 3		24
41	Mar 7		A	Mansfield Town	2434	L 0 - 1		
42	10		A	Rushden & Diamonds	928	L 1 - 2	Henry 6	24
43	14		H	Kidderminster Harriers	385	L 0 - 1		24
44	17		A	Kettering Town	867	L 0 - 1		
45	21		A	Barrow	1390	L 0 - 2		
46	28		A	Forest Green Rovers	898	L 1 - 4	**Keehan** 5	Rel
47	April 4		H	Altrincham	337	W 2 - 0	Wheeler 25 **Keehan** 41	24
48	11		H	Weymouth	456	W 1 - 0	Breach 70	24
49	13		A	Ebbsfleet United	1098	L 1 - 2	Jirbandey 41	24
50	18		A	Northwich Victoria	487	L 0 - 3		24
51	21		H	Kettering Town	343	L 1 - 2	**Keehan** 71 (pen)	
52	26		H	York City	802	D 1 - 1	**Keehan** 87	24

Average Home Att: 824 (867) **Goals** 38 103

Best Position: 22nd **Worst:** 24th

Goalscorers: Keehan 9, Standing 5, Taylor 5, Gargan 3, Fenelon 2, Wheeler 2, Breach 1, Charles 1, Cox 1, Cullip 1, Foreman 1, Henry 1, Jirbandey 1, St Aimie 1, Tabiri 1. Own Goals 3.

Rel - Relegated.

BANKS	BREACH	BARNESS	GRAVES	WALLIS-TAYLOR	GEARD	STANDING	KEEHAN	RICHARDS	FRASER	TAYLOR	FENELON	RUDDY	ELLIOTT	ROWLAND	COX	CULLIP	LYONS	BAIDOO	MAYO	SACKEY	WHEELER	GARGAN	THOMAS	BELL	A WILKINSON	TABIRI	RIVERS	FOREMAN	KLEIN-DAVIES	LIBURD	ST AIMIE	CHARLES	STORRIE	HALL	FISK	S WILKINSON	BUTTERS	HENRY	SUTTON	OSBORN	ROONEY	
1	6	2	5	3	11	7	8	14	22	10	9	29	15	12	16	4	23	24	25	21	19	27	30	33	20	34	24	21	35	31	22	26	23	34	31	20	25	22	14	27	10	
X	X	X	X	X	X	X	X	X	X	X	S	U	U	U	U																											1
X	X	X	X	X	X	X	X	X	X	X	S	U	U	S	U																											2
X	X	X	X	X	U	X	X	X	X	X	X	U	U	U	U																											3
X	X	X	U	X	U	X	X	X	X	X	X	U			S	X	U																									4
X	X	X	U	X	X	X	X		U	X	X	U		S	S	X																										5
X	X	X	S	X	X	X	X			X	X	U		S	S	X	U																									6
X		X	X	X	U	X	X	X		X	U	U	X	X	X		U																									7
X		X	U	X	U	X	X	X		X		U	S	X	X		S	X																								8
X	X	X		U	S	X	X			X		U	X	X	X		X	S	X																							9
X	X	X	U	X	U	X	X			X		U			S	X		X	X	X	S																					10
X	X	X	U	X	S	X	X			X		U		X	U	X		U	X			X																				11
X	X	X		X	U	X	X			X		U	S	X	S			S	X			X	X																			12
X	X	X		U		X	X			X		S	U	X	S	X		S	X			X	X																			13
	X	X	U	S			X			X	S	X	X	S	X	X			X			X	X																			14
	X	X	U	S			X			X	S	X	S	X	X	X				U		X	X																			15
X	**X**	**X**	**X**	**U**			**X**			**X**	**S**		**U**	**X**	**X**					**U**		**X**	**X**																			16
X	X	X		U		X	X			X	S			X	U	X				S		X	X																			17
X	**X**	**X**		**X**			**X**			**X**			**S**	**X**	**X**						**S**		**X**	**X**	**U**																	18
X	**X**	**X**		**X**			**X**	**S**		**X**			**X**	**X**	**X**						**S**			**X**	**X**																	19
X	X	X		U			X	S			X		X		X					S			X	S		X																20
X	X	X		X		X	X	U		X	S		S	X		X						X	X	U																		21
X	X	X	U	X		X	X	U		X	S		S			X					X		X	U		X																22
X	U	X	U	X		X	X			X	S				S	X				S	X		X			X																23
X	X	X	U	X		X	X				S				S	X	S					X	X			X	U															24
X	X	X	U	X		X	X				X				S	X							X		U	X																25
X	**X**			**X**		**X**	**X**				**X**				**S**	**X**	**U**				**X**					**X**	**X**	**U**														26
X	X	X	U	X		X	X				X	U			S	X					S		X			X	X	U														27
X	X	X	U	X		X	X				X	U			S	X					X		X			X		S														28
X	X	X	U	X			X					U			S	X					X		X			X	U	X	X	U												29
X	X	X	S	X			X					U			X						X					X	S	X	X	S												30
X	**X**	**X**		**X**		**X**	**X**					**U**			**U**	**X**					**X**						**U**	**U**		**U**	**X**	**X**										31
X	X	X		X			X								S	X												X	X	S	X	X	U									32
X	**X**	**X**		**U**			**X**								**U**	**X**					**X**							**X**		**U**	**X**	**X**	**U**	**X**								33
X	X	X				X									S						X						U	S	X	U	X	X		X	X	X						34
X	X	X				X	X								S	X												S	X	U	X	X		U	X	X						35
X	X	X		U			X								X	X												S		U	X	X		U	X	X	X					36
X	X	X		U		X	X								X	X					X						S	U	S		X	X			X							37
X	X	X		U		X	X					U			X	X											U	X	X					U	X		X	S				38
X	X	X		X		S	X								X	X					X						S	X	X					U			X	U				39
X	X					X	X					U			X	X					X						S	U	X					U	X	X	X	S				40
X	U	X				X	X								S	X					X						S	X						U	X	X	X	X				41
X	X	X				X	X								S	X												X						U	X	X	X	X				42
X	X	X					X								X	X					X						S	S					U	U	X	X	X	X	S			43
X	X	X					X								X	X					S				S		X	X		U			S		X	X	U	X				44
X	X	X					X								X	X					X				S		X	X					S	X	X			S	U	U		45
X		X				X	X								X									U	X		X	S					X	X					S	S	X	46
X	X					X	X									X					X				S		X	S					X	U	X				S		X	47
X	X	X				X	X														X				U		X	U					S	X	X				S	U	X	48
X	X	X				X	X														X			U			X	U					X	S	X				S	S	X	49
X						X									X	X								S	X		X	X					X	U	X				S			50
X		X				X	X								X	X								S	X		X	S					X						S	U	X	51
X		X				X	X									X					S			U	X		X	S					X	U	X				S		X	52
Total League Appearances																																										
44	38	43	4	22	4	35	44	6	4	19	8	2	4	9	18	33	1	2	6	1	15	8	14	0	4	9	10	10	8	0	5	5	6	4	16	8	7	4	0	0	6	**X**
0	0	0	2	2	2	1	0	1	0	0	9	1	5	4	17	0	2	3	0	3	4	0	0	3	3	0	6	9	1	2	0	0	3	1	0	0	0	3	8	2	0	**S**
0	2	0	14	7	6	0	0	2	1	0	1	18	4	2	5	0	3	1	0	1	0	0	0	5	2	0	4	5	0	5	0	0	2	11	0	0	1	1	1	3	0	**U**
Total Cup Appearances																																										
6	6	5	1	4	0	2	6	0	0	3	1	0	1	3	3	3	0	0	0	0	3	1	2	2	1	1	1	1	0	0	2	2	0	1	0	0	0	0	0	0	0	**X**
0	0	0	0	0	0	0	0	1	0	0	1	0	1	0	1	0	0	0	0	0	2	0	0	0	0	0	0	0	0	0	0	0	0	0	0	0	0	0	0	0	0	**S**
0	0	0	0	2	0	0	0	0	0	0	0	1	1	0	2	0	1	0	0	1	0	0	0	0	1	0	1	2	0	2	0	0	1	0	0	0	0	0	0	00		**U**

Also played: DAVIS X(5,6). BEDA U(7,9,19) X(8,18). COMPTON X(15,16,17, 20). S BARTON U(16,17,18,19,20,21). APPS S(19). CLARK U(19,26,28) S(25). HINSHELWOOD X(20,23,24,25,26). PEARSON X(30,31,32,33). BUSS U(32,33,37). WINTERTON U(34,35,36,39,41). SAUNDERS U(42). JIRBANDEY X(46,47,49,50,51). O BARTON U(46,47). BANKS-SMITH X(48). TIMMS X(50,52) U(51). TIDEY U(50).

LEWES

CURRANT SQUAD AS OF BEGINING OF 2008-09 SEASON

GOALKEEPERS	HT	WT	D.O.B	AGE	P.O.B	CAREER	APPS	GOA
JJ Banasco-Zaragoza						Lewes		
Rikki Banks	6'03"	13 08	13/5/86	23	Brighton	C.Palace, Crawley (L) 2/06, Hendon (SL) 3/06, Worthing c/s 06, Lewes 6/08	44	0
DEFENDERS								
Anthony Barness	5'11"	12 01	25/3/73	36	Lewisham	Charlton, Chelsea £350,000 9/92, Middlesbrough (2ML) 8/93, Southend (L) 2/96, Charlton £165,000 8/96 Rel c/s 00, Bolton 7/00 Rel c/s 05, Plymouth 7/05 Rel 1/07, Yeovil (Trial) 2/07, Grays 3/07 Rel 5/07, Lewes 8/07	43	0
Chris Breach	5'11"	12 07	19/4/86	23	Brighton	Brighton Rel c/s 07, Bognor (L) 3/06, Bognor (L) 12/06, Bognor 8/07, Lewes 5/08	38	1
DannyCullip	6'01"	12 07	17/9/76	32	Bracknell	Oxford U Rel c/s 96, Kettering (L) 10/95 (95/96 3,0), Fulham 7/96, Brentford £75,000 2/98, Brighton (L) 9/99 £50,000 10/99, Sheffield United £250,000 12/04, Watford (SL) 3/05, Nottingham Forest Undisc 8/05, QPR 1/07 Rel 11/07, Gillingham 2/08, Lewes 7/08	33	0
Sam Fisk			5/2/88	21		Hassocks, Australia, Hassocks 9/08, Lewes 1/09	16	0
Grant Hall			29/10/91	17		Lewes, Gillingham (Trial) 8/09	5	0
Andy Pearson	5'11"	13 08	19/9/89	19	Brighton	Brighton Rel 5/09, Worthing (L) 10/08, Lewes (L) 1/09, Bognor Regis (SL) 2/09, Lewes c/s 09	2	0
William Peauroux						Three Bridges, Ebbsfleet, Horsham (Dual) 11/08 Perm, Lewes 7/09		
Ryan Timms						Southwick, Lewes	2	0
Andrew Wilkinson			26/2/90	19		Lewes, Eastbourne T (Dual) 5/08, Horley (L)	7	0
MIDFIELDERS								
Scott Chamberlain	5'09"	10 08	15/1/88	21	Eastbourne	Brighton Rel 1/09, Bognor (L) 2/07, Eastbourne B (L) 8/07, Bognor (5ML) 9/07, Bognor 1/09, Finland 1/09, Bognor 2/09, Lewes c/s 09		
Sam Crabb			25/10/87	21	Eastbourne	Eastbourne U, Eastbourne B (Dual) 3/08 Perm c/s 08, Eastbourne U (Dual) c/s 08, Lewes c/s 09		
Joe Keehan			7/1/87	22		Brighton (Yth), Whitehawk, Worthing 1/04, Crawley, Eastbourne (L) 12/05 Perm 1/06, Worthing (3ML) 11/06 Perm 2/07, Horsham YMCA c/s 07, Worthing 1/08, Lewes 7/08	44	8
Scott Kirkwood			4/5/85	24		Brighton (Yth), Crawley 7/02, Bognor 9/04 Rel 7/06, Horsham YMCA c/s 06, Hastings U 7/07, Worthing 1/08, Lewes 6/09		
Ben Osborn			13/1/91	18		Lewes	2	0
Dan Royce	5'09"	11 13	26/11/89	19	Chichester	Brighton Rel 5/09, Burgess Hill (WE) 11/07, Havant & W (L) 10/08, Lewes 7/09		
Ryan Storrie			26/2/91	18		Lewes, Southampton (Trial)	9	0
Ross Sutton			20/7/92	17		Lewes	8	0
Jack Walder						Lewes		
David Wheeler			4/10/90	18		Lewes	19	1
FORWARDS								
Dan Beck	5'10"	10 11	14/11/83	25	Worthing	Brighton & HA, Bognor (2ML) 8/03, Bognor (2ML) 8/04, Eastbourne B 11/04, Bognor 1/05 Rel 9/08, Burgess Hill 9/08, Bognor Regis 3/09, Lewes 7/09		
Freddie Foreman						Brighton (Yth), Lewes	19	0
Louis Pople						St Francis Rangers, Burgess Hill 8/07, Lewes c/s 09		
Tim Rivers						Lewes	16	0

LOANEES	HT	WT	DOB	AGE	POB	From - To	APPS	GOA
(M)James Fraser	5'09"	12 07	26/4/89	20	Brighton	Bristol R 7/08 - Tiverton (L) 9/08, Bognor (L) 12/08	4	0
(D)Kerry Mayo	5'10"	12 08	21/9/77	31	Cuckfield	Brighton 9/08 -	6	0
(F)Sam Gargan	6'03"	11 12	24/6/88	21	Hurstpierrepoint	Brighton (3ML) 9/08 - Eastbourne B (L) 1/09, Eastbourne B (L) 3/09, Rel 5/09, Sutton U 8/09	8	3
(D)Aswad Thomas	5'10"	11 06	9/8/89	20	Westminster	Charlton (3ML) 9/08 - Woking 6/09	14	0
(M)Jack Compton	5'08"	10 07	2/9/88	20	Portsmouth	Brighton 10/08 - Havant & W 12/08	3	0
(D)Adam Hinshelwood	5'10"	12 10	8/1/84	25	Oxford	Brighton 10/08 - Rel 5/09	4	0
(M)Joe Tabiri	5'10"	11 07	16/10/89	19	London	Barnet (2ML) 10/08 - Grays (L) 1/09	9	1
(F)Josh Klein-Davies	5'11"	13 09	6/7/89	20	Bristol	Bristol R (2ML) 12/08 - Bath C (L) 3/09, Rel 4/09, Weymouth (Trial) 7/09, Weston-Super-Mare 8/09	9	0
(M)Kieron St Aimie	6'01"	13 00	4/5/89	20	Brent	Barnet 1/09 - Rel 2/09, Thurrock 3/09, Hitchin 3/09, Maidenhead 8/09	5	0
(F)Elliot Charles						Barnet 1/09 - Hemel Hempstead (SL) 3/09	5	0
(D)Guy Butters	6'03"	14 02	30/10/69	39	Hillingdon	Havant & W (2ML) 1/09 -	7	0
(M)Shaun Wilkinson	5'07"	11 00	12/9/81	27	Portsmouth	Havant & W (2ML) 1/09 -	8	0
(M)Rhys Henry						Southend 2/09 - Rel 5/09	7	1
(M)Luke Rooney			28/12/90	18	Bermondsey	Gillingham 3/09 -	6	0
(D)Josh Jirbandey			5/6/91	18		Peterborough 3/09 - Hastings U 8/09	5	1
(F)Geoff Banks-Smith	5'06"		5/4/91	18		Brentford 3/09 -	1	0

DEPARTURES	HT	WT	DOB	AGE	POB	From - To	APPS	GOA
(F)Shabazz Baidoo	5'08"	10 07	13/4/88	21	Hackney	Dag & Red 9/08 - Rel 10/08, Croydon A 10/08	5	0
(M)Matt Geard						Horsham 7/08 - Horsham YMCA 10/08	6	0
(F)Scott Taylor	5'10"	11 06	5/5/76	33	Chertsey	Grays 7/08 - Staines 11/08	19	5
(M)Emmanuel Sackey						Brentwood 9/08 - Croydon Ath 11/08, Fisher 1/09	4	0
(D)Craig Richards	5'11"	12 01	24/11/86	22	Southampton	Salisbury c/s 08 - Rel 12/08	7	0
(F)Tom Lyons						Three Bridges 12/08 - Rel 12/08, Newport C 3/09	3	0
(G)Seb Barton						ex Eastbourne B 10/08 - Ashford T 12/08	0	0
(M)Louis Clark						Yth - Rel	1	0
(G)Jake Buss						Rel 1/09	0	0
(M)Seb Wallis-Taylor			3/6/87	22	Paphos	Bognor 5/08 - Bognor 3/09	24	0
(D)Zac Beda					Brighton	Brighton 9/08 - Burgess Hill	1	0
(G)Chris Winterton	5'10"	12 06	18/11/88	20	Eastbourbe	Eastbourne B 1/09 - Rel 3/09 Finland	0	0
(G)Dean Ruddy			12/10/82	26		Dover 8/08 - Rel 3/09	3	0
(F)Chamal Fenelon						Havant & W 5/08 - Tonbridge A (L) 9/08, Whitehawk (2ML) 1/09, Seaford 3/09	17	2
(M)Michael Standing	5'10"	10 05	20/3/81	28	Shoreham	Oxford U 7/08 - Rel 5/09	36	3
(M)Stefan Cox						Luton 1/08 - Rel c/s 09, Horsham (L) 2/08	35	0
(G)Ollie Barton						Worthing 3/09 -	0	0
(D)Steve Elliott			24/12/87	21		Lewes - Hastings U (L) 3/09	9	0
(D)Tom Graves						Horsham 5/08 - Horsham (L) 10/08	6	0
(M)Josh Apps						Yth - Rel	0	0
(M)Louis Bell						Bromley 10/08 - Croydon Ath (Dual) 12/08, Horsham (Dual) 2/09	3	0
(M)Ollie Rowland			6/8/82	27		Burgess Hill 7/08 -	13	0
(M)Jay Tidey						Yth -	0	0
(F)Danny Davis	5'10"	11 04	3/10/80	28	Brighton	Horsham c/s 08 -	2	0
(F)Jay Liburd						ex Braintree 12/08 -	2	0
(F)Callum Saunders						Peacehaven 3/09 -	0	0

LEWES

Founded: 1885

Nickname: Rooks

Club Colours: Red and black shirts, black shorts, black socks.

Change Colours: Sky blue shirts, white shorts, sky blue socks.

Club Sponsor: TBA.

Previous League: Isthmian League.

Ground Address: The Dripping Pan, Mountfield Road, Lewes, East Sussex, BN7 2XD

Telephone: 01273 472 100

Facsimile: 01273 483 210

E-mail: carole.bailey@lewesfc.com

Website: www.lewesfc.com

SIMPLE DIRECTIONS:

By Road: M23 to A23 to A27. Follow A27 for five miles until first roundabout take first exit to Lewes. Follow road until you reach traffic lights at Lewes Prison. Turn right into Winterbourne Hollow and Bell Lane to mini roundabout Turn left into Southover High Street. Cross two mini roundabouts to Mountfield Road, ground on your right.

Capacity: 3,000

Seats: 400

Covered: 1,400

Clubhouse: Bar and tea bar.

Club Shop: Yes

no image available

PROGRAMME EDITOR

James Boyes

Tel: (M) 07962 113 550

Email: james.boyes@lineone.net

CLUB STATISTICS

RECORDS

Attendance: 2,500 v Newhaven, Sussex County Lge, 26.12.47.

Victory: Not known.

Defeat: Not known.

Career Goalscorer: 'Pip' Parris - 350.

Career Appearances: Terry Parris - 662

Transfer Fee Paid: £2,000 for Matt Allen.

Transfer Fee Received: £2,500 from Brighton for Grant Horscroft.

SENIOR HONOURS

Mid Sussex League Champions 1910-11, 13-14.

Sussex County League Champions 1964-65.

Sussex Senior Cup Winners 1964-65, 70-71, 84-85, 2000-01, 05-06.

Athenian League Div.2 Champions 1967-68.

Athenian League Div.1 Champions 1969-70.

Isthmian Division One South Champions 2003-04.

Blue Square South Champions 2007-08.

PREVIOUS

Leagues: Mid Sussex 1886-1920. Sussex County 1920-65. Athenian 1965-77. Isthmian 1977-2003.

MAIDENHEAD UNITED

Back Row (L-R): Bradley Quamina, Lewis Ochoa, Reis Stanislaus, Warren Carter, Adam Carpenter, Brandon Martin, Pat Sappleton. **Middle:** Martin Ireland (Coach), Max Bangura (Physio), Kieran Knight, Daniel Brown, Arian Taj, Kieron St. Aimie, Jamal Fyfield, Alex Wall, Nevin Saroya, Mark Nisbet (Captain), James Hamsher, Jake Brooks, Dereck Brown (Assistant Manager), Jon Urry (Kitman). **Seated:** Sam Collins, Luke Barney, Staforde Palmer, Johnson Hippolyte (Manager), Bobby Behzadi, Jack Bradshaw, Dean Mason.

CLUB PERSONNEL

Chairman: Peter Griffin.
Vice-Chairman: Robert Hussey.
Company Secretary: Peter Griffin.
Additional Directors: Una Loughrey, Ken Chandler, Mark Stewart, Steve Jinman, Suzanne Loughrey, Graham Alfred.

Secretary: Ken Chandler
2 Tithe Close, Holyport, Maidenhead, Berks SL6 2YT
(H): 01628 636 078
(M): 07726 351 286
Email: kenneth.chandler@btinternet.com

Commercial Manager: Roy Bannister
(M): 07930 115 748
Email: roybannister2002@yahoo.com
Press Officer: Steve Jinman
(H): 0208 222 8441 M: 07909 655 409
Email: sjinman@hotmail.com

Manager: Johnson Hippolyte.
Assistant Manager: Dereck Brown.
Coach: David Gumbs & David Clarke.
Club therapist: Chris Barton.

A lively start, which only included two league defeats by November, saw Maidenhead in second place and an experienced manager in charge. Johnson Hippolyte had been very successful at Yeading and knew the right players and tactics for Blue Square success, so there were high hopes for a special season at York Road.

An F.A.Cup defeat in their first game at Bashley was a disappointment, as was their exit from the F.A.Trophy when losing at home to Chesham United, but consistency in the league saw United favourites for the play offs at the mid way stage.

Many clubs in the country found that a sensible review of their weekly spending underlined the fact that changes should be made, and Maidenhead's manager was informed that his whole squad would have to be made available on the transfer list. So, having spent time bringing his players together, full marks must go to the management for keeping the club in touch with the vital top five places throughout the campaign.

In fact, apart from a last day defeat to second placed Hampton & Richmond Borough when it was too late to finish higher than sixth,'The Magpies had closed the season with an unbeaten run of seven games including five victories. Keeping playing standards so high was even more praiseworthy as it had been learnt that the club's facilities had not been passed for promotion.

MAIDENHEAD UNITED

BEST LGE ATT.: **1,298** v AFC Wimbledon
LOWEST: **157** v Fisher Athletic

No.	Date	Comp	H/A	Opponents	Att:	Result	Goalscorers	Pos
1	Aug 9	BSS	A	Bromley	438	W 2 - 1	Newman 12 64 (pen)	
2	12		H	Bath City	369	D 0 - 0		
3	16		H	Braintree Town	322	W 2 - 1	**Pacquette** 3 85	6
4	23		A	Bognor Regis Town	451	W 4 - 2	**Pacquette** 27 Newman 41 (pen) Binns 70 78	5
5	25		H	St Albans City	426	W 1 - 0	**Pacquette** 79	
6	30		A	Weston-s-Mare	212	D 2 - 2	Surey 54 **Pacquette** 87	3
7	Sept 2		A	Fisher Athletic	218	W 1 - 0	Nicholls 20	
8	**9**	**SS S1**	**H**	**Havant & Waterlooville**	**171**	**L 1 - 2**	**Tiryaki 90**	
9	13		A	AFC Wimbledon	3039	L 1 - 3	**Pacquette** 88	6
10	20		H	Bishop's Stortford	361	W 3 - 2	Smith 4 **Pacquette** 29 Newman 89	5
11	**27**	**F.A.C. 2Q**	**A**	**Bashley**	**312**	**L 1 - 2**	**Newman 81**	
12	Oct 4		H	Dorchester Town	343	W 2 - 1	Behzadi 15 **Pacquette** 64	
13	18		A	Thurrock	250	W 2 - 1	Behzadi 21 Newman 73	4
14	21		A	Hampton & Richmond B	390	L 0 - 1		
15	25		H	Worcester City	451	W 5 - 0	Nicholls 3 Baptiste 10 Binns 37 **Pacquette** 59 72	
16	Nov 1		A	Team Bath	135	W 2 - 0	Newman 82 (pen) El Abd 90 (og)	
17	8		H	Chelmsford City	782	L 0 - 2		2
18	15		H	Eastleigh	401	L 1 - 4	Smith 37	3
19	18		H	Newport County	315	L 0 - 1		
20	**22**	**F.A.T 3Q**	**H**	**Chesham United**	**256**	**L 2 - 4**	**Baptiste 27 Surey 82**	
21	29		H	Bath City	500	L 0 - 1		5
22	Dec 6		H	Weston-s-Mare	258	D 0 - 0		6
23	20		H	Bromley	364	W 4 - 0	Nicholls 15 Baptiste 56 88 **Pacquette** 86	5
24	26		A	Hayes & Yeading	331	L 0 - 2		8
25	Jan 1		H	Maidenhead United	564	W 2 - 0	**Pacquette** 63 65	
26	17		H	AFC Wimbledon	1298	L 0 - 4		6
27	24		A	Bishop's Stortford	342	L 0 - 2		8
28	27		H	Havant & Waterlooville	213	W 1 - 0	Tyriaki 57	
29	31		A	Welling United	505	D 1 - 1	**Pacquette** 44	
30	Feb 14		A	Newport County	673	W 1 - 0	**Pacquette** 66	5
31	17		A	Braintree Town	600	W 2 - 0	Smith 65 Burgess 86 (og)	
32	21		H	Team Bath	304	L 0 - 2		5
33	24		H	Fisher Athletic	157	W 1 - 0	Tyriaki 66	
34	28		A	Eastleigh	552	D 0 - 0		5
35	Mar 3		H	Thurrock	188	D 1 - 1	Tyriaki 76	
36	7		A	Chelmsford City	1203	L 1 - 2	Okay 90 (og)	6
37	14		H	Basingstoke Town	293	L 1 - 2	James 57	6
38	16		A	Worcester City	479	D 1 - 1	Stevenson 45	
39	21		A	Dorchester Town	361	W 3 - 0	**Pacquette** 43 69 Tyriaki 56	6
40	28		H	Welling United	342	W 2 - 0	**Pacquette** 47 55	6
41	April 4		A	Havant & Waterlooville	626	D 3 - 3	Tyriaki 14 36 **Pacquette** 85 (pen)	6
42	11		H	Bognor Regis Town	228	W 2 - 0	Tyriaki 8 77	6
43	13		A	St Albans City	375	W 2 - 1	Bradshaw 16 Tyriaki 74	
44	18		A	Basingstoke Town	409	W 1 - 0	Tyriaki 48	6
45	25		H	Hampton & Richmond B	436	L 0 - 3		6

Average Home Att: **425 (364)** **Goals** **61 54**

Best Position: 2nd **Worst:** 8th

Goalscorers: Pacquette 20, Tyriaki 11, Newman 7, Baptiste 4, Binns 3, Nicholls 3, Smith 3, Behzadi 2, Bradshaw 1, James 1, Stevenson 2, Surey 1. Own Goals 3.

GORE	T SMITH	BERNARD	HINDS	COOPER	STERLING	A SMITH	NICHOLLS	PACQUETTE	NEWMAN	BINNS	NISBET	SUREY	BRADSHAW	JAMES	BEHZADI	CARTER	BADDELEY	FYFIELD	TIRYAKI	HAMSHER	CLARKE	BAPTISTE	WILLIAMS	S SMITH	SAPPLETON	SAROYA	STEVENSON	HONG	COLLINS	TAJBAKSH	BARNES	ERDELYI	AITEOUAKRIM	
X	X	X	X	X	X	X	X	X	X	X	S	S	S	U	U																			**1**
X	X	X	X		X	X	X	X	X	X	X	S	U	U	S	U																		**2**
X	X	X	X		X	X	X	X	X	X		X	S	S	S	U	U																	**3**
X		X	X		X	X	X	X	X	X		X	X	U	S	U		S	S															**4**
X		X			X	X	X	X	X	X	X	X	X		S	U		S	S	U														**5**
X		X			X	X	X	X		X	X	X	X	S	S	U		S	X	U														**6**
X	X		S	X	X		X	X		X	U	X	S	S	X			X	X	U														**7**
X			**X**	**X**		**S**	**X**		**X**		**X**		**X**	**X**	**X**	**U**	**U**	**X**	**S**	**X**	**S**													**8**
X	X	X	X	X	X	U	X	X	X	X	U				X	U		S	S															**9**
X	X	X	X		X	X		X	X	X	X				X	U		S	S	U	S													**10**
X	**X**	**S**		**X**	**X**	**X**	**X**	**X**	**X**		**U**		**S**		**X**	**U**		**X**	**S**	**X**	**U**													**11**
X	X	X	S		X	X	X	X	S	X	X				X	U		U	S			X												**12**
X	X	X	S		X	X	X	X	X		X	S			X	U		X	S		U													**13**
X	X	U	U		X	X	X	X	X	X	X	S			X	U		X				S												**14**
X	X	U	S		X	X	X	X	S	X	X	X			S	U		X				X												**15**
X	X	U	S		X	X	X		S	X	X	X			S	U		X	X			X												**16**
X	X	U			X	X	X	X	S	X	X	X			S	U		X				X	S											**17**
X	X	U	U		X	X	X	X	S	X	X	X			S			X				X	S											**18**
	U	U	S		X	X	X	X	S	X	X	X			X			X				S	X	X										**19**
	U	**X**	**X**		**X**	**X**	**S**		**S**	**X**	**X**	**X**			**X**	**U**					**U**	**X**	**X**	**X**										**20**
X	U	X			X	X	X		X	X	U	X			X	U					S	S	X		X									**21**
X	U	X	U			X	X		X	X	X	X			X	U					U	X	S		X									**22**
X	S	U	U		X		X	S	X	X	S	X			X		X					X	X		X									**23**
X	S		U		X	X	X	X		X	S	X			X	U	X					X	S			X								**24**
X	U		S			U	X	X	X	X	X	X			X	U		X	S			X				X								**25**
X	U		X			S	X	X	X		X	X			X	U	S	X			S	X				X								**26**
X	S		X			X	X	X	X	X	S	X			X			X	S		U	U				X								**27**
X	S		X			X	X	X		X	U	X		U	X			X	X		S	U				X								**28**
X	S		X			X	X	X	U	X	S	X		S	X			X	X		U					X								**29**
X	X		S			X	X	X	S			X		U	X			X	X		S	U			X	X								**30**
X	X		X				X	X	X			X		U	X	U		X	S		S	X			S	X								**31**
X	X				S		X		X		X	X		X	X	U		X	X		S					X	S	U						**32**
X	X				X		X		S		X	X		S				X	X	U	X	S				X	X		U					**33**
X	X				X		X				X	X	U		X	U		X	X	S	S	S				X	X							**34**
X	S				X		X				X	X	X	S	U				X	X	U	X				X	X		S					**35**
X	X				X		X				X	X	S	S	X	U		X	X	S		U				X	X							**36**
X						X	X				X	X	X	X	U			X	X	X	U					X	S			S	S			**37**
X					X	X	X				X		U	X	X			U	S	X	X					X	X		S	S				**38**
					X	X	X	S			X		S	X	X	U	U	X	X	X	X									S		X		**39**
U					X	X	X	X			X		S		X		U	X	X	X	X									S	S	X		**40**
U					X	X	X	X			X				X			X	X	X	X					U				S	U	X	S	**41**
X					X	X	X	X			X	X	U		X			X	X		S					S				U	X		S	**42**
X						S	X	X			X	X	X		X	U		X	X		U					X				S	X		S	**43**
X					S	X	X	X			X		X		X	U		X	X		S					X				S			X	**44**
X					X	S	X	X			X		S		X	U			X		S					X			X	X	U		X	**45**
Total League Appearances																																		
38	19	12	11	3	30	29	41	30	17	24	29	29	7	4	29	0	2	26	19	6	5	12	3	1	4	18	5	0	1	1	2	3	2	**X**
0	6	0	8	0	2	3	0	2	8	0	5	4	7	7	9	0	1	5	10	2	11	5	4	0	1	1	2	0	2	7	2	0	3	**S**
2	5	7	5	0	0	2	0	0	1	0	4	0	4	6	3	26	3	2	0	5	7	4	0	0	0	1	0	1	1	1	2	0	0	**U**
Total Cup Appearances																																		
2	1	1	2	2	2	2	2	1	2	1	2	1	1	1	3	0	0	2	0	2	0	1	1	1	0	0	0	0	0	0	0	0	0	**X**
0	0	1	0	0	0	1	1	0	1	0	0	0	1	0	0	0	0	0	2	0	1	0	0	0	0	0	0	0	0	0	0	0	0	**S**
0	1	0	0	0	0	0	0	0	0	0	1	0	0	0	0	3	1	0	0	0	2	0	0	0	0	0	0	0	0	0	0	0	0	**U**

MAIDENHEAD UNITED

CURRENT SQUAD AS OF BEGINING OF 2009-10 SEASON

GOALKEEPERS	HT	WT	D.O.B	AGE	P.O.B	CAREER	Apps	Gls
Adam Carpenter						Maidenhead, Chalfont Wasps (L), Bracknell (L)		
Warren Carter						Holyport, Maidenhead 8/08, Northwood (L) 3/09	0	0
Chris Tardif	5'11"	12 07	20/6/81	28	Guernsey	Portsmouth Rel c/s 04, Newport IOW (L) 3/00, Bournemouth (SL) 8/02, Havant & W (L) 10/03, Wycombe (Trial) 3/04, Oxford U 7/04 Rel 9/07, Eastleigh 10/07 Rel 10/07, Basingstoke 12/07 Rel 3/08, Maidenhead 3/08, Farnborough 5/08, Bognor Regis 8/08 Rel 2/09, Winchester 3/09, Worcester (Dual) 3/09, Maidenhead 6/09		
DEFENDERS								
Tom Baddeley			24/2/90	19		Brentford (Scholar), Thatcham (WE) 1/08 Maidenhead 8/08, Bracknell (L) 9/08, Burnham (L) 2/09, Burnham (L) 3/09	3	0
Bobby Behzadi			8/2/81	28	London	Stevenage, Wealdstone (L) 1/00, Hayes 3/00, Yeading 8/01, Maidenhead 1/07	38	2
Jack Bradshaw						Stevenage Rel 5/09, Tiptree (L) 8/07, Maidenhead (4ML) 1/08, Maidenhead (3ML) 8/08, Ware (L) 12/08, Maidenhead (SL) 2/09, Maidenhead 8/09	14	1
Jamal Fyfield			17/3/89	20		L.Orient, Maidenhead 8/07	31	0
Brandon Martin	5'09"	12 01	13/1/91	18		L.Orient (Scholar) Rel c/s 09, Ware (WE) 2/09, Maidenhead 8/09		
Mark Nisbet			29/11/86	22		Flackwell Heath, Maidenhead 7/06	34	0
Nevin Saroya	6'03"	13 01	15/9/80	28	Hillingdon	Brentford, Grays 10/00, Hampton & R 1/01, Yeading/Hayes & Yeading 8/01 Rel 12/08, Maidenhead 12/08	19	0
MIDFIELDERS								
Steve Barnes	5'04"	10 09	5/1/76	33	Harrow	Welling, Birmingham 10/95, Brighton (2ML) 1/98, Barnet 10/98 Rel c/s 00, Welling (L) 3/00, Hayes c/s 00, St Albans 12/00, Harrow 12/00, Welling 3/01, Chesham 8/01, Welling 9/01, Time Out, Maidenhead 3/09	4	0
Jake Brooks						Maidenhead		
Daniel Brown						Northwood, Maidenhead 8/09		
David Clarke			2/9/71	37	Nottingham	Notts County, Eastwood T, Harrow, Dover £5,000 2/98, Chesham (L) 3/01 Kingstonian £10,000 6/01, Yeading c/s 03, Maidenhead (Pl/Coach) 10/06	16	0
Sam Collins	6'00"	12 06	25/6/89	20	London	MK Dons, Maidenhead (L) 11/06, Kettering (3ML) 9/07, Hendon (L) 11/07, Wivenhoe (L) 8/08 Perm, Hendon 12/08, Maidenhead 2/09, Canvey Island (Trial) 6/09, Maidenhead 8/09	3	0
Jamie Hamsher						Sutton, Northwood c/s 06, Maidenhead, Clanfield (L) 12/07, Godalming (L) 12/08	8	0
Gavin James						Wycombe, Beaconsfield SYCOB, Maidenhead 8/07, Wealdstone (L) 10/08, Bracknell (L) 11/08, Burnham (L) 12/08	11	1
Lewis Ochoa	5'10"	11 02	24/6/91	18	London	Brentford (Scholar) Rel c/s 09, Wycombe (Trial) 3/09, Maidenhead 8/09		
Bradley Quamina	5'11"		28/6/85	24		Yeading Rel 8/05, USA Scholarship, Yeading/Hayes & Yeading 1/06, Woking 5/07 Rel 5/09, Maidenhead 6/09		
FORWARDS								
Lee Barney						Maidenhead		
Dean Mason			28/2/89	20	Islington	Barnet, AFC Wimbledon 8/08 Rel 5/09, Northwood (L) 10/08, Northwood (L) 12/08, Walton Casuals (L) 3/09, Maidenhead 8/09		
Stafforde Palmer						Hayes/Hayes & Yeading, Northwood (L) 12/08, Maidenhead (3ML) 6/09		
Kieron St Aimie	6'01"	13 00	4/5/89	20	Brent	QPR Rel 1/08, Oxford U (L) 10/07, Barnet 1/08 Rel 2/09, Grays (L) 9/08, Stevenage (L) 11/08, Lewes (L) 1/09, St Albans (Trial), Thurrock 3/09, Hitchin 3/09, Maidenhead 8/09		
Reis Stanislaus						Woking (Yth), Maidenhead 8/09		
Aryan Tajbakhsh						Kentish Town, Northwood (L) 11/08 Perm, Maidenhead 3/09	8	0
Alex Wall						Thatcham, Maidenhead 8/09		

LOANEES	HT	WT	DOB	AGE	POB	From - To	APPS	GOA
(F)Manny Williams			13/11/81	27	London	Woking (2ML) 11/08 - Weston-Super-Mare (3ML) 1/09, Rel 5/09, Havant & W 6/09	7	0
(F)Belal Aiteouakrim			12/4/85	24	London	AFC Wimbledon 3/09 - Rel 5/09	5	0

DEPARTURES	HT	WT	DOB	AGE	POB	From - To	APPS	GOA
(F)Tyrone Sealey						Stevenage 2/08 - Harrow, Slough 3/09		
(D)Grant Cooper	6'02"		16/9/77	31	London	Kings Lynn 3/07 - Rel 1/09, Bishops Stortford (L) 12/08 Bishops Stortford 1/09	3	0
(M)Dale Binns			8/7/81	28	London	Lewes 5/08 - Hayes & Yeading 2/09	24	3
(D)Narada Bernard	5'02"	10 05	30/1/81	28	Bristol	Weymouth 2/08 - Bishops Stortford (L) 1/09 Perm 2/09	12	0
(D)Jermaine Hinds			27/12/83	25	London	Dulwich H 12/07 - Rel 2/09	19	0
(F)Lee Newman			19/3/84	25	Sussex	Eastbourne B 9/06 - Rel 3/09, Jailed 4/09	25	6
(M)Freddy Okyere						Yeading (Yth) c/s 07 - Waltham Forest 3/09 Rel 3/09		
(F)Rocky Baptiste	6'02"	11 11	7/7/72	37	Clapham	Havant & W 9/08 - Rel 3/09, AFC Wimbledon 3/09	17	3
(D)Tyron Smith			4/8/86	23		Basingstoke 5/08 - Rel 3/09	25	2
(F)Jon Stevenson						Halesowen T 2/09 - Rel 3/09, Thurrock 3/09	7	1
(G)Shane Gore	6'01"	12 00	28/10/81	27	Ashford	East Thurrock 5/08 - Rel 5/09, Luton 8/09	38	0
(D)Dominic Sterling			8/7/76	33	Isleworth	Canvey Island 5/06 - Rel 5/09, Staines 7/09	32	0
(F)Richard Pacquette	6'00"	12 06	23/1/83	26	Paddington	Havant & W 3/08 - Rel 5/09, Histon (L) 2/09, York C 5/09	32	20
(M)Ashley Nicholls	5'11"	11 11	30/10/81	27	Ipswich	Boston U 4/08 - Rel 5/09, Bishops Stortford 5/09	41	3
(M)Ben Surey	5'10"	11 00	18/12/82	26	Camberley	Gravesend 5/08 - Rel 6/09, Travelling	33	1
(F)Mustafa Tiryaki						Turkey c/s 08 - Potters Bar (L) 11/08, Godalming (L) 12/08, Cheltenham (Trial) 5/09, Havant & W 7/09	29	10
(G)Miklos Erdelyi						ex Honved 1/09 -	3	0
(G)Kieran Hudson						Yth -		
(G)Steve Smith			3/6/79	30		Aylesbury 11/08 -	1	0
(D)Pat Sappleton			16/4/82	27	London	Godalming T 11/08 -	5	0
(M)Ashley Smith			22/12/83	25		Flackwell Heath c/s 06 - Hampton & R 8/09	32	1
(M)Luke Dexter						Yth - Bracknell (SL) 8/08		
(M)Marvin Hong						Yth -	0	0

MAIDENHEAD UNITED

Formed: 1870

Nickname: Magpies.

Club Colours: Black & white striped shirts, black shorts, red socks.

Change Colours: Red shirts, shorts and socks.

Club Sponsor: Pharmalink Consulting.

Previous League: Southern League

Ground address: York Road, Maidenhead, Berks SL6 1SF

Telephone: 01628 636 314

Mobile: 07726 351 286

Social Club: 01628 624 739

Email: kenneth.chandler@btinternet.com

Website: www.maidenheadunitedfc.co.uk

Simple Directions: From Maidenhead BR drive eastwards down Bell St. Ground is 500 yards. Ground is 5 miles from Jct 7 on the M4.

Capacity: 4,500 **Seats**: 400 **Covered**: 2,000 **Floodlights**:Yes

Clubhouse: Open week days, evenings and matchdays.

Club Shop: Yes.

Local Radio: Star FM. Thames Valley F.M & BBC Radio Berkshire.

Local Press: Maidenhead Advertiser and Maidenhead Express.

no image available

PROGRAMME EDITOR

Steve Jinman

(H) 0208 222 8441 (M) 07909 655 409

Email: sjinman@hotmail.com

CLUB STATISTICS

RECORDS

Attendance: 7,920 v Southall F.A.Amateur Cup Q/F 07.03.36

Victory: 14-1 v Buckingham Town F.A.Amateur Cup 06.09.52

Defeat: 0-14 v Chesham United (a) Spartan Lg 31.03.23

Career Goalscorer: George Copas - 270 1924-35

Career Appearances: Bert Randall - 532 1950-64

Record Transfer Fee Paid: Undisclosed

Received: £5,000 from Norwich City for Alan Cordice 1979

SENIOR HONOURS

Berks & Bucks Senior Cup (x19)

PREVIOUS

Leagues: Southern 1894-1902. West Berks 1902-04.
Gt West Suburban1904-22. Spartan 1922-39.
Gt West Comb. 1939-45. Corinthian 1945-63. Athenian 1963-73.
Isthmian 1973-2004. Conference South 2004-06. Southern 2006-07.

Name: Maidenhead F.C. and Maidenhead Norfolkians.

NEWPORT COUNTY

Back Row (L-R): Jamal Easter, Ian Hillier, Richard Evans, Nathan Davies, Chris Hartland, Kevin Stephens, Kris Leek, Tommy Cosh (Physio). **Middle row:** Bobby Morris (Back room staff), Tony Gilbert (Kit Manager), Steve Jenkins (Player Coach), Dave Collins, Glyn Thompson, Kieran Blackburn, Scott James, Nick Skelton, Anthony Church, Phil Walsh, Russell Jones (Masseur), Kevin Morris (Back room staff). **Front row:** Rob Duffy, Martyn Giles, Adie Harris, Craig Hughes, Dean Holdsworth (Manager), Chris Blight (Chairman), Danny Rose, Paul Keddle, Kevin Cooper, Paul Hall.

CLUB PERSONNEL

Chairman: Chris Blight.

Company Secretary: John Allison.

Additional Directors: Matt Southall,

John Collingbourne, John Bowkett.

Secretary: Mike Everett

13 Dale Road, Newport NP19 9DZ

(H): 01633 669 572

(B): 01633 292 130

(M): 07889 359100

Email: mike.everett@uk.atlas-elektronik.com

Commercial Manager: Phil Morgan

(B): 01633 662 262

Email: office@newport-county.co.uk

Press Officer: Tim Harris

(M): 07767 415 415

Email: timharris@yahoo.co.uk

Manager: Dean Holdsworth.

Coach: Fraser Skimming.

Club therapist: John Fitzgerald.

The excellent support given to 'The Exiles' at Newport Stadium always gives the home club and its management a distinct advantage and with the well known Dean Holdsworth at the helm, the South Wales club was expected to make a promotion challenge last season.

In reality the results were disappointing, as just two victories in the first seventeen league games sent them down to nineteenth place with no relief from the F.A.Cup in which they lost to Dorchester Town at home after a replay.

After another disappointment in the F.A.Trophy in which a victory away to Andover was followed by a replay defeat at Rushden & Diamonds, the club entered the New Year with the manager's new signings settling down to some encouraging form. A run of five victories in six undefeated games lifted spirits and County's league placing to eleventh but possibly the celebrations came too soon as four more defeats were suffered immediately and the relegation worries were back again.

Finally, Newport's strange season, apparently with no continuity to it, finished on a high with only one defeat in the last ten games and a final place in the top ten. Supporters will remember those matches and the exciting form shown. An excellent attendance of 809 watched the last league fixture against Thurrock and who would argue that four figure attendances wouldn't be a regular occurrence watching a successful Newport County side next season.

NEWPORT COUNTY

BEST LGE ATT.: 2,546 v AFC Wimbledon
LOWEST: 540 v Eastleigh

No.	Date	Comp	H/A	Opponents	Att:	Result	Goalscorers	Pos
1	Aug 9	BSS	H	AFC Wimbledon	2546	L 1 - 4	Collins 80	
2	12		A	Eastleigh	787	D 3 - 3	Cooper Rose 80	
3	16		A	Chelmsford City	1093	D 0 - 0		19
4	23		H	Dorchester Town	852	D 4 - 4	Rose 6 Harris 37 Easter 85 Hughes 90	17
5	25		A	Team Bath	563	L 0 - 2		
6	30		H	Hampton & Richmond B	931	W 1 - 0	Hughes 64	
7	Sept 3		H	Havant & Waterlooville	859	L 0 - 2		
8	**9**	**SS S1**	**A**	**Dorchester Town**	**178**	**W 5 - 4***	**Cooper 35, Duffy 60, Walsh 90, Rose 104, Hall 113**	
9	13		A	Bishop's Stortford	414	D 1 - 1	Duffy 57 (pen)	16
10	20		H	St Albans City	886	L 0 - 1		20
11	**27**	**F.A.C. 2Q**	**A**	**Dorchester Town**	**242**	**D 2 - 2**	**Duffy 61 (pen) Rose 84**	
12	**Oct 1**	**F.A.C. 2Q r**	**H**	**Dorchester Town**	**653**	**L 1 - 2**	**Reid 40**	**18**
13	4		H	Bromley	746	W 3 - 0	Bignot 20 **Reid** 28 (pen) Hughes 57	
14	18		A	Braintree Town	350	L 2 - 3	Roberts 39 **Reid** 45	17
15	20		A	Weston-s-Mare	528	D 1 - 1	Rose 90	
16	25		H	Welling United	800	D 0 - 0		16
17	**28**	**SS S2**	**A**	**Bath City**	**241**	**L 1 - 4**	**Reid 35**	
18	Nov 1		A	Basingstoke Town	350	D 0 - 0		18
19	8		H	Hayes & Yeading	679	L 1 - 5	**Reid** 26	
20	15		A	Havant & Waterlooville	601	D 1 - 1	Cochlin 28	19
21	18		A	Maidenhead United	315	W 1 - 0	**Reid** 6	
22	**22**	**F.A.T 3Q**	**A**	**Andover**	**264**	**W 3 - 0**	**Rose 40 Reid 53 Hughes 90**	
23	29		H	Bishop's Stortford	654	L 0 - 1		17
24	Dec 6		A	Thurrock	309	D 0 - 0		18
25	**13**	**F.A.T. 1R**	**H**	**Rushden & Diamonds**	**603**	**D 1 - 1**	**Reid 73 (pen)**	
26	**16**	**F.A.T 1R r**	**A**	**Rushden & Diamonds**	**421**	**L 0 - 2**		
27	20		A	AFC Wimbledon	2945	L 0 - 3		19
28	26		H	Worcester City	822	W 1 - 0	Harris 8	18
29	Jan 3		H	Chelmsford City	902	W 3 - 1	**REID** 3 (42 64 77)	
30	17		A	Fisher Athletic	249	W 3 - 1	Butterworth 32 **Reid** 37 Giles 48	16
31	19		A	Worcester City	759	D 0 - 0		
32	24		H	Basingstoke Town	844	W 3 - 0	Cook 45 Rose 63 **Reid** 83	14
33	28		H	Weston-s-Mare	913	W 1 - 0	Cook 63	
34	31		A	Bath City	1137	L 1 - 2	**Reid** 47	14
35	Feb 11		H	Bognor Regis Town	618	W 2 - 1	Rose 15 Cochlin 56	11
36	14		H	Maidenhead United	673	L 0 - 2		
37	21		A	Bromley	561	L 1 - 2	Rose 59 (pen)	
38	25		H	Eastleigh	540	L 0 - 1		15
39	28		A	Hayes & Yeading	311	L 0 - 2		
40	Mar 3		A	Hampton & Richmond B	409	W 1 - 0	Cochlin 36	
41	7		H	Braintree Town	714	W 2 - 1	**Reid** 67 Cochlin 82	12
42	18		H	Bath City	734	L 0 - 4		
43	21		A	St Albans City	494	D 1 - 1	Foley 80	15
44	28		A	Bognor Regis Town	362	W 1 - 0	**Reid** 63	14
45	April 4		H	Fisher Athletic	641	W 4 - 0	Giles 5 Foley 46 72 Rose 74	12
46	11		A	Dorchester Town	519	W 1 - 0	**Reid** 77	12
47	13		H	Team Bath	758	W 4 - 2	**Reid** 14 20 Cochlin 28 Rose 56	
48	18		H	Thurrock	809	D 1 - 1	**Reid** 85	10
49	25		A	Welling United	520	W 2 - 0	Foley 61 79	10

Average Home Att: 853 (999) **Goals** 64 67

Best Position: 10th **Worst:** 20th

Goalscorers: Reid 20, Rose 11, Foley 5, Cochlin 5, Hughes 4, Duffy 3, Cooper 2, Cook 2, Giles 2, Harris 2, Bignot 1, Butterworth 1, Collins 1, Easter 1, Hall 1, Roberts 1, Walsh 1.

THOMPSON	STEPHENS	COLLINS	DAVIES	HILLIER	GILES	ROSE	HARRIS	DUFFY	EASTER	COOPER	WALSH	HALL	SKELTON	A CHURCH	JENKINS	R EVANS	N CHURCH	HUGHES	VICKERS	COLBORNE	HARTLAND	LEEK	JAMES	BIGNOT	ROBERTS	REID	OSEI	ARMITAGE	COCHLIN	B EVANS	MANSHIP	TURK	KLEIN-DAVIES	COOK	BUTTERWORTH	ROGERS	MOHAMED	BLACKBURN	FOLEY	SMITH	LYONS	
X	X	X	X	X	X	X	X	X	X	X	S	S	S	U	U																											**1**
X	X	X	X		X	S	X	X	S	X	X	S	X	U		X	U																									**2**
X	X	X	X	X	X	X	X	S	S		X	X	U	S			U	X																								**3**
X	X	X		X	X	X	X	S	S	U	X	X		X	U		U	X																								**4**
X	X	X	S	X		X	X	S	S		X	X	X	X	U		U	X																								**5**
X	X	X	X			X	S	X		U	S	X		X	X		S	X	X	U																						**6**
	X	X	X			X	S	X		S	S	X		X	X		U	X	X	U																						**7**
	X	**X**				**S**	**X**	**X**		**X**	**S**	**X**		**X**	**X**		**X**		**X**	**U**	**X**	**S**																				**8**
U	X	X	X		S	X	U	X		X	S	X		X	X				X			S																				**9**
X	X	X	X		S	X	S	X		S	U	X		X	X			X	X				U																			**10**
X			**U**		**X**	**X**	**X**	**X**		**X**		**S**			**U**	**X**		**S**	**X**		**U**	**U**	**U**	**X**	**X**	**X**																**11**
X			**S**		**X**	**X**	**X**	**X**		**S**		**S**			**U**			**X**	**X**	**U**	**U**	**X**	**U**	**X**	**X**	**X**																**12**
X			X		X	X	X	S		S		X			U			X	X			S	U	X	X	X																**13**
X			X		X	X	X	S		U		X			U			X	X			S	U	X	X	X																**14**
X					X	X	X	S		X		X			U			X	X			S	U	X	X	X	S															**15**
X					X	X	X	S		X		X			U			X	X			S	U	X	X	X	S															**16**
X					**X**	**X**	**X**	**S**		**X**					**X**					**U**	**X**	**X**	**U**	**S**		**X**		**S**														**17**
X			X		X	X	X	X		X					S				X	U			U	X		X	S	U	X													**18**
X			X		U	X	X	X		S					X			S	X				U	X		X	X		X	S												**19**
X			X			X		X							X			X	X	U			U	X		X	X	U	X	U	U											**20**
X			X			X		X							X			X	X	U			U	X		X	X	S	X	U	S											**21**
X					**S**	**X**		**X**		**X**					**X**			**X**	**X**			**X**	**U**	**X**		**X**	**U**	**U**	**X**		**U**											**22**
X					U	X		X		X					X			X	X				U	X		X		S	X			X	S	S								**23**
X					X	X	S	S		X					X			X		U			U	X		X			X			X	S	X								**24**
X					**X**	**X**	**X**			**X**					**U**			**X**	**U**				**U**	**X**		**X**		**U**	**X**			**X**	**U**	**X**								**25**
X					**X**	**X**	**X**	**S**		**X**					**U**			**X**	**X**			**U**	**U**	**X**		**X**			**X**			**X**	**S**									**26**
X					X	X	X	S		X								X	X			S	U	X		X			X			X	U	S								**27**
X					X	X	X			X					U			X	U				U	X		X		U	X			X	S	X								**28**
X					X	X		X		X					X				U	U		X	U			X		U	X		U	X		X								**29**
X	U				X					X					X				S			X	U			X		S	X		S	X		X	X	X						**30**
X					X	X				S					X				S			X	U			X		S	X		U	X		X	X	X						**31**
X	S				X	X				S					X				S				U			X		U	X			X		X	X	X	X					**32**
X	U				X	X				X					X				U			S				X		U	X			X		X	S	X	X					**33**
X	U		U		X	X				X					X				U			X				X		U	X			X		X			X	U				**34**
X	S		U		X	X				X					X				S			X				X		S	X			X		X		X		U				**35**
X	S		U		X	X				S					X				X			X						S	X			X				X	X	U	X			**36**
X	S				X	X				X					X				X			X						S			U	X		X			X	U	X	S		**37**
X	S		X		X	X									X				X			X							X			X		X				U	X	S		**38**
X	X		X		X	X													U			S		X		X		S	X			X		X				U	X	U		**39**
X	X		S		X	X													U			X		X				X	X			X		X				U	X	U	U	**40**
X	X		S			X				S									U			X		X		S		X	X			X		X				U	X	X		**41**
X	X		S		S	X				X					U							X		X				S	X			X		X				U	X	X		**42**
X			X		X	X				S					U							X		X				X	X			X		X				U	X	S	U	**43**
X			X		X	X				X					U							S		X		S		X	X			X		X				U	X		U	**44**
X			X		X	X				X					S							S		X		X			X			X		X				U	X	U	S	**45**
X			X		X	X									U							X		X		X			X		S	X		X				U	X	U	U	**46**
			X		X	X									U					U		X		X		X			X		U	X		X				X	X	S	U	**47**
X			X		X	X									U					U		X		X		X		S	X		U	X		X				U	X			**48**
X			X		X	X									X									X		X		U	X		U	X		X				U	X	S	S	**49**
																																										50
Total League Appearances																																										
39	13	9	22	4	31	40	13	12	1	19	4	11	2	6	20	1	0	16	17	0	0	15	0	23	4	25	3	4	28	0	0	25	0	22	3	6	5	1	14	2	0	**X**
0	5	0	4	0	3	1	4	9	4	9	4	2	1	1	2	0	1	1	4	0	0	10	0	0	0	2	3	10	0	1	3	0	3	2	1	0	0	0	0	5	2	**S**
1	3	0	3	0	2	0	1	0	0	3	1	0	1	2	14	0	5	0	7	9	0	0	17	0	0	0	0	8	0	2	7	0	1	0	0	0	0	15	0	4	5	**U**
Total Cup Appearances																																										
6	1	1	0	0	5	6	6	4	0	6	0	1	0	1	3	1	1	4	5	0	2	3	0	5	2	6	0	0	3	0	0	2	0	1	0	0	0	0	0	0	0	**X**
0	0	0	1	0	1	1	0	2	0	1	1	2	0	0	0	0	0	1	0	0	0	1	0	1	0	0	0	1	0	0	0	0	1	0	0	0	0	0	0	0	0	**S**
0	0	0	1	0	0	0	0	0	0	0	0	0	0	0	4	0	0	0	1	3	2	2	6	0	0	0	1	2	0	0	1	0	1	0	0	0	0	0	0	0	0	**U**

Also Played: SAK X(7) U(8). TUCKER X(9). HART X(17). HARRISON X(17).

NEWPORT COUNTY

CURRENT SQUAD AS OF BEGINING OF 2009-10 SEASON

GOALKEEPERS	HT	WT	D.O.B	AGE	P.O.B	CAREER	Apps	Gls
Kieron Blackburn			24/6/88	21	Newport	Newport C, Dinas Powys, Ton Pentre, Newport C 1/09	1	0
Glyn Thompson	6'02"	13 01	24/2/81	28	Telford	Shrewsbury, Fulham £50,000 10/99, Mansfield (3ML) 1/00, Shrewsbury (L) 1/01, Northampton (2ML) 11/02, Northampton 3/03 Rel c/s 04, Walsall 8/04, Koge (Den), Rushden & D (Trial) 2/05, Waterford U (Trial) 2/05, Stafford R 1/05, Chesterfield 3/05 Rel c/s 05,	39	0
DEFENDERS								
Paul Bignot	6'01"	12 03	14/2/86	23	Birmingham	Crewe, Kidderminster (2ML) 10/06, Kidderminster 6/07 Rel 2/09, Newport C (3ML) 9/08, Newport C 2/09	23	1
Paul Cochlin			23/8/83	26	Cardiff	Cardiff Civil Service, UWIC Inter Cardiff, Team Bath, Cwmbran, Carmarthen 6/05, Merthyr 7/05, Newport C 12/05 Rel 6/08, Almondsbury (L) 11/07, Cirencester (L) 12/07, Bath C 6/08, Newport C 10/08	28	5
Aaron Cook	6'01"	11 05	6/12/79	29	Caerphilly	Portsmouth, C.Palace 12/98 Rel c/s 99, Havant & W 7/99, Bashley 1/02, Salisbury 3/04, Newport C (SL) 11/08 Perm 4/09	24	2
Gary Colborne			12/9/90	19	Newport	Newport C	0	0
Martyn Giles	6'00"	12 00	10/4/86	23	Cardiff	Cardiff C Rel c/s 03, Newport C (L) 10/02, Port Talbot 7/03, Morecambe 12/03 Rel 2/04, Barry T 3/04 Rel c/s 04, Carmarthen 8/04, Hereford 7/06 Rel c/s 07, Injured, Newport C 6/08	34	2
Matt Smith	5'10"	12 00	5/10/88	20	Newport	Cardiff Rel 5/08, Newport C (L) 3/08, Newport C 1/09, Cinderford (L) 1/09	7	0
Gary Warren			16/4/84	25		Mangotsfield, Team Bath c/s 07, Newport C 5/09		
MIDFIELDERS								
Takumi Ake			26/4/84	25		Hendon 3/06, Team Bath c/s 07, Newport C 6/09		
Scott Armitage						Newport C	14	0
Kevin Cooper	5'10"	10 04	8/2/75	34	Derby	Derby, Stockport (SL) 3/97, Stockport 8/97, Wimbledon 3/01, Wolves 3/02, Sunderland (2ML) 1/04, Norwich (SL) 3/04, Cardiff 7/05 Rel 1/08, Yeovil (L) 9/06, Walsall (SL) 2/07, Tranmere (L) 10/07, Chesterfield 2/08 Rel c/s 08, Newport C 7/08	28	1
Nathan Davies			26/5/82	27	Pontypool	Newport C	26	0
Sam Foley	6'00"	10 08	17/10/86	22	Upton	Cheltenham Rel c/s 08, Bath C (L) 3/08, Kidderminster 8/08, Redditch (2ML) 10/08, Newport C (SL) 2/09 Perm 4/09	14	4
Kris Leek			11/3/88	21	Newport	Newport C, Clevedon T (L) 8/07, Clevedon T (L) 10/08	25	0
Ricky Manship			17/11/90	19	Church Village	Newport C	3	0
Scott Rogers	5'11"	11 00	23/5/79	30	Bristol	Exeter (Jun), Bristol C (Trainee), Tiverton 7/97, Forest Green 8/03, Weston-super-Mare (L) 11/05, Bath C 3/06, Newport C (L) 1/09, Newport C 4/09	6	0
Daniel Rose	5'07"	10 01	21/2/88	21	Bristol	Man Utd, Oxford U (SL) 1/07, Oxford U 8/07 Rel 4/08, Newport C 7/08	41	8
Wayne Turk			21/1/81	28	Gloucestershire	Oxford U (Trainee), Cirencester, Salisbury 7/00, Newport C (SL) 11/08 Perm 4/09	25	1
FORWARDS								
Chris Hartland			20/6/90	19	Abergavenny	Newport C, Cinderford (L) 1/09	0	0
Dave Gilroy	5'11"	11 05	23/12/82	26	Yeovil	Bristol R Rel 1/04, Clevedon (L) 1/02, Bath C (6WL) 2/02, Forest Green (L) 8/03, Clevedon (L) 9/03, Weston-s-Mare 1/04, Chippenham (L) 11/04, Chippenham £1,000 2/05, Bath C 5/07, Newport C 4/09		
Charlie Henry			1/7/87	22	Stevenage	Arlesey, Wycombe 11/05, Grays 3/06 Rel c/s 06, Haverhill R 7/06, Cambridge C 10/06, Dorchester 6/07, Havant & W 11/07, Newport C 6/09		
Tom Lyons	6'01"	11 04	22/2/88	21		C.Palace (Trainee) Rel c/s 07, Blackpool (Trial) c/s 07, Burgess Hill 9/07, Crawley (Trial) 10/07, Worthing 10/07, Horsham YMCA 12/07 Lewes 8/08, Farnborough 10/08, Three Bridges 11/08, Lewes 12/08 Rel 12/08, Newport C 3/09	2	0

Craig Reid	5'10"	11 10	17/12/88	20	Coventry	Ipswich (Scholar), Coventry Rel c/s 06, Tamworth (L) 3/06, Falkirk (Trial) 7/06, Dunfermline (Trial) 7/06, Cheltenham 1/07 Rel c/s 08, Grays NC 8/08, Newport C (3ML) 9/08 Perm 12/08	27	16

LOANEES	HT	WT	DOB	AGE	POB	From - To	APPS	GOA
(G)Erwin Sak			15/2/90	19	Lubin, Pol	Cardiff 9/08 -	1	0
(G)Tony Tucker			12/10/80	28		Redbridge (One Game) 9/08 - Billericay 10/08	1	0
(F)Josh Klein-Davies	5'11"	13 09	6/7/89	20	Bristol	Bristol R 11/08 - Lewes (2ML) 12/08, Bath C (L) 3/09, Rel 4/09, Weymouth (Trial) 7/09, Weston-Super-Mare 8/09	3	0
(F)Steve Butterworth						Dartford 1/09 - Rel 5/09, AFC Hornchurch 7/09	4	1
(F)Kaid Mohamed	5'11"		23/7/84	25	Cardiff	Forest Green 1/09 - Rel c/s 09	5	0

DEPARTURES	HT	WT	DOB	AGE	POB	From - To	APPS	GOA
(D)Nick Skelton			25/9/86	22	Basildon	Redbridge 6/08 - Rel 8/08	3	0
(D)Paul Keddle			18/11/83	25	Brecon	Carmarthen 6/08 - Rel 8/08, Merthyr 8/08		
(G)Nicky Church			31/5/86	23	Newport	Cwmbran Celtic 8/08 - Rel	1	0
(M)Danny Wring						Team Bath c/s 08 - Mangotsfield 7/08 Rel 11/08, Clevedon 11/08		
(F)Jemal Easter	5'08"	11 00	15/11/87	21	Cardiff	Carmarthen 8/08 - Rel 8/08, Carmarthen 9/08	5	1
(D)Ian Hillier	6'02"	11 13	26/12/79	29	Neath	Luton 10/01 7/05 - Rel 9/08, Re-signed Rel 4/09, Neath Ath 4/09	4	0
(D)Dave Collins	8/5/83	26	CorkRedbridge 6/08 - Rel 9/08			9	1	
(M)Anthony Church			29/9/87	21	Newham	Redbridge 7/08 - Rel 9/08, Ilkeston 10/08, Boston U 7/09	7	0
(M)Richard Evans	5'09"	11 08	19/6/83	26	Cardiff	Shrewsbury 8/06 - Rel 10/08, Bath C 10/08	1	0
(F)Rui Branguina						Oliviera do Bairro (Port) 9/08 - Rel 10/08		
(F)Paul Hall	5'08"	12 00	3/7/72	37	Manchester	Walsall 7/08 - Rel 10/08, Stratford T 11/08	13	0
(D)Justyn Roberts	6'00"	10 04	12/2/86	23	Lewisham	Rushden & D (L) 9/08 Perm 9/08 - Rel 10/08, Tooting & M Rel 5/09, Sutton U 7/09	4	1
(M)Leon Osei						Dorchester 10/08 - Rel 11/08	6	0
(F)Phil Walsh					Bristol	Bath C 6/08 - Tiverton (3ML) 9/08 Undisc 12/08, Dorchester 3/09	8	0
(F)Craig Hughes			18/12/78	30	Rhondda	Carmarthen 11/05 - Rel 1/09, Carmarthen 1/09	17	3
(F)Robert Duffy	6'01"	12 04	2/12/82	26	Swansea	Oxford U 7/08 - Mansfield 1/09	21	1
(M)Adie Harris			21/2/81	28		Bath C 6/08 - Weston-Super-Mare 4 fig 1/09	17	2
(D)Callum Hart	6'00"	11 00	21/12/85	23	Cardiff	ex Weymouth 10/08 - Farnborough 2/09, Weymouth 3/09	0	0
(D)Ashley Vickers	6'03"	13 10	14/6/72	37	Sheffield	Weymouth 3/08 - Dorchester (Pl/Coach) 3/09	21	0
(G)Scott James			29/8/89	20	Newport	Cinderford 2/08 - Cinderford 3/09	0	0
(D)Kevin Stephens	5'10"	12 05	28/7/84	25	Enfield	Redbridge 6/08 - Enfield T 9/08, Boreham Wood 10/08, Newport C 1/09 Rel 3/09, Boreham Wood 3/09	18	0
(D)Stephen Jenkins	6'02"	13 01	16/7/72	37	Merthyr	Worcester 10/06 (Pl/Coach) 6/08 - Lllanelli (Pl/Ass Man) 5/09	22	0
(M)Ben Evans						Yth - Clevedon (SL) 1/09, Clevedon 6/09	1	0
(D)Dan Harrison						Yth - Cinderford (L) 10/08	0	0

NEWPORT COUNTY

Formed: 1998

Nickname: The Exiles.

Club Colours: Amber shirts, black shorts, black socks.

Change Colours: White striped shirts, white shorts, white socks.

Club Sponsor: Acorn.

Previous League: Southern League

Ground address: Newport Stadium, Langland Way, Newport, South Wales NP19 4PT

Telephone: 01633 662 262

Mobile: 07889 359 100

Fax: 01633 666 107

Email: office@newport-county.co.uk

Website: www.newport-county.co.uk

Simple Directions: From Severn Bridge on M4 take first exit signed Newport (jct 24) tand follow signs to Newport International Sports Village. Turn left into Langland Way (Carcraft)and take next left into stadium car park.

Capacity: 4,300 **Seats:** 1,236 **Covered:** 3,236 **Floodlights:** Yes

Clubhouse: Open matchdays offering comprehensive meal menu and Sky Sports.

Club Shop: Open matchdays.

Local Radio: Red Dragon, Real Radio and BBC Wales.

Local Press: South Wales Argus and South Wales Echo

no image available

PROGRAMME EDITOR

Ray Taylor

M: 07770 751189

Email: raynafc@aol.com

CLUB STATISTICS

RECORDS

Attendance: 4,616 v Swansea City, FA Cup 1st Rnd 11.11.2006.
Victory: 9-0 v Pontlottyn Blast Furnance (A) Welsh Cup 01.09.90
Defeat: 1-6 v Stafford Rangers (A) 06.01.96
Career Goalscorer: Chris Lillygreen 93
Career Appearances: Mark Price 275 (222 lg +53 Cup)
Transfer Fee Paid:
£5,000 to Forest Green Rovers for Shaun Chapple.
Received: £5,000 from Merthyr Tydfil for Craig Lima

SENIOR HONOURS

Hellenic League Champions 1989-90.
Hellenic League Cup Winners 1989-90.
Gloucestershire Senior Cup Winners 1993-94.
Southern League Midland Division Champions 1994-95.
Gwent F.A.Senior Cup Winners 1996-97, 97-98, 98-99, 99-2000, 00-01, 01-02, 03-04, 04-05.

PREVIOUS

Leagues: Hellenic 1989-90. Southern 1990-2004.
Names: Newport AFC after demise of Newport County in 1988-89 Changed back again in 1999.

ST. ALBANS CITY

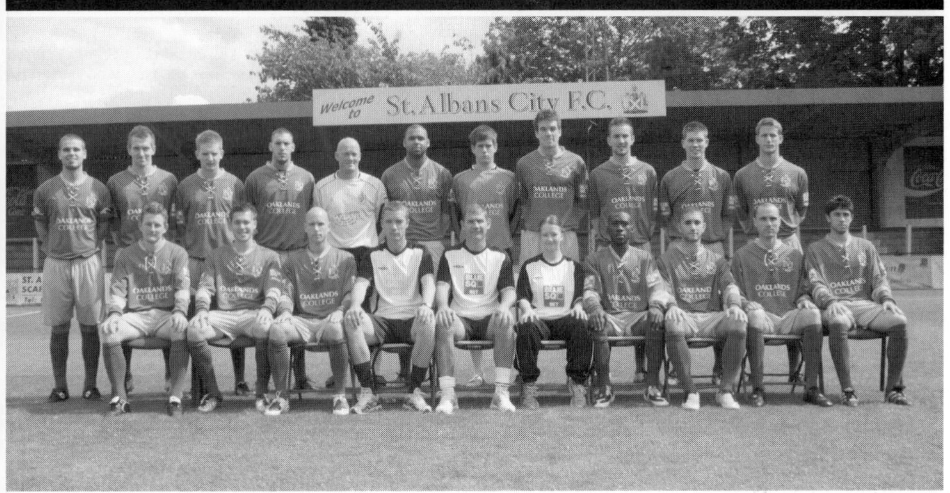

CLUB PERSONNEL

Chairman: John Gibson.

Vice-Chairman: Alisdair McMillin.

Company Secretary: Bill Nicholson.

Additional Directors: Karen Gibson.

Secretary: Steve Eames

c/o the club.

(B): 01727 864 296

(H): 01727 767 252

(M): 07805 769 083

steveeames@sacfc.co.uk

Commercial Manager: Nick Archer.

(M): 07802 817 843

Email: nick.archer@gsp-stalbans.co.uk

Press Officer: As secretary.

Manager: Steve Castle.

Club therapist: Zac Chandler.

St Albans City had been one of the favourites to struggle in season 2008-2009 following the previous poor campaign, so manager Steve Castle was probably lucky that supporters were not expecting too much. However, a poor start was still disappointing as City had to wait for the seventh game for the first victory.

The first F.A.Cup tie can sometimes give relief from the fight for points, but a 0-0 home draw against Harlow Town was followed by a replay defeat and morale was no better. This was a turning point however, as an immediate run of six consecutive victories took 'The Saints' up to fifth position.

Football really is a 'funny old game' and apart from winning an F.A.Trophy replay on penalties against Dartford before losing the next tie at Stevenage Borough, St Albans slumped with a massive twelve league games without a victory. Supporters will never understand how a club can change fortunes so quickly in such dramatic fashion.

Just to show they could turn on the form again, a 3-0 victory over Basingstoke Town was the signal for City to play five fixtures, which included a home game with A.F.C.Wimbledon, without letting in a single goal! A final position of twelfth was perhaps about right for a topsy turvey season in which St Albans finished with only one victory in the last six games. With their form fluctuating from the superb to the depressing, Saints supporters will be wondering which St Albans team will be turning up next season.

ST ALBANS CITY

BEST LGE ATT.: **1,105** v Eastleigh
LOWEST: **222** v Basingstoke Town

No.	Date	Comp	H/A	Opponents	Att:	Result	Goalscorers	Pos
1	Aug 9	BSS	H	Havant & Waterlooville	522	D 1 - 1	S Martin 2	
2	11		A	Worcester City	944	L 0 - 2		
3	16		A	Dorchester Town	490	D 1 - 1	**Hakim** 9	15
4	23		H	Chelmsford City	623	L 1 - 2	**Hakim** 80	16
5	25		A	Maidenhead United	426	L 0 - 1		
6	30		H	Eastleigh	408	W 5 - 0	S.Martin 6 **Hakim** 10 B.Martin 42 Suliaman 68 Cohen 81	
7	Sept 2		H	Bishop's Stortford	448	W 2 - 0	Quilter 72 Clarke 90	
8	6		A	Team Bath	160	L 0 - 2		15
9	**9**	**SS S1**	**H**	**Hayes & Yeading**	**165**	**L 0 - 1**		
10	13		H	Thurrock	373	L 0 - 2		15
11	20		A	Newport County	886	W 1 - 0	Hunt 87 (pen)	13
12	**27**	**F.A.C. 2Q**	**H**	**Harlow Town**	**404**	**D 0 - 0**		
13	**Oct 1**	**F.A.C. 2Q r**	**A**	**Harlow Town**	**299**	**L 2 - 3**	**Cousins 75 Cohen 78**	
14	4		A	Basingstoke Town	280	W 2 - 1	Hunt 58 B.Martin 67	12
15	18		H	Bognor Regis Town	389	W 1 - 0	Hurrell 22	10
16	21		A	Welling United	413	W 1 - 0	Hunt 21 (pen)	
17	25		H	Bath City	472	W 2 - 1	S.Martin 61 **Hakim** 82	
18	Nov 1		A	Bromley	373	W 3 - 2	**Hakim** 30 55 Burgess 66	6
19	8		H	Fisher Athletic	443	W 4 - 1	Cohen 54 **Hakim** 57 62 Quilter 90	6
20	15		H	Hayes & Yeading	587	D 1 - 1	**Hakim** 77	5
21	**22**	**F.A.C. 3Q**	**H**	**Dartford**	**525**	**D 0 - 0**		
22	**25**	**F.A.C. 3Q r**	**A**	**Dartford**	**542**	**D 1 - 1***	**Quilter 33 (Won 4-2 on pens)**	
23	29		A	Braintree Town	400	L 0 - 1		9
24	Dec 6		H	Worcester City	424	L 0 - 2		9
25	**13**	**F.A.T. 1R**	**A**	**Stevenage Borough**	**737**	**L 1 - 4**	**Cohen 81**	
26	20		A	Havant & Waterlooville	541	L 0 - 2		9
27	26		H	Hampton & Richmond B	609	D 2 - 2	**Hakim** 48 Lake 53 (og)	10
28	Jan 1		A	Hanpton & Richmond B.	687	D 0 - 0		
29	17		H	Bromley	514	L 4 - 5	B.MARTIN 3 (43 52 72) Charge 90	11
30	24		A	Bath City	676	L 0 - 1		11
31	27		H	Welling United	248	L 2 - 3	**Hakim** 63 Hurrell 73	
32	31		A	Weston-s-Mare	273	D 1 - 1	Everitt 20	13
33	Feb 14		A	Bishop's Stortford	602	D 1 - 1	**Hakim** 63	
34	21		A	Hayes & Yeading	256	L 1 - 2	Shields 45	14
35	24		H	Basingstoke Town	222	W 3 - 0	**Hakim** 6 Cohen10 Fisher 33	
36	28		A	Bognor Regis Town	245	W 5 - 0	Fisher 12 **HAKIM** 3 (37 65 69) Hunt 48 (pen)	11
37	Mar 7		H	Team Bath	447	D 0 - 0		
38	10		H	AFC Wimbledon	1105	D 0 - 0		
39	14		A	Fisher Athletic	137	W 4 - 0	Hunt 58 B.Martin 63 S.Martin 75 88	11
40	21		H	Newport County	494	D 1 - 1	S.Martin 5	10
41	24		H	Dorchester Town	311	W 2 - 0	**Hakim** 13 Cohen 16	
42	27		A	Thurrock	300	D 0 - 0		10
43	31		A	Eastleigh	567	L 0 - 3		
44	April 4		H	Weston-s-Mare	393	W 3 - 0	**Hakim** 22 Martin B 33 Martin S 77	10
45	10		A	Chelmsford City	1459	D 1 - 1	B.Martin 70	
46	13		H	Maidenhead United	375	L 1 - 2	Hunt 19	
47	18		H	Braintree Town	385	L 0 - 3		11
48	25		A	AFC Wimbledon	4722	L 0 - 3		12

Average Home Att: 466 (448) **Goals** 60 59

Best Position: 5th **Worst:** 16th

Goalscorers: Hakim 18, Martin B 8, Martin S 7, Cohen 6, Hunt 6, Quilter 3, Fisher 2, Hurrell 2, Burgess 1, Charge 1, Cousins 1, Clarke 1, Everitt 1, Shields 1, Suliaman 1.Own Goals 1.

BASTOCK	FISHER	COUSINS	BOWDITCH	B MARTIN	QUILTER	SULAIMAN	RIDGWAY	HAKIM	S MARTIN	HUNT	YOUNGS	PROTHEROE	TWOMEY	ARCHER	ADAMS	HICKS	CLARKE	JINADU	COHEN	RIECK	BAILEY	THURLBOURNE	MORTIMER	FRATER	EFFIONG	HURRELL	BYFIELD	OHAM-STRACHAN	MACKIE	PALMER	EVERITT	BARONET	GRAY	MUNDAY	NICHOLLS	SEEBY	CHARGE	SHIELDS	JACKAMAN	BUTCHER	ASAMOAH	
X	X	X	X	X	X	X	X	X	X	X	S	U	U	U	U																											**1**
X	X	X	X	X	X	X	X	X	X	X	S	S		U	U	S																										**2**
X	X	X	X	X	X	X	X	X	X	X	U			S		S	S	U																								**3**
X	X	X	X	X	X		X	X	S	X	S			S	U	X	X	U																								**4**
X	X	X	X	X	X		X	X	S	X	S		U	U			X	S	X																							**5**
X	X	X	X	X	X	X	S	X	X	X		X		U			U		S	S																						**6**
X	X	X	X	X	X	X	U	X	X	X				U			S		S	U	X																					**7**
X	X	X	X	X	X	X	S	X	X	X		X		U			U		S		S																					**8**
X	**X**	**X**	**X**	**X**		**X**	**U**	**X**	**S**	**X**				**S**	**U**		**S**		**X**	**X**	**X**																					**9**
X	X	X	X	X	X	X		U	X	X				S	U		S		X	U	X																					**10**
X	X		X	X	X	X		X	X	X		X				S	U		S	U	X	S																				**11**
X	**X**	**S**	**U**	**X**	**X**			**X**	**S**	**X**		**X**			**U**	**X**	**X**		**S**	**U**	**X**	**X**	**U**																			**12**
X	**X**	**X**	**X**	**X**	**S**			**X**	**S**	**X**					**U**	**X**	**X**		**S**		**X**	**X**	**U**	**U**	**U**																	**13**
X	X	X	X	X	X			X	S	X					U	U	X		X		X			S		U																**14**
X	X	X		X	U			X	X	X							S		X			X		X		X	U	U	U													**15**
X	X	X		X	S			S	X	X							X		X			X	U	X		X		U	S													**16**
X	X	X		X	S			S	X	X							X		X			X		X		X		U	S	U												**17**
X	X	X		X	X	U		X	X	X									X			X		X		S	U	U	U													**18**
X	X	X		X	X			X		X									X		S	X	U			X			S	U	X											**19**
X	X	X		X	X	S		X		X									X		U	X		X		X				U	S		S									**20**
X	**X**	**X**		**X**	**X**	**X**		**X**	**S**	**S**									**X**			**X**		**X**		**X**	**U**				**U**		**S**									**21**
X	**X**	**S**		**X**	**X**	**X**		**X**	**S**	**X**									**X**			**X**		**X**		**U**	**U**				**X**		**S**									**22**
X	X	U		X	X	X				X									X			X		X		S			S	U	X		X	S								**23**
X	X	X		X	X	X		X	S	X									X			X		X	S	U								S								**24**
X	**X**	**U**		**X**	**X**	**X**		**X**	**S**	**X**							**S**		**X**			**X**		**X**		**S**					**X**				**U**							**25**
X	X	U		X	X	S		X	X	X							X							X		X					X		S	U	S							**26**
X	X	X		X		U		X	X	X							X		X					X							S		U	S	U	X						**27**
X	X	X		X	S	X		X	S	X							X		X					X		S					U			U		X						**28**
X	X	X		X	S	X		X	X	X							X							X		S			U		U					X	S					**29**
X	X	X		X	X	X		X	X	X													S	X		S			U		X					U	S					**30**
X	X	X		X	X	U		X	S	X									X				X	X		S					X					S	U					**31**
X	X	X		X	X	X		X	S	X									X				U						U		X					X	U					**32**
X		X			X	X		X		X									X				U	X	U		U				X					S	X	X				**33**
X	X	X		X	X	X		X	S	X									X				U	X	U											U		X				**34**
X	X	X		X	X	X		X	S	X									X				S		S				X	U						U		X				**35**
X	X			X	X	X		X	S	X									X		X		S		S				X							U		X				**36**
X	X	X			X	X			X	X									X		X		U	U	S				X							U		X				**37**
	X	X		S	X	X		X	U	X									X		X		U	U					X							U		X		X		**38**
	X	X		X	X	X		X	S	X									X		X		U	S	U						S							X		X		**39**
	X	X		X	X	X		X	X	X									S		X			U	U				S		U							X		X		**40**
	X	X		X	X	X		X	X	X									S		X			S	U				S		U							X		X		**41**
U		X		X	X	X		X	X	X									S		X		S	U					S		X							X		X		**42**
	X	X		X	X	X		X	S										X		X		S	U					S		X							X		X		**43**
X	X			X	U	X		X	X	X									S		S		S	X					X		X							X		U		**44**
X	X	U		X	X	X		S	X	X									X				U	X	U				X		X											**45**
X		X		X	X	X		X	S	X									X		S		S	X	U				X		X											**46**
X		X			X	X			X	X									X				X	X	S				X	U	X								U		S	**47**
X		X			X	X		X	X										X		X		S		S		U		X		X		X								S	**48**
Total League Appearances																																										
36	37	36	11	37	35	30	5	35	24	40	0	3	0	0	0	1	9	0	27	0	13	8	2	19	0	6	0	0	9	0	14	0	2	0	0	4	1	12	0	6	0	**X**
0	0	0	0	1	4	2	2	3	13	0	4	1	0	3	0	3	4	1	8	1	4	1	8	3	6	6	0	0	8	0	3	0	2	3	1	2	2	0	0	0	2	**S**
1	0	3	0	0	2	3	1	1	1	0	1	1	2	6	5	1	3	2	0	3	1	0	9	5	7	2	4	4	5	6	4	0	1	2	1	6	2	0	1	1	0	**U**
Total Cup Appearances																																										
6	6	3	2	6	4	4	0	6	0	5	0	1	0	0	0	2	2	0	4	1	3	5	0	3	0	1	0	0	0	0	2	0	0	0	0	0	0	0	0	0	0	**X**
0	0	2	0	0	1	0	0	0	6	1	0	0	0	1	0	0	2	0	2	0	0	0	0	0	0	1	0	0	0	0	0	0	2	0	0	0	0	0	0	0	0	**S**
0	0	1	1	0	0	0	1	0	0	0	0	0	0	0	3	0	0	0	0	1	0	0	2	1	1	1	2	0	0	0	1	0	0	0	1	0	0	0	0	0	0	**U**

ST ALBANS CITY

CURRENT SQUAD AS OF BEGINING OF 2009-10 SEASON

GOALKEEPERS	HT	WT	D.O.B	AGE	P.O.B	CAREER	Apps	Gls
Paul Bastock	5'11"	14 00	19/5/70	39	Leamington Spa	Coventry (Trainee), Cambridge Utd 3/88, Sabah (Mal) c/s 89, Kettering (L) 3/90, Kettering 7/90, Fisher (L), Boston Utd 8/92, Scarborough 10/04, Dag & Red 10/04, St Albans 11/04 Rel 5/07, Rushden & D 5/07 Rel 2/08, St Albans 2/08	36	0

DEFENDERS	HT	WT	D.O.B	AGE	P.O.B	CAREER	Apps	Gls
Alex Bailey	5'09"	10 07	21/9/83	25	Newham	Arsenal, Chesterfield Rel 5/07, Halifax NC 10/07, St Albans 9/08 Rel 11/08, St Albans 3/09	17	0
Adam Everitt			28/6/82	27	Hemel Hempstead	Hemel Hempstead, Harrow c/s 00, Luton, Harrow 10/01, Hayes 6/03 Rel 5/05, Yeading (Trial) c/s 05, Yeading 9/05, Cambridge C 5/07, Eastleigh Undisc 10/07 Rel 5/08, AFC Hornchurch 8/08, Bromley 8/08, St Albans 11/08	17	1
James Fisher			13/4/84	25	London	Chelsea (Yth), Wembley, Wealdstone 8/02, Ruislip Manor, Northwood 12/07, St Albans 2/08	37	2
Ryan Frater			20/1/84	25	Herts	St Albans (Yth), Hitchin, Chelsea (Trial) 3/03, Dunstable 11/04, Bedford T (Trial) c/s 05, Stotfold 8/05, Hitchin 2/06, St Albans 12/07, Welling (Trial) 6/09	22	0
Jason Mitchell						Witham T, Maldon T, St Albans 8/09		
Mark Peters	6'00"	13 03	6/7/72	37	Rhyl	Man City Rel c/s 92, Norwich 9/92 Rel c/s 93, Peterborough 8/93, Mansfield 9/94 Rel c/s 99, Bromsgrove (SL) c/s 96, Rushden & D 7/99, L.Orient 9/03 Rel c/s 05, Aldershot (L) 11/04, Aldershot (Trial) 7/05, Cambridge U 8/05 Rel 5/08, Kings Kynn 7/08, St Albans (Pl/Man) 6/09		

MIDFIELDERS	HT	WT	D.O.B	AGE	P.O.B	CAREER	Apps	Gls
Danny (DJ) Green						Harlow Rel 3/09, Cheshunt (Dual) 1/08, Bishops Stortford 3/09, St Albans 8/09		
Craig Mortimer						St Albans, Northwood (L) 10/08	10	0
Jonathan O'Donnell						Watford (Yth), MK Dons (Yth), Hemel Hempstead, St Albans 7/09		
James Quilter						Tottenham (Yth), Brentford, Southend, Dag & Red, Heybridge, Cambridge C Rel 11/03, Bishops Stortford, Takeley, Manford Way, St Albans 1/08	39	2
Darren Quinton	5'08"	9 11	28/4/86	23	Romford	Cambridge U Rel 3/09, CRC (L) 12/06, Braintree 3/09, St Albans 8/09		
Soloman Shields	5'10"	12 00	14/10/89	19	Leyton	L.Orient Rel 5/09, St Albans (2ML) 2/09, Hayes & Yeading (Trial) 7/09, St Albans 8/09	12	1
Jamie Thurlbourne						Ely, Newmarket 7/07, Haverhill R 11/07, Wisbech 7/08, Newmarket 9/08, St Albans c/s 09		
Luke Thurlbourne						Southend Rel 5/09, St Albans (2ML) 9/08, St Albans 7/09	9	0

FORWARDS	HT	WT	D.O.B	AGE	P.O.B	CAREER	Apps	Gls
Daniel Chillingworth	6'00"	12 06	13/9/81	27	Cambridge	Cambridge U, Cambridge C (SL) 3/01, Cambridge C (2ML) 8/01, Darlington (L) 11/01, Walsall (Trial) 11/04, L.Orient (L) 12/04, Rushden & D 7/05, Notts County (SL) 2/06, Cambridge U 1/07 Rel 5/08, St Albans (L) 12/07, Injured, St Albans 8/09		
Gary Cohen	5'11"	11 02	20/1/84	25	Leyton	Watford 7/02, Scarborough 2/03 Rel c/s 03, Gretna 8/03, Workington (SL) 8/04, Grimsby (7ML) 7/05 Perm 1/06 Rel c/s 07, St Albans 8/08	35	5
Inih Effiong						St Albans, Northwood (L) 10/08	6	0
Paul Hakim			18/6/82	27	London	Wingate & F, Cheshunt, Slough 11/02, Wingate & F 12/02, Dag & Red (Trial) c/s 04, B.Stortford 8/04, St Albans 7/05, Stevenage 1/07, Woking (L) 9/07, St Albans 1/08	38	16
Jamie-Lee O'Donoghue						Yeading, Brimsdown, St Albans c/s 09		
Drew Roberts					Luton	Leighton Corinthians, AFC Houghton, Leighton T, Barton R, Bedford 3/03, Kettering 7/04, Aylesbury 12/04, Histon 11/05 Rel 5/07, Hemel Hempstead 5/07, Cambridge C 2/08, St Albans 8/09		

LOANEES	HT	WT	DOB	AGE	POB	From - To	APPS	GOA
(D)Gordon Rieck						Southend 8/08 - Great Wakering (L) 10/08	1	0
(F)Bradley Gray	5'11"	11 07	5/7/90	19	Swindon	L.Orient 11/08 - AFC Hornchurch (L) 1/09, Dulwich Hamlet (L) 2/09, St Albans (L) 3/09 Rel 5/09, Salisbury 7/09	4	0
(F)Danny Charge						Dag & Red 1/09 -	3	1
(G)Lee Butcher			11/10/88	20	Waltham Forest	Tottenham 3/09 - Grays (L) 4/09	6	0

DEPARTURES	HT	WT	DOB	AGE	POB	From - To	APPS	GOA
(M)Jamie Eames			11/6/89	20	St Albans	Stevenage c/s 08 - Colney Heath, Cambridge C 2/09		
(M)Sean Ridgway	5'11"	12 02	10/12/86	22	London	Manley (Aust) 7/08 - Rel 9/08, Enfield T 9/08 Rel 1/09	7	0
(F)Tom Youngs	5'09"	10 07	31/8/79	30	Bury St Edmunds	Cambridge C 8/08 - Mildenhall 9/08, Norwich U 6/09	4	0
(F)Hamsa Twomey			25/9/88	20		Yth - Rel 9/08	0	0
(M)James Archer			25/1/89	20		Yth - Bognor 9/08	3	0
(M)Rodney Hicks			4/11/86	22		Halesowen T 8/08 - Rel 10/08, Northwood 10/08, Hitchin 10/08 Rel 11/08, Northwood, Wealdstone 2/09	4	0
(M)Ben Bowditch	5'10"	12 00	19/2/84	25	Bishops Stortford	Cambridge C 8/08 - Rel 10/08, Bishops Stortford 7/09	11	0
(D)Lee Protheroe			5/11/75	33		Chelmsford c/s 08 - Rel 10/08, Welling 11/08	4	0
(D)Jonathan Munday			13/4/88	21		Grays 11/08 - Sutton U 1/09, Hitchin 2/09	3	0
Sam Hurrell						ex Chelsea 10/08 - Welling 2/09	12	2
(F)Lee Clarke	5'11"	10 08	28/7/83	26	Peterborough	Peterborough (SL) 1/04 Perm 7/04 - Rel 4/09, Welling 5/09	13	1
(M)Hector Mackie						Potters Bar 10/08 - Weymouth 6/09	17	0
(D)Scott Cousins	5'10"	11 06	12/7/83	26	Edgware	Hendon 8/04 - Carshalton 6/09	36	0
(D)Ben Martin	6'07"	13 08	25/11/82	26	Harpenden	Swindon 8/04 - Chelmsford 7/09	38	8
(F)Simon Martin			8/7/79	30	London	Hayes & Yeading (L) 1/08 Perm 2/08 - Rel c/s 09, Slough 8/09	37	7
(D)Chris Seeby			20/11/84	24	St Albans	Watford (Jun) - Northwood (L) 3/09, Northwood c/s 09	6	0
Ryan Baronet						Yth -	0	0
Robin Nicholls						Yth -	1	0
Luke Jackaman						Yth -	0	0
Kwame Asamoah						Yth -	2	0
(G)Christopher Adams						Stevenage 8/08 - St Neots	0	0
(G)Austin Byfield						Yth -	0	0
(G)Jake Palmer						Berkhamstead 10/08 -	0	0
(D)Tobi Jinadu			14/7/84	25		Heybridge 8/08 -	1	0
(D)Troy Oham-Strachan						Yth -	0	0
(D)Hassan Sulaiman			26/9/85	23	London	Crawley 7/07 -	32	1
(M)Jonathan Hunt	5'10"	11 12	2/11/71	37	Camden	ex Peterborough 2/08 -	40	7

ST. ALBANS CITY

Formed: 1908

Nickname: The Saints.

Club Colours: Royal blue shirts, amber shorts, royal blue socks.

Change Colours: Red shirts, red shorts, red socks.

Club Sponsor: Oaklands College.

Previous League: Isthmian League

Ground address: Clarence Park, York Road, St. Albans, Herts AL1 4PL

Telephone: 01727 864 296

Fax: 01727 866 235

Email: secretary@sacfc.co.uk

Website: www.sacfc.co.uk

Simple Directions: Exit M25 jct 22 and follow A1081 towards St Albans, at 5th roundabout turn right into Alma Road. At the lights turn right into Stanhope Road and straight on at next lights into Clarence Road. Ground is 200 yards on left.

Capacity: 6,000 **Seats:** 904 **Covered:** 1,900 **Floodlights:** Yes

Clubhouse: Open matchdays and open for functions.

Club Shop: Fully stocked.

Local Radio: BBC Three Counties, Chiltern Radio.

Local Press: St Albans Observer

no image available

PROGRAMME EDITOR

Steve Eames

(H) 01727 767 252 (M) 07805 769 083

(B) 01727 864296

Email: steveeames@sacfc.co.uk

CLUB STATISTICS

RECORDS

Attendance: 9,757 v Ferryhill Athletic F.A.Amateur Cuo 1926

Victory 14-0 v Aylesbury United (H) Spartan League 19.10.12

Defeat 0-11 v Wimbledon (H) Isthmian League 1946

Career Goalscorer: W.H.(Billy) Minter - 356

Top scorer for 12 consecutive seasons from 1920 -1932.

Career Apperances: Phil Wood - 900 (1962-85

Transfer Fee Paid:

£6,000 to Yeovil Town for Paul Turner Auguat 1957.

Transfer Fee Received:

£92,759 from Southend United for Dean Austin 1990.

SENIOR HONOURS

Isthmian Champions 1923-24, 26-27, 27-28.

Athenian League Champions (2)

London Senior Cup 1970-71.

PREVIOUS

Leagues: Herts County 08-10 Spartan 08-20 Athenian 20-23.

Isthmian. Conference.

STAINES TOWN

CLUB PERSONNEL

Chairman: Alan Boon.

Secretary: Steven Parsons

3 Birch Green, Staines, Middlesex TW18 4HA

(H) 01784 450 420

(M): 0787 667 2458

Email: catspar57@aol.com

Commercial Manager: Angie Payne.

(M): 07825 067 232

Email: angie@stainestownfootballclub.co.uk

Press Officer: Stuart Moore.

(M): 07803 207 661

Email: stuartmr@uk.ibm.com

Manager: Steve Cordery.

Club therapist: Gareth Workman.

Having lost their second league fixture of the season, Staines promptly won the next five fixtures, moved up to second place and never dropped below third all season. The frustratingly good form of leaders Dover Athletic really limited the other challengers to play-off ambitions, but consistent results saw 'The Swans' consolidate in second place.

Cup football didn't play a very important part in the season for Staines, who beat Cheshunt away 3-0 in the F.A.Cup before losing a thriller 3-5 to Hayes & Yeading away after a replay. In the F.A.Trophy they were drawn against the league leaders Dover Athletic and lost 0-2 at home. 'The Swans' were free to concentrate on the league!

League form was consistent throughout the season and only once did Staines lose two consecutive games. This 'blip' was followed by a run of twenty four games with just one defeat, away to Harrow Borough. Two original runs gave 'The Swans' five games with clean sheets over the Christmas holiday period and seven consecutive draws of which four were at home, from 14th March to 10th April, but at no time did they lose their second place in the table.

As the top placed play-off club, Staines had the home advantage and produced two very business like performances to keep a clean sheet against Sutton United (3-0) and Carshalton Athletic with, senior non-league football's top marksman Richard Jolly, were beaten 1-0 with an extra time goal. A tremendous season had been rewarded with promotion and the 'Swans' fans could look forward to Blue Square football for the first time.

STAINES TOWN

BEST LGE ATT.: 591 v Ashford Town
LOWEST: 150 v Harlow Town

No.	Date	Comp	H/A	Opponents	Att:	Result	Goalscorers	Pos
1	Aug 16	Ryman P.	H	Billericay Town	277	W 1 - 0	Sargent 16	
2	20		A	Horsham	236	L 1 - 2	Elliott 36	
3	23		A	Tonbridge Angels	411	W 2 - 1	Onochie 29 Thomas 38	7
4	25		H	Harrow Borough	232	W 1 - 0	Onochie 65	
5	30		A	AFC Hornchurch	274	W 2 - 0	Thomas 45 Sargent 56	4
6	Sept 2		H	Boreham Wood	228	W 4 - 1	ONCHIE 3 (15 61 66) Thomas 54	
7	6		H	Dartford	451	W 2 - 1	Kersey 70 Onochie 78	3
8	9		A	Sutton United	410	D 1 - 1	Charles-Smith 57	2
9	**13**	**F.A.C. 1Q**	**A**	**Cheshunt**	**236**	**W 3 - 0**	**Thomas 2 Kersey 36 Scarlett 63**	
10	20		A	Ramsgate	327	D 1 - 1	**Butler** 56	2
11	23		H	Hendon	266	W 2 - 0	**Butler** 30 75	
12	**27**	**F.A.C 2Q**	**H**	**Hayes & Yeading**	**305**	**D 0 - 0**		
13	**30**	**F.A.C. 2Qr**	**A**	**Hayes & Yeading**	**348**	**L 3 - 5**	**Butler 20 72 Onochie 67**	
14	Oct 4		A	Canvey Island	351	D 2 - 2	Sargent 24 Fenton 90	2
15	**18**	**F.A.T. 1Q**	**H**	**Dover Athletic**	**320**	**L 0 - 2**		
16	25		A	Carshalton Athletic	314	W 3 - 1	Scarlett 23 **Butler** 69 Onachie 74	2
17	28		A	Wealdstone	280	L 3 - 4	Sargent 53 66 Newton 87	
18	Nov 8		H	Dover Athletic	491	L 2 - 3	J.Thomas 19 Onochie 61	2
19	15		A	Tooting & Mitcham United	321	W 2 - 1	Thomas 54 **Butler** 59 (pen)	
20	18		H	Hastings United	211	W 2 - 0	Charles-Smith 68 Ramsay 88 (og)	
21	29		A	Margate	403	W 2 - 1	Taylor 18 McDonald 42	3
22	Dec 6		A	Billericay Town	371	D 1 - 1	**Butler** 82	3
23	20		A	Boreham Wood	131	W 2 - 0	Taylor 53 **Butler** 70	2
24	27		H	Ashford Town	591	W 3 - 0	Newton H 36 Cook 37 **Butler** 47	2
25	Jan 17		A	Dartford	1148	D 0 - 0		2
26	24		H	Ramsgate	288	W 2 - 0	Grifiths 45 **Butler** 82	2
27	31		A	Hendon	181	W 2 - 0	Newton 53 **Butler** 55	2
28	Feb 7		H	Sutton United	376	W 3 - 1	Newton 19 Taylor 24 Griffiths 88	2
29	10		H	Maidstone United	302	W 3 - 1	Sargent 74 (pen) **Butler** 90 H.Newton 90	
30	14		H	Canvey Island	282	W 2 - 1	Taylor 12 H.Newton 88	2
31	17		A	Harrow Borough	146	L 1 - 2	**Butler** 22	
32	21		A	Maidstone United	332	D 0 - 0		2
33	24		H	Harlow Town	150	W 1 - 0	Gordon 84	
34	28		H	Carshalton Athletic	349	W 4 - 1	**Butler** 9 Ifura 19 Taylor 67 Newton 68	2
35	Mar 7		A	Harlow Town	327	W 2 - 0	Ifura 44 **Butler** 70	
36	10		H	Heybridge Swifts	192	W 3 - 2	Taylor 27 47 **Butler** 38	
37	14		A	Dover Athletic	2019	D 0 - 0		2
38	17		H	Tonbridge Angels	283	D 2 - 2	Risbridger 6 77	
39	21		A	Wealdstone	388	D 2 - 2	Griffiths 45 **Butler** 37 (pen)	2
40	24		H	Horsham	255	D 0 - 0		
41	28		A	Hastings United	393	D 1 - 1	Onochie 16	2
42	April 4		H	Tooting & Mitcham	308	D 0 - 0		2
43	10		H	AFC Hornchurch	308	D 2 - 2	Newton 19 90	2
44	13		A	Ashford Town	250	L 0 - 2		
45	18		A	Heybridge Swifts	121	L 2 - 3	Ifura 70 Griffiths 89	2
46	25		H	Margate	384	W 4 - 1	Brown 8 **BUTLER** 3 (11 33 54)	2
47	**28**	**Play Off S-F**	**H**	**Sutton United**	**738**	**W 3 - 0**	**Newton 22 Griffiths 47 Chabann 85**	
48	**May 3**	**Play-Off F**	**H**	**Carshalton Athletic**	**1198**	**W 1 - 0***	**Taylor 110**	

Average Home Att: 296 (348) **Goals** 85 48

Best Position: 2nd **Worst:** 7th

Goalscorers: Butler 21, Onochie 10, Newton 10, Taylor 8, Sargent 6, Thomas 6, Griffiths 4, Charles-Smith 2, Ifura 2, Kersey 2, Risbridger 2, Scarlett 2, Brown 1, Chabann 1, Cook 1, Elliott 1, Fenton 1, Gordon 1, Ifura 1, McDonald 1. Own Goals 1.

CURRENT SQUAD AS OF BEGINING OF 2009-10 SEASON

GOALKEEPERS	HT	WT	D.O.B	AGE	P.O.B	CAREER	Apps	Gls
James Courtnage			18/3/84	25		Brentford (Trainee), Watford (Trainee), Hampton, Aylesbury, Hemel Hempstead, Hertford (L), Leyton Pennant 2/03, Enfield c/s 03, Leyton 2/04, Walton & H 9/04, Hendon 1/05, Staines c/s 05, Bracknell (Dual) 10/06		
Louis Wells			22/2/82	27		Hayes, Aldershot 6/06, Maidenhead 8/07, Uxbridge 3/08, Staines c/s 08		
DEFENDERS								
Marc Cumberbatch						C.Palace (Yth), Colchester (Yth), Barnet, Ashford T (L) 11/03, Wealdstone (L) 2/04, Erith & B 8/04, Ashford T 2/05, Dover 11/05 Rel 1/06, Leyton, Dulwich H 12/07, Staines 3/09		
Danny Gordon			20/12/81	27	Aylesbury	Aylesbury, Staines 7/04		
Marien Ifura			7/9/84	24		QPR (Sch) Rel c/s 04, Aylesbury (SL) 3/03, Farnborough (3ML) 9/03 (03/04 6,0), Hendon (L) 1/04, Kingstonian 9/04, Staines 1/05, Studying, Windsor & E 11/06, Staines 3/08		
Simon Jackson			4/4/85	24	Lewisham	Charlton (Sch) Rel 03/04, Woking 8/04 Rel 5/07, Fisher (L) 2/07, Fisher c/s 07, Bognor Regis 8/08, Sutton U 10/08, Staines 8/09		
Lee Kersey	5'09"	11 07	12/8/79	30	Harlow	Tottenham Rel c/s 99, Norwich (Trial) 7/99, Barnsley (Trial) 9/99, Enfield 11/99, Stevenage 2/00, Chesham 3/00 Rel 5/02, Chelmsford 8/02, QPR (Trial) 1/03, Heybridge S (L) 1/03 4 fig 2/03, Windsor & E 6/04, Maidenhead 12/04, Windsor & E 9/05, AFC Wimbledon 8/06 Rel 5/07, Time Out, Beaconsfield SYCOB 9/07, Maidenhead 10/07, Staines 8/08		
Marlon Patterson	5'09"	11 10	24/6/83	26	London	Millwall (Trainee), Chelsea (Trainee), Crawley 8/02, Fisher 1/03, Billericay, Fisher 12/03, Carshalton 3/04, Dulwich Hamlet 12/04, Crashalton 7/05, Hayes & Yeading 7/06, Dag & Red NC 8/07, Welling (3ML) 9/07, Grays (SL) 2/08, Bishops Stortford (L) 11/08,		
Dave Sargent			22/12/77	31		Watford (Yth), Wycombe (Yth), Hendon, Hayes, Northwood 10/97, St Albans, AFC Wimbledon c/s 04 Rel c/s 06, Staines 6/06		
Dominic Sterling			8/7/76	32	Isleworth	Wimbledon, Wealdstone, Hayes 7/00, Aldershot 7/02 Rel 6/04, Canvey Island 6/04, Maidenhead 5/06 Rel 5/09, Staines 7/09		
David Woozley	6'00"	12 10	6/12/79	29	Ascot	C.Palace, Bournemouth (L) 9/00, Torquay (L) 8/01, Torquay 3/02, Oxford U 7/04, Yeovil (L) 3/05, Aldershot (Trial) 7/05, Crawley 8/05 Rel 8/07, Farnborough 8/07, Staines 6/09		
MIDFIELDERS								
Chris Bourne						Southend (Yth), Canvey Island, Billericay (L), Welling (L), Brentwood, Heybridge 9/08, Staines 7/09		
Darti Brown			10/6/77	32	London	Willesden Constantine, Yeading, Wembley, Harrow, Yeading 3/03, Maidenhead 12/06 Rel 6/08, Staines 7/08		
James King						Staines		
Gareth Risbridger	5'10"	11 05	31/10/81	27	High Wycombe	Marlow (Yth), Yeovil c/s 98, Southend 7/01 Rel 1/02, Dover (L) 10/01, Salisbury 2/02, Aylesbury 3/02, Staines 12/03		
Andre Scarlett	5'04"	09 06	11/1/80	29	Wembley	Luton Rel c/s 01, Chelmsford 8/01, Boreham Wood, Hemel Hempstead, Stevenage, Wealdstone, Hitchin 3/02, Chesham 7/02, Staines 12/05		
Dean Thomas			20/9/87	21		Staines, Bracknell (L) 8/07		
FORWARDS								
Richard Butler			1/5/85	24	Ashford	Ashford T (Middx), AFC Wimbledon 8/04, St Albans 11/07, Staines 2/08		
Marc Charles-Smith			1/7/84	25		Leatherhead, Staines c/s 07, Boreham Wood (L) 3/09		
Leroy Griffiths	5'11"	13 05	30/12/76	32	London	Sutton U, Banstead, Corinthian C, Hampton & Richmond 2/00, QPR £40,000 5/01 Rel 7/03, Farnborough (L) 8/02, Margate (L) 11/02, Farnborough 8/03, Grays 9/03, Fisher 5/05 Rel 5/07, Aldershot (3ML) 1/06, Grays (SL) 2/07, Havant & W 7/07, Corinthian Casuals 10/07, Lewes 10/07, Gillingham (6WL) 11/07 Perm 1/08 Rel c/s 08, Eastleigh 8/08, Staines 8/08		
Howard Newton			16/3/82	27	Hammersmith	Epsom & E, Hitchin, Wembley, Staines, Hampton & R, Sutton U, Dag & Red, Harrow 9/04, Staines 7/06		
Eliot Onochie			15/3/82	27		Tottenham (Yth), Wimbledon (Yth), Tooting & M, C.Palace (Trial) c/s 04, Croydon A, Kingstonian, Staines 10/04 Harrow 2/05, Boreham Wood 10/07, Staines 3/08		
Scott Taylor	5'10"	11 06	5/5/76	33	Chertsey	Staines, Millwall £15,000 2/95, Bolton £150,000 3/96, Rotherham (2ML) 12/97, Blackpool (L) 3/98, Tranmere £50,000 10/98 Rel c/s 01, Stockport 8/01, Blackpool 1/02, Plymouth £100,000 12/04, MK Dons £100,000 1/06, Brentford (L) 3/07, Rochdale (L) 10/07, Grays 1/08 Rel c/s 08, Lewes 7/08, Staines 11/08		

STAINES TOWN

Formed: 1892

Nickname: The Swans

Club Colours: Blue shirts, blue shorts, azure socks.

Change Colours: White shirts, white shorts, red socks.

Club Sponsor: AT&T (GB) Ltd - Electrical Wholesalers of Brentford.

Previous League: Southern League

Ground address: Wheatsheaf Park, Wheatsheaf Lane, Staines, TW18 2PD

Telephone: 01784 225 943 / 01784 463 100

Mobile: 07876 672 458

Fax: 01784 225 947

Email: catspar57@aol.com

Capacity: 3,000 **Seats:** 300 **Covered:** 850 **Floodlights:** Yes

Simple Directions: Ground is located at the Thames Club. Turn left off B376 (Lakeham Road) approx. one mile from town centre, bus and railway stations.

Clubhouse: All facilities plus modern sports bar

Club Shop: All souvenirs available. Contact Ray Moore c/o club

Local Press: Staines & Ashford News, Middx Chronicle,Informer + Staines Guardian

Local Radio: County Sound, GLR,Capital and Radio Wey

no image available

PROGRAMME EDITOR

Steven Parsons

Tel: (M) 0787 667 2458

Email: catspar57@aol.com

CLUB STATISTICS

RECORDS

Attendance: 2,750 v Banco di Roma, Barassi Cup 1975 (70,000 watched the second leg)

Victory: 14-0 v Croydon (A) Isthmian Div 1 19.03.94

Defeat: 1-18 v Wycombe Wanderers (A) Gt. Western Suburban.Lg. 27.12.09

Career Goalscorer: Alan Gregory 122

Career Appearances: Dickie Watmore 840

SENIOR HONOURS

Spartan League Champions 1959-60.

Athenian League Division 2 Champions 1971-72.

Isthmian League Division 1 Champions 1974-75 88-89

Middlesex Senior Cup 1975-76, 76-77, 77-78, 88-89, 90-91, 94-95, - 97-98.

Barssi Cup 1975-76.

Isthmian Full Members Cup1994-95.

Isthmian League Premier Play-off Winners 2008-09.

PREVIOUS

Names:Staines Albany & St Peters Institute merged in 1895.
Staines 1905-18. Staines Lagonda 1918-25.
Staines Vale (Second World War)

Leagues:(since 1920) Hounslow & Dist 1919-1920.
Spartan 1924-35,58-71. Middx Senior 1943-52. Parthenon 1952-53.
Hellenic 1953-58. Athenian 1971-73.

THURROCK

CLUB PERSONNEL

Chairman: Tommy South.

Company Secretary: Norman Posner.

Additional Directors: Harry South.

Secretary: Norman Posner

1 Chase House Gardens, Hornchurch,

Essex RM11 2PJ

(H): 01708 458 301

Email: normpos@aol.com

Commercial Manager: Gary Reed

(M): 07894 092 427

Press Officer: Tony Flood

(M): 07525 493 785

Email: thurrockpressoffice@gmail.com

Manager: Hakan Hayrettin.

Club therapist: Craig Turner BSc HPC CSP

After the first month of the season Thurrock had not managed to collect a single point and must have lined themselves up as relegation certainties. As it turned out, it would have been a safe bet, but a little burst at the beginning of November actually produced four victories and a draw to take them up to fourteenth place and this gave their supporters reasonable hope.

A short run in the F.A.Cup can sometimes lift morale when league games are becoming a pain, but 'Fleet' suffered a shattering home defeat by a 0-5 scoreline against Boreham Wood. The Chairman was so upset by the performance that he offered to reimburse the 90 brave supporters who had attended. The F.A.Trophy also only concerned Thurrock for one game, as they lost by the only goal of the tie at Basingstoke.

The New Year saw Thurrock quickly sink down to twentieth position, as goals became very difficult to score, although Che Stadhart bravely chipped away in a side usually under pressure themselves, and did well to accumulate twelve senior goals including one golden run of five in five games early in the season.

Finishing in twentieth place, the club steeled themselves for the drop, but thanks to Team Bath stepping down from senior football, the Essex club were saved, but they know there must be wholesale improvements if the club is to avoid another difficult season.

THURROCK

BEST LGE ATT.: 1,173 v AFC Wimbledon
LOWEST: 196 v Dorchester Town

No.	Date	Comp	H/A	Opponents	Att:	Result	Goalscorers	Pos
1	Aug 9	BSS	H	Eastleigh	231	L 0 - 1		
2	12		A	AFC Wimbledon	2786	L 1 - 2	Anderson 15	
3	16		A	Team Bath	125	L 1 - 4	Araba 32	21
4	23		H	Welling United	328	L 1 - 2	Masade 35	22
5	25		A	Bishop's Stortford	323	L 1 - 2	**Stadhart** 25	
6	30		H	Havant & Waterlooville	261	L 2 - 3	Orilonishe 19 **Stadhart** 25	
7	Sept 2		H	Hampton & Richmond B	243	D 3 - 3	Orilonishe 8 **Stadhart** 22 58	
8	6		A	Hayes & Yeading	238	L 1 - 2	McLeish 63	22
9	**9**	**SS S1**	**H**	**Welling United**	**81**	**W 2 - 0**	**Bryant 22, Orilonishe 59**	
10	13		A	St Albans City	373	W 2 - 0	**Stadhart** 68 Flynn 88	20
11	20		H	Dorchester Town	196	W 1 - 0	**Stadhart** 66	19
12	**27**	**F.A.C. 2Q**	**H**	**Boreham Wood**	**90**	**L 0 - 5**		
13	Oct 4		A	Weston-s-Mare	204	L 1 - 2	Docker 18	20
14	**7**	**SS S2**	**H**	**Hayes & Yeading**	**68**	**D 3 - 3***	**McKenzie 25, Wright 30, Stadhart 90 + 3 (Won 5-4 on pens)**	
15	18		H	Maidenhead United	250	L 1 - 2	Swaine 27	20
16	21		A	Braintree Town	449	W 2 - 1	McKenzie 35 52	
17	25		H	Bognor Regis Town	196	D 1 - 1	Flynn 45	17
18	Nov 1		A	Fisher Athletic	200	W 3 - 0	McKenzie 25 42 Hart 73	16
19	**4**	**SS S3**	**A**	**Kettering Town**	**438**	**L 1 - 4**	**McKenzie 78**	
20	8		H	Basingstoke Town	443	W 6 - 0	Wright 37 Howard 43 Orilonishe 54 70 Bryant 88 90	15
21	15		H	Worcester City	224	W 2 - 0	**Stadhart** 15 McKenzie 51	14
22	**22**	**F.A.T 3Q**	**A**	**Basingstoke Town**	**280**	**L 0 - 1**		
23	29		A	Bromley	427	D 3 - 3	Swaibi (og) 31 McKenzie 46 66	15
24	Dec 6		H	Newport County	309	D 0 - 0		15
25	13		A	Dorchester Town	357	L 3 - 4	McKenzie 2 Wright 45 Bryant 83	
26	20		A	Eastleigh	509	D 1 - 1	Orilonishe 9	15
27	27		H	Chelmsford City	812	L 0 - 1		15
28	Jan 1		A	Chelmsford City	2014	L 2 - 3	**Stadhart** 27 89	
29	17		H	Weston-s-Mare	300	L 0 - 1		18
30	24		A	Hampton & Richmond B	786	L 1 - 3	Kechmere 51	
31	27		A	Bognor Regis Town	254	D 1 - 1	Bryant 77	
32	31		H	Fisher Athletic	202	W 2 - 1	Paine 25 Bryant 57	18
33	Feb 21		H	AFC Wimbledon	1173	L 0 - 1		20
34	28		H	Bromley	320	D 1 - 1	**Stadhart** 67	20
35	Mar 3		A	Maidenhead United	188	D 1 - 1	**Stadhart** 17	
36	7		A	Worcester CIty	588	L 0 - 2		20
37	14		H	Hayes & Yeading	286	L 0 - 1		20
38	21		A	Havant & Waterlooville	574	D 2 - 2	St Aimee 11 Knight 87	20
39	24		H	Team Bath	204	L 1 - 2	Swaine 90	
40	28		H	StAlbans City	300	D 0 - 0		20
41	31		A	Bath City	409	D 2 - 2	Hughes 77 Orilonishe 90	
42	April 4		A	Basingstoke Town	354	L 0 - 1		20
43	10		A	Welling United	620	D 0 - 0		
44	13		H	Bishop's Strtford	334	L 1 - 3	Flynn 20	
45	18		A	Newport County	809	D 1 - 1	Flynn 81	20
46	21		H	Braintree Town	255	W 1 - 0	Orilonishe 78	
47	25		H	Bath City	288	W 2 - 0	**Stadhart** 52 Malik 61	20

Average Home Att: 341 (325) **Goals** 60 73

Best Position: 14th **Worst:** 22nd

Goalscorers: Stadhart 13, McKenzie 10, Orilonishe 8, Bryant 6, Flynn 4, Wright 3, Swaine 2, Anderson 1, Araba 1, Docker 1, Hart 1, Howard 1, Hughes 1, Knight 1, Lechmere 1, Malik 1, Masade 1, McLeish 1, Paine 1, St Aime 1. Own Goals 1.

YOUNG	CLARK	ANDERSON	SWAINE	PAINE	LETTEJALLOW	HENRY	ORILONISHE	STADHART	ARABA	GREENE	READ	GILBERT	MASADE	HUSSEIN	FLYNN	SPENCER	DOCKER	BRYANT	MCLEISH	HUGHES	BLACKMORE	WRIGHT	TAYLOR	MCKENZIE	LECHMERE	WOOLLEY	HART	HOWARD	GILBEY	SAMBROOK	CAMPANA	KNIGHT	BEANEY	ALLEN	RICHARDS	FITZGERALD	LALITE	ST AIMIE	DEAN	STEVENSON	MALIK	
X	X	X	X	X	X	X	X	X	X	X	S	U	U	U																												1
X	X	X	X	X	X	X	X	X	X	S	S	U		U																												2
X	X	X	X	X	X	U	X	X	X	X	S	S		U	X																											3
X	X	X	X	X	X	S	X	X	X	U		S	X	U	X																											4
X	X	X		X	X	S	X	X	U	X		S	X	U	X																											5
X	X		X	X	X		X	X	U		U	U	U		X	X	X	X	S																							6
X	X	S	X	X	X		X	X	U					U	X	X	X	X	S	S																						7
	X	X		X	X		X	X	S			U		U	X	X	X	X	S	S	X																					8
	X		**X**	**X**	**S**		**X**	**X**	**S**			**U**		**U**	**X**	**X**	**X**	**X**	**S**	**X**	**X**																					**9**
	X	U		X	S		X	X	U					U	X	X	X	X	S	X	X	X																				10
	X	U		X	X		X	X						U	X			X	X	X	X	X	S	S	U																	11
		X		**X**	**X**		**X**	**X**	**S**		**U**	**U**		**X**			**X**	**X**		**X**		**X**	**U**	**S**	**X**																	**12**
			X	X	X		X	X	S			U		U		X	X	X	S	S	X	X			X																	13
			X	**X**	**X**		**X**	**S**				**U**		**U**		**X**	**X**	**S**	**X**	**S**	**X**	**X**		**X**	**X**																	**14**
	X		X	X	X		X	X						U	U		X	X	S	S	X	X		S	X																	15
	X		X	X			X							U	X		U	X	U	X		X	U	X	U	X	X															16
	X	U	X	X			X	S							X			X		X		X	U	X	S	X	X															17
	X	U	X	X			X	X				U			X	U				S		X	U	X		X	X	X														18
	X	**U**	**X**	**X**			**X**								**X**	**U**				**X**		**X**	**U**	**X**	**U**	**X**	**X**	**X**	**U**													**19**
	X	U	X	X			X	X							X			S		S		X		X	U	X	X	X		S												20
	X	U		X			X	X							X	U				U		X		X	S	X	X	X	U	X												21
	X	**U**	**X**	**X**			**X**	**X**							**X**	**S**				**S**		**X**		**X**	**S**	**X**	**X**		**U**	**X**												**22**
	X	S		X			X	X							X	X				U		X		X	U	X	U	X			X	U										23
	X	U	X	X			X	X								S						X		X	U	X	S	X	U	X	X											24
	X		X				S	X							X	U		S				X		X		X	X	X		X	X	U	S									25
	U	U	X	X			X	X			S				X			X				X				X			U	X	X		X									26
	U		X	X			X	X			U				X			X				X			U	X		S	U	X	X		X									27
	X	U	X	X			X	X							X			S				X			U	X			U	X	X	S	X									28
	X	U	X	X			X	X			U							X		X	X	X			S	U				X		S	X									29
		U	X	X			X	X										X		X	X	X			X				U	X	S	S	X	S								30
	U		X	X				X			U	X						X		X	X	X			X	U					X	U	X	U								31
	S		X	X				X			U				X			X		X	X	X			X	U	X	X	U					S								32
	X	U	X	X				S							X			X		X					X	X	S	X	U						X	X						33
	X	X		X				S				U			X			X		X					X	X	U	X	S			S			X	X						34
	X	X		X				X				U			X			X		X	U				U	X	X		U							X	X					35
	X	X		X			X	X				U						X		X	U				S	X	X		S			S					X	X				36
	X	X		X			X	X				X						S		X	U					X	X		U			S			S		X	X				37
	X	U	X	U			X	X				X			X					S					S	X	X					S					X	X	X			38
	X	U	X	U			X	X				X			X					U					X	X			U			S					X	X	X			39
	X	X	X				X	X				U			X					X			U		X	X			U			X					U		X			40
		X	X	X			X	X							X			S		X					X	X						S							X	X	S	41
	X	X	X	U			X	U							X			U		X					X	X						U					U	X	X	X		42
	X	X	X	U			X	X							X			X		S						X			U			X					X		X	S	S	43
	X	X	X	U			X	X							X			X		X						X			S			S					X		X	S	U	44
	X	U	X	X			X	U							X			X							U	X	X		U								X		X		X	45
	X	U	X	X			X	S							X			X							U	X	X		U			U					X		X		X	46
	X		X	X			X	S				U			X			X		S					S	X	X		U								X		X		X	47

Total League Appearances

YOUNG	CLARK	ANDERSON	SWAINE	PAINE	LETTEJALLOW	HENRY	ORILONISHE	STADHART	ARABA	GREENE	READ	GILBERT	MASADE	HUSSEIN	FLYNN	SPENCER	DOCKER	BRYANT	MCLEISH	HUGHES	BLACKMORE	WRIGHT	TAYLOR	MCKENZIE	LECHMERE	WOOLLEY	HART	HOWARD	GILBEY	SAMBROOK	CAMPANA	KNIGHT	BEANEY	ALLEN	RICHARDS	FITZGERALD	LALITE	ST AIMIE	DEAN	STEVENSON	MALIK	
7	35	15	32	35	11	2	36	34	4	3	0	4	2	0	32	6	6	24	1	17	9	19	0	8	11	26	14	9	0	8	7	2	6	0	2	3	10	4	10	2	4	**X**
0	1	2	0	0	1	2	1	5	2	1	4	3	0	0	0	1	0	5	6	9	0	0	1	2	6	0	2	1	3	1	1	10	1	2	1	0	0	0	0	2	2	**S**
0	3	16	0	5	0	1	0	2	4	1	5	11	2	12	1	3	1	1	1	3	3	0	4	0	10	3	2	0	16	0	0	5	0	1	0	0	2	0	0	0	1	**U**

Total Cup Appearances

YOUNG	CLARK	ANDERSON	SWAINE	PAINE	LETTEJALLOW	HENRY	ORILONISHE	STADHART	ARABA	GREENE	READ	GILBERT	MASADE	HUSSEIN	FLYNN	SPENCER	DOCKER	BRYANT	MCLEISH	HUGHES	BLACKMORE	WRIGHT	TAYLOR	MCKENZIE	LECHMERE	WOOLLEY	HART	HOWARD	GILBEY	SAMBROOK	CAMPANA	KNIGHT	BEANEY	ALLEN	RICHARDS	FITZGERALD	LALITE	ST AIMIE	DEAN	STEVENSON	MALIK	
0	3	1	4	5	2	0	5	3	0	0	0	0	0	1	3	2	3	2	1	3	2	4	0	3	2	2	2	1	0	1	0	0	0	0	0	0	0	0	0	0	0	**X**
0	0	0	0	0	1	0	0	1	2	0	0	0	0	0	0	1	0	1	1	2	0	0	0	1	1	0	0	0	0	0	0	0	0	0	0	0	0	0	0	0	0	**S**
0	0	2	0	0	0	0	0	0	0	0	1	3	0	2	0	1	0	0	0	0	0	0	2	0	1	0	0	0	2	0	0	0	0	0	0	0	0	0	0	0	0	**U**

Also Played: STEPHENSON S(1,2). LINCOLN X(2). LODGE S(3,4) X(5). SAMUELS S(5). PUGH S(12). JUSTHAM U(12). ZULMATASHVILI U(17). TYBURSKI U(33). HAMMATT U(35). LEMONIUS U(40). OKTAY U(45).

THURROCK

CURRENT SQUAD AS OF BEGINING OF 2009-10 SEASON

GOALKEEPERS	HT	WT	D.O.B	AGE	P.O.B	CAREER	Apps	Gls
Adam Rafis						Leyton Pennant, Ford U 3/03, London APSA, Romford, Barking 7/07, Aveley 11/07, Concord R, Thurrock c/s 09		
Joe Woolley			20/9/89	19		Charlton (Yth), Grays c/s 08 Rel 8/08, Thurrock 10/08	26	0
DEFENDERS								
Phil Anderson			1/3/87	22		Southend, Aldershot 7/06 Rel 5/07, Thurrock c/s 07	17	1
Ryan Andrews						West Ham (Scholar), Dover, Hastings U 11/07, East Thurrock 1/08, Sittingbourne 2/08, Thurrock c/s 09		
Kenny Clark						Dag & Red, Heybridge (L) 3/06, Thurrock 6/06	36	0
Lee Flynn	5'09"	11 05	4/9/73	35	Hampstead	Boreham Wood, Wingate & F, Romford, Hendon, Hayes 7/95, Barnet 1/01 £13,500, Stevenage 5/03 Rel 4/04, Dag & Red 5/04, St Albans (L) 10/05, Cambridge C (L) 12/05, St Albans (L) 1/06, St Albans 3/06 Rel 3/07, Thurrock 3/07	32	4
Matthew Paine	6'01"	12 12	22/12/87	21	Bexley	Colchester, Thurrock (SL) 1/07, Thurrock c/s 07	35	1
Rob Swaine						Billericay, Thurrock 9/07	32	2
MIDFIELDERS								
Matt Bodkin	5'06"	10 11	16/9/86	22	Chatham	Notts Forest Rel c/s 04, Gillingham 8/04, Welling 8/05, Grays 12/06 Rel 2/09, Thurrock (L) 1/07, Dartford (L) 8/07, Thurrock (SL) 9/07, Eastleigh (6ML) 8/08, Dover 2/09 Rel 5/09, Thurrock 5/09		
Reiss Gilbey						Thurrock	3	0
Leon Lalite						Barnet, Stevenage, Waltham Forest, Harlow 12/03, Thurrock 3/09	10	0
Lamar Lemonius						Thurrock	0	0
Greg Lincoln	5'09"	10 13	23/3/80	29	Cheshunt	Arsenal Rel c/s 01, York C (Trial) 4/01, Cambridge U (Trial) 7/01, Stevenage 9/01 Rel 9/01, Hull C (Trial) 9/01, Torquay (Trial) 9/01, Margate 10/01 Rel 10/01, Hammarby IF (Swe), Northampton T 7/02 Rel c/s 04, Redbridge 8/04, Chelmsford 7/05, Cambridge C 12/05, Thurrock 5/07	1	0
Junior Luke						Potters Bar, Dulwich Hamlet 11/07, Leyton 12/07, Potters Bar, Leyton 1/09, Waltham Forest 7/09, Thurrock 8/09		
Fola Orilonshe			14/7/86	23		Waltham Forest, Thurrock 8/07	37	7
FORWARDS								
David Bryant			9/6/82	27		Dag & Red, Maldon, Aveley, Thurrock 3/07, Braintree 5/08 Rel 8/08, Thurrock 8/08	29	5
David Knight						Thurrock	12	1
Paul Olima			6/8/86	23	Dublin	St Patricks, Taunton 9/06, Dag & Red, Waltham Forest 8/07, Arlesey 11/07, Ilford 2/08, Walton Casuals, Grays 11/08, Walton Casuals (L) 12/08 Perm, Croydon Ath 1/09, Hitchin 2/09, Thurrock c/s 09		

PLAYING SQUAD

LOANEES	HT	WT	DOB	AGE	POB	From - To	APPS	GOA
(M)Baimass Lettejallow	5'09"	10 12	16/4/84	25	London	Dag & Red (3ML) 8/08 - Bishops Stortford (L) 1/09, Bishops Stortford c/s 09	12	0
(M)Rhys Henry						Southend 8/08 - Harlow (L) 9/08, Lewes (L) 2/09, Rel 5/09	4	0
(F)Hakeem Araba			12/2/91	18		Dag & Red (3ML) 8/08 - Redbridge (L) 11/08, Redbridge (L) 1/09	6	0
(F)Anton Stephenson						Tilbury, Walton Casuals 3/07, Eton Manor, Tilbury 6/08, Thurrock (L) 8/08 , Concord R 1/09, Sevenoaks T Rel 3/09	2	0
(M)Danny Hart	5'10"	11 09	26/4/89	20	London	Barnet 10/08, (SL) 1/09 -	16	1
(M)Charlie Howard	6'00"	15 00	26/11/89	19	London	Gillingham 10/08 -	10	1
(M)Harley Dean	6'03"	12 12	26/7/91	18		Dag & Red (SL) 3/09 -	10	0

DEPARTURES	HT	WT	DOB	AGE	POB	From - To	APPS	GOA
(M)Ebenezer Masade						Thamesmead 8/08 - Slade Green, Margate 11/08, Harrow 1/09, Horsham 2/09	2	1
(M)Nicky Greene						Sutton U 8/08 - Rel 9/08, Fisher 10/08, Bromley 8/09	4	0
(G)Andrew Young						Bishops Stortford 7/08 - Dartford 9/08	7	0
(G)Eliot Justham						East Thurrock, Waltham Forest, Leyton 1/09	0	0
(F)Danny Lodge			31/3/86	23		Grays 10/08	3	0
(M)Jon Docker			12/2/86	23	London	Dorchester 8/08 - Welling 10/08 Rel 11/08, Hitchin 2/09, Billericay 3/09	6	1
(F)Aaron McLeish						Bedfont Green 8/08 - Rel 11/08	7	1
(M)David Pugh						Haversham (L) 10/07, Boreham Wood 11/08	0	0
(F)Leon McKenzie			18/10/84	24		Waltham Forest 6/06 - Rel 12/08, Luton (Trial) 12/08, Grays 12/08 Rel 1/09, Bishops Stortford 7/09	10	8
(D)Michael Spencer						Enfield 8/08 - Fisher 12/08	7	0
(D)Andrew Sambrook	5'10"	11 09	13/7/79	30	Chatham	Fisher 11/08 - AFC Wimbledon 1/09, Welling 5/09	9	0
(M)Alex Campana	5'11"	12 01	11/10/88	20	Harrow	Wivenhoe 11/08 - Rel 2/09, Enfield T 2/09	8	0
(D)Mark Wright			20/1/87	22	London	Fisher 9/08 - Bishops Stortford 2/09	19	2
(M)Kenny Beaney			27/7/86	23		Beckenham 12/08 - Bromley 2/09	7	1
(F)Oliver Allen	5'09"	10 05	7/9/86	22		Retirement 1/09 - Rel 2/09, Billericay 3/09	2	0
(F)Alexander Read			17/5/88	21		Eton Manor c/s 07 - Enfield T 3/09	4	0
(F)Jamie Richards						Harlow 2/09 - Harlow 3/09, Boreham Wood 5/09	3	0
(M)Kieron St Aimie	6'01"	13 00	4/5/89	20	Brent	Barnet 3/09 - Hitchin 3/09, Maidenhead 8/09	4	1
Lorcan Fitzgerald						ex West Ham 2/09 - Ireland 3/09	3	0
(M)Bryan Hammatt						Enfield Town 2/09 - Ware, Aveley 3/09	0	0
(F)Craig Hughes	6'00"	11 09	26/11/87	21	Canterbury	Heybridge 10/07 - AFC Sudbury (L) 12/08, AFC Sudbury 6/09	26	1
(G)Nedjet Hussain						Margate c/s 07 - Bishops Stortford c/s 09	0	0
(G)David Blackmore	6'01"	13 00	23/3/89	20	Chelmsford	West Ham 1/09 -	9	0
(D)Jake Gilbert						Yth - Boreham Wood 11/08, Holmer Green (Dual) 11/08, Hemel Hempstead (L) 12/08	7	0
(M)Sam Lechmere						West Ham (Trial) 11/08	17	1
(M)Wesley Samuels							1	0
(F)Jon Stevenson						Maidenhead 3/09 -	4	0
(F)Chris Taylor			16/3/88	21		Waltham Forest 8/06 -	1	0
Hasan Oktay						Thurrock (Ass Man)	0	0
Tchokounte Malik							6	1
Luke Tyburski							0	0
Grigoli Zulmatashvili							0	0
(F)Che Stadhart			25/9/76	32	London	Welling 3/07 - Retired c/s 09	39	12

THURROCK

Formed: 1985

Nickname: Fleet.

Club Colours: Yellow shirts, green shorts, yellow socks.

Change Colours: Sky blue shirts, claret shorts, claret socks.

Club Sponsor: Direct Flooring.

Previous League: Isthmian League

Ground address: Thurrock Hotel, Ship Lane, Grays, Essex RM19 1YN.

Telephone: 01708 865 492

Mobile: 07956 393 156

Fax: 01708 868 863

Email: nompos@aol.com

Website: www.thurrock-fc.com

Simple Directions: M25 or A13 to Dartford tunnel roundabout. Ground is fifty yards on right down Ship Lane.

Capacity: 4,500 **Seats**: 300 **Covered**: 1,000 **Floodlights**:Yes

Club Shop: Yes.

Clubhouse: Hotel facilities.

LocalRadio: BBC Essex Essex Radio

Local Press: Thurrock Gazette. Echo.

no image available

PROGRAMME EDITOR

Norman Posner

(H) 01708 458 301

Email: normpos@aol.com

CLUB STATISTICS

RECORDS

Attendance: 2,572 v West Ham United Friendly 1998

Victory: 10-0 v Stansted (H) 1986-87

v East Ham U 1987-88 (A) both Essex Senior League.

Defeat: 0-6 v St Leonards Stamco (A) F.A.Trophy 1996-97 and Sutton United (H) 1997-88 Isthmian League.

Career Goalscorer: George Georgiou - 106

Career Appearances: Jimmy McFarlane - 632

Transfer Fees Paid: Not known.

Received: Not known.

SENIOR HONOURS

Isthmian League Division 2 Champions 1991-92 .

Essex Senior Cup 2003-04, 05-06.

PREVIOUS

Name: Purfleet.

Leagues: Essex Senior 1985-89. Isthmian 1989-2004.

WELLING UNITED

no up-to-date image available

CLUB PERSONNEL

Chairman: Paul Websdale.

Vice-Chairman: Steve Pain.

Company Secretary: Barrie Hobbins.

Additional Directors: Eric Brackstone.

Secretary: Barrie Hobbins

(H): 0208 304 2006

(B): 0208 301 1196

(M): 07949 180 816

Email: barry.hobbins@hotmail.co.uk

Press Officer: Paul Carter

(M): 07863 347 587

Manager: Andy Ford.

Assistant Manager: Lee Protheroe.

Coach: Keith Levett.

Club therapist: Dave Lawson.

A 4-0 away victory on the opening day of the season and a hat trick for Ryan Martin was the best possible start, and on the coach journey back from Bath there must have been some conjecture regarding a great campaign ahead. Indeed, after five games with four victories and a draw plus the emergence of Charlie Sheringham, an exciting young striker, third in The Blue Square South seemed a very good place to be.

Maybe a little over confidence crept in, but seven games later without another win,'The Wings' were down to ninth and had been knocked out of the F.A.Cup by Whyteleafe away in a replay. Welling supporters had to get used to their team's inconsistency but they must have been pleased with just two defeats in the next fifteen games including an F.A.Trophy replay victory over A.F.C.Totton which led to a splendid 2-0 win against Weymouth.

The run finished at Hednesford Town in a 3-4 thriller, but this defeat was the start of another puzzling change of form. Sherringham had enjoyed a goalscoring spell of ten in ten games during the good run but 'The Wings' only managed one victory in the next eight games, although Sheringham did score four of the ten goals scored as the team struggled.

Local supporters must have finished the season as nervous wrecks as they celebrated great victories against top clubs Hampton & Richmond Borough (H) 4-0 and A.F.C. Wimbledon (A) 1-0 before drawing 0-0 at home to struggling Thurrock and losing to Maidenhead United (A) 0-2 and Havant & Waterlooville (A) 0-1. The crazy campaign came to and end with 'The Wings' in a very respectable seventh place - but what could it have been?

WELLING UNITED

BEST LGE ATT.: 1,625 v AFC Wimbledon
LOWEST: 389 v Hayes & Yeading

No.	Date	Comp	H/A	Opponents	Att:	Result	Goalscorers	Pos
1	Aug 9	BSS	A	Bath City	628	W 4 - 0	MARTIN 3 (14 45 60) Pinnock 83	
2	12		H	Braintree Town	519	W 1 - 0	Martin 74	
3	16		H	Basingstoke Town	531	D 1 - 1	Cobbs 25	
4	23		A	Thurrock	328	W 2 - 1	**Sheringham** 27 Cobbs 35	3
5	25		H	Fisher Athletic	805	W 3 - 0	Martin 21 **Sheringham** 36 (pen) 54	
6	30		A	Hayes & Yeading	239	L 1 - 2	**Sheringham** 56 (pen)	5
7	Sept 2		A	Bognor Regis Town	275	D 0 - 0		
8	6		H	Dorchester Town	560	D 0 - 0		7
9	**9**	**SS S1**	**A**	**Thurrock**	**81**	**L 0 - 2**		
10	13		A	Eastleigh	812	L 2 - 4	Healey 17 Braham-Barrett 80	
11	20		H	Worcester City	534	L 1 - 3	Quinn 37 (pen)	9
12	**27**	**F.A.C. 2Q**	**H**	**Whyteleafe**	**326**	**D 1 - 1**	**Martin 5**	
13	**Oct 1**	**F.A.C. 2Q r**	**A**	**Whyteleafe**	**206**	**L 0 - 2**		
14	4		A	Bishop's Storford	372	W 1 - 0	Andrews 73	9
15	18		H	Weston-s-Mare	550	W 2 - 0	Anderson 3 Blackburn 31	8
16	21		H	St Albans City	413	L 0 - 1		
17	25		A	Newport County	800	D 0 - 0		
18	Nov 1		A	Worcester City	769	W 1 - 0	Baker 32	8
19	8		H	Eastleigh	501	W 3 - 2	Baker 12 36 Anderson 86	
20	16		H	AFC Wimbledon	1625	S 2 - 2	**Sheringham** 23 51	
21	**22**	**F.A.T 3Q**	**H**	**AFC Totton**	**309**	**D 1 - 1**	**Sheringham 10**	
22	**25**	**F.A.T.3Q r**	**A**	**AFC Totton**	**232**	**W 2 - 1**	**Smith 5 Sinclair 83**	
23	29		A	Dorchester Town	366	D 1 - 1	Hill 32 (og)	8
24	Dec 6		H	Chelmsford City	780	L 1 - 3	**Sheringham** 54	8
25	**16**	**F.A.T. 1R**	**H**	**Weymouth**	**262**	**W 2 - 0**	**Sheringham 1 Ademola 18**	
26	20		H	Bath City	621	W 2 - 1	**Sheringham** 17 Fazackerly 25	7
27	26		A	Bromley	739	W 3 - 1	**Sheringham** 72 Sinclair 76 Ademola 81	6
28	Jan 1		H	Bromley	1255	W 3 - 1	**Sheringham** 30 (pen) 70 Fazackerley 52	
29	**13**	**F.A.T. 2R**	**A**	**Hednesford Town**	**346**	**L 3 - 4**	**Sheringham 37 84 Ming 56**	
30	17		H	Bishop's Stortford	529	L 1 - 3	Johnson 9	5
31	20		H	Team Bath	426	D 1 - 1	Tome 20 (og)	
32	24		A	Chelmsford City	1408	L 0 - 2		6
33	27		A	St Albans City	248	W 3 - 2	Ming 9 **Sheringham** 34 (pen) 87	
34	31		H	Maidenhead United	505	D 1 - 1	**Sheringham** 33	5
35	Feb 17		A	Hampton & Richmond B	475	L 0 - 2		7
36	24		H	Hayes & Yeading	389	L 0 - 2		
37	28		A	Braintree Town	556	D 1 - 1	Stevens 88	9
38	Mar 7		H	Havant & Waterlooville	485	W 2 - 1	**Sheringham** 56 Ademola 66	8
39	10		A	Basingstoke Town	223	D 0 - 0		
40	14		H	Hampton & Richmond B	605	W 4 - 0	Ademola 23 Baker 42 (pen) 76 Parkinson 90	7
41	21		A	AFC Wimbledon	337	W 1 - 0	Ming 73	7
42	28		A	Maidenhead United	342	L 0 - 2		8
43	April 4		H	Bognor Regis Town	556	W 4 - 1	Ming 38 Hurrell 45 Ademola 52 **Sheringham** 76	8
44	6		A	Havant & Waterlooville	557	L 0 - 1		
45	10		H	Thurrock	620	D 0 - 0		
46	13		A	Fisher Athletic	175	W 5 - 0	Andrews10 Johnson 12 Protheroe 50 Hurrell 62 **Sheringham** 75 (pen)	
47	18		A	Weston-s-Mare	261	W 3 - 0	Ming 37 Johnson 45 **Sheringham** 82	8
48	21		A	Team Bath	91	W 1 - 0	**Sheringham** 59	
49	25		H	Newport County	620	L 0 - 2		7

Average Home Att: 639 (515) **Goals** 70 53

Best Position: 3rd **Worst:** 9th

Goalscorers: Sheringham 23, Martin 6, Baker 5, Ming 5, Ademola 5, Johnson 3, Anderson 2, Andrews 2, Cobbs 2, Fazackerly 2, Hurrell 2, Sinclair 2, Blackburn 1, Braham-Barrett 1, Healey 1, Parkinson 1, Pinnock 1, Protheroe 1, Quinn 1, Smith 1, Stevens 1. Own Goals 2.

TURNER	SINCLAIR	BRAHAM-BARRETT	QUINN	MA MCENTEGART	G ANDREWS	GREEN	COBBS	HEALY	MARTIN	SHERINGHAM	DOR SMITH	SCHOBURGH	PINNOCK	S ANDREWS	BLACKBURN	JOHNSON	CHAPPELL	WHITE	STEVENS	O SMITH	NURSE	ANDERSON	GROSS	MI MCENTEGART	BAKER	MING	FAZACKERLEY	DOCKER	MORGAN	PARKINSON	BILAL	MASTERS	PROTHEROE	RICHARDS	ADEMOLA	DEL SMITH	DAYES	WILKINSON	MITTEN	ARTER	HURRELL	
X	X	X	X	X	X	X	X	X	X	X	S	S	S	U	U																											**1**
X	X	X	X	X	X	X	X	X	X	X	S		S	U	S	U																										**2**
X	X	X	X	X	X	X	X	X	X	X	S		S	U	U		U																									**3**
X	X	X	X	X	X	X	X	X	X	X	U		S	U	S		S																									**4**
X	X	X	X	X		X		S	X	X	X	S	U	U	X	S	X																									**5**
X		X	X	X	U	X	S	X	X	X	S		S	U	X	X	X																									**6**
U		X	X	X	U	X	X	X	X	X	S		S	X	S	X	X																									**7**
U		X	X	X	U	X	S	X	X		X	S	S	X	X	X	X																									**8**
U		**X**	**S**	**U**	**X**	**S**	**X**	**X**	**S**		**X**		**X**	**X**	**X**	**X**	**X**	**X**																								**9**
X		X	X	X	X	X	S	X	X		S			U	X	X	U		X	S																						**10**
X		X	X	X	X		X	X	S		S		S	U	X	X	U			X	X																					**11**
X	**X**	**X**	**X**	**X**	**U**	**X**	**S**	**S**	**X**	**X**	**S**		**U**			**X**	**U**		**U**	**X**	**X**																					**12**
																																										13
X	X	X	X	X	X	X	X		U	X			X		U	X	U		S		S																					**14**
X	X			X	X	X	X	S		X					X	X	U		S			X	X	U																		**15**
X	X		U	X	X	X	X			X					X	X			S			X	X	U	S	S																**16**
X	X		X	X	U	U	X			X					X	X	U		U			X	U		X	X																**17**
X	X		X	X	S		X			X					X	X						X	U		X	X	S	S	U													**18**
X	X		X	X	S	U	X			X					X	X						S	S		X	X	X	U														**19**
X	X			X			X			X					X	X							S	U	X	X	X		U	X	U											**20**
U	**X**		**X**	**X**			**X**			**X**					**X**	**X**			**S**	**S**					**X**		**X**		**S**			**X**	**X**	**U**								**21**
																																										22
	X		U	X	U		X			X	S				X	X									X	S	X			X		X	X	U								**23**
	X		U		X		X			X					U	X				U						X	X			X		X	X	S	X							**24**
U	**X**		**X**	**U**	**X**		**X**			**X**	**U**				**X**					**U**						**X**	**X**					**X**	**X**		**X**							**25**
U	X		X	X			X			X	U				X				U							X	X			S		X	X		X	S						**26**
	X	U	X		X			X	S				X				U							X	X			S		X	X		X	U								**27**
	X		X	U	X		X			X					X	S			U							X	X			S		X	X		X	S						**28**
	X		**X**	**S**	**X**					**X**	**U**				**X**	**X**			**U**	**X**						**X**	**X**		**U**			**X**	**X**			**S**						**29**
	X		X	X	S		X			X	S					X			U	X							X		U	S		X	X			X						**30**
	X		U	U	X		X			X	S				X	X			U	S						X	X			X		X				X						**31**
	X		X		X		X			X					X	X			S	X						X	X			S		X				U	S					**32**
	S			U	X		X			X					X	X			S	X						X	X			X						U	X	X	U			**33**
				X	X		X			X					X	S			S	X						X	X		U	X			X			U		X	U			**34**
	X		U	X	X		X			X					X	U									X	X	U			X					X		U	X	U			**35**
	X		U	U	X		X			X					X										S	X	X			X			X		X			U	X			**36**
	X		X	S	X		X			X					X				S						X	X	X			U			U		X			U	X			**37**
	X			U	X		X			X					X				S							X	X			X				U	X			U	X	X		**38**
	X		S	U	X					X					X				U						S	X	X			X					X			U	X	X	X	**39**
	X		X	U	X					U					X	S			S						X	X	S			X					X				X	X	X	**40**
	X		X		X					S					X	S			U						X	X	U			X					X			U	X	X	X	**41**
			X	U	X					S					X	S									X	X	S			X			X		X			U	X	X	X	**42**
			X	X	X					S					U	X									X	X	S			X			U		X			U	X	X	X	**43**
	S		X	X	X					X					S	X									X	X	S			X			U		X			U	X		X	**44**
	X		X	U	X					X					X	X			S							X	S			X			S		X			U	X		X	**45**
	X		X	U	X					X						X			U						S	X	X			X			X	S				S	X		X	**46**
	X		X	U	X		S			X						X			U	U						X	X			X			X					X			X	**47**
	X		X	U	X		S			X						X			U	U					S	X	X			X			X					X			X	**48**
	X		X	U	X		X			X						X			U						S	X	X			X			S					X	U		X	**49**
Total League Appearances																																										
15	32	11	30	24	31	12	28	9	9	35	2	0	1	2	28	25	4	0	1	5	1	4	2	0	12	27	20	0	0	20	0	8	12	0	15	2	1	6	11	6	11	**X**
0	2	0	1	1	3	0	5	2	1	3	11	3	8	0	4	6	1	0	10	2	1	1	2	0	6	2	6	1	0	5	0	0	2	2	0	2	1	1	0	0	0	**S**
3	0	0	6	14	5	2	0	0	1	1	2	0	1	8	5	2	6	0	12	3	0	0	2	3	0	0	2	1	4	1	1	0	3	2	0	4	1	9	4	0	0	**U**
Total Cup Appearances																																										
1	4	2	4	2	3	1	3	1	1	4	1	0	1	1	4	4	1	1	0	2	1	0	0	0	1	2	3	0	0	0	0	3	3	0	1	0	0	0	0	0	0	**X**
0	0	0	1	1	0	1	1	1	1	0	1	0	0	0	0	0	0	0	1	1	0	0	0	0	0	0	0	0	1	0	0	0	0	0	0	1	0	0	0	0	0	**S**
3	0	0	0	2	1	0	0	0	0	0	2	0	1	0	0	0	1	0	2	1	0	0	0	0	0	0	0	0	1	0	0	0	0	1	0	0	0	0	0	0	0	**U**

WELLING UNITED

CURRENT SQUAD AS OF BEGINING OF 2009-10 SEASON

GOALKEEPERS	HT	WT	D.O.B	AGE	P.O.B	CAREER	Apps	Gls
Charlie Mitten	6'02"	12 07	9/10/74	34	Woolwich	Thamesmead T, Dover 3/96, Margate (3ML) 9/96, Gillingham 10/99 Rel c/s 01, Margate 7/01, Gravesend NC 2/04 Rel 11/04 Welling 11/04 Rel 5/05, Margate 7/05, Folkestone I c/s 07, Welling 1/09	11	0
DEFENDERS								
Graeme Andrews						Bearsted, Dover, Welling 7/08	34	2
Michael Dean						Welling 7/09		
Michael Haswell			23/8/83	26	London	Wimbledon (Junior), Southend (Yth), Grays c/s 01, Romford 1/02, Grays 3/02, Wingate & F c/s 02, Harlow 7/04, Chelmsford 1/05, AFC Wimbledon 6/06 Rel 5/09, Grays 6/09 Rel 8/09, Welling 8/09		
Sam Hurrell			13/7/88	21	Hillingdon	North Greenford, Chelsea Rel c/s 07, L.Orient (Trial), Bradford C (Trial), Chelsea (Youngsters Coach) 2/08, St Albans 10/08, Welling 2/09	11	2
Ryan Johnson			15/1/87	22	Dartford	QPR, Maidenhead (L) 9/05, Dag & Red (2ML) 1/06, Maidenhead (SL) 3/06, Bournemouth (Trial) 5/06, Maidenhead 8/06, Slade Green 10/07, Welling 8/08, Sittingbourne (L) 8/08	31	3
Steve King						Hornchurch, Brentwood, Bishops Stortford 7/08, Brentwood (L) 1/09, Brentwood (Trial) 6/09, Welling 7/09		
Cedric Ngakam						Waltham Forest, Ebbsfleet (Trial) 7/08, Dulwich Hamlet 9/08, Welling 8/09		
Lee Protheroe			5/11/75	33		Walthamstow Pennant, St. Margaretsbury, Ruislip Manor, Yeading c/s 96, Enfield £5,000 7/98, Aldershot 6/00, Canvey Island 6/02, Gravesend (L) 11/03, Gravesend 4/04 Rel 4/06, Margate (SL) 3/06, Margate 5/06 Rel c/s 07, Chelmsford c/s 07, St Albans c/s 08 Rel 10/08, Welling 11/08 (Pl/Ass Man) 5/09	14	1
Andrew Sambrook	5'10"	11 09	13/7/79	30	Chatham	Gillingham (AS), USA Scholarship (Hartwick College) c/s 97, Gillingham 3/01 Rel 6/01, Rushden & D 8/01 Rel c/s 05, Grays 7/05, Fisher 7/08, Thurrock 11/08, AFC Wimbledon 1/09, Welling 5/09		
MIDFIELDERS								
Dean Cracknell	5'10"	12 04	12/10/83	25	Hitchin	Watford (Ass Sch), Northampton Rel 2/04, Stevenage 3/04 Rel c/s 04, Aylesbury 7/04, Barnet 1/05, B.Stortford 2/05, St Albans 5/05 Hemel Hempstead 5/07, St Albans 1/08, Cambridge C 3/08, Brackley 6/08, Welling 7/09		
Louis Fazackerley			24/7/84	25	Winchester	Fulham Rel c/s 04, Northampton (Trial) c/s 04, Farnborough (Trial) c/s 04, Sutton U 8/04, Eastbourne B 11/04, Leyton 7/06, Bishops Stortford 8/07, Bromley 5/08, Welling 10/08	26	2
Anthony Finn			27/11/82	26	Manchester	Hayes, Gravesend Rel 2/04, Edgware, Northwood 8/04, Colliers Wood, Met Police 3/06, AFC Wimbledon 6/07 Rel 5/09, Welling U 6/09		
Ben Greenhalgh						Welling		
Rob Hughes	5'08"	11 10	6/9/80	28	Sutton	Fulham, Aston Villa (Trial), Bromley, Molesey 2/03, Lewes, Horsham 10/03, Banstead 3/04, Farnborough 8/04 (04/05 11,0) Rel 5/05, Berkhamstead T (L) 2/05,Yeading (Trial) 7/05, Oxford U 7/05 Rel 11/05, Sutton U 12/05, Yeading 1/06, Croydon A, Bromley (Dual) 10/07, Sutton U 11/07 Rel 6/08 Injured, Welling 7/09		
Jeff Minton	5'06"	11 10	28/12/73	35	Hackney	Tottenham Rel c/s 94, Brighton 7/94 Rel c/s 99, Port Vale 7/99, Rotherham 3/01 Rel c/s 01, L.Orient 7/01 Rel c/s 02, Southend (Trial) 7/02, Grays 8/02, Canvey Island 8/02, Chelmsford 7/06 Rel 6/09, Welling 7/09		
Jack Parkinson						Tonbridge A (Yth), VCD Ath, Welling 7/08, Margate (L) 10/08	25	1
Ayden Richards						Welling	2	0
FORWARDS								
Lee Clarke	5'11"	10 08	28/7/83	26	Peterborough	Yaxley, Peterborough Undisc 10/01, Kettering (SL) 3/03, Kettering (2ML) 8/03, St Albans (SL) 1/04, St Albans 7/04 Rel 4/09, Welling 5/09		
Jake Hobbs	5'10"		10/2/91	18		Blackpool (Scholar) Rel c/s 09, Gillingham (Trial) 4/09, Welling 7/09		
James Lawson	5'09"	10 03	21/1/87	22	Basildon	Southend Rel c/s 07, Grimsby (L) 9/06, Bournemouth (L) 1/07, Dag & Red (L) 2/07, Grays 8/07, Chelmsford (3ML) 10/07 Perm 1/08, Welling 6/09		
Lheureux Menga					Angola	Dag & Red, Gainsborough, Dinnington, Shepshed D, Stocksbridge PS 12/08, Shepshed D 3/09, Welling 8/09		
James Morgan						Welling	0	0
Richard Stevens						Welling	11	1

LOANEES	HT	WT	DOB	AGE	POB	From - To	APPS	GOA
(D)Adam Gross	5'10"	10 09	16/2/86	23	Greenwich	Grays 10/08 - Dartford (L) 11/08, Rel 1/09	4	0
(M)Jerome Anderson			8/12/88	20		Stevenage 10/08 -	5	2
(F)Moses Ademola						Brentford 11/08, 12/08, (2ML) 2/09 - Woking (6ML) 7/09	15	4
(G)Clark Masters	6'03"	13 12	31/5/87	22	Hastings	Southend (2ML) 11/08 -	8	0
(F)Adam Burchell						Gillingham 11/08 - Dartford (WE) 3/09		
(G)David Wilkinson	5'11"	12 00	17/4/88	21	Croydon	C.Palace (3ML) 1/09 - Rel 5/09	7	0
Billy Chattaway						Dulwich H 2/09 -		
(M)Harry Arter	5'09"	11 07	23/12/89	19	Sidcup	Charlton (SL) 3/09 - Woking 5/09	6	0

DEPARTURES	HT	WT	DOB	AGE	POB	From - To	APPS	GOA
(M)Ross Lover						Cray W 7/08 - Rel 8/08		
(M)Seb Schoburgh						Dulwich H 7/08 - Sittingbourne, Maidstone 10/08, Fisher 1/09	3	0
(D)Craig Braham-Barrett						East Thurrock 5/08 - Peterborough £10,000 10/08, Kettering (L) 1/09, Grays 8/09	11	1
(F)Ryan Martin			25/11/82	26		Margate 8/08 - Rel 10/08, Carshalton 11/08	10	5
(F)Sol Pinnock						Fisher 7/08 - Rel 10/08, Walton & H, Dulwich H 12/08, Croydon Ath 2/09	9	1
(M)Chris Nurse			7/5/84	25	Croydon	Stevenage 9/08 - Rel 10/08, Halesowen T, Tamworth 1/09, Rochester Rhinos (USA) 3/09	2	0
(F)Joe Healy	6'00"	12 04	26/12/86	22	Sidcup	Beckenham 7/08 - Rel 10/08, Beckenham 10/08, Margate 12/08	11	1
(D)Frankie Chappell						Folkestone I 6/08 - Folkestone I (3ML) 10/08 Dual 1/09	5	0
(M)Jon Docker			12/2/86	23	London	Thurrock 10/08 - Rel 11/08, Hitchin 2/09, Billericay 3/09	1	0
(M)Ellis Green			30/6/86	23	Greenwich	Eastleigh 9/07 - Rel 12/08, Croydon Ath, Tooting & M 12/08, Ramsgate 1/09	12	0
(G)Jamie Turner					Kent	Tonbridge A 7/05 - Ramsgate (L) 12/08 Perm 1/09, Maidstone 5/09	15	0
(G)Scott Andrews						Bearsted c/s 08 - Rel 1/09	2	0
(G)Michael McEntegart			17/1/90	19	Adelaide, Aust	Millwall (Yth) - Tooting & M 2/09	0	0
(M)Rob Quinn	5'11"	11 02	8/11/76	32	Sidcup	AFC Wimbledon 5/08 - Rel 5/09, Cray W 6/09	31	1
(M)Lee Blackburn	5'08"	10 05	1/10/85	23	Romford	Crawley 6/08 - Rel 5/09	32	1
(D)Matthew McEntegart						Chippenham 7/08 - Rel 5/09, Hemel Hempstead 6/09	25	0
(M)Dorian Smith						Charlton 8/08 - Rel 5/09, Harrow (L) 1/09	13	0
(M)Orlando Smith (Mucu)					Jamaica	Chipstead 8/07 - Rel 5/09, Ashford T (2ML) 2/09	7	0
(F)Charlie Sheringham	6'01"	11 06	17/4/88	21	Chingford	Cambridge C 6/08 - Bishops Stortford 5/09	38	19
(M)James Baker						Chelmsford 2/09 - Billericay 5/09	18	5
(D)Tony Sinclair			5/3/85	24		Fisher 8/07 - Woking 6/09	34	1
(D)Sonny Cobbs						Brighton 7/08 - Sutton U 6/09	33	0
(M)Sanchez Ming						Fisher 10/08 - Rel 7/09	29	4
(M)Spencer Knight					Herts	Chelmsford 6/09 - Rel 7/09		
(D)Gavin Dayes	6'01"	13 03	8/6/84	25	London	Grays 1/09 -	2	0
(M)Anton Douglas						Crawley 1/09 -		
(F)Delando Smith						Sutton U 12/08 -	4	0
White						Yth -	0	0
Junior Bilal						Yth -	0	0

WELLING UNITED

Formed: 1963

Nickname: Theh Wings.

Club Colours: Red shirts, red shorts, white socks.

Change Colours: Yellow and blue shirts, blue shorts, yellow and blue socks.

Club Sponsor: TBA.

Previous League: Southern League

Ground address: Park View Road Ground, Welling, Kent DA16 1SY

Telephone: 0208 301 1196

Mobile: 077823 47432

Fax: 0208 301 5676

Email: barrie.hobbins@hotmail.co.uk

Website: www.wellingunited.com

Simple Directions: M25 then A2 towards London. Take Welling turn off and ground is one mile.

Welling BR 3/4 mile.

Capacity: 4,000 **Seats:** 1,070 **Covered:** 1,500 **Floodlights:** Yes

Clubhouse: Open on match days.

Club Shop: Fully stocked.

Local Radio: Radio Kent Radio Invicta R.T.M.

Local Press: Kentish Times, Kent Messenger, Bexleyheath & Welling Mercury

no image available

PROGRAMME EDITOR

Paul Carter

(M): 07863 347 587

CLUB STATISTICS

Records

Attendance: 4,100 v Gillingham F.A.Cup

Victory: 7-1 v Dorking 1985-86

Defeat: 0-7 v Welwyn Garden City 1972-73

Career Goalscorer: Not known.

Career Appearances: Not known.

Record Transfer Fee Paid: £30,000 to Enfield for Gary Abbott.

Received: £95,000 from Birmingham City for Steve Finnan 1995.

SENIOR HONOURS

Southern League Champions 1985-86.

Kent Senior Cup 1985-86, 98-99, 08-09.

London Senior Cup 1989-90.

London Challenge Cup 1991-92.

PREVIOUS

Leagues: Eltham & Dist.1963-71. London Spartan 1971-77.

Athenian 1978-81. Southern 1981-86, 2000-04.

Conference 1986-2000

Grounds: Butterfly Lane, Eltham 1963-78.

WESTON-SUPER-MARE

CLUB PERSONNEL

Chairman: Paul Bliss.

Vice Chairman: Dennis Usher.

Company Secretary: William Hammill.

Chief Executive & Managing Director: Paul Bliss.

Additional Directors: Paul Macey, Oliver Bliss.

Secretary: Richard Sloane.

Correspondence to the Club.

(B): 01934 621 618

(M): 07711 078 589

Email: wsmsecretary@hotmail.co.uk

Press Officer: Simon Stephens

(H): 01934 413 280

(M): 07947 732 492

Email: wsmfcest1948@btopenworld.com

Manager: Andy Gurney.

Club therapist: Dave Callow.

Supporters of the Weston club may have wondered whether a spell at a lower level might just give the management a chance to re build and perhaps benefit from a more successful campaign. As, at the end of the last two seasons their relegation had only been saved by the merger of Hayes F.C. and Yeading F.C. and then the demotion of Cambridge City, did they really want another season of pain?

After two games and two victories over Bishop's Stortford and Havant & Waterlooville, perhaps any such thoughts were banished and a new look Weston-super-Mare could be enjoyed. Indeed, after eight games and only one defeat, 'The Seagulls' were in eighth position and feeling good after a 1-1 draw at A.F.C.Wimbledon in front of a crowd of 2,934.

There was no cup excitement to please the fans or boost the club funds as Chesham United won 2-0 at The Woodspring Stadium in the F.A.Cup and A.F.C. Sudbury travelled to the West Country to win 2-1 in the F.A.Trophy. This defeat featured in a particularly bad spell and just two victories in September, October and November brought about the dismissal of manager Tony Ricketts in December.

Captain Andy Gurney took responsibility but results didn't improve very much, although the supporters could celebrate the fact that 'The Gulls' were not going to be needing any outside help to avoid relegation this year. Enough points were won to reach the comparative safety of seventeenth in the table. Blue Square South football would be at The Woodspring Stadium by right and perhaps, with some hard work and team building in the summer, the club's luck may change for good.

WESTON-SUPER-MARE

BEST LGE ATT.: **1,238** v AFC Wimbledon
LOWEST: **185** v Bishop's Stortford

No.	Date	Comp	H/A	Opponents	Att:	Result	Goalscorers	Pos
1	Aug 9	BSS	H	Bishop's Stortford	185	W 2 - 1	**Brown** 37 Gurney 82	
2	11		A	Havant & Waterlooville	620	W 3 - 2	Wells10 **Brown** 59 Gurney 61	
3	16		A	Hampton & Richmond B	365	L 1 - 4	R.Havard 26	8
4	23		H	Worcester City	426	D 1 - 1	Gurney 14	10
5	25		A	Dorchester Town	482	W 2 - 1	McGregor 23 Mullings 77	
6	30		H	Maidenhead United	212	D 2 - 2	**Brown** 4 43 (pen)	
7	Sept 1		H	Eastleigh	254	D 1 - 1	Wells 23	
8	6		A	AFC Wimbledon	2934	D 1 - 1	McGregor 2	8
9	**9**	**SS S1**	**A**	**Eastleigh**	**173**	**D 4 - 4***	**Byles 6 (og) Gurney 10 Mullings 102 Palmer 112 (Lost 4-5 on pens)**	
10	13		A	Bromley	345	L 0 - 3		10
11	20		H	Chelmsford City	308	L 1 - 4	Wells 90	11
12	**27**	**F.A.C 2Q**	**H**	**Chesham United**	**190**	**L 2 - 4**	**McKeever 40 48**	
13	Oct 4		H	Thurrock	204	W 2 - 1	Mullings 24 Holgate 68	20
14	18		A	Welling United	550	L 0 - 2		
15	20		H	Newport County	528	D 1 - 1	Mullins 73	
16	Nov 2		H	Bath City	428	L 0 - 1		13
17	8		A	Braintree Town	423	D 1 - 1	Havard 19	14
18	11		A	Basingstoke Town	320	W 1 - 0	McGregor 60	
19	15		A	Bognor Regis Town	220	D 1 - 1	**Brown** 45	13
20	**22**	**F.A.T 3Q**	**H**	**AFC Sudbury**	**218**	**L 1 - 2**	**Brown 89**	
21	29		H	Basingstoke Town	267	L 0 - 3		14
22	Dec 6		A	Maidenhead United	258	D 0 - 0		14
23	20		A	Bishop's Stortford	281	L 1 - 2	McGregor 29	16
24	26		H	Team Bath	360	L 0 - 1		17
25	Jan 3		H	Hampton & Richmond B	311	L 0 - 3		18
26	17		A	Thurrock	300	W 1 - 0	Wells 60	
27	24		H	Fisher Athletic	231	W 3 - 1	Rand 45 Mullings 48 Williams 80	14
28	28		A	Newport County	913	L 0 - 1		
29	31		H	St Albans City	273	D 1 - 1	Williams 56	
30	Feb 14		H	Bognor Regis Town	251	L 1 - 2	**Brown** 85	16
31	21		H	Braintree Town	254	W 3 - 1	Compton 13 Rand 18 Dean Grubb 67	17
32	24		A	Bath City	466	L 0 - 3		
33	28		A	Fisher Athletic	89	W 2 - 0	Williams 19 McGregor 45	16
34	Mar 7		H	AFC Wimbledon	1238	D 1 - 1	Williams 67 (pen)	
35	14		A	Eastleigh	502	L 0 - 1		16
36	17		A	Team Bath	101	W 2 - 1	**Brown** 45 McGregor 54	
37	21		H	Bromley	305	W 2 - 1	Kite 9 **Brown** 51	16
38	23		H	Havant & Waterlooville	264	L 0 - 1		
39	28		H	Hayes & Yeading	281	L 1 - 2	Evans 29	16
40	April 4		A	St Albans City	393	L 0 - 3		17
41	7		A	Hayes & Yeading	255	L 0 - 3		
42	11		A	Worcester City	577	W 2 - 1	Wells 21 McGregor 63 (pen)	17
43	13		H	Dorchester Town	275	D 2 - 2	Partridge 28 McGregor 47	
44	18		H	Welling United	261	L 0 - 3		16
45	25		A	Chelmsford City	1665	L 1 - 4	Mullings 72	17

Average Home Att: 339 (325) **Goals** 50 78

Best Position: 8th **Worst:** 20th

Goalscorers: Brown 9, McGregor 8, Mullings 6, Wells 5, Williams 4, Havard R 2, McKeever 2, Rand 2, Compton 1, Evans 1, Grubb, Dean 1, Holgate 1, Kite 1, Palmer 1, Partridge 1. Own Goals 1.

NORTHMORE	WILLSHIRE	MCGREGOR	MULLINGS	GURNEY	COMYN-PLATT	WELLS	PALMER	HOLGATE	BROWN	DEAN GRUBB	HAVARD	ARMSTRONG	PADDOCK	JOHNSON	HARRISON	GREEN	ABRAHAM	MCKEEVOR	MIDDLETON	PURNELL	QUISTIN	CLARK	RAND	THORNE	DAYLE GRUBB	PARINELLO	PARTRIDGE	HARRIS	WILLIAMS	COMPTON	BARTLETT	KITE	EVANS	GROVES	LAFFORD	
X	X	X	X	X	X	X	X	X	X	X	S	S	S	U	U																					1
X	U	S	X	X	X	X	S	X	X	X	X	U	S			X	X																			2
X	X	S	X	X	X	X	S	X	X	X	X	U	U			X	S																			3
X	X	X	X	X	X	X	X	S	X	S	S		U			X	U	X																		4
X	X	X	X	U	X	X		S	X	X	S		S			X	X	X	U																	5
X	X	X	X	S	X	X	S	S	X	X	U		U			X	X	X																		6
X		S	X	X	X	X	S	X	X	X	S		X			X	U	X		U																7
X	U	X	X	S	X	X	X	X	X	U	S		X			X	X	U																		8
X	**X**	**S**	**X**	**X**		**S**	**S**	**X**	**U**	**X**	**X**		**X**			**U**	**X**	**X**			**X**															**9**
X	U	X	X	S	X	X	X	S	X	X	U		X			X	X	S																		10
X	U	S	X		X	X	S		X	X	X		X			X	X	X		U	U															11
X	**X**	**S**	**X**	**S**	**X**	**X**	**X**	**X**	**X**	**S**			**X**			**X**		**X**																		**12**
X		X	X	X	X	X	U	X	S	S	U		U			X	X	X			X															13
X	X	X	X	X	X	X	U	X		X	S		U			U	S	X			X															14
X	U		X	X	X	X	X	X	U	U	X		S				X	X			X	S														15
X		S	X	X	X	X	X	X	U	S	X		U			U	X	X			X															16
X	U	X	X		X	X	X	X	S		X		S			X	X	U			X															17
X		X	X		X	X	X	X	U		X	S	U			X	X	S			X															18
X	U	X	X	S		X	X	X	X		S	U	X			X	X				X															19
X		**X**	**X**	**X**		**X**	**X**		**X**		**S**	**U**	**X**	**U**		**X**	**X**	**S**			**X**		**U**													**20**
X	S	X	X	U		X	X	X	X	X		U	X			X		S			X		S													21
X	X	X				X	S	X	X	X		U	X			X		X				S	X	U	U											22
X	X	X	S			X	U	X	X	X	U		S			X		X					X		U	X										23
X	S	X	S		X	X	U	X	X	X	S		U			X		X					X			X										24
X	X	X	S		X	X		X	U	X	S		U			S		X					X			X	X									25
X	U	U	X		X	X		S	U	S						X		X					X			X	X	X	X							26
X	U	S	X		X	X		U	S	X						X							X		U	X	X	X	X							27
X	U	S	X	S	X	X		X	S	X						X							X		U	X	X		X							28
X	X	S	X			X			U	X		U				X							X	U	U	X	X	X	X							29
X	U	X	X		X	X			S	S						X							X	U	U	X		X	X	X						30
X	U	X	X		X	X			S	S						X						U	X		S	X		X	X	X						31
X	S	X			X	X			S	X				U		X							X	U	U	X		X	X	X						32
	X	X		U	X	X			S	S										X			X		U	X		X	X	X	X	U				33
X	X	X			X	X			S	U						S				U			X			X		X	X	X	X	S				34
X		X		S		X			X	S						X				U		U	X			X		X	X	S	X	X				35
X		X			X	X			X														X			X		X	X		X	X				36
X	S	X			X	X			X											U			X		U	X	S	X	X	S	X	X				37
X	X			X		X			X		S			S						U		S	X	U	X	X	X	X			X					38
X	S				X	X			X		S	U										U		S	X	X	X	X				X	X	X		39
X	X	X				X		S	X			U								U		S	X				X	X			X	X	X	S		40
X	X	X				X		S	X			S								U		U				X		X		S	X	X	X	X		41
X		X				X		X	S			S		U								U	X		S	X	X	X		X	X	X				42
X		X	S			X		X	S														X			X	X	X		X	X	X	S			43
		S	X						S			X		X						X		X		U	X	X	X	X		X			X	S	U	44
X	X	X	X			X						U		U								S	X	U	X	X	X			X			X	S		45

Total League Appearances

40	16	29	26	10	29	41	10	20	22	18	7	1	7	1	0	25	12	14	0	2	8	1	21	0	4	22	12	18	12	9	10	8	5	2	0	X
0	5	9	4	6	0	0	6	7	12	8	11	4	6	1	0	2	2	3	0	0	0	5	1	1	2	0	1	0	0	3	0	1	1	3	0	S
0	12	1	0	3	0	0	4	1	6	3	4	9	9	4	1	2	2	2	1	8	1	5	0	7	9	0	0	0	0	0	0	1	0	0	1	U

Total Cup Appearances

3	2	1	3	2	1	2	2	2	2	1	1	0	3	0	0	2	2	2	0	0	2	0	0	0	0	0	0	0	0	0	0	0	0	0	0	X
0	0	2	0	1	0	1	1	0	0	1	1	0	0	0	0	0	0	1	0	0	0	0	0	0	0	0	0	0	0	0	0	0	0	0	0	S
0	0	0	0	0	0	0	0	0	1	0	0	1	0	1	0	1	0	0	0	0	0	0	1	0	0	0	0	0	0	0	0	0	0	0	0	U

WESTON-SUPER-MARE

CURRENT SQUAD AS OF BEGINING OF 2009-10 SEASON

GOALKEEPERS	HT	WT	D.O.B	AGE	P.O.B	CAREER	Apps	Gls
Kevin Sawyer			14/4/80	29	Swindon	Cirencester, Salisbury 8/02, Cirencester Undisc 8/06, Gloucester 5/07, Weston-Super-Mare (L) 3/08, Weston-Super-Mare 5/09		
DEFENDERS								
Scott Bartlett			30/5/79	30	Salisbury	Bournemouth (Jun), Amesbury T, Cirencester, Salisbury 2/00 Rel 2/09, Weston-Super-Mare 2/09	10	0
Clayton Fortune	6'03"	13 10	10/11/82	26	Forest Gate	Tottenham, Bristol C 4/01 Rel 6/06, Port Vale (SL) 11/05, Derby (Trial) 7/06, L.Orient 8/06 Rel c/s 08, Port Vale (SL) 11/06, Darlington 7/08 Rel c/s 09, Rushden & D (L) 11/08, Weston-Super-Mare 7/09		
Mike Green	5'09"	11 04	18/12/84	24	Gloucester	Southampton, Chippenham (L) 12/03 (L) 3/04, Forest Green 3/04 Rel 4/05, Cinderford c/s 05, Bath C 6/06, Clevedon (3ML) 8/07 Dual 11/07, Weston-Super-Mare 12/07	27	0
Eric Laborieux						Bordeaux (Fra) (Yth), Fairford T 3/09, Weston-Super-Mare 8/09		
Tomaso Parinello						Bristol R Rel 2/09, Weston-Super-Mare (2ML) 12/08, Weston-Super-Mare 2/09	22	0
Craig Rand	6'01"	11 00	24/6/82	27	Bishop Auckland	Sheff Wed, Whitby 3/02, Stocksbridge PS 12/02, Spennymoor 5/03, Thornaby 10/03, Durham 8/04, Team Bath 10/05, Weston-Super-Mare 11/05	22	2
MIDFIELDERS								
Jack Compton	5'08"	10 07	2/9/88	20	Portsmouth	West Brom, Weymouth (L) 2/08, Brighton 8/08 Rel 12/08, Lewes (L) 10/08, Havant & W 12/08, Weston-Super-Mare 2/09	12	1
Dayle Grubb						Weston-Super-Mare	6	0
Andy Gurney	5'10"	11 06	25/1/74	35	Bristol	Bristol R Rel c/s 97, Torquay 7/97, Reading £100,000 1/99 Rel c/s 01, Swindon 7/01, Swansea Undisc 9/04, Swindon (4ML) 8/05 Perm 1/06 Ret 11/06, Clevedon T 12/06, Weston-Super-Mare 2/07, Havant & W 5/07, Weston-Super-Mare 12/07, Newport C 2/08 Rel 5/08, Weston-Super-Mare (Pl/Ass Man) 5/08	16	3
Adie Harris			21/2/81	28		Cardiff, Llanelli, Merthyr, Haverfordwest, Hornchurch 7/04, Haverfordwest c/s 05, Bath C 7/05, Haverfordwest 6/06 Rel 11/06, Bath C 12/06, Newport C 6/08, Weston-Super-Mare 4 fig 1/09	18	0
Leon Jeanne	5'08"	11 01	17/11/80	28	Cardiff	QPR Rel 3/01, Cardiff 7/01 Rel 5/02, Newport C 8/02 Rel 10/02, Port Talbot, Barry T 1/03 Rel 6/03, Dinas Powys, Barry T 11/03, Merthyr, Grange Quins 8/04, Neath A 5/05, Maesteg Park, Carpenter Arms, Weston-Super-Mare 7/09		
Mark McKeever	5'11"	11 08	16/11/78	29	Derry	Peterborough, Sheff Wed 4/97, Bristol R (2ML) 12/98, Reading (L) 3/99, Bristol R (L) 2/01, Bristol R 3/01 Rel c/s 03, Weston-Super-Mare 8/03, Gloucester (L), Bath C 5/06, Mangotsfield (2ML) 1/08, Weston-Super-Mare 3/08	17	0
Darren Mullings	6'01"	12 00	3/3/87	22	Bristol	Bristol R, Clevedon (L) 12/06, Torquay 6/07 Rel 5/08, Tiverton (L) 11/07, Weston-Super-Mare 8/08	30	5
Ben Wells	5'09"	10 07	26/3/88	21	Basingstoke	Swindon, Basingstoke (L) 9/06, Basingstoke 7/07, Weston-Super-Mare 7/08	41	4
FORWARDS								
Marvin Brown	5'09"	11 01	16/7/83	26	Bristol	Bristol C Rel 6/04, Torquay (L) 9/02, Cheltenham (3ML) 1/03, Forest Green 8/04, Tamworth 9/04 Rel 10/04, Exeter (Trial) 2/05, Weymouth 2/05, Yeovil 3/05 Rel c/s 05, Weston-Super-Mare 5/05, Salisbury 3/07, Weston-Super-Mare 7/08	34	8
Ashan Holgate	6'02"	12 00	9/11/86	22	Swindon	Swindon Rel c/s 07, Salisbury (L) 3/06, Newport C (L) 10/06, Macclesfield (SL) 1/07, Weston-Super-Mare 8/07 , Eastleigh 12/07, Cirencester (L) 2/08, Weston-Super-Mare 3/08	27	1
Josh Klein-Davies	5'11"	13 09	6/7/89	20	Bristol	Bristol C (Scholar), Bristol R Rel 4/09, Yate T (L) 11/07, Luton (L) 8/08, Newport C (L) 11/08, Lewes (2ML) 12/08, Bath C (L) 3/09, Weymouth (Trial) 7/09 Weston-Super-Mare 8/09		
Josh Llewellyn			27/4/87	22		Derby, Hayes, Team Bath c/s 06, Weston-Super-Mare 5/09		
Marc McGregor	5'09"	11 10	30/4/78	31	Southend	Oxford U Rel c/s 97, Endsleigh c/s 97, Forest Green 8/98, Cirencester (L) 10/98, Nuneaton £35,000 6/00, Weston Super-Mare (L) 8/02, Macclesfield (Trial) 1/03, Tamworth 8/03, Chippenham (L) 9/03, Weston-Super-Mare (L) 10/03, Weston-Super-Mare (L) 12/03, Weston-Super-Mare 3/04, Hinckley U 5/05, Weston-Super-Mare 5/06	38	8

LOANEES	HT	WT	DOB	AGE	POB	From - To	APPS	GOA
(F)Manny Williams			13/11/81	27	London	Woking (3ML) 1/09 - Rel 5/09, Havant & W 6/09	12	4
(D)Alex Kite	6'00"	12 05	7/3/89	20	Kent	Bristol R 2/09 - Gloucester (L) 7/09	9	1
(D)Tom Evans						Swindon 3/09 - Rel 5/09	6	1

DEPARTURES	HT	WT	DOB	AGE	POB	From - To	APPS	GOA
(G)Ryan Harrison			6/12/85	23		Llanelli 8/08 - Rel 8/08, Oxford C 8/08, Weymouth 6/09	0	0
(D)Bradley Middleton						Cardiff C 8/08 - Rel 9/08, Bridgwater T 10/08	0	0
(D)Cedric Abraham			1/6/82	27		Halesowen T 8/08 - Rel 12/08, Fisher 12/08, Hednesford 3/09	14	0
(M)Ludovic Quistin			24/5/84	25	Gualaloup, WI	Hednesford 9/08 - Rel 12/08, Fisher 12/08, Grays NC 2/09, AFC Hornchurch (L) 2/09, Hednesford 3/09	8	0
(F)Ryan Havard			19/10/82	26		Taunton 8/08 - Rel 11/08 Re-signed 11/08, Mangotsfield (L) 1/09, Langford Rovers (Dual) 3/09	18	3
(M)Dean Grubb	5'09"	11 11	4/10/87	21	Weston-Super-Mare	Bristol C 8/07 - Gloucester 3/09, Weymouth 5/09 Rel 7/09	26	1
(D)Charlie Comyn-Platt	6'02"	12 00	2/10/85	23	Manchester	Rochdale 10/07 - ECU Joondalup (Aust) 3/09	29	0
(G)Ryan Northmore	6'01"	13 01	5/9/80	28	Plymouth	Team Bath 6/05 - Weston (Yth Man) 5/09, Dorchester 8/09	40	0
(D)Ben Willshire	5'08"	10 07	5/10/86	22		Taunton 6/07 - Rel 5/09	21	0
(M)James Palmer	5'07"	11 04	30/3/88	21	Bristol	Bristol R - Gloucester (L) 1/09, Gloucester 6/09	16	0
(F)Matt Groves	5'08"	11 07	11/12/88	20	Bristol	Bristol R 3/09 - Weymouth 7/09	5	0
(D)Adrian Williams	6'02"	13 02	16/8/71	38	Reading	Swindon 6/09 - Rel 8/09		
(G)Luke Purnell			1/6/90	19		Weston St Johns - Yate T (L) 11/08	2	0
(D)Mark Armstrong			5/4/90	19		Yth -	5	0
(D)Sam Johnson			22/9/89	19		Yth -	2	0
(D)Ryan Paddock	6'03"	12 06	8/10/88	20	Newport	Bristol R 8/08 - Bishops Cleeve (L) 1/09	13	0
(M)Ben Carpenter						Weston-Super-Mare		
(M)David Thorne			24/9/89	19		Cardiff (Yth) -	1	0
(F)Sam Clark			6/6/90	18		Yth -	6	0
(F)Scott Partridge	5'09"	11 00	13/10/74	34	Leicester	Sheffield FC 12/08 -	13	1
Steve Lafford						Yth -	0	0

WESTON SUPER MARE

Formed: 1899

Nickname: Seagulls.

Club Colours: White shirts, black shorts, black socks.

Change Colours: Royal blue shirts, royal blue shorts, royal blue socks.

Club Sponsor: TBA.

Previous League: Southern League.

Ground address: Woodspring Stadium, Winterstoke Road,Weston-super-Mare BS24 9AA.

Telephone: 01934 621 618

Fax: 01934 622 704

Email: wsmafc@hotmail.co.uk

Website: www.westonsupermarefc.co.uk

Simple Directions: From Junction 21 of the M5 take A370 along dual carriageway to 4th roundabout and follow Winterstoke Road.

Capacity: 3,000 **Seats**: 278 **Covered**: 2,000 **Floodlights**: Yes

Clubhouse: Open daily Mid week evenings

Club Shop: Yes.

Local Radio: Somerset Sound and Radio Bristol

Local Press: Bristol Evening Post and Western Daily press

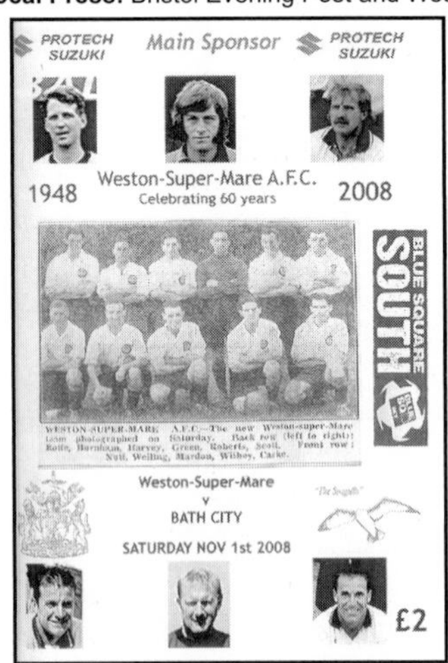

PROGRAMME EDITOR

Phil Sheridan

(M): 07963 166 031

Email: phil.sheridan29@btopenworld.com

CLUB STATISTICS

RECORDS

Attendance: 2,623 v Woking F.A.Cup 1st Rd Replay 23.11.93

Victory: 11-0 v Paulton Rovers

Defeat: 1-12 v Yeovil Town Reserves

Career Goalscorer: Matt Lazenby -180

Career Appearances: Harry Thomas - 740

Transfer Fee Paid: None

Received: £20,000 from Sheffield Wednesday for Stuart Jones

SENIOR HONOURS

Western League Champions 1991-92.

Somerset Senior Cup Winners 1923-24, 26-27.

PREVIOUS

Leagues: Somerset Senior. Western League.

Previous Name: Borough of Weston-super-Mare.

WEYMOUTH

Back: Brian Glover, Justin Roberts, Jefferson Louis, Ashley Vickers, Sido Jombarti, Joel Kitamarike, Scott Doe. **Middle:** Carol Nicholas (Assistant Therapist), Gavin McCallum, Stuart Bevon, Conal Platt, Dani Rodrigues, Jon Stewart, Anton Robinson, Jason Matthews, Kyle Critchel, Lewis Ironside, Callum Crawley, James Coutts, Stuart Douglas (Therapist). **Front:** Danny Phillips, Paulo Vernazza, Jason Tindall (Manager), Simon Weatherston, Marcus Browning (Coach), Nick Crittenden, Narada Barnard, Trevor Challis.

CLUB PERSONNEL

Chairman: Ian Ridley.

Company Secretary: Ian Winsor.

Additional Directors: Paul Cooks, Shaun Hennessey, Connor Kinsella.

Secretary: Phil Searle.

12 Chepstow Close, Chippenham, Wiltshire SN14 0XP

(B&M): 07968 025 113

Email: phil@digitalscape.co.uk

Commercial Manager: Carol Biggs.

(M): 07917 681 825.

Press Officer: Ian Ridley.

(M): 07887 508 331

Manager: Matt Hale.

Assistant Manager: Ian Hutchinson.

Club therapist: Roger Hoare.

Another desperate season for loyal Weymouth supporters finished in disaster, as the club dropped down to the Blue Square South with little pride left and the new owners and board facing yet another frantic rebuilding job.

All this after a start to the season that produced three victories in the first four games and a place in the top three. As things went from bad to worse off the field, three well known and respected managers tried to help. John Hollins, Alan Lewer and briefly Bobby Gould, who all took up the challenge but found there were too many aspects out of their control at the famous Dorset club.

Two first match defeats in the major cup competitions did nothing to lift spirits and a depressing low point was the selection of the youth team to face Rushden & Diamonds, but the loyal fans did their best for the youngsters and their beloved 'Terras'. After a depressing dip in numbers in mid season the home attendance figures didn't drop below four figures in their desperate end of season bid for survival in the Premier Division.

As a club with traditionally loyal support, Weymouth fans will be hoping that old favourite Matty Hale will build a side that will at least challenge for a quick return. Remarkably, attendances were over the thousand mark for the last five home league games at a time when only four goals (one an 'own-goal') were scored in the last sixteen league matches. Those special supporters deserve a very special season.

WEYMOUTH

BEST LGE ATT.: 3,711 v Kettering Town
LOWEST: 696 v Woking

No.	Date	Comp	H/A	Opponents	Att:	Result	Goalscorers	Pos
1	Aug 9	BSP	H	Grays Athletic	1059	W 3 - 1	Robinson 17 Reed 35 McPhee 78	
2	12		A	Oxford United	4547	W 1 - 0	**Beavon** 17	
3	16		A	Stevenage Borough	1357	D 1 - 1	Malcolm 28	3
4	23		H	Lewes	1172	W 2 - 0	Malcolm 42 Mchee 69	
5	25		A	Forest Green Rovers	1132	L 1 - 4	Doe 71	6
6	30		H	Cambridge United	1367	D 2 - 2	McPhee 71 Malcolm 83	7
7	Sept 2		A	Salisbury City	1382	L 0 - 1		
8	6		H	Histon	1003	L 2 - 5	Malcolm 24 Bygrave 49	
9	13		A	Burton Albion	11435	D 1 - 1	Malcolm 34	16
10	20		H	Kidderminster Harriers	1014	L 1 - 2	Joseph-Dubois 15	18
11	23		H	Crawley	1005	D 2 - 2	McPhee 22 Malcolm 54	18
12	27		A	Northwich Victoria	700	W 3 - 2	Welch 52 (og) **Beavon** 81 (pen) Coutts 90	13
13	Oct 4		H	Eastbourne Borough	931	W 3 - 2	**Beavon** 17 (pen) McPhee 29 Joseph-Dubois 90	12
14	7		A	Woking	1802	D 1 - 1	**Beavon** 58	
15	11		A	Cambridge United	3981	L 0 - 1		14
16	18		H	Altrincham	926	W 2 - 0	McPhee 34 Williams 83	11
17	**25**	**F.A.C. 4Q**	**H**	**AFC Hornchurch**	**904**	**L 1 - 2**	**Beavon 9**	
18	Nov 1		A	Kettering Town	1607	W 1 - 0	Coutts 87	10
19	**4**	**SS S3**	**H**	**Torquay United**	**621**	**L 0 - 3**		
20	8		A	Rushden & Diamonds	1002	L 0 - 1		11
21	15		H	Wrexham	1207	L 1 - 3	**Beavon** 90	11
22	18		H	Woking	696	D 1 - 1	Coutts 49	
23	22		A	Barrow	1350	W 1 - 0	Joseph-Dubois 52	
24	29		H	Mansfield Town	931	D 1 - 1	McPhee 21	
25	Dec 6		A	Ebbsfleet United	1005	L 0 - 1		10
26	9		H	Oxford United	822	D 2 - 2	**Beavon** 39 51	
27	**16**	**F.A.T. 1R**	**A**	**Welling United**	**262**	**L 0 - 2**		**11**
28	20		A	Mansfield Town	1841	L 1 - 2	**Beavon** 20 (pen)	
29	26		H	Torquay United	2323	L 0 - 1		11
30	Jan 17		A	Kidderminster Harriers	1569	W 2 - 0	**Beavon** 43 56	13
31	24		H	Northwich Victoria	1105	W 3 - 0	**Beavon** 5 (pen) 10 Phillips 32	
32	27		A	Grays Athletic	415	D 1 - 1	**Beavon** 8	
33	Feb 10		A	Torquay United	1743	W 2 - 0	Williams 45 **Beavon** 88	
34	14		H	Stevenage Borough	1226	L 0 - 3		13
35	21		H	Rushden & Diamonds	967	L 0 - 9		14
36	28		A	York City	2349	L 0 - 2		15
37	Mar 8		A	Crawley Town	901	L 2 - 4	Vincent 18 Raynor 38 (og)	
38	10		H	Salisbury City	1004	L 0 - 4		15
39	14		A	Altrincham	70	L 0 - 4		16
40	17		H	Burton Albion	848	L 0 - 5		
41	21		H	Kettering Town	3711	L 0 - 2		16
42	29		H	Barrow	1264	L 0 - 3		18
43	April 4		A	Eastbourne Borough	1075	L 0 - 3		20
44	11		A	Lewes	456	L 0 - 1		21
45	13		H	Forest Green Rovers	1183	D 1 - 1	Akurang 33	
46	18		H	Ebbsfleet United	1007	L 0 - 2		22
47	21		A	Histon	1016	L 1 - 2	Akurang 45	
48	24		H	York City	1122	L 0 - 2		
49	26		A	Wrexham	2756	L 0 - 2		23

Average Home Att: 1213 (1411) **Goals** 46 94

Best Position: 3rd **Worst:** 23rd

Goalscorers: Beavon 15, McPhee 7, Malcolm 6, Coutts 3, Joseph-Dubois 3, Akurang 2, Williams 2, Bygrave 1, Doe 1, Phillips 1, Reed 1, Robinson 1, Vincent 1. Own Goals 2.

BARNARD 25	SANDWITH 3	MAWER 2	REED 14	GAIA 16	ROBINSON 8	WILLIAMS 11	BEAVON 10	DOE 12	MALCOLM 4	MCPHEE 7	KNOWLES 1	BYGRAVE 5	COUTTS 6	JOSEPH-DUBOIS 9	WEBB 23	CUTLER 13	REIFFER 18	RICHARDSON 19	FRAMPTON 20	VINCENT 21	TRIBE 17	COLLINS 22	MCKECHNIE 24	PHILLIPS 23	BROWNING 4	DIXON 25	EVANS 1	HOYTE 7	CROOK 12	APPIAH 16	HART 10	HYDE 11	PALMER 8	CRITCHELL 3	GILL 23	ONIBUJE 27	LEGZDINS 25	MERELLA 16	COOKE 29	AKURANG 28	GWINNETT 30	
X	X	X	X	X	X	X	X	X	X	X	U	U	U	U	U																											1
X	X	X	X	X	X	X	X	X	X	X	U	U	S	S	U																											2
X	X	X	X	X	X	X	X	X	X	X	U	U	S	U	U																											3
X	X	X	X	X	X	X	X	X	X	X	U	U	S		S	S																										4
X	X	X	X	X	X	X	X	X	X	X	U	U	S		S	S																										5
X	X	X	X	X	X	X	X	X	X	X	U	S			U	S	U																									6
X			X	X	X	X	X	X	X	X	U	X	X		U	U	U	U																								7
X	X		X	X	X	X	X	X	X	X	U	X	S	S	U	S																										8
X	X			X	X	X		X	X	X	U	X	X	S	X	S	U	U																								9
X	X	X	X	X	X	X		X	X	X	U		U	X	U	S																										10
X	X	X	X		X	X		X	X	X	U		S	X	U	X	U																									11
X	X	X	X		X	X	S	X	X	X	U	U	S	X	U	X																										12
	X	X	X	S	X	X	X	X	X	X	X	S	U	S	U	X																										13
X	X	X	X	X	X	X	X		S	X	U	X	U	S	U	X																										14
X	X	X	X	X	X	S	X	X	S	X	U	U		X	U	X																										15
U	X	X	X	X	S	X	X	X	S	X	X	S	U	X		X																										16
U	**X**	**X**		**X**	**X**	**X**	**X**	**X**	**X**	**X**	**X**	**U**	**S**	**S**	**U**	**X**	**U**		**U**																							17
U	X	S	X	X	X	X	X	X	X	X	X	X	S	U	U																											18
X	**X**	**X**	**X**			**X**	**S**	**X**		**S**	**U**	**X**		**X**	**X**	**X**			**U**	**X**	**S**																					19
U	X	X	X		X	X	X	X		X	X	X	X		U				U	U																						20
U	X	X	X	X	X	S	X	X		X	X	X	X	U	U	U																										21
U	X	U	X	X	X	X	X	X		X	X	X	X	S	U	U																										22
U	X	X	X		X	X	X	X			X	X	U	X	U	X				U		S																				23
U	X	X	X	U	X	X		X		X	X	X	S	X	S	X						U																				24
	X	X	X	U	X	S	X	X		X	X	X		X	U	X						U																				25
	X	S	U	X	X	X	X	X		X	X	X		S	U	X						X																				26
		X	**X**		**X**	**X**	**X**	**X**		**X**	**X**	**X**	**U**	**S**	**S**	**X**				**U**		**X**	**S**																			27
	X	U		X	X	X	X	X		X	X	X	S	X	U	X					U		U																			28
	X	X	U	X	X	X	X			X	X		X	X		X				U	U		U																			29
	X	X	U	X	X	X	X	X		X	X		X	S									U	X	S	U																30
	X	X	S	X	X	X	X	X		X	X		X			S						S		X	U	U																31
	X	X	U	X	X	X	X	X		X	X		X			U						S		X	U	U																32
	X	X	X	X		X	X	X		X	X		X								U	U	U	X	U	U																33
	X	X	X	X		X	X	X		X	X		X							U		U	U	X	U	U																34
																	X	S		X	X	X	X			X																35
		X	X															X		X	S	X	S			X	X	X	X	X												36
			X										X			X		S		X	U	U	U			X	X	X	X	X	X	X	S									37
		X	X										X			X		S		X		U	U			S	X	X	X	X	X	X	S									38
		X														X		S		X	S	X	S				X	X	X		X	X	X									39
													X			X		S		X	U		S			U	X	X	X	X	X	X	X									40
		X											X			X		S	U	U						U	X	X	X			X	X	X	X	S						41
		X											X			X			U						U		U	X				X	S	X	X	S	X	X	X	X		42
		X											X			X						X			X		U	X			S		S	X	X	S	X	X	U	X		43
			X										X			X						X			X		U	X			S		X	X	X	S	X	U	U	X		44
		X	X										X					S				X					U	X			S			X	X	X	X	X	S	X		45
		X	X										X	U											S		U	X			X			X	X	X	X	S	X	X	S	46
		X	X										X	S				U				X					U	X						X	X	X	X	X	U	X	S	47
		X											X	S		X		U	S								U	X						X	X	X	X	X		X	X	48
													X	S		X	U	U	X						X			X							X	X	X	X	S	X	X	49
Total League Appearances																																										
14	30	34	31	24	28	28	26	29	14	30	17	13	23	10	1	22	1	1	1	6	1	8	1	5	3	3	6	14	6	4	5	6	4	8	9	5	8	6	2	8	2	**X**
0	0	2	1	1	1	3	1	0	3	0	0	3	10	11	3	7	0	7	1	0	2	3	3	0	2	1	0	0	0	0	3	0	4	0	0	4	0	1	2	0	2	**S**
7	0	2	4	2	0	0	0	0	0	0	14	7	6	5	20	4	5	5	3	5	5	6	7	0	5	7	7	0	0	0	0	0	0	0	0	0	0	1	3	0	0	**U**
Total Cup Appearances																																										
1	2	3	2	1	2	3	2	3	1	2	2	2	0	1	1	3	0	0	0	1	0	1	0	0	0	0	0	0	0	0	0	0	0	0	0	0	0	0	0	0	0	**X**
0	0	0	0	0	0	0	1	0	0	1	0	0	1	2	1	0	0	0	0	0	1	0	1	0	0	0	0	0	0	0	0	0	0	0	0	0	0	0	0	0	0	**S**
1	0	0	0	0	0	0	0	0	0	0	1	1	1	0	1	0	1	0	2	1	0	0	0	0	0	0	0	0	0	0	0	0	0	0	0	0	0	0	0	0	0	**U**

Also played: IRONSIDE U(10,11,25,26,29). PRODOMO X(35) U(39). BANSENDE X(35) U(39,40). AGERA X(35) U(36,48) S(49). ROBINS X(35) U(45). DADSON X(35) U(36). OOLE S(35). TUBBS S(35). NEISH U(35). PERRETT U(35). STRICKLAND X(36). SIBLEY U(36). RYAN X(39,40,41).

WEYMOUTH

CURRENT SQUAD AS OF BEGINING OF 2009-10 SEASON

GOALKEEPERS	HT	WT	D.O.B	AGE	P.O.B	CAREER	APPS	GOA
Simon Evans						Andover, Dorchester 8/06 Rel 4/08, Weymouth 2/09	6	0
Ryan Harrison			6/12/85	23		Swansea (Sch), Canvey Island 10/04, Hastings T 12/04, Wrexham 2/05, Forest Green 7/05 Rel c/s 07, Havant & W (L) 5/07, Llanelli 5/07 Rel 5/08, Weston-Super-Mare 8/08 Rel 8/08, Oxford C 8/08, Weymouth 6/09		
Michael Neish						Weymouth	0	0
DEFENDERS								
Ollie Barnes						Bristol C Rel c/s 06, Bristol R 7/06 Rel c/s 07, Gloucester (L) 1/07, Salisbury 7/07 Rel 5/08, Team Bath (SL) 3/08, Worcester 7/08 Rel 4/09, Weymouth 8/09		
Scott Brice						Bristol R (Trainee), Yate T c/s 05, Weymouth 6/09		
Kyle Critchell	6'00"	12 02	18/1/87	22	Dorchester	Southampton, Torquay (3ML) 10/06, Chesterfield 1/07, Weymouth 6/07, Wrexham 6/08 Rel 6/09, York C (2ML) 1/09, Weymouth (L) 3/09, Weymouth 6/09	8	0
Jamie Frampton						Weymouth	2	0
Nathan Loader						Team Bath (Yth), Weymouth 7/09		
Sam Poole						Weymouth	1	0
Callum Robins						Weymouth	1	0
Matt Townley			20/10/83	25	Essex	Southampton (Yth), Bath C, Team Bath, Mangotsfield (L) 11/08, Weymouth 7/09		
Jordan Vincent						Weymouth	6	1
MIDFIELDERS								
Bostry Bansende						Weymouth	1	0
Shola Dadson						Dag & Red, Weymouth 9/08	1	0
Andy Harris	5'10"	12 05	26/2/77	32	Springs, SA	Liverpool Rel c/s 96, Southend 7/96 Rel c/s 99, L.Orient 7/99 Rel c/s 03, Chester 6/03 Rel 5/05, Forest Green (3ML) 2/05, Weymouth 7/05, Eastleigh (L) 9/06 Perm 10/06 Rel 5/09, Weymouth 5/09		
Hector Mackie			10/5/88	21	Inverness	Waltham Forest, Tottenham (Trial), Redbridge 4/05, Welling, Stevenage 7/06, Cambridge C (L) 8/06, Wealdstone (L) 12/06, Diss T (L) 2/07, Welling (L) 3/07, St Albans 7/07, Potters Bar 10/07, St Albans 10/08, Weymouth 6/09		
Ryan McKechnie						Weymouth	4	0
Aiden Perrett						Weymouth	0	0
Carl Preston						Bournemouth Rel c/s 09, Poole T (WE) 1/09, Eastleigh (Trial) 7/09, Weymouth 7/09		
Ben Reiffer						Weymouth	1	0
Tom Richardson						Weymouth	8	0
Martin Slocombe			8/11/88	20	Weston-S-Mare	Bristol C Rel c/s 08, Bath C 8/08, Weymouth 7/09		
Dean Smith			21/1/83	26		West Ham (Scholar), Stevenage, Thurrock, Team Bath, Weymouth 5/09		
Matt Thorne			23/12/86	22		Bristol R, Bristol Manor Farm, Team Bath, Cirencester (L) 9/08, Weymouth 6/09		
Ollie Tribe						Weymouth	3	0
FORWARDS								
Joe Arnold			20/5/88	21		Derby, Swindon, Team Bath c/s 06, Gloucester (L) 1/09, Weymouth 8/09		
Daniel Bennett						Weymouth		
Matthew Cooper			7/9/87	21		Trowbridge, Frome, Team Bath (L) 12/06 Perm 1/07, Weymouth 7/09		
Ryan Gazet Du Chattelier			17/2/91	18		Portsmouth, Bognor Regis (L) 3/09, Weymouth (3ML) 7/09		
Matt Groves	5'08"	11 07	11/12/88	20	Bristol	Bristol R Rel 3/09, Chippenham (SL) 3/08, Tiverton (L) 8/08, Mangotsfield (3ML) 12/08, Weston-Super-Mare 3/09, Weymouth 7/09		
Jordan Metters						Bristol C (Yth), Weymouth 7/09		
Tom Piotroski			20/1/89	20		Reading (Scholar), Team Bath c/s 08, Newport C (Trial) 6/09, Weymouth (Trial) 7/09, Weymouth 8/09		
Tyler Sibbick						Team Bath (Yth), Weymouth 8/09		

LOANEES	HT	WT	DOB	AGE	POB	From - To	APPS	GOA
(M)Jordan Collins			7/12/88	20		Cambridge U (SL) 11/08 - Rel 5/09, Ebbsfleet 7/09	11	0
(D)Kenny Strickland	5'10"	11 05	10/10/90	18	Ormskirk	Man Utd 2/09 - Farsley Celtic (L) 3/09, Rel c/s 09	1	0
(M)Billy Crook			23/8/90	19		Peterborough 2/09 -	6	0
(F)Kwesi Appiah	5'11"	12 08	12/8/90	19	Peterborough	Peterborough 2/09 -	4	0
(F)Jake Hyde	6'01"	12 03	1/7/90	19	Slough	Swindon 3/09 - Rel 5/09	6	0
(D)David Ryan	6'00"	11 07	16/2/91	18		Blackburn 3/09 - Rel c/s 09	3	0
(F)Cliff Akurang	6'02"	12 03	27/2/81	28	Ghana	Barnet (SL) 3/09 - Rushden & D (SL) 7/09	8	2
(G)Adam Legzdins	6'01"	14 02	28/11/86	22	Stafford	Crewe 3/09 -	8	0

DEPARTURES	HT	WT	DOB	AGE	POB	From - To	APPS	GOA
(G)Richard Barnard	6'01"	12 13	27/12/80	28	Frimley	Carshalton 8/08 - Farnborough 12/08	14	0
(D)Adam Bygrave	5'09"	12 02	24/2/89	20		Reading 5/08 - Histon £5,000 1/09	16	1
(M)Joshua Webb			23/1/90	19		Reading (Scholar) 5/08 - Rel 1/09, Farnborough 1/09	4	0
(F)Michael Malcolm	5'10"	11 07	13/10/85	23	Harrow	Thurrock 1/08 - Crawley (2ML) 11/08 Perm 1/08	17	6
(M)Anton Robinson	6'00"	11 06	17/2/86	23	Brent	Fisher 3/07 - Bournemouth Undisc 2/09	29	1
(G)Danny Knowles	6'00"	12 00	7/1/86	23	Sidcup	Grays 7/08 - Rel 2/09, Woking 2/09 Rel 5/09, Eastbourne B 5/09	17	0
(F)Ryan Williams	5'04"	11 02	31/8/78	31	Chesterfield	Aldershot 5/08 - Rel 2/09, Mansfield 2/09	31	2
(D)Santos Gaia	6'00"	12 04	8/9/78	30	Sao-Mateus-Es	Grays 5/08 - Rel 2/09, Crawley 2/09 Rel 5/09, Truro C 5/09	25	0
(F)Chris McPhee	5'11"	11 09	20/3/83	26	Eastbourne	Ebbsfleet 7/08 - Rel 2/09, Kidderminster 2/09	30	7
(D)Kevin Sandwith	5'11"	13 06	30/4/78	31	Workington	Chester 7/08 - Rel 2/09, Oxford U 2/09	30	0
(G)Joe Prodomo						Christchurch 2/09 -	1	0
(F)Lee Phillips	5'10"	12 00	16/9/80	28	Penzance	Rushden & D 1/09 - Rel 2/09, Cambridge U 3/09	5	1
(D)Scott Doe			6/11/88	20		Swindon 6/07 - Rel 2/09, Dag & Red 3/09	29	1
(D)Steve Reed	5'08"	12 02	18/6/85	24	Barnstaple	Cambridge U 7/08 - Rel 4/09, Macclesfield 5/09	32	1
(M)Marcus Browning	6'00"	12 10	22/4/71	38	Bristol	Bournemouth (Pl/Coach) 8/07 - Rel c/s 08 Re-signed 1/09, Bath C 7/09	5	0
(D)Gavin Hoyte	6'04"	12 06	24/6/86	23	Bedford	Cambridge U 2/09 - Grays 7/09	14	0
(M)Dean Grubb	5'09"	11 11	4/10/87	21	Weston-S-Mare	Gloucester 5/09 - Rel 8/09		
(D)Cameron Mawer	5'10"	11 06	21/2/86	23	Stevenage	Grays 7/08 - Grays 8/09	36	0
(M)Sam Cutler			11/2/90	19	Sidcup	Cambridge U 5/08 - Grays 8/09	29	0
(M)James Coutts	5'06"	09 07	15/4/87	22	Weymouth	Bournemouth 7/07 - Rel c/s 09	33	3
(F)Stuart Beavon			5/5/84	25	Reading	Didcot T 1/07 - Wycombe (SL) 2/09, Wycombe c/s 09	27	14
(D)Raiff Gwinnett			9/11/90	18		Torquay 4/09 - Bath C 8/09	4	0
(D)Scott Dixon						Yth -	4	0
(D)Callum Hart	6'00"	11 00	21/12/85	23	Cardiff	Farnborough 3/09 -	8	0
(M)Stephen Cooke	5'08"	09 08	15/2/83	26	Walsall	Stourport 3/09 -	4	0
(M)Ben Gill	5'09"	10 11	9/10/87	21	Harrow	Crawley 3/09 -	9	0
(M)Lewis Ironside			15/4/90	19	Weymouth	Yth -	0	0
(M)Dominic Merella					Chorley	Burscough 3/09 - Burscough c/s 09	7	0
(F)Tamu Agera						Ebbsfleet 2/09 -	2	0
(F)Pierre Joseph-Dubois			12/2/88	21	Paris, Fra	Crawley 5/08 -	21	3
(F)Fola Onibuje	6'05"	14 09	25/9/84	24	Lagos, Ghana	Accrington 3/09 -	9	0
(F)Jermaine Palmer			28/8/86	23	Nottingham	Quorn NC 3/09 -	8	0
(F)James Sibley						Yth -	0	0
(F)Charlie Tubbs						Yth -	1	0

WEYMOUTH

Founded: 1890.

Nickname: The Terras.

Club Colours: Claret/ sky blue shirts, white shorts, claret and sky blue socks.

Change Colours: Sky blue shirts, navy shorts, sky blue socks.

Club Sponsor: TBA.

Previous League: Southern League.

Ground Address: Wessex Stadium, Radipole Lane, Weymouth DT4 9XJ

Telephone: 01305 785 558

Fax: 01305 766 658

General email address: office@weymouthfc.net

Official website: www.theterras.co.uk

SIMPLE DIRECTIONS: Arriving from Dorchester on A354, turn right following signs for Granby Industrial estate at Safeway roundabout.Ground on right as you enter estate

By Rail: Nearest Railway Station is Weymouth (2 miles)

CAPACITY: 6,600 **Seats:** 800 **Covered:** All Four Sides

Clubhouse: Matchdays and Functions. **Refreshments:** Two refreshment bars.

Club Shop: Yes.

THE TERRA
FORWARD TOGETHER
BLUE SQUARE PREMIER
v GRAYS ATHLETIC

CLUB STATISTICS

RECORDS

Attendance: 4,995 v Manchester United (ground opening) 21.10.97

Victory: Not known.

Defeat: Not known.

Career Goalscorer: W 'Farmer' Haynes 275

Career Apperances: Tony Hobsons 1,076

Transfer Fee Paid:

£15,000 to Northwich Victoria for Shaun Teale.

Transfer Fee Received:

£100,000 from Tottenham Hotspur for Peter Guthrie 1988

SENIOR HONOURS

Southern League Champions 1964-65, 65-66.

Dorset Senior Cup (27)

PREVIOUS LEAGUES

Dorset. Western 1907-23, 28-49.

Southern 1923-28, 49-79.

Alliance Premier 1979-89.

PROGRAMME EDITOR

Hilary Billimore

Email: hbillimore@tiscali.co.uk

WOKING

CLUB PERSONNEL

Chairman: Shahid Azeem.

Additional Directors: Phil Ledger J.P., Peter Jordan, David Taylor, Jane Spong, Peter Sheppard.

Secretary: Phil Ledger J.P.

Tel: Club: 01483 772 470

(H): 01483 725 295. (M): 07831 271 369.

E-mail: football@wokingfc.co.uk

correspondence to Secretary at club.

Commercial Manager: Geoff Chapple.

(M): 07768 853 443

Email: geoff.chapple@wokingfc.co.uk

Press Officer: David Holmes & John Moore.

Email: press@woking.co.uk

Manager: Graham Baker.

Assistant Manager: Jimmy Dack.

Head of Youth Development: Graham Baker.

Club therapist: Steve Snelling.

The Blue Square Premier Division certainly contained its share of clubs whose off field problems overshadowed the results on the field and Woking, a Surrey club with some great cup memories of not so long ago, suddenly appeared to be in the news on a regular basis for all the wrong reasons.

A club appointing three managers in a season cannot be good for the players, fans or the board of directors. It was Kim Grant who started the campaign in charge at Kingfield Stadium but a poor opening spell with not one victory in the first seven games saw Phil Gilchrist take over team matters. A short burst of improved results at the end of September lifted spirits but an F.A.Cup defeat at Ebbsfleet United was followed by a home F.A.Trophy loss to Salisbury City and with league results slumping again in April, Youth Team coach Graham Baker was given responsibility for Premier league survival.

Chairman David Taylor had offered to stand down after the first managerial change, but when the club was finally relegated after a desperate end of season battle that only produced two victories in the last ten games, he felt it was definitely time to go back to the terrace and enjoy the club once again.

Woking had been in the top flight of the Conference for sixteen seasons with some wonderful memories and some exciting and brilliant non-league players, but it is obviously time to rebuild and find the right team off the field to back up a manager capable of bringing back 'the good old days'

WOKING

BEST LGE ATT.: 3,791 v Oxford United
LOWEST: 751 v Kidderminster Harriers

No.	Date	Comp	H/A	Opponents	Att:	Result	Goalscorers	Pos
1	Aug 9	BSP	H	Altrincham	1645	L 1 - 2	Ledgister	
2	12		A	Torquay United	2881	L 1 - 2	Sole 35	
3	16		A	Burton Albion	1456	L 2 - 3	Pattison 19 Sole 21	24
4	23		H	Forest Green Rovers	1617	L 0 - 1		24
5	25		A	Oxford United	4314	D 0 - 0		24
6	30		A	Kettering Town	1493	L 0 - 1		24
7	Sept 2		H	Lewes	1604	D 1 - 1	Sole 85	
8	6		A	York City	2307	L 0 - 2		24
9	13		H	Grays Athletic	1619	W 3 - 1	**Domoraud** 48 Lorraine 58 Ledgister 90	22
10	20		A	Ebbsfleet United	1498	L 0 - 2		22
11	23		H	Salisbury City	1369	W 1 - 0	Marum 58	22
12	27		H	Histon	1797	W 1 - 0	**Domoraud** 56	21
13	Oct 4		A	Mansfield Town	2563	W 1 - 0	Sole 58 (pen)	19
14	7		H	Weymouth	1802	D 1 - 1	Ledgister 80	
15	11		H	York City	2341	L 0 - 2		19
16	18		A	Grays Athletic	581	D 1 - 1	Lorraine 87	20
17	**25**	**F.A.C. 4Q**	**H**	**Ebbsfleet United**	**1462**	**D 2 - 2**	**Domoraud 8 Marum 9**	
18	**28**	**F.A.C. 4Q r**	**A**	**Ebbsfleet United**	**869**	**L 0 - 1**		
19	Nov 1		H	Stevenage Borough	1955	L 0 - 1		20
20	**8**	**SS 3**	**H**	**Bognor Regis Town**	**460**	**W 3 - 0**	**Vernazza 14, Miles 2 (19, 77)**	
21	15		A	Eastbourne Borough	1105	D 0 - 0		20
22	18		A	Weymouth	696	D 1 - 1	Lorraine 50	
23	22		H	Torquay United	2452	D 2 - 2	Marum 6 Vernazza 22	20
24	**Dec 2**	**SS S4**	**A**	**Salisbury City**	**297**	**W 3 - 0**	**Denton 34, Pattison 38, Domoraud 60**	
25	6		A	Histon	1249	L 0 - 1		20
26	9		H	Rushden & Diamonds	1119	D 1 - 1	Denton 17	
27	**16**	**F.A.T 1R**	**H**	**Salisbury City**	**506**	**L 1 - 2**	**Marum 51**	
28	20		A	Lewes	694	W 2 - 0	**Domoraud** 42 71	20
29	26		H	Crawley Town	1910	D 0 - 0		21
30	28		A	Wrexham	4803	D 1 - 1	Denton 72	
31	Jan 1		A	Crawley Town	1525	D 2 - 2	**Domoraud** 26 Spence 57	21
32	**14**	**SS QFS**	**H**	**Forest Green Rovers**	**499**	**D 2 - 2***	**Marum 19, Sam-Yorke 93 (Lost 4-5 on pens)**	
33	17		A	Cambridge United	2696	L 1 - 4	Sole 90	21
34	24		H	Ebbsfleet United	1471	W 1 - 0	Ledgister 70	19
35	27		H	Eastbourne Borough	1101	L 0 - 4		
36	31		H	Northwich Victoria	1092	W 4 - 1	**DOMORAUD** 3 (17 39 79) Lambu 88	
37	Feb 14		H	Kettering Town	1414	L 0 - 1		18
38	17		A	Salisbury City	923	L 0 - 1		
39	21		A	Altrincham	943	L 0 - 1		20
40	24		A	Stevenage Borough	1965	L 0 - 1		
41	28		H	Burton Albion	1813	D 0 - 0		20
42	Mar 7		H	Barrow	1529	W 1 - 0	Bozanic 22	
43	14		H	Wrexham	1676	D 1 - 1	Elvins 53	19
44	21		A	Kidderminster Harriers	1594	L 0 - 2		22
45	30		H	Cambridge United	1775	L 0 - 1		
46	April 1		H	Kidderminster Harriers	751	L 1 - 5	Bozanic 66	22
47	4		A	Barrow	1424	W 1 - 0	Marum 88	22
48	7		A	Northwich Victoria	450	L 0 - 2		22
49	11		A	Forest Green Rovers	1109	W 2 - 0	Rhodes 18 Marum 90	20
50	13		H	Oxford United	3791	L 0 - 2		
51	18		H	Mansfield Town	2096	D 2 - 2	Miles 44 Anderson 67	21
52	26		A	Rushden & Diamonds	1676	L 1 - 3	Kamara 10	

Average Home Att: 1728 (1753) **Goals** 48 66

Best Position: 18th **Worst:** 24th

Goalscorers: Domoraud 10, Marum 7, Sole 5, Ledgister 4, Denton 3, Lorraine 3, Miles 3, Bozanic 2, Pattison 2, Vernazza 2, Anderson 1, Elvins 1, Kamara 1, Lambu 1, Rhodes 1, Sam-Yorke 1, Spence 1.

WORNER 12	KONAN 13	HUTCHINSON 5	BUNCE 3	MILES 6	SALAU 7	VERNAZZA 16	MARUM 10	WILLIAMS 9	EL KHOLTI 8	PATTISON 11	SAM-YORKE 18	LEDGISTER 19	LORRAINE 2	LAMBU 15	GINDRE 1	SOLE 24	QUAMINA 4	MOON 20	PIDGELEY 40	DOMORAUD 21	THORPE 25	GILCHRIST 22	SPENCE 17	PENTNEY 25	DENTON 30	MAGUNDA 27	EASTWOOD 29	KAMARA 31	BOZANIC 23	ELVINS 17	MCNERNEY 28	POWELL 32	SINTIM 29	ANDERSON 25	BOSSMAN 26	KNOWLES 1	HYDE 7	RHODES 32	
X	X	X	X	X	X	X	X	X	X	X	S	S	S	U	U																								1
X	X	X	X	X		X	X		X	X	S	X	U	U	U	X	S																						2
X	X	X	X	X	S	X	X	S	X	X			S	X	U	X		U																					3
U	X	X	X	X		X	X	S	X	X	S		U	X		X	S		X																				4
U	X	X		X	U	X		X	X	S	X		X	S		X	X	U	X																				5
U	X	X	S	X	U	X	S	X	X	S	X		X			X	X		X																				6
U	X	X	X		U	X		S		X	S			X		X	X		X	X	X	U																	7
U	X	X	X	X	U		S	S		X	X			X		X	X	S	X	X																			8
U	S	X	X	X			X	X		S	U	S	X	X		X	X		X	X																			9
U	S	X	X	X			X	S		U	S	X	X	X		X	X		X	X																			10
U	X	X	U	X			X			X	U	S	X	X		X	X	S	X	X																			11
U	X	X	S	X			X			X	S	S	X	X		X	X	U	X	X																			12
U	X	X	S	X			X	U			S	X	X	X		X	X	U	X	X																			13
U	X	X	X				X	S		S	X	X	X	X		X	X	S	X			U																	14
U	X	X	X	X			X	U		S	S	X	X	X		X	X	S	X																				15
U	X			X		X	X	S	X	X		X	X			X		S	X	S		U	X																16
U	X	X	U	X		X	X		X	U	U	X	X			S	X	U		X			S	X															17
U	X	X	S	X		X	X		X	U	U	X	X			S	X	U		X			S	X															18
	X	X	X	X		U	X		X	U		S		X		S	X		X	X			X	U															19
	U	X	X	X		X	X		X	S		S		X			X	S	X	X			X	U															20
	X	X	X	X		X	X		X	X	U	U					S	U	X	X			X	U															21
	X		X			X	X		X	X	U	U	X			S	X	U	X	X			X	U															22
	X		X	X		X	X		X	X	S	U	X	S	X	U		U		X			X																23
	U		X	X		X			X	X		S	X		X	S	X			X			X		X	S	U												24
			X	X		U	S		X	X		U	X		X		X			X			X		X	X	U	S											25
			X	X		X	X		X	X		U	X		U	S	X			S			U		X	X	X												26
			X	X		X	X		S	X		U	X		U	U	X			X			S		X	X	X												27
	X		X	X			X			X	S	X		U	U	X				X			X		U	X	X	U											28
	X		X	X			X			X	U	X			U	X	S			X			X		U	X	X	U											29
	X		X						U	X	X	X		S	U		X	U		X			X		S	X	X	X											30
	X		X				U			X	S	X	S	S	U		X			X			X		X	X	X	X											31
	X		X	U			X			X	S	S	X	X	U			U		X			X		X	X	X												32
	S		X			S	X			X		X	X	X	U	S				X			X		U	X	X	X											33
	X			X		X	X					X	X	S	U		X	S		X					U	S	X	X	X										34
	X			X			X			X		X	X	S	U		X	U		X					S	S	X	X	X										35
U	S			X			S			X		X	X	S			X	X		X					U	X	X	X	X										36
U	X			X			S		X	X		X					X	U		X							X	X	X	X	U	U							37
U	X					S	X		X	X		X	X				X	S		X		U					X	X		X			U						38
U	X					X	S			X		X	X					X		X							X	X	X		S		U	X	S				39
U						X	S		U	X			X					S		X								X	X	X	S		X	X	X	X			40
U	X					X	S			X		S	X					U										U	X	X			X	X	X	X	X		41
	X			X			S			X			X	S				U		X								U	X	X			S	X	X	X	X		42
U	X			X			U			X		S	X	S						X									X	X			S	X	X	X		X	43
U	X			X		X	S			X		S	X	U						X									X	X			S	X	X	X			44
U				U		U	X			X		S	X	X			X			X								X	X	S			X	X		X			45
U				U		S	X			X		S	X	X			X			X								X	X	S			X	X		X			46
U	X			X		X	S			X			X	X				S		X									X		U		S	X	X	X			47
X	X					X	S			X		S	X	X			U			X								X	X				U	X	X			S	48
U	X					S	S	U		S			X	X			X			X									X				X	X		X	X	X	49
U	X			U			S	S		X		S	X	X			X			X									X				X	X		X	X		50
	X	S		X		X	X			S		X	X	S			X	U		X									X				U	X		X			51
U	X		X			X					S	X	X	U			X	S		X								X	X		S			X		X			52
Total League Appearances																																							
4	37	17	22	30	1	21	26	4	15	34	5	19	33	19	2	17	28	2	16	35	1	0	11	0	3	8	12	14	18	7	0	0	6	14	7	12	4	2	X
0	4	1	3	0	1	4	14	8	0	7	12	12	3	10	0	4	4	10	0	2	0	0	0	0	2	2	0	1	0	2	3	0	4	0	1	0	0	1	S
27	0	0	1	3	4	3	2	3	2	2	5	5	2	5	11	1	1	13	0	0	0	4	1	3	5	0	1	4	0	0	2	1	4	0	0	0	0	0	U
Total Cup Appearances																																							
0	3	3	4	5	0	5	5	0	4	3	0	2	5	2	1	0	5	0	1	6	0	0	3	2	3	2	2	0	0	0	0	0	0	0	0	0	0	0	X
0	0	0	1	0	0	0	0	0	1	1	1	3	0	0	0	3	0	1	0	0	0	0	3	0	0	1	0	0	0	0	0	0	0	0	0	0	0	0	S
2	2	0	1	1	0	0	0	0	0	2	2	1	0	0	2	1	0	3	0	0	0	0	0	1	0	0	1	0	0	0	0	0	0	0	0	0	0	0	U

WOKING

CURRENT SQUAD AS OF BEGINING OF 2009-10 SEASON

GOALKEEPERS	HT	WT	D.O.B	AGE	P.O.B	CAREER	APPS	GOA
Matt Pegler						Aldershot (Yth), Woking c/s 09		
Ross Worner			3/10/89	19		Woking	4	0
DEFENDERS								
Ricky Anane	5'08"	11 02	18/2/89	20	Manchester	Bradford C (Yth), Bury Rel c/s 09, Workington (L) 2/09, Fleetwood (SL) 3/09, Woking 7/09		
Luke Baker						Woking		
Jon Boardman	6'02"	13 11	27/1/81	28	Reading	C.Palace cc 01/02, Woking (SL) 3/01, Torquay (Trial) 8/01, Margate (L) 10/01, Colchester (Trial) 12/01, Woking (L) 2/02 Perm 3/02, Rochdale 5/05 Rel 1/07, Dag & Red 1/07, Woking 6/09		
Tom Hutchinson	6'01"	12 06	23/2/82	27	Kingston	Sutton U, Fulham 8/98, Dundee 8/02, Woking 1/06	18	0
Joseph McNerney						Woking	3	0
Tony Sinclair			5/3/85	24		Gillingham (Yth), Beckenham, Maidstone 8/06 Rel 8/06, Beckenham, Fisher 3/07 Rel 5/07, Welling 8/07, Woking 6/09		
Daniel Sintim			19/5/91	18		Woking	10	0
Aswad Thomas	5'10"	11 06	9/8/89	20	Westminster	Charlton Rel c/s 09, Accrington (SL) 1/08, Barnet (L) 8/08, Lewes (3ML) 9/08, Woking 6/09		
MIDFIELDERS								
Harry Arter	5'09"	11 07	23/12/89	19	Sidcup	Charlton, Staines (L) 12/08, Ipswich (Trial) 1/09, Welling (L) 3/09, Woking 6/09		
Matt Ferdinando						Woking		
Billy Hussey						Woking		
Jerome Maledon			24/2/88	21		Woking Rel 8/08, Basingstoke (L) 3/06, Carshalton (SL) 1/07, Basingstoke 10/08, Woking 6/09		
Charlie Moon			14/11/88	20		Woking	12	0
Matthew Powell						Woking	0	0
Mark Ricketts	6'00"	11 02	7/10/84	24	Sidcup	Charlton Rel c/s 06, MK Dons (3ML) 11/05, Gravesend/Ebbsfleet 8/06, Woking 6/09		
Sam Sloma	5'08"	11 06	29/10/82	26	London	Wimbledon, Hampton & R (L) 12/01, Aylesbury c/s 02, Wingate & F 12/02 Rel 2/06, Milwaukee Wave United (USA) (L) (2005), Wealdstone 2/06, Thurrock (Dual) 3/06, Dag & Red 7/06, Grays 6/08 Rel 1/09, Chelmsford 2/09 Rel 5/09, Woking 6/09		
FORWARDS								
Moses Ademola	5'06"		18/7/89	20	Bermondsey	Cray W (Yth), Croydon A, Brentford Undisc 7/08, Welling (L) 11/08 Recalled 1 day, Welling (L) 12/08, Welling (2ML) 2/09, Woking (6ML) 7/09		
Anson Cousins						Woking		
Luke Medley	6'01"	13 03	21/6/89	20	Greenwich	Tottenham (Scholar), Bradford C Rel c/s 08, Cambridge C (L) 1/08, Barnet 7/08, Havant & W (SL) 3/09, Woking (6ML) 7/09		
Delano Sam-Yorke			20/1/89	20		Woking	17	0
Giuseppe Sole			8/1/88	21		Woking, Basingstoke (L) 3/06, Ebbsfleet (SL) 1/09	21	5

PLAYING SQUAD

LOANEES	HT	WT	DOB	AGE	POB	From - To	APPS	GOA
(G)Lenny Pidgeley	6'04"	14 09	7/2/84	25	Isleworth	Millwall (3ML) 8/08 - Rel 5/09	16	0
(D)Daniel Spence			22/10/89	19		Reading (2ML) 10/08 - Salisbury (L) 1/09, Salisbury 7/09	11	1
(G)Carl Pentney			3/2/89	20	Leicester	Leicester 10/08 -	0	0
(D)Joe Magunda						Leicester (2ML) 11/08 - Rel c/s 09, Kings Lynn 6/09	10	0
(G)Simon Eastwood			24/7/89	20	Huddersfield	Huddersfield (3ML) 11/08 -	12	0
(F)Tom Denton			26/6/89	20	Luton	Huddersfield (2ML) 11/08 - Wakefield (SL) 3/09	5	2
(M)Oliver Bozanic	6'00"	12 00	8/1/89	20	Melbourne, Aust	Reading (SL) 1/09 - Cheltenham (6ML) 7/09	18	2
(F)Rob Elvins	6'02"	12 04	17/9/86	22	Alvechurch	Aldershot (2ML) 2/09 - Rel c/s 09, Worcester 7/09	9	1
(F)Kelvin Bossman	6'00"					Reading (SL) 2/09 -	8	0
(D)Joe Anderson			13/10/89	19		Fulham (2ML) 2/09 -	14	1
(M)Alex Rhodes	5'09"	10 04	23/1/82	27	Cambridge	Rotherham (SL) 3/09 - Rel 5/09, Oxford U 5/09	3	1

DEPARTURES	HT	WT	DOB	AGE	POB	From - To	APPS	GOA
(F)Tony Thorpe	5'09"	12 06	10/4/74	35	Leicester	Barton R 8/08 - Brackley 9/08, Stamford 12/08	1	0
(M)Adekunle Salau						Peckham 8/08 - Rel 10/08	2	0
(G)Nick Gindre			24/7/84	25	Leatherhead	Walton & H 1/07 - Rel 1/09, Croydon A (L) 11/08, AFC Wimbledon 2/09	2	0
(D)Phil Gilchrist	5'11"	13 12	25/8/73	36	Stockton	Leicester Academy (Coach) 5/08 Man 9/08 - Sacked 4/09	0	0
(G)Danny Knowles	6'00"	12 00	7/1/86	23	Sidcup	Weymouth 2/09 - Rel 5/09, Eastbourne B 5/09	12	0
(D)Abdelhalim El Kholti	5'10"	11 00	17/10/80	28	Annemasse (Fr)	Rushden & D 6/08 - Rel 5/09	15	0
(D)Michael Kamara						Fisher 12/08 - Rel 5/09	15	1
(D)Patrece Konan	6'01"	11 05	17/3/83	26	Abidjan, IVC	Les Sables d'Olonne (Fra) 7/08 - Rel 5/09	41	0
(D)Colin Miles	6'00"	13 10	6/9/78	30	Edmonton	Port Vale 8/08 - Rel 5/09	30	1
(M)Micah Hyde	5'10"	11 02	10/11/74	34	Newham	Gillingham 2/09 - Rel 5/09, Barnet 7/09	4	0
(M)Goma Lambu	5'03"	9 08	10/11/84	24	Ghana	Dulwich Hamlet 8/06 - Rel 5/09	29	1
(M)Joel Ledgister	6'00"	12 04	29/9/87	21		Oxford U 7/08 - Rel 5/09	31	4
(M)Matt Pattison			24/3/84	25	Surrey	Farnborough 6/07 - Rel 5/09, Rushden & D 6/09	41	1
(M)Paulo Vernazza	6'00"	11 10	1/11/79	29	Islington	Weymouth 8/08 - Rel 5/09	25	1
(F)Liam Marum	6'03"	12 00	17/11/87	21	London	Cambridge U 1/07 - Rel 5/09, Eastbourne B 5/09	40	4
(F)Manny Williams			13/11/81	27	London	Maidenhead 5/08 - Rel 5/09, Maidenhead (2ML) 11/08, Weston-Super-Mare (3ML) 1/09, Havant & W 6/09	12	0
(D)Paul Lorraine			12/10/83	24		AFC Wimbledon 5/07 - AFC Wimbledon 5/09	36	3
(D)Danny Bunce			30/4/86	23		Cambridge U 7/06 - Rel 6/09, Chelmsford 7/09	25	0
(M)Bradley Quamina	5'11"		28/6/85	24		Yeading/Hayes & Yeading 5/07 - Rel 5/09, Maidenhead 6/09	32	0
(F)Wilfried Domoraud	6'00"	13 10	18/8/88	21	Maisons-Alfort (Fra)	Yeovil 9/08 - Rel c/s 09	37	8

WOKING

Founded: 1889.

Nickname: The Cards.

Club Colours: Red & white shirts, black shorts, white socks.

Change Colours: Yellow shirts, yellow shorts, yellow socks.

Club Sponsor: Calor Gas

Previous League: Isthmian

Ground Address:	Kingfield Stadium, Kingfield Road, Woking, Surrey GU22 9AA.
Tel No:	01483 772 470
Fax:	01483 888 423
Mobile:	07831 271 369
General email address:	admin@wokingfc.co.uk
Official website:	www.wokingfc.co.uk

SIMPLE DIRECTIONS

By Road	M25 exit 10 or 11, Woking FC signposted from outskirts of town wfc is opposite the well signposted Leisure Centre.
Parking:	Big car park at Leisure Centre and a car park at the football club

Capacity:	6,000
Seats:	2,500
Covered:	3,900

Clubhouse:	Excellent clubhouse open on matchdays.
Refreshments:	Available on matchdays
Club Shop:	Club shop in the Bellway Stand now open on matchdays. Tel: 01483 772 470

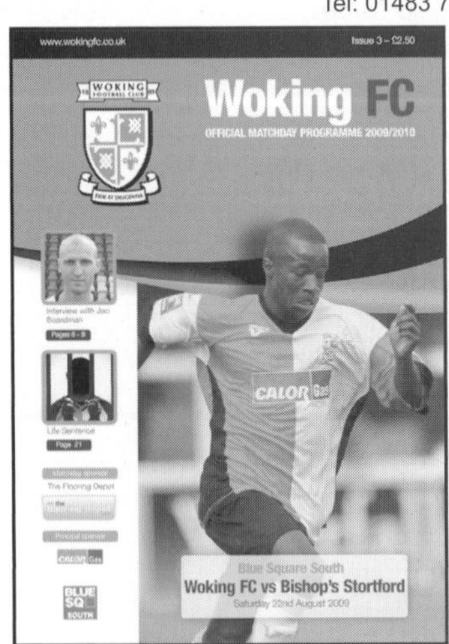

PROGRAMME EDITOR

Jane Spong/Brian Caffarey
Tel: (B) 01483 772 470
Email: programme@wokingfc.co.uk

CLUB STATISTICS

RECORDS

Attendance: 6,000 v Swansea F.A. Cup 1978-79
v Coventry City F.A.Cup 1996-97
Victory: 17-4 v Farnham 1912-13
Defeat 0-16 v New Crusaders 1905-06
Career Goalscorer: Charlie Mortimore - 331 1953-65
Career Appearances: Brian Finn - 564 1962-74
Transfer Fee Paid:
£60,000 paid to Crystal Palace for Chris Sharpling
Transfer Fee Received:
£150,000 from Bristol Rovers for Steve Foster.

SENIOR HONOURS

Surrey Senior Cup 1912-13, 26-27, 55-56, 56-57, 71-72, 90-91, 93-94, 95-96, 99-00, 03-04.
F.A. Amateur Cup Winners 1957-58.
Isthmian League Cup Winners 1990-91.
Isthmian League Champions 1991-92.
F.A.Trophy Winners 1993-94, 94-95, 96-97.
Vauxhall Championship Shield Winners 1994-95.
GLS Conference Cup Winners 2004-05.

PREVIOUS

League: Isthmian 1911-92.
Grounds: Wheatsheaf, Ive Lane (pre 1923).

WORCESTER CITY

Back Row (L-R): Martin Obrey, Rob Elvins, Kevin Spencer, Wayne Daniel, Mark Clyde, Shabir Khan, Steve Ball, Ernie North.
Middle Row: Pete O'Connell, Jack Connolly, Aaron Moses-Garvey, Louis Bridges, Jake Meredith, Richard Mace, Jordan Fitzpatrick, Chris Cornes, Matt Dinsmore, Kevin Gardiner.
Front Row: Graham Ward, Martin Butler, Richard Dryden, Carl Heeley, Tom Kemp, Gary Walker.

CLUB PERSONNEL

Chairman: Anthony Hampson.

Vice Chairman: Jim Painter.

Additional Directors: Dave Boddy, David Hallmark,

Colin Layland, Cliff Slade, Keith Stokes-Smith.

Secretary: Joe Murphy.

11 Middlewood Close, Wharf Lane, Solihull B91 2TZ.

Tel: 07837 086 205.

Email: joemurphy77@yahoo.co.uk

Commercial Manager: Phlip Williamson.

(B): 01905 23003

Press Officer: Anthony Hampson.

(M): 07530 411 126.

Email: awghampson@hotmail.com

Manager: Richard Dryden.

Club therapist: Steve Ball.

A generally unhappy season at least finished with City still in the Blue Square South, the Board still working towards a new ground and supporters hoping for an all round new look for the famous Midland outfit. Their geographical position meant that switching from Northern to Southern Divisions was always a possibility which could either be considered refreshing or a nuisance!

City were back in the South last season and two victories in the first two fixtures seemed to be a good omen, but although the season never really threatened relegation it wasn't a comfortable campaign. With league form fluctuating, a cup run could have livened up the season but it was not to be. Tamworth won 1-0 at St George's Lane in The F.A.Cup and A.F.C. Wimbledon also travelled to the Midlands to win 3-1 in The F.A.Trophy.

Off the field, the Chairman and his board held off a challenge for power and the long standing plans for developing the club continued to be discussed. Goals were not coming easily for Richard Dryden's squad, in fact only twice (early in the season) did City score three in a match and in nineteen of their forty four games they failed to score.

Worcester City are proud of their famous non-league club and they are prepared to give their support to 'their city team' when it is deserved. They knew last season had been a difficult one, but even when the last ten games had brought just three goals and four points, a crowd of 608 watched the 0-0 draw in the last match of the season. Those supporters deserve better and hopefully they won't have to wait too long.

WORCESTER CITY

BEST LGE ATT.: **1,725** v AFC Wimbledon
LOWEST: **479** v Maidenhead United

No.	Date	Comp	H/A	Opponents	Att:	Result	Goalscorers	Pos
1	Aug 9	BSS	A	Bognor Regis Town	436	W 2 - 1	Barnes 20 **Adaggio** 90	
2	11		H	St Albans City	944	W 2 - 0	**Adaggio** 21 Dinsmore54	
3	16		H	Hayes & Yeading	824	L 0 - 3		7
4	23		A	Weston-s-Mare	426	D 1 - 1	**Adaggio** 37	9
5	25		H	Bath City	915	L 0 - 1		
6	30		A	Bromley	505	W 2 - 0	**Adaggio** 1 Wilding 4	9
7	Sept 2		A	Basingstoke Town	312	D 0 - 0		
8	**9**	**SS S1**	**A**	**Bognor Regis Town**	**168**	**L 0 - 2**		
9	13		H	Braintree Town	703	D 2 - 2	Dinsmore 49 (pen) Barnes 81	12
10	15		H	Fisher Athletic	580	D 1 - 1	Richards 8	
11	20		A	Welling United	534	W 3 - 1	**Adaggio** 36 Wilding 56 84	8
12	**27**	**F.A.C. 2Q**	**H**	**Tamworth**	**898**	**L 0 - 1**		
13	Oct 4		H	AFC Wimbledon	1725	W 3 - 2	**Adaggio** 1 Wilding 15 Price 24	8
14	18		A	Havant & Waterlooville	651	W 2 - 0	Smith 40 (og) **Adaggio** 48	7
15	20		H	Team Bath	703	L 0 - 2		
16	25		A	Maidenhead United	451	L 0 - 5		
17	Nov 1		H	Welling United	769	L 0 - 1		10
18	8		A	Hampton & Richmond B	549	W 2 - 1	Dinsmore 33 Davies 78	9
19	15		A	Thurrock	224	L 0 - 2		10
20	**22**	**F.A.C 3Q**	**H**	**AFC Wimbledon**	**895**	**L 1 - 3**	**Wilding 62**	
21	29		H	Chelmsford City	647	L 0 - 1		12
22	Dec 6		A	St Albans City	424	W 2 - 0	Dinsmore 55 Wilding 62	12
23	20		H	Bognor Regis Town	588	D 1 - 1	Barnes 45	12
24	26		A	Newport County	822	L 0 - 1		12
25	Jan 17		A	Dorchester Town	433	L 1 - 3	Ward 25	13
26	19		H	Newport County	759	D 0 - 0		
27	24		H	Havant & Waterlooville	714	D 2 - 2	Dodd 14 **Adaggio** 63	13
28	27		A	Team Bath	107	W 2 - 0	**Adaggio** 11 Davies 60	
29	31		H	Bishop's Stortford	644	L 1 - 2	**Adaggio** 66	12
30	Feb 14		H	Bromley	635	W 1 - 0	Dodd 37	10
31	21		A	Fisher Athletic	147	W 1 - 0	Wilding 73	10
32	24		A	AFC Wimbledon	2695	L 0 - 2		
33	28		H	Hampton & Richmond B	667	L 1 - 2	**Adaggio** 40	12
34	Mar 7		H	Thurrock	588	W 2 - 0	**Adaggio** 25 (pen) 90	11
35	10		A	Hayes & Yeading	219	L 1 - 3	**Adaggio** 70	
36	14		A	Bishop's Stortford	403	L 0 - 3		12
37	16		H	Maidenhead United	479	D 1 - 1	Spencer 75	14
38	21		H	Eastleigh	577	L 0 - 1		
39	24		A	Braintree Town	425	D 1 - 1	Barnes 17	
40	28		H	Dorchester Town	493	D 0 - 0		15
41	April 4		A	Chelmsford City	1055	L 0 - 2		15
42	11		H	Weston-s-Mare	577	L 1 - 2	Dinsmore 75	16
43	13		A	Bath City	484	L 0 - 1		
44	18		A	Eastleigh	648	L 0 - 1		17
45	25		H	Basingstoke Town	608	D 0 - 0		16

Average Home Att: 721 (843) **Goals** 39 58

Best Position: 7th **Worst:** 20th

Goalscorers: Adaggio 14, Wilding 7, Dinsmore 5, Barnes 4, Davies 2, Dodd 2, Price 1, Richards 1, Spencer 1, Ward 1. Own Goals 1.

MCDONNELL	WARD	KHAN	RICHARDSON	BARNES	PRICE	DODD	BAMPTON	OWEN	ADAGGIO	DINSMORE	WALKER	RICHARDS	WOOD	FITZPATRICK	LESTER	TYACK	WILDING	BROWN	CLARKE	DAVIES	WRIGHT	MCGRATH	JEPHCOTT	HEELEY	KEMP	POLAN	CURTIS	BRIDGES	CONNOLLY	SPENCER	TARDIFF	DRYDEN	
X	X	X	X	X	X	X	X	X	X	X	S	S	S	U	U																		1
X	X	X	X	X	X	X		X	X	X	X	S	S	U	U	U																	2
X	X	X	X	X	X			X	X	X	X	S	S	S	U	U	X																3
X	X	X	X	X	X			X	X	X	X	S	S	S		U	X	U															4
X	X	X	X	X	X			X	X	X	X	U	U	U		U	X	U															5
X	X	X	X	X	X	X		S	X	X	U	S	S	X			X	U															6
X	X	X	X	X	X			U	X	X	S	U	X	X		U	X	U															7
	X	**X**	**X**	**X**	**X**		**X**	**X**	**X**	**X**	**U**	**S**	**X**	**S**				**U**	**X**	**S**													**8**
	X	X	X	X	X				X	X	U	X	S	X		S		S	X	X	U												9
X	X	X	X	X	X				X	X	S	X	S	X		S		U	U	X													10
X	X	X	X	X			X		X	X		S	S	S			X	U		X	U	X											11
X	**X**	**X**	**X**	**X**	**U**		**X**		**X**	**X**	**U**	**U**	**S**	**S**			**X**			**X**	**U**	**X**	**U**										**12**
X	X	X	X	X	X	S	X		X	S	S	U	U				X			X		X											13
X	X	X	X	X	X	S			X		X	U	S	S			X			X		X		U									14
X	X	X		X	X	S	X		X	S	S	X	U	U			X			X		X											15
X	X	X	X	X	X	S	X		X	S	U	S		U			X			X		X											16
X	X	X	X	X	X	S	X		X	S	S	U		U			X			X		X											17
X	X	X	X		S	X			X	X	X	X	U	U			X	U		S		X											18
X	X	X	X	S	U	S	S		X	X	X	X		U			X			X		X											19
X	**X**	**X**	**X**	**X**	**S**	**X**	**X**		**X**	**S**	**X**			**U**			**X**			**U**		**X**		**U**									**20**
X	X	X	X	X	S	S	X		X	S	X			U			X			U		X			X								21
X	X	X	X	X	S	S	X		X	X	X	U		U			X					S			X								22
X	X	X	X	X	S	U	X		X	X	X			U			X			U		S			X								23
X	X	X	X	X	X	U			X	X	X			U			X			S				S	X								24
X	X	X	X	X	U	X			X	X	X			S			X			U				U	X	S							25
X	X	X	X	X	S	X			X	X	X			U			X			S				U	X	U							26
X	X	X	X	X	S	X			X	X	X			U			X			U				U	X	U							27
X	X		X	X	X	X			X	X	X			S			X			S				U	X	S							28
X	X			X	X	X			X	X				S		U	X	S		X				U	X	U	X						29
X		X		X		X			X		X			X		U	X	S		X				S	X	U	X	S					30
X	X	X	X	X		S	S		X		X			X			X	U		X				U	X			U					31
X	X	X	X	X		X	S		X		X			X			X	U		X				U				S					32
X	X	X	X	X	S	X			X		X			X			X	U		X								U	U				33
X	X	X	X	X	S	X	U		X		X			S			X	U		X				U	X								34
X	X		X		X	X	X		X		X			S			X	S		X				U	X			U					35
X	X	X	X		S	X	X		X		X			X			X	X		S				S				U		U			36
		X	X	X	X	X			X		X			X			X	U		X				S				U		S	X		37
X	X	X	X	X	X	S	U		X		X			X			X	U		X				S									38
X	X	X	X	X	X	S	X		X		S			X			X			X				U									39
X	X	X	X	X	X	S	X		X	S	S			U			X			X					X					U			40
X	X	X	X	X	S	X	X		X	X	X			S			X			S				U						U			41
X	X		X	X	X	X	X			X	X			S			X			X				U					S	S			42
X	X		S	U		S	X		X	X	U			X			X			X				X					X	X		U	43
X	X		X	X	U	S	X		X	X	S			X			X			X				U					U	X			44
X	X		X	X	U	S			X	X	X			X			X			X				U					S	X		U	45
Total League Appearances																																	
40	40	35	38	37	23	18	17	5	41	25	27	5	1	15	0	0	38	1	1	24	0	9	0	1	14	0	2	0	1	3	1	0	X
0	0	0	1	1	10	15	3	1	0	6	9	7	9	11	0	2	0	4	0	6	0	2	0	5	0	2	0	2	2	2	0	0	S
0	0	0	0	1	4	2	2	1	0	0	4	6	4	15	3	7	0	13	1	4	2	0	0	15	0	4	0	5	2	3	0	2	U
Total Cup Appearances																																	
2	3	3	3	3	1	1	3	1	3	2	1	0	1	0	0	0	2	0	1	1	0	2	0	0	0	0	0	0	0	0	0	0	X
0	0	0	0	0	1	0	0	0	0	1	0	1	1	2	0	0	0	0	0	1	0	0	0	0	0	0	0	0	0	0	0	0	S
0	0	0	0	0	1	0	0	0	0	0	2	1	0	1	0	0	0	1	0	1	1	0	1	1	0	0	0	0	0	0	0	0	U

WORCESTER CITY

CURRENT SQUAD AS OF BEGINING OF 2009-10 SEASON

GOALKEEPERS	HT	WT	D.O.B	AGE	P.O.B	CAREER	Apps	Gls
Richard Mace						Cambridge U (Yth), Worcester 7/09		
Jake Meredith			9/12/87	21		Aston Villa (Yth), Birmingham (Yth), Team Bath c/s 07, Worcester 5/09		
DEFENDERS								
Mark Clyde	6'01"	12 00	27/12/82	26	Limavady, NI	Wolves Retired 2/07, Kidderminster (L) 9/02, Worcester 7/09		
Wayne Daniel			12/12/76	32	Birmingham	St Gerards, Paget R 10/00, Boldmere St Michaels 5/02, Stafford R 6/02, Worcester 6/09		
Richard Dryden						Worcester (Man)	0	0
Carl Heeley						Worcester (Pl/Ass Man)	6	0
Tom Kemp	6'03"		16/1/87	22	Ashby	Derby (Jun), Lincoln C Rel 11/06, Tamworth (3ML) 8/06, Tamworth 12/06, Grays 2/07, Kettering 6/07, Halesowen T (L) 8/08 Perm, Worcester 11/08	14	0
Shabir Khan			10/11/85	23		Worcester	35	0
Kevin Spencer						Tamworth, Kettering 6/07 Rel 8/08, Halesowen T (L) 10/07, Worcester (L) 11/07, Solihull Moors 8/08 Rel 10/08, Stratford T, Worcester 3/09	5	1
MIDFIELDERS								
Louis Bridges						Worcester	2	0
Jordan Fitzpatrick	6'00"	12 00	15/6/88	21	Stourbridge	Wolves (Scholar), Hereford 9/06 Rel c/s 08, Bromsgrove (L) 3/08, Worcester 8/08	26	0
Sam Tyack						Worcester	2	0
Gary Walker			10/2/88	21		Walsall, Worcester, Malvern (L) 3/07, Evesham (Dual) 9/07	36	0
Graham Ward	5'08"	11 09	25/2/83	26	Dublin	Wolves, Cambridge U (Trial) 3/03, Bournemouth (Trial) 4/03, Kidderminster Free 8/03 Rel c/s 04, Cheltenham 8/04, Rel c/s 05, Burton (L) 3/05, Tamworth 5/05, Worcester (L) 10/06 Perm	40	1
FORWARDS								
Marco Adaggio	5'08"	12 04	6/10/87	21	Malaga, Sp	Shrewsbury, AFC Telford (L) 1/06, Bangor C 1/07, Stafford R 8/07 Rel c/s 08, Worcester 8/08	41	14
Martin Butler	5'11"	11 09	15/9/74	34	Wordsley	Walsall, Cambridge U £22,500 8/97, Reading £750,000 2/00, Rotherham £150,000 8/03, Walsall 5/06, Grimsby (3ML) 10/07 Perm 1/08 Rel 10/08, Burton 2/09 Rel c/s 09, Worcester 7/09		
Matthew Dinsmore						Worcester	31	5
Rob Elvins	6'02"	12 04	17/9/86	22	Alvechurch	West Brom, Cheltenham (L) 9/06, York C (2ML) 1/07, Aldershot 6/07 Rel c/s 09, Woking (2ML) 2/09, Worcester 7/09		
Aaron Moses-Garvey	5'08"	11 13	6/9/89	19	Birmingham	Birmingham Rel c/s 09, Hinckley (L) 10/08, Worcester 7/09		
Dan Polan						Worcester	2	0
Craig Wilding	5'10"	11 11	30/10/81	27	Birmingham	Chesterfield, York 4/02, Kidderminster (Trial) 7/03, Stafford R 8/03, Redditch 7/05, Worcester 6/06386		

LOANEES	HT	WT	DOB	AGE	POB	From - To	APPS	GOA
(M)Michael McGrath			4/9/85	23		Kidderminster (3ML) 9/08 - Rel 1/09, Oxford U (Trial) 1/09, Galway Utd 2/09	11	0

DEPARTURES	HT	WT	DOB	AGE	POB	From - To	APPS	GOA
(M)Dave Burtoft						Hinckley U 2/08 - Atherstone c/s 08		
(G)James Lester						Southampton - Bognor Regis NC 8/08	0	0
(M)Rapinder Gill						Willenhall, Bromsgrove 3/07 - Bromsgrove 9/08, Hednesford Rel c/s 09		
(F)Mark Owen						Evesham 7/08 - Evesham 9/08, Stourport 11/08, Evesham 6/09	6	0
(G)David Clarke						Gresley R NC 9/08 - Rugby T 9/08, Belper 1/09, Rushall O 3/09, Atherstone T 6/09	1	0
(D)Jemiah Richards			10/5/86	23	Birmingham	Stafford R 7/08 - Bromsgrove 12/08	12	1
(F)Troy Wood			12/4/88	21		Yth - Rel 12/08, Evesham (L) 11/08 Perm 12/08 Rel 1/09, Bromsgrove 1/09	10	0
(D)John Curtis	5'10"	11 07	3/9/78	30	Nuneaton	ex QPR 1/09 - Wrexham 2/09, Northampton 7/09	2	0
(D)Ollie Barnes						Salisbury 7/08 - Rel 4/09, Weymouth 8/09	38	4
(D)Jamie Price	5'07"	11 00	22/7/88	21	Hereford	Gloucester 11/07 - Rel 4/09	33	1
(F)Matthew Dodd						Sutton Coldfield Undisc 7/08 - Rel 4/09	33	2
(M)Rob Davies	5'09"	11 03	24/3/87	22	Tywyn	Oxford U 9/08 - Rel 4/09	30	2
(D)Jon Richardson	6'01"	12 02	29/8/75	34	Nottingham	Exeter 6/08 - Rel 5/09	39	0
(G)Chris Tardif	5'11"	12 07	20/6/81	28	Guernsey	Winchester (Dual) 3/09 - Maidenhead 6/09	1	0
(G)Danny McDonnell			7/9/73	35		Halesowen T 5/00 - Rel 7/09	40	0
(G)Michael Wright						Yth -	0	0
(M)David Bampton	5'08"	11 00	5/5/85	24	Swindon	Tamworth 5/08 -	20	0
(F)Avun Jephcott							0	0
Jack Connolly						Yth -	3	0
(D)Craig Brown						Yth - Rel 4/09	5	0

WORCESTER CITY

Formed: 1902

Nickname: City.

Club Colours: Blue & white striped shirts, royal blue shorts, white socks.

Change Colours: Sky & navy shirts, navy shorts, sky blue socks.

Club Sponsor: M Pinches Transport.

Previous League: Southern League.

Ground address: St George's Lane, Barbourne, Worcester WR1 1QT

Telephone: 01905 23003

Mobile: 07837 086 205

Fax: 01905 26668

Email: joemurphy77@yahoo.co.uk

Website: www.worcestercityfc.co.uk

Simple Directions: M5 Jct 6 (Worcester North) follow signs for Worcester and turn right at first lights. St George's Lane is 3rd left. One mile from Foregate Station BR

Capacity: 4.004 **Seats:** 1,125 **Covered:** 2,000 **Floodlights:**Yes

Clubhouse: Open every evening and all day at weekends.

Club Shops: Two

Local Radio: Radio Wyvern, Classic Hits, BBC Hereford & Worcester

Local Press: Worcester Standard , Worcester Evening News

PROGRAMME EDITOR
c/o the club

CLUB STATISTICS

RECORDS

Attendance: 17,042 v Sheffield United F.A.Cup 4th Rd 24.0159

Victory: 18-1 v Bilston, Birmingham League 21.11.31

Defeat: 0-10 v Wellington, Birmingham League 29.08.20

Career Goalscorer: John Inglis - 189 (1970-77)

Career Appearances: Bobby McEwan - 596 (1959-75)

Record Transfer Fee Paid:
£8,500 to Telford United for Jim Williams 1981

Received: £27,000 from Everton for John Barton

SENIOR HONOURS

Birmingham League Champions 1913-14, 24-25, 28-29, 29-30.
Southern League Cup Winners 1939-40, 2000-01.
Southern League Division One Champions 1967-68, 1976-77.
Birmingham Senior Cup Winners 1975-76.
Southern League Champions 1978-79.
Worcestershire Senior Cup Winners (x26) Last win 1996-07.

PREVIOUS

Leagues: West Midlands 1902-38. Southern 1938-79, 85-2004. Alliance 1979-85.

Grounds: Severn Terrace, Thorneloe, Flagge Meadow.

SPONSORED BY:

UNIBOND

President:
N White F.S.C.A.

Chairman:
M Harris

Vice Chairman:
K Brown

Secretary & Press Officer:
P Bradley
7 Guest Road,
Prestwich,
Manchester M25 7DJ
Tel: 0161 798 5198
Fax: 0161 773 0930

NORTHERN PREMIER LEAGUE

	Premier Division	P	W	D	L	F	A	GD	Pts
1	Eastwood Town	42	25	12	5	82	37	45	87
2	Ilkeston Town	42	23	13	6	59	34	25	82
3	Nantwich Town	42	22	10	10	83	41	42	76
4	Guiseley	42	22	10	10	98	60	38	76
5	Kendal Town	42	21	11	10	85	63	22	74
6	FC United of Manchester	42	21	9	12	82	58	24	72
7	Bradford Park Avenue	42	20	12	10	74	52	22	72
8	Hednesford Town	42	21	6	15	78	52	26	69
9	Ashton United	42	16	10	16	71	75	-4	58
10	North Ferriby United	42	16	6	20	67	65	2	54
11	Frickley Athletic	42	13	15	14	50	58	-8	54
12	Ossett Town	42	15	8	19	71	74	-3	53
13	Marine	42	15	6	21	54	75	-21	51
14	Buxton	42	13	10	19	56	58	-2	49
15	Matlock Town	42	12	13	17	65	74	-9	49
16	Boston United	42	12	13	17	38	52	-14	49
17	Worksop Town	42	12	12	18	48	87	-39	48
18	Cammell Laird	42	12	11	19	58	70	-12	47
19	Whitby Town	42	12	10	20	58	71	-13	46
20	Witton Albion	42	12	6	24	53	73	-20	42
21	Leigh Genesis	42	11	7	24	42	88	-46	40
22	Prescot Cables	42	5	12	25	52	107	-55	27

PROMOTION PLAY-OFFS - SEMI-FINALS

Ilkeston Town	4 - 3*	Kendal Town
Nantwich Town	2 - 1*	Guiseley

PROMOTION PLAY-OFF - FINAL

Ilkeston Town	2 - 1*	Nantwich Town

	1	2	3	4	5	6	7	8	9	10	11	12	13	14	15	16	17	18	19	20	21	22
1 Ashton United		3-0	2-1	4-1	1-1	2-2	2-1	0-2	2-2	1-0	1-1	1-2	2-0	2-0	3-2	0-1	1-1	2-1	2-2	3-3	5-1	6-2
2 Boston United	0-1		1-2	1-1	1-0	0-1	0-1	2-3	2-2	1-2	0-0	1-0	1-1	2-1	0-2	0-5	0-2	3-2	5-0	2-0	0-0	0-1
3 Bradford P.A	6-4	1-1		1-0	1-2	0-2	2-0	1-0	2-2	3-0	0-1	2-2	2-1	2-0	3-2	0-0	3-1	2-0	4-0	3-2	0-2	1-1
4 Buxton	1-2	0-1	1-1		3-0	0-0	0-1	1-1	2-1	0-3	0-2	2-2	0-0	0-2	4-1	0-2	2-1	0-0	2-2	3-0	2-1	2-0
5 Cammell Laird	1-2	0-0	1-2	0-1		1-0	2-1	2-0	5-4	1-1	0-1	2-3	2-1	3-2	2-2	0-1	1-2	0-1	1-1	2-2	1-2	2-1
6 Eastwood Town	2-1	1-0	1-1	2-1	4-1		4-2	4-2	1-3	2-1	2-2	1-1	2-0	4-0	1-0	3-1	5-0	2-0	1-1	1-1	2-1	4-0
7 FC Utd of Manc.	4-0	0-1	1-1	1-1	5-5	0-1		2-0	2-1	3-0	3-1	1-3	2-4	3-2	3-3	0-0	4-0	3-2	2-0	3-1	5-3	0-0
8 Frickley Athletic	3-0	0-0	3-4	1-0	1-1	0-0	1-3		2-2	0-0	1-1	2-1	0-0	0-0	3-1	0-4	0-0	2-2	3-1	1-0	2-0	0-3
9 Guiseley	3-1	3-1	1-3	1-3	2-0	2-1	2-2	2-3		1-2	1-1	3-2	3-1	4-0	1-1	2-2	2-0	0-1	4-0	1-3	2-0	6-0
10 Hednesford T.	2-1	0-1	3-1	2-1	4-1	0-1	2-2	1-0	2-2		0-1	3-3	1-2	1-2	4-0	2-0	0-2	0-3	4-1	1-3	2-0	5-0
11 Ilkeston Town	2-1	1-1	0-0	1-0	2-1	1-0	0-1	1-0	0-1	0-1		1-1	3-1	5-0	2-2	3-2	1-0	2-1	3-0	1-0	3-1	3-3
12 Kendal Town	5-1	3-0	5-0	3-2	4-2	2-0	1-2	1-1	1-4	4-1	1-1		2-0	1-2	2-2	1-3	3-2	2-3	5-1	3-3	1-0	0-0
13 Leigh Genesis	3-0	0-0	2-1	0-7	2-1	0-4	0-2	2-0	2-4	1-3	1-2	1-2		0-0	0-2	0-8	0-3	0-6	2-1	2-4	0-2	1-2
14 Marine	1-1	3-1	0-4	2-0	0-0	1-2	2-3	1-2	2-0	0-3	0-2	0-1	0-1		2-1	0-0	1-0	2-1	3-6	2-2	0-2	6-2
15 Matlock Town	2-1	0-2	0-4	0-2	2-0	1-1	2-1	1-2	2-2	2-0	1-1	0-0	5-0	4-0		2-3	3-2	1-3	2-2	2-0	1-0	2-2
16 Nantwich Town	3-1	5-0	1-0	3-2	0-1	2-2	3-0	2-2	0-2	1-3	0-1	4-0	1-1	0-3	1-1		4-0	2-0	3-2	3-1	2-0	3-1
17 North Ferriby U.	1-2	0-2	2-2	4-2	2-0	2-2	0-2	4-1	1-2	2-1	0-0	1-2	1-2	1-2	6-3	1-1		4-1	5-0	1-0	1-2	5-0
18 Ossett Town	3-1	0-0	1-2	1-1	2-2	0-3	0-4	2-0	1-4	1-1	1-3	5-1	0-2	4-5	3-2	2-1	0-1		1-1	6-2	4-2	1-0
19 Prescot Cables	1-1	2-2	1-1	2-0	1-4	1-5	4-3	0-2	3-6	0-5	0-2	0-1	2-0	1-2	2-2	2-0	1-2	2-3		2-4	1-3	0-1
20 Whitby Town	1-2	1-0	1-0	0-2	0-3	1-3	0-0	2-2	0-2	0-3	3-0	2-3	2-2	2-0	2-0	0-0	1-2	5-2	3-0		1-0	0-2
21 Witton Albion	4-2	1-2	1-4	4-1	2-3	1-2	2-1	1-1	1-2	0-2	2-0	1-3	1-3	1-3	2-0	0-2	2-1	1-1	0-0	0-0		2-3
22 Worksop Town	1-1	1-1	1-1	2-3	1-1	1-1	0-3	3-1	0-4	2-7	0-1	0-2	2-1	1-0	0-1	0-4	2-1	1-0	3-3	1-0	2-2	

UNIBOND LEAGUE CHALLENGE CUP

PRELIMINARY ROUND

FC Halifax Town 2 Wakefield 1 *(Sept 30)* Att: 335

FIRST ROUND

Bamber Bridge 2 Chorley 1 *(Oct 28)* Att: 152
Belper Town 4 Gresley Rovers 2 *(Sept 30)* Att: 150
Brigg Town 0 **Sheffield** 5 *(Sept 30)* Att: 78
Clitheroe 2 **Garforth Town** 4 *(Nov 4)* Att: 122
Goole 2 **Stocksbridge Park Steels** 3 *(Sept 30)* Att: 91
FC Halifax Town 1 **Curzon Ashton** 2 *(Oct 18)* Att: 697
Harrogate Railway A. 0 **Durham City** 2 *(Sept 29)* Att: 105
Kidsgrove Ath. 3 Willenhall 3 *aet* (4-3p) *(Oct 1)* Att: 89
Leek Town 0 **Rushall Olympic** 1 *(Sept 30)* Att: 107
Loughborough Dyn. 4 Carlton Town 1 *(Sept 30)* Att: 65
Newcastle Blue Star 2 Ossett Albion 1 *(Sept 29)* Att: 48
Radcliffe Borough 2 Lancaster City 0 *(Sept 30)* Att: 81
Retford United 2 Glapwell 1 *(Sept 30)* Att: 119
Rossendale United 0 **Woodley Sports** 2 *(Oct 21)* Att: 47
Salford City 2 Mossley 0 *(Sept 16)* Att: 106
Shepshed Dynamo 4 Quorn 0 *(Sept 30)* Att: 107
Spalding United 3 Grantham Town 0 *(Sept 30)* Att: 86
Stamford 6 Lincoln United 4 *aet (Oct 4)* Att: 159
Warrington Town 0 **Colwyn Bay** 2 *(Sept 30)* Att: 101
Trafford 1 **Skelmersdale United** 3 *(Sept 30)* Att: 90

SECOND ROUND

Loughborough Dynamo 3 Stamford 1 *(Oct 28)* Att: 94
Spalding United 1 Shepshed Dynamo 0 *(Oct 28)* Att: 79
Woodley Sports 2 Radcliffe Borough 1 *(Oct 28)* Att: 73
Kidsgrove Athletic 3 Rushall Olympic 0 *(Oct 28)* Att: 80
Belper 1 **Stocksbridge Pk Steels** 3 *aet (Nov 18)* Att: 146
Retford Town 2 **Newcastle Blue Star** 3 *(Nov 18)* Att: 93
Sheffield 3 Durham City 2 *(Nov 18)* Att: 164
Colwyn Bay 2 **Skelmersdale United** 6 *(Nov 17)* Att: 115
Curzon Ashton 0 **Garforth Town** 1 *(Nov 17)* Att: 55
Bamber Bridge 2 Salford City 1 *(Nov 25)* Att: 102

THIRD ROUND

Buxton 2 **Matlock Town** 3 *aet (Jan 14)* Att: 238
Frickley Athletic 0 **Garforth Town** 1 *(Nov 25)* Att: 145
Guiseley 2 Bradford Park Avenue 0 *(Nov 25)* Att: 153
Kendal Town 4 Nantwich Town 1 *(Nov 25)* Att: 109
Loughborough Dynamo 1 **Ilkeston** 2 *(Nov 25)* Att: 92
Ossett Town 0 **Worksop Town** 3 *(Nov 25)* Att: 88
Prescot Cables 2 **Marine** 2 *aet* (1-4p) *(Nov 25)* Att: 153
Sheffield 5 North Ferriby United 2 *(Nov 25)* Att: 110
Spalding United 1 **Boston United** 6 *aet (Dec 16)* Att: 255
Stocksbridge PS 0 **Eastwood Town** 1 *(Nov 25)* Att: 72
Witton Albion 2 Cammell Laird 1 *(Dec 16)* Att: 102
Woodley 3 FC United of Manchester 0 *(Dec 2)* Att: 366
Skelmersdale Utd 10 Bamber Bridge 0 *(Dec 2)* Att: 117
Whitby Town 7 Newcastle Blue Star 2 *(Dec 17)* Att: 115
Ashton United 3 Leigh Genesis 1 *aet (Jan 12)* Att: 125
Kidsgrove Athletic 1 **Hednesford Town** 3 *(Jan 21)* Att: 92

FOURTH ROUND

Eastwood Town 0 **Boston United** 4 *(Jan 13)* Att: 233
Guiseley 3 Ashton United 0 *(Jan 27)* Att: 99
Hednesford 2 **Skelmersdale Utd** 3 *(Jan 27)* Att: 146
Witton Albion 2 Marine 1 *(Jan 27)* Att: 110
Worksop Town 1 **Matlock Town** 3 *(Jan 28)* Att: 183
Ilkeston Town 3 Sheffield 0 *(Jan 3)* Att: 270
Garforth Town 1 **Whitby Town** 3 *(Jan 3)* Att: 125
Woodley Sports 2 **Kendal Town** 3 *aet (Jan 3)* Att: 126

QUARTER-FINALS

Witton Albion 2 **Guiseley** 3 *aet (Feb 10)* Att: 119
Boston United 3 **Ilkeston Town** 4 *aet (Feb 18)* Att: 519
Kendal Town 1 **Skelmersdale United** 5 *(Feb 2)* Att: 152
Whitby 3 Matlock Town 3 *aet* (4-2p) *(Feb 24th)* Att: 132

SEMI-FINALS

Guiseley 5 Skelmersdale United 0 *(Mar 10)* Att: 123
Whitby Town 3 **Ilkeston Town** 5 *aet (Mar 11)* Att: 183

FINAL

(Apr 7th at Curzon Ashton)

Guiseley 3 Ilkeston Town 2 Att: 227

UNIBOND LEAGUE PRESIDENT'S CUP

(First Division teams)

FIRST ROUND

Brigg Town 3 Spalding United 2 *(Sept 23)* Att: 69
Chorley 1 Clitheroe 1 *aet* (3-2p) *(Sept 23)* Att: 159
Durham City 2 Garforth Town 1 *(Sept 16)* Att: 113
Glapwell 0 **Shepshed Dynamo** 4 *(Sept 23)* Att: 108
Gresley Rovers 4 Leek Town 0 *(Sept 23)* Att: 142
Ossett Albion 3 **FC Halifax Town** 4 *(Sept 23)* Att: 248
Sheffield 2 Goole 1 *(Sept 23)* Att: 211
Skelmersdale 4 Kidsgrove Athletic 3 *(Sept 23)* Att: 168
Woodley Sports 3 **Salford** 3 *aet* (4-1p)*(Oct 14)* Att: 84
(Woodley Sports expelled)

SECOND ROUND

Chorley 2 Lancaster City 0 *(Oct 14)* Att: 112
Colwyn Bay 0 **Trafford** 3 *(Oct 13)* Att: 195
Durham City 2 **Newcastle Blue Star** 4 *(Dec 23)* Att: 137
Curzon Ashton 2 **Salford City** 3 *(Nov 10)* Att: 87
Shepshed Dynamo 4 Carlton Town 2 *(Oct 14)* Att: 63
Grantham Town 1 **Stamford** 4 *(Oct 14)* Att: 139
Gresley Rovers 1 **Willenhall Town** 3 *(Oct 14)* Att: 131
Lincoln United 6 Brigg Town 2 *(Oct 14)* Att: 90
Mossley 2 Radcliffe Borough 1 *(Oct 14)* Att: 103
FC Halifax Town 3 Sheffield 1 *(Nov 11)* Att: 382
Quorn 3 Loughborough Dynamo 1 *(Oct 14)* Att: 154
Retford United 4 Stocksbridge PS 3 *(Oct 14)* Att: 121
Rossendale 3 **Bamber Bridge** 4 *aet (Nov 4)* Att: 64
Rushall Olympic 1 **Belper Town** 2 *(Sept 23)* Att: 69
Skelmersdale United 1 Warrington 0 *(Nov 25)* Att: 134
Wakefield 5 Harrogate Railway Ath 1 *(Oct 14)* Att: 111

THIRD ROUND

Chorley 1 **Mossley** 2 *(Dec 16)* Att: 70
FC Halifax Town 0 **Retford United** 2 *(Dec 16)* Att: 295
Lincoln United 2 **Stamford** 2 *aet* (6-5p) *(Dec 16)* Att: 70
(Lincoln United expelled)
Bamber Bridge 1 **Trafford** 4 *(Dec 23)* Att: 103
Newcastle Blue Star 4 Wakefield 3 *(Jan 21)* Att: 45
Salford City 2 **Skelmersdale United** 4 *(Jan 13)* Att: 121
Belper 4 **Willenhall Town** 4 *aet* (2-3p) *(Jan 27)* Att: 79
Shepshed Dynamo 2 **Quorn** 3 *(Jan 27)* Att: 110

QUARTER-FINALS

Skelmersdale 3 Newcastle Blue Star 0 *(Feb 17)* Att: 149
Quorn 0 Stamford 0 *aet* (4-3p) *(Feb 17)* Att: 103
Willenhall Town 1 **Trafford** 3 *(Feb 17)* Att: 54
Mossley 2 Retford United 1 *(Feb 17)* Att: 124

SEMI-FINALS

Skelmersdale United 0 **Quorn** 2 *(Mar 7)* Att: 192
Trafford 2 Mossley 1 *(Mar 17)* Att: 157

FINAL

Quorn 0 **Trafford** 2 *(April 21 at Quorn)* Att: 186

CHAIRMAN'S CUP

(Div One North v Div One South champions)

(April 28th at Durham City)

Durham City 2 Retford United 1 Att: 388

NORTHERN PREMIER LEAGUE DIVISION ONE NORTH

		P	W	D	L	F	A	GD	Pts
1	Durham City	40	25	12	3	98	41	57	87
2	Skelmersdale United	40	26	8	6	96	51	45	86
3	Newcastle Blue Star	40	21	10	9	93	54	39	73
4	Colwyn Bay (-3)	40	23	7	10	72	49	23	73
5	Curzon Ashton	40	20	8	12	66	44	22	68
6	Ossett Albion	40	19	9	12	76	61	15	66
7	Lancaster City	40	19	8	13	69	64	5	65
8	FC Halifax Town	40	17	12	11	71	52	19	63
9	Wakefield	40	16	8	16	65	62	3	56
10	Mossley	40	16	6	18	63	70	-7	54
11	Bamber Bridge	40	16	5	19	69	78	-9	53
12	Clitheroe	40	15	7	18	64	76	-12	52
13	Woodley Sports	40	16	3	21	57	74	-17	51
14	Chorley	40	13	8	19	56	66	-10	47
15	Trafford	40	13	7	20	72	83	-11	46
16	Garforth Town	40	13	5	22	77	99	-22	44
17	Radcliffe Borough	40	12	6	22	51	66	-15	42
18	Harrogate Railway	40	13	3	24	58	82	-24	42
19	Warrington Town	40	11	8	21	50	73	-23	41
20	Salford City	40	10	6	24	59	107	-48	36
21	Rossendale United	40	8	10	22	53	83	-30	34

PROMOTION PLAY-OFFS - SEMI-FINALS

Skelmersdale United	0 - 1	Curzon Ashton
Newscastle Blue Star	2 - 2*	Colwyn Bay

Newcastle Blue Star won 4-2 on penalties.

PROMOTION PLAY-OFF - FINAL

Newcastle Blue Star	4 - 1	Curzon Ashton

	DIVISION ONE NORTH	1	2	3	4	5	6	7	8	9	10	11	12	13	14	15	16	17	18	19	20	21
1	Bamber Bridge		1-1	0-5	2-5	1-0	0-5	2-5	1-3	2-3	2-3	0-2	1-4	1-4	3-0	3-1	4-1	0-0	2-0	2-0	3-3	2-1
2	Chorley	3-1		0-2	2-3	0-1	1-3	0-0	4-1	2-2	1-2	1-1	1-0	2-4	2-0	3-2	2-2	4-1	1-1	1-3	1-3	2-3
3	Clitheroe	3-3	1-1		3-0	1-0	1-3	1-2	3-1	4-3	0-5	0-2	3-3	4-2	1-2	3-2	4-1	0-6	2-2	3-0	3-2	2-3
4	Colwyn Bay	0-1	2-1	3-0		1-1	0-2	3-1	2-1	3-2	4-1	6-1	4-1	4-0	1-0	1-0	1-1	1-2	0-1	3-2	3-1	1-1
5	Curzon Ashton	0-1	4-1	0-1	0-1		1-0	0-1	1-0	3-1	1-1	0-1	2-1	2-0	3-1	4-1	2-1	0-4	3-3	2-1	1-3	3-0
6	Durham City	3-2	3-1	3-1	0-0	2-2		1-1	5-2	1-0	6-0	6-1	2-2	3-0	4-2	4-0	2-1	0-0	2-0	1-0	4-1	5-0
7	FC Halifax Town	0-3	3-1	4-0	1-1	1-2	0-0		5-1	2-1	0-0	2-0	3-3	1-1	1-1	1-2	7-1	3-0	2-2	3-2	1-0	0-1
8	Garforth Town	3-4	1-0	3-4	2-3	3-2	0-3	2-2		4-1	3-1	3-1	2-3	2-4	1-4	2-3	2-5	3-6	2-1	1-0	1-1	3-1
9	Harrogate Railway	1-5	0-1	1-0	0-1	1-3	2-1	2-0	2-1		2-3	1-2	1-2	0-5	2-1	1-0	1-3	2-4	4-2	0-1	2-3	2-1
10	Lancaster City	1-0	1-0	1-0	1-3	0-1	3-3	2-0	3-1	1-2		0-0	1-4	3-2	0-1	1-0	3-5	2-5	3-0	1-1	2-3	3-2
11	Mossley	2-2	0-1	1-0	1-3	0-2	1-3	3-1	3-4	1-1	1-1		0-5	5-3	0-2	3-0	2-3	0-1	3-1	1-2	4-1	3-2
12	Newcastle Blue Star	0-2	0-0	1-1	1-1	0-1	2-2	3-0	6-1	5-0	1-2	1-1		4-2	2-1	5-0	2-0	0-4	1-3	1-0	3-1	2-2
13	Ossett Albion	1-0	1-2	1-2	2-0	1-1	0-1	2-2	2-1	2-0	2-1	3-0	2-1		2-1	3-1	3-1	1-1	2-3	1-1	2-1	4-3
14	Radcliffe Borough	3-2	1-2	0-1	2-2	1-4	4-2	1-4	0-2	1-0	1-1	1-0	0-3	0-2		1-3	6-0	1-1	1-2	0-2	0-1	0-2
15	Rossendale United	2-3	0-1	2-2	0-1	1-0	1-1	1-0	2-2	2-2	1-1	0-3	1-4	1-1	0-2		4-5	2-3	2-2	3-0	3-2	0-1
16	Salford City	1-0	1-6	1-1	1-3	1-1	0-1	0-1	0-4	2-0	0-4	0-4	1-2	1-1	2-2	3-1		0-1	2-6	1-2	3-1	2-3
17	Skelmersdale Utd	3-2	2-1	3-0	3-0	3-1	1-1	2-1	3-3	2-4	1-3	4-2	1-2	2-0	2-1	2-2	4-1		2-0	2-0	1-1	2-1
18	Trafford	1-2	5-0	4-0	6-1	0-5	3-3	1-2	0-5	1-0	2-3	3-1	2-4	0-2	1-0	2-4	5-2	2-4		1-3	0-1	0-2
19	Wakefield	3-1	3-0	3-2	1-0	2-2	1-1	1-4	3-1	3-6	1-2	0-2	1-1	2-2	1-1	2-2	8-1	2-1	0-1		1-0	2-1
20	Warrington Town	0-3	1-3	1-0	0-1	2-2	1-2	1-1	5-0	0-2	0-2	0-1	0-4	1-1	2-4	1-1	1-0	0-4	2-2	2-1		1-0
21	Woodley Sports	2-0	1-0	1-0	1-0	0-3	3-4	2-3	0-0	2-1	2-1	1-4	2-4	0-3	0-1	2-0	0-3	2-3	3-1	2-4	1-0	

NORTHERN PREMIER LEAGUE DIVISION ONE SOUTH

		P	W	D	L	F	A	GD	Pts
1	Retford United	38	24	9	5	88	34	54	81
2	Belper Town	38	24	9	5	79	41	38	81
3	Stocksbridge PS	38	23	6	9	92	44	48	75
4	Carlton Town	38	20	10	8	83	50	33	70
5	Rushall Olympic	38	20	8	10	63	42	21	68
6	Glapwell	38	21	5	12	78	58	20	68
7	Stamford	38	15	16	7	65	51	14	61
8	Shepshed Dynamo	38	16	8	14	61	61	0	56
9	Leek Town	38	14	12	12	63	60	3	54
10	Lincoln United	38	14	9	15	58	65	-7	51
11	Sheffield	38	14	8	16	67	69	-2	50
12	Quorn	38	13	9	16	54	63	-9	48
13	Grantham Town	38	12	11	15	49	65	-16	47
14	Loughborough Dynamo	38	11	13	14	45	58	-13	46
15	Kidsgrove Athletic	38	12	5	21	49	62	-13	41
16	Willenhall Town	38	10	8	20	55	74	-19	38
17	Spalding United	38	10	7	21	41	82	-41	37
18	Goole (-11)	38	13	5	20	62	85	-23	33
19	Gresley Rovers	38	6	7	25	41	78	-37	25
20	Brigg Town	38	3	5	30	41	92	-51	14

PROMOTION PLAY-OFFS - SEMI-FINALS

Belper Town	1 - 0	Rushall Olympic
Stocksbridge Park Steels	5 - 2	Carlton Town

PROMOTION PLAY-OFF - FINAL

Belper Town	0 - 1	Stocksbridge Park Steels

DIVISION ONE SOUTH		1	2	3	4	5	6	7	8	9	10	11	12	13	14	15	16	17	18	19	20
1	Belper Town		2-1	1-0	3-1	2-0	2-0	4-0	3-1	4-1	1-2	2-1	2-0	1-1	2-2	3-0	4-1	0-0	2-2	4-2	3-1
2	Brigg Town	1-2		2-3	0-1	0-2	1-1	1-2	0-1	0-2	2-2	0-2	2-3	2-4	3-3	2-0	1-2	1-2	1-3	1-3	1-2
3	Carlton Town	5-1	5-0		2-1	4-2	5-1	2-0	2-1	6-2	0-1	0-0	2-4	1-3	1-2	3-3	0-0	3-0	3-3	0-2	3-2
4	Glapwell	4-0	3-2	0-0		6-2	2-1	3-1	3-0	1-3	3-2	1-0	3-1	0-1	3-1	2-3	4-2	2-0	2-1	0-1	3-0
5	Goole	0-5	4-3	2-1	1-1		1-4	3-1	0-1	1-2	3-3	2-1	2-3	1-2	1-2	2-1	3-2	1-2	1-3	0-3	5-1
6	Grantham Town	1-1	3-0	0-3	0-5	0-0		2-0	2-1	2-0	1-3	0-0	1-1	0-0	1-0	1-1	4-2	0-0	3-3	1-2	1-2
7	Gresley Rovers	0-1	1-2	0-2	1-2	1-3	1-3		3-3	1-1	1-2	1-1	1-2	0-4	0-3	2-5	0-1	5-0	3-2	0-2	2-1
8	Kidsgrove Athletic	0-1	5-2	2-4	2-5	3-3	0-1	2-1		1-2	2-0	0-0	2-0	2-4	3-0	0-2	1-0	0-1	1-2	0-1	0-2
9	Leek Town	1-1	3-0	2-2	6-0	3-1	0-2	2-2	1-0		0-0	1-1	1-0	1-2	0-0	2-2	3-4	0-0	3-4	2-2	4-3
10	Lincoln United	2-3	1-1	1-4	5-0	1-2	1-0	1-1	1-4	1-0		1-1	0-1	0-3	1-4	1-0	0-2	0-4	3-5	3-2	3-4
11	Loughborough Dynamo	0-4	1-1	0-1	2-1	2-1	4-0	2-0	2-1	2-2	1-1		1-1	1-4	1-1	2-1	1-5	0-2	0-0	0-2	0-1
12	Quorn	1-1	4-0	2-0	1-1	3-1	3-2	2-1	0-2	2-2	0-2	1-3		0-3	1-4	1-3	3-5	3-1	4-1	1-3	2-3
13	Retford United	2-3	3-0	1-2	3-3	5-0	0-0	0-1	4-1	3-2	3-1	3-0	0-0		2-1	3-0	4-3	5-0	1-1	2-1	0-0
14	Rushall Olympic	1-1	3-1	0-1	2-0	0-1	2-3	3-1	4-2	2-0	0-0	2-2	1-0	1-3		3-2	1-0	2-0	2-0	3-1	2-2
15	Sheffield	1-1	0-2	2-2	0-4	2-0	2-0	1-4	1-0	1-2	3-2	2-3	3-1	3-2	1-3		0-2	7-0	3-1	3-5	2-1
16	Shepshed Dynamo	3-0	2-0	0-3	1-1	4-2	1-1	2-0	1-1	0-1	0-3	1-2	2-0	1-3	1-0	1-1		3-2	1-1	2-0	1-1
17	Spalding United	0-4	3-2	1-2	1-2	1-4	5-1	1-1	0-1	1-2	0-1	3-5	1-1	0-5	1-0	2-1	1-2		0-1	1-3	2-2
18	Stamford	1-2	2-1	2-2	3-1	4-1	2-1	1-0	0-0	2-1	1-1	3-0	1-1	0-0	0-1	2-2	0-0	1-1		2-2	2-0
19	Stocksbridge PS	1-0	5-1	2-2	3-0	2-3	7-1	4-0	3-1	4-1	1-3	4-1	0-0	1-0	0-1	1-1	3-0	8-0	1-1		4-1
20	Willenhall Town	1-3	2-1	2-2	1-4	1-1	2-4	2-2	1-2	0-2	2-3	2-0	0-1	0-0	0-1	1-2	6-1	1-2	0-2	2-1	

ASHTON UNITED

Founded: 1878
Nickname: Robins

Manager: Danny Johnson

Club Colours: Red & white halves/black/red.

Change: Navy & sky stripes/navy/sky.

Best Seasons - League: 21st Conference North 2004-05.

Ground address: Hurst Cross, Surrey Street, Ashton-u-Lyne 0L68 DY

Tel No: 0161339 4158 (office) 01613 301511 (Social Club) 0161 339 4158 (Fax)

Official Website: www.ashtonunited.com

Capacity: 4,500 **Seats:** 250 **Covered:** 750 **Floodlights:** Yes

Simple Directions: From M62 jct 20 take A627 to Oldham. Keep to right and leave at Ashton sign, take A627 at next island then keep to left and take slip road to Ashton. At island follow Stalybridge/Park road sign straight for three miles to ground at Hurst Cross

Midweek Home Matchday: Monday

Clubhouse: Open 11am -11 pm Snacks on matchdays

Club Shop: Yes. Contact: Ken Lee (0161 330 9800)

CLUB PERSONNEL

Chairman: David Aspinall
Additional Directors:
David Aspinall, Tony Collins, John Milne, Terry Hollis, Eric Stafford, Jackie Tierney, Michael Cummings, Denise Pinder, Jim Pinder, Tony Robinson, Ronnie Thomasson, Jan Sutherland.
Secretary: Bryan Marshall
330 Manchester Road East, Little Hulton, Worsley, Manchester M38 9WH
Tel No: 0161 950 3167 (H)
07944 032 362 (M)
Programme Editor: Ken Lee
Tel No: 0161 330 9800

CLUB STATISTICS

Record	**Attendance**:	11,000 v Halifax Town, F.A.Cup 1st Rd.1952
	Victory:	11-3 v Stalybridge Celtic, Manchester Intermediate Cup 1955
	Defeat:	1-11 Wellington Town , Cheshire League 1946-47
Goalscorer:	**Career Appearances**:	Micky Boyle 462
Record Transfer Fee	**Paid**:	£9,000 to Netherfield for Andy Whittaker 1994
	Received:	£15,000 from Rotherham United for Karl Marginson 1993
Senior Honours:		N.P.L. Div 1 Cup 94-95 Manchester Senior Cup (4) Manchester Prem Cup (5) Manchester Challange Shield 92-93 Manchester Junior Cup: (3)
Previous Leagues:		Manchester, Lancs Comb 12-33 48-64 66-68, Midland 64-66 Cheshire County 23-48 68-82 N.W.Co82-92
Name:		Hurst 1878-1947 **Ground:** Rose Hill 1878-1912

Back Row: Russell Batchelor (Physio), Anthony Jackson (Coach), Joe Reedy, Ross Thaker, Chris Middleton, Nick Prescott, Alex Frost, Terry Smith, Gareth Johnson, Callum Flanagan, Matty O'Neill, Gareth Richards, Ian Kearney, Nathan Kilcourse, Dave Haworth (Coach)
Front Row: Robbie Talbot, Ben Smith, Iain Howard, Ryan Moore, Danny Caldecott, Danny Johnson (Manager), Craig Robinhson (Captain), Martin Piana, Pat McFadden, Ian Bennett, Astley Mulholland

ASHTON UNITED

BEST LGE ATT.: 1,561 v FC Utd of Manchester
LOWEST: 122 v Ossett Town

No.	Date	Comp	H/A	Opponents	Att:	Result	Goalscorers	Pos
1	Aug 16	Unibond P.	H	North Ferriby United	128	D 1 - 1	Chapman 8	
2	19		A	Leigh Genesis	140	L 0 - 3		
3	23		A	Boston United	1209	W 1 - 0	Deegan 50	13
4	25		H	Buxton	272	W 4 - 0	Fitzpatrick (pen) Moore 67 Deegan 70 B Smith 84	
5	30		H	MatlockTown	152	W 3 - 2	Robinson 16 B.Smith 36 Fitzpatrick 54	5
6	Sept 2		A	Cammell Laird	149	W 2 - 1	Deegan 79 B Smith 90	
7	8		H	Marine	160	W 2 - 0	Deegan 30 B.Smith 54	1
8	**13**	**F.A.C 1Q**	**H**	**Kendal Town**	**118**	**L 2 - 3**	**Deegan 40 Robinson 73**	
9	20		A	Prescot Cables	237	D 1 - 1	Robinson 34	3
10	22		H	Kendal Town	150	L 1 - 2	**Howard** 54 (pen)	
11	27		A	Hednesford Town	408	L 1 - 2	Talbot 59	
12	Oct 4		H	Ossett Town	122	W 2 - 1	**Howard** 56 Deegan 60	
13	7		A	Eastwood Town	314	L 1 - 2	**Howard** 26	
14	11		A	Marine	322	D 1 - 1	**Howard** 68	7
15	13		H	Nantwich Town	188	L 0 - 1		
16	**18**	**F.A.T.1Q**	**H**	**Lincoln United**	**108**	**W 2 - 1**	**Talbot 8 Kearney 49**	
17	25		H	Worksop Town	150	W 6 - 2	**Howard** 4 Talbot 10 (pen) Smith 34 Flannagan 70 72 Bennett 76	6
18	28		A	Frickley Athletic	162	L 0 - 3		
19	**Nov 1**	**F.A.T. 2Q**	**H**	**Ilkeston Town**	**142**	**L 0 - 2**		
20	10		H	Hednesford Town	187	W 1 - 0	**Howard** 84 (pen)	7
21	15		H	Cammell Laird	132	D 1 - 1	Smith 90	7
22	18		A	Guiseley	244	L 1 - 3	Dennis 86	
23	22		A	North Ferriby United	198	W 2 - 1	Deegan 18 Bennett 45	7
24	29		A	Buxton	261	W 2 - 1	Bennett 23 Kennedy 55	4
25	Dec 20		H	Ilkeston Town	130	D 1 - 1	**Howard** 85	6
26	27		H	F.C.United	1561	W 2 - 1	Deegan 27 Finnigan 64	
27	Jan 17		H	Guiseley	157	D 2 - 2	Ellis 44 (og) Bennett 61	8
28	24		H	Prescot Cables	133	D 2 - 2	**Howard** 26 (pen) 71	8
29	31		A	Ilkeston Town	341	L 1 - 2	Bennett 67	10
30	Feb 14		H	Whitby Town	134	D 3 - 3	Frost 24 Smith 75 **Howard** 83 (pen)	10
31	16		A	Bradford P.A.	349	L 4 - 6	SMITH 4 (38 67 73 87)	11
32	21		A	Nantwich Town	320	L 1 - 3	McFaddon 46	
33	23		H	Bradford PA	295	W 2 - 1	Lees 17 Bennett 90	
34	28		A	Worksop Town	156	D 1 - 1	Thornley 34	
35	Mar 7		H	Leigh Genesis	182	W 2 - 0	Bennett 52 Thornley 89	10
36	10		A	Witton Albion	165	L 2 - 4	Thornley 11 Dougan 67	
37	14		H	Boston United	208	W 3 - 0	Smith 59 Richards 87 Deegan 90	10
38	21		A	Whitby Town	243	W 2 - 1	Lees 64 Deegan 71	9
39	25		A	F.C.United	1714	L 0 - 4		
40	28		H	Frickley Athletic	137	L 0 - 2		9
41	April 4		A	Ossett Town	110	L 1 - 3	Richards 38	9
42	10		A	Kendal Town	312	L 1 - 5	**Howard** 45 (pen)	9
43	13		H	Witton Albion	225	W 5 - 1	**Howard** 32 (pen) Richards 54 69 Deegan 63 73	
44	18		H	Eastwood Town	273	D 2 - 2	Richards 43 **Howard** 60 (pen)	9
45	25		A	Matlock Town	365	L 1 - 2	Richards 56	9

Average Home Att: **242 (157)** **Goals** **75 80**

Best Position: 1st **Worst:** 13th

Goalscorers: Howard 13, Deegan 12, Smith B 12, Bennett 8, Richards 6, Thorney 4, Robinson 3, Talbot 3, Fitzpatrick 2, Lees 2, Chapman 1, Dennis 1, Dougan 1, Finnigan 1, Flanagan 1, Kearney 1, Kennedy 1, McFaddon 1, Moore 1. Own Goals 1.

BOSTON UNITED

Founded: 1933
Nickname: The Pilgrims

Manager: Ron Scott & Paul Hurst.

Club Colours: Amber & black stripes/black/black.

Change: All white.

Best Season - League: 11th Football League Division 3/League 2 2003-04/05-06.

Ground address: Jakemans Stadium, York Street, Boston, Lincolnshire, PE21 6JN

Telephone: 01205 364 406. Fax: 01205 354 063

Website: www.bufc.co.uk

Capacity: 6,645 **Seats:** 1,323 **Covered:** 6,645

Simple Directions: A1 to A17 Sleaford to Boston, over railway crossing. Bear right at the Eagle Pub to lights. Over Haven Bridge, straight along Adams Way (dual carriageway) Turn right at traffic lights into Main Ridge then right again in to York Street. (this opposite Eagle Fisheries) Ground is signposted after railway crossing.

Midweek Home matchday: Tuesday

Clubhouse:. Yes - 01205 362 967

Club Shop: Yes

CLUB PERSONNEL

Chairman: David Newton.

Additional Directors:
Neil Kempster (Vice Chairman)
Chris Cook

Secretary: John Blackwell
Jakemans Stadium,
York Street, Boston,
Lincolnshire, PE21 6JN
Tel: 01205 364 406
(H): 01205 365 652
(M): 07860 663 299

Programme
Editor: Craig Singelton.
(B) 01205 363 264
(M) 07966 952 694

CLUB STATISTICS

Record	**Attendance:** 10,086 v Corby Town floodlights inaugaration 1955.
	Victory: 12-0 v Spillsbury Town 1992-93 Grace Swan Cup.
Goalscorer:	**Career Appearances:** Billy Howells - 500+
	Goals in a Career: Chris Cook - 181.
Record Transfer Fee	**Paid:** £14,000 for Micky Nuttell from Wycombe Wanderers.
	Received: £50,000 for David Norris from Bolton Wanderers 2000.

Senior Honours: Conference Champions 2001-02. Southern League Champions 1999-2000. Northern Premier League Champions 1972-73, 73-74, 76-77, 77-78. NPL Cup 1973-74, 75-76. United Counties League Champions 1965-66. West Midlands League Champions 1966-67, 67-68. Central Alliance League Champions 1961-62.

Previous Leagues Central Alliance, West Midlands, United Counties, Northern Premier, Southern, Conference, Football League.

Back Row (L-R): Ollie Ryan, David Farrell, Liam Parker, Lee Beeson, Michael Wood, Adam Millson.
Middle: Jon Froggatt, Matt Bloomer, Tom Matthews, Chris Wright, Stewart Talbot, Ryan Clarke, Kieran Leabon.
Front: Tony Pascu, Danny Steadman, Steve Welsh (assistant manager), Wes Parker (captain), Tommy Taylor (manager), Jon Rowan, Liam Green.

BOSTON UNITED

BEST LGE ATT.: **1,625** v FC Utd of Manchester
LOWEST: **621** v Frickley Athletic

No.	Date	Comp	H/A	Opponents	Att:	Result	Goalscorers	Pos
1	Aug 20	Unibond P.	H	Ossett Town	1334	W 3 - 2	Froggatt 14 **Ryan** 27 39	
2	23		H	Ashton United	1209	L 0 - 1		16
3	25		A	F.C.United	2825	W 1 - 0	**Ryan** 34	
4	30		A	Pressed Steel	270	D 2 - 2	Froggatt 38 Leabon 64	10
5	Sept 3		H	Worksop Town	1058	L 0 - 1		
6	6		H	Guiseley	1062	D 2 - 2	Rowan 59 75	12
7	**13**	**F.A.C. 1Q**	**H**	**Glapwell**	**867**	**W 6 - 1**	**Melton 21 Leabon 26 RYAN 3 (33 39 52 pen) Rowan 82 (pen)**	
8	20		A	Matlock Town	499	W 2 - 0	Rowan 24 **Ryan** 39	11
9	23		A	Buxton	408	W 1 - 0	**Ryan** 65	
10	**27**	**F.A.C. 2Q**	**H**	**Stamford**	**1125**	**W 2 - 0**	**Froggatt 14 49**	
11	Oct 4		H	Bradford PA	1162	L 1 - 2	Haran 90	11
12	8		H	Hednesford Town	1090	L 1 - 2	**Ryan** 15	
13	**11**	**F.A.C. 3Q**	**A**	**Southport**	**792**	**W 2 - 0**	**Clarke 1 Rowan 56 (pen)**	
14	14		A	Marine	224	L 1 - 3	Talbot 79	14
15	**18**	**F.A.T. 1Q**	**H**	**Kidsgrove Athletic**	**797**	**W 6 - 1**	**Millson 32 Talbot 41 85 Ryan 47 Rowan 49 (pen) 53**	
16	**25**	**F.A.C 4Q**	**H**	**Cambridge United**	**1956**	**L 2 - 3**	**Leabon 25 Ryan 56**	
17	29		A	Worksop Town	230	D 1 - 1	**Ryan** 31	14
18	**Nov 1**	**F.A.T. 2Q**	**A**	**Clitheroe**	**359**	**W 4 - 2**	**Rowan 5 68 Parker 16 76**	
19	8		A	Guiseley	456	L 1 - 3	Rowan 38 (pen)	17
20	15		H	North Ferriby United	1069	L 0 - 2		19
21	19		H	Frickley Athletic	621	L 2 - 3	**Ryan** 44 Rowan 46	
22	**26**	**F.A.T. 3Q**	**A**	**F.C.United**	**936**	**W 3 - 1**	**Ryan 32 Parker 44 61**	
23	29		H	Whitby Town	949	W 2 - 0	Froggatt 52 **Ryan** 89	19
24	Dec 6		A	Witton Albion	265	W 2 - 1	Farrell 67 **Ryan** 73	15
25	9		A	Ilkeston Town	270	D 1 - 1	**Ryan** 89 (pen)	
26	**13**	**F.A.T 1R**	**H**	**AFC Telford United**	**895**	**L 1 - 2**	**Rowan 90**	
27	20		A	Frickley Athletic	306	D 0 - 0		16
28	26		H	Eastwood Town	1270	L 0 - 1		
29	Jan 3		H	Nantwich Town	987	L 0 - 5		17
30	10		H	FC United	1625	L 0 - 1		17
31	17		A	Whitby Town	301	L 0 - 1		18
32	20		A	Eastwood Town	485	L 0 - 1		
33	24		H	Kendal Town	971	W 1 - 0	King 39	16
34	31		H	Buxton	1008	D 1 - 1	Froggatt 41	18
35	Feb 21		H	Witton Albion	1106	D 0 - 0		19
36	24		A	Cammel Laird	112	D 0 - 0		
37	28		H	Matlock Town	1080	L 0 - 2		20
38	Mar 3		A	Leigh Genesis	93	D 0 - 0		
39	7		A	Kendal Town	182	L 0 - 3		19
40	11		H	Prescot Cables	749	W 5 - 0	Rowan 3 22 MILLER 3 (29 41 51)	
41	14		A	Ashton United	208	L 0 - 3		19
42	16		A	Bradford P.A.	486	D 1 - 1	Miller 75	
43	21		H	Marine	933	W 2 - 1	Miller 18 Elender 61	17
44	28		A	North Ferriby United	437	W 2 - 0	Clarke 49 Millson 60	15
45	April 4		H	Leigh RMI	1212	D 1 - 1	Parker 39	15
46	11		A	Hednesford Town	520	W 1 - 0	Beck 88	14
47	13		H	Ilkeston Town	1100	D 0 - 0		
48	18		A	Ossett Town	286	D 0 - 0		18
49	21		A	Nantwich Town	514	L 0 - 5		
50	25		H	Cammell Laird	1522	W 1 - 0	Froggatt 6 (pen)	16

Average Home Att: **1,101** **Goals** **64 62**

Best Position: 10th **Worst:** 20th

Goalscorers: Ryan 17, Rowan 13, Froggatt 7, Miller 5, Parker 5, Leabon 3, Talbot 3, Clarke 2, Melton 2, Millson 2, Beck 1, Ellender 1, Farrell 1, Haran 1, King 1.

BRADFORD (P.A.)

Founded: 1907 Reformed 1988
Nickname: Avenue

Manager: Lee Sinnott.

Club Colours: Green & white stripes/white/white.

Change: Red & black stripes/red/red.

Best Season: 2nd Football League 2nd Division 1913-1914

Ground address: Horsfall Stadium, Cemetery Rd, Bradford, West Yorks BD6 2NG

Tel No: 01274 604 578

Capacity: 5,000 **Seats:** 1,247 **Covered:** 2,000 **Floodlights:** Yes.

Simple Directions: M62 Jct 26 Along A6036 (Halifax). Then in approx one mile turn left into Cemetery Road (by Kings Head Pub). Ground is 150 yards on left.

Midweek Home Matchday: Monday

Clubhouse: Yes

Club Shop: Yes

CLUB PERSONNEL

Chairman: Dr.John Dean

Additional Directors:
R Blackburn, K Hainsworth,
M Nelson.

Secretary: Steven Burnett.
21, Edward Turner Close,
Low Moor,
Bradford BD12 0AS
Tel: Home/Fax:01274 418092
Mob: 07863 180787

Programme
Editor: Mark Nelson.
Tel: 07904 224 125

CLUB STATISTICS

Record	**Attendance**: 2,100 v Bristol City, FA Cup 1st Round - 2003
Victory:	11-0 v Derby Dale F.A. Cup 1908 **Defeat:** 0-7 v Barnsley 1911
Goalscorer:	Len Shackleton 171 1940-46 **Career Appearances**: Tommy Farr 542 1934-50
Record Transfer Fee	**Paid**: £24,500 to Derby County for Leon Leuty 1950
	Received: £34,000 from Derby County for Kevin Hector 1966
Senior Honours:	Div 2 R-up 1914 3rd Div N Champions 1928 West Riding Senior Cup(9)
	West Riding Co.Cup (2) N.W.Co Champs 94-95 NPl Div 1 Champions 00-01
Previous Leagues	Southern 07-08 Football League 08-70 NPL 70-74 W.Riding Co Am. 88-89
	Central Midlands 89--90 N.W.Co 90-95
Grounds:	Park Avenue 07-73 Valley Parade: 73-74 Manningham Mills 88-89
	Bramley RLFC McLaren Field 85-93 Batley 93-96

BRADFORD PARK AVENUE

BEST LGE ATT.: 1,077 v FC Utd of Manchester
LOWEST: 175 v Prescot Cables

No.	Date	Comp	H/A	Opponents	Att:	Result	Goalscorers	Pos
1	Aug 16	Unibond P.	H	Prescot Cables	175	W 4 - 0	Rudd 30 50 Hall 57 65	
2	19		A	Matlock Town	403	W 4 - 0	Connors 34 Ruffer 40 Hall 54 **Bett** 90	
3	23		A	Hednesford Town	478	L 1 - 3	Hall 59	
4	25		H	Worksop Town	481	D 1 - 1	Connors 64	10
5	30		A	Eastwood Town	420	D 1 - 1	Patterson 38	
6	Sept 1		H	F.C.United	1077	W 2 - 0	Patterson 16 59	7
7	9		A	Frickley Athletic	353	W 4 - 3	Heath 18 (og) Patterson 40 Rudd 60 90	3
8	**13**	**F.A.C 1Q**	**A**	**Bedlington Terriers**	**161**	**W 1 - 0**	**Patterson 12**	
9	20		H	Ilkeston Town	425	L 0 - 1		6
10	24		A	Whitby Town	289	L 0 - 1		
11	**27**	**F.A.C. 2Q**	**A**	**Droylsdon**	**425**	**L 1 - 2**	**Rudd 48**	
12	Oct 4		A	Boston United	1162	W 2 - 1	Hall 21 41	
13	6		H	Frickley Athletic	495	W 1 - 0	Connors 42	
14	11		A	North Ferriby United	326	D 2 - 2	**Bett** 45 Connors 88	5
15	**18**	**F.A.T. 1Q**	**H**	**Clitheroe**	**294**	**L 1 - 2**	**Moseley 80**	
16	22		A	Ilkeston Town	112	D 0 - 0		
17	25		H	Cammell Laird	380	L 1 - 2	**Bett** 49	7
18	27		H	Matlock Town	334	W 3 - 2	Pacey14 (og) Patterson 81 Hall 90	
19	Nov 8		A	Kendal Town	281	L 0 - 5		7
20	11		A	Buxton	117	D 1 - 1	Murphy 82	
21	15		H	Marine	536	W 2 - 0	Hall 10 **Bett** 75	6
22	22		H	WItton Albion	441	L 0 - 2		
23	Dec 6		A	Nantwich Town	603	L 0 - 1		10
24	20		A	Witton Albion	300	W 4 - 1	Patterson 4 75 Holden 31 Hall 47	
25	26		A	Guiseley	729	W 3 - 1	Patterson 7 James 79 **Bett** 90	
26	Jan 1		H	Guiseley	745	D 2 - 2	**Bett** 18 42	
27	3		H	North Ferriby United	391	W 3 - 1	**Bett** 39 (pen) 45 Hall 90	
28	24		H	Eastwood Town	620	L 0 - 2		9
29	31		A	Marine	350	W 4 - 0	Connors 7 Campbell 27 Hall 55 **Bett** 56	7
30	Feb 21		H	Ashton United	349	W 6 - 4	Campbell 13 **BETT** 3 (21 27 41) Hall 75 90	
31	21		A	Prescot Cables	317	D 1 - 1	**Bett** 37 (pen)	6
32	23		A	Ashton United	205	L 1 - 2	**Bett** 37 (pen)	
33	28		H	Hednesford Town	505	W 3 - 0	Campbell 47 59 Hall 87	5
34	Mar 2		H	Buxton	398	W 1 - 0	Whitehouse 4	
35	14		H	Leigh Genesis	469	W 2 - 1	Hall 19 Campbell 20	5
36	16		H	Boston United	486	D 1 - 1	Haran 68	
37	21		A	Cammell Laird	147	W 2 - 1	**Bett** 13 Hall 35	4
38	23		H	Ossett Town	389	W 2 - 0	Campbell 2 **Bett** 16	
39	28		H	Nantwich Town	520	D 0 - 0		4
40	April 1		A	Worksop Town	187	D 1 - 1	**Bett** 20	
41	10		H	Whitby Town	585	W 3 - 1	Davidson 53 Hall 62 James 68	
42	13		A	Ossett Town	356	W 2 - 1	Davidson 4 **Bett** 85	
43	18		H	Kendal Town	679	D 2 - 2	Stamer 45 Haran 90	4
44	21		A	Leigh Genesis	301	L 1 - 2	Haran 81	
45	25		A	F.C.United	3719	D 1 - 1	**Bett** 85	7

Average Home Att: **499** **Goals** **77 55**

Best Position: 3rd **Worst:** 10th

Goalscorers: Bett 20, Hall 17, Patterson 9, Campbell 6, Connors 5, Rudd 5, Haran 3, Davidson 2, James 2, Holden 1, Moseley 1, Murphy 1, Ruffer 1, Stamer 1, Whitehouse 1. Own Goals 2.

BURSCOUGH

Founded: 1946
Nickname: Linnets

Manager: Andy Gray.

Club Colours: Green/green/white.

Change: All pale blue.

Best Season: 8th Conference North, 2007-08.

Ground address: Victoria Park, Bobby Langton Way, Mart Lane, Burscough, Lancashire L40 0SD.

Tel: 01704 893 237

Capacity: 2,500 **Seats:** 270 **Covered:** 1,000 **Floodlights:** Yes.

Simple Directions: M6 Jct 27 follow signs through Parbold A5209, right into Junction Lane (signed Burscough & Martin Mere) to lights, right into A59 to Burscough village. Then second left over canal bridge into Mart Lane to ground. Only 200 yards from Burscough (BR).

Midweek Home Matchday: Tuesday

Clubhouse: Barons Club outside ground.

Club Shop: Yes.

CLUB PERSONNEL

Chief Executive:
Nick Killeen

Additional Directors:
Chris Lloyd, Stuart Heaps.

Secretary: Keith Maguire.
"Fairholme", 218 Bescar Lane, Scarisbrick,
Nr Ormskirk, Lancashire,
L40 9QT
Tel: (H): 01704 880 587
(M): 07970 030 588

CLUB STATISTICS

Record

Attendance: 4,798 v Wigan Athletic F.A. Cup 3rd Qualifying Round 1950-51
Victory: 10-0 V Cromptons Rec 1947 & Nelson 1948-49 both Lancs.Comb.
Defeat: 0-9 v Earltown, Liverpool Co Comb. 1948-49.
Goalscorer in a Game : Louis Bimpson 7
Season: Johnny Vincent - 60 1953-64 **Career**: Wes Bridge - 188
Career Appearances: Not known.

Senior Honours

NWC Div.1 Champions 1982-83. F.A.Trophy Winners 2002-03.
NPL Premier Champions 2006-07.
Liverpool Challenge Cup (3). Liverpool Non-League Senior Cup (2).

PREVIOUS

Leagues: Liverpool Co.Comb. 1946-53. Lancs Comb. 1953-70
Cheshire Co 1970-82. N.W.Co 1982-98. NPL 1998-07. Conf 2007-09.

Back Row left to right, Mal Liptrott (coach), Farrell Kilbane, Neil Fitzhenry, Dominic Morley, Mike Tomlinson, Tony McMillan, Paul Gedman, Ryan Bowen, Mel Singleton(physio). Front Row left to right, Kevin Leadbeater, Joey Dunne (coach), Chris Price (captain), Liam Watson (manager), Steve McEwan, Neil Robinson, Own Rimmer (mascot).
NB: UNFORTUNATELY A RECENT PHOTO WAS NOT AVAILABLE AT THE TIME OF GOING TO PRESS.

BURSCOUGH

BEST LGE ATT.: **1,407** v Stafford Rangers
LOWEST: **201** v Redditch United

No.	Date	Comp	H/A	Opponents	Att:	Result	Goalscorers	Pos
1	Aug 9	BSN	H	King's Lynn	389	D 1 - 1	Evans 72	
2	11		A	Hyde United	303	W 1 - 0	Grogan 21	
3	16		A	Tamworth	609	L 2 - 6	Grogan 36 Smart 86	11
4	23		H	Farsley Celtic	250	D 0 - 0		13
5	25		A	Workington	377	L 1 - 4	Roscoe 77	
6	30		H	Solihull Moors	255	L 1 - 2	Grogan 82	18
7	Sept 2		H	Vauxhall Motors	242	L 0 - 1		
8	6		A	Hucknall Town	279	W 2 - 0	Moogan 11 (pen) Roberts 47	16
9	**9**	**SS N1**	**H**	**Blyth Spartans**	**160**	**L 1 - 4**	**Moogan 53**	
10	13		A	Alfreton Town	307	L 0 - 2		17
11	20		H	Gainsborough Trinity	310	L 0 - 2		19
12	**27**	**F.A.C.2Q**	**A**	**Buxton**	**442**	**L 0 - 1**		
13	Oct 4		A	Hinckley United	470	W 1 - 0	Wade 87	17
14	18		H	AFC Telford United	495	L 0 - 2		18
15	21		A	Fleetwood Town	515	L 1 - 3	Heler 51	
16	2		H	Harrogate Town	350	L 0 - 2		
17	Nov 8		A	Gateshead	334	L 1 - 4	Evans 73	21
18	15		H	Stalybridge Celtic	358	L 0 - 2		21
19	**22**	**F.A.T 3Q**	**H**	**Hinckley United**	**251**	**W 2 - 1**	**Parry 25 Heler 80**	
20	29		A	Redditch United	164	W 2 - 1	Davies 3 Heler 36	20
21	Dec 6		H	Hyde United	362	D 2 - 2	Heler 70 Moogan 78 (pen)	20
22	**16**	**F.A.T 1R**	**A**	**Kidderminster Harriers**	**685**	**L 2 - 3**	**Wade 59 Heler 70**	
23	20		A	King's Lynn	860	D 0 - 0		20
24	26		H	Southport	1133	L 2 - 3	Davies 86 Moogan 90	
25	Jan 17		A	Stafford Rangers	494	W 2 - 0	Moogan 14 (pen) Heler 78	20
26	20		H	Droylsden	270	L 0 - 1		
27	24		H	Hinckley United	331	D 1 - 1	Grogan 90	20
28	27		H	Fleetwood Town	385	D 1 - 1	Heler 90	
29	31		A	Droylsden	295	L 1 - 3	Stepian 64	21
30	Feb 14		H	Gateshead	343	L 2 - 4	Stafford 61 Parry 78	21
31	17		A	Harrogate Town	272	L 0 - 2		
32	21		A	Blyth Spartans	495	W 2 - 0	Davies 1 Parry 28	20
33	24		H	Alfreton Town	233	L 1 - 3	Wilson 43	
34	26		H	Stafford Rangers	1407	W 2 - 0	Davies 46 Wade 57	19
35	Mar 3		A	Gainsborough Trinity	211	W 4 - 0	Wade 19 36 Yates 54 Heler 68	
36	7		A	Vauxhall Motors	225	L 0 - 2		
37	14		H	Redditch United	201	W 1 - 0	Moogan 90	17
38	17		A	Southport	978	L 0 - 3		
39	24		H	Tamworth	309	L 0 - 1		20
40	28		A	Solihull Moors	196	L 2 - 3	Hine 39 Davies 65	
41	April 4		H	Hucknall Town	259	L 2 - 3	Davies 6 Moogan 14 (pen)	20
42	11		A	Farsley Celtic	235	L 1 - 5	Hine 61	21
43	13		H	Workington	274	W 2 - 1	Hine 23 Moogan 31	
44	18		A	Stalybridge Celtic	361	L 0 - 4		Rel.
45	21		A	AFC Telford United	1642	L 0 - 3		
46	25		H	Blyth Spartans	402	L 2 - 3	Wade 27 Yates 77	

Average Home Att: 408 (434) **Goals** 48 89

Best Position: 11th **Worst:** 21st

Goalscorers: Heler 8, Moogan 8, Davies 6, Wade 6, Grogan 4, Hine 3, Parry 3, Evans 2, Yates 2, Roberts 1, Roscoe 1, Smart 1, Stafford 1, Stepian 1, Wilson 1.

Rel. - Relegated.

BUXTON

Founded: 1877
Nickname: The Bucks

Manager: John Reed
Club Colours: All royal blue.
Change: All red.
Best Season - League: 4th Northern Premier League 1980-1981
Ground address: The Silverlands, Buxton, Derbyshire. SK17 6QH
Tel.No: 01298 23197
Capacity: 4,000 **Seats**: 490 **Covered**: 2,500 **Floodlights**: Yes
Simple Directions: FROM STOCKPORT (A6): Turn left at first roundabout, turn right at next roundabout, right at traffic lights (London Road pub) to Buxton Market Place. After two sets of pedestrian lights turn right at Royles shop then turn immediate left and follow road approx 500 metres to ground (opposite police station.) FROM BAKEWELL (A6): Turn left at roundabout on to Dale Road and follow road to traffic lights – then as above. FROM MACCLESFIELD/CONGLETON/LEEK: Follow road to Burbage traffic lights and take right fork in the road at the Duke of York pub (Macclesfield Road.) Then at next traffic lights turn left (London Road pub) and follow as above. FROM ASHBOURNE (A515): Go straight on at first traffic lights (London Road pub) and follow directions as above.
Midweek Home Matchday: Monday
Clubhouse: Open match Days. Available for hire. **Club Shop:** Yes.
Local Radio: High Peak radio
Local Press: Buxton Advertiser

CLUB PERSONNEL

Chairman: Tony Tomlinson.

Additional Directors:
C Brindley, B Goodwin,
J Bainbridge, G Taylor,
D Belfield, T Hoban, S Dakin.

Secretary: Don Roberts.
49 Market Street, Buxton,
Derbyshire SK17 6LF.
Tel: 07967 822 448.

Programme
Editor: Mike Barton.
Tel: 07773 947 869

CLUB STATISTICS

Record Attendance: 6,000 v Barrow F.A. Cup 1st Round 1951-1952
Career Goalscorer:: Mark Reed 116 in 176+19 appearances. (Still playing for the club).
Career Appearances: David Bainbridge 642 (591+51). Retired in 2007.
Record Transfer Fee **Paid**: £5,000 to Hyde United for Gary Walker .
Received: £3,000 from Rotherham United for Ally Pickering.
Senior Honours: Northen Premier League Division One 2006-07 Derbyshire Senior Cup (9). Northern Premier League Cup R-Up 1990-1991 Presidents Cup 1980-81, 06-07, Manchester League 1931-32 Cheshire League 1971-72 R-Up 62-63.
Northern Counties East Champions 2005-06 N.Co.Presidents Cup 2005-06.
Previous Leagues: Combination 1891-99 Manchester League 1899 Northern Premier League. Northern Counties East.

Back Row (L-R): Kay Morgan (Physio), Charlie Cresswell (Goalkeeping Coach), Grant Black, Joe Wilcox, Danny Reet, Scott Hartley, Gregg Anderson, Ryan Pugh, Jon Froggatt, Tommy Agus, Christain Millar, Sam Liversedge, Robert Porter and Tony Hoban (Kit Men).
Front Row: Kieran Lugsden, Scott Maxfield, Michael Towey, John Reed (Manager), Gavin Knight, Neil Stevens, Steve Ridley, Indy Aujla.

BUXTON

BEST LGE ATT.: 2,090 v FC Utd of Manchester
LOWEST: 215 v Kendal Town

No.	Date	Comp	H/A	Opponents	Att:	Result	Goalscorers	Pos
1	Aug 16	Unibond P.	A	Whitby Town	359	W 2 - 0	Towey 21 **Knight** 89	
2	19		H	Ilkeston Town	372	L 0 - 2		
3	23		H	F.C.United	2090	L 0 - 1		17
4	25		A	Ashton United	272	L 1 - 4	Hulme 78	
5	30		H	Cammell Laird	387	W 3 - 0	Jones 11 Towey 14 **Knight** 27	15
6	Sept 2		A	Hednesford Town	462	L 1 - 2	Towey 38	
7	9		H	Witton Albion	314	W 2 - 1	**Knight** 76 85	15
8	**13**	**F.A.C. 1Q**	**H**	**Bootle**	**412**	**W 3 - 1**	**Knight 12 57 Baife 87**	
9	20		A	North Ferriby United	254	L 2 - 4	**Knight** 74 Maxfield 82	11
10	23		H	Boston United	408	L 0 - 1		
11	**27**	**F.A.C. 2Q**	**H**	**Burscough**	**442**	**W 1 - 0**	**Wiggins-Thomas 50**	
12	Oct 4		H	Leigh Genesis	378	D 0 - 0		17
13	7		A	Prescot Cables	213	L 0 - 2		
14	**11**	**F.A.C. 3Q**	**H**	**Blyth Spartans**	**556**	**L 0 - 1**		
15	14		H	Hednesford Town	283	L 0 - 3		
16	**18**	**F.A.T. 1Q**	**H**	**Carlton Town**	**302**	**W 5 - 3**	**Towey 3 Matthews 16 Wood 43 Knight 73 82**	
17	22		A	Worksop Town	233	W 3 - 2	**Knight** 15 84 Ellis 81	
18	25		H	Marine	326	L 0 - 2		17
19	**Nov 1**	**F.A.T. 2Q**	**H**	**Skelmersdale United**	**345**	**L 0 - 1**		
20	4		A	Guiseley	254	W 3 - 1	Towey 45 86 **Knight** 51	
21	8		A	Cammel Laird	175	W 1 - 0	Turley 88	14
22	11		H	Bradford Park Avenue	272	D 1 - 1	Reed 16 (pen)	
23	15		A	Nantwich Town	603	L 2 - 3	Turley 8 McCoughtrie 77	14
24	22		H	Prescot Cables	308	D 2 - 2	**Knight** 45 58	15
25	29		H	Ashton United	281	L 1 - 2	Turley 25	
26	Dec 6		A	Marine	375	L 0 - 2		16
27	13		A	Eastwood Town	530	L 1 - 2	Reed 45 (pen)	17
28	20		H	North Ferriby United	280	W 2 - 1	Wood 85 Towey 87	
29	26		H	Nantwich Town	489	L 0 - 2		
30	Jan 17		A	Ossett Town	202	D 1 - 1	Reed 50	16
31	24		H	WorksopTown	302	W 2 - 0	**Knight** 45 Turley 78	15
32	31		A	Boston United	1008	D 1 - 1	**Knight** 45	
33	Feb 14		A	Witton Albion	380	L 1 - 4	Bowker 61	17
34	21		H	Frickley Athletic	341	D 1 - 1	Stevens 69	17
35	28		A	F.C.United	2158	D 1 - 1	Reed 7	16
36	Mar 2		A	Bradford P.A.	398	L 0 - 1		
37	7		H	Guiseley	302	W 2 - 1	Reed 1 17	17
38	11		A	Matlock Town	413	W 2 - 0	Stevens 30 Towey 53	
39	14		A	Ilkeston Town	554	L 0 - 1		16
40	21		H	Eastwood Town	472	D 0 - 0		16
41	28		H	Ossett Town	302	D 0 - 0		17
42	April 4		A	Frickley Athletic	264	L 0 - 1		19
43	7		H	Kendal Town	215	D 2 - 2	Reed 21 **Knight** 5	
44	11		H	Matlock Town	702	W 4 - 1	REED 3 (10 25 56) Stevens 80	
45	13		A	Leigh Genesis	257	W 7 - 0	**Knight** 23 Bowker 37 Reed 42 61 Turley 48 Anderson 55 Towey 73	
46	18		H	Whitby Town	462	W 3 - 0	M.Reed 48 62 D.Reed 84	13
47	25		A	Kendal Town	521	L 2 - 3	**Knight** 66 Stevens 80	14

Average Home Att: 442 (439) **Goals 65 64**

Best Position: 11th **Worst:** 19th

Goalscorers: Knight 19, Reed 14, Towey 9, Turley 5, Stevens 4, Bowker 2, Wood 2, Anderson 1, Baife 1, Elis 1, Hulme 1, Jones 1, McCoughtrie 1, Matthews 1, Maxfield 1, Reed D 1, Wiggins-Thomas 1.

DURHAM CITY

Founded: 1918
Re-formed: 1949
Nickname: City

Manager: Lee Collings

Club Colours: Yellow/blue/white.

Change: Red & blue stripes/red/blue.

Best Seasons - League: 1st Northern Premier League Division 1 North 2008-09

Ground address: Arnott Stadium, Belmont Industrial Estate, Durham. DH1 1GG

Tel: Office/Fax: 0191 386 9616 (Soccer Arena on non-match days).

Capacity: 2,700 **Seats:** 270 **Covered**: 750 **Floodlights**: Yes

Simple Directions: Leave the A1M at J62 (signed Durham City) At the top of the slip road turn left. After about 1/2 mile bear left (signed Belmont + Dragonville). At the top of the slip road turn left. At traffic lights turn left then take the 2nd left, the stadium is on your right.

Midweek Home Matchday: Tuesday

Clubhouse: Two bars and function rooms.

Club Shop: No

CLUB PERSONNEL

Chairman: Stewart Dawson

Additional Directors:
Gerard O'Connor,
Trevor Cartner,
Richard Rodden,
Austin Carney.

Secretary: Daniel Day
186 Braemar Rd., Roseberry Estate, Billingham, Cleveland. TS23 2AR
Tel: (H/F): 01642 899506
(M): 07882 321 095

CLUB STATISTICS

Record Attendance:	2,750 v Whitley Bay F.A. Vase S-F 2001-02
Career Goalscorer:	Lee Ludlow - 45 in a season.
Career Appearances:	Joe Raine - 552
Record Transfer Fee Paid:	Not known
Record Transfer Fee Received:	Not known
Senior Honours:	Northern League 1994-95, 2007-08. NPL Div.1 North 2008-09.
Previous Leagues:	Victory 1918-19, N.Eastern 1919-21, 1928-38, Football League 1921-28. Wearside 1938-39, 50-51. Northern 1951-2008.
Previous Grounds:	Holiday Park 1921-38, Ferens Park 1949-94 (club disbanded in 1938)

Back Row (L-R): Ritchie Pitt (Ass Man), M.Walton, A.Benjiman, M.Laws, C.Carr, R.Wilkinson, C.Turns, Howarth (not signed) M.Riches, G.Brown, C.Smith, S.Bell, L.Collings (Manager).
Front Row (L-R): N.Bonar, P.Brayson, T.English, S.Capper, S.Elliott, S.Morris, D.Newby, L.Dodds, K.Dixon.

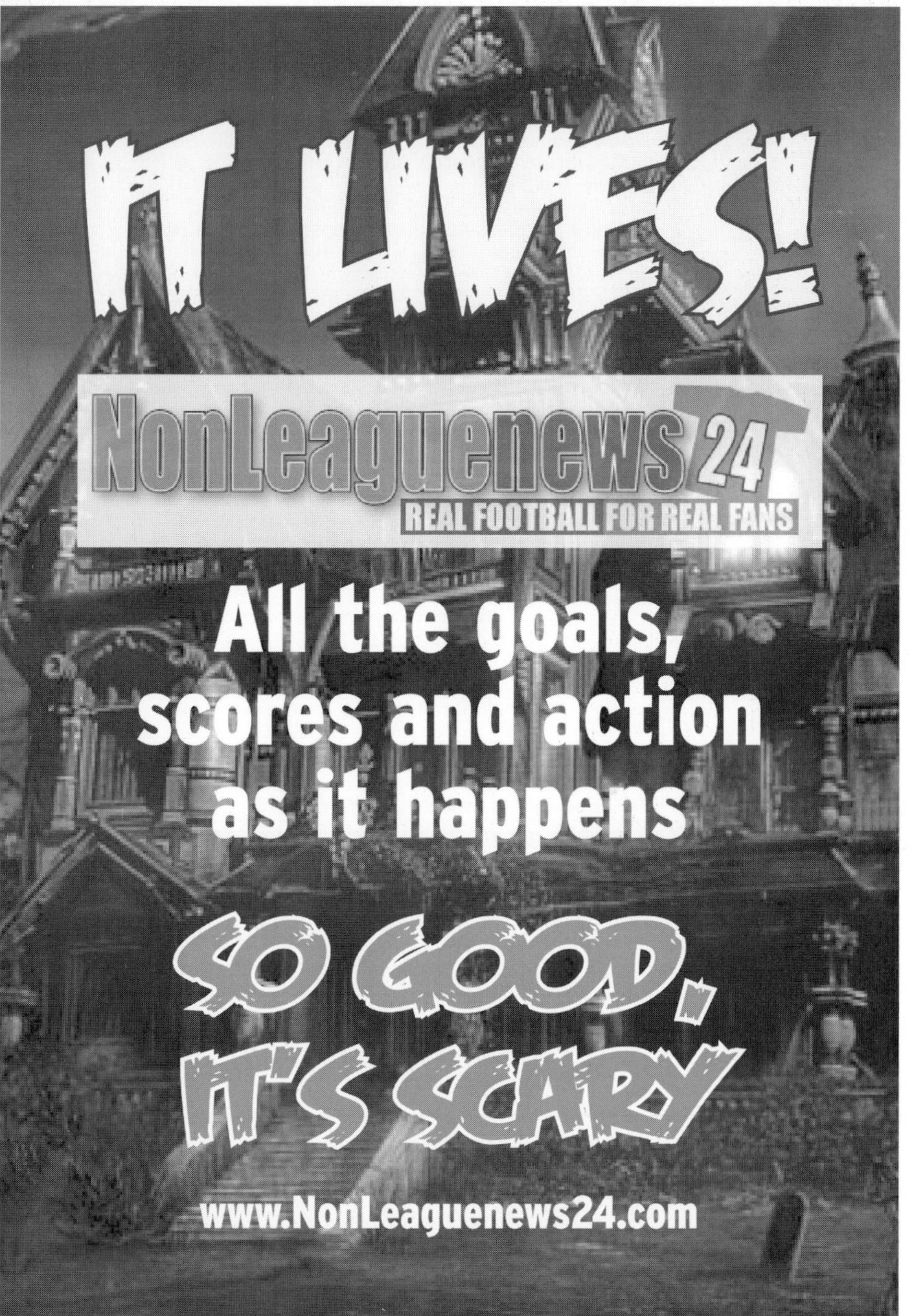
IT LIVES!
NonLeaguenews 24
REAL FOOTBALL FOR REAL FANS
All the goals, scores and action as it happens
SO GOOD, IT'S SCARY
www.NonLeaguenews24.com

F.C. UNITED of MANCHESTER

Founded: 2005
Nickname: F.C.

Manager: Karl Marginson.
Club Colours: Red/white/black.
Change: All blue.
Best Season - League: 6th Northern Premier Premier Division 2008-09
Ground address: Groundsharing with Bury F.C., Gigg Lane, Bury B19 9HR
Tel No: 0161 273 8950 (Office). 0161 764 4881 (Club)
Capacity: 11,669

Simple Directions: All Main Routes: Exit M60 at junction 17 (s/p A56 Whitefield, Salford). At roundabout follow signs to `Whitfield A56, Radcliffe (A665), Bury A56' onto the A56. After 0.3 miles go straight over double traffic lights passing McDonalds on LHS (s/p Bury A56, Radcliffe A665). At lights after 0.8 miles (just after the `Bull's Head' pub) bear right (s/p Bury A56). Straight on at lights after 1.0 miles (s/p Town Centre). After 1.0 miles turn right (s/p Football Ground) into Gigg Lane. Ground is on RHS after 0.1 miles. From North and East (via M66): Exit M66 at junction 2 and follow signs to `Bury A58, Football Ground' onto the A58 Rochdale Road. After 0.5 miles turn left at traffic lights by the Crown Hotel (s/p Football Ground) onto Heywood Street. After 0.4 miles turn right at second mini-roundabout (s/p Football Ground, Manchester, Salford B6219) into Wellington Road. At next mini-roundabout turn left into Market Street. Straight on over mini-roundabout after 0.1 miles and right at T-junction after 0.2 miles into Gigg Lane.

Midweek Home Matchday: Wednesday
Clubhouse: Social facilities available.
Club Shop: Open match days. Online shop: www-fc-utd.co.uk
Local Radio: BBC Manchester.
Local Press: Manchester Evening News, Saturday News Pink

CLUB PERSONNEL

General Manager:
Andy Walsh
Committee: Adam Brown, Alan Hargrave, Martin Morris, Phil Sheeran, Mike Sherrard, Scott Fletcher, John Manning, Ian Robertson, Jules Spencer, Vasco Wackrill, Alison Watt.
Secretary:
Lindsey Robertson.
FC United of Manchester,
Hope Mills, 113 Pollard Street,
Ancoats, Manchester. M4 7JA.
Tel. 0161 273 8950
(F): 0161 273 7598
(M): 07968 903565
Programme Editor: See secretary

CLUB STATISTICS

Record	**Attendance:** 6,023 v Great Harwood Town - 22.04.2006
	Career Goalscorer: Rory Patterson - 99 (2005-08).
	Career Appearances: Simon Carden - 158 - 128 starts 30 sub - (2005-09)
	Record Victory :10-2 v Castleton Gabriels - 10.12.2005.
	Record Defeat: 0-3 v Atherton Collieries - 29.11.2006
	0-3 v Nantwich - 07.02.2009
Senior Honours:	North West Counties Div 2 2005-06 and Div 1 2006-07
Previous Leagues:	North West Counties 2005-07.

Back Row (L to R): Debbie Wilson (U18 physio), Not Known, A Griffiths (assistant kit manager), N Swirad, A Ibrahim, B Deegan, A Tong, S Ashton, G Shenton, T Moses, C Lomax, S Garner, S Carden, J Cottrell, S Rhoades (physio), G Hayden (kit manager).
Front Row: S Williams, C Roca, R King, A Carden, D Warrender, K Lenaghan (goalkeeping coach), R Soule (assistant manager), K Marginson (manager), D Lyons (head of player development), D Brown (first team coach), D Chadwick (club captain), B Morris, D Stott, R Nugent, J Mack.

F.C. UNITED OF MANCHESTER

BEST LGE ATT.: 3,719 v Bradford Park Avenue
LOWEST: 1,550 v Ilkeston Town

No.	Date	Comp	H/A	Opponents	Att:	Result	Goalscorers	Pos
1	Aug 16	Unibond P.	H	Matlock Town	2344	D 3 - 3	**Wilson** 16 (pen) 19 C.Baguley 88	
2	19		A	Cammell Laird	569	L 1 - 2	**Wilson** 20	
3	23		A	Buxton	2090	W 1 - 0	J.Baguley 64	9
4	25		H	Boston United	2825	L 0 - 1		
5	30		H	Whitby Town	2071	W 3 - 1	**WILSON** 3 (13 66 68)	9
6	Sept 1		A	Bradford PA	1077	L 0 - 1		14
7	9		A	Prescott Cables	704	L 3 - 4	**Wilson** 70 79 (pen) C.Baguley 77	17
8	**13**	**F.A.C. 1Q**	**A**	**Nantwich Town**	**1783**	**D 0 - 0**		
9	**17**	**F.A.C. 1Q r**	**H**	**Nantwich Town**	**1012**	**L 3 - 4**	**S.Carden 57 Self 73 Wilson 89**	
10	20		H	Worksop Town	2033	D 0 - 0		17
11	23		A	Ossett Town	544	W 4 - 0	Roca 10 83 **Wilson** 33 85	
12	Oct 4		H	Witton Albion	2201	W 5 - 3	**Wilson** 1 4 C.Baguley 12 40 Wright 66	10
13	15		H	Kendal Town	1801	L 1 - 3	C.Baguley 43	
14	**18**	**F.A.T. 1Q**	**H**	**Radcliffe Borough**	**1227**	**W 1 - 0**	**A.Turner 90**	
15	21		A	Frickley Athletic	840	W 3 - 1	Garner 31 **Wilson** 33 Williams 82	
16	25		A	Whitby Town	1079	D 0 - 0		12
17	29		H	Ilkeston Town	1550	W 3 - 1	**Wilson** 14 Roca 55 81	10
18	**Nov 1**	**F.A.T. 2Q**	**A**	**Worksop Town**	**599**	**W 3 - 0**	**Wilson 13 (pen) 67 Chadwick 49**	
19	12		H	Cammell Laird	1714	D 5 - 5	S.Carden S 20 **Wilson** 23 70 C.Baguley 80 Robinson 89	
20	16		A	Guiseley	1283	D 2 - 2	C.Baguley 5 **Wilson** 84	
21	19		H	Eastwood Town	1636	L 0 - 1		
22	**26**	**F.A.T 3Q**	**H**	**Boston United**	**936**	**L 1 - 3**	**Dieyte 68**	
23	29		H	Hednesford Town	1945	W 3 - 0	**Wilson** 13 70 Wright 85	11
24	Dec 6		A	Eastwood Town	820	L 2 - 4	S.Carden 85 Wilson 90	11
25	20		H	Marine	2122	W 3 - 2	T.Turner 20 C.Baguley 36 Robinson 88	
26	27		A	Ashton United	1561	L 1 - 2	T.Turner 90	
27	Jan 3		A	Worksop Town	443	W 3 - 0	S.Carden 39 T.Turner 68 76	
28	10		A	Boston United	1625	W 1 - 0	**Wilson** 85	11
29	17		H	Prescot Cables	2945	W 2 - 0	S.Carden 45 75	
30	24		A	Witton Albion	1030	L 1 - 2	Whitman 57	10
31	27		A	Leigh Genesis	1302	W 2 - 0	Wright 17 J.Baguley 69	
32	31		H	Guiseley	1986	W 2 - 1	Wright 87 T.Turner 88	5
33	Feb 7		A	Nantwich Town	1547	L 0 - 3		5
34	14		H	Leigh Genesis	1850	L 2 - 4	Chappell 64 Lomax 85	6
35	21		A	Kendal Town	1010	W 2 - 1	Wright 12 S.Carden 28	5
36	28		H	Buxton	2158	D 1 - 1	Tong 52	8
37	Mar 8		A	Matlock Town	1038	L 1 - 2	Roca 9	
38	14		H	Frickley Athletic	1849	W 2 - 0	Warrender 29 S.Carden 44	9
39	17		A	North Ferriby United	376	W 2 - 0	Roca 62 (pen) S.Carden 75	
40	21		A	Hednesford Town	1077	D 2 - 2	A.Carden 65 Garner 90	7
41	25		H	Ashton United	1714	W 4 - 0	ROCA 3 (2 54 (pen) 88) Lomax 34	
42	28		A	Marine	1146	W 3 - 2	S.Carden 33 Lomax 44 61	
43	April 1		H	Ossett Town	1665	W 3 - 2	Marsh 38 Tong 39 S.Carden 66	
44	4		H	North Ferriby United	3120	W 4 - 0	Wright 4 Moses 20 S.Carden 27 Roca 71	4
45	13		H	Nantwich Town	2840	D 0 - 0		
46	18		A	Ilkeston Town	1313	W 1 - 0	Williams 90	3
47	25		H	Bradford PA	3719	D 1 - 1	Tong 8	6

Average Home Att: **2195** **Goals** **90 64**

Best Position: 3rd **Worst:** 17th

Goalscorers: Wilson 24, S.Carden 12, Roca 10, C.Baguley 8, Wright 6, T.Turner 5, Lomax 4, Tong 3, J.Baguley 2, Garner 2, Robinson 2, Williams 2, A.Carden 1, Chadwick 1, Chappell 1, Dieyte 1, Marsh 1, Moses 1, Self 1, A.Turner 1, Warrender 1, Whitman 1.

FRICKLEY ATHLETIC

Founded: 1910
Nickname: The Blues

Manager: Billy Heath

Club Colours: Blue with white trim/blue/blue.

Change: White with black trim/black/black.

Best Seasons - League: Alliance (Conference) Runners-up 1985-86.

Ground address: Tech5 Stadium, Westfield Lane, South Elmsall, Pontefract WF9 2EQ. **Tel No/Fax:** 01977 642 460

Capacity: 2,087 **Seats**: 490 **Covered**: 700 **Floodlights**:Yes

Simple Directions: From A1and A638. Left at Superdrug warehouse, right at T junction and left up Westfield Lane. Left into Oxford Road opposite Westfield Hotel. Ground at bottom on right.

Midweek Home Matchday: Tuesday

Clubhouse: On ground, open matchdays

Club Shop: Yes.

Local Radio: Radio Sheffield, Radio Hallam, Radio Leeds and Ridings F.M.

Local Press: South Yorks Times, Hemsworth & South Elmsall Express.

CLUB PERSONNEL

Chairman: Peter Bywater

Additional Directors:
Gareth Dando,
Steve Shorthouse,
Barry Johnson.

Secretary: Steve Pennock,
3 Kingsley Crescent,
Armthorpe,
Doncaster DN3 3JG
(H) 01302 835 956
(M) 07985 291 074

Programme Editor:
Darren Haynes
Tel: 01924 366 462

CLUB STATISTICS

Record	**Attendance**: 6,500 v Rotherham United F.A. Cup 1st Rd 1971
	Career Goalscorer: K.Whiteley
	Transfer Fee Paid: £1,800
	Transfer Fee Received: £12,500 from Boston United for Paul Shirtliff
	& £12,500 from Northampton Town for Russ Wilcox
Senior Honours:	Alliance Runners-up 1985-86 Midland Co Lg R-up 1972-73
	Hallamshire Senior Cup (10)
Previous Leagues:	Sheffield, Yorkshire 1922-24, Midland Counties, 1924-33, 34-60, 70-76,
	Cheshire Co. 1960-70, NPL 1976-80, and Conference 1980-87
Previous Name:	Frickley Colliery

FRICKLEY ATHLETIC F.C. – 2008/2009 SQUAD

FRICKLEY ATHLETIC

BEST LGE ATT.: 840 v FC Utd of Manchester
LOWEST: 162 v Ashton United

No.	Date	Comp	H/A	Opponents	Att:	Result	Goalscorers	Pos
1	Aug 16	Unibond P.	A	Witton Albion	322	D 1 - 1	Pell 34	
2	19		H	Whitby Town	300	W 1 - 0	**Morris** 50	
3	23		H	Marine	241	D 0 - 0		7
4	25		A	Ilkeston Town	495	L 0 - 1		
5	30		H	Hednesford Town	329	D 0 - 0		14
6	Sept 2		A	North Ferriby United	219	L 1 - 4	**Morris** 75 (pen)	
7	6		A	Leigh Genesis	165	L 0 - 2		17
8	9		H	Cammell Laird	353	L 3 - 4	Towler 1 3 **Morris** 49 (pen)	18
9	**13**	**F.A.C. 1Q**	**H**	**Skelmersdale United**	**240**	**W 1 - 0**	**Walsh 72**	
10	20		A	Kendal Town	191	D 1 - 1	**Morris** 30	20
11	23		H	Eastwood Town	295	D 0 - 0		
12	**27**	**F.A.C. 2Q**	**H**	**Clitheroe**	**271**	**W 1 - 0**	**Jones 61**	
13	Oct 4		H	Cammell Laird	225	D 1 - 1	Groome 89	18
14	6		A	Bradford PA	495	L 0 - 1		
15	**11**	**F.A.C. 3Q**	**A**	**Fleetwood Town**	**722**	**L 0 - 2**		
16	14		A	Whitby Town	249	D 2 - 2	Davies 48 **Morris** 81 (pen)	
17	**19**	**F.A.T 1Q**	**H**	**Nantwich Town**	**187**	**L 0 - 2**		
18	21		H	F.C.United	840	L 1 - 3	Hilton 41	21
19	28		H	Ashton United	162	W 3 - 0	White 9 **Morris** 32 57	18
20	Nov 8		H	Ilkeston Town	226	D 1 - 1	Pell 89	18
21	15		A	Prescott Cables	225	W 2 - 0	Towler 48 56	
22	19		A	Boston United	821	W 3 - 2	**Morris** 8 37 White 24	
23	22		H	Matlock Town	279	W 3 - 1	**Morris** 10 70 White 54	12
24	Dec 6		A	Matlock Town	229	W 2 - 1	Clarke 7 **Morris** 9	12
25	20		A	Boston United	306	D 0 - 0		16
26	26		A	Ossett Town	280	L 0 - 2		
27	Jan 1		H	WorksopTown	408	L 0 - 3		
28	17		A	Hednesford Town	481	L 0 - 1		14
29	24		H	North Ferriby United	230	D 0 - 0		13
30	31		A	Nantwich Town	531	D 2 - 2	Clarke 18 O'Loughlin 57 (og)	
31	Feb 17		H	Guiseley	251	D 2 - 2	White 14 **Morris** 42	
32	21		A	Buxton	341	D 1 - 1	Clarke 35	
33	24		H	Kendal Town	174	W 2 - 1	White 10 Clarke 79	
34	28		A	Marine	293	W 2 - 1	Towler 20 Walsh 31	13
35	Mar 4		A	Worksop Town	174	L 1 - 3	Knox 45	
36	7		H	Witton Albion	284	W 2 - 0	**Morris** 36 Knox 69	
37	14		A	F.C.United	1849	L 0 - 2		13
38	17		A	Guiseley	258	W 3 - 2	Groome 13 Towler 59 70	
39	21		H	Nantwich Town	235	L 0 - 4		13
40	24		H	Leigh Genesis	228	D 0 - 0		
41	28		A	Ashton United	137	W 2 - 0	Knox 58 Towler 85	12
42	April 4		H	Buxton	254	W 1 - 0	Towler 53	12
43	10		H	Ossett Town	470	D 2 - 2	Towler 6 Clarke 19	
44	13		A	Eastwood Town	940	L 2 - 2	Towler 61 Wilburn 78	
45	18		A	Cammell Laird	139	L 0 - 2		12
46	25		H	Prescot Cables	215	W 3 - 1	**Morris** 64 66 Towler 90	11

Average Home Att: 286 (258) **Goals 52 60**

Best Position: 7th **Worst:** 21st

Goalscorers: Morris 16, Towler 12, Clarke 5, White 5, Knox 3, Groome 2, Pell 2, Walsh 2, Davies 1, Hilton 1, Jones 1, Wilburn 1. Own Goals 1.

GUISELEY

Founded: 1909

Manager: Steve Kittrick

Club Colours: White with navy trim/navy/navy.

Change: Yellow/blue/blue.

Best Seasons - League: 3rd Northern Premier Premier Division 1998-99

Ground address: Nethermoor Park, Otley Road, Guiseley, Leeds LS20 8BT

Tel No: 01943 873223 (Office). 01943 872872 (Club)

Capacity: 3,000 **Seats**: 427 **Covered**: 1,040 **Floodlights**: Yes

Simple Directions: From M1(South/East)M1/M621 towards Leeds City Centre continue on M621 to Jct.2 Follow brown Headingley Stadium signs onto A65 (Ilkley). From M62(West) Jct 28 follow airport signs to junction of A65 at Rawdon.Turn left at roundabout onto A65 through to Guiseley centre. Ground a quarter of mile past traffic lights on the right opposite new houses.

Midweek Home Matchday: Tuesday

Clubhouse: Open before and after all games. Tel No: 01943 874 534

Club Shop: Yes, full range.

Local Press: Yorkshire Evening Post, Bradford Telegraph & Argus, Airedale & Wharfdale Observer and Wharfe Valley Times

CLUB PERSONNEL

Chairman: Philip Rogerson

Additional Directors:
Stuart Allen, Gary Douglas,
John Gill, Steve Parkin.

Secretary: Adrian Towers,
58 Manville Road, Keighley,
W. Yorks. BD22 6AT
Tel: 07946 388 739

Programme
Editor: Rachel O'Connor
0113 250 6205

CLUB STATISTICS

RECORD **Attendance:** 2,486 v Bridlington Town F.A. Vase S-F 1st Leg 89-90

Senior Honours:
Northern Premier League Division One Champions 1993-94.
F.A.Vase Winners 1990-91.
Northern Counties East League Champions 1990-91.

Previous Leagues:
West Riding Co.Amateur, West Yorks, Yorkshire 1968-82.
Northern Counties East 1982-91.

Back Row (L-R): Steve Kittrick (Manager), Wayne Benn (Asst Manager), Danny Ellis, Steve Burton, Ryan Crossley, Piotr Skiba, Lee Crooks, Tom Morgan, James Hanson, Danny Husband, Lee Pugh, Mark Whitehouse, Damian Dunne, Jordan Yorath, Martin Stringfellow (Physio).
Front Row: David Brown, Adam Muller, Alex Callery, Bailey Camfield, Dave Merris, Anthony Lloyd, Dean Walters, Brice Tianai, James Cotterill.

GUISELEY

BEST LGE ATT.: **1,283** v FC Utd of Manchester
LOWEST: **240** v Ilkeston Town

No.	Date	Comp	H/A	Opponents	Att:	Result	Goalscorers	Pos
1	Aug 16	Unibond P.	H	Cammell Laird	255	W 2 - 0	Burton 27 (pen) Brown 90	
2	20		A	North Ferriby United	214	W 2 - 1	Lloyd 14 58	
3	23		A	Prescot Cables	186	W 6 - 3	Crossley 29 Crooks 35 Merris 38 Brown 50 Whitehouse 53 54	1
4	25		H	Matlock Town	408	D 1 - 1	Burton 58	
5	30		H	Witton Albion	352	W 2 - 0	Whitehouse 16 63	1
6	Sept 6		A	Boston United	1062	D 2 - 2	Burton 37 Lloyd 66	2
7	**16**	**F.A.C.1Q**	**A**	**Selby Town**	**220**	**W 4 - 0**	**Muller 58 Bambrook 66 Brown 86 Burton 90**	
8	20		H	Eastwood Town	366	W 2 - 1	Burton 16 **Hanson** 67	2
9	**27**	**F.A.C 2Q**	**H**	**Garforth Town**	**447**	**D 2 - 2**	**Merris 31 Hanson 37**	
10	**30**	**F.A.C.2Qr**	**A**	**Garforth Town**	**244**	**W 3 - 1**	**Burton 67 Bown 74 Tiani 82**	
11	Oct 4		A	Ilkeston Town	603	W 1 - 0	Burton 72	3
12	7		A	Matlock Town	275	D 2 - 2	Ellis 14 Taylforth 57	
13	**11**	**F.A.C. 3Q**	**H**	**Sheffield F.C.**	**431**	**D 3 - 3**	**Ovington 11 Brown 19 35**	
14	**15**	**F.A.C.3Qr**	**A**	**Sheffield F.C.**	**451**	**L 1 - 2**	**Burton 60**	
15	**18**	**F.A.T 1Q**	**H**	**Ossett Town**	**272**	**L 0 - 1**		
16	21		H	Whitby Town	289	L 1 - 3	Bolder 83	5
17	25		A	Ossett Town	204	W 4 - 1	Whitehouse 2 Muller 69 Burton 80 Denney 81	5
18	Nov 1		A	Kendal Town	188	W 4 - 1	Denney 13 Burton 39 Whitehouse 60 Bolder 78	4
19	4		H	Buxton	254	L 1 - 3	**Hanson** 72	
20	8		H	Boston United	456	W 3 - 1	Whitehouse 55 Fitzgerald 61 Denney 90	3
21	12		A	Worksop Town	171	W 4 - 0	Callery 12 Bolder32 Ellis 50 Fitzgerald 56 (pen)	
22	16		H	F.C.United	1283	D 2 - 2	**Hanson** 6 Lloyd 90	
23	18		H	Ashton United	244	W 3 - 1	Frost (og) 5 Brown 55 Burton 78	
24	22		A	Marine	289	L 0 - 2		2
25	29		H	Nantwich Town	301	D 2 - 2	Muller 3 Brown 74	2
26	Dec 6		A	Hednesford Town	579	D 2 - 2	Denney 59 Harvey 65 (og)	2
27	20		A	Cammell Laird	112	L 4 - 5	Bambrook 20 Muller 21 Fitzgerald 54 Bolder 87	
28	26		H	Bradford P.A.	729	L 1 - 3	Bambrook 87	
29	1		A	Bradford P.A.	745	D 2 - 2	**Hanson** 10 28	
30	Jan 17		A	Ashton United	157	D 2 - 2	Fitzgerald 35 Bambrook 59	8
31	24		H	Ossett Town	328	L 0 - 1		5
32	31		A	F.C. United	1986	L 1 - 2	Wright 16 (og)	
33	Feb 17		A	Frickley Athletic	251	D 2 - 2	Roddy 9 **Hanson** 11	
34	21		H	Leigh Genesis	292	W 3 - 1	Fitzgerald 7 Cotterill 65 Muller 74	7
35	28		H	Prescot Cables	313	W 4 - 0	Bambrook 58 65 **Hanson** 75 82	
36	Mar 7		A	Buxton	302	L 1 - 2	Bambrook 16	
37	14		H	Kendal Town	290	W 3 - 2	Dovey 21 Crossley 89 **Hanson** 90	8
38	17		H	Frickley Athletic	256	L 2 - 3	**Hanson** 88 Lloyd 89 (pen)	
39	21		A	Leigh Genesis	122	W 4 - 2	Ellis 13 Muller 29 71 Bambrook 87	8
40	24		A	Eastwood Town	577	W 3 - 1	Muller 61 Crossley 73 **Hanson** 87	
41	26		H	Ilkeston Town	240	D 1 - 1	Lloyd 90 (pen)	
42	28		H	Hednesford Town	307	L 1 - 2	**Hanson** 26	8
43	April 4		A	Nantwich Town	672	W 2 - 0	**Hanson** 10 Walshaw 48	8
44	10		H	Worksop Town	338	W 6 - 0	Bolder 2 Muller 27 72 Walshaw 32 Merris 45 Thompson 87	
45	13		A	Whitby Town	404	W 2 - 0	Muller 43 Lloyd 75	
46	18		H	Marine	334	W 4 - 0	Lloyd 19 Walshaw 29 **Hanson** 29 Ellis 90	6
47	21		H	North Ferriby United	357	W 2 - 0	Lloyd 6 (pen) **Hanson** 57	
48	25		A	Witton Albion	380	W 2 - 1	**Hanson** 47 Walshaw 80	4
49	28	Play-Off SF	A	Nantwich Town	930	L 1 - 2*	Muller 70	

Average Home Att **408 (336)** **Goals** **112 71**

Best Position: 1st **Worst:** 8th

Goalscorers: Hanson 17, Muller 12, Burton 11, Lloyd 9, Bambrook 8, Brown 8, Whitehouse 7, Bolder 5, Fitzgerald 5, Denney 4, Ellis 4, Walshaw 4, Crossley 3, Merris 3, Whitehouse 2, Callery 1, Cotterill 1, Crooks 1, Dovey 1, Ovington 1, Roddy 1, Taylforth 1, Thompson 1, Tiani 1. Own Goals 2.

HUCKNALL TOWN

Founded: 1987
Nickname: The Town

Manager: Bryan Chambers.
Club Colours: Yellow & black, black/yellow.
Change: All white.
Best Season - League: 10th Conference North 2004-05.
Ground address: Watnall Road, Hucknall, Notts NG15 6EY
Tel: 0115 963 0206. **Fax:** 0115 963 0716. **Social Club:** 0115 956 1253
Capacity: 3,013 Seats: 500 Covered: 900 Floodlights: Yes
Simple Directions: M1 Jct 27. A608 to lights, right onto A611 to Hucknall. Right at roundabout (new by-pass) over next roundabout and right into Watnall Road at next roundabout. Ground on right.
Midweek Home Matchday: Tuesday
Clubhouse: Open midday and evenings daily.
Club Shop: Yes.
Local Press: Hucknall & Bulwell Dispatch, Nottingham Evening Post and Nottingham Football Post.

CLUB PERSONNEL

Chairman: David Gamble.
Additional Director:
John Coleman (Vice Chairman).
Peter Chapamn,
Glen Lathall, Dave Green.
Secretary: Tony Knowles 55 Stonechurch View, Annesley, Nottinghamshire, NG15 0AZ
(H) 01623 483648
(M) 07801 976175
(B) 0115 844 0451
Programme Editors: Terry Brumpton.
Tel: 07771 802 048

CLUB STATISTICS

Record	**Attendance**: 1,841 v Bishop's Stortford F.A.Trophy S-Final 2004-05
	Victory: 12-1 v Teversal Notts Sen. Cup 89-90
	Defeat: Not known.
	Career Goalscorer: Maurice Palethorpe approx. 400 (1980-90)
	Career Appearances: Dave McCarthy 282 Paul Tomlinson 240
	Transfer Fee Paid: Not known.
	Received: £10,000 from Brentford for Stuart Nelson 2003-2004
Senior Honours	Northern Premier Champions 2003-2004
	Northern Counties East Champions 1997-1998, Lg Cup (3)
	Central Midland Lge 1989-90 1990-91
	Central Midlands League Cup Winners (3) Notts Sen Cup (5)
Previous	**Leagues**: Bulwell & Dist. 1946-59, 60-65. Central Alliance 1959-60.
	Notts Spartan 1965-70. Central Midlands 1989-92.
	Northern Counties East 1992-97. N.P.L. 97-2004. Conference 2004-09.

Back Row (L-R): Rebecca Storer,(assistant physio) Reuben Wiggins-Thomas, Alistair Asher, Curtis Shaw, Russell Cooke, Greg Smith, Liam Hearns, Ben Saunders, Jermaine Hollis, Olivia Waldron (assistant physio).
Front: John Whetton, Paul Dempsey, Danny Mayman, Tony Knowles (kit manager), Chris Timons, Andy Legg (Player Manager), James Cullingworth, Jason Truscott (Head Physio), Danny Bacon, Stephen Akers.

HUCKNALL TOWN

BEST LGE ATT.: **475** v Redditch United
LOWEST: **132** v Vauxhall Motors

No.	Date	Comp	H/A	Opponents	Att:	Result	Goalscorers	Pos
1	Aug 12	BSN	H	Gainsborough Trinity	329	L 1 - 2	Wilson 80	
2	16		H	Stalybridge Celtic	337	L 2 - 3	Kettle 5 **Bacon** 81	21
3	23		A	Harrogate Town	351	D 0 - 0		22
4	25		H	Droylsden	314	D 1 - 1	**Bacon** 24	
5	30		A	Blyth Spartans	404	L 0 - 3		22
6	Sept 2		A	Redditch United	214	D 2 - 2	**Bacon** 32 83	
7	6		H	Burscough	279	L 0 - 2		22
8	**9**	**SS N1**	**H**	**Hinckley United**	**192**	**L 1 - 3**	**Holmes 5**	
9	13		A	Southport	823	L 0 - 3		22
10	16		A	Fleetwood Town	702	W 3 - 1	Wilson 4 51 (pen) Ward 82	
11	20		H	Workington	291	D 0 - 0		22
12	**27**	**F.A.C. 2Q**	**H**	**Cradley Town**	**230**	**W 3 - 0**	**Ricketts 32 Timons 35 Robertson 85**	
13	Oct 4		A	Farsley Celtic	300	L 0 - 4		22
14	**12**	F.A. Cup **3Q**	**A**	**Newcastle Blue Star**	**290**	**L 0 - 4**		
15	18		H	Hinckley United	303	L 1 - 2	**Bacon** 48	22
16	21		A	Stafford Rangers	403	D 0 - 0		
17	25		H	Hyde United	214	L 0 - 1		22
18	Nov 1		A	AFC Telford United	1803	L 1 - 3	Mitchell 21	22
19	8		H	King's Lynn	339	L 1 - 2	**Bacon** 14	
20	15		A	Vauxhall Motors	174	W 3 - 2	O'Brien 7 **Bacon** 29 Shaw30	22
21	**22**	**F.A.T. 3Q**	**A**	**Stourbridge**	**176**	**L 2 - 3**	**Ricketts 13 Bacon 51**	
22	29		H	AFC Telford United	365	L 0 - 5		22
23	Dec 6		A	Hinckley United	417	L 0 - 4		22
24	20		H	Fleetwood Town	271	W 3 - 2	Ricketts 43 Wilson 70 O'Brien 81	22
25	26		A	Alfreton Town	571	L 0 - 5		22
26	Jan 13		H	Alfreton Town	365	D 1 - 1	Ricketts 4	
27	17		A	Tamworth	1132	D 1 - 1	Kettle 49	22
28	20		A	Stalybridge Celtic	336	D 2 - 2	**Bacon** 74 Sucharewycz 90	
29	24		H	Southport	354	D 0 - 0		
30	27		H	Stafford Rangers	241	W 3 - 1	Ricketts 4 Wilson 25 **Bacon** 49	22
31	Feb 14		A	Hyde United	301	L 0 - 2		22
32	21		A	Gateshead	605	L 0 - 1		22
33	24		H	Redditch United	475	L 0 - 2		
34	28		A	King's Lynn	921	D 0 - 0		22
35	Mar 7		H	Solihull Moors	266	L 0 - 2		
36	14		A	Gainsborough Trinity	319	D 2 - 2	Wiggins-Thomas 34 Ricketts 46	22
37	21		H	Tamworth	356	L 2 - 3	Ricketts 24 32	22
38	24		H	Farsley Celtic	139	L 1 - 2	Wilson 19	
39	28		H	Blyth Spartans	239	D 1 - 1	Bonnick 78	22
40	31		H	Vauxhall Motors	132	L 0 - 1		
41	April 4		A	Burscough	259	W 3 - 2	Spriggs 8 Wilson 50 Hawes 90	22
42	6		A	Workington	255	L 0 - 1		
43	11		H	Harrogate Town	222	D 1 - 1	Walters 30	Rel.
44	13		A	Droylsden	307	L 1 - 5	**Bacon** 71	
45	18		A	Solihull Moors	200	L 1 - 3	Bonnick 20	22
46	25		H	Gateshead	347	D 2 - 2	Walters 81 Bonnick 83	22

Average Home Att: **294 (405)** **Goals** **45 92**

Best Position: 20th **Worst:** 14th

Goalscorers: Bacon 11, Ricketts 8, Wilson 7, Kettle 2, O'Brien 2, Bonnick 2, Walters 2, Hawes 1, Holmes 1, Mitchell 1, Robertson 1, Shaw 1, Spriggs 1, Sucharewycz 1, Timons 1, Ward 1, Wiggins-Thomas 1.

Rel. - Relegated.

KENDAL TOWN

Founded: 1919
Nickname: Town

Manager: Lee Ashcroft

Club Colours: Black & White stripes/white/white.

Change: All blue.

Best season - League: 11th Northern Premier Premier Division 2007-08

Ground address: Lakelands Radio Stadium,Parkside Road, Kendal, Cumbria LA9 7BL. Tel: 01539 727 472 / 722 469.

Capacity: 2,490 **Seats**:450 **Covered**: 1000 **Floodlights**: Yes

Simple Directions: M6 Junction 36, via A590/591/A6 to Kendal (South). At first traffic lights turn right, left at roundabout, right into Parkside Road. Ground on right over brow of hill.

Midweek Home Matchday: Tuesday

Club Shop: Yes.

Clubhouse: Open matchdays. Pies and pasties available.

Local Press: Westmorland Gazette & Lancaster Evening Post.

Local Radio: Cumbria, The Bay & Lakeland.

CLUB PERSONNEL

Chairman: David Willan
Additional Directors:
Craig Campbell,
Roy Nicholson,
John Wharton, Steve Dixon,
Graham O'Callaghan,
Meril Tummey, M Sorenson.

Secretary: Craig Campbell,
22 Hawesmead Drive,
Kendall, Cumbria LA 9 5HD
Tel Nos: 01539 722 593 (H)
07980 660 428 (M)

Programme Editor: Meril Tummy.
Tel: 07967 1118339

CLUB STATISTICS

Record	**Attendance:** 5,184 v Grimsby Town F.A. Cup1st Round 1955
	Career Goalscorer:Tom Brownlee
Record Transfer Fee	**Paid**: Undisclosed to Bradford City for Tom Brownlee 1966
	Received: £10,250 from Manchester City for Andy Milner 1995
	Victory: 11-0 v Great Harwood 22.3.47.
	Defeat: 0-10 v Stalybridge Celtic 1.9.84.
Senior Honours:	Westmorland Senior Cup (12) Lancashire Senior Cup: 2002-2003
Previous	**Names:** Netherfield.
	Leagues: Westmorland; North Lancs; Lancs Combination 45-68; Northern Premier 68-83; North West Counties 83-87

Back row (L-R): Chris Dixon (kit man), Paul Byrne, Matt Moss, George Melling, Craig Hobson, David Newnes, Jack Summerfield (physio), Tom Newton, Danny Wisdom, Mark Wane, Matt Bell, Glen Steel, Ben Ashcroft.
Front Row: James Nicholl (goalkeeper coach), Alex Taylor, David Foster, Lee Mulvaney, Ian Kilford (ass manager), Tony Hallam (c), Dave Willan (chairman), Lee Ashcroft (manager), Warren Beattie, Callum Warburton, Kieran Walmsley, Mike O'neil (fitness coach).

KENDAL TOWN

BEST LGE ATT.: **1,010** v FC Utd of Manchester
LOWEST: **130** v Leigh Genesis

No.	Date	Comp	H/A	Opponents	Att:	Result	Goalscorers	Pos
1	Aug 16	Unibond P.	A	Ilkeston Town	393	D 1 - 1	Kilford 35	
2	19		H	Marine	223	L 1 - 2	Murt 59	
3	23		H	Eastwood Town	196	W 2 - 0	A.Taylor 39 Ashcroft 64	8
4	25		A	Whitby Town	302	W 3 - 2	**HOBSON** 3 (3 4 45)	
5	30		A	Nantwich Town	562	L 0 - 4		12
6	Sept 6		A	North Ferriby United	206	W 2 - 1	Moore 10 (og) Osman 22	10
7	9		H	Cammell Laird	188	W 4 - 2	Cole 2 27 Ashcroft 10 Mullvaney	
8	**13**	**F.A.C 1Q**	**A**	**Ashton United**	**118**	**W 3 - 2**	**Taylor 22 Osman 68 Ashcroft 75 (pen)**	
9	20		H	Frickley Athletic	191	D 1 - 1	**Hobson** 80	
10	22		A	Ashton United	150	W 2 - 1	**Hobson** 65 79	
11	**27**	**F.A.C. 2Q**	**H**	**Mossley**	**208**	**L 1 - 2**	**Hobson 54**	**5**
12	Oct 4		A	Worksop Town	161	W 2 - 0	Cole 49 (pen) Taylor 56	
13	11		H	Worksop Town	247	D 0 - 0		4
14	15		A	F.C.United	1801	W 3 - 1	Osman 1 64 Cole 51	
15	**18**	**F.A.T 1Q**	**A**	**Stamford**	**210**	**L 0 - 3**		**4**
16	25		A	Matlock Town	265	D 0 - 0		
17	28		H	Witton Albion	301	W 1 - 0	Ashcroft 31	3
18	Nov 1		H	Guiseley	188	L 1 - 4	**Hobson** 32	2
19	8		H	Bradford PA	281	W 5 - 0	Wordsworth 11 **HOBSON** 3 (47 88 90) Wisdom 84	
20	15		A	Hednesford Town	564	D 3 - 3	Taylor 10 Hallam 12 Osman 22	
21	Dec 13		H	Whitby Town	180	D 3 - 3	Osman 29 90 Cole 78	7
22	20		H	Ossett Town	167	L 2 - 3	Osman 28 **Hobson** 33	
23	26		A	Cammell Laird	161	W 3 - 2	Taylor 58 Osman 60 **Hobson** 90	11
24	Jan 17		H	Matlock Town	192	D 2 - 2	Connerton 43 Osman 83 (pen)	11
25	24		A	Boston United	971	L 0 - 1		
26	27		H	Nantwich Town	130	H 1 - 3	Osman 60 (pen)	11
27	31		A	Ossett Town	133	L 1 - 5	Taylor 15	
28	Feb 14		H	Hednesford Town	205	W 4 - 1	Kilford 37 Taylor 41 44 Wisdom 52	
29	17		A	Leigh Genesis	120	W 2 - 1	Osman 45 **Hobson** 65	10
30	21		H	F.C.United	1010	L 1 - 2	Cole 64 (pen)	
31	24		A	Frickley Athletic	174	L 1 - 2	Cole 45	9
32	31		A	WittonAlbion	293	W 3 - 1	Beattie 61 Taylor 64 Wisdom 75	7
33	Mar 7		H	Boston United	162	W 3 - 0	Taylor 26 87 Cole 34 (pen)	
34	10		H	Leigh Genesis	132	W 2 - 0	Cole 9 **Hobson** 83	7
35	14		A	Guiseley	290	L 2 - 3	Cole 24 (pen) Mulvaney 89	
36	17		H	Prescot Cables	180	W 5 - 1	Wordsworth 14 Cole 35 Taylor 85 Newnes 90 (pen) Osman 90	5
37	21		H	North Ferriby United	201	W 3 - 2	FOSTER 3 (11 14 57)	
38	24		A	Prescot Cables	172	W 1 - 0	Foster 61	5
39	28		A	Eastwood Town	518	D 1 - 1	**Hobson** 54	7
40	April 4		H	Ilkeston Town	262	D 1 - 1	Cole 90	
41	7		A	Buxton	215	D 2 - 2	Taylor 89 Walmsley 90	6
42	10		H	Ashton United	312	W 5 - 1	Cole 23 26 Hallam 60 Foster 64 **Hobson** 78	
43	13		A	Marine	313	W 1 - 0	**Hobson** 71	5
44	18		A	Bradford P.A.	679	D 2 - 2	**Hobson** 81 Osman 89	
45	25		H	Buxton	521	W 3 - 2	Taylor 16 Hallam 26 Wisdom 88	5
46	**28**	**Play-Off SF**	**A**	**Ilkeston Town**	**653**	**L 3 - 4**	**Hallam 2 Foster 43 Taylor 82**	

Average Home Att: **260 (257)** **Goals** **92 74**

Best Position: 2nd **Worst:** 12th

Goalscorers: Hobson 19, Cole 14, Osman 14, Taylor A 14, Foster 6, Ashcroft 4, Hallam 4, Wisdom 4, Connerton 2, Kilford 2, Mulvaney 2, Beattie 1, Murt 1, Newnes 1, Walmsley 1, Wisdom 1, Wordsworth 1. Own Goals 1.

KING'S LYNN

Founded: 1879
Nickname: Linnets

Manager: Carl Heggs.

Club Colours: Yellow/blue/blue.

Change: White/black/black.

Best Season - League: 17th Conference North 2008-09.

Current Ground address: The Walks Stadium, Tennyson Road, King's Lynn PE30 5PB

Tel: 01553 760 060. **Fax:** 01553 762 159

Capacity: 8,200 **Seats:** 1,200 **Covered:** 5,000 **Floodlights:** Yes

Simple Directions: At mini roundabout arriving from A10/A47 take Vancouver Avenue. Ground on left after half a mile

Midweek home matchday: Tuesday

Clubhouse: Normal licensing hours with extensions on matchdays.

Club Shop: Full range of merchandise.

CLUB PERSONNEL

Chairman: Ken Bobbins.

Additional Directors:
T Coates (Vice Chairman)
C Nichols, J Suckling,
N Featherby, S Pomfret,
M Chinn

Secretary: Martin Davis.
Ely Villa, 7 grebe Close,
Sutton Bridge, Spalding
PE12 9RY.
(H) 01406 350 870
(M) 07885 144 039

Programme Editor: See Secretary

CLUB STATISTICS

Record	**Attendance**: 12,937 v Exeter City F.A. Cup 1st Rd.1950-51
	Victory: 17-0 v Beccles 1929-30
	Defeat: 0-11 v Aston Villa F.A. Cup 1905-06
	Goalscorer: Malcolm Lindsey 321
	Career Appearances: Mick Wright 1,152 (British Record)
	Transfer Fee Paid: £5,000 to Halesowen Town for Lyndon Rowland Nov. 99
	Received: £60,000 from Southampton for Mark Paul 1998-99
Senior Honours	Southern League Division One East 2003-04.
	Southern League Cup 2004-05.
Previous	**Name**: Lynn Town.
	Leagues: Norfolk & suffolk, Eastern Cos 1935-39 48 -54 UCL 46-48 Midland Co's 54-58 NPL 80-81.Southern.

KING'S LYNN

BEST LGE ATT.: **1,326** v Hinckley United
LOWEST: **656** v Harrogate Town

No.	Date	Comp	H/A	Opponents	Att:	Result	Goalscorers	Pos
1	Aug 9	BSN	A	Burscough	389	D 1 - 1	Weaver 26	
2	12		H	Redditch United	1168	D 1 - 1	Joachim 41	
3	16		H	Droylsden	1035	D 2 - 2	**Defty** 33 Bloomfield 89	15
4	23		A	Alfreton Town	501	D 1 - 1	**Defty** 54	
5	25		H	Hinckley United	1326	D 1 - 1	Bloomfield 52	
6	30		A	Stalybridge Celtic	489	D 1 - 1	**Defty** 59	14
7	Sept 2		A	Stafford Rangers	476	D 0 - 0		
8	6		H	Fleetwood Town	1143	W 1 - 0	Frew 18	11
1	**9**	**SS N1**	**H**	**Tamworth**	**510**	**L 1 - 2**	**Joachim 78**	
9	13		H	Hyde United	1095	W 4 - 1	**Defty** 6 Camm 36 Frew 84 Bloomfield 90	8
10	20		A	Harrogate Town	548	L 0 - 4		10
11	**27**	**F.A.C. 2Q**	**H**	**Worksop Town**	**1080**	**W 2 - 1**	**France 10 Bloomfield 89**	
12	Oct 4		A	Blyth Spartans	433	W 4 - 2	Peters 29 Frew 33 Turner 59 Mitchell 72	9
13	**11**	**F.A.C. 3Q**	**A**	**Wroxham**	**502**	**W 2 - 0**	**Defty 55 68**	
14	18		H	Farsley Celtic	1121	L 1 - 4	Mitchell 73	13
15	21		H	Tamworth	742	L 1 - 2	Turner 64	
16	**25**	**F.A.C 4Q**	**H**	**Kidderminster Harriers**	**1460**	**L 1 - 5**	**Francis 66**	
17	Nov 1		H	Solihull Moors	970	W 3 - 0	Joachim 35 82 **Defty** 39 (pen)	13
18	8		A	Hucknall Town	339	W 2 - 1	Joachim 53 Graham 79	10
19	15		A	Southport	853	L 1 - 2	Frew 11	12
20	19		A	Gateshead	264	L 2 - 3	Frew 10 16	
21	**22**	**F.A.T 3Q**	**H**	**Stafford Rangers**	**749**	**W 3 - 2**	**Joachim 18 Weaver 42 Thomas 55**	
22	29		H	Stafford Rangers	924	D 2 - 2	Weaver 48 Frew 76	12
23	Dec 6		A	Workington	325	D 1 - 1	**Defty** 70	13
24	**13**	**F.A.T 1R**	**A**	**Workington**	**240**	**L 3 - 4**	**Frew 41 Graham 51 Vipond 68 (og)**	
25	20		H	Burscough	860	D 0 - 0		12
26	26		A	Gainsborough Trinity	526	L 0 - 2		12
27	Jan 1		H	Gainsborough Trinity	1051	D 2 - 2	Graham 8 Francis 30	
28	3		H	King's Lynn	932	D 1 - 1	Graham 85	
29	17		A	Farsley Celtic	309	D 1 - 1	Fisk 77	11
30	24		H	Blyth Spartans	1041	L 2 - 3	**Defty** 62 Joachim 64	14
31	27		A	Tamworth	617	L 0 - 2		
32	31		H	Gateshead	968	W 2 - 0	Hocking 56 (og) Graham 84	14
33	Feb 14		H	Southport	972	D 0 - 0		12
34	21		A	Redditch United	332	W 2 - 1	**Defty** 4 9	11
35	24		H	Harrogate Town	656	L 2 - 3	Frew 62 Francis 67	
36	28		H	Hucknall Town	921	D 0 - 0		12
37	Mar 7		A	AFC Telford United	1990	D 1 - 1	Dwyer 83	13
38	10		A	Solihull Moors	164	D 1 - 1	Thomas 55	
39	14		H	Vauxhall Motors	939	D 1 - 1	Dwyer 30	13
40	21		A	Hyde United	305	W 1 - 0	Fisk 90	13
41	28		H	Stalybridge Celtic	962	W 1 - 0	Joachim 62	13
42	30		A	Droylsden	278	L 0 - 1		
43	April 4		A	Fleetwood Town	909	L 0 - 3		14
44	11		H	Alfreton Town	1007	L 0 - 4		14
45	13		A	Hinckley United	397	L 0 - 1		
46	18		H	Workington	884	L 1 - 3	**Defty** 81	16
47	25		A	Vauxhall Motors	174	W 3 - 1	Smith 2 **Defty** 42 Kelly 75	17

Average Home Att: **1038 (1148)** **Goals** **61 72**

Best Position: 8th **Worst:** 17th

Goalscorers: Defty 13, Frew 9, Joachim 8, Graham 5, Bloomfield 4, Francis 3, Thomas 3, Weaver 3, Fisk 2, Mitchell 2, Turner 2, Camm 1, Dwyer 1, France 1, Kelly 1. Own Goals 2.

MARINE

Founded: 1894
Nickname: Mariners

Manager: Kevin Lynch.

Club Colours: White/black/black.

Change: Yellow/green/green.

Best Seasons - League: 1st Northern Premier Premier Division 1993-94, 1994-95

Ground address: Arriva Stadium, College Road, Crosby, Liverpool L23 3AS

Tel/Fax No: 0151 924 1743

Capacity: 3,185 **Seats**: 400 **Covered**: 1,400 **Floodlights**:Yes)

Simple Directions: College Road is off A565 (Liverpool-Southport road) in Crosby. Ground is ten minutes walk from Crosby & Blundellsands (Mersey Rail).**Bus**: No 92

Midweek Home Matchday: Tuesday

Clubhouse: Open daily with concert hall (250 seats) and members lounge (100).

Club Shop: Full range of products.

CLUB PERSONNEL

Chairman: Paul Leary.
Additional Directors:
David Wotherspoon (President), Brian Lawlor (Vice Chairman), John Wildman (Hon Secretary), Geoff Kewley & Mark Prescott (Hon Treasurers), Dave Rannard, Richard Cross, Paul Eustace, John Hall, Peter McCormack, Dave McMillan.

Secretary: John Wildman,
4 Ashbourne Avenue,
Blundell-sands, Liverpool.
L23 8TX
Tel No: (H) 0151 924 5248

Programme Editor: Dave Rannard
Tel No: 0151 474 9848

CLUB STATISTICS

Record	**Attendance**: 4,000 v Nigeria Friendly 1949
Victory:	14-0 v Sandhurst, FA Cup 1st Qual., 01.10.1938.
Defeat:	2-11 v Shrewsbury Town F.A. Cup 1st Rd 1995
Goalscorer:	Paul Meachin 200
Career Appearances:	Peter Smith 952
Record Transfer Fee	**Paid**: £6,000 to Southport for Jon Penman Oct.1985
	Received: £20,000 from Crewe Alexandra for Richard Norris 1996
Senior Honours:	F.A.Amateur Cup R-up 31-32, NPL Champions 93-94 94-95 R-Up 85-86 91-92, Lancashire Trophy: (3), Lancashire Junior Cup 78-79, Lancs Amateur Cup (5), Lancs Sen Cup (6), Liverpool Non-Lg Cup (3) and Liverpool Challenge Cup (3)
Previous Leagues	Liverpool Zingari, Liverpool Co.Comb, Lancs. Comb.35-39 46-69 Cheshire Co.69-79.
Previous Ground:	Waterloo Park (1894-1903).

Front Row (Left to Right): Peter McShane, Kieran Molyneux, Stephen Johnson, Jame Rainford, Lee Parle, Steve Hussey, Kevin Lynch (Manager), James Olsen, Tom Grice, Neil Prince, Wayne McDermott, Neil Black
Middle Row (Left to Right): Gary Dobson (Physio), Phil Brazier (Assistant Manager), Ian Latham, Anthony Lipson, Stephen Brown, Joe Fowler, Kevin Atherton, Sean Lake, John Shaw, Michael Jackson, Tony Davies, Joe McMahon, Joe Doyle, Peter Cumiskey (Player/Coach), Tony Abbott (Coach), Neil Coomber (Physio), Barry Simms (Fitness Coach)
Back Row: (Left to Right): Geoff Kewley, Mark Prescott, Dave Rannard, John Wildman (Secretary), Dave McMillan, Brian Lawlor (Vice Chairman), Paul Leary (Chairman), Richard Cross, Paul Eustace.

MARINE

BEST LGE ATT.: **1,146** v FC Utd of Manchester
LOWEST: **210** v Eastwood Town

No.	Date	Comp	H/A	Opponents	Att:	Result	Goalscorers	Pos
1	Aug 16	Unibond P.	H	Worksop Town	304	W 6 - 2	**Cumiskey** 1 Brookfield 6 Walcott 49 Atherton 57 Lynch 72 McNichols 88	
2	19		A	Kendal Town	223	W 2 - 1	**Cumiskey** 26 Atheryon 68	
3	23		A	Frickley Athletic	241	D 0 - 0		2
4	25		H	Cammell Laird	460	D 0 - 0		
5	30		A	Ossett Town	118	W 5 - 4	Woolcroft 22 Artherton 34 79 Parle 50 Tuck 90	
6	Sept 2		H	Nantwich Town	305	D 0 - 0		
7	6		H	Ilkeston Town	293	L 0 - 2		5
8	8		A	Ashton United	160	L 0 - 2		10
9	**13**	**F.A.C. 1Q**	**H**	**Worksop Town**	**295**	**L 1 - 5**	**McMahon 22**	
10	20		A	Witton Albion	327	W 3 - 1	Bigland 53 82 Tuck 90	
11	23		H	Leigh Genesis	252	L 0 - 1		
12	Oct 4		H	Matlock Town	330	W 2 - 1	Hussey 37 O'Donnell 74	6
13	7		A	Nantwich Town	540	W 3 - 0	O'Donnell 39 **Cumiskey** 81 90	
14	11		H	Marine	322	D 1 - 1	O'Donnell 34	
15	14		H	Boston United	224	W 3 - 1	Hussey 29 (pen) Lawless 41 O'Donnell 90	
16	**18**	**F.A.T 1Q**	**A**	**Brigg Town**	**131**	**W 5 - 1**	**Arnold 21 Lynch 30 McMahon 45 81 Lawless 84**	
17	25		A	Buxton	326	W 2 - 0	O'Donnell 17 Hussey 90	2
18	28		A	Leigh Genesis	129	D 0 - 0		
19	**Nov 1**	**F.A.T. 2Q**	**H**	**Durham City**	**206**	**L 1 - 2**	**Cumiskey 74**	
20	8		H	Whitby Town	336	D 2 - 2	Hussey 44 (pen) Lawless 53	4
21	15		A	Bradford PA	536	L 0 - 2		5
22	22		H	Guiseley	289	W 2 - 0	Lawless 55 Tuck 90	3
23	29		A	North Ferriby United	178	W 2 - 1	Adam 43 Tomlinson 71	3
24	Dec 6		H	Buxton	375	W 2 - 0	Tuck 18 Lawless 76	3
25	20		A	F.C.United	2122	L 2 - 3	**Cumiskey** 35 (pen) 52	4
26	26		H	Prescot Cables	360	L 3 - 6	Lawless 20 Brazier 51 78	
27	Jan 17		H	Witton Albion	413	L 0 - 2		7
28	24		A	Hednesford Town	502	W 2 - 1	Hussey 40 (pen) 74	4
29	31		H	Bradford PA	350	L 0 - 4		8
30	Feb 17		H	Ossett Town	225	W 2 - 1	Brookfield 19 **Cumiskey** 39	9
31	24		H	Frickley Athletic	281	L 1 - 2	Tuck 33	10
32	Mar 7		A	Whitby Town	281	L 0 - 2		11
33	9		A	Eastwood Town	438	L 0 - 4		
34	14		H	Hednesford Town	273	L 0 - 3		11
35	17		H	Eastwood Town	210	L 1 - 2	**Cumiskey** 19	
36	21		A	Boston United	933	L 1 - 2	Doyle 5	12
37	25		A	Worksop Town	171	L 0 - 1		
38	28		H	F.C.United	1146	L 2 - 3	**Cumiskey** 35 McDermott 36	13
39	31		A	Prescot Cables	259	W 2 - 1	**Cumiskey** 37 Davies 90	
40	April 4		A	Matlock Town	283	L 0 - 4		13
41	10		A	Cammell Laird	252	L 2 - 3	Farley 15 O'Donnell 55	13
42	13		H	Kendal Town	313	L 0 - 1		14
43	18		A	Guiseley	334	L 0 - 4		
44	21		A	Ilkeston Town	341	L 0 - 5		
45	25		H	North Ferriby United	408	W 1 - 0	**Cumiskey** 82	

Average Home Att: 356 (332) **Goals** 61 83

Best Position: 2nd **Worst:** 14th

Goalscorers: Cumiskey 12, Hussey 6, O'Donnell 6, Lawless 6, Tuck 5, Atherton 4, McMahon 3, Bigland 2, Brazier 2, Brookfield 2, Lynch 2, Adam 1, Arnold 1, Davies 1, Doyle 1, Farley 1, McDermott 1, McNichols 1, Parle 1, Tomlinson 1, Walcott 1, Woolcroft 1.

MATLOCK TOWN

Founded: 1885
Nickname: The Gladiators

Manager: Mark Atkins

Club Colours: All Royal Blue.

Change: All yellow.

Best Seasons - League: 2nd Northern Premier Premier Division 1983-84

Ground address: Causeway Lane, Matlock, Derbyshire DE4 3AR

Tel No & Fax: 01629 583 866

Capacity: 5,500 **Seats:** 560 **Covered:** 1,200 **Floodlights**: Yes

Simple Directions: On A615, ground is 500 yds from town centre and Matlock (BR)

Midweek Home Matchday: Tuesday

Clubhouse: Gladiators Social Club on ground.

Club Shop: Yes.

CLUB PERSONNEL

Chairman: Tom Wright
Additional Directors:
S Baker, P Bates, J Beaumont, KF Brown, S Else, Mrs C Else, P Eyre, S Greenhough, D Reynolds, I Richardson, A Smith, GM Tomlinson, Mrs LH West, T Weston.
Secretary: Keith Brown
1 Malvern Gardens, Matlock, Derbys. DE4 3JH
Tel No: 01629 584 231 (H)
07831 311 427 (M)
Programme Editor:
Mike Tomlinson
Tel No: 01629 583 763

CLUB STATISTICS

Record	**Attendance**: 5,123 v Burton Albion F.A. Trophy 1975
	Victory: 10-0 v Lancaster City (A) 1974
	Defeat: 0-8 v Chorley (A) 1971
	Goalscorer: Peter Scott
	Career Appearances: Mick Fenoughty
	Transfer Fee Paid: £2,000 for Kenny Clark 1996
	Received: £10,000 from York City for Ian Helliwell
Senior Honours:	F.A. Trophy Winners 1974-75 NPL R-up 83-84 Div1 R-up 03-04 Derbys.Senior Cup (7) R-up (10) Anglo Italian Non-League Cup 1979
Previous Leagues	Mid.Co 1894-96, Matlock & Dist., Derbys.Sen , Central Alliance 24-25 47-61, Central Comb. 34-35, Chesterfield & Dist. 46-47 & Midland Counties 61-69

MATLOCK TOWN

BEST LGE ATT.: **1,036** v FC Utd of Manchester
LOWEST: **210** v Ossett Town

No.	Date	Comp	H/A	Opponents	Att:	Result	Goalscorers	Pos
1	Aug 16	Unibond P.	A	F.C.United	234	D 3 - 3	**Hannah** 7 40 Cropper 69	
2	19		H	Bradford P A	403	L 0 - 4		
3	23		H	Whitby Town	263	W 2 - 0	**Hannah** 72 80 (pen)	12
4	25		A	Guiseley	408	D 1 - 1	Cropper 55	
5	30		A	Ashton United	152	L 2 - 3	Warne 63 **Hannah** 90	16
6	Sept 2		H	Eastwood Town	410	D 1 - 1	**Hannah** 35	
7	10		A	Worksop Town	230	W 1 - 0	Barraclough 89 (pen)	15
8	**13**	**F.A.C. 1Q**	**A**	**Ilkeston Town**	**495**	**L 1 - 4**	**Warne 26**	
9	20		H	Boston United	499	L 0 - 2		15
10	23		A	Hednesford Town	373	L 0 - 4		
11	27		H	Cammell Laird	259	W 2 - 0	Barraclough 10 Cropper 90	
12	Oct 4		A	Marine	330	L 1 - 2	Williams 66 (og)	15
13	7		H	Guiseley	275	D 2 - 2	Cropper 8 47	
14	11		A	Ossett Town	169	L 2 - 3	Barraclough 22 Cropper 83	
15	14		H	North Ferriby United	220	W 3 - 2	**Hannah** 5 61 Pacey 40	
16	**18**	**F.A.T.1Q**	**H**	**Warrington Town**	**242**	**L 0 - 1**		
17	25		H	Kendal Town	265	D 0 - 0		14
18	27		A	Bradford PA	334	L 2 - 3	**Hannah** 53 Cropper 56	
19	Nov 1		H	Prescot Cables	267	D 2 - 2	**Hannah** 68 (pen) 71 (pen)	14
20	8		H	Nantwich Town	294	L 2 - 3	Cropper 53 **Hannah** 61	15
21	11		A	North Ferriby United	181	L 3 - 6	Donnelly-Jackson 50 72 Barraclough 75	
22	15		H	Ossett Town	210	L 1 - 3	Barraclough 39	16
23	22		A	Frickley Athletic	279	L 1 - 3	Cropper 64	18
24	29		H	Worksop Town	249	D 2 - 2	Donnelly-Jackson 75 76	18
25	Dec 6		H	Frickley Athletic	229	L 1 - 2	Barraclough 35	19
26	13		A	Prescot Cables	184	D 2 - 2	King 6 Cropper 90	19
27	26		A	Ilkeston Town	779	D 2 - 2	**Hannah** 45(pen) 56 (pen)	
28	Jan 17		A	Kendal Town	192	D 2 - 2	Warne 35 55	21
29	24		A	Leigh Genesis	302	W 5 - 0	Donnelly-Jackson 20 Flint 28 Benger 37 63 Cropper 50	19
30	14		H	Ilkeston Town	415	D 1 - 1	Featherstone 7	
31	Feb 21		A	Whitby Town	266	L 0 - 2		20
32	28		A	Boston United	1060	W 2 - 0	Cropper 68 Donnelly Jackson 76	
33	Mar 3		A	Witton Albion	234	L 0 - 2		
34	8		H	F.C.United	1036	W 2 - 1	Cropper 35 Donnelly-Jackson 90	
35	11		A	Buxton	413	L 0 - 2		
36	14		A	Nantwich Town	763	D 1 - 1	Featherstone 38	20
37	21		H	Witton Albion	330	W 1 - 0	Davidson 45	19
38	28		A	Cammell Laird	121	D 2 - 2	Donnelly-Jackson 45 **Hannah** 58	16
39	April 4		H	Marine	283	W 4 - 0	DAVIDSON 3 (10 38 82 pen) Clarke 85	16
40	7		A	Eastwood Town	648	L 0 - 1		
41	10		A	Buxton	702	L 1 - 4	Wood 82	20
42	13		H	Hednesford Town	486	W 2 - 0	**Hannah** 12 Donnelly-Jackson 64	
43	18		A	Leigh Genesis	105	W 2 - 0	**Hannah** 42 Wood 74	17
44	25		H	Ashton United	365	W 2 - 1	Warne 68 Benger 85	15

Average Home Att: 322 (293) **Goals** 66 79

Best Position: 12th **Worst:** 21st

Goalscorers: Hannah 17, Cropper 13, Donnelly-Jackson 9, Barraclough 6, Warne 5, Davidson 4, Benger 3, Featherstone 2, Pacey 2, Wood 2, Clarke 1, Flint 1, King 1. Own Goals 1.

NANTWICH TOWN

Founded: 1884
Nickname: 'Dabbers'

Manager: Steve Davis

Club Colours: All Green.

Change: Red & white/red/red.

Best Season - League: 3rd Northern Premier Premier 2008-09.

Ground address: Weaver Stadium, Waterlode, Kingsley Fields, Nantwich, Cheshire. CW5 5BS. Tel: 01270 621 771.

Capacity: 3500 **Seats:** 350 **Covered standing:** 495 **Floodlights:** Yes

Simple Directions: M6 Jct 16 .A500 for Natwich (about 8 miles) continue on A52 pver railway crossing, then second right into Jackson Avenue. From Chester use A51. Three miles from Crewe B.R.

Midweek Home Matchday: Tuesday

Clubhouse: Open Matchdays **Club Shop:** Yes. Contact: Sarah Laws

Local Radio: BBC Radio Stoke, Signal Radio.

Local Press: Nantwich Chronicle, Nantwich Guardian, The Sentinel.

CLUB PERSONNEL

Chairman: Clive Jackson

Additional Directors:
A Pye, N Clarke, P Temmin, C Jackson, J Brydon, J Morris, R Melling, R Tilley, E Beeson, B Lycett.

Secretary: Bernard Lycett.
Rivington, Clay Lane,
Haslington. CW1 5SE
Tel: (H/F): 01270 584 066
(B): 01782 425 590
(M) 07876 230 280

Programme Editor: Neil Southern
Tel: 01270 621 771

CLUB STATISTICS

Record
Attendance: 5,121 v Winsford United, Cheshire Senior Cup 2nd Rd 1920-21
Career Goalscorer: Bobby Jones 60 . In Season: Gerry Duffy 42 in 1961-62
Record Transfer Fee Received: £4,000 from Stafford Rangers for D.Dawson
Record Victory: 15-0 v Ashton United , Manchester League 1966-67
Record Defeat: 0-12 v Chirk F.A.Cup 2nd Qualifying Round 1889-90

Senior Honours: F.A. Vase 2005-06. Cheshire Senior Cup 1975-1976 and Runners-Up (5)

Previous Leagues: 1891-92 Shropshire & Dist League, 1892-94 The Combination, 1894-95 Cheshire Junior League, 1895-97 Crewe & Dist Junior League, 1897-1900 North Staffordshire & Dist League, 1900-01 Cheshire League, 1901-10 The Combination, 1910-12 Manchester League, 1912-14 Lancashire Combination, 1919-38 Cheshire County League, 1938-39 Crewe & Dist League, 1946-47 Crewe Amateur Combination, 1947-48 Crewe & Dist League, 1948-65 Mid-Cheshire League, 1965-68 Manchester League Division One, 1968-82 Cheshire County League, 1982-2007 North West Counties

Back Row (L-R): L-R. Michelle Pennell (Physio). Dave Walker. Michael Lennon. Alan Naggington. Charlie O'Loughlin. Glyn Blackhurst. Lee Jones (G/K). Liam Shotton. Nick Linford. Darren Tinson. Peter Heler. Gyorgy Kiss. Nathan Southern. Paul Kelly (Physio).
Front Row: Dave Tickle. Andy Taylor. Ryan Green. Richard Smith. Phil Parkinson (Captain). Steve Davis (Head Coach). Peter Hall (Assistant Head Coach). Danny Griggs. Adam Beasley. Robin Gibson. Ashley Carter. Rob Hawthorne.
Not included due to unavailability: Dave Whittaker. Mark Beeston. Omar Mamood.

NANTWICH TOWN

BEST LGE ATT.: **1,547** v FC Utd of Manchester
LOWEST: **355** v Ossett Town

No.	Date	Comp	H/A	Opponents	Att:	Result	Goalscorers	Pos
1	Aug 16	Unibond P.	A	Hednesford Town	468	L 0 - 2		
2	23		A	Worksop Town	181	W 4 - 0	Tickle 3 LENNON 3 (21 72 76 pen)	14
3	25		H	Prescot Cables	694	W 3 - 2	Shotton 1 43 Gibson 53	
4	30		H	Kendal Town	562	W 4 - 0	Blackhurst 2 Shotton 20 Heler 28 Walker 85	6
5	Sept 2		A	Marine	305	D 0 - 0		
6	6		A	Whitby Town	302	D 0 - 0		8
7	9		H	Leigh Genesis	547	D 1 - 1	Blackhurst 75	8
8	**13**	**F.A.C.1Q**	**H**	**F.C. United**	**1783**	**D 0 - 0**		
9	**17**	**F.A.C.1Qr**	**A**	**F.C. United**	**1012**	**W 4 - 3**	**WALKER 3 (9 47 68pen) O'Loughlin 49**	
10	20		A	Ossett Town	170	L 1 - 2	Blackhurst 34	11
11	**27**	**F.A.C. 2Q**	**H**	**F.C. Halifax Town**	**1091**	**W 4 - 1**	**Naggington 16 Blackhurst 57 Walker 68 (pen) 85**	
12	Oct 4		A	Eastwood Town	345	L 1 - 3	Naggington 45	14
13	7		H	Marine	540	L 0 - 3		
14	**11**	**F.A.C. 3Q**	**A**	**Whitley Bay**	**749**	**W 5 - 1**	**LENNON 4 (12 65 73 78) Griggs 85**	
15	13		A	Ashton United	188	W 1 - 0	Walker 30	12
16	**18**	**F.A.T 1Q**	**A**	**Frickley Athletic**	**187**	**W 2 - 0**	**Griggs 4 Whittaker 78**	
17	21		H	Witton Albion	612	W 2 - 0	Walker 8 Naggington 86	
18	**25**	**F.A.C. 4Q**	**A**	**Fleetwood Town**	**874**	**L 3 - 4**	**Lennon 20 Carter 45 Walker 60 (pen)**	
19	28		A	Prescot Cables	172	L 0 - 2		13
20	**Nov 1**	**F.A.T. 2Q**	**A**	**Rugby Town**	**238**	**W 3 - 1**	**Walker 14 Carter 44 50**	
21	4		H	Ossett Town	355	W 2 - 0	Carter 16 Walker 60	
22	8		A	Matlock Town	294	W 3 - 2	Griggs 36 **Lennon** 47 69	8
23	15		H	Buxton	603	W 3 - 2	Whittaker 70 Griggs 72 Gibson 81	9
24	**22**	**F.A.T. 3Q**	**A**	**Warrington Town**	**232**	**W 1 - 0**	**Blackhurst 25**	
25	29		A	Guiseley	301	D 2 - 2	**Lennon** 7 Whiitaker 45	10
26	Dec 6		H	Bradford PA	603	W 1 - 0	Walker 90	9
27	**16**	**F.A.T.1R**	**A**	**Hednesford Town**	**264**	**L 2 - 3**	**Whittaker 27 Comes (og) 50**	
28	20		H	Eastwood Town	692	D 2 - 2	Carter 50 **Lennon** 75	9
29	26		A	Buxton	489	W 2 - 0	Walker 12 **Lennon** 78	
30	Jan 1		H	Cammell Laird	932	L 0 - 1		
31	3		A	Boston United	987	W 5 - 0	Carter 65 **LENNON** 3 (81 87 90) Walker 90	6
32	17		A	Ilkeston Town	396	L 2 - 3	McPherson 38 **Lennon** 83	10
33	24		H	Whitby Town	603	W 3 - 1	**Lennon** 34 Walker 35 65	6
34	27		A	Kendal Town	130	W 3 - 1	**Lennon** 41 Walker 43 MacPherson 53	
35	31		H	Frickley Town	531	D 2 - 2	Walker 11 **Lennon** 85	4
36	Feb 7		H	FC United	1547	W 3 - 0	**Lennon** 13 (pen) 86 Carter 60	3
37	14		A	Cammell Laird	202	W 1 - 0	Carter 26	3
38	21		H	Ashton United	578	W 3 - 1	Whittaker 25 McPherson 85 Walker 88	2
39	28		H	North Ferriby United	750	W 4 - 0	**Lennon** 5 Whittaker 16 56 MacPherson 83	
40	Mar 14		H	Matlock Town	783	D 1 - 1	Whittaker 5	2
41	17		A	Leigh Genesis	100	W 8 - 0	**Lennon** 3 43 O'Loughlin 20 McPherson 21 Gibson 59 Heald 62 (og) Walker 65 Kinsey 89	
42	21		A	Frickley Athletic	235	W 4 - 0	Walker 40 (pen) **Lennon** 42 50 Whittaker 72	2
43	28		A	Bradford P.A.	520	D 0 - 0		3
44	31		A	Witton Albion	401	W 2 - 0	Carter 47 **Lennon** 51	
45	April 4		H	Guiseley	672	L 0 - 2		3
46	7		H	Hednesford Town	490	L 1 - 3	Marshall 84 (og)	3
47	13		A	F.C.United	2840	D 0 - 0		
48	15		H	Ilkeston Town	537	L 0 - 1		
49	18		A	North Ferriby United	184	D 1 - 1	Carter 29	7
50	21		H	Boston United	514	W 5 - 0	Walker 32 46 **Lennon** 9 55 Kinsey 90	
51	25		H	Worksop Town	794	W 3 - 1	Walker 15 (pen) **Lennon** 34 90	3
52	28	Play-Off SF	H	Guiseley	930	W 2 - 1*	**Lennon** Walker 113	
53	May 2	Play-Off F.	A	Ilkeston Town	1784	L 1 - 2	**Lennon** 31	

Average Home Att: **664** **Goals** **110 57**

Best Position: 2nd **Worst:** 14th

Goalscorers: Lennon 34, Walker 25, Carter 10, Whittaker 9, Blackhurst 5, Griggs 5, McPherson 4, Gibson 3, Naggington 3, Shotton 3, Kinsey 2, O'Loughlin 2, Heler 1, Tickle 1. Own Goals 3.

NORTH FERRIBY UNITED

Founded: 1934
Nickname: United

Manager: Neil Allison.

Club Colours: Green/white/green.

Change: Yellow/black/yellow.

Best Seasons: League: 5th Northern Premier League 2005-2006

Ground address: Grange Lane, Church Road, N.Ferriby, East Yorks.HU14 3AA

Tel/Fax No: 01482 634 601. Club: 01482 633 089.

Capacity: 3,000 **Seats:** 250 **Covered**: 1,000 **Floodlights:**Yes

Simple Directions: Main Leed-Hull road A630 M62. North Ferriby is 8 miles west of Hull. Go through North Ferriby past Duke of Cumberland Hotel, right down Church Road

Ground half a mile on left. One mile from North Ferriby BR

Midweek Home Matchday: Tuesday

Clubhouse: Open matchdays.

Club Shop: Yes.

CLUB PERSONNEL

Chairman: Les Hare
Additional Directors:
Colin Wicks (Vice Chairman)
Steve Tather, Mike Bonewell,
Alan Sage, Steve Turtle,
Jim White, Phil Withers.

Secretary: Steve Tather,
39 Northfielld, North Ferriby,
E.Yorks. HU14 3RG
Tel No: 01482 634 444 (H)
(M) 07976 556 952

Programme
Editor: James Chestney
Tel: 07837 975 924

CLUB STATISTICS

Record	**Attendance:** 1,927 v Hull City, Charity Game 2005
	Victory: 9-0 v Hatfield Main N.Co.East 1997-98
	Defeat: 1-7 v North Shields N.C.E. 1991
	Goalscorer: Andy Flounders 50 (season) 1998-99
	Goalscoring in Career: Mark Tennison 161
	Appearances: Paul Sharp 497 (1996-2006)
	Transfer Fee Paid: Not Known
	Received: £60,000 from Hull City for Dean Windass
Senior Honours:	F.A.Vase Finalists 1996-97 N.Co.East Champions 99-00 R-up 97-98
	E.Riding Senior Cup: (11) Unibond Div 1 Champions 2004-05
Previous Leagues	East Riding Church, East Riding Amateur, Yorks 69-82, N.Co.East

Back Row (L-R): Callum Russell, Ricky Foster, Niel Allison (Manager), John Anderson (ass Manager), Liam Chapman, Paul Foot (Captain). **Middle Row:** Colin Hunter, Brewster Frizzell, Chris Bolder, Mark Wilberforce, Steve Wilson, Russell Fry, Matty Bloor, David Cooke. **Front Row:** Alex Davidson, Kevin Larvin, Danny Moore, Martin Woodmansey (Physio), Gary Bradshaw, Rob Northen, Andy Jackson.

NORTH FERRIBY UNITED

BEST LGE ATT.: **437** v Boston United
LOWEST: **143** v Hednesford Town

No.	Date	Comp	H/A	Opponents	Att:	Result	Goalscorers	Pos
1	Aug 16	Unibond P.	A	Ashton United	128	D 1 - 1	Chapman 86 (og)	
2	20		H	Guiseley	214	L 1 - 2	**Bradshaw** 87	
3	23		H	Witton Albion	197	L 1 - 2	**Bradshaw** 13	19
4	25		A	Eastwood Town	330	L 0 - 5		
5	30		A	Ilkeston Town	421	L 0 - 1		20
6	Sept 2		H	Frickley Athletic	219	W 4 - 1	Fry 24 65 Davidson 36 72	
7	6		H	Kendal Town	206	L 1 - 2	**Bradshaw** 36 (pen)	20
8	9		A	Ossett Town	104	W 1 - 0	**Bradshaw** 60	
9	**17**	**F.A.C. 1Q**	**A**	**Consett**	**175**	**D 4 - 4**	**Denton 20 42 Fry 75 Torpey 78**	
10	20		H	Buxton	254	W 4 - 2	Larvin 9 Fry 23 Davidson 53 **Bradshaw** 70 (pen)	13
11	**23**	**F.A.C. 1Qr**	**H**	**Consett**	**135**	**W 6 - 1**	**Bradshaw 5 Jackson 36 DAVIDSON 3 (43 49 78) Torpey 80**	
12	**27**	**F.A.C. 2Q**	**H**	**Newcastle Blue Star**	**134**	**L 1 - 4**	**Bradshaw 86**	
13	Oct 4		A	Hednesford Town	405	W 2 - 0	Torpey 78 **Bradshaw** 90	13
14	7		H	Worksop Town	189	W 5 - 0	DAVIDSON 3 (7 70 73) **Bradshaw** 30 Hunter 84	
15	11		H	Bradford PA	326	D 2 - 2	Larvin 63 Davidson 69	9
16	14		A	Matlock Town	220	L 2 - 3	Hunter 44 Davidson 58	
17	**18**	**F.A.T 1Q**	**A**	**Spalding United**	**154**	**D 0 - 0**		
18	25		A	Prescot Cables	166	W 2 - 1	Russell 67 **Bradshaw** 87	8
19	28		H	Ossett Town	167	W 4 - 1	Bloor 26 Fry 45 **Bradshaw** 51 Torpey 71	
20	**Nov 1**	**F.A.T. 2Q**	**A**	**Chasetown**	**377**	**D 1 - 1**	**Bradshaw 1**	
21	**4**	**F.A.T. 2Qr**	**H**	**Chasetown**	**111**	**L 1 - 4**	**Bradshaw 2**	
22	8		A	Leigh Genesis	70	W 3 - 0	Torpey 8 Larvin 64 Russell 74	6
23	11		H	Matlock Town	181	W 6 - 3	Benger 2 (og) Fry 6 **Bradshaw** 12 37 Foot 19 Hunter 86	
24	15		A	Boston United	1069	W 2 - 0	Jackson 25 Hunter 80	3
25	22		H	Ashton United	198	L 1 - 2	**Bradshaw** 61	
26	29		H	Marine	178	L 1 - 2	**Bradshaw** 42 (pen)	8
27	Dec 20		A	Buxton	280	L 1 - 2	Davidson 72	8
28	26		H	Whitby Town	212	W 1 - 0	Russell 82	
29	Jan 1		A	Whitby Town	397	W 2 - 1	**Bradshaw** 23 Cooke 77	
30	3		A	Bradford P.A.	391	L 1 - 3	Fry 3 (pen)	7
31	17		A	Cammell Laird	114	W 2 - 1	Russell 5 Davidson 28	4
32	24		A	Frickley Athletic	230	D 0 - 0		3
33	31		H	Prescot Cables	154	W 5 - 0	RUSSELL 3 (17 71 84) Fry 29 Chapman 54	3
34	Feb 21		H	Cammell Laird	209	W 2 - 0	Bird 85 Russell 90	4
35	24		A	Nantwich Town	750	L 0 - 4		7
36	Mar 3		H	Hednesford Town	143	W 2 - 1	Bird 11 48	
37	7		H	Eastwood Town	340	D 2 - 2	Fry 25 Hunter 34	5
38	14		A	Witton Albion	245	L 1 - 2	Foot 37	6
39	17		H	F.C. United	376	L 0 - 2		
40	21		A	Kendal Town	201	L 2 - 3	Hunter 38 Fry 48	10
41	28		H	Boston United	437	L 0 - 2		
42	31		H	Ilkeston Town	198	D 0 - 0		
43	April 4		A	F.C. United	3120	L 0 - 4		10
44	10		H	Leigh Genesis	197	L 1 - 2	Bloor 2	10
45	13		A	Worksop Town	173	L 1 - 2	Fry 14	
46	18		H	Nantwich Town	184	D 1 - 1	Fry 86	10
47	21		A	Guiseley	357	L 0 - 2		
48	25		A	Marine	408	L 0 - 1		10

Average Home Att: 228 (169) **Goals** 80 79

Best Position: 3rd **Worst:** 20th

Goalscorers: Bradshaw 18, Davidson 13, Fry 12, Russell 8, Hunter 6, Torpey 5, Bird 3, Larvin 3, Bloor 2, Denton 2, Foot 2, Jackson 2, Chapman 1, Cooke 1. Own Goals 2.

OSSETT TOWN

Founded: 1936
Nickname: Town

Manager: Simon Collins

Club Colours: Red/white/red.

Change: Blue/white/blue.

Best Seasons - League: 10th Northern Premier League 2006-2007

Ground address: Ingfield, Prospect Road, Ossett, Wakefield, WF5 9HA

Tel No: 01924 280 028

Capacity: 4,000 **Seats:**360 **Covered**: 1,000 **Floodlights:**Yes

Simple Directions: From M1 Junction 40: Take A638 signposted Dewsbury / Batley, Take first left off A638 onto Wakefield Road, sixth left turn into Dale Street (B6120), signposted Ossett Town Centre, to traffic lights. Turn left at lights. The Ground is on left hand side opposite the bus station. The entrance to the Ground is just before the Coop petrol station.

Midweek Home Matchday: Tuesday

Clubhouse: Open every evening plus Friday lunchtimes and all day Saturdays.

Club Shop: Yes.

CLUB PERSONNEL

Chairman: Graham Firth

Additional Directors:
Simon Turfrey (CEO Football)
Martin Voakes (Vice Chairman)

Secretary: Trevor Jowett
Ingfield, Prospect Road,
Ossett WF5 9HA.
Tel: 01924 280 028
07770 266 115

Programme
Editor: Simon Turfrey
Tel: 01924 280 028

CLUB STATISTICS

Record	**Attendance**: 2,600 v Manchester United friendly 1988
	Victory: 10-1 v Harrogate RA (H) N.Co.E. 27.04.93.
	Defeat: 0-7 v Easington Colliery F.A.Vase 08.10..83
	Goalscorer: Dave Leadbetter. **Career Appearances**: Steve Worsfold
Record Transfer Fee	**Paid**: Not known.
	Received: £1,350 from Swansea Town for Dereck Blackburn
Senior Honours:	West Riding County Cup 58-59 81-82 N.Co.East R-Up 98-99 (promotion)
Previous Leagues	Leeds 36-39, Yorkshire 45-82 and Northern Counties East 83-99

OSSETT TOWN

BEST LGE ATT.: **544** v FC Utd of Manchester
LOWEST: **104** v North Ferriby United

No.	Date	Comp	H/A	Opponents	Att:	Result	Goalscorers	Pos
1	Aug 16	Unibond P.	H	Hednesford Town	175	D 1 - 1	Thompson 15	
2	20		A	Boston United	1334	L 2 - 3	Briggs 26 Longstaff 52	
3	23		A	Cammell Laird	130	W 1 - 0	Holt 77 (og)	10
4	25		H	Leigh Genesis	131	L 0 - 2		
5	30		H	Marine	270	L 4 - 5	Greaves 6 Hardy 14 29 **Savory** 67	21
6	Sept 3		A	Whitby Town	244	L 2 - 5	Greaves 26 85	
7	6		A	Witton Albion	329	D 1 - 1	Daly 90	18
8	9		H	North Ferriby United	104	L 0 - 1		19
9	**13**	**F.A.C. 1Q**	**A**	**Garforth Town**	**151**	**L 0 - 1**		
10	20		H	Nantwich Town	170	W 2 - 1	**Savory** 27 61	18
11	23		H	F.C.United	544	L 0 - 4		
12	Oct 4		A	Ashton United	122	L 1 - 2	Wharton 17 (og)	20
13	7		A	Ilkeston Town	374	L 1 - 2	**Savory** 12	
14	11		H	Matlock Town	159	W 3 - 2	Lee 15 **Savory** 17 Davidson 90	
15	**18**	**F.A.T 1Q**	**A**	**Guiseley**	**272**	**W 1 - 0**	**Davidson 26**	
16	25		H	Guiseley	204	L 1 - 4	Davidson 26	19
17	28		A	North Ferriby United	167	L 1 - 4	Davidson 50	
18	**Nov 1**	**F.A.T 2Q**	**H**	**Bedworth United**	**110**	**W 1 - 0**	**Lee 84**	
19	4		A	Nantwich Town	355	L 0 - 2		
20	8		H	Witton Albion	190	W 4 - 2	**Savory** 42 O'Brien 49 Lee 59 81	20
21	11		H	Eastwood Town	155	L 0 - 3		
22	15		A	Matlock Town	210	W 3 - 1	Briggs 41 (pen) Lee 55 **Savory** 65	18
23	18		H	Whitby Town	151	W 6 - 2	O'Brien 5 86 Riorden 31 **Savory** 55 Lee 56 Greaves 87	
24	**22**	**F.A.T. 3Q**	**H**	**Fleetwood Town**	**151**	**W 3 - 1**	**Baldry 11 Hay 73 Savory 89**	**16**
25	29		H	Prescot Cables	122	D 1 - 1	Greaves 18	16
26	Dec 6		A	Worksop Town	123	L 0 - 1		17
27	**16**	**F.A.T. 1R**	**A**	**Ilkeston Town**	**205**	**L 2 - 3**	**Savory 3 Davidson 16**	
28	20		A	Kendal Town	167	W 3 - 2	**Savory** 6 Baldry 10 Davidson 84	
29	26		H	Frickley Athletic	280	W 2 - 0	Lee 16 **Savory** 42	
30	Jan 17		H	Buxton	202	D 1 - 1	Baldry 53	13
31	24		A	Guiseley	328	W 1 - 0	**Savory** 11	12
32	31		H	Kendal Town	133	W 5 - 1	Greaves 23 **SAVORY** 3 (12 29 70) Lee 40	12
33	Feb 21		A	Marine	225	L 1 - 2	O'Brien 5	12
34	24		A	Leigh Genesis	59	W 6 - 0	O'Brien 11 Baldry 14 44 Lee 69 **Savory** 79 Greaves 90	
35	28		H	Cammell Laird	108	D 2 - 2	Greaves 22 73	12
36	Mar 7		A	Hednesford Town	412	W 3 - 0	**Savory** 34 71 Greaves 51	12
37	14		A	Prescot Cables	157	W 3 - 2	**Savory** 39 (pen) 50 (pen) Greaves 84	
38	17		H	Ossett Town	179	W 1 - 0	O'Brien 24	
39	21		H	Ilkeston Town	154	L 1 - 3	O.Brien 24	11
40	23		A	Bradford P.A.	389	L 0 - 2		
41	28		A	Buxton	302	D 0 - 0		11
42	April 1		A	F.C.United	1665	L 2 - 3	**Savory** 2 31 (pen)	
43	4		H	Ashton United	110	W 3 - 1	Greaves 10 Tonks 78 **Savory** 83	11
44	10		A	Frickley Atheltic	470	D 2 - 2	Lee 16 **Savory** 90	11
45	13		H	Bradford PA	356	L 1 - 2	Lee 78	
46	18		H	Boston United	286	D 0 - 0		11
47	25		A	Eastwood Town	2000	L 0 - 2		12

Average Home Att: **199 (155)** **Goals** **78 79**

Best Position: 10th **Worst:** 21st

Goalscorers: Savory 25, Greaves 12, Lee 11, O'Brien 7, Davidson 6, Baldry 6, Briggs 2, Hardy 2, Hay 2, Riorden 1, Daly 1, Longstaff 1, Thompson 1, Tonks 1. Own Goals 2.

RETFORD UNITED

Founded: 1987
Nickname: Badgers

Manager: Peter Duffield

Club Colours: Black & White Stripes/black/black.

Change: All yellow.

Best Season - League: 1st Northern Premier Division One South 2007-08, 08-09.

Ground address: Cannon Park, Leverton Road, Retford, Notts DN22 6QF.

Tel: Office/Fax: 01777 869468 Club: 01777 710300

Club website: www.retfordunited.co.uk

Capacity: 2,000 **Seats**: 150 **Covered**: 300 **Floodlights**: Yes

Simple Directions: From A1 take A620 past Ranby prison and into Retford. At large roundabout take 3rd exit. Pass Morrisons superstore to lights. Right at first set of lights and left at next. Follow Leverton Rd out of town. Ground on right after two bridges.

Midweek Home Matchday: Tuesday

Clubhouse: Yes

Club Shop: Yes

CLUB PERSONNEL

Chairman: Bill Wyles

Committee: S Payling, G Brittian, A Legg, J Lewis

Secretary: Annie Knight
16, Willand Court, Retford,
Notts. DN22 7GD
(H): 01777 719 600
(M): 07825 047 799

Programme
Editor: Jon Knight
07825 047 766

CLUB STATISTICS

Record
Attendance: 1527 v Doncaster Rovers (Friendly) July 2006
500 v Belper Town (League) February 2009
922 v Alfreton Town (Cup) October 2008
Career Goalscorer: Andy Powell – 126 (1990-1995)
Career Appearances: Steve Hardy – 272 (1987-1996)
Transfer Fee Paid: N/A **Transfer Fee Received:** N/A

Senior Honours: Northern Premier Division One South 2007-08, 08-09. NCEL Premier Division 2006-07. NPL Chairmans Cup 2007-08. NCEL Presidents Cup Winners 2006-07. NCEL Wilkinson Sword Trophy 2005-06. Central Midlands Supreme Division 2003-04. Central Midlands Division One 2001-02. Central Midlands League Cup 2001-02, 2003-04. Central Midlands Floodlit Cup 2003-04. Nottinghamshire Alliance Division One 2000-01. Nottinghamshire Senior Cup 2008-09.

Previous Leagues: Gainsborough & District Football League. Nottinghamshire Football Alliance. Central Midlands League. Northern Counties East League

The Retford squad celebrate winning the Northern Premier Division One South title and with it promotion to the Premier League.

STOCKSBRIDGE PARK STEELS

Founded: 1986
Nickname: Steels

Manager: Gary Marrow

Club Colours: Yellow/royal blue/yellow.

Change: All red.

Best Seasons: League: 3rd Northern Premier Division One North 2008-09.

Ground address: Look Local Stadium, Bracken Moor Lane, Stocksbridge, Sheffield.

Tel/Fax No: 0114 288 8305. Club: 0114 288 2045.

Club Website: www.stocksbridgepsfc.co.uk

Capacity: 3,500 **Seats**: 400 **Covered**:1,500 **Floodlights**: Yes

Simple Directions: M1 jct 35a (from S), 36 (from N), A616 to Stocksbridge. On arrival in Stocksbridge turn left into Nanny Hill under the Clock Tower.Ground is 500 yds up the hill on left.

Midweek Home Matchday: Tuesday

Clubhouse: Open every day lunchtime & evenings. No food but separate food bar for matchdays.

Club Shop: Full range of products.

Local Press: Look Local, The Green Un & The Star.

CLUB PERSONNEL

Chairman: Allen Bethel
Committee: M Grimmer, A Horsley, P Kenney, M Kenney, R Sellers, J Newton, P Birkinshaw, W Fieldsend, T Grayson, W Cefferty.

Secretary: Michael Grimmer
48 Hole House Lane,
Stocksbridge,
Sheffield. S36 1BT
(H/F): 0114 288 6470
(B): 0114 283 6608
(M): 07801 626 725

Programme Editor: Edwin O'Sullivan
0114 288 4218

CLUB STATISTICS

Record	**Attendance:** 2,050 v Sheffield Wednesday Opening Floodlights, October 1991
	Career Goalscorer: Trevor Jones 145
	Match: Paul Jackson 10 v Oldham Town 2002-2003 (F.A. Cup Record).
	Career Appearances: Not known
Record Transfer Fee	**Received:** £15,000 from Wolverhampton Wanderers for Lee MIlls
	Victory: 17-1 v Oldham Town F.A.Cup. 2002-2003
	Defeat: 0-6 v Shildon
Senior Honours:	Northern Co's East Prem Div 93-94, R-up 95-96, Div 1 91-92, Lg Cup 94-95;
	Sheffield Senior Cup 1951-52 92-93 95-96,98-99.
Previous Leagues:	**Leagues:** Sheffield Amateur/ Sheffield Association/Yorkshire 1949-82.
	Northern Counties East 1986-96.
	Ground: Stonemoor 49-51 52-53
	Names: Stocksbridge Works & Oxley Park merged in 1986

WHITBY TOWN

Founded: 1926
Nickname: Seasiders

Manager: Harry Dunn.

Club Colours: All royal blue.

Change: All white.

Best Season - League: 4th Northern Premier League 2004-2005

Ground address: Turnbull Ground, Upgang Lane, Whitby, NorthYorks YO21 3HZ.

Tel No: 01947 604 847 / 603 193

Capacity: 2,680 **Seats**: 622 **Covered**: 1,372 **Floodlights**:Yes

Simple Directions: Take A174 road from town centre.

Midweek Home Matchday: Wednesday

Clubhouse: Open every evening and weekend lunchtimes.

Club Shop: Yes..

Local Radio: Yorkshire Coast Radio.

Local Press: Whitby Gazette & Northern Echo.

CLUB PERSONNEL

Chairman: Graham Manser
Committee: P J Tyreman, A J Spenceley, M Agar, J Nellist, B Lonsdale, G Osbourne, M Osbourne, C Bone, D Griffiths, J Smith, M Green.
Secretary: John Tyreman.
17 Wellclose Terrace,
Whitby, North Yorkshire
YO21 3AR
Tel: (H): 01947 605 153
Programme Editor:
Alison Booth
Tel: 07968 188 587

CLUB STATISTICS

Record	**Attendance**: 4,000 v Scarborough North Riding Cup 18.04 65
	Victory: 11-2 v Cargo Fleet Works 1950
	Defeat: 3-13 v Willington 24.03.28
	Career Goalscorer: Paul Pitman 382
	Career Appearances: Paul Pitman 468
Record Transfer Fee	**Paid:** £2,500 to Newcastle Blue Star for John Grady 1990
	Received: £5,000 from Gateshead for Graham Robinson 1997
Senior Honours:	F.A.Vase Winners 96-97 F.A.Amateur Cup Finalists: 64-65 NPL Div 1 97-98 Northern Lg 92-93 96-97 R-up (5) Rothmans National Cup 75-76 77-78 N.Riding Senior Cup (5)
Previous Leagues:	Northern League 1926-97 **Previous Name**: Whitby United (pre 1950)

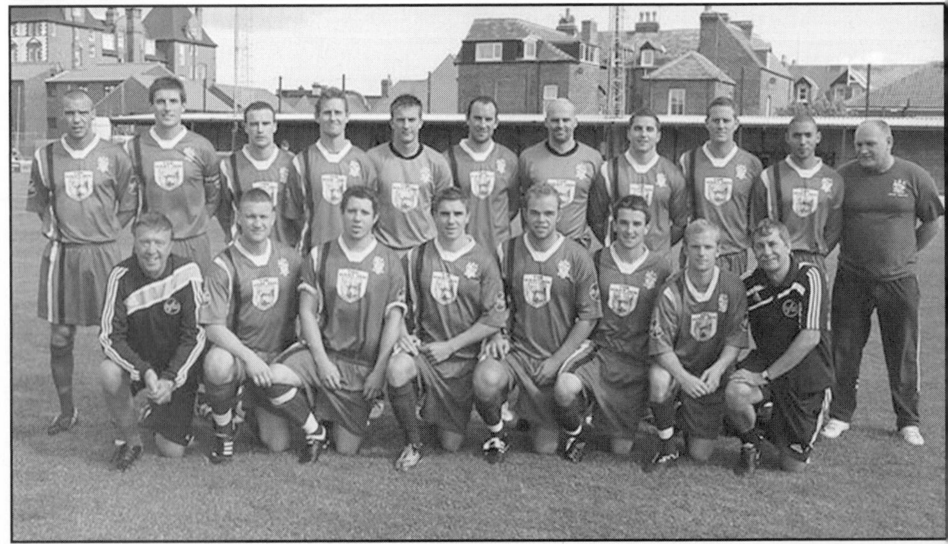

WHITBY TOWN

BEST LGE ATT.: **1,079** v FC Utd of Manchester
LOWEST: **227** v Hednesford Town

No.	Date	Comp	H/A	Opponents	Att:	Result	Goalscorers	Pos
1	Aug 16	Unibond P.	H	Buxton	359	L 0 - 2		
2	19		A	Frickley Athletic	300	L 0 - 1		
3	23		A	Matlock Town	263	L 0 - 2		21
4	25		H	Kendal Town	302	L 2 - 3	Raw 31 Nogan 61	
5	30		A	F.C.United	2071	L 1 - 3	Hackworth 31	22
6	Sept 3		H	Ossett Town	244	W 5 - 2	Brunskill 11 Huggins 25 Raw 47 **Charlton** 56 Forster 61	
7	6		H	Nantwich Town	302	D 0 - 0		19
8	**13**	**F.A.C. 1Q**	**H**	**Dunston Federation B**	**244**	**W 3 - 2**	**Brunskill 1 Charlton 6 Raw 32**	
9	20		A	Leigh Genesis	151	W 4 - 2	**Charlton** 40 72 Brunskill 51 Hackworth 88	
10	24		H	Bradford P.A.	289	W 1 - 0	Brunskill 83	15
11	**27**	**F.A.C. 2Q**	**H**	**Blyth Spartans**	**403**	**D 2 - 2**	**Garvie 1 Thompson 90**	
12	**30**	**F.A.C. 2Qr**	**A**	**Blyth Spartans**	**408**	**L 2 - 5**	**Beadle 6 Huggins 64**	
13	Oct 4		H	Prescot Cables	246	W 3 - 0	Huggins 56 Garvie 82 Beadle 85	12
14	11		A	Cammell Laird	118	D 2 - 2	**Charlton** 65 83	12
15	14		H	Frickley Athletic	249	D 2 - 2	Beadle 29 Raw 42	
16	**18**	**F.A.T. 1Q**	**H**	**Trafford**	**223**	**W 3 - 2**	**Huggins 61 Beadle 80 Scott 88**	
17	21		A	Guiseley	197	W 3 - 1	Scott 24 Rae 43 Raw 53	
18	25		H	F.C.United	1079	D 0 - 0		11
19	**Nov 1**	**F.A.T. 2Q**	**A**	**Stocksbridge PS**	**153**	**W 2 - 0**	**Rae 42 Hackworth 82**	
20	8		A	Marine	336	D 2 - 2	Lake 45 (og) Hackworth 78	13
21	15		H	Leigh Genesis	263	D 2 - 2	Scott 32 Hackworth 61 (Pen)	13
22	18		A	Ossett Town	151	L 2 - 6	Hackworth 18 Forster 64	
23	**26**	**F.A.T. 3Q**	**H**	**Stalybridge Celtic**	**176**	**L 0 - 3**		
24	29		A	Boston United	949	L 0 - 2		14
25	Dec 13		A	Kendal Town	180	D 3 - 3	Brunskill 49 Raw 70 Hackworth 88	
26	20		H	Worksop Town	248	L 0 - 2		18
27	26		A	North Ferriby United	212	L 0 - 1		
28	Jan 1		H	North Ferriby United	397	L 1 - 2	Brunskill 84	
29	17		H	Boston United	301	W 1 - 0	Beadle 10	16
30	24		A	Nantwich Town	603	L 1 - 3	Rae 90	17
31	27		A	Prescot Cables	177	W 4 - 3	**Charlton** 23 Rae 26 45 Raw 88	
32	31		H	Cammell Laird	237	L 0 - 3		16
33	Feb 14		A	Ashton United	134	D 3 - 3	Farthing 38 Brunskill 42 Raw 73	15
34	21		H	Matlock Town	266	W 2 - 0	Flint 1 (og) **Charlton** 72	
35	28		A	Eastwood Town	602	D 1 - 1	Rae 58	15
36	Mar 4		H	Eastwood Town	229	L 1 - 3	Todd 66 (og)	
37	7		H	Marine	281	W 2 - 0	Raw 30 Brunskill 84	
38	14		A	Worksop Town	165	L 0 - 1		17
39	17		A	Ilkeston Town	368	L 0 - 1		
40	21		H	Ashton United	243	L 1 - 3	Scott 69	18
41	25		A	Witton Albion	220	D 0 - 0		18
42	April 1		H	Hednesford Town	227	L 0 - 3		
43	4		A	Hednesford Town	434	W 3 - 1	**Charlton** 40 Thompson 52 87	
44	10		A	Bradford PA	585	L 2 - 3	**Charlton** 60 Price 74 (og)	
45	13		H	Guiseley	404	L 0 - 2		19
46	18		A	Buxton	462	L 0 - 3		20
47	22		H	Witton Albion	333	W 1 - 0	Bishop 81	
48	25		H	Ilkeston Town	504	W 3 - 0	Huggins 44 Hackworth 73 **Charlton** 90	19

Average Home Att: 333 (283) **Goals** 70 87

Best Position: 11th **Worst:** 22nd

Goalscorers: Charlton 11, Raw 9, Brunskill 8, Hackworth 8, Rae 7, Beadle 5, Huggins 5, Scott 4, Thompson 3, Forster 2, Garvie 2, Nogan 1, Farthing 1. Own Goals 3.

WORKSOP TOWN

Founded: 1861
Nickname: Tigers

Manager: Peter Rinkcavage.

Club Colours: All Amber & black.

Change: Sky blue/white/sky blue.

Best Season - League: 17th Conference North 2004-2005

Ground address: Ilkeston Town FC, New Manor Ground, Awsworth Road, Ilkeston, Derbyshire DE7 8JF

Tel/Fax No: 0115 944 2949. Club: 0115 932 4094.

Capacity: 3,029 **Seats**: 550 **Covered**: 2,000 **Floodlights**:Yes

Simple Directions: From M1 Junction 26, take A610 signposted Ripley. Leave the A610 at the first exit on to the A6096 signed Awsworth/Ilkeston. At the next island join the Awsworth by-pass, signed A6096 Ilkeston. Continue for approx. half a mile and turn right into Awsworth Road. Small signpost marked Cotmanhay. The ground is half a mile down this road on the left hand side.

Midweek Home Matchday: Wednesday

Clubhouse: Yes.

Club Shop: Yes.

Local Press: Worksop Guardian, Green Un, Sheffield Star.

Local Radio: Radio Sheffield, Radio Hallam, Trust AM, Trax FM

CLUB PERSONNEL

Chairman : John Hepworth

Additional Directors:
Keith Ilett (President),
Chris Smith, Chris Pridmore

Secretary: Keith Illett
2 Mount Avenue, Worksop.
S81 7JL
Tel: (H/F): 01909 487 934
(M): 07734 144 961

Programme
Editor: Steve Jarvis
Tel: 07740 845 803

CLUB STATISTICS

Record	**Attendance**: 2,263 v Sheffield United, friendly - 2005 (Sandy Lane) 8,171 v Chesterfield, FA Cup - 1925 (Central Ave)
Victory:	20-0 v Staveley 01.09.84
Defeat:	1-11 v Hull City Reserves 1955-56
Career Goalscorer:	Kenny Clark 287 **Career Appearances**: Kenny Clark 347
Record Transfer Fee	**Paid**: £5,000 to Grantham Town for Kirk Jackson **Received:** £47,000 from Sunderland for Jon Kennedy 2000
Senior Honours:	NPL Prem Div R-up 98-99, NPL Div 1 R-up 97-98, Sheff & Hallamshire Senior Cup (9)
Previous Leagues:	Midland Counties 1896--98 1900-30 49-60 61-68 69-74 Sheff Association 1898-99 1931-33, Central Combination 33-35, Yorkshire 35-39. Central Alliance 1947-49 60-61 NPl 68-69 74-2004. Conference North 2004-07.

WORKSOP TOWN

BEST LGE ATT.: 443 v FC Utd of Manchester
LOWEST: 123 v Ossett Town

No.	Date	Comp	H/A	Opponents	Att:	Result	Goalscorers	Pos
1	Aug 16	Unibond P.	A	Marine	304	L 2 - 6	Jackson 26 **Sanasy** 69	
2	20		H	Eastwood Town	342	D 1 - 1	Dempsey 85	
3	23		H	Nantwich Town	181	L 0 - 4		20
4	25		A	Bradford P.A.	481	D 1 - 1	Rowland 42	
5	30		H	Leigh Genesis	155	W 2 - 1	Wilson 53 Jackson 90	17
6	Sept 3		A	Boston United	1058	W 1 - 0	**Sanasy** 76	
7	10		H	Matlock Town	230	L 0 - 1		15
8	**13**	**F.A.C. 1Q**	**A**	**Marine**	**295**	**W 5 - 1**	**Sanasy 47 71 Cockerill 52 Jackson 57 White 80**	
9	20		A	F.C.United	2033	D 0 - 0		16
10	24		H	Ilkeston Town	332	L 0 - 1		
11	**27**	**F.A.C. 2Q**	**A**	**King's Lynn**	**1080**	**L 1 - 2**	**Jackson 47**	
12	Oct 4		H	Kendal Town	161	L 0 - 2		19
13	7		A	North Ferriby United	189	L 0 - 5		
14	11		A	Kendal Town	247	D 0 - 0		20
15	15		H	Prescot Cables	143	W 3 - 2	**Sanasy** 23 Glass 53 Boyce 65	
16	**18**	**F.A.T. 1Q**	**A**	**Witton Albion**	**219**	**W 1 - 0**	**Sanasy 64**	
17	22		H	Buxton	233	L 2 - 3	Townsend 25 Robinson 56	
18	25		A	Ashton United	150	L 2 - 6	Jackson 61 **Sanasy** 67	20
19	29		H	Boston United	230	D 1 - 1	**Sanasy** 13	
20	**Nov 1**	**F.A.T. 2Q**	**H**	**F.C.United**	**599**	**L 0 - 3**		
21	8		A	Hednesford Town	483	L 0 - 5		21
22	12		H	Guiseley	171	L 0 - 4		
23	15		A	Witton Albion	250	W 3 - 2	White 12 Adam 42 Galloway 84	20
24	22		A	Eastwood Town	427	L 0 - 4		21
25	29		A	Matlock Town	249	D 2 - 2	Adam 43 Hussey 45 (pen)	21
26	Dec 6		H	Ossett Town	123	W 1 - 0	**Sanasy** 90	20
27	9		A	Cammell Laird	108	L 1 - 2	Adam 65	
28	20		A	Whitby Town	248	W 2 - 0	White 41 56	19
29	26		H	Hednesford Town	267	L 2 - 7	Maguire 65 (og) Adam 65	
30	Jan 1		A	Frickley Athletic	408	W 3 - 0	Adam 13 Glass 62 Townsend 71	
31	3		H	F.C.United	443	L 0 - 2		20
32	24		A	Buxton	302	L 0 - 3		20
33	31		A	Leigh Genesis	102	W 2 - 1	Jones 30 Glass 56	17
34	Feb 21		A	Ilkeston Town	510	D 3 - 3	Glass 21 (pen) 75 (pen) White 772	
35	28		H	Ashton United	156	D 1 - 1	White 77	18
36	Mar 4		H	Frickley Athletic	174	W 3 - 1	White 23 Callery 45 Adam 63	
37	7		A	Prescot Cables	227	W 1 - 0	Holmes 9	
38	14		H	Whitby Town	165	W 1 - 0	Adam 89	15
39	17		A	Ossett Town	179	L 0 - 1		15
40	25		H	Marine	171	W 1 - 0	Callery 72	14
41	April 1		H	Bradford PA	187	D 1 - 1	Tomlinson 82	
42	4		H	Cammell Laird	181	D 1 - 1	White 47	14
43	10		A	Guiseley	338	L 0 - 6		15
44	13		H	North Ferriby United	173	W 2 - 0	**Sanasy** 40 Denton 90	
45	18		H	Witton Albion	251	D 2 - 2	**Sanasy** 14 Callery 18	15
46	25		A	Nantwich Town	794	L 1 - 3	Adam 23	17

Average Home Att: 213 (305) **Goals** 55 91

Best Position: 14th **Worst:** 21st

Goalscorers: Sanasy 11, Adam 8, White 8, Glass 5, Jackson 5, Callery 3, Townsend 2, Boyce 1, Cockerill 1, Dempsey 1, Denton 1, Gallaway 1, Holmes 1, Hussey 1, Jones 1, Robinson 1, Rowland 1, Tomlinson 1, Wilson 1. Own Goals 1.

A.F.C. FYLDE

Formed 1988

Manager: Mick Fuller
Colours: All white.
Change: Rd & blue halves/blue/blue.
Best Season - League: 1st North West Counties Premier 2008-09.
Ground: Kellamergh Park, Bryning Lane, Warton, Preston. PR4 1TN
Tel: Office: 01772 635880 Fax: 01772 679600
Capacity: **Seats:** Yes **Cover:** Yes **Floodlights:** Yes

Directions: EXIT via Junction 3 M55 (signposted A585 Fleetwood/Kirkham). Up approach and turn left towards signs for Kirkham.In around 3/4 mile you will approach a roundabout. Then follow the signs for Wrea Green and Lytham St. Annes (2nd exit) B5259.After another 500 yards you will approach a new roundabout (go straight on) and 1/4 mile you will go over main Preston/Blackpool railway bridge and drop down almost immediately to a small mini roundabout (pub on left called Kingfisher). Carry on straight over this and up to main roundabout (another 200 yards) at junction of main Preston/Blackpool A583. Go straight over roundabout and drive on into Wrea Green Village.At 2nd mini roundabout in the centre of the village (Church on right l) take left turn into Bryning Lane, signposted on The Green (small white signpost) to Warton (2 miles).The Green will now be on your right as you exit out of the village and in around 1.8 miles you will come to the Birley Arms Pub on your left. Turn immediately left into The Birley Arms Pub Car park and continue to drive through the car park down until you reach access road and park in the Main Club Car Park located behind the Main Stand. Approximate mileage from motorway to the ground is 5 miles and will take around 10 minutes to travel in a car.

Midwee Home Matches: Tuesday.
Clubhouse: Yes.
Club Shop: Yes.

CLUB PERSONNEL

Chairman: Dai Davies.
Additional Directors:
Stuart King

Secretary: Eric Picton
c/o AFC Fylde Head Office, No1 Clifton Fields, Lytham Road, Clifton, Preston. PR4 0XG
Tel. (H) 01772 686264
07545 735154

Programme
Editor: Martin Booker
Tel: 07525 323 775

CLUB STATISTICS

Records: **Attendance:** 1,053 v Needham Market, FA Vase Semi-Final 1st lge, 22.03.08.

Senior Honours: West Lancashire Champions 1999-00, 00-01, 01-02, 03-04, 04-05, 05-06, 06-07.
F.A. Vase 2007-08.
North West Counties Champions 2008-09.

PREVIOUS **Names:** Wesham FC and Kirkham Town amalgamated in 1988 to form, Kirkham & Wesham > 2008.
Leagues: West Lancashire. North West Counties 2007-09.

BAMBER BRIDGE

Re-formed 1952
Nickname : Brig

BAMBER BRIDGE FOOTBALL CLUB
Unibond League First Division North
BAMBER BRIDGE
versus
GARFORTH TOWN
Tuesday 18th August 2009
7.45pm Kick-Off
OFFICIAL MATCH PROGRAMME

Manager: Tony Greenwood.

Colours: White/black/black.

Change: All red.

Best Season - League: 1st Northern Premier Premier 1995-1996

Ground: QED Stadium, Irongate, Brownedge Road, Bamber Bridge, Preston, Lancs. PR5 6UX

Tel.No: Club Office: 01772 909 690 Social Club : 01772 909 695

Capacity: 3,000 **Seats:** 554 **Cover:** 800 **Floodlights:** Yes

Directions: M6 jct 29 then A6 (Bamber Bridge bypass) towards Walton-le-Vale to roundabout. A6 London Road to next roundabout, third exit marked Bamber Bridge (Brownedge Road) and first right. Ground 100 yards on left at end of road.

Midwee Home Matches: Tuesday

Clubhouse: Open all day matchdays, every evening and Sunday lunchtime.Hot and cold snacks on sale in refreshments cabin on matchdays.

Club Shop: Yes.

CLUB PERSONNEL

Chairman: Terry Gammans.
Additional Directors:
Dennis Allen (President),
Dave Spencer (Treasurer),
Geoff Wright (Club Secretary)
George Halliwell (Director of Football and Football Secretary),
Gerry Lawson (Trustee).
Secretary: George Halliwell.
26 The Laund, Leyland, Preston
PR26 7XX
Tel Nos: 01772 454 762 (H)
07929 042 954 (M)
Programme Editor: Dave Rowland
Tel: 01772 312 987

CLUB STATISTICS

RECORDS:	**Attendance:** 2,300 v Czech Republic, Pre Euro 96 Friendly
	Victory: 8-0 v Curzon Ashton N.W.Co. 94-95 **Defeat**: Unknown
	Transfer Fee Paid: £10,000 to Horwich RMI for Mark Edwards.
	Fee Received: £15,000 from Wigan Athletic for Tony Black 1995
Senior Honours:	NPL Premier Champions 1995-96, Div 1 R-up 1994-95,
	NPL Challenge Cup 1995-96
	ATDC Lancs Trophy 1994-95 N.W.Co R-up 1992-93
PREVIOUS	**Leagues:** Preston & Disrict 1952-90 and North West Counties 1990-93
	Grounds: King George V Ground, Higher Wallton1952-86

Back Row: (L-R) Phil Robinson, Craig Sargeson, James Heywood, Colin McAllister, Martin Moran, Mike Hale, Sean O'Neill, Phil Denney, Shane Oldfield, Phil Eastwood, Gus Muncaster.
Front Row: Neil Reynolds, Ryan - Zico Black, Chris Marlow, Tony Greenwood (Manager), Neil Crowe (Assistant Manager), Lee Pryers, Mitchell Bailey, Ashley Dunn.

CHORLEY

Formed: 1883
Nickname:The Magpies

Manager: Steve Waywell

Colours: Black & white/black/black.

Change: All sky blue.

Best Season - League: 18th Conference 1988-1989

Ground address: Victory Park, Duke Street, Chorley, Lancs PR7 3DU

Tel: 01257 263 406. Club: 01257 275 662.

Directions: From jct 6 of M61 to Chorley turm left into Pilling Lane after Yarrow BridgeHotel. First right into Ashley Street.Ground is second left.

Capacity: 4,100 Cover: 2,800 Seats: 900

Clubhouse: 01257 275 662. Open matchdays and other evenings by arrangement

Club Shop: Open on matchdays in social club

Midweek matchday: Tuesday.

Local Press: Lancs Evening Post, Chorley Guardian, Chorley Citizen & LancashireTelegraph

Local Radio: BBC Radio Lancashire

CLUB PERSONNEL

Chairman: Ken Wright

Additional Directors:
Brian Pilkington, Tony Garner, Geoff Haslam, Peter Hardcastle, Brian Haslam.

Secretary: John Gibbons
2, The Asshawes Heath, Charnock, Chorley. PR6 9JW
Tel: (H) 01257 480161
(B) 01257 263406
(F) 01257 241625
07969 066574

Programme
Editor: John Newman
Tel: 07816 955 778

CLUB STATISTICS

CLUB RECORDS	**Attendance:** 9,679 v Darwen, F.A.Cup 1931-32.
	Goalscorer: Peter Watson. 371 (1958-1966)
	Fee Paid: £16,000 to Marine for Brian Ross 1995.
	Fee Received: £30,000 from Newcastle U for David Eatock 1996
HONOURS	Northern Premier Lg 87-88, Cheshire Co. Lg 75-76 76-77 81-82, Lancs F.A.Trophy Winners (14) R-Up(16) Lancs Comb. (11) R-up 6., League Cup (3), Lancs Lg 1896-97 98-99 Lancs Alliance 1892-93 (R-Up 94-95), Lanc s Junior (14)
PREVIOUS	**Leagues**:Lancs Alliance 1890-94; Lancs18 94-1903; Lancs Comb1903-68 69-70; Northern Premier 68-69, 70-72, 82-88; Cheshire County 70-82; GMV Conference 88-90.
	Grounds: Dole Lane 1883-1901; Rangletts Park 01-05; St George's Park 05-20

CLITHEROE

Formed: 1877
Nickname:The Blues

Manager: Peter Smith.

Colours: Blue & white hoops/royal blue/navy blue.

Change: Black & amber stripes/black/black.

Best Seasons - League: 12th Northern Premier Divison One North 2008-09.

Ground : Shawbridge, off Pendle Road,Clitheroe Lancashire BB7 1DZ

Tel No: & Fax: 01200 444 487.

Midweek matchday: Tuesday

Directions: M6 jct 31. A59 to Clitheroe (17 miles) at fifth roundabout turn left after half a mile at Pendle Road. Ground is one mile behind Bridge Inn on the right.

Capacity: 2,400 **Seats**: 250 **Cover** 1,400 **Floodlights** Yes

Clubhouse: Open on match days, Snacks available. Club Tel No: 01200 423344

CLUB PERSONNEL

Chairman: Carl Garner
Additional Directors:
Colin Wilson, Anne Barker, Andrew Jackson.
Secretary: Colin Wlson,
4 Moss Street, Clitheroe,
Lancs BB7 1DP
Tel/Fax: 01200 424 370
Mobile: 07949 031 039
Programme
Editor: Chris Musson
Tel: 01254 245 461

CLUB STATISTICS

CLUB RECORDS
Attendance: 2,050 v Mangotsfield .F.A.Vase Seimi-Final 95-96.
Goalscorer: Don Francis
Appearances: Lindsey Wallace 670
Transfer Fee Received: £45,000 from Crystal Palace for Carlo Nash

SENIOR HONOURS
Lancs Challenge Trophy 1984-85.
North West Counties Champions 1984-85. East Lancs Floodlit Trophy 1994-95.

PREVIOUS
Leagues: Blackburn& District , Lancs Combination 03-04 05-10 25-82.
North West Counties.

COLWYN BAY

Founded: 1885
Nickname: Seagulls

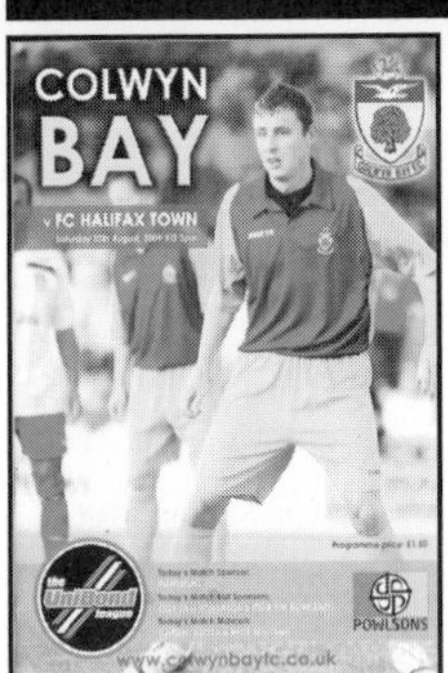

Manager: Neil Young.

Club Colours: Sky blue & claret/claret/sky blue.

Change: All white.

Best Seasons - League: 6th Northern Premier Premier Division 1993 -1994

Ground address: Llanelian Road, Old Colwyn, North Wales LL29 8UN

Tel No.01492 514 581

Capacity: 2,500 **Seats**: 250 **Covered**: 700 **Floodlights**: Yes

Simple Directions: Take A55 North Wales Expressway. Exit Jct.22 signposted to Hen Golwyn/Old Colwyn. At end of slip road turn left then straight on at roundabout and into Llanelian Road. Ground half a mile on left.

Midweek Home Matchday: Tuesday

Clubhouse: Open matchdays only.

Club Shop: Yes.

CLUB PERSONNEL

MD: Darren Cartwright

Additional Directors:
Geoffrey Cartwright,
Grant McIndoe, Roger Skinner,
Martin Cartwright,
Mark Williams.

Secretary: Grant McIndoe
15, Maes Onnen, Rhuddlan,
Denbighshire.LL18 2YL
Tel: (H): 01745 590 923
07769 538 012

Programme
Editor: Andrew Wynn

CLUB STATISTICS

Record	**Attendance:** 5,000 v Borough United at Eirias Park 1964
	Career Goalscorer: Peter Donnelly
	Career Appearances: Bryn A. Jones
Record Transfer Fee	**Paid**: Not known.
	Received: Not known.
Senior Honours:	Northern Premier League Div.1 Champions 1991-1992
Previous Leagues:	N.Wales Coast 1901-21 33-35, Welsh National 1921-30
	N.Wales Comb. 1930-31. Welsh Lg. (North) 1945-84. N.W. Co 1984-91.

NB: UNFORTUNATELY A RECENT PHOTO WAS NOT AVAILABLE AT THE TIME OF GOING TO PRESS.

CURZON ASHTON

Founded: 1963

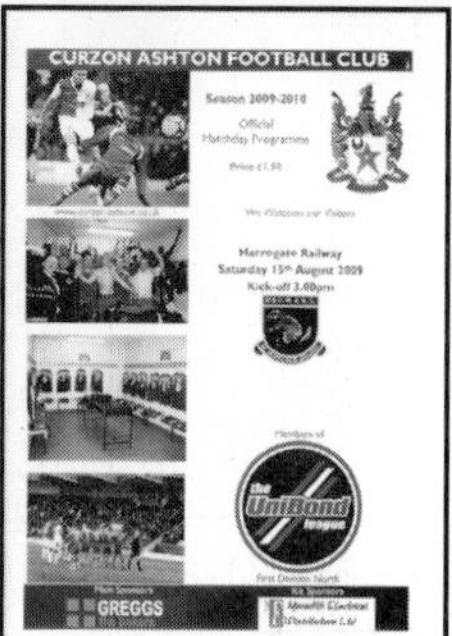

Manager: Gary Lowe

Club Colours: All royal blue.

Change: All red.

Best Seasons - League: 4th Northern Premier Division One North 2007-08

Ground address: Tamesside Stadium, Richmond Street, Ashton-under-Lyme, Lancashire OL7 9HG Tel No: 0161 330 6033

Club Website: www.curzon-ashton.co.uk

Capacity: 5,000 **Seats:** 504 **Covered**: Yes **Floodlights**: Yes

Simple Directions: M60 (from Stockport) jct 23 left off slip road. In second lane from left , through lightsonto A6140 to Ashton.Left at lights with cinema on right, over bridge and mini roundabout and ground is at bottom of road. Cars park on right, coaches park on left.

Midweek Home Matchday: Monday

Clubhouse: Yes with large function room for hire.

Club Shop: Yes.

Local Radio: G.M.GR. (BBC Manchester)

Local Press: Manchester Evening News, Saturday News Pink, Ashton Reporter and Ashton Advertiser

CLUB PERSONNEL

Chairman: Harry Galloway

Additional Directors:
Harry Twamley, Ronnie Capstick, Simon Shuttleworth, Robert Hurst, Paul Price, James Newall, Roy Jackson, Steve Ball, Ian Seymour, Ron Walber.

Secretary: Robert Hurst
The Tameside Stadium,
Richmond Street,
Ashton-under-Lyne.
OL7 9HG
Tel: (H) 0161 775 3883
(B): 0161 330 6033 (Ground)
(F): 0161 339 8802
07713 252310

Programme Editor: See secretary.

CLUB STATISTICS

Record	**Attendance:** 1,826 v Stamford F.A.Vase Semi-Final.
	Career Goalscorer:Alan Sykes. **Career Appearances:** Alan Sykes:
	Victory:: 7-0 v Ashton United. **Received:** 0-8 v Bamber Bridge
Senior Honours:	Manchester Premier Cup (5)
Previous Leagues:	Manchester Amateur, Manchseter > 1978 , Cheshire County, N.W. Counties
	Northern Premier League 1987-97 N.W.Counties 1997-2007.

Back Row (L-R): Chris Worsley, Adam Jones, Andrew Lundy, Phil Edghill, Dave Carnell, Daryl Weston, Matthew Russell, Chris Curley, Paul Riley (Trainer).
Front Row: Martin Rothwell (Physio), Michael Norton, Hasim Deen, Matthew Wood, Michael O'Connor, David Birch, Alex Elliott.

F.C. HALIFAX TOWN

Formed: 2008

Manager: Neil Aspin

Club Colours: All blue.

Change: Orange/black/orange & black.

Best Season - League: 8th Northern Premier Division One North 2008-09.

Ground address: The Shay Stadium, Shay Syke, Halifax. HX1 2YS

Tel: Office: 01422 341 222 Fax: 01422 349 487

Capacity: 9,500

Simple Directions: M62, Junction 24. Head towards Halifax on A629 and the Town Centre

After 3-4 miles, ground is on the right (Shaw Hill) Signposted The Shay.

Midweek Home Matchday: Tuesday

Clubhouse: Open normal licensing hours.

Club Shop: At The Shay

CLUB PERSONNEL

Chairman: David Bosmworth

Additional Directors:
Bobby Ham, Stuart Peacock.

Secretary: Hayley Horne
The Shay Stadium, Shay
Syke, Halifax. HX1 2YS
Tel: (B) 01422 341 222
(F) 01422 349 487

Programme
Editor: G Stainton.
Tel: 01422 341 222.

CLUB STATISTICS (AS HALIFAX TOWN)

Records
Attendance: 36,885 v Tottenham Hotspur F.A.Cup 5th Rd. 14.02.53
Victory: 12-0 v West Vale Ramblers F.A.Cup 1st Qual. Rd 1913-14
Defeat: 0-13 v Stockport County Div.3 North 1933-34
Career Goalscorer: Albert Valentine
Career Appearances: John Pickering

Senior Honours: Conference Champions 1997-98

Previous
Names: Halifax Town 1911 - 2008
Leagues: Yorkshire Comb.1911-12, Midland League 1912-21, Football League-Division 3 North 1921-58, Division 3, 1958-63, 69-76, 98-02. Division 4 1963-69 76-93 Conference 1993-98, 02-08.

Grounds: Sandhall Lane 1911-15 Exley 1919-20.

Back Row: Dan Cochrane, Nicky Gray, James Riley, Phil Senior, Jonathan Hedge, Steve Payne, Paul Sykes, Sam Jerome

Middle Row: Trevor Storton Assistant Manager, James Dean, Mark Whitehouse, Luke Smith, Neil Ross, Ross Clegg, Alan Russell-Cox Physio, Kevin Gillespie Fitness Coach

Front Row: Richard Marshall, Aaron Hardy, Daniel Lowe, Ryan Crossley, Neil Aspin Manager, Tom Baker, Scott Phelan, Mark Peers, Mark Hollis

GARFORTH TOWN

Founded: 1964
Nickname: The Miners

Manager: Simon Clifford

Club Colours: Yellow & green/blue/white & blue.

Change: Blue & white/white/blue.

Best Seasons - League: 10th Northern Premier Division One North 2007-2008

Ground address: Genix Healthcare Stadium, Cedar Ridge , Garforth,

Leeds LS25 2PF.

Tel: Office 0113 287 7145 Fax: 0113 286 4083

Capacity: 3,000 **Covered**: 200 **Floodlights**: Yes

Simple Directions: M1 Jct 47 take Garforth turning A 642 and turn left after 200 yards into housing estate opposite White House Stadium at end of Lane.

Midweek Home Matchday: Tuesday

Clubhouse: Full Licensed Hours **Club Shop:** Yes

CLUB PERSONNEL

Chairman: Tom Murray

Committee:

Norman Hebbron – President
Simon Clifford – Owner
Gillian Clifford – General Secretary
Peter Taylor – Treasurer
George Williams – Gen. Manager
Steve Nichol – Match Secretary

Secretary: Steve Nichol.
35 Lambton Drive,
Hetton-le-Hole, Tyne & Wear.
DH5 0EW
Tel: (H): 0191 517 0419
(M): 07984 786 782

Programme Editor: George Williams.
Tel: 0113 287 7145

CLUB STATISTICS

Record Attendance:	1,385 v Tadcaster Albion (Socrates Debut) League Record
Career Goalscorer:	Simeon Bambrook 67
Career Appearances:	Philip Matthews 1982-1993
Record Transfer Fee Paid:	Not known
Record Transfer Fee Received:	Not known
Senior Honours:	Northern Counties East Division 1 1997-98.
Previous Leagues:	Leeds Sunday Combination 1964-72 West Yorks League 1972-78 Yorks League 1978-83. Northern Counties 1983-2007.
Previous Names:	Garforth Miners 1964-1985.

HARRODGATE RAILWAY ATH.

Founded: 1935
Nickname: The Rail

Manager: Phil Sharpe.

Club Colours: Red/green/red.

Change: White/black/white.

Best Season - League: 12th Northern Premier Div. One/One North 2006-07/07-08

Ground address: Station View, Starbeck, Harrogate, North Yorks. HG2 7JA

Tel Nos: 01423 883 104

Capacity: 3,500 **Seats**: 800 **Covered**: 600 **Floodlights:** Yes:

Simple Directions: A59 Harrogate to Knaresborough Road. Turn left after one and a half miles just before railway level crossing. Ground is 150 yards up the lane.

Midweek Home Matchday: Monday

Clubhouse: Full facilities available.

Shop: No. But club merchandise available.

CLUB PERSONNEL

Chairman: Dennis Bentley

Additional Directors:
David Shepherd
Paddy Hall
David Green

Secretary: David Shepherd
99 The Avenue, Starbeck,
Harrogate.HG1 4QG
Tel: (H): 01423 886 293
(M): 07816 986 799

Programme Editor: See secretary.

CLUB STATISTICS

Record **Attendance:** 3,500 v Bristol City F.A.Cup 2nd Round 2002-2003

Career Goalscorer: Not known

Career Appearances: Not known

Record Transfer Fee Paid: Not known

Received: £1,000 from Guiseley for Colin Hunter.

Senior Honours: N.Co.East Div 1 1989-1999 Div 2 North Lg & Cup 1983-84

Previous Leagues: West Yorks., Harrogate & District, Yorkshire 55-73 80-82 N.Co East 82-06

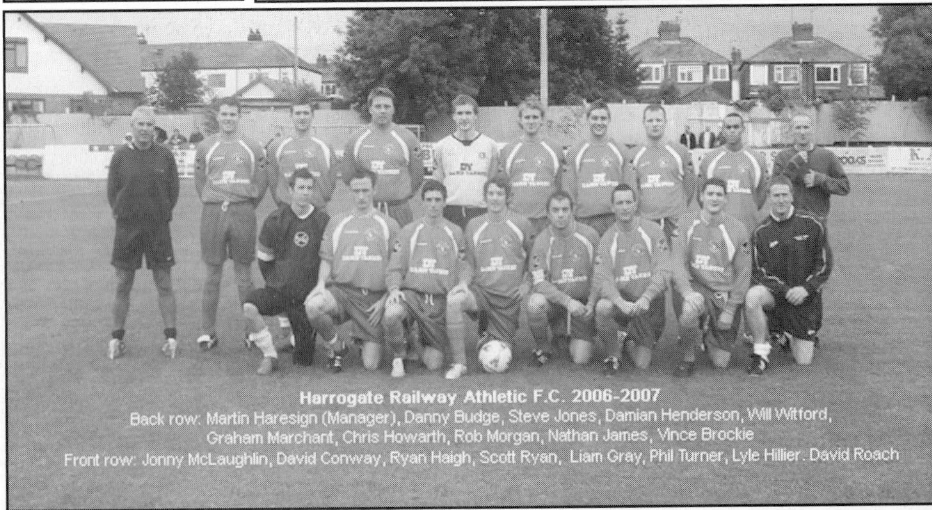

Harrogate Railway Athletic F.C. 2006-2007
Back row: Martin Haresign (Manager), Danny Budge, Steve Jones, Damian Henderson, Will Witford, Graham Marchant, Chris Howarth, Rob Morgan, Nathan James, Vince Brockie
Front row: Jonny McLaughlin, David Conway, Ryan Haigh, Scott Ryan, Liam Gray, Phil Turner, Lyle Hillier. David Roach

NB: UNFORTUNATELY A RECENT PHOTO WAS NOT AVAILABLE AT THE TIME OF GOING TO PRESS.

LANCASTER CITY

Founded: 1905
Nickname: Dolly Blues

Manager: Tony Hesketh

Club Colours: Blue/white/blue.

Change: Yellow or white/blue or white/white.

Best Seasons - League: 13th Conference North 2004-2005

Ground address: Giant Axe, West Road, Lancaster LA1 5PE

Tel: Office: 01524 382 238 Fax: 01524 841 710 Club: 01524 843 500

Capacity: 3,064 **Seats**: 513 **Covered**: 900 **Floodlights**: Yes

Simple Directions: M6 jct 33 follow into city, left at lights immediately after Waterstones bookshop. Second right past railway station on right, follow down hill and ground is first right.

Midweek Home Matchday: Tuesday

Clubhouse: The Dolly Blue Tavern just outside the ground.

Club Shop: Yes

Local Press: Lancaster Guardian, Morecambe Visitor, Lancashire Evening Post and Lancaster Citizen.

Local Radio: Red Rose, Radio Lancaster and Bay Radio.

CLUB PERSONNEL

Chairman: Ian Sharp

Additional Directors:
Stuart Houghton (Vice-Chairman/Financial Director), Mick Hoyle (Chief Executive Officer), David Needham (Director), John Bagguley (President), Norman Wilson & Steve Ball (Vice-Presidents), Eric Williams (Non-Executive)

Secretary: Barry Newsham
c/o Club.
(H): 01524 32430
(F): 01524 841 710
(B): 01524 382 238
07759 530 901

Programme Editor: See Secretary.

CLUB STATISTICS

Record	**Attendance**: 7,500 v Carlisle United F.A.Cup 1936
Victory:	8-0 v Leyland Motors(A) 83-84
Defeat:	0-10 v Matlock Town NPL Div 1 73-74
Career Goalscorer:	David Barnes 130
Career Appearances:	Edgar J.Parkinson 591
Record Transfer Fee	**Paid**: £6,000 to Droylsden for Jamie Tandy
	Received: £25.000 from Birmingham City for Chris Ward
Senior Honours:	N.P.L. Division One Champions 1995-96, Lancashire Junior Cup (ATS Challenge Trophy): 27-8 28-9 30-1 33-4 51-2 74-5 R-up (5)
Previous Leagues:	Lancs Comb. 05-70 NPL 70-82, NW Co 82-87 NPL 87-04. Conf North 04-07.

Front Row (L-R): Ian Flannery, Rob Henry, Phil Brown (Assistant Manager), Ian Sharp Chairman,Tony Hesketh (Manager) Roger Sharrock, Andrew Teague. **Middle Row:** David Rhodes Physio, Mike Rushton, Hughie Sharkey Kitman, Adam Farrell, Mark Jackson,Chris Ward, Seydou Bamba, Michael Stringfellow Captain, Paul Jarvis, Dominic Ward, Kevin McGuffog (Physio), Guy Heffernan, Derek Bull (Coach). **Back Row:** Max Rothwell, Jordan Connerton, Alex Kenyon, Mark Thornley, Rob Wilson, Martin Fearon, Aaron Helliwell, Neil Marshall.

LEIGH GENESIS

Founded:1896
Nickname: Railwaymen

Manager: Gary Flitcroft.
Club Colours: White & black/black & white/white & black.
Change: Blue & white/blue & white/white & blue.
Best Season - League: 5th Conference 2000-01
Current Ground address: Leigh Sports Village Stadium, Atherleigh Way, Leigh, Lancashire WN7 4JY.
Tel: 0800 634 2878 (Office)
Capacity: 8,000 **Seats:** 2,000 **Covered:** 4,000 **Floodlights:** Yes
Simple Directions: Leave the M6 at Junction 22 At the end of the slip road turn off the roundabout onto Winwick Lane. Continue to the end of that road (approximately 2 miles) and turn right. Continue straight on through the first set of traffic lights. At the second set of traffic lights (opposite Texaco garage) turn right onto the East Lancashire Road (A580). Turn left at the first set of traffic lights (signposted Pennington Flash) onto Atherleigh Way. Continue forward through the traffic lights to a mini-roundabout Leigh Sports Village Stadium is situated on the right.
Midweek home matchday: Wednesday
Clubhouse: Yes
Club Shop: At the ground
Local Radio: Radio Lancs, Red Rose Radio and G.M. R.
Local Press: Bolton Evening News

CLUB PERSONNEL

Chairman: Alan Leach
Additional Directors:
Gary Culshaw, Stan Walker, William Taylor.

Secretary: Donna Middleton
c/o Leigh Genesis F.C.
Leigh Sports Village Stadium.
Tel: (B) 0800 634 2878.
07970 987 847.

Programme Editor: See Secretary

CLUB STATISTICS

Record	**Attendance**: 8,500 v Wigan Athletic, Lancs Jnr.Cup 1954
	Victory: 19-1 Nelson. Lancs Comb. 1964
	Defeat: 1-9 v Brandon United F.A.Cup
Career Goalscorer:	Neil McLachlan
Career Appearances:	Neil McLachlan
Record Transfer Fee	**Paid**: £6,000 to Prescot Cables for Peter Cumiskey
	Received: £75,000 from Crewe Alexandra for Steve Jones
Senior Honours:	N.P.L. Champions 1999-2000, N.P.L. League Cup 99-00, Div 1 R-Up 96-97, Lancs F.A.Cup 84-85 and Lancs Trophy 02-03
Previous Leagues:	Lancs Alliance 1891-97, Lancs Lg 1897-1900, Lancs Comb., 17-18 19-39, 46-68, Cheshire Co 68-82, N.W.Co 82-83 N.P.L. 83-2000
Names:	Horwich RMI, Leigh RMI. **Previous Grounds**: Grundy Hill, Horwich until 1994.

MOSSLEY

Founded:1903
Nickname: Lilywhites

Manager: Chris Wilcock
Club Colours: White/black/white.
Change: Orange/black/orange.
Best Season - League: 1st Northern Premier Premier Division 1978-79, 79-80.
Ground address: Seel Park, Market Street, Mossley, Lancs OL5 0ES.
Tel: Office/Fax: 01457 832 369 Club: 01457 836 104
Capacity: 4,500 **Seats**: 200 **Covered**:1,500 **Floodlights**: Yes
Simple Directions:
From north; M60 J.23, then A635 to Ashton-U-Lyne, A670 Mossley to town centre .Ground behind market place. From south: M6 Junc 19, A556, M56 to Junc3, A5103 to M'chester, then Mancunian Way (A57M) to A635. Follow Ashton signs 5m, the Mossley signs via A670 to town centre.
Rail: Mossley BR. Buses 153 from Manchester, 343 from Oldham, 350 from Ashton
Midweek Home Matchday: Tuesday
Clubhouse: Open evenings and matchdays.
Club Shop: Yes.
Local Radio: BBC GMR (Key 103) 96.2 Revolution
Local Press: Oldham Evening Chronicle, Mossley & Saddleworth Reporter, Manchester Evening News, Tameside Advertiser and Pink Final.

CLUB PERSONNEL

Chairman: Alan Barrow
Additional Directors:
Mike Chamley, Mark Griffin.

Secretary: Harry Hulmes
7 Market Street, Mossley,
Ashton-u-Lyne, Lancs.
OL5 0ES
Tel: (H/F) 01457 836 079
07944 856 343

Programme
Editor: John Cawthorne
0161 303 7929

CLUB STATISTICS

Record	**Attendance:** 7,000 v Stalybridge Celtic 1950
	Career Goalscorer: David Moore 235 - 1974-84
	Career Appearances: Jimmy O'Connor 613 - 1972-87
Record Transfer Fee	**Paid**: £2,300 for Phil Wilson from Altrincham - 1980
	Received: £25,000 from Everton for Eamonn O'Keefe.
Senior Honours:	Northern Premier League Champions 1978-79, 79-80.
	Challenge Cup 1978-79.
Previous	**Leagues:** Ashton. South East Lancs. Lancs Comb. 1918-19.
	Cheshire County 1919-72. Northen Premier. N.West Counties.
	Names: Park Villa 03-04. Mossley Juniors.

Back row (L-R): Nathan McDonald, Jordan Goodeve, Sam Walker, Gareth Wager.
Middle row: Kayleme Baxter, Andy Watson, Graham Kay, Peter Collinge, Matthew Wrigley, Nick Boothby, Jonathan Jackson.
Front row: Lee Merricks (coach), Kurtis Noble, Ben Richardson, Matt Easter, Chris Willcock (manager), Danny Egan, Dan Schwarz, Leon Henry, John Flanagan (assistant manager).

OSSETT ALBION

Founded: 1944
Nickname: Albion

Manager: Eric Gilchrist
Club Colours: Old gold/black/old gold.
Change: All white.
Best Season - League: 6th Northern Premier Division One North 2007-08, 08-09.
Ground address: The Warehouse Systems Stadium, Dimple Wells, Ossett, Yorkshire.
Tel: Office/Fax: 01924 280 450 Club: 01924 273 618.
Capacity: 3,000 **Seats**: 2 **Covered**: 750 **Floodlights**: Yes
Simple Directions:
M1 jct 40. Take Wakefield road, right at Post House Hotel down Queens Drive. Right at end then second left down Southdale Rd. Right at end, then first left into Dimple Wells (cars only). Coaches take second left following the road for 200yds bearing left twice. Four miles from both Wakefield and Dewsbury BR stations. Buses 116 and 117
Midweek Home Matchday: Tuesday
Clubhouse: Three bars & catering facilities. Open seven days a week
Club Shop: Full range of souvenirs.
Local Radio: Radio Leeds and Ridings Radio
Local Press: Wakefield Express

CLUB PERSONNEL

Chairman: Eric J Gilchrist.
Additional Directors:
A Lightfoot, S Chambers, Miss L Burns, Miss G Patterson, K Fletcher, S Wilkinson, S Garside, N Yarrow, Mrs S Langdale, P Young.
Secretary: Andrew Lightfoot
24 Garden Close, Ossett, West Yorkshire, WF5 0SQ
Tel: (H); 01924 276 898
(M): 07711 309 923
Programme Editor:
Neville Wigglesworth.
Tel: 01924 275 630

CLUB STATISTICS

Record	**Attendance:** 1,200 v Leeds United Opening of floodlights 1986
	Career Goalscorer:John Balmer
	Career Appearances: Peter Eaton 800+ (22years)
Record	**Victory:** 12-0 v British Ropes (H) Yorks League 2 6/5/59
	Defeat: 2-11 v Swillington (A) W.Yorks Lge Div 1 25/4/56
Senior Honours:	N.C.E. Premier Champions 1998-99, 03-04. Div 1 1986-87.
	N.C.E. League Cup 1983-84, 02-03. W. Riding County Cup (4)
Previous	**Leagues**: Heavy Woollen Area 1944-49. West Riding Co. Amtr 1949-50; West Yorks 1950-57 Yorks 1957-82. North Co. East. **Ground:** Fearn House

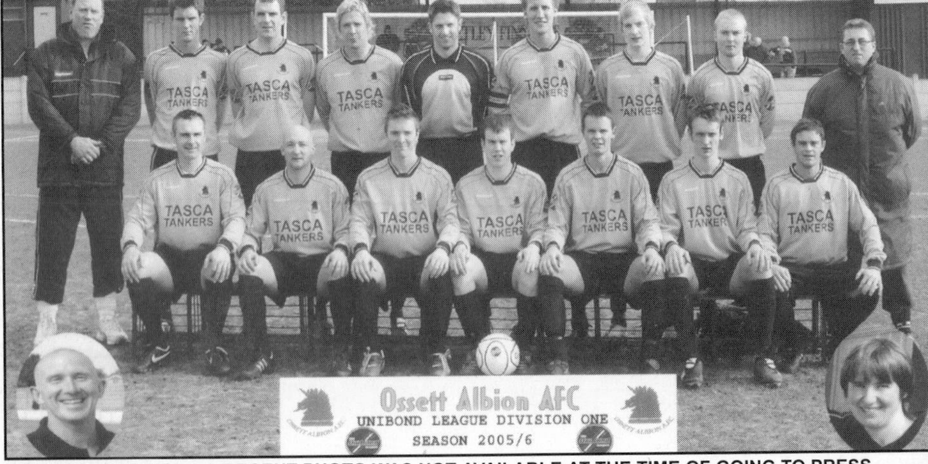

NB: UNFORTUNATELY A RECENT PHOTO WAS NOT AVAILABLE AT THE TIME OF GOING TO PRESS.

PRESCOT CABLES

Founded: 1866
Nickname: Tigers

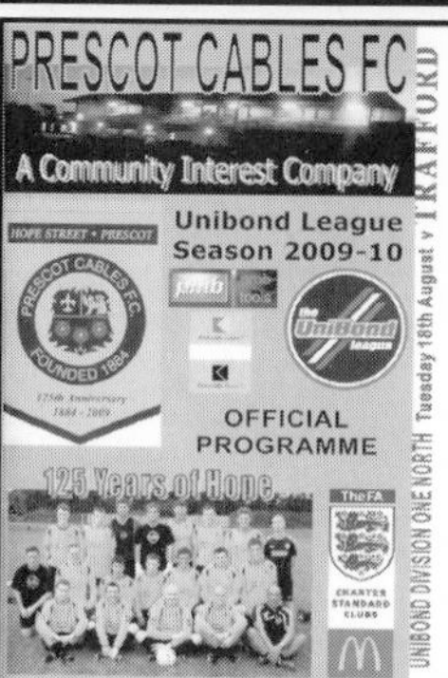

Manager: Joe Gibiliru.

Club Colours: Black & amber stripes/black/black.

Change: All red.

Best Seasons - League: 5th Northern Premier Prmier Division 2004-2005.

Ground address: Valerie Park, Eaton Street, Prescot. L34 6HD

Tel/Fax No: 0151 430 0507

Website: www.prescotcablesfc.co.uk

Capacity: 3,000 **Seats**: 500 **Covered:** 600 **Floodlights:** Yes

Simple Directions: M62 Jct 7 A57 to Prescot. Take 3rd exit at roundabout after two and half miles. Turn right after another half mile. Right at Hope & Anchor pub, into Hope Street.

Midweek Home Matchday: Tuesday

Clubhouse: Open matchdays with refreshments.

Club Shop: Fully stocked. Orders can be made from website above.

CLUB PERSONNEL

Chairman: Tony Zeverona

Additional Directors:
D Lace, D Bellairs,
D Williams, E Williams,
P Kneale, K Derbyshire,
M Flaherty, N Parr,
F Weston.

Secretary: Doug Lace
20 Cable Road,
Prescot L35 5AW
Tel: 0151 426 6440 (H).
07753 143 273

Programme
Editor: Paul Watkinson
Tel: 0151 426 4593

CLUB STATISTICS

Record	**Attendance:** 8,122 v Ashton National 1932
	Victory: 18-3 v Great Harwood 1954-55
	Defeat: 1-12 v Morecambe 1936-37
	Goalscorer: Freddie Crampton
	Career Appearances: Harry Grisedale
	Transfer Fee Paid: N/A **Received:** N/A
Senior Honours:	N.W.Co Champions 2002-03 Liverpool Non-League Cup (4) Liverpool Challenge Cup (6) Lane's Combination Champions 1956-57 N.W.Co.Cup Winners 1947-48
Previous Leagues	Liverpool Co Comb., Lancs Comb.1897-98 18-20 27-33 36-37, Mid Cheshire 1977-78 Cheshire County 1978-82 N.W.Co.1982-2003

RADCLIFFE BOROUGH

Founded: 1949
Nickname: Boro

Manager: Gerry Luczka

Club Colours: All blue.

Change: All maroon.

Best Season - League: 9th Northern Premier Premier 2004-05

Ground address: Stainton Park Pilkington Rd, Radcliffe, Lancs. M26 3PE

Tel: Office: 0161 724 8346 Club: 0161 724 5937

Fax: 0161 723 3178

Capacity: 3,000 **Seats**: 350 **Covered**: 1,000 **Floodlights**: Yes

Simple Directions: M62 Jct 17 follow signs for Whitefield and Bury. Take A665 to Radcliffe, through town centre. Right into Unsworth Street (opposite Turf Hotel). Ground half a mile on left.

Midweek Home Matchday: Tuesday

Clubhouse: On ground-food available

Club Shop: Yes.

Local Radio: GMR, Piccadilly Tower and F.M. Bolton

Local Press: Radcliffe Times, Bolton Evening News & Manchester Evening News.

CLUB PERSONNEL

Chief Executive:
David Murgatroyd

Additional Director:
Graham Fielding
(Company Secretary)

Secretary: Graham Fielding
c/o Radcliffe Borough Football Club, Stainton Park, Pilkington Road, Radcliffe, Manchester. M26 3PE
Tel: (B): 0161 724 8346
(F): 0161 723 3178

Programme Editor:
John Walker.
Tel: 0782 4647 289

CLUB STATISTICS

Record	**Attendance:** 2,495 v York City F.A.Cup 1st Rd 2000-01
	Career Goalscorer: Ian Lunt 147
	Career Appearances: David Bean 401
	Transfer Fee Paid: £5,000 to Buxton for Gary Walker 1991
	Received: £20,000 from Shrewsbury Town for Jody Banim 2003
Senior Honours:	N.P.L. Div One Champions 1996-97. N.W.Co 1984-85.
Previous	**Leagues**: S.E. Lancs, Manchester 1953-63 Lancs Combination 1963-71. Cheshire Co. 1971-82. N.W.Co. 1982-87.

Back Row (L-R): Kevin Glendon (Manager), Ronnie Evans (Asst. Manager), Simon Garden, Simon Kelly, Danny Hurst, Richard Landon, David Bean, Karl Marginson, Davy Luker, David Felgate, Roy Davies (physio). **Front Row:** Tony Whealing, Steven Spencer, Richard Battersby, Jody Banim, Bernard Manning Jnr. (Chairman), Chris Denham, James Price, Jason Astley, Gary Simpson.

NB: UNFORTUNATELY A RECENT PHOTO WAS NOT AVAILABLE AT THE TIME OF GOING TO PRESS.

ROSSENDALE UNITED

Founded: 1898
Nickname: The Stags

Manager: John Hughes.

Club Colours: Royal blue & white stripes/royal blue/royal blue.

Change: Tangerine/black/tangerine.

Best Season - League: 9th Northern Premier Div. One/One North 2006-07/07-08

Ground address: Dark Lane, Staghills Road, Newchurch, Rossendale BB4 7UA

Tel: 01706 215 119. Club: 01706 213 296.

Capacity: 2,500 **Seats**:500 **Covered**:Yes **Floodlights**:Yes

Simple Directions: M60 Junc 18, M66 north following signs for Burnley, then A682 to Rawstenstall, take 2nd exit sign Burnley A682, at 1st lights turn right into Newchurch Rd, 1.5 miles turn right into Staghills Rd. Ground is 800 yards right.

Midweek Home Matchday: Tuesday

Clubhouse: Evenings and Matchdays. Hot Snacks. Sky TV, Pool and hall.

Club Shop: Yes.

Local Radio: Red Rose Radio Lancashire.

Local Press: Lancs Evening Telegraph & Rossendale Free Press.

CLUB PERSONNEL

Chairman: Steve Hobson

Additional Direcotrs:
Wendy Ennis,
Andrew Connolly,
Dave Hancock,

Secretary : Wendy Ennis
4, Brow Edge, Rawtenstall,
Lancs. BB4 7TT
(H): 01706 212 634
(B): 01706 215 119
(M): 07804 362 171

Programme
Editor: Dave Rogan
Tel: 01282 415 099

CLUB STATISTICS

Record	**Attendance:** 12,000 v Bolton Wanderers F.A.Cup 2nd Round 1971
	Career Goalscorer: Bob Scott: 230
	Career Appearances: Johhny Clark 770 1947-65
Record Transfer Fee	**Paid**: £3,000 to Buxton for Jimmy Clarke 1992
	Received: £1,500 from Huddersfield Town for Dave O'Neill 1974
	Victory: 17-0 v Ashton Town Lancs. Comb. 1911-12
	Defeat: 0-14 v Morecambe Lancs. Comb. 1967-1968
Senior Honours:	N.W.Co League DIV.1 1988-1989 2000-2001.
Previous	**Leagues**: N.E.Lancs. Combination, Lancs Cobination 1898-1899 1901-1970. Central Lancs 1899-1901, Cheshire County 1970-1982 North West Counties 1982-89 1993-2001.

Back Row (L-R): Papis Dieyte, Jack Brierley, Robert Flint, Tom Smith, Tom Brocklehurst, Chris Lawton, Andrew Charlesworth, Paul Socha, Kanganl Ndiwa.
Front Row: Demaine Cousins, Matt Walsh, Sean Pearson, Jason Hart, Danny Ellis, Danny Finch, Alex Leke.

SALFORD CITY

Founded: 1940
Nickname: Ammies

Manager: Paul White.

Club Colours: Tangerine/black/tangerine.

Change: All sky blue.

Best Season - League: 20th Northern Premier Division One North 2008-09.

Ground address: Moor Lane, Kersal, Salford, Manchester M7 3PZ. Tel: 0161 792 6287.

Capacity: 8,000 **Seats:** 260 **Covered:** 600 **Floodlights**: Yes

Directions: M62 to Junction 17 (Prestwich, Whitefield). Take A56 Bury New Road towards Manchester. Continue through four sets of traffic lights. Turn right into Moor Lane. Ground 500 yards on left. Take first left after ground (Oaklands Road), first left again into Nevile Road and follow along to main entrance.

Midweek Home Matchday: Tuesday.

Clubhouse: Open matchdays only.

Club Shop: No

CLUB PERSONNEL

Chairman: Darren Quick

Additional Direcotrs:
Bill Taylor, Ged Carter, George Russell, Dave Russell, Paul Raven, Terry Gaskell, Barbara Gaskell, Mark Geoarge, Pete Byrom, Val Carter, Derek Brent, John Simpson.

Secretary : Bill Taylor
23, Westwood Drive,
Pendlebury, Salford.
M27 4JJ
Tel: (H/F) 0161 736 1840
07989 800 231

Programme Editor: As Secretary.

CLUB STATISTICS

Record **Attendance:** 3,000 v Whickham F.A.Vase 1980.
4,058 v FC Utd of Manchester, NWC Div.1, 03.10.06
(Played at The Willows, Salford R.L.F.C.)
Career Goalscorer: Not known.
Career Appearances: Not known.
Victory: Not known.
Defeat: Not known.

Senior Honours: Manchester Football League Premier 1975, 1976, 1977, 1979.
North West Counties League Cup 2006.

Previous **Leagues:** Manchester 1963-80. Cheshire County 1980-82.
North West Counties 1982-2008.
Names: Salford Central, 1940-63 Salford Amateurs 1963 until merger with Anson Villa, Salford F.C. >1990.

Back Row (L-R): Adrian Bellamy, Phil McGahey, Martin Campbell, Kenny Tudor, Simon Myerscough, Steve Brackenridge.
Front: Neil Davies, Jon Robinson, Mark Dwyer, Lathan Forrester, Lee Mc Nally.

SKELMERSDALE UNITED

Founded: 1882
Nickname: Skem

Manager: Tommy Lawson

Club Colours: All royal blue.

Change: All red.

Best Seasons - League: 11th Northern Premier Premier Division 1971-72.

Ground address: Skelmersdale & Ormskirk College Stadium, Stormy Corner, Selby Place, off Stathem Road, Stanley Industrial Estate, Skelmersdale, Lancs.WN8 8EF. **Tel/Fax No**: 01695 722 123

Capacity: 2,300 **Seats**: 240 **Covered**: 500 **Floodlights**: Yes

Simple Directions: M58 Jct 4 to Skem. Over roundabout into Glenburn Road, left into Neverstitch Rd. at roundabout and then first right at next two roundabouts into Staveley Road. Sharp left into Stathem Rd with ground 500 yds on left in Selby Place.

Midweek Home Matchday: Tuesday

Clubhouse: Matchdays.

Club Shop: Yes

Local Radio: Radio Merseyside, Radio Lancashire

Local Press: Advertiser/Champion

CLUB PERSONNEL

Chairman: Frank Hughes

Additional Directors:
Mr W Bennett, Mrs L Boardman, Mr W Boardman, Mr D Bolderston, Mr T Garner, Mr A Gore, Mr P Griffiths, Mr J Johnson, Mr S Johnson, Mr B Jones, Mr P McGee, Mr J Sewell, Mr M Sewell.

Secretary: Bryn Jones.
34 Bromilow Road,
Skelmersdale Lancs, WN8 8TU. (H): 01695 724 647
(M) 07904 911 234

Programme Editor: See chairman

CLUB STATISTICS

Record	**Attendance:** 7,000 v Slough Town F.A.Amateur Cup Semi-Final 1967
	Career Goalscorer: Stuart Rudd 230
	Career Appearances: Robbie Holcroft 422 including 398 consecutive
	Transfer Fee Paid: £2,000 for Stuart Rudd.
	Transfer Fee Received: £4,000 for Stuart Rudd.
Senior Honours:	F.A.Amateur Cup Winners 1970-71. Lancs Junior Cup (2)
	Barassi Anglo-Italioan Cup 1970-1971, Lancs Non-League Cup (2)
Previous Leagues:	Liverpool Co.Comb., Lancs. Comb. 1891-93 1903-07 21-24 55-56 76-78
	Cheshire County: 1968-1971 1978-1982 N.P.L. 1971-1976 N.W.Co. 1983-2006

TRAFFORD

Founded: 1990
Nickname: The North

Manager: Garry Vaughan.

Club Colours: All white.

Change: All yellow.

Best Season - League: 5th Northern Premier Division One 2000-01

Ground address: Shawe View, Pennybridge Lane, Flixton, Urmston, Manchester M41 5DL **Tel/Fax No:** 0161 747 1727

Capacity: 2,500 **Seats:** 292 **Covered:** 740 **Floodlights:** Yes

Simple Directions: M60 Jct 9 B5158 towards Urmston. At first roundabout take first exit.Then right at first lights into Moorside Rd. At next roundabout take second exit into Bowfell Rd. Next lights sharp left, then immediately right into Pennyridge Lane next to Bird -in-Hand pub parking on left after 100 yards.

Midweek Home Matchday: Tuesday

Clubhouse: Yes

Club Shop: Yes

CLUB PERSONNEL

Chairman: Tom Walmsley

Additional Directors: D Brown, G Foxall, D Law, D Murray, B Whitten.

Secretary : Graham Foxall
90, Grosvenor Road,
Urmston, Manchester
M41 5AQ
Tel: (H): 0161 747 4502
(M): 07796 864 151

Programme Editor: Dave Murray.
Tel: 07780 784 268

CLUB STATISTICS

Record
Attendance: 803 v Flixton, Northern Premier Div.One 1997-98.
2,238 v FC Utd of Manchester, FAC Preliminary Rnd, 02.09.07 (Played at Moss Lane - Altrincham FC)
Career Goalscorer: Garry Vaughan - 88.
Career Appearances: Garry Vaughan - 293.
Victory: Not known.
Defeat: Not known.

Senior Honours:
North West Counties Division One Champions 1996-97, 2007-08.
Manchester Challenge Trophy 2004-05.

Previous
Leagues: Mid Cheshire 1990-92,
North West Counties 1992-97, 2003-08
Northern Premier 1997-2003.
Names: North Trafford 1990-94.

Back Row (L-R): G. Vaughan (Manager), K. Harrop, R. Marley, T. Read, B. McCartney, S.Woodford, G. Barker, J. Williamson, S. Roscoe, L. Greenhalgh (Ass. Manager).
Front Row: I. Hall, S. Gallanders, S. Barlow, D. White, S. Metcalfe, G. Thomas, M. Knight, S. Payne.

WAKEFIELD

Re-Formed: 2006

Manager: Ronnie Glavin

Club Colours: All niki blue.

Change: All niki amber.

Best Season - League: 1st Northern Premier Premier Division 1987-88, 88-89.

Ground address: Wakefield Sports Club, Eastmoor Road,Wakefield WF1 3RR

Tel: Office/Fax: 01924 365 007 Club: 01924 372 038

Capacity: 2,500 **Seats**: 460 **Covered**: 700 **Floodlights**:Yes

Simple Directions: From M1 Juction 41 take A650(Wakefield) then at third roundabout takeA642 (Garforth). After fuirst roundabout take first right (North Avenue). Then left at T Junction and ground is 80 yards on the right.

Midweek Home Matchday: Tuesday

Clubhouse: Yes **Club Shop:** Yes

Local Radio: Radio Leeds, Radio Sheffield,Pulse FM, Huddersfield FM & Ridings FM.

Local Press: Huddersfield Examiner, Huddersfleld & District Chronicle, Wakefield Express

CLUB PERSONNEL

Chairman: Alan Blackman

Additional Directors:
Pete Belvis, Paul David, Peter Maude, Peter Matthews, Daniel Brownhill, Marcus Pound.

Secretary: Peter Matthews, 'Hillandale', Slant Gate, Highburton, Huddersfield HD 8 0QN
(H/F): 01484 603 629
(M): 0794 382 9818

Programme Editor: Dan Brownhill
07921 156 561

CLUB STATISTICS

Record	**Attendance**:	5,134 v Barking Amateur Cup 3rd proper 01.02.69
		18,000 at West Ham for F.A.Cup 3rd Rd 03.01.99
	Victory:	12-0 v Ecclesfield Red Rose 09.06.97
	Defeat:	1--7 v Altrincham 25.04.98
	Career Goalscorer:	Mick Pamment 305
	Career Appearances:	Ray Dennis 762
Record Transfer Fee	**Paid**:	Not known
	Received:	£60,000 for Michael Reynolds (Ayr United 98)
Senior Honours:	F.A.Vase R-up 87-88 NPL Div 1 R-up 90-91 N.Co E 87-88 88-89 R-up 85-86	
	Sheffield & Hallamshire Senior Cup (8)	
Previous	**Leagues**:	Huddersfield, Yorkshire 69-82, Northern Counties East 82-89
	Name:	Emley 1903-2002. Wakefield-Emley 2002-05.
	Ground:	Emley Welfare Sports Ground. Wakefield Trinity R.L.F.C.

Photo courtesy of Wakefield Express.

WARRINGTON TOWN

Founded: 1948
Nickname: The Town

Manager: Joey Dunn.

Club Colours: Yellow & blue/blue/blue.

Change: Red & white/red/red.

Best Season - League : 3rd Northern Premier Division One 1994-95.

Ground address: Cantilever Park, Common Lane, Latchford, Warrington WA4 2RS

Tel No: 01925 631 932 (Club) 01925 653044 (Office)

Capacity: 2,000 **Seats**: 350 **Covered**: 650 **Floodlights**: Yes

Simple Directions: M6 junction 20, then A50 towards Warrington. After 2 miles turn left immediately after swing bridge into Station Road, ground 600yds on left. From town centre travel 1 mile south on A49, left at lights into Loushers Lane, ground quarter mile on right. Two miles from Warrington Bank Quay (BR)

Midweek Home Matchday: Tuesday **Club Shop:** Yes.

Clubhouse: Weekdays 1-11pm, Sat.12-11pm, Sun. 12-11pm Bar food on matchdays

Local Radio: Wire Radio and Hospital Radio

Local Press: Warrington Guardian

CLUB PERSONNEL

Chairman: Dave Hughes
Additional Directors:
Gary Skentelbery, Richard Sutton, Jeff Greenwood, Bill Carr, Martin Simcock, Kevin Read, David Mowat, Ken Lacey.

Secretary: Geoff Bell
19, Yarmouth Road, Gt
Sankey, Warrington.
WA5 3EJ
Tel: (H) 01925 721 242
07841 175 268
Programme
Editor: Paul Roach
01352 752 489

CLUB STATISTICS

Record	**Attendance:** 2,600 v Halesowen Town F.A.Vase Semi-Final 1st Leg 1985-86
	Career Goalscorer: Steve Hughes 167
	Career Appearances: Neil Whalley
Record Transfer Fee	**Paid**: £50,000 from P.N.E. for Liam Watson
	Received: £60,000 from Preston North End for Liam Watson
Senior Honours:	N.W.C. Lge 1989-90. Lg Cup 85-86 87-88 88-89.
	Div 2 00-01
Previous	**Leagues:** Warrington & Dist. 49-52; Mid-Cheshire 52-78; Cheshire Co. 78-82; N.W.C. 82-90; N.P.L 90-97.
	Name: Stockton Heath 1949-62.

Back Row (L-R): Mike Walsh Assistant Manager,Jamie Holme,Scott Williams,Anthony Kielty,Richard Mottram, Andy Alston, Carl Rendell,Calvin Daives,Francis Smith.
Front row: Chris Fitzsimmons,Matthew Farrell, Paul Williams,Manager Paul Moore, Anthony Daniels, Billy Webb,Phillip Hadland,James Thomas.

WOODLEY SPORTS

Founded: 1970
Nickname: Sports

Manager: Trevor MacFarlane.

Club Colours: Red & blue/blue/blue.

Change: White/green/green.

Best Season - League: 4th Northern Premier Division One 2005-2006

Ground address: The Neil Rourke, Lambeth Stadium, Lambeth Grove, Woodley, Stockport SK6 1QX

Tel: Office/Fax: 0161 406 6896 Club: 0161 494 6429.

Floodlights: Yes

Simple Directions: M60 Jct 25, follow signs (A560) Bredbury, take left filter at lights which brings you onto A560 Stockport Road for approx 1 mile, turn left at Lowes Arms into Mill Street which goes into Mill Lane. Second right over bridge into Woodlands Avenue, then first left into Lambeth Grove. Ground 200 yards ahead.

Midweek Home Matchday: Tuesday

CLUB PERSONNEL

Chairman: Tony Whiteside
Additional Directors:
Rod Haslam,
Dave Parsonage,
John Rourke,
Darrin Whittaker, Peter Ross.

Secretary: Rod Haslem,
62 Marina Drive, Bredbury,
Stockport,SK6 2P.
(H) 0161 355 2407
(B/F): 0161 406 6896
(M): 07772 223 115

Programme Editor: See secretary

CLUB STATISTICS

Record	**Attendance:** 1,500 v Stockport County
Senior Honours:	NWC Div 2 99-00. Cheshire Senior Cup 2003-04,
Previous	**Leagues**: Lancashire & Cheshire, Manchester, North West Counties.

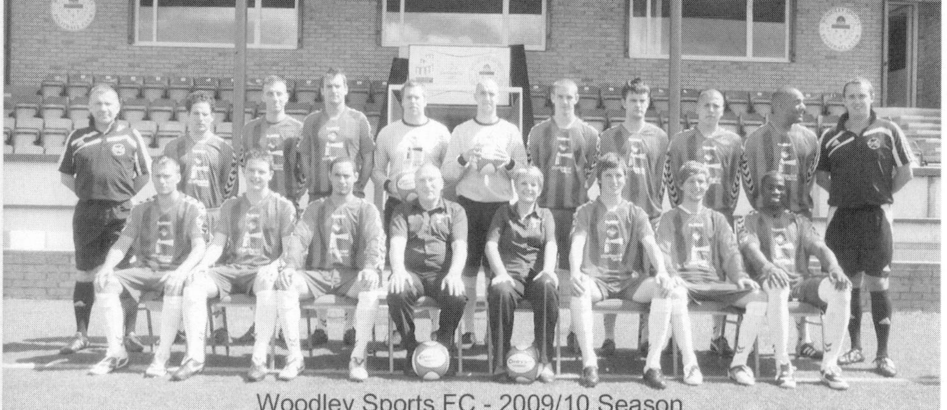

Woodley Sports FC - 2009/10 Season

back row (l-r) Trevor Macfarane-Manager, Russell Headley, Mike Clark, Gary Furnival, Ben Connett, Dominic Ingram-Hughes, Matt Cotton, Rob Parsonage, Antoni Sarcevic, Levi Kennedy, Gareth McClelland-Ass Manager/Coach
Front row (l-r) Mark Haslam, Tom Sellers, Danny Queeley, Bob&Anne Wallace-Sponsors, Gary Gee, Tom Bane, Gavin Salmon

BELPER TOWN

Formed: 1883
Nickname: Nailers

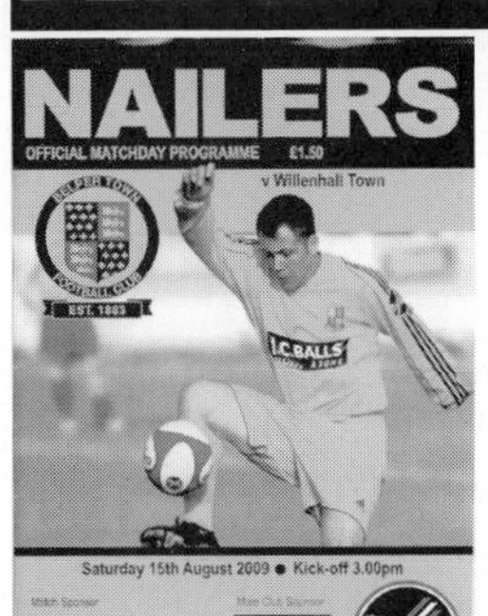

Managers: Andy Carney & Danny Hudson

Colours: Yellow/black/black.

Change: All white.

Best Season - League: 9th Northern Premier Premier Division 2005-06.

Ground Address: Christchurch Meadow, Bridge Street, Belper DE56 1BA.

Tel/fax No: 01773 825 549

Directions: From M1 North, Jnct 28 onto A38 towards Derby, turn off at A 610 (Ripley/Nottingham), then fourth exit at roundabout towards Ambergate. At junction with A6 (Hurt Arms Hotel) left to Belper. Ground on right past traffic lights. 400 yards from Belper (BR)

Capacity: 2,650 **Seats**: 500 **Cover**: 850

Floodlights: Yes

Midweek home matchday: Tuesday

Clubhouse: Open matchdays and for functions with bar and hot and cold food available.

Shop: Yes.

Local Press: Belper News, Derby Evening Telegraph, Belper Express

Local Radio: BBC Radio Derby.

CLUB PERSONNEL

Chairman: Phil Varney

Additional Directors:
Stephen Boxall (Vice Chairman), Dave Laughlin (Company Secretary), Christopher Balls, Rex Barker, Alan Benfield, Graham Boot, Christopher Briddon, Andrew Carter, David Winterbotham.

Secretary: David Laughlin
Lorne Cottage, 1 Top Hagg Lane,
Fritchley, Derbyshire. DE56 2HJ
Tel: Home/Fax: 01773 856 556
(M): 07768 010 604

Programme Editor: See secretary

CIUB STATISTICS

RECORD
Attendance: 3,200 v Ilkeston Town, 1955
Goalscorer: Mick Lakin 231
Appearances: Craig Smithurst 678
Fee Received: £2,000 for Craig Smith from Hinckley United
Fee Paid: £2,000 to Ilkeston Town for Jamie Eaton. 2001
Victory: 15-2 v Nottingham Forest 'A'1956
Defeat: 0-12 v Goole Town 1965

Senior Honours
Northern Counties East Lge 84-85, Midland Counties Lg 79-80;
Central Alliance Lge 58-59; Derbys Senior Cup 58-59 60-61 62-63 79-80

Previous
Leagues: Central Alliance 57-61; Midland Co's 61-82,
Northern Counies East 1982-97
Grounds: Acorn Ground prior to 1951

Back Row (L-R): Andy Carney (Joint Manager), Adam Burley, Richard Haigh, Mark Barnard, Dean Oliver, Richard Adams, Leigh Walker, Tom Pressman, Tom Naylor, Asa Ingall, Jon Sainthouse, Gary Middleton (Coach), Paul Bennett (Kit Manager).
Front Row: Simon Barraclough, Mickey Harcourt, Ben Walker, Lee Stevenson, James Colliver, Chris Balls (Sponsor), Danny Hudson (Joint Manager), Lewis Trimmer, Anthony Wilson, Luke Fedorenko, Katie Pilgrim. (Physiotherapist)

BRIGG TOWN

Formed: 1864
Nickname: Zebras

Manager: Steve Housham

Colours: Black & white stripes/black/red.

Change: Sky blue/maroon/sky blue.

Best Season - League: 8th Northern Premier Division One 2004-05, 05-06.

Ground: The Hawthorns, Hawthorn Avenue, Brigg DN20 8PG*

Tel: 01652 652 767. Office: 01652 651 605.

Capacity: 2,500 **Seats**: 370 **Cover**: 2 Stands **Floodlights**: Yes

Directions: From M180 Junc 4 Scunthorpe East, A18 through Brigg leaving on Wrawby Rd, left into recreation ground and follow road into BTFC.

*SATNAV postcode DN20 8DT

Website: www.briggtownfc.co.uk

Clubhouse: Licensed club open matchdays **Shop**: Contact: Kiron Brown (01652 656189)

Midweek Matchday: Tuesday

Local Radio: Radio Humberside

Local Press: Scunthorpe Evening Telegraph

CLUB PERSONNEL

Chairman: Kiron Brown

Committee: Martin North, John Martin, Bob Taylor, Jack Dunderdale, Mark Cawkwell, Carl Atkinson, Mike Smith, Simon Harris, Tim Harris, Kenny Bowers.

Secretary: Martin North
"Beau View", 24 Manley Gardens, Brigg, North Lincs. DN20 8LW
Tel: (H) 01652 651 468
07891 122 242

Programme
Editor: Michael Harker
01302 852 404

CLUB STATISTICS

RECORD	**Attendance:** 2,000 v Boston U. 1953 (at Brocklesby Ox)
	Goalscorer: Not known.
	Appearances: Not known.
	Victory: Not known.
	Defeat: Not known.
HONOURS	F.A. Challenge Vase 1995-96 02-03; Northern Counties East Prmier 2000-01, Lincolshire League Champions (8) , League Cup (5); Midland Counties League1977-78 Lincolnshire `A' Snr Cup (4) Lincolnshire `B' Snr Cup (5),
PREVIOUS	**Leagues:** Lincolshire 1948-76; Midland Counties 1976-82. Northern Counties East 1982-2004.
	Grounds: Old Manor House Convent, Station Road (pre1939); Brocklesby Ox 1939-59

Back Row (L-R): Sam West, Neal Spafford, Jason Maxwell, Adam Smith, Caroline Smith (sponsor) Paul Metcalf, Sam Thorne, ChrisRogers, Rob Zant, Mick Smith (sponsor) Scott Hellewell, Matty Mckay, Steve Hutchinson, Luke Smith, Mark Anderson, Steve Davis. **Front Row:** Audrey Mcguigan (Sports Rehabilitator) Daniel Barrett, Alan Lamb, Andy Taylor, Julian Capuano, Dave Andrews (Asst. Mgr) Lee Roy Cochrane, Steve Housham (Manager) Jonathan Pickess, Tommy Spall, Stuart Ainsley, Jimmy Snee (Trainer).

CAMMELL LAIRD

Founded: 1907
Nickname: Lairds

Manager: Derek Ward

Club Colours: All royal blue.

Change: Red & black stripes/black/black.

Best Season - League: 18th Northern Premier Premier Division 2008-09.

Ground address: Kirklands, St Peter's Road, Rock Ferry, Birkenhead, Merseyside CH42 1PY. 0151 645 3121 (Office). 0151 645 5991 (Club)

Club Website: www.camelllairdfc.co.uk

Capacity: 2,000 **Seats**: 150 **Covered**: Yes **Floodlights**: Yes

Simple Directions: From M6 take M56 towards Chester and then M53 towards Birkenhead. Exit jct 5 towards Birkenhead on A4. After aprox.4 miles take B 5136 signposted New Ferry. After a mile turn right into Procter Road. Club is at bottom of the road on the left.

Midweek Home Matchday: Tuesday

Clubhouse: Yes **Tel Nos**: 0151 645 3121/5991

Club Shop: Yes (matchdays and online)

Local Radio: Radio Merseyside

Local Press: Wirral Globe

CLUB PERSONNEL

Chairman: John Lynch

Additional Directors:
Ray Steele, Ian Doran,
George Higham,
Paul Connelly.

Secretary: Anthony R Wood.
Lairds Sports Club,
St. Peter`s Road, Rock Ferry,
Birkenhead. CH42 1PY
0151 645 3121 (H)
07931 761 429

Programme
Editor: Gary Langley
07891 457 511

CLUB STATISTICS

Record	**Attendance:** 1,700 v Harwich & Parkeston 5th Round F.A.Vase 1990-91
	Career Goalscorer: Not Known.
	Career Appearances: Not known.
Record Transfer Fee	**Paid**: N/A
	Received: N/A
Senior Honours:	N.W.Counties Champions 2005-2006 Div 2 League Cup & Trophy Treble 04-05
	West Cheshire Champions (19) Cheshire Amateur Cup (11).
	Wirral Senior Cup.
Previous	**Leagues**: West Cheshire, North West Counties.

CARLTON TOWN

Founded: 1904
Nickname: Town

Manager: Tommy Brookbanks.

Club Colours: Royal blue with stripe/royal & yellow/yellow.

Change: Sky blue/navy & sky blue/sky blue.

Best Season - League: 4th Northern Premier Division One South 2008-09.

Ground address: Bill Stokeld Stadium, Stoke Lane, Gedling, Nottingham NG4 2QP

Tel:Office/Fax: 0115 940 3192 Club: 0115 940 2531

Capacity: 1000 **Seats**:164 **Covered**: 100 **Floodlights**: Yes

Simple Directions: A612 Nottingham to Southwell road. Stoke Lane is situated off A612 between Gedling & Burton Joyce. Ground can only be accessed from the new A612 Gedling By Pass which runs from The Business Park at Netherfield to Burton Joyce. Ground is situated at the mid point traffic lights and is visible from the new road.

Midweek Home Matchday: Tuesday

Clubhouse: Yes.

Club Shop: No

CLUB PERSONNEL

Chairman: Michael Garton.

Additional Directors:
Terry Fowler, Roger Smith,
Tom Brookbanks, Gary Stones,
Mark Steggles, Jenny Shaw,
Bob Sharpe,
Tim Bee, Ian White.

Secretary: Nicola Burton
4 Perlethorpe Drive,
Hucknall, Nottingham.
NG15 7UH
Tel: (H) 0115 952 8042
07591 502 285

Programme Editor: Ashley Winfield
Tel: 0115 958 1735.

CLUB STATISTICS

Record	**Attendance:** 1,000 Radio Trent Charity Match
Senior Honours:	Northern Counties East Division One Champions 2005-06.
	Central Midlands Supreme Champions 2002-03.
	Notts Alliance Div 1 1992-93. Division 2 1984-85.
Previous	**Leagues**: Notts Alliance and Central Midlands
	Name: Sneinton

Back Row (L-R): Alan Sewell (Coach), Gary Stones (Coach), Tremaine Walters, Danny Blair, Steve Chaplin, Danny Cane, Alessandro Barcherini, Phil Bignall, Martin Ball, Steve Fenton, Fabian Smith, Paul Shelton (Secretary), Stuart Scott (Physio).
Front Row: Aidan Brady, Simon Wilkinson, Willis Francis, Terry Hawkridge, Dave Nairn (Asst Manager), Mike Martin (Capt), Tom Brookbanks (Manager), Darryl Thomas, Dean Gent, Marquin Smith, Dominic Thomas.

CHASETOWN

Founded: 1954
Nickname: The Scholars

Manager: Charlie Blakemore

Club Colours: Royal blue/royal/white.

Change Colours: All bright red.

Best Season - League: 3rd Southern Division 1 Midlands 2006-07

Ground address: The Scholars, Church Street, Chasetown, Walsall WS7 8QL

Tel. 01543 682 222 Fax: 01543 684 609

Capacity: 2,000 **Seats**: 151 **Covered**: 220 **Floodlights**: Yes

Simple Directions: M6 toll road, exit Jct 6 Burntwood, left at first island, left at second island onto B5011, over toll road bridge, left at island at bottom of road, continue up the hill Highfields Road, cross over mini island at top into Church Street, pass Church on left and School on right, ground on left at the end of the street. **A5** from Tamworth, turn right at main traffic lights, Brownhills and continue on B5011 as above. As from **M6 Jct 11**/Cannock, turn left at lights at Brownhills and continue as above.

Midweek Home Matchday: Tuesday

Clubhouse: Open Daily **Club Shop:** Yes.

Local Radio: BBC Radio W.M.

Local Press: Express & Star, Burntwood Mercury/Burntwood Post.

CLUB PERSONNEL

Chairman: John Donnelly

Additional Committee:
Michael Joiner (Chief Executive), Brian Baker (President), Janice Brookes (Treasurer), Laurence Hawkes, John Goddard, Alan Smith (Vice Chairman), Robert Brookes, Barbara Hawkes, Colin Faunch, David Birt, Fred Humphries, John Richards, Russell Brown, Mark Prince, John Franklin, Michael Hampton.

Secretary: John Richards
36 Highfield Avenue,
Burntwood, Staffs. WS7 9AP
(H): 01543 675 569
(B): 01543 682 222
(BF): 01543 684 609
(M): 07866 902 093

Programme Editor: Russell Brown
Tel: 01543 682 222

CLUB STATISTICS

Record	**Attendance:** 2,134 v Blyth Spartans 4th Q..Rd F.A.Cup 2005-2006
	Career Goalscorer: Tony Dixon 197
	Career Appearances: 469 +15 subs
Record Transfer Fee	**Paid:** N/A **Received:** £200 fromTelford United for Chris Aullet
	Victory: 14-1 v Hanford, Walsall Senior Cup 1991-1992
	Defeat: 1-8 V Telford United Res, W.Mids Lg.
Senior Honours:	W.Mids Champions 1978, Lg.Cup (2) Walsall Senior Cup (2)
	Staffs Senior Cup R-Up 91-92 Midland Alliance Champions 2005-06
Previous Leagues:	Cannock Youth 54-58 Lichfield & District 58-61 Staffs.Co. 61-72
	West Mids.72-94 Midland Alliance 1994-2006. Southern 2006-09.
Previous Name:	Chase Terrace Old Scholars 54-72 **Previous Ground**: Burntwood Rec.

GLAPWELL

Formed: 1985
Nickname: The Well

CLUB PERSONNEL

Chairman: Dr Colin Hancock.
Managment Committee:
Debbie Davies, Malc Holmes, Brian Smith, Phil Davies, Bernard Wale, Adam Adin, Paul Harrison, Bill Taylor, Gary Brown.

Secretary: Malc Holmes
57 Sterland Street, Brampton,
Chessterfield, Derbyshire
S40 1BP.
(H): 01246 558 892
(M): 07986 224 289

Programme
Editor: Brian Smith
07828 915 427

Manager: John Gaunt.

Colours: Black & white stripes/black/black.

Change: All yellow.

Best Season - League: 6th Northern Premier Division One South 2008-09.

Ground: Hall Corner, Bolsover Road, Glapwell, Chesterfield. S44 5PZ

Tel: Office/Fax: 01623 812 213

Capacity: 1,500 **Seats: 300** **Covered:** Yes **Floodlights:** Yes

Simple Directions: M1 Jct 29 Take A617 towards Mansfield. Take filter lane left to Bolsover Road after pub Ground facing- use entrance next to garden centre.

Midweek Home Matchday: Tuesday.

Clubhouse: Yes.

Club Shop: Yes.

CLUB STATISTICS

HONOURS Central Midlands Division One 1989-90.

Supreme Division 1993-94.

Derbyshire Senior Cup 1997-98.

PREVIOUS **Leagues:** Sutton & Skegby 1985-89. Central Midlands 1989-96.

Northern Counties East 1996-2008.

Back Row (L-R): M Holmes (Sec), P Harrison (Press Officer), M Ottley, I Streather, D Rimington, L Matthewson, C Cockerill, N Grayson, D Reet, M Varley, D Lester (Phsio), M Hill.
Front : S Wright, A Grayson, R Smith, J Willaims, T Gibbons (DIFS- sponsor), K Gee (asst Manager), L McJannett (manager) D Davies, I Brown, J Burdett, M Fox.

GOOLE

Founded: 1997
Nickname: The Badgers

Manager: Nigel Danby

Club Colours: Red & white/red/red.

Change: All yellow.

Best Season - League: 7th Northern Premier Division One South 2006-07

Ground address: Victoria Plaesure Gardens, Marcus Road, Goole DN14 6WW

Tel: 01405 762 794.

Capacity: 3,000 **Seats**:200 **Covered**:800 **Floodlights**: Yes

Simple Directions: M62 to jct 36 then follow signs to town centre. Right at 2nd lights into Boothferry Road, after 300 yards turn right into Carter St.Ground at end.

Midweek Home Matchday: Tuesday.

Clubhouse: Matchdays Only.

Club Shop: Manager: Eric Lawton.

CLUB PERSONNEL

Chairman: Des O'Hearne.

Additional Directors:
E Lawton, P O'Hearne.

Secretary:
Terrence Reddhall
Victoria Pleasure Grounds,
Marcus Street,
Goole. DN14 6WW
(M): 07792 962 855
(F): 01405 765 775 (ring first)

CLUB STATISTICS

Record

Attendance: 976 v Leeds United 1999
Career Goalscorer: Kevin Severn (1997-2001)
Career Appearances: Phil Dobson 187 1999-2001
Transfer Fee Paid: Not known.
Transfer Fee Received: Not known.

Senior Honours: N.Co.East Champions 2003-2004 N.Co. East Division One 1999-2000 Central Midlands 2997-2998

Previous Leagues: Central MIdlands 1997-1998 Northern Counties East 2000-2004

Back row, left to right: Vill Powell, Niall O'Brien, Mick Goddard, Danny Farthing, Greg Archer, Sam Beard, Craig Parry, Leo Fortune-West, Jamie Ward, Rob Pacey, Nicky Darker, Tom Osborne.
Front Row: Mick Norbury (Assistant Manager), Colin Naylor (Physio), Karl Rose, Adam Lee, Jason Kitchen, Des O'Hearne (Chairman), Jay Sobers, Luke Jeffs, Nigel Danby (Manager).

GRANTHAM TOWN

Founded: 1874
Nickname: Gingerbreads

Manager: Wayne Hallcro & Jimmy Albans.

Club Colours: Black & white stripes/black/black.

Change: Green/green or white/green.

Best Season - League: 2nd Southern League 1973-74

Ground address: South Kesteven Sports Stadium, Trent Road, Grantham, Lincolnshire NG31 7XQ.

Tel: Office: 01476 402 224. Fax: 01476 419 392

Capacity: 7,500 **Seats**:750 **Covered**:1,950 **Floodlights**:Yes

Simple Directions: Midway between A1 and A52 on edge of Earlsfield Industrial Estate from A1take A607 to Earlsfield Industrial Estate and continue into Trent Rd.

Midweek Home Matchday: Tuesday

Clubhouse: Open evenings and weekends.

Club Shop: Wide range of products.

CLUB PERSONNEL

Chairman: Darron Quinn

Additional Directors:
Roger Booth
(Vice Chairman),
Barry Palmer, Steve Boam,
Peter Railton.

Secretary: Patrick Nixon.
72 Huntingtower Road,
Grantham,
Lincs. NG31 7AU
(H): 01476 419 391
(F): 01476 419 392
(M): 07747 136 033

CLUB STATISTICS

Record	**Attendance**: 3,695 v Southport F.A.Trophy 97-98
	Victory: 13-0 v Rufford Colliery (H) F.A.Cup 15.09.34
	Defeat: 0-16 v Notts County Rovers(A) Midland Am.Alliance 22.101892
	Goalscorer: Jack McCartney 416
	Career Appearances: Chris Gardner 664
Record Transfer Fee	**Paid**: Undisclosed for Mario Ziccari
	Received: £20,000 from Nottingham Forest for Gary Crosby
Senior Honours:	Southern Lg R-up 90-91 Mid Div Champions 97-98 Eastern Div R-up 2001-02, Lincs Senior Cup (20 R-up (5) Linc Co Sen Cup(2) R-up 80-81
Previous Leagues	Mid Am Alliance, Central Al l11-25 59-61 Midland Co. 25-59 61-72 Southern 72-79 NPL 79-85.

Back row (L to R): Michael Stahlberger, Nathan Beardsley, Billy Stubbs, Gio Carchedi, Dan French, Jack Simmons, Steve Norris, Gary Hateley, Ryan Clarke, Adam Jones, Lee Potts, Ricky Hanson, Garath Pritchard, Sam Kirton. **Middle row (L to R):** Danny Steadman, David Brown, Sam Saunders, Dave Frecklington, Dan Reidy, Iain Screaton, Mick Barthorpe (Staff), Andy Norbury (Goalkeeping Coach), Danny Brooks, Nigel Marshall (Physio), Paul Albans (Kit Man), Chris Gray, Rob Norris, Martin Wormall, Lee Marshall, Robert Hughes. **Front Row (L to R):** Ted Neville (Staff), Andy Drummond (Coach), Jimmy Albans (Joint Manager), George Freeston (President), Ted Foxall (Business Advisor), Pete Railton (Director), Darron Quinn (Chairman), Roger Booth (Vice-Chairman), Barry Palmer (Director), Pat Nixon (Secretary), Wayne Hallcro (Joint Manager), Dennis Rhule (Coach).

KIDSGROVE ATHLETIC

Founded: 1952
Nickname: The Grove

Managers: Peter Ward.

Club Colours: All blue.

Change: Green & white trim/green/green.

Best Season - League: 8th Northern Premier Division One 2006-07

Ground address: The Seddon Staium, Hollinwood Road, Kidsgrove, Staffordshire ST7 1DH.

Tel: Office/Fax/Club: 01782 782 412

Capacity: 4,500 **Seats**: 1,000 **Covered**: 800 **Floodlights**: Yes

Simple Directions: From M6 Jct 16 take A500 towards Stoke then second junction onto A34 towards Manchester. Turn right at first lights down hill and right at lights into Cedar Rd. Take second right into Lower Ash Rd and third left into Hollinwood Rd and ground. BR Kidsgrove (5mins)

Midweek Home Matchday: Tuesday

Clubhouse: Yes with food matchdays. Hall seats 180, with Sky TV.

Club Shop: Yes .

Local Radio: Radio Stoke, Signal Radio

Local Press: Staffordshire Evening Sentinel

CLUB PERSONNEL

Chairman: Michael Fitzjohn

Additional Directors:
David James,
Ernie Langford, John Rowley,
Karl Holness.

Secretary: Linda Gillan
18 Church Street, Rookery,
Stoke-on-Trent.ST7 4RS
Tel: (H) 01782 787 368
(F) 01782 782 412
(M) 07917 166 334

Programme Editor: Steve Green
Tel: 07732 997 513

CLUB STATISTICS

Record	**Attendance:** 1,903 v Tiverton Town F.A.Vase Semi-Final 1998
	Career Goalscorer: Scott Dunndas 53 1997-1998
	Career Appearances: Not Known.
	Transfer Fee Paid: £10,000 for Steve Walters from Stevenage Borough.
	Transfer Fee Received: `£3,000 for Ryan Baker 2003-04.
	Victory: 23-0 v Cross Heath W.M.C. Staffs Cup 1965
	Defeat:: 0-15 v Stafford Rangers, Staffs Senior Cup - 20.11.01
Senior Honours:	NWC Div. 1 97-98, 01-02; NWC Chall. Cup 97-98; Mid Cheshire Lg (4). Lg Cup (3).
Previous	**Leagues:** Burslem & Tunstall 1953-63, Staffordshire County 63-66, Mid Cheshire Lge. 66-90, North West Counties 1990-2002.
	Ground: Vickers & Goodwin 1953-60

LEEK TOWN

Founded: 1946
Nickname: The Blues

Manager: Wayne Johnson

Club Colours: All blue.

Change: Red & black stripes/black/black.

Best Seasons - League: 19th Conference 1998-99

Ground address: Harrison Park, Macclesfield Road, Leek, Cheshire ST13 8LD

Tel/Fax No: 01538 399 278

Capacity: 3,600 **Seats:** 625 **Covered**: 2,675 **Floodlights**:Yes

Simple Directions: Opposite Coutaulds Chemical works on A523 Macclesfield to Buxton road half a mile out of Leek heading towards Macclesfield.

Midweek Home Matchday: Tuesday

Clubhouse: Open matchdays. Functions by request.

Club Shop: Yes.

CLUB PERSONNEL

Chairman: Andrew Wain.
Additional Directors:
A Reeves, T Reynolds, S Reynolds, M Howson, C Hermiston

Secretary: Brian Wain
223 New Inn Lane,
Trentham, Stoke on Trent.
ST4 8PS
01782 657 693
07967 204 470

Programme Editors:
Steve & Tracy Reynolds
07940 370 872

CLUB STATISTICS

Record	**Attendance**: 5,312 v Macclesfield Town F.A.Cup 1973-74
Goalscorer:	Dave Sutton 144
Career Appearances:	Gary Pearce 447
Record Transfer Fee	**Paid**: £2,000 to Sutton Town for Simon Snow.
	Received: £30,000 from Barnsley for Tony Bullock.
Senior Honours:	F.A.Trophy R-up 89-90 NPL 96-97 R-up 93-94 Staffs Sen. Cup 95-96 R-up (3)
Previous	**Leagues:** Staffs Co, Manchester 51-54 57-73, W.Mids (B'ham) 54-56, Cheshire Co 73-82. N.W.Co 82-87, NPL 87-94 95-97, Southern 94-95. Conference 97-99.

Back Row (L-R): Leon Ashman, Mark Ruddock, Carl Allen, Steve Hodgson, Damain Smith, Jon Evans, Steve Brannan. **Middle Row:** Alex Morris, Pete Johnson, Ken Ashford (Physio), Wayne Corden, Oliver Edwards. **Front Row:** Chris Fullalove, Luke Robinson, Andy Taylor (captain), Wayne Johnson (Manager), Matt Johnson, Dan Cope, Ashley Miller.

LINCOLN UNITED

Founded: 1938
Nickname: United

Manager: Seamus Lawless.

Club Colours: White/red/red.

Change: Yellow/blue/yellow.

Best Seasons - League: 14th Northern Premier Premier 2004-05.

Ground address: Ashby Avenue, Hatsholme, Lincoln LN6 0DY.

Tel: Office/Fax: 01522 696 400 Club: 01522 690 674

Capacity: 2,714 **Seats**: 400 **Covered**: 1,084 **Floodlights**:Yes

Simple Directions: From A46 onto Lincoln relief road (A446) right at second round-about for Birchwood (Skellingham Road). Then first right after 30mph sign into Ashby Avenue. Ground in 200 yards opposite old peoples' home.

Midweek Home Matchday: Tuesday

Clubhouse: Open daily.

Club Shop: Yes.

Local Press: Lincolnshire Echo and Lincoln Standard

CLUB PERSONNEL

Chairman: Chris Geeson

Additional Directors:
C Bestford, P McHugh,
D Sweeney, A Adams.

Secretary: John Wilkinson
175, Rookery Lane, Lincoln.
LN6 7PJ
Tel: 07773 284 017

Programme
Editor: See secretary.

CLUB STATISTICS

Record	**Attendance**: 2,000 v Crook Town F.A.Amateur Cup 1st Round 1968
	Victory: 12-0 v Pontefract Colls 1995
	Defeat: 0-7 v Huddersfield Town F.A.Cup 1st Rd 16.11.91
	Career Goalscorer: Tony Simmons 215
	Career Appearances: Steve Carter 447
Record Transfer Fee	**Paid**: 1,000 to Hucknall Town for Paul Tomlinson Dec. 2000
	Received: 3,000 from Charlton Athletic for Dean Dye july 1991
Senior Honours:	N.Co.East Prem Champions 1994-95, Div 1 1985-86, 92-93
	Lincs Sen Cup R-up 97-8
Previous	**Leagues**: Lincs 45-38, 60-67, Lincoln 46-60, Yorks 67-82, N.Co East 82-86 92-95. Central Midlands: 82-92. Northern Counties East 1992-95.
	Grounds: Skew Bridge (40s), Co-op Sports Ground to mid 60s) Hartsholme Cricket Club (to 82).
	Name: Lincoln Amateurs until 1954.

LOUGHBOROUGH DYNAMO

Founded: 1955
Nickname: Dynamo

Managers: John Folwell.

Club Colours: Gold/black/gold.

Change: Green & white hoops/white/green & white hoops.

Best Season - League: 14th Northern Premier Division One South 2008-09.

Ground address: Nanpantan Sport Ground, Nanpantan Road, Loughborough, Leics. LE11 3YE. Tel: Office/Fax: 01509 237 148

Capacity: 1,500 **Seats:** 250 **Covered:** Yes **Floodlights:** Yes

Simple Directions: From M1: At Junction 23 turn towards Loughborough (A512). At 1st set of traffic lights turn right on to Snells Nook Lane. At 1st crossroads ("Priory" pub on left) turn left on to Nanpantan Rd. Turn (1st) right after 0.75 miles on to Watermead Lane. The ground is at the end of the lane.

Midweek Home Matchday: Tuesday.

Clubhouse: Open Matchdays.

Club Shop: No.

CLUB PERSONNEL

Chairman: Frank Fall

Committee:
Keith Hawes, Greg Blood.

Secretary: Brian Pugh
15, Coe Avenue, Thorpe
Acre, Loughborough,
Leicestershire. LE11 4SE
Tel: 07775 825 321

Programme
Editor: Rob Smith
07966 545 543

CLUB STATISTICS

Senior Honours: Leicestershire Senior League 2003-04.
Leicestershire Senior Division One 2001-02.
Leicestershire Senior Cup 2002-03, 03-04.

Previous Leagues: Loughborough Alliance 1957-66. Leicestershire & District 1966-71.
East Midlands 1971-72. Central Alliance 1972-89.
Leicestershire Senior 1989-2004. Midland Alliance 2004-08.

Back Row (L-R): J.P. Considine (Coach) Scott Clamo, Lewis Allen, Jake Betts, Lawrence Hale, Rich Bredice, Matt Nurse, Rick Nurse, Calum Ross, Matt Nurse, Alex Johnson, Lucy Goss (Physio).
Front Row: Reece Lester, Ryan Collis, Karl Noble, John Folwell (Manager), Keith Hawes (Sponsor) Mike McLarnon (Asst Manager), Karl Brennan, Neil Morgan, Jamie Allen, Andy Harrison.

MARKET DRAYTON TOWN

Founded: 1969

Managers: Simon Line.

Club Colours: All red.

Change: All dark blue.

Best Season - League: 1st Midland Alliance 2008-09.

Ground address: Greenfields Sports Ground, Greenfield Lane,

Market Drayton. TF9 3SI.

Tel: Office: 01630 655 088 Fax 01630 658 859

Simple Directions: Take the A41 to Ternhill Island, turn right on A53 for Newcastle –u-Lyne. Straight on at first island (by Muller factory). At next island turn right to town centre (by Gingerbread Inn). Approx 200yds take 2nd right into Greenfields Lane. Ground 150 yards on right, car park opposite.

From Stoke-on-Trent take A53 for Shrewsbury, at Gingerbread Inn turn left for town centre then as above.

Midweek Home Matchday: Tuesday.

Clubhouse: Yes.

CLUB PERSONNEL

Chairman: Alex Mutch
Committee:
Clive Jones, Ron Ebrey,
Frank Hodgkiss,
Doug Goodhead,
Jackie Davies, Roy Blase,
Graham Machin.

Secretary: Brian Garratt
"Garlow", 4 Quarry Bank
Road, Market Drayton.
TF9 1DR
Tel: (H) 01630 654618
(F) 01630 658 859
(M) 07854 725 957
Programme
Editor: Simon Line
Tel: 01630 656 763

CLUB STATISTICS

Senior Honours: West Midlands (Reginal) Champions 2005-06.

Midland Alliance Champions 2008-09.

Previous **Leagues:** West Midlands (Regional) > 2006.

Midland Alliance 2006-09.

Names: Little Drayton Rangers > 2003.

MICKLEOVER SPORTS

Founded: 1948
Nickname: Sports

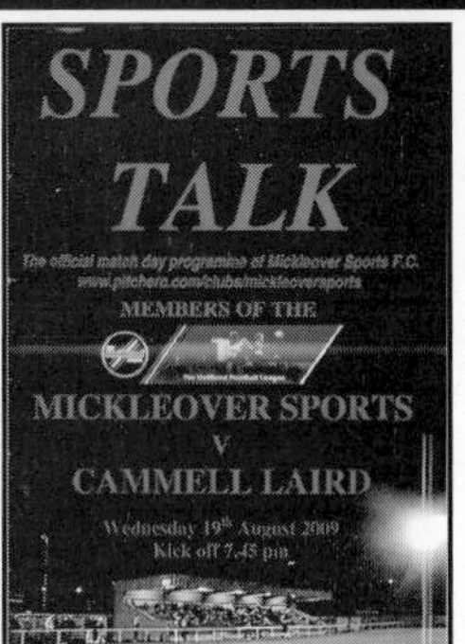

Managers: Richard Pratley.

Club Colours: Red/black/red.

Change: All blue.

Best Season - League: 1st Northern Counties East Premier Division 2008-09.

Ground address: Mickleover Sports Club, Station Road, Mickleover,

Derby. DE3 9FB

Tel: Office: 01332 512 826 Fax 01332 600 301

Capacity: 1,500 **Seats**: 280 **Covered**: 500 **Floodlights**: Yes

Simple Directions: M1 NORTH - J28. A38 to Derby. At Markeaton Island right A52 Ashbourne, 2nd left Radbourne Lane, 3rd Left Station Road 50 yds.

M1 SOUTH – J25. A52 to Derby. Follow signs for Ashbourne, pick up A52 at Markeaton Island (MacDonalds) then as above.

FROM STOKE A50 – Derby. A516 to A38 then as above.

Midweek Home Matchday: Wednesday.

Clubhouse: Yes.

CLUB PERSONNEL

Chairman: Johnathan Green
Additional Directors:
Keith Jenkinson,
Ken Blackshaw, Roger Lee,
Kevin Haddon,
Charles Divers,
Dave Chambers,
Alan Brown, James Edge.
Secretary:
Anthony John Shaw
80, Onslow Road,
Mickleover, Derby. DE3 9JG
Tel: (H) 01332 512 826
Bus/Fax: 01332 600 301
07966 197246
Programme
Editor: Steve Pritchard
Tel: 07531 706 491

CLUB STATISTICS

Record	**Attendance:** Not known.
	Career Goalscorer: Not known.
	Career Appearances: Not Known.
	Victory: Not known.
	Defeat: Not known.
Senior Honours:	Central Midlands Supreme Division Champions 1998-99.
	Northern Counties East Division One Champions 2002-03.
	Northern Counties East Premier Division Champions 2008-09.
Previous	**Leagues:** Central Midlands > 1999.
	Northern Counties East 1999-2009.

QUORN

Founded: 1924
Nickname: Reds

Manager: Dougie Keast

Club Colours: All Red.

Change: Yellow/blue/white.

Best Season - League: 12th Northern Premier Division One South 2007-08, 08-09.

Ground address: Farley Way Stadium, Farley Way, Quorn, Leics. LE12 8RB.

Tel No: 01509 620 232

Club Website: www.quornfc.com

Capacity: 1,550 **Seats**: 350 **Covered**: 250 **Floodlights**: Yes

Simple Directions: M1 Jct 23 follow signs to Loughborough and turn right at second roundabout towards Leicester A6. Right at fourth roundabout to Quorn then left at first lights and ground is on left

Midweek Home Matchday: Tuesday

Clubhouse: Yes

CLUB PERSONNEL

Chairman: Stuart Turner

Additional Directors: Reg Molloy, Les Caunt, Stewart Warrington, John Unwin, Jake Nooney, Mavis Turner, Margaret Berry, Peter Clarke, Terry Brookes, Ivan Kirk, Andrew Webb, Hilary Simpson, Jane Penny, Jim Simpson.

Secretary: Reg Molloy
96, Grange Drive, Melton Mowbray, Leicestershire.
LE13 1HA
(H/F): 01664 564 665
(M) 07729 173 333

Programme Editor: Stuart Warrington
Tel: 07988 721 796

CLUB STATISTICS

Record	**Attendance:** Not known
	Career Goalscorer: Not known.
	Career Appearances: Not known.
	Transfer Fee Paid: Not known.
	Transfer Fee Received: Not known.
Senior Honours:	Leicestershire Senior Cup 1940 1952 1954.
	Leicestershire Senior League 2000-01.
Previous	**Leagues**: Leicestershire Senior and Midland Alliance.
	Names: Quorn Methodists.

Back Row (L-R): DANNY WRIGHT, MICHAEL PAPPAROZZI, LIAM TURNER, RUSSELL PEEL, CRAIG JONES, CAMERON KEAST, PHIL GILCHRIST, MATT LANGHAM, JOE JONAS.
Front Row: TOM INGRAM, ASH WHITE, KRIS MATTHEWS, ANTHONY MARRIOTT, PHIL MILLER, ASH ROBINSON, JULIAN JOACHIM.

RUSHALL OLYMPIC

Founded: 1951
Nickname: The Pics

Manager: Neil Kitching.

Club Colours: Black & gold stripes/black/black.

Change: Navy & red trim/red/red.

Best Season - League: 5th Southern Division One Midlands 2007-08.

5th - Northern Premier Division One South 2008-09.

Ground address: Dales Lane off Daw End Lane, Rushall, Nr. Walsall WS4 1LJ

Tel/fax No: 01922 641 021

Capacity: 2,500 **Seats**: 200 **Covered**: 200 **Floodlights**: Yes

Simple Directions: From Rushall cemtre (A461) take B4154 signed Aldridge. Approx one mile on right opposite Royal Oak Public house in Daw End Lane.

Midweek Home Matchday: Tuesday

Clubhouse: Yes.

Club Shop: Yes.

CLUB PERSONNEL

Chairman: John C Allen.
Committee:
Nick Allen (Vice Chairman),
Pete Athersmith (Secretary),
Brian Greenwood (President),
Ray Barrow (Treasurer),
Peter Brough, Edwin Venables,
Ray Jones, Bob Thomas, Darren Stockall.

Secretary: Peter Athersmith.
46 Blakenall Lane,
Leamore,Walsall. West
Midlands WS3 1HG
(H/F): 01922 445 252
(M): 07909 792 422

Programme
Editor: Darren Stockall
07870 236 013

CLUB STATISTICS

Record	**Attendance:** 2,000 v Leed United Ex Players
	Career Goalscorer: Graham Wiggin
	Career Appearances: Alan Dawson - 400+
Record Transfer Fee	**Paid**: Not known
	Received: Not known
Senior Honours:	Midland Alliance 2004-05.
	West Midlands 1979-80.
Previous	**Leagues**: Walsall Amateur 1952-55 Staffs Co (South) 1956-78.
	West Midlands 1978-94. Midland Alliance 1994-05. Southern 2005-08.
	Grounds: Rowley Place 51-75 and Aston University 76-79

SHEFFIELD (WORLD'S FIRST FOOTBALL CLUB) Founded: 1857

Manager: Christopher Dolby

Club Colours: Red & black/black/red.

Change: All blue.

Best Seasons - League: 4th Northern Premier Division One South 2007-08.

Ground address: The Bright Finance Stadium (Coach & Horses), Sheffield Road, Dronfield, Sheffield S18 2GD.

Office: 01246 292 622 Fax: 01246 292 633

Club: 01246 413 269

Capacity: 1,456 **Seats**: 250 **Covered**: 500 **Floodlights**: Yes

Simple Directions: M1 Jct 29 to A617 towards Chesterfield. Turn right into dual carriageway (A61) at traffic island. Over two more traffic islands and follow signs to Dronfield/Gosforth Valley. At entrance to Dronfield, the ground is behind the Coach & Horses pub at the foot of the hill on the right

Midweek Home Matchday: Tuesday

Clubhouse: Licensed Bar open on Matchdays

Club Shop: Yes

CLUB PERSONNEL

Chairman: Richard Tims

Additional Directors:
I. Cameron, P. Hancock, J. Harrison

Secretary: Stephen Hall
c/o the club.
(H): 0114 2205 026
(B): 01246 292 622
(F): 01246 292 633
(M): 07761 207 447

Programme Editor: Craig Williamson
0114 2581 108

CLUB STATISTICS

Record — **Attendance:** 2,000 v Barton Rovers F.A.Vase S-Final 76-77
Career Goalscorer: Not known **Career Appearances**: No tknown
Record Transfer Fee Paid: £1000 David Wilkins 2006 to Arnold Town
Record Transfer Fee Received: £1000 Mick Godber from Alfreton 2002

Senior Honours:
F.A.Amateur Cup: Winners 1902-03
N.Co.East Div 1 Champions 1988-89 1990-91
N.Co East League Cup Winners 2000/01, 2004/05
Sheffield & Hallamshire Senior Cup 1993-94 2004-05 2005-06

Previous League: Yorkshire League 1949-1982

Previous Grounds: Abbeydale Park, Dore 1956-1989, Sheffield Amateur Spts Stadium, Hillsborough Park 1989-91, Sheffield International Stadium 1991-94, Sheffield Sports Stadium Don Valley 1994-97.

Players progressing to Football League Premiership - Sam Sodje (Reading 2000/01), Richard Peacock (Hull City 1997).

Back Row (L-R): Darren Spooner – GK Coach; Will Senior; Kirk Jackson; Ben Leonard; Tom Cross; Jon Hobson; Gavin Smith; Danny Macpherson; Greg Wright; Paul Smith; James Smith – Trainer. **Front Row:** Michael Jenkins – Physio; Daryl Winter; Jordan Eagers; Steve Woolley; Matt Roney; Andy Gascoigne; Joel Purkiss; Billy Dempsey; Matt Outram; Ian Turner – Physio Assistant.

SHEPSHED DYNAMO

Founded: 1994
Nickname: Dynamo

Manager: Dave Stinger

Club Colours: Black & white stripes/black/black.

Change: All yellow.

Best Season - League: 10th Southern League 1998-99

Ground address: The Dovecote, Butt Hole Lane, Shepshed,

Leicestershire LE12 9BN.

Tel No: 01509 650 992

Capacity: 2,050 **Seats**: 570 **Covered**: 400 **Floodlights**: Yes

Simple Directions: M1 J 23, A512 towards Ashby, right at first lights, right at garage in Forest Street, right into Butthole Lane opposite Black Swan. Five miles from Loughborough (BR)

Midweek Home Matchday: Tuesday

Clubhouse: Yes **Club Shop:** Yes.

Local Radio: Radio Leicester, Leicester Sound, Oak F.M.

Local Press: Loughborough Echo, Leicester Mercury

CLUB PERSONNEL

Chairman: Shaun Taylor.

Additional Directors:
D Wheatley, S Taylor, E Anderson, M Voce, J Sharples, B Reed, G Williamson, A McMillan, K Freer.

Secretary: Dave Wheatley.
9 Holcombe Close,
Whitwick, Leics.
LE67 5BR.
(H/F): 01530 814 959
(B): 07799 083 703
(M): 07725 302 287

Programme Editors: Ben Reed
Tel: 01858 440 032

CLUB STATISTICS

Record	**Attendance:** 2,500 v Leicester City (friendly) 1996--1997
	Career Goalscorer: Lee McGlinchey - 107
	Career Appearances: Lee McGlinchey - 255
Record Transfer Fee	**Paid**: None
	Received: None
Senior Honours:	Southern Lge Midland Div. R-up 83-84, N.C.E. Lge 82-83, Lge Cup 82-83; Midland Counties Lge 81-82, Lge Cup 81- 82; Leicestershire Senior Cup (7); Midland Alliance Winners 1995-96
Previous Leagues:	Leicestershire Senior 07-16 19-27 46-50 51-81, Midland Counties 81-82, Northern Counties (East) 82-83, Southern 83-88, Northern Premier 88-93, Midland Combination 93-94, Midland Alliance 94-96. Southern 1996-04

Back Row (L-R): Back Row (L-R) Chris Tullin, Danny Gaunt, Thea Moussa, Mark Williams, Nick Jupp, Luke Barlone, Robert Webb, Reece Styche, Adam Goodby, Nathan Morris, David Timmins.
Front Row: Jamie Capes (Physio), Adam Jones, Rhys Powell, Chad Sheppard, Dave Stringer (Manager), Jimmy Ginnelly (Co-Manager), Dominic Reece, Ben Ashby, Ebenezer Ofori.

SPALDING UNITED

Founded: 1921
Nickname: Tulips

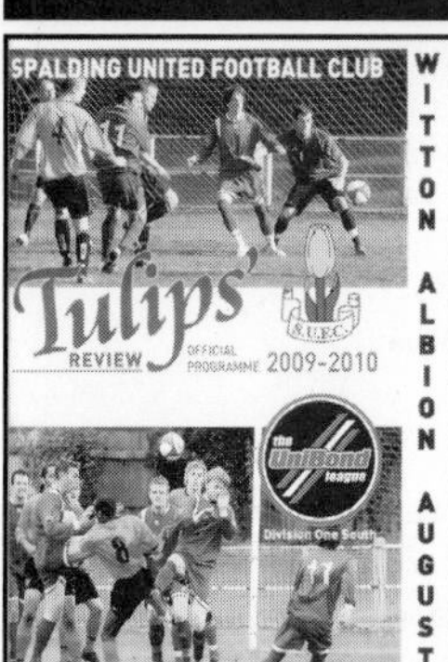

Manager: Mark Hone.

Club Colours: All Royal blue.

Change: Orange/black & orange/black.

Best Season - League: 6th Southern Midlands Division 1989-90.

Ground address: Sir Halley Stewart Playing Field, Winfrey Avenue, Spalding, Lincs. PE11 1DA

Tel: Office: 01733 769 771 Club/Fax: 01775 713 328

Capacity: 2,700 **Seats**:300 **Covered**:500 **Floodlights**:Yes

Simple Directions: Town centre off A16, adjacent to bus station. 250 yds from Spalding (BR) station

Midweek Home Matchday: Tuesday

Clubhouse: Open matchdays and functions

Club Shop: Yes.

Local Radio: Radio Lincolnshire

Local Press: Lincolnshire Free Press, Spalding Target and Spalding Guardian

CLUB PERSONNEL

Chairman: Chris Toynton

Additional Directors: Graham Chappell, Ray Tucker, Audrey Fletcher.

Secretary: Audrey Fletcher, The Castle, Horseshoe Road, Spalding, Lincs. PE11 3BE
(H): 01775 714 039
(B/F): 01775 769 771
(M): 07778 411 916

Programme Editor: Ray Tucker
Tel: 01775 725 253

CLUB STATISTICS

Record	**Attendance:** 6,972 v Peterborough F.A. Cup 1982
	Career Goalscorer: Not known.
	Career Appearances: Not known.
Record Transfer Fee	**Paid**: Not known.
	Received: Not known.
Senior Honours:	Utd Counties Lg 54-55 74-75 87-88 98-99 R-up 50-53(x3) 72-73 75-76 96-97; N.C.E.Lg 83-84; Lincs Snr Cup 52-53
Previous:	**Leagues:** Peterborough; U.C.L. 31-55 68-78 86-88 91-99; 03-04 Eastern Co's 55-60; Central Alliance 60-61; Midland Co's 61-68; N.C.E.F.L. 82-86; Southern 88-91, 99-03, N.P.L. Div 1 2004-05.

Spalding United squad: Alan Biley (Manager), Ian Lochhead (Assistant Manager), David Hone, Dan Holyoak, Richard Roberts, Luke McShane, Nicky Hurst, David Blake, Simon Ward (Coach), Pete Foskett (Physio), (Seated) Matty O'Neill, Ashley Caress, Andy Stanhope (Captain), Ricky Miller, Kev Ward, Lewis Allen, Shaun Carey and Davy Shepherd.
Picture courtesy of: Jim Scott www.photoimagery.co.uk

STAMFORD

Manager: Tuncay Korkmaz.

Colours: Red with white trim/red with white trim/red.

Change: All navy blue.

Best Seasons - League: 8th Southern League Premier Division 2006-2007

Ground address: Vic Couzens Stadium, Kettering Road,Stamford Lincs. PE9 2JS

Tel No: 01780 763 079.

Capacity: 2,000 **Seats**: 250 **Covered**: 1,250 **Floodlights**:Yes

Simple Directions: Off A43 Kettering Rd, one mile east of A1. 200 yards from station.

Midweek Home Matchday: Tuesday

Clubhouse: Open matchdays and for functions.

Club Shop: Full range of products.

Local Radio: Rutland Radio, BBC Radio Lincolnshire & BBC Radio Cambridgeshire

Local Press: Stamford Mercury, Peterborough Evening Telegraph,

Herald & Post and Rutland Times.

CLUB PERSONNEL

Chairman: Bob Feetham

Committee:
Richard Jacobs – Vice Chairman,
John Drewnicki, Ken Joynson,
Dave Salisbury, Roger Twiddy,
Guy Walton (Chief Executive).

Secretary: Phil Bee.
3 Launde Gardens,
Stamford, Lincs. PE9 2RP.
(H): 01780 756 665
(M): 07709 356131

Programme
Editor: John Burrows
07710 290 000

CLUB STATISTICS

Record	**Attendance:** 4,200 v Kettering Town F.A.Cup 3rd Qualifying Round 1953
	Career Goalscorer:Bert Knighton 248
	Career Appearances: Dick Kwiatkowski 462
Record	**Victory:**: 13-0 v Peterborough Reserves, Northants League 1929-1930
	Defeat: 0-17 Rothwell F.A.Cup 1927-1928
Senior Honours:	F,.A.Vase Winners 1979-80, United Co. Champions (7),
	Lincolnshire Senior Cup, Senior Shield, Lincs Senior A Cup (3).
Previous	**Leagues**: Peterborough, Northants (UCL) 08-55, Central Alliance 55-61,
	MId Co 61-72. UCL 72-98, Southern 1998-07.

Back row (L-R): Ross Watson, Michael Stevenson, Lee Ellison, David Burton-Jones, Chris Wright, Danny Bircham, Miles Chamberlain, Paul Malone, Sam Bettinson, Adrian Tilley. **Middle Row** : Kieran Scarff (Assistant Manager), Dave Toone (Kit man), Ian Evley (Goalkeeping coach), David Cobb, Lee Beeson, Scott Woods, Karl Gibbs, Ben Sedgemore, Dave Farrell, Andy Ellis, Seth Burkett, Becky Moss (Physio), Tuncay Korkmaz (Manager), Giles Lawrence (Assistant Kit Man), Rodney Sadd (DISC representative). **Front Row:** Roger Twiddy (Director), Phil Bee (Secretary), Dave Salisbury (Director), Peter Lane (Commercial Manager), Guy Walton (Chief Executive), Richard Jacobs (Vice Chairman), Sandee Lane (Commercial Manager), John Drewnicki (Director), Ken Joynson (Director), Keith Scarber (200 Club Manager). Photo: Geoff Atton.

WILLENHALL TOWN

Founded: 1953
Nickname: The Lockmen

Willenhall Town fc
the lockmen
Aspray
Willenhall Town v Goole AFC
Aspray

Manager: Shaun Cunnington.

Club Colours: All red.

Change: All navy.

Best Seasons - League: 4th Southern League Premier Division1984-1985.

Ground address: Noose Lane, Willenhall, West Midlands WV13 3BB.

Tel/Fax No: 01902 636 586.

Capacity: 5,000 **Seats**:324 **Covered**: 500 **Floodlights**:Yes

Simple Directions: M6 jct 10 follow 'new' Black Country route then 'Keyway'. On leaving 'Keyway' follow signs to Wolverhampton (A454). At Neachells Public House turn right into Neachells Lane and first right again into Watery Lane. At island turn left into Noose Lane and ground is 200 yards on left.

Midweek Home Matchday: Tuesday.

Club Shop: Full range of products.

CLUB PERSONNEL

Chairman: Jason Bott.
Committee: Simon Haynes, Chris Blue, Geoff Toy, Shaun Tibbott, Les Burrows, Steve Siddaway, Dave Cooper.

Secretary: Simon Haynes
6 Ingledew Close,
Briarsleigh, Walsall,
West Midlands WS2 0NF
Tel: (H) 01902 411758
(B) 01922 402428
(F) 01922 404983
(M) 07906 561750

Programme Editor: Matthew Wood
Tel: 07835 312 613

CLUB STATISTICS

Record	**Attendance:** 3,454 V Crewe Alexandra F.A.Cup 1st Round 1981 **Career Goalscorer**:Gary Matthews **Career Appearances**:Gary Matthews
Record	**Victory:** 11-1 v Bridgnorth Town 2001-2002: **Defeat:** Not known
Senior Honours:	Staffs Prem Lg 74-75 W.Mids Div 1 75-76 W.Mids Premier Div 77-78 F.A.Vase Finalists 19080-81Souther Lg Midland Div 83-84 MfFL Cup 94-95 Midland Alliance R-Up 2006-07
Previous: and 1991-94	**League:** Wolverhampton Amateur/ Staffs County/ West Midland 1975-78 Midkland Allliance 1994-2004. Northern Premier Division One 2004-05. Southern League 1982-1991, 2005-08.

NB: UNFORTUNATELY A RECENT PHOTO WAS NOT AVAILABLE AT THE TIME OF GOING TO PRESS.

Photo: Marshall's Sports Service (01384 274 877).

WITTON ALBION

Founded: 187
Nickname: The Albion

Manager: Gary Finley.

Club Colours: Red & white stripes/red/white.

Change: All yellow.

Best Season - League 10th Conference 1991-92

Ground address: Wincham Park, Chapel Street, Wincham, Northwich CW9 6DA.

Tel No: /Fax: 01606 43008

Capacity: 4,500 **Seats:** 650 **Covered**: 2,300 **Floodlights:** Yes

Simple Directions: M6 jct 19 Take A556 towards Northwich. After 3 miles turn onto A559 at beginning of dual carriageway . After 3/4 mile turn left opposite Black Greyhound Inn. Ground 1/2 mile on left after crossing canal bridge.

Midweek Home Matchday: Tuesday

Clubhouse: Concert Room and Vice Presidents club open matchdays, Tuesdays, Thursdays and Friday evenings. Contact: Mike Worthington. Tel 01606 43008

Club Shop: Yes

CLUB PERSONNEL

Chairman: Mark Harris

Additional Directors:
Paul Worthington,
Laura Edgeley,
Graham Pickering.

Secretary: Peter Riley
11 Hedgerow Drive,
Ashwood Park, Wincham,
Northwich. CW9 6QX
Tel: (H): 01606 331 916
(M): 07813 620 161

Programme
Editor: Stewart Cain
Tel: 07722 067 735

CLUB STATISTICS

Record	**Attendance:**	3,940 V Kidderminster Harriers F.A. Trophy Semi-Final 13.04.91 at Wincham Prak
	Victory:	13-0 v Middlewich (H)
	Defeat:	0-9 v Macclesfield Town (A) 18.09.65
	Goalscorer:	Frank Fidler 175 (1947-1950)
	Career Appearances:	Alf Ashley 556 (1946-1958)
Record Transfer Fee	**Paid:**	£12,500 to Hyde United for Jim McCluskie 1991
	Received:	£11,500 from Chester City for Peter Henderson
Senior Honours:		N.P.L. Champions 1990-91 Cheshire County Senior Cup (7) F.A.Trophy Runners-Up 91-92
Previous	**Leagues:**	Lancashire Comb., Cheshire Co.>79, N.P.L.79-91 & Conf 91-94

Back Row (L-R): Mike Moseley, Brian Pritchard, Joe Clegg, Lee Neville, Dylan Adams, Peter Moogan (Team Assistant)
Middle Row: Vijay Anthwal (Club Doctor), Steve Foster, Stuart Rudd, Callum Tai-Hogan, Lee Neville, Brad Maylett, Andy Hadzik, Ed Robinson (Physio).
Front Row: Steve Hall, Paul Booth (Captain), Gary Finley (Manager), Mark Harris (Chairman), Neil Murphy, Phil Doran.
Players Missing From Photo : Steve Brodie, Peter Heler, Greg Smith & Jordan King. PHOTO COURTESY OF THE "NORTHWICH GUARDIAN"

SOUTHERN LEAGUE

SPONSORED BY:
BRITISH GAS BUSINESS

Founded: 1894

Chairman:
Ken Turner

Secretary:
Jason Mills
secretary@southern-football-league.co.uk

	Premier Division	P	W	D	L	F	A	GD	Pts
1	Corby Town	42	25	9	8	85	38	47	84
2	Farnborough	42	23	14	5	67	36	31	83
3	Gloucester City	42	21	12	9	80	45	35	75
4	Cambridge City	42	21	10	11	62	40	22	73
5	Hemel Hempstead Town	42	21	7	14	71	48	23	70
6	Oxford City	42	19	10	13	76	55	21	67
7	Merthyr Tydfil	42	19	10	13	66	55	11	67
8	Chippenham Town (-3)	42	20	8	14	64	51	13	65
9	Evesham United	42	16	13	13	48	39	9	61
10	Halesowen Town (-3)	42	19	6	17	65	73	-8	60
11	Brackley Town	42	15	12	15	69	62	7	57
12	Tiverton Town	42	16	9	17	51	50	1	57
13	Swindon Supermarine	42	15	12	15	59	61	-2	57
14	Bashley	42	15	12	15	52	58	-6	57
15	Bedford Town	42	14	8	20	44	55	-11	50
16	Stourbridge	42	13	11	18	62	78	-16	50
17	Rugby Town	42	11	10	21	63	71	-8	43
18	Clevedon Town	42	11	10	21	51	80	-29	43
19	Banbury United	42	11	8	23	43	83	-40	41
20	Hitchin Town	42	10	10	22	57	79	-22	40
21	Yate Town	42	9	9	24	54	91	-37	36
22	Mangotsfield United	42	10	6	26	39	80	-41	36

PROMOTION PLAY-OFFS - SEMI-FINALS

Farnborough	0 - 0*	Hemel Hempstead Town
	4 - 3p	
Gloucester City	3 - 1	Cambridge City

PROMOTION PLAY-OFF - FINAL

Farnborough	0 - 1	Gloucester City

	1	2	3	4	5	6	7	8	9	10	11	12	13	14	15	16	17	18	19	20	21	22
1 Banbury United		1-0	4-0	3-1	2-2	0-5	3-1	0-4	0-6	0-2	1-5	2-1	3-0	1-4	1-1	1-1	1-0	2-1	2-0	1-5	0-3	3-0
2 Bashley	1-0		1-0	1-1	0-0	2-1	1-0	0-3	0-0	1-0	1-1	1-3	2-1	4-0	0-1	1-3	3-2	3-1	4-1	2-2	0-3	1-1
3 Bedford Town	3-0	0-2		0-0	1-1	2-0	0-0	1-5	1-1	0-2	1-1	1-0	1-2	5-0	3-1	1-0	3-1	2-0	2-1	1-0	1-1	1-1
4 Brackley Town	1-2	2-4	2-0		2-0	1-0	1-1	5-0	2-1	1-1	2-3	4-1	3-2	1-2	3-1	2-2	2-1	2-2	3-0	0-3	1-2	0-1
5 Cambridge City	3-1	5-0	1-0	1-0		0-1	0-1	3-2	2-3	0-2	2-1	3-0	1-0	3-1	0-2	3-0	1-0	3-2	2-0	0-1	1-0	2-2
6 Chippenham T.	1-0	2-3	1-0	3-1	3-1		2-1	3-1	1-0	1-1	2-2	2-1	1-2	1-1	1-1	1-0	0-2	1-1	1-2	3-1	1-0	3-0
7 Clevedon Town	1-1	0-0	2-1	2-2	1-0	3-2		1-3	2-0	1-1	1-4	1-2	0-3	1-2	2-3	1-5	0-1	1-0	2-0	1-2	1-2	4-3
8 Corby Town	5-0	3-1	1-2	2-0	0-0	3-0	4-0		0-0	3-1	1-2	1-2	0-0	2-0	1-1	2-1	0-1	2-0	0-0	2-1	1-4	1-1
9 Evesham Utd	2-0	2-2	0-1	1-1	0-1	2-0	0-0	1-1		0-0	2-2	0-0	4-1	2-1	3-1	0-2	0-1	1-0	0-1	1-0	1-1	4-1
10 Farnborough	1-0	1-1	3-1	2-2	1-1	2-0	3-1	3-3	2-1		2-1	1-1	1-0	1-0	3-1	0-1	0-2	2-1	4-0	1-0	1-0	2-0
11 Gloucester City	1-1	3-0	0-1	0-1	2-1	2-0	0-1	1-3	2-0	0-0		1-2	2-1	4-1	5-2	1-1	2-2	3-0	4-0	3-1	2-1	4-0
12 Halesowen T.	2-1	2-0	2-1	3-2	2-2	2-2	3-5	0-5	3-1	0-1	1-2		2-1	3-2	2-0	2-0	5-2	0-4	1-3	2-4	0-1	5-3
13 Hemel Hemp. T.	1-0	0-0	1-0	2-1	0-1	1-1	0-0	0-1	4-0	3-1	2-1	1-1		4-2	3-0	1-0	0-1	3-1	4-3	1-1	0-1	1-0
14 Hitchin Town	2-0	1-1	0-0	0-1	1-1	2-1	2-2	2-2	1-2	1-3	1-1	0-1	2-1		3-2	2-2	0-4	1-1	2-2	0-1	0-1	3-1
15 Mangotsfield U.	1-0	1-0	3-2	0-3	0-3	0-4	2-0	0-3	0-0	0-2	0-1	0-1	0-1	2-1		0-3	2-2	0-2	1-2	2-1	3-2	1-2
16 Merthyr Tydfil	3-0	0-2	3-0	1-4	1-1	2-0	2-2	0-2	1-0	1-1	2-1	2-0	3-2	3-2	1-0		2-2	3-3	4-1	1-2	1-2	2-1
17 Oxford City	3-0	2-0	1-0	3-0	1-0	2-2	5-3	0-1	0-1	2-2	1-1	4-1	2-3	2-3	4-0	1-4		3-2	1-1	1-2	3-0	4-0
18 Rugby Town	0-0	2-3	3-0	3-3	2-3	0-1	4-0	0-2	0-1	2-3	1-3	0-2	0-5	4-3	2-1	3-0	1-1		4-0	0-0	2-0	2-2
19 Stourbridge	1-1	1-1	3-1	0-1	1-1	1-2	6-1	0-2	0-2	0-3	1-1	2-2	1-6	1-0	4-1	1-2	2-0	1-1		2-1	3-0	8-4
20 Swindon S.	4-4	3-2	2-1	4-4	0-2	1-3	0-1	1-4	1-1	1-1	0-1	1-0	1-4	0-4	2-1	0-0	1-1	3-1	1-1		1-0	3-0
21 Tiverton Town	2-0	2-1	0-2	2-1	1-2	1-2	3-2	0-2	0-1	0-2	2-2	3-0	1-1	3-1	0-0	0-1	2-2	0-1	1-1	1-1		3-2
22 Yate Town	3-1	1-0	3-1	0-0	0-3	1-3	2-1	0-2	0-1	2-2	0-2	1-2	2-3	2-1	2-1	4-0	2-3	2-4	2-4	0-0	0-0	

DIVISION ONE MIDLANDS

		P	W	D	L	F	A	GD	Pts
1	Leamington	42	32	5	5	114	44	70	101
2	Nuneaton Town	42	28	8	6	85	31	54	92
3	Atherstone Town	42	24	13	5	82	45	37	85
4	Chasetown	42	25	9	8	67	31	36	84
5	Chesham United	42	22	10	10	70	38	32	76
6	Sutton Coldfield Town	42	24	4	14	79	62	17	76
7	Bury Town	42	22	9	11	88	41	47	75
8	Leighton Town	42	18	13	11	57	46	11	67
9	Marlow	42	19	9	14	65	53	12	66
10	Aylesbury United	42	19	7	16	65	58	7	64
11	Romulus	42	17	10	15	60	42	18	61
12	AFC Sudbury	42	17	10	15	66	65	1	61
13	Bromsgrove Rovers	42	15	8	19	58	53	5	53
14	Bedworth United	42	14	7	21	50	66	-16	49
15	Soham Town Rangers	42	13	7	22	48	79	-31	46
16	Stourport Swifts	42	10	10	22	46	74	-28	40
17	Barton Rovers	42	12	4	26	50	79	-29	40
18	Arlesey Town	42	11	5	26	40	70	-30	38
19	Rothwell Town	42	8	12	22	35	79	-44	36
20	Woodford United	42	9	7	26	38	80	-42	34
21	Dunstable Town (-13)	42	11	3	28	54	89	-35	23
22	Malvern Town	42	2	10	30	27	119	-92	16

PROMOTION PLAY-OFFS - SEMI-FINALS

Atherstone Town	0 - 5	Chasetown
Nuneaton Town	2 - 1	Chesham United

PROMOTION PLAY-OFF - FINAL

Nuneaton Town	1 - 0	Chasetown

	1	2	3	4	5	6	7	8	9	10	11	12	13	14	15	16	17	18	19	20	21	22
1 AFC Sudbury		0-0	0-3	2-2	4-2	2-1	2-1	1-1	2-0	1-0	4-2	0-4	1-1	0-0	1-2	1-1	1-1	1-2	3-1	1-1	2-0	0-1
2 Arlesey Town	2-3		0-1	2-0	1-3	1-2	1-2	3-2	0-0	0-2	3-2	1-4	0-2	1-2	0-1	1-3	1-0	3-0	0-1	0-1	0-2	2-0
3 Atherstone T.	2-0	3-3		3-5	5-0	1-0	2-0	2-0	2-1	3-3	2-1	0-0	1-1	7-1	1-1	0-2	2-2	5-0	2-0	1-1	3-2	2-2
4 Aylesbury Utd	0-3	1-0	1-1		0-1	1-3	1-2	1-2	3-0	2-1	4-0	1-2	0-0	5-1	0-3	0-4	2-1	2-0	4-1	1-0	3-0	1-0
5 Barton Rovers	3-2	1-2	0-1	1-2		1-3	1-1	1-2	1-1	0-1	3-0	0-2	1-2	0-0	3-1	2-1	3-2	0-1	1-2	2-5	2-3	0-1
6 Bedworth Utd	3-4	1-0	1-4	1-1	0-2		0-1	0-4	1-0	1-3	3-0	1-1	0-1	3-0	0-3	1-2	0-2	1-0	1-0	1-1	2-3	3-3
7 Bromsgrove R.	2-0	5-0	0-1	3-1	1-0	4-1		0-1	1-2	1-2	2-0	1-3	0-1	2-1	0-2	0-4	0-0	2-1	0-2	7-0	2-0	1-2
8 Bury Town	2-0	1-0	1-1	1-0	0-2	0-1	0-0		2-0	0-1	3-1	2-2	4-0	7-0	1-0	0-1	1-1	8-0	5-0	7-2	0-2	2-0
9 Chasetown	3-1	0-0	0-2	2-1	2-1	2-0	2-1	3-0		0-0	1-3	2-0	0-0	4-0	4-1	1-1	3-0	2-0	0-0	4-1	1-2	1-0
10 Chesham Utd	3-2	3-1	0-1	2-3	8-1	0-0	1-1	2-2	0-2		2-1	1-2	2-1	3-0	3-3	0-0	0-1	0-0	1-0	2-1	0-1	4-0
11 Dunstable Town	1-3	4-0	1-2	2-1	4-2	2-0	3-1	3-7	0-1	0-1		0-4	2-4	4-0	1-1	0-1	3-2	3-2	2-3	0-0	0-1	2-0
12 Leamington	3-5	3-1	3-0	1-2	4-1	4-1	2-0	2-1	1-3	2-0	2-0		3-3	8-0	7-2	2-1	2-1	1-0	3-1	1-0	0-3	7-1
13 Leighton Town	3-0	2-0	0-0	1-0	1-0	2-1	1-1	0-1	1-1	0-1	1-1	2-5		3-0	2-0	0-1	1-1	3-0	2-0	1-3	0-0	1-0
14 Malvern Town	1-2	0-1	1-3	1-1	2-2	2-0	0-4	1-1	0-3	1-4	0-1	0-3	2-2		1-1	0-3	0-2	0-0	1-2	1-2	0-2	1-1
15 Marlow	1-0	1-0	3-1	0-4	2-1	1-0	2-1	0-0	1-2	1-0	2-0	0-1	0-1	9-1		1-1	1-1	2-0	2-0	0-0	1-0	0-2
16 Nuneaton Town	3-1	4-1	2-2	3-0	2-0	0-0	2-1	4-1	1-1	0-1	6-1	0-2	2-1	3-1	2-4		2-0	0-1	2-0	3-1	3-0	2-0
17 Romulus	2-0	3-2	1-1	0-1	0-1	3-0	2-0	1-2	0-1	0-0	3-0	1-2	2-0	7-0	2-1	0-2		1-0	2-2	1-1	3-0	1-2
18 Rothwell Town	1-1	2-2	1-2	1-1	1-0	1-3	2-2	0-7	1-2	0-1	3-2	0-6	3-1	0-0	2-0	2-2	0-2		1-2	3-1	1-1	1-1
19 Soham Town R.	3-3	0-1	2-1	1-1	2-0	3-3	1-0	0-2	0-3	1-3	3-2	2-3	3-4	4-2	1-1	0-2	0-3	1-0		1-3	0-1	0-3
20 Stourport Swifts	0-1	2-0	1-2	1-2	2-3	0-2	0-0	1-1	0-2	1-1	1-0	1-2	0-2	2-1	2-1	0-4	0-1	1-1	1-2		1-2	2-3
21 Sutton Coldfield	1-4	1-2	1-2	4-2	2-0	0-3	3-3	2-1	0-3	0-5	2-0	3-3	2-1	5-2	4-1	1-2	2-1	4-1	4-0	3-1		2-1
22 Woodford Utd	0-2	0-2	1-2	1-2	1-2	1-2	1-2	0-3	0-2	1-3	3-0	0-2	2-2	2-0	0-6	0-1	0-1	0-0	1-1	1-2	0-8	

DIVISION ONE SOUTH & WEST

		P	W	D	L	F	A	GD	Pts
1	Truro City	42	29	8	5	120	49	71	95
2	Windsor & Eton	42	26	7	9	77	44	33	85
3	AFC Totton	42	23	13	6	89	39	50	82
4	Beaconsfield SYCOB	42	24	9	9	77	44	33	81
5	Didcot Town	42	21	10	11	91	52	39	73
6	Thatcham Town	42	20	8	14	74	58	16	68
7	Bridgwater Town	42	19	8	15	69	56	13	65
8	North Leigh	42	17	10	15	68	64	4	61
9	AFC Hayes	42	18	7	17	80	92	-12	61
10	Paulton Rovers	42	16	10	16	65	62	3	58
11	Cinderford Town	42	15	11	16	71	75	-4	56
12	Gosport Borough	42	15	10	17	64	67	-3	55
13	Uxbridge	42	15	9	18	76	72	4	54
14	Cirencester Town	42	14	10	18	78	79	-1	52
15	Abingdon United	42	15	7	20	63	77	-14	52
16	Slough Town	42	11	12	19	62	91	-29	45
17	Burnham	42	12	9	21	52	83	-31	45
18	Bishops Cleeve	42	10	13	19	51	71	-20	43
19	Andover	42	10	12	20	58	102	-44	42
20	Taunton Town	42	9	9	24	50	85	-35	36
21	Bracknell Town	42	9	8	25	39	75	-36	35
22	Winchester City (-3)	42	10	8	24	47	84	-37	35

PROMOTION PLAY-OFFS - SEMI-FINALS

AFC Totton	2 - 1	Beaconsfield SYCOB
Windsor & Eton	0 - 2	Didcot Town

PROMOTION PLAY-OFF - FINAL

AFC Totton	1 - 2	Didcot Town

	1	2	3	4	5	6	7	8	9	10	11	12	13	14	15	16	17	18	19	20	21	22
1 Abingdon Utd		3-1	2-1	0-2	1-2	1-0	2-0	2-1	1-2	0-2	3-2	2-2	4-1	1-1	2-0	1-1	2-1	1-3	1-4	1-2	0-2	2-0
2 AFC Hayes	4-4		1-1	4-1	3-1	2-1	1-2	1-4	3-2	0-0	4-3	0-3	4-3	0-4	2-2	2-1	5-2	4-2	1-7	1-3	5-1	0-1
3 AFC Totton (P)	4-1	6-0		3-1	0-0	5-0	3-1	3-0	1-1	3-3	2-0	3-1	3-3	4-0	2-3	4-2	3-0	3-2	0-2	3-2	4-1	1-1
4 Andover	1-2	2-2	0-0		2-1	1-1	2-2	2-1	2-2	0-2	2-0	0-5	1-2	0-3	3-5	1-2	4-3	1-6	1-9	0-3	3-1	0-3
5 Beaconsfield SYCOB	4-0	3-2	2-0	4-0		3-1	4-0	1-0	3-0	3-1	2-3	1-1	0-0	4-3	2-1	0-0	4-0	2-3	2-0	1-0	1-0	1-1
6 Bishops Cleeve	0-3	2-2	1-1	0-2	1-2		1-2	2-0	2-0	1-2	1-2	2-2	1-0	0-0	4-3	0-4	2-0	1-0	0-1	3-1	4-0	0-1
7 Bracknell Town	1-0	2-0	0-1	1-1	1-2	3-1		2-1	1-2	1-2	0-2	0-1	0-0	0-1	0-3	0-0	0-1	0-4	1-3	5-1	1-1	3-2
8 Bridgwater Town	2-0	3-1	1-2	2-1	3-2	0-0	3-0		3-0	2-2	2-2	1-1	1-2	1-0	1-1	6-0	1-2	2-1	1-1	3-2	3-0	0-2
9 Burnham	4-1	1-1	0-5	1-1	0-1	0-0	1-0	0-1		2-0	4-0	0-3	1-1	0-6	1-0	3-0	3-3	1-3	2-6	1-1	1-0	0-2
10 Cinderford Town	1-3	2-3	0-2	5-0	1-1	3-3	3-2	0-4	1-2		2-1	2-1	2-3	1-3	0-0	4-1	1-1	2-2	1-4	1-4	4-0	1-5
11 Cirencester T.	2-2	1-2	2-4	3-3	0-1	5-2	0-0	2-2	2-3	1-2		2-1	1-1	4-1	1-2	4-1	2-0	4-3	2-5	3-2	3-0	3-1
12 Didcot Town	5-4	4-0	0-1	3-1	3-3	6-0	3-0	1-2	6-2	0-2	0-0		1-0	2-1	3-0	2-0	5-0	0-0	3-4	1-1	2-2	0-1
13 Gosport Boro'	2-2	0-3	2-0	1-1	1-2	1-4	1-2	5-0	2-1	2-1	0-3	1-3		3-1	1-0	2-1	4-1	1-0	2-4	0-1	1-2	1-2
14 North Leigh	2-0	2-1	0-2	3-1	1-0	1-1	2-0	2-4	3-0	1-1	2-1	0-3	2-1		1-2	6-1	1-1	0-4	0-1	1-0	1-0	0-1
15 Paulton Rovers	2-0	2-1	0-0	2-2	2-1	3-2	3-2	0-1	2-4	2-3	3-1	1-2	1-3	4-1		1-2	3-2	0-1	0-1	2-1	2-1	0-1
16 Slough Town	0-3	2-3	0-0	4-3	2-2	1-1	0-0	2-1	2-2	2-3	3-2	2-3	2-1	1-1	1-0		2-2	1-1	3-3	1-2	4-0	3-2
17 Taunton Town	2-2	1-4	0-1	1-2	0-2	1-0	2-1	1-2	3-0	0-2	1-1	1-0	1-1	2-2	2-2	2-3		1-2	1-3	1-0	3-0	1-3
18 Thatcham Town	1-3	2-0	0-5	1-1	4-2	1-1	3-2	1-0	1-0	2-0	3-1	1-1	4-2	1-2	0-2	3-1	3-1		0-5	1-0	3-0	1-2
19 Truro City	4-0	3-1	0-0	4-0	1-2	0-0	4-0	3-1	3-0	3-2	1-1	2-4	1-3	2-2	1-1	2-1	3-0	0-0		3-2	5-0	4-2
20 Uxbridge	2-0	2-3	2-2	2-3	1-3	3-3	5-0	1-2	3-2	1-1	2-2	3-2	1-1	3-3	1-1	4-0	1-0	1-0	5-2		1-4	0-2
21 Winchester Cit	3-1	1-2	0-0	1-2	1-0	0-2	1-1	1-1	2-1	3-2	1-3	1-2	0-1	2-2	1-1	3-1	1-2	1-1	1-2	3-2		1-2
22 Windsor & Eton	1-0	0-1	2-1	2-2	0-0	3-0	2-0	2-0	2-0	1-1	3-1	3-0	2-2	4-0	1-1	6-2	2-1	1-0	0-4	1-2	2-4	

Southern League action from:
Corby Town v Banbury United (above) and
Bedford Town v Bashley (left).

Photos: Peter Barnes.

BGB SOUTHERN LEAGUE CUP

PRELIMINARY ROUND

Chippenham Town 2 Oxford City 2 *aet* (5-4p) *(Sep 23)* Att: 205
Sutton Coldfield 1 **Halesowen Town** 1 *aet* (5-6p) *(Sep 23)* Att: 103

FIRST ROUND

Abingdon United 1 Banbury United 1 *aet* (5-3p) *(Oct 28)* Att: 75
Andover 2 Farnborough 2 *aet* (3-0p) *(Oct 28)* Att: 116
Atherstone Town 2 Nuneaton Town 2 *aet* (4-3p) *(Oct 28)* Att: 378
Aylesbury United 3 Burnham 0 *(Oct 27)* Att: 67
Barton Rovers 0 **Dunstable Town** 3 *(Oct 28)* Att: 62
Beaconsfield SYCOB 4 Marlow 1 *(Oct 27)* Att: 88
Bracknell Town 0 **Windsor & Eton** 1 *(Nov 18)* Att: 67
Bridgwater Town 4 Taunton Town 3 *aet (Oct 28)* Att: 346
Bromsgrove Rovers 0 **Romulus** 1 *(Nov 11)* Att: 60
Bury Town 2 AFC Sudbury 0 *(Oct 28)* Att: 402
Chasetown 1 **Leamington** 3 *(Nov 11)* Att: 352
Chippenham Town 1 **Brackley Town** 2 *(Oct 28)* Att: 187
Corby Town 0 **Rothwell Town** 1 *(Oct 11)* Att: 232
Didcot Town 1 **Swindon Supermarine** 2 *(Oct 28)* Att: 139
Evesham United 0 **Gloucester City** 3 *(Oct 28)* Att: 37
Gosport Borough 1 AFC Totton 0 *(Oct 28)* Att: 133
Hemel Hempstead Town 3 Bedford Town 0 *(Nov 18)* Att: 108
Hitchin Town 4 Arlesey Town 0 *(Nov 18)* Att: 128
Leighton Town 3 Slough Town 0 *(Oct 28)* Att: 38
Malvern Town 1 **Cirencester Town** 2 *(Oct 18)* Att: 63
Mangotsfield United 3 Clevedon Town 1 *(Oct 28)* Att: 72
Merthyr Tydfil 4 Bishops Cleeve 2 *aet (Oct 28)* Att: 112
Paulton Rovers 0 **Yate Town** 1 *(Oct 27)* Att: 99
Rugby Town 1 **Bedworth United** 2 *(Nov 11)* Att: 169
Soham Town Rangers 3 **Cambridge City** 4 *aet (Oct 28)* Att: 162
Stourport Swifts 3 **Cinderford Town** 4 *aet (Oct 28)* Att: 46
Halesowen Town 1 Stourbridge 0 *(Oct 28)* Att: 329
Thatcham Town 2 **Chesham United** 4 *aet (Nov 11)* Att: 41
Tiverton Town 3 **Truro City** 4 *aet (Oct 28)* Att: 301
Uxbridge 3 **AFC Hayes** 4 *aet (Oct 28)* Att: 54
Winchester City 3 **Bashley** 4 *(Oct 28)* Att: 156
Woodford United 0 **North Leigh** 1 *(Oct 29)* Att: 39

SECOND ROUND

AFC Hayes 2 **Chesham United** 4 *(Nov 25)* Att: 68
Andover 2 Bashley 1 *(Nov 25)* Att: 68
Atherstone Town 2 Leamington 1 *(Dec 2)* Att: 226
Aylesbury United 1 **Windsor & Eton** 2 *(Nov 26)* Att: 97
Brackley Town 3 Romulus 2 *aet (Nov 25)* Att: 105
Cinderford Town 4 Merthyr Tydfil 3 *(Nov 25)* Att: 75
Gloucester City 3 Abingdon United 0 *(Nov 25)* Att: 74
Gosport Borough 1 **Beaconsfield SYCOB** 2 *(Nov 25)* Att: 76
Hemel Hempstead 4 **Dunstable Town** 4 *aet* (4-5p) *(Dec 2)* Att: 89
Leighton Town 1 **Bury Town** 3 *(Nov 25)* Att: 69
Mangotsfield United 1 **Yate Town** 2 *(Nov 25)* Att: 79
North Leigh 4 Rothwell Town 0 *(Nov 25)* Att: 43
Bedworth United 2 Halesowen Town 0 *(Nov 25)* Att: 60
Hitchin Town 1 Cambridge City 0 *(Dec 9)* Att: 112
Swindon Supermarine 1 Cirencester Town 0 *(Nov 26)* Att: 100
Truro City 0 **Bridgwater Town** 3 *(Nov 25)* Att: 231

THIRD ROUND

Brackley Town 3 North Leigh 0 *(Jan 13)* Att: 98
Bury Town 2 Hitchin Town 0 *(Jan 13)* Att: 163
Chesham United 4 Beaconsfield SYCOB 1 *aet (Jan 13)* Att: 156
Cinderford Town 2 **Bridgwater Town** 2 *aet* (3-5p) *(Jan 13)* Att: 51
Gloucester City 3 Yate Town 0 *(Jan 13)* Att: 130
Halesowen Town 0 **Atherstone Town** 2 *(Jan 13)* Att: 145
Dunstable Town 1 **Windsor & Eton** 2 *(Jan 13)* Att: 46
Swindon Supermarine 6 Andover 2 *(Feb 17) (at Andover)* Att: 92

QUARTER-FINALS

Atherstone Town 2 Brackley Town 0 *(Feb 26)* Att: 172
Bridgwater Town 2 Gloucester City 1 *(Feb 17)* Att: 297
Bury Town 3 Chesham United 1 *(Feb 17)* Att: 201
Swindon Supermarine 3 Windsor & Eton 0 *(Feb 25)* Att: 74

SEMI-FINALS

Bridgwater Town 3 Swindon Supermarine 0 *(Mar 5)* Att: 184
Atherstone Town 2 Bury Town 2 *aet* (3-1p) *(Mar 12)* Att: 220

FINAL *(played over two legs)*

(April 7th) **Atherstone Town** 2 Bridgwater Town 1 Att: 325
(April 21st) Bridgwater Town 1 **Atherstone Town** 3 Att: 533

BANBURY UNITED

Founded: 1933
Re-Formed: 1965
Nickname: Puritans

Manager: Billy Jeffrey

Club Colours: Red with gold trim/red/red

Change Colours: White/blue/blue

Best Season - League: 7th - Southern Premier 2005-06

Ground address: Spencer Stadium, off Station Road, Banbury, Oxon. OX16 5TA

Tel No: 01295 263 354. Fax: 01295 276 492

Capacity: 6,500 Seats: 250 Covered: 50 Floodlights:Yes

Simple Directions: M40 jct11 follow signs for Banbury then to BR station at eastern end of town. Turn right down narrow lane just before station forecourt

Midweek Home Matchday: Tuesday

Clubhouse: Open matchdays and week-ends. Hot & Cold food.

Club Shop: Yes.

CLUB PERSONNEL

Chairman: Paul Jones.
Additional Directors:
David Bennett, Richard Cox.

Secretary: Barry.Worsley.
c/o SOL Systems, Unit 4,
Mallorie House, Beaumont
Rd, Banbury 0X16 1RH
(H) 01295 265638
(B) 01295 255536
(M) 07941 267567
(F) 01295 276492,
bworsley@btinternet.com

Programme Editor:
David Shadbolt
djshadbolt@tiscali.co.uk

CLUB STATISTICS

Record	**Attendance**: 7,160 v Oxford City F.A.Cup 3rd Qualifying Road 30.10.48
	Victory: 12-0 v RNAS CULHAM Oxon. Senior Cup 45-46
	Defeat: 2-11 v W.B.A. 'A' Birmingham Combination 38-39
Career Goalscorer:	Dick Pike (1935-48) Tony Jacques (65-76) both 222
Career Appearances:	**In Career:** Jody McKay 576
Record Transfer Fee	**Paid:** £2,000 to Oxford United for Phil Emsden
	Received: £20,000 from Derby County for Kevin Wilson 1979
Senior Honours:	Hellenic Premier 99-00, Oxford Senior Cup 78-9 87-8 03-04 R-up (7) and Birmingham Senior Cup R-up 48-9 59-60
Previous	**Leagues**: Banbury Jnr 33-34, Oxon. Sen. 34-35 Birmingham Comb. 35-54 West Mids 54-66 Southern 66-90 Hellenic 1991-2000
	Name: Banbury Spencer

Back Row (L-R): Stevie Howkins, Troy Bryan, Luke Bennett, Joe Murrell, Kameron Abbassi, James Peppiatt, Scott Bridges.
Front Row: Ollie Stanbridge, Tom Breward, Craig Pearman, Mark Essex (captain), Lewis Travers, Nicky Gordon, Stefan Morley, Dan Drummond.

BANBURY UNITED

BEST LGE ATT.: 625 v Brackley Town
LOWEST: 101 v Merthyr Tydfil

No.	Date	Comp	H/A	Opponents	Att:	Result	Goalscorers	Pos
1	Aug 16	Southern P.	H	Oxford City	430	W 1 - 0	**Gordon** 41 (pen)	
2	19		A	Stourbridge	144	D 1 - 1	**Gordon** 32 (pen)	
3	23		A	Rugby Town	257	D 0 - 0		10
4	25		H	Swindon Supermarine	336	L 1 - 5	Stanbridge 15	
5	30		A	Bashley	315	L 0 - 1		18
6	Sept 2		H	Cambridge City	213	D 2 - 2	Bridges S 13 Breward 75	
7	**13**	**F.A.C. 1Q**	**A**	**Chippenham Town**	**421**	**L 0 - 2**		
8	20		H	Farnborough	386	L 0 - 2		21
9	Oct 4		A	Yate Town	164	L 1 - 3	Bridges S 75	
10	7		H	Gloucester City	235	L 1 - 5	Hawkins 16	
11	11		H	Bedford Town	285	W 4 - 0	Forington 35 Bridges S 41 82 Bennett 70	20
12	**18**	**F.A.T. 1Q**	**H**	**Burnham**	**217**	**L 0 - 1**		
13	Nov 1		H	Halesowen Town	245	W 2 - 1	**Gordon** 17 (pen) Bridges S 60	17
14	4		A	Clevedon Town	115	D 1 - 1	**Gordon** 46	
15	8		A	Chippenham Town	391	L 0 - 1		14
16	15		H	Mangotsfield United	267	D 1 - 1	**Gordon** 62 (pen)	15
17	18		A	Tiverton Town	253	L 0 - 2		
18	25		A	Evesham United	107	L 0 - 2		
19	29		A	Hemel Hempstead	189	L 0 - 1		16
20	Dec 6		H	Hitchin Town	310	L 1 - 4	**Gordon** 69	21
21	20		A	Merthyr Tydfil	361	L 0 - 3		22
22	27		A	Swindon Supermarine	254	D 4 - 4	**Gordon** 28 49 Travers 29 Bulman 75 (og)	21
23	Jan 1		H	Brackley Town	625	W 3 - 1	Halsey 22 **Gordon** 36 Stringfellow 48	
24	3		A	Oxford City	444	L 0 - 3		20
25	17		A	Cambridge City	290	L 1 - 3	**Gordon** 30	21
26	20		H	Corby Town	151	L 0 - 4		
27	27		A	Gloucester City	215	D 1 - 1	Groves 31	
28	31		H	Yate Town	216	W 3 - 0	Redknapp 47 **Gordon** 72 (pen) Groves 90	18
29	Feb 14		H	Evesham United	264	L 0 - 6		19
30	17		H	Rugby Town	201	W 2 - 1	Travers 12 Bridges P 90	
31	21		H	Clevedon Town	316	W 3 - 1	Travers 25 Groves 33 **Gordon** 72	18
32	28		A	Farnborough	602	L 0 - 1		18
33	Mar 3		A	Bedford Town	228	L 0 - 3		
34	7		H	Chippenham Town	284	L 0 - 5		
35	10		A	Halesowen Town	213	L 1 - 2	**Gordon** 21	
36	14		A	Mangotsfield United	168	L 0 - 1		19
37	17		H	Stourbridge	170	W 2 - 0	Gardner 24 Redknapp 47	
38	21		H	Tiverton Town	308	L 0 - 3		18
39	28		A	Hitchin Town	314	L 0 - 2		20
40	April 4		H	Hemel Hempstead	215	W 3 - 0	Bridges P 6 Redknapp 58 Stone 90	20
41	11		H	Bashley	324	W 1 - 0	Stone 26	20
42	13		A	Brackley Town	636	W 2 - 1	**Gordon** 42 (pen) Stone 78	
43	18		H	Merthyr Tydfil	101	D 1 - 1	Stone 32	18
44	25		A	Corby Town	1969	L 0 - 5		19

Average Home Att: 280 (323) **Goals** 43 86

Best Position: 10th **Worst:** 22nd

Goalscorers: Gordon 14, Bridges S 4, Groves 4, Stone 4, Redknapp 3, Travers 3, Bridges P 2, Bennett 1, Breward 1, Forington 1, Gardner 1, Halsey 1, Hawkins 1, Stanbridge 1, Stringfellow 1. Own Goals 1.

BASHLEY

Founded: 1947
Nickname: The Bash

Manager: Steve Riley

Club Colours: Gold/black/black

Change Colours: White/green/green

Best Seasons - League: 4th Southern Premier 1991-92.

Ground address: Bashley Road Ground, Bashley Road, New Milton Hampshire. BH25 5RY **Tel No**: 01425 620 280. Fax: 01425 638 376.

Capacity: 4,250 **Seats**: 250 **Covered**:1,200 **Floodlights**: Yes

Simple Directions: A35 Lyndhurst towards Christchurch, turn left down B3058 towards New Milton, ground on left in Bashley village. Half hour walk from New Milton (BR) station. New Cargo Bus service C32 (New Milton-Lymington).

Midweek Home Matchday: Tuesday

Clubhouse: Usual Licensing Hours with food available.

Club Shop: Matchdays

Local Radio: 2CR FM & BBC Radio Solent

Local Press: Bournemouth Echo, Southern Pink & New Milton Advertiser Southampron Echo.

CLUB PERSONNEL

Chairman: Andy Gotteland

Additional Directors:
Richard Millbery (Treasurer),
Pat Bowring,
Gary Parsons, Phil Barry.

Secretary: Dave Grant.
46 Spring Road,
Bournemouth, Dorset BH1
4PS. (H) 01202 391 466

Programme
Editor: Richard Milbery
rw_milberry@lineone.net

CLUB STATISTICS

Record	**Attendance:** 3,500 v Emley F.A.Vase S-Final 1st Leg 1987-1988
	Career Goalscorer: Richard Gillespie - 134
	Career Appearances: John Bone - 829
	Win: 21-1 v Co-operative (a) Bournemouth League 1964
	Defeat:2-20 v Air Speed (a) Bournemouth League 1957
Record Transfer Fee	**Paid**: £7,500 to Newport (IOW)for Danny Gibbons and to Dorchester Town for David Elm.
Received:	£15,000 from Salisbury City for Craig Davis,from Eastleigh for Paul Sales and from AFC Bournemouth foir Wade Elliott
	Victory: 21-1 v Co-Operative (A) Bournemoutth League1964
	Defeat: 2-20 v Air Special (A) Bournemouth League 1957
Senior Honours:	Southern League Div 1 South & West 2006-07 Southern Division 89-90. Wessex League 86-87 87-88 88-89 Southern Leagure Divison 1.
Previous Leagues:	Bournemouth 1953-83 Hants 1983-86 Wessex 1986-89 Southern 1989-04 Isthmian 2004-06.

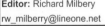

Back row (L-R): Matt Finlay, Gary Middleton, Joe Fisher, Matt Parnell, Steve Hollick, Jordan Rose, David Elm, Jeremy Tarr, Pete Castle, Chris Ferrett, Nic Eastham.
Front row: Phil Waters, Richard Gillespie, Marc Fairbrother, John Edwards (physio), Paul Gazzard, Steve Riley (manager), James Rowe, Martin Doolan (assistant manager), Charlie Knight, Aidan Sainsbury, Justin Keeler, Lee Burch.

BASHLEY

BEST LGE ATT.: 537 v Farnborough
LOWEST: 211 v Hemel Hempstead

No.	Date	Comp	H/A	Opponents	Att:	Result	Goalscorers	Pos
1	Aug 16	Southern P.	A	Clevedon Town	195	D 0 - 0		
2	19		H	Mangotsfield United	265	L 0 - 1		
3	23		H	Halesowen Town	290	L 1 - 3	Fisher 78	19
4	25		A	Chippenham Town	451	W 3 - 2	**Gillespie** 10 Finlay 39 Parnell 61	
5	30		H	Banbury United	315	W 1 - 0	Tarr 70	12
6	Sept 2		A	Gloucester City	236	L 0 - 3		
7	6		H	Stourbridge	273	W 4 - 1	**Gillespie** 28 69 Tarr 36 Eastham 71	9
8	**13**	**F.A.C. 1Q**	**A**	**Calne Town**	**125**	**W 5 - 0**	**Knight 20 Gillespie 34 (pen) 57 Parnell 75 Knowles 82**	
9	20		A	Cambridge City	297	L 0 - 5		14
10	**27**	**F.A.C. 2Q**	**H**	**Maidenhead United**	**312**	**W 2 - 1**	**Gillespie 7 Eastham 79**	
11	Oct 4		H	Corby Town	291	L 0 - 3		17
12	7		A	Hemel Hempstead T	187	D 0 - 0		
13	**11**	**F.A.C. 3Q**	**A**	**Basingstoke Town**	**356**	**D 2 - 2**	**Parnell 48 Gillespie 90 (pen)**	
14	**14**	**F.A.C. 3Qr**	**H**	**Basingstoke Town**	**349**	**L 0 - 3**		
15	**18**	**F.A.T. 1Q**	**A**	**Mangotsfield United**	**134**	**W 2 - 0**	**Eastham 50 Keeler 90**	
16	25		H	Tiverton Town	285	L 0 - 3		18
17	**Nov 1**	**F.A.T. 2Q**	**A**	**Yate Town**	**148**	**W 3 - 1**	**Rowe 40 Gillespie 57 76**	
18	11		H	Swindon Supermarine	238	D 2 - 2	Parnell 58 Tarr 89	
19	15		H	Merthyr Tydfil	307	L 1 - 3	**Gillespie** 40 (pen)	21
20	**22**	**F.A.T 3Q**	**A**	**Eastleigh**	**424**	**W 2 - 0**	**Rowe 7 Allen 71**	
21	29		H	Yate Town	227	D 1 - 1	Allen 65	21
22	Dec 6		A	Oxford City	214	L 0 - 2		22
23	**16**	**F.A.T.1R**	**H**	**Tiverton Town**	**165**	**D 2 - 2**	**Keeler 52 Tarr 88**	
24	20		H	Bedford Town	260	W 1 - 0	Allen 14	19
25	**23**	**F.A.T. 1Rr**	**A**	**Tiverton Town**	**436**	**L 1 - 2**	**Keeler 43**	
26	27		H	Chippenham Town	389	W 2 - 1	Rowe 46 Knight 54	
27	Jan 1		A	Farnborough Town	821	D 1 - 1	Allen 34 (pen)	
28	10		A	Halesowen Town	423	L 0 - 2		18
29	17		H	Gloucester City	300	D 1 - 1	Allen 36	
30	24		A	Mangotsfield United	145	L 0 - 1		18
31	27		H	Hemel Hempstead	211	W 2 - 1	**Gillespie** 64 67	
32	31		A	Corby Town	251	L 1 - 3	Parnell 87	
33	Feb 14		A	Tiverton Town	333	L 1 - 2	Finley 73	17
34	17		H	Clevedon Town	246	W 1 - 0	**Gillespie** 72 (pen)	
35	21		A	Stourbridge	229	D 1 - 1	**Gillespie** 71	17
36	28		H	Cambridge City	342	D 0 - 0		17
37	Mar 7		H	Brackley Town	262	D 1 - 1	Moss 75	17
38	11		A	Swindon Spermarine	149	L 2 - 3	Allen 64 **Gillespie** 90	
39	14		A	Merthyr Tydfil	301	W 2 - 0	**Gillespie** 60 Allen 67	17
40	17		A	Hitchin Town	228	D 1 - 1	Allen 48	
41	21		H	Evesham United	248	D 0 - 0		17
42	24		A	Evesham United	80	D 2 - 2	Moss 6 Allen 70	
43	28		H	Oxford City	302	W 3 - 2	Allen 38 Ballard 48 (og) Moss 62	16
44	31		A	Rugby Town	158	W 3 - 2	Tarr 21 Allen 25 Knight 45	
45	April 4		A	Yate Town	147	L 0 - 1		16
46	11		A	Banbury United	324	L 0 - 1		16
47	13		H	Farnborough	537	W 1 - 0	Moss 47	
48	15		A	Brackey Town	157	W 4 - 2	Moss 38 47 Knowles 48 Kelly 65	
49	18		A	Bedford Town	308	W 2 - 0	Knowles 44 **Gillespie** 73	14
50	21		H	Hitchin Town	241	W 4 - 0	Kelly 52 **Gillespie** 54 Knight 82 Keeler 90	
51	25		H	Rugby Town	334	W 3 - 1	Parnell 27 Ferrett 41 **Gillespie** 89	14

Average Home Att: 293 (326) **Goals 71 69**

Best Position: 9th **Worst:** 22nd

Goalscorers: Gillespie 19, Allen 11, Moss 6, Parnell 6, Tarr 5, Keeler 4, Knight 4, Eastham 3, Knowles 3, Rowe 3, Kelly 2, Finlay 2, Fisher 1. Parnell 1, Own Goals 1.

BEDFORD TOWN

Founded: 1908
Reformed 1989
Nickname: The Eagles

CLUB PERSONNEL

Chairman: David Howell

Additional Directors:
Dave Swallow,
Gerry Edmunds,
Dave Redman, Tony Luff,
Mick Hooker.

Secretary:
Dave Swallow.
c/o the club.
01234 854 973
(M) 07939 812965

Programme Editor:
As Secretary.

Manager: Lee Howarth.

Club Colours: Blue with white trim/blue/blue.

Change Colours: Yellow/navy/yellow.

Best Season - League: 22nd Conference South 2006-07

Ground address: The Eyrie, Meadow Lane, Cardington, Bedford MK44 3SB

Tel No: 01234 831558 Fax: 01234 831990

Capacity: 3,000 **Seats**: 300 **Covered:** 1,000 **Floodlights**:Yes

Simple Directions: From the A1 at the Sandy roundabout take A603 through Moggerhanger and Willington and the ground is situated just before the Bedford by-pass on the right.

Midweek Home Matchday: Tuesday

Clubhouse: Large function room with bar and food.

Club Shop: Well stocked.**Contact:** Gerry Edmonds.

Local Radio: Chiltern Radio and Three Counties.

Local Press: Beds Times and Beds on Sunday

SOUTHERN CLUB STATISTICS

Record	**Attendance**	:3,000 v Peterborough United Ground opening 06.08.93
	Victory:	9-0 v Ickleford and v Cardington
	Defeat:	0-5 v Hendon
	Career Goalscorer:Jason Reed	
	Career Appearances: Eddie Lawley	
Senior Honours:	Southern League Play Off Winners 2005-2006, Isthmian Div 1 R-up 00-01 Div 2 98-909 Bedfordshire Senior Cup 94-95	
Previous Leagues:	South Midlands: 91-94, Predecessors: Utd Co.1908-39, Southern 46-82, Isthmian 94-2004, Southern 200 5-2006, Conference South 2006-07.	
Grounds:	Allen Park, Queens Park, Bedford Park Pitch 1991-93 (for predecessors): London Rd., Gasworks, Queens Park, The Eyrie, Raleigh St	

Back row (L-R): Chris Gibbons (Physio), Tony Battersby, Jon Darby, Dan Walker, Stuart Wall, Mike Armitt, Scott Priestnall, Graham Clark, Aaran Cavill, Ian Draycott, Jonathan Woolf, Lee Howarth (Manager). **Front Row:** Callum Lewis, Joe Power, Rob Miller, Eddie Lawley (Captain), Craig Daniel, Jamie Cole, Andrew Phillips, Lewis McBride.

BEDFORD TOWN

BEST LGE ATT.: **589** v Cambridge City
LOWEST: **228** v Banbury United

No.	Date	Comp	H/A	Opponents	Att:	Result	Goalscorers	Pos
1	Aug 16	Southern P.	H	Evesham United	382	D 1 - 1	Aladetoun	
2	19		A	Hemel Hempstead T	229	L 0 - 1		
3	23		A	Oxford City	275	L 0 - 1		16
4	25		H	RugbyTown	441	W 2 - 0	Cavell 36 Gentle 62	
5	30		A	TivertonTown	316	W 2 - 0	Gentle 5 **Phillips** 80	8
6	Sept 2		H	Brackley Town	291	D 0 - 0		
7	6		H	Chippenham Town	383	W 2 - 0	Gentle 26 Daniel 53	7
8	**13**	**F.A.C. 1Q**	**A**	**Wealdstone**	**312**	**D 2 - 2**	**Phillips 19 41**	
9	20		A	Gloucester City	270	W 1 - 0	**Phillips** 71	6
10	**27**	**F.A.C. 2Q**	**H**	**AFC Wimbledon**	**1296**	**D 2 - 2**	**Gentle 11 Clark 89**	
11	**30**	**F.A.C. 2Qr**	**A**	**AFC Wimbledon**		**L 0 - 3**		
12	Oct 4		H	Halesowen Town	463	W 1 - 0	**Phillips** 20	4
13	7		A	Hitchin Town	550	D 0 - 0		
14	11		A	Banbury United	285	L 0 - 4		6
15	**18**	**F.A.T. 1Q**	**H**	**Corby Town**	**374**	**L 1 - 2**	**Phillips 19**	
16	25		H	Corby Town	453	L 1 - 5	Cavell 33	9
17	Nov 8		H	Yate Town	307	D 1 - 1	**Phillips** 26	8
18	11		A	Farnborough Town	710	L 1 - 3	Cavell 52	10
19	15		A	Stourbridge	211	L 1 - 3	Oujda 35	
20	22		H	Clevedon Town	301	D 0 - 0		
21	29		A	Swindon Supermarine	181	L 1 - 2	Gould 90	12
22	Dec 6		H	Merthyr Tydfil	278	W 1 - 0	Gould 22	11
23	13		H	Mangotsfield United	273	W 3 - 1	Daniel 8 Darby 49 **Draycott** 74	
24	20		A	Bashley	280	L 0 - 1		11
25	27		A	Rugby Town	340	L 0 - 3		13
26	Jan 1		H	Cambridge City	589	D 1 - 1	Daniel 9	
27	17		A	Brackley Town	248	L 0 - 2		15
28	20		H	Bedford Town	358	W 5 - 0	Battersby 45 56 (pen) Cavell 51 **Phillips** 77 Wall 79	
29	31		A	Halesowen Town	344	L 1 - 2	**Draycott** 23	14
30	Feb 10		A	Evesham United	94	W 1 - 0	Battersby 34	
31	21		A	Chippenham Town	441	L 0 - 1		14
32	24		A	Corby Town	240	W 2 - 1	Wall 18 **Draycott** 22	
33	28		H	Gloucester City	379	D 1 - 1	**Draycott** 58	14
34	Mar 3		H	Banbury United	228	W 3 - 0	Daniel 46 Lewis 57 Clark 70	
35	7		A	Yate Town	163	L 1 - 3	**Draycott** 63	14
36	10		H	Farnborough	322	L 0 - 2		
37	14		H	Stourbridge	292	W 2 - 1	**Draycott** 16 Daniel 78	14
38	21		A	Clevedon Town	179	L 1 - 2	**Draycott** 75	14
39	24		H	Hemel Hempstead	319	L 1 - 2	**Draycott** 1	
40	29		A	Merthyr Tydfil	312	L 0 - 3		
41	31		H	Oxford City	286	W 3 - 1	Woolf 29 31 Clark 60	
42	April 4		H	Swindon Supermarine	315	W 1 - 0	Battersby 62 (pen)	14
43	11		H	Tiverton Town	294	D 1 - 1	Gould 9	14
44	13		A	Cambridge City	506	L 0 - 1		
45	18		H	Bashley	308	L 0 - 2		15
46	25		A	Mangotsfield United	156	L 2 - 3	Darby 59 Battersby 77 (pen)	15

Average Home Att: **346 (367)** **Goals** **49 64**

Best Position: 4th **Worst:** 16th

Goalscorers: Draycott 8, Phillips 8, Daniel 5, Battersby 5, Cavell 4, Gentle 4, Clark 3, Gould 3, Darby 2, Wall 2, Woolf 2, Aladetoun 1, Lewis 1, Oujda 1.

BRACKLEY TOWN

Founded: 1890
Nickname: Saints

CLUB PERSONNEL
Chairman: Sara Crannage
Additional Directors:
Phil Hedges, Francis Oliver,
Phil Lines.

Secretary: Pat Ashby,
17 Manor Road,
Woodford Halse,
Daventry, Northamptonshire
NN11 3QP
07969 825 636

Programme
Editor: Brian Martin
brainmartin2905@aol.com

Manager: Jon Brady.

Club Colours: Red & white stripes/red/red & white.

Change Colours: Yellow/yellow/yellow.

Best Seasons - League: 8th Southern League Premier 2007-08.

Ground address: St James Park, Churchil Way, Brackley, Northants NN13 7EJ

Tel No: 01280 704 077

Capacity: 3,500 **Seats**:300 **Covered**:1,500 **Floodlights**: Yes

Simple Directions: Churchill Way, East off A 43 at South end of town.

Midweek Home Matchday: Tuesday

Clubhouse: Fully licensed. Lounge & main hall. Food available. Open all week.

Club Shop: Yes, selling club merchandise,programmes and badges etc.

Local Press: Brackley Advertiser, Banbury Guardian and Herald & Post

Local Radio: Fox F.M., Touch FM & Radio Northampton

CLUB STATISTICS

Record
Attendance: 960 v Banbury United, F.A. 2005-2006
Career Goalscorer:Paul Warrington 320
Career Appearances: Terry Muckelberg 350
Transfer Fee Paid: N/A
Received: £2,000 from Oxford City for Phil Mason 1998

Senior Honours:
United Counties R-up 88-89 (Div 1 83-84); Northants Snr Cup R-up 88-89;
Hellenic Lg Prem 96-97, 2003-04 Div 1 Cup 82-83. Southern Div.1 M 2006-07.

Previous
Leagues:Banbury&District; North Bucks; Hellenic 1977-83; United Co.1983-94;
Hellenic 1994-97,Southern 1997-99.
Ground: Banbury Road, Manor Road, Buckingham Road (up to 1974).

NB: UNFORTUNATELY A RECENT PHOTO WAS NOT AVAILABLE AT THE TIME OF GOING TO PRESS.

BRACKLEY TOWN

BEST LGE ATT.: **636** v Banbury United
LOWEST: **120** v Mangotsfield United

No.	Date	Comp	H/A	Opponents	Att:	Result	Goalscorers	Pos
1	Aug 16	Southern P.	A	Merthyr Tydfil	303	W 4 - 1	Winters 21 87 **Mackey** 61 74	
2	19		H	Farnborough Town	352	D 1 - 1	Winters 20	
3	23		H	Clevedon Town	232	D 1 - 1	Winters 64	8
4	25		A	Corby Town	320	L 0 - 2		
5	30		H	Hitchin Town	236	L 1 - 2	**Mackey** 33	17
6	Sept 2		A	Bedford Town	291	D 0 - 0		
7	6		H	Cambridge City	303	W 2 - 0	**Mackey** 18 (pen) Hadland 74	11
8	**13**	**F.A.C. 1Q**	**A**	**Leyton**	**80**	**W 4 - 2**	**Winters 13 Mackey 18 38 Spencer 55**	
9	20		A	Stourbridge	237	W 1 - 0	Winters 39	8
10	**27**	**F.A.C. 2Q**	**A**	**Stourbridge**	**199**	**D 1 - 1**	**Mackey 45**	
11	**30**	**F.A.C. 2Qr**	**H**	**Stourbridge**	**187**	**W 1 - 0**	**Hadland 78**	
12	Oct 4		H	Swindon Supermarine	207	L 0 - 3		10
13	**11**	**F.A.C. 3Q**	**A**	**Boreham Wood**	**216**	**W 1 - 0**	**Cracknell 86 (pen)**	
14	14		A	Halesowen Town	407	L 2 - 3	Thorpe 51 Wenass 79	
15	**18**	**F.A.T. 1Q**	**A**	**Whitstable Town**	**170**	**W 4 - 3**	**Thorpe 13 42 Cracknell 56 (pen) Peirson 65**	
16	**25**	**F.A.C 4Q**	**A**	**Hampton & Richmond B**	**582**	**W 1 - 0**	**Green 56**	
17	**Nov 1**	**F.A.T. 2Q**	**A**	**Northwood**	**115**	**W 4 - 1**	**Perpetuini 57 Cracknell 67 (pen) Mackey 86 88**	
18	**8**	**F.A.C. 1R**	**A**	**Eastwood Town**	**960**	**L 1 - 2**	**Winters 20**	
19	15		A	Yate Town	171	D 0 - 0		18
20	**22**	**F.A.T. 3Q**	**A**	**Cray Wanderers**	**112**	**W 3 - 0**	**Mackey 61 Winters 81Cracknell 85 (pen)**	
21	Dec 2		H	Mangotsfield United	120	W 3 - 1	**Mackey** 11 Cracknell 36 (pen) Harper 40	
22	6		A	Gloucester City	225	W 1 - 0	Winters 37	
23	9		A	Rugby Town	170	D 3 - 3	Gardner 27 57 Winters 90	
24	**16**	**F.A.T 1R**	**A**	**Basingstoke Town**	**221**	**L 1 - 3**	**Mackey 64**	
25	20		H	Chippenham Town	260	W 1 - 0	Allen 14	13
26	27		H	Corby Town	328	W 5 - 0	**MACKEY** 3 (9 63 71) Sandy 13 37	
27	Jan 1		A	Banbury United	625	L 1 - 3	Blossom 87	
28	3		H	Merthyr Tydfil	252	D 2 - 2	Sandy 1 29	11
29	17		H	Bedford Town	248	W 2 - 0	Spencer 32 Winters 72	11
30	20		H	Evesham United	268	W 2 - 1	Cracknell 57 Sandy 87	
31	24		A	Farnborough Town	721	D 2 - 2	Spencer 6 23	10
32	27		H	Halesowen Town	208	W 4 - 1	Brown 5 Winters 13 Sandy 15 31	
33	Feb 14		A	Mangotsfield United	151	W 3 - 0	**Mackey** 10 48 Hadland 22	
34	21		A	Cambridge City	362	L 0 - 1		11
35	24		A	Hemel Hempstead	150	L 1 - 2	Spencer 47	
36	28		H	Stourbridge	204	W 3 - 0	Sandy 27 Rawle 59 Winters 70	9
37	Mar 7		A	Bashley	262	D 1 - 1	Winters 51	10
38	10		H	Rugby Town	217	D 2 - 2	Sandy 33 67	
39	14		H	Yate Town	204	L 0 - 1		12
40	17		A	Clevedon Town	87	D 2 - 2	Winters 38 Spencer 61	
41	21		A	Oxford City	423	L 0 - 3		13
42	24		A	Tiverton Town	248	L 1 - 2	Sandy 15	
43	28		H	Gloucester City	307	L 2 - 3	**Mackey** 35 Winters 40	13
44	31		H	Hemel Hempstead	221	W 3 - 2	**Mackey** 2 Sandy 7 Winters 82	
45	April 4		A	Evesham United	136	D 1 - 1	Blossom 85	12
46	8		A	Swindon Supermarine	119	D 4 - 4	Cracknell 11 31 (pen) Winters 21 **Mackey** 39	
47	11		A	Hitchin Town	363	W 1 - 0	Rawle 47	11
48	13		H	Banbury United	636	L 1 - 2	**Mackey** 39	
49	15		H	Bashley	157	L 2 - 4	Spencer 40 **Mackey** 85	
50	18		A	Chippenham Town	371	L 1 - 3	Rawle 23	11
51	21		H	Oxford City	264	W 2 - 1	Rawle 12 **Mackey** 36	
52	25		H	Tiverton Town	210	L 1 - 2	**Mackey** 31	11

Average Home Att: **249 (278)** **Goals** **90 74**

Best Position: 8th **Worst:** 18th

Goalscorers: Mackey 24, Winters 18, Sandy 12, Cracknell 8, Spencer 7, Rawle 4, Hadland 3, Thorpe 3, Blossom 2, Gardner 2, Allen 1, Brown 1, Green 1, Harper 1, Peirson 1, Perpetuini 1, Wenass 1.

CAMBRIDGE CITY

Founded: 1908
Nickname: Lilywhites

CLUB PERSONNEL

Chairman: Kevin Satchell

Additional Directors:
Terry Dunn (Vice Chairman),
Ken Ledran (Co. Secretary),
Roger de Ste Croix,
Gill Wordingham.

Secretary: Andy Dewey
50 Doggett Road,
Cambridge, CB1 9LF
(H): 01223 245 694
(M): 07720 678 585

Programme Editor: Steve Warne.
ccfc.editor@googlemail.com

Manager: Gary Roberts.

Club Colours: White/black/black.

Change Colours: Light blue/light blue/light blue.

Best Performance - League: 2nd Conference South 2004-2005

Ground address: City Ground, Milton Road,Cambridge CB4 1UY

Tel No: 01223 357973. Fax: 01223 351582

Capacity: 2,000 **Seats:** 533 **Covered:** 1,400 **Floodlights**: Yes

Simple Directions: On A1309 (Cambridge to Ely) at beginning of road behind Westbrook centre.

Midweek Home Matchday: Monday.

Club Shop: Sells all club accessories

Local Press: Cambridge Evening News

Local Radio: BBC Radio Cambridge

CLUB STATISTICS

Record	**Attendance** : 12,058 v Leytonstone F.A.Amateur Cup 1st Rd 1949-50
	Career Goalscorer: Gary Grogan
	Appearances in career: Mal Keenan
Record Transfer Fee	**Paid**: £ 8,000 to Rushden & Diamonds for Paul Coe
	Received: £100,000 from Millwall for Neil Harris 1998
Senior Honours:	Southern Lg 62-3 R-up 70-71 , Southern Div 85-6 R-up 69-70
	Southern Lg Cup R-up 98-9 Suffolk Sen Cup (09-10) East Anglian Cup (9)
Previous	**Leagues**: Bury & Dist.,08-13 19-20 E Anglian 08-10 Southern Olympian 11-14
	Southern Amateur 13--35 Spartan 35-50 Athenian 50-58 Southern 1958-2004
	Name : Cambridge Town 1908-1951

Back row (L-R): Gary Roberts, Laurie Stewart, Neil Midgley, Steve Gentle, Zac Barrett, Dave Theobald, Lee Chaffey, James Krause, Joe Miller.
Front Row: Pat Bexfield, Robbie Nightingale, Adrian Cambridge, Ashley Fuller, Craig Radcliffe, Stephen Smith, Tom Pepper.

CAMBRIDGE CITY

BEST LGE ATT.: 506 v Bedford Town
LOWEST: 182 v Merthyr Tydfil

No.	Date	Comp	H/A	Opponents	Att:	Result	Goalscorers	Pos
1	Aug 16	Southern P.	A	Chippenham Town	434	L 1 - 3	Calliste 69	
2	18		H	Corby Town	295	W 3 - 2	Neilson 44 Calliste 48 Roberts 64	
3	23		H	Merthyr Tydfil	182	W 3 - 0	Theobald 35 **Midgeley** 72 Neilson 87	5
4	25		A	Hitchin Town	503	D 1 - 1	Neilson 76	
5	30		H	Mangotsfield United	264	L 0 - 2		9
6	Sept 2		A	Banbury United	213	D 2 - 2	**Midgeley** 52 Neilson 61	
7	6		A	Brackley Town	303	L 0 - 2		14
8	**13**	**F.A.C. 1Q**	**H**	**Lowestoft Town**	**391**	**W 2 - 0**	**Calliste 44 Neilson 78**	
9	20		H	Bashley	297	W 5 - 0	CALLISTE 3 (26pen 69 85) **Midgeley** 28 Fuller 47	9
10	**27**	**F.A.C. 2Q**	**H**	**Worthing**	**357**	**D 1 - 1**	**Theobald 56**	
11	**30**	**F.A.C. 2Qr**	**A**	**Worthing**	**250**	**L 1 - 2**	**Spendlove 86**	
12	Oct 4		H	Rugby Town	302	W 3 - 2	Theobald 58 Calliste 65 Smith 83	7
13	7		A	Farnborough	751	D 1 - 1	Smith S 89	
14	11		A	Hemel Hempstead	307	W 1 - 0	**Midgeley** 87 (pen)	5
15	**18**	**F.A.T. 1Q**	**H**	**Canvey Island**	**312**	**D 1 - 1**	**Sharp 70**	
16	**21**	**F.A.T. 1Qr**	**A**	**Canvey Island**	**245**	**D 0 - 0***	**Cambridge City won 4-2 after penalties**	
17	25		H	Swindon Supermarine	361	L 0 - 1		7
18	**Nov 4**	**F.A.T. 2Q**	**A**	**Dover Athletic**	**509**	**W 3 - 2**	**Fuller 3 Midgeley 6 Calliste 30**	
19	8		H	Stourbridge	334	W 2 - 0	Calliste 10 S.Smith 4	5
20	15		A	Clevedon Town	161	L 0 - 1		7
21	**22**	**F.A.T 3Q**	**H**	**Hastings United**	**302**	**W 1 - 0**	**Midgeley 67**	
22	29		H	Tiverton Town	301	W 1 - 0	Neilson 76	7
23	Dec 6		A	Evesham United	166	W 1 - 0	Chaffey 21	7
24	**13**	**F.A.T 1R**	**H**	**Kettering Town**	**432**	**L 1 - 4**	**Haniver 5**	
25	20		H	Oxford City	319	W 1 - 0	Bloomfield 89	7
26	27		H	Hitchin Town	432	W 3 - 1	Cambridge 40 Theobald 55 Neilson 90	6
27	Jan 1		A	Bedford Town	589	D 1 - 1	**Midgeley** 70	
28	3		H	Chippenham Town	405	L 0 - 1		6
29	17		H	Banbury United	290	W 3 - 1	Fuller 20 Bloomfield 58 Roach 90	4
30	24		A	Corby Town	325	D 0 - 0		8
31	26		H	Farnborough Town	357	L 0 - 2		
32	31		A	Rugby Town	293	W 3 - 2	Gentle 15 Cambridge 18 Chaffey 89	6
33	Feb 17		A	Yate Town	161	W 3 - 0	Neilson 20 **Midgeley** 50 (pen) 53 (pen)	
34	21		H	Brackley Town	362	W 1 - 0	Krause 90	3
35	24		A	Halesowen Town	278	D 2 - 2	**Midgeley** 39 51	
36	28		A	Bashley	342	D 0 - 0		3
37	Mar 7		A	Stourbridge	257	D 1 - 1	Frew 16	
38	9		H	Hemel Hempstead	335	W 1 - 0	**Midgeley** 49	
39	14		H	Clevedon Town	339	L 0 - 1		5
40	16		H	Halesowen Town	278	W 3 - 0	Frew 9 Gentle 50 65	
41	21		A	Gloucester City	275	L 1 - 2	Frew 9	6
42	24		A	Merthyr Tydfil	243	D 1 - 1	**Midgeley** 35 (pen)	
43	28		H	Evesham United	359	L 2 - 3	Neilson 20 Gentle 74	6
44	30		H	Gloucester City	301	W 2 - 1	Theobald 18 Neilson 64	
45	April 4		A	Tiverton Town	292	W 2 - 1	Gentle 44 Frew 77	5
46	11		A	Mangotsfield United	190	W 3 - 0	**Midgeley** 34 (pen) Frew 70 Gentle 83	4
47	13		H	Bedford Town	506	W 1 - 0	Theobald 5	
48	15		A	Swindon Spermarine	142	W 2 - 0	**Midgeley** 15 (pen) Frew 24	
49	18		A	Oxford City	442	L 0 - 1		4
50	25		H	Yate Town	480	D 2 - 2	Theobald 72 Neilson 75	4
51	**28**	**Play-Off SF**	**A**	**Cambridge City**	**745**	**L 1 - 3**	**Nielson 59**	

Average Home Att: 338 (372) **Goals** 72 50

Best Position: 3rd **Worst:** 14th

Goalscorers: Midgeley 15, Neilson 12, Calliste 9, Gentle 6, Theobald 7, Frew 4, Chaffey 2, Fuller 3, Smith 3, Bloomfield 2, Cambridge 2, Roberts 2, Haniver 1, Krause 1, Roach 1, Sharp 1, Spendlove 1, Theobald 1.

CHIPPENHAM TOWN

Founded: 1873
Nickname: The Bluebirds

Manager: Adie Mings.

Club Colours: Royal blue/royal blue/blue.

Change Colours: White/white/white.

Best Season - League: 2nd Southern Premier 2004-2005

Ground address: Hardenhuish Park, Bristol Road, Chippenham SN14 6LR

Tel: 01249 650 400. Fax:. 01249 650 400,

Capacity: 3,000 **Seats**:300 **Covered**: 1,000 **Floodlights**: Yes

Simple Directions: M4 Jct 17. A 350 into Chippenham. Follow signs for Trowbridge and Bath to Bumpers Farm roundabout. Then left onto A420 towards town. Ground 800 yds on left.

Midweek Home Matchday: Tuesday

Clubhouse: Matchdays.

Club Shop: Yes.

Local Press: Chippenham News, Wilts Gazette and Wiltshire Chronicle

CLUB PERSONNEL

Chairman: TBA

Additional Directors:
Chris Blake, John Applegate (Finance), Doug Webb (President), Sandie Webb, Simon Eason.

Secretary: George McCaffery.
The Firs, 68A Pickwick Road, Corsham,
Wiltshire SN13 9DB
(H) 01249 701 262
(M) 07925 975 275
(B) 01249 650 400

Programme Editor: As Secretary.

CLUB STATISTICS

Record	**Attendance**: 4,800 v Chippenham United. Western League 1951
	Victory: 9-0 v Dawlish Town (H) Western League
	Defeat: 0-10 v Tiverton Town (A) Western League
	Career Goalscorer: Dave Ferris
	Career Appearances: Ian Monnery
Senior Honours:	Western League 1951-52 Wiltshire Senior Cup and Wiltshire Senior Shield (4)
Previous Leagues:	Hellenic, Wiltshire Senior, Wiltshire Premier, Western.

CHIPPENHAM TOWN

BEST LGE ATT.: 602 v Farnborough
LOWEST: 272 v Hemel Hempstead

No.	Date	Comp	H/A	Opponents	Att:	Result	Goalscorers	Pos
1	Aug 16	Southern P.	H	Cambridge City	434	W 3 - 1	Halliday 34 Gullick 63 **Pratt** 67	
2	19		A	Chippenham Town	139	L 0 - 2		
3	23		A	Hemel Hempstead	238	D 1 - 1	Gullick 44	13
4	25		H	Bashley	451	L 2 - 3	Seavill 26 Halliday 90	
5	30		A	Rugby Town	211	W 1 - 0	Allison 29	
6	Sept 2		H	Stourbridge	371	L 1 - 2	Holly 90	
7	6		A	Bedford Town	383	L 0 - 2		17
8	**13**	**F.A.C. 1Q**	**H**	**Banbury United**	**421**	**W 2 - 0**	**Allison 58 Pratt 90 (pen)**	
9	20		H	Halesowen Town	491	W 2 - 1	Gullick 4 22	13
10	**27**	**F.A.C. 2Q**	**A**	**Truro City**	**710**	**D 1 - 1**	**Holly 81**	
11	**30**	**F.A.C. 2Qr**	**H**	**Truro City**	**498**	**W 4 - 2***	**Pratt 80 114 Harvey 105 White 120**	
12	Oct 4		A	Gloucester City	380	L 0 - 2		16
13	**11**	**F.A.C. 3Q**	**A**	**Ashford Town (Middx)**	**277**	**L 0 - 1**		
14	14		H	Clevedon Town	411	W 2 - 1	Williams 8 White 32	
15	**18**	**F.A.T.1Q**	**H**	**Fleet Town**	**318**	**W 2 - 1**	**Holly 35 42**	
16	25		A	Merthyr Tydfil	338	L 0 - 2		11
17	**Nov 1**	**F.A.T. 2Q**	**A**	**Heybridge Swifts**	**169**	**D 0 - 0**		
18	**4**	**F.A.T. 2Qr**	**H**	**Heybridge Swifts**	**223**	**L 0 - 2**		
19	8		H	Banbury United	391	W 1 - 0	Belle 48	12
20	11		A	Oxford City	207	D 2 - 2	Slack 26 Harvey 56	
21	15		A	Farnborough	1017	L 0 - 2		13
22	23		H	Hitchin Town	413	D 1 - 1	**Pratt** 52	
23	29		A	Mangotsfield Town	273	W 4 - 0	Allison 45 **Pratt** 61 Harvey 67 Slack 71	11
24	Dec 2		H	Yate Town	321	W 3 - 0	Adams 15 Holly 50 **Pratt** 70	
25	6		H	Corby Town	395	W 3 - 1	**Pratt** 45 81 Holly 46	8
26	20		A	Brackley Town	183	L 0 - 1		10
27	27		A	Bashley	389	L 1 - 2	Lye 10	10
28	Jan 1		H	Tiverton Town	562	W 1 - 0	Kite 55	
29	3		A	Cambridge City	405	W 1 - 0	**Pratt** 80	8
30	17		A	Stourbridge	270	W 2 - 1	Adams 32 Allison 64	7
31	22		H	Evesham United	438	W 1 - 0	Allison 31	7
32	27		A	Clevedon Town	198	L 2 - 3	Seavill 26 **Pratt** 87 (pen)	
33	31		H	Gloucester City	468	D 2 - 2	Williams 74 **Pratt** 88	8
34	Feb 14		H	Merthyr Tydfil	442	W 1 - 0	**Pratt** 26 (pen)	6
35	21		H	Bedford Town	441	W 1 - 0	Lye 83	
36	28		A	Halesowen Town	468	D 2 - 2	**Pratt** 69 Seavill 83	7
37	Mar 3		H	Hemel Hempstead	272	L 1 - 2	Seavill 45	
38	7		A	Banbury United	284	W 5 - 0	Bennett 20 (og) **Pratt** 51 70 (pen) Martin 53 Sercombe 82	
39	10		H	Oxford City	333	L 0 - 2		
40	14		H	Farnborough	602	D 1 - 1	Adams 1	7
41	17		H	Swindon Supermarine	464	W 3 - 1	**Pratt** 13 70 Seedel 68	
42	21		A	Hitchin Town	309	L 1 - 2	Lamb 12	7
43	28		A	Corby Town	232	L 0 - 3		7
44	31		A	Yate Town	255	W 3 - 1	Seedel 3 Palmer 22 **Pratt** 89	
45	April 4		H	Mangotsfield Town	405	D 1 - 1	Palmer 81	7
46	11		H	Rugby Town	345	D 1 - 1	Gullick 82	9
47	13		A	Tiverton Town	301	W 2 - 1	Adams 15 35	
48	18		H	Brackley Town	371	W 3 - 1	Adams 18 Gullick 57 Powell 82	9
49	25		A	Swindon Supermarine	353	W 3 - 1	**Pratt** 14 (pen) Gullick 28 Powell 31	8

Average Home Att: 420 (490) **Goals 73 56**

Best Position: 6th **Worst:** 17th

Goalscorers: Pratt 20, Adams 6, Gullick 7, Holly 6, Allison 5, Seavill 4, Harvey 3, Halliday 2, Lye 2, Palmer 2, Powell 2, Seedel 2, Slack 2, White 2, Williams 2, Belle 1, Kite 1, Lamb 1, Martin 1, Sercombe 1. Own Goal 1.

CLEVEDON TOWN

Founded: 1880
Nickname: Seasiders

Manager: Nick Tucker.

Club Colours: Pale blue and white stripes/dark blue/pale blue.

Change Colours: White/black/white or black.

Ground Address: Hand Stadium, Davis Lane, Clevedon BS21 6TG.

Tel. No.: 01275 871 600. Fax: 01275 871 601.

Capacity: 3,500 **Seats**: 300 **Covered**: 1,600 **Floodlights**:Yes

Simple Directions: M5 Jct 20 - follow signs for Hand Stadium; first left into Central Way (at island just after motorway), 1st left at mini-roundabout into Kenn Rd, 2nd left Davis Lane; ground half mile on right. Or from Bristol (B3130) left into Court Lane (opposite Clevedon Court), turn right after one mile, ground on left. Nearest BR station: Nailsea & Backwell. Buses from Bristol.

Midweek Home Matchday: Tuesday

Clubhouse: Open every day and evening. Separate function suite & lounge bar. Hot food available. Matchday refreshment bar within ground sells confectionary, teas & hot food

Club Shop: Sells all types of souvenirs, programmes and replica kit. Exchanges welcome.

Local Radio: Radio Bristol, Star 107.,7 FM

Local Press: Clevedon Mercury, Evening Post and Western Daily Press

CLUB PERSONNEL

Chairman: John Croft.

Additional Directors:
Russell Conybeare,
Graham Moody.

Secretary: Brian Rose.
53 Butterfield Park, Clevedon
B21 5EE.
(H): 01275 877 833
(F): 01275 877 833
(M): 07768 100 632

Programme
Editor: Dave Wright
smallwavedave@hotmail.com

CLUB STATISTICS

Record	**Attendance:** 1,600 v Bristol City (Friendly) 27.07.98 at Teignmouth Road, 2,300 v Billingham Synthonia , F.A.Amateur Cup 1952-53 **Career Goalscorer**: Not known **Career Appearances**: Not known
Record	**Victory:**: 18-0 v Dawlish Town (H) Western Premier Division 24.04.93 **Defeat:** 3-13 v Yate YMCA (A) Bristol Combination 1967-1968
Senior Honours:	Southern League, Midland Division 98-99, Western League 92-93 Somerset Senior Cup 1901-02, 1904-05, 1928-29, 2000-01, 2001-02. Somerset Prem Cup (4)
Previous Leagues:	**Leagues:** Weston & District, Somerset Senior, Bristol Charity, Bristol & District, Bristol Suburban, Western 74-93 **Grounds:** Dial Hill (until early 1890's); Teignmouth Road (until 1991) **Names:** Clevedon FC, Ashtonians (clubs merged in 1974)

Back Row (L-R): John Roberts (Kit Manager), Jake Harris, Craig Loxton, Leighton Burrows, Danny Greaves, Dan O'Brien, Matt Driscoll, Chris Collins, Josh Brigham, Mike Williams (Chief Scout), Sylvia Durham (Physio).
Front: Adam Callan, Chris Pearce, Rhys Jones, Kevin Davies (Captain), Wayne Powell (Manager), Alan Bull (Assistant Manager), Kyle Bassett, Simon Heal, Lewis Powell.
Not present: Jamie Adams, Tom Hooper, Lee Jenkins, Hanin Romhdane, Rhys Williams, Jim Humphries (Assistant Kit Manager)

CLEVEDON TOWN

BEST LGE ATT.: 365 v Oxford City
LOWEST: 87 v Brackley Town

No.	Date	Comp	H/A	Opponents	Att:	Result	Goalscorers	Pos
1	Aug 16	Southern P.	H	Bashley	195	D 0 - 0		
2	20		A	Swindon Supermarine	146	W 1 - 0	Powell 15	
3	23		A	Brackley Town	232	D 1 - 1	Powell 19	11
4	25		H	Tiverton Town	211	L 1 - 2	**Brigham** 48	
5	30		A	Stourbridge	131	L 1 - 6	Bassett 76	19
6	Sept 2		H	Evesham United	122	L 0 - 2		15
7	**13**	**F.A.C. 1Q**	**H**	**Bridport**	**161**	**W 4 - 1**	**Peckham 8 Brigham 36 87 Prosser 79**	
8	23		A	Hemel Hempstead	203	D 0 - 0		16
9	**27**	**F.A.C. 2Q**	**A**	**Bath City**	**486**	**W 2 - 0**	**Powell 39 (pen) Bassett 43**	
10	Oct 4		H	Hitchin Town	122	L 1 - 2	Powell 24	18
11	11		A	Mangotsfield United	184	L 0 - 2		19
12	14		A	Chippenham Town	411	L 1 - 2	Adams 43 (og)	
13	**18**	**F.A.T. 1Q**	**A**	**Evesham United**	**110**	**L 0 - 4**		
14	25		H	Farnborough	228	D 1 - 1	**Brigham** 65	20
15	Nov 4		H	Banbury United	115	D 1 - 1	Prosser 51	
16	8		A	Corby Town	262	L 0 - 4		20
17	11		H	Merthyr Tydfil	154	L 1 - 5	Driscoll 64	
18	15		H	Cambridge City	161	W 1 - 0	**Billing** 46	16
19	22		A	Bedford Town	301	D 0 - 0		16
20	29		H	Gloucester City	93	L 1 - 4	Powell 86	17
21	Dec 6		A	Rugby Town	178	L 0 - 4		20
22	20		H	Halesowen Town	187	L 1 - 2	Powell 32	
23	27		A	Tiverton Town	420	L 2 - 3	Sheppard 38 Peckham 90	22
24	Jan 17		A	Evesham United	133	D 0 - 0		22
25	24		H	Swindon Supermarine	168	L 1 - 2	**Billing** 79	22
26	27		H	Chippenham Town	198	W 3 - 2	Bassett 15 Sheppard 32 Wring 72	
27	31		A	Hitchin Town	254	D 2 - 2	**Brigham** 87 Small 90	22
28	Feb 14		A	Farnborough	526	L 1 - 3	Sheppard 43	22
29	17		A	Bashley	246	L 0 - 1		
30	21		A	Banbury United	316	L 1 - 3	Easter 2	22
31	28		H	Hemel Hempstead	133	L 0 - 3		22
32	Mar 7		H	Corby Town	148	L 1 - 3	Easter 31	
33	10		A	Merthyr Tydfil	339	D 2 - 2	Easter 10 Peckham 21	
34	14		A	Cambridge City	339	W 1 - 0	**Billing** 60	22
35	17		H	Brackley Town	87	D 2 - 2	Bassett 6 **Brigham** 70 (pen)	
36	21		H	Bedford Town	179	W 2 - 1	Molineaux 38 88	21
37	28		H	Rugby Town	169	W 1 - 0	Loxton 79	19
38	31		H	Mangotsfield United	239	L 2 - 3	Easter 89 Molineux 90	
39	April 4		A	Gloucester City	300	W 1 - 0	Small 21	19
40	7		A	Oxford City	164	L 3 - 5	**Brigham** 30 **Billing** 68 Walsh 73 (pen)	
41	11		H	Stourbridge	201	W 2 - 0	Peckham 77 **Billing** 79	19
42	13		A	Yate Town	242	L 1 - 2	**Billing** 62	
43	18		A	Halesowen Town	381	W 5 - 3	Shepherd 12 Wring 21 Walsh 34 **Billing** 90 Bassett 90	
44	21		H	Yate Town	202	W 4 - 3	Shepherd 63 86 Easter 75 Walsh 88	
45	25		H	Oxford City	365	L 0 - 1		18

Average Home Att: 175 (202) **Goals 55 87**

Best Position: 11th **Worst:** 22nd

Goalscorers: Billing 7, Brigham 7, Powell 6, Sheppard 6, Bassett 5, Easter 5, Peckham 4, Molyneaux 3, Walsh 3, Prosser 2, Small 2, Wring 2, Driscoll 1, Loxton 1. Own Goal 1.

DIDCOT TOWN

Founded: 1907
Nickname: Railwaymen

CLUB PERSONNEL

Chairman: John Bailey

Additional Committee:
Mick Cox , Steve Clare
Justin Lambourne, Pete Aplin,
Dave Warwick, Peter Cox,
Mark Roberts, Peter Chalk,
Jaquie Chalk, Paul Leach,
Mark Buckmaster,
Mark Beauchamp.

Secretary: Pat Horsman.
64 High Street, Milton,
Abingdon OX14 4EJ
(M) 07882 154 612

Programme Editor: Joffy Chinnock
joffy@hotmail.co.uk

Manager: Stuart Peace.

Club Colours: Red with white sleeves/white/red.

Change Colours: Gold/black/black.

Best Season - League: 3rd Southern Division One South & West 2007-08.

Ground address: Npower Loop Meadow Stadium, Bowmont Water, Didcot OX11 7GA Tel No: 01235 813 138. Fax: 01235 816 352.

Capacity: 5,000 **Seats**: 250 **Covered**: 200 **Floodlights**: Yes

Simple Directions: from A34 take Milton interchange on Didcot road for a mile. At roundabout take perimeter road and cross three roundabouts before turning right at Avon Way.

Midweek Home Matchday: Tuesday.

Club Shop: Yes.

Clubhouse: Full faciliites available every evening and from mid day at week-ends and holidays. Function rooms available.

Local Radio: Fox FM.

Local Press: Oxford Mail & Didcot Herald.

CLUB STATISTICS

Record	**Attendance:** 1,512 v Jarrow Roofing F.A.Vase S-Final 2005
	Career Goalscorer: I. Concanon
	Career Appearances: Not known.
Record Transfer Fee	**Paid**: N/A
	Received: N/A
Senior Honours:	F.A.Vase Winners 2004-2005 Hellenic Champions 1953-54 2005-2006 Hellenic Cup Winners (6) Division One Champions 1976-77 1987-88 Runners Up 2004-05 Berks & Bucks Senior Trophy 2001-02 2002-03 2005-6 Hellenic League Cup (6)
Previous Leagues:	Metropolitan 1957-1963 Hellenic 1963-2006

The ZAMARETTO League

EVESHAM UNITED

Founded: 1945
Nickname: The Robins

CLUB PERSONNEL

Chairman: Jim Cockerton
Committee:
Steve Lane (Vice Chairman),
Malcolm Davis (President),
Roger Westmacott (Secretary/Treasurer),
David Wright, Bob Prater,
Bernard Jordan, Morris Allan,
Simon Parry
Secretary: Mike Peplow.
2 College Mews,
Somers Road, Malvern,
Worcs. WR14 1JD
(H): 01684 561 770
(M): 07889 011539
Programme Editor: As Secretary

Manager: Paul West.

Club Colours: Red & white stripes/red/red

Change Colours: All sky blue

Best Season - League: 9th Southern Premier Division 2008-09.

Ground address: Sharing with Worcester City at St George's Lane, Worcester, WR1 1QT **Tel No**: 01905 23003

Capacity: 2,000 **Seats**: 350 **Covered**: 600 **Floodlights**:Yes

Simple Directions: M5 Jct 6 (Worcester North) follow signs for Worcester and turn right at first lights. St George's Lane is 3rd left. One mile from Foregate Station BR

Midweek Matchday: Tuesday

Clubhouse: Worcester City's facilities are available on matchdays.

Club Shop: Yes.

Local Radio: Classic Gold, BBC Hereford & Worcs, FM102 The Bear.

Local Press: Evesham Journal, Worcester Evening News, Gloucester Echo.

CLUB STATISTICS

Record	**Attendance**: 2,338 v W.B.A. friendly 18.07.92
	Victory: 11-3 v West Heath United. **Defeat:** 1-8 v Ilkeston Town
	Career Goalscorer: Sid Brain
	Career Appearances: Rob Candy
	Record Transfer Fee Paid: £1,500 to Hayes for Colin Day 1992
	Received: £5,000 from Cheltenham Town for Simon Brain.
Senior Honours:	F.A.Amateur Cup R-up 1923-24, Worcs. Senior Urn (2) R-up 90-91
	Midland Comb Prem 1991-92, Div 1 65-66, 67-68, 68-69
Previous Leagues:	Worcester, Birmingham Comb., Midland Combination 1951-55, 1965-92
	West Midlands Regional 1955-62
Grounds:	The Crown Meadow (pre-1968) Common Road (1968-2006)

STANDING : M BRENNAN, M ALLAN, R WESTMACOTT, L SHEEHAN, A WATSON, J CLARKE, S LUCKETT, P BONA, N VAUGHAN, J KNOTT, S HANDS, S FITTER, O HAY, M OWEN, D SCHEPPELL, B JORDAN, B PRATER

SEATED : T HADLEY, D WRIGHT, M HANDS, M HAYDEN, D HODNETT, P WEST (MANAGER), J COCKERTON (CHAIRMAN), L WEST (ASSITANT MANAGER), S LUTZ (CAPTAIN), A DAVIES, D LENNON, D SUTTON, T FISHER

EVESHAM UNITED

BEST LGE ATT.: 395 v Cambridge City
LOWEST: 71 v Mangotsfield United

No.	Date	Comp	H/A	Opponents	Att:	Result	Goalscorers	Pos
1	Aug 16	Southern P.	A	Bedford Town	382	D 1 - 1	**Scheppel** 90 (pen)	
2	19		H	Chippenham Town	139	W 2 - 0	Hay 20 **Scheppel** 88	
3	23		H	Gloucester City	207	D 2 - 2	Hands 67 75	9
4	25		A	Halesowene Town	602	L 1 - 3	Hay 57	
5	30		H	Farnboorugh	208	D 0 - 0		14
6	Sept 2		A	Clevedon Town	122	L 0 - 2		
7	6		A	Swindon Supermaraine	207	D 1 - 1	Hay 56	16
8	**13**	**F.A.C 1Q**	**A**	**Leamington**	**712**	**W 3 - 0**	**Lutz 52 Hayden 67 Owen 86**	
9	20		H	Yate Town	107	W 4 - 1	Etheridge 35 Owen 53 Davis 74 Lutz 77	11
10	**28**	**F.A.C. 2Q**	**H**	**Nuneaton Town**	**252**	**D 2 - 2**	**Owen 8 Hands 32**	
11	**30**	**F.A.C. 2Qr**	**A**	**Nuneaton Town**	**508**	**W 2 - 1**	**Owen 25 Hayden 88**	
12	Oct 4		A	Mangotsfield United	166	D 0 - 0		12
13	7		H	Tiverton Town	132	D 1 - 1	Owen 82	
14	**11**	**F.A.C. 3Q**	**H**	**Chasetown**	**407**	**W 2 - 0**	**Owen 88 Lennon 90**	
15	**18**	**F.A.T. 1Q**	**H**	**Clevedon Town**	**110**	**W 4 - 0**	**Scheppel 17 Owen 25 Fifer 55 Hay 82**	
16	**25**	**F.A.C. 4Q**	**H**	**Rushden & Diamonds**	**609**	**W 2 - 0**	**Scheppel 18 81**	
17	**Nov 1**	**F.A.T 2Q**	**A**	**Stourbridge**	**198**	**L 1 - 2**	**Owen 9**	
18	**8**	**F.A.C 1R**	**A**	**Torquay United**	**2275**	**L 0 - 2**		
19	11		A	Stourbridge	196	W 2 - 0	Coillins 61 (og) **Scheppel** 63	12
20	15		A	Rugby Town	205	W 1 - 0	**Scheppel** 23	11
21	22		A	Corby Town	349	D 0 - 0		11
22	25		H	Banbury United	107	W 2 - 0	Wood 16 Lennon 51	
23	Dec 6		H	Cambridge City	395	L 0 - 1		12
24	13		H	Hitchin Town	151	W 2 - 1	Wood 8 Hands 15	11
25	20		A	Hemel Hempstead	201	L 0 - 4		12
26	27		H	HalesowenTown	392	D 0 - 0		12
27	Jan 13		H	Oxford City	111	L 0 - 1		
28	17		H	Clevedon Town	133	D 0 - 0		13
29	20		A	Brackley Town	268	L 1 - 2	Slack 25	
30	24		A	Chippenham Town	438	L 0 - 1		15
31	17		H	Mangotsfield United	71	W 3 - 1	Slack 52 Hay 65 Luckett 85	
32	21		A	Tiverton Twn	327	W 1 - 0	Slack 56 (pen)	
33	Feb 10		H	Bedford Town	94	L 0 - 1		
34	14		A	Banbury United	264	W 6 - 0	ROBINSON 3 (26 42 53) Slack 60 **Scheppel** 67 Lennon 70 (pen)	13
35	21		H	Swindon Supermarine	138	W 1 - 0	Robinson 51	13
36	24		A	Merthyr Tydfil	378	L 0 - 1		
37	28		A	Yate Town	190	W 1 - 0	Slack 39	12
38	Mar 7		A	Oxford City	304	W 1 - 0	Lennon 64	
39	10		H	Stourbridge	105	L 0 - 1		
40	14		H	Rugby Town	139	W 1 - 0	Robinson 75	10
41	17		A	Gloucester City	210	L 0 - 2		
42	22		A	Bashley	248	D 0 - 0		11
43	24		H	Bashley	80	D 2 - 2	Clarke 32 **Scheppel** 68	
44	28		A	Cambridge City	359	W 3 - 2	Lutz 30 Slack 56 64	10
45	31		H	Corby Town	140	D 1 - 1	Luckett 54	
46	April 4		H	Brackley Town	136	D 1 - 1	Lennon 80	8
47	11		A	Farnborough	722	L 1 - 2	Ager 75	10
48	13		H	Merthyr TYdfil	211	L 0 - 2		
49	18		H	Hemel Hempstead	124	W 4 - 1	Slack 30 Haydon 5 Lennon 55 Clarke 90	10
50	25		A	Hitchin Town	534	W 2 - 1	Clark 45 Ager 83	9

Average Home Att: 164 **Goals 64 46**

Best Position: 8th **Worst:** 16th

Goalscorers: Scheppel 9, Owen 8, Slack 8, Lennon 6, Hay 5, Robinson 5, Hands 4, Clark 3, Hayden 3, Lutz 3, Ager 2, Luckett 2, Wood 2, Davis 1, Etheridge 1, Fifer 1. Own Goals 1.

FARNBOROUGH

Founded:1967 - Reformed 2007
Nickname: Boro

Manager: Steve King.
Club Colours: Yellow & blue/yellow/yellow.
Change Colours: White with pink & gold trim/white/white.
Best Season - League: As Farnborough Town 5th Conference 1991-92.
As Farnborough - 2nd Southern Premier Division 2008-09.
Ground address: Cherrywood Road, Farnborough, Hants. GU14 8UD
Tel No:01252 541 469 Fax: 01252 372 640.
Capacity: 4,163 **Seats:** 627 **Covered:** 1,350 **Floodlights:** Yes
Simple Directions: From M3 exit 4. Take A325 towards Farnborough, right into Prospect Avenue (club is signposted). Second right into Cherrywood Road and ground is on the right.
Midweek Home Matchday: Wednesday
Clubhouse: Open daily.
Club Shop: All types of leisurewear Contact: 01252 541745
Local Radio: BBC Southern Counties and County Sound
Local Press: Farnborough News

CLUB PERSONNEL

Chairman: Simon Hollis.
Additional Committee:
Simon Hollis, Amanda Hollis.

Secretary: Steven Duly,
Cherrywood Road,
Farnborough, Hampshire
GU14 8UD
01252 541469
(F): 01252 372640
(M): 07922 666 621

Programme
Editor: Chris Harris.
(B) 01252 541 469
(M) 07855 903 888

CLUB STATISTICS

Record	**Attendance**: As Farnborough Town - 3,581 v Brentford F.A.Cup 22.01.95 As Farnborough - 951 v Fleet Town Southern Div.1 S&W 26.12.07. **Victory:** As F.T. - 11-0 v Chertsey Town (H) Spartan League 72-73 As Farnborough - 7-0 v Newport IOW (A) Southern Div.1 S&W 01.12.07. **Defeat:** As F.T. - 2-10 v Worpleston (H) Surrey Senior Lg Div 1 68-69. As Farnborough - 0-3 v Fleet Town (A) Southern Div.1 S&W 24.03.08. **Career Goalscorer**: Simon Read - 209 (1986-1994). For Farnborough - Rob Saunders - 23 (2007-08). **Career Appearances**:Brian Broome - 529 (1980-1994). For Farnborough - Nic Ciardini - 52 (2007-08) **Transfer Fee Paid**: Undisclosed. For Farnborough - Undisclosed to Eastleigh for Ian Oliver January 2008. **Received:** £50,000 from Dover Athletic for David Leworthy August 1993. For Farnborough - N/A.
Senior Honours:	As F.T. Southern League Prem Div 90-91 93-94 Isthmian Prem 00-01 Div 1 84-85 Hampshire Senior Cup 74-75 81-82 83-84 85-86 90-91 03-04 As Farnborough - Southern Division One South & West 2007-08.
Previous Leagues:	Surrey Senior 68-72 Spartan 72-76 Athenian 76-77 Isthmian 77-89 99-01 Alliance Premier /Conference 89-90 91-93 94-99 Southern 90-91 93-94. Conference South 01-07. As Farnborough - None.
Previous Grounds:	Queens Road. Farnborough. As Farnborough - None.

Back Row (L-R): Steve Laidler, Rob Saunders, Dave Woozley, Marcus Richardson, Mark Gamble.
Middle Row: Steve Duly (Chief Executive), Ryan Scott, David Ray, Michael Barima, Ian Oliver, Lyall Beazley, Nic Ciardini, Paul Massaquoi, Nick Burton, Connor Hamilton, Simon Hollis (Chairman), Neale Dent.
Front Row: Roger Peirce (Kit Manager), Darren Wheeler, Paul Harkness, Steve Snelling (Physiotherapist), Francis Vines (Manager), Carl Plunkett (Coach), Leigh Rumbold, Michael Charles, Jack Taylor (Assistant Physiotherapist).

FARNBOROUGH

BEST LGE ATT.: 2,230 v Corby Town
LOWEST: 419 v Stourbridge

No.	Date	Comp	H/A	Opponents	Att:	Result	Goalscorers	Pos
1	Aug 16	Southern P.	H	Rugby Town	520	W 2 - 1	**Charles** 87 89	
2	19		A	Brackley Town	352	D 1 - 1	Doyle 85	
3	23		A	Tiverton Town	436	W 2 - 0	Rumbold 19 Richardson 90	2
4	25		H	Hemel Hempstead T	571	W 1 - 0	**Charles** 42	
5	30		A	Evesham United	208	D 0 - 0		1
6	Sept 2		H	Yate Town	552	W 2 - 0	Woozley 62 Richardson 90	
7	6		H	Gloucester City	700	W 2 - 1	Wheeler 16 Rose 66 (og)	1
8	**13**	**F.A.C 1Q**	**H**	**Slough Town**	**571**	**W 1 - 0**	**Saunders 75 (pen)**	
9	20		A	Banbury United	386	W 2 - 0	Wheeler 56 (pen) Harkness 89	1
10	**27**	**F.A.C. 2Q**	**A**	**Eastleigh**	**687**	**L 0 - 1**		
11	Oct 4		A	Oxford City	382	D 2 - 2	Rumbold 50 Woozley 62	1
12	7		H	Cambridge City	751	D 1 - 1	**Charles** 3	
13	11		H	Merthyr Tydfil	1148	L 0 - 1		1
14	**18**	**F.A.T. 1Q**	**H**	**Marlow**	**348**	**W 4 - 0**	**Saunders 15 Rumbold 31 M.Charles 74 Barima 84**	
15	25		A	Clevedon Town	228	D 1 - 1	Richardson 52	3
16	**Nov 1**	**F.A.T. 2Q**	**A**	**Soham Town Rovers**	**188**	**W 5 - 0**	**Charles 14 GAMBLE 3 (24 30 49) Scott 40**	
17	8		A	Halesowen Town	432	W 1 - 0	**Charles** 18	2
18	11		H	Bedford Town	710	W 3 - 1	Giles 11 29 Woozley 24	
19	15		H	Chippenham Town	1017	W 2 - 0	**Charles** 46 62	1
20	**22**	**F.A.T 3Q**	**A**	**Braintree Town**	**212**	**D 1 - 1**	**Burton 42**	
21	**25**	**F.A.T 3Qr**	**H**	**Braintree Town**	**321**	**W 6 - 2**	**Roget 4 (og) Woozley 70 Wheeler 76 Gamble 82 Richardson 88 89**	
22	29		A	Hitchin Town	385	W 3 - 1	**Charles** 2 Scott 42 Richardson 87	1
23	Dec 6		H	Mangotsfield United	623	W 3 - 1	Gamble 4 Scott 40 Richardson 86	1
24	**16**	**F.A.T 1R**	**H**	**Wingate & Finchley**	**304**	**W 3 - 1**	**Charles 2 Wheeler 47 Richardson 88**	
25	20		A	Swindon Supermarine	495	D 1 - 1	Gamble 90	
26	27		A	Hemel Hempstead T	503	L 1 - 3	Saunders 70	1
27	Jan 1		H	Bashley	821	D 1 - 1	Saunders 75 (pen)	
28	3		A	Rugby Town	306	W 3 - 2	**Charles** 48 Rumbold 69 Gamble 74	1
29	**13**	**F.A.T. 2R**	**H**	**Stevenage Borough**	**705**	**L 0 - 2**		
30	17		A	Yate Town	267	D 2 - 2	**Charles** 82 Richardson 88	1
31	20		H	Stourbridge	419	W 4 - 0	**Charles** 12 Ray 45 Richardson 47 Saunders 85 (pen)	
32	24		H	Brackley Town	721	D 2 - 2	Saunders 71 Ray 89	1
33	26		A	Cambridge City	357	W 2 - 0	**Charles** 33 Sigere 50	
34	31		H	Oxford City	713	L 0 - 2		1
35	Feb 14		H	Clevedon Town	526	W 3 - 1	Wilde 55 Woozley 82 Laidler 90	1
36	21		A	Gloucester City	431	D 0 - 0		1
37	28		H	Banbury United	602	W 1 - 0	**Charles** 32	1
38	Mar 7		H	Halesowen Town	1044	D 1 - 1	**Charles** 2	
39	10		A	Bedford Town	322	W 2 - 0	Richardson 35 (pen) Gamble 47 (pen)	
40	14		A	Chippenham Town	602	D 1 - 1	Rumbold 40	1
41	21		H	Corby Town	2230	D 3 - 3	Calliste 8 Gamble 61 Richardson 90	1
42	28		A	Mangotsfield United	259	W 2 - 0	Gamble 20 Caliste 44	1
43	31		H	Tiverton Town	524	W 1 - 0	Laidler 34	
44	April 4		H	Hitchin Town	707	W 1 - 0	Wilde 65	1
45	8		A	Corby Town	668	L 1 - 3	**Charles** 79	
46	11		H	Evesham United	722	W 2 - 1	Harkin 15 Whisken 50	1
47	13		A	Bashley	537	L 0 - 1		
48	18		H	Swindon Supermarine	1149	W 1 - 0	**Charles** 59	2
49	21		A	Merthyr Tydfil	329	D 1 - 1	Ray 62	
50	25		A	Stourbridge	461	W 3 - 0	**Charles** 4 Gamble 64 Ray 90	2
51	**28**	**Play-Off SF**	**H**	**Hemel Hempstead**	**701**	**D 0 - 0***	**Won 4-3 on penalties**	
52	**May 2**	**Play-Off F**	**H**	**Gloucester City**	**1715**	**L 0 - 1**		

Average Home Att: **799** **Goals** **87 44**

Best Position: 1st **Worst:** 2nd

Goalscorers: Charles 20, Richardson 12, Gamble 11, Saunders 6, Rumbold 5, Woozley 5, Ray 4, Wheeler 4, Scott 3, Calliste 2, Giles 2, Laidler 2, Wilde 2, Barima 1, Burton 1, Doyle 1, Harkin 1, Harkness 1, Sigere 1, Whisken 1. Own Goals 2.

HALESOWEN TOWN

Founded: 1873
Nickname: Yeltz

CLUB PERSONNEL

Chairman: Guy Simpson.

Additional Directors:
Kelly Gentles (Co.Secretary).

Secretary: Andrew While
27 Penfields Road,
Stourbridge,West Midlands
DY8 4LB
(H): 01384 838 448
(M): 07976 769 972

Programme Editor: Bob Pepper
robrjp1@btinternet.com

Manager: Morell Maison.

Club Colours: Blue/white/blue.

Change Colours: Red and black/black/white.

Best Season - League: 2nd Southern Premier 1996

Ground address: The Grove, Old Hawne Lane, Halesowen, West Midlands B63 3TB **Tel No:** 0121 550 9433, Fax: 0121 550 8011

Capacity: 3150 **Seats:** 525 **Covered** 930 **Floodlights**: Yes

Simple Directions: M5 jct 3 A456 (signed to Kidderminster) then turn right at first island (signed A459 Dudley). Left at next island (signed A458 Stourbridge) then at next island take third left into Grammar School Lane, then Old Hawne Lane.

Midweek Home Matchday: Wednesday

Clubhouse: Open every day. **Club Shop:** Yes

Local Radio: BBC West Midlands,B.R.M.B., Beacon.

Local Press: Sports Argus, Express & Star,Birmingham Mail, Halesowen News Stourbridge & Halesowen Chronicle.

CLUB STATISTICS

Record
Attendance: 5,000 v Hendon F.A.Cup 1st Rd Proper 1954
Victory: 13-1 v Coventry Amateurs ,Birmingham Senior Cup 1956
Defeat: 0-8 v Bilston, West Midlands League 07.04.62
Career Goalscorer: Paul Joinson 369 **Appearances**: Paul Joinson 608
Record Transfer Fee Paid: £ 7,250 to Gresley Rovers for Stuart Evans
Received: £40,000 from Rushden & Diamonds for Jim Rodwell

Senior Honours:
Southern Premier League R-up 1996 Midland Div 89-90
Western Div 2001-02 Birmingham Sen Cup 83-4 97-8 R-up (2)
Staffs Sen Cup 88-89 R-up 83-4 FA.Vase 84-85 85-86 R-up 83-3
Worcs Sen Cup 51-52 61-62 02-03 04-05 R-up 2005-06

Previous Leagues: West Mids.1892-1905 06-11 46-86 Birmingham Comb. 1911-1939

2008-09 Squad
(August 2008)

Top row: Rob Woodbine, Micheal Briscoe, Justin Rowe, Zema Abbey, Tom Kemp, Nick Bussey, Jermaine Palmer, Dwane Lee, Tom Bryant, Alex Cowley
Bottom row: Aaron Cornwall, Dino Metalis, Mark Danks, Jay Denny, Morell Maison, Darren Caskey, Dean Smith, Jack Allward, Daryl Taylor, Dean Brennan

HALESOWEN TOWN

BEST LGE ATT.: **1,273** v Stouridge
LOWEST: **160** v Merthyr Tydfil

No.	Date	Comp	H/A	Opponents	Att:	Result	Goalscorers	Pos
1	Aug 16	Southern P.	H	Tiverton Town	423	L 0 - 1		
2	19		A	Rugby Town	287	W 2 - 0	Briscoe 57 Palmer 72	7
3	23		A	Bashley	290	W 3 - 1	Denney 12 Rowe 60 **Danks** 72	
4	25		H	Evesham United	602	W 3 - 1	Rowe 45 Palmer 69 83	5
5	30		A	Hemel Hempstead	252	D 1 - 1	Brennan 27	
6	Sept 2		H	Oxford City	454	W 5 - 2	Cowley 19 Rowe 61 Palmer 84 (pen) Kemp 88 Denney J 90	5
7	**13**	**F.A.C. 1Q**	**A**	**Meir KA**	**214**	**D 1 - 1**	**Rowe 51**	
8	**16**	**F.A.C. 1Qr**	**H**	**Meir KA**	**308**	**W 8 - 1**	**DENNY 3 (3 23 83) Rowe 12 59 Palmer 15 34 (pen) Clegg 44 (og)**	
9	20		A	Chippenham Town	481	L 1 - 2	Palmer 71	5
10	**27**	**F.A.C. 2Q**	**H**	**Gainsborough Trinity**	**502**	**W 3 - 0**	**Smith 18 Cornwall 34 Abbey 88**	
11	Oct 4		A	Bedford Town	463	L 0 - 1		8
12	**11**	**F.A.C. 3Q**	**H**	**Maidstone United**	**872**	**L 1 - 4**	**Denney 27**	
13	14		H	Brackley Town	407	W 3 - 2	Caskey 10 Dent 61 Kemp 65	
14	**18**	**F.A.T. 1Q**	**A**	**Durham City**	**202**	**D 4 - 4**	**DANKS 3 (8 35 90) Capper 80 (og)**	
15	**21**	**F.A.T. 1Qr**	**H**	**Durham City**	**311**	**L 0 - 1**		
16	25		A	Gloucester City	366	W 2 - 1	**Danks** 2 (pen) Rowe 86	4
17	Nov 1		A	Banbury United	245	L 1 - 2	Caskey 71 (pen)	
18	8		H	FarnboroughTown	432	L 0 - 1		7
19	15		A	Hltchin Town	325	W 1 - 0	Cornwall 21	5
20	18		H	Mangotsfield Town	357	W 2 - 0	Nurse 11 Cornwall 15	
21	22		H	Yate Town	409	W 5 - 3	Allward 7 Palmer 58 Barreto 64 Gouveia 75 88	
22	29		A	Corby Town	417	W 2 - 1	**Danks** 15 45	2
23	Dec 6		H	Swindon Supermarine	509	L 2 - 4	**Danks** 19 (pen) 89 (pen)	3
24	20		A	Clevedon Town	187	W 2 - 1	Denney 56 80	3
25	27		A	Evesham United	392	D 0 - 0		5
26	Jan 1		H	Stourbridge	1273	L 1 - 3	Barretto 49	
27	10		H	Bashley	423	W 2 - 0	**Danks** 18 Denney 89	
28	17		A	Oxford City	292	L 1 - 4	Gunn 28 (og)	3
29	20		H	Merthyr Tydfil	160	W 2 - 1	**Danks** 85 89 (pen)	
30	24		H	Rugby Town	426	L 0 - 4		3
31	27		A	Brackley Town	208	L 1 - 4	**Danks** 72 (pen)	
32	31		H	Bedford Town	344	W 2 - 1	Murray 8 Hamilton 83	4
33	Feb 14		H	Gloucester City	434	L 1 - 2	Cornwall 12	5
34	21		A	Mangotsfield United	221	W 1 - 0	Shittu 49	4
35	24		H	Cambridge City	278	D 2 - 2	Shittu 9 Thomas 83	
36	28		H	Chippenham Town	468	D 2 - 2	Denney 15 Caskey 37 (pen)	5
37	Mar 7		A	Farnborough Town	1044	D 1 - 1	Shittu 60	7
38	10		H	Banbury United	213	W 2 - 1	Johnson 88 Springfellow 90 (og)	
39	14		H	Hitchin Town	408	W 3 - 2	Cornwall 50 64 Daval 77	3
40	16		A	Cambridge City	278	L 0 - 3		
41	21		A	Yate Town	183	W 2 - 1	Cornwall 25 (pen) Clarke 65	4
42	28		A	Swindon Supermarine	238	L 0 - 1		5
43	April 4		H	Corby Town	294	L 0 - 5		6
44	7		A	Tiverton Town	143	L 0 - 3		
45	11		H	Hemel Hempstead	320	W 2 - 1	Darby 63 Taylor 65	6
46	13		A	Stourbridge	791	D 2 - 2	Deakin 13 (pen) 74 (pen)	
47	18		H	Clevedon Town	381	L 3 - 5	Loney 1 Taylor 5 Darby 24	
48	25		A	Merthyr Tydfil	422	L 0 - 2		10

Average Home Att: **444 (451)** **Goals** **82 85**

Best Position: 2nd **Worst:** 10th

Goalscorers: Danks 13, Denney 10, Palmer 8, Cornwall 7, Rowe 7, Caskey 3, Shittu 3, Barreto 2, Darby 2, Deakin 2, Gouveia 2, Kemp 2, Taylor 2, Abbey 1, Allward 1, Brennan 1, Briscoe 1, Clarke 1, Cowley 1, Daval 1, Dent 1, Hamlton 1, Johnson 1, Loney 1, Murray 1, Nurse 1, Smith 1, Thomas 1. Own Goals 2.

HEDNESFORD TOWN

Founded: 1880
Nickname: The Pitmen

CLUB PERSONNEL

Chairman: Stephen Price.

Additional Directors:

Carole Price.

Secretary: Terry McMahon.

c/o the club.

(M) 07901 822 040.

Programme

Editor: Michael Johnson.

Email: bigmickj10@aol.com

Manager: Dean Edwards.

Club Colours: White/black/black.

Change Colours: Dark blue/white/white.

Best Season: - League: 3rd Conference 1995-1996

Ground Address: Keys Park, Park Road, Hednesford, Cannock, WS12 2DZ.

Tel/Fax: 01543 422870/ 428180

CAPACITY: 6,039 **Seats:** 1,010 **Covered:** 5,334 **Floodlights: Yes**

SIMPLE DIRECTIONS: M6 Jct.11 to Cannock (or M6 toll jct T7). Follow signs for A460 (Rugeley). After crossing A5 at Churchbridge Island continue to follow A460 (Rugeley) over five islands and pick up signs for HTFC, Keys Park.

Midweek Home Matchday: Tuesday

Clubhouse: Open matchdays evening.

Club Shop: Open throughout the week.

Local Press: Express & Star, Sporting Star, Chase Post, Cannock Mercury, Evening Mail & Birmingham Post **Local Radio:** Radio WM

CLUB STATISTICS

RECORD

Attendance: At Keys Park: 3,169 v York City F.A.Cup 3rd Rd 13.01 97
Victory: 12-1 v Redditch U. B'ham Comb. 52-53.
Defeat: 0-15 v Burton B'ham Comb. 52-53
Career Goalscorer: Joe O'Connor (post war) 230 in 430 games
Career Apps: Kevin Foster 463
Transfer Fee Paid: £12,000 to Macclesfield Town for Steve Burr
Transfer Fee Received: £50,000 from Blackpool for Kevin Russell

SENIOR HONOURS: F.A.Trophy 2004. Welsh Cup R-up 91-92. Southern Prem.94-95 Lg Cup R-Up 86-87. Southern Midland Div 1 R-up 91-92. Staffs Senior Cup (2). B'ham Senior Cup 35-36.

PREVIOUS Leagues: Walsall & Dist, B'ham Comb. 06-15,45-53. West Midlands 19-39, 53-72,74-84 Midland Counties 72-74. Southern 84-95 Conference 95-01. Southern 01-05 **Names**: None

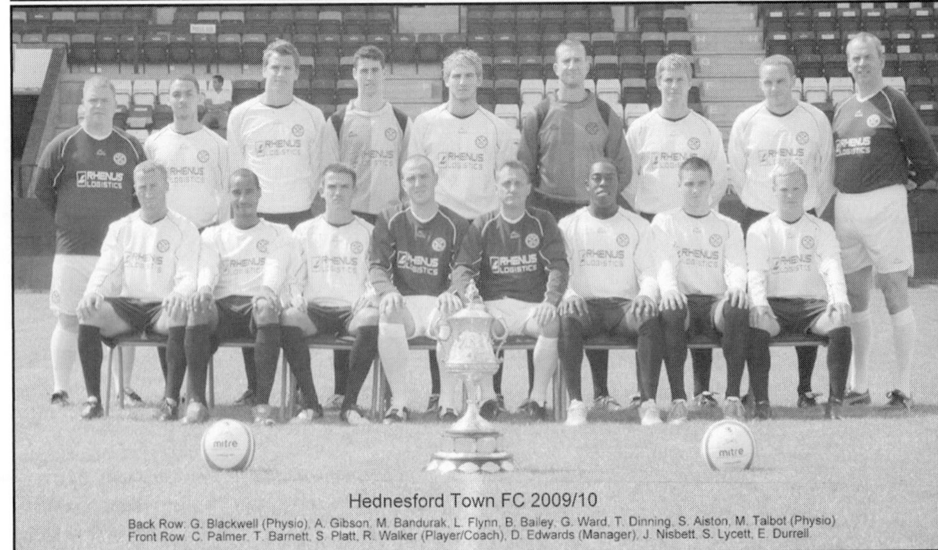

Hednesford Town FC 2009/10

Back Row: G. Blackwell (Physio), A. Gibson, M. Bandurak, L. Flynn, B. Bailey, G. Ward, T. Dinning, S. Aiston, M. Talbot (Physio)
Front Row: C. Palmer, T. Barnett, S. Platt, R. Walker (Player/Coach), D. Edwards (Manager), J. Nisbett, S. Lycett, E. Durrell

HEDNESFORD TOWN

BEST LGE ATT.: **1,077** v FC Utd of Manchester
LOWEST: **122** v Eastwood Town

No.	Date	Comp	H/A	Opponents	Att:	Result	Goalscorers	Pos
1	Aug 16	Unibond P.	A	Ossett Town	175	D 1 - 1	Brisco 75	
2	19		H	Nantwich Town	468	W 2 - 0	Briscoe 6 **Dyer** 34	
3	23		H	Bradford PA	478	W 3 - 1	Barnett 7 **Dyer** 45 74	3
4	25		A	Witton Albion	481	W 2 - 1	**Dyer** 2 Sheppard 90	
5	30		A	Frickley Athletic	329	D 0 - 0		4
6	Sept 2		H	Buxton	462	W 2 - 1	Barnett 26 Harvey 90	
7	9		A	Eastwood Town	387	L 1 - 2	Marshall 35	5
8	**13**	**F.A.C. 1Q**	**H**	**Atherstone Town**	**410**	**L 1 - 2**	**Barnett 10**	
9	20		A	Cammell Laird	225	D 1 - 1	Durrell 88	4
10	23		H	Matlock Town	373	W 4 - 0	BARNETT 3 (30 64 87) Durrell 81	
11	27		H	Ashton United	408	W 2 - 1	Draper 41 Durrell 57	2
12	Oct 4		H	North Ferriby United	405	L 0 - 2		2
13	8		A	Boston United	1090	W 2 - 1	**Dyer** 22 Barnett 55	
14	11		H	Witton Albion	401	W 2 - 0	Barnett 22 **Dyer** 58 (pen)	
15	14		A	Buxton	283	W 3 - 0	**Dyer** 11 Durrell 46 Maguire 62	
16	**18**	**F.A.T. 1Q**	**H**	**Quorn**	**338**	**W 3 - 1**	**Dyer 3 87 Barnett 21**	
17	25		A	Ilkeston Town	541	W 1 - 0	Barnett 88	1
18	28		H	Cammell Laird	307	W 4 - 1	Barnett 7 **Dyer** 22 Marshall 55 Durrell 87	1
19	**Nov 1**	**F.A.T. 2Q**	**A**	**Stamford**	**245**	**W 4 - 3**	**Draper 7 34 Durrell 10 Dyer 89**	
20	8		H	Worksop Town	483	W 5 - 0	**DYER** 3 (31 50 76) Draper 37 70	
21	10		A	Ashton United	187	L 0 - 1		
22	15		H	Kendal Town	564	D 3 - 3	Platt18 (pen) Barnett 84 Burley 90	1
23	**22**	**F.A.T 3Q**	**A**	**Hyde United**	**275**	**D 1 - 1**	**Dyer 25**	**1**
24	**25**	**F.A.T.3Qr**	**H**	**Hyde United**	**263**	**W 5 - 0**	**Williams (og) 14 Draper 33 Dyer 46 Barnett 60 Hall 83**	
25	29		A	F.C.United	1945	L 0 - 3		1
26	Dec 6		H	Guiseley	579	D 2 - 2	Durrell 47 Hall 72	1
27	**16**	**F.A.T. 1R**	**H**	**Nantwich Town**	**264**	**W 3 - 2**	**Durrell 67 Dyer 50 60**	
28	20		H	Prescot Cables	490	W 4 - 1	Barnett 35 52 Durrell 72 85	1
29	26		A	Worksop Town	267	W 7 - 2	BARNETT 3 (19 48 61) DURRELL 3 (35 85 90) **Dyer** 40	
30	**Jan 13**	**F.A.T 2R**	**H**	**Welling United**	**346**	**W 4 - 3**	**DURRELL 3 (9 16 26) Barnett 30**	
31	17		H	Frickley Athletic	481	W 1 - 0	Barnett 94	1
32	24		H	Marine	502	L 1 - 2	Durell 37	2
33	**31**	**F.A.T 3R**	**A**	**Forest Green Rovers**	**768**	**L 0 - 1**		
34	Feb 7		A	Leigh Genesis	344	W 3 - 1	**DYER** 3 (25pen 31 46)	2
35	14		A	Kendal Town	205	L 1 - 4	Draper 78	2
36	21		H	Eastwood Town	122	L 0 - 1		3
37	24		H	Ilkeston Town	351	L 0 - 1		
38	28		A	Bradford P.A.	505	L 0 - 3		
39	Mar 3		A	North Ferriby United	143	L 1 - 2	Durrell 5	
40	7		H	Ossettt Town	412	L 0 - 3		
41	14		A	Marine	273	W 3 - 0	Briggs 18 Lewis 58 **Dyer** 62	4
42	21		H	F.C.United	1077	D 2 - 2	Lewis 28 **Dyer** 75 (pen)	6
43	28		A	Guiseley	307	W 2 - 1	**Dyer** 41 73	7
44	April 1		A	Whitby Town	227	W 3 - 0	**Dyer** 39 Marshall 60 Barnett 90	
45	4		H	Whitby Town	434	L 1 - 3	Marshall 38	6
46	7		A	Nantwich Town	490	W 3 - 1	Barnett 1 18 **Dyer** 56 Durrell 87	
47	11		H	Boston United	520	L 0 - 1		7
48	13		A	Matlock Town	486	L 0 - 2		
49	18		A	Prescot Cables	247	W 5 - 0	Barnett 7 45 **Dyer** 12 Durrell 48 86	
50	25		H	Leigh Genessis	467	L 1 - 2	Durrell 61	8

Average Home Att: **466 (372)** **Goals** **99 66**

Best Position: 1st **Worst:** 8th

Goalscorers: Dyer 29, Barnett 25, Durrell 21, Draper 7, Marshall 4, Briscoe 2, Lewis 2, Hall 2, Burley 1, Harvey 1, Maguire 1, Platt 1, Sheppard 1, Briggs 1.

HEMEL HEMPSTEAD TOWN

Founded: 1885
Nickname: The Tudors

CLUB PERSONNEL

Chairman: David Boggins.

Additional Directors/Committee:
Brendan Glynn (President), Laurie McParland (Vice President), David Stanley (Secretary), Chris Brooks, Andy Smith, Bev Darvill, John Adams, Mick Dorer.

Secretary: Dean Chance.
104 Turners Hill, Adeyfield,
Hemel Hempstead HP2 4LN
(M) 07983 452 688

Programme Editor: Tony Conway
Email: tc@g7bc.com

Managers: Dennis Greene.

Club Colours: All Red.

Change Colours: Green/green/white.

Best Season - League: 5th Southern Premier 2006-07, 08-09.

Ground address: Vauxhall Road, Adeyfield Road, Hemel Hempstead HP2 4HW

Tel/Fax No: 01442 259777

Capacity: 3,152 **Seats**:300 **Covered**:900 **Floodlights**: Yes

Simple Directions: Leave MI at junction 8 and follow dual carriageway over two roundabouts. From outside lane take first right then left at mini roundabout.Take third turning right at next large roundabout intio ground car park.

Midweek Home Matchday: Tuesday

Clubhouse: Open 7-11 pm weekdays 12-11pm weekends & bank holidays
Tea bar with hot snacks open on matchdays.

Club Shop: Yes.

Local Radio: Local Radio, Sports Talk, Chiltern and Three Counties Radio.

Local Press: Hemel Gazette and The Herald

CLUB STATISTICS

Record	**Attendance:** 2,000 v Watford 1985
	at Crabtree Lane 3,500 v Tooting & Mitcham U Amateur Cup 1962
	Career Goalscorer: Dai Price
	Career Appearances:John Wallace 1012
Record	**Transfer Fee Paid**: Not known
	Transfer Fee Received: Not known
Senior Honours:	Ryman League Division 3 1998-1999 Herts Senior Cup (7)
	Herts Charity Cup (6) Athenian League Diov 1 R-Up 64-65
Previous Leagues:	Spartan 1922-52. Delphian 1952-63. Athenian 1963-77. Isthmian 1977-04.
Name:	Crabtree Lane

NB: UNFORTUNATELY A RECENT PHOTO WAS NOT AVAILABLE AT THE TIME OF GOING TO PRESS.

HEMEL HEMPSTEAD TOWN

BEST LGE ATT.: 684 v Gloucester City
LOWEST: 150 v Brackley Town

No.	Date	Comp	H/A	Opponents	Att:	Result	Goalscorers	Pos
1	Aug 16	Southern P.	A	Mangotsfield United	208	W 1 - 0	Dillon 63	
2	19		H	Bedford Town	229	W 1 - 0	Sippetts 57	
3	23		H	Chippenham Town	238	D 1 - 1	Yeboah 55	3
4	25		A	Farnborough Town	571	L 0 - 1		
5	30		H	Halesowen Town	252	D 1 - 1	Wales 54	
6	Sept 3		A	Corby Town	305	D 0 - 0		
7	6		A	Rugby Town	206	W 5 - 1	Sippetts 48 75 Martin 55 Dillon 77 Wales 82	6
8	**13**	**F.A.C. 1Q**	**H**	**Harrow Borough**	**199**	**D 1 - 1**	**Deeney 42 (pen)**	
9	**16**	**F.A.C. 1Qr**	**A**	**Harrow Borough**	**121**	**W 2 - 1**	**Sippetts 4 Edgeworth 88**	
10	20		H	Clevedon Town	203	D 0 - 0		6
11	**27**	**F.A.C 2Q**	**H**	**Ware**	**202**	**L 1 - 2**	**Dillon 16**	
12	Oct 4		A	Stourbridge	183	W 6 - 1	Sippetts 22 Dillon 37 Edgeworth 56 67 Bowden-Haaase 61 Martin 71	5
13	7		H	Bashley	197	D 0 - 0		
14	11		H	Cambridge City	307	L 0 - 1		8
15	**18**	**F.A.T. 1Q**	**H**	**AFC Hayes**	**147**	**W 6 - 0**	**Roberts 17 (pen) 31 Dillon 26 Sippetts 38 Deeney 41 Yeboah 80**	
16	**Nov 1**	**F.A.T 2Q**	**A**	**Concord Rangers**	**117**	**W 3 - 1**	**Edgeworth 8 Martin 10 Roberts 90 (pen)**	
17	8		A	Swindon Supermarine	169	W 4 - 1	**Roberts** 17 47 (pen) Edgeworth 81 Herron 89	6
18	15		H	Tiverton Town	215	L 0 - 1		9
19	**22**	**F.A.T 3Q**	**H**	**Heybridge Swifts**	**168**	**W 5 - 1**	**Roberts 45 Edgeworth 49 Wales 69 Sippetts 78 Dillon 86**	
20	29		H	Banbury United	189	W 1 - 0	Dillon 69	9
21	Dec 6		A	Yate Town	170	W 3 - 2	Thomas 85 88 Edgeworth 90	9
22	9		A	Oxford City	155	W 3 - 2	Dillon 16 Yeboah 53 Thomas 73	
23	**13**	**F.A.T 1R**	**A**	**Forest Green Rovers**	**509**	**L 1 - 5**	**A.Thomas 79**	
24	20		H	Evesham United	201	W 4 - 0	**Roberts** 70 Thomas 64 Sinclair 89 Wales 90	5
25	27		H	Farnborough Town	503	W 3 - 1	Dillon 20 Martin 32 Thomas 90	4
26	Jan 1		A	Hitchin Town	442	L 1 - 2	**Roberts** 73	
27	17		H	Corby Town	311	L 0 - 1		8
28	20		A	Gloucester City	160	L 1 - 2	Bowden-Haase 27	
29	28		A	Bashley	211	L 1 - 2	Bowden-Haase 54	
30	31		H	Stourbridge	240	W 4 - 3	Dillon 5 39 **Roberts** 50 Thomas 85	9
31	Feb 14		H	Oxford City	221	L 0 - 1		10
32	21		H	RugbyTown	280	W 3 - 1	Bowden-Haase 3 **Roberts** 22 Thomas 49	
33	24		H	Brackley Town	150	W 2 - 1	Bowden-Haase 20 Martin 67	
34	28		A	Clevedon Town	133	W 3 - 0	Thomas 28 85 Dillon 69	6
35	Mar 3		A	Chippenham Town	272	W 2 - 1	Dillon 57 Thomas 67	
36	7		H	Swindon Spermarine	354	D 1 - 1	Griffin 78 (og)	
37	9		A	Cambridge City	335	L 0 - 1		
38	14		A	Tiverton Town	270	D 1 - 1	Herron 40	6
39	17		H	Mangotsfield United	158	W 3 - 0	Hilliard 22 73 Thomas 28	
40	21		H	Merthyr Tydfil	307	W 1 - 0	Wales 52	5
41	24		A	Bedford Town	319	W 2 - 1	Thomas 24 Edgeworth 90	
42	28		H	Yate Town	327	W 1 - 0	Thomas 45	4
43	31		A	Brackley Town	221	L 2 - 3	Edgeworth 10 **Roberts** 78 (pen)	
44	April 4		A	Banbury United	215	L 0 - 3		4
45	7		A	Merthyr Tydfil	203	L 2 - 3	**Roberts** 39 52	
46	11		A	Halesowen Town	320	L 1 - 2	**Roberts** 31 (pen)	5
47	13		H	Hitchin Town	351	W 4 - 2	Thomas 2 **Roberts** 9 (pen) Martin 51 Bowden-Haase 62	
48	18		A	Evesham United	124	L 1 - 4	Dillon 67	5
49	25		H	Gloucester City	684	W 2 - 1	**Roberts** 7 Thomas 36	5
50	**28**		**A**	**Farnborough**	**701**	**D 0 - 0**	**Lost 3-4 on pens**	

Average Home Att: 282 (221) **Goals 90 60**

Best Position: 3rd **Worst:** 10th

Goalscorers: Roberts 16, Thomas 16, Dillon 14, Edgeworth 9, Sippetts 7, Bowden-Haase 6, Martin 6, Wales 5, Yeboah 3, Deeney 2, Herron 2, Hillard 2, Sinclair 1. Own Goals 1.

LEAMINGTON F.C.

Nickname: The Brakes

Manager: Jason Cadden.

Club Colours: Gold & black stripes/black with white trim/black.

Change Colours: Blue with white trim/blue with white trim/blue.

Best Seasons: League: 1st Southern Division One Midlands 2008-09.

Ground address: New Windmill Ground, Harbury Lane, Whitmarsh, Leamington, Warwickshire CV33 9JR **Tel/Fax No**: 01926 430406

Capacity: 5,000 **Seats**: 120 **Covered**:720 **Floodlights**:Yes

Simple Directions: Via M40 follow signs to Leamington Spa. On outskirts turn rifght at roundabout towards Harbury. Over traffic lights towards Harbury (with Leamington to left and Tachbrook to right). Ground is about two miles on left.

Midweek Home Matchday: Tuesday

Clubhouse: Fully equipped new building **Club Shop:** Yes

CLUB PERSONNEL

Chairman: Jim Scott.
Additional Directors:
Shaun Brady
Nigel Hodgkins
Harvey Hunt, Nic Sproul,
Russell Davis.

Secretary: Richard Edy.
3 ustcliffClose, Hunt End,
Redditch, Worcs B97 5NZ.
(M) 07588 701 261

Programme
Editor: Verian Thomas
programme@leamingtonfc.co.uk

CLUB STATISTICS

Record	**Attendance:** 1,380 v Retford United - 17.02.07.
	Career Goalscorer: Josh Blake - 166
	Career Appearances: Josh Blake - 314
	Transfer Fee Paid: Not known.
	Transfer Fee Received: Not known.
	Victory: Not known.
	Defeat: Not known.
Senior Honours:	Champions Midland Alliance 2006-07 Mid.Allance Cup 05-06 Champions Mid Comb. 2004-05 R-up 03-04 Div 1 R-up 2001-02 Div 2 Champions 2001-02. Southern Div.1 Midlands Champions 2008-09.
Previous Leagues:	Combination and Midlannd Alliance

Back Row (L-R): Natalie Wilson (physio) Paul Eden (coach), Steve Palmer, Luke Corbett, Mykel Beckley, Stuart Herlihy, Richard Morris, Richard Anstiss, Chris Kiely, Adam Cooper, Liam Reynolds, James Husband, Keith Orme (coach).**Front Row:** Chris Murphy, Jai Stanley, Ryan Parisi, Reis Ashraf, Morton Titterton (Assistant Manager) Guy Sanders (Club Captain), Jason Cadden (Manager), Josh Blake, Mark Bellingham, Martin Hier, Marcus Jackson.

The ZAMARETTO
League

MERTHYR TYDFIL

Founded: 1945
Nickname: The Martyrs

Manager: Gary Shephard.

Club Colours: White/black/black.

Change Colours: Blue/blue/blue.

Best Season - League: 4th Conference 1991-92

Ground address: Penndarren Park, Merthyr Tydfil, Mid Glamorgan CF47 8RF.

Tel No: 01685 384102/371395. Fax: 01685 382882

Capacity: 10,000 **Seats:** 1,500 **Covered**: 5,000 **Floodlights:** Yes

Simple Directions: From South: A470 Express Way to Merthyr Centre to Pontmorlais (traffic lights) turn left then right. First right at Catholic Church and right again into Park Terrace.

Midweek Home Matchday: Tuesday

Clubhouse: Daily from 6.30-11,00pm. Two club cafes on matchdays for hot food.

Club Shop: Fully stocked.

CLUB PERSONNEL

Chairman: Unknown at time of going to press.

Secretary: Anthony Hughes.
4 Brynmorlais, Penydarren,
Merthyr Tydfil CF47 9YE
(H): 01685 359 921
(M): 07737 022 293

Programme
Editor: John Strand
jstrand@salisburyclose.fsnet.co.uk

CLUB STATISTICS

Record	**Attendance**: 21,000 v Reading F.A.Cup 2nd Rd 1949-50
	Victory: 11-0 v Rushden 1987
	Defeat: 2-9 v Altrincham 1993
	Goalscorer:
	Career Appearances:
Record Transfer Fee	**Paid**: £10,000 to Cardiff City for Robbie James 1992
	Received: £12,000 from Exeter City for Ray Pratt 1981
Senior Honours:	Welsh League: 1948-49, 49-50, 51-52. Welsh F.A.Cup 1947-48, 48-49, 50-51, 86-87. Southern League (5) Midland Div 87-88. Premier Champions 1988-89
Previous Leagues	Southern Lg. 46-49,and Conference 89-95

Photo courtesy of: The Merthyr Express

MERTHYR TYDFIL

BEST LGE ATT.: **686** v Corby Town
LOWEST: **203** v Hemel Hempstead

No.	Date	Comp	H/A	Opponents	Att:	Result	Goalscorers	Pos
1	Aug 16	Southern P.	H	Brackley Town	303	L 1 - 4	**Steins** 44	
2	19		A	Yate Town	226	L 0 - 4		
3	23		A	Cambridge City	282	L 0 - 3		22
4	25		H	Stourbridge	315	W 4 - 1	SHEPHARD 3 (28 63 67) Griffiths M 88	
5	30		A	Oxford City	217	W 4 - 1	Shephard 2 23 **Steins** 18 Keddle 28	16
6	Sept 2		H	Swindon Supermarine	286	L 1 - 2	Williams 87	
7	6		A	Corby Town	262	L 1 - 2	Shephard 27	20
8	**13**	**F.A.C 1Q**	**A**	**Poole Town**	**231**	**L 0 - 3**		
9	20		H	Hitchin Town	262	W 3 - 2	O'Sullivan 7 Jones 10 Shephard 46	
10	Oct 4		A	Tiverton Town	305	W 1 - 0	Griffiths M 81	11
11	7		H	Mangotsfield United	294	W 1 - 0	**Steins** 82	
12	11		A	Farnborough	1148	W 1 - 0	**Steins** 74	7
13	**18**	**F.A.T. 1Q**	**H**	**Bishop's Cleeve**	**273**	**W 4 - 1**	**Keddle 4 M.Jones 21 85 Harris 90**	
14	25		H	Chippenham Town	336	W 2 - 0	Keddle 61 Shephard 78	5
15	**Nov 1**	**F.A.T.2Q**	**A**	**Andover**	**180**	**L 2 - 3**	**Shephard 34 55**	
16	8		H	Gloucester City	328	W 2 - 1	Griffiths D 29 **Steins** 34	4
17	11		A	Clevedon Town	154	W 5 - 1	Rewbury 19 Thomas 56 O'Sullivan 58 **Steins** 64 Clarke 82 (pen)	
18	15		A	Bashley	307	W 3 - 1	Hartsham 3 11 **Steins** 73	2
19	29		H	Rugby Town	282	D 3 - 3	Griffiths D 53 Griffiths M 77 Evans 78	4
20	Dec 6		A	Bedford Town	278	L 0 - 1		4
21	20		H	Banbury United	361	W 3 - 0	Williams 8 Thomas 36 Peppiatt 69 (og)	4
22	27		A	Stourbridge	379	W 2 - 1	O'Sullivan 13 Williams 85	2
23	Jan 3		A	Brackley Town	252	D 2 - 2	Shephard 37 43 (pen)	2
24	17		A	Swindon Supermarine	259	D 0 - 0		2
25	20		A	Halesowen Town	334	L 0 - 2		
26	24		H	Yate Town	362	W 2 - 1	Rewbury 65 **Steins** 84	2
27	27		H	Tiverton Town	289	L 1 - 2	Keddle 51	
28	31		A	Mangotsfield United	201	W 3 - 0	Thomas 3 Jones 32 Keddle 68	
29	Feb 14		A	Chippenham Town	442	L 0 - 1		3
30	21		H	Corby Town	686	L 0 - 2		7
31	24		H	Evesham United	378	W 1 - 0	Griffiths M 63	
32	28		A	Hitchin Town	288	D 2 - 2	**Steins** 62 67	4
33	Mar 7		A	Gloucester City	315	D 1 - 1	Griffiths D 2	
34	10		H	Clevedon Town	339	D 2 - 2	**Steins** 5 45	
35	14		H	Bashley	301	L 0 - 2		8
36	21		A	Hemel Hempstead	307	L 0 - 1		9
37	24		H	Cambridge City	243	D 1 - 1	Griffiths M 11	9
38	29		H	Bedford Town	312	W 3 - 0	Rewbery 31 53 Morgan 68	
39	April 4		A	Rugby Town	274	L 0 - 3		9
40	7		H	Hemel Hempstead	203	W 3 - 2	Hartshorn 23 **Steins** 69 Jones 80	
41	11		H	Oxford City	274	D 2 - 2	Jones 11 Cullimore 87	7
42	13		A	Evesham United	211	W 2 - 0	Williams 2 Jones 90	
43	16		A	Banbury United	101	D 1 - 1	Harris 87	7
44	21		H	Farnborough	329	D 1 - 1	Thomas 90	
45	25		H	Halesowen Town	422	W 2 - 0	M.Griffiths 29 Keddle 38	7

Average Home Att: 329 (371) **Goals** 72 62

Best Position: 2nd **Worst:** 22nd

Goalscorers: Steins 13, Shephard 12, Jones 7, Griffiths M 6, Keddle 6, Rewbury 4, Thomas 4, Williams 4, Grifiths D 3, Hartshorn 3, O'Sullivan 3, Harris 2, Clarke 1, Cullimore 1, Evans 1, Morgan 1. Own Goal 1.

NUNEATON TOWN

Formed: 2008
Nickname: The Boro

CLUB PERSONNEL

Chairman: Ian Neale.

Additional Directors:
Paul Roberts.

Secretary: Graham Wilson.
3 Stanford Court,
Whitestone, Nuneaton CV11
4TZ. (M) 07702 449 162.

Programme
Editor: As Secretary.

Manager: Kevin Wilkin.
Club Colours: Blue & white stripes/blue/blue.
Change Colours: Red & black halves/red/black.
Beat Season - League: As Nuneaton Borough - 2nd Conference 1983-84, 1984-85. As Nuneaton Town - 2nd Southern Division One Midlands 2008-09.
Ground address: Liberty Way, Nuneaton,Warwickshire CV11 6RR
Tel: 02476 385738. Fax: 02476 342995. (M) 07917 237 171.
Simple Directions: From the South,West and North West, exit the M6 at Junction 3 and follow the A444 into Nuneaton. At the Coton Arches roundabout turn right into Avenue Road which is theA4254 signposted for Hinckley. Continue along the A4254 following the road into Garrett Street, then Eastboro Way, then turn left into Townsend Drive. Follow the road round before turning left into Liberty Way for the ground. **From the North**, exit the M1 at Junction 21 and follow the M69. Exit at Junction 1 and take the 4th exit at roundabout onto A5 (Tamworth, Nuneaton). At Longshoot Junction turn left onto A47, continue to roundabout and take the 1st exit onto A4254, Eastboro Way. Turn right at next roundabout into Townsend Drive, then right again into Libery Way.
Midweek Home Matchday: Tuesday
Local Radio: Mercia Sound, BBC CWR
Local Press: Nuneaton Telegraph & Weekly Tribune

CLUB STATISTICS (AS NUNEATON BOROUGH)

Record	**Attendance** :22,114 v Rotherham United F.A.Cup 3rd Rd 1967
	Victory: 11-1 45-46 & 55-56 **Defeat:** 1-8 55-56 & 68-69
	Career Goalscorer: Paul Culpin 201 (Career) 55 (Season 92-93)
	Career Appearances: Alan Jones 545 (62-74)
	Fee Paid: £35,000 to Forest Green Rovers for Marc McGregor 2000
	Fee Received: £80,000 from Kidderminster H for Andy Ducross 2000
Senior Honours:	Alliance Runners-up 83-4-84-5 Southern Premier 98-99 R-up 66-7 74-75
	Midland Div 81-2 92-3 Birmingham Senior Cup (7)
Previous Leagues:	Central Amateur 1937-38 B'ham Comb. 1938-52 West Mids 1952-58.
	Southern 1958-79, 81-2, 88-90, 03-04. Conference 79-81, 82-88, 99-03, 04-08.
Previous Names:	Nuneaton Borough1937-2008.

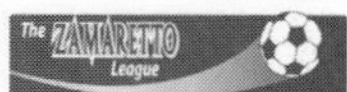
The ZAMARETTO League

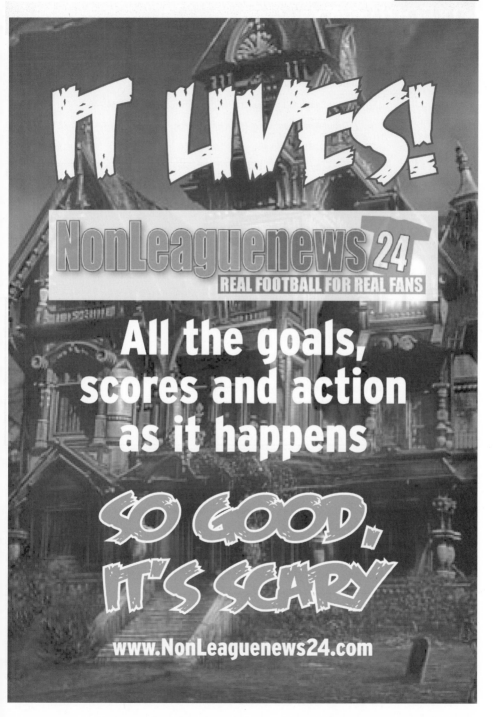

OXFORD CITY

Founded: 1882
Nickname: City

CLUB PERSONNEL

Chairman: Brian Cox.

Additional Directors:
Paul Cotterell (Vice Chairman),
Colin Taylor (Managing Director),
John Shepperd (Secretary),
Paul Townsend.

Secretary: John Shepherd.
20 Howe Close, Wheatley,
Oxford OX33 1SS
(H): 01865 872 181
(M): 07748 628 911

Programme
Editor: ColinTaylor.
ctoxford@btinternet.com

Manager: Justin Merritt.

Club Colours: Blue & white hoops /blue/white.

Change Colours: All yellow.

Best Season - League: 2nd Isthmian Premier 1934-35, 1945-46.

Ground address: Court Place Farm, Marsh Lane, Marston, Oxford OX3 0NQ

Tel/Fax: 01865 744 493

Capacity: 3,000 **Seats**: 300 **Covered**: 400 **Floodlights**: Yes

Simple Directions: From London M40 or A40 take ring road to North of Oxford . then first slip road and follow signs to John Radcliffe Hospital and Court Farm Stadium. Ground on left aftyer leaving flyover.

Midweek Home Matchday: Tuesday

Clubhouse: Open matchdays with snacks.

Club Shop: Yes

CLUB STATISTICS

Record	**Attendance:** 9,500 v Leytonstone F.A. Amateur Cup 1950 (White House)
	Career Goalscorer: John Woodley
	Career Appearances: John Woodley
Record Transfer Fee	**Paid**: £3,000 to Woking for S.Adams
	Received: £15,000 from Yeovil Town for Howard Forinton
Senior Honours	F.A.Amateur Cup 1905-06. Oxford Senior Cup (x31).
Previous	**Leagues**: Spartan South Midlands 2005-06, Isthmian1907-88, 94-2005. South Midlands 1990-93.
	Grounds: The White House 1882-1988. Cuttleslowe Park 1990-91. Pressed Steel 1991-93.

NB: UNFORTUNATELY A RECENT PHOTO WAS NOT AVAILABLE AT THE TIME OF GOING TO PRESS.

OXFORD CITY

BEST LGE ATT.: **444** v Banbury United
LOWEST: **155** v Hemel Hempstead

No.	Date	Comp	H/A	Opponents	Att:	Result	Goalscorers	Pos
1	Aug 16	Southern P.	A	Banbury United	430	L 0 - 1		
2	19		H	Hitchin Town	210	L 2 - 3	Romeo 64 Salisbury 69 (pen)	
3	23		H	Bedford Town	275	W 1 - 0	Baird 34	16
4	25		A	Gloucester City	302	D 2 - 2	Faulcenbridge 59 Romeo 86	21
5	30		H	Merhyr Tydfil	217	L 1 - 4	Thomas 47 (og)	
6	Sept 2		A	Halesowen Town	454	L 2 - 5	Davis 12 Faulcenbridge 45	
7	**13**	**F.A.C. 1Q**	**A**	**Bracknell Town**	**111**	**L 0 - 2**	**Bracknell Town disqualified for ineligable player**	
8	20		H	Rugby Town	237	W 3 - 2	Baird 2 39 Lyon 50	19
9	**27**	**F.A.C. 2Q**	**H**	**Tiverton Town**	**257**	**W 2 - 1**	**Faulkner 61 Lyon 86**	
10	Oct 4		H	Farnborough Town	382	D 2 - 2	Brookes 4 Faulconbridge 88	
11	7		A	Corby Town	314	W 1 - 0	**Faulkner** 25	15
12	**11**	**F.A.C 3Q**	**H**	**Chesham United**	**257**	**W 2 - 1**	**Redknapp 58 Faulkner 62**	
13	**18**	**F.A.T 1Q**	**H**	**Aylsbury United**	**299**	**W 3 - 1**	**Jackman 6 Brookes 40 56**	
14	**25**	**F.A.C 4Q**	**H**	**Eastbourne Borough**	**564**	**L 0 - 1**		
15	**Nov 1**	**F.A.T. 2Q**	**A**	**Dartford**	**749**	**D 3 - 3**	**Gardner 20 Gunn 53 Jackman 89**	
16	**4**	**F.A.T. 2Qr**	**H**	**Dartford**	**219**	**L 2 - 4**	**Faulkner 13 Salisbury 87(pen)**	
17	11		H	Chippenham Town	207	D 2 - 2	Gardner 11 **Faulkner** 17	11
18	15		H	Swindon Spermarine	256	L 1 - 2	Lyon 90	
19	18		A	Yate Town	143	W 3 - 2	Gunn 3 Lyon 48 Pond 80 (pen)	
20	29		A	Stourbridge	201	L 0 - 2		16
21	Dec 6		H	Bashley	214	W 2 - 0	Brookes 2 Faulconbridge 64	14
22	9		H	Hemel Hempstead Town	155	L 2 - 3	Pond 60 Davis 89	
23	20		A	Cambridge City	319	L 0 - 1		16
24	27		H	Gloucester City	265	D 1 - 1	Pond 77 (pen)	
25	Jan 3		H	Banbury United	444	W 3 - 0	**Faulkner** 46 Pond 60 Lyon 75	16
26	13		A	Evesham United	111	W 1 - 0	**Faulkner** 6	
27	17		H	Halesowen Town	292	W 4 - 1	Gunn 6 Brookes 44 Fisher 47 79	12
28	24		A	Hitchin Town	327	W 4 - 0	Fisher 17 21 Baird 53 Gunn 64	
29	27		H	Corby Town	206	L 0 - 1		
30	31		A	Farnborough Town	713	W 2 - 0	Savage 37 (pen) Fisher 89	12
31	Feb 14		A	Hemel Hempstead	221	W 1 - 0	Pond 82	
32	17		A	Mangotsfield United	127	D 2 - 2	Gunn 15 Faulconbridge 30	
33	21		H	Yate Town	242	W 4 - 2	Fisher 31 Pond 33 (pen) Gunn 53 **Faulkner** 65	
34	28		A	Rugby Town	272	D 1 - 1	Pond 37	10
35	Mar 3		A	Tiverton Town	175	D 2 - 2	Faulconbridge 41 72	
36	7		H	Evesham United	304	L 0 - 1		
37	10		A	Chippenham Town	333	W 2 - 0	Lamb 21(og) **Faulkner** 54	
38	14		A	Swindon Supermarine	211	D 1 - 1	**Faulkner** 48	9
39	17		H	Tiverton Town	194	W 3 - 0	Baird 42 80 Bell 79	
40	21		H	Brackley Town	423	W 3 - 0	Fisher 30 67 Faulconbridge 54	8
41	28		A	Bashley	302	L 2 - 3	Faulconbridge 7 25	
42	31		A	Bedford Town	286	L 1 - 3	Pond 8	
43	April 4		H	Stourbridge	327	D 1 - 1	Gunn 28	10
44	7		H	Clevedon Town	164	W 5 - 3	**FAULKNER** 3 (19 50 77) Lyon 56 Bell 87	
45	11		A	Merthyr Tydfil	274	D 2 - 2	Fisher 62 Faulconbridge 73	8
46	13		H	Mangotsfield United	294	W 4 - 0	Pond 3 23 Bell 22 Malone 85	
47	18		H	Cambridge City	442	W 1 - 0	**Faulkner** 84	6
48	21		A	Brackley Town	264	L 1 - 2	Faulconbridge 7	
49	25	42	A	Clevedon Town	365	W 1 - 0	Bell 82	6

Average Home Att: **274 (272)** **Goals** **88 70**

Best Position: 6th **Worst:** 21st

Goalscorers: Faulkner 14, Faulconbridge 12, Pond 10, Fisher 9, Gunn 7, Baird 6, Lyon 6, Brookes 5, Bell 4, Romeo 2, Davis 2, Gardner 2, Jackman 2, Salisbury 2, Malone 1, Redknapp 1, Savage 1. Own Goals 2.

RUGBY TOWN

Formed: 1956
Nickname: The Valley

CLUB PERSONNEL

Chairman: Brian Melvin.

Additional Directors:
Mike Yeats (Corporate),
Les Leeson (Stadium),
Danny Lorden (Stadium),
Lisa Melvin (Financial), Darren Knapp (Health & Safety), Jim Melvin.

Secretary: Doug Wilkins.
298 Rocky Lane, Great Barr,
Birmingham, B42 1NQ
(H) 0121 681 1544
(F): 0121 681 1544
(M): 07976 284 614

Programme Editor: As Secretary.

Manager: Tony Dobson.

Club Colours: Sky blue/white/white.

Change Colours: All orange.

Best Season - League: 15th Southern Premier Division 2005-06, 07-08.

Ground address: Butlin Road, Rugby, Warwicks. CV21 3SD

Tel No: 01788 844 806. Fax: 01788 866 923.

Capacity: 6,000 **Seats:** 750 **Covered**: 1,000 **Floodlights:** Yes

Simple Directions: Ground is off Clifton (B5414) on the north side of Rugby.

One mile from Rugby station.

Midweek Home Matchday: Tuesday

Clubhouse: Open every evening and week end lunchtimes.

Club Shop: Yes.

CLUB STATISTICS

Record Attendance: 3,961 v Northampton Town F.A.Cup 1984

Victory: 10-0 v Ilkeston Town F.A.Trophy 04.09.85 **Defeat:** 1-11 v Ilkeston Town (A) 18.04.98

Goalscorer: Danny Conway 124 **Career Appearances**: Danny Conway 374

Record Transfer Fee **Paid**: £3,500 for R. Smith, I. Crawley and G.Bradder
Received: £15,000 from Northampton Town for T.Angus.

Senior Honours: F.A.Vase Winners 82-83 Southern League Midland Division 86-87
Birmingham Senior Cup: 88-89 91-92

Previous Leagues: Rugby & District, 56-63 Coventry & Partnership, North Warwicks 63-69
United Counties 69-75 and West Midlands 75-83

Names: Valley Sports 1956-1971. Valley Sports Rugby 1971-1973. VS Rugby 1973-2000. Rugby United 2000-2005.

RUGBY TOWN

BEST LGE ATT.: **410** v Corby Town
LOWEST: **158** v Bashley

No.	Date	Comp	H/A	Opponents	Att:	Result	Goalscorers	Pos
1	Aug 16	Southern P.	A	Farnborough	520	L 1 - 2	Olaoye 16	
2	19		H	Halesowen Town	287	L 0 - 2		
3	23		H	Banbury United	257	D 0 - 0		20
4	25		A	Bedford Town	441	L 0 - 2		
5	30		H	Chippenham Town	211	L 0 - 1		22
6	Sept 2		A	Hitchin Town	313	D 1 - 1	Curtis 75	
7	6		H	Hemel Hempstead T	206	L 0 - 5		22
8	**13**	**F.A.C. 1Q**	**A**	**Friar Lane & E**	**210**	**D 0 - 0**		
9	**16**	**F.A.C. 1Qr**	**H**	**Friar Lane & E**	**176**	**W 5 - 3**	**Purton 4 Kolodynski 20 42 Dykes 60 (pen) 70**	
10	20		A	Oxford City	237	L 2 - 3	King 32 Gordon 60	22
11	**27**	**F.A.C. 2Q**	**H**	**Long Eaton United**	**223**	**W 5 - 1**	**Musgrove 32 Kolodynski 65 71 King 83 Gearing 89**	
12	Oct 4		A	Cambridge City	302	L 2 - 3	Fitzharris 15 Stone 69	22
13	7		H	Stourbridge	169	W 4 - 0	Gordon 9 **Kolodynski** 22 43 Purton 87	
14	**11**	**F.A.C 3Q**	**A**	**Bishop's Stortford**	**411**	**L 1 - 2**	**King 73**	
15	**18**	**F.A.T. 1Q**	**A**	**Lancaster City**	**166**	**D 3 - 3**	**Kolodynski 67 (pen) Stone 71 Taylor 80**	
16	**21**	**F.A.T. 1Qr**	**H**	**Lancaster City**	**131**	**W 2 - 0**	**Musgrove 27 Taylor 90**	
17	25		A	Yate Town	165	W 4 - 2	**Kolodynski** 16 61 Stone 45 87	22
18	**Nov 1**	**F.A.T. 2Q**	**H**	**Nantwich Town**	**238**	**L 1 - 3**	**Musgrove 25 (pen)**	
19	8		A	Tiverton Town	358	W 1 - 0	Musgrove 86	19
20	15		H	Evesham United	205	L 0 - 1		22
21	22		H	Gloucester City	193	L 1 - 3	Morley 19	
22	29		A	Merthyr Tydfil	282	D 3 - 3	**KOLODYNSKI** 3 (19pen 38 54)	22
23	Dec 6		H	Clevedon Town	178	W 4 - 0	**KOLODYNSKI** 3 (21 89 90) Musgrove 53	19
24	9		H	Brackley Town	170	D 3 - 3	**Kolodynski** 23 59 Purton 25	
25	20		A	Mongotsfield United	173	W 2 - 0	Musgrove 61 74	
26	27		H	Bedford Town	340	W 3 - 0	Stone 2 **Kolodynski** 7 64	14
27	Jan 1		A	Corby Town	369	L 0 - 2		
28	3		H	Farnborough	306	L 2 - 3	Stone 18 Bicel 79	15
29	17		H	Hitchin Town	253	W 4 - 3	**Kolodynski** 21 53 Morley 80 Staff 84	
30	21		A	Halesowen Town	426	W 4 - 0	**Kolodynski** 5 74 Gordon 26 Staff 79	14
31	27		A	Stourbridge	173	D 1 - 1	Stone 89	
32	31		H	Cambridge City	293	L 2 - 3	Gordon 12 **Kolodynski** 35	15
33	Feb 14		H	Yate Town	231	D 2 - 2	Metitri 65 (og) Nicell 86 (pen)	15
34	17		A	Banbury United	201	L 1 - 2	Gearing 62	
35	21		A	Hemel Hempstead	280	L 1 - 3	Gordon 9	16
36	28		H	Oxford City	272	D 1 - 1	Musgrove 32	15
37	Mar 7		H	Tiverton Town	173	W 2 - 0	Turner 34 Gearing 87	15
38	10		A	Brackley Town	217	D 2 - 2	Pearson 6 90	
39	14		A	Evesham United	139	L 0 - 1		15
40	21		H	Swindon Supermarine	220	D 0 - 0		16
41	25		A	Gloucester City	267	L 0 - 3		
42	28		A	Clevedon Town	169	L 0 - 1		17
43	31		H	Bashley	158	L 2 - 3	**Kolodynski** 30 Staff 38	
44	April 4		H	Merthyr Tydfil	274	W 3 - 0	Pearson 8 **Kolodynski** 36 87	17
45	11		A	Chippenham Town	345	D 1 - 1	**Kolodynski** 90 (pen)	17
46	13		H	Corby Town	410	L 0 - 2		
47	18		H	Mangotsfield United	312	W 2 - 1	**Kolodynski** 3 (pen) 24	6
48	22		A	Swindon Spermarine	147	L 1 - 3	**Kolodynski** 49	
49	25		A	Bashley	334	L 1 - 3	Staff 45	

Average Home Att: **244 (272)** **Goals** **80 83**

Best Position: 6th **Worst:** 22nd

Goalscorers: Kolodynski 31, Musgrove 8, Stone 7, Gordon 5, Pearson 4, Staff 4, Gearing 3, King 3, Purton 2, Dykes 2, Morley 2, Nicell 2, Taylor 2, Curtis 1, Fitzharris 1, Olaoye 1, Turner 1. Own Goal 1.

STOURBRIDGE

Founded: 1876
Nickname: The Glassboys

Manager: Gary Hackett.

Club Colours: Red & white stripes/red/red.

Change Colours: Yellow/green/yellow.

Previous Name: Stourbridge Standard

Best Season - League: 14th Southern League Premier Division 1982-83

Ground address: War Memorial Athletic Ground, High Street, Amblecote, Stourbridge, W.Mids. DY8 4HN Tel No: 01384 394 040

Capacity: 2,000 **Seats**: 250 **Covered**: 750 **Floodlights**: Yes

Simple Directions: From Stourbridge ringroad, take A491 signposted Wolverhampton, and ground is 300 yards on left opposite Royal Oak pub. Buses 311 and 246 from Dudlley and 256 from Wolverhampton pass the ground.

Midweek Home Matchday: Tuesday

Clubhouse: Open matchdays and training evenings. **Club Shop:** Yes

Local Radio: Beacon Radio

Local Press: Stourbridge News and Express & Star

CLUB PERSONNEL

Chairman: Ian Pilkington.

Additional Directors/Committee:
Hugh Clark (President), Stephen Hyde, Sharon Dimmock, Nigel Gregg, Geoff Tomason, Pauline Wiley, Jonathan Martin, Sharon Hyde.

Secretary: Nick Pratt.
91 Rangeways Road,
Kingswinford DY6 8NU.
(M) 07799 070 596

Programme Editors: Nigel Gregg
ng004f7624@blueyonder.co.uk

CLUB STATISTICS

Record	**Attendance:** 5,726 v Cardiff City Welsh Cup Final 1st Leg 1974
	Career Goalscorer: Ron Page 269
	Career Appearances: Ron Page 427
	Transfer Fee Received: £20,000 From Lincoln C. for Tony Cunningham 1979
Senior Honours:	Welsh Cup R-Up 73-74, Southern League Mid.Div. 90-91, Lg Cup 92-93, Div 1 North 73-74, Mid Alliance 01-02 02-03, B'ham Senior Cup (3) R-Up (4), Worcs Senior Cup (9) Hereford Sen. Cup 54-55 and Worcs Junior Cup 27-28
Previous Leagues:	West Midlands (ex Birmingham League.) 1892-1939, 1954-71 Birminghamham Comb.ination 45-53 and Southern League 19 71-2000

Back Row (L-R): Lee Williams, Kalum Evitts, Alex Cowley, Joe Williams, James Dyson, Ross Collins, Mark Clifton (Coach), Matt Jones, Sam Smith, Lewis Solly, Jon Ford, Nathan Bennett, Craig Slater, Morris Brookes (Kit manager), Nick Ingram, Dreniz Bala, Sean Evans.
Front Row: Ryan Rowe, Ryan Mahon, Sam Rock, Drew Canavan, Gary Hackett (manager), Ian Pilkington (Chairman), Richard Drewett (Physio), Linden Dovey, Aaron Drake, Adam Bastable, Ben Billingham, Chris Rabone.
Mascot: Ryan Pratt. Photo courtesy of http://jamesmarshphotography.co.uk

STOURBRIDGE

BEST LGE ATT.: 791 v Halesowen Town
LOWEST: 131 v Clevedon Town

No.	Date	Comp	H/A	Opponents	Att:	Result	Goalscorers	Pos
1	Aug 16	Southern P.	A	Gloucester City	245	L 0 - 4		
2	19		H	Banbury United	144	D 1 - 1	Morley (og)	
3	23		H	Corby Town	185	L 0 - 2		21
4	25		A	Merthyr Tydfil	315	L 1 - 4	**Broadhurst** 70	
5	30		H	Clevedon Town	131	W 6 - 1	Slater 6 **Broadhurst** 28 Martin 30 45 Bennett 52 74	20
6	Sept 2		A	Chippenham Town	371	W 2 - 1	**Broadhurst** 47 Rostill 66	
7	6		A	Bashley	273	L 1 - 4	Collins 49	18
8	**13**	**F.A.C.1Q**	**H**	**Rainworth M.W.**	**183**	**D 0 - 0**		
9	20		H	Brackley Town	237	L 0 - 1		20
10	**27**	**F.A.C 2Q**	**H**	**Brackley Town**	**199**	**D 1 - 1**	**Dyson 63 (pen)**	
11	**30**	**F.A.C. 2Qr**	**A**	**BrackleyTown**	**187**	**L 0 - 1**		
12	Oct 4		H	Hemel Hempstead	183	L 1 - 4	Dyson 34	20
13	7		A	Rugby Town	169	L 0 - 4		
14	11		A	Swindon Supermarine	171	D 1 - 1	**Broadhurst** 51	
15	**18**	**F.A.T. 1Q**	**H**	**Salford City**	**162**	**W 6 - 0**	**Bennett 6 Canavan 12 Burns 40 (og) Broadhurst 53 Slater 80 Dovey 87**	
16	25		H	Hitchin Town	207	W 1 - 0	Rock 63	
17	**Nov 1**	**F.A.T. 2Q**	**H**	**Evesham United**	**198**	**W 2 - 1**	**Broadhurst 10 Dovey 63**	
18	8		A	Cambridge City	334	L 0 - 2		22
19	11		H	Evesham United	195	L 0 - 2		
20	15		H	Bedford Town	211	W 3 - 1	Bennett 13 Hines 71 (pen) **Broadhurst** 82	
21	**22**	**F.A.T 3Q**	**H**	**Hucknall Town**	**176**	**W 3 - 2**	**Hines 21 (pen) Broadhurst 86 90**	
22	29		H	Oxford City	201	W 2 - 0	**Broadhurst** 50 64	
23	Dec 6		A	Tiverton Town	328	D 1 - 1	Bennett 74	15
24	**16**	**F.A.T 1R**	**H**	**Stalybridge Celtic**	**148**	**L 1 - 6**	**Canavan 37**	
25	20		H	Yate Town	182	W 8 - 4	Collins 28 Martin 29 Bennett 50 ROCK 3 (59 75 84) **Broadhurst** 70 Hines 88	
26	27		H	Merthyr Tydfil	379	L 1 - 2	Bennett 45	15
27	Jan 1		A	Halesowen Town	1273	W 3 - 1	**Broadhurst** 32 73 Langford 48	
28	13		A	Mangotsfield United	123	W 2 - 1	Hines 61 Langford 74	
29	17		H	Chippenham Town	270	L 1 - 2	Hines 69 (pen)	14
30	20		A	Farnborough Town	419	L 0 - 4		
31	27		H	Rugby Town	173	D 1 - 1	**Broadhurst** 51 (pen)	
32	31		A	Hemel Hempstead	240	L 3 - 4	**Broadhurst** 30 Slater 37 Winsper 75	16
33	Feb 21		H	Bashley	229	D 1 - 1	Canavan 60	
34	28		A	Brackley Town	204	L 0 - 3		15
35	Mar 4		A	Corby Town	180	D 0 - 0		
36	7		H	Cambridge City	257	D 1 - 1	Langford 82	
37	10		A	Evesham United	105	W 1 - 0	Langford 50	
38	14		A	Bedford Town	292	L 1 - 2	Drake 32	16
39	17		A	Stourbridge	170	L 0 - 2		
40	21		H	Mangotsfield United	184	W 4 - 1	**BROADHURST** 3 (24 75 84 pen) Drake 90	15
41	24		A	Hitchin Town	248	D 2 - 2	**Broadhurst** 32 Benjamin 77	
42	28		H	Tiverton Town	228	W 3 - 0	Benjamin 20 Rock 70 Dovey 86	16
43	30		H	Swindon Supermarine	180	W 2 - 1	**Broadhurst** 68 (pen) Langford 89	
44	April 4		A	Oxford City	327	D 1 - 1	**Broadhurst** 26	15
45	7		H	Gloucester city	236	D 1 - 1	**Broadhurst** 38 (pen)	
46	11		A	Clevedon Town	201	L 0 - 2		15
47	13		H	Halesowen Town	791	D 2 - 2	**Broadhurst** 77 (pen) Slater 84	
48	18		A	Yate Town	167	W 4 - 2	Hadley 1 Dovey 78 Rock 80 Drake 82	16
49	25		H	Farnborough	461	L 0 - 3		16

Average Home Att: 251 **Goals 75 87**

Best Position: 14th **Worst:** 22nd

Goalscorers: Broadhurst 24, Bennett 7, Rock 6, Langford 5, Dovey 4, Hines 5, Drake 3, Martin 3, Slater 3, Benjamin 2, Collins 2, Dyson 2, Canavan 2, Hadley 1, Hines 1, Rostill 1, Slater 1, Winsper 1. Own Goals 2.

SWINDON SUPERMARINE

Founded: 1992
Nickname: Marine

Manager: Mark Collier.

Club Colours: Blue & white/blue/white.

Change Colours: All red.

Best Season - League: 12th Southern League Premier Division 2007-08.

Ground address: Hunts Copse, South Marston, Swindon, Wilts SN3 4SY.

Tel No: 01793 828 778. Fax: 01793 790685

Capacity: 3,000 **Seats**: 300 **Covered**: 300 **Floodlights**: Yes

Simple Directions: On A361 Swindon/Highworth road, adjoining South Marston Ind. Estate.Six miles from Swindon (BR) - buses in direction of Highworth, Fairford & Lechdale. If lost ask for Honda!

Midweek Home Matchday: Wednesday

Clubhouse: Yes. **Club Shop:** Yes.

Local Radio: BBC Wiltshire Sound G.W.R.F.M.

Local Press: Swindon Advertiser

CLUB PERSONNEL

Chairman: TBA.
Additional Directors/Committee:
Steve Moore
Keith Yeomans (Executive)
Mark Bisset (Executive)
Mark Carter
Secretary: Judi Moore,
8 Callas Rise,Wanborough,
Swindon SN4 0AQ
(H): 01793 790 685
(F): 01793 790 685
(M): 07785 970 954

Programme
Editor: Keith Yeomans
supermarinefc@aol.com

CLUB STATISTICS

Record	**Attendance:** 1,550 v Aston Villa
	Career Goalscorer: Damon York 136
	Career Appearances: Damon York 298 + 16 1990-1998
Record Transfer Fee	**Paid**: £1,000 to Hungerford Town for Lee Hartson
	Received: Not known.
Senior Honours:	Hellenic Lge - Premier Div. 97-98, 00-01, R-up 95-96 98-99; Div. One 85-86 86-87; Hellenic Challenge Cup 96-97, 99/00.Wiltshire Senior Cup 82-83, 86-87, 89-90.
Previous	**Leagues:** Wiltshire Lge., Hellenic League to 2001
	Names: Vickers Armstrong 46-81,Supermarine 82-91 (merged 1992), Penhill Youth Centre 70-84, Swindon Athletic 84-89 (merged)
	Grounds: Supermarine: Vickers Airfield (until mid-1960s); Swindon Ath.: Merton 70-84; `Southbrook', Pinehurst Road 84-92

SWINDON SUPERMARINE

BEST LGE ATT.: **495** v Farnborough
LOWEST: **119** v Brackley Town

No.	Date	Comp	H/A	Opponents	Att:	Result	Goalscorers	Pos
1	Aug 16	Southern P.	A	Hitchin Town	271	W 1 - 0	Cook 63	
2	20		H	Clevedon Town	146	L 0 - 1		
3	23		H	Mangotsfield United	147	W 2 - 1	Allen 39 Boteng 44	6
4	25		A	Banbury United	336	W 5 - 1	Cook 37 Horgan 48 Taylor 55 Hopper 75 84	
5	30		H	Corby Town	165	L 1 - 4	Edenborough 14	6
6	Sept 2		A	Merthyr Tydfil	286	W 2 - 1	Taylor 56 Boateng 80	
7	6		H	Evesham United	207	D 1 - 1	Harris 444	
8	**13**	**F.A.C. 1Q**	**A**	**Thatcham Town**	**103**	**L 0 - 1**		
9	20		A	Tiverton Town	318	D 1 - 1	Draycott 33 (pen)	4
10	Oct 4		A	Brackley Town	207	W 3 - 0	Draycott 42 52 **Griffin** 80	2
11	8		H	Yate Town	197	W 3 - 0	Draycott 42 Henry 84 Hopper 89	
12	11		H	Stourport	171	D 1 - 0	Edenborough 86	2
13	**18**	**F.A.T.1Q**	**A**	**Bracknell Town**	**102**	**W 4 - 2**	**Edenborough 15 Griffin 40 85 Stanley 46**	
14	25		A	Cambridge City	361	W 1 - 0	**Griffin** 35	1
15	**Nov 1**	**F.A.T. 2Q**	**H**	**Maidstone United**	**333**	**W 2 - 0**	**Cook 44 Taylor 60**	
16	8		H	Hemel Hempstead	169	L 1 - 4	McKay 38	3
17	11		A	Bashley	238	D 2 - 2	**Griffin** 18 59	
18	15		A	Oxford City	258	W 2 - 1	Taylor 57 Davis 85 (og)	4
19	**22**	**F.A.T 3Q**	**H**	**Bromley**	**229**	**W 1 - 0**	**Stanley 23**	
20	29		H	Bedford Town	181	W 2 - 1	**Griffin** 49 Darby 87 (og)	
21	Dec 6		A	Halesowen Town	509	W 4 - 2	**Griffin** 24 81 Cook 28 65 (pen)	
22	**17**	**F.A.T. 1R**	**H**	**Eastbourne Borough**	**302**	**W 1 - 0**	**Edenborough 74**	
23	20		H	Farnborough	495	D 1 - 1	Cook 13	2
24	27		H	Banbury United	254	D 4 - 4	Henry 10 58 McKay 65 **Griffin** 73	3
25	Jan 1		A	Gloucester City	382	L 1 - 3	Henry 47	
26	**13**	**F.A.T 2R**	**A**	**Uxbridge**		**W 6 - 1**	**Allen 28 Griffin 32 Cook 36 74 Edenborough 57 Hopper 69**	
27	17		H	Merthyr Tydfil	259	D 0 - 0		5
28	24		A	Clevedon Town	168	W 2 - 1	Harris 19 Stanley 57	5
29	**31**	**F.A.T 3R**	**A**	**Ebbsfleet United**	**3750**	**L 0 - 2**		
30	Feb 21		A	Evesham United	138	L 0 - 1		12
31	28		H	Tiverton Town	178	W 1 - 0	Stanley 46	
32	Mar 7		A	Hemel Hempstead	354	D 1 - 1	Harris 49	10
33	11		H	Bashley	149	W 3 - 2	Harris 5 Henry 46 **Griffin** 84	
34	14		H	Oxford City	211	D 1 - 1	**Griffin** 12	9
35	17		A	Chippenham Town	464	L 1 - 3	Edenborough 40	
36	21		A	Rugby Town	220	D 0 - 0		10
37	24		A	Yate Town	179	D 0 - 0		
38	28		H	Halesowen Town	238	W 1 - 0	**Griffin** 37	9
39	30		A	Stourbridge	180	L 1 - 2	Draycott 60	
40	April 1		H	Hitchin Town	127	L 0 - 4		
41	4		A	Bedford Town	315	L 0 - 1		11
42	6		A	Mangotsfield United	124	L 1 - 2	Stanley N 82	
43	8		H	Brackley Town	119	D 4 - 4	Hopper 4 Harris 19 Draycott 66 Edenborough 84	
44	11		A	Corby Town	361	L 1 - 2	**Griffin** 78	13
45	13		H	Gloucester City	301	L 0 - 1		
46	15		H	Cambridge City	142	L 0 - 2		
47	18		A	Farnborough	1149	L 0 - 1		13
48	22		H	Rugby Town	147	W 3 - 1	Harris 21 Stanley N 63 **Griffin** 86	
49	25		H	Chippenham Town	353	L 1 - 3	Stanley 42	

Average Home Att: **207 (162)** **Goals** **73 66**

Best Position: 1st **Worst:** 13th

Goalscorers: Griffin 16, Cook 8, Edenborough 7, Stanley 7, Draycott 6, Harris 6, Henry 5, Hopper 5, Taylor 4, Allen 2, Boeteng 2, McKay 2, Horgan 1. Own Goals 2.

TIVERTON TOWN

Founded: 1920
Nickname: Tivvy

Manager: Martyn Rogers.

Club Colours: All Yellow

Change Colours: All white

Best Season- League: 8th Southern Premier 2004-2005

Ground address: Ladysmead, Bolham Road, Tiverton, Devon EX16 6SG

Tel No:01884 252 397 **Fax:** 01884 252 397

Capacity: 3,500 **Seats** 520 **Covered:** 2,300 **Floodlights:** Yes

Simple Directions: Leave M5 at jct 27. Take second Tiverton turning off A361 at end of dual carriageway. Turn left then over new roundabout and left at next roundabout. Ground is now on you right.

Midweek Home Matchday: Tuesday

Clubhouse: Two large bars with hot and cold food.

Club Shop: Yes, fully stocked.

CLUB PERSONNEL

Chairman: Dave Wright

Additional Directors/Committee:
Peter Buxton (Vice Chairman)
Kimm Smith (Treasurer)
Ramsay Findlay (Football Secretary)
John Smith (General Secretary)

Secretary: Ramsey Findlay.
35 Park Road, Tiverton,
Devon EX16 6AY
(H): 01884 256 341
(M): 07761 261 990
(F-club): 01884 252 397

Programme Editor: Alan Reidy
Email:
alanreidy@hotmail.com

CLUB STATISTICS

Record	**Attendance**:	3,00 v Leyton Orient F.A.Cup First Round Proper 1994-95
	Victory:	7-1 v Cirencester Town (Southern League) 2001
	Defeat:	2-6 v Stafford Rangers (A) Southern League 2001-2002
	Career Goalscorer:	Phil Everett
	Career Appearances:	Not known
	Transfer Fee Paid:	to Clevedon for Steve Peters
	Transfer Fee Received:	from Coventry City for Jason Smith
Senior Honours:	F.A.Vase Winners (2) Western League Champions (5)	
	Devon Senior Cup 55-56 65-6 East Devon Senior Cup ((7)	
	Southern League Cup 2006-07	
Previous Leagues	Devon & Exeter and Western.	

TIVERTON TOWN

BEST LGE ATT.: **446** v Gloucester City
LOWEST: **143** v Oxford City

No.	Date	Comp	H/A	Opponents	Att:	Result	Goalscorers	Pos
1	Aug 16	Southern P.	A	Halesowen Town	423	W 1 - 0	Pugh 76	
2	19		H	Gloucester City	446	D 2 - 2	Gardner 29 Rudge 80	
3	23		H	Farnborough	436	L 0 - 2		14
4	25		A	Clevedon Town	211	W 2 - 1	Knighton 27 47	
5	30		H	Bedford Town	316	L 0 - 2		13
6	Sept 2		A	Mangotsfield United	214	L 2 - 3	Pugh 16 73	
7	6		A	Hitchin Town	298	W 1 - 0	Pugh 90	10
8	**13**	**F.A.C. 1Q**	**A**	**Wimborne Town**	**389**	**W 1 - 0**	**Hopkinson 16**	
9	20		H	Swindon Supermarine	318	D 1 - 1	Knighton 41	10
10	**27**	**F.A.C.2Q**	**A**	**Oxford City**	**257**	**L 1 - 2**	**Wyatt 89**	
11	Oct 4		H	Merthyr Tydfil	305	L 0 - 1		14
12	7		A	Evesham United	132	D 1 - 1	Jarvis 29	
13	11		H	Yate Town	288	W 3 - 2	Knighton 56 Fraser 69 (pen) Jarvis 90	9
14	**18**	**F.A.T 1Q**	**H**	**North Leigh**	**344**	**W 5 - 2**	**WALSH 3 (23 34 38) Willis 56 Knighton 71**	
15	25		A	Bashley	285	W 3 - 0	**Walsh** 18 Saunders 38 Jarvis 86	8
16	**Nov 1**	**F.A.T. 2Q**	**A**	**Wealdstone**	**100**	**W 2 - 1**	**Jarvis 27 Walsh 71**	
17	8		H	Rugby Town	358	L 0 - 1		10
18	15		A	Hemel Hempstead	215	W 1 - 0	Hopkinson 11	8
19	18		H	Banbury United	253	W 2 - 0	**Walsh** 41 61	
20	**22**	**F.A.T 3Q**	**A**	**Bishop's Stortford**	**271**	**D 0 - 0**		
21	**26**	**F.A.T. 3Qr**	**H**	**Bishop's Stortford**	**290**	**W 1 - 0**	**Rudge 17**	
22	29		A	Cambridge City	301	L 0 - 1		8
23	Dec 6		H	Stourbridge	328	D 1 - 1	Wyatt 88	10
24	**16**	**F.A.T 1R**	**A**	**Bashley**	**165**	**D 2 - 2**	**Hopkinson 1 Walsh 22**	
25	20		A	Corby Town	240	W 4 - 1	Wyatt 36 Booth 52 **Walsh** 84 Jarvis 90	9
26	**23**	**F.A.T 1Rr**	**H**	**Bashley**	**436**	**W 2 - 1**	**Walsh 32 Jarvis 63**	
27	27		H	Clevedon Town	420	W 3 - 2	Wyatt 6 Faux Alex 48 Booth 73	
28	Jan 1		A	Chippenham Town	562	L 0 - 1		
29	**11**	**F.A.T 2R**	**H**	**Kettering Town**	**604**	**D 1 - 1**	**Hopkinson 77**	
30	**14**	**F.A.T 2Rr**	**A**	**Kettering Town**	**816**	**D 1 - 1***	**Rudge 83 Kettering Town won 4-1 on penalties**	
31	17		H	Mangotsfield United	328	D 0 - 0		10
32	20		A	Yate Town	127	D 0 - 0		
33	24		A	Gloucester City	285	L 1 - 2	**Walsh** 16	11
34	27		A	Merthyr Tydfil	289	W 2 - 1	Hopkinson 1 Gardner 71	
35	31		H	Evesham United	327	L 0 - 1		11
36	Feb 14		H	Bashley	333	W 2 - 1	Rudge 4 Mudge 27	9
37	21		H	Hitchin Town	375	W 3 - 1	Booth 12 **Walsh** 33 Mudge 45 (pen)	8
38	28		A	Swindon Supermarine	178	L 0 - 1		13
39	Mar 3		H	Oxford City	175	D 2 - 2	Saunders 42 Mudge 63	
40	7		A	Rugby Town	173	L 0 - 2		
41	14		H	Hemel Hempstead	408	D 1 - 1	Wyatt 5	13
42	17		A	Oxford City	194	L 0 - 3		
43	21		A	Banbury United	308	W 3 - 0	Jarvis 9 27 Mudge 72	12
44	24		H	Brackley Town	248	W 2 - 1	Mudge 18 Saunders 57	
45	28		A	Stourbridge	228	L 0 - 3		12
46	31		A	Farnborough	524	L 0 - 1		
47	April 4		H	Cambridge City	292	L 1 - 2	Knighton 69 (pen)	13
48	7		H	Halesowen Town	143	W 3 - 0	Pugh 27 Gardner 62 Knighton 85	
49	11		A	Bedford Town	294	D 1 - 1	Knighton 86 (pen)	12
50	13		H	Chippenham Town	301	L 1 - 2	Knighton 32 (pen)	
51	18		H	Corby Town	372	L 0 - 2		12
52	25		A	Brackley Town	210	W 2 - 1	Connery 66 Hopkinson 90	12

Average Home Att: **351 (314)** **Goals** **67 59**

Best Position: 8th **Worst:** 14th

Goalscorers: Walsh 12, Knighton 9, Jarvis 8, Hopkinson 6, Mudge 5, Pugh 5, Wyatt 5, Rudge 4, Booth 3, Gardner 3, Saunders 3, Connery 1, Faux Alex 1, Fraser 1, Willis 1.

TRURO CITY

Founded: 1889
Nickname: City

CLUB PERSONNEL

Chairman: Kevin Heaney
Additional Committee:
Chris Webb (Vice Chairman)
Marina Heaney

Secretary: Ian Anear.
31 Tremayne Close,
Devoran,Truro, Cornwall
TR3 6QE
(H): 01872 862 366
(B): 01872 225 400
(B/F): 01872 225 402
ian.anear@gmail.com

Programme Editor: As Secretary.

Manager: Sean McCarthy.

Club Colours: All white.

Change Colours: All gold.

Best Season - League: 1st Southern League Division 1 Midlands 2008-09

Ground address: Treyew Road, Truro, Cornwall TR1 2TH

Tel: 01872 225400/278853. Fax: 01872 225 400.

Simple Directions: Leave M5 at Junction 30 and join A30. Travel via Okehampton, Launceston, & Bodmin. At end of dua carriageway (windmills on right hand side) take left hand turning signposted Truro. After approximately 7 miles turn right at traffic lights, cross over three roundabouts following signs for Redruth. Approximately 500 metres after roundabout marked 'Arch Hill' ground is situated on left hand side.

Midweek Home Matchday: Tuesday

Clubhouse: Yes.

CLUB STATISTICS

Record
Attendance: 1,400 v Aldershot F.A.Vase.
Career Goalscorer: Not Known.
Career Appearances: Not Known.

Senior Honours:
South Western 1960-61, 69-70, 92-93, 95-96, 97-98.
Cornwall Senior Cup x 15.
Western League Premier 2007-08. Division One 2006-07.
FA Vase Winners 2006-07. Southern League Division One Champions 2008-09.

Previous Leagues: Cornwall County. Plymouth & District.
Cornwall Senior Cup (15). South Western 1951-75, 78-2006.
Cornwall Combination 1975-78. Western 2006-08.

The ZAMARETTO League

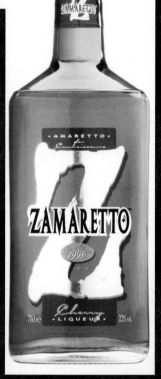

A.F.C.SUDBURY

Founded: 1999
Nickname: Yellows

CLUB PERSONNEL
Chairman: Keith Morris.
Additional Directors/Committee:
Brian Tatum (Finance/Co. Secretary), Peter Scott (Vice Chairman), Danny Crosbie, Michael Mills, Mark Pearman, David Webb.

Secretary: Davis Webb.
6 Melford Road, Sudbury,
Suffolk CO10 1LS
(H): 01787 372 352
(M): 07885 327 510
dave-afc@supanet.com

Programme Editor: Liz Wood
Email:
liz@lizcollins1234.wanadoo.co.uk

Manager: Nicky Smith.

Club Colours: Yellow with blue flash/blue with yellow flash/yellow.

Change: Red with white flash/red with white flash/red.

Best Seasons- League: 2nd Isthmian Division One North 2007-08.

Ground address: Kingsmarsh Stadium, Brundon Lane, Sudbury, Suffolk CO10 1LX

Tel No: 01787 376 213

Club Website: www.afcsudbury.com

Capacity: 2,500 **Seats**: 200 **Covered**: 1500 **Floodlights**: Yes

Simple Directions: Follow Halstead/Chelmsford road from Sudbury centre for a mile. First right after railway bridge at foot of steep hill and first right again after left hand bend.

Midweek Home Matchday: Tuesday

Clubhouse: Match days and Training Evenings **Club Shop:** Yes

Local Radio: BBC Suffolk Radio

Local Press: Suffolk Free Press East Anglian Daily Times

CLUB STATISTICS

Record	**Attendance:** 1,800	
	Career Goalscorer: Gary Bennett - 172	
	Career Appearances: Paul Betson - 376	
Record Transfer Fee	**Paid**: Not known.	**Received:** Not known.
Senior Honours:	Eastern Counties League 2000-01, 01-02, 02-03, 03-04, 04-05.	
	Suffolk Premier Cup 2002-03-04	
Previous Leagues:	Eastern Counties 1999-2006. Isthmian 2006-08.	
Names:	Sudbury Town (1874) and Sudbury Wanderers (1958) merged in 1999	

Back Row (L-R): Assistant Manager Chris Tracey, Danny Shipton, Steve Joyce, Curtis Haynes-Brown, Ollie Blackwell, Danny Brown, Marcus Hunt, Sheridan Driver, Jamie Ricks, Danny Stokes, manager Nicky Smith.
Front: James Rowe, Neil Cogger, Sam Clarke, Liam Jones, Gareth Heath, Luke Hammond, Nathan Speed
Photo: Suffolk Free Press.

ARLESEY TOWN

Founded: 1891
Nickname: The Blues

CLUB PERSONNEL

Chairman: Manny Cohen.
Additional Committee:
David Dainton (Vice Chairman)
Ken Gear (Fixtures Secretary),
Maurice Crouch (President),
Jeff Brown (Treasurer),
Trevor Flint (Press Officer).
Secretary: Keith Broughton
9, Davis Row, Arlesey
Bedfordshire SG15 6RB
(H): 01462 734 324
(M): 07786 275 929

Programme Editor: Tony Smith
cricketfants@sky.com

Manager: Lee Cowley.

Club Colours: Light & dark blue/dark blue/dark blue.

Change: Yellow & black/black/black.

Best Seasons - League: 8th Isthmian Division One North 2003-2004.

Ground address: Chateau Roux Stadium, Hitchin Road, Arlesey,Beds. SG15 6RD

Tel: 01462 734 504. Fax: 01462 734 504

Capacity: 2,920 **Seats**: 150 **Covered**: 600 **Floodlights**: Yes

Simple Directions: A1 take A507 to Shefford, at 3rd roundabout turn left, 1st left follow road through village, ground 1.5 miles on left.

Midweek Home Matchday: Tuesday

Clubhouse: Open daily 7- 11.00, Sat 12p.m.-11.30, Sun 12-2.30 7-11.30

Members bar ,wide screen for Sky TV, function suite and hot food available.

Club Shop: Yes. Old programmes, leisure wear, replica shirts and various souvenirs

CLUB STATISTICS

Record	**Attendance:** 2,000 v Luton TownReserves Beds Senior Cup 1906
	Career Goalscorer: Not known.
	Career Appearances: Gary Marshall
Record Transfer Fee	**Paid**: None.
	Received: Undisclosed for Dave Kitson from Cambridge
Senior Honours:	FA Vase Winners 1994-5; Isthmian League (Ryman) Div 3 Champions 00-01, Beds Sen Cup 65-6 78-9 96-7, S Mids Prem Div (5) Utd Co Prem Div 84-85,
Previous Leagues:	**Leagues:** Biggleswade & Dist.; Beds. Co. (S. Mids) 22-26 ,27-28; Parthenon; London 58-60; Utd Co's 1933-36 1982-92. Spartan South Midlands 1992-2000. Isthmian 2000-04, 06-08. Southern 2004-07.

NB: UNFORTUNATELY A RECENT PHOTO WAS NOT AVAILABLE AT THE TIME OF GOING TO PRESS.

ATHERSTONE TOWN

Formed: 2004
Nickname: The Adders

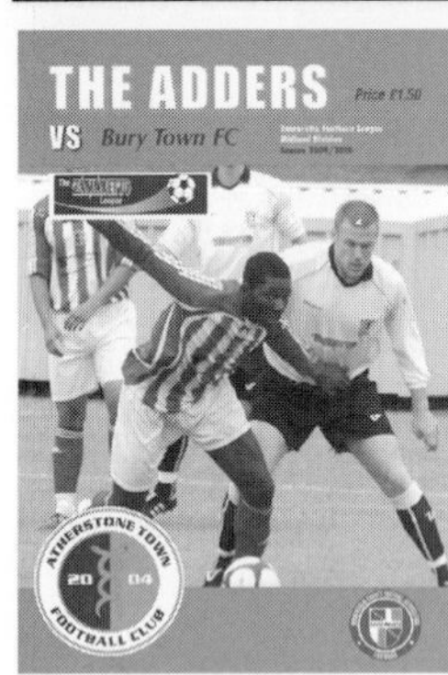

Manager: Daren Fulford.

Club Colours: Red & white stripes/black/red.

Change: Yellow/black/black.

Best Seasons - League: 1st Midland Alliance 2007-08.

Ground address: Sheepy Road, Atherston, Warwickshire CV9 1HD.

Tel: 01827 717 829

Simple Directions: From junction 10 M42 join the A5 towards Nuneaton/Atherstone (South). After 3.7 miles at roundabout sign posted B4116 SheepyMagna/Twycross turn left into Holly Lane. At next roundabout turn right into Rowland Way, in 300 yards past Gypsy Lane turn through red gates on the right into club carpark.

Midweek Home Matchday: Tuesday

Clubhouse: Yes.

CLUB PERSONNEL

Chairman: Adrian Burr.

Additional Directors:
Graham Reed
Howard Kerry

Secretary: Peter Lowe.
83 Claremont Road,
Tamworth B79 6EW
(M) 07738 604 391

Programme Editor: As Secretary.

CLUB STATISTICS

Record	**Attendance:** Not known.
	Career Goalscorer: Not known.
	Career Appearances: Not known.
Transfer Fee	**Paid**: Not known.
	Received: Not known.
Senior Honours:	Midland Alliance 2007-08.
	Midland Combintion 2005-06. Division One 2004-05.
Previous	**Leagues:** Midland Combination 2004-06.
	Midland Alliance 2006-08.

Front Row (L-R): Jordan Brown, Conor Fulford, Lyndon Weller, Steve Johnson (youth/reserves physio), Shylo Thomas, Stuart Hendrie, Chris Woodhall. **Middle:** John Cole (sports therapist), Kieran Robinson, Will Holyland, Adam Henchcliffe, Nathan Woakes, Dave Clarke, Chris Sturridge-Packer, Grant Roscorla, Giavanni Dainty, Wayne Chapman (youth/reserves coach). **Front:** Mark Grainger (youth/reserves manager), Shawn Boothe, Luke Edwards, Dave Haywood (assistant manager), Daren Fulford (manager), Niki Preston, Tom Weale, Brendan Murphy, Dave Brandon (coach).
Not present for photocall: Marcus Ebdon, Matt Brown, Dean Rathbone, Luke Keen

AYLESBURY UNITED

Founded: 1897
Nickname: The Ducks

CLUB PERSONNEL
Chairman: Graham Read
Additional Directors/Committee:
John Newman (Vice Chairman), Ken Turnbull, Chris Dann, Luke Brown, Ron Syratt, Brian Metcalf, Martin Shaw, Andy Foster,Wendy Brandon.

Secretary: Steve Baker.
10 Miles End, Aylesbury,
Bucks HP21 8PR
(M) 07768 353 265

Programme Editor: Luke Brown
luke@aylesburyunited.co.uk

Manager: Tony Thompson

Club Colours: Green & white/green/white.

Change Colours: All tangerine.

Best Season - League: 20th Conference 1988-89.

Ground address: Leighton Town FC, Lake Street, Leighton Buzzard LU7 1RX

Capacity: 2,800 **Seats**:155 **Covered**: 300 **Floodlights**: Yes

Simple Directions: From bypass (A505) take A4146 (Billington Rd) towards Leighton Buzzard, straight overfirst roundabout then straight over mini-r'bout. After aprox 50 yards take first left into car park which is opposite the Morrisons petrol stattion. Half a mile from Leighton Buzzard (BR) station. Buses from Luton, Aylesbury and Milton Keynes.

Midweek Home Matchday: Wednesday

Clubhouse: Normal licensing hours.Snack bar on matchdays - full range of hot snacks & drinks

Club Shop: No

Local Radio: BBC Three Counties Mix96

Local Press: Bucks Herald and Bucks Advertiser

CLUB STATISTICS

Record Attendance :	6,000 v England 1988
Career Goalscorer:	Cliff Hercules 301
Career Appearances:	Cliff Hercules 651+18
Record Transfer Fee	**Paid**: £15,000 to Northampton Town for Glenville Donegal 1990
	Received: Undisclosed fee for Jermaine Darlington from Q.P.R. 1999
Senior Honours:	Southern League 87-88 Mids Div R-up 84-85 Southern Div R-up 79-80 . Isthmian R-up 1998-99.
	Berks & Bucks Sen Cup (4) Isth Cup 94-95
Previous Leagues:	Bucks Contiguous 1897-1903, South Eastern 03-07 Spartan 07-51 Delphian 51-63 Athenian 63-76,
	Southern 76-88 GMV Conference 88-89 Conference 88-99 Isthmian 89-2004
Grounds:	Printing Works Ground 1897-1903 Wendover Rd /The Stadium Turnfurlong Rd 35-85 (same ground -name changed).
	Shared grounds 85-86

BARTON ROVERS

Founded: 1898
Nickname: Rovers

Manager: Gary Fitzgerald.

Club Colours: Royal blue and white stripes with royal blue reverse/royal/royal with white bands.

Change Colours: Yellow with black trim/black/yellow with white bands.

Best Season - League: 8th Southern Division One East 2004-05

Ground address: Sharpenhoe Road, Barton-le-Clay, Bedford, MK45 4SD

Tel No: 01582 707 772. Fax: 01582 882 398.

Capacity: 4,000 **Seats**:160 **Covered:** 1,120 **Floodlights**: Yes

Simple Directions: M1 Jct 12, from London exit turn right, take 2nd right through Harlington and Sharpenhoe. Entrance to ground 44 yds on right down concrete drive entering village. 4.5 miles from Harlington (BR), 6 miles from Luton (BR), good bus or taxis service from Luton.

Midweek Home Matchday: Tuesday

Clubhouse: Yes. **Club Shop:** Yes.

Local Radio: Radio Chiltern, Radio Beds & Three Counties Radio.

Local Press: Luton News, The Herald and Beds on Sunday

CLUB PERSONNEL

Chairman: Malcolm Bright

Committee:
Darron Whilley (Vice Chairman),
Richard Carey,
Nick Rhodes (Press Secretary),
John Gray Jnr, Julie Gray,
Darrell Thornton, Paul Reardon,
Chris Larkin, Gary Hanley.

Secretary: Chris Sterry.
13 Ashwell Avenue, Sundon Park, Luton, Beds. LU3 3AU
(H): 01582 751 013
(F): 01582 751 013
(M): 07745 217 175

Programme Editor:
Nick Rhodes
nicholas.rhodes@tesco.net

CLUB STATISTICS

Record	**Attendance:** 1,900 v Nuneation Borough 4th. Q.Rd F.A.Cup 1976
	Career Goalscorer:Richard Camp 152 1989-1998
	Career Appearances::Tony McNally 598 (1988-2005)
Record Transfer Fee	**Paid**: £1,000 to Hitchin Town for for B.Baldry 1980
	Received: £1,000 from Bishop's Stortford for B.Baldry 1981
Senior Honours:	Isthmian Lge Div 2 R-Up 94-95South Midlands League (8) ;
	Beds Senior Cup (7), R-up (5); Beds Premier Cup 95-96, R-up (5)
Previous Leagues:	Luton & District 1947-1954 South Midlands 1954-1979 Isthmian1979-2004

Photo: Gordon Whittington.

BEACONSFIELD SYCOB

Re-Formed 1994
Nickname: The Rams

Manager: Joe Mitchell.

Club Colours: Red & white quarters/black/red & white.

Change Colours: Yellow/yellow/yellow.

Best Season - League: 4th Southern League Division 1 South & West 2008-09.

Ground address: Holloways Park, Windsor Road, Beaconsfield, Bucks. HP9 2SE

Tel. 01494 676 868

Simple Directions: Leave junction 2 of the M40, take the A355 towards Slough. 50 yards off the roundabout on the A355, take the slip road on the right with sign to the Club. Turn right through the gate and the clubhouse is 200 yards on the right.

Midweek Home Matchday: Monday

Clubhouse: Open evenings & matchdays. Full facilities for bookings.

CLUB PERSONNEL

Chairman: Fred Deanus.
Additional Directors:
Paul Hughes (Vice Chairman)
Robin Woolman

Secretary: Robin Woolman
13 East Crescent, Windsor,
Berks. SL4 5LD
(H): 01753 853 607
(F): 01753 865 081
(M): 07778 832 019

Programme
Editor: Stephen Cleare
spvcleare@hotmail.com

CLUB STATISTICS

Record	**Attendance:** 300 v Chesham United, Berks & Bucks Cup 1985.
	Career Goalscorer: Allan Arthur.
	Career Appearances: Allan Arthur.
Transfer Fee	**Paid**: Not Known
	Received: Not Known
Senior Honours:	Spartan South Midlands 2000-01, 03-04, 07-08.
	Berks & Bucks Senior Trophy 2003-04.
Previous	**Names:** Slough YCOB and Beaconsfield United merged in 1994.
	Leagues: Spartan South Midlands 1994-2004, 07-08. Southern 2004-07.

BEDWORTH UNITED

Founded: 1896
Nickname: Greenbacks

CLUB PERSONNEL
Chairman: David Taylor
Additional Directors:
Roy Whitehead (President)
Bill Haywood (Treasurer)
Graham Bloxham, Steven Collins, Bob Howe, Scott Hennerley, John Roberts, Glen Moran.

Secretary: Graham Bloxham
43 Mount Pleasant Road,
Bedworth, Warwicks.
CV12 8EX
(H): 02476 317 940
(M): 07748 640 613

Programme Editor: David Taylor.
david@sas02.co.uk

Manager: Liam O'Neill.

Club Colours: Green/green/green with white trim.

Change Colours: All yellow.

Best Seasons- League: 5th Southern League Premier 1982-83.

Ground address: The Oval, Coventry Road, Bedworth CV12 8NN

Tel/Fax No: 02476 314 752

Capacity: 7,000 **Seats**:300 **Covered**: 300 **Floodlights**:Yes

Simple Directions: M6 jct 3, into Bedworth on B4113 Coventry to Bedworth road, ground 200yds past Bedworth Leisure Centre on this road.Coaches should park at the Leisure Centre. Buses from Coventry and Nuneaton pass ground. Nerarest BR is Bedworth (5 mins walk)

Midweek Home Matchday: Tuesday

Clubhouse: Social club open every day 7.30-11pm & w/e noon-3pm. Hot and cold bar food

Club Shop: Full range of souvenirs & programmes. Contact : Ron Kemp & Paul Sylvester.

Local Radio: Mercia Sound BBC CWR

Local Press: Heartland Evening News, Weekly Tribune, Bedworth Echo and Coventry Evening Telegraph

CLUB STATISTICS

Record — **Attendance:** 5,127 v Nuneatyon Boro.Southern Lg. Midland Div 23.02.82
Career Goalscorer:Peter Spacey 1949-1969
Career Appearances: Peter Spacey

Record Transfer Fee — **Paid**: £1,750 to Hinckley Town for Colin Taylor 1991-1992
Received: £30,000 from Plymouuth Argyle for Richard Landon
Senior Honours: Birmingham Comb.(2) 48-50, Birmingham Snr Cup(3) 78-79 80-82, Midland Floodlit Cup 81-82 92-93

Previous — **Leagues:** Birmingham Comb. 47-54; West Mids (at first Birmingham) Lg 54-72 West Midlands.
Name: Bedworth Town 47-68
Ground: British Queen Ground 11-39

BIGGLESWADE TOWN

Founded: 1874
Nickname: The Waders

CLUB PERSONNEL

Chairman:
Maurice Dorrington

Additional Directors:
B Doggett, Mick Jarvis, Brian Mader, David Doggett, Annette Dorrington, R J Dorrington, Terry Baldwin, D Simpson, Barry Skinner.

Secretary: Andy McDonnell.
2 Hereford Grove,
Biggleswade SG18 8HX.
(M) 07879 802 105

Programme Editor: David Simpson.
simpson_david@hotmail.co.uk

Manager: Chris Nunn

Club Colours: Green & white stripes/green/white.

Change Colours: Sky blue and white stripes/sky blue/sky blue.

Best Season - League: 1st Spartan South Midlands Premier Division 2008-09

Ground address: The Carlsberg Stadium, Langford Road, Biggleswade SG18 9JJ.

Simple Directions: Leave the A1 at the Sainsbury Roundabout at Biggleswade and head for the town centre. At the roundabout adjacent to St. Andrews Church, take the second exit and proceed to traffic lights. Turn right onto Hitchin Street and follow the road until you pass under the A1. Ground is 100 yards on the right.

Midweek Home Matchday: Tuesday

Clubhouse: Open matchdays.

CLUB STATISTICS

Record	**Attendance:** 2,000
	Career Goalscorer: Not known.
	Career Appearances: Ray Fitzgerald.
	Transfer Fee Paid: Not known.
	Received: Not known.
Senior Honours:	Spartan South Midlands Premier Champions 2008-09.
Previous	**Leagues:** Biggleswade & District. Bedford & District. Spartan South Midlands 1951-55, 80-2009. Eastern Counties 1955-63. United Counties 1963-80.

BROMSGROVE ROVERS

Founded: 1885
Nickname: Rovers or Greens

CLUB PERSONNEL

Chairman: Tom Herbert

Company Secretary: S Daniels.

Secretary: Brian Hewings.
21 Carol Avenue,
Bromsgrove B61 8RN.
(H): 01527 831 182

Programme Editor: Mr & Mrs A Jones
andybrfc1jones@aol.com

Manager: J Snape.

Club Colours: Green & white stripes/green/green.

Change Colours: Yellow with green trim/yellow/yellow.

Best Season - League: 2nd Conference 1992-1993

Ground address: Victoria Ground, Birmingham Rd, Bromsgrove, Worcs. B61 0DR
Tel No: 01527 876949. Fax: 01527 876 265.

Capacity: 4,893 **Seats**:394 **Covered**: 1,344 **Floodlights**:Yes

Simple Directions: Ground is situated on the north side of Bromsgrove on the Birmingham Road, off the A38 Bromsgrove by pass. The M5 and M42 join theA38 to the north of the town making it easy to get to the ground without havingto go into town.

Midweek Home Matchday: Tuesday

Clubhouse: Victoria Club (01527 878260) - Serves hot & cold food. Big screenTV, pool table & darts. Open matchdays and week-day evenings.

Club Shop: Selling replica clothing & souvenirs. Contact Tracy Kite (01527 876949)

Local Radio: Radio Wyvern

Local Press: Bromsgrove Advertiser and Bromsgrove Standard

CLUB STATISTICS

Record
Attendance: 7,389 v Worcester City 1957
Career Goalscorer:Chris Hanks 238 1983-1984
Career Appearances: Shaun O'Meara 763 1975-1994

Record Transfer Fee
Paid: £3,000 to Solihull Borough for Recky Carter
Received: Undisclosed from Peterbrough United for Scott Cooksey Dec 93

Senior Honours:
Vauxhall Conference League Cup 1994-95, 95-96. Southern League Premier 1991-92. League Cup 1992-93. Midland Division 1985-86. Worcester Senior Cup (8). Birmingham Senior Cup 1946-47.

Previous:
Leagues: Birmingham League 1898-08, 53-65. Birmingham Combination 1908-53. West Midlands 1965-72. Southern League - Northern Div. 1973-79. Midland Div. 1979-86. Premier Div. 1986-92. GMVC 1992-97. Southern 1997-01. Midland Alliance 2001-02.
Grounds: Old Station Road 1885-87, Recreation Ground 1887-88, Churchfields 1888-97,Well Lane 1897-1910.

Back Row (L-R): James Smith, Mark Benbow, Wayne Dyer, Chris McHale, Neil Davis, Joe Williams, Chris Taylor, Tim Clarke, Dean Coleman, Daire Doyle, Carl Heeley, Riad Erraji, Kevin Banner, Nigel Clement (Coach).
Front Row: Ron Mellor (Coach), John Snape (Player / Coach), Liam McDonald, Delton Francis, Nathan Lamey, Tom Herbert (Chairman), Rod Brown (Manager), Mark Taylor (Captain), Richard Burgess, Paul Carty, Paul Lloyd, Steve Ball (Physio).

BURNHAM

Founded: 1878
Nickname: The Blues

CLUB PERSONNEL

Chairman: Malcolm Higton.

Additional Committee:
R. H. Saunders (Vice Chairman/Treasurer)
T. R. Saunders, M. J. Boxall,
K.W. Ambrose.

Secretary: Trevor Saunders.
61 Disraeli Crescent,
High Wycombe,
Bucks.
HP13 5EW
(H): 01494 447 604
(M): 07711 856 780

Programme Editor: Michael Boxall.
saunderstrevor@hotmail.com

Manager: Jamie Jarvis.

Club Colours: Blue & white quarters /blue/blue.

Change Colours: Red & black quarters/black/red.

Best Season - League: 3rd Southern Division One West 2006-07

Ground address: The Gore, Wymers Wood Road, Burnham, Slough SL1 8JB

Tel No: 07771 677 337. Fax: 01628 668 654.

Capacity: 2,500 **Floodlights**: Yes

Simple Directions: North west of village centre, two miles from Burnham BR station, two miles from M4 junction 7 & 5 miles from M40 junction 2,100yds north of Gore crossroads - fork right into Wymers Wood Rd and ground is immediately on right.

Midweek Home Matchday: Tuesday

Clubhouse: Open every evening and lunch times at weekends.

Club Shop: Yes.

Local Radio: Star FM, BBC THames Valley and Swan F.M.

Local Press: Slough Observer and Buckingham Advertiser

CLUB STATISTICS

Record	**Attendance:**	2,380 v Halesowen Town F.A.Vase 2.4.83.
Career	**Goalscorer:**	Fraser Hughes 65 1969-1970
Career	**Appearances:**	Not Known
Record	**Victory:**	18-0 v High Duty Alloys 1970-1971
	Received:	1-10 v Ernest Turner Sports 1963-1964
Senior Honours:	Athenian Lg R-up (2) , Hellenic Lg 75-76 98-99 Div 1 R-up 72-73, Lg Cup 75-76 98-99, Div 1 Cup 71-72,	
Previous Leagues:	**Leagues:** Hellenic 71-77; Athenian 77-84; London Spartan 84-85; Southern 85-95; Hellenic 95-99	
	Name: Burnham & Hillingdon 1985-87 **Ground:** Baldwin Meadow (until 20's)	

BURY TOWN

Founded: 1872
Nickname: The Blues

CLUB PERSONNEL
Chairman: Russell Ward
Committee:
Adrian Lewis (Vice Chairman),
Wendy Turner (Secretary),
Andy Gould,
Trevor Collins (Director of Football),
Doug Howlett, David Scarfe,
Philip Smailes, Bernard Turner,
Brian Wadsworth,
Christopher Ward.

Secretary:
Mrs Wendy Turner
64 Winthrop Road, Bury St. Edmunds, Suffolk IP33 3UF
(H/F): 01284 753 688
(M): 07795 661 959

Programme Editor: Christopher Ward
cpward@burytownfc.co.uk

Manager: Richard Wilkins

Club Colours: All blue.

Change Colours: All red.

Best Season- League: 4th Southern Division South 1988-89.

Ground address: Ram Meadow, Cotton Lane, Bury St. Edmunds IP33 1XP

Tel: 01284 754721

Capacity: 3,500 **Seats**: 300 **Covered**: 1,500 **Floodlights**: Yes

Simple Directions: Follow signs to town centre from A14. At second roundabout take first left into Northgate Street then left into Mustow Street at T junction at lights and left again into Cotton Lane. Ground is 350 yards on right.

Midweek Home Matchday: Tuesday

Clubhouse: Match days and training nights **Club Shop:** Yes

Local Radio: BBC Suffilk or SGR FM

Local Press: East Anglian Daily Times, Bury Fre Press and The Green Un.

CLUB STATISTICS

Record	**Attendance:** 2,500 v Enfiled F.A.Cup 1986
	Career Goalscorer: Doug Tooley
	Career Appearances: Doug Tooley
	Transfer Fee Paid: £1,500 to Chelmsford City for Mel Springett
	Transfer Fee Received: £5,500 from Ipswich Town for Simon MIlton
Senior Honours:	Eastern Counties Champions 1963-1964.
	Suffolk Premier Cup (9)
Previous Leagues:	Norfolk & Suffolk Border. Essex & Suffolk Border. Eastern Co. 1935-64, 76-87, 97-06.
	Metropolitan 1964-71. Southern 1971-76, 87-97.
	Isthmian 2006-08.
Names:	Bury St.Edmunds 1895-1902 Bury United 1902-1906 Bury Town (1995) Ltd

Back Row (L-R): Michael Steward, Gavin Johnson, Sam Nunn, Marcus Garnham, Dean Greygoose, Roscoe Hipperson, Lee Smith, Liam Barrett, Steve Bugg.
Front Row: Ryan Foster, Scott Chaplin, Sam Reed, Lee Reed, Stuart Walker, James Patterson.

CHESHAM UNITED

Founded: 1919
Nickname: The Generals

CLUB PERSONNEL

Chairman:
Charles Manchester

Additional Directors:
A. Calder, M. Dickson, M. Dragisic, R. Goldhawk, M. Gould, M.Warrick, B. McCarthy.

Secretary: Alan Lagden
5 Mill Close, Chesham, Buckinghamshire HP5 1QL.
(H): 01494 782 022

Programme Editor: Dave Jeffries
dave@chesslive.org.uk

Manager: Andy Leese.

Club Colours: Claret/sky blue/sky blue.

Change Colours: Yellow/black/yellow.

Best Season - League: 1st Isthmian Premier 1992-93.

Ground: The Meadow, Amy Lane, Amersham Rd, Chesham, Bucks. HP5 1NE

Tel No: 01494 783 964 **Fax**: 01494 794 244

Capacity: 5,000 **Seats**: 284 **Covered**: 2,500 **Floodlights:** Yes

Simple Directions: M25 Jct 18 to Amersham. A416 to Chesham go down to roundabout at foot of Amersham Hill then sharp left.

Midweek Home Matchday: Tuesday

Clubhouse: Open every evening and matchdays. Available for hire.

Club Shop: Open matchdays (Mike Elliott)

CLUB STATISTICS

Record	**Attendance**: 5,000 v Cambridge United 3rd Rd F.A.Cup 05.12.79
	Victory: Not known
	Defeat: Not known
	Goalscorer: John Willis
	Career Appearances: Martin Baguley 600+
Record Transfer Fee	**Paid**: Undisclosed
	Received: £22,000 from Oldham Athletic for Fitz Hall
Senior Honours:	F.A.Amateur Cup R- Up 1967-68 Isthmian League Champions 1992-93
	Div 1 86-87 96-97 Berks & Bucks Senior Cup (12) R-up (2)
Previous Leagues	Spartan 17-47 Corinthian 47-63 Athenian 63-73 Isthmian 73-2004

NB: UNFORTUNATELY A RECENT PHOTO WAS NOT AVAILABLE AT THE TIME OF GOING TO PRESS.

HITCHIN TOWN

Founded: 1865
Re-formed: 1928
Nickname: Canaries

Manager: Colin Payne.

Club Colours: Yellow/green/green

Change Colours: Green/yellow/yellow

Best Season - League: 2nd Isthmian League 1968-69

Ground address: Top Field, Fishponds Road, Hitchin SG5 1NJ

Tel No: 01462 459 028 (matchdays only)

Capacity: 5,000 Seats: 500 Covered:1,250 Floodlights: Yes

Simple Directions: On A505 near town centre opposite a large green.

One mile from Hitchin BR.

Midweek Home Matchday: Tuesday

Clubhouse: Open every day.

Club Shop: Yes

Local Radio: Chiltern, BBC Three Counties

Local Press: Hitchin Comet, Herts on Sunday

CLUB PERSONNEL

Chairman: Terry Barratt.

Additional Directors/Committee:
Andy Melvin (Managing Director), Mark Burke (Company Secretary), Roy Izzard, Neil Jensen(Media officer), Mrs Chris Morrell(Catering Manager), John Morrell, Frank King(Supporters Club Chairman), Chris Newbold(Supporters Club Secretary) Fred Andrews(Com. Manager), Stewart Virgo (Supporters Trust).

Secretary: Roy Izzard.
2 Bedford Road, Ickleford,
Hitchin,Herts SG5 3XH
(H): 01462 433 171
(B): 01462 454 545
(M): 07803 202 498

Programme Editor: Neil Jensen
neil.jensen@db.com

CLUB STATISTICS

Record

Attendance : 7,878 v Wycombe Wanderers. F.A.Amateur Cup 3rd Rd 8.02.56
Victory: 13-0 v Cowley 0 and v R.A.F.Uxbridge both Spartan Lg.1929-30
Defeat: 0-10 v Kingstonian (A) 65-66 and v Slough Town (A) 79-80
Career Goalscorer: Paul Giggle 214
Career Appearances: **In Career**: Paul Giggle 769 (68-86)
Transfer Fee Paid: £2,000 To Potton United for Ray Seeking
Received: £30,000 from Cambridge United for Zema Abbey. Jan 2000

Senior Honours:
A.F.A.Senior Cup 1931-32. London Senior Cup 1969-70.
Isthmian Division 1 Champions 1992-93.
Herts Senior Cup (x19 - a record .

Previous Leagues:
Spartan 1928-39. Herts & Middx. 1939-45. Athenian 1945-63.
Isthmian 1964-2004.

LEIGHTON TOWN

Founded: 1885
Nickname: Reds

CLUB PERSONNEL
Chairman: Iain McGregor
Additional Directors/Committee:
Bruce Warner (Vice Chairman),
Roy Parker (Fixture Secretary),
Andrew Parker ,
Alec Irvine (Treasurer),
James Ullyett, Terry Migliori, Jim Snee,
Jamie Green, Vicky Janes, Chris Blair.

Secretary: Jim Snee
32 Brooklands Avenue,
Leighton Buzzard, LU7 3QX.
(H): 01525 382 409
(M): 07912 678 038

Programme Editor: James Ullyett
james_ullyett@hotmail.com

Manager: Sean Downey.

Club Colours: Red & white stripes/red/red

Change Colours: Yellow/black/yellow.

Best Season - League: 8th Southern Lge Div. 1 West/Midland 2005-06/2008-09.

Ground address: Lake Street, Leighton Buzzard, Beds LU7 1RX.

Tel: 01525 373 311.

Capacity: 2,800 **Seats**:155 **Covered**: 300 **Floodlights**: Yes

Simple Directions: From bypass (A505) take A4146 (Billington Rd) towards Leighton Buzzard, straight overfirst roundabout then straight over mini-r'bout. After aprox 50 yards take first left into car park which is opposite the Morrisons petrol stattion. Half a mile from Leighton Buzzard (BR) station. Buses from Luton, Aylesbury and Milton Keynes.

Midweek Home Matchday: Tuesday

Clubhouse: Normal licensing hours.Snack bar on matchdays - full range of hot snacks & drinks

Club Shop: No

Local Radio: Chiltern, Mix 96.

Local Press: Leighton Buzzard Observer, The Citizen

CLUB STATISTICS

Record
Attendance: 1,522 v Aldershot Town Isthmian Div 3 30.01.93
Career Goalscorer: Not Known. **Career Appearances**: Not known.
Transfer Fee Paid: Not known.
Transfer Fee Received: Not known.
Victory: 1-0 v Met Railway 1925-26 (H) Spartan League
Defeat: 0-12 v Headington United (A) 18.10.47 Spartan Lreague.

Senior Honours:
South Midlands League Champions 1966-67, 91-92. Isthmian League Div.2 Champions 2003-04.
Beds Senior Cup 1926-27, 67-68, 68-69, 69-70, 92-93.

Previous Leagues:
Leagues: Leighton & Dist; South Midlands 22-24 26-29 46-54 55-56 76-92;
Spartan 22-53 67-74; United Counties 74-76. Isthmian
Name: Leighton United 1922-63
Ground: Wayside

NB: UNFORTUNATELY A RECENT PHOTO WAS NOT AVAILABLE AT THE TIME OF GOING TO PRESS.

MARLOW

Founded: 1870
Nickname: The Blues

CLUB PERSONNEL

Chairman: Terry Staines.

Additional Directors: Ray Frith.

Secretary: Paul Burdell.
69 Wycombe Road,
Marlow,
SL7 3HZ
(H): 01628 890 540
(M): 07961 145 949

Programme Editor: Terry Staines
terry.staines@ntlworld.com

Manager: Kevin Stone

Club Colours: Royal Blue with white trim/royal/royal.

Change Colours: Red/red/red.

Best Season - League: 3rd Isthmian Premier 1993-1994

Ground address: Alfred Davies Memorial Ground, Oak Tree Road, Marlow SL7 3ED **Tel No**: 01628 483 970. Fax: 01628 477 032.

Capacity: 3,000 **Seats**:250 **Covered**:600 **Floodlights**: Yes

Simple Directions: A404 to Marlow (from M4 or M40), then A4155 towards town centre.Turn right into Maple Rise (by ESSO garage), ground in road opposite (Oak Tree Rd).1/2 mile from Marlow (BR). 1/4 mile from Chapel Street bus stops

Midweek Home Matchday: Tuesday

Clubhouse: Open matchdays and most evenings. Smack bar on matchdays.

Local Radio: Radio Berkshire & Thames Valley Radio

Local Press: Bucks Free Press, Maidenhead Advertiser and Evening Post.

CLUB STATISTICS

Record	**Attendance:** 3,000 v Oxford United F.A.Cup 1st Round 1994
	Career Goalscorer: Kevin Stone
	Career Appearances: Mick McKeown 500+
Record Transfer Fee	**Paid**: £5,000 to Sutton United for Richard Evans
	Received: £8,000 from Slough Town for David Lay
Senior Honours:	Isthmian League Division 1 Champions 1987-88. League Cup 1992-93. Berks & Bucks Senior Cup (x11)
Previous	**Leagues:** Reading & District. Spartan 1908-10, 28-65. Great Western Suburban. Athenian 1965-84. Isthmian 1984-2004.
	Name: Great Marlow
	Grounds: Crown Ground 1870-1919. Star Meadow 1919-24.

Back Row (L-R): Mark Skoyles (physio), Jeff Lamb, Aaron Couch, Sam Wadieh, Chris Elsegood, Johnny Isaac, Andy Martinus, Adam Harman, Christian Peirce, Simon Lane, Philip Nugent.
Front Row: Sam Arhin, Jon Case, Kieron Drake, Simon Herbert, Seb Neptune, Ian MacTaggart, Daniel Stone, Jermaine Roche.

ROMULUS

Founded: 1979
Nickname: The Roms

CLUB PERSONNEL
Chairman: Keith Higman.
Addtional Committee:
Roger Evans, Keith Higham, Paul Dockerill, Phil Hobson, John Dockerill, Tom Clarke, Kevin Kingham, Craig Seaman, Richard Evans, Keith Brown, Peter Morgan, Gerry Harris.

Secretary: Andy Fitchett.
7 Saveker Drive, Sutton Coldfield B76 1FT.
(M) 07502 036 593

Programme Editor: Paul Dockerill
pauldockerill@btconnect.com

Manager: Richard Evans and Keith Brown.

Club Colours: Red & white/red /red.

Change Colours: Black & green/black/green.

Best Seasons - League: 10th Southern Division One Midlands 2007-08.

Ground : Sharing with Sutton Coldfield - Central Ground, Coles Lane, Sutton Coldfield, West Midlands B72 1NL.

Tel/fax: 0121 354 2997.

Capacity: 4,500 **Seats**:200 **Covered**: 500 **Floodlights**: Yes

Simple Directions: From M42 J.9, take A4097 (Minworth sign), at island. Follow signs to Walmley Village. At traffic lights. Turn right (B4148), after shops turn left at lights. Into Wylde Green Road, over railway bridge turn right into Eastern Road, which becomes Coles Lane.

Midweek Home Matchday: Tuesday.

Clubhouse: Yes.

Club Shop: Yes.

Local Radio: BRMB and Radio WM.

Local Press: Sutton Coldfield News, Sutton Observer and Sports Argus.

CLUB STATISTICS

Record **Attendance:** Not Known.

Career Goalscorer: Not Known. **Career Appearances**: Not Known.

Transfer Fee Paid: Not Known. **Transfer Fe Received:** Not Known.

Senior Honours: Midland Combination 2003-04.

Previous Leagues: Midland Combination 1999-04. Midland Alliance 2004-07.

Back Row (L-R): Steve Johnson (GK Coach), Tom Franklin, Davion Hamilton, Marcus Brown, Lei Brown, Tyrone Fagan, Matt Sargeant, Leo Brown, Jerome Grandison, Dave Barnett, Colm Tiernan, Peter Folkes, Keith Brown (Joint Manager)
Front Row: Trevor Burroughs (Coach), Danny Douglas, Nick Heath, Tom Wilmore, Luke Wilson, Leon Blake, Robbie Banks, Ashley Jackson, Richard Evans Jnr, Alan Ward, Richard Munday, Paul Hunter (Fitness Coach).

ROTHWELL TOWN

Founded: 1895
Nickname: The Bones

CLUB PERSONNEL
Chairman: Peter Bradley
Additional Committee:
Neil Griffin (Secretary/Treasurer), David Rudkin, Neil Barratt, Alan Trusler, Ian Rice, Pino Colonna (Vice President), Stuart Andrews (President), Derrick Smith, Martyn Cherry, Jim McInally (Director of Football), Roger Barratt (Vice President), Stuart Martin.

Secretary: Neil Griffin.
10 Saxondale,
Kettering NN16 9JN
(H): 01536 358 740
(B): 01536 411 920

Programme Editor: David Rudkin
(M): 07725 146 210

Manager: Rob Dunion.

Club Colours: White with blue trim/white with blue trim/white with blue trim..

Change Colours: Yellow/black/black.

Best Season- League: 10th Southern Division One West 2004-05

Ground address: Home Close, Cecil Street, Rothwell, Northants. NN14 2EZ

Tel No: 01536 710 694

Capacity: 3,500 **Seats**:264 **Covered**:1,264 **Floodlights**: Yes

Simple Directions: A14/A6 to Rothwell. At town centre r'about turn into BridgeStreet (right if northbound, left if southbound), take 3rd left into TreshamStreet, ground is at top on left. 3 miles from Kettering (BR); Rothwell is served by Kettering to Market Harborough buses

Midweek Home Matchday: Tuesday

Clubhouse: Rowellian Social Club, open evenings and weekend lunchtimes.Crisps and rolls available on matchdays (hot food and drinks in ground). 'Top of the Town Ballroom'for 200.

Club Shop: Sells various souvenirs including metal badges.

Local Radio: BBC Radio Northants and KCBC.

Local Press: Northants Evening Telegraph, Chronicle & Echo and Herald & Post.

CLUB STATISTICS

Record	**Attendance:** 2,508 v Irthlingborough Diamonds , Utd.Co. 1971
	Career Goalscorer: Not known
	Career Appearances: Not known
Record Transfer Fee	**Paid**: Undisclosed for Andy Wright (Aylesbury United) 1992
	Received: Undisclosed for Matty Watts (CharltonAthletic) 1990
Senior Honours:	Northants Snr Cup 1899-1900 23-24 59-60 88-89 95-96 01-02 R-Up (3)
	United Counties Lg 92-93 94-95 R-Up (5)
Previous Leagues:	**Leagues:** Northants 1896-1911 21-33, Kettering Amateur 11-21 33-48, 02-03 Leics.Senior 48-50, United Counties 50-56 61-94. Central Alliance 56-61
	Grounds: Harrington Rd, Castle Hill
	Name: Rothwell Town Swifts

Back row (L-R): Mick Tolton (Snr) (Coach), Kevin Byrne, Jon Stead, Richard Challinor, Craig Attwood, David Blake, Tom Smith, Paul Rice, Ian Batchelor, Adam Sturgess, Andy Brown, Stephen Purton, Michael Boyle-Chong, Pete Sneddon. **Middle:** Ian Rice (Groundsman), Dick Goode (Vice Chairman), Tony Gaziano (Sponsor), Pino Collona (Sponsor), Peter Bradley (Chairman), Ian Jackson (Manager), Pete Foskett (Assistant Manager), Neil Griffin (Director of Football & Secretary), John Jones (Kit Manager). **Front:** Fazel Korayi, Mick Tolton, Adam Bridgeford, Chris Hynes, Robert Ritchie-Smith, Martin Flannigan. Not present: Ben Greasley, Ian Baker, Ryan Collis.

SLOUGH TOWN

Founded: 1890
Nickname: The Rebels

Manager: Steve Bateman.

Club Colours: Amber/navy blue/amber.

Change Colours: Red & black shirts/black/red.

Best Season - League : 5th Conference 1992-93.

Ground address: Ground sharing with Beaconsfield SYCOB. Holloways Park, Slough Road, Beaconsfield, Bucks HP9 2SG

Tel No: 01494 676 868

Capacity: 3,500 **Seats** 200 **Covered**: Yes **Floodlights:** Yes

Simple Directions: Leave M40 at Junction 2, take A355 towards Slough, only 50 yards off the roundabout on the A355 is slip road on right with sign giving Club name. Turn right through gate and clubhouse is 200 metres on the right. The ground is 'signposted' from both sides of the carriageway (A355).

Midweek Home Matchday: Tuesday

Clubhouse: Yes.

Club Shop: Yes.

CLUB PERSONNEL

Chairman: Steve Eatserbrook

Additional Directors/Committee:
Roy Merryweather (General Manager), Glen Riley, Alan Harding, Mike Lightfoot, Gary Thomas, Chris Sliski, Kevin Merryweather (Club Safety Officer)

Secretary: Gary Thomas
25 Northcroft, Slough,
Berkshire SL2 1HR
(H): 01753 646477
(M): 07989 434371

Programme Editor: Glen Riley.
programme@sloughtownfc.net

CLUB STATISTICS

Record	**Attendance**: At Slough: 8,000 Schoolboys Slough v Liverpool 1976
	Victory: 17-0 v Railway Clearing House 1921-22
	Defeat: 1-11 v Chesham Town 1909-1910
	Goalscorer: Tory Norris 84 1925-26
	Career Appearances: Terry Reardon 458 1964-81
Record Transfer Fee	**Paid**: £18,000 from Farnborough Town for Colin Fielder
	Received: £22,000 from Wycombe Wanderers for Steve Thompson
Senior Honours:	F.A.Amateur Cup R-Up 1972-73 Isthmian League Champions 80-81 89-90 Athenian League (3) Berks & Bucks Senior Cup: (10)
Previous Leagues:	Southern Alliance 1892-93, Berks & Bucks 1901-05, Gt Western Subebian 1906 19 Spartan 1920-39 Herts & Middx 1940-45, Corinthiian 46-63, Athenian 63-73 Isthmian 73-90 94-95 Conference 90-94.

Back Row (L-R):
Paul Lillywhite (Kit Man), Simon Sweeney, Roy Gumbs, Simon Martin, Danny Jordan, Dean Harper, Steve Jackman, Ricky Perks, Graeme Edwards, Nathan Bowden-Haase, Tommy Hayes, Tyron Sealey, Grant Avis, Kevin McGoldrick (Physio)

Front Row (L-R):
Chris Herron, Kyle Jeffrey, Paul Edgeworth, Robbie Kean, Darren Salton (Asst. Manager), Steve Bateman (Manager), John Lawford (Coach), Craig O'Connor, Ryan Fenton, Danny Murphy, Steve Sinclair (Not pictured: Jamie Jackson, Dean Sinclair)

SOHAM TOWN RANGERS

Founded: 1947
Nickname: Town or Rangers

CLUB PERSONNEL
Chairman: Colin Murfitt
Additional Committee:
Karen Prewett (Secretary),
Lisa Moore (Treasurer),
Walter Gray (Vice Chairman),
Bill Gray (Vice Chairman),
Graham Eley (Groundsman),
Brian Eley (Fixtures Secretary),
Malcolm Howe (Steward),
Mark Bailey, Mick Gipp, Dave Thomas,
Bett Hornby, Andy Burford, Vince Mallett.

Secretary: Karen Prewett,
10 Blackthorn Court, Soham,
Ely, Cambs. CB7 5DT
(H): 01353 721 788
(M): 07917 417 516

Programme
Editor: Fred Parker
fred@fredparker.plus.com

Manager: Ian Benjamin.

Club Colours: Green with white trim/green with white trim/green & white.

Change Colours: Royal blue/royal blue/royal blue.

Best Season - League: 1st Eastern Counties Premier 2007-08.

Ground address: Julius Martin Lane, Soham, Ely, Cambs. CB7 5EQ.

Tel: 01353 720 732.

Capacity: 2,000 **Seats:** 250 **Covered:** 1,000 **Floodlights:**Yes

Simple Directions: A142 between Newmarket and Ely. At roundabout at northern end of by-pass turm left towards town centre and then right at the corner shop into Julius Martina Lane. Ground is on the left.

Midweek Home Matchday: Tuesday

Clubhouse: Three barsand function room for hire.

Club Shop: Yes

CLUB STATISTICS

Record	**Attendance:** 3,000 v Pegasus, FA Amateur Cup 1963.
	Career Goalscorer: Not known
	Career Appearances: Not known
Transfer Fee	**Paid**: Not known.
	Received: Not known.
Senior Honours:	Eastern Counties Premier 2007-08.
Previous	**Leagues:** Peterborough & District. Eastern Counties 1963-2008.
	Names: Soham Town and Sham Rangers merged in 1947

STOURPORT SWIFTS

Founded: 1882
Nickname: Swifts

Manager: Neil Hunt

Club Colours: Black & gold stripes/black/black.

Change: Light blue/light blue/light blue.

Best Seasons - League: 8th Southern Division 1 West 2001-02.

Ground address: Walshes Meadow, Harold Davis Drive, Stourport on Severn, Worcestershire DY13 0AA.

Tell No: 01299 825 188

Capacity: 2,000 **Seats**:250 **Covered**: 150 **Floodlights**:Yes

Simple Directions: Follow one-way system through Stourport sign posted Sports Centre.Go over River Severn Bridge, turn left into Harold Davie Drive. Ground is at rear of Sports Centre. Nearest rail station is Kidderminster.

Midweek Home Matchday: Tuesday

Clubhouse: Open matchdays. Hot snacks available. **Club Shop:** Yes

Local Radio: Hereford & Worcester

Local Press: Kidderminster Shuttle

CLUB PERSONNEL

Chairman: Chris Reynolds

Additional Committee: Roy Crowe (President), Ian Sword, John McDonald, Steve Saunders, Martin Goode, Matt Guise, Chris Knight.

Secretary: Laura McDonald. 65 Princess Way, Stourport on Severn DY13 0EL. (M) 07793 768 793.

Programme Editor: TBA.

CLUB STATISTICS

Record	**Attendance:** 2,000
	Career Goalscorer: Gary Crowther
	Career Appearances: Ian Johnson
Record Transfer Fee	**Paid**: N/A
	Received: N/A
	Victory: 10-0 **Defeat**: 1-7
Senior Honours:	Midland A lliance 2000-01.
Previous Leagues:	**Leagues:** Kidderminster/ Worcester/ West Midland Regional, Midland Football Alliance 1998-2001
	Grounds: Bewdley Rd; Moor Hall Park; Feathers Farm; Olive Grove; Hawthorns.

Back Row (L-R): Lewis Fathers, Alex Lavery, Jamie Insall, Neil Hunt (Manager), Troy Wood, Jamie Price, Nic Clayton.
Middle Row: Richard Tomkins, Dene Wittal Williams, Andy Jones, Paul Evans, Stephen Towers ,Nathan Jukes, Mark Benbow.
Back Row: Julian Triana, Ben Pattison, Chris Duggan, Richard Colwell (Assistant Manager), Dane Aldington, Luke Whittington.

SUTTON COLDFIELD TOWN

Founded: 1897
Nickname: Royals

CLUB PERSONNEL
Chairman: Tom Keogh
Additional Directors:
Bernard Bent (President),
Bernard Cheek, Paul Jones,
Ken Hawkins, Andy Taylor,
Bill Worship (Vice President),
Chris Rogers (Treasurer),
Andy Truelove (Yth Development).

Secretary: Alan Fleming.
28 Manor Road,
Streetly,W.Mids. B74 3NG
(H): 0121 353 5383
(M): 07970 573 638

Programme Editor: Lyn Coley
lyncoley@blueyonder.co.uk

Manager: Chris Keogh.

Club Colours: All blue

Change Colours: All yellow

Best Seasons - League: 17th Southern Premier Division 1983-84

Ground address: Central Ground, Coles Lane, Sutton Coldfield B72 1NL

Tel/Fax No: 0121 354 2997

Capacity: 4,500 **Seats**:200 **Covered**: 500 **Floodlights**: Yes

Simple Directions: A 5127 into Sutton, right at Odeon cinema (Holland Rd), then first right into Coles Lane - ground 150 yds on left. 10 mins walk from SuttonColdfield (BR), bus 104 from B'ham.

Midweek Home Matchday: Monday

Clubhouse: Fully carpeted brick built lounge & concert room Open daily, food available

Club Shop: Selling metal badges, scarves, hats, pens, rosettes, progs. Contact: Bill Portman

Local Radio: BRMB and Radio WM

Local Press: Sutton Coldfield News, Sutton Observer and Sports Argus.

CLUB STATISTICS

Record	**Attendance:** 2,029 v Doncaster Rovers F.A.Cup 1980-1981
	Career Goalscorer: Eddie Hewitt 288
	Career Appearances: Andy Ling 550
Record Transfer Fee	**Paid**: £1,500 to Gloucester C for Lance Morrison , to Burton Albion for Micky Clarke and to Atherstone United for Steve Farmer 1991
	Received: £25,000 from W.B.A. for Barry Cowrill 1979
Senior Honours:	Southern League Midland Div R-up 82-83, West Midlands Lg 79-80 Midland Comb.(2) (R-up (2), Staffs Sen. Cup R-up 89-90, Worcs Sen. Cup SF 88-89,
Previous Leagues:	**Leagues:** Central Birmingham, Walsall Sen, Staffs Co., BirminghamCom 50-54 West Mids (Regional) 54-65 79-82, Midlands Comb. 65-79.
	Name: Sutton Coldfield FC 1879-1921
	Grounds: Meadow Plat 1879-89/ Coles Lane 90-1919

WOODFORD UNITED

Founded: 1946
Nickname: Reds

CLUB PERSONNEL

Chairman: Andrew Worrall

Additional Directors/Committee:
R. Adams (Vice Chairman)
D. Grogan (Treasurer)
Y. Worrall (Safety Officer)
G. Allen (Committee).
P. Shrimpton (Committee)

Secretary: David Allen.
25 Townsend, Woodford Halse, Daventry NN11 3QL
(M) 07889 847 428

Programme Editor: David Allen
allend@freenet.co.uk

Manager: Phil Mason.

Club Colours: All Red.

Change Colours: Yellow/black/yellow.

Best Season - League: 8th Southern Division 1 Midlands 2006-07

Ground address: Byfield Road, Woodford Halse, Daventry, Northants NN11 3QR.

Tel: 01327 263 734

Capacity: 3,000 **Seats**:252 **Covered**: 252 **Floodlights**:Yes

Simple Directions: Off A361 Daventry to Banbury road the ground is on Woodford road out of Byfield.

Midweek Home Matchday: Tuesday

Clubhouse: Full facilities. **Club Shop:** No

CLUB STATISTICS

Record

Attendance: 1,500 v Stockport County

Career Goalscorer: Not Known. **Career Appearances**: Not Known

Transfer Fee Not Known **Record Transfer Fee Paid**: Not Known

Received: Not Known

Senior Honours: United Counties 2005-2006 Division Two 1973-1974.

Previous Leagues: Central Northants Combination 1946-1970 United Counties 1971-2006.

NB: UNFORTUNATELY A RECENT PHOTO WAS NOT AVAILABLE AT THE TIME OF GOING TO PRESS.

A.F.C. HAYES

Founded: 1974
Nickname: The Brook

CLUB PERSONNEL

Chairman: B. Stone

Additional Directors/Committee:
Dave Swan, Keith Gavin (Treasurer), Dave Ball (President and Historian), John Handell (Vice Present), Ken Aldridge, P.Squires (Director), B.Crump (Football Sec./Vice Chairman), P.Betts

Secretary: Barry Crump.
19 Bradenham Road, Hayes, Middlesex UB4 8LP
(H): 020 8841 3959
(M): 07966 468 029

Programme Editor: Dave Swan
daveswan03@hotmail.com

Manager: Dave Welch.

Club Colours: Blue & white Stripes/blue/blue.

Change Colours: All red.

Best Season - League: 9th Southern Division One South & West 2008-09.

Ground address: Farm Park, Kingshill Avenue, Hayes, Middlesex UB4 8DD.

Tel No: 020 8845 0110

Capacity: 2,000 **Seats**: 150 **Covered**: 200 **Floodlights**: Yes

Simple Directions: From North Circular Road take A40 Western Avenue then left at the Target Roundabout towards Hayes. Turn right at traffic lights into Kingshill Avenue and the Ground is one mile on right.

Midweek Home Matchday: Tuesday. **Club Shop:** No

Clubhouse: Open Week days 7-11pm and Week Ends 12 noon-11pm.

Local Press: Hayes Gazette

CLUB STATISTICS

Record **Attendance:** Not Known

Career Goalscorer: Not Known **Career Appearances**: Not Known

Transfer Fee **Paid**: Not Known

Received: Not Known

Senior Honours: Spartan South Midlands Premier South 1997-1998 and Premier Division Runners-Up 1999-2000 and 2003-2004

Previous Leagues: Spartan South Midlands and Isthmian.

Name: Brook House

A.F.C. TOTTON

Founded: 1886
Nickname: Stags

Manager: Stuart Ritchie.

Club Colours: All blue.

Change Colours: Pink/black/black.

Best Season - League: 3rd Southern League Division One 2008-09.

Ground address: Testwood Park, Testwood Place, Totton, Southampton, Hampshire SO40 3BE **Tel:** 02380 868 981

Capacity: 2,500 **Seats:** 200 **Covered:** 250 **Floodlights:** Yes

Simple Directions: From M27 Junction 3, take A271 then A35 dual carriageway. Take next slip road signed A36 Totton & go under road. At next roundabout take 3rd exit into Library Road then left into Testwood Road after Police Station. Testwood Place is 2nd left & ground entrace is 50 yards on the left.

Midweek Home Matchday: Tuesday.

C lubhouse: Open for matches and training evenings. **Club Shop:** No

CLUB PERSONNEL

Chairman: Alan Davis
Additional Committee:
Paul Malden, Alf Peckham, Geoffrey Gook. Clive Bratcher (President), Richard Vowles (Accountant), Sean McGlead, Ann Dunwell, Pat Coombs, Ken Dunwell, Valerie Devoy, Angie Cox, Les Tanner, Mick Budny, Terry Bagshaw.

Secretary: John Heskins.
141 Testwood Lane, Totton,
Southampton SO40 3AR.
(M) 07825 621 509

Programme Editor: Steve Coombs.
Email:
programme@afctotton.co.uk

CLUB STATISTICS

Record	**Attendance:** 600 v Windsor & Eton, FA Cup 4th Qual. 1982-83
	Career Goalscorer: Not known.
	Career Appearances: James Sherlington.
Senior Honours:	Wessex Premier 2007-08. Hampshire League 1981-82, 84-85.
Previous	**Leagues**: Hampshire 1982-86. Wessex 1986-2008.
	Names: Totton FC until merger with Totton Athletic in 1979.

Back Row (L-R): Stuart Ritchie, Neil Champion, Jonathan Richardson, Anthony Lloyd, Matt Troon, Floyd Hamodu, Gareth Byres, Steve Marwood, Ross Bottomley, Sean New.
Front Row: Graham Mills, Adam Barfoot, Matt Jones, Ashley Jarvis, Jamie Austin, Nathaniel Sherborne, Mike Gosney, James Roden. Photo: Graham Brown.

ABINGDON UNITED

Founded: 1946
Nickname: The U's

CLUB PERSONNEL

Chairperson:
Mrs Deborah Blackmore

Additional Committee:
Alf White (Vice Chairman/Health & Safety Officer),Pat Evans (President), Shirley Evans (Catering Manager), Bill Fletcher (Press Officer), Doreen White (Booking Secretary), Darren Edwards (Youth Development Officer), Chris Druce (Groundsman), Chris Janes (Website Officer) Robin Yuill, Derek Turner (Hon Vice President), Steve Clarkson, Pete Hunt.

Secretary: John Blackmore.
91 Gainsborough Green,
Abingdon, Berks OX14 5JL
(H): 01235 203167
(M): 07747 615691

Programme Editor: Bill Fletcher
billfletcher@fsbdial.co.uk

Manager: Andy Slater.

Club Colours: Yellow/yellow/yellow.

Change Colours: Red/red/red.

Best Season - League: 11th Southern Div 1 South & West 2006-2007

Ground address: The North Court, Northcourt Road, Abingdon,Oxon. OX14 1PL

Tel. 01235 203 203

Capacity: 2,000 **Seats**:158 **Covered**:258 **Floodlights**: Yes

Simple Directions: Take A4183 main road towards Oxford from town centre. Ground is on left after one mile.

Midweek Home Matchday: Tuesday

Clubhouse: Open evening pub hours every night and weekend lunchtimes with lounge bar and function room.

Local Radio: BBC Radio Oxford and FOX FM

Local Press: Oxford Mail

CLUB STATISTICS

Record	**Attendance:**	1,500 v Oxford United Friiendly 1994
	Career Goalscorer:	Not known.
	Career Appearances:	Not known.
Senior Honours:	Hellenic Lg Div 1Cup 65-66, Div 1 Champions 1981-82	
	Berks & Bucks Sen. Cup R-Up 83-84 04-05 Berks & Bucks Senior Trophy (2)	
Previous Leagues:	North Berks 1949-58. Hellenic 1958-2006.	

NB: UNFORTUNATELY A RECENT PHOTO WAS NOT AVAILABLE AT THE TIME OF GOING TO PRESS.

ANDOVER

Re-Formed 1983
Nickname: The Lions

Manager: Andy Leader.

Club Colours: Red & black/black/black.

Change Colours: Yellow/white/white.

Best Season - League: 6th Southern League 1991-1992

Ground address: The Portway Stadium, West Portway Industrial Estate, Andover, Hants SP10 3LF Tel No: 01264 351 302

Capacity: 3,000 **Seats**: 250 **Covered**: 250 **Floodlights**: Yes

Simple Directions: Situated on the western outskirts of town. Follow signs to Portway Industrial Estate two miles from Andover BR.

Midweek Home Matchday: Tuesday

Clubhouse: Matchdays and Private Functions.

Club Shop: No

Local Radio: Radio Spire F.M.

Local Press: Andover Advertiser

CLUB PERSONNEL

Chairman: John Smith

Additional Directors: Ray Emery, Alan Mussell, Martin Mitty, Bob Haynes.

Secretary: John Gorman. 6 Overton House, London Road, Overton RG25 3TD. (M) 07804 949 369

Programme Editor: As secretary

CLUB STATISTICS

Record	**Attendance:** 1,100 v Leicester City. Ground Opening.
	Career Goalscorer:Tommy Muchalls
	Career Appearances: Pete Pollard
Record Transfer Fee	**Paid**: Not Known
	Received: Not Known
Senior Honours:	Wessex League Champions 2001 & 2002, Cup 2002
	Hants Senior Cup (5) N. Hants Sen Cup (6)
Previous Leagues:	Salisbury & Dist, Hants 1896-98 1899-1901, 1902-1962.
	Southern Lg: 1898-99, 1971-93 1998-99 Western 1962-71
	Wessex 1993-98, 99-2006

NB: UNFORTUNATELY A RECENT PHOTO WAS NOT AVAILABLE AT THE TIME OF GOING TO PRESS.

BEDFONT GREEN

Founded: 1965
Nickname: The Peacocks

Manager: Dennis Bainborough

Club Colours: Navy/navy/navy.

Change Colours: White/red/red.

Best Season- League: 1st Combined Counties Premier Division 2008-09.

Ground address: Stag Meadow, Windsor & Eton FC, St Leonards Road, Windsor SL4 3DR. Tel: 01753 876 0656.

Capacity: 4,500 Seats: 400 Covered: 550 Floodlights: Yes

Simple Directions: A332 from M4 Jct. Third left at roundabout then into St L eonards Rd at light at T junction. Ground 500 yards on right on B3022 opposite Stag & Hounds pub.

Midweek Home Matchday: Tuesday

Clubhouse: Yes.

CLUB PERSONNEL

Chairman: Doug White

Additional Committee:
Bob Betts, Lynn Newman,
Lawrence Brimicombe,
David Prodger,
Paul Spencer.

Secretary: Stewart Cook.
295 Feltham Hill Road,
Ashford, Middlesex
TW15 1LT
(M) 07946 170 277.

Programme Editor: David Prodger.
Email: dprodger@odyssey-group.com

CLUB STATISTICS

Record	**Career Appearances**: John Skeen
Senior Honours:	Surrey Intermediate Premier Champions 2003-04. Combined Counties Premier Champions 2008-09.
Previous	**Names:** Amalgamated with Bedfont United in 1972 to create Bedfont Green of today. **Leagues**: West Middlesex Sunday. Hounslow & District. Woking & District 1986-99. Guildford & Woking All.1999-2001. Surrey Intermediate 2001-09.

BISHOP'S CLEEVE

Founded: 1892
Nickname: Villagers

CLUB PERSONNEL

Chairman: David Walker

Additional Committee:
Dave Lewis (Safety Officer & Treasurer), Hanif Tai (Ground Development Officer), Bob Weaver(Website Manager), Lyn Weaver(Catering Manageress), Richard Mitchell(Matchday Manager), Malcolm Eustace(Maintenance Manager), John Pickup.

Secretary: Nigel green, 'Caramea', Tewksbury Road, Eckington, Worcs WR10 3AW.(M) 07919 518 880.

Programme Editor: John Pickup
johnpickup@blueyonder.co.uk

Manager: Paul Collicutt.

Club Colours: Blue/blue/blue.

Change Colours: White/white/white.

Best Season- League: 12th Southern Division 1 Midlands 2007-08.

Ground address: Kayte Lane, Bishop's Cleeve, Cheltenham, Glos. GL52 3PD

Tel: 01242 676 166

Capacity: 1,500 **Seats**: 50 **Covered**: 50 **Floodlights**: Yes

Simple Directions: Pass Racecourse North of Cheltenham on the A534 then turn right at Traffic lights and left into Kayte Lane. Ground is half a mile on left.

Midweek Home Matchday: Wednesday

Clubhouse: Full facilities including bar, dance floor, television,etc.

Club Shop: Yes.

Local Radio: BBC Radio Gloucestershire and Severn Sound.

Local Press: Gloucestershire Echo and Western Daily Press.

CLUB STATISTICS

Record	**Attendance:** 1,300 v Cheltenham Town July 2006
	Career Goalscorer: Kevin Slack
	Career Appearances: John Skeen
	Record Transfer Fee Paid N/A **Received:** N/A
Senior Honours:	Glos. Jumior Cup North, Glos Sen.Amateur Cup North (x3)
	Hellenic League Div 1 1986-87. Prem. Lge Cup 1988.
Previous Leagues:	Cheltenham, North Gloucestershire and Hellenic 1983-2006
Grounds:	Stoke Road and ground sharing with Moreton Town F.C., Wollen Sports F.C. Highworth Town & Forest Green Rovers F.C.

NB: UNFORTUNATELY A RECENT PHOTO WAS NOT AVAILABLE AT THE TIME OF GOING TO PRESS.

BRACKNELL TOWN

Founded: 1896
Nickname: The Robins

CLUB PERSONNEL
Chairman: Ian Watson.
Additional Directors:
Ian Nugent, Tony Hardy, Brian Ashworth, Mick Bradly.

Secretary: Tony Hardy.
139 Helmsdale, Crown Wood, Bracknell, Berkshire RG12 0TB
(H): 01344 441 888
(M): 07920 726 501

Programme Editor: Robert Scully
robscully@ntlworld.com

Manager: Kerthney Carty.

Club Colours: All red

Change Colours: All blue

Best Season - League: 3rd Isthmian Division One 1986-87

Ground address: Larges Lane, Bracknell, Berks. RG12 9AN.

Tel No: 01344 412 305.

Capacity: 2,500 **Seats**: 190 **Covered**:400 **Floodlights**: Yes

Simple Directions: Off A329 just before Met Office r'bout by Bracknell College, ground 200 yards. From Bracknell (BR)/bus station - right out of station, follow path over bridge, left down steps and follow cycle path ahead, after 300yds follow curve over footbridge, right and follow lane to end, left and ground on left after bend.

Midweek Home Matchday: Tuesday

Clubhouse: Members Bar open 11am-11 pm Mon-Sat: &12-3 & 7-10.30 pm Sunday.

Club Shop: Yes with full range of products.

Local Radio: Radio Berkshire.

Local Press: Bracknell News and Bracknell Times.

CLUB STATISTICS

Record	**Attendance:** 2,500 v Newquay F.A.Amateur Cup 1971
	Career Goalscorer:Justin Day
	Career Appearances: James Woodcock
Senior Honours:	Isthmian Lg Div 3 93-94; Berks & Bucks Senior Cup Runners-up 2003-04
Previous Leagues:	Great Western Combination.; Surrey Senior 63-70; London Spartan 70-75 and Isthmian 1984-2004

NB: UNFORTUNATELY A RECENT PHOTO WAS NOT AVAILABLE AT THE TIME OF GOING TO PRESS.

BRIDGWATER TOWN 1984

Founded: 1984
Nickname: The Robins

CLUB PERSONNEL
Chairman: Alan Hurford.
Additional Committee:
Keith Setter (President)
Gordon Nelson (Treasurer)
Alan Slade (Asst, Treasurer/Secretary),
Roland Rich, Eddie Pike, Keith Feltham,
Lin Godfrey, Ian Moore, Heather Little,
Shaun Ryall, Winston Davey, Pat Barker,
Robin Mobsby, Howard Pike,
Ben Norman, Rick Norman.

Secretary: Roger Palmer.
c/o Bridgwater Town FC,
(B): 01278 446 899
(M): 07596 033 277
palmer449@btinternet.com

Programme
Editor: As Secretary.

Managers: Craig Laird.

Club Colours: Red & white/white/white.

Change Colours: Blue & white/white/white.

Best Seasons - League: 6th Southern Division One South & West 2007-08.

Ground address: Fairfax Park, College Way, Bath Road, Bridgwater, Somerset TA6 4TZ. Tel/Fax No: 01278 446 899

Capacity: 2,500 **Seats**: 128 **Covered**: 500 **Floodlights**: Yes

Simple Directions: M5 jct 23 following signs to Glastonbury (A39) turn rght on A39 to Bridgwater . Follow signs for Bridgwater College via College Way Ground on right after Rugby club. One Mile from Bridgwater BR.

Midweek Home Matchday: Tuesday

Clubhouse: Open on Matchdays.

Club Shop: Refreshments only.

Local Radio: Orchard FM.

CLUB STATISTICS

Record **Attendance:** 1,112 v Taunton Town 26.02.97

Senior Honours: Somerset Senior Cup 1993-94 1995-95 Western Lg Premier R-Up 2006--07

Western Lg Div 1 Champions 95-96 Somerset Senior League (3)

Previous Leagues: Somerset Senior and Western League **Previous Name**: Bridgwtater Town

Back Row (L-R): Craig Laird (Manager), Piers Govier, Jak Martin, Ross McErlain,Steve Orchard, Brett Trowbridge,Stuart Wood, Tom Manley, Mike Taylor, Mike Mackay, Matt Pitcher,Pete Monks, Danny Phillips (Assistant Manager), Amy Callow (Physio)
Front Row: Lee Morgan,Mitch O'Donnell, Andy Proctor, Craig Laird (Jnr), Chris Young, Anton Olondo, Natt Pepperell.

CINDERFORD TOWN

Founded: 1922
Nickname: The Foresters

Talk Of The Town
Season 2009 - 2010
The Official Matchday Programme for Cinderford Town Football Club
kwbellgroup

Manager: Mike Davis.

Club Colours: Black & white/black/black.

Change Colours: Green & White stripes/green/green.

Best Season - League: 9th Southern Div.1 Western 1999-00, Midlands 2006-07

Ground address: The Causeway, Hildene, Cinderford, Glos. GL14 2QH.

Tel No: 01594 827 147 / 822 039

Capacity: 3,500 **Seats**:250 **Covered**:1,000 **Floodlights**:Yes

Simple Directions: From Gloucester take A40 to Ross-on-Wye, then A48 - Chepstow. In 8miles turn right at Elton garage onto A4151 signed Cinderford, thru Littledean, up steep hill, right at cross-roads, second left into Latimer Rd. Ground 5 mins walk from town centre

Midweek Home Matchday: Tuesday.

Clubhouse: Open daily 2 bars, kitchen, 2 skittle alleys, darts, dancehall,committee room

Club Shop: Souvenirs, club badges, ties, mugs , scarves and pennants (Contact: Dave Gettings)

Local Radio: Radio Gloucester and Severn Sound

Local Press: The Forester, Gloucester Citizen and Western Daily Press

CLUB PERSONNEL

Chairman: Ashley Saunders

Additional Directors/Committee:
Ken McNally, Ray Read (Safety Officer), Chris Parsons (Director of Football), Alan Jones, Beryl Reed, Tina Jones, Robert Knight, Chris Warren, Barry Turner, S.Tait.

Secretary: Robert Maskell.
36 Westerley Close,
Cinderford, Glos. GL14 3EB
(H) 01594 822 772.

Programme Editor: Liam Maskell.
liammaskell@googlemail.com

CLUB STATISTICS

Record	**Attendance:** 4,850 v Minehead , Western League 1955-1956
	Career Goalscorer: Not known
	Career Appearances: Russel Bowles 528
Record	**Victory**: 13-0 v Cam Mills 1938-1939
	Defeat: 0-10 v Sutton Coldfield 1978-1979
Senior Honours:	Hellenic Lg Premier Champions 94-95, Premier Lg.Cup 94-95, Glos Snr Amtr Cup (Nth) (6), R-up (3); Western Lg Div 2 56-57; Glos Jnr Cup (Nth) 80-81; Midland Comb. 81-82; Glos.Sen Cup Winners 00-01
Previous	**Leagues:** Glos Northern Snr 22-39 60-62, Western 46-59, Warwickshire Comb 63-64,West Midlands 65-69, Gloucestershire County 70-73 85-89, Midland Comb. 74-84,Hellenic 90-95
	Grounds: Mousel Lane, Royal Oak.

NB: UNFORTUNATELY A RECENT PHOTO WAS NOT AVAILABLE AT THE TIME OF GOING TO PRESS.

CIRENCESTER TOWN

Founded: 1889
Nickname: Centurions

Manager: Adi Viveash

Colours: Red & black stripes/black/red

Change Colours: All navy and sky blue.

Best Season - League: 7th Southern Premier 2004-05

Ground address: The Corinium Stadium, Kingshill Lane, Cirencester GL7 1HS.

Tel. No: 01285 654 543. Fax: 01285 654 474.

Capacity: 4,500 **Seats**: 550 **Covered**: 1250 **Floodlights:** Yes

Simple Directions: Leave North South bypass(A417(T)/A419)T) at Stow in the Wold turn off. Turn towards Stow. Right at lights then right again at next junction, London Road and first left onto Kingshill Lane. Ground about a mile on right.

Midweek Home Matchday: Tuesday

Clubhouse: Open seven days a week. Two bars, function rooms. Catering available, food bar on matchdays. Also Indoor full size Training Arena.

Club Shop: At the bar.

Local Press: Wilts & Glos Standard and Swindon Advertiser.

CLUB PERSONNEL

Chairman: Stephen Abbley.

Additional Committee:
Alan Sykes (President)
Ian Stewart
Robert Saunders
Alan Lloyd
David Bougen

Secretary: Kathie Chambers
c/o of the club.
(B): 01285 654 543
(BF): 01285 654 474

Programme Editor: Mark O'Brien
obrienm2uk@aol.com

CLUB STATISTICS

Record	**Attendance**: 2,600 v Fareham Town 1969.
	Transfer Fee Paid: £4,000 to Gloucester City for Lee Smith.
	Received: Not known
Senior Honours:	Glos. Senior Amateur Cup 1989-90 Hellenic Lg.Premier Champions 1995-96
	Glos. County Cup 1995-96.
Previous	**Leagues:** Hellenic
	Ground: Smithfield Stadium

Back Row (L-R): Eddie Leather, Andy Minturn, Ben Pugh, Ked Metiteri, Tom King, Aaron Stevens, Nathan Hailsey, Rob Dean, Harry Etheridge.
Front Row: Sean Bailey, Lee Spalding, Steve Davies, Oggy Hunt, Gary Thorne, Adi Viveash, Dan Thompson, Matt Williams, Adam Heath, Julian Alsop.

FROME TOWN

Founded: 1904
Nickname: The Robins

CLUB PERSONNEL

Chairman: Gavin Hares
Additional Committee: Jeremay Alderman, Terry Wolff, Gary Collinson, Colin Carpenter, Roger Smith, Ivan Carver, Robin Strange, Carla Travis, Brian Stevens, Clive Lewis, Richard Hudson.

Secretary: Ian Pearce, 7 Friars Close, Dulton Marsh, Westbury, Wiltshire BA13 4BS
(M) 07811 511 222.

Programme Editor: Andrew Meaden.
programmes@amprintcopy.co.uk

Manager: Andrew Crabtree.

Club Colours: Red/red/red.

Change Colours: Blue/blue/blue.

Best Season - League: 1st Western League Premier 1978-79.

Ground address: Aldersmith Stadium, Badgers Hill, Berkley Road, Frome, Somerset BA11 2EH. Tel/Fax: 01373 464 087.

Capacity: 2,000 **Seats**: 150 **Covered**: 200 **Floodlights**: Yes

Simple Directions: Ground is on the Westbury Road one mile from town centre and from Frome BR.

Midweek Home Matchday: Wednesday.

Clubhouse: Yes.

CLUB STATISTICS

Record	**Attendance:** 8,000 v Leyton Orient, FA Cup 1st Round 1958.
	Career Goalscorer: Not known. **Career Appearances**: Not known.
	Victory: Not known. **Defeat:** Not known.
Senior Honours:	Somerset County League Champions 1906-07, 08-09, 10-11.
	Western League Division 1 Champions 1919-20, 2001-02.
	Wiltshire Premier Division Champions 1962-63.
	Western League Premier Champions 1978-79.
	Somerset Senior Cup 1932-33, 33-34, 50-51.
	Somerset Premier Cup Winners 1966-67, 68-69 (shared), 82-83, 2008-09.
Previous Leagues:	Wiltshire Premier 1904. Somerset Senior 1906-19. Western 1919, 1963-2009.

Back row (L-R): Ian Pearce (Club Secretary), Derek Graham (Assistant Manager), Shaun Baker (Kit Manager), Terry Wolff (Vice-Chairman), Andrew Crabtree (Manager), Steve Hunt, Dan Harvey, Alex Lapham, Ed Quelch, Josh Payne, Paul Farrell, Greg Lake, Mike Whittington, Matt Cowler, Brian Stevens, Gavin Hares (Chairman), Richard Hudson (Treasurer), Lloyd Chamberlain (Reserve Team Manager).
Front row (L-R): Gavin Eyres, Jamie Cheeseman, Ashley Clarke, Simon Millard, Simeon Allison, Jeremy Alderman (Main Club Sponsor), Roger Smith (Main Club Sponsor), Shaun Percival, Matt Peters, Ian Kennedy.
Picture courtesy of Official Club Photographer: Charlie Hadfield.

GOSPORT BOROUGH

Founded: 1944
Nickname: The ' Boro'

Manager: Alex Pike

Club Colours: Yellow/blue/yellow.

Change Colours: White/red/red.

Best Season - League: 7th Southern Premier Division 1982-83, 88-89.

FA Amateur Cup: 3rd Round 1947-48, 66-67.

Ground address: Privett Park, Privett Road, Gosport, Hampshire PO12 0SX.

Tel Nos: 023 9250 1042 (Matchdays only).

Club website: www.gosportboroughfc.co.uk

Capacity: 4,500 **Seats**: 450 **Covered**: 600 **Floodlights**: Yes

Simple Directions: Exit M27 at jct 11 then take A32 Fareham to Gosport road. At Brockhurst roundabout (after 3 miles) right into Military road past HMS Sulton then left into Privett Road at next roundabout. Ground is 300 yards on left.

Midweek Home Matchday: Monday.

Clubhouse: Open daily.

Club Shop: Yes.

Local Radio: BBC Radio Solent, 107.4 The Quay.

Local Press: The News, The Daily Echo.

CLUB PERSONNEL

Chairman: Mark Hook

Additional Committee:
Kevin Blenkinsopp
(Vice Chairman),
Paul Hook (Treasurer)

Secretary: Brian Cosgrave.
2 Cavanna Close, Gosport,
Hampshire PO13 0PE
(H/F): 01329 314 117
(M): 07984 960 537

Programme
Editor: Nigel Miller.
programme@gosportboroughfc.co.uk

CLUB STATISTICS

Record
Attendance: 4,770 v Pegasus (F.A.Amateur Cup 1951)
Career Goalscorer: Ritchie Coulbert - 192
Career Appearances: Tony Mahoney - 765
Victory: 14-0 v Cunliffe Owen, Hampshire League - 1945-46
Defeat: 0-9 v Gloucester City, Southern Prem 1989-90
0-9 v Lymington & N.M., Wessex 1999-00.
1-10 v Andover, Wessex Lge Cup, 1999-00.

Senior Honours:
Hampshire League 1945-46, 76-77, 77-78.
Wessex League 2006-07, Hampshire Senior Cup 1987-88.
Wessex League Cup 1992-93.

Previous Leagues: Portsmouth 1944-45 Hampshire 1945-78 Southern 1978-92. Wessex 1992-07
Name: Gosport Borough Athletic

Gosport skipper Craig Davis in action against Taunton Town on the opening day of the 2009/10 season. Photo Keith Fuller

HUNGERFORD TOWN

Formed:1886
Nickname : The Crusaders

Manager: Alan Clark.

Club Colours: White/blue/white.

Change Colours: Blue/blue/blue.

Best Season - League: 3rd Isthmian Division Two 1979-80, 80-81, 81-82.

Ground address: Bulpitt Lane, Hungerford RG17 0AY.

Tel No: 01488 682 939. 0870 300 4041.

Capacity: 2,500 **Seats:** 170 **Covered:** 400 **Floodlights:** Yes

Simple Directions: M4 jct 14 to A4. Turn right and then left before Bear Hotel. Through town centre on A338 and left into Priory Road then left again into Bulpit Lane. Over crossroads and ground is on the left.

Midweek Home Matchday: Tuesday

Clubhouse: Full facilities.

Club Shop: Yes (Opens on request).

CLUB PERSONNEL

Chairman: Nigel Warwick.
Additional Directors/Committee:
Ken Holmes, Ron Tarry, John Smyth, Mick Butler, John Sopp, Ray Brown, Steve Puffett, Terry Wild, Jim McCafferty.

Secretary:
Norman Matthews.
72 Chiltonway, Hungerford, Berks. RG17 0JF.
(M) 07768 761 795.

Programme Editor: John Smyth.
john.smyth@saxon-brands.com

CLUB STATISTICS

Record	**Attendance** : 1,684 v Sudbury Town, FA Vase Semi-final, 1988-89.
	Career Goalscorer: Ian Farr - 268.
	Career Appearances: Dean Bailey and Tim North - 400+
	Transfer Fee Paid: £4,000 to Yeovil Town for Joe Scott.
	Fee Received: £3,800 from Barnstaple Town for Joe Scott.
Senior Honours:	Hellenic League Division 1 Champions 1970-71
	Hellenic League Premier Champions 2008-09. League Cup 2006-07, 07-08.
	Berks & Bucks Senior Cup 1981-82.
	Isthmian representatives in Anglo Italian Cup 1981.
Previous Leagues:	Newbury & District. Swindon & District. Hellenic 1958-78, 2003-09.
	Isthmian 1978-2003.

Back Row (L-R): Mick Butler (match co-coordinator) Ricky Allaway, Ritchie Saunders, Kevin Halliday, Paul Bedwell, Richard Witt, Mark Scott, Nick McCrae, Tom Fila, Toby Clark, Alan Clark (Manager).
Front Row: Chris Blackford, Shaun Wimble, Nick Roache, Tom Melledew, James Lewis, Bradley Clark, Steve Cook, Wayne Probet (physio).

MANGOTSFIELD UNITED

Formed:1950
Nickname : The Field

Manager: Phil Bater.

Club Colours: Sky blue/maroon/sky blue.

Change Colours: Yellow/black/yellow.

Best Season - League: 9th Southern Premier Divison 2006-2007

Ground address: Cossham Street, Mangotsfield, Bristol BS16 9EN

Tel No: 0117 956 0119. Fax: 01179 567424.

Capacity: 2,500 **Seats:** 300 **Covered:** 800 **Floodlights:**Yes

Simple Directions: M4 Jct 19 A4174 marked Downend. Follow signs to Mangotsfield. Left by church towards Pucklechurch. Ground quarter of mile on right.

Midweek Home Matchday: Tuesday

Clubhouse: Open 12.30-11 Snacks hot food on matchdays. Lounge bar for functions.

Club Shop: Yes

CLUB PERSONNEL

Chairman: Mike Richardson

Additional Directors/Committee:
Mike Hamilton, Pat McKeown, Roger Gray (Chief Exec.), Peter Selway, Alan Williams, Peter Brown, Chris Stone (Vice Chair).

Secretary: Steve Porter.
40 Colliers Break, Emersons Green, Bristol BS16 7EE
(H): 0117 308 742
(M): 07787 225 957

Programme Editor: Bob Smale
bob_smale@yahoo.co.uk

CLUB STATISTICS

Record	**Attendance** : 1,253 v Bath City F.A.Cup 1974
	Victory: 17-0 v Hanham Sports (H) 1953 Bristol & District League
	Defeat: 3-13 v Bristol City United (Bristol & District Div 1)
	Career Goalscorer: John Hill
	Career Appearances: John Hill - 600+
Senior Honours:	Southern League Division One West 2004-205. Western League 1990-91
	Somerset Prem. Cup: 1987-88.
	Glouscestershire Sen.Cup: 1968-69 75-76 02-03.
	Glouscestershire F.A.Trophy (6)
Previous Leagues:	Bristol & District 50-67, Avon Premier Comb. 67-72 and Western 1972-2000

Back Row (L-R): Lee Williams (Physio), Rob Scott, Richard Kear, Danny Bryant, James Simpson, Mitchell Page, Dan Hughes, Scott Hendy, Josh Clapham, Nick Sloane, Alex Ball, Tom Collett, Mitch Tippins.
Front: Simon Bryant, Geraint Bater, Simon Dew, Paul Milsom (Manager), Neil Arndale, Spencer Thomas (Ass. Manager), Mark Pocock, Leon Maloney, Andy Finsh, Daine O'Connor.

NORTH LEIGH

Founded: 1908
Nickname: The Millers

CLUB PERSONNEL

Chairman: Peter King

Additional Committee:
Barry Norton (Press Officer)
M. Burnell (Safety Officer)
Steve Smith (Press Officer)
Phil Horne (Welfare Officer)
Pete Dix (Disciplinary Secretary)
Wayne Reynolds (Club Steward)
Stacey McDonough (Treasurer)
John Franks (Hospitality Officer).

Secretary: Keith Huxley.
The Orchard, Cote,
Bampton, Oxon OX18 2EG.
(M) 07775 818 066

Programme Editor: Mike Burnell
michael.burnell1@ntlworld.com

Manager: Mark Gee

Club Colours: Yellow/black/yellow.

Change Colours: Sky blue/sky blue/white.

Best Season - League: 8th Southern Division 1 South & West 2008-09.

Ground address: Eynsham Hall Park, North Leigh, Witney, Oxon OX29 6PN

Tel: 01993 881 427. Fax: 01993 880 458.

Capacity: 2,000 **Seats**: 100 **Covered**: 200 **Floodlights**: Yes

Simple Directions: Ground is situated off A4095 Witney to Woodstock road, three miles east of Witney. Entrance 300 yards east of main park entrance.

Midweek Home Matchday: Tuesday.

Clubhouse: Open matchdays.

Club Shop: No.

CLUB STATISTICS

Record	**Attendance:** 426 v Newport County, FAC 3rd Qualifying Round, 16.10.04.
	Career Goalscorer: P Coles.
	Career Appearances: P King.
Record Transfer	**Fee Paid**: N/A
	Received: N/A
Senior Honours:	Hellenic Premier 2001-02, 02-03, 07-08.
	Oxon Charity Cup (2)
Previous	**Leagues**: Witney & District. Hellenic 1990-2008.

PAULTON ROVERS

Founded: 1881
Nickname: The Robins/Rovers

Manager: Andy Jones

Club Colours: Maroon/maroon/maroon.

Change Colours: White/white/white.

Best Season- League: 2nd Southern League Divison 1 South & West 2006-07

Ground address: Athletic Ground, Winterfield Road, Paulton, Bristol, Somerset BS39 7RF **Tel/Fax No**: 01761 412 907

Capacity: 5,000 **Seats**: 253 **Covered**: 2,500 **Floodlights**: Yes

Simple Directions: From A39 at Farrington Gurney, follow A 362 marked Radstock for two miles. Turn left at roundabout, take B3355 to Paulton and ground is on right.

Midweek Home Matchday: Monday

Clubhouse: Three bars with full social facilities to hire. Lounge, skittle alley and dancehall available to hire.

Club Shop: Yes.

Local Press: Bath Evening Chronicle, Bristoil Evening Post, Western Daily Press and Somerset Gaurdian.

CLUB PERSONNEL

Chairman: David Bissex

Additional Directors/Committee:
Tracy Curtis, Lar Rogers (President), Paul Rowlands (Social Chairman), Les Rogers (Treasurer), Rob Filer , Tim Pow (Vice President)

Secretary: Andrew Harris.
11 Matthews Close,
Stockwood, BS14 8NL
(M) 07760 377 302

Programme Editor: Tracy Curtis.
tracy.curtis.2000@btinternet.com

CLUB STATISTICS

Record	**Attendance:**	2,000 v Crewe Alexandra F.A.Cup 1906-1907
	Career Goalscorer:	Graham Colbourne
	Career Appearances:	Steve Tovey
Record	**Transfer Fee Paid:**	Not known.
	Received:	Not known.
Senior Honours:		Western League Premier Division Runners-Up 2003-2004 Div 2 R-Up 1900-01 Somerset Senior Cup (12)
Previous Leagues:		Wiltshire Premier, Somerset Senior, Western
Grounds:		Chapel Field, Cricket Ground and Recreation Ground.

Back Row (L-R): Colin Parsons (Kit Manager), Stuart Tovey, Danny Boys, Mike Trought, Rob Claridge, Kyle Phillips, Courtney Redwood, Jason Hughes, Ollie Price, Chris Lane, Ricky Hulbert, Bob Stokes (Physio).
Front Row L-R: Darren James (Physio), Dan Flower, Josh Jefferies, Rob Cousins, Andrew Jones (Manager), Dan Cleverley (Club Captain), Steve Tovey (Asst Manager), Ben Cleverley (Vice Captain), Jon French, Dean Pendry, Peter Sheppard.

TAUNTON TOWN

Founded: 1947
Nickname: The Peacocks

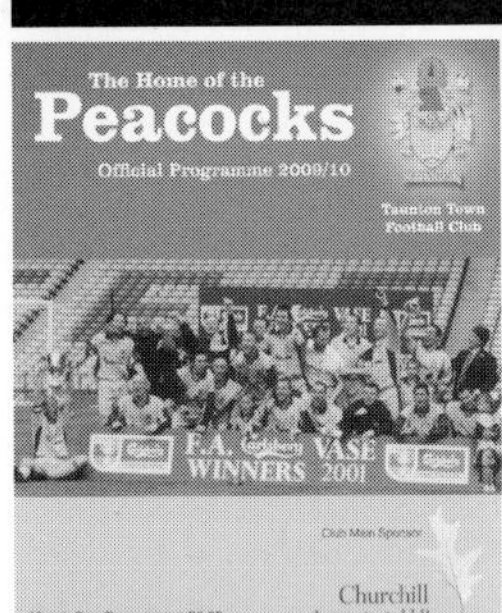

Manager: Paul West.

Club Colours: Sky blue/sky blue/sky blue.

Change Colours: Yellow/yellow/yellow.

Best Season- League: 5th Southern Division 1 South & West 2006-07

Ground address: Wordsworth Drive, Taunton, Somerset TA1 2HG

Tel No: 01823 278 191. Fax: 01823 254 909.

Capacity: 2,500 **Seats**: 300 **Covered**:1,000 **Floodlights**: Yes

Simple Directions: Leave M5 Jct 25, follow signs to town centre. At traffic lights bear left and then straight on through through second lights into Wordsworth Drive; ground on left. 25 mins walk from Taunton (BR); turn left out of station and follow road right through town centre bearing left into East Reach. Follow road down and turn right into Wordsworth Drive shortly after Victoria pub.

Midweek Home Matchday: Tuesday

Clubhouse: Social club to accomodate 300 with full bar facilities. Plus separate bar and hall for private functions.. Hot snacks also always on sale matchdays.

Club Shop: Yes

Local Radio: Orchard FM & Radio Bristol.

Local Press: Somerset County Gazette and Taunton Times.

CLUB PERSONNEL

Chairman: Tom Harris

Additional Directors:
Martin Dongworth
John Eastment
Stanley Petty
Harold Needs

Secretary:
Martin Dongworth.
1 Ilford Court, Wiltshire
Close, Taunton TA1 4JT.
(H): 01823 322 850
(M): 07791 948 686
mpdongworth@somerset.gov.uk

Programme Editor: As Secretary.

CLUB STATISTICS

Record	**Attendance:** 3,284 v Tiverton Town F.A.Vase Semi-Final1999
	Career Goalscorer: Tony Payne
	Goalscorer in a Season: Reg Oram 67
	Career Appearances:: Tony Payne
Record	**Victory:** 12-0 v Dawlish Town (a) F.A.Cup Preliminary Round 28.8.93
	Received: 0-8 v Cheltenham Town (A) F.A.Cup 2nd Qualifying Round 28.9.91
Senior Honours:	FA Vase Winners 2000-01.
	Western League Champions 1968-69, 89-90, 95-6, 98-9, 99-00, 00-01.
	Somerset Prem.Cup Winners 2002-03, 05-06.
Previous	**Leagues**: Western 1954 -1977. Southern 1977-1983. Western 1983-2002.

Back row (L-R): Charlie Welch, Danny Lane, Stuart Nelson, Scott Thomas, Lee Bridson, Nathan Whatley, Simon Cooper, Sam Jones, Chris Kite, Jamie Price, Jason Burt, Shaun Anthony.
Front row: Matt Naylor, Lee Groves, Paul Short, Martin Dongworth, Tom Harris, Ian Jones, Dave Anthony, Alex Pounde.

THATCHAM TOWN

Founded: 1895

CLUB PERSONNEL

Chairman: Eric Bailey

Additional Committee:
Sylvia Bailey (Treasurer), Steve Berry, Alan Lovegrove, Peter Woodage, Alan Rashbrook, Maurice Brown, Jim Goslin, Charlie Heaver, John Haines, Les Winkworth, Karen Churchill, Anita Kent.

Secretary: Steve Berry.
29 Hurford Drive, Thatcham
RG19 4WA.
(M) 07775 602 083

Programme Editor: Alan Lovegrove.
mail@alanlovegrove.wanadoo.co.uk

Manager: Gary Ackling

Club Colours: Blue & white stripes/ blue/blue.

Change Colours: Red/black/red.

Best Season - League: 6th Southern Division 1 South & West 2006-07, 08-09.

Ground address: Waterside Park, Crookham Hill, Thatcham, Berks. RG19 4PA

Tel: 01635 862 016.

Club Website: www.thatchamtowntc.co.uk

Capacity: 3,000 **Seats**: 300 **Covered**: 300 **Floodlights**: Yes

Simple Directions: From M4 jct 13 take A34 to Newbury. Left onto A4 towards Reading and turn right in Thatcham following signs to the B.R. station. Ground is on left before the station.

Midweek Home Matchday: Tuesday

Clubhouse: Open every evening and iunchtimes **Club Shop:** Yes

CLUB STATISTICS

Records — **Attendance:** 1,400 v Aldershot F.A.Vase.

Senior Honours: — Wessex League 1995-96. Hellenic League 1974-75.

Previous — **Leagues**: Hellenic 1974-82. Athenian 1982-84. London Spartan 1984-86. Wessex 1986-2006.

Grounds: Station Road 1946-1952 Lancaster Close 1952-1992

NB: UNFORTUNATELY A RECENT PHOTO WAS NOT AVAILABLE AT THE TIME OF GOING TO PRESS.

UXBRIDGE

Founded: 1871
Nickname: The Reds

Manager: Tony Choules.

Club Colours: Red/white/red.

Change Colours: White/white/white.

Best Season - League: 4th Southern League Div 1 East 2004-05.

Ground address: Honeycroft, Horton Road, West Drayton, Middlesex UB7 8HX

Tel No: 01895 443 557. Fax: 01895 445 830.

Capacity: 3,770 **Seats**: 339 **Covered**: 760 **Floodlights**: Yes

Simple Directions: From West Drayton (BR) turn right then1st right (Horton Road).Ground one mile on left. From Uxbridge (LT) take 222 or U3 bus to West Drayton station, then follow as above. By road, ground 1 mile north of M4 jct 4 taking road to Uxbridge and leaving by first junction and turning left into Horton Rd - ground 500yds on right. Nearest Railway station is West Drayton.

Midweek Home Matchday: Tuesday

Clubhouse: Open every evening and week end & bank holiday lunchtimes

Tel No: 01895 443 557.

Local Radio: Capital, G.L.R. and Star F.M.

Local Press: Uxbridge Gazette & Leader and Uxbridge Recorder.

CLUB PERSONNEL

Chairman: Alan Holloway

Additional Committee:
A. Odell (President), R. Stevens, D.Tucker (Treasurer), M. Burell (Match Secretary), C. Rycraft (Assistant Match Sec.), D. Marshall (Commercial Manager), G. Hiseman (Administrator), D. Gill (Press Officer), R. Turton (PA Ancouncer).

Secretary: Roger Stevens.
9 Bourne Avenue,
Hillingdon, Middlesex.
UB8 3AR
(H): 01895 236 879
(M): 07773 513 405

Programme Editor: Graham Hiseman.
bbpublications@tiscali.co.uk

CLUB STATISTICS

Record	**Attendance:** 1,000 v Arsenal opening of floodlights 1981
	Career Goalscorer:Phil Duff 153
	Career Appearances:: Roger Nicholls 1054
Record Transfer Fees	**Paid**: Not known.
	Received: Not known.
Senior Honours:	F.A Amateur Cup R-up 1897-98; London Chall. Cup 93-94 96-97 98-99, R-up 97-98; IsthLge Div 2 S. R-up 84-85; Athenian Lge Cup R-up 81-82, Middx Sen.Cup 1893-94 95-96 1950-51, 2000-01 R-up 97-98;
Previous	**Leagues:** Southern 1894-99; Gt Western Suburban 1906-19, 20-23; Athenian 1919-20, 24-37, 63-82; Spartan 37-38; London 38-46; Gt Western Comb. 39-45;Corinthian 46-63. Isthmian. **Name:** Uxbridge Town 23-45
	Grounds: RAF Stadium 23-48 and Cleveland Road 48-78

Back Row (L to R): Johnnie Dyer, Chris Fermie, Charlie Hill, Gavin Brown, Damian Panter, Wayne Carter. **Middle Row L-R:** Stuart Everley (Physio), Tommy Howe, Ryan Wharton, Frazer Toms, Rob Bullivant, Mark Dennison, Paul McCarthy, David Everley, Ryan O'Toole, Lee Tunnell, Ashleigh Drum (Physio). **Front Row L-R:** Dave Lawrence, David Warner, Rob Tidbury (Goalkeeping Coach), Scott Tarr (Assistant Manager), Tony Choules (Manager), Gary Farrell (Coach), Kevin Warner, Dave Thomas. (Photograph by Roy Green)

V.T. FC

Founded: 1916
Nickname: The Boatmen

Manager: David Diaper.

Club Colours: Red/white/red.

Change Colours: All white.

Best Season - League: 2nd Wessex Premier 2007-08, 08-09.

Ground address: VT Group Sportsground, Portsmouth Road, Sholing, Southampton SO19 9PW.

Tel No: 02380 403 829.

Capacity: **Seats**: Yes **Covered**: Yes **Floodlights**: Yes

Simple Directions: Exit jct 8 M27 follow signs for Hamble. Second exit to Ham at Windover roundabout. Take right hand lane andsecond exit at mini roundabout. After150 yards turn right to Portsmouth Road and after half a mile look out for large lay by on left. The entrance to ground is opposite next bus stop.

Midweek Home Matchday: Tuesday

Clubhouse: Yes.

CLUB PERSONNEL

Chairman: Trevor Lewis

Additional Committee:
Bill Boyle, Arthur Fox, Mrs Chris Lewis, David Diaper, Malcolm Stokes, Kevin Harnelt, Ray Tyrell, Len Lacey, Charlie Ducellier.

Secretary:
Colin Chamerlain.
3 Squires Walk, Weston,
Southampton SO19 9GJ
(M) 07770 452 660

Programme Editor: Mrs Chris Lewis
chrislewis@tsicali.co.uk

CLUB STATISTICS

Records	**Attendance:** 150
	Career Goalscorer: George Diaper - 100+
Senior Honours:	Hampshire Premier Champions 2000-01, 03-04.
Previous	**Names:** Woolston Works. Thornycrofts (Woolston) 1918-52. Vospers 1960-2003.
	Leagues: Hampshire 1991-2004. Wessex 2004-09.

WINDSOR & ETON

Founded:1892
Nickname: The Royalists

CLUB PERSONNEL

Chairman:
Peter Simpson OBE

Additional Directors:
Kevin Stott (Vice Chairman)
Abbas Shams

Secretary: Steve Rowland
C/o Club
(M): 07887 770 630

Programme
Editors: Dan Gomm.
wefcprogramme@hotmail.co.uk

Manager: Keith Scott.

Club Colours: Red with green trim/red with green trim/red.

Change Colours: Yellow with green trim/yellow with green trim/yellow.

Best Season - League: 5th Isthmian Premier Division 1984-85.

Ground address: Stag Meadow, St Leonards Rd., Windsor, Berkshire, SL4 3DR

Tel No: 01753 860 656. Fax 01753 860 656.

Capacity: 4,500 Seats: 400 Covered: 550 Floodlights: Yes

Simple Directions: A332 from M4 Jct. Third left at roundabout then into St L eonards Rd at light at T junction. Ground 500 yards on right on B3022 opposite Stag & Hounds pub.

Midweek Home Matchday: Tuesday

Clubhouse: Yes **Club Shop:** Yes

LocalRadio: BBC Radio Berkshire and Star FM

Local Press: Windsor & Eton Express and Windsor Observer

CLUB STATISTICS

Record	**Attendance**: 8,500 (Charity Match)
	Career Appearances: Kevin Mitchell
Record Transfer Fee	**Paid**: 9,000 to Slough Town for Keith White
	Received: 45,000 from Barnet for Michael Banton & Michael Barnes
Senior Honours:	Isthmian Div 1 83-84 Div 2 R-up 21-22 Athenian Lg 79-80 80-81 Berks & Bucks Senior Cup (11) R-up (6)
Previous Leagues:	Southern, West Berks, Great Western Suburban, Athenian 22-29 63-81
	Spartan 29-32 Gt Western Comb., Corinthian 45-50 Metropolitan 50-60 Delphian 60-63 Athenian
Ground:	Ballon Meadow 1892-1912

NB: UNFORTUNATELY A RECENT PHOTO WAS NOT AVAILABLE AT THE TIME OF GOING TO PRESS.

YATE TOWN

Founded: 1946
Nickname: The Bluebells

CLUB PERSONNEL

Chairman: Peter Jackson.
Committee:
Robert Lomas (Treasurer), John Burns (Commercial Manager), Peter Crowley, Barry Neal, Colin Pick, John Powell, Michael Powell, Roger Pullin, Malcolm Robinson, Derek Smith, Ian Summers, Colin Roddan.

Secretary: Terry Tansley.
1 Tyning Close, Yate, Bristol
BS37 5PN
(H): 01454 324 305
(F): 01454 324 305
(M): 07875 272 126

Programme Editor: As Secretary.

Manager: Dave Mogg

Club Colours: White/navy/white.

Change Colours: Navy blue/white/navy blue.

Previous Grounds: Yate Airfield 50-54 Newmans Field 54-60 Sunnyside Lane 60-84

Best Seasons - League: 6th Southern Premier 2006-07.

Ground address: Lodge Road, Yate, Bristol BS37 7LE

Tel No: 01454 228 103

Capacity: 2,000 **Seats**: 236 **Covered**: 400 **Floodlights**: Yes

Simple Directions: M4 jct 18 A46 towards Stroud then A432 to Yate. Turn right at Green Goose Way and at first roundabout into link road and Yate shopping centre. Turn right at third main traffic lights into North Road, then first left into Lodge Road.

Midweek Home Matchday: Tuesday

Clubhouse: Open every evening and lunchtimes at weekends.

Club Shop: Yes

CLUB STATISTICS

Records

Attendance: 2,000 v Bristol R v Rovers Past Vaughan Jones Testimonial 1990

Victory: 13-3 Clevedon, Bristol Premier Combination 1967-68

Career Goalscorer: Kevin Thaws

Career Appearances: Gary Hewlett

Transfer Fee Paid: £2,000 to Chippenham Town for Matt Rawlings 2003

Received: £15,000 from Bristol Rovers for Mike Davis

Senior Honours: Hellenic League Champions 1987-88, 88-89. Glos. F.A.Senior Cup 2004-2005, 2005-06.

Previous Leagues: Glos. County 1968-83. Hellenic 1983-89, 2000-03. Southern 1989-2000.

Previous Name: Yate YMCA 1946-70

Back Row (L-R): KYLE SHALLCROSS, NEIL WARD*, SCOTT THOMAS,EDD VAHID, STUART WOOD*, CALLUM STEWART,JON McALINDON,JASON BURT, REEKO BEST*
Front Row: MARK REYNOLDS, DAVID PEARSE*,ROB DUMPHY* ARON ROBBINS, ASHLEY DERRICK, MARC HUGHES, CRAIG RIMMER*, TOM WARREN.
* no longer with club. Not in photo: Lee Matthews, Adam White, Sam Duggan, Zayne Simpson.

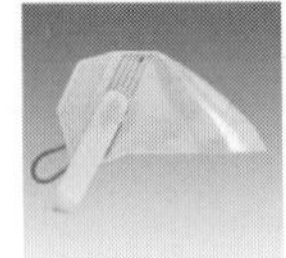

Ryman football league

SPONSORED BY:
RYMAN

Founded: 1905

President & Chairman:
Alan C.F. Turvey FCIM

Competition Secretary:
Bruce Badcock
Unit 14-15,
Wisdon Facilities Centre,
42 Hollands Road,
Haverhill, Suffolk CB9 8SA
Telephone: 01440 768840
Mobile: 07921 940784
Fax: 01440 768841
E-mail:
leaguesecretary@isthmian.co.uk

ISTHMIAN LEAGUE

		P	W	D	L	F	A	GD	Pts
1	Dover Athletic	42	33	5	4	91	34	57	104
2	Staines Town	42	23	13	6	75	41	34	82
3	Tonbridge Angels	42	20	13	9	82	54	28	73
4	Carshalton Athletic	42	19	11	12	64	63	1	68
5	Sutton United	42	18	13	11	57	53	4	67
6	AFC Hornchurch	42	19	8	15	60	51	9	65
7	Wealdstone	42	18	8	16	70	56	14	62
8	Dartford (P)	42	17	11	14	62	49	13	62
9	Tooting & Mitcham United	42	16	10	16	57	57	0	58
10	Ashford Town (Mx)	42	18	2	22	64	66	-2	56
11	Billericay Town	42	15	11	16	54	66	-12	56
12	Canvey Island	42	16	7	19	65	70	-5	55
13	Horsham	42	16	7	19	49	60	-11	55
14	Harrow Borough	42	14	12	16	56	73	-17	54
15	Maidstone United	42	14	11	17	46	51	-5	53
16	Hendon	42	15	6	21	69	65	4	51
17	Hastings United	42	14	7	21	52	68	-16	49
18	Boreham Wood	42	12	12	18	48	61	-13	48
19	Margate	42	13	7	22	51	64	-13	46
20	Harlow Town (-3)	42	13	6	23	61	77	-16	42
21	Heybridge Swifts	42	10	11	21	41	63	-22	41
22	Ramsgate (-4)	42	8	11	23	47	79	-32	31

PROMOTION PLAY-OFFS - SEMI-FINALS

Staines Town	3 - 0	Sutton United
Tonbridge Angels	2 - 3	Carshalton Athletic

PROMOTION PLAY-OFF - FINAL

Staines Town	1 - 0	Carshalton Athletic

	1	2	3	4	5	6	7	8	9	10	11	12	13	14	15	16	17	18	19	20	21	22
1 AFC Hornchurch		1-3	1-1	1-4	1-0	0-2	2-0	1-0	3-1	2-0	1-2	1-2	2-3	3-0	0-0	3-0	3-0	0-2	2-1	3-0	1-0	1-0
2 Ashford Tn (Mx)	2-0		5-1	0-1	1-0	1-1	1-0	1-2	0-2	0-0	5-4	0-2	0-1	3-0	1-0	0-1	0-3	2-0	2-1	1-7	7-0	2-1
3 Billericay Town	1-0	2-0		1-1	2-4	2-2	0-1	2-3	2-2	1-1	1-0	4-2	2-0	0-1	1-1	3-2	2-2	1-1	1-0	1-1	2-1	3-2
4 Boreham Wood	1-3	3-1	0-2		0-1	1-2	0-0	2-3	2-0	1-2	2-0	0-1	1-0	0-2	0-1	1-2	1-1	0-2	1-3	0-2	2-0	2-0
5 Canvey Island	3-2	1-0	4-0	4-0		0-1	2-3	0-3	1-3	3-1	5-2	1-1	2-0	2-4	0-1	0-4	2-0	2-2	0-0	3-2	3-1	1-1
6 Carshalton Ath.	2-2	1-0	3-1	0-2	2-2		0-2	0-1	3-1	2-3	2-2	1-0	0-0	1-5	0-3	2-1	3-3	1-3	0-2	0-3	0-1	3-2
7 Dartford	3-3	4-2	2-0	3-0	4-0	2-3		0-2	1-1	0-1	0-2	1-0	1-1	4-0	1-0	0-1	4-0	0-0	2-3	2-2	3-1	2-2
8 Dover Athletic	2-1	3-2	2-1	1-2	2-1	2-2	4-2		2-0	4-0	3-2	3-0	2-1	2-1	3-0	1-0	4-1	0-0	6-0	3-0	3-0	3-1
9 Harlow Town	4-1	2-5	3-0	3-3	3-0	1-2	1-2	1-4		3-0	0-1	3-5	0-1	0-1	2-3	1-1	1-1	0-2	1-1	0-2	0-2	2-0
10 Harrow Borough	1-2	0-1	3-1	1-1	2-4	1-5	2-1	3-0	1-4		1-1	4-2	0-0	6-1	1-1	3-2	0-1	2-1	0-0	2-3	0-0	0-3
11 Hastings United	2-4	1-2	5-2	1-1	2-0	0-1	0-0	0-1	3-2	0-2		2-1	0-1	0-2	0-4	1-1	3-1	1-1	0-2	0-1	0-3	2-1
12 Hendon	1-2	0-3	0-1	1-1	2-0	1-2	3-0	0-2	5-0	7-0	4-0		1-1	3-1	2-0	1-2	3-1	0-2	0-0	1-3	2-2	1-4
13 Heybridge Swifts	0-0	0-1	2-2	1-2	2-3	0-1	0-0	1-1	0-2	2-2	0-2	0-2		1-0	0-2	3-2	3-1	3-2	0-2	1-5	1-1	0-1
14 Horsham	0-0	2-0	0-1	2-2	3-0	2-3	0-3	1-2	1-4	1-0	0-2	1-2	2-0		3-1	2-0	1-0	2-1	1-2	0-0	0-0	0-2
15 Maidstone Utd	0-0	2-1	0-1	1-1	0-0	0-2	1-2	0-2	1-2	0-2	0-1	3-2	0-2	1-1		1-1	3-2	0-0	1-0	0-1	2-0	2-1
16 Margate	0-2	2-0	3-1	3-1	0-4	2-2	2-2	0-2	3-0	2-3	2-3	2-2	2-1	0-1	0-2		1-0	1-2	2-0	0-0	2-0	0-1
17 Ramsgate	1-2	0-3	1-0	2-0	2-2	1-2	0-1	0-0	1-2	0-2	0-1	1-5	3-2	2-2	1-2	2-0		1-1	3-1	2-3	1-4	2-2
18 Staines Town	2-2	3-0	1-0	4-1	2-1	4-1	2-1	2-3	1-0	1-0	2-0	2-0	3-2	0-0	3-1	4-1	2-0		3-1	2-2	0-0	2-2
19 Sutton United	2-1	3-1	0-1	1-1	1-0	1-1	1-0	1-0	3-0	2-2	2-1	1-0	1-1	2-1	2-2	2-0	1-1	1-1		3-3	0-0	3-2
20 Tonbridge Angels	0-1	3-2	3-2	1-1	3-0	1-0	4-1	0-2	2-0	1-1	3-3	5-1	2-1	4-0	2-2	1-0	2-2	1-2	1-3		0-2	1-2
21 Tooting & M. Utd	2-0	3-2	0-0	1-2	3-1	1-2	0-2	1-1	4-2	1-1	1-0	1-0	2-3	0-2	2-0	2-1	3-0	1-2	4-2	2-2		2-3
22 Wealdstone	1-0	3-1	1-2	1-1	2-3	1-1	0-0	1-2	1-2	6-0	1-0	2-1	3-0	1-0	3-2	2-0	0-1	4-3	4-0	0-0	0-3	

ISTHMIAN LEAGUE DIVISION ONE NORTH

		P	W	D	L	F	A	GD	Pts
1	Aveley	42	29	9	4	81	40	41	96
2	East Thurrock United	42	30	5	7	112	50	62	95
3	Brentwood Town	42	26	10	6	77	32	45	88
4	Waltham Abbey	42	25	7	10	85	45	40	82
5	Concord Rangers	42	23	10	9	83	34	49	79
6	Northwood	42	22	12	8	65	39	26	78
7	Wingate & Finchley	42	19	10	13	67	51	16	67
8	Redbridge	42	18	10	14	61	50	11	64
9	Ware	42	19	4	19	69	75	-6	61
10	Chatham Town	42	18	6	18	58	60	-2	60
11	Tilbury	42	16	10	16	62	53	9	58
12	Enfield Town	42	17	7	18	71	68	3	58
13	Great Wakering Rovers	42	16	10	16	56	62	-6	58
14	Cheshunt	42	17	5	20	60	71	-11	56
15	Leyton	42	12	15	15	63	56	7	51
16	Maldon Town (-3)	42	13	9	20	48	63	-15	45
17	Ilford	42	12	5	25	27	68	-41	41
18	Thamesmead Town	42	10	10	22	46	73	-27	40
19	Potters Bar Town (-1)	42	9	10	23	52	73	-21	36
20	Waltham Forest	42	9	7	26	39	81	-42	34
21	Witham Town	42	6	9	27	37	103	-66	27
22	Hillingdon Borough	42	4	4	34	35	107	-72	16

PROMOTION PLAY-OFFS - SEMI-FINALS

Brentwood Town	1 - 4	Waltham Abbey
East Thurrock United	0 - 1	Concord Rangers

PROMOTION PLAY-OFF - FINAL

Waltham Abbey	1 - 1	Concord Rangers

Waltham Abbey won 5-4 on penalties.

	1	2	3	4	5	6	7	8	9	10	11	12	13	14	15	16	17	18	19	20	21	22
1 Aveley		1-3	4-3	3-1	2-1	3-1	1-0	3-2	4-1	2-0	1-1	1-1	1-1	3-2	2-0	3-0	1-2	0-0	0-2	2-2	3-0	3-1
2 Brentwood Town	2-3		2-0	0-2	1-1	2-3	3-0	0-0	1-0	2-0	2-0	8-2	1-1	3-0	2-0	1-0	2-0	2-3	1-0	2-0	3-0	0-0
3 Chatham Town	1-2	1-1		5-1	1-4	0-3	1-1	1-2	0-1	1-0	2-0	0-2	1-1	2-4	1-0	2-0	1-4	1-0	3-0	0-2	2-0	2-0
4 Cheshunt	2-3	1-3	1-0		0-0	3-4	0-1	0-2	2-0	0-0	2-3	0-3	1-2	4-2	1-2	2-0	1-0	4-0	1-0	3-3	0-1	2-1
5 Concord Rangers	0-1	0-0	5-0	1-0		0-1	3-0	4-0	1-0	2-2	2-0	3-0	1-1	1-0	1-3	3-0	1-1	2-3	3-1	1-2	2-2	2-2
6 East Thurrock Utd	2-3	1-2	1-0	5-0	1-1		2-0	3-0	4-0	4-2	4-2	2-1	1-0	0-2	1-0	3-0	4-2	2-2	5-0	7-0	1-4	5-0
7 Enfield Town	4-7	2-2	1-3	2-3	2-1	2-2		1-0	3-0	0-1	0-4	2-2	0-1	3-1	2-2	2-2	1-0	2-0	0-1	2-1	2-0	2-0
8 Great Wakering R.	0-1	1-2	1-1	3-0	0-2	4-0	2-1		0-0	3-1	3-3	0-2	2-2	2-1	1-0	2-1	2-0	2-2	2-1	2-3	1-4	2-1
9 Hillingdon Boro'	0-1	0-4	3-4	1-2	1-3	1-3	1-4	1-2		1-2	0-4	0-2	1-4	1-3	0-4	0-2	3-2	2-3	1-0	0-4	1-3	2-1
10 Ilford	0-1	0-0	0-1	0-1	0-1	0-3	0-3	3-0	1-0		2-0	2-1	0-1	2-0	0-1	0-2	1-0	0-1	1-0	1-4	0-0	1-0
11 Leyton (R)	0-2	0-0	1-2	1-1	0-0	1-1	4-0	2-1	4-0	3-0		2-0	2-2	0-0	2-2	2-0	1-1	1-2	5-1	2-3	2-2	0-2
12 Maldon Town	1-0	0-1	2-3	3-1	0-1	1-2	0-5	1-1	2-0	0-1	1-0		1-0	1-1	1-2	0-1	0-3	1-2	4-0	1-2	2-1	0-1
13 Northwood	0-0	3-2	2-1	1-1	0-3	1-2	4-0	1-0	3-0	3-0	3-0	2-0		2-1	0-0	2-0	3-1	0-2	1-0	2-1	1-1	5-0
14 Potters Bar Town	1-1	1-2	0-1	1-2	2-1	2-4	2-1	0-3	3-3	1-1	0-2	0-0	0-1		2-3	4-0	1-4	2-2	0-2	1-0	1-4	0-0
15 Redbridge	1-1	1-1	2-0	1-0	0-6	0-3	3-1	1-1	4-1	5-0	3-2	2-2	1-2	1-1		1-0	1-3	0-3	1-1	0-1	1-0	3-0
16 Thamesmead T.	0-2	2-3	0-0	4-5	0-5	2-3	1-3	2-2	3-1	3-0	0-0	2-0	2-1	1-1	1-1		0-0	2-2	1-2	2-1	1-1	2-3
17 Tilbury	0-0	1-0	2-0	3-0	0-1	0-1	2-4	2-1	0-0	5-1	1-0	1-1	2-2	3-2	0-1	1-1		2-0	1-1	2-0	0-3	1-1
18 Waltham Abbey	1-2	1-3	1-2	2-0	1-0	0-1	1-0	5-0	3-1	8-1	3-1	3-0	0-1	3-0	1-0	3-0	3-1		3-0	3-0	2-2	5-1
19 Waltham Forest	0-2	0-1	1-1	0-1	0-5	1-4	0-6	2-2	4-1	0-1	1-1	2-2	0-1	0-1	1-0	0-2	3-2	1-2		5-3	1-3	1-0
20 Ware	1-2	1-3	1-2	1-4	2-4	2-1	1-3	0-1	3-2	3-0	1-1	0-1	5-1	1-0	0-2	2-1	1-4	2-1	4-2		1-0	3-1
21 Wingate & Finchley	0-1	0-1	1-0	4-1	0-2	2-2	3-2	2-0	4-3	1-0	0-1	1-2	1-1	2-1	1-0	3-1	2-0	1-1	2-1	1-1		5-1
22 Witham Town	0-3	0-3	1-6	0-4	2-3	2-10	1-1	0-1	1-1	1-0	3-3	2-2	1-0	1-5	1-6	1-2	1-3	0-2	1-1	0-1	2-0	

ISTHMIAN LEAGUE DIVISION ONE SOUTH

		P	W	D	L	F	A	GD	Pts
1	Kingstonian	42	26	8	8	91	48	43	86
2	Cray Wanderers	42	24	7	11	87	54	33	79
3	Fleet Town	42	21	15	6	82	43	39	78
4	Metropolitan Police	42	21	14	7	72	45	27	77
5	Worthing	42	21	13	8	77	48	29	76
6	Sittingbourne	42	19	13	10	63	54	9	70
7	Ashford Town	42	16	15	11	68	54	14	63
8	Merstham (-1)	42	18	10	14	57	54	3	63
9	Godalming Town	42	17	11	14	71	50	21	62
10	Croydon Athletic	42	16	14	12	67	54	13	62
11	Folkestone Invicta	42	16	11	15	54	46	8	59
12	Dulwich Hamlet (-3)	42	15	15	12	64	50	14	57
13	Eastbourne Town	42	17	6	19	66	72	-6	57
14	Walton & Hersham	42	13	11	18	46	55	-9	50
15	Leatherhead	42	14	8	20	57	74	-17	50
16	Whitstable Town	42	14	8	20	58	77	-19	50
17	Walton Casuals	42	12	8	22	43	60	-17	44
18	Whyteleafe	42	11	10	21	48	64	-16	43
19	Burgess Hill Town	42	10	13	19	49	66	-17	43
20	Corinthian-Casuals	42	11	10	21	61	91	-30	43
21	Chipstead	42	8	12	22	57	96	-39	36
22	Crowborough Athletic (-3)	42	4	4	34	42	125	-83	13

PROMOTION PLAY-OFFS - SEMI-FINALS

Cray Wanderers	1 - 0	Worthing
Fleet Town	0 - 1	Metropolitan Police

PROMOTION PLAY-OFF - FINAL

Cray Wanderers	1 - 0	Metropolitan Police

	1	2	3	4	5	6	7	8	9	10	11	12	13	14	15	16	17	18	19	20	21	22
1 Ashford Town		4-1	2-3	1-5	0-2	3-1	1-1	0-0	1-0	2-3	1-0	2-1	1-1	5-0	3-0	2-1	0-1	2-2	1-1	4-0	0-0	2-0
2 Burgess Hill Town	1-1		3-3	0-0	2-1	3-1	0-0	0-1	2-0	2-5	2-1	0-0	1-2	0-2	0-1	0-2	1-1	1-1	3-0	0-5	2-0	1-1
3 Chipstead	1-1	0-2		1-4	1-6	2-1	2-1	2-2	2-4	0-2	1-0	2-2	2-3	3-3	2-2	1-2	1-3	3-3	0-3	2-1	1-5	1-1
4 Corinthian-Casuals	3-2	3-3	2-1		1-8	5-1	0-5	2-1	3-3	1-1	1-1	0-3	2-5	1-0	2-2	1-0	1-3	2-4	0-6	1-2	2-2	0-3
5 Cray Wanderers	0-0	3-0	1-0	4-1		2-1	5-2	3-1	3-0	0-4	3-1	3-2	2-4	2-1	3-0	1-2	1-1	4-2	3-0	2-0	0-2	2-1
6 Crowborough Ath.	3-4	1-4	2-4	2-1	1-0		0-3	0-7	0-3	4-4	2-8	0-3	1-3	0-4	0-4	1-2	2-3	0-2	3-0	2-2	3-4	1-2
7 Croydon Ath.	5-1	2-1	3-0	1-0	0-0	1-0		0-0	0-1	0-3	1-1	3-1	3-3	2-0	0-2	0-1	2-3	1-1	1-2	1-2	0-0	1-1
8 Dulwich Hamlet	1-1	2-1	2-1	3-1	1-2	5-1	3-2		2-1	1-2	0-0	2-2	0-3	2-0	1-2	1-1	0-2	1-1	1-1	4-3	3-1	2-2
9 Eastbourne Town	0-2	2-1	1-0	2-0	2-1	2-0	2-3	0-0		1-2	2-2	2-1	2-4	2-4	2-3	2-5	2-1	0-1	0-2	3-0	3-2	2-4
10 Fleet Town	2-2	4-0	4-1	2-2	1-1	6-0	2-2	0-0	2-1		2-0	0-0	2-0	5-1	3-0	2-2	2-2	0-1	0-4	0-1	1-0	1-1
11 Folkestone Invicta	1-0	1-0	2-1	2-0	1-3	0-2	2-2	2-0	1-0	0-0		1-2	0-2	1-2	1-2	2-0	0-0	1-2	4-0	1-0	2-1	0-2
12 Godalming Town	2-0	1-1	4-2	0-2	2-1	8-0	1-2	0-0	1-3	1-1	1-1		1-2	2-0	1-2	1-0	2-3	2-1	1-0	4-0	2-0	0-1
13 Kingstonian	2-3	3-1	3-0	0-1	2-0	6-0	1-2	2-1	3-0	2-1	1-1	1-1		4-1	1-0	1-1	1-2	1-0	4-2	1-1	3-0	1-3
14 Leatherhead	1-5	2-2	2-0	4-1	1-1	2-2	1-2	0-3	0-1	2-0	3-2	1-1	0-2		2-1	1-2	3-0	0-2	2-1	1-2	3-1	0-1
15 Merstham	1-0	1-1	0-0	2-1	1-1	1-0	0-1	1-4	4-3	0-0	0-2	1-2	2-0	1-0		2-1	1-2	5-0	0-0	1-1	2-2	4-1
16 Metropolitan Police	1-2	2-0	2-2	0-0	5-0	1-0	1-1	1-1	2-2	1-2	2-1	3-1	2-2	3-3	1-0		1-1	3-1	1-0	4-1	0-0	1-1
17 Sittingbourne	1-1	1-1	3-2	2-1	1-3	2-2	1-1	2-3	1-1	1-3	0-1	1-0	0-4	2-2	0-1	1-2		1-0	3-1	3-0	3-1	0-1
18 Walton & Hersham	2-2	1-2	1-2	2-1	0-1	2-1	3-3	1-0	0-1	1-0	0-2	1-0	0-0	0-0	1-1	1-2	1-2		0-0	1-0	0-1	0-1
19 Walton Casuals	0-3	1-0	1-1	1-3	1-1	1-0	0-2	1-0	2-1	2-3	0-1	1-4	0-1	1-0	3-1	1-2	0-0	1-0		1-2	0-0	1-3
20 Whitstable Town	4-1	0-4	5-1	3-2	1-4	2-1	3-2	0-0	2-3	0-2	1-1	1-1	2-4	0-1	2-0	0-3	1-1	1-2	2-0		3-2	1-2
21 Whyteleafe	0-0	3-0	1-2	2-1	1-3	2-0	2-1	2-1	1-2	0-2	1-1	2-3	0-2	0-2	0-1	1-2	1-2	2-1	1-0	0-0		1-4
22 Worthing	0-0	1-0	1-1	1-1	4-1	2-0	1-2	1-2	2-2	1-1	1-2	1-4	4-1	6-0	4-2	2-2	0-1	2-1	2-1	4-1	1-1	

RYMAN ISTHMIAN LEAGUE CUP 2008-09

FIRST ROUND

Brentwood Town 0 **Potters Bar Town** 1 *(Nov 18)* Att: 56
Great Wakering Rovers 0 **East Thurrock United** 1 *(Nov 18)* Att: 60

SECOND ROUND

AFC Hornchurch 4 Potters Bar Town 0 *(Dec 2)* Att: 135
Ashford Town 1 **Thamesmead Town** 2 *aet (Dec 2)* Att: 99
Aveley 3 Maidstone United 1 *(Dec 1)* Att: 79
Billericay Town 4 Enfield Town 1 *(Dec 2)* Att: 123
Boreham Wood 2 **Waltham Abbey** 3 *(Dec 2)* Att: 40
Burgess Hill Town 3 Hastings United 2 *(Dec 9)* Att: 84
Concord Rangers 5 East Thurrock United 3 *(Jan 20)* Att: 106
Crowborough Athletic 0 **Eastbourne Town** 4 *(Dec 2)* Att: 101
Croydon Athletic 0 **Sutton United** 2 *(Dec 2)* Att: 136
Dartford 3 Margate 2 *(Dec 2)* Att: 306
Dover Athletic 4 Canvey Island 1 *(Dec 2)* Att: 214
Dulwich Hamlet 3 Cray Wanderers 2 *aet (Jan 20)* Att: 82
Folkestone Invicta 1 **Tilbury** 2 *(Dec 2)* Att: 115
Godalming Town 1 Walton & Hersham 0 *(Dec 2)* Att: 89
Harlow Town 4 Cheshunt 2 *(Nov 25)* Att: 118
Hendon 0 **Harrow Borough** 2 *(Dec 3)* Att: 80
Heybridge Swifts 2 Maldon Town 1 *aet (Dec 2)* Att: 93
Hillingdon Borough 0 **Kingstonian** 3 *(Dec 2)* Att: 71
Ilford 0 **Redbridge** 1 *(Jan 14)* Att: 37
Leatherhead 0 **Ashford Town (Middx)** 2 *(Dec 2)* Att: 58
Leyton 0 **Ware** 2 *(Nov 25)* Att: 27
Merstham 2 **Tonbridge Angels** 5 *(Dec 2)* Att: 87
Northwood 4 Corinthian Casuals 1 *(Dec 2)* Att: 71
Ramsgate 4 Chatham Town 0 *(Dec 2)* Att: 127
Sittingbourne 0 **Whitstable Town** 1 *(Dec 1)* Att: 104
Tooting & Mitcham United 2 **Carshalton Athletic** 5 *(Jan 13)* Att: 166
Walton Casuals 1 **Fleet Town** 6 *(Dec 16)* Att: 81
Wealdstone 5 Metropolitan Police 2 *(Dec 2)* Att: 73
Whyteleafe 0 **Chipstead** 3 *(Dec 2)* Att: 60
Wingate & Finchley 0 **Staines Town** 3 *(Dec 2)* Att: 37
Witham Town 0 Waltham Forest 5 *(Nov 25) (Waltham Forest expelled)* Att: 54
Worthing 1 **Horsham** 2 *(Dec 2)* Att: 172

THIRD ROUND

AFC Hornchurch 2 Witham Town 0 *(Jan 20)* Att: 141
Ashford Town (Middx) 2 Kingstonian 1 *aet (Jan 27)* Att: 114
Aveley 1 **Dover Athletic** 4 *(Jan 27)* Att: 92
Burgess Hill Town 1 **Dulwich Hamlet** 3 *(at Dulwich Hamlet) (Jan 27)* Att: 59
Carshalton Athletic 3 Tonbridge Angels 0 *(Jan 20)* Att: 104
Concord Rangers 1 **Dartford** 3 *(Jan 27)* Att: 163
Eastbourne Town 4 Chipstead 0 *(Jan 21)* Att: 60
Godalming Town 1 **Harrow Borough** 2 *(Jan 13)* Att: 61
Harlow Town 3 Heybridge Swifts 2 *aet (Jan 13)* Att: 120
Northwood 2 Fleet Town 0 *(Jan 13)* Att: 66
Staines Town 2 Wealdstone 1 *aet (Jan 13)* Att: 194
Sutton United 2 **Horsham** 3 *aet (Jan 27)* Att: 116
Thamesmead Town 0 **Ramsgate** 4 *(Jan 7)* Att: 58
Waltham Abbey 2 **Billericay Town** 3 *(at Billericay Town) (Jan 27)* Att: 138
Ware 2 **Redbridge** 5 *(Jan 27)* Att: 63
Whitstable Town 1 **Tilbury** 2 *(Jan 13)* Att: 100

FOURTH ROUND

Billericay Town 1 AFC Hornchurch 0 *(Feb 10)* Att: 172
Carshalton Athletic 5 Eastbourne Town 1 *(Jan 27)* Att: 98
Dulwich Hamlet 0 **Dover Athletic** 2 aet *(Feb 10)* Att: 91
Harlow Town 1 **Harrow Borough** 2 *(Jan 27)* Att: 113
Horsham 3 Dartford 2 *aet (Feb 18)* Att: 188
Redbridge 1 **Ashford Town (Middx)** 2 *(Feb 24)* Att: 38
Staines Town 5 Northwood 2 *aet (Jan 27)* Att: 117
Tilbury 3 Ramsgate 0 *(Feb 24)* Att: 45

QUARTER-FINALS

Billericay Town 3 Dover Athletic 1 *(Feb 24)* Att: 201
Carshalton Athletic 2 **Ashford Town (Middx) 3** *(Mar 3)* Att: 81
Harrow Borough 4 Horsham 1 *(Feb 24)* Att: 55
Tilbury 1 Staines Town 1 *aet* (4-2p) *(Mar 3)* Att: 41

SEMI-FINALS

Harrow Borough 3 Ashford Town (Middx) 1 *(Mar 17)* Att: 82
Tilbury 2 Billericay Town 0 *(Mar 17)* Att: 189

FINAL *(April 8th at Staines Town)*

Harrow Borough 0 **Tilbury** 2 Att: 284

THE NATIONAL STRIKEFORCE 2008-2009
Goals scored in The F.A.Cup, F.A.Trophy and League games for clubs in Steps1,2 & 3
(including play-offs denoted by +1 +2 or+3)

		Lge	FAC	FAT	Total	Pens	Hat Tricks
RICHARD JOLLY	**(CARSHALTON ATHLETIC)**	**31+2**	**4**		**37**	**2**	
Michael Lennon	(Nantwich Town)	27+2	5		34	3	
Jon Main	(AFC Wimbledon)	33	1		34	6	3
Steve Morison	(Stevenage Borough)	22+2	1	7	32	3	1
David Kolodynski	(Rugby Town)		26	4	1	31	2
Ross Dyer	(Hednesford Town)	21	7	3	28	2	
Andy Mangan	(Forest Green Rovers)	26		1	27	5	3
Lee Novak	(Gateshead)	26+1			27	2	2
James Constable	(Oxford United)	23	2	1	26	6	
Carl Rook	(Tonbridge Angels)	24	1	1	26	3	2
Tyrone Barnett	(Hednesford Town)	21	1	3	25		
Alex Sykes	(Gloucester City)	21	1	3	25	11	1
Dave Walker	(Nantwich Town)	17+1	6	1	25	4	1
Leon Broadhurst	(Stourbridge)	20		4	24	5	1
Paul Clayton	(Alfreton Town)	17+1	4	2	24		
Fran Collin	(Dover Athletic)	21	1	2	24	4	
Ben Mackey	(Brackley Town)	17	3	4	24	1	1
Josh Scott	(Hayes & Yeading)	23	1		24	4	
Gareth Sheldon	(Tamworth)	23	1		24	3	
Richard Brodie	(Barrow)			3			
	(York City)	15		5	23		
Byron Harrison	(Ashford Town - Middx)	21	1	1	23	3	1
Ian Holmes	(Eastwood Town)	21	2		23	4	1
Ben Mackey	(Brackley Town)	16	3	4	23	1	1
Aiden Savoury	(Ossett Town)	21		2	23	3	1
Charlie Sheringham	(Welling United)	19		4	23	5	
Adam Warlow	(Fleetwood Town)	19	3	1	23		
Kyle Wilson	(F.C.United)	21	1	1	23	3	1
Richard Butler	(Staines Town)	20		2	22	2	2
Steve Diggin	(Corby Town)	19		3	22	1	2
Elliott Durrell	(Hednesford Town)	17		5	22		
Charlie Griffin	(Salisbury City)	21		1	22	1	
Matt Barnes-Homer	(Kidderminster Harriers)	20	1		21		
Warren McBean	(Bromley)	21			21	2	
Jack Midson	(Histon)	19	1	1	21		
Mark Bett	(Bradford P.A.)	20			20	3	1
Richard Brodie	(York City)	15		5	20		
Andy Brown	(A.F.C. Telford United)	16	1	3	20	2	1
Michael Charles	(Farnborough Town)	17		3	20		
Richard Pacquette	(Maidenhead United)	20			20	1	
Dave Pratt	(Chippenham Town)	17	3		20	3	
Justin Richards	(Kidderminster Harriers)	16	2	2	20	3	
Chris Simm	(Hyde United)	19		1	20	4	1
Graham Arnison	(Workington)	15		4	19	3	
Richard Gillespie	(Bashley)	13	4	2	19	4	
Liam Hearn	(Alfreton Town)	18		1	19		2
Craig Hobson	(Kendal Town)	18	1		19	2	1
Gavin Knight	(Buxton)	15	2	2	19		
Greg Pearson	(Burton Albion)	18		1	19	7	
Craig Reid	(Newport County)	16	1	2	19	2	1
Tim Sills	(Torquay United)	14+1	4		19	2	
Paul Vines	(Tooting & Mitcham)	18	1		19	1	1
Gary Bradshaw	(North Ferriby United)	14	2	2	18	3	
Billy Bricknell	(Billericay Town)	15	2	1	18		
Danny Carey-Bertram	(Bath City &	2					
	AFC Telford United)	10+1		5	18	1	
Steve Daly	(Southport)	14		4	18		
Paul Hakim	(St Albans City)	18			18	1	1
Danny Hockton	(Bromley)	6					
	(Braintree Town)	12			18		
Ciaran Kilheeney	(Southport)	16		2	18	2	
Gareth Seddon	(Kettering Town)	15	3		18	4	
Craig Watkins	(Havant & Waterlooville)	12	1	5	18		
Tom Winters	(Brackley Town)	16	1	1	18		
Lawrence Yaku	(Hampton & Richmond B)	15+2	1		18	1	

A.F.C. HORNCHURCH

Re-Formed: 2005
Nickname: The Urchins

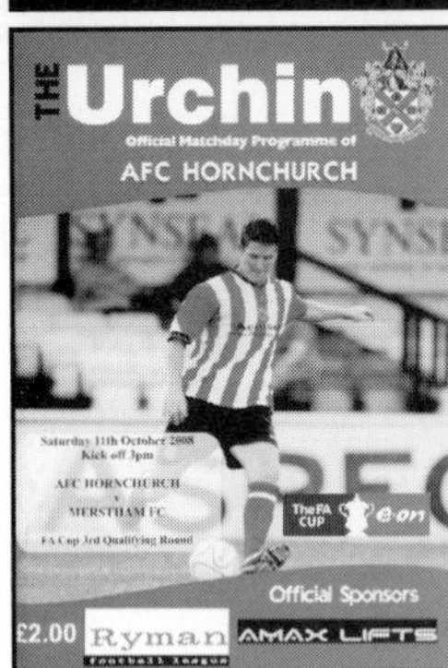

Manager: Colin McBride

Colours: Red & white sttripes/black/red

Best Season - League: 17th Conference South 2003-2004

Ground address: The Stadium, Bridge Avenue, Upminster, Essex RM14 2LX.

Tel Nos: 01708 220080 (clubhouse) 01708 250501 (Office) 01708 220080 (FAX)

Club Website: www.afchornchurch.com

Capacity: 3,500 **Seats**: 800 **Covered**: 1,400 **Floodlights**: Yes

Simple Directions: Bridge Avenue is off A124 between Hornchurch and Upminster

Nearest BR Station: Upminster **Underground Station**: Upminster Bridge (District)

Midweek Home Matchday: Tuesday

Clubhouse: Open Daily **Club Shop:** Yes

Local Radio: Essex Radio, Time FM

Local Press: Romford Recorder

CLUB PERSONNEL

Chairman: Grant Beglan.

Secretary: Kerry Street.
97 Rosedale Road
Romford
Essex RM1 4QR
(M) 0775 834 8244

Press Officer: As secretary

Programme
Editor: As secretary

CLUB STATISTICS

Record — **Attendance:** 3,500 v Tranmere Rovers 2nd Rd F.A.Cup 2003-2004

Senior Honours: Since club was re-formed. Essex League Champions 2005-2006 (Record points total 64) and League Cup and
Memorial Trophy winners.
Isthmian Division 1 North 2006-07.

Previous — **Leagues**: Athenian, Istthmian, Conference South, Essex Senior

Peterborough's Sergio Torres tries to get past A.F.C. Hornchurch's Donny Barnard and Mark Janney during their F.A. Cup 1st Round tie. Photo: Alan Coomes.

A.F.C. HORNCHURCH

BEST LGE ATT.: **810** v Dartford
LOWEST: **152** v Boreham Wood

No.	Date	Comp	H/A	Opponents	Att:	Result	Goalscorers	Pos
1	Aug 16	Ryman P.	A	Ramsgate	315	W 2 - 1	Parker 17 **Green** 21	
2	19		H	Carshalton Athletic	309	L 0 - 2		
3	23		H	Dover Athletic	487	W 1 - 0	Curley 35	8
4	25		A	Heybridge Swifts	202	D 0 - 0		
5	30		H	Staines Town	274	L 0 - 2		12
6	Sept 2		A	Tooting & Mitcham U	346	L 0 - 2		
7	6		A	Margate	501	W 2 - 0	Goodfellow 50 Lee 67	12
8	**13**	**F.A.C 1Q**	**A**	**Saffron Walden**	**33**	**W 2 - 0**	**Styles 37 Wall 55**	
9	20		H	Billericay Town	506	D 1 - 1	Tomlinson 79	14
10	23		A	Canvey Island	363	L 2 - 3	Parker 15 Janney 70	
11	**27**	**F.A.C 2Q**	**A**	**Bromley**	**581**	**W 1 - 0**	**Janney 19 (pen)**	
12	Oct 4		A	Ashford Town (Mddx)	192	L 0 - 2		16
13	7		H	Wealdstone	252	W 1 - 0	**Green** 56	
14	**11**	**F.A.C. 3Q**	**H**	**Merstham**	**473**	**W 2 - 0**	**Green 29 85 (pen)**	
15	14		H	Tonbridge Angels	282	W 3 - 0	Styles 6 Janney 50 Lee 73	14
16	**18**	**F.A.T.1Q**	**A**	**Maidstone United**	**384**	**D 1 - 1**	**Green 37**	
17	**21**	**F.A.T. 1Qr**	**H**	**Maidstone United**	**257**	**L 1 - 2**	**Wall 89**	
18	**25**	**F.A.C. 4Q**	**A**	**Weymouth**	**904**	**W 2 - 1**	**Lee 47 Parker 90**	
19	28		A	Dartford	923	D 3 - 3	Parker 13 **Green** 17 41	14
20	**Nov 9**	**F.A.C 1R**	**H**	**Peterborough United**	**3000**	**L 0 - 1**		
21	15		A	Hastings United	604	W 4 - 2	Lee 16 Shave 74 Janney 40 (pen) 50	13
22	18		H	Hendon	233	L 1 - 2	Shave 44	
23	22		A	Horsham	212	D 0 - 0		12
24	29		H	Sutton United	359	W 2 - 1	Lee 45 Parker 69	11
25	Dec 6		H	Ramsgate	254	W 3 - 0	Shave 56 87 Styles 71	9
26	9		H	Boreham Wood	152	L 1 - 4	Parker 43	
27	20		H	Tooting & Mitcham U	303	W 1 - 0	Wall 73	8
28	27		A	Harlow Town	392	L 1 - 4	Tomlinson 60	9
29	Jan 17		H	Margate	313	W 3 - 0	Wall 3 61 Lee 75	8
30	24		A	Billericay Town	532	L 0 - 1		10
31	31		H	Canvey Island	371	W 1 - 0	**Green** 5	8
32	Feb 14		H	Ashford Town	192	L 1 - 3	Janney 49	10
33	17		H	Heybridge Swifts	212	H 2 - 3	Styles 20 Wall 29	
34	21		A	Harrow Borough	158	W 2 - 1	Spencer 4 Wall 13	8
35	28		H	Maidstone United	414	D 0 - 0		10
36	Mar 3		A	Dover Athletic	907	L 1 - 2	Janney 73 (pen)	
37	7		A	Tonbridge Angels	184	W 1 - 0	**Green** 66	7
38	10		A	Carshalton Athletic	119	D 2 - 2	Janney 60 (pen) 86	
39	14		A	Boreham Wood	168	W 3 - 1	Parker 29 63 Tomlinson 75	7
40	21		H	Dartford	810	W 2 - 0	Styles 16 Lee 90	6
41	24		A	Wealdstone	325	L 0 - 1		8
42	29		A	Hendon	245	W 2 - 1	Parker 9 Kirby 51 (og)	
43	31		A	Maidstone United	301	D 0 - 0		
44	April 4		H	Hastings United	322	L 1 - 2	Janney 77	7
45	10		A	Staines Town	308	D 2 - 2	**Green** 47 67	7
46	13		H	Harlow Town	397	W 3 - 1	Abraham 37 **Green** 49 Wall 90	
47	16		H	Harrow Borough	312	W 2 - 0	**Green** 49 Lee 90	
48	18		H	Horsham	372	W 3 - 0	Parker 30 Curley 52 82	4
49	25	42	A	Sutton United	832	L 1 - 2	Curly 48	6

Average Home Att: 339 (456) **Goals** 69 56

Best Position: 4th **Worst:** 16th

Goalscorers: Green 13, Janney 10, Parker 10, Lee 8, Wall 8, Styles 5, Curley 4, Shave 4, Tomlinson 3, Abraham 1, Goodfelow 1, Spencer 1. Own Goals 1.

ASHFORD TOWN (Middlesex)

Founded: 1964
Nickname: Tangerines

Manager: Mark Butler.

Club Colours: Tangerine & white stripes/black/white.

Previous League: Southern

Best Season - League: 6th Isthmian Premier Division 2007-08.

Ground address: Short Lane Stadium, Stanwell, Staines, Middlesex TW19 7BH

Tel No: 01784 245908. Fax: 01784 253 913.

Capacity: 2,550 **Seats**:250 **Covered**: 250 **Floodlights**: Yes

Simple Directions: M25 jct 13, A30 towards London, third left at footbridge after Ashford Hospital crossroads - ground signposted after 1/4 mile on right down Short Lane, two miles from Ashford (BR) & Hatton Cross (tube) stations.

Midweek Home Matchday: Tuesday

Clubhouse: Open seven days a week with refreshments always available

Club Shop: No

CLUB PERSONNEL

Chairman: Bob Parker
Secretary: Alan Connstable, 3 Craigwell Close, Chertsey Lane, Staines, Middlesex.TW18 3NP
Tel No: (H) 01784 440613
(M) 07956 930719
alanc52@aol.com
Press Officer: Terry Ryan
Tel No: (Day) 01932 425845
(H) 01932 350867
(M) 0789 464 2826
terry@terry-ryan.co.uk
Programme Editor: As secretary

CLUB STATISTICS

Record	**Attendance:** 992 v AFC Wimbledon - Isthmian Premier 26.09.06
	Career Goalscorer: Andy Smith
	Career Appearances: Alan Constable 650
Record Transfer Fee	**Paid**: None
	Received: £10,000 for Dannie Bulman from Wycombe Wanderers 1997.
Senior Honours:	Combined Counties League Champions 94-95, 95-96, 96-97, 97-8, 99-00. Middlesex Prem. Cup 06-07, R-up 89-90. Middlesex Charity Cup 2000-01. Isthmian Lge Cup 06-07.
Previous :	**Leagues:** Hounslow & Dist. 64-68; Surrey Intermediate 68-82; Surrey Premier 82-90 Combined Counties League 90-00 Isthmian 2000-01 - 03-4
	Ground: Clockhouse Lane Rec

Back Row (L-R): Alan Constable (Secretary), Pat Munns (Goakeeper Coach), Tori (Barmaid), Glynn Stephens (Reserve Team Manager), Gavin Smith, Byron Harrison, Scott Weight, Jon Palmer, Ricky Wellard, Paul Burgess, Craig Ross, Danny Cox, Adam Logie, Ricard Joseph, Paul Johnson, Russell Canderton, Billy Jeffreys, Matt Holley, Gary Ross (coach), Emma (Barmaid), Andy Tomkins (Physio), Gareth Coates (Webmaster), Bob Parker (Chairman). **Front:** Scott Todd, Darren Deegan, Wes Goggin, Stuart Bamford, Warren Harris, Rory Gleeson (Assistant Manager), Mark Butler (Manager), Symon James, Scott Harris, Brett Cooper, Gavin Bamford, Vinnie O'Sullivan.

ASHFORD TOWN (Middlesex)

BEST LGE ATT.: 320 v Dartford
LOWEST: 75 v Heybridge Swifts

No.	Date	Comp	H/A	Opponents	Att:	Result	Goalscorers	Pos
1	Aug 16	Ryman P.	A	Hastings United	408	W 2 - 1	Harris S 30 60	
2	19		H	Wealdstone	278	W 2 - 1	**Harrison** 13 69	
3	23		H	Tooting & Mitcham	170	W 7 - 0	Johnson 9 Harris W 29 Logie 45 **Harrison** 52 61 Wellard 57 (pen) Smith 90	1
4	25		A	Hendon	240	W 3 - 0	**Harrison** 26 Harris S 45 55	
5	30		H	Canvey Island	247	W 1 - 0	**Harrison** 31	
6	Sept 2		A	Heybridge Swifts	119	W 1 - 0	Logie 6	
7	6		A	Dover Athletic	1009	L 2 - 3	Johnson 2 12	1
8	9		H	Harlow Town	200	L 0 - 2		3
9	**13**	**F.A.C 1Q**	**A**	**Raunds Town**	**154**	**W 3 - 0**	**S.HARRIS 3 (31 35 49)**	
10	20		H	Margate	178	L 0 - 1		4
11	23		A	Carshalton Athletic	207	L 0 - 1		
12	**27**	**F.A.C. 2Q**	**A**	**Arlesey Town**	**129**	**W 4 - 1**	**Welland 21 (pen) Harrison 54 W.Harris 84 86**	
13	Oct 4		H	AFC Hornchurch	192	W 2 - 0	Wellard 30 Johnson 90	5
14	**11**	**F.A.C. 3Q**	**H**	**Chippenham Town**	**277**	**W 1 - 0**	**Harris S 50**	
15	14		A	Boreham Wood	96	L 1 - 3	Logie 76	
16	**18**	**F.A.T. 1Q**	**A**	**Wingate & Finchley**	**80**	**D 1 - 1**	**Harrison 89**	
17	**21**	**F.A.T. 1Qr**	**H**	**Wingate & Finchley**	**52**	**L 2 - 4**	**Todd 83 Palmer 90**	
18	**25**	**F.A.C. 4Q**	**H**	**Forest Green Rovers**	**425**	**D 0 - 0**		
19	**28**	**F.A.C. 4Qr**	**A**	**Forest Green Rovers**	**425**	**L 0 - 4**		
20	Nov 1		H	Tonbridge Angels	144	L 1 - 7	Harris W 57	9
21	15		H	Billericay Town	130	W 5 - 1	Logie 10 W.HARRIS 3 (25 37 90) **Harrison** 88	8
22	18		A	Harrow Borough	115	W 1 - 0	**Harrison**	
23	22		A	Maidstone United	274	L 1 - 2	S.Harris 26	
24	29		H	Ramsgate	120	L 0 - 3		8
25	Dec 6		H	Hastings United	131	W 5 - 4	SMITH 3 (2 8 32) **Harrison** 16 47	6
26	16		A	Sutton United	334	L 1 - 3	Johnson 45	
27	20		H	Heybridge Swifts	75	L 0 - 1		9
28	27		A	Staines Town	591	L 0 - 3		10
29	Jan 3		H	Hendon	278	L 0 - 2		11
30	17		H	Dover Athletic	283	L 1 - 2	Harris S 29	12
31	24		A	Margate	357	L 0 - 2		14
32	31		H	Carshalton Athletic	167	D 1 - 1	**Harrison** 10	15
33	Feb 14		A	AFC Hornchurch	192	W 3 - 1	**HARRISON** 3 (19 43 81)	14
34	21		H	Dartford	320	W 1 - 0	**Harrison** 51	13
35	28		A	Horsham	195	L 0 - 2		14
36	Mar 7		H	Boreham Wood	118	L 0 - 1		
37	14		H	Sutton United	172	W 2 - 1	Pigden 29 Joseph 63	15
38	19		A	Harlow Town	225	W 5 - 2	Pigden 35 **Harrison** 69 Joseph 52 Harris W 75 79	
39	21		A	Tonbridge Angels	429	L 2 - 3	W.Harris 52 **Harrison** 58 (pen)	12
40	24		A	Tooting & Mitcham	223	L 2 - 3	**Harrison** 30 54 (pen)	
41	28		H	Harrow Borough	110	D 0 - 0		13
42	31		A	Wealdstone	343	L 1 - 3	Smith 6	
43	April 4		A	Billericay Town	320	L 0 - 2		17
44	7		H	Horsham	121	W 3 - 0	S.Harris 60 **Harrison** 78 90 (pen)	
45	11		A	Canvey Island	294	L 0 - 1		15
46	13		H	Staines Town	250	W 2 - 0	Wellard 55 Smith 64	
47	16		H	Maidstone United	202	W 1 - 0	Palmer 90	12
48	21		A	Dartford	883	L 2 - 4		
49	25		A	Ramsgate	181	W 3 - 0	Jefferies 21 Harris S 66 Joseph 73	10

Average Home Att: 198 (225) **Goals 75 76**

Best Position: 1st **Worst:** 14th

Goalscorers: Harrison 23, Harris S 12, Harris W 10, Johnson 5, Logie 4, Smith 4, Wellard 4, Joseph 3, Palmer 2, Pigden 2, Smith 2, Jefferies 1, Todd 1.

AVELEY

Founded: 1927
Nickname: The Millers

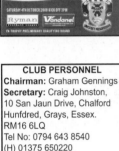

Manager: Rod Stringer

Club Colours: All royal blue.

Best Seasons - League: 1st Isthmian Division 1 North 2008-09.

Ground address: Mill Field, Mill Road, Aveley Essex RM15 4SJ

Tel No: 01708 865 940

Capacity: 4,000 **Seats**: 400 **Covered**: 400 **Floodlights**: Yes

Simple Directions: London - Southend A1306, turn into Sandy Lane at Aveley.

Rainham or Purfleet BR stations then bus No. 723 to the ground.

Bus from Rainham No 324

Midweek Home Matchday: Monday

Clubhouse: Normal pub hours. Bar snacks and hot food available. **Club Shop:** No

Local Radio: Radio Essex, Essex Radio and Time FM.

Local Press: Thurrock Gazette and Romford Recorder

CLUB PERSONNEL

Chairman: Graham Gennings
Secretary: Craig Johnston, 10 San Jaun Drive, Chalford Hunfdred, Grays, Essex. RM16 6LQ
Tel No: 0794 643 8540
(H) 01375 650220
(M) 0794 643 8540
Fax No: (H) 01375 650220 (call first)
craigjohnson@aveleyfc.freeserve.co.uk
Press Officer: Terry King
Tel No: 01708 557596
(H) 01708 557596
(M) 0798 990 2271
Fax No: (H) 01708 557596
Programme Editor: As Secretary

CLUB STATISTICS

Record	**Attendance:** 3,741 v Slough Town F.A.Amateur Cup 27.02.71
	Career Goalscorer: Jotty Wilks 214
	Career Appearances: Ken Riley 422
Record	**Victory:** 11-1 v Histon 24.08.63
	Defeat: 0-8 v Orient Essex
Senior Honours:	Athenian League Champions 1970-71.
	Thameside Trophy Winners 1980, 2005, 07.
	Isthmian League Division 1 North Champions 2008-09.
Previous Leagues:	**Leagues:** Thurrock Com 46-49; London 49-57; Delphian 57-63; Athenian 63-73
	Isthmian 1973-2004 Southern 2004-2006

Action from Aveley's FA Trophy match with Ilford. Above, Aveley's Christian Wheeler tries to go around Ilford 'keeper Rob Budd, whilst below Ilford's James Hughes clears the danger. Photos: Alan Coomes.

BILLERICAY TOWN

Founded:1880
Nickname: Town or Blues

CLUB PERSONNEL

Chairman: Steve Kent

Secretary: Ian Ansell
c/o BTFC
Tel No: 020 8496 6713
(H) 020 8500 9778
(M) 0795 897 8154
Fax No: (H) 020 8500 9778
ian.ansell@walthamforest.gov.uk
secretary@billericaytown.co.uk

Press Officer: Simon Williams
Tel No: (H) 01268 729825
simon@onemoredown.net
press.officer@billericaytown.co.uk

Programme Editor: Gary Clark
programme.editor@billericaytown.co.uk

Managers: Brian Statham.

Club Colours: Royal Blue/white/royal blue.

Best Season - League: 4th Isthmian Premier Division 2006-2007

Ground address: New Lodge, Blunts Wall Road, Billericay CM12 9SA

Tel No: 01277 652 188. Fax: 01277 655 177.

Capacity: 3,500 **Seats:** 424 **Covered:** 2,000 **Floodlights:** Yes

Simple Directions: From Shenfield (A129)right at first lights then 2nd right. From Basildon (A129) over first lights in town, then left at next lights and second right.

Midweek Home Matchday: Tuesday

Clubhouse: Open every evening except Mondays and open weekend lunchtime.

Club Shop: Open matchdays. Contact: John Richardson - c/o club

Local Radio: BBC Radio Essex, Essex Radio and Essex FM

Local Press: Evening Echo, Billericay Gazette and Billericay Recorder.

CLUB STATISTICS

Record
Attendance: 3,841 v West Ham Utd. Opening Floodlights 1977
3,193 v Farnborough T. F.A.Vase SF 1976
Victory: 11-0 v Stansted (A) Essex Senior .League. 05.05.76
Defeat: 3-10 v Chelmsford City (A) Essex Senior Cup 04.01.93
Career Goalscorer: Freddie Claydon 273 **Season**: Leon Gutzmore 51 (97-8)
Career Appearances: J.Pullen 418
Transfer Fee Paid: Undisclosed
Received: £22,500 + from W.H.U. for Steve Jones Nov. 1992

Senior Honours:
F.A.Vase Winners 75-76 76-77 78-79, Isthmian Div 1 R-up 80-81 97-98 Arthenian Lg 78-79
Essex Senior Cup 75-76 R-up (4) Essex Sen Trophy (2)

Previous
Leagues: Romford & Dist. 1890-1914, Mid Essex 18-47, S.Essex Comb. 47-66 Essex Olympian 66-71
Essex Senior 71-77. Athenian 77-79
Ground: New Lodge, Blunts Wall Road, Billericay CM12 9SA

Back Row (L-R): Jamie Dormer, Russell Pond, Harrison Chatting, Jo Flack, Nick Muir, Jack Edwards, Dean Etchells, Luca Frankis. **Middle Row:** Gary Ling (Physio), Fiston Manuella, Spencer Knight, James Baker, Jack West, Andy Walker, Mal Downing (Goalkeeping coach), Danny Fowler, Lawrence Yiga, Ian Wiles, Sam West, Marvin Hamilton. **Front Row:** Dave Wareham, Billy Bricknell, Ashley Dumas, Brian Statham (Manager), Ian Cousins (Captain), Barry Lakin (Assistant Manager), Michael Shinn, Greg Oates, Chris Sullivan.
Not pictured: Wayne Semanshia, Bradley Thomas.

BILLERICAY TOWN

BEST LGE ATT.: 532 v AFC Hornchurch
LOWEST: 79 v Dartford

No.	Date	Comp	H/A	Opponents	Att:	Result	Goalscorers	Pos
1	Aug 16	Ryman P.	A	Staines Town	277	L 0 - 1		
2	19		H	Tooting & Mitcham U	409	W 2 - 1	Flack 26 (pen) **Bricknell** 85	
3	23		H	Wealdstone	386	W 3 - 2	**Bricknell** 55 74 Shave 89	6
4	25		A	Canvey Island	577	L 0 - 4		
5	30		H	Carshalton Athletic	358	D 2 - 2	Cleary 57 **Bricknell** 68	
6	Sept 2		A	Hendon	221	W 1 - 0	Woods-Garness 8	
7	6		H	Harrow Borough	375	D 1 - 1	**Bricknell** 39	9
8	9		A	Tonbridge Angels	344	L 2 - 3	**Bricknell** 33 Shave 42	13
9	**13**	**F.A.C. 1Q**	**H**	**Clacton**	**337**	**W 4 - 1**	**Bricknell 6 90 Flack 87 (pen) Woods-Garness 89**	
10	20		A	AFC Hornchurch	506	D 1 - 1	**Bricknell** 5	12
11	23		H	Sutton United	342	W 1 - 0	**Bricknell** 18	
12	**27**	**F.A.C. 2Q**	**A**	**Sutton United**	**410**	**L 1 - 3**	**Wareham 78**	
13	Oct 4		H	Dartford	79	L 0 - 1		11
14	14		A	Hastings United	343	L 2 - 5	Wareham 35 Ferguson 71	
15	**18**	**F.A.T .1Q**	**A**	**Concord Rangers**	**291**	**L 1 - 3**	**Bricknell 2**	
16	25		H	Ramsgate	473	D 2 - 2	**Bricknell** 75 Flack 89	
17	Nov 2		H	Margate	336	W 3 - 2	Smith 29 Dean 30 **Bricknell** 73	12
18	15		A	Ashford Town	130	L 1 - 5	**Bricknell** 76	16
19	22		A	Boreham Wood	160	W 2 - 0	Ferguson 49 **Bricknell** 67	14
20	26		A	Horsham	134	W 1 - 0	Flack 85	
21	29		H	Maidstone United	505	D 1 - 1	**Bricknell** 72	
22	Dec 6		H	Staines Town	371	D 1 - 1	Woods-Garness 7	11
23	20		H	Hendon	408	W 4 - 2	**Bricknell** 19 66 Flack 21 51	10
24	Jan 13		A	Dover Athletic	922	L 1 - 2	Heffer 66	
25	17		A	Harrow Borough	178	L 1 - 3	Walters 19 (og)	13
26	24		H	AFC Hornchurch	532	W 1 - 0	Dumas 81	11
27	31		A	Sutton United	499	W 1 - 0	Lynvall 30	11
28	Feb 14		A	Dartford	1092	L 0 - 2		12
29	16		A	Tooting & Mitcham	232	D 0 - 0		
30	21		H	Horsham	419	L 0 - 1		15
31	28		A	Ramsgate	280	L 0 - 1		15
32	Mar 3		A	Wealdstone	288	W 2 - 1	Dormer 58 Wareham 72	
33	7		H	Hastings United	453	W 1 - 0	Duncan 2	10
34	10		H	Canvey Island	402	L 2 - 4	Flack 47 (pen) 70	
35	14		A	Harlow Town	354	L 0 - 3		12
36	21		H	Dover Athletic	502	L 2 - 3	Flack 35 Hodges 49	14
37	24		A	Heybridge Swifts	211	D 2 - 2	Shave 18 Hodges 56	
38	28		A	Margate	395	L 1 - 3	Shave 11	14
39	31		H	Harlow Town	305	D 2 - 2	Burbidge 12 68	
40	April 4		H	Ashford Town	320	W 2 - 0	Flack 52 Okojie 84	13
41	7		H	Tonbridge Angels	372	D 1 - 1	Flack 23	
42	11		A	Carshalton Athletic	266	L 1 - 3	Hunter 58	14
43	13		H	Heybridge Swifts	380	W 2 - 0	Shave 48 65	
44	18		H	Boreham Wood	425	D 1 - 1	Wareham 46	12
45	25		A	Maidstone United	357	W 1 - 0	Burbridge 35	11

Average Home Att: **388 (548)** **Goals** **60 73**

Best Position: 6th **Worst:** 16th

Goalscorers: Bricknell 18, Flack 11, Shave 6, Wareham 4, Burbridge 3, Woods-Garness 3, Ferguson 2, Hodges 2, Cleary 1, Dean 1, Dormer 1, Dumas 1, Duncan 1, Heffer 1, Hunter 1, Lynvall 1, Okojie 1, Smith 1. Own Goals 1.

BOGNOR REGIS TOWN

Founded: 1883
Nickname: The Rocks

Manager: Darin Kilpatrick

Club Colours: White with green trim/green/white.

Change Colours: Azure blue/navy/azure.

Best Seasons - League: 9th Conference South 2005-06.

Ground address: Nyewood Lane, Bognor Regis PO21 2TY.

Tel No: 01243 822 235.

Capacity: 4,100 **Seats**: 350 **Covered**: 2,600 **Floodlights**: Yes

Simple Directions: West along sea front from pier past Aldwick shopping centre then turn right into Nyewood Lane.

Midweek Home Matchday: Tuesday

Clubhouse: Yes

Club Shop: Yes

Local Press: Bognor Regis Guardian, Bognor Regis Observer, Brighton Argus and Portsmouth Evening News

Local Radio: Radio Sussex,Ocean Sound, Radio Solent,Southern Sound &Spirit FM

CLUB PERSONNEL

Chairman: Dominic Reynolds
Secretary: Simon Cook.
c/o Bognor Regis Town FC
(H): 01243 864 237
(B): 01293 610 801
(M): 07974 229 405
sajcook2@aol.com

Press Officer: Roger Nash
(M): 07751 594 285

Programme
Editor: Nigel Folland
nigel folland@btinternet.com

CLUB STATISTICS

Record
Attendance: 3,642 v Swansea City 1st Rd replay F.A.C 1984
Victory: 24-0 v Littlhampton W.Sussex Lg. 1913-14
Defeat: 0-19 v Shoreham W.Sussex Lg 1906-07
Career Goalscorer: Kevin Clements - 206
Career Appearances: Mick Pullen - 967 (20 seasons
Transfer Fee Paid: £2,000 for Guy Rutherford 95-96
Received: £10,500 from Brighton & Hove for John Crumplin and Geoff Cooper and from Crystal Palace for Simon Rodger

Senior Honours Sussex Senior Cup (9). Sussex Professional Cup 1973-74

Previous Leagues: West Sussex 1896-1926, Brighton & H.& D. 26-27, Sussex Co 1927-72, Southern Lg 1972-81. Isthmian 1982-2004. Conference 2004-09.

NB: UNFORTUNATELY A RECENT PHOTO WAS NOT AVAILABLE AT THE TIME OF GOING TO PRESS.

BOGNOR REGIS

BEST LGE ATT.: **1,000** v AFC Wimbledon
LOWEST: **200** v Braintree Town

No.	Date	Comp	H/A	Opponents	Att:	Result	Goalscorers	Pos
1	Aug 9	BSS	H	Worcester City	436	L 1 - 2	Jackson 89	
2	12		A	Hampton & Richmond B	430	D 0 - 0		
3	16		A	AFC Wimbledon	2741	L 1 - 3	Jackson 44	
4	23		H	Maidenhead United	451	L 2 - 4	Burke 49 Watson 73	19
5	25		A	Eastleigh	907	L 1 - 2	Waterman 56	
6	30		H	Bishop's Stortford	319	L 0 - 2		21
7	Sept 2		H	Welling United	275	D 0 - 0		
8	6		A	Chelmsford City	1215	L 0 - 2		21
9	**9**	**SS S1**	**H**	**Worcester City**	**168**	**W 2 - 0**	**Gaisie 13 Gatting 19**	
10	13		A	Team Bath	101	L 0 - 1		22
11	20		H	Fisher Athletic	220	W 2 - 1	Gaisle 19 64	21
12	**27**	**F.A.C. 2Q**	**A**	**Burgess Hill Town**	**426**	**D 0 - 0**		
13	**30**	**F.A.C.2R r**	**H**	**Burgess Hill Town**	**319**	**L 0 - 2**		
14	Oct 4		H	Bath City	302	L 0 - 0		21
15	**14**	**SS S2**	**A**	**Lewes**	**222**	**W 2 - 0**	**Gaisie 10 Clarke 90**	
16	18		A	St Albans City	389	L 0 - 1		22
17	21		H	Bromley	255	D 1 - 1	Clarke 57	
18	25		A	Thurrock	196	D 1 - 1	Clarke 40	22
19	Nov 1		H	Braintree Town	200	L 0 - 2		22
20	**8**	**SS S3**	**A**	**Woking**	**460**	**L 0 - 3**		
21	15		H	Weston-s-Mare	220	D 1 - 1	Hughes 71	
22	**22**	**F.A.T. 3Q**	**A**	**Ramsgate**	**247**	**W 2 - 0**	**McEnery 36 Jupp 84**	
23	29		A	Fisher Athletic	200	W 1 - 0	McEnery 66	22
24	Dec 6		H	Hampton & Richmond B	328	L 0 - 1		22
25	9		A	Dorchester Town	344	L 0 - 1		
26	**16**	**F.A.T. 1R**	**H**	**Ebbsfleet United**	**299**	**L 0 - 2**		
27	20		A	Worcester City	588	D 1 - 1	Smith 71	22
28	26		H	Havant & Waterlooville	458	L 1 - 5	Castles 3	22
29	Jan 1		A	Havant & Waterlooville	971	D 2 - 2	Pearce13 (pen) 44	
30	3		H	AFC Wimbledon	1000	L 1 - 5	Pearce 75	22
31	17		A	Basingstoke Town	371	D 0 - 0		21
32	24		H	Hayes & Yeading	333	D 1 - 1	Pearce 42 (pen)	21
33	27		H	Thurrock	254	D 1 - 1	Downes 90	
34	31		A	Braintree Town	459	D 1 - 1	Downes 18	22
35	Feb 7		H	Basingstoke Town	351	L 2 - 3	Downes 47 Lynch 67	
36	11		A	Newport County	618	L 1 - 2	Cox 22	
37	14		A	Weston-s-Mare	251	W 2 - 1	Downes 25 Lynch 90	22
38	21		H	Chelmsford City	451	W 2 - 1	Downes 40 Lynch 54	21
39	24		A	Bromley	206	L 0 - 1		
40	28		H	St Albans City	245	L 0 - 5		
41	Mar 7		A	Bath City	497	W 1 - 0	Du Chattellier	
42	14		H	Team Bath	328	W 3 - 0	Hughes 20 Du Chattelier 30 Downes 88	
43	21		A	Bishop's Stortford	492	L 0 - 2		21
44	24		H	Newport County	362	L 0 - 1		21
45	April 4		A	Welling United	556	L 1 - 4	Downes 25	Rel.
46	11		A	Maidenhead United	228	L 0 - 2		21
47	13		H	Eastleigh	442	W 1 - 0	Smith 58	
48	18		H	Dorchester Town	400	D 0 - 0		22
49	25		A	Hayes & Yeading	325	L 1 - 3	Wallis-Taylor 3	21

Average Home Att: 363 (377) **Goals** 39 73

Best Position: 19th **Worst:** 22nd

Goalscorers: Downes 7, Gaisie 4, Pearce 4, Clarke 3, Lynch 3, McEnery 3, Du Chattellier 2, Hughes 2, Jackson 2, Jupp 2, Smith 2, Burke 1, Cox 1, Castles 1, Gatting 1, Wallis-Taylor 1, Waterman 1, Watson 1.

Rel. - Relegated.

BOREHAM WOOD

Founded: 1948
Nickname: The Wood

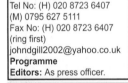

Manager: Ian Allinson.

Club Colours: White/black/black.

Best Season - League: Isthmian Premier Division Runners Up 1997-1998

Ground address: Meadow Park, Broughinge Road, Boreham Wood, WD6 5AL.

Tel No: 0208 953 5097. Fax: 0208 207 7982.

Capacity: 4,502 **Seats**: 600 **Covered**: 1,568 **Floodlights**: Yes

Simple Directions: A1 towards London from M25, 1st turn for Boreham Wood, head for town-centre, into Brook Road at roundabout before town centre, Broughinge Rd is first right. 1 mile from Elstree & Boreham Wood station (Thameslink), or bus 292 or107 to McDonalds (5 minutes walk)

Midweek Home Matchday: Tuesday.

Clubhouse: Open norman licensing hours with snacks available. Function Room (250) for hire. **Club Shop:** Full selection of products. Contact: Jeff Weston

Local Radio: Chiltern Radio

Local Press: Boreham Wood Times, Watford Observer and Herts Advertiser.

CLUB OFFICIIALS

Chairman: Danny Hunter

Secretary: Dell Ward
38 Beresford Gardens,
Enfield,
Middlesex EN1 1NN
Tel No: (H) 020 8363 7345
(M) 0786 766 1592
Fax No: (Day) 020 8207 7982
ddelldell@aol.com

Press Officer: John Gill
Tel No: (H) 020 8723 6407
(M) 0795 627 5111
Fax No: (H) 020 8723 6407
(ring first)
johndgill2002@yahoo.co.uk

Programme Editors: As press officer.

CLUB STATISTICS

Record	**Attendance:** 4,030 v Arsenal (Friendly) 13.07.01
	Career Goalscorer: Mickey Jackson
	Career Appearances: Dave Hatchett 714
Record Transfer Fee	**Paid**: Not known.
	Received: £5,000 from Dagenham & Redbridge for Steve Heffer
Senior Honours:	Isthmian Lg. Prem Div R-Up 97-98 Div I Champions 94-95, 00-01 Southern Lg. Div 1 East Champions 2005-2006 Isthmian Lg. Div 2 76-77 Athenian Lg. 73-74, Herts SeniorCup 71-72 ,98-99 01-02 R-up (8), London Challenge Cup 97-98
Previous :	**Leagues:** Mid Herts 48-52, Parthenon 52-57, Spartan 56-66, Athenian 66-74
	Ground: Eldon Avenue 1948-63
	Names: Boreham Wood Rovers and Royal Retournez, amalgamated in 1948

Back Row (L-R): Ryan Kirby, Marc Charles-Smith, Jon Wordsworth, Simon Overland, Anthony Anstead, Kevin Stephens, Greg Morgan, Curtis Ujah, Sean Sonner, Laura Dalby (Physiotherapist).
Front Row: Raphael Sylvester, Billy Hawes, Jon Clements, Joe Reynolds, Paul Burrows (First Team Coach), Wes Daly (Club Captain), Ian Allinson (Team Manager), Mario Noto, Lewis Cook, Lee Allinson.

BOREHAM WOOD

BEST LGE ATT.: **453** v Dartford
LOWEST: **96** v Ashford Town (Middx)

No.	Date	Comp	H/A	Opponents	Att:	Result	Goalscorers	Pos
1	Aug 16	Ryman P.	A	Tooting & Mitcham	295	W 2 - 1	Donnelly 7 Ofori 90	
2	19		H	Hastings United	109	W 2 - 1	Morgan 24 Ofori 85	
3	23		H	Ramsgate	135	D 1 - 1	Donnelly 48	4
4	25		A	Wealdstone	354	D 1 - 1	Barber 8	
5	30		H	Dover Athletic	218	L 2 - 3	Archer 77 (pen) **Allinson** 89	7
6	Sept 2		A	Staines Town	228	L 1 - 4	Watters 25	
7	6		A	Carshalton Athletic	258	W 2 - 0	Buchanan 7 Watters 53	8
8	9		H	Maidstone United	137	L 0 - 1		
9	**13**	**F.A.C. 1Q**	**H**	**Biggleswade United**	**75**	**W 3 - 0**	**Buchanan 31 Allinson 63 Archer 79**	
10	20		H	Harlow Town	163	W 2 - 0	Noto 38 Morgan 72	9
11	23		A	Heybridge Swifts	130	W 2 - 1	Noto 56 Archer 78	
12	**27**	**F.A.C 2Q**	**A**	**Thurrock**	**90**	**W 5 - 0**	**Allinson 3 Wordsworth 11 Archer 18 48 Watters 51**	
13	Oct 4		A	Harrow Borough	169	D 1 - 1	**Allinson** 68 (pen)	9
14	**11**	**F.A.C. 3Q**	**H**	**Brackley Town**	**416**	**L 0 - 1**		
15	14		H	Ashford Town (Middx)	96	W 3 - 1	Mason 54 59 Buchanan 74	
16	**18**	**F.A.T 1Q**	**H**	**Burgess Hill**	**89**	**W 2 - 0**	**Buchanan 45 Allinson 90 (pen)**	
17	25		A	Tonbridge Angels	367	D 1 - 1	Archer 86	6
18	**Nov 1**	**F.A.T 2Q**	**H**	**Uxbridge**	**77**	**L 1 - 2**	**Mason 85**	
19	11		H	Margate	122	L 1 - 2	Ofori 13	
20	15		H	Horsham	118	L 0 - 2		9
21	18		A	Canvey Island	235	L 0 - 4		
22	22		H	Billericay Town	160	L 0 - 2		13
23	29		A	Dartford	906	L 0 - 3		15
24	Dec 6		H	Tooting & Mitcham U	124	W 2 - 0	Sonner 3 **Allinson** 67	14
25	9		A	AFC Hornchurch	152	W 4 - 1	Watters 16 McFarlane 26 (og) Mason 75 Sonner 81	
26	20		H	Staines Town	131	L 0 - 2		13
27	27		A	Hendon	175	D 1 - 1	Sonner 60	14
28	Jan 13		A	Ramsgate	162	L 0 - 2		
29	17		H	Carshalton Athletic	138	L 1 - 2	Watters 35	16
30	24		A	Harlow Town	295	D 3 - 3	Watters 57 Noto 75 Daly 90	15
31	31		H	Heybridge Swifts	132	W 1 - 1	**Allinson** 90	
32	Feb 7		A	Maidstone United	319	D 1 - 1	Wordsworth 72	13
33	10		A	Hastings United	249	D 1 - 1	Noto 77	
34	14		H	Harrow Borough	158	L 1 - 2	Clements 90	13
35	17		H	Wealdstone	214	W 2 - 0	Sonner 78 Daly 85 (pen)	
36	21		A	Margate	453	L 1 - 3	Sonner 69	12
37	28		H	Tonbridge Angels	160	L 0 - 2		12
38	Mar 7		A	Ashford Town	118	W 1 - 0	Noto 24	
39	10		H	Sutton United	119	L 1 - 3	**Allinson** 8 (pen)	
40	14		H	AFC Hornchurch	168	L 1 - 3	Lee 77	14
41	21		A	Sutton United	893	D 1 - 1	Abbassi 52 (og)	15
42	28		H	Canvey Island	137	L 0 - 1		15
43	April 4		A	Horsham	194	D 2 - 2	Sonner 31 68	
44	11		A	Dover Athletic	1346	W 2 - 1	Sonner 26 Noto 69	16
45	15		H	Hendon	220	L 0 - 1		
46	18		A	Billericay Town	425	D 1 - 1	**Allinson** 80	18
47	25		H	Dartford	453	D 0 - 0		18

Average Home Att: **162 (308)** **Goals** **59 66**

Best Position: 4th **Worst:** 18th

Goalscorers: Allinson 9, Sonner 8, Archer 6, Noto 6, Watters 6, Buchanan 4, Mason 4, Ofori 3, Daly 2, Donnelly 2, Morgan 2, Wordsworth 2, Barber 1, Clements 1, Lee 1. Ownn Goals 2.

CANVEY ISLAND

Founded: 1926
Nickname: The Gulls

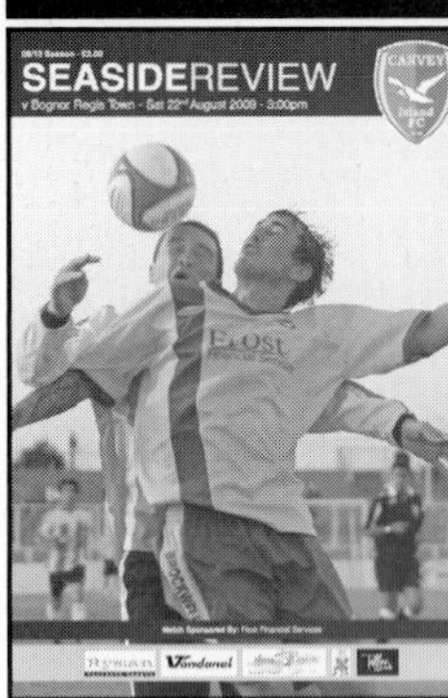

Manager: John Batch
Club Colours: Yellow & royal blue/royal blue/yellow & royal blue.
Best Seasons: League: 14th Conference 2005-2006
Ground address: The Brockwell Stadium, Park Lane, Canvey Island, Essex SS8 7PX
Tel No: 01268 682 991. Fax: 01268 695 281
Capacity: 4,100 **Seats**: 500 **Covered**: 827 **Floodlights**: Yes
Simple Directions:
By Road: A130 from A13 or A127 at Sadlers Farm roundabout. One mile through town centre, first right past old bus garage.
By Rail: Nearest station: Benfleet (BR). Three miles from ground on Fenchurch St line from London.Then bus 3 or 151 to the stop after the Admiral Jellicoe pub.
Midweek Home Matchday: Tuesday
Clubhouse: Open Tuesday & Thursday evenings, matchdays and private functions.
Club Shop: Sells full range of club products which can also be purchased online at www.canveyislandfc.com.
Local Radio: BBC Essex & Essex FM
Local Press: Evening Echo

CLUB PERSONNEL
Chairman: George Frost
Secretary: Gary Sutton
58 Lottem Road, Canvey Island,Essex SS8 7HX
(H) 01268 696836
(M) 0779 002 5828
Fax No: (Club) 01268 695281
gary.sutton@db.com
Press Officer: Chris Sutton
(M) 0774 092 1532
chris.sutton@talksport.co.uk
Programme
Editor: Glen Eckett
gleneckett@another.com

CLUB STATISTICS

Record	**Attendance:** 3,553 v Aldershot Town Isthmian League 2002-2003
	Career Goalscorer: Andy Jones
	Season's Top Scorer: Lee Boylan
	Career Appearances: Steve Ward
Record Transfer Fee	**Paid**: £5,000 to Northwich Victoria for Chris Duffy
	Received: £4,500 to Farnborough Town for Brian Horne
Senior Honours:	F.A.Trophy Winners 2000-2001 R-Up 2001-2002 Isthmian Champions 2003-04 Isthmian Divison 1 Champions 1993-1994 Essex Sen. Cup 98-99 00-01 01-02
Previous Leagues:	Southend & District, Thurrock & Thamesid Combination, Parthenon, Metropolitan, Greater London 64-71 Essex Senior 71-95 Isthmian 95-04 Conference 2004-2006.

Back Row (L-R): Tony West (Physio), Kevin Dobinson, Greg Cohen, Chris Moore, Ben Patten, Richard Halle, James Russell, Richard Bastin, Andrew West, Leon Gordon, Reiss Noel, Gabriel Fanibuyan, Jay Curran, John Batch (Manager). **Front Row:** Danny Kerrigan, Ian Luck, Ryan Edgar, Craig Davidson, James Rowe, Nick Reynolds, Stuart Batch, Danny Curran, Jon Edwards, Frank Everett.

CANVEY ISLAND

BEST LGE ATT.: **785** v Dartford
LOWEST: **235** v Boreham Wood

No.	Date	Comp	H/A	Opponents	Att:	Result	Goalscorers	Pos
1	Aug 16	Ryman P.	H	Horsham	377	L 2 - 4	Moore 19 J.Curran 85	
2	19		A	Maidstone United	452	D 0 - 0		
3	23		A	Margate	537	W 4 - 0	**Gordon** 22 Young 59 Lee 60 J.Curran 86	10
4	25		H	Billericay Town	577	W 4 - 0	Lee 14 Moore 26 Luck 40 **Gordon** 88	
5	30		A	Ashford Town (Middx)	247	L 0 - 1		9
6	Sept 2		H	Tonbridge Angels	315	W 3 - 2	Halle 45 Davidson 46 (pen) Lee 90	
7	6		H	Hendon	363	D 1 - 1	Curran 13	
8	9		A	Harrow Borough	143	W 4 - 2	**Gordon** 22 63 Davidson 39 (pen) Corbell 84	6
9	**13**	**F.A.C. 1Q**	**H**	**Dunstable Town**	**242**	**L 1 - 5**	**Fanibuyan 36**	
10	20		A	Sutton United	544	L 0 - 1		8
11	23		H	AFC Hornchurch	363	W 3 - 2	Davidson 66 Antoine 69 Curran 70	
12	Oct 4		H	Staines Town	351	D 2 - 2	Davidson 34 Antoine 71	
13	11		A	Ramsgate	282	D 2 - 2	Curran 59 Moore 90	8
14	14		A	Wealdstone	303	W 3 - 2	Curran 27 44 Lee 90	
15	**18**	**F.A.T.1Q**	**A**	**Cambridge City**	**312**	**D 1 - 1**	**Moore 57**	
16	**21**	**F.A.T.1Qr**	**H**	**Cambridge City**	**245**	**D 0 - 0**	**Cambridge City won 4-2 after penalties**	
17	25		H	Dover Athletic	573	L 0 - 3		5
18	Nov 1		A	Harlow Town	285	L 0 - 3		8
19	8		H	Hastings United	324	W 5 - 2	Ainsley 11 Antoine 3145 **Gordon** 33 88	6
20	15		A	Carshalton Athletic	297	D 2 - 2	**Gordon** 63 Ainsley 88 (pen)	6
21	18		H	Boreham Wood	235	W 4 - 0	Davidson 21 61 Fanibuyan 9 Ainsley 47	
22	22		H	Tooting & Mitcham U	387	W 3 - 1	Ainsley 22 Moore 29 Edwards 38	5
23	29		A	Heybridge Swifts	216	W 3 - 2	Davidson 50 Fanibuyan 52 60	4
24	Dec 6		A	Horsham	204	L 0 - 3		4
25	13		H	Maidstone United	316	L 0 - 1		5
26	20		A	Tonbridge Angels	446	L 0 - 3		6
27	27		H	Dartford	785	L 2 - 3	Oliva 64 Fanibuyan 71	6
28	Jan 17		A	Hendon	123	L 0 - 2		7
29	24		H	Sutton United	328	D 0 - 0		8
30	31		A	AFC Hornchurch	371	L 0 - 1		10
31	Feb 7		H	Harrow Borough	259	W 3 - 1	**Gordon** 3 Fanibuyan 25 Moore 38	7
32	14		A	Staines Town	282	L 1 - 2	Halle 31	7
33	21		H	Ramsgate	319	W 2 - 0	**Gordon** 42 Davidson 44	7
34	28		A	Dover Athletic	1083	L 1 - 2	Curran 56	7
35	Mar 3		H	Margate	310	L 0 - 4		
36	5		H	Wealdstone	342	D 1 - 1	Curran 77	8
37	10		A	Billericay Town	402	W 4 - 2	Halle 23 Curran 26 **Gordon** 49 Antione 60	
38	14		A	Hastings United	364	L 0 - 2		8
39	21		H	Harlow Town	310	L 1 - 3	**Gordon** 72	10
40	28		A	Boreham Wood	137	W 1 - 0	Antoine 81	10
41	April 4		H	Carshalton Athletic	300	L 0 - 1		11
42	11		H	Ashford Town	294	W 1 - 0	Dobinson 84	10
43	13		A	Dartford	1053	L 0 - 4		
44	18		A	Tooting & Mitcham	302	L 1 - 3	**Gordon** 72	13
45	25		H	Heybridge Swifts	354	W 2 - 0	Antione 35 43	12

Average Home Att: **371** **Goals** **67 76**

Best Position: 4th **Worst:** 13th

Goalscorers: Gordon 12, Curran J 10, Antoine 8, Davidson 8, Fanibuyan 6, Moore 6, Ainsley 4, Lee 4, Halle 3, Corbett 1, Dobinson 1, Edwards 1, Luck 1, Oliva 1, Young 1.

CARSHALTON ATHLETIC

Founded: 1905
Nickname: Robins

CLUB PERSONNEL
Chairman: Harry Driver
Secretary: Paul Dipre
c/o the club.
Tel No: 020 8642 2551
(H) 01306 611 667
(M) 0776 600 2660
Fax No: 020 8643 0999
pauldipre@carshaltonathletic.co.uk
Press Officer: Peter Randall
Tel No (M) 0774 236 8826
peter.randall1@btinternet.com
Programme
Editor: Simon Fuller
Tel No: (M) 0771 571 6061
leovialli@hotmail.com

Manager: Hayden Bird

Club Colours: Red/red/red.

Best Season - League: 19th Conference South 2004-2005.

Ground: War Memorial Sports Ground, Colston Avenue, Carshalton, SM5 2PN

Tel No: 0208 642 2551. Fax: 0208 643 0999.

Capacity: 8,000 **Seats**: 240 **Covered**: 4,500 **Floodlights**: Yes

Simple Directions: Turn right out of Carshalton Station exit, turn right again and then left into Colston Avenue.

Midweek Home Matchday: Tuesday

Clubhouse: Open daily evenings and midday. Bookings taken 020 8642 8658

Club Shop: Yes

Local Press: Sutton Comet, Croydon Advertiser, Sutton Guardian and Sutton Borough Post

Local Radio: BBC Southern Counties

CLUB STATISTICS

Record	**Attendance**: 7,800 v Wimbledon London Senior Cup
	Victory: 13-0 v Worthing Lg Cup 28.02.91
	Defeat: 0-11 v Southall, Athenian League - March 1963.
	Career Goalscorer: Jimmy Bolton - 242
	Career Appearances: Jon Warden - 504
Record Transfer Fee	**Paid**: £15,000 to Enfield for Curtis Warmington
	Received: £30,000 from Crystal Palace for Ian Cox
Senior Honours:	Surrey Senior Cup (3) Runners-Up (5) Surrey Senior Shield 75-76 R-Up (2) London Challenge Cup 91-92
Previous Leagues:	Southern Suburban (pre 1911) Surrey Senior 22-23 London 23-46 Corinthian 46-56 Athenian 56-73. Isthmian

Back Row (L-R): Hayden Bird (manager), Jeff Evans (coach), David Graves, Jamie England, Matt Gray, Adrian Toppin, Richard Stroud, Matt Reed, Liam Harwood, Bashir Alimi, Lewis Gonsalves, Tony Quinton, Micky Reid (physiotherapist), Gerry Wrafter (kit manager). **Front row:** Wes Daly, Charlie Ide, Karl Beckford, Antonio Gonnella, Simon Cooper, Frankie Sawyer, Richard Jolly, Adrian Stone.

CARSHALTON ATHLETIC

BEST LGE ATT.: 1,078 v Sutton United
LOWEST: 119 v AFC Hornchurch

No.	Date	Comp	H/A	Opponents	Att:	Result	Goalscorers	Pos
1	Aug 16	Ryman P.	H	Margate	285	W 2 - 1	Stevens 60 **Jolly** 75	
2	19		A	AFC Hornchurch	309	W 2 - 0	Alimi 51 **Jolly** 69	
3	23		A	Harrow Borough	140	W 5 - 1	Carpenter 6 **JOLLY** 4 (pen 22 27 49)	2
4	25		H	Horsham	354	L 1 - 5	Carpenter 34	
5	30		A	Billericay Town	358	D 2 - 2	**Jolly** 46 73	6
6	Sept 2		A	Dartford	798	W 3 - 2	**Jolly** 72 Day 78 (og) Kadi 90	
7	6		H	Boreham Wood	258	L 0 - 2		5
8	9		A	Hastings United	329	W 1 - 0	**Jolly** 20	5
9	**13**	**F.A.C. 1Q**	**H**	**Eastbourne Town**	**247**	**W 4 - 1**	**Stevens 8 JOLLY 3 (39 49 69)**	
10	20		A	Tooting & Mitcham U	561	W 2 - 1	**Jolly** 51 Kadi 56	
11	23		H	Ashford Town (Middx)	207	W 1 - 0	**Jolly** 21	
12	**27**	**F.A.C 2Q**	**H**	**Leiston**	**311**	**L 1 - 2**	**Jolly 71**	
13	Oct 4		H	Dover Athletic	528	L 0 - 1		4
14	11		A	Wealdstone	334	D 1 - 1	Kadi 68	4
15	14		A	Ramsgate	186	W 2 - 1	Carpenter 5 52	
16	**18**	**F.A.T 1Q**	**A**	**Hastings United**	**320**	**L 1 - 3**	**Kadi 49**	
17	25		H	Staines Town	314	L 1 - 3	**Jolly** 70	3
18	28		H	Heybridge Swifts	139	D 0 - 0		
19	Nov 15		H	Canvey Island	297	W 2 - 0	**Jolly** 78 85	4
20	18		A	Maidstone United	278	W 2 - 0	Kadi 42 England 36	
21	22		A	Harlow Town	242	W 2 - 1	Stevens 45 Power 60	2
22	29		H	Hendon	307	W 1 - 0	**Jolly** 18	2
23	Dec 6		A	Margate	365	D 2 - 2	**Jolly** 40 45	2
24	20		H	Dartford	413	L 0 - 2		4
25	27		H	Sutton United	1078	L 0 - 2		4
26	Jan 17		A	Boreham Wood	138	W 2 - 1	**Jolly** 57 60	5
27	24		H	Tooting & Mitcham	376	L 0 - 1		5
28	31		A	Ashford Town (Middx)	167	D 1 - 1	**Jolly** 40	5
29	Feb 10		A	Horsham	109	W 3 - 2	**Jolly** 15 England 50 Martin 80	
30	14		A	Dover Athletic	1095	D 2 - 2	Stevens 72 Gonsalves 90	4
31	21		H	Wealdstone	321	W 3 - 2	**Jolly** 8 Graves 77 Clarke 72	4
32	24		A	Tonbridge Angels	302	L 0 - 1		
33	28		A	Staines Town	349	L 1 - 4	**Jolly** 27	4
34	Mar 7		H	Ramsgate	249	D 3 - 3	Ide 18 Alimi 28 **Jolly** 80	5
35	10		H	AFC Hornchurch	119	D 2 - 2	Martin 28 Ide 29	
36	14		H	Tonbridge Angels	366	L 0 - 3		5
37	17		H	Hastings United	160	D 2 - 2	Stevens 2 **Jolly** 50	
38	21		A	Heybridge Swifts	130	W 1 - 0	Harwood 75	
39	28		H	Maidstone United	323	L 0 - 3		5
40	31		H	Harrow Borough	151	L 2 - 3	**Jolly** 76 Stevens 88	
41	April 4		A	Canvey Island	300	W 1 - 0	**Jolly** 82	5
42	11		H	Billericay Town	266	W 3 - 1	Ide 47 England 71 **Jolly** 84 (pen)	5
43	13		A	Sutton United	12	D 1 - 1	Ide 88	
44	16		H	Harlow Town	281	W 3 - 1	Ide 14 **Jolly** 65 Kadi 87 (pen)	5
45	25		A	Hendon	274	W 2 - 1	**Jolly** 48 Ide 50	4
46	**28**	**Play-Off SF**	**A**	**Tonbridge Angels**	**1249**	**W 3 - 2**	**Jolly 22 85 Ide 49**	
47	**May 2**	**Play-Off F**	**A**	**Staines Town**	**1198**	**L 0 - 1***		

Average Home Att: 323 (348) **Goals** 73 70

Best Position: 2nd **Worst:** 6th

Goalscorers: Jolly 37, Ide 7, Kadi 6, Stevens 6, Carpenter 4, England 3, Alimi 2, Martin 2, Clarke 1, Gonsalves 1, Graves 1, Harwood 1, Power 1. Own Goals 1.

CRAY WANDERERS

Founded: 1860
Nickname: The Wands

CLUB PERSONNEL
Chairman: Gary Hillman
Secretary: John de Palma
76 Elm Grove, Orpington, Kent
BR6 0AD
Tel No: (H) 01689 819418
(M) 0778 603 8822
john.depalma@abbey.com
Press Officer: Jerry Dowlen
Tel No: 020 7204 8038
(H) 01689 859029
(M) 0771 315 8461
jerry.dowlen@btopenworld.net
Programme
Editor: Greg Mann
Tel No: (H) 020 8916 0997
(M) 0794 113 9997
greg25old@aol.com

Manager: Ian Jenkins.

Club Colours: Amber/black/black.

Best Season - League: 2nd Isthmian Division 1 South 2008-09.

Ground address: c/o Bromley F.C. Hayes Lane, Bromley, Kent BR2 9EF
Tel No: 020 8460 5291. Fax: 020 8313 3992

Capacity: 5,000 **Seats**: 1,300 **Covered**: 2,500 **Floodlights**: Yes

Simple Directions: One mile from Bromley South (BR). Buses 316, 146 and 119 pass the ground. Junction 4 off M25 then A21 towards London.

Midweek Home Matchday: Tuesday

Clubhouse: Open Matchdays

Club Shop: Yes

Local Radio: Radio Kent

CLUB STATISTICS

Record	**Attendance:** 1,523 v Stamford F.A.Vase 6th Round 1979-1980
	Career Goalscorer: Ken Collishaw 274
	Career Appearances: John Dorey 500 1961-1972
Record	**Victory** : 15-0 v Sevenoaks 1894-1895
	Defeat : 1-11 v Bromley 1920-1921
Senior Honours:	Kent Senior Trophy 92-93 03-04 Kent Amateur Cup (4) Kent Lg (5)
Previous Leagues:	**Previous Leagues**: Kent (4 spells) latest 34-38, W.Kent, London, Kent Amateur, S.London All., Aetolian 59-64, Gtr London 64-66, Metropolitan 66-71, Lon Metropolitan 71-75 London Spartan 75-78
	Grounds: Star Lane, Tothills, Twysden, Fordcroft, Grassmeade and St Mary Cray.

Top: Dartford 'keeper Andrew Young, gets up above his defence and Harlow's Ryan Kirby in the 1st Qualifying Round of the F.A. Trophy.

Middle: Dartford's James White (8) heads clear.

Left: Adam Flanagan, Dartford, cuts out the cross meant for Harlow's Tashan Adiyinka.

Photos: Alan Coomes.

DARTFORD

Founded: 1888
Nickname: The Darts

Manager: Tony Burman
Club Colours: White/ black/black.
Best Season- League: 3rd Alliance, 1984-85.
Ground address: Princes Park Stadium, Grassbanks, Darenth Road, Dartford DA1 1RT. Tel: 01322 299 990. Fax: 01322 299 996.
Capacity: 4,097 **Seats**: 640 **Covered**: All sides **Floodlights**: Yes
Simple Directions: 1) Fast track bus route from Dartford Town Centre to Princes Park bus stop outside ground. **2)** Ten minute walk from Dartford Town Centre. **3) By Car:** From Dartford Town Centre leave by A226 (Lowfield Street), up to junction with Princes Road controlled by traffic lights. Turn left into Princes Road, up to next traffic lights and junction with Darenth Road, turn right and entrance to gound is second road on the left.
Email Address: info@dartfordfc.co.uk
Midweek Home Matchday: Tuesday
Clubhouse: Yes. **Club Shop:** At ground.
Local Radio: Radio Kent. Time 106.8 FM
Local Press: Dartford Times, Dartford Messenger & News Shopper.

CLUB PERSONNEL

Chairman: David Skinner
Secretary: Peter Martin.
10 Pembroke Place,
Sutton-at-Hone, Dartford, Kent
DA4 9HR
(H) 01322 864038
(M) 0797 605 4202
Fax No: 01322 864038
peter@martinpe.freeserve.co.uk
Press Officer: Nicola Collett
Tel: 01322 299 990
niccollett@yahoo.co.uk
Programme
Editor: Tony Jaglo.
Tel No: (M) 0783 081 6958
tonyjaglo@tiscali.co.uk

CLUB STATISTICS

Record	**Attendance:** 11,004 v Leyton Orient F.A.Cup 1948 (Watling Street) 4,097 v Horsham YMCA (Ryman League Div 1South) 11/11/06 and v Crystal Palace Pre-season Friendly 20/7/07 **Career Appearances**:: Steve Robinson 692
Record Transfer Fee	**Paid**: £6,000 to Chelmsford City for John Bartley **Received:** £25,000 from Redbridge Forest for Andy Hessenthaler
Senior Honours:	Southern Lg 1930-31, 31-32, 73-74, 83-84, R-up 87-88, 88-89, Eastern Div 30-31,31-32, Southern Div 80-81, Southern Lg Div 2 1896-97, Lg Cup 76-77, 87-88, 88-89, Championship Shield 83-84, 87-88, 88-89; Kent Lg 1995-96, Lg Cup 24-25,Kent Snr Cup 29-30, 34-35, 38-39, 69-70, ;FA Trophy R-up 1974. Isthmian Division One North 2007-08.
Previous Leagues:	**Leagues:** Kent League 1894-96 1897-98 1899-1902 1909-14 21-26 93-96; Southern League 1996-2006 **Grounds:** The Brent/ Westgate House, Potters Meadow, Engleys Meadow, Summers Meadow, Watling St, then groundshares with Cray Wanderers, Erith & Belverdere, Purfleet, Gravesend & Northfleet and Thurrock.

Back row (L-R): Danny Barber, John Beales, Adam Flanagan, Rob Haworth, James White, Allan Tait. **Middle Row:** Leanne Taylor (Asst Physio); Dave Phillips (Physio), Kiran Dingri, Jamie Day,Lee Burns, Jay May, Den Ibrahim, Andrew Young, Tony Kessell, Elliot Bradbrook, Jamie Coyle, Karl Dent, John Macrae (Goalkeeper Coach). **Front Row:** Adam Burchell, Hussein Isa, Ryan Hayes, Paul Hennessy (ReserveTeanm Manager), Tony Burman (First Team Manager), Paul Sawyer (Asst Manager/Coach), Billy Burgess, Lee Noble, Adam Gross.

DARTFORD

BEST LGE ATT.: 2,013 v Maidstone United
LOWEST: 733 v Heybridge Swifts

No.	Date	Comp	H/A	Opponents	Att:	Result	Goalscorers	Pos
1	Aug 16	Ryman P.	A	Hendon	389	L 0 - 3		
2	19		H	Dover Athletic	1004	L 0 - 2		
3	23		H	Hastings United	1781	L 0 - 2		21
4	25		A	Harlow Town	594	W 2 - 1	Howard 1 Haworth 19	
5	30		H	Wealdstone	986	D 2 - 2	Dafter 11 Haworth 37	
6	Sept 2		H	Carshalton Athletic	798	L 2 - 3	Day 64 Guest 88	
7	6		A	Staines Town	451	L 1 - 2	Butterworth 27	21
8	9		H	Heybridge Swifts	733	D 1 - 1	White 90	19
9	**13**	**F.A.C. 1Q**	**H**	**Hastings United**	**830**	**W 3 - 2**	**Cass 15 Butterworth 48 Dafter 55**	
10	20		H	Horsham	1006	W 4 - 0	Cass 31 40 Noble 44 48	17
11	23		A	Maidstone United	667	W 2 - 1	Butterworth 16 Haworth 22	
12	**27**	**F.A.C. 2Q**	**H**	**Hampton & Richmond B**	**1057**	**L 0 - 1**		
13	Oct 4		A	Billericay Town	719	W 1 - 0	Noble 18	13
14	11		H	Margate	1379	L 0 - 1		13
15	**18**	**F.A.T 1Q**	**H**	**Harlow Town**	**851**	**W 2 - 1**	**Flanagan 14 Hayes 49**	
16	25		A	Tooting & Mitcham U	586	W 2 - 0	**McDonald** 44 Haworth 75	
17	28		H	AFC Hornchurch	923	D 3 - 3	**McDonald** 50 Haworth 68 Day 70	
18	**Nov 1**	**F.A.T. 2Q**	**H**	**Oxford City**	**749**	**D 3 - 3**	**McDonald 3 (2 34 47)**	
19	**4**	**F.A.T. 2Qr**	**A**	**Oxford City**	**219**	**W 4 - 2**	**McDonald 2 60 Coyle 29 Noble 43**	
20	8		A	Harrow Borough	325	L 1 - 2	**McDonald** 29	16
21	15		H	Sutton United	1082	L 2 - 3	Dafter 48 Haworth 90	17
22	18		A	Tonbridge Angels	703	L 1 - 4	**McDonald** 10	
23	**22**	**F.A.T 3Q**	**A**	**St. Albans City**	**525**	**D 0 - 0**		
24	**25**	**F.A.T. 3Qr**	**H**	**St Albans City**	**542**	**D 1 - 1**	**Haworth 78 St Albans City won 4-2 on penalties.**	
25	29		H	Boreham Wood	906	W 3 - 0	**McDonald** 22 82 Harvey 79 (og)	17
26	Dec 6		H	Hendon	926	W 1 - 0	Osborne 74 (pen)	15
27	13		A	Dover Athletic	1208	L 2 - 4	Haworth 9 71	15
28	20		A	Carshalton Athletic	413	W 2 - 0	Osborne 48 (pen) Noble 82	14
29	27		A	Canvey Island	785	W 3 - 2	**McDonald** 3 (44 45 58)	
30	30		A	Ramsgate	412	W 1 - 0	Day 45	
31	Jan 17		H	Staines Town	1148	D 0 - 0		9
32	24		A	Horsham	418	W 3 - 0	Hayes 23 **McDonald** 50 88	6
33	31		H	Maidstone Uited	2013	W 1 - 0	Haworth 63	6
34	Feb 7		A	Heybridge Swifts	376	D 0 - 0		6
35	14		H	Billericay Town	1092	W 2 - 0	Cass 71 Guest 89	5
36	21		A	Ashford Town	320	L 0 - 1		6
37	28		H	Tooting & Mitcham U	1320	W 3 - 1	Hayes 6 Haworth 9 69	6
38	Mar 3		A	Hastings United	334	D 0 - 0		
39	7		A	Margate	745	D 2 - 2	Osbourne 60 Gross 76	6
40	14		H	Harrow Borough	1139	L 0 - 1		
41	21		A	AFC Hornchurch	610	L 0 - 2		7
42	24		H	Harlow Town	828	D 1 - 1	May 39	
43	28		H	Tonbridge Angels	1380	D 2 - 2	Woods-Garness 14 Flanagan 47	7
44	April 4		A	Sutton United	727	L 0 - 1		9
45	11		A	Wealdstone	664	D 0 - 0		9
46	13		H	Canvey Island	1053	W 4 - 0	Flanagan, Haworth Hayes Noble	
47	18		H	Ramsgate	1105	W 4 - 0	Haworth 37 60 Hayes 57 Noble 70	
48	21		H	Ashford Town	883	W 4 - 2	Coyle Flanagan (pen) May Noble	
49	25		A	Boreham Wood	453	D 0 - 0		8

Average Home Att: 1118 **Goals 75 59**

Best Position: 5th **Worst:** 21st

Goalscorers: McDonald 16, Haworth 15, Noble 8, Hayes 5, Cass 4, Flanagan 4, Butterworth 3, Dafter 3, Day 3, Guest 2, Osborne 3, May 2, Coyle 2, Gross 1, Howard 1, White 1, Woods-Garness 1. Own Goals 1.

HARROW BOROUGH

Founded: 1933
Nickname: Boro

Manager: David Howell

Club Colours: Red with white trim/red/red

Best Season - League: Isthmian Premier Champions 1983-84.

Ground Address: Earlsmead, Carlyon Avenue,South Harrow, Middlx HA2 8SS

Telephone: 0844 561 1347 Fax: 0208 423 0159

Official website: www.harrowboro.com

Capacity: 3,070 **Seats:** 350 **Covered:**1,000 **Floodlights:** Yes

SIMPLE DIRECTIONS: Underground to Northolt Central Line and140 bus to Northolt Park BR or South Harrow (Piccadilly Line) then 114 or H10 to King Rd junction. By road leave A40 at MacDonalds roundabout towards Northolt station (A312 north) left at lights right at Eastcote Arms pub. Ground 5th turning on right.

Midweek Home Matchday: Tuesday

Clubhouse: Open daily normal pub hours.

Club Shop: Yes contact c/o club

Local Press: Harrow Observer & Harrow Times

Local Radio: None

CLUB PERSONNEL

Chairman: Peter Rogers

Secretary: Peter Rogers
Tel No: 020 8423 0157
(H) 020 8248 8003
(M) 0795 618 5685
Fax No: 020 8423 0159
peter@harrowboro.co.uk

Press Officer: As chairman.

Programme
Editor: As chairman

CLUB STATISTICS

RECORD	**Attendance**: 3,000 v Wealdstone F.A.C.1st Qualifying Round 1946
	Victory: 13-0 v Handley Page (A) 18.10.41
	Defeat: 0-8 on five occasions
	Career Goalscorer: Dave Pearce 153
	Career Appearances: Steve Emmanuel 522 Colin Payne 557 Les Currell 582
SENIOR HONOURS:	Isthmian Champions 1983-84 Athenian Div 2 R-Up 63-64 Middx Sen Cup 82-83 92-93 Middx Premier Cup 81-82 Middx Sen. Charity Cup 79-80 92-93 05-06, 06-07
PREVIOUS	**Names:** Roxonian 1933-38 Harrow Town 38-66
	Leagues: Harrow & District 1933-34 Spartan 34-40 45-58 W.Middx Comb 40-41 Middlesex SeniorCU. 41-45 Delphian 56-63 Athenian 63-75

Back Row: (L-R): Jerome Hall, Jamie Lawrence, Danny Leech, Kai Williams, Gary Ross, Andray Baptiste, Jonathan Constant, Bobby Highton, Eugen George Burlacu, Chad Smith (Physiotherapist).
Front Row: David Howell (Manager), Darren Grieves, Daniel McGonigle, Simon Dahl, Wayne Walters (Captain), Lee Hall, Josiah Hunte, Ismael Ehui, Ken Charlery (First Team Coach). Photo by Stuart Emmerson / Harrow Observer.

HARROW BOROUGH

BEST LGE ATT.: 580 v Wealdstone
LOWEST: 101 v Heybridge Swifts

No.	Date	Comp	H/A	Opponents	Att:	Result	Goalscorers	Pos
1	Aug 16	Ryman P.	A	Dover Athletic	906	L 0 - 4		
2	19		H	Heybridge Swifts	101	D 0 - 0		
3	23		H	CarshaltonAthletic	140	L 1 - 5	Grieves 90	20
4	25		A	Staines Town	232	L 0 - 1		
5	30		H	Ramsgate	137	L 0 - 1		24
6	Sept 2		A	Hastings United	328	W 2 - 0	Constant 6 (pen) Williams 62	
7	6		A	Billericay Town	375	D 1 - 1	Grieves 27	
8	9		H	Canvey Island	143	L 2 - 4	Grieves 6 Constant 90 (pen)	21
9	**13**	**F.A.C. 1Q**	**A**	**Hemel Hempstead**	**199**	**D 1 - 1**	**Walters 30**	
10	**16**	**F.A.C. 1Qr**	**H**	**Hemel Hempstead**	**121**	**L 1 - 2**	**Constant 64**	
11	20		H	Maidstone United	230	D 1 - 1	Constant 80	20
12	23		A	Harlow Town	202	L 0 - 3		
13	Oct 4		H	Boreham Wood	189	D 1 - 1	Walters 37	
14	15		A	Hendon	130	L 0 - 7		22
15	**18**	**F.A.T. 1Q**	**H**	**Chatham Town**	**101**	**W 2 - 1**	**Hall 29 Shroot 30**	
16	28		A	Tooting & Mitcham U	191	D 1 - 1	Shroot	
17	**Nov 1**	**F.A.T. 2Q**	**H**	**Hastings United**	**111**	**L 2 - 3**	**Clarke 47 Highton 79**	
18	8		H	Dartford	325	W 2 - 1	Morelese 65 Shroot 69	21
19	15		A	Margate	374	W 3 - 2	Morlese 29 62 Shroot 68	19
20	18		H	Ashford Town (Middx)	115	L 0 - 1		
21	22		A	Tonbridge Angels	421	D 1 - 1	Clark 1	19
22	29		H	Horsham	124	W 6 - 1	Shroot 25 87 Leech 45 Jones 46 57 Highton 77	19
23	Dec 6		H	Dover Athletic	246	W 3 - 0	Shroot 5 76 Clarke 41	18
24	13		A	Heybridge Swifts	102	D 2 - 2	Shroot 52 **Noel** 44	17
25	20		H	Hastings United	163	D 1 - 1	Shroot 70	17
26	27		A	Wealdstone	780	L 0 - 6		18
27	Jan 17		H	Billericay Town	178	W 3 - 1	Constant 36 Hall L 65 Clarke 76	18
28	20		H	Harlow Town	162	L 1 - 4	Constant 30	19
29	Feb 7		A	Canvey Island	259	L 1 - 2	Constant 46	20
30	14		A	Boreham Wood	158	W 2 - 1	Hall 43 Whiteley 47	
31	17		H	Staines Town	146	W 2 - 1	Clarke 77 **Noel** 90	
32	21		H	AFC Hornchurch	158	L 1 - 2	Clarke 36	18
33	28		A	Sutton United	465	D 2 - 2	Clarke 48 McGonigle 86	18
34	Mar 7		H	Hendon	211	H 4 - 2	**NOEL** 4 (3 27 65 90)	
35	14		A	Dartford	1139	W 1 - 0	Fenton 36	16
36	21		H	Tooting & Mitcham U	174	D 0 - 0		
37	24		H	Suttton United	165	D 0 - 0		
38	28		A	Ashford United	110	D 0 - 0		18
39	31		A	Carshalton Athletic	151	W 3 - 2	**Noel** 21 57 Hall 86	
40	April 4		H	Margate	203	W 3 - 2	Watts 47 **Noel** 52 Jinadu 89	14
41	11		A	Ramsgate	176	W 2 - 0	**Noel** 21 Clarke 81	13
42	13		H	Wealdstone	580	L 0 - 3		
43	16		A	AFC Hornchurch	312	L 0 - 2		
44	18		H	Tonbridge Angels	202	L 2 - 3	Smith 1 Walters 76	15
45	21		A	Maidstone United	218	W 2 - 0	**Noel** 75 Clarke 88	
46	25		A	Horsham	225	L 0 - 1		14

Average Home Att: 187 (210) **Goals** 62 79

Best Position: 13th **Worst:** 22nd

Goalscorers: Noel 11, Shroot 10, Clarke 9, Constant 7, Hall 4, Grieves 3, Morelese 3, Walters 3, Highton 2, Jones 2, Fenton 1, Jinadu 1, Leech 1, McGonicle 1, Smith 1, Watts 1, Whiteley 1, Williams 1.

HASTINGS UNITED

Founded: 1894
Nickname : The U's

CLUB PERSONNEL
Chairman: David Walters
Secretary: Tony Cosens.
31 Sheerwater Crescent,
Hastings, East Sussex
TN34 2NY
Tel No: 01424 444635
(H) 01424 424209
(M) 0771 265 4288
richardcosens@btinternet.com
Press Office: Sean Adams
Tel No: (H) 01424 437533
(M) 0776 462 5739
hastingspaddy@aol.com
Programme
Editor: Simon Rudkins
Tel No: (H) 01424 719146
(M) 0770 335 8399
Fax No: (H) 01424 719146
simonrudkins@hotmail.com

Managers: Tony Dolby.

Club Colours: Claret/claret/claret.

Best Season- League: 5th Southern Premier 1998-1999

Ground address: The Pilot Field, Elphinstone Road, Hastings TN34 2AX

Tel No: 01424 444635.

Capacity: 4,050 **Seats**: 800 **Covered**: 1,750 **Floodlights**: Yes

Simple Directions: From A1 turn left at 3rd mini roundabout into St Helens Road. Then left after one mile into St Helens Park Rd. leading into Downs Rd. Turn left at T junction at end of road. Ground is 200yds on right.

Midweek Home Matchday: Tuesday

Clubhouse: Open matchdays **Club Shop:** Sells full range of club products

Local Radio: BBC Southern Counties, Southern Sound and Arrow F.M.

Local Press: Hastings Observer and The Argus.

CLUB STATISTICS

Records
Attendance: 4,888 v Nottingham Forest (Friendly) 23.06.96
Goalscorer in a Season: Terry White 33 1999-2000
Transfer Fee Paid: £8,000 to Ashford Town for Nicky Dent
Received: £30,000 from Nott'm Forest for Paul Smith

Senior Honours: Southern Lg.Cup 94-95 Southern Div 1 91-92 Div 2 R-Up 08-09

Previous Leagues: South Eastern 04-05 Southern 05-10 Sussex County 21-27 52- 85
Southern Amateur 27-46 Corinthian 46-48
Ground: Bulverhy the Recreation (pre 76)
Name: Hastings & St Leonards Amateurs, Hastings Town>2002

BackRow (L-R): John Lambert (Manager), Marc Whiteman, Ben Radley, Sam Adams, Scott Ramsay, Chris May, Nathan Russell, Rhys Whyborne, Sam Crabb, Gren Nessling, Mark Stapley (Reserve team assistant manager).
Front Row: Loraine Western (Physio), Antonio Gonnella, Frankie Sawyer, Scott Marshall, Paddy Cody, Danny Spice, Jack Franklin, Matt Maclean, Milton Miltiadou, Paul Nessling, Keith Miles (Reserve team manager).

HASTINGS UNITED

BEST LGE ATT.: 759 v Maidstone United
LOWEST: 249 v Boreham Wood

No.	Date	Comp	H/A	Opponents	Att:	Result	Goalscorers	Pos
1	Aug 16	Ryman P.	H	Ashford United	408	L 1 - 2	Whiteman 90	
2	19		A	Boreham Wood	109	L 0 - 2		
3	23		A	Dartford	1004	W 2 - 0	Gonnella 13 Adams 64	15
4	25		H	Maidstone United	759	L 0 - 4		
5	30		A	Sutton United	469	L 1 - 2	Gonella 25	20
6	Sept 2		H	Harrow Borough	328	L 0 - 2		
7	6		A	Harlow Town	313	W 1 - 0	Whiteman 90	17
8	9		H	Carshalton Athletic	329	L 0 - 1		17
9	**13**	**F.A.C. 1Q**	**A**	**Dartford**	**830**	**L 2 - 3**	**Adams 42 Radley 45**	
10	20		H	Dover Athletic	645	L 0 - 1		19
11	24		A	Horsham	225	W 2 - 0	**Sawyer** 13 69	
12	Oct 4		A	Margate	453	W 3 - 2	White 17 Adams 31 Whiteman 90	15
13	11		H	Tooting & Mitcham	462	L 0 - 3		17
14	14		H	Billericay Town	348	W 5 - 2	**Sawyer** 5 (27 42 49 60 77)	
15	**18**	**F.A.T 1Q**	**H**	**Carshalton Athletic**	**320**	**W 3 - 1**	**Sawyer 34 Ramsay 40 88**	
16	25		A	Heybridge Swifts	232	W 2 - 0	Ballard 49 Ramsay 90	10
17	28		H	Ramsgate	419	W 3 - 1	Warren 11 **Sawyer** 63 Ramsay 90	
18	**Nov 1**	**F.A.T. 2Q**	**A**	**Harrow Borough**	**111**	**W 3 - 2**	**Leech 3 (og) Adams 27 Franklin 87**	
19	8		A	Canvey Island	324	L 2 - 5	White 65 Gonella 81	10
20	15		H	AFC Hornchurch	604	L 2 - 4	McPharland 13 (og) Ballard 16	14
21	18		A	Staines Town	211	L 0 - 2		
22	**22**	**F.A.T. 3Q**	**A**	**Cambridge City**	**302**	**L 0 - 1**		
23	29		H	Wealdstone	435	W 2 - 1	Gray 45 (og) Gonnella 60	12
24	Dec 6		A	Ashford Town	131	L 4 - 5	**Sawyer** 37 Gonnella 40 Jirbandi 50 Darby 67	16
25	20		A	Harrow Borough	163	D 1 - 1	**Sawyer** 32	16
26	27		H	Tonbridge Angels	722	L 0 - 1		16
27	Jan 3		A	Maidstone United	431	W 1 - 0	Gonella 75	18
28	17		H	Harlow Town	429	W 3 - 2	Adams 41 **Sawyer** 76 MacLean 79	11
29	24		A	Dover Athletic	1205	L 2 - 3	**Sawyer** 37 72	13
30	31		H	Horsham	443	L 0 - 2		16
31	Feb 10		H	Boreham Wood	249	D 1 - 1	**Sawyer** 18	
32	14		H	Margate	388	D 1 - 1	Whyborne 31	16
33	17		A	Tooting & MItcham	330	L 0 - 1		16
34	28		H	Heybridge Swifts	377	L 0 - 1		17
35	Mar 3		H	Dartford	334	D 0 - 0		
36	7		A	Billericay Town	453	L 0 - 1		
37	14		H	Canvey Island	364	W 2 - 0	Adams 37 Carey 45	18
38	17		A	Carshalton Athletic	160	D 2 - 2	Gonella 5 Ramsay 23	
39	21		A	Ramsgate	260	W 1 - 0	Adams 73 (pen)	16
40	24		A	Hendon	162	L 0 - 4		
41	28		H	Staines Town	393	D 1 - 1	Adams 85 (pen)	16
42	April 4		A	AFC Hornchurch	322	W 2 - 1	MacLean 33 62	16
43	11		H	Sutton United	370	L 0 - 2		18
44	13		A	Tonbridge Angels	736	D 3 - 3	Adams 38 (pen) **Sawyer** 88 Whyborne 90	
45	18		H	Hendon	523	W 2 - 1	Whyborne 15 MacLean 78	16
46	25		A	Wealdstone	444	L 0 - 1		17

Average Home Att: **444 (515)** **Goals** **60 75**

Best Position: 10th **Worst:** 20th

Goalscorers: Sawyer 16, Adams 8, Gonella 7, Ramsay 5, MacLean 4, Whiteman 3, Whybone 3, Ballard 2, White 2, Carey 1, Darby 1, Franklin 1, Jirbani 1, McPharland 1, Radley 1, Warren 1. Own Goals 3.

HENDON

Founded: 1908
Nickname: Dons or Greens

Manager: Gary McCann.

Club Colours: Green/green/white.

Best Season - League: Isthmian Premier Champions 1964-65, 1972-73.

Ground address: Wembley F.C., Vale Farm, Watford Road, Sudbury, Wembley, Middlesex HA0 3HG.

Tel: 020 8908 3553 **Fax:** 020 8908 6116

Capacity: 2,450 **Seats:** 350 **Covered:** 950

Simple Directions: 400 yards from Sudbury Town station (underground) or 10 minutes walk from North Wembley BR.

Midweek Home Matchday: Tuesday

Clubhouse: Yes

Local Press: Hendon Times, Kilburn Times, Barnet Press, Hampstead & Highgate Express

Local Radio: Capital, GLR LBC.

CLUB PERSONNEL

Chairman: Vacant

Secretary: Graham Etchell, c/o the club
Tel No: 020 8908 3553
(M) 0797 369 8552
Fax No: 020 8908 6116
hendonfc@freenetname.co.uk

Press Officer:
David Balheimer
(M) 0777 580 9951
ballheimerdavid@hotmail.com

Programme Editor: As secretary

CLUB STATISTICS

RECORD	**Attendance**: 9,000 v Northampton Town F.A.Cup 1st Rd 1952
	Victory: 13-1 v Wingate Middlessex County Cup 2.2.57
	Defeat: 2-11 v Walthamstowe Avenue. Athenian League 9.11.35
	Career Goalscorer: Freddie Evans 176 (1929-35)
	Career Appearances: Bill Fisher 787 (1940-1964)
	Transfer fee received: £30,000 for Iain Dowie from Luton Town.
Senior Honours:	European Amateur Champions 1972-73. F.A.Amateur Cup Winners 59-60 64-65 71-72 R-up 54-5 65-6 Isthmian League 64-5 72-3 Premier Inter League Cup R-up 86-7Athenian Lg (3)London Senior Cup 63-4 68-9 Middx Sen Cup (14)
Previous Names:	Christ Church Hampstead to 1908 Hampstead Town to 1933 Golders Green to 1946 Leagues:Finchley & District 08-11 Middlesex League 1910-11 London League 1911-14 Athenian 14-63

BackRow (L-R): Glenn Garner, Yacine Hamada, Harry Hunt, Casey Maclaren, Peter Dean, Lee O'Leary, James Reading, Berkley Laurencin, Marc Leach, Mark Kirby, Sam Berry, Craig Vargas, Dave Diedhiou, James Bent.
Front Row: James Parker, Wayne O'Sullivan, Jamie Busby, James Burgess, Freddie Hyatt (Assistant Manager), Gary McCann (Manager), Mark Findlay (Sports Therapist), Roy Harwood (Coach), Kevin Maclaren, Wayne Jackson, Lubomir Guentchev, Danny Dyer.

HENDON

BEST LGE ATT.: **389** v Dartford
LOWEST: **123** v Canvey Island

No.	Date	Comp	H/A	Opponents	Att:	Result	Goalscorers	Pos
1	Aug 16	Ryman P.	H	Dartford	389	W 3 - 0	**Haule** 14 Bent 31 Bangura 79	
2	19		A	Margate	474	D 2 - 2	**Haule** 2 Busby 43	
3	23		A	Sutton United	499	L 0 - 1		11
4	25		H	Ashford Town (Middx)	240	L 0 - 3		
5	30		A	Maidstone United	403	L 2 - 3	Bangura 16 **Haule** 90	18
6	Sept 2		H	Billericay Town	221	L 0 - 1		
7	6		A	Canvey Island	363	D 1 - 1	Bent 55	18
8	9		H	Dover Athletic	279	L 0 - 2		18
9	**13**	**F.A.C 1Q**	**A**	**Royston Town**	**303**	**W 4 - 2**	**Mapes 13 38 Guentchev 39 Busby 54**	
10	20		H	Wealdstone	280	L 1 - 4	Diedhiou 78	
11	23		A	Staines Town	266	L 0 - 2		
12	**27**	**F.A.C 2Q**	**A**	**Dulwich Hamlet**	**353**	**D 2 - 2**	**Hudson 23 Hunt 78**	
13	**Oct 2**	**F.A.C.2Qr**	**H**	**Dulwich Hamlet**	**139**	**W 2 - 1**	**Diedhiou 8 Hunt 22**	
14	4		A	Tooting & Mitcham U	339	L 0 - 1		22
15	**11**	**F.A.C. 3Q**	**H**	**AFC Telford United**	**277**	**L 1 - 2**	**Haule 90 (pen)**	
16	15		H	Harrow Borough	130	W 7 - 0	Hunt 19 80 **Haule** 25 O'Leary 51 Burgess 67 Garner 72 Mapes 75	
17	**18**	**F.A.T. 1Q**	**A**	**Margate**	**362**	**W 1 - 0**	**Hunt 3**	
18	**Nov 2**	**F.A.T. 2Q**	**H**	**Sutton United**	**269**	**L 1 - 2**	**Hunt 17**	
19	8		A	Ramsgate	229	W 5 - 1	O'Leary 42 59 **Haule** 46 Bent 75 Mapes 90	20
20	15		H	Tonbridge Angels	188	L 1 - 3	Garner 87	21
21	18		A	AFC Hornchurch	233	W 2 - 1	Garner 75 Guentchev 90	
22	22		H	Margate	149	L 1 - 2	Hunt 25	20
23	26		H	Heybridge Swifts	137	D 1 - 1	O'Leary 68	
24	29		A	Carshalton Athletic	307	L 0 - 1		21
25	Dec 6		A	Dartford	926	L 0 - 1		21
26	16		A	Harlow Town	161	W 5 - 3	HUNT 3 (7 55 76) Garner 45 Busby 85	
27	20		A	Billericay Town	405	L 2 - 4	Byfield 42 **Haule** 75	21
28	27		H	Boreham Wood	175	D 1 - 1	Collins 90	21
29	Jan 3		A	Ashford Town (Middx)	278	W 2 - 0	Bent 45 Byfield 90	20
30	17		H	Canvey Island	123	W 2 - 0	Hunt 34 Halle 77 (og)	
31	24		A	Wealdstone	433	L 1 - 2	Busby 6	19
32	31		H	Staines Town	181	L 0 - 2		20
33	Feb 7		A	Dover Athletic	976	L 0 - 3		21
34	14		H	Tooting & Mitcham	192	D 2 - 2	Howell 52 (og) Parker 83	
35	21		A	Heybridge Swifts	163	W 2 - 1	**Haule** 85 90	21
36	28		H	Harlow Town	184	W 5 - 0	**Haule** 6 Dean 24 85 O'Leary 24 Busby 40	21
37	Mar 7		A	Harrow Borough	211	L 2 - 4	Parker 6 Busby 54	
38	14		H	Ramsgate	180	W 3 - 1	Garner 43 Collins 65 Busby 90	19
39	21		A	Horsham	263	W 2 - 1	Vargas 45 Hunt 90	19
40	24		H	Hastings United	162	W 4 - 0	Busby 9 Collins 41 Garner 70 **Haule** 72	18
41	28		H	AFC Hornchurch	245	L 1 - 2	**Haule** 64	
42	31		H	Sutton United	202	D 0 - 0		
43	April 4		A	Tonbridge Angels	475	L 1 - 5	Busby 82	19
44	11		H	Maidstone United	227	W 2 - 0	Busby 29 88	17
45	15		A	Boreham Wood	220	W 1 - 0	**Haule**	
46	18		A	Hastings United	523	L 1 - 2	Garner 12	17
47	21		H	Horsham	169	W 3 - 1	Busby 2 K.MacLaren	
48	25		H	Carshalton Atletic	274	L 1 - 2	Burgess 90	16

Average Home Att: **206 (271)** **Goals** **80 75**

Best Position: 11th **Worst:** 22nd

Goalscorers: Haule 13, Busby 12, Hunt 12, Garner 7, O'Leary 5, Bent 4, Mapes 4, Collins 3, Bangura 2, Burgess 2, Byfield 2, Dean 2, Diedhiou 2, Guentchev 2, Parker 2, Hudson 1, MacLaren K 1, Vargas 1. Own Goals 2.

HORSHAM

Founded: 1881
Nickname: Hornets

CLUB PERSONNEL

Chairman: Kevin Borrett

Secretary : John Lines
River Cottage, Chesworth Close, Horsham, West Sussex RH12 5AL
Tel No: (H) 01403 267 711
(M) 0772 141 8889
linesj@tesco.net

Press Officer:
Adam Hammond
Tel No: 01403 265 608
(H) 01403 217 316
adam@horshampress.co.uk

Programme Editor: As press officer

Manager: John Maggs

Club Colours: Amber and green halves/green/amber.

Best Season - League: 8th Isthmian Premier 2006-07

Ground address: Horsham YMCA F.C., Gorings Mead, Horsham RH13 5BP.

Tel/fax No: 01403 252 689.

Capacity: 1,575 **Seats**: 150 **Covered**: 200 **Floodlights**: Yes

Simple Directions: From the east, take A281 (Brighton Road) and the ground is on the left and signposted opposite Gorings Mead.

Midweek Home Matchday: Tuesday

Clubhouse: Open matchdays and functions.

Local Radio: BBC Southern Counties Radio and Radio Mercury

Local Press: West Sussex County Times

CLUB STATISTICS

Record	**Attendance:** 8,000 v Swindon F.A.Cup 1st Round November 1966
	Career Goalscorer: Mick Browning
	Career Appearances: Mark Stepney
Record	**Victory:** 16-1 v Southwick Sussex Co. League 1945-1946
	Defeat: 1-11 v Worthing ,Sussex Senioe Cup 1913-1914:
Senior Honours:	Athenian League Div 1 72-73 Isthmian Div 1 R-Up 2005-06
	Sussex Senior Cup (7)
Previous	**Leagues:** W Sussex Sen; Sussex County 26-51; Metropolitan 51-57; Corinthian 57-63; Athenian 63-73
	Grounds: Horsham Park, Hurst Park, Springfield Park

Back Row (L-R): Michael Dale, Andy Howard, Eddie French, Same Page, EvanArchibald. **Middle:** Andy Marfleet (Physio) Jacob Mingle, Matt Whitefoot, Jack Page, Paul Seuke, Lee Farrell, Ian Payne, Reggie Savage (now with Heybridge) DarrenEtheridge (Kit man). **Front:** Rob Frankland (Coach) Danny Hutchings, Liam Baitup, Lee Carey, John Maggs (Manager) Mark Knee, Lee Carney, Gary Charman, Mark Hawthorne, (Assistant Manager).

HORSHAM

BEST LGE ATT.: **418** v Dartford
LOWEST: **109** v Carshalton Athletic

No.	Date	Comp	H/A	Opponents	Att:	Result	Goalscorers	Pos
1	Aug 16	Ryman P.	A	Canvey Island	377	W 4 - 2	**Archibald** 13 81 Bateup 40 Carney 79	
2	20		H	Staines Town	239	W 2 - 1	Haddow 27 Eldridge 84	
3	23		H	Heybridge Swifts	260	W 2 - 0	**Archibald** 39 Carney 79	1
4	25		A	CarshaltonAthletic	354	W 5 - 1	Carney 1 Charman 4 Bateup 48 Eldridge 71 Knee 83	
5	30		H	Harlow Town	287	L 1 - 4	Charman 14	3
6	Sept 2		A	Dover Athletic	948	L 1 - 2	Mingle 39	
7	6		H	Sutton United	373	L 1 - 2	Carey 71	6
8	9		A	Ramsgate	238	D 2 - 2	**Archibald** 13 Carey 38	
9	**14**	**F.A.C. 1Q**	**H**	**Colliers Wood**	**258**	**W 1 - 0**	**Archibald 29**	
10	20		A	Dartford	1008	L 0 - 4		10
11	23		H	Hastings United	225	L 0 - 2		
12	**27**	**F.A.C 2Q**	**A**	**Folkestone Invicta**	**345**	**W 2 - 1**	**Howard 36 Archibald 72**	
13	Oct 4		A	Tonbridge Angels	490	L 0 - 4		14
14	**11**	**F.A.C. 3Q**	**H**	**Paulton Rovers**	**297**	**W 2 - 1**	**Mingle 38 Sigere 80**	
15	15		H	Maidstone United	233	W 3 - 1	**Archibald** 13 Knee 33 Farrell 68	13
16	**19**	**F.A.T. 1Q**	**H**	**Sittingbourne**	**199**	**W 4 - 2**	**Haddow 31 Sigere 45 Farrell 76 Nwachukwu 90**	
17	**25**	**F.A.C. 4Q**	**A**	**Stevenage Borough**	**1051**	**D 2 - 2**	**Sigere 33 Farrell 45**	
18	**29**	**F.A.C. 4Qr**	**H**	**Stevenage Borough**	**640**	**L 1 - 4**	**Carney 33**	
19	**Nov 1**	**F.A.T. 2Q**	**H**	**Cray Wanderers**	**158**	**L 1 - 2**	**Sigere 89**	
20	8		H	Margate	278	W 2 - 0	Charman 5 Farrell 7	13
21	15		A	Boreham Wood	118	W 2 - 0	Acheampong 53 **Sigere** 80 (pen)	9
22	19		H	Wealdstone	193	L 0 - 1		
23	22		H	AFC Hornchurch	212	D 0 - 0		10
24	26		H	Billericay Town	134	L 0 - 1		
25	29		A	Harrow Borough	307	L 1 - 6	**Archibald** 60 (Pen)	
26	Dec 6		H	Canvey Island	204	W 3 - 0	**Sigere** 71 89 Peauroux 83	13
27	20		H	Dover Athletic	362	L 1 - 2	**Sigere** 3	15
28	27		A	Tooting & Mitcham U	378	W 2 - 0	Carney 29 Charman 50	13
29	Jan 17		A	Sutton United	545	L 1 - 2	Eldridge 36	14
30	24		H	Dartford	418	L 0 - 3		16
31	31		A	Hastings United	443	W 2 - 0	Carney 17 Seanla 90	13
32	Feb 7		H	Ramsgate	243	W 1 - 0	Savage 39	12
33	10		H	Carshalton Athletic	109	L 2 - 3	Peauroux 28 Seanla 85	
34	14		H	Tonbridge Angels	312	D 0 - 0		11
35	21		A	Billericay Town	419	W 1 - 0	Budd 28	10
36	28		H	Ashford Town	195	W 2 - 0	Savage 52 Seanla 55	
37	Mar 7		A	Maidstone United	305	D 1 - 1	Seanla 64	9
38	14		A	Margate	401	W 1 - 0	Savage 7	9
39	21		H	Hendon	263	L 1 - 2	Seanla 7	11
40	24		A	Staines Town	255	D 0 - 0		
41	28		A	Wealdstone	449	L 0 - 1		12
42	31		A	Heybridge Swifts	87	L 0 - 1		
43	April 4		H	Boreham Wood	194	D 2 - 2	Acheampong 20 Davies 56	12
44	7		A	Ashford Town	121	L 0 - 3		
45	11		A	Harlow Town	370	W 1 - 0	Charman 31	12
46	13		H	Tooting & Mitcham	289	D 0 - 0		
47	18		A	AFC Hornchurch	372	L 0 - 3		14
48	21		A	Hendon	169	L 1 - 3	Davies	

Average Home Att: **239 (554)** **Goals** **61 71**

Best Position: 1st **Worst:** 16th

Goalscorers: Archibald 8, Sigere 8, Carney 6, Charman 5, Seanla 5, Farrell 4, Eldridge 3, Savage 3, Acheampong 2, Bateup 2, Carey 2, Davies 2, Haddow 2, Knee 2, Mingle 2, Peauroux 2, Budd 1, Howard 1, Nwachukwu 1.

KINGSTONIAN

Founded: 1885
Nickname: The K's

Manager: Alan Dowson
Club Colours: Red & white hoops/black/black.
Best Season - League: 5th Conference 1999-2000
Ground address: Kingsmead Stadium, Kingston Road, Kingston upon Thames, Surrey KT1 3PB **Tel No**; 0208 8547 3528. Fax: 020 8397 0433
Capacity: 4,262 **Seats**: 1,080 **Covered**: 2,538 **Floodlights**: Yes
Simple Directions: Take Cambridge Rd. from town centre (A2043) to Malden Rd. From A3 turn off at New Malden and turn left onto A2043. Ground is 1 mile on left which is half a mile from Norbiton (BR) .
Midweek Home Matchday: Monday
Clubhouse: Three Bars. Capacity 400 with a banqueting centre available daily.
Club Shop: Yes
Local Radio: County Sound,1566 MW, BBC Southern Counties, SCR 104.8 FM, 95.3 FM and Radio Jackie 107.8 FM.
Local Press: Surrey Comet, Kingston Informer, Kingston Guardian, Esher News & Mail and Kingston, Surbiton and New Malden Times.

CLUB PERSONNEL

Chairmen: Mark Anderson & Malcolm Wainwright

Secretary: Gerry Petit.
149 Bridge Road,
Chessington, Surrey KT9 2RT
Tel No: 020 8397 0433
(H) 020 8397 0433
(M) 0785 937 7778
Fax No: (H) 020 7636 8098/020 8397 0433
gandjpetit149@tiscali.co.uk

Press Officer: Ali Kazemi
Tel No: (M) 0771 945 9259
Fax No: (H) 0709 236 8070

Programme
Editor: Robert Wooldridge
(M) 0788 407 4668
floiing@aol.com

CLUB STATISTICS

Record	**Attendance:** 4,582 v Chelsea (Friendly)
	Career Goalscorer: Johnnie Wing 295 - 1948-62
	Career Appearances: Micky Preston 555 - 1967-85
	Transfer Fee Paid: £18,000 to Rushden & Diamonds for David Leworthy 1997
	Received: £150,000 from West Ham United for Gavin Holligan1999
	Victory: 15-1 v Delft - 1951
	Defeat: 0-11 v Ilford Isthmian 13.02.37
Senior Honours:	F.A.Trophy Winners 98-99 99-00 F.A.Am Cup Winners 1932-33
	Isthmian Champions 1933-34 36-37 97-98. Division 1 South 2008-09. Athenian League (x2). London Senior Cup (3) Surrey Sen Cup (x3)
Previous Leagues:	Kingston & Dist., West Surrey, Southern Suburban, Athenian 1919-29
	Isthmian 29-98 Conference 98-01
	Grounds: Several to 1921 Richmond Rd21-89
	Names: Kingston & Suburton YMCA 85-87 Saxons 87 -90 Kingston Wanderers 1893-1904 Old Kingstonians 1908-1919

Back Row (L-R): Paul Ferrie (backroom), Jamie Street (backroom), Carl Wilson-Denis, Simon Huckle, Francis Duku, Ian Pearce, Neil Lampton, Adam Thompson, Christian Jolley, Mark Francis (backroom), Alan Smith (backroom).
Middle Row: Gerry Petit (secretary), Wayne Finnie, Steve Tyson, Martin Tyler (coach), Josh Willis, Alan Dowson (manager), Luke Garrard, Mark Hams (assistant manager), Rob Sheridan, Max Hustwick, Paul Horsecroft (backroom).
Front Row: Lewis Cook, Luke Pigden, Bobby Traynor, Jon Coke, Tommy Williams, Dean Lodge, Jamie Beer, Tom Dilloway, Liam Collins.

MAIDSTONE UNITED

Re-Formed 1992
Nickname: The Stones

Managers: Alan Walker & Lloyd Hume.

Club Colours: Amber/black/amber.

Best Season - League: 15th Isthmian Premier 2008-09.

Ground address: Ashford Town F.C., The Homelands, Ashford Road, Kingsnorth, Ashford, Kent TN26 1NJ.

Tel/Fax: 01233 611 838

Simple Directions: Jct 10 off M20 onto A2070 towards Breneitt & Lydd Airport. Dual carriageway to junction of old A2070.Ground one mile on left through Kingsnorth four miles south of Ashford.

Capacity: 3,200 **Seats:** 500 **Covered:**1,250 **Floodlights:** Yes

Midweek Home Matchday: Tuesday

Clubhouse: Open matchdays and for special functions.

Club Shop: Yes

Local Press: Kent Messenger Adscene

Local Radio: BBC Radio Kent (96.7), CTR 105.6 FM

CLUB PERSONNEL

Chairman: Paul Bowden-Brown

Secretary: Darren Lovell,
573 Lordswood Lane,
Chatham, Kent. ME5 8NP
Tel No: 01634 672086
(H) 01634 672086
(M) 0777 374 5577
darren.lovell1@btinternet.com

Press Officer: Ian Tucker
Tel No: 0796 850 5888
mufcprogramme@btopenworld.com

Programme Editor: As press officer.

CLUB STATISTICS

Record	**Attendance:** 1,589 v Gillingham (friendly)
	Career Goalscorer: Richard Sinden - 98
	Career Appearances: Aaron Lacy - 187
Record	**Victory:** 12-1 v Aylesford, Kent League 1993-1994
	Defeat: 2-8 v Scott Sports 1995-1996
	Transfer fee paid: £2,000 for Steve Jones - 2000
Senior Honours:	Kent League Champions 2001-2002 League & Cup 2005-2006
	Kent Senior Trophy 2002-2003. Isthmian Division 1 South 2006-07
Previous Leagues:	Kent County League, and Kent League
Grounds:	London Road 1992-2001 Central Park 2001-2002

Back Row (L-R): Peter Norris (kit man), James Peacock, Peter Hawkins, Jimmy Bottle, Meshach Nugent, Tom Parkinson, Richard Knell, Lynden Rowland, Jamie Turner, Alan Pouton, Roland Edge, Nick Barnes, Jay Saunders, Alan Rogers (goalkeeper coach), Narada Pascal. **Front row:** Nicki Collins (physio), Tim Warden (trainer), Dan Stubbs, Antonio Gonnella, Ashley Ulph, Nathan Paul, Paul Bowden-Brown (chairman), James Pinnock, Dean Hernandez-Bradshaw, Ant Bodle, Ashley Dann, Lloyd Hume (manager).

MAIDSTONE UNITED

BEST LGE ATT.: **689** v Dover Athletic
LOWEST: **218** v Harrow Borough

No.	Date	Comp	H/A	Opponents	Att:	Result	Goalscorers	Pos
1	Aug 16	Ryman P.	A	Heybridge Swifts	244	W 2 - 0	Cox 25 Saunders 60	
2	19		H	Canvey Island	452	D 0 - 0		
3	23		H	Harlow Town	365	L 1 - 2	Bradbrook 38	12
4	25		A	Hastings United	759	W 4 - 0	PINNOCK 3 (13 78 85) Edge 89	
5	30		H	Hendon	403	W 3 - 2	Pinnock 10 Watson 12 **Blackman** 85	5
6	Sept 2		A	Ramsgate	430	W 2 - 1	Nugent 7 **Blackman** 89	
7	6		H	Tonbridge Angels	574	L 0 - 1		
8	9		A	Boreham Wood	137	W 1 - 0	**Blackman** 29	4
9	**13**	**F.A.C 1Q**	**H**	**Tooting & Mitcham U**	**355**	**W 2 - 1**	**Saunders 21 Bradbrook 23**	
10	20		A	Harrow Borough	230	D 1 - 1	Nugent 31	5
11	23		H	Dartford	667	L 1 - 2	Cox 29	
12	**27**	**F.A.C 2Q**	**H**	**Fisher Athletic**	**389**	**W 3 - 2**	**Paul 25 Pinnock 65 Lewid 90**	
13	Oct 4		H	Sutton United	435	W 1 - 0	Selley 35 (pen)	6
14	**11**	**F.A.C. 3Q**	**A**	**Halesowen Town**	**872**	**W 4 - 1**	**Nugent 43 Saunders 45 Blackman 45 Selley 78 (pen)**	
15	15		A	Horsham	233	L 1 - 3	Selley 36 (pen)	
16	**18**	**F.A.T. 1Q**	**H**	**AFC Hornchurch**	**384**	**D 1 - 1**	**Pinnock 58**	
17	**25**	**F.A.C. 4Q**	**H**	**AFC Wimbledon**	**1719**	**L 0 - 1**		
18	28		A	Margate	586	W 2 - 0	Selley 37 Nugent 59	6
19	**Nov 1**	**F.A.T. 2Q**	**A**	**Swindon Supermarine**	**333**	**L 0 - 2**		
20	8		H	Tooting & Mitcham United	375	W 2 - 0	Pinnock 19 Selley 90	4
21	15		A	Wealdstone	660	L 2 - 3	Pinnock 56 Nugent 89	5
22	18		H	Carshalton Athletic	278	L 0 - 2		
23	22		H	Ashford Town	274	W 2 - 1	**Blackman** 84 Pinnock 90	6
24	29		A	Billericay Town	505	D 1 - 1	Saunders 76	6
25	Dec 6		H	Heybridge Swifts	256	L 0 - 2		7
26	13		A	Canvey Island	316	W 1 - 0	Edge 56	6
27	20		H	Ramsgate	331	W 3 - 2	**Blackman** 40 85 Bradbrook 75	5
28	27		A	Dover Athletic	2545	L 0 - 3		5
29	Jan 3		H	Hastings United	431	L 0 - 1		6
30	17		A	Tonbridge Angels	948	D 2 - 2	Saunders 80 Hawkins 90	6
31	31		A	Dartford	2013	L 0 - 1		9
32	Feb 7		H	Boreham Wood	319	D 1 - 1	**Blackman** 50 (pen)	9
33	10		A	Maidstone United	302	L 1 - 3	Pinnock 52	
34	14		A	Sutton United	596	D 2 - 2	**Blackman** 67 (pen) Berry 77	8
35	21		H	Staines Town	332	D 0 - 0		9
36	28		A	AFC Hornchurch	414	D 0 - 0		11
37	Mar 7		H	Horsham	305	D 1 - 1	Pinnock 60	
38	10		A	Harlow Town	200	W 3 - 2	Saunders 50 73 **Blackman** 81	
39	14		A	Tooting & Mitcham U	391	L 0 - 2		11
40	21		H	Margate	411	D 1 - 1	**Blackman** 62	9
41	28		A	Carshalton Athletic	323	W 3 - 0	Nugent 23 Royston 34 **Blackman** 75	9
42	31		H	AFC Hornchurch	301	D 0 - 0		
43	April 4		H	Wealdstone	377	W 2 - 1	Nugent 11 61	8
44	11		A	Hendon	227	L 0 - 2		8
45	13		H	Dover Athletic	689	L 0 - 2		
46	18		A	Ashford Town	202	L 0 - 1		10
47	21		H	Harrow Borough	218	L 0 - 2		
48	25	42	H	Billericay Town	357	L 0 - 1		15

Average Home Att: **388 (444)** **Goals** **56 59**

Best Position: 4th **Worst:** 15th

Goalscorers: Blackman 12, Pinnock 11, Nugent 8, Saunders 7, Selley 5, Bradbrook 3, Edge 2, Cox 2, Berry 1, Hawkins 1, Lewis 1, Paul 1, Royston 1, Watson 1.

MARGATE

Founded: 1896
Nickname: The Gate

Manager: Terry Yorath

Club Colours: Royal Blue/royal blue/royal & white

Best Season - League: 8th Conference 2001-02

Ground address: Hartsdown Park, Hartsdown Road, Margate, Kent CT9 5QZ

Tel No: 01843 221 769. Fax: 01843 221 769.

Capacity: 3,000 **Seats:** 350 **Covered:** 1750 **Flooodlights:** Yes

Simple Directions: Follow M2 towards Ramsgate and into A299 Thanet Way and after 16.2 miles take second exit off roundabout into A28. Follow signs for Margate. After BP petrol station turn right into B2052, continue round left hand bend and turn right at end into Hartsdown Road. Ground is on left.

Midweek Home Matchday: Tuesday

Clubhouse: Yes.

Club Shop: Yes.

CLUB PERSONNEL
Chief Exec: Keith Piper
Secretary: Ken Tomlinson
65 Nash Road,
Margate, Kent CT9 4BT
Tel No: 01843 291040
(H) 01843 291040
(M) 0771 003 3566
Fax No: (H) 01843 291040
ken.tomlinson@margate-fc.com
Press Officer: Keith Piper
(M) 0796 836 7318
office@margate-fc.com
Programme
Editor: Steve Ball
Tel No: (H) 01843 587396
steve.ball@margate-fc.com

CLUB STATISTICS

Record	**Attendance**: 14,500 v Spurs F.A.Cup 3rd Rd 1973
	Victory: 8-0 v Stalybridge Celtic (H) 2001-02 v Tunbridge Wells(H) 66-7 v Chatham Town (H) 87-88
	Defeat: 0-11 v AFC Bournemouth (A) F.A.Cup 20.11.71
Goalscorer:	(Season) Jack Palethorpe 66 1929-30 **Career Appearances**: Bob Harrop
Record Transfer Fee	**Paid**: £5,000 to Dover Athletic for Steve Cuggy
	Received: Undisclosed from St Johnstone for Martin Buglione
Senior Honours:	Southern League 1935-36, 2000-02. Div 1 1962-63. Div 1 South 1977- 78.
Previous Leagues:	Kent 1911-23, 24-28, 29-33, 37-38, 46-59. Southern 1933-37, 59-2001 Conference 2001-04.

MARGATE

BEST LGE ATT.: 1,339 v Dover Athletic
LOWEST: 355 v Tonbridge Angels

No.	Date	Comp	H/A	Opponents	Att:	Result	Goalscorers	Pos
1	Aug 16	Ryman P.	A	Carshalton Athletic	285	L 1 - 2	Parkinson 14	
2	19		H	Hendon	474	D 2 - 2	Wilson 69 Smith 78	
3	23		H	Canvey Island	537	L 0 - 4		19
4	25		A	Dover Athletic	1512	L 0 - 1		
5	30		H	Heybridge Swifts	439	W 2 - 1	Coleman 36 Young 62	
6	Sept 2		A	Harlow Town	265	D 1 - 1	Young 73	
7	6		H	AFC Hornchurch	501	L 0 - 2		19
8	9		A	Tooting & Mitcham U	292	L 1 - 2	Peters 17	20
9	**13**	**F.A.C 1Q**	**A**	**Worthing**	**338**	**L 1 - 5**	**Wilson 51**	
10	20		A	Ashford Town	178	W 1 - 0	Power 59	18
11	23		H	Tonbridge Angels	355	D 0 - 0		
12	Oct 4		H	Hastings United	453	L 2 - 3	**Pratt** 7 Stubbs 80	16
13	11		A	Dartford	1379	W 1 - 0	Gregory 17	
14	**18**	**F.A.T. 1Q**	**H**	**Hendon**	**362**	**L 0 - 1**		
15	25		H	Wealdstone	428	L 0 - 1		18
16	28		H	Maidstone United	586	L 0 - 2		
17	Nov 1		A	Billericay Town	336	L 2 - 3	Peters 40 Stubbs 48	15
18	8		A	Horsham	278	L 0 - 2		18
19	11		A	Boreham Wood	122	W 2 - 1	Wheatley 19 Wilson 33	
20	15		H	Harrow Borough	374	L 2 - 3	Takaloo 8 **Pratt** 64	18
21	22		A	Hendon	149	W 2 - 1	Wilson 73 Takaloo77	18
22	29		H	Staines Town	403	L 1 - 2	Stubbs 60	18
23	Dec 6		H	Carshalton Athletic	365	D 2 - 2	Wilson 25 Quian 67	19
24	20		H	Harlow Town	355	W 3 - 0	Takaloo 45 Shittu 68 70	18
25	27		A	Ramsgate	1082	L 0 - 2		19
26	Jan 3		H	Dover Athletic	1339	L 0 - 2		21
27	13		A	Sutton United	404	L 0 - 2		
28	17		A	AFC Hornchurch	313	L 0 - 3		21
29	24		H	Ashford Town	357	W 2 - 0	**Pratt** 38 90	21
30	31		A	Tonbridge Angels	471	L 0 - 1		21
31	Feb 7		H	Tooting & Mitcham U	407	W 2 - 0	Wilson 46 Peters 88	19
32	14		A	Hastings United	388	D 1 - 1	Wheatley 19	19
33	21		H	Boreham Wood	453	W 3 - 1	Young 47 Peters 62 Healy 71	17
34	28		A	Wealdsone	376	L 0 - 2		18
35	Mar 3		A	Canvey Island	310	W 4 - 0	Lacy 44 **Pratt** 45 Peters 72 (pen) Wilson 79	
36	7		H	Dartford	745	D 2 - 2	Osbourne 39 (og) **Pratt** 67	
37	14		H	Horsham	401	L 0 - 1		21
38	21		A	Maidstone United	411	D 1 - 1	**Pratt** 16	20
39	28		H	Billericay Town	395	W 3 - 1	Alaile (og) Robinson 25 Wilson 59	
40	April 4		A	Harrow Borough	203	L 2 - 3	**Pratt** 3 Wheatley 45	20
41	11		A	Heybridge Swifts	173	L 2 - 3	Gregory 48 Peters 52	20
42	13		H	Ramsgate	1010	W 1 - 0	Young 83	
43	18		H	Sutton United	620	W 2 - 0	Healy 38 **Pratt** 84	19
44	25		A	Staines Town	384	L 1 - 4	**Pratt** 90	

Average Home Att: 524 (531) **Goals 52 70**

Best Position: 15th **Worst:** 21st

Goalscorers: Pratt 10, Wilson 8, Peters 6, Young 4, Stubbs 3, Takaloo 3, Wheatley 3, Gregory 2, Healy 2, Pratt 2, Shittu 2, Coleman 1, Lacy 1, Parkinson 1, Power 1, Quian 1, Robinson 1, Smith 1. Own Goals 2.

SUTTON UNITED

Founded: 1898
Nickname: The U's

CLUB PERSONNEL

Chairman: Bruce Elliott

Secretary: Gerard Mills.
c/o the club.
(M) 0793 270 2375

Press Officer: Tony Dolbear
(Me) 0796 650 7023
pr@suttonunited.net

Programme Editor: Lyall Reynolds
(M): 07764 450 051
suttoneditor@hotmail.com

Manager: Paul Doswell.

Club Colours: Amber and Chocolate quarters/amber/amber.

Best Season - League: 7th Conference 1986-87.

Ground address: Borough Sports Ground, Gander Green Lane, Sutton, Surrey SM1 2EY. **Tel No**: 0208 644 4440 **Fax:** 0208 644 5120

Capacity: 7,032 **Seats:** 765 **Covered:** 1,250 **Floodlights**:Yes

Simple Directions: Gander Green Lane runs between A232 (Cheam Road - turn by Sutton Cricket club) and A217 (Oldfields Road - turn at The Gander Public House). Ground opposite The Plough 50 yards from W.Sutton BR. Bus: No 413

Midweek Home Matchday: Tuesday.

Club Shop: All club accessories on matchdays.

Local Press: Sutton Advertiser, Sutton Guardian, Sutton Independent and S.Comet

Local Radio: Radio Jackie

CLUB STATISTICS

Record	**Attendance**: 14,000 v Leeds United F.A.Cup 4th Rd 24.01.70
	Victory: 11-1 v Clapton 1966 & Leatherhead 82-83 Isthmian League
	Defeat: 0-13 V Barking Athenian League1925-26
	Career Goalscorer: Paul McKinnon 279
	Career Appearances:: Larry Pritchard 781 (65-84)
	Transfer Fee Paid: Undisclosed to Malmo for Paul McKinnon in 1983
	Fee Received: 100,000 from Bournemouth for Efan Ekoku in 1990
Senior Honours:	Anglo Italian Semi-Pro Cup 1979. Isthmian Champions (x3) Athenian Champions (x3). London Senior Cup (x2) Surrey Senior Cup (x15) London Senior Cup (x2).
Previous Leagues:	Sutton Jnr,Southern Sub.,Athenian 21-63, Isthmian 63-86 91-99 00-04 Conf.99-00. Conf. South 04-08.
Grounds:	Western Rd, Manor Lane, London Rd and The Find

Back Row (L-R): Steve McKimm (Player Coach), Kevin Scriven, Sam Gargan, Karim El-Salahi, Paul Smith, Sonny Cobbs. **Middle row:** Billy Hawes, Anthony Joseph, Sam Stannard, Billy Dunn, Jason Goodliffe (Team Captain), Justyn Roberts, Steffan Payne, Kenny Beaney, Billy Chattaway, Ebenezer Masabe. **Front row:** Alan Bray, Bentley Graham, Danny Phillips, Alan Payne (Assistant Manager), Clive Baxter (Kit Manager), Paul Doswell (Manager), Bob Childs (Physio), Bradley Woods-Garness, James Hawes, Matt Hann.

SUTTON UNITED

BEST LGE ATT.: **1,251** v Carshalton Athletic
LOWEST: **334** v Ashford Town (Middx)

No.	Date	Comp	H/A	Opponents	Att:	Result	Goalscorers	Pos
1	Aug 16	Ryman P.	A	Harlow Town	376	D 1 - 1	**McCallum** 11	
2	19		H	Ramsagate	447	D 1 - 1	Palmer 67	
3	23		H	Hendon	499	W 1 - 0	**McCallum** 38 (pen)	9
4	25		A	Tooting & Mitcham U	546	L 2 - 4	**McCallum** 88 90	
5	30		H	Hastings United	469	W 2 - 1	**McCallum** 22 D.Smith 50	
6	Sept 2		A	Wealdstone	371	L 0 - 4		
7	6		A	Horsham	373	W 2 - 1	Wilde 59 **McCallum** 90	10
8	9		H	Staines Town	410	D 1 - 1	**McCallum** 30	10
9	**13**	**F.A.C. 1Q**	**H**	**Cray Wanderers**	**325**	**W 3 - 1**	**McCallum 3 West 43 Dundas 70**	
10	20		H	Canvey Island	544	W 1 - 0	Dunn 87	11
11	23		A	Billericay Town	342	L 0 - 1		
12	**27**	**F.A.C. 2Q**	**H**	**Billericay Town**	**410**	**W 3 - 1**	**Dunn 56 Webb73 McCallum 84**	
13	Oct 4		A	Maidstone United	435	L 0 - 1		12
14	**11**	**F.A.C. 3Q**	**A**	**Ware**	**474**	**W 2 - 1**	**West 81 Dunn 83**	
15	14		H	Heybridge Swifts	377	D 1 - 1	Dundas 87	
16	**18**	**F.A.T. 1Q**	**H**	**Tooting & Mitcham**	**511**	**W 2 - 0**	**Dunn 66 Hann 87**	
17	**25**	**F.A.C. 4Q**	**A**	**Aylesbury United**	**545**	**W 1 - 0**	**Hann 67**	
18	**Nov 2**	**F.A.T 2Q**	**A**	**Hendon**	**269**	**W 2 - 1**	**Dundas 25 McCullum 39**	
19	**8**	**F.A.C. 1R**	**H**	**Notts County**	**2041**	**L 0 - 1**		
20	11		H	Tonbridge Angels	414	D 3 - 3	Eribenne 26 (pen) 71 Dundas 68	
21	15		A	Dartford	1082	W 3 - 2	Hughes 16 Eribenne 44 55	15
22	18		H	Dover Athletic	569	W 1 - 0	Eribenne 19	
23	**22**	**F.A.T 3Q**	**A**	**Wingate & Finchley**	**149**	**D 1 - 1**	**Downer 33**	
24	**25**	**F.A.T 3Qr**	**H**	**Wingate & Finchley**	**212**	**D 2 - 2**	**Eribenne 29 Palmer 84 Wingate won 4-3 on pens**	
25	29		A	AFC Hornchurch	359	L 1 - 2	Dunn 63	13
26	Dec 6		H	Harlow Town	636	W 3 - 0	Hughes 19 Dunn 53 68	12
27	13		A	Ramsgate	195	L 1 - 3	Eribenne 20	13
28	16		H	Ashford Town (Middx)	334	W 3 - 1	Dundas 6 **McCallum** 55 Hann 81	
29	20		H	Wealdstone	499	W 3 - 2	West 11 Palmer 76 Wilde 86 (pen)	7
30	27		A	Carshalton Athletc	1078	W 2 - 0	Hughes 6 Dunn 78	7
31	Jan 13		H	Margate	404	W 2 - 0	Palmer 89 **McCallum** 90	
32	17		H	Horsham	545	W 2 - 1	Munday 15 Dunn 62	4
33	24		A	Canvey Island	328	D 0 - 0		4
34	31		H	Billericay Town	499	L 0 - 1		4
35	Feb 7		A	Staines Town	376	L 1 - 3	Hughes 10	4
36	14		H	Maidstone United	596	D 2 - 2	**McCallum** 8 58	6
37	21		A	Tonbridge Angels	615	W 3 - 1	Legge 44 (og) **McCallum** 79 Dundas 87	5
38	24		H	Tooting & Mitcham United	479	D 0 - 0		
39	28		H	Harrow Borough	465	D 2 - 2	Graham 52 Hann 72	5
40	Mar 7		A	Hebridge Swifts	184	W 2 - 0	Homici 10 Dundas 55	
41	10		A	Boreham Wood	119	W 3 - 1	Homici 32 Eribenne 70 **McCallum** 81	
42	14		A	Ashford United	172	L 1 - 2	Hughes 58	4
43	21		H	Boreham Wood	893	D 1 - 1	Dundas 90	4
44	24		A	Harrow Borough	165	D 0 - 0		
45	28		A	Dover Athletic	1404	L 0 - 6		4
46	31		A	Hendon	202	D 0 - 0		
47	April 4		H	Dartford	727	W 1 - 0	Watts 83 (pen)	4
48	11		A	Hastings United	542	W 2 - 0	Hamici 25 El-Salahi 68	4
49	13		H	Carshalton Athletic	1251	D 1 - 1	**McCallum**	
50	18		A	Margate	620	L 0 - 2		6
51	25		H	AFC Hornchurch	832	W 2 - 1	Phillips 39 Watts 74 (pen)	5
52	**28**	**Play Off S-F**	**A**	**Staines Town**	**738**	**L 0 - 3**		

Average Home Att: **566** **Goals** **73 64**

Best Position: 4th **Worst:** 15th

Goalscorers: McCallum 16, Dunn 9, Dundas 8, Eribenne 8, Hughes 5, Hann 4, Palmer 4, Homici 3, West 3, Watts 2, Wilde 2, Downer 1, El-Salahi 1, Graham 1, Munday 1, Phillips 1, Smith D 1, Webb 1. Own Goals 1.

TONBRIDGE ANGELS

Formed: 1948
Nickname: Angels

Manager: Tommy Warrilow.

Club Colours: Blue and white/blue/blue.

Best Season- League: 3rd Isthmian Premier 2008-09.

Ground address: Longmead Stadium, Darenth Avenue, Tonbridge, Kent. TN10 3JW **Tel No**: 01732 352 417

Midweek Home Matchday: Tuesday

Capacity: 2,487 **Seats**: 750 **Covered**: 1,500 **Floodlights**: Yes

Simple Directions: From Tonbridge BR through High Street, then north up Shipbourne Rd (A227 Gravesend road) to 2nd mini roundabout (The Pinnacles Pub), left into Darenth Avenue and ground is at bottom on far side of car park.

Clubhouse: Open match evenings and Saturday afternoons. Tel No: 01732 352 417

Club Shop: Yes full range of products.

Local Radio: Mercury, Radio Kent and K.F.M.

Local Press: Kent Messenger, Ciourier and Sevenoaks Leader.

CLUB PERSONNEL

Chairman: Steve Chrucher

Secretary & Press Officer: Charlie Cole
30 Faraday Ride, Tonbridge.
Kent TN10 4RL
(H) 01732 354 985
(M) 0782 570 2412
chcole1063@aol.com

Programme Editor: Geoff Curtis
curtis.g10@ntlworld.com

CLUB STATISTICS

Records	**Attendance:** 2,281 v AFC Wimbledon, FA Trophy 2nd Rnd, 12.01.08.
	At Angel Ground: 8,236 v Aldershot in F.A.Cup 1st Rd 24.11 19 51
	Season's Goalscorer: Jon Main 44 (including 7 hat tricks)
	Career Appearances: Mark Giham
	Received: £7,500 from Charlton Athletic for Paul Emblem
	Victory: 11-1 v Worthing F.A.Cup 1951
	Defeat: 2-11 v Folkestone Kent Senior Cup 1949
	Senior Honours: Southern League Cup R-Up (2) Kent Senior Cup 64-65 74-75
Previous Leagues:	Southern 48-80 Kent 1989-1993 Southern 1993-2004
Grounds:	The Angel 1948-1980 (Record Att. 8,236 v Aldershot F.A.Cup 1951)
Names:	Tonbridge Angels, Tonbridge F.C. Tonbridge A.F.C.

Back Row (L-R): John Westcott, Tim Olorunda, Kirk Watts, Michael Phillips, Ade Olorunda, Stuart Myall.
Middle Row:- Melvyn Slight (Medical Staff) Jamie Cade, Luke Piscina, Lewis Hamilton, Lee Worgan, Leon Legge, Simon Glover, Fraser Logan, Terry Sedge (Coach)
Front Row:- Alan Rogers (Goalkeeping Coach), James Donovan, Anthony Storey, Cliff Cant (Assistant Manager), Tommy Warrilow (Manager) Phil Starkey, Tommy Tyne, Bob Gott (Kitman).

TONBRIDGE ANGELS

BEST LGE ATT.: **948** v Maidstone United
LOWEST: **260** v Harlow Town

No.	Date	Comp	H/A	Opponents	Att:	Result	Goalscorers	Pos
1	Aug 16	Ryman P.	A	Wealdstone	387	D 0 - 0		
2	19		H	Harlow Town	260	W 2 - 0	Logan 40 **Rook** 46 (pen)	
3	23		H	Staines Town	411	L 1 - 2	Olorunda 62	13
4	25		A	Ramsgate	337	W 3 - 2	Logan 41 44 Westcott 45	
5	30		H	Tooting & Mitcham U	433	L 0 - 2		11
6	Sept 2		A	Canvey Island	315	L 2 - 3	Cade 17 **Rook** 39	
7	6		A	Maidstone United	373	W 1 - 0	Cade 90	11
8	9		H	Billericay Town	344	W 3 - 2	McSweeney 14 (og) Cade 31 **Rook** 55 (pen)	8
9	**13**	**F.A.C. 1Q**	**H**	**Dover Athletic**	**797**	**L 1 - 2**	**Rook 35**	
10	20		H	Heybridge Swifts	381	W 2 - 1	Watts 12 **Rook** 77	6
11	23		A	Margate	355	D 0 - 0		
12	Oct 4		H	Horsham	490	W 4 - 0	**ROOK** 3 (8 21 30) Cade 77	9
13	14		A	AFC Hornchurch	282	L 0 - 3		
14	**18**	**F.A.T 1Q**	**H**	**Ramsgate**	**372**	**L 2 - 3**	**Rook 48 Twyman 89 (og)**	
15	25		H	Boreham Wood	367	D 1 - 1	**Rook** 76	8
16	Nov 1		A	Ashford Town (Middx)	144	W 7 - 1	LEGGE 3 (10 34 66) Oluronda 39 Storey 55 70 (pens) Logan 75	5
17	11		A	Sutton United	414	D 3 - 3	Gooding 32 Cade 45 El-Saiahi 45 (og)	
18	15		A	Hendon	188	W 3 - 1	**Rook** 4 Cade 65 69	3
19	18		H	Dartford	703	W 4 - 1	**ROOK** 3 (3 45 82) Tyne70	
20	22		H	Harrow Borough	421	D 1 - 1	Storey 59	4
21	29		A	Dover Athletic	1108	L 0 - 3		5
22	Dec 6		H	Wealdstone	347	W 1 - 0	Legge 60	5
23	13		A	Harlow Town	220	W 2 - 0	Glover 59 **Rook** 85	4
24	20		H	Canvey Island	446	W 3 - 0	Storey 25 (pen) Cade 42 **Rook** 88	3
25	27		A	Hastings United	722	W 1 - 0	Hamilton 42	3
26	Jan 3		H	Ramsgate	489	D 2 - 2	Legge 40 **Rook** 62	3
27	17		H	Maidstone United	948	D 2 - 2	Westcott 5 **Rook** 30	3
28	24		A	Heybridge Swifts	182	W 5 - 1	Lee 26 72 **Rook** 42 48 Westcott 55	3
29	31		H	Margate	471	W 1 - 0	Cade 63	3
30	Feb 14		A	Horsham	312	D 0 - 0		3
31	21		H	Sutton United	615	L 1 - 3	Legge 89	3
32	24		H	Carshalton Athletic	302	W 1 - 0	Legge 32	
33	28		A	Boreham Wood	160	W 2 - 0	Storey 23 Gooding 88	3
34	Mar 7		H	AFC Hornchurch	442	L 0 - 1		
35	14		A	Carshalton Athletic	366	W 3 - 0	Clarke 7 Cade 46 65	3
36	17		A	Staines Town	283	D 2 - 2	Legge 81 Gooding 90	
37	21		H	Ashford Town	429	W 3 - 2	**Rook** 87 Ferguson 89 Logan 89	3
38	28		A	Dartford	1380	D 2 - 2	Gooding 3 Booth 18	3
39	April 4		H	Hendon	475	W 5 - 1	Gooding 9 32 Storey 41 **Rook** 58 Clarke 86	3
40	7		A	Billericay Town	372	D 1 - 1	**Rook** 26 (pen)	
41	10		A	Tooting & Mitcham U	470	D 2 - 2	Cade 52 Booth 77	3
42	13		H	Hastings United	736	D 3 - 3	Booth 29 **Rook** 44 76	
43	18		A	Harrow Borough	202	W 3 - 2	Dayes 6 **Rook** 7 Booth 12	3
44	25		H	Dover Athletic	858	L 0 - 2		3
45	**28**		**H**	**Carshalton Athletic**	**1249**	**L 2 - 3**	**Booth, Rook**	

Average Home Att: **494 (518)** **Goals** **85 57**

Best Position: 3rd **Worst:** 13th

Goalscorers: Rook 27, Cade 12, Legge 8, Gooding 6, Storey 6, Logan 5, Booth 4, Westcott 3, Clarke 2, Lee 2, Olorunda 2, Dayes 1, Ferguson 1, Glover 1, Hamilton 1, Tyne 1, Watts 1. Own Goals 4.

TOOTING MITCHAM UNITED

Founded: 1932
Nickname: The Terrors

CLUB PERSONNEL

Chairman: Steve Adkins

Secretary: Nigel Sarson.
The Hub, Bishopsford Road,
Morden, Surrey SM4 6BF
Tel No: 020 8648 3248 or
020 8685 6193
(H) 020 8640 5348
Fax No: 020 8685 6190
football@thehubbattmufc.co.uk

Press Officer: Nigel Wood
Tel No: (M) 0795 783 2732
nigelathome@talk21.com

Programme Editor: Michael Woods
michael@mwoods38.freeserve.co.uk

Manager: Billy Smith

Club Colours: Black & white stripes/black/red.

Best Season - League: Isthmian League Champions 1957-58, 1959-60

Ground address: Imperial Fields, Bishopsford Road, Morden, Surrey SM4 6BF

Tel No: 020 8648 3248 / 020 8685 6193

Capacity: 3,500 **Seats**: 600 **Covered**: 1,200 **Floodlights**: Yes

Simple Directions: From M25 J8, A217 north, ground 1 mile past the Rose Hill roundabout. From Mitcham town centre follow signs to Rose Hill and Sutton, ground 1/2 mile on the left.Ground 1/4 mile down London Road and Bishopsford Road from Mitcham Tramlink station (wimbledon to Croydon). Buses 118 and 280. Morden tube station 1 mile away by bus 118.

Midweek Home Matchday: Tuesday

Clubhouse: Cafe/Bar open daily and family friendly facilties

Club Shop: Open Matchdays, selling replica shirts and other club clothing, merchandise and memorabilia.

Local Radio: Capital

Local Press: South London Press, Wimbledon News , Wandsworth Borough News, Surrey Comet.

CLUB STATISTICS

Record	**Attendance:** 17,500 v Q.P.R. FAC 2nd Round 1956-1957 (At Sandy Lane) at Imperial Fields: 2,637 v AFC Wimbledon Ryman Div 1 April 2005 **Career Appearances**: Danny Godwin 470 **Career Goalscorer**: Alan Ives 92 **Transfer Fee Paid**: £9,000 to Enfield for David Flint **Received:** £10,000 from Luton Townn for Herbie Smith **Victory**: 11-0 v Welton Rovers F.A.Amateur Cup 1962-1963 Defeat: 1-8 v Kingstonian Surrey Senior Cup 1966-1967
Senior Honours:	Isthmian Champions 1975-78, 59-60. Isthmian Div.2 2000-01. Full Members Cup 1992-93. Athenian Champions 1949-50, 54-55. London Senior Cup 1942-43, 48-49, 58-59, 59-60, 06-07, 07-08. Surrey Senior Cup 1937-38, 43-44, 44-45, 52-53, 59-60, 75-76, 76-77, 77-78, 06-07. South Thames Cup 1969-70. Surrey Senior Shield 1951-52, 60-61, 61-62, 65-66.
Previous Leagues:	London 1932-37 Athenian 1937-56
Ground:	Sandy Lane, Mitcham.

TOOTING MITCHAM UNITED

BEST LGE ATT.: **948** v Heybridge Swifts
LOWEST: **191** v Harrow Borough

No.	Date	Comp	H/A	Opponents	Att:	Result	Goalscorers	Pos
1	Aug 16	Ryman P.	H	Boreham Wood	295	L 1 - 2	**P.Vines** 63	
2	19		A	Billericay Town	409	L 1 - 2	**P.Vines** 43	
3	23		A	Ashford Town (Midx)	170	L 0 - 7		22
4	25		H	Sutton United	546	W 4 - 2	McLeod 18 Abbey 50 Byatt 64 Stevens 79	
5	30		A	Tonbridge Angels	433	W 2 - 0	Legg 21 (og) Grant 69	14
6	Sept 2		H	AFC Hornchurch	346	W 2 - 0	Grant 63 Byatt 89	
7	6		A	Heybridge Swifts	176	D 1 - 1	Pinnock 60	13
8	9		H	Margate	292	W 2 - 1	Bouadji 3 Byatt 45	9
9	**13**	**F.A.C. 1Q**	**A**	**Maidstone United**	**355**	**L 1 - 2**	**P.Vines 80**	
10	20		H	Carshalton Athletic	381	L 1 - 2	Pitterson 83	11
11	23		A	Wealdstone	306	W 3 - 0	**P.Vines** 67 77 Antonia 90	4
12	27		A	Ramsgate	243	W 4 - 1	**P.Vines** 6 Antonio 35 J.Vines 70 Pinnock 88	
13	Oct 4		H	Hendon	339	W 1 - 0	Antonio 16	3
14	11		A	Hastings United	462	W 3 - 0	Antonio 2 Howell 72 Byatt 84	
15	**18**	**F.A.T 1Q**	**A**	**Sutton United**	**511**	**L 0 - 2**		
16	25		H	Dartford	586	L 0 - 2		4
17	28		H	Harrow Borough	191	D 1 - 1	J.Vines 45	
18	Nov 8		A	Maidstone United	375	L 0 - 2		5
19	15		H	Staines Town	321	L 1 - 2	Pitterson 88	
20	22		A	Canvey Island	387	L 1 - 3	Sullivan 20	
21	29		H	Harlow Town	239	W 4 - 2	**P.Vines** 3 (19 16 68) Sullivan 90	7
22	Dec 6		A	Boreham Wood	124	L 0 - 2		8
23	16		A	Dover Athletic	2780	L 0 - 3		
24	20		A	AFC Hornchurch	303	L 0 - 1		11
25	27		H	Horsham	378	L 0 - 2		15
26	Jan 17		H	Heybridge Swifts	948	L 2 - 3	**P.Vines** 51 (pen) Vines J 78	
27	24		A	Carshalton Athletic	376	W 1 - 0	Antonio 80	12
28	31		H	Wealdstone	314	L 2 - 3	**P.Vines** 18 Antonio 45	14
29	Feb 7		A	Margate	407	L 0 - 2		14
30	14		A	Hendon	192	D 2 - 2	Goode 14 Antonio 41	15
31	17		H	Billericay Town	232	D 0 - 0		
32	21		H	Hastings United	330	W 1 - 0	**P.Vines** 86	14
33	24		A	Sutton United	479	D 0 - 0		
34	31		A	Dartford	1320	L 1 - 3	**P.Vines** 88 (pen)	
35	Mar 7		H	Dover Athletic	488	D 1 - 1	**P.Vines** 79	14
36	14		H	Maidstone United	391	W 2 - 0	McDonald 25 Watts 89	13
37	21		A	Harrow Borough	174	D 0 - 0		13
38	24		H	Ashford Town (Middx)	223	W 3 - 2	**P.Vines** 1 McDonald 5 Goode 20	
39	28		H	Ramsgate	281	W 3 - 0	McDonald 21 Marshall 31 **P.Vines** 37	11
40	April 4		A	Staines Town	308	D 0 - 0		10
41	10		H	Tonbridge Angels	470	D 2 - 2	Howell 84 McDonald 88 (pen)	11
42	13		A	Horsham	289	D 0 - 0		
43	18		H	Canvey Island	302	W 3 - 1	McDonald 44 **P.Vines** 49 87	9
44	25		A	Harlow Town	330	W 2 - 0	McDonald 10 **P.Vines** 89	9

Average Home Att: **376** **Goals** **58 61**

Best Position: 3rd **Worst:** 22nd

Goalscorers: P. Vines 19, Antonio 7, McDonald 6, Byatt 4, Pinnock 3, J.Vines 3, Goode 2, Grant 2, Howell 2, Pitterson 2, Abbey 1, Bouadji 1, McLeod 1, Marshall 1, Stevens 1, Sullivan 1, Watts 1. Own Goals 1.

WALTHAM ABBEY

Founded: 1944
Nickname: The Abbotts

CLUB PERSONNEL

Chairman: Joe Collins

Secretary: Derek Bird
17 Fishers Close, Waltham Cross, Essex EN8 7NL.
(M) 0754 364 7066
secretary@wafc.net

Press Officer: As secretary.

Programme Editor: As secretary

Manager: Lee Johnson.

Club Colours: Green & white Hoops/white/green.

Best Season - League: 4th Isthmian Division 1 North 2008-09.

Ground address: Capershotts, Sewardstone Road, Waltham Abbey, Essex EN9 1LU.

Tel/Fax No: 01992 711 287

Capacity: 2,000 **Seats**: 300 **Covered**: 500 **Floodlights**: Yes

Simple Directions: Exit M 25 at Jct 26 and take 2nd left at roundabout into Honey Lane (A121). At the Sewardstone roundabout, take third right into Sewardstone Road which takes you over the M25. Ground is first right before cemetery.

Midweek Home Matchday: Tuesday

Clubhouse: Yes **Club Shop:** no

CLUB STATISTICS

Senior Honours:
London Spartan League Senior Champions 1979.
London Spartan League Division 1 Champions 1978.
London Senior Cup Winners 1999.
Essex Senior Cup Winners 2004-05.

Previous
Leagues: Spartan, Esex & Herts Border League, Essex Senior.
Names: Abbey Sports and amalgamated with Beechfield Sports in 1974 to form Beechfield. Renamed as Waltham Abbey in 1976.

NB: UNFORTUNATELY A RECENT PHOTO WAS NOT AVAILABLE AT THE TIME OF GOING TO PRESS.

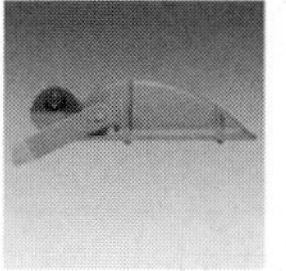

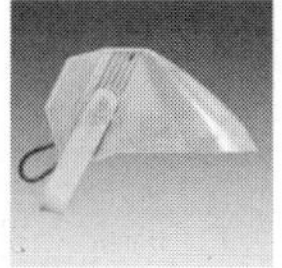

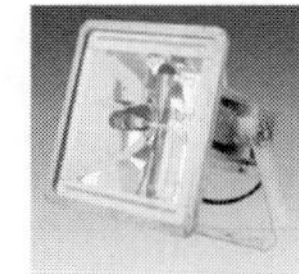

WEALDSTONE

Founded: 1899
Nickname: The Stones

Manager: Gordon Bartlett.

Club Colours: Blue with white trim/blue with white trim/blue and white.

Best Season - League: Conference Champions 1984-85.

Ground address: Grosvenor Vale, Ruislip, Middlesex HA4 6JQ.

Tel: 01895 637487. Fax: 020 8930 7143

Capacity: 2,300 **Seats:** 300 **Covered:** 450 **Floodlights:** Yes

Simple Directions: From the M25: Take Junction 16 Off M25 onto A40. Then come off at The Polish War Memorial junction A4180 sign posted to Ruislip, continue on West End Road, right into Grosvenor Vale after approx 1.5 miles, the ground is at the end of the road.

Midweek Home Matchday: Tuesday.

Clubhouse: Yes.

Local Press: Harrow Observer.

Local Radio: None give reports.

CLUB PERSONNEL

Chairman: Howard Krais

Secretary: Paul Fruin
c/o 31 Jersey Avenue,
Stanmore, Middlesex HA7 2JG
(M) 0779 003 8095
Fax No: 020 8930 7143
paul@pfruin.orangehome.co.uk

Press Officer: Nick DuGard
(M) 0777 819 8905
nickdugard@fsmail.net

Programme
Editor: Adam Gloor
0776 468 8386
Email: adamgloor@aol.com

CLUB STATISTICS

Record	**Attendance**: 13,504 v Leytonstone, 4th Rd replay. F.A. Amateur Cup 05.03.49 (at Lower Mead Stadium) **Victory:** 22-0 v The 12th London Regiment (The Rangers) F.A.Amateur Cup 13.10.23 **Defeat**::14 v Edgware Town (A) London Senior Cup 09.12.44 **Career Goalscorer**: George Duck 251 **Career Appearances**: Charlie Townsend 514 **Transfer FeesPaid:** £15,000 to Barnet for David Gipp **Transfer Fee Received**: £70,000 from Leeds United for Jermaine Beckford.
Senior Honours:	F.A.Trophy Winners 84-85 F.A.Amateur Cup 65-66 Conference 84-85 Isthmian Div 3 96-97 Southern Lg Southern Div 81-82 Div 1 South 73-4 Athenian Lg 51-2 London Sen Cup 61-2 Middx Sen Cup 11
Previous Leagues:	Willesden & Dist. 1899-1906 08-13 London 1911 -22 Middx 13-22 Spartan 22-28 Athenian 28-64 Isthmian 64-71,95-06 Southern 71-79 ,81-82 88-95. Conference 79-81 82-88

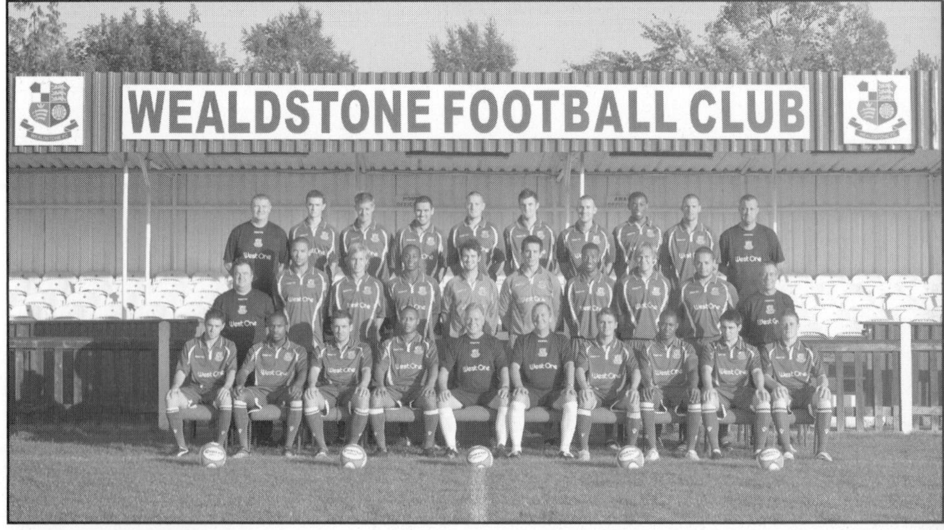

WEALDSTONE

BEST LGE ATT.: 780 v Harrow Borough
LOWEST: 254 v Boreham Wood

No.	Date	Comp	H/A	Opponents	Att:	Result	Goalscorers	Pos
1	Aug 16	Ryman P.	H	Tonbridge Angels	387	D 0 - 0		
2	19		A	Ashford Town (Midx)	278	L 1 - 2	Alexander 72	
3	23		A	Billericay Town	386	L 2 - 3	Chappell 34 Hughes 38	17
4	25		H	Boreham Wood	254	D 1 - 1	**Ashe** 6	
5	30		A	Dartford	986	D 2 - 2	Hughes 13 25	19
6	Sept 2		H	Sutton United	371	W 4 - 0	Massey 54 60 Chappell 84 **Ashe** 89	
7	6		H	Ramsgate	344	L 0 - 1		16
8	**13**	**F.A.C.1Q**	**H**	**Bedford Town**	**312**	**D 2 - 2**	**Gray 67 Hughes 84 (pen)**	
9	**16**	**F.A.C 1Qr**	**A**	**Bedford Town**	**349**	**D 1 - 1**	**Clarke 66 Bedford Town won 4-2 after pens**	
10	20		A	Hendon	280	W 4 - 1	Boyce 15 **Ashe** 50 53 Hughes 90	16
11	23		H	Tooting & Mitcham U	306	L 0 - 3		
12	Oct 4		A	Harlow Town	342	L 0 - 2		18
13	7		A	AFC Hornchurch	252	L 0 - 1		
14	11		H	Carshalton Athletic	334	W 1 - 1	Gray 64	19
15	14		H	Canvey Island	303	L 2 - 3	James 5 30	
16	**18**	**F.A.T. 1Q**	**H**	**Croydon Athletic**	**195**	**W 1 - 0**	**O'Leary 44**	
17	25		A	Margate	428	W 1 - 0	**Ashe** 69	17
18	28		H	Staines Town	280	W 4 - 3	Montgomery 21 James 33 Gray 45 48	
19	**Nov 1**	**F.A.T. 2Q**	**H**	**Tiverton Town**	**100**	**L 1 - 2**	**Hicks 61**	
20	8		A	Heybridge Swifts	139	W 1 - 0	O'Leary 19	12
21	15		H	Maidstone United	660	W 3 - 2	Sorvell 1 Montgomery 46 Haule 66	10
22	19		A	Horsham	193	W 2 - 0	Montgomery 7 Haule 77	
23	22		H	Dover Athletic	448	L 1 - 2	Keister 10 (og)	
24	29		A	Hastings United	435	L 1 - 2	Chappell 20	10
25	Dec 6		A	Tonbridge Angels	347	W 2 - 1	Hicks 32 Massey 54	10
26	20		A	Sutton United	499	L 2 - 3	Locke 6 Spendlove 71	
27	27		H	Harrow Borough	780	W 6 - 0	**Ashe** 14 62 Gray 21 42 Leech (og) 48 Chappell 54	8
28	Jan 17		A	Ramsgate	282	D 2 - 2	Haule 30 38	10
29	24		H	Hendon	433	W 2 - 1	**Ashe** 68 Ngoyi 83	
30	31		A	Tooting & Mitcham	314	W 3 - 2	Forbes 43 **Ashe** 85 Spendlove 90	7
31	Feb 14		H	Harlow Town	394	L 1 - 2	Chappell 10	9
32	17		A	Boreham Wood	214	L 0 - 2		
33	21		A	Carshalton Athletic	321	L 2 - 3	**Ashe** 22 (pen) Gonsalves 23 (og)	11
34	28		H	Margate	376	W 2 - 0	Haule 55 Martin 53	9
35	Mar 3		H	Billericay Town	288	L 1 - 2	Forbes 28	
36	7		A	Canvey Island	342	D 1 - 1	Chappell 28	11
37	14		H	Heybridge Swifts	384	W 3 - 0	Gray 6 Ngoyi 16 **Ashe** 56	10
38	21		A	Staines Town	388	D 2 - 2	**Ashe** 37 (pen) 55	8
39	24		H	AFC Hornchurch	325	W 1 - 0	**Ashe** 2	
40	28		H	Horsham	449	W 1 - 0	**Ashe** 23	6
41	31		H	Ashford Town (Midx)	343	W 3 - 1	O'Leary 4 Ngoyi 47 75	
42	April 4		A	Maidstone United	377	L 1 - 2	Ngoyi 14	6
43	11		H	Dartford	664	D 0 - 0		6
44	13		A	Harrow Borough	580	W 3 - 0	NGOYI 3 (36 38 46pen)	
45	18		A	Dover Athletic	1024	L 1 - 3	Ngoyi 75	7
46	25		H	Hastings United	444	W 1 - 0	Ngoyi 39	7

Average Home Att: 408 (289) **Goals 75 61**

Best Position: 6th **Worst:** 19th

Goalscorers: Ashe 15, Ngoyi 10, Gray 7, Chappell 6, Hughes 5, Haule 5, James 3, Massey 3, Montgomery 3, O'Leary 3, Forbes 2, Hicks 2, Spendlove 2, Alexander 1, Boyce 1, Clarke 1, Locke 1, Martin 1, Sorvell 1. Own Goals 3.

BRENTWOOD TOWN

Founded: 1972
Nickname: Blues

Manager: Carl Griffiths

Club Colours: Sky Blue/navy/navy.

Best Seasons - League: 3rd Isthmian Division 1 North 2008-09.

Ground address: The Arena, Brentwood Centre, Doddinghurst Road, Brentwood, Essex CM15 9NN.

TFax: 01708 437 904

Capacity: 1,000 **Seats**: 50 **Covered**: 250 **Floodlights**: Yes

Simple Directions: From High St.(Wilson's Corner) turn north into Ongar Road, then at third moin roundabout turn right into Doddinghurst Road.

Midweek Home Matchday: Tuesday

Clubhouse: Tuesday, Thursday evenings and matchdays **Club Shop:** No

CLUB PERSONNEL

Chairman: Keith Woodcock

Secretary: Ray Stevens,
Woodside, 7 Woodlands Ave,
Hornchurch, Essex
RM11 2QT
Tel No: 01708 456677
(M) 0776 800 6370
Fax No: 01708 437904
r.w.stevens@btinternet.com

Press Officer: Ken Hobbs
(M) 0795 823 2829
khobbs1057@aol.com

Programme Editor: As secretary.

CLUB STATISTICS

Record	**Attendance:** 472 v West Ham - 27.07.04
Senior Honours:	Champions Essex Senior League 2001-02, 06-07.
	Essex Senior Lge Cup 1975-76, 78-79, 90-91, 06-07.
	Essex Olympian Lge Cup 1967-68
Previous Leagues:	Romford & District, South Essex Combination, London & Essex Border, Olympian. Essex Senior.
Names:	Manor Athletic, Brentwood Athletic, Brentwood F.C.
Grounds:	King George's Playing Fields (Hartswood). Larkins Playing Fields 1957-93

CHESHUNT

Founded: 1946
Nickname: Ambers

Manager: Bob Dearie.

Club Colours: Amber/black/amber or black.

Best Seasons - League: 16th Southern Premier 2005-06, 06-07.

Ground address: Cheshunt Stadium, Theobalds Lane, Cheshunt, Herts EN8 8RU.

Tel/fax No: 01992 633 500.

Capacity: 3,500 **Seats**: 424 **Covered**: 600 **Floodlights**: Yes

Simple Directions: M25, junction 25 take A10 north towards Hertford. Third exit at roundabout towards Waltham Cross A121. First exit at roundabout towards Cheshunt B176. Under railway bridge then left onto Theobalds Lane. Ground 800 yards on right.

Midweek Home Matchday: Tuesday

Clubhouse: Bar and Function Hall **Club Shop:** No

Local Press: Waltham and Cheshunt Mercury, East Herts Herald, Lea Valley Star.

CLUB PERSONNEL

Chairman: Vince Sartori

Secretary: Alex Kalinic
89 Eleanor Road, Waltham Cross, Herts EN8 7DN
(M) 075 483 1800

Press Officer: Jim Tuite
(M) 0795 632 4525
jim@cheshuntfc.com

Programme Editor: As press officer

CLUB STATISTICS

Record **Attendance**: 5,000 v Bromley F.A.Amateur Cup 2nd Rd 28.01.50
Victory: 11-0 v Royal Ordnance Factories (A) 1946-47 London League Div 1
Defeat: 0-10 v Eton Manor, London League 17.04..56
Goalscorer: Eddie Sedgwick 148 (1967 to 72 & 80)
Career Appearances: John Poole 526 (1970 to 76 & 79 to 83)

Record Transfer Fee **Paid**: Undisclosed for Darrell Cox from Boreham Wood 2006
Received: £10,000 from Peterborough United for Lloyd Opara

Senior Honours: Isthmian league div 2 winners 2003, r/up 1982, div 3 r/up 1994
Athenian league prem winners 1976, r/up 1974, div 1 winners 1968, div 2 r/up 1966
Spartan league winners 1963. London league prem winners 1950, r/up 1957, div 1 winners 1948, 1949, r/up 1947. London Charity Cup winners 1974. Herts Charity Cup winners 2006, 2008
East Anglian Cup winners 1975, r/up 1976.

Previous Leagues London 1947-51 56-59. Delphian 1952- 55. Aetolian 1960-62
Spartan 1963-64 88-93. Athenian 1965-76. Isthmian 77-87 94-05 09-date. Southern 2006-08.

Back Row (L-R): Caroline Manning, Alfie Norman, Matt Cook, Ricky Light, Neil Ameh, Darren Williams, Bradley Harrison, Stuart Pack, Christiaan Beaupierre, Adem Salih, Tom Tresadern, Bob Dearie, Rebecca Cornish, Barry Green. **Front Row:** Boniek Forbes, Glen Adams, Reece Lyons, Graeme Dearie, Glen Parry, Chris Meikle, Aaron Churchouse, Charlie Hoy, Gary Schillachi.

CONCORD RANGERS

Founded: 1967
Nickname: Rangers

Managers: Danny Scopes and Danny Cowley

Club Colours: Yellow/blue/blue.

Best Seasons - League: 5th Isthmian Division 1 North 2008-09.

Ground address: Thames Road, Canvey Island, Essex SS8 0HH

Tel/fax: 01268 515 750.

Capacity: 1,500 **Seats**: Yes **Covered**: Yes **Floodlights**: Yes

Simple Directions: A 130 onto Canvey Island. Turn right into Thorney Bay Road. Then right again into Thames Road.

Midweek Home Matchday: Tuesday

Clubhouse: Yes **Club Shop:** No

CLUB PERSONNEL

Chairman: Antony Smith

Secretary: Chris Crerie
c/o the club.
(M) 0790 952 8818
Fax No: 01268 534666
concordrangers@btinternet.com

Press Officer: Antony Smith
(M) 0776 887 2625
asmith@aspectcontracts.co.uk

Programme Editor: As secretary

CLUB STATISTICS

Records	**Attendance**: 1,500 v Lee Chapel North, F.A.Sunday Cup 1989-90.
Senior Honours:	Essex Intermediate Division 2 Champions 1990-91.
	Essex Senior League 1997-98, 2003-04, 07-08.
Previous Leagues:	Southend & District. Southend Alliance.
	Essex Intermediate 1988-91.
	Essex Senior 1991-2008.
Previous Ground:	Waterside.

EAST THURROCK UNITED

Founded: 1969
Nickname: Rocks

CLUB PERSONNEL

Chairman: Brian Mansbridge

Secretary: Mick Stephens,
39 New Park Road, Benfleet,
Essex SS7 5UR
Tel No: 01268 458571
(M) 0797 921 4350
Fax No: (H) 01268 458571
mickygatta@blueyonder.co.uk

Press Officer: Peter Lambert
(M) 0788 400 2514

Programme Editor: Neil Speight
(M) 0788 531 3435
neil.speight@nqe.com

Manager: John Coventry

Club Colours: Amber/black/black

Best Season - League: 12th Isthmian Premier 2005-06

Ground address: Rookery Hill, Corringham, Essex SS17 9LB

TelNo: 01375 644 166. Fax: 01375 384 159

Capacity: 4,000 **Seats:** 160 **Covered:** 1,000 **Floodlights:** Yes

Simple Directions: From A13 London -Southend road, take A1014 at Stanford -le-Hope for two and a half miles. Ground on left. Two miles from Basildon & S-le-H BR

Midweek Home Matchday: Tuesday

Clubhouse: Open all day seven days a week.

Club Shop: No

Local Radio: BBC Essex

Local Press:Thurrock Gazette and Thurrock Recorder.

CLUB STATISTICS

Record	**Attendance**: 1,215 v Woking F.A.Cup 2003
	Victory: 7-0 v Coggeshall (H) 1984 Essex Senior League
	Defeat: 0-9 v Eton Manor (A) 1982 Essex Senior League
	Career Goalscorer: Graham Stewart 102
	Career Appearances: Glen Case 600+
	Received: £22,000 from Leyton Orient for Greg Berry
Senior Honours:	Isthmian Division 3 Champions 1999-2000.
	E.Anglian Cup 2002-03.
Previous Leagues:	South Essex Comb. Greater London, Metroplitan 72-75 London
	Spartan 75-79 Essex Senior 79-92 Isthmian 92-2004 Southern 2004-05.
Previous Name:	Corrington Social (pre 1969 Sunday side)
Previous Grounds:	Billet, Stanford-le-Hope 70-73 74-76 Grays Athletic 73-74, Tilbury F.C. 77-82
	New Thames Club 82-84.

ENFIELD TOWN

Founded: 2001
Nickname: 'ET's or Towners

Manager: Steve Newing.

Club Colours: White/royal blue/white.

Best Seasons - League: 3rd Southern Division 1 East.

Ground address: Groundsharing with Brimsdown Rovers at Brimsdown Social Club, Goldsdown Road, Enfield EN3 7RP. Tel/Fax No: 020 8804 5491

Capacity: 2,300 **Seats**: 250 **Covered**: 300 **Floodlights**: Yes

Simple Directions: Off Green Street which is off Hertford Road (A1010) Buses 191 or 307 or Liverpool Street to Brimsdown (BR) or Southbury Rd

Midweek Home Matchday: Tuesday

Clubhouse: Yes **Club Shop:** No

Local Press: Enfield Gazette, Enfield Advertiser and Enfield Independant

CLUB PERSONNEL

Chairman: Paul Millington
Secretary: Peter Coath
33 Ashford Crescent, Enfield, Middlesex EN3 7HX
Tel No: 0800 616 961
(H) 020 8292 4495
(M) 0794 937 8931
Fax No: 020 7918 1291
(H) 020 8292 4495
qscp@lineone.net
Press Officer: Ciaron Glennon
(M) 0773 095 3813
ciaran.glennon@btopenworld.com
Programme Editor: As press officer

CLUB STATISTICS

Record	**Attendance:** 562 v Enfield, Middlesex Charity Cup 2002-2003
	Career Goalscorer: Dan Clarke - 68
	Career Appearances: Stuart Snowden - 147
Record	**Victory:** 7-0 v Ilford (a) 29.04.03
Senior Honours:	Essex Senior Champions 2002-03.
Previous	**Leagues**: Essex Senior League and Isthmian League
	Name: Broke away from Enfield F.C. in 2001

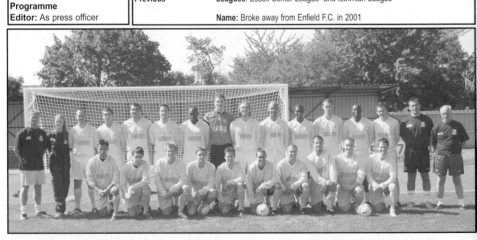

NB: UNFORTUNATELY A RECENT PHOTO WAS NOT AVAILABLE AT THE TIME OF GOING TO PRESS.

GREAT WAKERING ROVERS

Founded: 1919
Nickname: Rovers

Manager: Iain O'Connell

Club Colours: Green & White Stripes/white/green.

Best Season - League: 12th Isthmian Division 1 North 2006-07

Ground address: Burroughs Park, Little Wakering Hall Lane, Gt.Wakering, Southend, Essex SS3 0HH Tel No: 01702 217 812

Capacity: 2,500 **Seats**: 150 **Covered**:300 **Floodlights**: Yes

Simple Directions: A127 towards Southend and follow signs for Shoeburyness for about four miles.. Turnleft to Gt Wakering onn B1017 at Bournes Green. Go down High Street for half a mile and ground is on the left.

Midweek Home Matchday: Tuesday

Clubhouse: Open every evening, Sat 11-11, Sun 12-3 & 7.30-10.30p.m. Hot meals, snacks etc matchdays only.

Club Shop: No

Local Radio: Essex F.M.

Local Press: Evening News

CLUB PERSONNEL

Chairman: Roy Ketteridge

Secretary: Roger Sampson, 37 Lee Lotts, GreatWakering, Esssex SS3 0HA
Tel No: 01702 218794
(H) 01702 218794
(M) 0783 785 6482
Fax No: (H) 01702 216098
rogersampson@talktalk.net

Press Officer:
Norman Johnson
(M) 0790 55 9852
nobbysarover@blueyonder.co.uk

Programme Editor: As press officer.

CLUB STATISTICS

Records — **Attendance:** 1,150 v Southend United (Friendly) 19.07.06

Victory: 9-0 v Eton Manor 27.12.1931

Defeat: 1-7 v Bowers United ,Essex Senior 01.04.98

Senior Honours: Isthmian League Division 3. Essex Senior League 1994-95.

Previous: **Leagues:** Southend & Dist. 19-81, Southend All. 81-89, Essex I'mediate 89-92, Essex Senior 1992-1999, Isthmian 1999-2004 Southern 2004-2005

Ground: Gt Wakering Rec

Back Row (L-R): Jimmy Webb, James Nolan, Ty Benjamin, Stewart Moore, Dan williams, Ben Hudson.
Middle Row: Jack O'Connor, Freskim Rushti, Dominic Binns, Adam Holmes, Louis Godwin-Green, Richard McKinney, Matt Toms, Michael Fox, Danny Heath (Reserve team manager).
Front Row: Billy Johnson, Lewis Sparrow, Cleve Taylor (Physio), Ryan Wilkinson.

HARLOW TOWN

Founded: 1879
Nickname: Hawks

CLUB PERSONNEL

Chairman: Simon Morgan

Secretary: Jim Aldridge
Tel No: 01279 400909
(M) 0788 153 8922
Fax No: 01279 405889
jimaldridge@hotmail.co.uk

Press Officer: Billy Shaw
(M)0798 442 0494
billyontheradio@yahoo.co.uk

Programme Editor: As press officer

Manager: Glen Alzapiedi

Club Colours: Red/red/red.

Best Season - League: 15th Isthmian Premier 2007-08.

Ground address: Barrows Farm Stadium, off Elizabeth Way, The Pinnacles, Harlow, Essex CM19 5BE. Tel: 01279 445 319. Fax: 01279 635 846.

Capacity: 3,500 **Seats**: 500 **Covered**: 500 **Floodlights**: Yes

Simple Directions: If coming into Harlow from the M11 (North or South) exit at Junction 7 and follow the A414 until the first roundabout where you turn left onto the A1169. Follow the A1169 signed for Roydon until you see the ground ahead of you at the Roydon Road roundabout. Go straight over the roundabout and the entrance to the ground is on the left.

If coming into town from the west on the A414 turn right at the first roundabout (the old ground was straight ahead) signed Roydon A1169. Follow the A1169 for approx 1 mile and the entrance to the ground is on the right.

Midweek Home Matchday: Tuesday

Clubhouse: Function Suite available. **Club Shop:** Yes

Local Radio: Essex Radio, BBC Essex Ten 17

Local Press: Harlow Citizen, Harlow Star and Harlow Herald & Post

CLUB STATISTICS

Record	**Attendance:** 9,723 v Leicester City F.A.Cup 3rd Round Replay 08.01.80
	Goalscore in a Season: Dick Marshall 64 - 1928-29
	Career Appearances: Norman Gladwin 639 (1949-1970)
Record	**Victory:** 14-0 v Bishop's Stortford - 11.04.1925.
	Defeat: 0-11 v Ware(A) Spartan Div 1 (East) 06.03.48
Senior Honours:	Isthmian League Div 1 78-79 R-up 82-83, Div 2 North 88-89, Athenian Lg Div 1 71-72, Essex Snr Cup 78-79,
Previous Leagues:	**Leagues:** East Herts (pre-1932); Spartan 32-39 46-54; London 54-61; Delphian 61-63; Athenian 63-73; Isthmian 73-92; Inactive 92-93. Southern 2004-06.
	Grounds: Marigolds 1919-22; Green Man Field 22-60

NB: UNFORTUNATELY A RECENT PHOTO WAS NOT AVAILABLE AT THE TIME OF GOING TO PRESS.

HEYBRIDGE SWIFTS

Founded: 1880
Nickname: Swifts

CLUB PERSONNEL

Chairman: Nick Bowyer

Secretary: Peter Pask
7 Maple Avenue, Heybridge,
Maldon, Essex CM9 4BP
Tel No: 01621 857 336
(M) 0777 093 0556
Fax No: 01621 857336 (ring first)
hsfcadmin@tiscali.co.uk

Press Officer: Noel Tilbrook
(M) 0780 243 4508
noel@steponsafety.co.uk

Programme Editor: As press officer

Manager: Wayne Bond

Club Colours: Black & white stripes/black/black.

Best Season - League: 2nd Isthmian Premier Division 2005-06.

Ground address: Scraley Road, Heybridge, Maldon, Essex CM9 8JA

Tel No: 01621 852 978

Club Website: www.heybridgeswifts.com

Capacity: 3,000 **Seats:** 550 **Covered:** 1,200 **Floodlights:** Yes

Simple Directions: Leave Maldon on the main road to Colchester, pass through Heybridge then turn right at sign to Tolleshunt Major (Scraley Road). The ground is on the right.

Midweek Home Matchday: Tuesday

Clubhouse:.Two bars open every evening

Club Shop: Open matchdays.

CLUB STATISTICS

Record	**Attendance**: 2,477 v Woking F.A.Trophy 1997
Career Goalscorer:	Julian Lamb 115 (post war) Dave Matthews 112 (Isthmian)
Career Appearances:	Hec Askew 500+ John Pollard 496
Record Transfer Fee	**Paid**: £1,000 for Dave Rainford and for Lee kersey.
	Received: £35,000 from Southend United for Simon Royce.
Senior Honours:	Isthmian Div 1 R-Up 95-96 Div 2 North 89-90 Essex Senior Lg (3)
	E.Anglian Cup 93-94 94-95 Essex Junior Cup 31-32
Previous Leaguess:	Essex & Suffolk Border , North Essex, South Essex & Essex Senior 1971-84

NB: UNFORTUNATELY A RECENT PHOTO WAS NOT AVAILABLE AT THE TIME OF GOING TO PRESS.

ILFORD

Re-Formed: 1987
Nickname: The Foxes

CLUB PERSONNEL

Chairman: Roger Chilvers
Secretary: Roger Chivers
50 Harrow Road, Barking,
Essex IG11 7RA
(M) 0771 028 5571
Fax No: (H) 020 8591 1751
rogerchilvers@aol.com
Press Officer: Len Llewellyn
Tel No: 01277 363103
Fax No: (H) 01277 363103
exseniorlenl@aol.com
Programme Editor: As press officer

Manager: Chris Wood

Club Colours: Blue and white/blue/blue and white.

Best Seasons - League: 1st Isthmian Premier 1906-07, 1920-21, 1921-22.

Ground address: Cricklefield Stadium, 486 High Road, Ilford, Essex. IG1 1UE

Tel/Fax No: 020 8514 8352

Capacity: 3,500 **Seats**: 216 **Covered**: Yes **Floodlights**: Yes

Simple Directions: Five minutes walk from Seven Kings Station, opposite 'The Cauliflower' pub. Or 86 Bus.

Midweek Home Matchday: Wednesday

Clubhouse: Open lunchtimes and evenings every day. Snacks available.

Club Shop: No

Local Radio: Time F.M. and BBC Essex.

Local Press: Ilford Recorder.

CLUB STATISTICS

Record **Attendance:** 17,000 Ilford Boys v Swansea Boys (Schools Trophy Final)

Senior Honours:
FA Amateur Cup 1928-29, 29-30.
Isthmian League Champions 1906-07, 20-21, 21-22.
Essex Senior Cup x 14 (record number of wins).
London Senior. Cup x 7

Previous Leagues: Isthmian. Spartan, Essex Senior, Isthmian, Southern

Back Row (L-R): Victor Omogbehin, Jurrel McCarthy, George Dawson, Aaron Scott, Pape Diagne, Derek Hawtin, Callum McGeehan. Middle Row: Richard Pike, Des Gallen, Anton Trice, Junior Konadu, Tony Russell, Harry Chalk, Jason Sam-Franks, Roy Holliwell, Junior Appiah. Front Row: **John Hughes, Bradley Drisdale, Neil Matthews, Lucelta Eugeen (Physio), Colin Walton (Asst. Manager), Roger Chilvers (Chairman), Chris Wood (Manager), Michael Thompson (Coach), Jamie Pooley, Michael Noble, John Sparks.**

LEYTON

Founded: 1868
Nickname: Lilywhites

CLUB PERSONNEL

Chairman:
Costas Sophocleous

Secretary:
Stephen Bellanoff
c/o the club
Tel/fax: 020 8539 1780
leytonfc@btconnect.com

Press Officer:
As secretary

Programme
Editor: Tony Hardy
(M) 0778 637 4815
leytonfc@btconnect.com

Manager: Tony Levoli.

Club Colours: White/royal blue/white.

Best Seasons - League: 5th Isthmian Premier.

Ground address: Leyton Stadium, 282 Lea Bridge Road, Leyton, E10 7LD

Tel/fax: 020 8539 1780.

Capacity: 2,500 **Seats:** Yes **Covered:** Yes **Floodlights:** Yes

Simple Directions: Lea Bridge Road is the A104 and ground is next to Hare & Hounds pub. Leyton (Central Line) then bus 58 or158 to Lea Bridge Road.

Midweek Home Matchday: Tuesday

Clubhouse: Open every evening and weekends at lunchtime.

Club Shop: Yes

CLUB STATISTICS

Senior Honours:
Essex Senior Cup Winners 1896-97, 97-98, 99-1900, 00-01, 02-03, 29-30, 30-31, 34-35.
London Senior Cup Winners 1903-04
F.A. Amateur Cup Winners 1926-27, 27-28.
100,000 watched their Amateur Cup Final with Walthamstow Avenue at Wembley in 1951-52, which they lost.
Athenian Champions 1928-29, 65-66, 66-67.
As Leyton Wingate Athenian Champions 1976-77, 81-82.
Isthmian Division Two North 1984-85.

Previous
Names: Leyton 1891-1973. Leyton Wingate 1976-87. Leyton 1992 -
Leagues: Leyton & District Alliance. South Essex. Essex Intermediate. Essex Senior. London Spartan.

LOWESTOFT TOWN

Founded: 1884
Nickname: The Blues

CLUB PERSONNEL

Chairman: Gary Keyzor

Secretary: Terry Lynes.
31 Avondale Road,
Lowestoft,
Suffolk NR32 2HU.
Tel: 01502 564 034
(M) 0793 087 2947

Press Officer & Programme Editor:
As secretary

Manager: Micky Chapman and Ady Gallagher.

Club Colours: All blue.

Best Seasons - League: 1st Eastern Counties Premier (x12) most recently 2008-09

Ground address: Crown Meadow, Love Road, Lowestoft NR32 2PA.

Tel No: 01502 573 818.

Capacity: 3,000 **Seats:** 466 **Covered:** 500

Simple Directions: Just off A12. Ten minutes from Lowestoft BR.

Midweek Home Matchday: Tuesday

Clubhouse: Yes

Club Shop: Yes

CLUB STATISTICS

Record — **Attendance:** 5,000 v Watford, FA Cup 1st Round 1967.

Senior Honours:
Eastern Counties Champions 1935-36 (shared), 37-38, 62-63, 64-65, 65-66, 66-67, 67-68, 69-70, 70-71, 77-78, 2005-06, 08-09.
Suffolk Senior Cup Winners 1902-03, 22-23, 25-26, 31-32, 35-36, 46-47, 47-48, 48-49, 55-56.

Previous — **Names:** Original club merged with Kirkley in 1887 to form Lowestoft and became Lowestoft Town in 1890.
Leagues: North Suffolk 1897-1935. Eastern Counties 1935-2009.

Back Row (L-R): Michael Ling (physio), Martin McNeil, Bradley Hough, Ady Gallagher (joint manager), Andy Reynolds (part hidden), Marcus Saunders, Ally McKenna, Ross King, Matty Potter, Gerry Lawrence (committee), Russell Stock, Gary McGee (part hidden), Dale Cockrill, Craig Fleming (coach), Jamie Stokeld, Micky Chapman (joint manager).
Front Row: Emma Scoggins (physio), Darren Cockrill, Neil Plaskett, Richard Woodrow, Carl Poppy, Jamie Godbold, Reece Hunn, Damian Hilton, Jack Marsden.

MALDON TOWN

Founded: 1946
Nickname: Blues

CLUB PERSONNEL

Chairman: Ed Garty

Secretary: Tony Delaney
32 Peartree Lane
Danbury, Chelmsford
Essex CM3 4LS
(M) 0777 099 6202

Press Officer and Programme Editor:
As secretary

Manager: Stuart Nethercott.

Club Colours: Blue & white hoops/blue/blue.

Best Seasons- League: 20th Isthmian Premier 2005-06.

Ground address: Wallace Binder Ground, Park Drive, Maldon CM9 6XX

Tel No: 01621 853 762.

Capacity: 2,800 **Seats:** 155 **Covered:** 300 **Floodlights:** Yes

Simple Directions: From M25 jct. 28 travel north on A12 until A414 to Maldon. Turn right at Safeways roundabout, then over next two roundabouts. Ground on right.

Midweek Home Matchday: Tuesday

Clubhouse: Open to visitors on match days with variety of food.

CLUB STATISTICS

Record	**Attendance**: 1,163 v AFC Sudbury .F.A.Vase Semi-Final April 2003
	Victory: 10-1 v Dartford (a)
	Career Appearances: Jack Judd
	Transfer Fee Received: £5,000 from Millwall for Neil Harris
Senior Honours:	Essex Senior League 1984-85. Eastern Co.Div 1 1996-97.
Previous Leagues:	Mid Essex, N.Essex, Essex & Suffolk Border, Essex Senior.
Previous Ground:	Fambridge Road (pre 1994)

NB: UNFORTUNATELY A RECENT PHOTO WAS NOT AVAILABLE AT THE TIME OF GOING TO PRESS.

NORTHWOOD

Founded: 1899
Nickname: Woods

CLUB PERSONNEL

Chairman: Ian Barry

Secretary: Alan Evans
46 Webster Gardens,
Ealing, W5 5ND
Tel No: 020 8825 6869
(H) 020 8566 2880
(M) 0796 074 4349
Fax No: (H) 020 8825 6944
alan.evansnfc@btopenworld.com

Press Officer: Robin Piper
Tel No: (M) 0797 633 1276
robin.piper@antalis.co.uk

Programme Editor: Ken Green
(M) 0798 470 7398
ken.green01@ntlworld.com

Manager: Dave Anderson

Club Colours: Red/red/red.

Best Season - League 17th Isthmian Premier 2004-05.

Ground address: Northwood Park, Chestnut Avenue, Northwood, Middx. HA6 1HR

Tel No: 01923 827 148 Fax: 020 8825 6944

Capacity: 3,075 **Seats** 308 **Covered**: 932 **Floodlights:** Yes

Simple Directions: A404 (Pinner-Rickmansorth) Chestnut Avenue, A third of a mile from Northwood Hill station (Metropolitan Line). Right out of station to roundabout, left into Pinner Road, left into Chestnut Avenue after 300 yards.

Midweek Home Matchday: Tuesday

Clubhouse: Weekends and most week days. Hot food available.

Club Shop: No

CLUB STATISTICS

Record	**Attendance**: 1,642 v Chelsea. Friendly July 1997
	Victory: 15-0 v Dateline (H) Middlesex Intermediate Cup 1973
	Defeat: 0-8 v Bedfont Middx. Lg 1975
	Goalscorer: Season - Lawrence Yaku 61 (1999-00)
	Career Appearances: Chris Gell 493 +
Senior Honours:	Middlesex Premier Cup 1994-95. Isthmain Lg Div 1 North Champions 2002-03. Isthmian Charity Shield Winners 2002
Previous Name:	Northwood Town
Previous Leagues	Harrow & Wembley 32-69, Middlesex 69-78 , Hellenic 79-84
	London Spartan 84-93. Isthmian 1993-05. Southern League 2005-07

NB: UNFORTUNATELY A RECENT PHOTO WAS NOT AVAILABLE AT THE TIME OF GOING TO PRESS.

POTTERS BAR TOWN

Founded: 1960
Nickname: Grace or Scholars

CLUB PERSONNEL

Chairman: Peter Waller

Secretary: Alan Evans
45 Etchingham Park Road
Finchley, London N8 2EB
Tel No: (M) 0783 363 2965
potters_bar_sec@hotmail.co.uk

Press Officer: As secretary

Programme
Editor: Peter Broomfield
(M) 07775 345 126
Email: peterbsfl@yahoo.co.uk

Manager: Adam Lee

Club Colours: Maroon/maroon/maroon.

Best Seasons - League: 14th Isthmian Division 1 North 2006-07.

Ground address: The South Mimms Travel Stadium, Parkfield, Watkins Rise, off The Walk, Potters Bar, Herts. EN6 1QN

Tel No: 01707 654 833

Capacity: 2,000 **Seats**: 150 **Covered**: 250 **Floodlights**: Yes

Simple Directions: M25 Jct 24 enter Potters Bar along Southgate Road (A111) turn right into High Street at first lights (A1000) then left into The Walk after half a mile. Ground 200 yards on right.(opposite Potters Bar cricket club)

Midweek Home Matchday: Tuesday

Clubhouse: Training Nights, Matchdays and week-ends.

Club Shop: Contact Jeff Barnes (01707 662399) for details of club badges, pennants, car stickers etc.

Local Press: Welwyn & Hatfield Times (Potters Bar edition)

CLUB STATISTICS

Record — **Attendance:** 4,000 Charity Match.1997 268 for club v Wealdstone FACup 98

Senior Honours: South Midlands League Premier Division Champions 1996-97.
Spartan South Midlands League Premier Champions 2004-05.

Previous — **Leagues**: Barnet & District 1960-65. North London Combination 1965-68.
Herts Senior County 1968-91.
Spartan and Spartan South Midlands 1991-2005. Southern 2005-2006.

NB: UNFORTUNATELY A RECENT PHOTO WAS NOT AVAILABLE AT THE TIME OF GOING TO PRESS.

REDBRIDGE

Re-Formed: 2004
Nickname: Motormen

CLUB PERSONNEL

Chairman: Jimmy Chapman

Secretary: Bob Holloway.
94 Stanley Road, Hornchurch,
Essex RM12 4JW
(M) 0789 069 9907
bobholloway@redbridgefc.com

Press Officer: Adam Silver
Tel No: (M) 0779 688 0824
adammichaelsilver@hotmila.com

Programme Editor: As press officer.

Manager: Jay Devereux

Club Colours: Blue/blue/white.

Best Seasons - League: 22nd Conference South 2004-05.

Ground address: Oakside Stadium, Station Rd., Barkingside, Ilford, Essex IG6 1NB.

Tel/fax No: 020 8550 3611

Capacity: 3,000 **Seats**: 316 **Covered**: 1,000 **Floodlights:** Yes

Simple Directions: A12 from London. Turn left off Eastern Ave into Horns Rd, Barkingside (Greengate). Right into Craven Gardens, right again into Carlton Drive and left into Station Road. Go over bridge and ground is on right..

Midweek Home Matchday: Tuesday

Clubhouse: Large bar open Tues/Thurs/Sat and any other match day.

Club Shop: Yes

CLUB STATISTICS

Record — **Attendance:** F.A.Amateur Cup Semi-Final v Bishop Auckland 58.000 at St James Park, Newcastle.

Goalscorer: Jeff Wood 196

Career Appearances: Roger Bird

Senior Honours: London Senior Cup (x5) Essex Senior Trophy (x3) EsseX Senior Cup(x5)

Previous Leagues Spartan. Aetolian. Metropolitan. Essex Senior. Isthmian

Back Row (L-R): Simon Peddie, Ben Turner, Jon Higgs, Fabio Jesus, Mason Durrell, Jake Whincup, Brian Alidjah, Theo Daniels, Carl Bruce. **Middle Row:** Sonny Read, Nathaniel Hibbert, Aaron Hunwicks, Ashley Marsh(coach), Jay Deverux(manager), Dave Ross(coach), Carl Conway,Andy Edmunds, Sonny Adams. **Front Row:** Joel Palmer, Ricki Mackin, Tom Laxton, Mark Nougher, Leon Diaczuk, George Alder.

ROMFORD

Founded: 1876
Nickname: Boro

CLUB PERSONNEL

Chairman: Steve Gardener

Secretary: Colin Ewenson
103 Clockhouse Lane,
Romford, Essex RM5 3QS
(M) 0797 371 7074

Press Officer:
Steve Gardener
(M) 0771 177 1053
spgardener@aol.com

Programme Editor:
Ron May and Keith Preston
prestonruf@aol.com

Manager: Paul Martin

Club Colours: Blue & yellow hoops/blue/blue.

Best Seasons - League: 1st Southern League Premier Division 1966-67.

Ground address: Aveley FC, The Mill Field, Mill Road, Aveley RM15 4TR.

Tel: 01708 865 940.

Capacity: 4,000 **Seats**: 400 **Covered**: 400 **Floodlights**: Yes

Simple Directions: London - Southend A1306, turn into Sandy Lane at Aveley.

Rainham or Purfleet BR stations then bus No. 723 to the ground.

Bus from Rainham No 324

Midweek Home Matchday: Tuesday

Clubhouse: Normal pub hours. Bar snacks and hot food available.

CLUB STATISTICS

Records — **Attendance:** 820 v Leatherhead, Isthmian Div. 2.
Career Goalscorer: Danny Benstocks.
Career Appearances: S. Horne - 234.

Senior Honours: Essex Senior League Champions 1995-96, 2008-09.
Isthmian Division 2 Champions 1996-97.

Previous — **Names:** Original club founded 1876 folded during WW1.
Reformed in 1929 folded again in 1978. Reformed in 1992.
Leagues: Athenian 1931-39. Isthmian 1945-59, 97-2002. Southern 1959-78.
Essex 1992-96, 2002-09.

THAMESMEAD TOWN

Founded: 1970
Nickname: The Mead

Manager: Keith McMahon

Club Colours: Green and white/green/green and white.

Best Seasons - League: 18th Isthmian Division 1 North 2008-09.

Ground address: Bayliss Avenue, Thamesmead, London SE28 8NJ.

Tel: 020 8311 4211.

Capacity: 400 **Seats**: 125 **Covered**: 125 **Floodlights**: Yes

Simple Directions: From Dartford Tunnel A2 to London, exit Danson interchange and follow signs for Thamesmead and Abbey Wood. From Abbey Wood BR go north east along Harrow Manor Way into Crossways at 3rd roundabout. Bayliss Avenue is third on right. Bexley bus 272 stops in Crossway near Bayliss Avenue.

Midweek Home Matchday: Tuesday

Clubhouse: Full facilities open daily.

CLUB PERSONNEL

Chairman: Barry Stokley
Secretary:
Miss Kellie Discipline
77 Glebelands, Dartford, Kent
DA1 4RY
Tel No: (H) 01322 526184
(M) 0781 125 4792
kelliedt@tinyworld.co.uk
Press Officer: Kevin White
(M) 0797 398 1633
kevwhite35@hotmail.com
Programme
Editor: Albert Panting
(M) 0795 719 4640
gianpaulo.panting@btinternet.com

CLUB STATISTICS

Record	**Attendance:** 400 v Wimbledon, ground opening, 1988
	Victory: 9-0 v Kent Police, Kent League 19.04.94.
	Career Goalscorer: Delroy D'Oyley..
Senior Honours:	Kent Premier 2007-08
	Kent Senior Trophy 2004-2005
Previous	**Leagues**: Spartan 1987-91. Kent 1991-2008.

Back row (L-R): Alan Martin, Alan Woodward, Pedro Knight, Rikki Cable, Lee Cobourn, Chris Conneally, James Brown, Lew Watts, Richard Dimmock, Keith McMahon, Charlie McCarthy
Front row: Haribingi Grant, Junior Baker, Marc Merridan, Curtis Williams, Scot Mulholland, Nick Smith, Robbie Tarrant, Danny Moore, Peter Smith, Steve Wait.

TILBURY

Founded: 1900
Nickname: The Dockers

CLUB PERSONNEL

Chairman: Robin Nash

Secretary: Mark Southgate.
93 Falcon Avenue,
Grays. RM17 6SB
Tel No: 01708 686 269
(H) 01375 377 215
(M) 0797 952 5117
mark.southgate@purcom.com

Press Officer: Paul Tandy
(M) 0798 359 6499
paul_tandy@hotmail.com

Programme Editor: Mark Kettlety
(M) 0794 032 2612
sundayonly1@aol.com

Manager: Graham Chester

Club Colours: White/black/black

Best Season - League: 14th Isthmian Premier 1979-80

Ground address: Chadfields, St.Chads Road, Tilbury, Essex RM18 8NL

Tel No: 01375 843 093. Fax: 01375 859 496

Capacity: 4,000 **Seats**:350 **Covered**:1,000 **Floodlights**:Yes

Simple Directions: A13 Southend bound go left at Chadwell St Mary's turning, then right after 400 metres and right again at roundabout (signed Tilbury). Right into St Chads Road after five miles. First right into Chadfields for ground.

Midweek Home Matchday: Tuesday

Clubhouse: Open Daily

Club Shop: No

CLUB STATISTICS

Record	**Attendance:** 5,500 v Gorleston F.A.Cup 1949
	Career Goalscorer: Ross Livermore 282 in 305 games
	Career Appearances: Nicky Smith 424 (1975-1985)
Record	**Transfer Fee Received:** £2,000 from Grays Athletic for Tony Macklin 1990
	and from Dartford for Steve Connor (1985)
Senior Honours:	Isthmian Division One 1975-11976, Athenian League 1968-1969 and Essex **SeniorCup** (4) Runners-Up (5)
Previous Leagues:	Grays & Dist, also South Essex, Kent 27-31, London, South Essex Comb.(war time) Corinthian 50-57, Delphian 62-63, Athenian 6-73 Isthmian73-2004 Essex Senior 2004-2005

VCD ATHLETIC

Founded: 1916
Nickname: The Vickers

CLUB PERSONNEL

Chairman: Gary Rump

Secretary: Debbie Rump
c/o the club
(M) 0752 302 5369
debbierump@talktalk.net

Press Officer: Brian Norris
(M) 0774 602 8506
bnorris9@btinternet.com

Programme Editor: Adam Groom
(M) 0790 515 9105

Manager: Paul Foley.

Club Colours: Green and white hoops/white/white.

Best Season - League: 1st Kent League Premier Division 2006-07

Ground address: VCD Athletic Club, Old Road, Crayford DA1 4DN

Tel No: 01322 524 262.

Capacity: **Seats**: Yes **Covered**: Yes **Floodlights**:Yes

Simple Directions: Take A2 to Black Prince exit. On to roundabout and take 2nd exit (bourne Road) continue to the end of the road. Turn left. Take 1st right through width restrictors into Old Road. Ground is 400 yards on left.

Midweek Home Matchday: Tuesday

Clubhouse: Yes

CLUB STATISTICS

Record	**Victory:** 10-1 v Canterbury City 14.05.01
	Defeat: 0-5 v Deal Town 20.04 02
Senior Honours:	Kent County League Champions 1996-97.
	Ken League Champions 2008-09.
	West Kent Cup 1987-88.
Previous	**Names:** Vickers (Erith). Vickers (Crayford).
	Leagues: Dartford & District. Kent County. Kent 1997-2009.
	Grounds: Flamingo Park Sidcup (pre 1994).
	VCD Sports & Social Club. Old Road Crayford.

WALTHAM FOREST

Founded: 1995
Nickname: The Stags

Manager: Olowale Ojelabi

Club Colours: White/royal blue/royal blue

Best Season - League: 8th Southern Divison 1 East (As Waltham Forest)

Ground address: Cricklefield Stadium, 486 High Road, Ilford, Essex. IG1 1UE

Tel/Fax No: 0208 514 8352

Capacity: 3,500 **Seats**: 216 **Covered**: Yes **Floodlights**: Yes

Simple Directions: Five minutes walk from Seven Kings Station, opposite 'The Cauliflower' pub. Or 86 Bus.

Midweek Home Matchday: Wednesday

Clubhouse: Yes

CLUB PERSONNEL

Chairman: Isaac Johnson
Secretary: Andy Perkins
4 Chestnut Drive,
Wanstead, London E11 2TA
Tel No: 020 8520 3587
(H) 020 8530 4551
(M) 0774 898 3792
Fax No: 020 8520 3587
(H) 020 8530 4551
andrewpeterperkins@hotmail.co.uk
Press Officer: As secretary
Programme
Editor: Andrzej Perkins
(M) 0778 981 6303
forestgimp@hotmail.co.uk

CLUB STATISTICS

Previous

Leagues: Isthmian 2003-04.
Southern 2004-06.

Names: Leyton Pennant formed when Leyton and Walthamstow Pennant merged in 1995.
Changed to Waltham Forest in 2003.

NB: UNFORTUNATELY A RECENT PHOTO WAS NOT AVAILABLE AT THE TIME OF GOING TO PRESS.

WARE

Founded: 1892
Nickname: Blues

CLUB PERSONNEL

Chairman: Aiden Mynott

Secretary: Sean Mynott
68 Wheatsheaf Drive, Ware,
SG12 0XS
(M) 0781 209 7924
seanmynott@aol.com

Press Offcier: As secretary

Programme
Editor: Mark Kettlety
(M) 0794 032 2612
sundayonly1@aol.com

Manager: Paul Halsey

Club Colours: Blue & white stripes/blue/blue.

Best Season - League: 4th Isthmian Division 1 North 2007-08.

Ground address: Wodson Park, Wadesmill Road, Ware, Herts. SG12 0HZ

Tel No: 01920 463 247

Capacity: 3,300 **Seats**:500 **Covered**:312 **Floodlights**: Yes

Simple Directions: A10 off Jct A602 & B1001 turn right at roundabout after 300 yards and follow Ware sign, past Rank factory. Turn left at main road onto A1170 (Wadesmill Rd.) Stadium on right after 3/4 mile.

Midweek Home Matchday: Tuesday

Clubhouse: Open Matchdays **Club Shop:** Yes

Local Radio: Heartbeat F.M.

Local Press: Hertfordshire Mercury

CLUB STATISTICS

Record
Attendance: 3,800 v Hendon F.A.Amateur Cup 1956-1957
Career Goalscorer: M.Hibbert - 229
Goalscorer in a Season: Geirge Dearman - 98 1926-1927
Career Appearances: Gary Riddle 654
Victory: 10-1 v Wood Green Town
Defeat: 0-11 v Barnet

Senior Honours: Isthmian Divison 2 Champions 2005-2006 Herts Senior Cup (5) East Anglian Cup 1973-1974

Previous
Leagues: East Herts, North Middx 1907-08. Herts Co. 1908-25, Spartan 1925-55. Delphian 1955-63. Athenian 1963-75.
Grounds: Highfields, Canons Park, London Road, Presdales Lower Park 1921-26

Standing (L-R): Sara Ward (Physio), Barry Mason (Assistant Manager), Ben Andreos, Sam Rose, Steve Horsey, Michael Toner, Matt Turpin, Tom Hodge, Harry Ricketts, Grant Halsey, Ross Price, Kai Ramshaw, Matt Waldron, Dale Archer, Jason Coughlan, James Halsey, Stewart Margolis (Coach), Andy Crawford (Coach)
Sitting: Tamba Ngongou, Claudio Opondo-Mbai, Jimmie Berry, Glenn Harvey, Paul Halsey (Manager), Aiden Mynott (Chairman), Danny Wolf, Paul Abbott, Jermaine Ffolkes, Michael Sharman.

WINGATE & FINCHLEY

Founded: 1990
Nickname: Blues

Manager: David Norman

Physio: Matthew Guilliatt.

Club Colours: Azure blue/white/white.

Best Seasons - League: 7th Isthmian Div 1 North 2008-09.

Ground address: Harry Abraham Stadium, Summers Lane, Finchley, London N12 0PD **Tel No**: 020 8446 2217. www.wingatefinchley.com

Capacity: 8,500 **Seats**: 500 **Covered**: 500 **Floodlights**: Yes

Simple Directions: North Circular (A406) to junction with High Road Finchley (A1000). Go north and Summers Lane is 200 yds on right - parking for 80 cars. Bus 382 passes ground

Tube: to East Finchley (Northern Line) and then 263 bus to Summers Lane towards North Finchley

Midweek Home Matchday: Tuesday

Clubhouse: Open on match days plus a tea-bar. **Club Shop:** No.

Local Radio: LBC 1152 **Local Press**: Hendon & Finchley Times

CLUB PERSONNEL

Chairman: Aron Sharpe

President: Harvey Ackerman

Secretary: David Thrilling.
david.thrilling@soccerkits.com

Press Officer: Paul Lerman
Tel No: (H) 020 7433 1555
(M) 0773 628 2218
paullerman@hotmail.com

Programme Editor: As press officer.

CLUB STATISTICS

Record	**Attendance:** 9,555 Finchley v Bishop Auckland F.A.Amateur Cup 1949-1950
	Career Goalscorer: Marc Morris 578
	Career Appearances: Marc Morris 587 91975-1985)
Record	**Victory:**:9-0 v Sarrett Herts Co. 20.04 85
	Defeat: 0-9 v Edgware Istthmian Div 2 15.01.2000
Senior Honours:	**As Finchley**: Isthmian League Div. 3 R-up 98-99, Promoted (7th) 2001-02, London Senior Cup winners 94-95
	As Wingate: Middx SnrCup SF, Athenian Lg Div 2 69-70, Sth Midlands League Div 1 R-up 89-90, London Sen Cup 79-80
Previous Leagues:	**Leagues:** (as Wingate & Finchley) South Mids 89-95Finchley: London 02-12 14-15 23-25 30-39; Athenian 12-14 29-30 45-73; Isthmian73-91Wingate: Middx 46-52; London 52-62; Delphian 62-63; Athenian 63-75; Barnet Yth,Hendon & Dist. Sunday 75-84; Herts 84-89 Isthmian 94-04, Southern 05-06
	Names: Wingate (founded 46), Finchley (founded late 1800s) merged in 91

Back Row (L-R): Jimmy Martin, Dean Williams, Steve Velandia, Keiran Street, Callum Horton, Netanel Elraz, Tim Lees, Ola Williams, Andy Edmunds, Dean Nyman. **Middle:** Danny Nielsen, Daniel Stanton, Daniel Dlarke, Chris Milburn (physio) Richard Marchena (Reserve team manager) Ben Winston (Asst manager) Anthony Limbrick (Coach) Donald Buchanan (Coach) Joe O'brien, Chris Chase, Leon Skinner.
Front: Wayne Grant, Ahmet Rifat, Marc Weatherstone, Craig Ellis, Michael Stone (manager) Marvin Samuels (capt), Michael Sacks, Jerome Boyce, Bobby Aisien.

ASHFORD TOWN

Founded: 1930
Nickname: Nuts & Bolts

CLUB PERSONNEL

Chairman: Don Crosbie

Secretary: Elaine Orsbourne
13 Thornlea, Godinton Park,
Ashford Kent TN23 3JX
Tel No: 01233 625227
(H) 01233 646713
(M) 0775 989 1852
Fax No: 01233 612352
orsbournes@ntlworld.com

Press Officer: Sam Dixon
(M) 0790 311 2434
samdixon21@yahoo.co.uk

Programme
Editor: As press officer

Manager: Steve Lovell

Club Colours: Green/white/green and white hoops

Previous League: Kent

Best Season - League: 12th Southern Premier 1987-88.

Ground address: The Homelands, Ashford Road, Kingsnorth, Ashford, Kent. TN26 1NJ Tel/Fax No: 01233 611 838

Simple Directions: Jct 10 off M20 onto A2070 towards Breneitt & Lydd Airport. Dual carriageway to junction of old A2070. Ground one mile on left through Kingsnorth four miles south of Ashford.

Capacity: 3,200 **Seats:** 500 **Covered:**1,250 **Floodlights:** Yes

Midweek Home Matchday: Wednesday

Clubhouse: Open matchdays and for special functions.

Club Shop: Yes

Local Press: Kentish Express & Adscene

Local Radio: Radio Kent, Invicta Radio & KMFM

CLUB STATISTICS

Record Attendance :	3,363 v Fulham F.A.Cup 1st Rd 1994 (at present ground.)
Victory:	10-1 v Bury Town February 1964
Defeat:	0-8 v Crawley Town November 1964
Career Goalscorer:	Dave Arter 197 **Career Appearances**: Peter McRobert 765
Transfer Fees:Paid:	£7,000 for Jeff Ross & Dave Arter to Sittingbourne 1994
Received:	£25,000 for Jeff Ross & Dave Arter from Hythe Town
	for an individual: £20,000 from Sittingbourne for Lee McRobert
Senior Honours:	Kent League 1948-49 Kent Senior Cup (4)
Previous Leagues:	Kent 1930-59
Ground:	Essella Park (6,525 v C.Palace FAC 1959)

Back row (L-R): Daniel Brathwaite, James Humphreys, Danny Lye, Jamie Riley, Mark Lovell, Ryan Briggs, Andy Doerr.
Middle: Dave Hocking (coach/physio), John Ralph, Charlie Glyde, Anthony Hogg, Bradley Spice, Rod Udberg (coach).
Front: Paul Jones, Tony Browne, Jimmy Elford, Steve Lovell (Manager), Sean Ray, Lee Hockey, Mitchell Sherwood.

BURGESS HILL TOWN

Founded: 1882
Nickname: Hillians

Manager: Gary Croydon

Club Colours: Yellow & black/black/yellow

Best Season - League: 10th Isthmian Div 1 2004-2005

Ground address: Leylands Park, Maple Drive, Burgess Hill, West Sussex RH15 8DL

Tel/fax No: 01444 242 429

Capacity: 2,250 **Seats**: 307 **Covered**: Yes **Floodlights**: Yes

Simple Directions: Turn east from A273 London Road into Leylands Road, take 4th left signposted Leyland Park. Nearest station Wivelsfield

Midweek Home Matchday: Tuesday

Clubhouse: Bar & Social Facilities plus tea bar. **Club Shop:** Yes, full range.

Local Radio: Bright F.M. Southern F.M.

Local Press: Mid Sussex Times and The Argus

CLUB PERSONNEL

Chairman: Gary Croydon

Secretary: Tim Spencer
30 Condor Way, Burgess Hill,
RH15 9QA
Tel No: (H) 01444 244738
(M) 0781 264 2498
timspencer57@hotmail.com

Press Officer: Gary Newton
(M) 0790 157 2193
redeysports@hotmail.co.uk

Programme
Editor: Peter Ladds
(M) 0778 069 5113
peterladds@hotmail.com

CLUB STATISTICS

Record	**Attendance:** 2,005 v AFC Wimbledon Isthmian Div 1 2004-2005
	Career Goalscorer: Ashley Carr 208
	Career Appearances: Paul Williams 499
Record	**Transfer Fee Received:** Undisclosed four figure fee from Thurrock for Steve Harper
Senior Honours:	Sussex County League Championship (6)
	Sussex Senior Cup: 1883-84 , 84-85, 85-86.
Previous Leagues:	**Leagues:** Mid Sussex League, Sussex County >03, Southern League 2003-04

CHATHAM TOWN

Founded: 1882
Nickname: Chats

CLUB PERSONNEL

Chairman: Jeff Talbot

Secretary: Henry Longhurst
Address: 5 Cedar Grove, Hempstead, Gillingham, Kent ME7 3QT
(M) 0796 746 5554
Fax No: (H) 01634 371594
h.longhurst@sky.com

Press Officer: Steve Binks
(M) 0774 744 3223
stevebinks@btinternet.com

Programme Editor: John Crow
Tel No: (H) 01634 811507
(M) 0789 622 8454
crazyjohncrow@aol.com

Manager: Alex O'Brien

Club Colours: Red/black/black.

Best Seasons - League: 9th Southern South 1986-87.

Ground address: Maidstone Road Sports Ground, Maidstone Road, Chatham, Kent. ME4 6LR **Tel No**: 01634 812 194.

Capacity: 2,000 **Seats**: 600 **Covered:** 600 **Floodlights**: Yes

Simple Directions: M2, A229 Chatham turn-off, follow signs to Chatham, ground one and a half miles on right opposite garage. 1 mile from Chatham (BR).

Midweek Home Matchday: Tuesday 7.45

Clubhouse: Matchdays and functions **Club Shop:** Yes

CLUB STATISTICS

Record
Attendance: 5,000 v Gillingham 1980
Transfer Fee Received: £500

Senior Honours: Kent Lg (9) Kent Snr Cup 1888-89 1904-05 10-11 18-19, Kent Snr Shield 19-2

Previous
Leagues: Southern (several spells); Aetolian 59-64; Metropolitan 64-68; Kent (Several spells),
Names: Chatham FC; Medway FC (1970s)
Ground: Great Lines, Chatham 1882-90

NB: UNFORTUNATELY A RECENT PHOTO WAS NOT AVAILABLE AT THE TIME OF GOING TO PRESS.

CHIPSTEAD

Founded: 1906
Nickname: Chips

Manager: Mark Tompkins

Club Colours: Green & white hoops/black/black

Best Seasons - League: 15th Isthmian Division 1 South 2007-08

Ground address: High Road, Chipstead, Surrey CR5 3SF

Tel No: 01737 553 250

Capacity: 2000 **Seats**: 150 **Covered**: 200 **Floodlights**: Yes

Simple Directions: From the Brighton road northbound, go left into Church Lane and left into Hogcross Lane. High Road is on the right.

Midweek Home Matchday: Tuesday

Clubhouse: Yes

Club Shop: No

CLUB PERSONNEL

Chairman: Peter Philpott

Secretary: Derek Parsons
Low Wood 32 Canons Hill.
Old Coulsdon Surrey CR5 1HB
Tel No: 01932 257500
(H) 01737 552682
(M) 0788 078 8468
dellboy32@hotmail.com

Press Officer: Peter Philpott
(M) 0797 319 5192
peterphilpott@bulldog-sytems.com

Programme Editor: Terry Tiernan
(M) 0759 480 6875
terry.antell@btopenworld.com

CLUB STATISTICS

Record	**Attendance:** 1,170
	Career Goalscorer: Mick Nolan - 124.
Senior Honours:	Combined Counties Champions 1989-90, 2006-07.
Previous	**Leagues**: Surrey Intermediate 1962-82.
	Surrey Premier 1982-86.
	Combined Counties 1986-2007.

NB: UNFORTUNATELY A RECENT PHOTO WAS NOT AVAILABLE AT THE TIME OF GOING TO PRESS.

CORINTHIAN CASUALS

Founded: 1939
Nickname: Casuals

Manager: Brian Adamson

Club Colours: Chocolate & pink halves/navy blue/navy blue

Best Seasons - League: 5th Isthmian 1953-54 1959-60

Ground address: King George's Field, Queen Mary Close, Hook Rise South, Tolworth, Surrey, KT6 7NA **Tel No**: 0208 397 3368

Capacity: 2,000 **Seats**: 161 **Covered**: 700 **Floodlights**: Yes

Simple Directions: A3 to Tolworth (Charrington Bowl) roundabout. Hook Rise is the slip road immediately past the Toby Jug pub. Left under railway bridge after quarter of a mile and ground is on right. Half mile from Tolworth BR.

Midweek Home Matchday: Tuesday

Clubhouse: Evenings and Matchdays plus functions.

Club Shop: Club items in bar

Local Radio: County Sound & BBC Southern Counties

Local Press: South London Press and Surrey Comet

CLUB PERSONNEL

Chairman: Brian Vandervilt

Secretary: Phillip Pepperell
54 Ruskin Drive
Worcester Park
Surrey KT4 8LH
(M) 0795 090 4540
secretary@corinthian-casuals.com

Press Officer: Rob Cavallini
Tel No: (M) 0752 735 8365
press@corinthian-casuals.com

Programme Editor: As press officer

CLUB STATISTICS

Record	**Career Goalscorer**: Cliff West - 219 **Career Appearances**: Simon Shergold - 526
Senior Honours:	As Casuals: F.A.Amateur Cup Winners 1935-36. London Charity Cup (x6) Surrey Senior Cup 1929-30.
Previous	**Leagues**: Isthmian 1939-84. Spartan 1984-96. Combined Counties 1996-97. **Grounds**: Kennington Oval and shared with Kingstonian and Dulwich Hamlet **Names**: Casuals and Corinthians combined in 1939.

Back Row (L-R) : Mark Towse, Jamie Reive, Chris Horwood, Tom Jelley, Richard Price, David Ocquaye, Dan Jackson, Byron Brown, Martin Dunne, Paul Hunt, Paul Smith.
Front Row: Ryan Hughes, Matt Smith, Jason Haniff, Tyrone Myton, Dale Hennessey, Russell Banyard, Colin Harris.

CROYDON ATHLETIC

Founded: 1947
Nickname: The Rams

CLUB PERSONNEL

Chairman: Dean Fisher

Secretary: Bob Jenkins.
2 Warminster Way,
Mitcham, Surrey CR4 1AD.
Tel No: (H) 020 8687 2412
(M) 0772 932 1141
bjenkins@croydonathletic.co.uk

Press Officer: Karen Muir
Tel No: (M) 0775 292 6809
kmuir@croydonathletic.co.uk

Programme Editor: As secretary.

Manager: Tim O'Shea

Club Colours: Maroon with white flash/maroon/maroon

Best Seasons - League: 8th Isthmian Division One

Ground address: The Keith Tuckey Stadium, off Mayfield Road, Thornton Heath, Surrey CR7 6DN

Tel No: 020 8664 8343 Fax: 020 8664 8362

Capacity: 3.000 **Seats**: 163 **Covered**: 660 **Floodlights**: Yes

Simple Directions: Follow A23 from London & continue on A23 into Thornton Road. After roundabout take 1st on right into Silverleigh Road, left fork into Trafford Road which continues into Mayfield Road. To end and turn left and follow narrow road to ground. 1 mile from Norbury (BR). Buses 109, 60.

Midweek Home Matchday: Tuesday

Clubhouse: Open every evening and match days. **Club Shop:** Yes

Local Press: Croydon Advertiser

CLUB STATISTICS

Record

Attendance: 1,372 v AFC Wimbledon 2004-2005

Career Goalscorer: Marc Flemington

Career Appearances: James Gibson 300

Senior Honours: London Spartan Lg 1994-95. Isthmian League Div 3 2001-02

Previous

Leagues: Wandsworth Parthenon 1960-1964 Surrey Senior 1964-1977 London Spartan 1977-1979 Isthmian 1997-

Names: Wandsworth & Norwood amalgamated in 1986 and changed their name to Croydon Athletic in 1990

NB: UNFORTUNATELY A RECENT PHOTO WAS NOT AVAILABLE AT THE TIME OF GOING TO PRESS.

DULWICH HAMLET

Founded: 1889
Nickname: Hamlet

CLUB PERSONNEL

Chairman: Jack Payne

Secretary: John Leahy,
26 Newquay House,
Sancroft Street, Kennington,
London SE11 5UN
Tel No: (H) 020 7582 9296
(M) 0781 607 6582
Fax No: (H) 020 7582 9296

Press Officer:
John Lawrence
Tel No: (H) 020 8761 2091
john_lawrence@hotmail.co.uk

Programme Editor: As press officer

Manager: Gavin Rose

Club Colours: Navy blue & pink/navy blue/navy blue

Best Seasons - League: Isthmian Champions 1919-20 1925-26 1932-33 1948-49

Ground address: Champion Hill Stadium, Dog Kennel Hill, Edgar Kail Way, East Dulwich, London SE22 8BD **Tel No**: 0207 274 8707

Capacity: 3,000 **Seats**: 500 **Covered**: 1,000 **Floodlights**: Yes

Simple Directions: East Dulwich station, 200yds. Denmark Hill station, 10 mins walk. Herne Hill station then bus 37 stops near grd. Buses 40 & 176 from Elephant & Castle, 185 from Victoria

Midweek Home Matchday: Tuesday

Clubhouse: Open 7 days a week. Function rooms & meeting room available for hire Health Club, Gymnasium, Squash courts (020 7274 8707)

Club Shop: Sells programmes, pennants, badges, scarves, caps, replica shirts (by order only).

Local Press: South London Press and Southwark News

STATISTICS

Record — **Attendance:** 20,744 for F.A.Amateur Cup Final 1933 (Kingstonian v Stockton)
At refurbished ground: 1,835 v Southport F.A.Cup 1998-1999
Career Goalscorer: Edgar Kail 427 (1919-1933)
Career Appearances: Reg Merritt 576 (1950-1966)

Record Transfer Fee — **Paid**: Undisclosed for T.Eames (Wimbledon) and G.Allen (Carshalton Ath) 80
Received: £35,000 for Chris Dickson from Charlton Athletic 2007.

Senior Honours: Isthmian League (4) (R-up (7) Div 1 77-78; London Senior Cup (5) R-up(5); Surrey Senior Cup (16) R-up (16); London Chal. Cup 98-9 R-up(2)
FA Amateur Cup 1919-20, 31-32, 33-34, 36-37.

Previous Leagues: **Leagues:** Camberwell 1894-97; S/thern Sub 1897-1900 01-07; Dulwich 00-01; Spartan 07-08
Grounds: Woodwarde Rd 1893-95; College Farm 95-96; Sunray Avenue 96-1902; Freeman's Ground, Champion Hill 02-12; Champion Hill (old ground) 1912-92;
Sandy Lane (groundshare with Tooting & Mitcham F.C.) 91-92

EASTBOURNE TOWN

Founded: 1881
Nickname: Town

CLUB PERSONNEL

Chairman: Rupert Imich

Secretary: Mark Potter.
Flat 2, Carillon House,
18 Eversfield Road,
Eastbourne BN21 2AS
(M) 0772 084 6857
Fax No: (H) 01323 417336
markpotter@eastbournera.fsnet.co.uk

Press Officer: As Secretary

Programme Editor: Dave Pelling
(M) 0787 511 1647
pelling@hc26.freeserve.co.uk

Manager: Ady Colwell

Club Colours: Yellow/blue/white

Best Season - League: 13th Isthmian Division One South 2008-09.

Ground address: The Saffrons, Compton Place Road, Eastbourne, East Sussex BN21 1EA. Tel: 01323 723 734

Capacity: 3,000 **Seats**: 200 **Covered**: Yes **Floodlights**: Yes

Simple Directions: Turn South West off the A22 into Grove Road.

Midweek Home Matchday: Wednesday

Clubhouse: Yes, full facilities 01323 723 734 **Club Shop:** No

CLUB STATISTICS

Record **Attendance:** 7,378 v Hastings United 1953

Senior Honours: Sussex County League Champions 76-77 Sussex Senior Cup (12).
Sussex RUR Charity Cup (3) AFA Senior Cup (2)

Previous **Leagues**: Southern Amateur League19 07-1946 Corinthian 1960-1963
Athenian 1963-76 Sussex County 1976-2007

FLEET TOWN

Re-Formed: 1947
Nickname: The Blues

Manager: Andy Sinton

Club Colours: Sky blue & navy/sky blue & navy/sky blue & navy.

Best Season - League: 2nd Southern Division One South & West 2007-08.

Ground address: Calthorpe Park, Crookham Road, Fleet, Hants GU51 5FA.

Tel/fax No: 01252 623 804

Capacity: 2,000 **Seats**: 250 **Covered**: 250 **Floodlights**: Yes

Simple Directions: Leave the M3 at Junction 4A. Follow signs to Fleet via A3013. At 5th round about (a T-junction), turn left over railway bridge. Carry on past `Oatsheaf' pub on the right - ground is 1/4 mile further on right.

Midweek Home Matchday: Tuesday

Clubhouse: Yes, hot & cold food available **Club Shop:** Yes

CLUB PERSONNEL

Chairman: Graham Smith
Secretary: John Goodyear.
25 Velmead Road, Fleet,
Hants. GU52 7LJ
(M) 0796 870 1797
Fax No: 01252 622 008
goodyear.john@btinternet.com
Press Officer: Steve Cantle
(M) 0783 184 5643
stevecantle@hotmail.com
Programme
Editor: Matt Thorne
(M) 0776 011 0658
thornematthew@hotmail.com

CLUB STATISTICS

Record	**Attendance:** 1,336 v AFC Wimbledon - 08.01.05
	Career Goalscorer: Mark Frampton - 428
	Career Appearances: Mark Frampton - 250
Record Transfer Fee	**Paid**: £3,000 to Aldershot for Mark Russell
	Victory: 15-0 v Petersfield 26.12.94
	Defeat: 0-7 v Bashley - 12.04.04
Senior Honours:	Wessex Lg 94-95 Runners-Up 01-02, Lg Cup R-up 92-93, 01-02;
Previous Leagues:	**Leagues:** Hampsire 61-77, Athenian, Combined Co's, Chiltonian, Wessex 89-95, Southern 95-00, 02-04, 07-08. Wessex 2000-02. Isthmian 04-07.

FOLKESTONE INVICTA

Founded: 1936
Nickname: The Seasiders

CLUB PERSONNEL
Chairman: TBA
Secretary: Neil Pilcher
4 Sea View Close,
Capel-le-Ferne. Folkestone,
Kent CT18 7JW
Tel No: 020 7780 5020
(H) 01303 245066
(M) 0788 074 5772
neil.pilcher@xchanging.com
Press Officer: Andy Ingleston
(M) 0777 558 4196
aingleston@aol.com
Programme
Editor: Richard Murrill
(M) 0781 086 4228
richardmurrill@fsmail.net

Manager: Neil Cugley

Club Colours: Amber & black trim/black with amber trim/black.

Best Season - League: 13th Southern Premier 2001-02 Isthmian Premier 2005-06.

Ground Address: The Buzzlines Stadium, The New Pavilion, Cheriton Road, Folkestone, Kent CT19 5JU

Telephone & Fax: 01303 257461

Capacity 6,500 **Seats:** 900 **Covered:** 3,500 **Floodlights:** Yes

Simple Directions: On the A20 behind Morrisons food store, midway between Folkestone Central and West B.R. stations.

Midweek Home Matchday: Tuesday

Clubhouse: Stripes Club & Invicta Club

Club Shop: Yes

Local Press: Folkestone Herald

Local Radio: K.M.F.M. Invicta Radio & Radio Kent

CLUB STATISTICS

RECORD

Attendance: 2,332 v West Ham United (friendly) November 1996
Ground record 7,881 v Margate . Kent Senior Cup 1958
Victory: 13-0 v Faversham Town Kent League Division 1
Defeat: 1-7 v Crockenhill Kent League Division 1

PREVIOUS

Ground: South Rd, Hythe (pre 1991) County Lg.matches on council pitches
League: Kent 1990-98. Southern 1998-2004.

NB: UNFORTUNATELY A RECENT PHOTO WAS NOT AVAILABLE AT THE TIME OF GOING TO PRESS.

GODALMING TOWN

Founded: 1950
Nickname: The 'G's

Manager: Chuck Martini

Club Colours: Yellow /green/yellow

Best Season- League: 9th Southern Division One South & West 2008-09.

Ground address: Wey Court, Mead Row, Guildford, Surrey GU7 3JE

Tel No: 01483 417 520

Capacity: 3,000 **Seats**: 200 approx **Covered**: 400 approx. **Floodlights**: Yes

Simple Directions: A3100 from Guildford, pass the Manor Inn on the left and then a petrol station on the right. Wey Court is 50 yds on the right. A3100 From Godalming: pass the three Lions pub on the left and turn into Wey Court immediately after the Leathern Bottle pub.

Midweek Home Matchday: Tuesday

Clubhouse: Yes **Club Shop:** Yes

Local Radio: Radio Southern Counties and County Sound Radio.

Local Press: Surrey Advertiser.

CLUB PERSONNEL

Chairman: Kevin Young

Secretary: Mrs Jane Phillips.
135 Manor Road, Stoughton,
Guildford GU2 9NR
(M) 0788 993 3512
Fax No: 01483 572211
j.phillips12@ntlworld.com

Press Officer: Glenn Moulton
(M) 0779 033 2587
info@godalmingtownfc.co.uk

Programme Editor: As press officer

CLUB STATISTICS

Record	**Attendance:** 1,305 v AFC Wimbledon - 2002
Senior Honours:	Combined Counties Champions 1983-1984, 2005-2006
Previous	**Leagues**: Combined Counties.
	Names: Godalming & Farncombe United, Godalming & Guildford.

Courtesy of the Surrey Advertiser.

HORSHAM YMCA

Founded: 1898
Nickname : YM's

Chairman: Mick Browning

Secretary: Andy Flack
18 Tintagel Court
Arthur Road
Horsham
RH13 5NQ
(M): 0777 585 7392

Press Officer:
Mick Browning
(M) 0785 506 1696

Programme Editor: Alan Maguire
(M) 0778 598 6120
alan.maguire@hotmail.co.uk

Manager: Chris White.

Club Colours: White /black/red.

Change Colours: Sky & navy blue quarters/navy/navy.

Best Season - League: 9th Isthmian Division 1 South 2006-07

Ground address: Gorings Mead, Horsham, West Sussex RH13 5BP.

Tel: 01403 252 689

Club Website: www.horshamymcafc.com

Capacity: 1,575 **Seats**: 150 **Covered**: 200 **Floodlights**: Yes

Simple Directions: From the east, take A281 (Brighton Road) and the ground is on the left and signposted opposite Gorings Mead.

Midweek Home Matchday: Tuesday

Clubhouse: Open matchdays and functions.

Club Shop: No

Local Radio: Southern Counties and Radio Mercury

Local Press: West Sussex County Times and Evening Argus

CLUB STATISTICS

Record	**Attendance:** 950 v Chelmsford City F.A. Cup 2000
	Career Goalscorer: Danny Cherryman
	Career Appearances: Gerry Marsh, Peter Durrant & Jason Dumbrill all 500+
	Victory: 21-1 v Litttlehampton (Nick Flint 10) October 2003
Senior Honours:	Sussex League Champions 2004-2005, 05-06.
	SJohn O'Hara Cup 2001-02
Previous	**Leagues:**: Horsham & District. Brighton& Hove. Mid Sussex.
	Sussex County.

NB: UNFORTUNATELY A RECENT PHOTO WAS NOT AVAILABLE AT THE TIME OF GOING TO PRESS.

LEATHERHEAD

Founded: 1946
Nickname: The Tanners

Leatherhead FC
The Tanners
Matchday Programme 2009/10

Managers: Mick Sullivan

Club Colours: Green/white/green

Best Season - League: 7th Isthmian Premier 1977-78.

Ground address: Fetcham Grove, Guilford Road, Leatherhead, Surrey KT22 9AS

Tel No: 01372 360 151 Fax: 01372 272 366

Capacity: 3,400 **Seats**: 200 **Covered**:45 **Floodlights**: Yes

Simple Directions: M25 jct 9 to Leatherhead, follow signs to Leisure Centre, ground adjacent. Half mile from Leatherhead (BR)

Midweek Home Matchday: Tuesday

Clubhouse: Bar open 12.11pm matchdays. Full catering. Tel No : 01372 360151

Club Shop: Tel No: 01372 362 705

Local Radio: County Sound

Local Press: Leatherhead Advertiser and Surrey Advertiser

CLUB PERSONNEL

Chairman: Peter Ashdown
Secretary: Geoff Corner
20 Sunnymeade Avenue,
Carshalton Beeches, Surrey
SM5 4JF
(H) 0208 642 0827
(M) 0776 283 1142
gseacorner@btinternet.com
Press Officer:
Richard Wilkinson
(M) 0781 383 4739
richard.wilkinson@hmrc.gsi.gov.uk
Programme
Editor: Rod Ellis
(M) 0750 679 7789
rodellis83@hotmail.com

CLUB STATISTICS

Record	**Attendance:** 5,500 v Wimbledon 1976
	Goalscorer in a Season: Steve Lunn 46 1996-1997
	Career Appearances: P.Caswell 200
Record Transfer Fee	**Paid**: £1,500 to Croydon for B.Salkeld
	Received: £1,500 from Croydon for B.Salkeld
	Victory: 13-1 v Leyland Motors 1946-1947 Surrey Senior League
	Defeat: 1-11 v Sutton United
Senior Honours:	Isthmian League Cup 1977-78. Athenian Lg Div 1963-64. Surrey Snr Cup 1968-69.
Previous	**Leagues:** Surrey Snr 1946-50. Metropolitan 1950-51. Delphian 1951-58. Corinthian 1958-63. Athenian 1963-72.

MERSTHAM

Founded: 1905

CLUB PERSONNEL

Chairman: Ted Hickman

Secretary: Richard Baxter
2 Wood Street, Merstham,
Surrey RH1 3PF
Tel No: 01293 450809
(H) 01737 645748
(M) 0772 029 0027
Fax No: 01293 450572
richardbaxter01@hotmail.com

Press Officer: Kevin Austen
(M) 0791 185 3353
ka@merstham.co.uk

Programme Editor: Sarah Fish
(M) 0752 583 8823
sarah.fish@ntlworld.com

Manager: Graeme Banyard

Club Colours: Amber & black stripes/black/amber

Best Season- League: 8th Isthmian Division 1 South 2008-09.

Ground address: Moatside Stadium, Weldon Way, Merstham, Surrey RH1 3QB

Tel/Fax: 01737 644 046

Capacity: 2,500 **Seats**: 174 **Covered**: 100 **Floodlights**: Yes

Simple Directions: Leave Merstham village (A23) by School Hill take 5th right (Weldon Way) clubhouse and car park on right.Ten minutes walk from Merstham BR.

Midweek Home Matchday: Tuesday

Clubhouse: Open daily **Club Shop:** No

CLUB STATISTICS

Record — **Attendance:** 1,587 v AFC Wimbledon, 09.11.02

Senior Honours: Combined Counties Champions 2007-08.

Previous Leagues: Redhill & District. Surrey Senior 1964-78.
London Spartan 1978-84.
Combined Counties 1984-2008.

Photo: Alan Coomes.

METROPOLITAN POLICE

Founded: 1919
Nickname: The Blues

Manager: Jim Cooper

Physio: Paul Barrowcliff

Club Colours: All Blue

Best Season - League: 3rd Isthmian Divivision One 1981-82.

Ground address: Imber Court, East Molesey, Surrey KT8 0BT.

Tel No: 0208 398 7358

Capacity: 3,000 **Seats**: 297 **Covered**: 1,800 **Floodlights**: Yes

Simple Directions: From London A3 take A309 towards Scilly Isles roundabout then right into Hampton Court Way. Left at 1st roundabout into Imber Court Rd. Ground faces in 300 yards.

Midweek Home Matchday: Tuesday

Clubhouse: Four bars, dance hall, cafeteria open 9a.m. - 11p.m.

Club Shop: No

Local Radio: County Sounds

Local Press: Surrey Comet & Surrey Herald

CLUB PERSONNEL

Chairman: Des Flanders

Secretary: Tony Brooking
15 Westmoreland Avenue,
Hornchurch, Essex RM11 2EJ
Tel No: 0207 161 3056
(H) 01708 450715
(M) 0796 133 4523
tony.brooking@met.police.uk

Press Officer: Cliff Travis
Tel No: (H) 01932 782215
Fax No: (H) 01932 782215
cliffordtravis@hotmail.com

Programme Editor: As press officer

CLUB STATISTICS

Record	**Attendance:** 4,500 v Kingstonian F.A.Cup 1934
	Career Goalscorer: Mario Russo
	Career Appearances: Pat Robert
Record	**Victory:** 10-1 v Tilbury 1995
	Defeat: 1-11 v Wimbledon 1956
Senior Honours:	Spartan League (x7) Middlesex Senior Cup 1927-28.
	Surrey Senior Cup 1932-33.
Previous Leagues:	Spartan 1928-60. Metropolitan 1960-71. Southern 1971-78.

Back Row (L-R): Paul Barrowcliff, Anthony Smith, Russell Townsend,Micky Parma, Gareth Thomas, Gary Elliott, Jes Weeks, Dave Newman, Mat Cefai, Neil Williams, Andy Ottley, Charlie Moxham. **Middle:** Samantha Barker (reserve physio), Sam Downes (1st Physio)Scott Corbett, Ron Edwards, Scott Forrester, Justin Bowen, Gary Drewett, Mo Maan, Mark Rouse, James Greenaway, Micky Cobden, Rob George, Anthony Smith, Danny Platel, Chris Macpherson (Kit Manager)
Front: Sam Robinson, Craig Carley, Steve Potterill, Stuart Mackenzie, John Nicholson(Coach), Jim Cooper(Manager), Gavin MacphersonAssistant Manager), Steve Greene, Steve Sutherland, Stuart Harte, Steve Sergent.

RAMSGATE

Founded: 1945
Nickname: Rams

Manager: Jim Ward

Club Colours: All red.

Best Seasons - League: 5th Isthmian Premier 2007-08

Ground address: Southwood Stadium, Prices Avenue, Ramgate, Kent. CT11 0AN
Tel No: 01843 591662. Fax: 01843 591662

Capacity: 5,000 **Seats**: 400 **Covered**: 600 **Floodlights**: yes

Simple Directions: Approach Ramsgate from A299 (Canterbury/London) or A256 (Dover/Folkestone) to Lord of Manor roundabout then follow signs for Ramsgate along Cannterbury Road East and take second exit from first roundabout. From second roundabout take second exit towards Ramsgate then 3rd turning on left into St Mildreds Avenue and first left into Queen Bertha Road. After right hand bend take left into Southwood Avenue and then first left into Prices Avenue. Ground is at the end of Avenue.

Midweek Home Matchday: Tuesday

Clubhouse: Open five nights a week plus weekends. Hot & cold food available on match days. **Club Shop:** Yes. Open on first team match days.

Local Radio: Radio Kent & KMFM

Local Press: Thanet Times & Kent Messenger

CLUB PERSONNEL

Chairman: Richard Lawson
Secretary: Martin Able.
1 Parkside Villas, Tivoli Road, Margate, Kent CT 9 5PZ
Tel No: 020 8308 7883
(H) 01843 290272
(M) 0795 899 3959
Fax No: 020 8308 7845
secretary@ramsgate-fc.co.uk
Press Officer: Kevin Barham
(M) 0792 960 7258
fixtures@ramsgate-fc.co.uk
Programme Editor: Ayden Anderson
(M) 0774 544 191
media@ramsgate-fc.co.uk

CLUB STATISTICS

Record	**Attendance:** 5,200 v Margate 1956-57.
	Career Goalscorer: Mick Williamson
	Record Victory: 11-0 & 12-1 v Canterbury City Kent League 2000-01.
Senior Honours:	**Kent League Division 1 Champions 1949-50, 55-56, 56-57.**
	Kent League Premier Division Champions 1998-99, 2004-05.
	Isthmian Division 1 Champions 2005-06. Isthmian League Cup 2007-08.
	Kent Senior Cup 1963-64. Kent League Cup (x6). Kent Senior Trophy (x3)
Previous	**Names:** Ramsgate Athletic > 1972.
	Leagues: Kent 1949-59, 76-2005. Southern 1959-1976.

Back Row (L-R): Amy Lupton (Physio), Richard Langley (Coach), Ben Brown, Gary Lockyer, Ollie Gray, Will Graham, Sam Jones, Sam Mott, Brett Mills, Liam Quinn, Curtis Winnett, Matt Adams, Tom Tsangarides, Andy Hadden, Robbie Summers (Reserves Manager), Adrian Hubbard (Managers Assistant).
Front Row: Dean Powell, Jason Dolby, Ben Laslett, James Gregory, Foy Manoharan-Turner (Director), Richard Lawson (Chairman/MD), Jim Ward (Manager), Paul Jefcoate (Director), Gary Mickelborough, Rhys Lawson, Aaron Firth, Simon Pettit.
Not Pictured: Dan Allen, Shaun Alliston, Warren Schulz, Martin Jefferys (Asst Physio), Gary Toner (Physio).

SITTINGBOURNE

Founded:1886
Nickname: Brickies

SITTINGBOURNE
Football Club 2008-09
Ryman League Division One South
V KINGSTONIAN F.C.
Official Matchday Magazine £1.50

Manager: Gary Abbott

Club Colours: Red with black stripes/black/black

Best Season - League: 8th Southern Premier Division 1993-94, 1996-97.

Ground address: Bourne Park, Central Park Stadium, Eurolink,Sittingbourne, Kent. ME10 3SB Tel No: 01795 435 077

Capacity: 3,000 **Seats**: 300 **Covered**: 600 **Floodlights**: Yes

Simple Directions: Through Sittingbourne on main A2, club signposted clearly and regularly from both east and west. 1 mile from Sittingbourne BR station.

Midweek Home Matchday: Tuesday

Clubhouse: Yes

Club Shop: Wide variety of souvenirs etc.

Local Radio: BBC Radio and KMFM

Local Press: East Kent Gazette, Kent Messenger and Kent on Sunday

CLUB PERSONNEL

Chairman: Andy Spice

Secretary: John Pitts
4 Silverdale Grove,
Sittingbourne, Kent ME10 1UY
Tel No: 01795 476 809
(M) 0750 513 4135
Fax No: (H) 0709 211 2833
johncp49@hotmail.com

Press Officer: Peter Pitts
(M) 0778 590 6627
peterpitts@blueyonder.co.uk

Programme Editor: Grant Wilbur
(M) 0788 794 6971
grantcbt@hotmail.co.uk

CLUB STATISTICS

Record	**Attendance:** 5,951 v Tottenham Hotspur. Friendly 26.01.93
	Transfer Fee Paid: £20,000 to Ashford Town for Lee McRobert 1993
	Received: £210,000 from Millwall for Neil Emblen and Micharle Harle. 1993
Senior Honours:	Southern Lg Southern Div 92-93 95-96; Kent Lg (7) Lg Cup (4), Kent Senior Cup 01-02 28-29 29-30 57-58.
Previous:	**Leagues:** Kent 1894-1905 09-27 30-39 46-59 68-91, South Eastern 05-09, Southern 27-30 59-67
	Grounds: Sittingbourne Rec. Ground 1881-90, Gore Court Cricket Grd 90-92, The Bull Ground1892-1990
	Names: Sittingbourne United 1881-86

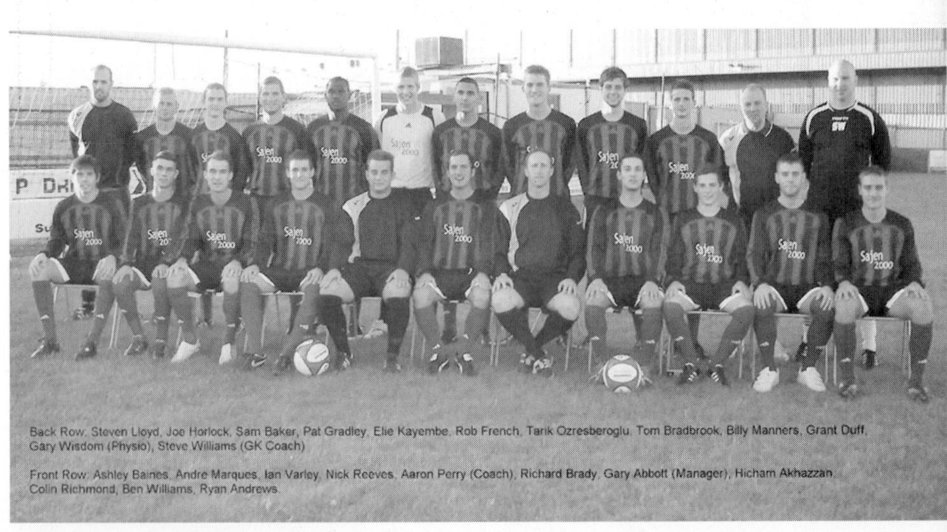

Back Row: Steven Lloyd, Joe Horlock, Sam Baker, Pat Gradley, Elie Kayembe, Rob French, Tarik Ozresberoglu, Tom Bradbrook, Billy Manners, Grant Duff, Gary Wisdom (Physio), Steve Williams (GK Coach)

Front Row: Ashley Baines, Andre Marques, Ian Varley, Nick Reeves, Aaron Perry (Coach), Richard Brady, Gary Abbott (Manager), Hicham Akhazzan, Colin Richmond, Ben Williams, Ryan Andrews.

WALTON & HERSHAM

Founded: 1896
Nickname: Swans

Manager: John Crumplin

Club Colours: All Red

Best Season - League: 2nd Isthmian Premier 1972-73.

Ground address: Sports Ground, Stompond Lane, Walton-on-Thames KT12 1HF

Tel. No: 01932 245 263

Capacity: 5,000 **Seats** 400 **Covered**: 2,500 **Floodlights:** Yes

Simple Directions: From Walton Bridge, go over and along New Zealand Avenue,down one way street and up A244 Hersham road. Ground second on right.

Midweek Home Matchday: Tuesday

Clubhouse: Open every evening.

Club Shop: Open matchdays.

CLUB PERSONNEL

Chairman: Alan Smith
Secretary: Michael Groom
15 Windsor Walk, Weybridge,
Surrey KT13 9AP.
Tel No: 01932 842982
(M) 0771 023 0694
Fax No: 01932 842982
mhgroom@aol.com

Press Officer: Mervyn Rees
(M) 0771 386 8117
merv@waltonandhershamfc.fsnet.co.uk

Programme
Editor: Mark Massingham
(M) 0798 550 7299
mark@waltonfc.freeserve.co.uk

CLUB STATISTICS

Records	**Attendance**: 10,000 v Crook Town F.A.Amateur Cup 6th Rd 1951-52
	Victory: 10-0 v Clevedon F.A.Amateur Cup 1960
	Defeat: 3-11 v Kingstonian, Surrey Shield 1958
	Goalscorer: Reg Sentance - 220 in 11 seasons
	Career Appearances: Terry Keen - 449 in 11 seasons.
	Transfer Fee Paid: £6,000
	Received: £150,000 from Bristol Rovers for Nathan Ellington 1999
Senior Honours:	F.A.Amateur Cup 1972-73. Barassi Cup 1973-74. Athenian League 1968-69. Surrey Senior Cup (6). London Senior Cup.
Previous Leagues	Surrey Senior. Corinthian 1945-50. Athenian 1950-71.

Back row, (L-R): Scott Hassell, Danny Green, Louis Clark, Richard Stroud, Jordan Cheadle, Matt Elverson, Jon Boswell, Stuart Booth, Zak Graham, Adrian Stone, Antony Hall.
Front Row: Jack Watkins, Craig Dunne, Adam Moriarty, Barry Moore, Aaron Nowacki, Phil Cramp, Tommo Carter, Paul Sears.

WALTON CASUALS

Founded: 1948
Nickname: The Stags

Manager: Spencer Collins

Club Colours: Tangerine/black/black

Best Season - League: 15th Isthmian Division One 2005-06.

Ground address: Franklyn Road Sports Ground, Waterside Drive, Walton-on-Thames, Surrey KT12 2JP

Tel No: 01932 787 749

Capacity: 2,000 **Seats**: 153 **Covered**: 403 **Floodlights**: Yes

Simple Directions: Left off Terrace Road at first major roundabout out of Walton centre. Ground is next to The Xcel Leisure Centre.

Midweek Home Matchday: Monday

Clubhouse: Open matchdays only. Hot food available.

Club Shop: Yes

CLUB PERSONNEL

Chairman: Graham James

Secretary: Gus Schofield
39 Molesey Park Road,
East Molesey, Surrey KT8 2LB
(M) 0782 469 6705
g.schofield1@ntlworld.com

Press Officer: Stuart Roberts
(H) 01932 845923
Fax No: 01932 220937
sroberts@cattronuk.com

Programme Editor: As Press Officer

CLUB STATISTICS

Record	**Attendance:** 1,748 v AFC Wimbledon Combined Counties League 12.04.04
	Career Goalscorer: Greg Ball - 77
	Career Appearances: Craig Carley - 234
Senior Honours:	Combined Counties League Champions 2004-05. League Cup 1999-2000.
Previous Leagues:	Surrey Intermediate, Surrey Senior, Suburban, Surrey Premier, & Co.Counties.

Back Row (L-R): Terry Collins, Dick Errington, Michael Cayford, Gary Meakin, John Ambridge, Steve Douglas, Liam Grier, Dom Worthington, Elliot Ransom, Craig Bradshaw, Jack Francis, Rob Ursell, Wes Harrison, Chris Kiganda, Spencer Collins, Tony Gale. **Front Row:** Victor Asombang, Rico Morris, Sonny Farr, Craig Lewington, John Morris, Matt Weston, Jamel Carr, Kane Sergant, James Kelch.

WHITSTABLE TOWN

Founded: 1886
Nicknames: Oysterman/Natives

THE BELMONT REVIEW
OFFICIAL MATCHDAY PROGRAMME
WHITSTABLE TOWN FOOTBALL CLUB
SEASON 2008-2009
RYMAN LEAGUE DIVISION ONE (SOUTH) £1
v CROYDON ATHLETIC
Tuesday 19th August 2008
Kick Off 7:45pm

Manager: Mark Munday

Club Colours: Red & white/white/red & white.

Best Season - League: 14th Isthmian Division One South 2007-08.

Ground address: Belmont Ground, Belmont Road, Belmont, Whitstable, Kent CT5 1QP

Tel No: 01227 266 012

Capacity: 2,000 **Seats**: 500 **Covered**: 1,000 **Floodlights**: Yes

Simple Directions: From Thanet Way (A299) turn left at Tesco roundabout and Millstrood Road. Ground at bottom of road, 400 yards from Whitstable BR station.

Midweek Home Matchday: Tuesday

Clubhouse: Open Matchdays and for functions.

Club Shop: Yes

CLUB PERSONNEL

Chairman: Joseph Brownett

Secretary: Alan Gower
110 Queens Road, Whitstable,
Kent CT5 2JJ
Tel No: (H) 01227 277875
(M) 0798 086 5637
agower@tiscali.co.uk

Press Officer: Anthony Rouse
(M) 0781 491 9830
tonyrouse@talktalk.net

Programme Editor: Andy Short
(M) 0791 702 1219
andy.short2@btinternet.com

CLUB STATISTICS

Record	**Attendance:** 2,500 v Gravesend& Northfleet F.A.Cup 19.10.87
	Career Goalscorer: Barry Godfrey
	Career Appearances: Frank Cox - 429 (1950-1960)
Senior Honours:	Kent Anmateur Cup 1928-29
	Champions Kent League 2006-2007
	Kent League Trophy Winners 2007
Previous Leagues:	East Kent 1897-1909, Kent 09-59, Aetolian 59-60, Kent Amateur 60-62 63-64.
	S.E.A.nglian 62-63, Greater London 64-6, Kent Premier 67-07.

NB: UNFORTUNATELY A RECENT PHOTO WAS NOT AVAILABLE AT THE TIME OF GOING TO PRESS.

WHYTELEAFE

Founded: 1946
Nickname: Leafe

CLUB PERSONNEL
Chairman: Mark Coote
Secretary: Edward Lucas
Braeside, Johns Road,
Tatsfield, Wetsreham, Kent.
TN16 2AP
(M) 0771 085 9034
Fax No: (H) 01959 572437
elucas001@aol.com
Press Officer: Brian Davis
(M) 0789 668 3812
briandavisleafe@hotmail.com
Programme
Editor: Chris Layton
(H) 01883 381 169
chris.layton@ntlworld.com

Manager: Stuart Massey

Club Colours: Green/black /black

Best Season - League: 5th Isthmian Division One South 2002-03

Ground address: 15 Church Road, Whyteleafe, Surrey CR3 0AR

Tel No: 0208 660 5491. Fax: 0208 645 0422.

Capacity: 5,000 **Seats**: 400 **Covered**: 600 **Floodlights**: Yes

Simple Directions: Five minutes walk from Whyteleafe (BR) - turn right from station, and left into Church Road.

Midweek Home Matchday: Tuesday

Clubhouse: Every evening & lunches at weekends. Hot & cold food, pool, darts, gaming machines.

Club Shop: Yes

Local Radio: Mercury

Local Press: Croydon Advertiser

CLUB STATISTICS

Record	**Attendance:** 2,210 v Chester City F.A. Cup 1999-2000
	Transfer Fee Paid: £1,000 to Carshalton Ath. for Gary Bowyer
	Received: £25,000 for Steve Milton
Senior Honours:	Isthmian Lge Div 2 South R-up 88-89;
	Surrey Sen.Cup 68-69
Previous	**Leagues**: Caterham & Edenbridge. Croydon.
	Thornton Heath & District.
	Surrey Intermediate (East) 1954-58.
	Surrey Senior 1958-75. Spartan 1975-81. Athenian 1981-84.

Back row, (L-R): Terry Douce(commercial manager), Tony Lidbury (President),Roger Hoyte (Fitness coach), Cedric Kabongo,Chris LaPierre,Sean Rivers, Billy Harding, Ricardo Williams,Gavin Dilley, Danny Rose, Rob Tolfrey, Jamie King , Adam Broomhead, Asher Hudson, Paul Scott, Mark Dickinson (coach), Paul Owens (Ground Manager), Edward Lucas (Secretary), Mark Coote (Chairman).
Front Row: Bernie Donnelly (Assistant Manager), Kris Barry, Michael Riley, Dean Eaton, Alhajie Jabbie, Ali Reeve, Robert Smith, Steve McNamara, Callum Maclean, Jason Goodchild, Stuart Massey (Manager).

WORTHING

Founded: 1886
Nickname: Rebels

CLUB PERSONNEL

Chairman: Dave Agnew & Mrs Deborah McKail

Secretary: Gareth Nicholas
c/o the club
Tel No: 01903 239575
(H) 01903 236449
Fax No: (H) 01903 234795
garethbnicholas@hotmail.co.uk

Press Officer: Morty Hollis
(M) 0774 765 7646

Programme Editor: Jon Justice
(M) 0782 571 1508
jon@worthingfc.com

Joint Managers: Simon Colbran

Club Colours: Red/red/red.

Best Performance - League: 2nd Isthmian Premier 1983-85.

Ground address: Woodside Road, Worthing, West Sussex BN14 7HQ

Tel No: 01903 239 575 Fax: 01903 234 795

Capacity: 3,650 **Seats:** 500 **Covered:** 1,500 **Floodlights:** Yes

Simple Directions: A24 or A27 to Grove Lodge roundabout. A24 (Town centre exit) and right into South Farm Rd. Over 5 roundabouts take last on right (Pavilion Road) before level crossing. Woodside Rd on right. ground on left. 1/2 mile from BR.

Midweek Home Matchday: Tuesday

Clubhouse: Open two hours before kick-off until 11.00p.m.

Local Press: Evening Argus, Worthing Herald

Local Radio: Southern FM, Splash FM & Southern Counties Radio

CLUB STATISTICS

Record	**Attendance**: 3,600 v Wimbledon F.A. Cup 14th November 1936
	Victory: 25-0 V Littlehampton (H) West Sussex League 1911-12
	Defeat: 0-14 v Southwick (A) Sussex County League 1946-47
	Career Goalscorer: Mick Edmonds - 276
	Career Appearances: Mark Knee - 414
Transfer Fees:	**Paid:** Undisclosed for Marc Rice (Havant & Waterlooville) 1998
	Received: £7,500 for Tim Read from Woking 1990
Senior Honours:	**Sussex League Champions 1920-21, 21-22, 26-27, 28-29, 30-31, 33-34, 38-39.**
	Sussex League West Champions 1945-46. Isthmian Division 2 Champions 1981-82, 92-93. Division 1 1982-83.
	Sussex Senior Cup (x21)
Previous Leagues:	West Sussex 1896-1904 05-14 19-20 Brighton Hove & Dist 19-20
	Sussex County 1920-40, 45-48. Corinthian 1948-63. Athenian 1963-77.

COMBINED COUNTIES LEAGUE

www.combinedcountiesleague.co.uk

Sponsored by: Cherry Red Records

Founded: 1978

Recent champions:

2004: AFC Wimbledon
2005: Walton Casuals
2006: Godalming Town
2007: Chipstead
2008: Merstham

Reserve Section		P	W	D	L	F	A	Pts
Bookham Res.		34	24	5	5	89	49	77
Badshot Lea Res.		34	24	3	7	92	52	75
Croydon Res.		34	23	5	6	103	41	74
Warlingham Res.	*-3*	34	17	11	6	71	52	59
Hanworth Villa Res.		34	18	2	14	79	67	56
Staines Lammas Res.	*-3*	34	18	4	12	85	62	55
South Park Res.		34	16	7	11	79	70	55
Crescent Rovers Res.		34	13	7	14	72	80	46
Knaphill Res.		34	11	12	11	55	50	45
Mole Valley SCR Res.		34	11	11	12	59	58	44
CB Hounslow United Res.		34	12	7	15	51	66	43
Hartley Wintney Res.	*-3*	34	13	4	17	64	75	40
Frimley Green Res.	*-1*	34	10	7	17	60	68	36
Westfield Res.		34	10	5	19	55	75	35
Farnham Town Res.		34	7	11	16	62	94	32
Worcester Park Res.		34	6	9	19	51	90	27
Farleigh Rovers Res.		34	7	5	22	42	69	26
Sheerwater Res.		34	5	7	22	50	101	22

Premier Division		P	W	D	L	F	A	Pts
Bedfont Green		**42**	**29**	**9**	**4**	**116**	**55**	**96**
North Greenford Utd		**42**	**22**	**13**	**7**	**99**	**66**	**79**
Chertsey Town		**42**	**23**	**8**	**11**	**96**	**58**	**77**
Epsom & Ewell		**42**	**22**	**11**	**9**	**85**	**55**	**77**
Camberley Town		**42**	**21**	**12**	**9**	**99**	**56**	**75**
Cove	*-1*	**42**	**19**	**14**	**9**	**81**	**56**	**70**
Badshot Lea		**42**	**21**	**6**	**15**	**87**	**91**	**69**
Raynes Park Vale		**42**	**20**	**4**	**18**	**80**	**80**	**64**
Ash United		**42**	**17**	**11**	**14**	**78**	**70**	**62**
Banstead Athletic		**42**	**18**	**7**	**17**	**78**	**80**	**61**
Molesey		**42**	**16**	**10**	**16**	**77**	**62**	**58**
Horley Town		**42**	**15**	**13**	**14**	**56**	**53**	**58**
Egham Town		**42**	**16**	**8**	**18**	**62**	**66**	**56**
Colliers Wood United		**42**	**15**	**8**	**19**	**81**	**73**	**53**
Bookham		**42**	**14**	**10**	**18**	**75**	**85**	**52**
Sandhurst Town		**42**	**14**	**9**	**19**	**63**	**82**	**51**
Wembley		**42**	**12**	**10**	**20**	**61**	**81**	**46**
Bedfont		**42**	**12**	**9**	**21**	**59**	**85**	**45**
Chessington & Hook		**42**	**10**	**14**	**18**	**61**	**78**	**44**
Guildford City		**42**	**11**	**11**	**20**	**55**	**95**	**44**
Hartley Wintney		**42**	**4**	**10**	**28**	**50**	**112**	**22**
Cobham		**42**	**4**	**7**	**31**	**48**	**108**	**19**

	Ash United	Badshot Lea	Banstead Athletic	Bedfont	Bedfont Green	Bookham	Camberley Town	Chertsey Town	Chessington & Hook United	Cobham	Colliers Wood United	Cove	Egham Town	Epsom & Ewell	Guildford City	Hartley Wintney	Horley Town	Molesey	North Greenford United	Raynes Park Vale	Sandhurst Town	Wembley
Ash United		3-0	1-2	0-1	1-4	4-0	0-4	3-6	2-0	3-1	1-0	1-1	0-1	2-1	3-1	3-1	2-2	1-1	1-1	2-0	1-0	3-0
Badshot Lea	2-1		3-1	1-5	2-3	3-2	5-3	0-6	1-3	2-1	3-3	2-2	2-1	3-4	3-0	3-1	3-2	2-1	2-2	2-3	0-1	4-2
Banstead Athletic	0-4	0-0		1-0	1-1	2-0	0-0	3-2	3-1	4-1	4-3	1-5	1-4	0-5	1-1	1-1	3-0	1-1	4-1	1-3	3-4	0-5
Bedfont	0-1	1-2	0-6	***P***	0-2	2-1	1-3	2-4	2-1	2-2	3-3	1-1	1-2	2-2	2-1	3-2	1-2	3-0	0-3	1-1	4-4	1-3
Bedfont Green	5-2	1-2	4-2	3-1	***R***	7-3	1-0	5-0	1-1	3-2	2-2	3-1	2-2	4-2	3-3	5-0	2-2	2-1	1-2	2-0	5-0	5-1
Bookham	2-0	2-3	0-4	3-2	1-3	***E***	4-4	1-1	1-2	4-2	2-1	0-0	3-2	0-1	6-1	2-1	3-2	2-1	1-1	1-4	2-1	2-2
Camberley Town	2-2	3-1	0-1	3-1	6-0	2-0	***M***	2-1	1-1	2-0	2-1	2-2	2-2	3-2	2-3	5-1	2-1	3-3	1-2	4-0	1-1	3-1
Chertsey Town	4-1	2-0	3-1	5-0	1-1	1-1	1-3	***I***	5-2	3-4	0-4	2-1	4-0	1-1	2-0	6-0	0-3	1-2	3-2	5-0	1-1	3-1
Chessington & Hook Utd	1-1	1-3	3-0	1-1	0-2	2-2	3-1	1-1	***E***	0-3	1-0	2-2	2-0	2-2	2-2	2-2	0-1	4-2	2-3	2-1	2-2	0-2
Cobham	1-2	2-2	2-1	0-3	1-4	2-3	0-6	0-2	1-2	***R***	1-2	2-2	0-1	0-2	1-3	1-1	0-3	1-4	0-2	0-2	2-3	0-3
Colliers Wood United	2-2	6-1	1-2	5-2	0-4	2-1	1-4	1-1	2-1	5-1		2-3	3-1	1-2	7-0	1-2	2-0	1-3	1-1	1-3	1-2	1-2
Cove	2-4	1-1	3-1	4-0	3-0	3-2	0-1	3-2	4-1	1-1	1-1	***D***	3-0	2-2	2-3	5-2	2-0	0-2	1-1	2-1	1-1	1-0
Egham Town	2-0	6-2	1-1	3-1	2-2	1-0	0-2	0-1	3-0	1-0	1-3	2-0	***I***	1-2	0-2	4-2	0-1	1-4	2-2	0-3	1-2	1-0
Epsom & Ewell	1-1	2-0	0-2	2-0	1-2	4-1	1-1	1-2	3-2	1-1	2-1	2-4	0-3	***V***	1-0	5-0	0-0	1-0	3-2	0-0	2-1	3-0
Guildford City	4-4	1-5	0-5	0-1	1-2	0-0	0-5	2-2	1-0	4-3	1-0	0-0	0-1	0-4	***I***	2-2	0-0	2-1	2-2	2-3	3-2	1-3
Hartley Wintney	0-5	3-4	1-2	2-3	1-2	2-1	1-3	0-2	2-4	3-0	1-2	0-3	1-1	0-0	0-3	***S***	0-2	0-4	1-2	2-2	1-1	1-2
Horley Town	1-1	4-1	4-3	0-1	1-3	1-1	0-0	2-0	1-1	2-0	1-2	0-1	2-2	2-3	1-1	1-1	***I***	0-4	2-3	2-1	1-0	2-1
Molesey	2-0	1-3	4-1	1-1	0-0	2-4	3-3	0-2	2-2	5-1	4-0	0-3	2-1	0-0	5-1	3-1	1-0	***O***	1-2	1-2	1-3	0-0
North Greenford United	5-2	0-3	3-2	2-2	2-3	3-2	3-3	0-2	4-1	2-2	2-1	6-1	3-3	4-1	3-1	4-0	0-0	3-1	***N***	2-1	2-0	4-3
Raynes Park Vale	5-2	3-2	2-0	1-0	2-5	0-3	2-1	0-3	3-2	4-5	1-3	0-3	2-0	3-5	3-0	2-3	1-3	3-1	3-2		0-1	4-1
Sandhurst Town	1-5	1-2	1-2	2-1	0-3	1-1	2-1	3-1	2-0	2-0	0-1	2-1	2-3	2-4	1-2	4-3	0-1	1-1	0-5	2-5		3-3
Wembley	1-1	1-2	2-5	0-1	0-4	3-5	2-0	1-2	1-1	2-1	2-2	0-1	1-0	0-5	2-1	2-2	1-1	0-2	1-1	1-1	3-1	

Division One	P	W	D	L	F	A	Pts
Staines Lammas	34	22	5	7	78	39	71
Hanworth Villa	34	21	7	6	79	44	70
Dorking	34	22	4	8	78	45	70
Mole Valley SCR	34	22	4	8	87	55	70
Knaphill	34	22	3	9	86	55	69
Worcester Park	34	20	7	7	72	38	67
Feltham	34	15	7	12	62	53	52
Farnham Town	34	16	3	15	85	74	51
Sheerwater	34	15	3	16	64	71	48
CB Hounslow United	34	13	6	15	48	52	45
Warlingham	34	12	8	14	62	70	44
Farleigh Rovers	34	11	8	15	49	61	41
Westfield	34	11	5	18	50	67	38
South Park	34	11	4	19	59	68	37
Crescent Rovers	34	8	9	17	48	70	33
Frimley Green	34	10	3	21	40	74	33
Coulsdon United	34	4	8	22	56	95	20
Chobham	34	2	4	28	43	115	10

LEMON RECORDINGS DIVISION ONE CUP

FIRST ROUND

Dorking 4 Hanworth 3
Worcester Park 4 Warlingham 1

SECOND ROUND

Coulsdon Utd 1 **Staines Lammas** 1 *aet* (1-3p)
Crescent 2 Dorking 1
Farnham Town 6 Frimley Green 0
Knaphill 3 CB Hounslow 1
Mole Valley 4 South Pk 2
Sheerwater 3 Feltham 1 *aet*
Westfield 2 **Farleigh Rovers** 2 *aet* (3-4p)
Worcester Park 4 Chobham 1
(at Colliers Wood United)

QUARTER-FINALS

Farnham Town 1 Crescent Rovers 1 *aet* (8-7p)
Mole Valley SCR 2 Farleigh Rovers 1 *aet*
Sheerwater 0 **Knaphill** 3
Staines Lammas 2 Worcester Park 1

SEMI-FINALS

Knaphill 1 **Staines Lammas** 2
Mole Valley SCR 3 Farnham Town 1

FINAL

(May 4th at Ashford Town (Middx))
Staines Lammas 1 Mole Valley SCR 0

RESERVES CUP

FINAL *(May 5th at Molesey)*
Bookham Res. 4 Crescent Rovers Res. 1

EL RECORDS PREMIER CUP

FIRST ROUND

Camberley Town 2 Hanworth Villa 1
CB Hounslow United 3 **Guildford City** 3 *aet* (3-4p)
Coulsdon United 3 Sandhurst Town 0
Epsom & Ewell 1 **Dorking** 2
Molesey 2 Frimley Green 1
Raynes Park Vale 2 Cove 2 *aet* (5-4p)
Staines Lammas 2 Farnham Town 1
Warlingham 4 Westfield 2

SECOND ROUND

Badshot Lea 1 **Wembley** 3 *aet*
Banstead Athletic 2 **Bedfont** 2 *aet* (1-4p)
Camberley Town 2 Hartley Wintney 1
Chessington & Hook Utd 1 **Chertsey Town** 1 *aet* (3-4p)
Cobham 0 **Raynes Park Vale** 1
Colliers Wood United 6 Chobham 2
Coulsdon United 2 **North Greenford United** 8
Farleigh Rovers 1 **Ash United** 4
Feltham 2 **Bookham** 4
Guildford City 2 Egham Town 1
Horley Town 4 Crescent Rovers 0
Mole Valley SCR 2 Knaphill 1
Sheerwater 0 **Molesey** 9
South Park 1 Bedfont Green 0
Staines Lammas 4 **Warlingham** 8
Worcester Park 4 Dorking 0

THIRD ROUND

Bedfont 0 **Bookham** 1
Camberley Town 2 North Greenford United 1
Chertsey Town 1 Raynes Park Vale 1 *aet* (3-0p)
Horley Town 5 Guildford City 2
Mole Valley SCR 2 **Wembley** 4
Molesey 2 Ash United 1
South Park 1 **Worcester Park** 4
Warlingham 2 **Colliers Wood United** 4

QUARTER-FINALS

Bookham 2 **Chertsey Town** 5
Camberley Town 1 Wembley 0
Colliers Wood United 0 **Molesey** 3
Worcester Park 1 Horley Town 0

SEMI-FINALS

Camberley Town 1 Molesey 0
Worcester Park 0 Chertsey Town 1 *(Chertsey expelled)*

FINAL

(April 24th at Carshalton Athletic)
Camberley Town 3 Worcester Park 0

	CBH	Chob	Coul	Cres	Dork	Farl	Farn	Felt	Frim	Han	Knap	Mole	Shee	Sth P	S Lam	Warl	West	Worc
CB Hounslow Utd		3-2	2-0	0-0	1-2	0-1	2-4	1-0	2-0	1-1	2-3	1-4	0-2	2-1	1-0	4-1	2-0	1-0
Chobham	0-6		1-9	1-1	0-4	4-2	6-1	0-1	1-3	0-1	1-4	0-2	1-6	1-3	2-2	1-4	1-2	1-2
Coulsdon United	0-0	4-4		4-4	1-2	1-1	1-5	0-0	2-4	1-3	0-2	1-5	1-3	2-1	0-3	0-0	1-4	3-2
Crescent Rovers	1-1	3-1	3-3	***D***	0-3	2-1	1-0	2-2	2-1	1-3	4-2	2-4	0-3	0-3	2-4	2-3	3-2	2-2
Dorking	3-1	4-1	4-0	5-3	***I***	4-0	3-6	1-1	0-1	2-2	2-3	2-0	3-1	1-0	1-0	3-1	4-0	0-5
Farleigh Rovers	2-3	2-1	3-0	2-0	0-3	***V***	1-3	0-1	5-1	3-2	3-2	2-1	1-1	1-1	0-1	1-1	1-4	2-2
Farnham Town	4-0	3-2	6-3	3-1	4-1	2-2	***I***	6-3	0-0	2-4	5-2	1-2	0-3	4-2	1-2	4-3	3-4	1-1
Feltham	1-0	2-0	5-0	1-0	1-3	3-1	4-1	***S***	5-2	1-1	1-2	1-2	4-0	3-1	2-5	2-2	2-1	2-2
Frimley Green	1-1	1-0	3-2	2-1	0-1	2-1	2-0	1-2	***I***	0-3	2-4	2-1	4-1	1-4	1-2	1-1	0-3	0-3
Hanworth Villa	1-0	8-1	2-1	2-1	1-1	1-1	1-0	2-1	2-1	***O***	2-2	8-2	3-0	4-0	1-0	2-3	5-4	0-2
Knaphill	4-1	4-0	3-3	3-0	1-1	3-1	4-2	2-0	2-0	2-0	***N***	1-3	0-4	5-1	0-1	2-1	4-1	5-1
Mole Valley SCR	4-1	4-1	4-3	2-0	0-1	2-3	1-5	3-1	3-0	5-4	4-0		6-0	2-0	3-1	1-1	2-0	3-1
Sheerwater	3-1	4-2	4-1	3-1	1-3	2-1	0-2	0-2	2-1	2-4	0-2	2-2	***O***	1-2	1-3	1-2	2-2	2-0
South Park	2-3	5-1	3-2	2-2	3-4	0-1	2-1	3-1	4-0	0-1	1-3	4-4	5-2	***N***	0-1	0-2	2-2	0-4
Staines Lammas	1-0	6-2	3-2	0-2	3-2	5-1	2-0	4-2	4-0	0-0	5-2	1-1	6-1	2-1	***E***	4-2	3-0	1-1
Warlingham	1-3	2-2	W-L	1-0	1-4	2-2	2-4	3-1	6-2	0-3	1-3	5-2	2-4	1-3	2-1		2-3	0-3
Westfield	1-1	4-2	1-2	0-1	1-0	0-1	3-1	2-4	1-0	0-2	1-5	0-2	0-2	3-0	0-0	1-1		0-4
Worcester Park	2-1	3-0	5-3	1-1	2-1	1-0	4-1	0-0	3-1	4-0	1-0	0-1	4-1	1-0	3-2	1-3	2-0	

PREMIER DIVISION

ASH UNITED

Founded: 1911 Nickname: United

Chairman: Vaughan Jones
Secretary: Gareth Watmore
69 Longacre
Ash
Aldershot
GU12 6RW
Tel: 07739 188 069
Manager: Paul Bonner
Prog Editor: Jim Avenell

Ground: Youngs Drive off Shawfield Road, Ash, GU12 6RE. Tel: 01252 320385/345757
Capacity: 2500 **Seats:** 152 **Covered:** 160
Midweek Matchday: Tuesday **Clubhouse:** Yes **Shop:** No
Colours(change): All green.
Previous Names: None
Previous Lges: Surrey Senior Lge
Records: **Att:** 914 v AFC Wimbledon Combined Co 02-03.
Goals: Shaun Mitchell (216). **Apps:** Paul Bonner (582)
Senior Honours: Combined Counties Champions 1981-82, 86-87, 98-99.
Aldershot Senior Cup 1998-99, 01-02.

10 YEAR RECORD

99-00	00-01	01-02	02-03	03-04	04-05	05-06	06-07	07-08	08-09
CC 2	CC 3	CC 2	CC 9	CCP 9	CCP 13	CCP 3	CCP 4	CCP 15	CCP 9

BADSHOT LEA

Founded: 1907 Nickname: Baggies

Chairman: Mark Board
Secretary: Mrs Nicky Staszkiewicz
12 Orchard Gardens
Aldershot
Hants
GU12 4HP
Tel: 07921 466 858
Manager: David Ford
Prog Editor: Peter Rapley

Ground: Farnborough FC, Cherrywood Rd, Farnborough GU14 8UD. Tel: 01252 541 469.
Capacity: 4,163 **Seats:** 620 **Covered:** 1,350
Midweek Matchday: Tuesday **Clubhouse:** Yes **Shop:** Yes
Colours(change): All claret and blue.
Previous Names:
Previous Lges: Surrey Intermediate. Hellenic.
Records: **Att:** 276 v Bisley, 16.04.07.
Senior Honours:

10 YEAR RECORD

99-00	00-01	01-02	02-03	03-04	04-05	05-06	06-07	07-08	08-09
				Hel1E 14	Hel1E 7	Hel1E 12	Hel1E 3	Hel P 11	CCP 7

BANSTEAD ATHLETIC

Founded: 1944 Nickname: A's

Chairman: Terry Molloy
Secretary: Terry Parmenter
90 Somerset Avenue
Chessington
Surrey
KT19 1PP
Tel: 07940 387 041
Manager: Dave Leaworthy
Prog Editor: See Secretary

Ground: Merland Rise, Tadworth, Surrey KT20 5JG. Tel: 01737 350 982
Capacity: 3500 **Seats:** 250 **Covered:** 800
Midweek Matchday: Tuesday **Clubhouse:** Yes **Shop:** Yes
Colours(change): Amber & black/black/black
Previous Names: None
Previous Lges: London Spartan League. Athenian League. Ishtmian.
Records: **Att:** 1400 v Leytonstone, FA Amateur Cup 1953.
Goals: Harry Clark. **Apps:** Dennis Wall.
Senior Honours: Surrey Snr Lg (6) 50-54 56-57 64-65, Lg Cup 57-58.
London Spartan LC 65-67, Athenian LC 80-82. Surrey Int. Lg 47-49, Cup 46-47 54-55.

10 YEAR RECORD

99-00	00-01	01-02	02-03	03-04	04-05	05-06	06-07	07-08	08-09
Isth2 10	Isth2 11	Isth2 5	Isth1S 16	Isth1S 18	Isth1S 17	Isth1S 20	CCP 6	CCP 17	CCP 10

BEDFONT

Founded: 1900 Nickname: Ochardmen

Chairman: Raymond Cook (Vice-Ch.)
Secretary: Les King
14 Harlequin Close
Isleworth
Middlesex
TW7 7LA
Tel: 0208 894 5525
Manager: Neil Shipperley
Prog Editor: See secretary

Ground: The Orchard, Hatton Road, Bedfont, Middlesex TW14 9QT. Tel: 0208 890 7264
Capacity: 1200 **Seats:** 100 **Covered:** 150
Midweek Matchday: Tuesday **Clubhouse:** Yes **Shop:** No
Colours(change): Yellow & blue/blue/blue
Previous Names: None
Previous Lges: Surrey Premier.
Records:
Senior Honours:

10 YEAR RECORD

99-00	00-01	01-02	02-03	03-04	04-05	05-06	06-07	07-08	08-09
CC 3	CC 4	CC 4	CC 5	CCP 6	CCP 6	CCP 6	CCP 22	CCP 20	CCP 18

BOOKHAM

Founded: 1921 Nickname:

Chairman: Simon Butler
Secretary: Bob Elcome (Vice Ch.)

Tel: 07824 884 046
Manager: Glyn Mandeville
Prog Editor: Daniel Carnota

Ground: Dorking FC, Mill Lane, Dorking, Surrey RH4 1DX. Tel: 01306 884 112
Capacity: 3000 **Seats:** 200 **Covered:** 600
Midweek Matchday: Tuesday **Clubhouse:** **Shop:**
Colours(change): Yellow/black/black
Previous Names: None
Previous Lges: Surrey County Senior League.
Records: **Att:** 81 v AFC Wallingford - 22.10.05.
Senior Honours:

10 YEAR RECORD

99-00	00-01	01-02	02-03	03-04	04-05	05-06	06-07	07-08	08-09
SuCP 11	SuCS 8	SuCS 4	SuCS 4	CC1 3	CC1 3	CC1 3	CCP 20	CCP 18	CCP 15

CAMBERLEY TOWN

Founded: 1895 Nickname: Reds or Town

Chairman: Ronnie Wilson
Secretary: Ben Clifford
63 Inglewood Avenue
Camberley
Surrey
GU15 1RS
Tel: 07876 552 210
Manager: Paul Barry
Prog Editor: Andy Vaughan

Ground: Krooner Park, Krooner Road, Camberley, Surrey GU15 2QW. Tel: 01276 65392
Capacity: 2000 **Seats:** 195 **Covered:** 350
Midweek Matchday: Tuesday **Clubhouse:** Yes **Shop:** Yes
Colours(change): Red and white stripes/red/red
Previous Names: None
Previous Lges: Surrey Senior Lge. Spartan Lge. Athenian Lge. Isthmian Lge.
Records: **Att:** 2066 v Aldershot Town, Isthmian Div.2 25/08/90.
Apps: Brian Ives.
Senior Honours: Surrey Senior Cup 1978-79. Aldershot Senior Cup (x3)

10 YEAR RECORD

99-00	00-01	01-02	02-03	03-04	04-05	05-06	06-07	07-08	08-09
Isth3 17	Isth3 20	Isth3 22	Isth2 16	Isth2 10	Isth2 12	Isth2 14	CCP 7	CCP 3	CCP 5

CHERTSEY TOWN

Founded: 1890 Nickname: Curfews

Chairman: Steve Powers
Secretary: Chris Gay
23 Richmond Close
Frimley
Camberley
GU16 8NR
Tel: 07713 473 313
Manager: Spencer Day
Prog Editor: See secretary

Ground: Alwyns Lane, Chertsey Surrey KT16 9DW. Tel: 01932 561 774
Capacity: 3,000 **Seats:** 240 **Covered:** 760
Midweek Matchday: Tuesday **Clubhouse:** Yes **Shop:** Yes
Colours(change): White/royal blue/white
Previous Names: None
Previous Lges: Metropolitan. Spartan. Athenian. Isthmian.
Records: **Att:** 2150 v Aldershot Town, Isthmian Div.2 04/12/93.
Goals: Alan Brown (54) 1962-63.
Senior Honours: Surrey Senior Champions 1959, 61, 62. Isthmian League Cup 1994.

10 YEAR RECORD

99-00	00-01	01-02	02-03	03-04	04-05	05-06	06-07	07-08	08-09
Isth1 21	Isth2 8	Isth2 17	Isth1S 24	Isth2 4	Isth2 6	Isth2 6	CCP 8	CCP 8	CCP 3

CHESSINGTON & HOOK UNITED

Founded: 1921 Nickname: Chessey

Chairman: Graham Ellis
Secretary: Chris Blackie
17 Finlays Close
Chessington
Surrey
KT9 1XG
Tel: 07748 877 704
Manager: Paul Norris
Prog Editor: Eric Wicks

Ground: Chalky Lane, Chessington, Surrey KT9 2NF. Tel: 01372 745 777
Capacity: 3000 **Seats:** 167 **Covered:** 600
Midweek Matchday: Tuesday **Clubhouse:** Yes **Shop:** No
Colours(change): All blue
Previous Names: Chessington United.
Previous Lges: Surrey Senior Lge. Surrey County Premier Lge.
Records:
Senior Honours:

10 YEAR RECORD

99-00	00-01	01-02	02-03	03-04	04-05	05-06	06-07	07-08	08-09
CC 14	CC 10	CC 11	CC 14	CCP 10	CCP 3	CCP 8	CCP 11	CCP 11	CCP 19

INS & OUTS

IN: Croydon (S – Kent League Premier Division), Dorking (P), Hanworth Villa (P)
OUT: Bedfont Green (P – Southern League Division One South & West), Cobham (R), Hartley Wintney (R)

COLLIERS WOOD UNITED

Founded: 1874 Nickname: The Woods

Chairman: Tony Eldridge
Secretary: Tony Hurrell
1 Inglewood
Pixton Way, Forestdale
Croydon
CR0 9LN
Tel: 07956 983947
Manager: Mark Douglas
Prog Editor: Chris Clapham

Ground: Wibandune Sports Gd, Lincoln Green, Wimbledon SW20 0AA. Tel: 0208 942 8062
Capacity: 2000 **Seats:** 102 **Covered:** 100
Midweek Matchday: Wednesday **Clubhouse:** Yes **Shop:** Yes
Colours(change): Blue & black/black/black
Previous Names: Vandyke Colliers United
Previous Lges: Surrey County Senior Lge.
Records: 90 v Epsom & Ewell, 14.11.2007.

Senior Honours: Surrey Co Prem Lge Champions 1997-98 (as Vandyke Colliers United)

10 YEAR RECORD

99-00	00-01	01-02	02-03	03-04	04-05	05-06	06-07	07-08	08-09
SuCP 2	SuCS 2	SuCS 5	SuCS 2	CC1 2	CCP 14	CCP 4	CCP 13	CCP 7	CCP 14

COVE

Founded: 1897 Nickname:

Chairman: P Wentworth
Secretary: Graham Brown
6 Longfield Close
Haley Estate
Farnborough
GU14 8HQ
Tel: 07713 250 093
Manager: Koo Dumbaya
Prog Editor: See secretary

Ground: Oak Farm Fields, 7 Squirrels Lane, Farnborough GU14 8PB. Tel: 01252 543 615
Capacity: 2500 **Seats:** 110 **Covered:** 200
Midweek Matchday: Tuesday **Clubhouse:** Yes **Shop:** No
Colours(change): Yellow/black/yellow
Previous Names: None
Previous Lges: Isthmian League. Hampshire.
Records: **Att:** 1798 v Aldershot Town, Isthmian Div.3 01/05/93.

Senior Honours: Combined Counties Lge Champions 2000-01. Lge Cup 81-82, 00-01. Aldershot Senior Cup (x5)

10 YEAR RECORD

99-00	00-01	01-02	02-03	03-04	04-05	05-06	06-07	07-08	08-09
CC 8	CC 1	CC 15	CC 23	CCP 24	CCP 20	CCP 16	CCP 18	CCP 4	CCP 6

CROYDON

Founded: 1953 Nickname: The Trams

Chairman: Dickson Gill
Secretary: Barry Feist
11 John Hunt Court
Clarence Road
Mottingham
SE9 4SH
Tel: 07931 655 113
Manager: Dickson Gill
Prog Editor: Vince Mitchell

Ground: Albert Road, South Norwood SE25 4QL. Tel: 0208 654 8555
Capacity: 6,000 **Seats:** 450 **Covered:** 1,000
Midweek Matchday: Wednesday **Clubhouse:** Yes **Shop:** Yes
Colours(change): Sky blue/sky blue/dark blue.
Previous Names: Croydon Amateurs > 1974.
Previous Lges: Surrey Senior. Spartan. Athenian. Isthmian. Kent 2006-09.
Records: **Att:** 1,450 v Wycombe Wanderers, FA Cup 4th Qual. 1975.
Goalscorer: Alec Jackson - 111. **Apps:** Alec Jackson - 452 (1977-88).
Senior Honours: Isthmian Division 1 1999-00. London Senior Cup 01-02.

10 YEAR RECORD

99-00	00-01	01-02	02-03	03-04	04-05	05-06	06-07	07-08	08-09
Isth1 1	Isth P 17	Isth P 22	Isth1S 18	Isth1S 21	Isth1 22	Isth2 10	Kent P 3	Kent P 12	Kent P 9

DORKING

Founded: 1880 Nickname: The Chicks

Chairman: Jack Collins
Secretary: Ray Collins
11 Richmond Way
Fetcham
Surrey
KT22 9NP
Tel: 07710 010241
Manager: Anthony Webb
Prog Editor: Bryan Bletso

Ground: Meadowbank, Mill Lane, Dorking Surrey RH4 1DX. Tel: 01306 884 112
Capacity: 3500 **Seats:** 200 **Covered:** 800
Midweek Matchday: Tuesday **Clubhouse:** Yes **Shop:** Yes
Colours(change): Green & white hoops/green & white/green
Previous Names: Guildford & Dorking (when club merged 1974). Dorking Town 77-82
Previous Lges: Corinthian Lge. Athenian Lge. Isthmian Lge.
Records: **Att:** 4500 v Folkstone Town FAC 1955 & v Plymouth Argyle FAC 1993.
Goals: Andy Bushell. **Apps:** Steve Lunn.
Senior Honours: Isthmian Div.2 1988-89.

10 YEAR RECORD

99-00	00-01	01-02	02-03	03-04	04-05	05-06	06-07	07-08	08-09
Isth3 19	Isth3 18	Isth3 8	Isth2 14	Isth2 2	Isth1 21	Isth2 9	CCP 16	CCP 22	CC1 3

EGHAM TOWN

Founded: 1886 Nickname: Sarnies

Chairman: Patrick Bennett
Secretary: Daniel Bennett
24 Burr Hill Lane
Chobham
Surrey
GU24 8QD
Tel: 07932 612 424
Manager: Steve Baker
Prog Editor: Paul Bennett

Ground: Runnymead Stadium, Tempest Road, Egham TW20 8HX. Tel: 01784 435 226
Capacity: 5500 **Seats:** 262 **Covered:** 3300
Midweek Matchday: Tuesday **Clubhouse:** Yes **Shop:** No
Colours(change): All red
Previous Names: Runnymead Rovers 1877-1905. Egham F.C. 05-63.
Previous Lges: Spartan Lge. Athenian Lge. Isthmian Lge. Southern Lge.
Records: Att: 1400 v Wycombe Wanderers, FAC 2nd Qual. 1972-73.
Goals: Mark Butler (153). **Apps:** Dave Jones (850+).
Senior Honours: Spartan Lge Champions 1971-72. Athenian Lge Div.2 Champions.

10 YEAR RECORD

99-00	00-01	01-02	02-03	03-04	04-05	05-06	06-07	07-08	08-09
Isth3 13	Isth3 13	Isth3 6	Isth1S 10	Isth1S 22	SthW 22	Isth2 5	CCP 10	CCP 12	CCP 13

EPSOM & EWELL

Founded: 1918 Nickname: E's

Chairman: Tony Jeffcoate
Secretary: Mrs Mayse Oakes
44 Royal Drive
Tattenham Corner
Epsom Downs
KT18 5PR
Tel: 07760 106 632
Manager: Lyndon Buckwell
Prog Editor: Richard Lambert

Ground: Banstead AFC, Merland Rise, Tadworth KT20 5JG. Tel: 01737 350 982
Capacity: 3400 **Seats:** 174 **Covered:** 800
Midweek Matchday: Tuesday **Clubhouse:** Yes **Shop:** No
Colours(change): Royal blue & white hoops/royal/royal & white.
Previous Names: Epsom T (previously Epsom FC) merged with Ewell & Stoneleigh in 1960
Previous Lges: Corinthian Lge. Athenian Lge. Surrey Senior Lge. Isthmian Lge.
Records: Att: 5000 v Kingstonian, FAC 2Q 15/10/49.
Goals: Tommy Tuite.
Senior Honours: Isthmian Lge Div.2 Champions 1977-78.

10 YEAR RECORD

99-00	00-01	01-02	02-03	03-04	04-05	05-06	06-07	07-08	08-09
Isth3 6	Isth3 7	Isth3 5	Isth1S 9	Isth1S 24	Isth2 14	Isth2 15	CCP 17	CCP 10	CCP 4

GUILDFORD CITY

Founded: 1996 Nickname: The City

Chairman: Chris Pegman
Secretary: Andrew Masters
3 Webster Court
Bramley
Guildford
GU2 8AW
Tel: 07834 956 475
Manager: Kevin Rayner
Prog Editor: Matt Howell

Ground: Spectrum Leisure Centre, Parkway, Guildford GU1 1UP. Tel: 01483 443 322
Capacity: 1100 **Seats:** 134 **Covered:** Yes
Midweek Matchday: Wednesday **Clubhouse:** Yes **Shop:** Yes
Colours(change): Red & white stripes/black/black
Previous Names: AFC Guildford 1996-2005. Guildford United 05-06.
Previous Lges: Surrey Senior.
Records: Att: 211 v Godalming & Guildford, 2004
Senior Honours: Combined Counties Div.1 Champions 2003-04

10 YEAR RECORD

99-00	00-01	01-02	02-03	03-04	04-05	05-06	06-07	07-08	08-09
SuCP 10	SuCS 4	SuCS 11	SuCS 9	CC1 1	CCP 12	CCP 17	CCP 21	CCP 2	CCP 20

HANWORTH VILLA

Founded: 1976 Nickname: The Vilans

Chairman: Gary Brunning
Secretary: Dave Brown
104 Park Road
Kingston
Surrey
KT2 5JZ
Tel: 020 8546 5979
Manager: Tony Buss
Prog Editor: As chairman

Ground: Rectory Meadows, Park Road, Hanworth TW13 6PN. Tel: 020 8831 9391
Capacity: 600 **Seats:** 100 **Covered:**
Midweek Matchday: Tuesday **Clubhouse:** **Shop:**
Colours(change): Red & white/red/red & white.
Previous Names:
Previous Lges: Hounslow & District Lge. West Middlesex Lge. Middlesex County League.
Records:
Senior Honours: Hounslow & District Div.1 & Premier Division Champions.
West Middlesex Div. 1 & Div. 2 Champions. Middlesex County Champions 2002-03, 04-05.

10 YEAR RECORD

99-00	00-01	01-02	02-03	03-04	04-05	05-06	06-07	07-08	08-09
MidCo 8	MidCo 6	MidCo 4	MidCo 1	MidCo 4	MidCo 1	CC1 7	CC1 6	CC1 2	CC1 2

HORLEY TOWN

Founded: 1896 Nickname: The Clarets

Chairman: Mark Sale
Secretary: Jim Betchley
The New Defence
Court Lodge Road
Horley
RH6 8RS
Tel: 07824 379 184
Manager: Ali Rennie
Prog Editor: Rob Cortazzi

Ground: The New Defence, Court Lodge Road, Horley RH6 8RS. Tel: 01293 822 000
Capacity: 1800 **Seats:** 101 **Covered:** Yes
Midweek Matchday: Tuesday **Clubhouse:** Yes **Shop:** Yes
Colours(change): Claret & sky blue/claret/claret
Previous Names: Horley >1975
Previous Lges: Surrey Senior Lge. London Spartan Lge. Athenian Lge. Surrey Co. Sen.
Records: Att: 15,00 v AFC Wimbledon, 2003-04. **Goalscorer:** Alan Gates.
Senior Honours: Surrey Senior League Champions 1976-77.

10 YEAR RECORD

99-00	00-01	01-02	02-03	03-04	04-05	05-06	06-07	07-08	08-09
			SuCS 3	CCP 17	CCP 7	CCP 5	CC1 2	CCP 5	CCP 12

MOLESEY

Founded: 1953 Nickname: The Moles

Chairman: Gary Mayne
Secretary: Tracey Teague
6 Joseph Locke Way
Esher
Surrey
KT10 8DU
Tel: 07939 387 277
Manager: Steve Webb
Prog Editor:

Ground: 412 Walton Road, West Molesey KT8 2JG. Tel: 020 8979 4283 (Clubhouse)
Capacity: 4,000 **Seats:** 400 **Covered:** 600
Midweek Matchday: Tuesday **Clubhouse:** Yes **Shop:** Yes
Colours(change): White/black/black.
Previous Names: None.
Previous Lges: Surrey Senior. Spartan. Athethian. Isthmian.
Records: Att: 1,255 v Sutton United, Surrey Senior Cup sem-final 1966.
Goalscorer: Michael Rose (139). **Apps:** Frank Hanley (453)
Senior Honours: Surrey Senior League 1957-58.

10 YEAR RECORD

99-00	00-01	01-02	02-03	03-04	04-05	05-06	06-07	07-08	08-09
Isth2 19	Isth2 15	Isth2 19	Isth1S 22	Isth1S 19	Isth1 16	Isth1 17	Isth1S 15	Isth1S 22	CCP 11

NORTH GREENFORD UNITED

Founded: 1944 Nickname: Blues

Chairman: John Bivens
Secretary: Mrs Barbara Bivens
1 The Green
Sarrett
Herts
WD3 6AY
Tel: 07915 661 580
Manager: Steve Ringrose
Prog Editor: Pat Hillier

Ground: Berkeley Fields, Berkley Ave, Greenford UB6. Tel: 0208 422 8923
Capacity: 2000 **Seats:** 150 **Covered:** 100
Midweek Matchday: Tuesday **Clubhouse:** Yes **Shop:** No
Colours(change): Blue & white/blue/blue
Previous Names: None
Previous Lges: London Spartan Lge.
Records: Att: 985 v AFC Wimbledon. **Goalscorer:** John Hill (98).
Senior Honours: None

10 YEAR RECORD

99-00	00-01	01-02	02-03	03-04	04-05	05-06	06-07	07-08	08-09
			CC 10	CCP 14	CCP 2	CCP 13	CCP 5	CCP 6	CCP 2

RAYNES PARK VALE

Founded: 1995 Nickname: The Vale

Chairman: Rick Cook
Secretary: David Brenen
22 The Crescent
Belmont
Sutton
SM2 6BJ
Tel: 07956 304566
Manager: Mark Williams
Prog Editor: Mike Woods

Ground: Prince George's Playing Field, Raynes Park SW20 9NB. Tel: 0208 540 8843
Capacity: 1500 **Seats:** 120 **Covered:** 100
Midweek Matchday: Wednesday **Clubhouse:** Yes **Shop:** No
Colours(change): Blue/blue/blue.
Previous Names: Raynes Park > 1995 until merger with Malden Vale.
Previous Lges: Surrey County Premier Lge. Isthmian.
Records: Att: 1871 v AFC Wimbledon (At Carshalton Athletic).
Senior Honours: Combined Counties Div.1 Champions 2002-03.

10 YEAR RECORD

99-00	00-01	01-02	02-03	03-04	04-05	05-06	06-07	07-08	08-09
CC 16	CC 16	CC 7	CC 8	CCP 16	CCP 9	CCP 9	CCP 15	CCP 19	CCP 8

SANDHURST TOWN

Founded: 1910 Nickname: Fizzers

Chairman: Ted Rogers
Secretary: Mike Ellsmore
67 Avocet Crescent
Sandhurst
Berkshire
GU47 0QD
Tel: 07986 484025
Manager: Jon Underwood
Prog Editor: Christine Bell

Ground: Bottom Meadow, Memorial Ground, Yorktown Rd, GU47 0XW. Tel: 01252 878 768
Capacity: 1000 **Seats:** 102 **Covered:** 100
Midweek Matchday: Tuesday **Clubhouse:** Yes **Shop:** No
Colours(change): Red/black/black.
Previous Names: None
Previous Lges: Reading & Dist. East Berks. Aldershot Senior. Chiltonian Lge.
Records: Att: 2,449 v AFC Wimbledon, Combined Counties 17.08.2002.
Senior Honours: Reading & District Premier Champions 1933-34. Division 1 1932-33. Aldershot FA Senior Invitation Challenge Cup 2000-01, 05-06.

10 YEAR RECORD

99-00	00-01	01-02	02-03	03-04	04-05	05-06	06-07	07-08	08-09
CC 17	CC 13	CC 13	CC 6	CCP 5	CCP 5	CCP 7	CCP 12	CCP 16	CCP 16

WEMBLEY

Founded: 1946 Nickname: The Lions

Chairman: Brian Gumm
Secretary: Mrs Jean Gumm
14 Woodfield Avenue
North Wembley
Middlesex
HA0 3NR
Tel: 07876 125 784
Manager:
Prog Editor: Richard Markiewicz

Ground: Vale Farm, Watford Road, Sudbury, Wembley HA0 3AG. Tel: 0208 904 8169
Capacity: 2450 **Seats:** 350 **Covered:** 950
Midweek Matchday: Tuesday **Clubhouse:** Yes **Shop:** No
Colours(change): Red & white/red/red
Previous Names: None
Previous Lges: Middlesex Lge. Spartan. Delphian. Corinthian. Athenian. Isthmian.
Records: Att: 2654 v Wealdstone, FA Amateur Cup 1952-53.
Goals: Bill Handraham (105). **Apps:** Spud Murphy (505)
Senior Honours: Middlesex Senior Cup 1983-84, 86-87.

10 YEAR RECORD

99-00	00-01	01-02	02-03	03-04	04-05	05-06	06-07	07-08	08-09
Isth2 13	Isth2 16	Isth2 18	Isth1N 23	Isth2 11	Isth2 13	Isth2 11	CCP 3	CCP 14	CCP 17

BEDFONT SPORTS

Founded: 2002 Nickname: The Eagles

Chairman: David Reader
Secretary: Terry Reader
126 Fernside Avenue
Hanworth
Middlesex
TW13 7BW
Tel: 07967 370 109
Manager: Anthony Yearsley/Jamie Cleary
Prog Editor: See secretary

Ground: Bedfont Sports Club, Hatton Road, Bedfont TW14 9QT.
Capacity: 3000 **Seats:** To come **Covered:** 200
Midweek Matchday: Tuesday **Clubhouse:** Yes **Shop:**
Colours(change): Red/black/red.
Previous Names: None
Previous Lges: Middlesex County.
Records:
Senior Honours: None

10 YEAR RECORD

99-00	00-01	01-02	02-03	03-04	04-05	05-06	06-07	07-08	08-09
					Midx1 2	MidxP 11	MidxP 3	MidxP 6	MidxP 3

CB HOUNSLOW UNITED

Founded: 1989 Nickname:

Chairman: Frank James
Secretary: Stephen Hosmer
27 St Georges Road
Hanworth
Middlesex
TW13 6RD
Tel: 07988 783 019
Manager: Roy Wright
Prog Editor: As secretary

Ground: Osterley S.C., Tentelow Lane, Norwood Green UB2 4LW. Tel: 0208 574 7055
Capacity: 1000+ **Seats:** 100 **Covered:** Yes
Midweek Matchday: Tuesday **Clubhouse:** **Shop:**
Colours(change): All blue
Previous Names:
Previous Lges: Middlesex County League
Records:
Senior Honours:

10 YEAR RECORD

99-00	00-01	01-02	02-03	03-04	04-05	05-06	06-07	07-08	08-09
							CC1 12	CC1 10	CC1 10

DIVISION ONE 2009-10

CHOBHAM

Founded: 1905 Nickname:

Chairman: Phil Walker
Secretary: Debbie Bexon
153 Hawthorn Road
Woking
Surrey
GU22 0BQ
Tel: 07875 482 731
Manager:
Prog Editor: Nik Hammond

Ground: Chobham Rec. Ground, Station Rd, Chobham, Surrey GU24 8AZ. 01276 857 876
Capacity: 100+ **Seats:** **Covered:**
Midweek Matchday: Tuesday **Clubhouse:** **Shop:**
Colours(change): All blue & yellow.
Previous Names: Chobham & Ottershaw 1998-2004.
Previous Lges: Surrey Senior. London Spartan. Surrey County Premier.
Records:
Senior Honours: Surrey County Premier Champions 1994-95, 95-96, 98-99.

10 YEAR RECORD

99-00	00-01	01-02	02-03	03-04	04-05	05-06	06-07	07-08	08-09
SuCP 5	SuCS 5	SuCS 13	SuCS 14	CC1 16	CC1 14	CC1 15	CC1 15	CC1 11	CC1 18

COBHAM

Founded: 1892 Nickname: Hammers

Chairman: Mark Leonard
Secretary: Ken Reed
39 Lavina Way
East Preston
Littlehampton
BN16 1EF
Tel: 07834 361 724
Manager: Ken Reed
Prog Editor: Mark Leonard

Ground: Leg O'Mutton Field, Anvil Lane, Cobham KT11 1AA. Tel: 07787 383 407
Capacity: 2500 **Seats:** 112 **Covered:** 212
Midweek Matchday: Tuesday **Clubhouse:** Yes **Shop:** No
Colours(change): Red & black/black/red.
Previous Names: None
Previous Lges: Kingston & District. Surrey Senior.
Records: **Att:** 2000 - Charity game 1975.
Senior Honours: Combined Counties League Cup Winners 2001-02.

10 YEAR RECORD

99-00	00-01	01-02	02-03	03-04	04-05	05-06	06-07	07-08	08-09
CC 11	CC 14	CC 18	CC 21	CCP 18	CCP 18	CCP 15	CCP 14	CCP 21	CCP 22

COULSDON UNITED

Founded: 1968 Nickname: Tops

Chairman: Robert Eason
Secretary: Mrs Dorothy Eason
25 Ninehams Close
Caterham
Surrey
CR3 5LQ
Tel: 07876 328 954
Manager: Terry Russell
Prog Editor: As secretary

Ground: Netherne CASC, Woodplace Lane, Coulsdon, Surrey CR5 1NE. 01737 557 509
Capacity: 1500 **Seats:** No **Covered:** Yes
Midweek Matchday: Tuesday **Clubhouse:** **Shop:**
Colours(change): All red.
Previous Names: Reedham Park. Netherne. Coulsdon Town. Merged with Salfords 2007.
Previous Lges: Surrey County Premier.
Records:
Senior Honours: Surrey County Premier Champions 1993-94.

10 YEAR RECORD

99-00	00-01	01-02	02-03	03-04	04-05	05-06	06-07	07-08	08-09
SuCP 14	SuCS 11	SuCS 9	SuCS 8	CC1 15	CC1 15	CC1 17	CC1 21	CC1 19	CC1 17

CRESCENT ROVERS

Founded: 1947 Nickname:

Chairman: Michael Critchfield
Secretary: Michael Bishop
64 Wolsey Crescent
New Addington, Croydon
Surrey
CR0 0PF
Tel: 01689 842 996
Manager:
Prog Editor: As secretary

Ground: Wallington S.&S.C. 34 Mollison Drive, Wallington, SM6 9BY. Tel: 020 8647 2558
Capacity: **Seats:** No **Covered:** No
Midweek Matchday: Thursday **Clubhouse:** **Shop:**
Colours(change): Green, white & black/black/black.
Previous Names:
Previous Lges: Surrey County Premier.
Records:
Senior Honours:

10 YEAR RECORD

99-00	00-01	01-02	02-03	03-04	04-05	05-06	06-07	07-08	08-09
SuCP 7	SuCS 13	SuCS 10	SuCS 6	CC1 13	CC1 7	CC1 10	CC1 17	CC1 15	CC1 15

CROYDON MUNICIPAL

Founded: 2009 Nickname: The Lions

Chairman: Ben McCarthy
Secretary: Leander Cox
13 Montpelier Road
Purley
Surrey
CR8 2QE
Tel: 07775 760 317
Manager: Ben McCarthy
Prog Editor: Andrew Martyniuk

Ground: Croydon Arena, Albert Road, Croydon SE25 4QL.Tel: 0208 647 2558
Capacity: 6,000 **Seats:** 450 **Covered:** 1,000
Midweek Matchday: Wednesday **Clubhouse:** Yes **Shop:** Yes
Colours(change): Black & yellow/black/yellow.
Previous Names: None.
Previous Lges: None.
Records: None.
Senior Honours: None.

10 YEAR RECORD

99-00	00-01	01-02	02-03	03-04	04-05	05-06	06-07	07-08	08-09

EVERSLEY

Founded: 1910 Nickname: The Boars

Chairman: Daniel Nevitt
Secretary: Paul Latham
3 Worldham House
Twyford Close
Fleet
GU51 1JX
Tel: 07875 885 647
Manager: Gavin Banks
Prog Editor: Antony Ings

Ground: ESA Sports Grd, Fox Lane, Everlsey RG27 0NS. Tel: 0118 973 2400
Capacity: **Seats:** Yes **Covered:** Yes
Midweek Matchday: Tuesday **Clubhouse:** Yes **Shop:**
Colours(change): Yellow/royal blue/royal blue.
Previous Names:
Previous Lges: Surrey Elite Intermediate 2008-09.
Records:
Senior Honours: Surrey Elite Intermediate Champions 2008-09

10 YEAR RECORD

99-00	00-01	01-02	02-03	03-04	04-05	05-06	06-07	07-08	08-09
									SuIP 1

FARLEIGH ROVERS

Founded: 1922 Nickname: Foxes

Chairman: Richard Bates
Secretary: Brett Fewell
20 Courtlands Close
South Croydon
Surrey
CR2 0LR
Tel: 07882 413 376
Manager: Dave Willcocks
Prog Editor: Matthew Durgan

Ground: Parsonage Field, Harrow Road, Warlingham CR6 9EX. Tel: 01883 626 483
Capacity: 500 **Seats:** 16 **Covered:** Yes
Midweek Matchday: Tuesday **Clubhouse:** **Shop:**
Colours(change): Black & red/black/black
Previous Names:
Previous Lges: Surrey County Premier.
Records:
Senior Honours: Surrey County Premier Champions 1982-83.

10 YEAR RECORD

99-00	00-01	01-02	02-03	03-04	04-05	05-06	06-07	07-08	08-09
SuCP 16	SuCS 14	SuCS 8	SuCS 10	CC1 7	CC1 5	CC1 9	CC1 8	CC1 18	CC1 12

FARNHAM TOWN

Founded: 1906 Nickname: The Town

Chairman: Geoff Chapple
Secretary: Sandra Charlton
12 Sabre Court
Aldershot
Hants
GU11 1YY
Tel: 07789 593 157
Manager: Simon Bates
Prog Editor: Charlotte Bowditch

Ground: Memorial Ground, West Street, Farnham GU9 7DY. Tel: 01252 715 305
Capacity: 1500 **Seats:** 50 **Covered:** 50
Midweek Matchday: Tuesday **Clubhouse:** **Shop:**
Colours(change): Claret & sky blue/claret & sky blue/sky blue.
Previous Names:
Previous Lges: Surrey Senior. Spartan League. London Spartan. Isthmian.
Records:
Senior Honours: Combined Counties League Champions 1990-91, 91-92.
Combined Counties League Division One Champions 2006-07.

10 YEAR RECORD

99-00	00-01	01-02	02-03	03-04	04-05	05-06	06-07	07-08	08-09
CC 10	CC 20	CC 14	CC 22	CCP 22	CCP 21	CCP 21	CC1 1	CC1 5	CC1 8

DIVISION ONE

INS & OUTS

IN: Bedfont Sports (P – Middlesex County League Premier Division), Cobham (R), Croydon Municipal (N), Eversley (P – Surrey Elite Intermediate League), Hartley Wintney (R). OUT: Dorking (P), Hanworth Villa (P)

FELTHAM

Founded: 1946 Nickname: The Blues

Chairman: Brian Barry
Secretary: Peter Morris
35 Shaftesbury Avenue
Feltham
Middlesex
TW14 9LN
Tel: 07717 170 822
Manager: Darren Lake
Prog Editor: As secretary

Ground: Bedfont FC, The Orchard, Hatton Road, Bedfont TW14 9QT. Tel: 020 8890 7264
Capacity: 1,200 **Seats:** 100 **Covered:** 150
Midweek Matchday: Wednesday **Clubhouse:** Yes **Shop:** No
Colours(change): Blue & white/blue/blue.
Previous Names: Feltham & Hounslow Borough 1991-95.
Previous Lges: Spartan. Athenian. Isthmian.
Records: **Att:** 1,938 v Hampton - Middx Senior Cup 1972-73.
Goalscorer: Paul Clarke (125). **Apps:** Colin Ryder (363).
Senior Honours: Isthmian Division Two Champions 1980-81.

10 YEAR RECORD

99-00	00-01	01-02	02-03	03-04	04-05	05-06	06-07	07-08	08-09
CC 15	CC 9	CC 10	CC 4	CCP 13	CCP 17	CCP 20	CC1 9	CC1 13	CC1 7

FRIMLEY GREEN

Founded: 1919 Nickname: The Green

Chairman: Craig Fennell
Secretary: Mark O'Grady
8 Rokes Place
Yateley
Hants
GU46 6FF
Tel: 01252 879 883
Manager:
Prog Editor: As secretary

Ground: Frimley Green Rec. Gd, Frimley Grn, Camberley GU16 6SY. Tel: 01252 835 089
Capacity: 2,000 **Seats:** No **Covered:** Yes
Midweek Matchday: Tuesday **Clubhouse:** **Shop:**
Colours(change): Blue & white/blue/blue.
Previous Names:
Previous Lges: Surrey Senior. Sparton. Surrey County Premier.
Records: 1,152 v AFC Wimbledon 2002-03.
Senior Honours:

10 YEAR RECORD

99-00	00-01	01-02	02-03	03-04	04-05	05-06	06-07	07-08	08-09
SuCP 4	SuCS 6	SuCS 2	CC 20	CCP 20	CCP 15	CCP 18	CC1 13	CC1 6	CC1 16

HARTLEY WINTNEY

Founded: 1897 Nickname: The Row

Chairman: Luke Mullen
Secretary: Gerald Wykes
140a Middlemoor Road
Frimley, Camberley
Surrey
GU16 8DF
Tel: 07720 474 214
Manager: Peter Gray
Prog Editor: Steve Shimwell

Ground: Memorial Playing Flds,Green Lane, Hartley Wintney RG27 8DL.Tel: 01252 843586
Capacity: 2000 **Seats:** 113 **Covered:** Yes
Midweek Matchday: Tuesday **Clubhouse:** **Shop:**
Colours(change): Orange/black/black.
Previous Names: None.
Previous Lges: Surrey Senior League.
Records: **Att:** 1,392 v AFC Wimbledon , 25.01.02.
Senior Honours: Combined Counties League Champions 1982-83.

10 YEAR RECORD

99-00	00-01	01-02	02-03	03-04	04-05	05-06	06-07	07-08	08-09
CC 20	CC 17	CC 6	CC 11	CCP 15	CCP 23	CC1 5	CC1 16	CC1 3	CCP 21

KNAPHILL

Founded: 1924 Nickname: The Knappers

Chairman: Terry Chapman
Secretary: Bryan Freeman
40 Fordwater Road
Chertsey
Surrey
KT16 8HL
Tel: 07876 162 904
Manager: Bob Pritchard
Prog Editor: Dave Freeman

Ground: Brookwood Country Park, Redding Way, Knaphill GU21 2AY. Tel:
Capacity: 750 **Seats:** No **Covered:** 50
Midweek Matchday: Tuesday **Clubhouse:** Yes **Shop:**
Colours(change): Red/black/red.
Previous Names:
Previous Lges: Woking & District. Surrey Intermediate (Western).
Records: **Att:** 134 v Westfield 26.12.2007. **Goalscorer:** Matt Baker - 24.
Senior Honours: Woking & District League Champions 1980-81.
Surrey Intermediate League (Western) Champions 2006-07.

10 YEAR RECORD

99-00	00-01	01-02	02-03	03-04	04-05	05-06	06-07	07-08	08-09
						SuI1 1	SuIP 1	CC1 7	CC1 5

MOLE VALLEY SCR

Founded: 1978 Nickname: The Commers

Chairman: Alan Salmon
Secretary: Darren Salmon
229 Sutton Common Road
Sutton
Surrey
SM3 9PY
Tel: 07891 308 771
Manager: Darren Salmon
Prog Editor: Michael Bolton

Ground: River Lane Sports Grd, River Lane, Leatherhead KT22 0AU. Tel: 07757 980497
Capacity: 500 **Seats:** No **Covered:** Yes
Midweek Matchday: Tuesday **Clubhouse:** Yes **Shop:** Yes
Colours(change): Red/red/red.
Previous Names: Inrad FC. Centre 21 FC . SCR Plough, SCR Grapes, SRC Litten Tree, SCR Kingfisher
Previous Lges: South Eastern Combination.
Records:
Senior Honours:

10 YEAR RECORD

99-00	00-01	01-02	02-03	03-04	04-05	05-06	06-07	07-08	08-09
									CC1 4

SHEERWATER

Founded: 1958 Nickname: Sheers

Chairman: Douglas Mulcahy
Secretary: Trevor Wenden
14 Byrefield Road
Guildford
Surrey
GU2 9UH
Tel: 01483 838 578
Manager: John Comer
Prog Editor: As Secretary

Ground: Sheerwater Rec., Blackmore Crescent, Woking GU21 5QJ
Capacity: 1000 **Seats:** 67 **Covered:** 25
Midweek Matchday: Tuesday **Clubhouse:** **Shop:**
Colours(change): All royal blue.
Previous Names:
Previous Lges: Surrey Senior. Surrey County Premier.
Records:
Senior Honours:

10 YEAR RECORD

99-00	00-01	01-02	02-03	03-04	04-05	05-06	06-07	07-08	08-09
SuCP 14	SuCS 16	SuCS 14	SuCS 12	CC1 17	CC1 10	CC1 12	CC1 11	CC1 16	CC1 9

SOUTH PARK

Founded: 1897 Nickname:

Chairman: Colin Puplett
Secretary: Nick Thatcher
9 New North Road
South Park
Reigate
RH2 8LZ
Tel: 07817613674
Manager: Ricky Kidd
Prog Editor: As secretary

Ground: King George's Field, Whitehall Lane, South Park RH2 8LG. Tel: 01737 245 963
Capacity: 700 **Seats:** 100 **Covered:** Yes
Midweek Matchday: Wednesday **Clubhouse:** **Shop:**
Colours(change): All red.
Previous Names: South Park & Reigate Town 2001-03.
Previous Lges: Redhill & District. Crawley & District.
Records: **Att:** 230 v Warlingham, 10.08.2007.
Senior Honours:

10 YEAR RECORD

99-00	00-01	01-02	02-03	03-04	04-05	05-06	06-07	07-08	08-09
							CC1 7	CC1 12	CC1 14

STAINES LAMMAS

Founded: 1926 Nickname:

Chairman: Ciaron Taylor
Secretary: Bob Parry
18 Hurstdene Avenue
Staines
Middlesex
TW18 1JQ
Tel: 0174 453 886
Manager: Nathan Wharf
Prog Editor: Clive Robertson

Ground: Laleham Rec. , The Broadway, Laleham, Staines TW18 1RZ Tel: 01784 465204
Capacity: 255 **Seats:** No **Covered:** No
Midweek Matchday: Tuesday **Clubhouse:** Yes **Shop:**
Colours(change): All blue.
Previous Names:
Previous Lges: Middlesex County League. Surrey County Senior.
Records: **Att:** 107 v Hanworth Villa, January 2006. **Goalscorer:** Jay Coombs - 270+
Senior Honours: Combined Counties Division 1 Champions 2007-08, 08-09.

10 YEAR RECORD

99-00	00-01	01-02	02-03	03-04	04-05	05-06	06-07	07-08	08-09
			SuCS 11	CC1 8	CC1 8	CC1 11	CC1 5	CC1 1	CC1 1

WARLINGHAM

Founded: 1896 Nickname: Hammers

Chairman: Steve Rolfe
Secretary: Les Badcock
29 Verdayne Gardens
Warlingham
Surrey
CR6 9RP
Tel: 01883 372 918
Manager:
Prog Editor: As chairman

Ground: Merstham FC, Moathside Grd, Weldon Way, Merstham RH1 3QB. T: 01737 644 046
Capacity: 2,500 **Seats:** 174 **Covered:** 100
Midweek Matchday: Tuesday **Clubhouse:** Yes **Shop:** No
Colours(change): Black & white stripes/black/black
Previous Names:
Previous Lges: Surrey South Eastern Combination
Records:
Senior Honours: Combined Counties Division One Champions 2005-06.

10 YEAR RECORD

99-00	00-01	01-02	02-03	03-04	04-05	05-06	06-07	07-08	08-09
					CC1 4	CC1 1	CC1 4	CC1 8	CC1 11

WESTFIELD

Founded: 1953 Nickname: The Field

Chairman: Steven Perkins
Secretary: Michael Lawrence
19 Ash Road
Barnsbury Estate
Woking
GU22 0BJ
Tel: 01483 722 184
Manager: David Robson
Prog Editor: Pat Kelly

Ground: Woking Park, off Elmbridge Lane, Kingfield, Woking GU22 9AE. Tel: 01483771106
Capacity: 1,000 **Seats:** 175 **Covered:** Yes
Midweek Matchday: Tuesday **Clubhouse:** Yes **Shop:**
Colours(change): Yellow/black/black.
Previous Names:
Previous Lges: Surrey Senior.
Records:
Senior Honours: Surrey Senior Champions 1972-73, 73-74.

10 YEAR RECORD

99-00	00-01	01-02	02-03	03-04	04-05	05-06	06-07	07-08	08-09
CC 9	CC 6	CC 12	CC 13	CCP 19	CCP 10	CCP 11	CC1 10	CC1 4	CC1 13

WORCESTER PARK

Founded: 1921 Nickname: The Skinners

Chairman: Sam Glass
Secretary: Steve Holmes
32 Green Lane
Worcester Park
Surrey
KT4 8AL
Tel: 07956 591 212
Manager: Mark Chapman
Prog Editor: Alan Pearce

Ground: Skinners Field, Green Lane, Worcester Park, Surrey KT4 8AJ Tel: 0208 337 4995
Capacity: **Seats:** No **Covered:** Yes
Midweek Matchday: Tuesday **Clubhouse:** **Shop:**
Colours(change): All blue.
Previous Names:
Previous Lges: Surrey County Premier.
Records:
Senior Honours: Surrey County Premier/Senior League Champions 1999-00, 00-01.

10 YEAR RECORD

99-00	00-01	01-02	02-03	03-04	04-05	05-06	06-07	07-08	08-09
SuIP 1	SuCS 1	SuCS 6	SuCS 5	CC1 9	CC1 6	CC1 4	CC1 3	CC1 9	CC1 6

BEDFONT F.C. - Back Row (L-R): Daniel Butler (Coach), Stephen Coulras, Victor Osubu, Ray Walsh, Mick Turtle (Manager), Marc Ryan, Mark Philpot, Luke Craig. **Front:** Ben Payne, Jamie Todd, Steve Potter (Capt), Carlos Newton, Alex Headland. Photo: Arthur Evans.

EAST MIDLAND COUNTIES LEAGUE

Sponsored by:

No sponsor

Founded: 2008

Recent champions:

N/A

B & M FASCIA & SOFFITTS LEAGUE CUP

PRELIMINARY ROUND

Blackwell Miners Welfare 0 **Bardon Hill Sports** 1

Heanor Town 1 **Dunkirk** 2

FIRST ROUND

Borrowash Victoria 3 Ellistown 1

Dunkirk 5 Bardon Hill Sports 1

Gedling Miners Welfare 2 St Andrews SC 0

Gedling Town 4 Barrow Town 2

Hinckley Downes 2 Greenwood Meadows 0

Holbrook Miners Welfare 1 Holwell Sports 0

Kirby Muxloe SC 2 Ibstock United 1 *aet*

Radford 4 Graham Street Prims 3

QUARTER-FINALS

Dunkirk 1 **Borrowash Victoria** 3

Gedling Town 3 Hinckley Downes 2

Holbrook Miners Welfare 2 Gedling Miners Welfare 1 *aet*

Kirby Muxloe SC 7 Radford 0

SEMI-FINALS

Borrowash Victoria 2 Gedling Town 1 *aet* *(at Radford)*

Holbrook Miners Welfare 1 Kirby Muxloe SC 0 *(at Borrowash Victoria)*

FINAL

(May 6th at Holwell Sports)

Borrowash Victoria 1 Holbrook Miners Welfare 0

Premier Division	P	W	D	L	F	A	Pts
Kirby Muxloe SC	34	23	6	5	83	38	75
Borrowash Victoria	34	21	9	4	80	37	72
Holbrook Miners Welfare	34	20	9	5	68	29	69
Gedling Town	34	20	7	7	84	49	67
Dunkirk	34	18	7	9	59	38	61
Barrow Town	34	18	4	12	67	58	58
Holwell Sports	34	17	6	11	68	42	57
Gedling Miners Welfare	34	15	4	15	55	60	49
St Andrews SC	34	13	6	15	64	64	45
Hinckley Downes	34	14	2	18	54	57	44
Greenwood Meadows	34	11	9	14	47	61	42
Heanor Town	34	12	4	18	53	63	40
Graham Street Prims	34	11	6	17	58	72	39
Radford	34	9	7	18	47	79	34
Ibstock United	34	8	9	17	34	61	33
Ellistown	34	8	8	18	57	72	32
Bardon Hill Sports	34	9	5	20	48	76	32
Blackwell Miners Welfare	34	3	4	27	20	90	13

	Bardon Hill Spts	Barrow Town	Blackwell MW	Borrowash Vics	Dunkirk	Ellistown	Gedling MW	Gedling Town	Graham St P.	Greenwood M.	Heanor Town	Hinck. Downes	Holbrook MW	Holwell Sports	Ibstock Utd	Kirby Muxloe SC	Radford	St Andrews SC
Bardon Hill Sports		3-3	3-1	2-4	0-2	4-0	1-1	1-4	3-2	4-3	3-1	0-2	1-1	1-0	2-0	0-3	2-3	2-3
Barrow Town	3-0		5-0	2-3	1-1	3-1	0-3	0-6	1-4	1-2	2-2	5-1	0-2	3-0	1-0	4-2	4-2	0-2
Blackwell Miners Welfare	2-1	1-4		0-2	0-2	5-4	0-1	0-4	0-3	0-2	0-3	0-2	0-3	0-3	1-5	2-2	0-3	2-1
Borrowash Victoria	4-0	3-3	3-1		1-1	3-1	2-0	5-0	0-0	7-0	2-1	3-1	1-1	1-0	1-0	0-1	2-2	2-1
Dunkirk	2-1	3-1	2-0	1-2		3-0	0-3	0-0	4-1	2-2	2-1	3-0	1-2	1-1	2-0	1-2	1-1	0-2
Ellistown	4-0	1-2	6-0	2-2	0-1		1-2	1-3	5-1	1-1	5-2	0-2	0-4	1-3	5-1	2-2	1-1	2-1
Gedling Miners Welfare	4-1	0-1	3-1	1-4	0-1	0-0		0-1	1-5	3-2	1-0	2-0	0-3	1-3	5-2	0-4	3-1	3-5
Gedling Town	2-1	0-1	1-1	1-2	3-3	0-2	3-0		5-3	3-0	6-1	3-2	0-3	1-1	4-0	4-3	4-3	6-2
Graham Street Prims	4-1	3-1	1-0	1-5	1-4	1-0	2-1	0-3		0-1	2-1	0-2	0-3	0-4	1-1	1-3	3-3	4-0
Greenwood Meadows	2-0	0-2	2-0	2-2	2-1	3-3	1-2	1-1	2-5		4-2	0-1	1-3	3-3	0-0	0-3	3-0	0-0
Heanor Town	1-3	2-0	3-0	2-0	3-0	1-0	1-2	1-1	2-2	0-2		3-2	1-0	1-0	0-1	1-2	3-4	1-2
Hinckley Downes	1-1	0-2	2-1	1-5	1-2	4-1	1-4	1-2	2-1	3-1	2-1		2-1	1-2	1-2	1-3	5-0	4-0
Holbrook Miners Welfare	4-1	0-4	0-0	2-2	2-0	4-2	2-1	1-2	1-1	5-2	2-2	2-1		2-1	1-1	0-0	6-0	1-1
Holwell Sports	2-0	4-1	4-0	2-2	0-2	5-1	4-2	2-0	4-3	0-1	1-2	3-1	0-1		3-1	2-2	3-0	2-2
Ibstock United	0-0	0-2	1-0	3-2	1-5	1-1	1-1	1-1	1-0	0-0	1-3	0-3	0-1	2-1		1-2	2-2	3-2
Kirby Muxloe SC	3-2	4-0	3-1	1-0	3-0	4-0	3-3	2-3	4-0	3-1	4-2	1-0	0-2	2-0	3-0		5-1	1-1
Radford	3-1	2-3	1-1	0-1	1-4	0-1	3-0	0-4	1-1	0-1	1-2	3-2	1-0	0-2	2-1	2-0		0-3
St Andrews SC	2-3	1-2	5-0	1-2	0-2	3-3	1-2	5-3	3-2	1-0	4-1	0-0	0-3	1-3	3-1	1-3	5-1	

INS & OUTS

IN: Anstey Nomads (P – Leicestershire Senior League Premier Division), Gresley (formerly Gresley Rovers) (R – Northern Premier League Division One South), Radcliffe Olympic (P – Central Midlands League Supreme Division). OUT: Kirkby Muxloe SC (P – Midland Alliance)

2009-10 CONSTITUTION

ANSTEY NOMADS
Secretary: Chris Hillebrandt. 22 The Leys, Kibworth, Leicestershire LE8 0NZ. Tel: 0794 685 6430.
Ground: Cropston Road, Anstey, Leicester LE7 7BP. Tel: 0116 236 4868
Colours: Red & white stripes/black/red.
Alternative: All white.

BARDON HILL SPORTS
Secretary: Adrian Bishop. 20 St Christopher's Rd, Ellistown, Coalville, Leicester LE67 1FE. Tel: 07999 879841
Ground: Bardon Close, Colville, Leicester LE67 4BS. Tel: 01530 815 569
Colours: White/royal blue/royal blue.
Alternative: All orange.

BARROW TOWN
Secretary: Alan Dawkins. 72 Beaumont Road, Barrow upon Soar LE12 8PJ. Tel: 07709 296 089.
Ground: Riverside Park, Bridge Street, Barrow Road, Quorn, Leicestershire LE12 8EN. Tel: 01509 620 650.
Colours: Red/black or red/black.
Alternative: Yellow/blue/blue.

BLACKWELL MINERS WELFARE
Secretary: Steve Harris. 6 Pennine Close, Newton, Alfreton DE55 5UD. Tel: 07505 366 136.
Ground: Primrose Hill Sports Ground, Primrose Hill, Blackwell, Alfreton DE55 5JF. Tel: 01773 811 295.
Colours: Red & white stripes/red/red.
Alternative: Purple/black/purple.

BORROWASH VICTORIA
Secretary: Ian Collins. 30 Margreave Road, Chaddesden, Derby DE21 6JD. Tel: 07733 055 212.
Ground: Robinsons Constructions Bowl, Borrowash Road, Spondon, Derby DE21 7PH. Tel: 01332 669688
Colours: Red & white stripes/black/black.
Alternative: All blue.

DUNKIRK
Secretary: Steve Throssell. 24 Kingfisher Wharfe, Castle Marina NG9 5LD. Tel: 07903 322 446.
Ground: Ron Steel Sports Ground, Trentside Lane, Old Lenton Lane, Clifton Bridge, Nottingham NG7 2SA
Tel: 0115 985 0803
Colours: Red/black/black. **Alternative:** All white.

ELLISTOWN
Secretary: Sue Matthews. 21 Federation Street, Enderby, Leicester LE19 4NP. Tel: 0116 286 5328.
Ground: 1 Terrace Road, Ellistown, Leicestershire LE67 1GD. Tel: 01530 230 159.
Colours: Yellow/royal blue/yellow.
Alternative: White/black/white.

GEDLING MINERS WELFARE
Secretary: Norman Hay. 182 Gedling Rd, Arnold, NG5 6NY. Tel: 07748 138 732.
Ground: Plains Social Club, Plains Road, Mapperley, Nottingham NG3 5RH. Tel: 0115 926 6300.
Colours: Yellow/blue/yellow. **Alternative:** All white.

GEDLING TOWN
Secretary: Graham Peck. 128 Granson Way, Washingborough, Lincoln LN4 1HF. Tel: 07815 458196
Ground: Riverside Stadium, Stoke Lane, Stoke Bardolf, Nottingham. Tel: 0115 940 2145.
Colours: Yellow/blue/yellow.
Alternative: Red & white/white/white.

GRAHAM ST PRIMS
Secretary: David Tice. Nothbank Cottage, Church Lane, Swarkstone DE73 7GT. Tel: 01332 704 064.
Ground: Asterdale Sports Ground, Borrowash Road, Spondon, Derbyshire DE21 7PH. Tel: 01332 704064
Colours: Red & white stripes/black/black.
Alternative: White/red/red.

GREENWOOD MEADOWS
Secretary: Mark Burton. 22 Staveley Way, Gamsron, NG2 6QR. Tel: 07712 530 706.
Ground: Lenton Lane Ground, Lenton Lane, Nr Clifton Bridge, NG7 2SA. Tel: 07712 530 706.
Colours: Green/black/black.
Alternative: Yellow/green/yellow.

GRESLEY (FORMERLY GRESLEY ROVERS)
Secretary: Reg Shorthouse. 95 Darklands Rd, Swadlincote DE11 0PQ. Tel: 07779 049 847.
Ground: The Moat Ground, Moat Street, Church Gresley DE11 0PQ. Tel: 01283 216 315.
Colours: Red/white/red. **Alternative:** White/red/white.

HEANOR TOWN
Secretary: Keith Costello. 45 Stainsby Ave, Heanor DE75 7EL. Tel: 07792 691 843.
Ground: The Town Ground, Mayfield Avenue, Heanor, Derbyshire DE75 7EN. Tel: 01773 713 742.
Colours: White/black/black.
Alternative: Red/white/white.

HINCKLEY DOWNES
Secretary: Ray Baggott. Tel: 01455 840 088.
Ground: The Greene King Stadium, Leicester Road, Hinckley, Leicestershire LE10 3DR. Tel: 01455 840088
Colours: Blue/blue/white.
Alternative: Yellow/black/black.

HOLBROOK MINERS WELFARE
Secretary: Chris Sadler. 16 Cornfield Ave, Broadmeadows, Sth Normanton DE55 3NN. Tel: 07813 680 458.
Ground: The Welfare Ground (Holbrook), Shaw Lane, Holbrook, Derbyshire DE56 0TG. Tel: 07966 792 011
Colours: All royal blue. **Alternative:** All white.

HOLWELL SPORTS
Secretary: Graham Parker. 1 Chapel Close, Melton Mowbray LE14 3HW. Tel: 07761 495 210.
Ground: Welby Road, Asfordby Hill, Melton Mowbray, Leicestershire LE14 3RD. Tel: 07523 427 450.
Colours: Yellow/green/yellow.
Alternative: Sky blue/black/black.

IBSTOCK UNITED
Secretary: Arthur Lakin. 43 Station Rd, Ibstock, LE67 6JL. Tel: 07515 752 772.
Ground: The Welfare Ground (Ibstock), Leicester Road, Ibstock, Leicestershire LE67 6HN. Tel: 01974 657 701.
Colours: Red & white/red/red.
Alternative: Blue/white/white.

RADCLIFFE OLYMPIC
Secretary: Michael Bradley. 148 Ring Leas, Cotgrave NG12 3NH. Tel: 07825 285 024.
Ground: The Recreation Ground, Wharfe Lane, Radcliffe on Trent NG12 2AN. Tel: 07825 285 024.
Colours: Navy blue & red/navy & red/navy.
Alternative: Red & black/black/red.

RADFORD
Secretary: Kirsty Lowe. 12 Kelfield Close, Old Basford, NG6 0EX. Tel: 07967 040 949.
Ground: Selhurst Street, Off Radford Road, Nottingham NG7 5EH. Tel: 0115 942 3250.
Colours: All claret. **Alternative:** All light blue.

ST ANDREWS
Secretary: Les Botting. 2 Neston Rd, Saffron Lane, Leicester LE2 6RD. Tel: 07793 500 937.
Ground: Canal Street, Aylestone, Leicester LE2 8LA. Tel: 0116 283 9298.
Colours: Black & white stripes/black/black.
Alternative: All blue.

EASTERN COUNTIES LEAGUE

www.ridgeonsleague.co.uk

Sponsored by: Ridgeons

Founded: 1935

Recent champions:
2004: AFC Sudbury
2005: AFC Sudbury
2006: Lowestoft Town
2007: Wroxham
2008: Soham Town Rangers

Premier Division	P	W	D	L	F	A	Pts
owestoft Town	40	32	4	4	114	46	100
RC	40	26	5	9	86	54	83
eedham Market	40	26	3	11	94	64	81
ereham Town	40	25	4	11	108	67	79
roxham	40	24	6	10	86	52	78
irkley & Pakefield	40	23	7	10	78	44	76
eiston	40	22	9	9	90	41	75
iptree United	40	20	5	15	90	72	65
tanway Rovers	40	19	7	14	81	65	64
alsham-le-Willows	40	15	9	16	60	62	54
ildenhall Town	40	16	5	19	75	81	53
elixstowe & Walton	40	16	1	23	75	110	49
iston Res.	40	14	6	20	77	88	48
ly City	40	12	6	22	59	82	42
ing's Lynn Res.	40	11	8	21	57	81	41
isbech Town	40	11	6	23	59	82	39
ivenhoe Town	40	12	2	26	65	105	38
oodbridge Town	40	9	10	21	52	77	37
orwich United	40	8	10	22	46	74	34
arwich & Parkeston	40	9	6	25	47	98	33
averhill Rovers	40	7	7	26	42	96	28

Whitton United - record expunged

LEAGUE CUP

PRELIMINARY ROUND
FC Clacton 3 Whitton United 2
Harwich & Parkeston 2 Ipswich Wanderers 1
Haverhill Rovers 3 Long Melford 0
King's Lynn Res. 1 **Norwich United** 4
Kirkley 4 Gorleston 1, **Lowestoft Town** 4 Diss Town 1
Mildenhall Town 3 Godmanchester Rovers 2 *aet*
Saffron Walden Town 2 Cornard United 0
Tiptree United 0 **Felixstowe & Walton United** 2
Wisbech Town 1 **March Town United** 3 *aet (at March)*

FIRST ROUND
CRC 3 Mildenhall 2, **Dereham Town** 3 Fakenham Town 1 *aet*
FC Clacton 3 Felixstowe & Walton United 2
Gt Yarmouth 3 **Debenham Leisure Centre** 6 *aet*
Halstead Town 1 Ely City 1 *aet* (5-4p)
Harwich & Parkeston 0 **Woodbridge Town** 1
Haverhill Rovers 0 **Saffron Walden Town** 1 *aet*
Histon Res. 6 Newmarket 2, Lowestoft Town 0 **Leiston** 2
March 0 **Wroxham** 3, Needham Market 0 **Stowmarket** 1
Stanway 1 Hadleigh 0, Swaffham 1 **Norwich United** 3 *aet*
Thetford Town 4 Downham Town 0
Walsham-le-Willows 0 **Kirkley & Pakefield** 1
Wivenhoe Town 7 Brantham Athletic 0

SECOND ROUND
Dereham Town 3 Debenham Leisure Centre 1
FC Clacton 3 **Halstead Town** 4
Kirkley & Pakefield 1 **Leiston** 1 *aet* (3-4p)
Saffron Walden Town 0 **CRC** 1 *aet*
Thetford Town 1 **Stowmarket Town** 2
Wivenhoe Town 0 **Histon Res.** 6
Woodbridge Town 0 **Stanway Rovers** 5
Wroxham 2 Norwich United 2 *aet* (5-4p)

QUARTER-FINALS
Halstead Town 0 **Leiston** 1
Stanway Rovers 4 Dereham Town 2
Stowmarket Town 1 **CRC** 4
Wroxham 2 **Histon Res.** 3

SEMI-FINALS
CRC 1 **Stanway Rovers** 4, **Leiston** 6 Histon Res. 4

FINAL *(May 4th at Diss Town)*
Stanway Rovers 2 Leiston 2 *aet* (4-2p)

	CRC	Der.	Ely	Fel.	Har.	Hav.	His.	KL	Kir.	Leis.	Low.	Mild.	Nee.	Nor.	Stan.	Tip.	Wal.	Whi.	Wis.	Wiv.	Woo.	Wro.
CRC		5-3	4-2	0-1	4-0	4-0	2-0	2-2	2-1	3-0	3-0	0-2	3-2	1-0	2-1	1-0	0-0	n/a	2-2	4-1	3-0	1-2
Dereham Town	4-0		5-2	4-3	6-1	3-0	3-0	1-2	2-1	0-3	1-2	3-2	2-2	6-3	1-2	3-0	3-1	n/a	1-4	5-1	0-0	1-1
Ely City	0-1	2-1		1-2	1-1	1-0	1-2	3-1	1-2	1-0	0-2	2-4	3-1	3-2	1-2	2-0	1-1	0-3	2-3	1-2	2-0	2-3
Felixstowe & Walton Utd	2-1	0-5	6-2	***P***	3-0	2-2	1-4	0-2	1-3	0-5	2-3	3-1	2-4	1-0	2-1	3-4	1-0	n/a	5-3	0-3	0-1	1-4
Harwich & Parkeston	0-3	0-4	1-1	1-3	***R***	3-2	1-0	4-2	2-3	1-3	2-2	3-0	2-2	0-2	1-5	1-1	1-1	0-6	0-1	3-2	1-0	0-1
Haverhill Rovers	4-5	0-1	4-2	2-1	2-0	***E***	3-2	2-1	0-3	0-2	1-6	1-4	0-3	3-0	1-3	1-1	0-2	3-3	0-3	1-3	3-1	1-3
Histon Res.	1-2	4-2	1-5	6-2	5-1	2-2	***M***	3-2	0-1	2-3	1-4	4-0	1-4	1-3	3-3	2-3	2-2	2-2	1-0	4-0	3-1	1-1
King's Lynn Res.	0-1	1-3	1-2	1-2	3-1	1-0	2-2	***I***	1-2	0-0	1-2	1-3	0-3	2-2	1-4	4-3	2-0	7-2	4-0	3-0	2-0	4-5
Kirkley & Pakefield	1-3	3-3	2-2	3-2	1-2	6-0	2-2	0-0	***E***	0-0	2-0	2-1	1-0	3-0	1-1	3-2	1-0	n/a	2-1	3-1	5-0	4-0
Leiston	1-3	0-1	0-0	6-0	7-0	4-0	3-0	2-0	1-0	***R***	3-1	3-3	5-1	1-1	3-3	3-3	2-4	5-0	1-0	2-0	1-1	0-2
Lowestoft Town	4-2	3-1	2-0	5-2	3-1	1-1	4-0	5-0	2-1	2-1		4-0	5-1	5-0	3-4	2-0	6-2	n/a	4-1	2-1	3-2	3-2
Mildenhall Town	1-2	2-4	2-1	1-2	4-2	2-0	0-4	3-2	0-0	1-5	1-3	***D***	1-3	1-2	2-3	2-1	1-2	8-2	3-1	6-1	2-2	3-1
Needham Market	0-3	2-1	4-3	4-3	3-1	4-1	4-1	2-0	1-2	1-0	0-5	2-1	***I***	3-1	4-3	2-1	5-2	4-1	2-0	4-0	3-0	2-2
Norwich United	1-2	0-2	3-1	3-0	2-1	0-0	0-2	0-0	2-0	1-2	0-1	1-1	1-2	***V***	0-2	2-3	2-2	n/a	1-2	1-3	0-0	0-1
Stanway Rovers	2-3	3-4	3-0	3-5	4-0	2-0	2-1	3-3	2-0	1-1	0-1	1-2	0-2	2-1	***I***	0-2	2-0	4-4	3-2	2-2	1-0	3-1
Tiptree United	2-4	0-2	5-1	7-2	3-2	3-2	6-2	3-1	1-2	1-5	2-3	3-2	3-4	2-2	3-2	***S***	1-0	n/a	2-1	2-1	5-0	3-1
Walsham-le-Willows	2-1	2-3	0-1	4-1	5-2	5-0	5-1	0-0	2-1	1-0	0-0	2-2	1-0	0-1	1-0	0-2	***I***	3-1	2-2	1-2	2-1	0-1
Whitton United	n/a	0-4	4-0	0-2	0-3	n/a	n/a	n/a	1-1	0-7	n/a	0-6	n/a	1-2	4-2	1-3	2-2	***O***	n/a	5-1	0-4	n/a
Wisbech Town	2-1	2-6	6-1	4-1	0-3	0-0	0-2	1-2	1-5	0-1	1-3	0-4	1-3	1-1	1-0	0-1	2-3	1-1	***N***	3-0	2-2	1-4
Wivenhoe Town	5-0	2-5	0-2	2-3	0-1	1-1	2-3	5-1	2-5	0-5	2-5	1-2	0-4	5-2	4-1	0-5	3-0	10-0	2-1		3-1	1-4
Woodbridge Town	2-2	2-3	0-0	2-3	3-1	3-1	3-2	1-2	1-0	2-3	1-1	4-1	2-1	2-2	1-2	1-1	0-2	n/a	1-3	4-2		3-0
Wroxham	1-1	4-0	3-1	3-2	1-0	3-1	3-0	6-0	0-1	1-3	1-2	0-2	1-0	5-1	0-0	1-0	6-1	n/a	1-1	3-0	4-2	

Division One	P	W	D	L	F	A	Pts
Newmarket Town	**38**	**29**	**4**	**5**	**85**	**29**	**91**
Hadleigh United	**38**	**26**	**4**	**8**	**79**	**40**	**82**
Debenham Leisure Centre	**38**	**25**	**3**	**10**	**91**	**36**	**78**
Halstead Town	**38**	**23**	**9**	**6**	**97**	**47**	**78**
Great Yarmouth Town	**38**	**22**	**7**	**9**	**79**	**46**	**73**
Gorleston	**38**	**21**	**8**	**9**	**87**	**59**	**71**
FC Clacton	**38**	**22**	**4**	**12**	**97**	**58**	**70**
Brantham Athletic	**38**	**20**	**6**	**12**	**81**	**57**	**66**
Diss Town	**38**	**17**	**8**	**13**	**78**	**63**	**59**
Godmanchester Rovers	**38**	**15**	**7**	**16**	**58**	**57**	**52**
Cornard United	**38**	**14**	**8**	**16**	**62**	**63**	**50**
Stowmarket Town	**38**	**13**	**11**	**14**	**52**	**67**	**50**
March Town United	**38**	**13**	**6**	**19**	**62**	**74**	**45**
Saffron Walden Town	**38**	**10**	**14**	**14**	**48**	**51**	**44**
Downham Town	**38**	**9**	**7**	**22**	**48**	**95**	**34**
Thetford Town	**38**	**9**	**6**	**23**	**55**	**84**	**33**
Ipswich Wanderers	**38**	**7**	**8**	**23**	**57**	**84**	**29**
Swaffham Town	**38**	**7**	**6**	**25**	**38**	**102**	**27**
Long Melford	**38**	**6**	**5**	**27**	**33**	**104**	**23**
Fakenham Town	**38**	**4**	**5**	**29**	**39**	**110**	**17**

DIVISION ONE CUP

PRELIMINARY ROUND

Diss Town 3 Great Yarmouth Town 0
Fakenham Town 0 **March Town United** 1
FC Clacton 0 Ipswich Wanderers 1
(Ipswich Wanderers expelled)
Saffron Walden Town 2 Godmanchester 2 *aet* (4-2p)

FIRST ROUND

Debenham Leisure Centre 3 Gorleston 0
Hadleigh United 2 Brantham Athletic 0
Halstead Town 2 **FC Clacton** 3
Long Melford 2 Saffron Walden Town 0
Newmarket Town 2 Cornard United 1
Stowmarket Town 0 **Diss Town** 3
Swaffham Town 2 **March Town United** 4
Thetford Town 1 **Downham Town** 2

QUARTER-FINALS

Debenham Leisure Centre 3 Downham Town 1
Diss Town 3 Long Melford 0
March Town United 0 **Hadleigh United** 6
Newmarket Town 1 FC Clacton 0

SEMI-FINALS

Diss Town 1 Debenham Leisure Centre 1 *aet* (3-1p)
Hadleigh United 2 Newmarket Town 0

FINAL

(April 22nd at Woodbridge Town)
Diss Town 1 Hadleigh United 0

Reserve Division North		P	W	D	L	F	A	Pts
Lowestoft Town Res.		26	24	2	0	110	26	74
Walsham-le-Willows Res.		26	18	3	5	75	35	57
Gorleston Res.	*-1*	26	17	2	7	78	42	52
Woodbridge Town Res.		26	13	6	7	66	51	45
Dereham Town Res.		25	13	5	7	61	38	44
Felixstowe & Walton Res.		26	11	5	10	56	50	38
Debenham LC Res.		25	10	6	9	45	47	36
Needham Market Res.		26	11	2	13	53	61	35
Thetford Town Res.		26	11	1	14	53	71	34
Ipswich Wanderers Res.		26	9	4	13	62	69	31
Diss Town Res.		26	6	7	13	38	50	25
Whitton United Res.		26	6	3	17	44	71	21
Stowmarket Town Res.		26	4	3	19	28	77	15
Leiston Res.		26	2	3	21	20	101	9

Dereham Town Res. v Debenham LC Res. - not played

Reserve Division South	P	W	D	L	F	A	Pts
Haverhill Rovers Res.	26	18	2	6	79	45	56
Maldon Town Res.	26	15	5	6	83	48	50
Tiptree United Res.	26	14	6	6	71	39	48
Brantham Athletic Res.	26	13	4	9	51	48	43
Braintree Town Res.	26	13	3	10	67	49	42
AFC Sudbury Res.	26	12	4	10	58	46	40
Stanway Rovers Res.	26	11	5	10	53	49	38
FC Clacton Res.	26	11	5	10	54	61	38
Halstead Town Res.	26	11	4	11	46	44	37
Hadleigh United Res.	26	11	2	13	69	72	35
Witham Town Res.	26	10	3	13	61	67	33
Long Melford Res.	26	8	6	12	39	53	30
Harwich & Parkeston Res.	26	6	6	14	49	69	24
Cornard United Res.	26	1	1	24	25	115	4

RESERVES CHAMPIONSHIP

(May 9th at Diss Town)
Lowestoft Town Res. 2 Haverhill Rovers Res. 1

CHELL TROPHY

FINAL *(April 29th at Hadleigh United)*
AFC Sudbury Res. 0 Tiptree Utd Res. 0 *aet* (4-2p)

	Bran.	Corn.	Deb.	Diss	Down.	FC Cl.	Fak.	God.	Gor.	GtY	Had.	Hal.	Ips.	Lg M.	Mar.	New.	Saf.	Stow.	Swa.	Thet.
Brantham Athletic		1-1	1-2	0-1	5-1	4-2	4-1	4-4	2-3	0-1	1-0	0-2	2-0	3-0	2-1	0-4	2-2	0-0	6-0	6-1
Cornard United	4-1		1-2	1-4	5-1	0-2	6-1	2-1	1-4	0-4	0-1	1-2	0-4	2-1	0-0	1-5	3-1	2-2	5-0	1-1
Debenham Leisure Centre	1-2	1-0		2-3	6-0	4-0	4-0	3-0	5-1	0-1	1-0	3-3	2-2	2-0	4-0	2-0	0-1	7-1	2-0	2-0
Diss Town	1-1	1-2	0-4		4-1	6-2	3-0	1-0	1-1	3-4	0-3	3-2	2-1	2-1	1-1	1-3	1-1	1-2	2-0	3-1
Downham Town	1-2	2-1	0-2	2-1	***D***	1-3	2-0	0-3	1-1	0-5	2-2	1-3	2-1	1-1	4-2	1-4	1-1	2-1	4-2	2-2
FC Clacton	3-4	3-1	3-0	3-3	3-1	***I***	1-1	1-0	7-0	4-1	3-2	4-1	3-0	7-0	1-3	1-2	1-1	5-1	2-0	2-1
Fakenham Town	2-9	0-2	0-2	1-4	2-4	0-7	***V***	2-0	1-2	0-2	1-2	0-1	6-3	4-0	1-1	0-1	0-4	1-1	0-2	3-2
Godmanchester Rovers	0-2	1-0	1-2	1-2	3-3	4-2	7-2	***I***	1-4	0-2	2-1	1-2	2-1	1-0	3-0	0-1	1-0	0-1	2-2	0-1
Gorleston	3-1	4-1	0-0	3-1	3-1	0-2	4-0	1-1	***S***	2-5	4-1	2-2	3-2	2-1	1-1	0-1	5-1	4-0	7-0	3-1
Great Yarmouth Town	4-0	0-0	3-0	1-1	1-2	1-0	2-1	1-1	0-1	***I***	1-2	1-1	3-1	5-1	4-1	0-3	0-0	0-0	2-1	2-1
Hadleigh United	2-1	0-0	4-3	3-1	2-0	4-2	2-0	4-0	4-0	2-1	***O***	1-1	0-3	6-1	1-0	2-3	1-0	3-3	3-1	3-1
Halstead Town	3-0	2-2	2-1	2-1	3-0	3-0	9-0	3-0	2-2	7-1	0-3	***N***	2-1	2-0	3-0	0-3	2-1	0-1	3-1	4-1
Ipswich Wanderers	1-3	2-6	2-1	2-5	2-2	1-1	2-2	2-2	0-1	0-4	0-1	1-7		1-0	1-2	0-2	4-0	1-1	0-1	4-0
Long Melford	0-3	1-1	0-5	0-3	2-1	4-2	2-1	0-3	1-4	0-5	0-3	0-2	2-2	***O***	1-4	1-4	2-1	2-5	0-0	2-1
March Town United	2-2	0-1	0-7	1-1	4-0	1-2	2-1	1-2	2-3	4-2	1-2	2-6	3-1	2-4	***N***	1-0	1-2	5-0	2-0	2-1
Newmarket Town	1-2	3-2	4-0	2-0	1-0	2-1	3-1	1-2	1-0	4-0	1-0	1-3	1-1	4-0	5-3	***E***	1-1	2-1	6-0	3-1
Saffron Walden Town	0-1	0-1	1-3	2-2	4-0	0-3	2-1	0-0	2-1	0-1	1-2	2-2	2-0	1-0	3-1	0-0		1-1	4-0	2-2
Stowmarket Town	2-1	2-0	0-1	3-2	3-1	0-1	2-0	1-2	3-2	0-3	0-1	3-3	2-5	1-1	2-1	0-1	1-1		2-2	2-0
Swaffham Town	0-1	2-4	0-2	0-4	2-1	1-3	2-2	2-4	2-2	1-4	0-4	3-2	2-1	3-1	0-1	1-2	2-2	2-0		0-3
Thetford Town	1-2	1-2	0-3	4-3	3-0	0-5	2-1	0-3	1-4	2-2	1-2	0-0	4-2	5-1	0-4	0-0	2-1	1-2	7-1	

CRC

Founded: Nickname:

Chairman: Brian Attmore
Secretary: Wayne Purser
The Trade Recruitment Stadium
Newmarket Road
Cambridge
CB5 8LN
Tel: 01223 729 203
Manager: Jez George
Prog Editor: Henry Millward

Ground: Newmarket Road, Cambridge CB5 8LN Tel: 01223 566 500
Capacity: 9,217 **Seats:** 200 **Covered:** Yes
Midweek Matchday: Wednesday **Clubhouse:** **Shop:** Yes
Colours(change): Amber & black/amber & black/amber. (All sky blue)
Previous Names: None.
Previous Lges:
Records:
Senior Honours:

10 YEAR RECORD

99-00	00-01	01-02	02-03	03-04	04-05	05-06	06-07	07-08	08-09
							ECP 17	ECP 13	ECP 2

DEBENHAM LC

Founded: Nickname:

Chairman: Stephen Anderson
Secretary: David Marshall
Debenham Leisure Centre
Gracechurch Street
Debeham
IP14 6BL
Tel: 01728 861 101
Manager: Mel Aldis
Prog Editor: As for Manager

Ground: Debenham Leisure C., Gracechurch St, Debenham IP14 6BL. Tel: 01728 861 101
Capacity: 1,000 **Seats:** 114 **Covered:** 114
Midweek Matchday: Tuesday **Clubhouse:** Yes **Shop:** No
Colours(change): Yellow/black/yellow. (All blue).
Previous Names: AFC Debenham.
Previous Lges: Suffolk & Ipswich.
Records: **Att:** 400. **Goalscorer:** Lee Briggs. **Apps:** Steve Nelson.
Senior Honours:

10 YEAR RECORD

99-00	00-01	01-02	02-03	03-04	04-05	05-06	06-07	07-08	08-09
		S&I 1 3			S&I S 2	EC1 10	EC1 5	EC1 9	EC1 3

DEREHAM TOWN

Founded: 1884 Nickname: Magpies

Chairman: Simon Barnes
Secretary: Ray Bayles
62 Church View Close
Sprowston
Norwich
NR7 8QA
Tel: 01603 789 905
Manager: Matt Henman
Prog Editor: Barnes Print

Ground: Aldiss Park, Norwich Road, Dereham, Norfolk NR20 3AL. Tel: 01362 690 460
Capacity: 3,000 **Seats:** 50 **Covered:** 500
Midweek Matchday: Tuesday **Clubhouse:** Yes **Shop:** Yes
Colours(change): White & black/black/black. (All green)
Previous Names: Dereham and Dereham Hobbies.
Previous Lges: Norwich District. Dereham & District. Norfolk & Suffolk. Anglian Comb.
Records: **Att:** 3000 v Norwich City, Friendly, 07/2001.
Senior Honours: Anglian Combination Div.1 Champions 1989-90. Premier 97-98. Norfolk Senior Cup 2005-06, 06-07.

10 YEAR RECORD

99-00	00-01	01-02	02-03	03-04	04-05	05-06	06-07	07-08	08-09
EC1 7	EC1 2	ECP 13	ECP 19	ECP 18	ECP 15	ECP 12	ECP 6	ECP 4	ECP 4

ELY CITY

Founded: 1885 Nickname: Robins

Chairman: Robert Button
Secretary: Derek Oakley
11 Frederick Talbot Close
Soham
Nr. Ely
CB7 5EY
Tel: 01353 722 141
Manager: Trevor Munns
Prog Editor: Barnes Print

Ground: Unwin Sports Ground, Downham Road, Ely CB6 2SH. Tel: 01353 662 035.
Capacity: 1,500 **Seats:** 150 **Covered:** 350
Midweek Matchday: Tuesday **Clubhouse:** Yes **Shop:** Yes
Colours(change): All red. (All blue).
Previous Names: None.
Previous Lges: Peterborough. Central Alliance.
Records: **Att:** 260 v Soham, Eastern Counties Div.1, 12.04.93.
Senior Honours: Cambridgeshire Senior Cup 1947-48. Eastern Counties Div.1 96-97.

10 YEAR RECORD

99-00	00-01	01-02	02-03	03-04	04-05	05-06	06-07	07-08	08-09
EC1 2	ECP 17	ECP 9	ECP 23	EC1 10	EC1 9	EC1 7	EC1 4	EC1 2	ECP 14

INS & OUTS

IN: Debenham Leisure Centre (P), Hadleigh United (P), Newmarket Town (P). OUT: Lowestoft Town (P – Isthmian League Division One North), Tiptree United (S – Essex Senior League), Whitton United (WS)

FELIXSTOWE & WALTON UNITED

Founded: 2000 Nickname: Seasiders

Chairman: Tony Barnes
Secretary: Adrian Hakes
26 Parkeston Road
Cricket Hill
Felixstowe
IP11 2NG
Tel: 01394 670 257
Manager: Glen Driver
Prog Editor: Chris Daynes

Ground: Town Ground, Dellwood Ave, Felixstowe IP11 9HT. Tel: 01394 282917.
Capacity: 2,000 **Seats:** 200 **Covered:** 200
Midweek Matchday: Tuesday **Clubhouse:** Yes **Shop:** Yes
Colours(change): Red & white stripes/black/black. (Yellow & blue/yellow/yellow).
Previous Names: Felixstowe Port & Town and Walton United merged in July 2000.
Previous Lges: None
Records:
Senior Honours:

10 YEAR RECORD

99-00	00-01	01-02	02-03	03-04	04-05	05-06	06-07	07-08	08-09
ECP 21	ECP 18	ECP 21	EC1 16	EC1 15	EC1 17	EC1 2	ECP 13	ECP 8	ECP 12

HADLEIGH UNITED

Founded: 1892 Nickname: Brettsiders

Chairman: Ken Ramsey
Secretary: Chris Rose
3 Aldercroft Road
Ipswich
Suffolk
IP1 6PL
Tel: 01473 740 607
Manager:
Prog Editor: As for Secretary

Ground: Millfield, Tinkers Lane, Duke St, Hadleigh IP7 5NG. Tel: 01473 822 165.
Capacity: 3,000 **Seats:** 250 **Covered:** 500
Midweek Matchday: Tuesday **Clubhouse:** Yes **Shop:**
Colours(change): White/navy/navy. (Red/navy/navy).
Previous Names: None
Previous Lges: Suffolk & Ipswich.
Records: Att: 518 v Halstead Town, FA Vase replay, 17.01.95.
Senior Honours: Suffolk & Ipswich Lge Champions 1953-54, 56-57, 73-74, 76-77, 78-79. Suffolk Senior Cup 68-69, 71-72, 82-83, 03-04. Eastern Counties Champions 93-94.

10 YEAR RECORD

99-00	00-01	01-02	02-03	03-04	04-05	05-06	06-07	07-08	08-09
EC1 8	EC1 6	EC1 14	EC1 4	EC1 18	EC1 16	EC1 21	EC1 9	EC1 5	EC1 2

HARWICH & PARKESTON

Founded: 1875 Nickname: Shrimpers

Chairman: Barry Vernon
Secretary: Andy Schooler
21 The Vineway
Harwich
Essex
CO12 4AX
Tel: 01255 504 590
Manager: Kevin Mather & Noel Gambling
Prog Editor: Carl Allan

Ground: Royal Oak, Main Road, Dovercourt, Harwich CO12 4AA. Tel: 01255 503 643.
Capacity: 5,000 **Seats:** 350 **Covered:** 1,000
Midweek Matchday: Tuesday **Clubhouse:** Yes **Shop:** No
Colours(change): Black & white stripes/black/red. (All red).
Previous Names: None.
Previous Lges: Essex County. Athenian. Isthmian.
Records:
Senior Honours: Eastern Counties Champions 1935-36. AFA Senior Cup 35-36, 36-37. Essex Co. 37-38. Athenian Div.2 64-65. Essex Senior Cup (x2). Essex Senior Trophy 89-90.

10 YEAR RECORD

99-00	00-01	01-02	02-03	03-04	04-05	05-06	06-07	07-08	08-09
ECP 20	ECP 19	ECP 18	ECP 22	EC1 2	ECP 11	ECP 21	ECP 18	ECP 18	ECP 20

HAVERHILL ROVERS

Founded: 1886 Nickname: Rovers

Chairman: Steve Brown
Secretary: Gary Brown
19 Cornish Hall End
Finchingfield
Essex
CM7 4HD
Tel: 01799 586 560
Manager: Peter Betts
Prog Editor: Steven Esdale

Ground: Hamlet Croft, Haverhill, Suffolk CB9 8EH. Tel: 01440 702 137.
Capacity: 3,000 **Seats:** 200 **Covered:** 200
Midweek Matchday: Tuesday **Clubhouse:** Yes **Shop:**
Colours(change): All red. (White/navy/navy).
Previous Names: None.
Previous Lges: East Anglian. Essex & Suffolk Border.
Records:
Senior Honours: Essex & Suffolk Border Champions 1947-48, 62-63, 63-64. Eastern Co. Lge Cup 64-65. Eastern Co. Champions 78-79. Suffolk Sen. Cup 95-96.

10 YEAR RECORD

99-00	00-01	01-02	02-03	03-04	04-05	05-06	06-07	07-08	08-09
EC1 14	EC1 7	EC1 3	EC1 10	EC1 11	EC1 5	EC1 8	EC1 2	ECP 10	ECP 21

HISTON RESERVES

Founded: Nickname:

Chairman: Gareth Baldwin
Secretary: Lisa Baldwin
c/o The Glassworld Stadium

Tel: 01223 237 373
Manager: Ossie Mintus
Prog Editor: As Secretary

Ground: The Glassworld Stadium, Bridge Road, Impington CB4 9PH. Tel: 01223 237 373.
Capacity: 3,250 **Seats:** 450 **Covered:** 1,800
Midweek Matchday: Wednesday **Clubhouse:** Yes **Shop:** Yes
Colours(change): Red & black/black/black. (Sky blue/navy/sky blue).
Previous Names: None.
Previous Lges: Cambridgeshire.
Records:
Senior Honours: Cambridgeshire League 1998/99, 00/01

10 YEAR RECORD

99-00	00-01	01-02	02-03	03-04	04-05	05-06	06-07	07-08	08-09
	CamP 1	EC1 2	ECP 13	ECP 13	ECP 19	ECP 13	ECP 15	ECP 19	ECP 13

KING'S LYNN RESERVES

Founded: Nickname:

Chairman: Ken Bobbins
Secretary: Martin Davis
Ely Villa
7 Grebe Close
Sutton Bridge
PE12 9AY
Tel: 01406 350 870
Manager: Keith Rudd
Prog Editor: As secretary

Ground: The Walks, Tennyson Road, King's Lynn PE30 5PB. Tel: 01553 760 060
Capacity: 8,200 **Seats:** 1,200 **Covered:** 5,000
Midweek Matchday: Wednesday **Clubhouse:** Yes **Shop:** Yes
Colours(change): Yellow/blue/blue. (All white).
Previous Names: None.
Previous Lges: United Counties Reserves Division.
Records:
Senior Honours:

10 YEAR RECORD

99-00	00-01	01-02	02-03	03-04	04-05	05-06	06-07	07-08	08-09
		EC1 6	EC1 2	ECP 15	ECP 18	ECP 15	ECP 19	ECP 14	ECP 15

KIRKLEY & PAKEFIELD

Founded: 1886 Nickname: The Kirks

Chairman: Robert Jenkerson
Secretary: Barrie Atkins
c/o K & P Community Sports & S.C

Tel:
Manager: Jon Reynolds
Prog Editor: Ben Atkins

Ground: K. & P. Community Sports & S. Club, Walmer Rd, NR33 7LE. Tel: 01502 513 549
Capacity: 2,000 **Seats:** 150 **Covered:** 150
Midweek Matchday: Wednesday **Clubhouse:** Yes **Shop:** Yes
Colours(change): Royal blue & maroon/royal/royal. (All silver).
Previous Names: Kirkley. Kirkley & Waveney 1929-33. Merged with Pakefield in 2007.
Previous Lges: Norfolk & Suffolk. Anglian Combination.
Records: **Att:** 1,125 v Lowestoft Town. **Goalscorer:** Barry Dale - 241.
Apps: Barry Dale - 495.
Senior Honours: Suffolk Senior Cup 1900-01, 01-02, 24-25, 00-01, 01-02.

10 YEAR RECORD

99-00	00-01	01-02	02-03	03-04	04-05	05-06	06-07	07-08	08-09
				EC1 5	EC1 3	ECP 14	ECP 7	ECP 6	ECP 6

LEISTON

Founded: 1880 Nickname:

Chairman: Andrew Crisp
Secretary: Michael Edwards
65 King Georges Avenue
Leiston
Suffolk
IP16 4JT
Tel: 01728 832 112
Manager: Carl Chenery
Prog Editor: James Mayhew

Ground: LTAA, Victory Road, Leiston IP16 4DQ. Tel: 01728 830 308.
Capacity: 2,500 **Seats:** 124 **Covered:** 500
Midweek Matchday: Wednesday **Clubhouse:** **Shop:**
Colours(change): All royal blue. (All white).
Previous Names: None.
Previous Lges: Suffolk & Ipswich.
Records: **Att:** 271 v AFC Sudbury, 13.11.04. **Goalscorer:** Lee McGlone - 60 (League).
Apps: Tim Sparkes - 154 (League).
Senior Honours:

10 YEAR RECORD

99-00	00-01	01-02	02-03	03-04	04-05	05-06	06-07	07-08	08-09
S&I S 7	S&I S 3	EC1 4	EC1 7	EC1 3	ECP 10	ECP 9	ECP 5	ECP 9	ECP 7

MILDENHALL TOWN

Founded: 1898 Nickname: The Hall

Chairman: Martin Tuck
Secretary: Brian Hensby
14 Sanderling Close
Mildenhall
Suffolk
IP28 7LE
Tel: 01638 715 772
Manager: Simon Charlton
Prog Editor: Frank Marshall

Ground: Recreation Way, Mildenhall, Suffolk IP28 7HG. Tel: 01638 713 449
Capacity: 2,00 **Seats:** 50 **Covered:** 200
Midweek Matchday: Tuesday **Clubhouse:** Yes **Shop:** Yes
Colours(change): Amber/black/black. (Sky blue & claret/sky blue & claret/sky).
Previous Names: None
Previous Lges: Bury & District. Cambridgeshire. Cambridgeshire Premier.
Records: Att: 450 v Derby County, Friendly, July 2001.
Senior Honours:

10 YEAR RECORD

99-00	00-01	01-02	02-03	03-04	04-05	05-06	06-07	07-08	08-09
ECP 6	ECP 15	ECP 11	ECP 10	ECP 12	ECP 6	ECP 5	ECP 2	ECP 5	ECP 11

NEEDHAM MARKET

Founded: 1919 Nickname:

Chairman: David Bugg
Secretary: Mark Easlea
15 Sanderling Way
Stowmarket
Suffolk
IP14 5FZ
Tel: 01449 672 731
Manager: Danny Laws
Prog Editor: Mark Coleman & Bev Dorling

Ground: Bloomfields, Quinton Road, Needham Market IP6 8DA. Tel: 01449 721 000
Capacity: 1,000 **Seats:** 250 **Covered:** 250
Midweek Matchday: Tuesday **Clubhouse:** Yes **Shop:** Yes
Colours(change): Red/black/red. (All blue).
Previous Names: None
Previous Lges: Suffolk & Ipswich.
Records: Att: 750 v Ipswich Town, Suffolk Premier Cup, 2007. **Goalscorer:** Alvin King.
Senior Honours: Suffolk Senior Cup 1989-90, 04-05. Suffolk & Ipswich Senior 95-96. East Anglian Cup 06-07.

10 YEAR RECORD

99-00	00-01	01-02	02-03	03-04	04-05	05-06	06-07	07-08	08-09
EC1 5	EC1 4	EC1 5	EC1 11	EC1 14	EC1 2	ECP 6	ECP 4	ECP 2	ECP 3

NEWMARKET TOWN

Founded: 1877 Nickname: The Jockeys

Chairman: Kevin Grainger
Secretary: Elaine Jenkins
140 New Cheveley Road
Newmarket

CB8 8BY
Tel: 01638 602 525
Manager: Karl Johnson
Prog Editor: As for Secretary

Ground: Sherbourn Stadium, Cricket Field Rd, Newmarket CB8 8BT. Tel: 01638 663 637.
Capacity: 2,750 **Seats:** 144 **Covered:** 250
Midweek Matchday: Tuesday **Clubhouse:** Yes **Shop:** Yes
Colours(change): Yellow & blue/blue/yellow & blue. (All red).
Previous Names: None
Previous Lges: Bury Senior. Ipswich Senior. Essex & Suffolk B. United Counties.
Records: Att: 2,701 v Abbey United (now Cambridge Utd) FA Cup, 01.10.49.
Senior Honours: Suffolk Senior Cup 1934-35, 93-94.
Suffolk Premier Cup 93-94, 94-95, 96-97. Eastern Counties Divi.1 Champions 2008-09.

10 YEAR RECORD

99-00	00-01	01-02	02-03	03-04	04-05	05-06	06-07	07-08	08-09
ECP 14	ECP 20	ECP 19	ECP 18	ECP 10	ECP 13	ECP 17	ECP 12	ECP 21	EC1 1

NORWICH UNITED

Founded: 1903 Nickname: Planters

Chairman: John Hilditch
Secretary: Keith Cutmore
54c St Augustines Street
Norwich
Norfolk
NR3 3AD
Tel: 01603 444 183
Manager: Paul Chick
Prog Editor: Barnes Print

Ground: Plantation Park, Blofield, Norwich NR13 4PL. Tel: 01603 716 963.
Capacity: 3,000 **Seats:** 100 **Covered:** 1,000
Midweek Matchday: Tuesday **Clubhouse:** Yes **Shop:** Yes
Colours(change): Yellow & blue/blue/blue. (All red).
Previous Names: Poringland & District > 1987.
Previous Lges: Norwich & District. Anglian Combination.
Records: Att: 401 v Wroxham, Eastern Co. Lge, 1991-92. **Goalscorer:** M. Money.
Apps: Tim Sayer.
Senior Honours: Anglian Comb. Senior Cup 1983-84.
Eastern Counties Div.1 Champions 90-91, 01-02.

10 YEAR RECORD

99-00	00-01	01-02	02-03	03-04	04-05	05-06	06-07	07-08	08-09
EC1 15	EC1 10	EC1 1	ECP 16	ECP 11	ECP 14	ECP 20	ECP 16	ECP 15	ECP 19

STANWAY ROVERS

Founded: 1956 Nickname: Rovers

Chairman: Roy Brett
Secretary: Paul Rogers
c/o Stanway Rovers FC

Tel: 01206 578 187
Manager: Steve Downey
Prog Editor: Mike Norfolk

Ground: Hawthorns, New Farm Road, Stanway, Colchester CO3 0PG. Tel: 01206 578 187
Capacity: 1,500 **Seats:** 100 **Covered:** 250
Midweek Matchday: Wednesday **Clubhouse:** Yes **Shop:** Yes
Colours(change): Gold & black/black/black. (Light blue/navy/navy).
Previous Names: None.
Previous Lges: Colchester & East Essex. Essex & Suffolk Border.
Records: **Att:** 210 v Harwich & P, Eastern Co. Lge Div.1, 2004.

Senior Honours: Eastern Counties Div.1 Champions 2005-06. League Cup 2008-09.

10 YEAR RECORD

99-00	00-01	01-02	02-03	03-04	04-05	05-06	06-07	07-08	08-09
EC1 3	EC1 3	EC1 7	EC1 5	EC1 4	EC1 6	EC1 1	ECP 14	ECP 7	ECP 9

WALSHAM-LE-WILLOWS

Founded: 1888 Nickname:

Chairman: Mike Powles
Secretary: Gordon Ross
c/o Walsham Sports Club Ground

Tel: 01359 259 298
Manager: Paul Smith
Prog Editor: Barnes Print

Ground: Walsham S. Club, Summer Rd, Walsham-le-Willows IP31 3AH. Tel: 01359 259298
Capacity: **Seats:** 100 **Covered:** 100
Midweek Matchday: Wednesday **Clubhouse:** Yes **Shop:**
Colours(change): Royal blue & yellow/royal/royal. (Yellow & blue/blue/yellow).
Previous Names: None
Previous Lges: Bury & District. Suffolk & Ipswich.
Records:

Senior Honours: Suffolk & Ipswich Senior Champions 2001-02, 02-03.
Suffolk Senior Cup 05-06. Eastern Counties Div.1 Champions 06-07.

10 YEAR RECORD

99-00	00-01	01-02	02-03	03-04	04-05	05-06	06-07	07-08	08-09
S&I S 3	S&I S 4	S&I S 1	S&I S 1	S&I S 2	EC1 4	EC1 5	EC1 1	ECP 16	ECP 10

WISBECH TOWN

Founded: 1920 Nickname: Fenmen

Chairman: Paul Brenchley
Secretary: Colin Grant
c/o Wisbech Town F.C.

Tel: 01945 584 176
Manager: Gary Setchell
Prog Editor: Spencer Larham

Ground: Fenland Park, Lerowe Road, Wisbech PE13 3QH. Tel: 01945 584 176
Capacity: **Seats:** **Covered:**
Midweek Matchday: Tuesday **Clubhouse:** **Shop:**
Colours(change): All red. (Yellow/green/yellow).
Previous Names: None
Previous Lges: East Midlands. Peterborough. United Co. Eastern Co. Midland. Southern.
Records: **Att:** 8,044 v Peterborough United, Midland League, 25.08.1957.
Goalscorer: Bert Titmarsh - 246 (1931-37). **Apps:** Jamie Brighty - 731.
Senior Honours: United Counties Champions 1946-47, 47-48. Southern Lge Div.1 61-62.
Eastern Counties Lge 71-72, 76-77, 90-91. East Anglian Cup 87-88.

10 YEAR RECORD

99-00	00-01	01-02	02-03	03-04	04-05	05-06	06-07	07-08	08-09
SthE 14	SthE 18	SthM 22	ECP 6	ECP 14	ECP 16	ECP 4	ECP 11	ECP 12	ECP 16

WIVENHOE TOWN

Founded: 1925 Nickname: The Dragons

Chairman: Carl Callan
Secretary: Dave Wignall
c/o Wivenhoe Town F.C.

Tel: 01206 825 380
Manager: Neil Northcott
Prog Editor: Richard Tweed

Ground: Broad Lane, Elmstead Road, Wivenhoe CO7 7HA. Tel: 01206 825 380.
Capacity: 2876 **Seats:** 161 **Covered:** 1300
Midweek Matchday: Tuesday **Clubhouse:** Yes **Shop:** Yes
Colours(change): Blue/white/blue. (Yellow/green/yellow).
Previous Names: Wivenhoe Rangers.
Previous Lges: Brightlingsea & Dist. Colchester & East Essx. Essx& Suff B. Essx Senior.
Records: **Att:** 1,912 v Runcorn, FA Trophy, 1st Round, Feb. 1990.
Goalscorer: (258 in 350 games). **Apps:** Keith Bain (538).
Senior Honours: Ishtmian Div.2 North 1987-88. Div.1 89-90. Essex Senior Trophy 87-88.

10 YEAR RECORD

99-00	00-01	01-02	02-03	03-04	04-05	05-06	06-07	07-08	08-09
Isth2 6	Isth2 5	Isth2 21	Isth1N 21	Isth1N 17	SthE 5	SthE 6	Isth1N 11	Isth1N 22	ECP 17

WOODBRIDGE TOWN

Founded: 1885 Nickname: The Woodpeckers

Chairman: John Beecroft
Secretary: Rob Bareham
c/o Woodbridge Town F.C.

Tel: 01394 385 308
Manager: Mark Scopes
Prog Editor: Richard Scott

Ground: Notcutts Park, Seckford Hall Road, Woodbridge IP12 4DA. Tel: 01394 385 308
Capacity: 3,000 **Seats:** 50 **Covered:** 200
Midweek Matchday: Wednesday **Clubhouse:** Yes **Shop:** No
Colours(change): Black & white stripes/black/black. (All red).
Previous Names: None.
Previous Lges: Ipswich & District. Suffolk & Ipswich.
Records: Att: 3,000 v Arsenal, for the opening of the floodlights, 02.10.90.

Senior Honours: Suffolk Senior Cup 1885, 77-78, 92-93, 93-94.
Ipswich & District Senior Champions 1912-13. Suffolk & Ipswich Senior 88-89.

10 YEAR RECORD

99-00	00-01	01-02	02-03	03-04	04-05	05-06	06-07	07-08	08-09
ECP 7	ECP 7	ECP 8	ECP 20	ECP 17	ECP 17	ECP 16	ECP 9	ECP 17	ECP 18

WROXHAM

Founded: 1892 Nickname: Yaghtsmen

Chairman: Tom Jarrett
Secretary: Chris Green
24 Keys Drive
Wroxham
Norfolk
NR12 8SS
Tel: 01603 783 936
Manager: David Batch
Prog Editor: Barnes Print

Ground: Trafford Park, Skinners Lane, Wroxham NR12 8SJ. Tel: 01603 783 538.
Capacity: 2,500 **Seats:** 50 **Covered:** 250
Midweek Matchday: Tuesday **Clubhouse:** Yes **Shop:** No
Colours(change): Blue & white stripes/blue/blue. (All red).
Previous Names: None
Previous Lges: East Norfolk. Norwich City. East Anglian. Norwich & Dist. Anglian Comb.
Records: Att: 1,011 v Wisbech Town, Eastern Co. Lge, 16.03.93.
Goalscorer: Matthew Metcalf. **Apps:** Stu Larter.
Senior Honours: Anglian Co. 1981-82, 82-83, 83-84, 84-85, 86-87. Eastern Co. D1 88-89.
Prem 91-92, 92-93, 93-94, 96-97, 97-98, 98-99, 06-07. N'folk Sen'Cup 92-93, 95-96, 97-98, 99-00, 03-04.

10 YEAR RECORD

99-00	00-01	01-02	02-03	03-04	04-05	05-06	06-07	07-08	08-09
ECP 2	ECP 6	ECP 2	ECP 2	ECP 3	ECP 5	ECP 8	ECP 1	ECP 3	ECP 5

BRANTHAM ATHLETIC

Founded: 1887 Nickname:

Chairman: Peter Crowhurst
Secretary: Graham Mower
1 Broughton Villa
Cattawade Strett
Brantham near Mannington
CO11 1SA
Tel: 07968 484 182
Manager: Tony Hall
Prog Editor: Andy Powell

Ground: Brantham Leisure Centre, New Village, Brantham CO11 1RZ. Tel: 01206 392 506
Capacity: 1,200 **Seats:** 200 **Covered:** 200
Midweek Matchday: Tuesday **Clubhouse:** Yes **Shop:**
Colours(change): All blue. (All white).
Previous Names: Brantham & Stutton United 1996-98.
Previous Lges: Eastern Counties. Suffolk & Ipswich.
Records: Att: 1,700 v VS Rugby, FA Vase 5R 1982-83.

Senior Honours: Suffolk & Ipswich Senior League 2007-08

10 YEAR RECORD

99-00	00-01	01-02	02-03	03-04	04-05	05-06	06-07	07-08	08-09
					S&I 1 2	S&I S 14	S&I S 4	S&I S 1	EC1 8

CORNARD UNITED

Founded: 1964 Nickname: Ards

Chairman: Neil Cottrell
Secretary: Chris Symes
22 Greenacres
Mile End
Colchester
CO4 5DX
Tel: 01206 851 627
Manager: As for Secretary
Prog Editor: As for Secretary

Ground: Blackhouse Lane, Great Cornard, Sudbury CO10 0NL. Tel: 07811 096 832
Capacity: 2,000 **Seats:** 250 **Covered:** 500
Midweek Matchday: Tuesday **Clubhouse:** Yes **Shop:** No
Colours(change): Royal blue & white/royal/royal. (Green/navy/navy).
Previous Names: None
Previous Lges: Sudbury S/day. Bury St Edmunds & D. Colchester. Essex. Suffolk Bord.
Records: Att: 400 v Colchester United 1997. **Goalscorer:** Andy Smiles.
Apps: Keith Featherstone.
Senior Honours: Essex & Suffolk Border League Champions 1988-89.
Eastern Counties Division One 89-90. Suffolk Senior Cup 89-90.

10 YEAR RECORD

99-00	00-01	01-02	02-03	03-04	04-05	05-06	06-07	07-08	08-09
EC1 10	EC1 11	EC1 11	EC1 13	EC1 12	EC1 11	EC1 17	EC1 15	EC1 18	EC1 11

DISS TOWN

Founded: 1888 Nickname: Tangerines

Chairman: Des Tebble
Secretary: Steve Flatman
31 Aldrich Way
Roydon
Diss
IP22 4FJ
Tel: 01379 641 406
Manager: Robert Taylor
Prog Editor: Gary Enderby

Ground: Brewers Green Lane, Diss, Norfolk IP22 4QP. Tel: 01379 651 223.
Capacity: 2,500 **Seats:** 280 **Covered:** Yes
Midweek Matchday: Tuesday **Clubhouse:** Yes **Shop:** Yes
Colours(change): Tangerine/navy/tangerine. (Blue/navy/navy).
Previous Names: None
Previous Lges: Norwich & District. Norfolk & Suffolk. Anglian Combination.
Records: Att: 1,731 v Atherton LR, FA Vase Semi Final, 19.03.94.
Apps: Des Tebble.
Senior Honours: Eastern Counties Div.1 Champions 1991-92. FA Vase winners 93-94.

10 YEAR RECORD

99-00	00-01	01-02	02-03	03-04	04-05	05-06	06-07	07-08	08-09
ECP 8	ECP 11	ECP 16	ECP 5	ECP 4	ECP 12	ECP 11	ECP 20	EC1 4	EC1 9

DOWNHAM TOWN

Founded: 1881 Nickname: Town

Chairman: David Green
Secretary: George Dickson
c/o Downham Town F.C.

Tel: 01366 388 424
Manager: Wayne Anderson
Prog Editor: Marie Nicholls

Ground: Memorial Field, Lynn Road, Downham Market PE38 9QE. Tel: 01366 388 424.
Capacity: 1,000 **Seats:** 60 **Covered:** Yes
Midweek Matchday: Tuesday **Clubhouse:** Yes **Shop:**
Colours(change): All red. (Navy & sky blue/navy/navy & sky blue).
Previous Names: None
Previous Lges: Peterborough League.
Records: Att: 325 v Wells Town, Norfolk Senior Cup, 1998-99.

Senior Honours: Peterborough Senior Cup 1962, 63, 67, 72, 87.
Peterborough League 63, 74, 79, 87, 88. Norfolk Senior Cup 64, 66.

10 YEAR RECORD

99-00	00-01	01-02	02-03	03-04	04-05	05-06	06-07	07-08	08-09
EC1 4	EC1 9	EC1 15	EC1 18	EC1 17	EC1 18	EC1 20	EC1 18	EC1 12	EC1 15

INS & OUTS

IN: Team Bury (P – Essex & Suffolk Border League Premier Division), Whitton United (R)
OUT: Debenham Leisure Centre (P), Hadleigh United (P), Newmarket Town (P)

FAKENHAM TOWN

Founded: 1884 Nickname: Ghosts

Chairman: Nigel Allen
Secretary: Paul Allen
c/o Fakenham Town F.C.

Tel: 01328 855 859
Manager: Mark King/Stuart Woodhouse
Prog Editor: Tony Miles

Ground: Clipbush Lane, Fakenham NR21 8SW. Tel: 01328 855 859 (clubhouse).
Capacity: 3,000 **Seats:** 264 **Covered:** 500
Midweek Matchday: Tuesday **Clubhouse:** Yes **Shop:** Yes
Colours(change): Amber & black/black/amber. (Blue & white/blue/blue).
Previous Names: None
Previous Lges: North Norfolk. Norwich & District. Norfolk & Suffolk. Anglian Combination.
Records: **Att:** 1,100 v Watford, official opening of new ground.

Senior Honours: Norfolk Senior Cup 1970-71, 72-73, 73-74, 91-92, 93-94, 94-95.

10 YEAR RECORD

99-00	00-01	01-02	02-03	03-04	04-05	05-06	06-07	07-08	08-09
ECP 11	ECP 13	ECP 14	ECP 14	ECP 22	EC1 10	EC1 11	EC1 10	EC1 17	EC1 20

FC CLACTON

Founded: 1892 Nickname: The Seasiders

Chairman: David Ballard
Secretary: Danny Coyle
c/o FC Clacton

Tel: 01255 432 590
Manager: David Coyle
Prog Editor: Karl fuller

Ground: Rush Green Bowl, Rush Green Rd, Clacton-on-Sea CO16 7BQ. Tel: 01255432590
Capacity: 3,000 **Seats:** 200 **Covered:** Yes
Midweek Matchday: Tuesday **Clubhouse:** Yes **Shop:** Yes
Colours(change): White & blue/blue/blue. (All red).
Previous Names: Clacton Town > 2007
Previous Lges: Eastern Counties. Essex County. Southern League.
Records: **Att:** 3,505 v Romford, FA Cup 1952 at Old Road.

Senior Honours: East Anglian Cup 1953-54, 99-00. Southern League Div.1 59-60. Eastern Counties Div.1 94-95, 98-99.

10 YEAR RECORD

99-00	00-01	01-02	02-03	03-04	04-05	05-06	06-07	07-08	08-09
ECP 4	ECP 5	ECP 4	ECP 11	ECP 6	ECP 8	ECP 22	ECP 21	EC1 10	EC1 7

GODMANCHESTER ROVERS

Founded: 1911 Nickname: Goody/Rovers

Chairman: Keith Gabb
Secretary: Sue Hirst
c/o Godmanchester Rovers F.C.

Tel: 0795 036 7417
Manager: Karl & David Hurst
Prog Editor: Nick Forshaw

Ground: Bearscroft Farm, Godmanchester, PE29 2LQ. Tel: 0795 036 7417.
Capacity: **Seats:** **Covered:** 150
Midweek Matchday: Wednesday **Clubhouse:** Yes **Shop:**
Colours(change): Sky blue/navy/navy. (Red/red/black).
Previous Names: None
Previous Lges: Cambridgeshire. Hunts County.
Records: **Att:** 138 v Cambridge City Reserves, Dec. 2003.

Senior Honours:

10 YEAR RECORD

99-00	00-01	01-02	02-03	03-04	04-05	05-06	06-07	07-08	08-09
			EC1 12	EC1 7	EC1 20	EC1 14	EC1 17	EC1 16	EC1 10

GORLESTON

Founded: 1887 Nickname:

Chairman: Anne Santon
Secretary: Martin Gaines
c/o Gorleston F.C.

Tel: 01493 602 802
Manager: Richard Daniels
Prog Editor: Jimmy Jones

Ground: Emerald Park, Woodfarm Lane, Gorleston NR31 9AQ. Tel: 01493 602 802.
Capacity: 5,000 **Seats:** 2,000 **Covered:** 4,000
Midweek Matchday: Tuesday **Clubhouse:** Yes **Shop:** Yes
Colours(change): Green & white stripes/green/green. (Red/black/black).
Previous Names: None
Previous Lges: Gt. Yarmouth & District. Norfolk & Suffolk. Anglian Combination.
Records: **Att:** 4,473 v Orient, FA Cup 1st Round, 29.11.51.

Senior Honours: Norfolk & Suff. Lge (x 7). Norfolk Senior Cup (x 14). Anglian Comb 68-69. Eastern Counties Champions 1952-53, 72-73, 79-80, 80-81. Div.1 95-96.

10 YEAR RECORD

99-00	00-01	01-02	02-03	03-04	04-05	05-06	06-07	07-08	08-09
ECP 13	ECP 2	ECP 5	ECP 15	ECP 20	ECP 21	EC1 18	EC1 14	EC1 8	EC1 6

GREAT YARMOUTH TOWN

Founded: 1897 Nickname:

Chairman: Stephen Brierley
Secretary: Colin Jones
c/o Great Yarmouth Town F.C.

Tel: 01493 843 373
Manager: Paul Tong
Prog Editor: Barnes Print

Ground: Wellesley, Sandown Road, Great Yarmouth NR30 1EY. Tel: 01493 843 373.
Capacity: 3,600 **Seats:** 500 **Covered:** 2,100
Midweek Matchday: Tuesday **Clubhouse:** Yes **Shop:** Yes
Colours(change): Amber & black stripes/black/black. (Blue & white/blue/blue).
Previous Names: None
Previous Lges: Norfolk & Suffolk.
Records: **Att:** 8,944 v Crystal Palace, FA Cup 1st Round 52-53.
Goalscorer: Gordon South - 298 (1927-47). **Apps:** Mark Vincent - 700 (84-05).
Senior Honours: Eastern Counties Champions 1968-69. Norfolk Senior Cup (x 12)

10 YEAR RECORD

99-00	00-01	01-02	02-03	03-04	04-05	05-06	06-07	07-08	08-09
ECP 12	ECP 8	ECP 17	ECP 8	ECP 16	ECP 22	EC1 13	EC1 13	EC1 11	EC1 5

HALSTEAD TOWN

Founded: 1879 Nickname: The Town

Chairman: Jimmy Holder
Secretary: Steve Webber
12 Ravens Avenue
Halstead
Essex
CO9 1NZ
Tel: 01787 476 959
Manager: Jody Brown
Prog Editor: Barnes Print

Ground: Rosemary Lane, Broton Ind. Est., Halstead CO9 1HR. Tel: 01787 472 082.
Capacity: 2,000 **Seats:** 400 **Covered:** 400
Midweek Matchday: Tuesday **Clubhouse:** Yes **Shop:** No
Colours(change): Black & white/black/black. (All blue).
Previous Names: None
Previous Lges: North Essex. Halstead & Dist. Haverhill. Essx & Suff. Border. Essx Senior.
Records: **Att:** 4,000 v Walthamstowe Avenue, Essex Senior Cup 1949.
Senior Honours: Eastern Counties Champions 1994-95, 95-96. Div.1 02-03.
Essex Senior Trophy 94-95, 96-97.

10 YEAR RECORD

99-00	00-01	01-02	02-03	03-04	04-05	05-06	06-07	07-08	08-09
ECP 18	ECP 22	EC1 13	EC1 1	ECP 6	ECP 3	ECP 18	ECP 22	EC1 6	EC1 4

IPSWICH WANDERERS

Founded: 1983 Nickname: Wanderers

Chairman: Ed Nicholls
Secretary: Mike Borrill
c/o Ipswich Wanderers F.C.

Tel: 01473 728 581
Manager: Steve Buckle
Prog Editor: Chris Hunton

Ground: SEH Sports Centre, Humber Doucey Lane, Ipswich IP4 3NR. Tel: 01473 728 581
Capacity: 2,000 **Seats:** 50 **Covered:** Yes
Midweek Matchday: Wednesday **Clubhouse:** Yes **Shop:** Yes
Colours(change): All blue. (All yellow).
Previous Names: Lancaster Ipswich.
Previous Lges:
Records: **Att:** 335 v Woodbridge, Eastern Counties Lge 1993-94.
Senior Honours: Eastern Counties Div.1 Champions 1997-98, 04-05.

10 YEAR RECORD

99-00	00-01	01-02	02-03	03-04	04-05	05-06	06-07	07-08	08-09
ECP 10	ECP 12	ECP 20	ECP 21	EC1 8	EC1 1	ECP 7	ECP 10	ECP 22	EC1 17

LONG MELFORD

Founded: 1868 Nickname: The Villagers

Chairman: Colin Woodhouse
Secretary: Richard Powell
14 North Rise
Great Cornard
Sudbury
CO10 0DE
Tel: 01787 377 969
Manager: Steve Rogers
Prog Editor: Andy Cussans

Ground: Stoneylands Stadium, New Road, Long Melford CO10 9JY. Tel: 01787 312 187.
Capacity: **Seats:** 106 **Covered:** 512
Midweek Matchday: Monday **Clubhouse:** Yes **Shop:**
Colours(change): Black & white stripes/black/black (All white).
Previous Names: None
Previous Lges: Essex & Suffolk Border.
Records:
Senior Honours: Essex & Suffolk Border Champions (x 5). Suffolk Senior Cup (x 8).

10 YEAR RECORD

99-00	00-01	01-02	02-03	03-04	04-05	05-06	06-07	07-08	08-09
			EC1 6	EC1 13	EC1 13	EC1 15	EC1 16	EC1 19	EC1 19

MARCH TOWN UNITED

Founded: 1885 Nickname: Hares

Chairman: Philip White
Secretary: Ray Bennett
47 Ellingham Avenue
March
Cambridgeshire
PE15 9TE
Tel: 01354 659 901
Manager: Brett Whaley
Prog Editor: Gary Wesley

Ground: GER Spts Grd, Robin Goodfellows Lane, March PE15 8HS. Tel: 01354 653 073
Capacity: 4,000 **Seats:** 500 **Covered:** 2,000
Midweek Matchday: Tuesday **Clubhouse:** Yes **Shop:**
Colours(change): All blue. (Black & amber/black/black).
Previous Names: None
Previous Lges: Peterborough. Isle of Ely. United Counties.
Records: Att: 7,500 v King's Lynn, FA Cup 1956.
Senior Honours: United Counties League Champions 1953-54. Eastern Counties 87-88.

10 YEAR RECORD

99-00	00-01	01-02	02-03	03-04	04-05	05-06	06-07	07-08	08-09
EC1 13	EC1 17	EC1 19	EC1 15	EC1 16	EC1 7	EC1 19	EC1 19	EC1 15	EC1 13

SAFFRON WALDEN TOWN

Founded: 1872 Nickname: The Bloods

Chairman: John Butchart
Secretary: Peter Rule
48 Church Street
Saffron Walden
Essex
CB10 1JQ
Tel: 01799 501 462
Manager: Marc Das
Prog Editor: Jim Duvall

Ground: 1 Catons Lane, Saffron Walden CB10 2DU. Tel: 01799 522 789.
Capacity: 3,500 **Seats:** 274 **Covered:** 120
Midweek Matchday: Wednesday **Clubhouse:** Yes **Shop:** No
Colours(change): Red & black/black/black. (Blue & white/blue/white).
Previous Names: Saffron Walden > 1967.
Previous Lges: Spartan. Herts County. Essex Senior. Isthmian. No league during 03-04.
Records: Goalscorer: Alec Ramsey - 192. **Apps:** Les Page - 538.
Senior Honours: Essex Senior League Champions 1973-74, 99-00.
Eastern Counties 82-83. Essex Senior Challenge Trophy 82-83, 83-84, 84-85.

10 YEAR RECORD

99-00	00-01	01-02	02-03	03-04	04-05	05-06	06-07	07-08	08-09
ESen 1	ESen 2	ESen 11	ESen 12		EC1 15	EC1 12	EC1 6	EC1 7	EC1 18

STOWMARKET TOWN

Founded: 1883 Nickname:

Chairman: Neil Sharp
Secretary: Mandy Griffin
c/o Stowmarket Town F.C.
Tel: 01449 612 533
Manager: Alan Johnson
Prog Editor: Nathan Morley

Ground: Greens Meadow, Bury Road, Stowmarket, Suffolk IP14 1JQ. Tel: 01449 612 533.
Capacity: 2,000 **Seats:** 200 **Covered:** 450
Midweek Matchday: Tuesday **Clubhouse:** Yes **Shop:** No
Colours(change): Gold/black/black. (All red).
Previous Names: Stowuplands Corinthians. Stowmarket Corinthians. Stowmarket FC.
Previous Lges: Ipswich & District. Essex & Suffolk Border.
Records: Att: 1,200 v Ipswich Town, friendly, July 1994.
Senior Honours: Suffolk Senior Cup (x 10).

10 YEAR RECORD

99-00	00-01	01-02	02-03	03-04	04-05	05-06	06-07	07-08	08-09
ECP 19	ECP 9	ECP 6	ECP 7	ECP 19	ECP 20	EC1 16	EC1 12	EC1 14	EC1 12

SWAFFHAM TOWN

Founded: 1892 Nickname: Pedlars

Chairman: Tony Hemeter
Secretary: Ray Ewart
19 Shepard Fold
Swaffham
Norfolk
PE37 7TR
Tel: 01760 724 581
Manager: Mick Simmons & Lester Kent
Prog Editor: Barnes Print

Ground: Shoemakers Lane, Swaffham, Norfolk PE37 7NT. Tel: 01760 722 700.
Capacity: 2,000 **Seats:** 50 **Covered:** 250
Midweek Matchday: Tuesday **Clubhouse:** Yes **Shop:**
Colours(change): Black & white stripes/black/black. (Tangerine/white/white).
Previous Names: None
Previous Lges: Dereham. Anglian Combination.
Records: Att: 250 v Downham Town, Eastern Counties League Cup, 03.09.91.
Senior Honours: Eastern Counties Div.1 Champions 2000-01.

10 YEAR RECORD

99-00	00-01	01-02	02-03	03-04	04-05	05-06	06-07	07-08	08-09
EC1 9	EC1 1	ECP 22	EC1 8	EC1 9	EC1 12	EC1 9	EC1 3	ECP 20	EC1 18

TEAM BURY

Founded: Nickname:

Chairman: Alan Collen
Secretary: Neil Reader
c/o Team Bury F.C.

Tel: 01284 754 721
Manager: Neil Reader & Dean Greygoose
Prog Editor:

Ground: Ram Meadow, Cotton Lane, Bury St Edmonds IP33 1XP. Tel: 01284 754 721
Capacity: 3,500 **Seats:** 300 **Covered:** 1,500
Midweek Matchday: Tuesday **Clubhouse:** Yes **Shop:** Yes
Colours(change): All blue. (Yellow/black/yellow).
Previous Names:
Previous Lges: Essex & Suffolk Border.
Records:

Senior Honours:

10 YEAR RECORD

99-00	00-01	01-02	02-03	03-04	04-05	05-06	06-07	07-08	08-09
								EsSuP 8	EsSuP 2

THETFORD TOWN

Founded: 1883 Nickname:

Chairman: Mick Bailey
Secretary: Bob Richards
60 Nunnery Drive
Thetford
Norfolk
IP24 3EN
Tel: 01842 764 282
Manager: Mark Scott
Prog Editor: Barnes Print

Ground: Recreation Ground, Mundford Road, Thetford IP24 1NB. Tel: 01842 766 120.
Capacity: 2,000 **Seats:** 400 **Covered:** 400
Midweek Matchday: Tuesday **Clubhouse:** Yes **Shop:** No
Colours(change): White/claret/claret & white. (Claret & blue/claret/claret & blue).
Previous Names: None
Previous Lges: Norfolk & Suffolk.
Records: Att: 394 v Diss Town, Norfolk Senior Cup, 1991.

Senior Honours: Norfolk Senior Cup 1947-48, 90-91. Norfolk & Suffolk League 54-55.

10 YEAR RECORD

99-00	00-01	01-02	02-03	03-04	04-05	05-06	06-07	07-08	08-09
EC1 18	EC1 15	EC1 18	EC1 17	EC1 19	EC1 19	EC1 22	EC1 11	EC1 13	EC1 16

WHITTON UNITED

Founded: 1926 Nickname: None

Chairman: Ruel Fox
Secretary: Phil Pemberton
c/o Whitton United F.C.

Tel: 01473 464 030
Manager: Ian Brown
Prog Editor: Ian Hart

Ground: King George V Playing F., Old Norwich Rd, Ipswich IP1 6LE. Tel: 01473 464 030
Capacity: 600 **Seats:** No **Covered:** 100
Midweek Matchday: Tuesday **Clubhouse:** Yes **Shop:** No
Colours(change): All green. (Yellow/yellow/white).
Previous Names: None
Previous Lges: Suffolk & Ipswich.
Records: Att: 528 v Ipswich Town, 29.11.95.

Senior Honours: Suffolk & Ipswich Lge 1946-47, 47-48, 65-66, 67-68, 91-92, 92-93. Suffolk Senior Cup 58-59, 62-63, 92-93.

10 YEAR RECORD

99-00	00-01	01-02	02-03	03-04	04-05	05-06	06-07	07-08	08-09
EC1 11	EC1 12	EC1 12	EC1 3	EC1 6	EC1 14	EC1 6	EC1 8	EC1 3	ECP Exp

ESSEX SENIOR LEAGUE

essexseniorfootballleague.moonfruit.com

Sponsored by: No sponsor

Founded: 1971

Recent champions:
2004:Concord Rgrs
2005: Enfield Town
2006: AFC Hornchurch
2007: Brentwood Town
2008: Concord Rgrs

	Bark	B'side	Basil.	Bow.	Burn.	Clap.	Enf.	Eton	Hull.	Lond.	Maur.	Romf.	Sawb.	South.	Stan.	Take.
Barking		1-1	0-4	0-4	1-1	3-0	1-3	1-0	1-2	1-1	5-1	0-5	1-1	2-2	1-2	1-4
Barkingside	2-1		2-1	0-3	3-0	3-0	0-1	1-1	4-1	2-2	4-1	0-6	5-4	4-3	1-2	0-2
Basildon United	1-2	0-1		1-0	3-2	3-1	0-2	4-3	3-1	3-4	2-0	1-5	3-1	0-1	2-0	1-3
Bowers & Pitsea	0-2	0-1	4-0		0-3	1-0	2-1	1-1	0-0	2-2	1-1	1-1	0-3	1-0	2-1	0-1
Burnham Ramblers	3-1	2-2	2-2	1-0		5-1	3-0	0-2	0-2	6-3	2-2	0-2	5-0	2-2	6-3	0-2
Clapton	4-5	2-1	0-3	1-4	1-0		0-3	1-5	2-0	1-3	4-1	2-2	1-4	0-1	2-4	0-3
Enfield	4-1	4-0	2-0	3-0	3-1	3-2		6-3	1-1	1-0	3-0	0-1	3-1	2-0	3-1	4-1
Eton Manor	2-0	3-3	1-1	0-2	0-1	3-1	1-0		2-2	4-0	3-1	0-1	1-1	0-2	0-1	0-2
Hullbridge Sports	1-0	2-3	2-1	1-1	0-5	3-0	2-3	0-0		1-0	4-1	1-2	2-2	2-2	2-1	1-3
London APSA	0-3	0-2	1-2	2-2	4-1	2-0	0-1	0-5	0-3		3-1	0-2	2-0	1-1	0-5	0-2
Mauritius Sports Assoc.	3-3	1-1	2-2	1-2	4-2	4-4	1-2	0-2	2-1	2-0		3-5	2-2	0-2	2-3	2-1
Romford	4-1	0-0	2-1	2-0	1-1	7-1	2-0	2-1	1-1	2-0	4-1		3-0	4-0	2-2	4-0
Sawbridgeworth Town	1-5	1-0	0-2	2-1	0-4	3-4	0-2	2-3	1-2	4-2	3-2	2-2		1-0	1-5	0-2
Southend Manor	1-0	6-1	5-1	2-0	2-2	3-3	2-1	1-2	3-2	5-0	4-0	3-1	2-0		5-2	4-4
Stansted	4-1	0-1	1-3	0-1	3-0	5-1	1-0	1-1	1-2	3-1	0-0	1-2	1-2	0-1		4-4
Takeley	1-1	1-0	0-3	2-0	1-2	4-1	2-1	2-3	1-0	0-1	2-1	2-2	3-1	3-0	1-0	

		P	W	D	L	F	A	Pts
Romford		30	21	8	1	79	25	71
Enfield		30	21	1	8	62	29	64
Takeley		30	19	4	7	59	37	61
Southend Manor		30	16	7	7	65	41	55
Barkingside		30	13	7	10	48	51	46
Eton Manor		30	12	8	10	52	40	44
Burnham Ramblers		30	12	7	11	62	50	43
Basildon United	*-3*	30	14	3	13	53	50	42
Hullbridge Sports		30	11	8	11	44	46	41
Stansted		30	12	4	14	57	50	40
Bowers & Pitsea	*-3*	30	11	7	12	35	35	37
Barking		30	8	7	15	45	62	31
Sawbridgeworth Town		30	8	5	17	43	70	29
London APSA	*-1*	30	7	5	18	34	67	25
Mauritius Spts Ass.		30	4	8	18	42	76	20
Clapton		30	5	3	22	40	91	18

GORDON BRASTED TROPHY

FIRST ROUND

Barking 0 **Burnham Ramblers** 1
Bowers & Pitsea 4 London APSA 0
Hullbridge Sports 0 **Eton Manor** 2
Romford 2 Basildon United 1
Sawbridgeworth Town 0 **Mauritius Sports Association** 5
Southend Manor 4 Clapton 2
Stansted 2 Barkingside 0
Takeley 2 **Enfield** 3

QUARTER-FINALS

Burnham Ramblers 2 Southend Manor 0
Enfield 4 Romford 2
Eton Manor 2 Bowers & Pitsea 0 *(at Bowers & Pitsea)*
Mauritius Sports Association 2 **Stansted** 5

SEMI-FINALS

Burnham Ramblers 3 Eton Manor 2
Stansted 1 **Enfield** 4

FINAL

(April 11th at Burnham Ramblers)
Burnham Ramblers 2 Enfield 1

LEAGUE CUP

(see next page for details of the group stage)

QUARTER-FINALS

(played over two legs)

Enfield 2 Romford 1, Romford 0 **Enfield** 2
Sawbridgeworth Town 2 Southend Manor 1, Southend Manor 2 **Sawbridgeworth Town** 2
Stansted 2 Barkingside 1, **Barkingside** 3 Stansted 1
Takeley 0 Burnham Ramblers 2, **Burnham Ramblers** 1 Takeley 0

SEMI-FINALS

(played over two legs)

Barkingside 3 Enfield 2, Enfield 1 **Barkingside** 2
Sawbridgeworth Town 0 Burnham Ramblers 3,
Burnham Ramblers 1 Sawbridgeworth Town 0

FINAL

(May 4th at Southend Manor)
Burnham Ramblers 0 **Barkingside** 2

ESSEX SENIOR LEAGUE CUP GROUP STAGE

GROUP A

	P	W	D	L	F	A	Pts
Stansted	6	4	2	0	16	10	14
Burnham Ramblers	6	2	3	1	13	12	9
Bowers & Pitsea	6	2	1	3	14	10	7
London APSA	6	0	2	4	5	16	2

Bowers & Pitsea 1 Burnham Ramblers 2
Bowers & Pitsea 1 London APSA 1
Bowers & Pitsea 2 Stansted 3
Burnham Ramblers 1 Bowers & Pitsea 5
Burnham Ramblers 4 London APSA 0
Burnham Ramblers 1 Stansted 1
London APSA 0 Bowers & Pitsea 3
London APSA 2 Burnham Ramblers 2
London APSA 1 Stansted 3
Stansted 3 Bowers & Pitsea 2
Stansted 3 Burnham Ramblers 3
Stansted 3 London APSA 1

GROUP B

	P	W	D	L	F	A	Pts
Takeley	6	5	0	1	21	4	15
Romford	6	4	0	2	13	13	12
Clapton	6	1	1	4	12	18	4
Basildon United	6	1	1	4	8	19	4

Basildon United 2 Clapton 2
Basildon United 2 Romford 0
Basildon United 0 Takeley 5
Clapton 7 Basildon United 2
Clapton 2 Romford 3
Clapton 0 Takeley 1
Romford 2 Basildon United 1
Romford 5 Clapton 1
Romford 2 Takeley 1
Takeley 3 Basildon United 1
Takeley 5 Clapton 0
Takeley 6 Romford 1

GROUP C

	P	W	D	L	F	A	Pts
Enfield	6	5	1	0	21	6	16
Southend Manor	6	2	1	3	12	18	7
Barking	6	1	3	2	9	11	6
Hullbridge Sports	6	1	1	4	6	13	4

Barking 0 Enfield 4
Barking 1 Hullbridge Sports 1
Barking 2 Southend Manor 2
Enfield 2 Barking 2
Enfield 2 Hullbridge Sports 0
Enfield 6 Southend Manor 0
Hullbridge Sports 0 Barking 3
Hullbridge Sports 1 Enfield 2
Hullbridge Sports 4 Southend Manor 2
Southend Manor 2 Barking 1
Southend Manor 3 Enfield 5
Southend Manor 3 Hullbridge Sports 0

GROUP D

		P	W	D	L	F	A	Pts
Sawbridgeworth T.		6	3	2	1	16	13	11
Barkingside		6	3	1	2	16	10	10
Eton Manor	*-3*	6	3	2	1	14	11	8
Mauritius Spts Ass.		6	0	1	5	5	17	1

Barkingside 1 Eton Manor 2
Barkingside 3 Mauritius Sports Association 1
Barkingside 2 Sawbridgeworth Town 2
Eton Manor 4 Barkingside 3
Eton Manor 2 Mauritius Sports Association 2
Eton Manor 3 Sawbridgeworth Town 3
Mauritius Sports Association 0 Barkingside 2
Mauritius Sports Association 0 Eton Manor 2
Mauritius Sports Association 0 Sawbridgeworth 3
Sawbridgeworth Town 1 Barkingside 5
Sawbridgeworth Town 2 Eton Manor 1
Sawbridgeworth 5 Mauritius Sports Association 2

BARKING

Founded: 1880 Nickname: The Blues

Chairman: Gillian Faherty
Secretary: John Faherty
265 Westrow Drive
Barking
Essex
IG11 9BU
Tel: 0776 458 7112
Manager: Steve Munday
Prog Editor: Norman Dean

Ground: Mayesbrook Park, Lodge Avenue, Dagenham RM8 2JR. Tel: 0776 458 7112.
Capacity: 2,500 **Seats:** 200 **Covered:** 600
Midweek Matchday: Tuesday **Clubhouse:** Yes **Shop:** Yes
Colours(change): All blue. (All yellow).
Previous Names: Barking Rov. Barking Woodville. Barking Institute. Barking T. Barking & East Ham Utd.
Previous Lges: Athenian. Isthmian. Southern.
Records: **Att:** 1,972 v Aldershot, FA Cup 2nd Rnd, 1978.
Goalscorer: Neville Fox - 241 (65-73). **Apps:** Bob Makin - 566.
Senior Honours: Athenian League Champions 1934-35. Isthmian League 78-79.
Essex Senior Cup 1893-94, 95-96, 1919-20, 45-46, 62-63, 69-70, 89-90.

10 YEAR RECORD

99-00	00-01	01-02	02-03	03-04	04-05	05-06	06-07	07-08	08-09
Isth2 7	Isth2 3	Isth1 21	Isth1N 12	Isth1N 23	SthE 6	SthE 5	ESen 6	ESen 9	ESen 12

BARKINGSIDE

Founded: 1898 Nickname:

Chairman: Jimmy Flanagan
Secretary: Jimmy Flanagan
66 Kingsland Road
Plaistow
London
E13 9PA
Tel: 0208 552 3995
Manager: Tony Fenn
Prog Editor: See secretary

Ground: Oakside Stadium, Station Road, Barkingside IG6 1NB. Tel 0208 550 3611.
Capacity: 3,000 **Seats:** 350 **Covered:** 850
Midweek Matchday: Monday **Clubhouse:** Yes **Shop:** No
Colours(change): Sky blue & white stripes/sky blue/sky blue. (All red & white).
Previous Names: None
Previous Lges: London. Greater London. Met London. Spartan, South Midlands.
Records: **Att:** 957 v Arsenal Reserves, London League, 1957.
Senior Honours: Greater London League 1964-65. Spartan League 96-97.
London Senior Cup 96-97. Spartan South Midlands Premier 98-99. Essex Senior Cup 08-09.

10 YEAR RECORD

99-00	00-01	01-02	02-03	03-04	04-05	05-06	06-07	07-08	08-09
ESen 3	ESen 3	ESen 13	ESen 9	ESen 11	ESen 4	ESen 4	ESen 3	ESen 3	ESen 5

BASILDON UNITED

Founded: 1963 Nickname:

Chairman: John Moran
Secretary: Richard Mann
29 Little Lullaway
Basildon
Essex
SS15 5HT
Tel: 01268 454 081
Manager: Jody Pervwell
Prog Editor: See secretary

Ground: The Stadium, Gardiners Close, Basildon SS14 3AW. Tel: 01268 520 268.
Capacity: 2,000 **Seats:** 400 **Covered:** 1,000
Midweek Matchday: Tuesday **Clubhouse:** Yes **Shop:** No
Colours(change): Amber & black/black/black. (Green & white).
Previous Names: Armada Sports.
Previous Lges: Grays & Thurrock. Greater London. Essex Senior. Athenian. Isthmian.
Records: **Att:** 4,000 v West Ham, ground opening 11.08.70.
Senior Honours: Essex Senior League Champions 1976-77, 77-78, 78-79, 79-80, 93-94.
Isthmian League Div.2 Champions 83-84.

10 YEAR RECORD

99-00	00-01	01-02	02-03	03-04	04-05	05-06	06-07	07-08	08-09
ESen 13	ESen 8	ESen 10	ESen 13	ESen 7	ESen 7	ESen 11	ESen 10	ESen 16	ESen 8

BETHNAL GREEN UNITED

Founded: 2000 Nickname:

Chairman: Mohammed Nural Hoque
Secretary: Akhtar Ahmed
25 James Hammett House
Ravenscroft Street
London
E2 7QH
Tel: 0794 902 2719
Manager: Justin Gardner
Prog Editor: Akhtar Ahmed

Ground: Mile End Stadium, Rhodeswell Rd, Poplar E14 7TW. Tel: 020 8980 1885.
Capacity: **Seats:** Yes **Covered:** Yes
Midweek Matchday: Wednesday **Clubhouse:** **Shop:**
Colours(change): Green & white. (Yellow & black).
Previous Names: None.
Previous Lges: Middlesex 2000-09.
Records:
Senior Honours: Middlesex League Champions 2008-09

10 YEAR RECORD

99-00	00-01	01-02	02-03	03-04	04-05	05-06	06-07	07-08	08-09
				Midx1 2	MidxP 7			MidxP 8	MidxP 1

BOWERS & PITSEA

Founded: 1946 Nickname:

Chairman: Barry Hubbard
Secretary: Lee Stevens
59 Cross Green
Lee Chapel South
Basildon
SS16 5QL
Tel: 07910 626 727
Manager: Colin Cook
Prog Editor: See Secretary

Ground: Len Salmon Stadium, Crown Ave., Pitsea, Bailson SS13 2BE. Tel: 01268 581 977.
Capacity: 2,000 **Seats:** 200 **Covered:** 1,000
Midweek Matchday: Wednesday **Clubhouse:** Yes **Shop:** Yes
Colours(change): All claret. (All sky blue).
Previous Names: Bowers United > 2004.
Previous Lges: Thurrock & Thameside Combination. Olympian.
Records: Att: 1,800 v Billericay Town, FA Vase.
Senior Honours: Essex Senior Champions 1980-81, 98-99.

10 YEAR RECORD

99-00	00-01	01-02	02-03	03-04	04-05	05-06	06-07	07-08	08-09
ESen 6	ESen 7	ESen 6	ESen 7	ESen 8	ESen 10	ESen 15	ESen 4	ESen 7	ESen 11

BURNHAM RAMBLERS

Founded: 1900 Nickname: Ramblers

Chairman: William Hannan
Secretary: Shaun Pugh
6 The Chase
South Woodham Ferrers
Essex
CM3 5PN
Tel: 07770 676 727
Manager: Gary Kimble
Prog Editor: Martin Leno

Ground: Leslie Fields Stadium, Springfield Rd., CM0 8AU. Tel: 01621 784 383
Capacity: 2,000 **Seats:** 156 **Covered:** 300
Midweek Matchday: Tuesday **Clubhouse:** Yes **Shop:** No
Colours(change): Royal blue & black stripes/black/royal blue. (All red).
Previous Names: None
Previous Lges: North Essex. Mid-Essex. Olympian. South East Essex.
Records: Att: 1,500 v Arsenal, opening of stand.
Senior Honours:

10 YEAR RECORD

99-00	00-01	01-02	02-03	03-04	04-05	05-06	06-07	07-08	08-09
ESen 3	ESen 14	ESen 3	ESen 8	ESen 12	ESen 2	ESen 5	ESen 5	ESen 8	ESen 7

CLAPTON

Founded: 1878 Nickname: Tons

Chairman: Dennis Wright
Secretary: Shirley Doyle
13 Thurlestone Road
West Norwood
London
SE27 0PE
Tel: 0798 358 8883
Manager: Wilfred Thomas
Prog Editor: Dennis Wright

Ground: The Old Spotted Dog, Upton Lane, Forest Gate E7 9NU. Tel: 0208 472 0822.
Capacity: 2,000 **Seats:** 100 **Covered:** 180
Midweek Matchday: Tuesday **Clubhouse:** Yes **Shop:** No
Colours(change): Red/white/black. (Blue/white/black).
Previous Names: None
Previous Lges: Southern (founder member). London. Isthmian (founder member).
Records: Att: 12,000 v Tottenham Hotspur, FA Cup, 1898-99.
First English club to play on the continent, beating a Belgian XI in 1890.
Senior Honours: FA Amateur Cup 1906-07, 08-09, 14-15, 23-24, 24-25.
Isthmian Lge Champions 10-11, 22-23. Div.2 82-83. Essex Senior Cup (x 4).

10 YEAR RECORD

99-00	00-01	01-02	02-03	03-04	04-05	05-06	06-07	07-08	08-09
Isth3 20	Isth3 21	Isth3 21	Isth2 9	Isth2 15	Isth2 16	Isth2 16	ESen 14	ESen 11	ESen 16

ENFIELD 1893 FC

Founded: 1893 Nickname:

Chairman: Steve Whittington
Secretary: Mark Wiggs
1 Trumper Road,
Stevenage
Herts
SG1 5JZ
Tel: 0754 593 9791
Manager: Kevin Lucas
Prog Editor: Mark Kettlety

Ground: Boxbourne Boro FC, Goff's Lane, Broxbourne EN7 5QW. Tel: 019991 624 281
Capacity: 500 **Seats:** 300 **Covered:** Yes
Midweek Matchday: Wednesday **Clubhouse:** Yes **Shop:**
Colours(change): White/blue/white. (Orange/black/white).
Previous Names: Enfield Spartans > 1900. Enfield > 2007.
Previous Lges: Tottenham & Dist. Nth Middx. London. Athenian. Isthmian. Alliance. S'then
Records: Att: 10,000 v Tottenham Hotspur, floodlight opening at Southbury Rd., 10.10.62.
Goals: Tommy Lawrence - 191 (1959-64). **Apps:** Andy Pape - 643 (85-92 93-99)
Senior Honours: Athenian 1961-62, 62-63. Isthmian 67-68, 68-69, 69-70, 75-76, 76-77, 77-78, 79-80, 94-95. FA Trophy 81-82, 87-88. Alliance 82-83, 85-86. FA Am. C. 66-67, 69-70

10 YEAR RECORD

99-00	00-01	01-02	02-03	03-04	04-05	05-06	06-07	07-08	08-09
Isth P 14	Isth P 18	Isth P 19	Isth P 23	Isth1N 24	Isth2 2	SthE 16	Isth1N 13	ESen 2	ESen 2

2009-10

INS & OUTS

IN: Bethnal Green United (Middlesex County League Premier Division), Tiptree United (S – Eastern Counties League Premier Division), Witham Town (R – Isthmian League Division One North). OUT: Romford (P – Isthmian League Division One North)

2009-10

ETON MANOR

Founded: 1901 Nickname: The Manor

Chairman: Reg Curtis
Secretary: Paul Norris
25 Greenacre Gardens
Walthamstow
London
E17 9EX
Tel: 0797 929 7971
Manager: Kevin Durrant
Prog Editor: See chairman

Ground: Barking FC, Mayesbrook Park, Lodge Ave, Dagenham RM8 2JR.
Capacity: 2,500 **Seats:** 200 **Covered:** 600
Midweek Matchday: Wednesday **Clubhouse:** Yes **Shop:**
Colours(change): Sky blue & navy. (All red with white piping/white/red).
Previous Names: Wildernes Leyton.
Previous Lges: London. Greater London. Metropolitan.
Records: **Att:** 600 v Leyton Orient, opening of floodlights.
Goalscorer: Dave Sams.
Senior Honours: Essex Senior League Cup 2007-08.

10 YEAR RECORD

99-00	00-01	01-02	02-03	03-04	04-05	05-06	06-07	07-08	08-09
ESen 12	ESen 15	ESen 15	ESen 16	ESen 9	ESen 12	ESen 13	ESen 11	ESen 4	ESen 6

HULLBRIDGE SPORTS

Founded: 1945 Nickname:

Chairman: Andy Burgess
Secretary: Mrs Beryl Petre
58 Grasmere Avenue
Hullbridge
Essex
SS5 6LF
Tel: 01702 230 630
Manager: Enrico Tritera
Prog Editor: See secretary

Ground: Lower Road, Hullbridge, Hockley Essex SS5 6BJ. Tel: 01702 230 420.
Capacity: 1,500 **Seats:** 60 **Covered:** 60
Midweek Matchday: Tuesday **Clubhouse:** Yes **Shop:** No
Colours(change): Royal blue & white/royal/royal. (All red).
Previous Names: None
Previous Lges: Southend & District. Southend Alliance.
Records: **Att:** 800 v Blackburn Rovers, FA Youth Cup 1999-00.
Senior Honours:

10 YEAR RECORD

99-00	00-01	01-02	02-03	03-04	04-05	05-06	06-07	07-08	08-09
ESen 10	ESen 12	ESen 12	ESen 15	ESen 16	ESen 15	ESen 14	ESen 12	ESen 14	ESen 9

LONDON APSA

Founded: 1993 Nickname:

Chairman: Zulfi Ali
Secretary: Zabir Bashir
Flat 5, Quiberon Court
45 Chadd Green
Plaistow
E13 0NJ
Tel: 07956 660 699
Manager: John Higley
Prog Editor: Fahim Shah

Ground: Terrance McMillian Stadium, Plaistow E13 8SO. Tel: 0207 511 4477
Capacity: 4,000 **Seats:** 400 **Covered:** 400
Midweek Matchday: Tuesday **Clubhouse:** **Shop:**
Colours(change): Green & white/green & white/green. (All blue).
Previous Names: Ahle Sunnah
Previous Lges: Asian League.
Records:
Senior Honours: None

10 YEAR RECORD

99-00	00-01	01-02	02-03	03-04	04-05	05-06	06-07	07-08	08-09
				ESen 15	ESen 13	ESen 9	ESen 13	ESen 17	ESen 14

MAURITIUS SPORTS & PENNANT

Founded: Nickname:

Chairman: Suresh Taurah
Secretary: Feizal Sobratty
68 Lynmouth Road
Walthamstow
London
E17 8AQ
Tel: 0208 923 9122
Manager: Hector Varela
Prog Editor: See secretary

Ground: Wadham Lodge S & S Club, Kitchener Rd E17 4JP. Tel: 020 8527 2444.
Capacity: **Seats:** **Covered:**
Midweek Matchday: Tuesday **Clubhouse:** Yes **Shop:** No
Colours(change): All white. (All blue).
Previous Names: Mauritius Sports merged with Walthamstow Avenue & Pennant 2007.
Previous Lges: London Intermediate.
Records:
Senior Honours: None

10 YEAR RECORD

99-00	00-01	01-02	02-03	03-04	04-05	05-06	06-07	07-08	08-09
		LonInt 9	LonInt 8					ESen 13	ESen 15

SAWBRIDGEWORTH TOWN

Founded: 1890 Nickname: Robins

Chairman: Steve Day
Secretary: Mrs Leslie Atkins
41 The Orchards
Sawbridgeworth
Herts
CM21 9BB
Tel: 07762 553 924
Manager: Pete Wickham
Prog Editor: Steve Tozer

Ground: Crofters End, West Road, Sawbridgeworth CM21 0DE. Tel: 01279 722 039.
Capacity: 2,500 **Seats:** 175 **Covered:** 300
Midweek Matchday: Tuesday **Clubhouse:** Yes **Shop:** No
Colours(change): Red & black/black/black. (Green/green/white).
Previous Names: Sawbridgeworth > 1976.
Previous Lges: Stortford. Spartan. Herts County. Essex Olympian.
Records: **Att:** 610 v Bishops Stortford.
Senior Honours: Essex Olympian League Champions 1971-72.

10 YEAR RECORD

99-00	00-01	01-02	02-03	03-04	04-05	05-06	06-07	07-08	08-09
ESen 7	ESen 13	ESen 7	ESen 6	ESen 3	ESen 8	ESen 6	ESen 8	ESen 12	ESen 13

SOUTHEND MANOR

Founded: 1955 Nickname: The Manor

Chairman: Robert Westley
Secretary: John Bastin
49 Leigh Hill
Southend-on-Sea
Essex
SS9 2DH
Tel: 01702 482 171
Manager: Russell Faulker/Stroyan Nelson
Prog Editor: See chairman

Ground: The Arena, Southchurch Pk, Lifstan Way, Southend SS1 2TH. Tel: 01702 615577
Capacity: 2,000 **Seats:** 500 **Covered:** 700
Midweek Matchday: Tuesday **Clubhouse:** Yes **Shop:** No
Colours(change): Yellow/black/yellow. (White/red/red).
Previous Names: None
Previous Lges: Southend Borough Combination. Southend & District Alliance.
Records: **Att:** 1,521 v Southend United, opening floodlights, 22.07.91.
Senior Honours: Essex Senior League Cup 1987-88, 89-90, 00-01.
Essex Senior League Champions 1990-91. Essex Senior Trophy 92-93.

10 YEAR RECORD

99-00	00-01	01-02	02-03	03-04	04-05	05-06	06-07	07-08	08-09
ESen 2	ESen 4	ESen 5	ESen 4	ESen 10	ESen 6	ESen 10	ESen 9	ESen 6	ESen 4

STANSTED

Founded: 1902 Nickname: Blues

Chairman: Terry Shoebridge
Secretary: Terry Shoebridge
2 Dawson Close
Saffron Walden
Essex
CB10 2AR
Tel: 01799 527 937
Manager: Terry Spillane
Prog Editor: Andy Taylor

Ground: Hargrave Park, Cambridge Road, Stansted CM24 8DL. Tel: 01279 812 897
Capacity: 2,000 **Seats:** 200 **Covered:** 400
Midweek Matchday: Tuesday **Clubhouse:** Yes **Shop:** No
Colours(change): All blue. (All red).
Previous Names: None.
Previous Lges: Spartan. London. Herts County.
Records: **Att:** 828 v Whickham, FA Vase, 1983-84.
Senior Honours: FA Vase Winners 1983-84.

10 YEAR RECORD

99-00	00-01	01-02	02-03	03-04	04-05	05-06	06-07	07-08	08-09
ESen 15	ESen 9	ESen 8	ESen 14	ESen 13	ESen 11	ESen 16	ESen 16	ESen 10	ESen 10

TAKELEY

Founded: 1903 Nickname:

Chairman: Pat Curran
Secretary: Lee Borham
4 Wintershutt Road
Little Canfield
Dunmow
CM6 1GE
Tel: 0798 412 0660
Manager: Don Watters
Prog Editor: David Edwards

Ground: Station Road, Takeley, Bishop's Stortford CM22 6SQ. Tel: 01279 870 404
Capacity: **Seats:** **Covered:**
Midweek Matchday: **Clubhouse:** **Shop:**
Colours(change): All royal blue. (White/black/white).
Previous Names: None.
Previous Lges: Essex Intermediate/Olympian.
Records:
Senior Honours: Essex Intermediate/Olympian 1987-88, 2001-02.

10 YEAR RECORD

99-00	00-01	01-02	02-03	03-04	04-05	05-06	06-07	07-08	08-09
EssxO 4	EssxO 6	EssxO 1	EssxO 2	EssxO 6	EssxO 8	EssxO 9	EssxO 3	EssxO 2	ESen 3

2009-10

TIPTREE UNITED

Founded: 1933 Nickname: The Jam-makers

Chairman: Ed Garty
Secretary: John Wisbey
103 Peace Road
Stanway
Colchester
CO3 0HW
Tel: 01206 564 222

Manager: Colin Wallington

Prog Editor: See Secretary

Ground: Chapel Road, Tiptree, Essex CO5 0RA. Tel: 07703 585 814.
Capacity: 2,500 **Seats:** 150 **Covered:** 300
Midweek Matchday: Tuesday **Clubhouse:** Yes **Shop:** No
Colours(change): Red with black trim/black/red with black trim. (All white).
Previous Names: None
Previous Lges: Essex & Suffolk Border. Essex Senior. Eastern Counties.
Records: Att: 1,920 v AFC Sudbury, FA Vase semi-final, 2002.

Senior Honours: Essex Senior Trophy 1980-81. Eastern Counties League 1981-82. Eastern Counties Div.1 99-00, 07-08.

10 YEAR RECORD

99-00	00-01	01-02	02-03	03-04	04-05	05-06	06-07	07-08	08-09
EC1 1	ECP 14	ECP 15	ECP 12	ECP 21	EC1 8	EC1 4	EC1 7	EC1 1	ECP 8

WITHAM TOWN

Founded: 1947 Nickname: Town

Chairman: Tony Last
Secretary: Mrs Alison Barker
15 Wentworth Crescent
Braintree
Essex
CM7 5QD
Tel: 01376 324 324

Manager: Danny Greaves

Prog Editor: David Cobb

Ground: Spicer McColl Stadium, Spa Road, Witham CM8 1UN.Tel: 01376 511 198
Capacity: 2,500 **Seats:** 157 **Covered:** 780
Midweek Matchday: Tuesday **Clubhouse:** Yes **Shop:** No
Colours(change): All blue. (All white).
Previous Names: None.
Previous Lges: Mid. Essex. Essex & Suff. B. Essex Senior 1971-87. Isthmian 1987-2009
Records: Att: 800 v Billericay Town, Essex Senior Lge, May 1976.
Goalscorer: Colin Mitchell. **Appearances:** Keith Dent.
Senior Honours: Essex Senior League Champions 1970-71, 85-86.

10 YEAR RECORD

99-00	00-01	01-02	02-03	03-04	04-05	05-06	06-07	07-08	08-09
Isth2 21	Isth3 8	Isth3 12	Isth2 7	Isth2 6	Isth2 5	Isth2 2	Isth1N 20	Isth1N 20	Isth1N 21

Barking F.C.

Swabridgeworth Town F.C.
Photos: Alan Coomes.

HELLENIC LEAGUE

www.hellenicleague.co.uk

Sponsored by:
FTL Futbol

Founded: 1953

Recent champions:
2004: Brackley Town
2005: Highworth Town
2006: Didcot Town
2007: Slimbridge
2008: North Leigh

Premier Division		P	W	D	L	F	A	Pts
Hungerford Town		42	29	9	4	103	38	96
Shortwood United		42	29	9	4	99	45	96
Witney United		42	28	7	7	105	55	91
Almondsbury Town	*-1*	42	28	7	7	106	41	90
Ardley United		42	23	11	8	85	58	80
Highworth Town		42	24	5	13	88	60	77
Chalfont Wasps		42	22	4	16	77	70	70
Reading Town		42	19	10	13	88	49	67
Kidlington		42	17	9	16	70	65	60
Pegasus Juniors		42	17	4	21	73	82	55
Wantage Town		42	17	3	22	71	69	54
Carterton		42	15	8	19	70	79	53
Hook Norton		42	14	10	18	69	81	52
Fairford Town		42	13	12	17	62	67	51
Marlow United		42	16	3	23	69	98	51
Flackwell Heath	*-3*	42	16	5	21	80	86	50
Old Woodstock Town		42	13	10	19	59	70	49
Shrivenham		42	12	4	26	49	87	40
Abingdon Town		42	11	5	26	43	86	38
Bicester Town		42	10	6	26	48	114	36
Milton United		42	8	6	28	52	105	30
Harrow Hill		42	4	7	31	46	107	19

Reserve Division One		P	W	D	L	F	A	Pts
North Leigh Res.	*-3*	30	22	3	5	104	38	66
Didcot Town Res.		30	19	5	6	78	40	62
Kidlington Res.	*-1*	30	18	5	7	70	49	58
Henley Town Res.		30	16	8	6	76	57	56
Highworth Town Res.		30	15	5	10	73	43	50
Binfield Res.		30	13	5	12	72	74	44
Swindon Supermarine Res.		30	14	2	14	63	81	44
Wantage Town Res.		30	12	6	12	73	82	42
Milton United Res.		30	12	4	14	73	68	40
Headington Amateurs Res.		30	13	1	16	86	88	40
Fairford Town Res.	*-1*	30	12	4	14	60	60	39
Finchampstead Res.		30	11	5	14	63	74	38
Cheltenham Saras Res.		30	9	5	16	50	69	32
Abingdon Town Res.		30	8	4	18	53	77	28
Wootton Bassett T. Res.		30	6	6	18	40	80	24
Carterton Res.		30	4	4	22	36	90	16

	Abingdon Town	Almondsbury Town	Ardley United	Bicester Town	Carterton	Chalfont Wasps	Fairford Town	Flackwell Heath	Harrow Hill	Highworth Town	Hook Norton	Hungerford Town	Kidlington	Marlow United	Milton United	Old Woodstock Town	Pegasus Juniors	Reading Town	Shortwood United	Shrivenham	Wantage Town	Witney United
Abingdon Town		0-3	1-2	2-1	0-1	4-2	1-0	1-3	2-1	1-4	2-0	0-2	2-2	1-0	2-2	0-2	1-2	0-4	2-2	1-0	0-5	2-5
Almondsbury Town	3-0		1-1	4-0	3-1	4-2	0-0	4-0	2-2	1-2	2-3	0-0	3-2	6-0	6-0	4-0	3-2	4-2	2-1	3-2	6-1	4-2
Ardley United	3-1	2-1		4-0	2-0	0-1	0-1	4-4	4-0	0-2	3-1	1-1	2-5	2-2	4-2	2-1	2-2	2-0	3-3	2-0	2-1	2-2
Bicester Town	2-3	1-0	2-4	***P***	0-4	0-1	4-2	1-0	4-3	0-4	1-1	0-5	0-0	1-3	2-1	3-5	1-6	0-0	1-3	2-0	0-4	1-4
Carterton	2-0	0-1	1-2	4-2	***R***	2-3	3-1	1-0	0-0	1-5	0-2	2-4	3-0	4-1	3-3	3-1	5-2	4-3	0-1	1-3	2-3	2-2
Chalfont Wasps	2-1	0-3	3-3	1-1	1-0	***E***	2-0	1-0	4-1	3-1	3-2	1-2	3-1	4-0	3-2	0-3	3-2	0-1	1-3	2-0	0-2	1-2
Fairford Town	2-1	2-0	0-2	6-2	0-0	1-2	***M***	1-2	1-1	6-1	1-1	1-1	2-1	1-0	0-1	1-1	2-2	2-2	0-2	1-0	6-1	2-3
Flackwell Heath	1-2	0-2	2-2	3-0	7-1	1-7	2-2	***I***	5-1	2-1	6-0	1-4	1-4	2-3	5-1	2-2	2-0	2-1	1-2	1-3	3-1	0-5
Harrow Hill	0-4	1-3	1-4	1-2	0-0	2-1	1-3	3-1	***E***	0-3	2-4	2-2	1-3	2-4	1-2	0-0	0-6	1-2	1-2	2-5	0-1	2-3
Highworth Town	2-0	0-2	0-1	4-2	1-0	4-0	6-0	2-1	2-1	***R***	2-2	2-1	2-2	3-2	2-1	1-0	3-1	3-2	2-3	5-0	0-3	1-3
Hook Norton	3-0	2-2	1-2	1-1	1-2	1-2	3-1	4-3	2-3	0-3		1-1	2-2	6-0	1-0	1-1	1-3	1-5	1-3	3-3	1-3	0-4
Hungerford Town	1-0	1-0	2-2	2-0	5-1	2-1	2-0	4-5	7-1	2-1	2-1	***D***	3-1	3-0	5-0	6-0	1-0	1-0	0-0	2-1	2-1	1-1
Kidlington	1-0	2-0	1-1	1-1	2-1	1-2	0-1	2-1	0-2	0-1	4-4	1-5	***I***	4-0	3-2	0-2	3-1	2-1	1-2	1-0	2-3	2-3
Marlow United	1-0	0-4	1-2	6-0	1-1	0-3	5-3	2-0	3-2	2-0	0-1	2-5	0-0	***V***	3-4	2-0	3-1	0-6	0-2	4-0	1-6	2-3
Milton United	2-0	0-1	3-4	2-4	1-2	1-1	0-2	1-1	2-1	1-5	1-2	1-2	1-3	2-4	***I***	1-2	3-0	1-1	0-3	0-2	2-1	2-2
Old Woodstock Town	2-2	1-2	0-2	6-1	2-2	2-1	1-1	3-1	2-0	0-0	0-2	0-3	1-2	1-3	3-2	***S***	0-1	2-1	2-3	0-0	2-3	1-2
Pegasus Juniors	1-0	1-4	2-0	1-2	2-3	2-0	0-0	1-2	1-0	1-2	0-2	0-6	2-1	3-2	4-0	2-4	***I***	1-1	1-4	2-1	4-1	3-0
Reading Town	1-0	1-2	0-1	2-0	3-2	6-0	2-0	2-0	2-2	6-1	3-0	2-2	2-2	1-2	5-0	2-1	3-0	***O***	1-1	8-0	1-3	1-0
Shortwood United	6-0	2-2	4-1	2-1	2-1	4-1	3-3	2-4	2-1	2-2	4-2	2-1	1-0	4-0	4-0	1-0	5-1	0-0	***N***	3-0	0-2	1-2
Shrivenham	6-1	0-5	1-0	3-1	1-2	2-3	0-3	0-1	1-0	2-1	0-1	0-1	0-2	2-1	3-1	0-2	2-3	0-0	1-1		0-3	1-4
Wantage Town	1-2	0-2	0-2	6-0	3-3	1-1	3-0	0-2	1-0	1-1	0-2	0-1	0-2	0-2	0-1	4-0	0-2	0-2	1-3	1-2		0-3
Witney United	1-1	2-2	2-1	0-1	3-0	0-5	3-1	3-0	5-1	2-1	1-0	3-0	1-2	3-2	3-0	1-1	4-2	4-0	0-1	7-2	2-1	

SBJ SPORTS INSURANCE TROPHY

(all teams in league)

PRELIMINARY ROUND

Ardley 4 Letcombe 0, Bisley Sports 0 **Highworth Town** 3
Carterton 2 Newbury 1
Cheltenham Saracens 0 **Kidlington** 3
Cirencester United 3 **Abingdon Town** 3 *aet* (2-3p)
Englefield Green Rovers 0 **Holyport** 2
Flackwell Heath 10 Headington Amateurs 3
Hardwicke 3 Clanfield 2, **Henley Town** 4 Purton 1
Hook Norton 1 **Wootton Bassett Town** 2
Launton 4 Winterbourne 1, **Lydney** 1 Cricklade Town 0
Milton United 2 Thame 1, **Old Woodstock** 3 Kintbury 1
Penn & Tylers Green 0 **Ascot United** 4
Pewsey Vale 0 **Tytherington Rocks** 1
Prestwood 5 **Finchampstead** 7 *aet*
Rayners Lane 1 **Binfield** 4, Reading Town 0 **Fairford** 1
Shrivenham 0 **Chalfont Wasps** 2
S. Kilburn 3 Malmesbury 2 *aet*, **Trowbridge** 2 Bicester 1
Wantage Town 1 Oxford City Nomads 0
Wokingham & Emmbrook 3 Easington Sports 0

FIRST ROUND

Ardley United 1 **Old Woodstock Town** 3 *aet*
Ascot United 2 **Shortwood United** 3
Binfield 2 South Kilburn 1
Chinnor 2 **Abingdon Town** 3
Fairford Town 0 **Marlow United** 2
Finchampstead 4 Harrow Hill 3
Flackwell Heath 2 **Almondsbury Town** 3
Henley 1 **Carterton** 3, **Highworth** 4 Pegasus Juniors 1
Hungerford 6 Holyport 1, Launton 0 **Kidlington** 7
Lydney Town 1 **Chalfont Wasps** 3
Tytherington Rocks 2 Trowbridge Town 1
Wantage Town 2 **Witney United** 2 *aet* (4-5p)
Wokingham & Emmbrook 2 **Milton United** 3
Wootton Bassett Town 1 Hardwicke 0

SECOND ROUND

Abingdon Town 0 **Old Woodstock Town** 2
Binfield 2 **Almondsbury Town** 3 *aet*
Carterton 3 Tytherington Rocks 0
Chalfont Wasps 4 Highworth Town 1
Kidlington 3 Finchampstead 0
Marlow United 2 Witney United 1
Milton United (scr.) v **Hungerford Town** (w/o)
Wootton Bassett Town 0 **Shortwood United** 2

QUARTER-FINALS

Almondsbury Town 2 Hungerford Town 2 *aet* (5-4p)
Carterton 2 Marlow United 1
Old Woodstock Town 2 Kidlington 0
Shortwood United 5 Chalfont Wasps 0

SEMI-FINALS

Carterton 2 Shortwood United 1
Old Woodstock Town 0 **Almondsbury Town** 2

FINAL

(May 4th at Shrivenham)
Almondsbury Town 1 Carterton 0

Division One East	P	W	D	L	F	A	Pts
Binfield	**34**	**29**	**3**	**2**	**89**	**18**	**90**
Ascot United	**34**	**25**	**4**	**5**	**91**	**35**	**79**
Newbury	**34**	**20**	**11**	**3**	**100**	**41**	**71**
Wokingham & Emmbrook	**34**	**20**	**6**	**8**	**86**	**44**	**66**
Holyport	**34**	**16**	**9**	**9**	**76**	**60**	**57**
South Kilburn	**34**	**15**	**8**	**11**	**68**	**62**	**53**
Henley Town	**34**	**13**	**13**	**8**	**65**	**43**	**52**
Chinnor	**34**	**14**	**9**	**11**	**51**	**48**	**51**
Thame United	**34**	**13**	**10**	**11**	**64**	**45**	**49**
Kintbury Rangers	**34**	**15**	**4**	**15**	**69**	**58**	**49**
Finchampstead	**34**	**12**	**12**	**10**	**64**	**43**	**48**
Penn & Tylers Green	**34**	**10**	**9**	**15**	**46**	**59**	**39**
Englefield Green Rovers	**34**	**9**	**9**	**16**	**52**	**73**	**36**
Rayners Lane	**34**	**8**	**7**	**19**	**45**	**63**	**31**
Launton Sports	**34**	**7**	**5**	**22**	**45**	**91**	**26**
Bisley Sports	**34**	**5**	**10**	**19**	**42**	**74**	**25**
Prestwood	**34**	**5**	**4**	**25**	**29**	**130**	**19**
Eton Wick	**34**	**1**	**5**	**28**	**25**	**120**	**8**

Reserve Division Two East	P	W	D	L	F	A	Pts
Rayners Lane Res.	18	15	2	1	59	14	47
Chalfont Wasps Res.	18	13	4	1	71	20	43
Holyport Res.	18	12	1	5	52	18	37
Newbury Res.	18	8	4	6	43	34	28
Ascot United Res.	18	5	5	8	23	34	20
Chinnor Res.	18	6	2	10	24	40	20
Thame United Res.	18	5	4	9	28	43	19
Penn & Tylers Green Res.	18	5	2	11	21	48	17
Kintbury Rangers Res.	18	3	4	11	22	55	13
Prestwood Res.	18	4	0	14	29	66	12

Reserve Division Two West		P	W	D	L	F	A	Pts
Ardley United Res.		16	13	1	2	51	15	40
Shrivenham Res.		16	11	1	4	55	16	34
Old Woodstock Town Res.		16	8	3	5	31	23	27
Hook Norton Res.		16	6	4	6	34	27	22
Witney United Res.	*-3*	16	7	3	6	34	41	21
Letcombe Res.		16	6	3	7	20	34	21
Clanfield Res.		16	5	2	9	35	54	17
Launton Sports Res.		16	4	4	8	29	40	16
Cirencester United Res.		16	1	1	14	12	51	4

	Ascot	Binf.	Bisley	Chin.	Eng.	Eton	Finch.	Henl.	Holy.	Kint.	Laun.	Newb.	Penn	Pres.	Rayn.	S Kil.	Tham	Wok.
Ascot United		0-1	2-0	1-1	3-1	3-1	1-1	5-1	7-1	3-0	5-0	2-1	2-1	6-1	3-2	5-0	2-1	2-1
Binfield	3-1	***D***	5-1	5-0	1-0	3-0	1-1	4-0	2-1	2-0	4-0	2-2	2-0	3-0	1-0	2-2	3-0	4-2
Bisley Sports	2-4	0-1	***I***	1-1	10-1	5-2	1-1	2-5	1-1	1-0	0-1	1-1	0-2	4-0	1-3	0-0	0-2	1-3
Chinnor	1-2	0-2	4-1	***V***	2-1	2-0	0-3	1-1	0-0	0-2	5-0	0-2	1-1	4-2	0-3	2-0	1-1	0-1
Englefield Green R.	0-1	0-6	3-0	2-2	***I***	3-0	1-0	2-2	2-4	3-4	2-0	1-5	1-1	5-2	3-0	1-2	1-3	1-1
Eton Wick	0-6	1-6	1-1	1-2	1-1	***S***	0-3	0-3	1-7	0-7	0-3	1-6	1-1	1-3	0-2	2-0	2-2	1-5
Finchampstead	4-2	0-1	1-1	0-1	2-2	3-0	***I***	0-4	2-1	4-0	2-0	1-4	5-1	11-0	0-3	0-2	1-2	2-0
Henley Town	0-0	1-4	0-0	0-1	4-0	5-0	1-5	***O***	1-1	1-1	0-0	1-1	1-1	5-0	1-1	5-0	1-1	1-1
Holyport	4-1	1-4	5-2	2-2	1-1	2-1	2-1	3-0	***N***	4-3	3-1	0-4	1-0	6-2	2-2	1-3	0-2	1-1
Kintbury Rangers	2-1	0-1	2-0	4-4	3-4	5-1	3-0	0-1	0-0		2-0	2-1	1-2	8-0	1-1	3-1	2-4	2-0
Launton Sports	1-3	0-3	0-1	1-3	1-3	3-3	1-1	1-3	2-4	4-3	***O***	2-5	1-0	2-2	5-0	3-6	3-2	0-1
Newbury	1-1	3-2	6-0	2-1	3-3	2-1	1-1	3-2	2-2	6-1	4-1	***N***	3-1	5-0	1-1	1-1	3-3	1-1
Penn/Tylers Green	0-3	0-2	2-2	0-2	3-1	4-1	2-2	0-4	4-2	0-2	2-0	0-2	***E***	0-0	1-0	3-1	1-1	3-4
Prestwood	0-4	0-1	1-0	0-3	2-1	5-1	0-2	0-3	0-3	0-3	2-1	1-12	1-1		1-5	1-4	1-5	1-6
Rayners Lane	1-2	1-2	3-1	1-3	0-1	3-0	1-1	0-3	0-3	3-1	2-4	1-2	1-3	0-0	***E***	0-2	0-1	1-4
South Kilburn	1-3	0-4	6-0	3-0	1-0	3-1	1-1	2-2	1-3	5-0	3-3	2-1	4-2	2-1	5-1	***A***	1-1	1-5
Thame United	0-1	0-2	1-1	2-0	3-1	6-0	1-1	1-0	2-5	0-2	6-1	1-2	0-1	7-0	1-1	1-1	***S***	0-1
Wokingham & E.	1-4	1-0	4-1	1-2	0-0	5-0	2-2	2-3	3-0	1-0	6-0	1-2	5-3	6-0	4-2	4-2	3-1	***T***

Division One West		P	W	D	L	F	A	Pts
Hardwicke		32	27	3	2	93	18	84
Malmesbury Victoria		32	21	6	5	91	45	69
Oxford City Nomads		32	20	4	8	80	51	64
Wootton Bassett Town		32	17	9	6	61	30	60
Letcombe		32	17	6	9	88	52	57
Purton		32	17	6	9	85	59	57
Winterbourne United		32	15	5	12	77	54	50
Lydney Town		32	14	7	11	45	45	49
Tytherington Rocks	*-1*	32	13	8	11	48	40	46
Headington Amateurs		32	11	8	13	72	64	41
Clanfield		32	11	6	15	51	63	39
Cheltenham Saracens		32	10	7	15	52	63	37
Easington Sports		32	9	6	17	45	69	33
Trowbridge Town		32	10	2	20	40	67	32
Cricklade Town		32	7	3	22	50	97	24
Cirencester United		32	4	3	25	34	130	15
Pewsey Vale		32	3	3	26	31	96	12

SOCCERKITS PLUS SUPPLEMENTARY CUP

(League Cup Preliminary and First Round losers)

PRELIMINARY ROUND

Bicester Town 0 **Reading Town** 6
Easington Sports 3 Lydney Town 0
Englefield Green Rovers 3 Clanfield 2 *aet*
Fairford Town 1 Winterbourne United 0
Holyport 0 **Cricklade Town** 1
Kintbury Rangers 2 Penn & Tylers Green 1
Prestwood 1 **Oxford City Nomads** 3
Thame United 0 **Trowbridge Town** 1
Wantage Town 6 Bisley Sports 0

FIRST ROUND

Ascot United 1 **South Kilburn** 5
Chinnor 2 Eton Wick 1 *(at Eton Wick)*
Competition abandoned due to inclement weather

CHAIRMAN'S CUP

FINAL *(May 2nd at Clanfield)*
Highworth Town Res. 3 Henley Town Res. 1

PRESIDENT'S CUP

FINAL *(May 5th at Witney United)*
Shriveham Res. 4 Witney United Res. 2

HIGHWORTH PRESS LTD FLOODLIGHT CUP

PRELIMINARY ROUND

Chalfont Wasps 0 **Ardley United** 1
Clanfield 0 **Hungerford Town** 7
Didcot Town Res. 1 **Shortwood United** 5
Harrow Hill 1 **Wootton Bassett Town** 2
Milton United 3 **Highworth Town** 4
Pewsey Vale 2 Swindon Supermarine Res. 0

FIRST ROUND

Abingdon Town 1 **Kidlington** 2 *aet*
Ardley United 2 Thame United 1
Bisley Sports 0 **Holyport** 2
Carterton 0 **Binfield** 0 *aet* (2-3p)
Flackwell Heath 4 Oxford City Nomads 1
Henley Town 2 **Marlow United** 3
Highworth Town 3 Reading Town 1
Hook Norton 3 Wantage Town 1
Lydney Town 0 **Almondsbury Town** 3
(at Almondsbury Town)
Malmesbury Victoria 3 Wootton Bassett Town 0
North Leigh Res. 1 **Cheltenham Saracens** 2
Old Woodstock Town 1 **Bicester Town** 1 *aet* (2-4p)
Pegasus Juniors 0 **Witney United** 2
Pewsey Vale 0 **Hungerford Town** 1
Shortwood United (w/o) v Newbury
Shrivenham 4 Fairford Town 1

SECOND ROUND

Almondsbury Town 0 **Witney United** 2
Ardley United 2 **Highworth Town** 5
Binfield 4 Flackwell Heath 1
Cheltenham Saracens 2 Shrivenham 1
Holyport 1 **Kidlington** 3
Hook Norton 4 Shortwood United 0
Malmesbury Victoria 1 **Hungerford Town** 4
Marlow United 3 Bicester Town 1

QUARTER-FINALS

Binfield 0 **Kidlington** 4
Highworth Town 1 **Hungerford Town** 1 *aet* (2-4p)
Marlow United 2 Cheltenham Saracens 1
Witney United 1 **Hook Norton** 2

SEMI-FINALS

Hungerford Town 3 Hook Norton 0
Kidlington 0 **Marlow United** 2

FINAL

(March 31st at Hungerford Town)
Hungerford Town 2 **Marlow United** 3 *aet*

	Chelt. S.	Ciren. U.	Clanf'ld	Crick.	Eas'gton	Hard.	Head.	Letc.	Lydney	Malm.	Ox. CN	Pewsey	Purton	Trowb.	Tyther.	Winter.	Woott.
Cheltenham Saracens	***D***	4-2	1-1	4-3	4-1	0-2	0-3	2-1	0-0	3-3	0-2	1-1	1-4	2-2	2-3	2-1	1-1
Cirencester United	3-2	***I***	1-1	0-6	2-0	0-7	0-6	2-3	0-1	1-5	4-7	0-2	2-9	0-2	0-2	0-6	0-3
Clanfield	1-0	3-0	***V***	6-0	0-3	2-4	2-2	2-1	0-1	1-6	1-4	1-0	3-1	5-0	2-3	0-3	1-1
Cricklade Town	1-3	1-1	4-1	***I***	7-1	0-2	1-4	1-5	1-4	0-5	0-4	2-1	1-3	5-3	0-3	3-5	3-5
Easington Sports	3-2	2-4	0-1	1-1	***S***	0-5	2-3	0-6	4-3	3-4	1-2	1-1	2-0	1-2	0-0	1-1	0-4
Hardwicke	4-0	5-0	2-1	4-1	1-0	***I***	6-0	1-2	4-1	3-1	3-0	7-0	1-1	2-1	1-0	3-0	1-0
Headington Amateurs	1-2	4-1	3-3	2-1	2-3	1-1	***O***	1-1	2-0	1-3	9-2	7-1	3-3	0-1	0-1	5-3	2-2
Letcombe	3-1	7-1	5-2	6-0	0-1	1-1	4-1	***N***	2-1	0-1	3-0	4-1	5-3	4-0	3-3	6-4	0-2
Lydney Town	3-2	2-1	2-2	4-0	W-L	1-3	2-1	3-3		0-1	1-2	1-0	2-3	1-0	0-3	2-0	1-0
Malmesbury Victoria	2-5	7-1	2-1	3-0	5-1	0-4	5-0	2-1	1-1	***O***	2-5	8-2	2-2	3-2	3-0	2-1	1-0
Oxford City Nomads	4-1	8-2	1-2	4-0	3-2	3-0	3-1	2-2	2-0	2-2	***N***	3-1	2-2	2-1	2-0	3-1	1-1
Pewsey Vale	2-3	2-2	1-3	0-1	0-3	0-3	3-1	3-4	0-1	0-3	2-1	***E***	0-6	0-1	0-2	2-5	2-5
Purton	2-1	5-1	1-0	2-1	1-1	1-4	3-4	2-0	4-1	2-1	1-2	5-0		3-1	4-2	0-1	2-5
Trowbridge Town	3-2	1-2	2-0	1-2	0-3	0-3	1-0	3-1	0-2	2-5	0-1	4-3	3-4	***W***	0-1	0-1	2-1
Tytherington Rocks	0-1	7-0	2-3	2-2	2-0	0-1	1-1	1-2	1-1	1-1	3-2	1-0	1-1	1-1	***E***	2-1	0-2
Winterbourne United	0-0	2-1	6-0	6-1	2-4	1-3	1-1	3-1	2-2	0-2	1-0	4-1	6-3	6-1	2-0	***S***	1-1
Wootton Bassett Town	1-0	8-0	1-0	2-1	1-1	0-2	2-1	2-2	1-1	0-0	2-1	3-0	0-2	1-0	2-0	2-1	***T***

ABINGDON TOWN

Founded: 1870 Nickname: The Abbots

Chairman: Tom Larman
Secretary: Wendy Larman
3 Belmont House
Wantage

OX12 9AS
Tel: 01235 763 985
Manager: Mark O'Hara
Prog Editor: Kenny More

Ground: Culham Road, Abingdon OX14 3HP. Tel: 01235 521 684.
Capacity: 3,000 **Seats:** 271 **Covered:** 1,771
Midweek Matchday: Tuesday **Clubhouse:** Yes **Shop:** Yes
Colours(change): Yellow & green/green/green.
Previous Names: Abingdon FC (merged with St Michaels in 1899) > 1928.
Previous Lges: Reading Senior. Reading & Dist. Oxfordshire Sen. Nth Berks. Spartan. Isthmian.
Records: **Att:** 4,000 v Swindon Town, Maurice Owen Benefit, 1950.

Senior Honours: Hellenic League Champions 1956-57, 58-59, 59-60, 86-87. Div.1 75-76. Berks & Bucks Senior Cup 58-59. Spartan Lge 88-89. Isthmian Lge Div.2 South 90-91.

10 YEAR RECORD

99-00	00-01	01-02	02-03	03-04	04-05	05-06	06-07	07-08	08-09
Isth3 15	Isth3 17	Isth3 16	Isth2 4	Isth2 9	Isth2 7	Hel P 18	Hel P 18	Hel P 19	Hel P 19

ALMONDSBURY TOWN

Founded: 1897 Nickname: Almonds

Chairman: Bob Jenkins
Secretary: David Jones
43 Cedar Close
Patchway
Bristol
BS34 5HD
Tel: 07903 655 723
Manager: Paul Weeks
Prog Editor: John Haile

Ground: Oakland Park, Almondsbury, Bristol BS32 4AG. Tel: 01454 612 220.
Capacity: 2,000 **Seats:** None **Covered:** None
Midweek Matchday: Wednesday **Clubhouse:** Yes **Shop:** No
Colours(change): Sky blue & white/navy/navy.
Previous Names: Almondsbury Greenway > 1987. Almondsbury Picksons > 1993.
Previous Lges: Gloucestershire County.
Records: **Att:** 2,100 v Newport AFC v Abingdon Utd, Hellenic Cup Final, 1989-90.

Senior Honours: Gloucester Co. Lge Champions 1976-77, 77-78, 78-79, 79-80, 80-81. Hellenic League 83-84. Div.1 88-89. Hellenic Lge Cup 83-84, 84-85, 08-09.

10 YEAR RECORD

99-00	00-01	01-02	02-03	03-04	04-05	05-06	06-07	07-08	08-09
Hel P 17	Hel P 19	Hel P 18	Hel P 17	Hel P 21	Hel P 9	Hel P 14	Hel P 5	Hel P 2	Hel P 4

ARDLEY UNITED

Founded: 1945 Nickname:

Chairman: Norman Stacey
Secretary: Norman Stacey
Ardley House
Somerton Road
Ardley
OX27 7NS
Tel: 01869 345 597
Manager: Kevin Brock
Prog Editor: Peter Sawyer

Ground: The Playing Fields, Oxford Road, Ardley OX27 7NZ. Tel: 07711 009 198.
Capacity: 1,000 **Seats:** 100 **Covered:** 200
Midweek Matchday: Tuesday **Clubhouse:** Yes **Shop:** No
Colours(change): All sky blue.
Previous Names: None
Previous Lges: Oxford Senior.
Records: **Att:** 278 v Kidlington, 29.08.05.

Senior Honours: Oxfordshire Senior League Champions (x 3). Hellenic League Div.1 Champions 1996-97, 97-98.

10 YEAR RECORD

99-00	00-01	01-02	02-03	03-04	04-05	05-06	06-07	07-08	08-09
Hel 1 2	Hel1W 3	Hel1W 3	Hel1W 5	Hel1W 5	Hel P 18	Hel P 10	Hel P 4	Hel P 13	Hel P 5

ASCOT UNITED

Founded: 1965 Nickname:

Chairman: Mike Harrison
Secretary: Mark Gittoes
3 Dorset Vale
Bracknell

RG42 3JL
Tel: 01344 862 184
Manager: Stuart Scammell
Prog Editor: Glen Griffiths

Ground: Ascot Racecourse, Car Park 10, Winkfield Rd, Ascot SL5 7RA. Tel: 07798 701995
Capacity: **Seats:** **Covered:**
Midweek Matchday: Wednesday **Clubhouse:** Yes **Shop:**
Colours(change): Yellow & blue/blue/yellow & blue.
Previous Names: None.
Previous Lges: Reading Senior.
Records: **Att:**121 v Binfield, 21.08.07.

Senior Honours: Reading Senior Champions 2006-07.

10 YEAR RECORD

99-00	00-01	01-02	02-03	03-04	04-05	05-06	06-07	07-08	08-09
		ReadS 12	ReadS 6	ReadS 6	ReadS 3	ReadS 4	ReadS 1	Hel1E 4	Hel1E 2

BICESTER TOWN

Founded: 1876 Nickname: Foxhunters

Chairman: Nick Rowles-Davies
Secretary: Nick Harverson
8 Hollow Furlong
Cassington

OX29 4ET
Tel: 01865 883 092
Manager: Paul Berry
Prog Editor: Phil Allen

Ground: Sports Ground, Oxford Road, Bicester OX26 2AD. Tel: 01869 241 036.
Capacity: 2,000 **Seats:** 150 **Covered:** 550
Midweek Matchday: Tuesday **Clubhouse:** Yes **Shop:** No
Colours(change): Red & black/black/black.
Previous Names: Slade Banbury Road > 1923.
Previous Lges: Oxford Senior.
Records: Att: 955 v Portsmouth, opening of floodlights, 01.02.94.

Senior Honours: Hellenic League Champions 1960-61, 79-80. Div.1 77-78.

10 YEAR RECORD

99-00	00-01	01-02	02-03	03-04	04-05	05-06	06-07	07-08	08-09
Hel P 15	Hel P 14	Hel P 20	Hel P 20	Hel P 14	Hel P 20	Hel1E 2	Hel P 14	Hel P 16	Hel P 20

BINFIELD

Founded: 1892 Nickname: Moles

Chairman: Rob Jones
Secretary: Rob Challis
49 St Mary's Road
Sindlesham
Wokingham
RG41 5DA
Tel: 01189 782 220
Manager: Steve McClurg
Prog Editor: As chairman

Ground: Stubbs Lane, Binfield RG42 5NR. Tel: 01344 860 822.
Capacity: **Seats:** **Covered:**
Midweek Matchday: Monday **Clubhouse:** Yes **Shop:**
Colours(change): All red.
Previous Names: None.
Previous Lges: Ascot & District. Great Western Combination. Reading & Dist. Chiltonian.
Records: Att: 1000+ Great Western Combination.

Senior Honours: Chiltonian League Championship 1995-96.
Hellenic Div.1E Champions 2008-09.

10 YEAR RECORD

99-00	00-01	01-02	02-03	03-04	04-05	05-06	06-07	07-08	08-09
ChiltP 11	Hel1E 10	Hel1E 14	Hel1E 8	Hel1E 5	Hel1E 5	Hel1E 8	Hel1E 11	Hel1E 9	Hel1E 1

CARTERTON

Founded: 1918 Nickname:

Chairman: Robert King
Secretary: John McCarthy
37 Cranwell Avenue
Oxon

OX18 3SB
Tel: 07835 623 843
Manager: Tim North
Prog Editor: As Secretary

Ground: Kilkenny Lane, Carterton, Oxfordshire OX18 1DY. Tel: 01993 842 410.
Capacity: 1,500 **Seats:** 75 **Covered:** 100
Midweek Matchday: Tuesday **Clubhouse:** Yes **Shop:** No
Colours(change): Red with green trim/green/red.
Previous Names: Carterton FC > 1982. Carterton Town > 2004
Previous Lges: Witney & District.
Records: Att: 650 v Swindon Town, July 2001. **Goalscorer:** Phil Rodney.

Senior Honours: Hellenic Div.1 Champions 1989-90, 93-94.

10 YEAR RECORD

99-00	00-01	01-02	02-03	03-04	04-05	05-06	06-07	07-08	08-09
Hel P 9	Hel P 10	Hel P 11	Hel P 3	Hel P 7	Hel P 6	Hel P 7	Hel P 12	Hel P 18	Hel P 12

FAIRFORD TOWN

Founded: 1891 Nickname: Town

Chairman: TBA
Secretary: William Beach
33 Park Close
Fairford
Glos
GL7 4LF
Tel: 01285 712 136
Manager: John Paget
Prog Editor: Andrew Meadon

Ground: Cinder Lane, London Road, Fairford GL7 4AX. Tel: 01285 712 071.
Capacity: 2,000 **Seats:** 100 **Covered:** 250
Midweek Matchday: Tuesday **Clubhouse:** Yes **Shop:** Yes
Colours(change): Red/white/red.
Previous Names: None.
Previous Lges: Cirencester & District. Swindon & District.
Records: Att: 1,525 v Coventry City, friendly, July 2000. **Goalscorer:** Pat Toomey.

Senior Honours: Hellenic League Div.1 A Champions 1971-72.

10 YEAR RECORD

99-00	00-01	01-02	02-03	03-04	04-05	05-06	06-07	07-08	08-09
Hel P 16	Hel P 9	Hel P 6	Hel P 6	Hel P 10	Hel P 8	Hel P 17	Hel P 13	Hel P 20	Hel P 14

INS & OUTS

IN: Ascot United (P – Division One East), Binfield (P – Division One East), Malmesbury Victoria (P – Division One West), Oxford City Nomads (P – Division One West).
OUT: Chalfont Wasps (R – Div. One East), Harrow Hill (R – Div. One West), Hungerford T. (P – Southern Lge Div. One South & West), Milton Utd (R – Div One East)

PREMIER DIVISION - 2009-10

FLACKWELL HEATH

Founded: 1907 Nickname: Heath

Chairman: Geoff Turner
Secretary: David Crisp
3 Melbourne Road
High Wycombe

HP13 7HE
Tel: 07928 727 665
Manager: Matt Flint
Prog Editor: As Chairman

Ground: Wilks Park, Magpie Lane, Heath End Rd, Flackwell Hth HP10 9EA. Tel: 01628 523 892
Capacity: 2,000 **Seats:** 150 **Covered:** Yes
Midweek Matchday: Tuesday **Clubhouse:** Yes **Shop:** No
Colours(change): All red.
Previous Names: None.
Previous Lges: Great Western Combination. Hellenic. Isthmian.
Records: **Att:** 1,500 v Oxford United, charity match, 1966. **Goalscorer:** Tony Wood. **Apps:** Lee Elliott.
Senior Honours: Wycombe Senior Cup Winners (x 12)

10 YEAR RECORD

99-00	00-01	01-02	02-03	03-04	04-05	05-06	06-07	07-08	08-09
Isth3 11	Isth3 4	Isth3 20	Isth2 3	Isth2 5	Isth2 9	Isth2 4	Isth1N 22	Hel P 9	Hel P 16

HIGHWORTH TOWN

Founded: 1893 Nickname: Worthians

Chairman: Darren Robbins
Secretary: Claire Haines
28 Lismore Road
Highworth
Swindon
SN6 7HU
Tel: 01793 763 841
Manager: Dave Webb
Prog Editor: Mike Markham

Ground: Elm Recreation Ground, Highworth SN6 7DD. Tel: 01793 766 263.
Capacity: 2,000 **Seats:** 150 **Covered:** 250
Midweek Matchday: Tuesday **Clubhouse:** Yes **Shop:** No
Colours(change): Red/black/red.
Previous Names: None.
Previous Lges: Swindon & District. Wiltshire.
Records: **Att:** 2,000 v QPR, opening of floodlights. **Goalscorer:** Kevin Higgs. **Apps:** Rod Haines.
Senior Honours: Wiltshire Senior Cup 1963-64, 72-73, 95-96, 97-98.
Hellenic League Champions 2004-05.

10 YEAR RECORD

99-00	00-01	01-02	02-03	03-04	04-05	05-06	06-07	07-08	08-09
Hel P 2	Hel P 8	Hel P 15	Hel P 4	Hel P 9	Hel P 1	Hel P 12	Hel P 15	Hel P 6	Hel P 6

HOOK NORTON

Founded: 1898 Nickname: Hooky

Chairman: Michael Barlow
Secretary: Garnet Thomas
39 Hereford Way
Banbury

OX16 1FT
Tel: 07866 035 642
Manager: Ben Spiero
Prog Editor: Mark Willis

Ground: The Bourne, Hook Norton OX15 5PB. Tel: 01608 737 132.
Capacity: 500 **Seats:** 500 **Covered:** 500
Midweek Matchday: Wednesday **Clubhouse:** Yes **Shop:**
Colours(change): White & royal blue/royal/white.
Previous Names: None.
Previous Lges: Chipping Norton Dist. Oxfordshire Jnr. Banbury & Dist. Oxfordshire Senior.
Records: **Att:** 244 v Banbury United, 12.12.98.

Senior Honours: Oxfordshire Senior Champions 1999-00, 00-01.
Hellenic Div.1 West Champions 2001-02.

10 YEAR RECORD

99-00	00-01	01-02	02-03	03-04	04-05	05-06	06-07	07-08	08-09
OxSen 1	OxSen 1	Hel1W 1	Hel P 12	Hel P 20	Hel1W 11	Hel1W 11	Hel1W 3	Hel P 14	Hel P 13

KIDLINGTON

Founded: 1909 Nickname:

Chairman: Geoff Talboys
Secretary: David Platt
57 Cherry Close
Kidlington
Oxon
OX5 1HJ
Tel: 07768 908 002
Manager: Gordon Geary
Prog Editor: Simon Dickens

Ground: Yarnton Road, Kidlington, Oxford OX5 1AT. Tel: 01865 841 526.
Capacity: **Seats:** Yes **Covered:** Yes
Midweek Matchday: Tuesday **Clubhouse:** Yes **Shop:** No
Colours(change): All green.
Previous Names: None.
Previous Lges: Oxford Senior.
Records: **Att:** 2,500 v Showbiz XI, 1973.

Senior Honours:

10 YEAR RECORD

99-00	00-01	01-02	02-03	03-04	04-05	05-06	06-07	07-08	08-09
Hel 1 12	Hel1W 11	Hel1W 10	Hel1W 7	Hel1W 12	Hel1W 3	Hel P 20	Hel P 9	Hel P 15	Hel P 9

MALMESBURY VICTORIA

Founded: Nickname: The Vic's

Chairman: Paul Neale
Secretary: Sue Neale
30 Gastons Road
Malmesbury
Wiltshire
SN16 0BE
Tel: 01666 823 560
Manager: Lee Marshall
Prog Editor: Andy Meaden

Ground: Flying Monk Ground, Gloucester Rd, Malmesbury SN16 0AJ. Tel: 01666 822 141.
Capacity: **Seats:** **Covered:**
Midweek Matchday: Tuesday **Clubhouse:** **Shop:**
Colours(change): Black & white/black/red.
Previous Names: None.
Previous Lges: Wiltshire Premier
Records: Att: 261 v Cirencester United, 25.08.02.
Senior Honours: Wiltshire League Champions 1999-00. Wiltshire Senior Cup 01-02.

10 YEAR RECORD

99-00	00-01	01-02	02-03	03-04	04-05	05-06	06-07	07-08	08-09
Wilt 1	Hel1W 4	Hel1W 12	Hel1W 14	Hel1W 14	Hel1W 17	Hel1W 13	Hel1W 4	Hel1W 16	Hel1W 2

MARLOW UNITED

Founded: 1977 Nickname: The Flying Blues

Chairman: Bernard Carvell
Secretary: Alan Turner
14 Seymour
Court Road
Marlow
SL7 3AY
Tel: 01628 487 832
Manager: Kevin Carvell
Prog Editor: As chairman

Ground: Wilks Park, Magpie Lane, Flackwell Hth HP10 9EA. Tel: 01628 523 892.
Capacity: 2,000 **Seats:** 150 **Covered:** Yes
Midweek Matchday: Tuesday **Clubhouse:** Yes **Shop:**
Colours(change): White & sky blue/sky blue/white.
Previous Names: None.
Previous Lges: Wycombe & District. Reading (Founder member).
Records: Att: 256 v Cookham Dean, 06.05.2006.
Senior Honours: Reading Senior Champions 2004-05.

10 YEAR RECORD

99-00	00-01	01-02	02-03	03-04	04-05	05-06	06-07	07-08	08-09
ReadP 1	ReadS 6	ReadS 11	ReadS 7	ReadS 3	ReadS 1	ReadS 2	Hel1E 7	Hel1E 2	Hel P 15

OLD WOODSTOCK TOWN

Founded: Nickname:

Chairman: Ted Saxton
Secretary: Louise Jordon
50a New Road
Woodstock
Oxon
OX20 1PD
Tel: 01993 810 641
Manager: Simon Lenagan
Prog Editor: Mark Cain

Ground: Bicester Town Sports Ground, Oxford Rd, Bicester OX20 1PD. Tel: 0869 241 036
Capacity: 2,000 **Seats:** 150 **Covered:** 550
Midweek Matchday: Wednesday **Clubhouse:** Yes **Shop:** No
Colours(change): Royal blue & red/royal/royal.
Previous Names: Old Woodstock and Woodstock Town merged in 1998.
Previous Lges: Oxfordshire Senior.
Records: Att: 258 v Kidlington, 27.08.01.
Senior Honours: Oxfordshire Senior Champions 1998-99.

10 YEAR RECORD

99-00	00-01	01-02	02-03	03-04	04-05	05-06	06-07	07-08	08-09
Hel 1 11	Hel1W 15	Hel1W 8	Hel1W 6	Hel1W 8	Hel1W 14	Hel1W 7	Hel1W 7	Hel1W 2	Hel P 17

OXFORD CITY NOMADS

Founded: 1936 Nickname: The Nomads

Chairman: Brian Cox
Secretary: Colin Taylor
24 Kellys Road
Wheatley
Oxford
OX33 1NT
Tel: 07817 885 396
Manager: Matty Hunt
Prog Editor: As for Secretary

Ground: Court Place Farm Stadium, Marsh Lane, Marston OX3 0NQ. Tel: 01865 744 493
Capacity: 3,000 **Seats:** 300 **Covered:** 400
Midweek Matchday: Wednesday **Clubhouse:** Yes **Shop:** Yes
Colours(change): Blue & white/blue/white.
Previous Names: Quarry Nomads > 2005.
Previous Lges: Chiltonian.
Records: Att: 334 v Headington Amateurs, 25.08.03.
Senior Honours: Hellenic Division East Champions 2002-03.

10 YEAR RECORD

99-00	00-01	01-02	02-03	03-04	04-05	05-06	06-07	07-08	08-09
ChiltP 12	Hel1E 4	Hel1E 11	Hel1E 1	Hel1W 7	Hel1W 15	Hel1E 11	Hel1E 12	Hel1W 9	Hel1W 3

PEGASUS JUNIORS

Founded: 1955 Nickname: The Redmen

Chairman: Roger Hesten
Secretary: Chris Wells
42 Queenswood Drive
Hampton Dene
Hereford
HR1 1AT
Tel: 07980 465 995
Manager: Steve Griffiths
Prog Editor: Kevin Bishop

Ground: Old School Lane, Hereford HR1 1EX. Tel: 07980 465 995 or 07931 971 765
Capacity: 1,000 **Seats:** 110 **Covered:** Yes
Midweek Matchday: Tuesday **Clubhouse:** Yes **Shop:**
Colours(change): All red.
Previous Names: None.
Previous Lges: Herefordshire.
Records: **Att:** 1,400 v Newport AFC, 1989-90.
Senior Honours: Herefordshire Lge Champions 1963-64. Herefordshire Senior Cup 71-72. Worcestershire Senior Urn 85-86. Hellenic Div.1 Champions 84-85, 98-99.

10 YEAR RECORD

99-00	00-01	01-02	02-03	03-04	04-05	05-06	06-07	07-08	08-09
Hel P 10	Hel P 15	Hel P 13	Hel P 18	Hel P 17	Hel P 16	Hel P 13	Hel P 17	Hel P 17	Hel P 10

READING TOWN

Founded: 1966 Nickname: Town

Chairman: Roland Ford
Secretary: Richard Grey
6 Milestone View Court
Lowfield Road
Caversham, Reading
RG4 6ND
Tel: 07970 253 785
Manager: Colin Millard
Prog Editor: Richard Wickson

Ground: Reading Tn Sports Ground, Scours Lane, Reading RG30 6AY. Tel: 0118 945 3555
Capacity: 2000 **Seats:** 120 **Covered:** 200
Midweek Matchday: Tuesday **Clubhouse:** Yes **Shop:** No
Colours(change): Red/black/red & black
Previous Names: Lower Burghfield, XI Utd, Vincents Utd, Reading Garage, ITS Reading T.
Previous Lges: Chiltonian Lge. Combined Counties.
Records: **Att:** 1067 v AFC Wimbledon, Combined Counties 03.05.03.
Senior Honours: Chiltonian League Champions 1994-95.

10 YEAR RECORD

99-00	00-01	01-02	02-03	03-04	04-05	05-06	06-07	07-08	08-09
CC 12	CC 19	CC 21	CC 15	CCP 3	CCP 19	CCP 10	CCP 9	CCP 13	Hel P 8

SHORTWOOD UNITED

Founded: 1900 Nickname: The Wood

Chairman: Peter Webb
Secretary: Mark Webb
7 Cotswold Cottages
Shortwood
Nailsworth
GL6 0SG
Tel: 01453 836 233
Manager: John Evans
Prog Editor: Paul Webb

Ground: Meadowbank, Shortwood, Nailsworth GL6 0SJ. Tel: 01453 833 936.
Capacity: 2,000 **Seats:** 50 **Covered:** 150
Midweek Matchday: Tuesday **Clubhouse:** Yes **Shop:** No
Colours(change): Red & white/black/black.
Previous Names: None.
Previous Lges: Gloucestershire County.
Records: **Att:** 1,000 v Forest Green Rovers, FA Vase 5th Rnd 1982.
Goalscorer: Peter Grant. **Apps:** Peter Grant.
Senior Honours: Gloucestershire Lge Champions 1981-82. Hellenic Lge Champions 84-85, 91-92. Gloucestershire Senior Cup (x 2).

10 YEAR RECORD

99-00	00-01	01-02	02-03	03-04	04-05	05-06	06-07	07-08	08-09
Hel P 11	Hel P 11	Hel P 9	Hel P 13	Hel P 19	Hel P 15	Hel P 15	Hel P 8	Hel P 5	Hel P 2

SHRIVENHAM

Founded: 1900 Nickname: Shrivy

Chairman: Robb Forty
Secretary: Emma Skilton
24 Rutland Road
New College Way
Swindon
SN3 2GY
Tel: 07845 693 274
Manager: Mark Love
Prog Editor: Matt Hirst

Ground: The Recreation Ground, Shrivenham SN6 8BJ. Tel: 07767 371 414.
Capacity: **Seats:** **Covered:**
Midweek Matchday: Wednesday **Clubhouse:** **Shop:**
Colours(change): Blue & white hoops/white/white.
Previous Names: None.
Previous Lges: North Berkshire.
Records: **Att:** 800 v Aston Villa, 21.05.2000.
Senior Honours: North Berkshire Champions 1997-98, 00-01. Hellenic Division 1 West 04-05.

10 YEAR RECORD

99-00	00-01	01-02	02-03	03-04	04-05	05-06	06-07	07-08	08-09
NBk 1 5	NBk 1 1	Hel1W 9	Hel1W 12	Hel1W 3	Hel1W 1	Hel P 8	Hel P 10	Hel P 8	Hel P 18

WANTAGE TOWN

Founded: 1892 Nickname: Alfredians

Chairman: Tony Woodward
Secretary: John Culley
7 The Medway
East Hanney
Wantage
OX12 0HY
Tel: 07921 243 263
Manager: Richard Bourne
Prog Editor: As chairman

Ground: Alfredian Park, Manor Road, Wantage OX12 8DW. Tel: 01235 764 781.
Capacity: 1,500 **Seats:** 50 **Covered:** 300
Midweek Matchday: Tuesday **Clubhouse:** Yes **Shop:** No
Colours(change): Green & white/white/white.
Previous Names: None.
Previous Lges: Swindon & District. North Berkshire. Reading & District.
Records: **Att:** 550 v Oxford United, July 2003.
Senior Honours: Hellenic Division 1 East 1980-81, 03-04. Oxon Senior Cup 82-83.

10 YEAR RECORD

99-00	00-01	01-02	02-03	03-04	04-05	05-06	06-07	07-08	08-09
Hel P 12	Hel P 16	Hel P 12	Hel P 21	Hel1E 1	Hel P 10	Hel P 9	Hel P 11	Hel P 12	Hel P 11

WITNEY UNITED

Founded: 2001 Nickname: The Blanketmen

Chairman: Steve Lake
Secretary: Adrian Bircher
13 Colwell Drive
Witney
Oxon
OX28 5NJ
Tel: 07824 999 119
Manager: Andy Lyne
Prog Editor: Richard Wickson

Ground: Polythene UK Stadium, Downs Road, Witney OX29 7WT. Tel: 01993 848 558.
Capacity: 3,500 **Seats:** 280 **Covered:** 2,000
Midweek Matchday: Tuesday **Clubhouse:** Yes **Shop:** Yes
Colours(change): Yellow/black/yellow.
Previous Names: None.
Previous Lges: None.
Records: **Att:** 628 v Oxford United, 26.02.08
Senior Honours: None.

10 YEAR RECORD

99-00	00-01	01-02	02-03	03-04	04-05	05-06	06-07	07-08	08-09
			Hel1W 15	Hel1W 4	Hel P 11	Hel P 6	Hel P 6	Hel P 4	Hel P 3

CHALFONT WASPS

Founded: 1922 Nickname: The Stingers

Chairman: Steve Waddington
Secretary: Bob Cakebread
8 Pheasant Walk
Chalfont St Peter
Bucks
SL9 0PW
Tel: 01494 873 469
Manager: Martin Stone
Prog Editor: Al Yeomans

Ground: Crossleys, Bowstridge Lane, Chlafont HP8 4QN. Tel: 01494 875 050.
Capacity: **Seats:** **Covered:**
Midweek Matchday: Tuesday **Clubhouse:** **Shop:**
Colours(change): Yellow & black stripes/black/black.
Previous Names: None.
Previous Lges: Chiltonian (Founder member)
Records: **Att:** 82 v Didcot Town, 17.12.2005.
Senior Honours: Hellenic Division 1 East Champions 2007-08.

10 YEAR RECORD

99-00	00-01	01-02	02-03	03-04	04-05	05-06	06-07	07-08	08-09
ChiltP 8	Hel1E 13	Hel1E 17	Hel1E 5	Hel1E 7	Hel1E 17	Hel1E 4	Hel1E 2	Hel1E 1	Hel P 7

CHINNOR

Founded: 1884 Nickname:

Chairman: Kevin Avery
Secretary: Richard Carr
54 Queens Road
Thame
Oxon
OX9 3NQ
Tel: 07786 115 089
Manager: As secretary
Prog Editor: As secretary

Ground: Station Road, Chinnor, Oxon OX39 4PV. Tel: 01844 352 579.
Capacity: 1,500 **Seats:** **Covered:**
Midweek Matchday: Tuesday **Clubhouse:** **Shop:**
Colours(change): Royal blue/blue/blue.
Previous Names: None.
Previous Lges: Wycombe & Dist. Chiltonian. Oxfordshire Senior.
Records: **Att:** 306 v Oxford Quarry Nomads, 29.08.2005.
Senior Honours:

10 YEAR RECORD

99-00	00-01	01-02	02-03	03-04	04-05	05-06	06-07	07-08	08-09
				Hel1E 11	Hel1E 9	Hel1E 16	Hel1E 15	Hel1E 15	Hel1E 8

DIVISION ONE EAST - 09-10

DIDCOT TOWN RESERVES

Founded: 1907 Nickname: Railwaymen

Chairman: John Bailey
Secretary: Pat Horsman
64 High Street
Milton
Abingdon
OX14 4EJ
Tel: 07882 154 612
Manager: Paul McKay
Prog Editor: Joffy Chinnock

Ground: Npower Loop Meadow Stadium, Didcot OX11 7GA. Tel: 01235 813 138
Capacity: 5,000 **Seats:** 250 **Covered:** 200
Midweek Matchday: Tuesday **Clubhouse:** Yes **Shop:** Yes
Colours(change): Red & white/white/red
Previous Names: N/A
Previous Lges: Hellenic Reserves
Records:
Senior Honours:

10 YEAR RECORD

99-00	00-01	01-02	02-03	03-04	04-05	05-06	06-07	07-08	08-09
			HelR1 1	HelR1 2	HelR1 3	HelR1 1	HelR1 8	HelR1 4	HelR1 2

ETON WICK

Founded: Nickname: The Wick

Chairman: Dave Jones
Secretary: Kevin Rhodes
71 Colenorton Crescent
Eton Wick
Windsor
SL4 6NW
Tel: 07701 098 365
Manager: Russell Last
Prog Editor: Terry Reeves

Ground: Haywards Mead, Eton Wick SL4 6JN. Tel: 01753 852 749.
Capacity: **Seats:** **Covered:**
Midweek Matchday: Wednesday **Clubhouse:** Yes **Shop:**
Colours(change): Amber/black/black.
Previous Names: None.
Previous Lges: Chiltonian. Combined Counties.
Records: Att: 500 v Andover, FA Vase, 1993.
Senior Honours: Chiltonian Div.1 Champions 1991-92. Premier 92-93, 98-99. Hellenic Division 1 East 04-05.

10 YEAR RECORD

99-00	00-01	01-02	02-03	03-04	04-05	05-06	06-07	07-08	08-09
ChiltP 2	Hel1E 5	Hel1E 10	Hel1E 6	Hel1E 4	Hel1E 1	Hel1E 10	Hel1E 18	Hel1E 17	Hel1E 18

FARNBOROUGH RESERVES

Founded: 2009 Nickname:

Chairman: Simon Hollis
Secretary: Steve Duley
Farnborough FC
Cherrywood Road
Farnborough
GU14 8UD
Tel: 07922 666 621
Manager: Craig Belgrave
Prog Editor: Chris Harris

Ground: Lion Park, Church Lane, Bisley GU24 9ER. Tel: 01252 541 469
Capacity: **Seats:** **Covered:**
Midweek Matchday: Tuesday **Clubhouse:** **Shop:**
Colours(change): All yellow.
Previous Names: Bisley Sports > 2005. Bisley > 2009.
Previous Lges: Surrey County Premier/Senior.
Records: Att: 252 v Hounslow Borough, 24.12.2005.
Senior Honours: Hellenic Division 1 East Champions 2006-07.

10 YEAR RECORD

99-00	00-01	01-02	02-03	03-04	04-05	05-06	06-07	07-08	08-09
SuCP 15	SuCS 9	Hel1E 7	Hel1E 12	Hel1E 12	Hel1E 18	Hel1E 7	Hel1E 1	Hel1E 8	Hel1E 16

FINCHAMPSTEAD

Founded: 1952 Nickname: Finches

Chairman: Richard Laughharne
Secretary: Nick Markham
12 Firtree Close
Sandhurst
Berks
GU47 8HU
Tel: 07793 866 324
Manager: Neil White
Prog Editor: Richard Whitchurch-Bennett

Ground: Memorial Park, The Village, Finchampstead RG40 4JR. Tel: 0118 973 2890.
Capacity: **Seats:** **Covered:**
Midweek Matchday: Tuesday **Clubhouse:** Yes **Shop:**
Colours(change): Sky blue & white/sky/sky.
Previous Names: None.
Previous Lges: Ascot & District. Reading & District. Chiltonian.
Records: Att: 425 v Sandhurst, 1958-59.
Senior Honours: Chiltonian Champions 1987-88. Reading Senior Challenge Cup 1986-87. Hellenic Div.1 East Champions 2001-02.

10 YEAR RECORD

99-00	00-01	01-02	02-03	03-04	04-05	05-06	06-07	07-08	08-09
ChiltP 4	Hel1E 7	Hel1E 1	Hel1E 3	Hel1E 8	Hel1E 4	Hel1E 13	Hel1E 14	Hel1E 14	Hel1E 11

HENLEY TOWN

Founded: Nickname: The Town

Chairman: Andy Bryan
Secretary: Tony Kingston
50 Birdhill Avenue
Reading
Berks
RG2 7JU
Tel: 07712 139 592
Manager: Roddy Slater
Prog Editor: Geoff Briggs

Ground: The Tringle, Mill Lane, Henley on Thams, Oxon RG9 4HB. Tel: 01491 411 083.
Capacity: 2,000 **Seats:** 60 **Covered:** 100
Midweek Matchday: Tuesday **Clubhouse:** Yes **Shop:** No
Colours(change): White/black/black.
Previous Names: None.
Previous Lges: Chiltonian.
Records: **Att:** 2000+ v Reading, 1922. **Goalscorer:** M. Turner.

Senior Honours: Hellenic Div.1 Champions 1963-64, 67-68. Chiltonian Div.1 87-88. Premier 99-00. Hellenic Div.1 East 00-01.

10 YEAR RECORD

99-00	00-01	01-02	02-03	03-04	04-05	05-06	06-07	07-08	08-09
ChiltP 1	Hel1E 1	Hel P 16	Hel P 10	Hel P 15	Hel P 14	Hel P 20	Hel1E 16	Hel1E 6	Hel1E 7

HOLYPORT

Founded: 1934 Nickname: The Villagers

Chairman: Tony Andrews
Secretary: Graham Broom
4 Rutland Place
Maidenhead
Berks
SL6 4JA
Tel: 07768 746 594
Manager: Jason Andrews
Prog Editor: Richard Tyrell

Ground: Summerleaze Village SL6 8SP. Tel: 07768 746594.
Capacity: **Seats:** **Covered:**
Midweek Matchday: Tuesday **Clubhouse:** **Shop:**
Colours(change): Claret/green/claret.
Previous Names: None.
Previous Lges: Maidenhead & District. Hayes & Giles.
Records: **Att:** 218 v Eton Wick, 2006.

Senior Honours: Norfolkian Senior Cup 1999-2000.

10 YEAR RECORD

99-00	00-01	01-02	02-03	03-04	04-05	05-06	06-07	07-08	08-09
			Hel1E 15	Hel1E 17	Hel1E 15	Hel1E 14	Hel1E 9	Hel1E 7	Hel1E 5

KINTBURY RANGERS

Founded: 1890 Nickname:

Chairman: Bert Newman
Secretary: Cheryl Angell
49 Glendale Avenue
Wash Common
Newbury
RG14 6TG
Tel: 07778 216 999
Manager: Craig Adey
Prog Editor: As secretary

Ground: Recreation Ground, Inkpen Road RG17 9TY. Tel: 01488 657 001.
Capacity: 1,500 **Seats:** **Covered:**
Midweek Matchday: Tuesday **Clubhouse:** Yes **Shop:**
Colours(change): Amber & black/black/amber.
Previous Names: None.
Previous Lges: North Berkshire.
Records: **Att:** 256 v Holyport, Sunday 28.08.2005.

Senior Honours: North Berkshire Champions 2001-02, 02-03, 03-04.

10 YEAR RECORD

99-00	00-01	01-02	02-03	03-04	04-05	05-06	06-07	07-08	08-09
	NBk 1 2	NBk 1 1	NBk 1 1	NBk 1 1	Hel1E 2	Hel1E 9	Hel1E 4	Hel1E 5	Hel1E 10

MILTON UNITED

Founded: 1909 Nickname: Miltonians

Chairman: Barry Griffiths
Secretary: Sharon Palmer
50 North Drive
Harwell, Didcot
Oxon
OX11 0PE
Tel: 07774 676 793
Manager: Bobby Wilkinson
Prog Editor: Pat Horsman

Ground: The Sportsfield, Milton Hill, Potash Lane, Oxon OX13 6AG. Tel: 01235 832 999.
Capacity: 2,000 **Seats:** 50 **Covered:** 100
Midweek Matchday: Monday **Clubhouse:** Yes **Shop:**
Colours(change): All sky blue & claret.
Previous Names: None.
Previous Lges: North Berks.
Records: **Att:** 608 Carterton v Didcot Town, League Cup Final, 07.05.05.
Goalscorer: Nigel Mott.
Senior Honours: Hellenic League Champions 1990-91.

10 YEAR RECORD

99-00	00-01	01-02	02-03	03-04	04-05	05-06	06-07	07-08	08-09
Hel P 19	Hel P 20	Hel1E 6	Hel1E 7	Hel1E 3	Hel P 13	Hel P 11	Hel P 7	Hel P 7	Hel P 21

INS & OUTS

IN: Chalfont Wasps (R), Didcot Town Res. (P – Reserve Division One), Milton United (R), Woodley Town (P – Reading League Senior Division)
OUT: Ascot United (P), Binfield (P), Englefield Green Rovers (W), Launton Sports (S – Division One West). Bisley Sports become Farnborough Res.

NEWBURY

Founded: 1887 Nickname:

Chairman: Keith Moss
Secretary: David Leno
16 Russell Road
Newbury

RG14 5LA
Tel: 07810 848 431
Manager: Steve Melledew
Prog Editor: As secretary

Ground: Faraday Road, Newbury RG14 2AD. Tel: 01635 401031 or 07790 592 154
Capacity: **Seats:** **Covered:**
Midweek Matchday: Tuesday **Clubhouse:** **Shop:**
Colours(change): Amber & black/amber & black/black.
Previous Names: Newbury Town. Old London Apprentice. O L A Newbury.
Previous Lges: Reading League.
Records: **Att:** 246 v Kintbury Rangers 27.12.08.
Senior Honours: Hellenic League 1978-79, 80-81. Athenian League 1982-83.

10 YEAR RECORD

99-00	00-01	01-02	02-03	03-04	04-05	05-06	06-07	07-08	08-09
			Read4 2	Read3 2	Read2 1	Read1 4	Read1 1	ReadS 2	Hel1E 3

PENN & TYLERS GREEN

Founded: 1905 Nickname:

Chairman: Tony Hurst
Secretary: Andreas Latta
Cherrytrees
Cock Lane
Tylers Green
HP10 8DS
Tel: 07810 850 475
Manager: John Farthing
Prog Editor: Fergus Sturrock

Ground: French School Meadows, Elm Road, Penn HP10 8LF. Tel: 01494 815 346.
Capacity: **Seats:** **Covered:**
Midweek Matchday: Tuesday **Clubhouse:** **Shop:**
Colours(change): Blue & white stripes/blue/blue.
Previous Names: None.
Previous Lges: Chiltonian (Founder member).
Records: **Att:** 125 v Chalfont Wasps, August 2000.
Senior Honours:

10 YEAR RECORD

99-00	00-01	01-02	02-03	03-04	04-05	05-06	06-07	07-08	08-09
ChiltP 9	Hel1E 15	Hel1E 9	Hel1E 2	Hel1E 10	Hel1E 3	Hel1E 6	Hel1E 13	Hel1E 11	Hel1E 11

PRESTWOOD

Founded: Nickname:

Chairman: Guy Stansbury
Secretary: Paul Bradley
42 Fairacres
Great Missenden
Bucks
HP16 0LE
Tel: 07711 633 103
Manager: Steve Simmons
Prog Editor: See chairman

Ground: Sprinters Sports Centre, Prestwood HP16 9QY. Tel: 01494 866 688.
Capacity: **Seats:** **Covered:**
Midweek Matchday: Tuesday **Clubhouse:** Yes **Shop:**
Colours(change): Claret & blue/claret & blue/claret.
Previous Names: None.
Previous Lges: Chiltonian.
Records: **Att:** 88 v Penn & Tylers Green, May 2004.
Senior Honours:

10 YEAR RECORD

99-00	00-01	01-02	02-03	03-04	04-05	05-06	06-07	07-08	08-09
ChiltP 14	Hel1E 11	Hel1E 8	Hel1E 14	Hel1E 13	Hel1E 16	Hel1E 18	Hel1E 17	Hel1E 16	Hel1E 17

RAYNERS LANE

Founded: Nickname: The Lane

Chairman: Richard Mitchell
Secretary: Tony Pratt
4 Stirling Close
Cowley
Uxbridge
UB8 2BA
Tel: 01895 233 853
Manager: Paul Leslie
Prog Editor: See chairman

Ground: The Farm Social Club, Rayners Lane, Sth Harrow HA2 0XH. Tel: 0208 868 8724.
Capacity: **Seats:** **Covered:**
Midweek Matchday: Tuesday **Clubhouse:** Yes **Shop:**
Colours(change): Yellow/green/yellow.
Previous Names: None.
Previous Lges: Spartan.
Records: **Att:** 550 v Wealdstone, 1983.
Senior Honours: Hellenic Division 1 Champions 1982-83.

10 YEAR RECORD

99-00	00-01	01-02	02-03	03-04	04-05	05-06	06-07	07-08	08-09
ChiltP 3	Hel1E 6	Hel1E 15	Hel1E 4	Hel1E 6	Hel1E 8	Hel1E 15	Hel1E 5	Hel1E 13	Hel1E 14

SOUTH KILBURN

Founded: Nickname:

Chairman: Dennis Woolcock
Secretary: Amanda Jennings
4 Carlton House
Canterbury Terrace
Kilburn
NW6 5DY
Tel: 07595 256 309
Manager: Mick Jennings
Prog Editor: See secretary

Ground: Vale Farm, Watford Road, Wembley HA0 3HE. Tel: 0208 908 6545
Capacity: **Seats:** **Covered:**
Midweek Matchday: Tuesday **Clubhouse:** **Shop:**
Colours(change): Black & white/black/black.
Previous Names:
Previous Lges: Middlesex County.
Records: **Att:** 65 v Rayners Lane 25.08.08.
Senior Honours:

10 YEAR RECORD

99-00	00-01	01-02	02-03	03-04	04-05	05-06	06-07	07-08	08-09
							Midx1 1	MidxP 2	Hel1E 6

THAME UNITED

Founded: 1883 Nickname: United

Chairman: Jake Collinge
Secretary: Jake Collinge
4 Arnold Way
Thame

OX9 2QA
Tel: 07753 502 955
Manager: Mark West
Prog Editor: See Chairman

Ground: AFC Wallingford, W'ford Sps Pk, Hithercroft Rd OX10 9RB. Tel: 01491 835 044
Capacity: 2,500 **Seats:** Yes **Covered:** Yes
Midweek Matchday: Tuesday **Clubhouse:** Yes **Shop:**
Colours(change): Red & black/black/black.
Previous Names: Thame F.C.
Previous Lges: Oxon Senior. Hellenic. South Midlands. Isthmian. Southern.
Records: **Att:** 1,035 v Aldershot, Isthmian Div.2, 04.04.94. **Goalscorer:** Not known. **Apps:** Steve Mayhew.
Senior Honours: Hellenic Champions 1961-62, 69-70. South Midlands Lge 90-91. Isthmian Div.2 94-95.

10 YEAR RECORD

99-00	00-01	01-02	02-03	03-04	04-05	05-06	06-07	07-08	08-09
Isth1 4	Isth1 5	Isth1 11	Isth1N 8	Isth1N 15	SthW 11	SthW 22	Hel P 20	Hel1E 10	Hel1E 9

WOKINGHAM & EMMBROOK

Founded: 2004 Nickname: Satsumas

Chairman: Glenn Duggleby
Secretary: Sally Blee
19 Clifton Road
Wokingham

RG41 1ML
Tel: 07714 732 790
Manager: Wayne Wanklyn
Prog Editor: Mike Bound

Ground: Cantley Park, Twyford Rd, Wokingham RG40 5QG. Tel: 07775 776 831
Capacity: 1,500 **Seats:** **Covered:**
Midweek Matchday: Tuesday **Clubhouse:** **Shop:**
Colours(change): Orange/black/black.
Previous Names: Club formed when Wokingham Town and Emmbrook Sports merged.
Previous Lges: Isthmian (Wokingham). Reading (Emmbrook Sports).
Records: **Att:** 305 v Binfield, 25.03.2005.
Senior Honours:

10 YEAR RECORD

99-00	00-01	01-02	02-03	03-04	04-05	05-06	06-07	07-08	08-09
					Hel1E 11	Hel1E 3	Hel1E 8	Hel1E 12	Hel1E 4

WOODLEY TOWN

Founded: 1904 Nickname: Town

Chairman: Mark Rozzler
Secretary: John Mailer
6 Waring Close
Lower Earley
Reading
RG6 4JE
Tel: 07883 341 628
Manager: Cyril Fairchild
Prog Editor: Jim Nightingale

Ground: East Park Farm, Park Lane, Charvil, Berks RG10 9TR. Tel: 07703 474 555.
Capacity: **Seats:** **Covered:**
Midweek Matchday: Wednesday **Clubhouse:** **Shop:**
Colours(change):
Previous Names:
Previous Lges: Wargrave & District. Reading & District. Reading.
Records:
Senior Honours: Reading Football League Senior Champions 2008-09. Berkshire Trophy Centre Senior Cup 08-09.

10 YEAR RECORD

99-00	00-01	01-02	02-03	03-04	04-05	05-06	06-07	07-08	08-09
Read1 3	Read1 2	ReadP 2	ReadS 12	ReadP 2	ReadS 7	ReadS 7			ReadS 1

CHELTENHAM SARACENS

Founded: 1964 Nickname: Saras

Chairman: Chris Hawkins
Secretary: Bob Attwood
179 Arle Road
Cheltenham

GL51 8LJ
Tel: 01242 515 855
Manager: Gerry Oldham
Prog Editor: See Secretary

Ground: Petersfield Park, Tewkesbury Road, Cheltenham GL51 9DY. Tel: 01242 584 134.
Capacity: **Seats:** **Covered:**
Midweek Matchday: Wednesday **Clubhouse:** Yes **Shop:** Yes
Colours(change): All navy blue.
Previous Names: None.
Previous Lges: Cheltenham.
Records: **Att:** 327 v Harrow Hill, 31.08.03.

Senior Honours: Glocestershire Senior Cup 1991-92. Hellenic Division 1 99-00.

10 YEAR RECORD

99-00	00-01	01-02	02-03	03-04	04-05	05-06	06-07	07-08	08-09
Hel 1 1	Hel P 17	Hel P 22	Hel1W 9	Hel1W 13	Hel1W 6	Hel1W 8	Hel1W 6	Hel1W 5	Hel1W 12

CIRENCESTER UNITED

Founded: 1969 Nickname: Herd

Chairman: Abderrahman Kartit
Secretary: Gordon Varley
95 Vaisey Road
Cirencester
Glocestershire
GL7 2JW
Tel: 07969 637 810
Manager: Chokri Kartit
Prog Editor: Neil Warriner

Ground: 29 Regt Army Base, South Cerney GL7 5RD. Tel: 07969 637 810
Capacity: **Seats:** **Covered:**
Midweek Matchday: Wednesday **Clubhouse:** **Shop:**
Colours(change): Red/black/black.
Previous Names: The Herd > 1990.
Previous Lges: Cirencester & District. Cheltenham.
Records: **Att:** 191 v Cirencester Academy, 28.12.98. **Goalscorer:** M Day.
Apps: J Stratford - 310.
Senior Honours:

10 YEAR RECORD

99-00	00-01	01-02	02-03	03-04	04-05	05-06	06-07	07-08	08-09
Hel 1 13	Hel1W 7	Hel1W 15	Hel1W 17	Hel1W 15	Hel1W 14	Hel1W 14	Hel1W 12	Hel1W 18	Hel1W 16

CLANFIELD

Founded: 1890 Nickname: Robins

Chairman: John Osborne
Secretary: John Osborne
70 Lancut Road
Witney

OX28 5AQ
Tel: 01993 771 631
Manager: Peter Osborne
Prog Editor: Terry Maycock

Ground: Radcot Road, Clanfield OX18 2ST. Tel: 01367 810 314.
Capacity: 2,000 **Seats:** No **Covered:** 300
Midweek Matchday: Wednesday **Clubhouse:** Yes **Shop:** No
Colours(change): All red.
Previous Names: None.
Previous Lges: North Berkshire. Witney & District.
Records: **Att:** 197 v Kidlington, August 2002.

Senior Honours: Hellenic Division 1 1969-70.

10 YEAR RECORD

99-00	00-01	01-02	02-03	03-04	04-05	05-06	06-07	07-08	08-09
Hel 1 14	Hel1W 9	Hel1W 14	Hel1W 19	Hel1W 18	Hel1W 10	Hel1W 17	Hel1W 17	Hel1W 12	Hel1W 11

CRICKLADE TOWN

Founded: 1897 Nickname: Crick

Chairman: Alisdair Ross
Secretary: Rebecca Ross
47 Melstock Road
Taw Hill
Swindon
SN25 1XE
Tel: 07970 066 581
Manager: Graham Jackson
Prog Editor: See Chairman

Ground: Cricklade Leisure Centre, Stone Lane, Cricklade SN6 6JW. Tel: 01793 750 011.
Capacity: **Seats:** **Covered:**
Midweek Matchday: Tuesday **Clubhouse:** **Shop:**
Colours(change): Green/black/green.
Previous Names: None.
Previous Lges: Wiltshire.
Records: **Att:** 170 v Trowbridge Town, 2003-04.

Senior Honours: Wiltshire League Champions 2000-01.

10 YEAR RECORD

99-00	00-01	01-02	02-03	03-04	04-05	05-06	06-07	07-08	08-09
	Wilt 1					Hel1W 12	Hel1W 8	Hel1W 10	Hel1W 15

EASINGTON SPORTS

Founded: 1946 Nickname: The Clan

Chairman: Steve Hill
Secretary: Neil Clarke
33 Hollies Court
Britannia Road
Banbury
OX16 5DR
Tel: 07789 751 488
Manager: Stuart Viggers
Prog Editor: Paul Dewar

Ground: Addison Road, Banbury, Oxon OX16 9DH. Tel: 01295 257 006.
Capacity: 1,000 **Seats:** No **Covered:** 30
Midweek Matchday: Tuesday **Clubhouse:** Yes **Shop:**
Colours(change): All red.
Previous Names: None.
Previous Lges: Oxfordshire Junior. Oxfordshire Senior. Warwick Combination.
Records: **Att:** 258 v Hook Norton, 29th August.

Senior Honours: Oxfordshire Senior Champions 1957-58, 58-59. Div.1 65-66. Oxfordshire Senior Ben Turner Trophy 70-71.

10 YEAR RECORD

99-00	00-01	01-02	02-03	03-04	04-05	05-06	06-07	07-08	08-09
Hel 1 8	Hel1W 6	Hel1W 13	Hel1W 10	Hel1W 6	Hel1W 5	Hel1W 16	Hel1W 13	Hel1W 6	Hel1W 13

HARROW HILL

Founded: 1932 Nickname: Harry Hill

Chairman: Reg Taylor
Secretary: Mark Rawlings
22 Mannings Road
Highmeade
Drybrooke
GL17 9HS
Tel: 07766 113 271
Manager: Tony Elliott
Prog Editor: See Secretary

Ground: Larksfield Road, Harrow Hill GL17 9JP. Tel: 01594 543 873.
Capacity: **Seats:** **Covered:**
Midweek Matchday: Wednesday **Clubhouse:** **Shop:**
Colours(change): Claret & sky blue/sky blue/sky blue.
Previous Names: None.
Previous Lges: Gloucestershire County.
Records: **Att:** 350 v Cinderford Town, 1992.

Senior Honours:

10 YEAR RECORD

99-00	00-01	01-02	02-03	03-04	04-05	05-06	06-07	07-08	08-09
Hel P 18	Hel P 18	Hel P 19	Hel P 21	Hel1W 18	Hel1W 11	Hel1W 8	Hel1W 2	Hel P 21	Hel P 22

HEADINGTON AMATEURS

Founded: 1949 Nickname: A's

Chairman: Donald Light
Secretary: Acting: Donald Light
64 Temple Road
Cowley
Oxford
OX4 2EZ
Tel: 07764 943 778
Manager: Shaun Pearce
Prog Editor: See Chairman

Ground: Barton Recreation Ground, Oxford OX3 9LA. Tel: 01865 760 489.
Capacity: **Seats:** **Covered:**
Midweek Matchday: Tuesday **Clubhouse:** Yes **Shop:**
Colours(change): All red.
Previous Names: None.
Previous Lges: Oxford City Junior. Oxfordshire Senior.
Records: **Att:** 250 v Newport AFC, 1991. **Goalscorer:** Tony Penge. **Apps:** Kent Drackett.

Senior Honours: Oxfordshire Senior League 1972-73, 73-74, 75-76, 76-77. Div.1 68-69.

10 YEAR RECORD

99-00	00-01	01-02	02-03	03-04	04-05	05-06	06-07	07-08	08-09
Hel 1 15	Hel1W 5	Hel1W 16	Hel1W 8	Hel1W 10	Hel1W 7	Hel1W 4	Hel1E 10	Hel1W 14	Hel1W 10

LAUNTON SPORTS

Founded: 1899 Nickname:

Chairman: Tony Cotter
Secretary: Paul Tulley
1 Forest Close
Launton

OX26 5DD
Tel: 07976 346 896
Manager: Duncan Currie
Prog Editor: Alison Simmons

Ground: The Playing Field, Bicester Road, Launton OX26 5DP. Tel: 01869 242 007.
Capacity: **Seats:** **Covered:**
Midweek Matchday: Tuesday **Clubhouse:** Yes **Shop:** Yes
Colours(change): Yellow/blue/yellow.
Previous Names: Launton.
Previous Lges: Lord Jersey. Oxfordshire Senior
Records: **Att:** 92 v Easington Sports.

Senior Honours: Oxfordshire Senior Div.1 Champions 1992-93.

10 YEAR RECORD

99-00	00-01	01-02	02-03	03-04	04-05	05-06	06-07	07-08	08-09
				OxSen 7	OxSen 7	OxSen 6	OxSen 3	Hel1W 13	Hel1E 15

INS & OUTS

IN: Harrow Hill (R), Launton Sports (S – Division One East), North Leigh Res. (P – Reserve Division One), Slimbridge (P – Gloucestershire County League)
OUT: Hardwicke (W), Malmesbury Victoria (P), Oxford City Nomads (P), Pewsey Vale (R – Wiltshire League Premier Division)

LETCOMBE

Founded: 1910 Nickname: Brooksiders

Chairman: Dennis Stock
Secretary: Des Williams
8 Larkdown
Wantage
oxon
OX12 8HE
Tel: 07765 144 985
Manager: Alan Gifford
Prog Editor: Russell Stock

Ground: Bassett Road, Letcombe Regis OX12 9JU. Tel: 07765 144 985.
Capacity: 1,500 **Seats:** 50 **Covered:** 50
Midweek Matchday: Wednesday **Clubhouse:** **Shop:**
Colours(change): All purple.
Previous Names: None.
Previous Lges: North Berkshire. Chiltonian.
Records: Att: 203 v Old Woodstock Town, 29.08.04.

Senior Honours: North Berkshire Div.1 Champions 1989-90. Chiltonian Div.1 90-91.

10 YEAR RECORD

99-00	00-01	01-02	02-03	03-04	04-05	05-06	06-07	07-08	08-09
Hel 1 7	Hel1W 12	Hel1W 17	Hel1E 9	Hel1E 2	Hel1E 12	Hel1W 9	Hel1W 15	Hel1W 3	Hel1W 5

LYDNEY TOWN

Founded: 1911 Nickname: The Town

Chairman: Pete Elliott
Secretary: Roger Sansom
17 Woodland Rise
Lydney
Glos
GL15 5LH
Tel: 07887 842 125
Manager: Neil Hook
Prog Editor: See Secretary

Ground: Lydney Rec., Swan Road, Lydney GL15 5RU. Tel: 01594 844 523.
Capacity: **Seats:** **Covered:**
Midweek Matchday: Tuesday **Clubhouse:** Yes **Shop:**
Colours(change): Black & white stripes/black/black.
Previous Names: None.
Previous Lges: Gloucestershire County.
Records: Att: 375 v Ellwood, 05.11.05.

Senior Honours: Gloucestershire County Champions 2005-06.
Hellenic Division 1 West Champions 2006-07.

10 YEAR RECORD

99-00	00-01	01-02	02-03	03-04	04-05	05-06	06-07	07-08	08-09
						GlCo 1	Hel1W 1	Hel P 10	Hel1W 8

NORTH LEIGH RESERVES

Founded: 1908 Nickname:

Chairman: Peter King
Secretary: Keith Huxley
The Orchard
Cote Bampton
Oxon
OX18 2EG
Tel: 07775 818 066
Manager: Paul Lewis
Prog Editor: Mike Burnell

Ground: Eynsham Hall Park Sports Ground OX29 6PN. Tel: 01993 881 427 (Match days)
Capacity: 2,000 **Seats:** 100 **Covered:** 200
Midweek Matchday: Tuesday **Clubhouse:** Yes **Shop:** No
Colours(change): Sky blue/sky blue/white.
Previous Names: N/A
Previous Lges: Hellenic Reserves.
Records: -

Senior Honours: None

10 YEAR RECORD

99-00	00-01	01-02	02-03	03-04	04-05	05-06	06-07	07-08	08-09
			HelR1 12	HelR1 4	HelR1 9	HelR1 13	HelR1 5	HelR1 5	HelR1 1

PURTON

Founded: 1923 Nickname: The Reds

Chairman: Alan Eastwood
Secretary: Jannice Kucynski
26 Manton Street
Swindon

SN2 2AL
Tel: 07816 648 949
Manager: Chris Pethick
Prog Editor: See Chairman

Ground: The Red House, Purton SN5 4DY. Tel: 01793 770 262 (Match days only)
Capacity: Unlimited **Seats:** No **Covered:** No
Midweek Matchday: Wednesday **Clubhouse:** Yes **Shop:**
Colours(change): All red.
Previous Names: None.
Previous Lges: Wiltshire. Wiltshire County.
Records: Att: 533 v Dorcan, April 1987.

Senior Honours: Wiltshire Champions 1945-46, 46-47, 47-48. Wiltshire County 85-86.
Hellenic Div.1 95-96, Div. 1 W 03-04. Wiltshire Senior Cup 38-39, 48-49, 50-51, 54-55, 87-88, 88-89, 94-95.

10 YEAR RECORD

99-00	00-01	01-02	02-03	03-04	04-05	05-06	06-07	07-08	08-09
Hel 1 9	Hel1W 13	Hel1W 4	Hel1W 3	Hel1W 1	Hel1W 13	Hel1W 15	Hel1W 16	Hel1W 11	Hel1W 6

SLIMBRIDGE

Founded: 1899 Nickname: The Swans

Chairman: Keith Sparrow
Secretary: Doug Reeves
35 Farm Lees
Charfield
Wotton-Under-Edge
GL12 8JA
Tel: 07957 483 827
Manager: James Cole
Prog Editor: Tim Blake

Ground: Wisloe Road, Cambridge, Glos GL2 7AF. Tel: 07957 483 827 or 07835 927 226
Capacity: **Seats:** Yes **Covered:** Yes
Midweek Matchday: Wednesday **Clubhouse:** Yes **Shop:** Yes
Colours(change): Blue/blue/white.
Previous Names: None
Previous Lges: Stroud & District. Gloucester Northern. Gloucestershire County.
Records: Since 2002-03. **Att:** 525 v Shortwood United, Hellenic Prem. 24.08.03.
Goals: Julian Freeman - 79 (from 122 apps.).
Senior Honours: Glos Northern Senior Cup 2000-01. Hellenic Div.1W Champions 02-03. Hellenic Premier Champions 06-07. Gloucestershire County Champions 2008-09.

10 YEAR RECORD

99-00	00-01	01-02	02-03	03-04	04-05	05-06	06-07	07-08	08-09
GIN2 2	GIN1 2	GlCo 2	Hel1W 1	Hel P 4	Hel P 4	Hel P 5	Hel P 1	GIN1 1	GlCo 1

TROWBRIDGE TOWN

Founded: 1880 Nickname:

Chairman: Andrew Mackinder
Secretary: Jo King
2 Holmeleaze
Steeple Ashton
Trowbridge
BA14 6EH
Tel: 07545 172 043
Manager: Chris Carr
Prog Editor: Andy Meadon

Ground: Wood Marsh Bradley Road, Trowbridge BA14 0SB. Tel: 07545 172043.
Capacity: 1,500 **Seats:** **Covered:**
Midweek Matchday: Tuesday **Clubhouse:** **Shop:**
Colours(change): Yellow & black/black/yellow & black.
Previous Names: Reformed in 1998.
Previous Lges: Wiltshire Intermediate. Wiltshire.
Records: **Att:** 369 v Tytherington Rocks, 28.08.05.
Senior Honours: Wiltshire League Champions 2003-04. Wiltshire Senior Cup 03-04.

10 YEAR RECORD

99-00	00-01	01-02	02-03	03-04	04-05	05-06	06-07	07-08	08-09
WiltIn 1	Wilt 6	Wilt 4	Wilt 5	Wilt 1	Hel1W 2	Hel1W 6	Hel1W 2	Hel1W 4	Hel1W 14

TYTHERINGTON ROCKS

Founded: 1896 Nickname: The Rocks

Chairman: Ted Travell
Secretary: Graham Shipp
21 Elmdale Crescent
Thornbury
Bristol
BS35 2JQ
Tel: 07811 318 424
Manager: Barry Granger
Prog Editor: Mark Brown

Ground: Hardwicke Playing Field, Tytherington GL12 8UJ. Tel: 07837 555 776.
Capacity: 1,500 **Seats:** **Covered:**
Midweek Matchday: Wednesday **Clubhouse:** Yes **Shop:**
Colours(change): Amber & black/black/black.
Previous Names: None.
Previous Lges: Gloucestershire County.
Records: **Att:** 400 v Thornbury Town, Senior Amateur Cup, 1948.
Senior Honours:

10 YEAR RECORD

99-00	00-01	01-02	02-03	03-04	04-05	05-06	06-07	07-08	08-09
GlCo 8	GlCo 4	GlCo 9	GlCo 5	GlCo 2	Hel1W 4	Hel1W 3	Hel1W 5	Hel1W 8	Hel1W 9

WINTERBOURNE UNITED

Founded: 1911 Nickname: The Bourne

Chairman: Robyn Maggs
Secretary: Geoff Endicott
27 Star Barn Road
Winterbourne
Bristol
BS36 1NU
Tel: 07778 678 823
Manager: Stewart Jones
Prog Editor: Mark Brown

Ground: Parkside Avenue, Winterbourne, Bristol BS36 1LX. Tel: 01454 850 059.
Capacity: **Seats:** **Covered:**
Midweek Matchday: Tuesday **Clubhouse:** Yes **Shop:**
Colours(change): All red.
Previous Names: None.
Previous Lges: Gloucestershire County.
Records: **Att:** 229 v Malmesbury Victoria, 29.08.2004.
Senior Honours: Gloucestershire County Champions 2000-01. Hellenic Division 1 West 05-06, 07-08.

10 YEAR RECORD

99-00	00-01	01-02	02-03	03-04	04-05	05-06	06-07	07-08	08-09
GlCo 9	GlCo 1	Hel1W 6	Hel1W 4	Hel1W 9	Hel1W 9	Hel1W 1	Hel1W 10	Hel1W 1	Hel1W 7

DIV 1 WEST - 09-10

WOOTTON BASSETT TOWN

Founded: 1882 Nickname:

Chairman: Paul Harrison
Secretary: Rod Carter
14 Blackthorn Close
Wootton Bassett
Swindon
SN4 7JE
Tel: 07957 996 283
Manager: Dave Turner
Prog Editor: Mark Smedley

Ground: Gerard Buxton Sport Ground, Rylands Way SN4 8AW. Tel: 01793 853 880.
Capacity: 2,000 **Seats:** None **Covered:** 350
Midweek Matchday: Tuesday **Clubhouse:** Yes **Shop:** No
Colours(change): Blue & yellow/blue/yellow.
Previous Names: None.
Previous Lges: Wiltshire.
Records: **Att:** 2,103 v Swindon Town, July 1991. **Goalscorer:** Brian 'Tony' Ewing. **Apps:** Steve Thomas.
Senior Honours: Wiltshire Champions 1987-88.

10 YEAR RECORD

99-00	00-01	01-02	02-03	03-04	04-05	05-06	06-07	07-08	08-09
Hel 1 3	Hel P 13	Hel P 19	Hel P 15	Hel P 16	Hel P 21	Hel1W 5	Hel1W 11	Hel1W 15	Hel1W 4

Step 5 Action.....

Spartan South Midlands League
Action from Biggleswade Town's 1-0 victory over Hertford Town.

Spartan South Midlands League
Kevin Kilroy heads Biggleswade Town into the lead during the title deciding game against Chalfont St Peter which the 'Waders' won 3-2 to take the title.

United Counties League
St Neots win this league match 3-0 against Newport Pagnell.

Photos: Gordon Whittington.

KENT LEAGUE

www.kentleague.com

Sponsored by: Bulmers

Founded: 1966

Recent champions:
2004: Cray Wanderers
2005: Ramsgate
2006: Maidstone United
2007: Whitstable Town
2008: Thamesmead Town

	Beck.	Croy.	Deal	Erith	E & B	Fav.	Green.	H. Bay	Holm.	Hythe	Lord.	Norton	Seven.	Slade G.	S Beng.	Tunb.	VCD
Beckenham Town	***P***	2-0	1-1	2-3	2-3	2-7	0-2	1-2	2-0	1-3	0-1	4-1	3-2	4-3	4-3	2-2	2-4
Croydon	2-1	***R***	3-1	1-3	2-0	2-1	0-1	1-2	0-3	1-2	5-2	2-0	3-0	4-1	8-0	0-1	0-0
Deal Town	1-1	2-4	***E***	0-0	0-1	0-3	1-2	2-1	0-4	1-0	3-3	4-0	3-0	2-1	4-0	1-3	1-1
Erith Town	2-1	0-0	1-1	***M***	1-3	0-1	1-2	1-3	0-1	4-1	2-0	0-0	2-1	0-2	6-0	0-0	3-1
Erith & Belvedere	3-2	3-2	1-5	2-3	***I***	2-1	1-1	1-2	0-2	0-2	1-0	0-0	2-1	0-3	10-2	0-0	0-1
Faversham Town	5-1	4-1	4-0	1-1	3-2	***E***	1-3	2-1	0-1	1-3	5-1	1-0	1-2	5-2	10-0	2-1	0-2
Greenwich Borough	3-2	0-2	2-1	3-3	2-0	1-2	***R***	1-0	1-3	1-1	2-3	0-1	2-1	3-2	4-0	2-1	0-4
Herne Bay	3-0	3-2	1-1	2-5	3-2	1-5	1-2		0-0	2-3	4-0	4-0	2-0	2-1	6-2	4-1	1-1
Holmesdale	3-2	1-1	3-2	1-1	0-2	0-1	1-1	4-0		3-1	1-0	3-2	2-1	2-2	6-0	3-3	0-1
Hythe Town	1-0	1-0	2-1	1-1	1-1	1-4	0-2	5-1	1-1	***D***	7-2	4-1	3-1	3-0	5-0	2-0	0-2
Lordswood	2-0	1-4	2-3	1-2	1-1	1-2	1-3	0-2	1-0	0-1	***I***	0-1	0-1	2-4	4-2	1-2	1-2
Norton Sports	2-1	1-0	1-4	0-1	3-4	2-1	3-5	0-1	2-1	1-4	4-3	***V***	2-2	1-2	5-0	3-1	1-2
Sevenoaks Town	2-2	0-1	3-2	3-3	1-3	1-5	4-2	1-3	0-1	3-2	5-1	0-2	***I***	1-1	2-1	1-2	0-5
Slade Green	1-3	1-0	2-1	1-0	0-4	1-1	2-3	3-1	0-3	2-5	1-1	0-1	1-2	***S***	5-0	1-3	0-2
Sporting Bengal United	1-5	1-3	0-7	0-7	1-9	1-3	2-3	1-3	2-3	1-3	1-5	1-3	0-2	2-5	***I***	1-5	1-2
Tunbridge Wells	3-1	1-3	2-2	1-2	2-4	3-1	0-1	0-4	1-0	1-2	4-1	1-1	2-1	1-2	4-0	***O***	1-0
VCD Athletic	5-0	1-1	1-0	3-1	1-2	1-0	1-0	2-3	0-1	0-1	4-2	1-0	3-0	4-1	9-0	2-1	***N***

Premier Division		P	W	D	L	F	A	Pts
VCD Athletic		**32**	**22**	**4**	**6**	**68**	**24**	**70**
Hythe Town		**32**	**21**	**4**	**7**	**71**	**39**	**67**
Greenwich Boro.	***-1***	**32**	**20**	**4**	**8**	**60**	**45**	**63**
Faversham Town		**32**	**20**	**2**	**10**	**83**	**40**	**62**
Holmesdale		**32**	**18**	**7**	**7**	**57**	**30**	**61**
Herne Bay		**32**	**19**	**3**	**10**	**68**	**50**	**60**
Erith Town	***+2***	**32**	**14**	**10**	**8**	**59**	**39**	**54**
Erith & Belvedere		**32**	**16**	**5**	**11**	**67**	**50**	**53**
Croydon		**32**	**15**	**4**	**13**	**58**	**40**	**49**
Tunbridge Wells		**32**	**13**	**6**	**13**	**53**	**50**	**45**
Norton Sports		**32**	**12**	**4**	**16**	**44**	**57**	**40**
Deal Town		**32**	**10**	**8**	**14**	**57**	**53**	**38**
Slade Green		**32**	**11**	**4**	**17**	**53**	**66**	**37**
Sevenoaks Town		**32**	**9**	**4**	**19**	**44**	**67**	**31**
Beckenham Town		**32**	**8**	**4**	**20**	**54**	**76**	**28**
Lordswood		**32**	**6**	**3**	**23**	**43**	**79**	**21**
Sporting Bengal Utd		**32**	**0**	**0**	**32**	**26**	**160**	**0**

CHALLENGE SHIELD

(Prem Div champions v Prem Div cup holders)

(August 2nd at Thamesmead Town)
Thamesmead Town 3 Erith Town 1

PREMIER DIVISION CUP

FIRST ROUND
(played over two legs)
Erith & B. 2 Tunbridge Wells 2, **Tunbridge Wells** 6 Erith & B. 4

SECOND ROUND
(played over two legs)
Croydon 2 Sevenoaks Town 0, Sevenoaks Town 2 **Croydon** 2
Faversham 1 Beckenham 0, Beckenham Town 1 **Faversham** 3
Herne Bay 1 Norton Sports 0, Norton Sports 0 **Herne Bay** 4
Holmesdale 2 Deal Town 0, Deal Town 1 **Holmesdale** 0
Hythe 10 Sporting Bengal 1, Sporting Bengal 2 **Hythe Town** 4
Lordswood 0 Erith Town 3, **Erith Town** 3 Lordswood 0
Slade Green 1 Greenwich 2, Greenwich 2 **Slade Green** 5
Tunbridge Wells 1 VCD 1, VCD 1 **Tunbridge Wells** 2

QUARTER-FINALS
(played over two legs)
Croydon 0 Herne Bay 0, Herne Bay 1 **Croydon** 2
Faversham 3 Holmesdale 2, Holmesdale 0 **FavershamTown** 0
Hythe 2 Slade Green 1, Slade Green 0 **Hythe Town** 4
Tunbridge W. 3 Erith Town 3, **Erith Town** 2 Tunbridge Wells 0

SEMI-FINALS
(played over two legs)
Croydon 4 Faversham Town 0, Faversham Town 0 **Croydon** 2
Hythe Town 3 Erith Town 1, **Erith Town** 4 Hythe Town 1

FINAL *(May 3rd at Welling United)*
Croydon 1 Erith Town 1 *aet* (3-1p)

Division One	P	W	D	L	F	A	Pts
Thamesmead Town Res.	22	15	0	7	45	24	45
Cray Wanderers Res.	22	13	1	8	46	27	40
Dartford Res.	22	11	4	7	39	26	37
Maidstone United Res.	22	11	3	8	32	22	36
Ashford Town Res.	22	11	3	8	36	27	36
Margate Res.	22	10	4	8	34	35	34
Erith & Belvedere Res.	22	10	3	9	30	24	33
Dover Athletic Res.	22	10	2	10	45	45	32
Whitstable Town Res.	22	8	3	11	25	33	27
Chatham Town Res.	22	7	5	10	36	43	26
Folkestone Invicta Res.	22	5	2	15	16	47	17
Sevenoaks Town Res.	22	3	6	13	20	51	15

Division Two		P	W	D	L	F	A	Pts
Holmesdale Res.		20	15	4	1	63	24	49
Herne Bay Res.		20	12	4	4	44	31	40
Hythe Town Res.		20	10	5	5	39	30	35
Faversham T. Res.		20	10	5	5	41	33	35
Tunbridge Wells Res.		20	10	3	7	45	44	33
Welling United Res.		20	10	2	8	46	32	32
Ramsgate Res.		20	8	3	9	48	40	27
VCD Athletic Res.		20	5	2	13	22	43	17
Deal Town Res.	*-3*	20	4	6	10	28	42	15
Greenwich B. Res.	*-3*	20	5	1	14	21	41	13
Lordswood Res.		20	2	3	15	28	65	9

DIVISION ONE/TWO CUP

FINAL *(May 2nd at Folkestone Invicta)*
Thamesmead Town Res. 4 Whitstable Town Res. 1

FLOODLIGHT CUP

FINAL *(May 6th at Faversham Town)*
Dartford Res. 1 Ashford Town Res. 0

2009-10

BECKENHAM TOWN

Founded: 1887 Nickname: Reds

Chairman: Chris McCarthy
Secretary: Peter Palmer
36 Inglewood
Pixton Way
Selsdon
CR0 9LP
Tel: 07774 728 758
Manager: Jason Huntley
Prog Editor: Sam Percival

Ground: Eden Park Avenue, Beckenham Kent BR3 3JL. Tel: 07774 728 758.
Capacity: 4,000 **Seats:** 120 **Covered:** 120
Midweek Matchday: Tuesday **Clubhouse:** Yes **Shop:** Yes
Colours(change): Red/red. (White/blue).
Previous Names: Stanhope Rovers.
Previous Lges: South East London Amateur. Metropolitan. London Spartan.
Records: **Att:** 720 v Berkhamsted, FA Cup 1994-95. **Goalscorer:** Ricky Bennett.
Apps: Lee Fabian - 985.
Senior Honours:

10 YEAR RECORD

99-00	00-01	01-02	02-03	03-04	04-05	05-06	06-07	07-08	08-09
Kent P 10	Kent P 7	Kent P 9	Kent P 10	Kent P 12	Kent P 10	Kent P 2	Kent P 11	Kent P 3	Kent P 15

CORINTHIAN

Founded: 1972 Nickname:

Chairman: R J Billings
Secretary: Sue Billings
c/o Corinthian FC
Tel:
Manager: Clive Billings
Prog Editor:

Ground: Gat Dawn Farm, Valley Road, Longfield DA3 8LY. Tel: 01474 573 118
Capacity: **Seats:** **Covered:**
Midweek Matchday: **Clubhouse:** **Shop:**
Colours(change): Green & white
Previous Names: Welling United Reserves
Previous Lges: Southern.
Records:
Senior Honours:

10 YEAR RECORD

99-00	00-01	01-02	02-03	03-04	04-05	05-06	06-07	07-08	08-09

DEAL TOWN

Founded: 1908 Nickname: Town

Chairman: Stuart McClusky
Secretary: Brian Pollard
c/o Deal Town F.C.
Tel: 07917 450 740
Manager: Derek Hares
Prog Editor: Colin Adams

Ground: Charles Sports Ground, St Leonards Road, Deal. CT14 9BB Tel: 01304 375 623.
Capacity: 2,500 **Seats:** 180 **Covered:** 180
Midweek Matchday: Tuesday **Clubhouse:** Yes **Shop:** Yes
Colours(change): Black & white/black. (Blue/blue).
Previous Names: Deal Cinque Ports FC > 1920
Previous Lges: Thanet. East Kent. Kent. Aetolian. Southern. Greater London.
Records: **Att:** 2,495 v Newcastle Town, FA Vase S-F, 26.03.200.
Senior Honours: Kent League 1953-54, 99-00. FA Vase 99-00. Kent Senior Cup (x2).

10 YEAR RECORD

99-00	00-01	01-02	02-03	03-04	04-05	05-06	06-07	07-08	08-09
Kent P 1	Kent P 15	Kent P 3	Kent P 4	Kent P 16	Kent P 13	Kent P 9	Kent P 8	Kent P 9	Kent P 12

ERITH & BELVEDERE

Founded: 1922 Nickname: Deres

Chairman: John McFadden
Secretary: Frank May
c/o Erith & Belvedere F.C.
Tel: 07778 987 579
Manager: Chris Cosgrove
Prog Editor: Martin Tarrant/Brian Spurrel

Ground: Welling FC, Park View Rd, Welling, DA16 1SY. Tel: 020 8304 0333.
Capacity: 4,000 **Seats:** 1,070 **Covered:** 1,000
Midweek Matchday: Tuesday **Clubhouse:** Yes **Shop:** Yes
Colours(change): Blue & white quarters/blue. (Red & white quarters/red.
Previous Names: Belvedere & District FC (Formed 1918 restructured 1922)
Previous Lges: Kent. London. Corinthian. Athenian. Southern.
Records: **Att:** 5,573 v Crook C.W., FA Amateur Cup 1949.
Goalscorer: Colin Johnson - 284 (61-71). **Apps:** Dennis Crawford - 504 (56-71).
Senior Honours: Kent League 1981-82. London Senior Cup 44-45.

10 YEAR RECORD

99-00	00-01	01-02	02-03	03-04	04-05	05-06	06-07	07-08	08-09
SthE 11	SthE 20	SthE 9	SthE 18	SthE 21	SthE 21	Kent P 4	Kent P 7	Kent P 7	Kent P 8

ERITH TOWN

Founded: 1959 Nickname: The Dockers

Chairman: Albert Putman
Secretary: Jim Davie
6 Dashwood Close
Broomfield Road
Bexleyheath
DA6 7NU
Tel: 07780 712 149
Manager: Steve O'Boyle
Prog Editor: Ian Birrell

Ground: Erith Sports Stadium, Avenue Road, Erith DA8 3AJ. Tel: 01322 350 271.
Capacity: 1,450 **Seats:** 1,006 **Covered:** 1,066
Midweek Matchday: Monday **Clubhouse:** Yes **Shop:** No
Colours(change): Red & black/black. (Yellow/white).
Previous Names: Woolwich Town 1959-89 and 1990-97.
Previous Lges: London Metropolitan Sunday. London Spartan.
Records: **Att:** 325 v Charlton Athletic, friendly. **Goalscorer:** Dean Bowey.
Senior Honours:

10 YEAR RECORD

99-00	00-01	01-02	02-03	03-04	04-05	05-06	06-07	07-08	08-09
Kent P 7	Kent P 11	Kent P 13	Kent P 15	Kent P 7	Kent P 15	Kent P 14	Kent P 14	Kent P 5	Kent P 7

FAVERSHAM TOWN

Founded: 1884 Nickname: Lillywhites

Chairman: Bob Mason
Secretary: Alan Trent
8 Chobham Chase
Faversham
Kent
ME13 7QD
Tel: 07709 937 518
Manager: Justin Luchford/Jimmy Strouts
Prog Editor: Mark Downs

Ground: Salters Lane, Faversham Kent ME13 8ND. Tel: 01795 591 900.
Capacity: 2,000 **Seats:** 200 **Covered:** 1,800
Midweek Matchday: Tuesday **Clubhouse:** Yes **Shop:**
Colours(change): White/black. (Yellow/black).
Previous Names: None.
Previous Lges: Metropolitan. Athenian.
Records:
Senior Honours: Kent League 1969-70, 70-71, 89-90.

10 YEAR RECORD

99-00	00-01	01-02	02-03	03-04	04-05	05-06	06-07	07-08	08-09
Kent P 17	Kent P 16	Kent P 16	Kent P 16				Kent P 12	Kent P 13	Kent P 4

FISHER

Founded: 1908 Nickname: The Fish

Chairman: Martin Eede
Secretary: Martin Eede
c/o Fisher F.C.
Tel: 07957 395 948
Manager: Gary Lisney
Prog Editor: TBA

Ground: Dulwich Hamlet FC, Edgar Kail Way, East Dulwich SE22 8BD
Capacity: 3,000 **Seats:** 500 **Covered:** 1,000
Midweek Matchday: Monday **Clubhouse:** Yes **Shop:** Yes
Colours(change): Black & white/black. (Red/red).
Previous Names: Fisher Athletic. Reformed as Fisher F.C. in 2009.
Previous Lges: N/A
Records: N/A
Senior Honours: None

10 YEAR RECORD

99-00	00-01	01-02	02-03	03-04	04-05	05-06	06-07	07-08	08-09

GREENWICH BOROUGH

Founded: 1928 Nickname: Boro

Chairman: Devon Hanson
Secretary: Steve Firkins
c/o Greenwich Borough FC
Tel: 07711 303 936
Manager: Steve Firkins/Jim Bajeux
Prog Editor: TBC

Ground: Harrow Meadow, Eltham Green Rd., Eltham, SE9 6BA. Tel: 07882 726 547.
Capacity: 2,500 **Seats:** **Covered:**
Midweek Matchday: Tuesday **Clubhouse:** Yes **Shop:** No
Colours(change): All red. (All blue).
Previous Names: London Borough of London.
Previous Lges: South London Alliance. Kent Amateur. London Spartan.
Records: **Att:** 2,000 v Charlton Athletic, turning on of floodlights, 1978.
Senior Honours: London Spartan League 1979-80. Kent Senior Trophy 84-85. Kent League 86-87, 87-88.

10 YEAR RECORD

99-00	00-01	01-02	02-03	03-04	04-05	05-06	06-07	07-08	08-09
Kent P 6	Kent P 9	Kent P 15	Kent P 14	Kent P 8	Kent P 9	Kent P 13	Kent P 5	Kent P 8	Kent P 3

INS & OUTS

IN: Corinthian (Formerly Welling United Reserves) (P - Kent League Division Two), Fisher (N)
OUT: Croydon (S – Comined Counties League Premier Division), VCD Athletic (P – Isthmian League Division One North), Slade Green (W).

2009-10

HERNE BAY

Founded: 1886 Nickname: The Bay

Chairman: John Bathurst
Secretary: Tony Day
c/o Herne Bay F.C.

Tel: 07789 655 768
Manager: Barry Morgan
Prog Editor: See Chairman

Ground: Winch's Field, Stanley Gardens, Herne Bay CT6 7BF. Tel: 01227 374 156
Capacity: 3,000 **Seats:** 200 **Covered:** 1,500
Midweek Matchday: Wednesday **Clubhouse:** Yes **Shop:** Yes
Colours(change): Blue & white strips/blue. (Red & gold/red).
Previous Names: None.
Previous Lges: East Kent. Faversham & Dist. Cantebury & Dist. Kent Am. Athenian.
Records: Att: 2,303 v Margate, FA Cup 4th Qual. 1970-71.

Senior Honours: Kent League 1991-92, 93-94, 96-97, 97-98.

10 YEAR RECORD

99-00	00-01	01-02	02-03	03-04	04-05	05-06	06-07	07-08	08-09
Kent P 12	Kent P 2	Kent P 7	Kent P 11	Kent P 10	Kent P 2	Kent P 7	Kent P 9	Kent P 6	Kent P 6

HOLMESDALE

Founded: 1956 Nickname:

Chairman: Ray Tolfrey
Secretary: Mark Hayes
563 Mierscourt Road
Rainham
Kent
ME8 8RB
Tel: 07816 650 748
Manager: Billy Hughes
Prog Editor: TBC

Ground: Holmesdale Sp.& Soc.Club, 68 Oakley Rd, Bromley BR2 8HQ. Tel: 020 8462 4440
Capacity: **Seats:** **Covered:**
Midweek Matchday: Tuesday **Clubhouse:** Yes **Shop:** Yes
Colours(change): Green & yellow/green. (All blue).
Previous Names: None.
Previous Lges: Thornton Heath & Dist. Surrey Inter. Surrey South Eastern. Kent County.
Records: Goals: M Barnett - 410 (in 429 apps).

Senior Honours: Kent County League 2006-07

10 YEAR RECORD

99-00	00-01	01-02	02-03	03-04	04-05	05-06	06-07	07-08	08-09
			KC1W 4	KC1W 4	KC1W 8	KC1W 1	KC P 1	Kent P 15	Kent P 5

HYTHE TOWN

Founded: 1992 Nickname: Town

Chairman: Paul Markland
Secretary: Martin Giles
21 Wych Elm Way
Hythe
Kent
CT21 6QE
Tel: 07908 763 101
Manager: Scott Porter
Prog Editor: Martin Whybrow

Ground: Reachfields Stadium, Fort Road, Hythe CT21 6JS. Tel: 01303 264 932.
Capacity: **Seats:** **Covered:**
Midweek Matchday: Tuesday **Clubhouse:** Yes **Shop:** No
Colours(change): Red & white/red. (Blue & white/blue).
Previous Names: Hythe Town > 1988. Hythe Town 1988 Ltd > 92. Hythe United 95- 01.
Previous Lges: Southern.
Records: Att: 2,147 v Yeading, FA Vase Semi-Final, 1990.

Senior Honours: Kent League 1988-89.

10 YEAR RECORD

99-00	00-01	01-02	02-03	03-04	04-05	05-06	06-07	07-08	08-09
Kent P 8	Kent P 14	Kent P 14	Kent P 8	Kent P 6	Kent P 6	Kent P 12	Kent P 6	Kent P 4	Kent P 2

LORDSWOOD

Founded: 1968 Nickname: Lords

Chairman: Ron Constantine
Secretary: Steve Lewis
Sunnybrook
Gorsewood Road
Hartley, Longfield
DA3 7DF
Tel: 07775 541 573
Manager: Kevin Metcalf
Prog Editor: Darell Harman

Ground: Martyn Grove, Northdane Way, Walderslade, ME5 9XX. Tel: 01634 669 138
Capacity: 600 **Seats:** 123 **Covered:** 123
Midweek Matchday: Tuesday **Clubhouse:** Yes **Shop:** No
Colours(change): Orange & black/black. (Blue & white/blue).
Previous Names: None.
Previous Lges: Rochester & Dist. Kent County.
Records:

Senior Honours: Kent League 1988-89.

10 YEAR RECORD

99-00	00-01	01-02	02-03	03-04	04-05	05-06	06-07	07-08	08-09
Kent P 11	Kent P 10	Kent P 11	Kent P 13	Kent P 13	Kent P 16	Kent P 8	Kent P 13	Kent P 16	Kent P 16

NORTON SPORTS

Founded: 1927 Nickname:

Chairman: Kevin James
Secretary: Colin Page
c/o Herne Bay FC
Winch's Field, Stanley Gardens
Herne Bay

Tel: 07970 549 355
Manager: Ben Taylor
Prog Editor: TBC

Ground: Herne Bay FC, Winch's Field, Herne Bay CT6 5SG. Tel: 01227 374 156
Capacity: 3,000 **Seats:** 200 **Covered:** 1,500
Midweek Matchday: Tuesday **Clubhouse:** Yes **Shop:** Yes
Colours(change): Blue & white/black. (All red).
Previous Names: Amalgamated with Teynham & Lynsted in 1998.
Previous Lges: Kent County.
Records:

Senior Honours: Kent County League 2007-08.

10 YEAR RECORD

99-00	00-01	01-02	02-03	03-04	04-05	05-06	06-07	07-08	08-09
					KC1E 1		KC P 3	KC P 1	Kent P 11

SEVENOAKS TOWN

Founded: 1883 Nickname: Town

Chairman: Tony Smart
Secretary: Eddie Diplock
23 Holly Bush Lane
Sevenoaks
Kent
TN13 3TH
Tel: 01732 454 280
Manager: Bob Pittaway & Derek Moore
Prog Editor: Vicki Jones

Ground: Greatness Park, Seal Road, Sevenoaks TN14 5BL. Tel: 01732 741 987.
Capacity: 2,000 **Seats:** 110 **Covered:** 200
Midweek Matchday: Tuesday **Clubhouse:** **Shop:**
Colours(change): Blue stripes/navy. (Green & white/white).
Previous Names: None.
Previous Lges: Sevenoaks League. Kent Amateur/County.
Records:

Senior Honours: Kent County 1984-85, 95-96, 02-03.

10 YEAR RECORD

99-00	00-01	01-02	02-03	03-04	04-05	05-06	06-07	07-08	08-09
		KC P 2	KC P 1	Kent P 11	Kent P 11	Kent P 16	Kent P 10	Kent P 11	Kent P 14

SPORTING BENGAL UNITED

Founded: 1996 Nickname: Bengal Tigers

Chairman: Suroth Miah
Secretary: Mahbub Hussain
119-123 Cannon Street Road
London

E1 2LX
Tel: 07947 161 887
Manager: Mamun Chowdhury
Prog Editor: See Secretary

Ground: Mile End Stadium, Rhodeswell Rd, Off Burdett Rd E14 4TW. Tel: 020 8980 1885.
Capacity: **Seats:** Yes **Covered:**
Midweek Matchday: Wednesday **Clubhouse:** **Shop:**
Colours(change): Blue/blue. (Yellow & orange/orange).
Previous Names: None.
Previous Lges: Asian League. London Intermediate.
Records: **Att:** 4,235 v Touring Phalco Mohammedan S.C.

Senior Honours: None.

10 YEAR RECORD

99-00	00-01	01-02	02-03	03-04	04-05	05-06	06-07	07-08	08-09
LonInt 4	LonInt 6	LonInt 7		Kent P 17	Kent P 14	Kent P 15	Kent P 17	Kent P 17	Kent P 17

TUNBRIDGE WELLS

Founded: 1886 Nickname: The Wells

Chairman: Joe Croker
Secretary: James Hitchell
c/o Tunbrideg Wells F.C.

Tel: 07980 243 508
Manager: Martin Larkin
Prog Editor: TBC

Ground: Culverden Stad., Culverden Down, Tunbridge Wells TN4 9SH. Tel: 01892 520517
Capacity: 3,750 **Seats:** 250 **Covered:** 1,000
Midweek Matchday: Wednesday **Clubhouse:** Yes **Shop:** No
Colours(change): Red/red. (Yellow/yellow).
Previous Names: None.
Previous Lges: Isthminan. London Spartan.
Records: **Att:** 967 v Maidstone United, FA Cup 1969. **Goalscorer:** John Wingate - 151.
Apps: Tony Atkins - 410.
Senior Honours: Kent League 1984-85.

10 YEAR RECORD

99-00	00-01	01-02	02-03	03-04	04-05	05-06	06-07	07-08	08-09
Kent P 14	Kent P 6	Kent P 8	Kent P 12	Kent P 14	Kent P 7	Kent P 10	Kent P 15	Kent P 10	Kent P 10

HOLMESDALE F.C.
Photo: Alan Coomes.

NORTON SPORTS F.C.
Photo: Alan Coomes.

MIDLAND COMBINATION

www.midcomb.com

Sponsored by:

No Sponsor

Founded: 1927

Recent champions:

2004: Romulus

2005: Leamington

2006: Atherstone Town

2007: Coventry Sphinx

2008: Coleshill Town

Premier Division		P	W	D	L	F	A	Pts
Loughborough University		40	31	3	6	96	34	96
Castle Vale		40	27	8	5	84	42	89
Southam United		40	24	10	6	83	36	82
Oldbury Athletic		40	26	4	10	101	55	82
Heather St John		40	18	12	10	68	45	66
Nuneaton Griff		40	18	10	12	64	51	64
Walsall Wood		40	18	9	13	59	50	63
Pilkington XXX		40	17	6	17	79	83	57
Coventry Copsewood		40	16	8	16	75	66	56
Heath Hayes		40	17	5	18	56	79	56
Cadbury Athletic		40	16	7	17	62	57	55
Knowle		40	13	11	16	50	64	50
Pershore Town	*-3*	40	13	10	17	59	81	46
GSA Sports		40	13	6	21	64	84	45
Massey-Ferguson		40	11	11	18	61	72	44
Brocton		40	11	8	21	60	71	41
Continental Star		40	11	7	22	70	84	40
Bartley Green	*-3*	40	11	8	21	58	81	38
Bolehall Swifts		40	10	7	23	43	71	37
Meir KA		40	9	8	23	52	87	35
Coton Green		40	5	12	23	59	110	27

TONY ALLDEN MEMORIAL CUP

(Prem Div champions v Challenge Cup holders)

(October 21st at Coleshill Town)

Coleshill Town 2 Loughborough University 0

	Bartley Green	Bolehall Swifts	Brocton	Cadbury Athletic	Castle Vale	Continental Star	Coton Green	Coventry Copsewood	GSA Sports	Heath Hayes	Heather St John	Knowle	Loughborough University	Massey-Ferguson	Meir KA	Nuneaton Griff	Oldbury Athletic	Pershore Town	Pilkington XXX	Southam United	Walsall Wood
Bartley Green		2-1	1-3	3-1	1-2	1-3	2-0	1-1	3-4	1-2	2-2	2-2	1-2	2-3	4-1	2-2	4-2	1-0	0-0	0-3	2-0
Bolehall Swifts	4-0		2-1	2-0	1-2	3-1	0-0	2-1	1-1	0-0	0-2	0-1	1-2	3-1	0-1	2-2	1-2	0-3	1-2	0-4	0-4
Brocton	0-1	2-1	***P***	2-2	2-3	3-3	3-3	4-2	1-0	3-0	1-2	1-2	0-1	1-0	3-3	1-3	0-3	2-2	3-4	1-3	3-1
Cadbury Athletic	4-1	3-4	2-1	***R***	1-1	3-2	5-0	1-2	0-1	0-2	2-1	4-1	0-1	1-1	3-1	4-1	0-3	2-0	1-0	0-2	1-3
Castle Vale	3-1	3-0	1-0	2-2	***E***	1-0	2-1	1-2	1-0	3-0	2-5	2-1	0-0	1-2	2-1	1-0	2-1	2-2	3-1	1-1	5-0
Continental Star	2-1	1-2	3-2	3-4	2-3	***M***	1-3	1-0	0-4	1-2	3-1	3-0	0-1	1-2	2-2	5-2	1-4	1-2	3-1	2-3	2-3
Coton Green	1-0	1-1	1-1	3-3	0-2	2-2	***I***	4-4	4-2	1-3	3-4	1-1	4-3	1-9	4-2	1-3	1-4	1-3	3-6	1-1	2-2
Coventry Copsewood	2-2	3-0	1-3	1-0	0-0	3-0	4-1	***E***	1-2	3-4	3-4	3-1	3-2	1-0	2-2	0-4	1-2	5-0	1-2	0-2	1-2
GSA Sports	2-2	2-2	1-0	0-3	1-2	4-1	1-1	2-2	***R***	0-2	0-3	4-2	0-2	1-3	1-2	2-3	2-2	2-3	2-1	1-6	1-0
Heath Hayes	1-0	2-0	2-0	0-1	2-1	1-3	2-1	1-2	4-2		0-3	2-1	0-2	0-0	2-1	2-3	3-6	1-1	4-2	1-1	0-3
Heather St John	1-4	4-0	2-1	0-0	2-2	1-1	3-2	1-1	4-0	2-3		2-2	0-1	0-1	3-2	0-0	2-1	3-0	0-1	0-1	0-0
Knowle	2-1	0-1	0-1	1-0	1-2	2-2	2-2	2-0	3-2	5-1	0-0	***D***	1-1	1-1	1-0	1-0	1-2	3-4	1-0	0-2	0-0
Loughborough University	4-1	4-0	0-0	3-1	2-3	2-1	6-2	2-1	4-0	4-0	2-0	7-0	***I***	2-0	4-0	2-0	0-2	6-1	3-0	1-3	2-1
Massey-Ferguson	0-1	3-2	0-2	1-1	1-4	3-3	3-0	2-4	2-3	2-2	1-2	3-0	2-1	***V***	1-1	1-1	1-5	0-2	1-4	0-3	2-1
Meir KA	0-2	1-3	4-3	0-2	0-4	3-4	1-0	1-5	4-0	4-1	0-2	0-0	0-2	3-3	***I***	0-2	1-4	1-2	2-2	0-4	1-0
Nuneaton Griff	2-0	1-0	3-1	1-2	0-2	1-0	2-1	1-0	0-4	0-1	0-0	0-1	1-2	2-2	1-2	***S***	2-0	5-0	4-1	2-0	2-1
Oldbury Athletic	4-1	3-1	2-1	2-0	0-3	1-0	6-2	2-3	3-0	5-0	1-1	2-3	0-3	2-1	2-1	2-2	***I***	2-1	2-3	2-1	6-1
Pershore Town	1-0	2-0	1-2	0-1	1-5	1-1	3-0	1-2	2-6	3-1	0-3	0-3	2-3	3-2	0-0	2-2	1-1	***O***	2-2	2-1	1-2
Pilkington XXX	8-3	1-0	4-2	2-1	0-2	3-4	2-1	1-4	3-2	3-1	0-3	4-1	1-3	2-1	4-2	0-0	1-4	1-1	***N***	3-4	1-2
Southam United	5-1	2-2	2-0	2-1	2-2	1-0	2-0	0-0	0-1	1-0	0-0	1-0	2-3	3-0	3-1	3-3	2-0	3-3	4-1		0-0
Walsall Wood	1-1	1-0	0-0	1-0	3-1	3-2	4-0	3-1	2-1	5-1	2-0	1-1	0-1	0-0	0-1	0-1	1-4	3-1	2-2	1-0	

Division One		P	W	D	L	F	A	Pts
Castle Vale JKS		30	21	4	5	82	29	67
Dosthill Colts		30	18	4	8	68	38	58
Stockingford AA		30	18	3	9	77	39	57
Fairfield Villa		30	17	5	8	76	31	56
Littleton		30	16	8	6	64	36	56
Earlswood Town		30	15	7	8	55	32	52
Archdale		30	16	4	10	66	51	52
Alveston		30	16	2	12	51	46	50
Brereton Social		30	14	6	10	60	49	48
West Midlands Police		30	12	5	13	55	55	41
Northfield Town		30	12	3	15	47	59	39
Droitwich Spa		30	9	8	13	43	59	35
Mile Oak Rovers		30	7	6	17	52	74	27
Thimblemill REC		30	6	2	22	41	91	20
Newhall United		30	3	7	20	33	85	16
Burntwood Town	*-3*	30	1	4	25	25	121	4

UNIQUE CATERING & MANAGEMENT PRESIDENT'S CUP

FIRST ROUND

Fairfield Villa (w/o) v Leamington Hibernian

SECOND ROUND

Alveston 1 Archdale 0
Castle Vale JKS 7 Littleton 2
Dosthill Colts 5 Mile Oak Rovers 2
Droitwich Spa 4 Newhall United 3
Fairfield Villa 5 Thimblemill REC 0
Northfield Town 0 **Earlswood Town** 1
Stockingford AA 10 Burntwood Town 1
West Midlands Police 7 Brereton Social 0

QUARTER-FINALS

Castle Vale JKS 2 Dosthill Colts 1
Droitwich Spa 4 Alveston 3 *aet*
Fairfield Villa 3 Earlswood Town 0
West Midlands Police 3 Stockingford AA 3 *aet* (8-7p)

SEMI-FINALS

(played over two legs)

Droitwich Spa 0 Fairfield Villa 2, **Fairfield Villa** 3 Droitwich Spa 1
West Midlands Police 3 Castle Vale JKS 2, **Castle Vale JKS** 5 West Midlands Police 3 *aet* (5-3p)

FINAL

(May 6th at Boldmere St Michaels)

Fairfield Villa 2 Castle Vale JKS 2 *aet* (6-5p)

ENDSLEIGH CHALLENGE CUP

PRELIMINARY ROUND

AFC Internazionale 2 **Castle Vale JKS** 2 *aet* (3-4p)
Alveston 0 **Chelmsley Town** 5
Clements '83 (w/o) v BNJS Mann & Co
Enville Athletic 2 Burntwood Town 0
Greenhill 1 **Thimblemill REC** 2
Kenilworth Town KH 0 **Shirley Town** 5
Lichfield City 4 Leamington Hibernian 0
Perrywood 2 **Henley Forest** 3
Shipston Excelsior 6 Coventry Amateurs 2.

FIRST ROUND

Archdale 0 **Castle Vale JKS** 1, **Brereton** 1 Mile Oak 0
Clements '83 0 **Coton Green** 3, Dosthill 1 **Littleton** 2
Earlswood 2 Chelmsley 1 *aet*, **Enville** 5 Shipston 1
Fairfield Villa 1 Shirley Town 1 *aet* (4-3p)
Feckenham 3 Hampton 2
Henley Forest 1 **West Midlands Police** 4
Lichfield City 2 **Stockingford AA** 4
Newhall 0 **Northfield** 4, Thimblemill 1 **Droitwich Spa** 4

SECOND ROUND

Bartley Green 2 **Coton Green** 4 *aet*
Castle Vale 5 Brocton 1
Castle Vale JKS 0 **Coventry Copsewood** 1
Continental Star 4 Northfield Town 1
Earlswood Town 2 **Walsall Wood** 3 *aet*
Enville Athletic 3 **Droitwich Spa** 3 *aet* (1-4p)
GSA 4 Pilkington XXX 0, **Heath Hayes** 3 Nuneton Griff 0
Heather SJ 3 Oldbury Ath 1, **Knowle** 2 Bolehall 1 *aet*
Loughborough University 4 Feckenham 1
Meir KA 3 Littleton 0
Pershore Town 1 Massey-Ferguson 1 *aet* (5-4p)
Southam United 1 **Cadbury Athletic** 2 *aet*
Stockingford AA 3 Brereton Social 2
West Midlands Police 3 Fairfield Villa 1

THIRD ROUND

Cadbury Athletic 1 Heath Hayes 0
Castle Vale 2 Meir KA 1
Contintental Star 0 **Heather St John** 4
Coton Green 7 West Midlands Police 2
Coventry Copsewood 4 Stockingford AA 3
Droitwich Spa 1 **Loughborough University** 2
GSA Sports 2 Walsall Wood 1
Pershore Town 1 Knowle 0

QUARTER-FINALS

Cadbury Athletic 1 Loughborough University 0
Coventry Copsewood 0 **Castle Vale** 1
GSA Sports 2 Coton Green 1
Heather St John 4 Pershore Town 2

SEMI-FINALS

(played over two legs)

Cadbury Athletic 0 Heather St John 0, Heather St John 0 **Cadbury Athletic** 1
Castle Vale 2 GSA Sports 0, GSA Sports 2 **Castle Vale** 2

FINAL

(May 4th at Solihull Moors)

Cadbury Athletic 1 **Castle Vale** 2

	Alv	Arc	Bre	Bur	Cas	Dos	Dro	Ear	Fair	Litt.	MO	New	Nor	Sto	Thi	WM
Alveston		1-5	2-0	7-0	0-7	0-2	1-0	3-1	0-1	2-2	3-0	4-1	3-0	0-2	5-0	1-0
Archdale	2-1		2-1	2-0	0-3	0-2	1-1	2-2	3-1	3-2	3-2	6-0	0-1	3-2	4-3	1-0
Brereton Social	0-2	2-2	***D***	6-1	3-5	1-0	1-1	2-0	0-1	0-0	3-2	4-0	5-0	1-5	1-0	3-2
Burntwood Town	2-0	2-3	2-2	***I***	1-4	1-4	0-3	0-4	0-4	0-2	3-8	2-2	1-3	1-3	1-4	0-3
Castle Vale JKS	0-2	4-2	3-1	3-1	***V***	1-2	2-0	0-0	0-0	3-0	1-1	4-0	3-1	3-0	6-0	3-2
Dosthill Colts	8-2	4-2	2-1	1-0	3-1	***I***	2-1	0-2	1-2	0-2	2-0	2-0	5-2	2-4	7-1	2-3
Droitwich Spa	2-2	0-2	1-1	3-0	0-7	2-2	***S***	1-3	0-4	0-4	3-2	1-0	2-0	1-5	3-0	1-1
Earlswood Town	0-1	1-0	2-3	9-0	1-1	1-1	2-1	***I***	1-0	0-1	3-0	1-1	0-0	2-1	3-1	3-2
Fairfield Villa	1-2	3-2	1-2	13-0	2-0	2-2	0-0	2-2	***O***	0-2	1-0	1-0	3-2	1-1	1-4	2-0
Littleton	0-3	3-1	2-1	7-1	3-2	0-2	5-2	1-0	1-2	***N***	1-1	3-0	4-2	3-1	6-1	0-0
Mile Oak Rovers	0-1	0-4	2-2	3-3	1-2	2-1	1-4	4-2	0-7	1-1		3-3	4-0	0-4	3-1	3-4
Newhall United	2-1	3-3	2-5	4-0	0-3	0-3	4-6	0-2	0-10	2-2	1-2	***O***	1-0	1-1	3-5	0-1
Northfield Town	1-0	1-3	2-3	3-0	2-3	1-3	1-0	0-4	2-1	1-1	1-0	3-0	***N***	2-4	6-2	5-1
Stockingford AA	6-0	4-3	1-2	7-0	0-2	2-0	3-0	0-1	4-0	3-2	3-0	4-1	0-0	***E***	5-3	0-1
Thimblemill REC	0-2	0-2	3-1	3-2	1-3	1-2	1-1	1-2	0-4	1-1	1-4	1-0	1-2	0-2		1-3
West Midlands Police	1-0	2-0	1-3	1-1	0-3	1-1	2-3	3-1	0-6	1-3	6-3	2-2	2-3	4-0	6-1	

Division Two	P	W	D	L	F	A	Pts
Shirley Town	**26**	**20**	**3**	**3**	**82**	**28**	**63**
Castle Vale Res.	**26**	**16**	**5**	**5**	**68**	**35**	**53**
Continental Star Res.	**26**	**13**	**7**	**6**	**61**	**48**	**46**
Worcester City Academy	**26**	**14**	**3**	**9**	**60**	**44**	**45**
Racing Club Warwick Res.	**26**	**12**	**7**	**7**	**68**	**52**	**43**
AFC Internazionale	**26**	**12**	**6**	**8**	**41**	**30**	**42**
Feckenham	**26**	**13**	**2**	**11**	**51**	**42**	**41**
Chelmsley Town	**26**	**10**	**4**	**12**	**44**	**48**	**34**
Greenhill	**26**	**9**	**6**	**11**	**26**	**40**	**33**
Droitwich Spa Res.	**26**	**9**	**4**	**13**	**37**	**49**	**31**
Enville Athletic	**26**	**7**	**3**	**16**	**60**	**86**	**24**
Perrywood	**26**	**6**	**5**	**15**	**44**	**60**	**23**
Leamington Hibernian	**26**	**7**	**0**	**19**	**31**	**78**	**21**
Cadbury Athletic Res.	**26**	**6**	**1**	**19**	**50**	**83**	**19**

Reserve Division		P	W	D	L	F	A	Pts
Chasetown Res.		28	22	4	2	71	21	70
Boldmere St Michaels Res.		28	20	3	5	84	30	63
Tamworth Res.		28	18	3	7	79	31	57
Quorn Res.		28	15	7	6	71	53	52
Bromsgrove Rovers Res.	*-3*	28	16	2	10	64	46	47
Coleshill Town Res.		28	12	6	10	64	53	42
Oadby Town Res.		28	12	2	14	51	64	38
Highgate United Res.		28	11	4	13	50	52	37
Gresley Rovers Res.		28	10	6	12	49	72	36
Coventry Sphinx Res.		28	8	4	16	57	77	28
Barwell Res.		28	7	5	16	47	66	26
Heather St Johns Res.	*-6*	28	8	7	13	35	60	25
Atherstone Town Res.	*-9*	28	8	6	14	49	55	21
Banbury United Res.		28	5	4	19	30	77	19
Walsall Wood Res.		28	4	5	19	33	77	17

CHALLENGE VASE

FIRST ROUND

BNJS Mann & Co v **Shirley Town** (w/o)
Cadbury Athletic Res. 3 Droitwich Spa Res. 2
Chelmsley Town 1 AFC Internazionale 0
Feckenham 2 **Leamington Hibernian** 2 *aet* (4-2p)
(Feckenham expelled)
Perrywood 0 **Continental Star Res.** 1
Racing Club Warwick Res. 0 **Castle Vale Res.** 2
Worcester City Academy 1 Enville Athletic 0

QUARTER-FINALS

Cadbury Athletic Res. 1 **Castle Vale Res.** 6
Chelmsley Town 3 Leamington Hibernian 1
Shirley Town 5 Continental Star Res. 2
Worcester City Academy 3 Greenhill 1

SEMI-FINALS

(played over two legs)
Chelmsley 1 Shirley 2, **Shirley Town** 2 Chelmsley Town 2
Worcester City Academy 5 Castle Vale Res. 0, Castle Vale Res. 1 **Worcester City Academy** 1

FINAL *(May 2nd at Pilkington XXX)*
Shirley Town 0 **Worcester City Academy** 1

	AFC Int.	Cadbury Res.	Castle V Res.	Chelmsley	Cont. S. Res.	Droitwich Res.	Enville Ath	Feckenham	Greenhill	L'gton Hibs	Perrywood	RC War. Res.	Shirley Town	Worc. City A..
AFC Internazionale		2-1	1-1	3-0	1-1	3-1	1-0	0-2	1-1	3-0	2-3	3-0	0-2	0-1
Cadbury Athletic Res.	0-2	***D***	1-4	1-5	3-2	2-0	4-2	2-3	3-1	2-1	1-3	2-3	1-1	3-7
Castle Vale Res.	2-1	5-3	***I***	3-1	1-2	1-1	4-1	3-2	1-1	2-0	2-0	3-3	1-3	4-2
Chelmsley Town	1-3	4-2	2-1	***V***	1-1	3-0	5-2	1-3	0-0	2-1	2-0	1-3	1-4	0-1
Continental Star Res.	3-2	2-0	0-3	2-2	***I***	1-0	6-4	1-1	1-1	5-1	1-1	3-5	0-6	2-1
Droitwich Spa Res.	1-2	2-1	1-2	2-1	2-1	***S***	2-1	1-0	0-1	4-1	1-0	1-5	2-2	2-5
Enville Athletic	3-1	7-3	1-7	2-2	2-6	2-2	***I***	3-2	4-0	0-3	2-0	2-6	2-6	3-2
Feckenham	1-2	5-1	4-1	0-1	2-3	1-0	4-3	***O***	0-3	4-0	1-7	3-1	0-1	2-0
Greenhill	0-0	3-1	0-6	0-2	1-6	0-1	3-0	0-2	***N***	1-2	2-1	0-0	0-5	1-2
Leamington Hibernian	2-1	0-6	0-5	1-3	2-3	3-1	2-7	2-1	0-1		2-3	1-3	0-5	2-4
Perrywood	1-2	3-1	2-2	2-0	1-4	1-1	5-5	0-1	0-4	1-2	***T***	1-1	3-5	0-3
Racing Club Warwick Res.	2-2	4-3	1-2	3-2	1-3	4-6	3-1	2-2	0-1	7-1	4-2	***W***	1-1	4-2
Shirley Town	1-3	5-1	0-1	5-1	4-2	3-2	3-0	0-3	2-0	3-0	6-3	2-0	***O***	5-0
Worcester City Academy	0-0	7-2	2-1	3-1	0-0	3-1	4-1	4-2	0-1	1-2	3-1	2-2	1-2	

MIDLAND COMBINATION DIVISION TWO CONSTITUTION 2009-10

AFC SMETHWICK . . . . Holly Lane Sports & Social Club, Holly Lane, Erdington, Birmingham B24 9LH 0121 373 0979
CADBURY ATHLETIC RESERVES . Cadbury Rec Ground, Bournville Lane, Bournville, Birmingham 0121 458 2000x3316/454 4264
CHELMSLEY TOWN . . . . The Pavilions, Coleshill Road, Marston Green, Birmingham B37 7HW 0121 779 5400
CONTINENTAL STAR RESERVES. . Oldbury Leis. Centre, Newbury Lane, Oldbury, Warley B69 1HE 0121 552 4497
DROITWICH SPA RESERVES . . . . . . Droitwich Spa Leisure Centre, Briar Mill, Droitwich WR9 0RZ 07860 591091
ENVILLE ATHLETIC. . . . . Enville Athletic Club, Hall Drive, Enville, Stourbridge DY7 5HB. 01384 872368
FECKENHAM. . . . . The Playing Fields, The Square, Mill Lane, Feckenham, Redditch B96 6HY. 01527 892611
GREENHILL. . . . . Dudley Sports FC, Dudley Sports & Social Club, Hillcrest Avenue, Brierley Hill DY5 3QH 01384 826420
HAMPTON . . . . Field Lane Sports Ground, Lugtrout Lane, Solihull B91 2RT . . . . None
HENLEY FOREST. . . . . Henley-in-Arden Sports & Social Club, Stratford Road, Henley-in-Arden B95 6AD 01564 792022
KENILWORTH TOWN KH. . . . . Gypsy Lane, off Rouncil Lane, Kenilworth CV8 1FA 01926 850851
KNOWLE RESERVES . . . . Hampton Road, Knowle, Solihull B93 0NX 01564 779807
LEAMINGTON HIBERNIAN . . . . Ajax Park, Hampton Road, Warwick CV34 6JP. 01926 495786
LICHFIELD CITY . . . . Brownsfield Park, Brownsfield Road, off Eastern Avenue, Lichfield WS13 6AY. None
PERRYWOOD . . . . Neel Park, Droitwich Road, Perdiswell, Worcester WR3 7SN 07808 768222
RACING CLUB WARWICK RESERVES. . . . . Hampton Road, Warwick CV34 6JP 01926 495786

IN: Hampton (P), Henley Forest (P), Kenilworth Town KH (P), Knowle Res. (P), Lichfield City (P)
OUT: BNJS Mann & Co (WN), Castle Vale Res. (P), Shirley Town (P), Worcester City Academy (W)
AFC Internazionale become AFC Smethwick

Division Three	P	W	D	L	F	A	Pts
Hampton	24	20	3	1	76	19	63
Henley Forest	24	16	3	5	79	28	51
Knowle Res.	24	12	9	3	46	25	45
Kenilworth Town KH	24	13	5	6	53	30	44
Lichfield City	24	13	4	7	64	36	43
Dosthill Colts Res.	24	12	3	9	53	51	39
Clements '83	24	7	8	9	30	32	29
Coton Green Res.	24	8	3	13	27	75	27
Chelmsley Town Res.	24	5	8	11	35	53	23
Coventry Amateurs	24	6	5	13	40	66	23
Shipston Excelsior	24	5	3	16	23	43	18
Littleton Res.	24	4	5	15	40	64	17
Evesham United A	24	3	5	16	21	65	14

CHALLENGE URN

FIRST ROUND
Clements '83 4 Dosthill Colts Res. 1
Coton Green Res. 0 **Chelmsley Town Res.** 4
Coventry Amateurs 2 **Shipston Excelsior** 3
Lichfield City 2 Hampton 1
Littleton Res. 1 **Henley Forest** 2
Nuneaton Town Res. v **Knowle Res.** (w/o)
QUARTER-FINALS
Henley Forest 2 Evesham United A 1 *aet*
Kenilworth Town KH 3 Knowle Res. 1
Lichfield City 4 Chelmsley Town Res. 0
Shipston Excelsior 1 **Clements '83** 2
SEMI-FINALS
(played over two legs)
Clements '83 0 Kenilworth Town KH 1, Kenilworth Town 0 **Clements '83** 3
Henley Forest 2 Lichfield City 1, Lichfield City 1 **Henley Forest** 1 *aet*
FINAL
(May 2nd at Stratford Town)
Clements '83 2 Henley Forest 1

	Che	Cle	Cot	Cov	Dos	Eve	Ham	Hen	Ken	Kno	Lic	Littl	Shi
Chelmsley Town Res.		1-1	1-4	1-1	2-2	4-0	2-3	0-6	3-3	0-3	1-2	2-3	1-0
Clements '83	1-2		2-1	2-1	1-2	4-0	0-3	1-1	1-4	0-0	1-3	4-0	1-0
Coton Green Res.	1-1	0-2	***D***	1-0	0-7	3-3	1-2	0-9	1-1	2-1	0-5	1-0	3-0
Coventry Amateurs	2-2	1-1	0-2	***I***	7-1	3-0	1-8	2-8	0-6	1-1	1-2	3-3	5-2
Dosthill Colts Res.	4-3	1-2	6-1	1-4	***V***	4-1	0-6	1-7	0-1	0-0	4-3	6-0	2-1
Evesham United A	2-0	1-1	0-1	2-1	0-3		0-6	1-4	1-0	2-2	1-5	1-1	0-1
Hampton	3-1	1-1	5-0	4-0	1-0	4-1	***T***	4-0	2-0	2-2	2-1	4-2	2-1
Henley Forest	5-1	1-0	5-1	4-2	4-0	3-2	0-1	***H***	1-1	0-1	2-2	3-1	6-0
Kenilworth Town KH	0-3	3-0	3-1	3-0	3-1	4-1	1-2	1-2	***R***	1-3	4-2	6-1	1-0
Knowle Res.	2-2	3-2	5-0	4-0	0-0	2-1	2-1	4-0	1-1	***E***	2-2	2-1	2-1
Lichfield City	0-0	1-1	9-0	6-0	2-3	5-0	1-5	1-3	1-2	1-0	***E***	2-1	2-0
Littleton Res.	1-2	1-1	6-0	1-2	2-4	3-0	1-4	0-5	2-2	2-3	3-5		4-1
Shipston Excelsior	4-0	1-0	2-3	1-3	0-1	1-1	1-1	1-0	1-2	3-1	0-1	1-1	

JACK MOULD TROPHY

(Division Two and Three clubs)

FIRST ROUND
Clements '83 0 **Henley Forest** 3
Continental Star Res. 2 **Shipston** 4
Coventry Ams 4 Leamington Hibs 2
Dosthill Colts Res. 2 Coton Green Res. 2 *aet* (10-9p)
Droitwich Spa Res. (w/o) v BNJS Mann & Co
Enville Athletic 0 **Hampton** 1
Greenhill 2 Feckenham 2 *aet* (4-2p)
Kenilworth Town KH 3 Shirley 1
Lichfield City 2 Castle Vale Res. 2 *aet* (5-4p)
Perrywood 3 Chelmsley Town Res. 2
Racing Club Warwick Res. 3 AFC Internazionale 2
Worcester City Academy 2 **Chelmsley Town** 5
SECOND ROUND
Cadbury Athletic Res. 5 Droitwich Spa Res. 4 *aet*
Chelmsley Town 1 **Lichfield City** 2
Coventry Amateurs 1 **Evesham United A** 3
Greenhill 1 Knowle Res. 0
Hampton 2 Kenilworth Town KH 1
Henley Forest 2 **Racing Club Warwick Res.** 3 *aet*
Littleton Res. 1 **Perrywood** 6
Shipston Excelsior 4 Dosthill Colts Res. 0
QUARTER-FINALS
Cadbury Athletic Res. 0 **Hampton** 1
Evesham A 4 **Perrywood** 4 *aet* (5-6p)
Lichfield City 3 Shipston Excelsior 0
Racing Warwick Res. 3 Greenhill 1
SEMI-FINALS
(played over two legs)
Hampton 0 Lichfield City 1, **Lichfield City** 3 Hampton 1
Perrywood 1 Racing Club Warwick Res. 1, **Racing Club Warwick Res.** 4 Perrywood 0
FINAL
(April 28th at Coventry Copsewood)
Racing Club Warwick Res. 4 Lichfield City 0

MIDLAND COMBINATION DIVISION THREE CONSTITUTION 2009-10

ARCHDALE RESERVES . . . . County Sports Ground, Claines Lane, Worcester WR3 7SS 07736 30967
BLACKWOOD . . . . Field Lane Sports Ground, Field Lane, Solihull B91 2RT . . . . Nor
CHELMSLEY TOWN RESERVES The Pavilions, Coleshill Road, Marston Green, Birmingham B37 7HW 0121 779 540
CLEMENTS '83 . . . . Mackadown Sports & Social, Mackadown Lane, Kitts Green, Birmingham B33 0JG 0121 783 992
COTON GREEN RESERVES. . . . . New Mill Lane, Fazeley, Tamworth B78 3RX . . . . Nor
COVENTRY AMATEURS . David Sinclair Sports Ground, Westwood Heath Road, Westwood Heath, Coventry . . . . Nor
DOSTHILL COLTS RESERVES . . . . Hermitage Hill, Polesworth, Tamworth B78 1HS 01827 89248
EARLSWOOD TOWN RESERVES. . . The Pavilions, Malthouse Lane, Earlswood, Solihull B94 5DX 07923 41550
INKBERROW. . . . . Sands Road, Inkberrow, Worcester WR7 4HJ . . . . Nor
LITTLETON RESERVES. . . . . Five Acres, Pebworth Road, North Littleton, Evesham WR11 8QL 07966 29797
NORTHFIELD TOWN RESERVES Shenley Lane Community Centre, Shenley Lane, Selly Oak, Birmingham B29 4HZ 0121 475 387
PERSHORE TOWN RESERVES King George V Playing Fields, King George's Way, Pershore WR10 1AA. 01386 55690
POLESWORTH . . . . Hermitage Hill, Polesworth, Tamworth B78 1HS 01827 89248
SHIPSTON EXCELSIOR . . . . Shipston Sports Club, London Road, Shipston-on-Stour CV36 4EP 01608 66113
STRATFORD TOWN A . . . . Knights Lane, Tiddington, Stratford-on-Avon CV37 7BZ 01789 26933
YOUNG WARRIORS . . . . Coventry Sphinx FC, Sphinx Drive, Off Siddeley Avenue, Coventry CV3 1WA. 02476 45136

IN: Archdale Res. (N), Blackwood (P - Sunday football), Earlswood Town Res. (N), Inkberrow (P - Stratford-on-Avon Alliance Divisic One), Northfield Town Res. (N), Pershore Town Res. (N), Polesworth (N), Stratford Town A (N), Young Warriors (P - Youth football)
OUT: Evesham United A (W), Hampton (P), Henley Forest (P), Kenilworth Town KH (P), Knowle Res. (P), Lichfield City (P), Nuneatc Town Res. (WN)

LEAGUE CONSTITUTION 2009-10 - PREMIER DIVISION

BARTLEY GREEN

Formed: 1959
Chairman: David Shepherd.
Secretary: Mark Wigley. 28 Hightree Close, Bartley Green, Birmingham, B32 3QP
Tel: (H) 0121 608 2972 (M) 07967 630 644.
Ground: Illey Lane, Halesowen B62 0HE.
Directions: From M5 junction 3, follow the A456 for Halesowen/Kidderminster for approx 1.5 miles to Grange Island. Turn left along the B4551 Bromsgrove Road for approx 400 yards, take the 1st left into Illey Lane and the ground is approximately 1 mile on the left hand side.
Hospitality: Bartley Green Social Club Jiggins Lane, Bartley Green. Turn left out of ground, go over Motorway Bridge to T junction, turn left along Kitwell Lane to mini roundabout, then turn right into Adams Hill, approx a 0.75 miles turn left into Jiggins Lane. The club is on the left (300 yards)
Floodlights: Yes.
Colours: Amber/amber & black/amber & black.
Honours: Midland Combination Div. Two Champions 05-06, Div. One 06-07.

BOLEHALL SWIFTS

Formed: 1953
Chairman: Mal Tooley.
Secretary: Mal Tooley. 7 Ninefoot Lane, Belgrave, Tamworth, Staffs, B77 2NA. Tel: (H) 01827 704 988 (B) 01675 468 218 (M) 07842 757786.
Ground: Rene Road, Bolehall, Tamworth B77 3NN Tel: 01827 62637
Directions: Take M42 north, leaving at J10. Turn left onto the A5 heading for Tamworth. Leave the A5 at the second exit, marked Glascote and Amington Industrial Estate. Turn right onto Marlborough Way until next island. Turn left at the island down the B5000 then take a right into Argyle Street (opposite the chip shop). At the T-junction, turn left into Amington Road. Drive over the canal bridge, take the second right into Leedham Avenue, then the right fork into Rene Road. The club is situated 150 yards on the right immediately after the school.
Floodlights: Yes.
Colours: Green & yellow/green/yellow.

BROCTON

Formed: 1937
Chairman: Brian Townsend
Secretary: Terry Homer.124 John Street, Chadsmoor, Cannock, Staffs, WS11 5HR
Telephone: (H) 01543 571964 (M) 07791 841774.
Ground: Silkmore Lane Sports Ground, Silkmore Lane, Stafford, ST17 4JH
Ground Telephone: 07791 841774 (Match Days Only)
Directions: From M6 J14 take A449 towards Stafford for 1.5 miles until reaching traffic lights by Esso petrol station. Turn right at lights into Rickescote Road, follow road round over railway bridge to mini island, at island bear left into Silkmore Lane. At next mini island take 4th exit for entrance to ground.
From Lichfield/Rugeley. After passing Staffs Police HQ at Baswick go downhill past BMW garage and pub to large island, take 1st exit into Silkmore Lane, at next mini island take 2nd exit into ground entrance
Do not turn into Lancaster Road or Silkmore Crescent as directed by Sat Navs
Hospitality: Spittle Brook, Queensville Bridge. At end of driveway go over Splitter Island and turn right at mini island, at next island take 2nd exit (Stafford Town Centre). Go over Railway Bridge, at bottom of bridge turn immediately right, travelling back on yourself. Spittle Brook is 100 yds on left at the end of the road.
Floodlights: Yes.
Colours: Green & White/White/Green.

CADBURY ATHLETIC

Formed: 1994
Chairman: John Peckham.
Secretary: Ron Thorn, 3 Kingshurst Road, Northfield, Birmingham B31 2LN Tel Nos: 0121 624 8288 (H) 07751 838715 (M)
Ground: Alvechurch FC, Lye Meadow, Redditch Road, Alvechurch, Worcestershire, B48 7RS Tel: 0121 445 2929.
Directions: M42 Junction 2, Follow signs for Redditch, taking dual carriageway. At 1st island turn right (Signposted Alvechurch), ground approximately 1km on right. Car Park entrance before ground.
Floodlights: Yes.
Colours: Purple/black/purple.

CASTLE VALE

Formed: 1964
Chairman: Gary Higgins.
Secretary: Shane Godwood. 78 Hawthorne Road, Castle Bromwich, Birmingham, B36 0HJ. Tel: (H) 0121 681 3711 (M) 07787 804153
Ground: Vale Stadium, Farnborough Road, Castle Vale, Warwick B35 7DA. Tel: 0121 747 6969.
Directions: Leave M6 J5 and turn right at island onto A452. At the island with the Spitfire sculpture turn right into Tangmere Drive, then right onto Farnborough Road. The ground is on the right hand side after approximately 1/2 mile.
Floodlights: Yes.
Colours: All red.

CASTLE VALE J.K.S.

Formed 1998
Chairman: Graham Crocker
Secretary: Pamela Crocker, 5 Turnhouse Road, Castle Vale, B35 6PT
Tel: (H) 0121 747 5970 (M) 07717 175361.
Ground: Vale Stadium, Farnborough Road, Castle Vale, Birmingham, B35 7DA. Tel: 0121 747 6969.
Directions: From M6 Junction 5 turn right at the island onto the A452 to island with Spitfire sculpture, turn right into Tangmere Drive, then right into Farnborough Road, Ground is on the right hand side after approximately 1/2 mile.
Floodlights: Yes.
Colours: Yellow & blue/yellow & blue/blue & white.
Honours: Midland Com. Div.1 Champions 2008-09.

CONTINENTAL STAR

Formed: 1975
Chairman: Keith John.
Secretary: Keith John. 11 Birmingham Road, Great Barr, Birmingham, B43 6NW. Tel: (H) 0121 358 2020 (M) 07956 429 046.
Ground: Oldbury Leisure Centre, Newbury Lane, Oldbury, B69 1HE Tel: 0121 552 4497.
Directions: M5 junction 2: Turn right at large islands towards Wolverhampton, turn left at 1st set of traffic lights into Newbury Lane, the ground is 150 yards on the right.
Floodlights: Yes.
Colours: Yellow & blue/blue/yellow.

INS & OUTS
In: Castle Vale JKS (P), Dosthill Colts (P), Pelsall Villa (S – West Midlands (Regional) League Premier Division), Racing Club Warwick (R – Midland Alliance)
Out: Coton Green (R), Loughborough University (P – Midland Alliance), Oldbury Athletic (S - West Midlands (Regional) League Premier Division)

COVENTRY COPSEWOOD

Formed: 1923 (Formerley Coventry Marconi)
Chairman: Robert Abercrombie.
Secretary: David Wilson. 60 Craven Avenue, Binley Woods, Coventry, CV3 2JT. Tel: (H) 02476 544 296 (M) 07807 969 327.
Ground: Copeswood Sports & Social Club, Allard Way, Copswood, Coventry. Tel: 02476 635 992.
Directions: From the M40, follow A46 signs to Coventry and Leicester. Stay on this road until very end. You reach a roundabout with a flyover. Go round the roundabout following M69 signs. This road takes you past Asda and you reach a set of traffic lights with a roundabout. Take second left turn off the roundabout, again following M69 signs onto Allard Way. Stay on Allard Way, go under the railway bridge and the ground is 400 yards on right.
Floodlights: Yes. **Colours:** All blue.
Honours: Midland Comb. Challenge Cup 2006-07.

DOSTHILL COLTS

Formed 1990
Chairman: Paul Billing
Secretary: David Brown, 82 Station Road, Polesworth, Staffs, B78 1BQ. Tel: (H) 01827 893501 (M) 07799 075828.
Ground: Bolehall Swifts F.C., Rene Road, Bolehall, Tamworth, Staffs, B77 3NN.
Directions: Exit M42 at Junction 10, take A5 towards Tamworth, exit A5 at 2nd exit (Glascote & Amington Industrial Estate). Turn right onto Marlborough Way, at next island turn left (B5000), turn right into Argyle Street (opposite chip shop). At T-junction, turn left into Amington Road, drive over canal bridge, turn 2nd right into Leedham Avenue. Take right fork into Rene Road. Club is situated 150 yards on right immediately after school.
Floodlights: Yes.
Colours: White/royal blue/red.

G.S.A. SPORTS

Formed: 1992
Chairman: Mr Cooksey Singh Nijjer
Secretary: Ms Kim Holland. 6 Pinehurst Drive, Kings Norton, Birmingham, B38 8TH. Tel: 07838 609287
Ground: Abbey Park Stadium, Glastonbury Crescent, Walsall WS3 2RQ
Floodlights: Yes
Colours: Red/Red/Red.

HEATH HAYES

Formed: 1965
Chairman: Paul Mallen.
Secretary: Mrs. Kathlyn Davies, 4 Prince Street, West Chadsmoor, Cannock, Staffs. WS11 5RT. **Tel:** 07969 203 063.
Ground: Coppice Colliery Ground, Newlands Lane, Heath Hayes, Cannock, Staffs. WS12 3HH. Tel: 07977 239 193.
Directions: From M6 Junction 11 take A4601 to Cannock, at 1st island turn right onto A460 to Rugeley/Cannock Business Parks. At double island (A5) straight on, still on A460, over next 2 islands, at 3rd island turn right onto A5190, signposted Lichfield, carry on past Texaco garage on the right, take next turn right into Newlands Lane, entrance to ground is 50 yards down lane on the left under green barrier. If using the M6 Toll motorway, leave at exit immediately after pay plaza, signposted A34 Walsall, Cannock & Rugeley, then follow the above directions from A5.
Floodlights: Yes.
Colours: Blue & white stripes/blue/white.

HEATHER ST. JOHN

Formed: 1949
Chairman: Paul Harrison.
Secretary: Kevin Williams. 3 Beech Tree Road, Coalville, Leicester, LE67 4JN. Tel: 07967 905808.
Ground: St John's Park, Ravenstone Road, Heather, Leics, LE67 2QJ Tel: 01530 263 986.
Directions: From Birmingham take M42, A42 north to Ashby De La Zouch, exit at junction 13, take the 5th exit, A511 to Coalville for 3 miles, at the roundabout take the 4th exit A447 for 3 miles. At the double mini island take 3rd exit to Heather, 1 mile at the mini island take 3rd exit, ground is 200 yards on the left. From Coventry/Warwick. A46 to M69 exit junction 1, to the A5 take the 2nd exit, then follow signs for Ibstock A447. At the mini island in Ibstock take 1st exit to Heather, 1 mile at the mini island take 3rd exit ground 200yards on the left.
Floodlights: Yes **Colours:** All royal blue.

KNOWLE

Formed: 1926
Chairman: Derek Adamson.
Secretary: Daniel Green. 315 Highters Heath Lane, Hollywood, Birmingham, B14 4TA
Tel: (H) 0121 244 5536 (M) 07798 713982
Ground: Studley FC, The Beehive, Abbeyfields Drive, Studley, Warks B80 7BE. Ground Telephone: 01527 853817
Directions: Leave M42 at junction 3. Take A435 towards Redditch, head south for 5 miles. Abbeyfields Drive is on the left hand side _ mile past 'The Boot' public house, adjacent to a sharp left hand bend
Floodlights: Yes
Colours: Red/Black/Black.

MASSEY FERGUSON

Formed: 1956
Chairman: Lindsey Bailey.
Secretary: Terry Borras. 4 Ashbridge Road, Allesley Park, Coventry, CV5 9LA. Tel: (H) 02476 276 646 (M) 07791 553 031.
Ground: Bannerbrook Park, Banner Lane, Tile Hill, Coventry CV4 9GF.
Directions: From M42 or M6 take the A45 to Coventry. At the first set of lights bear left onto Broad Lane. Travel down Broad Lane until you reach Vauxhall dealers on your right. Turn left opposite the Vauxhall Dealers into Banner Lane. Then take the third gate on your right signposted Sports Ground. Follow this road until you see the car park behind the main stand.
Floodlights: Yes.
Colours: Red/black/red.

MEIR K.A.

Formed: 1972
Chairman: Des Reaney.
Secretary: Chris Robinson, 12 The Broadway, Meir, Stoke-on-Trent ST3 5PE Tel: 07888 750 532.
Ground: Kings Park, Hilderstone Road, Meir Heath, Stoke-on-Trent Tel: 07888 750 532.
Directions: At M6 J14 take the A34 to Stone, then the A520 to Meir Heath, and B5066 into Hilderstone. The ground is on the right after approximately 1/2 mile.
Floodlights: Yes.
Colours: Amber/black/black.

NUNEATON GRIFF

Formed: 1974

Chairman: John Gore.

Secretary: Pete Kemp. 205 Haunchwood Road,Nuneaton, Warwicks. CV10 8DF. Tel: 02476 353 103 (H) 07931 297 935 (M)

Ground: The Pingles Stadium, Avenue Road, Nuneaton CV11 4LX. Tel: 02476 370 688.

Directions: At M6 J3 turn left onto A444 (Nuneaton). Stay on the A444 over the Bermuda Park, McDonalds and George Eliot Hospital roundabouts, until reaching the large roundabout with the footbridge over the road. Carry straight on and downhill, taking the right hand lane. At bottom you reach Coton Arches Island. Take the second exit (Avenue Road) and travel 1/2 mile to the Cedar Tree Pub traffic lights, turning left into the stadium car park service road.

Floodlights: Yes.

Colours: Blue & white/blue/ blue.

PELSALL VILLA

Formed: 1898

Chairman: Shaun Mason.

Secretary: Russell Storey. 1 Ninefoot Lane, Tamworth, Staffs B77 2NA. Tel: 07906 620 952.

Ground: The Bush Ground, Walsall Road, Walsall, WS3 4BP

Ground Telephone: 01922 692748

Directions: Leave M6 at junction 7 sign-posted A34 Birmingham. Take A34 towards Walsall to 1st Island, turn right (marked Ring Road) across 3 islands. At large island at the bottom of the hill, take last exit marked Lichfield. Up hill and across next island to traffic lights, continue to next set of lights and turn left (B4154 Pelsall). Go over Railway Bridge to Old Bush Public House, the ground is next to the public house signposted Pelsall Cricket Club

Floodlights: Yes.

Colours: White & red/red/white & red.

PERSHORE TOWN

Formed: 1988

Chairman: Colin Shepherd.

Secretary: Richard Terry. 9 River House, Common Road, Evesham, Worcs, WR11 4QY

Tel: (H) 01386 442 980 (M) 07834 315 113

Ground: King George V Playing Fields, King Georges Way, Pershore, Worcs WR10 1JP. Tel: 01386 556 902.

Directions: Leave the M5 J7 (Worcester South), taking the first left A44 to Pershore. On entering the town, at the second set of traffic lights turn left. The ground is 200 yards on the left hand side.

Floodlights: Yes.

Colours: Blue & white stripes/blue/blue.

PILKINGTON XXX

Formed: 2002

Chairman: Alan Rowlands.

Secretary: John McVey, 84 Clee Road,West Heath,Birmingham B31 3RF Tel: 07835 010 870.

Ground: Triplex Sports Ground, Eckersall Road, Kings Norton, Birmingham B38 8SR. Tel: 0121 458 4570.

Directions: Leave the M42 J2. At the roundabout take the third exit onto the A441 (Redditch Road). Stay on the A441 over two roundabouts and after about 4 1/2 miles turn left into Camp Lane. After 300 yards, the road changes to Eckersall Road. The ground is on the right.

Floodlights: Yes.

Colours: Green/black/green.

RACING CLUB WARWICK

Formed: 1919

Chairman: Andy Feasey.

Secretary: Lee Martin. 18 Burns Avenue, Warwick.

Tel: 07867 591 768.

Ground: Hampton Road, Warwick, CV34 6JP

Ground Telephone: 01926 495786.

Directions: M40 Junction 15, signposted Warwick. At roundabout with traffic lights take A429 to Warwick. Follow this road for _ mile and you will come to houses on your left. Take the 2nd turn on the left into Shakespeare Avenue. Follow to T-junction. Turn right into Hampton Road. Entrance to ground is 50 yards on left.

Floodlights: Yes.

Colours: Gold/black/black.

SOUTHAM UNITED

Formed: 1905

Chairman: Charles Hill.

Secretary: Charles Hill. 28 Millholme Close, Southam, CV47 1FQ Tel: (M) 07802 949 781.

Ground: Banbury Road Ground, Southam, Leamington Spa. Warwickshire CV47 2BJ. Tel: 01926 812 091.

Directions: Leave the M40 J12 (Gaydon). Turn right onto the B4451 at top of slip road. Southam is signposted. It is approximately 6 1/2 miles from motorway to the ground. As you approach Southam ignore signposts for town centre and go straight over at the first island, and right at the second island past the 24 hour garage (Banbury Road). The ground is 100 yards on the right.

Floodlights: Yes.

Colours: Yellow & royal blue/royal blue/ royal blue.

WALSALL WOOD

Formed: 1919

Chairman: TBA.

Secretary: Roger Merrick. 15 Vigo Terrace, Walsall Wood, Walsall, West Midlands, WS9 9LF. Tel: (H) 01543 378 873 (M) 07809 641926.

Ground: Oak Park, Lichfield Road, Walsall Wood, Walsall. WS9 9NP.

Tel: 01543 361 084.

Directions: From North using M6 south to junction 12, take A5 until large island just outside Brownhills (next island after the Turn pub on left), take A452 Chester Road North through Brownhills High Street to traffic lights at Shire Oak pub on right. Turn right onto A461 for Walsall, go to next traffic lights. Immediately after lights turn right onto Oak Park Leisure Centre car park (rear of Kentucky Fried Chicken). Proceed diagonally over car park and follow road round to ground entrance.

From South using M5/M6. Go onto M6 North and leave at junction 9. Take A4148 for Walsall. Proceed for about 2 miles over several islands until going down a hill alongside the Arboretum on the right. At large island at bottom of hill turn right onto A461 for Lichfield. Proceed for about 4 miles and go through Walsall Wood villagr (after Barons Court Hotel on right), up the hill after village, Oak Park is on the left opposite Fitness First, turn left and go diagonally across Oak Park Leisure Centre car park and follow road roubd to the ground entrance.

Floodlights: Yes.

Colours: Red/red/red & white.

IN: Castle Vale Res. (P), Coton Green (R), Shirley Town (P). OUT: Castle Vale JKS (P), Dosthill Colts (P) INS & OUTS

LEAGUE CONSTITUTION 2009-10 - DIVISION ONE

ALVESTON
Formed 1927
Chairman: Martin Beese
Secretary: Julie Collett.
26 Valletta Way, Wellesbourne, Warwickshire, CV35 9TB
Tel: (H) 01789 471102 (M) 07966 984811
Ground: The Home Guard Club, Main Road, Tiddington, Stratford Upon Avon, CV37 7AY
Tel: 01789 297718
Floodlights: Yes
Colours: Sky Blue/maroon/sky blue

ARCHDALE '73
Formed 1926
Chairman: Neil Cleaveley.
Secretary: R.T.Widdowson. 33 Mayfield Avenue, Worcester, WR3 8LA
Tel: (H) 01905 27866.
Ground: County Sports Ground, Claines Lane, Worcester, WR3 7SS
Social Club Tel: 07736 309670.
Floodlights: No
Colours: All white.

BRERETON SOCIAL
Formed: 1899
Chairman: David Mason
Secretary: Dennis Hibbs, 46 Handsacre Crescent, Rugeley, Staffs, WS15 4DQ
Tel: (H) 01543 307174 (M) 07970 016662.
Ground: Red Lion Ground, Armitage Lane, Brereton, Rugeley, Staffs. WS15 1ED. Tel: 01889 585 526.
Floodlights: Yes.
Colours: Red & White Stripes/red/red.

BURNTWOOD TOWN
Formed 1921
Chairman: David Cox
Secretary: Michael Gentles. 4 Californian Grove, Chase Terrace, Burntwood, Staffs, WS7 2BG
Tel: 07771 551244
Ground: Memorial Ground, Rugeley Road, Burntwood, Staffs, WS7 9BE
Tel: 07946 269153
Floodlights: No
Colours: Red & blue/blue/blue.

CASTLE VALE RESERVES
Formed 1964
Chairman: Gary Higgins
Secretary: Shane Godwood. 78 Hawthorne Road, Castle Bromwich, Birmingham, B36 0HJ
Tel: (H) 0121 681 3711 (M) 07787 804153
Ground: The Glades, Lugtrout Lane, Solihull, West Midlands, B91 2RX
Ground Telephone: 07825 940839
Floodlights: No
Colours: All red.

COTON GREEN
Formed 1982
Chairman: Andrew McMenemy.
Secretary: Steve Colyer. 26 Littlecote, Riverside, Tamworth, B79 7UJ
Tel: 01827 706 280 (M) 07917 206163
Ground: Red Lion Ground, Armitage Lane, Brereton, Rugeley, Staffs, WS15 1ED
Ground Telephone: 01889 585 526
Directions: From M6 Junction 11 follow A460 to Rugeley, on reaching large roundabout at Rugeley take A51 (signposted Lichfield). At end of dual carriageway in Brerton turn left at traffic lights into Armitage Lane. Entrance is 100 yards on right.
Floodlights: Yes
Colours: Red & White/Black/Black.

DROITWICH SPA
Formed 1986
Secretary and Chairman: David West.
3 Bagshott Road, Droitwich, WR9 8UH
Tel: (H) 01905 773 287 (B) 0121 565 6603
(M) 07860 591 091.
Ground: Droitwich Spa Leisure Centre, Briar Mill, Droitwich, WR9 8UE. Tel: 07860 591091
Floodlights: No
Colours: Red & black/black/black & red.

EARLSWOOD TOWN
Formed 1968
Chairman: Graham Ashford.
Secretary: Clive Faulkner. 21 St Thomas Close, Sutton Coldfield, West Midlands, B75 7QJ
Tel: (H) 0121 329 2436 (M) 07866 122254
Ground: The Pavilions, Malthouse Lane, Earlswood, Solihull, B94 5DX.Tel: 07923 415 501
Floodlights: No
Colours: Red & white Stripes/black/black.

FAIRFIELD VILLA
Formed 1959
Chairman: Patrick Eades.
Secretary: Charles Harris. Flat 3, 48 Stourbridge Road, Bromsgrove, Worcs, B61 0AH
Tel: (H) 01527 559 372 (M) 07880 777 673.
Ground: Recreation Ground, Stourbridge Road, Fairfield, Bromsgrove, Worcs, B61 9LZ
Tel: 01527 877 049.
Floodlights: No
Colours: All yellow.

LITTLETON
Formed 1890
Chairman & Secretary: Colin Emms.
Ivy Cottage, Cleeve Road, Middle Littleton, Evesham, Worcs, WR11 8JR. Tel: (H) 01386 832084
Ground: 5 Acres, Pebworth Road, North Littleton, Evesham, Worcs, WR11 8QL. Tel: 07813 021 905
Floodlights: No
Colours: Red/white/red.

MILE OAK ROVERS & YOUTH
Reformed 2003
Chairman: David Morton.
Secretary: Keith Lycett. 1 Price Avenue, Mile Oak, Tamworth, B78 3NL
Tel: (H) 01827 703389 (M) 07870 897625
Ground: Mile Oak Community Ground, Price Avenue, Mile Oak, Tamworth. Tel: 01827 289 614
Floodlights: No.
Colours: Blue & yellow/blue/blue.

NEWHALL UNITED
Formed 1926
Chairman: Robert Corner.
Secretary: Dave Foster. 25 Tudor Way, Newhall, Swadlincote, Derby, DE11 0HF
Tel: (H) 01283 214898 (M) 07974 423880
Ground: The Hadfields, Saint Johns Drive, Newhall Swadlincote, DE11 0SU.
Floodlights: No.
Colours: Blue & black/black/blue.

NORTHFIELD TOWN
Formed 1966
Chairman: Lynne Kirby.
Secretary: Harvey Ryder. 10 Meadow Brook Road, Northfield, Birmingham, B31 1NE
Te: (H) 0121 694 7571 (M) 07976 543 218.
Ground: Shenley Lane Community Association, 472 Shenley Lane, Selly Oak, Birmingham, B29 4HZ
Tel: 0121 475 3870
Floodlights: No
Colours: Yellow /royal blue/royal blue & yellow

SHIRLEY TOWN
Formed 2008
Chairman: Ian Gordon.
Secretary: Trevor Dunkley. 23 Turves Green, West Heath, Birmingham, B31 4AH
Tel: (B) 0121 643 3011 (M) 07889 124991
Ground: Tilehouse Lane, Shirley, B90 1PH
Floodlights: No
Colours: All red.

STOCKINGFORD AA
Formed 1948
Chairman& Secretary: Keith Lenton. 154 Malvern Avenue, Stockingford, Nuneaton, Warks, CV10 8NB
Tel: (H) 02476 327 363 (M) 07814 319 991
Ground: Stockingford Allotment Association Ltd, The Pavilion, Stockingford, Nuneaton, Warks
Tel: 02476 387 743.
Floodlights: No
Colours: White with red trim/red/red.

THIMBLEMILL PHOENIX (Previously Thimblemill R.E.C.)
Formed 1964
Secretary & Chairman: Peter Gardiner. 8 Vimy Road, Billesley, Birmingham, B13 0UA.
Tel: (H) 0121 443 1809 (M) 07956 840 121
Ground: Thimblemill Recreation & Entertainment Centre, Pavillion Sports Ground, Thimblemill Road, Smethwick, B67 6NR. Tel: 0121 420 3505
Floodlights: No
Colours: Royal blue/white/royal blue.

WEST MIDLANDS POLICE
Formed 1974
Chairman: Gez Moore.
Secretary: Simon Jones. 48 Gleneagles Road, Bloxwich, Staffs WS3 3UJ.
Tel: (H) 01922 494 191. (M) 07727 089 037.
Ground: Tally Ho Training Centre, Pershore Road, Edgbaston, Birmingham, B7 7RD. Tel: 0121 626 8228
Floodlights: No
Colours: Red & black/black/black.

MIDLAND ALLIANCE

www.midlandfootballalliance.co.uk

Sponsored by: Aspire

Founded: 1994

Recent champions:

2004: Rocester
2005: Rushall Olympic
2006: Chasetown
2007: Leamington
2008: Atherstone Town

		P	W	D	L	F	A	Pts
Market Drayton Town		42	31	6	5	111	31	99
Barwell		42	27	10	5	91	36	91
Coalville Town		42	25	7	10	88	51	82
Boldmere St Michaels		42	25	6	11	98	54	81
Tipton Town		42	23	9	10	82	44	78
Stratford Town		42	21	11	10	92	65	74
Coventry Sphinx		42	23	5	14	96	78	74
Shifnal Town	*-3*	42	20	10	12	73	56	67
Causeway United		42	19	7	16	62	47	64
Alvechurch		42	16	15	11	73	55	63
Coleshill Town		42	18	9	15	70	59	63
Bridgnorth Town		42	17	8	17	76	85	59
Highgate United		42	15	9	18	67	75	54
Studley		42	15	6	21	55	77	51
Friar Lane & Epworth		42	14	9	19	70	96	51
Cradley Town		42	14	8	20	69	81	50
Westfields		42	13	10	19	75	79	49
Biddulph Victoria		42	12	8	22	57	102	44
Oadby Town		42	9	10	23	43	73	37
Rocester		42	8	9	25	49	88	33
Racing Club Warwick		42	4	6	32	31	131	18
Oldbury United	*-1*	42	1	6	35	33	98	8

POLYMAC SERVICES LEAGUE CUP

FIRST ROUND

Alvechurch 4 Oldbury United 0
Boldmere St Michaels 2 Friar Lane & Epworth 1
Coalville Town 1 Racing Club Warwick 1 *aet* (4-3p)
Market Drayton Town 2 Tipton Town 2 *aet* (5-4p)
Stratford Town 0 **Shifnal Town** 1
Westfields 0 **Cradley Town** 1

SECOND ROUND

Alvechurch 4 Barwell 3
Biddulph Victoria 1 **Boldmere St Michaels** 3
Bridgnorth Town 2 **Highgate United** 2 *aet* (2-4p)
Coalville Town 4 Rocester 0
Coventry Sphinx 2 Coleshill Town 1
Market Drayton Town 3 Cradley Town 2
Oadby Town 1 Studley 0
Shifnal Town 2 Causeway United 2 *aet* (5-4p)

QUARTER-FINALS

Coventry Sphinx 5 Alvechurch 2 *aet*
Highgate United 3 Coalville Town 1
Oadby Town 0 **Boldmere St Michaels** 2
Shifnal Town 0 **Market Drayton Town** 3

SEMI-FINALS

(played over two legs)

Highgate United 0 Boldmere St Michaels 2, **Boldmere St Michaels** 3 Highgate United 1
Market Drayton Town 4 Coventry Sphinx 0, Coventry Sphinx 0 **Market Drayton Town** 1

FINAL

(May 5th at Walsall)

Market Drayton Town 2 Boldmere St Michaels 0

JOE McGORRIAN CUP

(League champions v League Cup holders)

(August 9th at Atherstone Town)

Atherstone Town 4 Shifnal Town 4 (5-4p)

	Alvechurch	Barwell	Biddulph	Boldmere	Bridgnorth	Causeway	Coalville	Coleshill	Cv. Sphinx	Cradley	Friar Lane	Highgate	M. Drayton	Oadby T.	Oldbury Utd	R Warwick	Rocester	Shifnal T.	Stratford	Studley	Tipton T.	Westfields
Alvechurch		0-1	6-0	0-3	1-1	2-2	1-1	3-0	1-3	1-2	1-1	3-2	0-1	2-1	2-1	0-0	3-1	1-1	0-2	2-0	0-1	2-1
Barwell	4-0		7-0	1-1	3-1	0-0	2-1	2-0	2-1	2-0	5-2	1-1	3-0	2-2	5-1	11-1	2-0	4-2	0-0	0-0	1-1	0-1
Biddulph Victoria	0-0	0-2		2-1	0-3	1-0	3-4	1-0	0-2	1-0	3-3	1-2	1-8	2-1	0-0	6-0	1-1	5-2	1-5	2-1	0-3	7-4
Boldmere St Michaels	2-1	1-2	5-0		2-3	2-3	3-2	3-1	1-2	0-0	4-1	1-2	2-1	4-0	1-0	2-0	4-2	4-1	5-1	2-1	3-2	0-2
Bridgnorth Town	3-0	3-0	1-1	0-5		1-2	3-2	1-1	2-0	3-4	4-1	2-1	2-6	4-1	3-2	1-0	4-1	0-4	2-1	3-0	0-0	2-1
Causeway United	1-2	0-1	2-0	0-0	3-2		0-1	2-0	1-2	3-2	6-1	3-2	0-1	0-1	2-1	1-0	2-1	0-1	3-0	3-0	0-1	3-2
Coalville Town	1-1	3-1	4-0	0-0	1-0	2-0		2-0	1-1	3-2	0-0	1-1	2-0	3-1	2-1	7-1	2-0	3-1	3-1	4-1	2-2	0-1
Coleshill Town	2-3	0-4	3-0	2-1	1-1	2-0	3-1		1-2	6-0	4-0	0-0	2-2	0-1	1-0	2-0	2-1	2-2	2-0	4-1	3-4	3-1
Coventry Sphinx	3-3	4-2	1-0	2-8	2-1	1-0	1-3	3-2		3-1	4-5	3-2	3-3	3-1	3-1	4-1	2-3	0-1	2-2	7-1	2-2	2-3
Cradley Town	0-1	0-2	6-2	2-3	2-4	1-1	3-1	1-1	0-2		4-0	2-2	1-4	2-1	4-0	1-4	2-3	2-1	2-1	0-4	0-0	3-2
Friar Lane & Epworth	1-2	1-2	3-1	0-3	3-3	2-0	1-2	3-3	0-4	0-3		0-2	1-1	1-0	3-0	6-0	3-1	2-3	4-3	1-2	0-1	2-1
Highgate United	1-1	1-2	4-2	0-2	5-3	2-2	0-6	0-3	5-1	3-2	1-3		0-2	2-1	2-0	0-0	0-1	1-1	2-6	1-0	3-2	1-2
Market Drayton Town	3-0	0-2	5-1	4-0	3-0	1-1	4-0	4-0	1-0	2-0	6-0	3-0		1-0	2-0	9-0	1-0	3-0	3-0	4-3	2-1	4-0
Oadby Town	1-1	0-0	0-3	2-3	3-0	0-3	4-2	0-0	0-1	3-3	1-2	0-1	0-2		3-1	2-2	2-1	0-3	0-1	1-1	0-4	1-0
Oldbury United	0-4	0-2	1-3	1-2	2-2	0-1	0-2	0-2	1-3	3-3	2-3	0-4	1-2	0-1		2-0	0-0	1-2	1-3	0-2	0-3	2-2
Racing Club Warwick	1-8	0-2	4-2	0-4	2-5	0-5	0-3	0-2	1-4	1-2	0-1	0-1	0-3	1-2	3-2		1-2	1-1	0-2	0-5	0-1	0-1
Rocester	1-4	0-1	0-0	1-2	1-0	1-4	1-2	2-3	1-4	0-2	1-1	4-2	0-0	2-2	4-1	1-4		0-1	2-2	3-1	0-4	1-1
Shifnal Town	0-0	3-0	0-0	2-2	3-0	2-1	0-3	0-2	2-0	2-1	4-0	3-1	0-2	2-1	2-1	0-0	3-1		1-2	1-1	2-0	2-2
Stratford Town	4-4	2-2	1-1	3-2	4-1	4-0	2-1	2-3	2-1	4-2	3-3	2-2	2-1	3-0	2-2	4-1	2-2	3-2		2-0	2-0	3-1
Studley	0-5	2-4	3-1	0-1	2-2	2-1	1-3	1-0	5-1	1-0	2-1	0-3	0-3	1-1	1-0	1-1	3-0	2-5	1-0		1-0	1-0
Tipton Town	0-0	0-1	2-0	2-1	4-0	0-0	3-0	3-0	1-4	0-1	1-1	3-2	1-1	2-0	5-2	7-1	3-1	2-1	0-4	3-1		3-2
Westfields	2-2	1-1	2-3	3-3	5-0	0-1	1-2	2-2	5-3	1-1	3-4	1-0	2-3	2-2	2-0	6-0	5-1	0-4	0-0	2-0	0-5	

2009-10

ALVECHURCH

Founded: 1929 Nickname: The Church

Chairman: Peter Eacock
Secretary: Stephen Denny
11 Shawhurst Croft
Hollywood
Birmingham
B47 5PB
Tel: 07710 012 733
Manager: S. Redhead & J. McWilliams
Prog Editor: Alan Deakin

Ground: Lye Meadow, Redditch Road, Alvechurch B48 7RS. Tel: 0121 445 2929.
Capacity: 3,000 **Seats:** 100 **Covered:** 300
Midweek Matchday: Tuesday **Clubhouse:** Yes **Shop:** No
Colours(change): Gold/black/black. (All blue).
Previous Names: Alvechurch FC >1992. Re-formed in 1994.
Previous Lges: Midland Combination
Records:
Senior Honours: Since 1994: Midland Combination Premier 2002-03.
Worcestershire Senior Urn 03-04, 04-05.

10 YEAR RECORD

99-00	00-01	01-02	02-03	03-04	04-05	05-06	06-07	07-08	08-09
MCmP 10	MCmP 7	MCmP 20	MCmP 1	MidAl 19	MidAl 15	MidAl 14	MidAl 10	MidAl 14	MidAl 10

BARWELL

Founded: 1992 Nickname: Kirkby Roaders

Chairman: David Laing
Secretary: Mrs Shirley Brown
101 Eskdale Road
Hinckley
LE10 0NW
Tel: 07961 905 141
Manager:
Prog Editor:

Ground: Kirkby Road Sports Ground, Kirkby Road, Barwell LE9 8FQ. Tel: 01455 843 067.
Capacity: 2,500 **Seats:** 256 **Covered:** 750
Midweek Matchday: Tuesday **Clubhouse:** Yes **Shop:** No
Colours(change): Yellow & green/green/yellow. (White & royal blue/royal/white).
Previous Names: Barwell Athletic FC and Hinckley FC amalgamated in 1992.
Previous Lges: Since 1992: None.
Records: **Goalscorer:** Andy Lucas. **Apps:** Adrian Baker.
Senior Honours: Since 1992: Midland Alliance League Cup 2005-06.

10 YEAR RECORD

99-00	00-01	01-02	02-03	03-04	04-05	05-06	06-07	07-08	08-09
MidAl 9	MidAl 3	MidAl 8	MidAl 12	MidAl 18	MidAl 13	MidAl 9	MidAl 6	MidAl 10	MidAl 2

BIDDULPH VICTORIA

Founded: 1969 Nickname: The Vics

Chairman: Terry Greer
Secretary: Siobhqan Perry
c/o Biddulph Victoria FC
Tel: 07801 028 829
Manager:
Prog Editor: John Shenton

Ground: Tunstall Road, Biddulph, Stoke on Trent ST8 7AQ. Tel: 01782 522 737.
Capacity: 2,500 **Seats:** 224 **Covered:** 224
Midweek Matchday: Tuesday **Clubhouse:** Yes **Shop:** No
Colours(change): Maroon & sky blue/maroon/maroon & sky. (Yellow & navy/navy/navy & yellow.
Previous Names: Knypersley Victoria > 2002.
Previous Lges: Leek & Moorlands. Staffordshire Co. Staffs Senior. West Midlands (Reg)
Records: **Att:** 1,100 v Port Vale (friendly) 1989. **Goalscorer:** John Burndred - 128.
Apps: Terry Stanway - 682.
Senior Honours:

10 YEAR RECORD

99-00	00-01	01-02	02-03	03-04	04-05	05-06	06-07	07-08	08-09
MidAl 12	MidAl 20	MidAl 20	MidAl 13	MidAl 16	MidAl 20	MidAl 17	MidAl 21	MidAl 12	MidAl 18

BOLDMERE ST. MICHAELS

Founded: 1883 Nickname: The Mikes

Chairman: Keith Fielding
Secretary: Rob Paterson
6 Salisbury House
Church Road
Erdington
B42 2DR
Tel: 07779 805 111
Manager: Rob Mallaband
Prog Editor: Alan Parsons

Ground: Trevor Brown Memorial Gd, Church Rd, Boldmere B73 5RY. Tel: 0121 373 4435
Capacity: 2,500 **Seats:** 230 **Covered:** 400
Midweek Matchday: Tuesday **Clubhouse:** Yes **Shop:** No
Colours(change): White/black/black. (All amber).
Previous Names: None.
Previous Lges: West Midlands (Regional). Midland Combination.
Records:
Senior Honours: AFA Senior Cup 1947-48.
Midland Combination Premier 1985-86, 88-89, 89-90.

10 YEAR RECORD

99-00	00-01	01-02	02-03	03-04	04-05	05-06	06-07	07-08	08-09
MidAl 5	MidAl 7	MidAl 13	MidAl 14	MidAl 15	MidAl 10	MidAl 10	MidAl 7	MidAl 4	MidAl 4

BRIDGNORTH TOWN

Founded: 1946 Nickname:

Chairman: Eric James Eagles
Secretary: Mark McIntyre
c/o Bridgnorth Town F.C.

Tel: 01952 583 995
Manager:
Prog Editor:

Ground: Crown Meadow, Innage Lane, Bridgnorth, WV16 5JU. Tel: 07870 546 726.
Capacity: **Seats:** **Covered:**
Midweek Matchday: **Clubhouse:** **Shop:** Yes
Colours(change): All blue. (All white).
Previous Names: None.
Previous Lges: Worcestershire Combination/Midland Combination. Southern. West Mids.
Records:

Senior Honours: Midland Combination 1979-80, 82-83. West Midlands (Regional) 07-08.

10 YEAR RECORD

99-00	00-01	01-02	02-03	03-04	04-05	05-06	06-07	07-08	08-09
MidAl 14	MidAl 9	MidAl 11	MidAl 16	MidAl 10	MidAl 22	MCmP 5	WMP 7	WMP 1	MidAl 12

CAUSEWAY UNITED

Founded: 1957 Nickname:

Chairman: Steve Hulston
Secretary: Frank Webb
10 Moorfield Drive
Halesowen

B63 3TG
Tel: 0121 550 5219
Manager: Carl Burley
Prog Editor:

Ground: War Mem. Ath. Gd, High St., Amblecote, Stourbridge DY8 4HN. Tel: 01384394040
Capacity: **Seats:** **Covered:**
Midweek Matchday: Tuesday **Clubhouse:** Yes **Shop:**
Colours(change): All blue. (All white).
Previous Names: None.
Previous Lges: West Midlands (Regional).
Records: Att: 150. **Apps:** Malcolm Power - 300+

Senior Honours: West Midlands (Regional) Premier 2001-02.

10 YEAR RECORD

99-00	00-01	01-02	02-03	03-04	04-05	05-06	06-07	07-08	08-09
WMP 2	WMP 5	WMP 1	MidAl 11	Isth P 17	MidAl 16	MidAl 19	MidAl 17	MidAl 6	MidAl 9

COALVILLE TOWN

Founded: 1994 Nickname: The Ravens

Chairman: Glyn Rennocks
Secretary: Robert Brooks
17 Ashland Drive
Coalville
Leicestershire
LE67 3NH
Tel: 07983 665 835
Manager: Adam Stevens
Prog Editor:

Ground: Owen Street Sports Ground, Owen St, Coalville LE67 3DA. Tel: 01530 833 365.
Capacity: 2,000 **Seats:** 240 **Covered:** 240
Midweek Matchday: Tuesday **Clubhouse:** Yes **Shop:** Yes
Colours(change): Black & white/white/white. (All maroon).
Previous Names: Ravenstoke Miners Ath. 1925-58. Ravenstoke FC 58-95. Coalville 95-98.
Previous Lges: Coalville & Dist. Amateur. North Leicester. Leicestershire Senior.
Records: Att: 1,500. **Apps:** Nigel Simms.

Senior Honours: Leicestershire Senior Cup 1999-00. Leicestershire Senior 01-02, 02-03.

10 YEAR RECORD

99-00	00-01	01-02	02-03	03-04	04-05	05-06	06-07	07-08	08-09
LeicS 11	LeicS 7	LeicS 1	LeicS 1	MidAl 8	MidAl 3	MidAl 8	MidAl 18	MidAl 8	MidAl 3

COLESHILL TOWN

Founded: 1894 Nickname:

Chairman: Paul Woodford
Secretary: William G Mort
c/o Coleshill Town FC

Tel: 0121 351 2931
Manager: Carl Adams
Prog Editor: As secretary

Ground: Pack Meadow, Packington Lane, Coleshill B46 3JQ. Tel: 01675 463 259.
Capacity: **Seats:** **Covered:**
Midweek Matchday: Tuesday **Clubhouse:** Yes **Shop:**
Colours(change): Green & white/white/green. (White & black/black/white).
Previous Names: None.
Previous Lges: Midland Combination.
Records:

Senior Honours: Midland Combination Div.2 1969-70. Premier 07-08.

10 YEAR RECORD

99-00	00-01	01-02	02-03	03-04	04-05	05-06	06-07	07-08	08-09
MCmP 19	MCmP 4	MCmP 10	MCmP 14	MCmP 18	MCmP 9	MCmP 11	MCmP 4	MCmP 1	MidAl 11

INS & OUTS
In: Kirkby Muxloe SC (P – East Midlands Counties Lge), Loughborough University (P – Midland Comb. Premier Div.), Malvern T. (R – Southern Lge Div. One Midlands)
OUT: Market Drayton Town (P – Northern Premier League Division One South), Oldbury United (F), Racing Club Warwick (R – Midland Combination Premier Division)

2009-10

COVENTRY SPHINX

Founded: 1946 Nickname: Sphinx

Chairman: Neil Long
Secretary: Jackie McGowan
c/o Coventry Sphinx FC
Sphinx Drive
Coventry
CV3 1WA
Tel: 07843 477 799
Manager: Danny McSheffrey
Prog Editor: See chairman

Ground: Sphinx Spts & Social Club, Sphinx Drive, Coventry CV3 1WA. Tel: 02476 451361
Capacity: **Seats:** **Covered:** Yes
Midweek Matchday: **Clubhouse:** Yes **Shop:**
Colours(change): Sky blue & white stripes/navy/navy or white. (All red).
Previous Names: Sphinx > 1995.
Previous Lges: Midland Combination.
Records:
Senior Honours: Midland Combination Premier 2006-07.

10 YEAR RECORD

99-00	00-01	01-02	02-03	03-04	04-05	05-06	06-07	07-08	08-09
MCmP 6	MCmP 5	MCmP 2	MCmP 7	MCmP 4	MCmP 2	MCmP 2	MCmP 1	MidAl 19	MidAl 7

CRADLEY TOWN

Founded: 1948 Nickname: Hammers

Chairman: Trevor Thomas
Secretary: David Attwood
4 Birch Coppice
Quarry Bank
Brierley Hill
DY5 1AP
Tel: 07708 659 636
Manager:
Prog Editor:

Ground: Beeches View, Beeches View Ave, Cradley B63 2HB. Tel: 01384 569 658.
Capacity: 1,000 **Seats:** 200 **Covered:** 350
Midweek Matchday: Tuesday **Clubhouse:** Yes **Shop:** No
Colours(change): Red & black/black/red. (Yellow/blue/blue).
Previous Names: Albion Haden United > 1975.
Previous Lges: Metropolitan. Brierley Hill. Kidderminster. W.Mids Am. Mid Comb. W.Mids.
Records: Att: 1,000 v Aston Villa, friendly. **Goalscorer:** Jim Nugent. **Apps:** R J Haywood.
Senior Honours: West Midlands (Regional) Div.1 1990-91.

10 YEAR RECORD

99-00	00-01	01-02	02-03	03-04	04-05	05-06	06-07	07-08	08-09
MidAl 19	MidAl 12	MidAl 22	MidAl 19	MidAl 22	MidAl 19	MidAl 21	MidAl 22	MidAl 22	MidAl 16

FRIAR LANE & EPWORTH

Founded: 2003 Nickname:

Chairman: Clive Gibbons
Secretary: Robert Beeson
11 Westfield Close
Rearsby
Leicester
LE7 4ZA
Tel: 07759 745 780
Manager:
Prog Editor:

Ground: Whittier Road, Off Knighton Lane, Aylestone Pk LE2 6FT. Tel: 0116 283 3629.
Capacity: **Seats:** **Covered:**
Midweek Matchday: **Clubhouse:** Yes **Shop:**
Colours(change): White/black/black. (Royal blue & yellow/royal/royal).
Previous Names: Friar Lane Old Boys merged with Epworth in 2004.
Previous Lges: Leicestershire Senior.
Records:
Senior Honours: FLOB: Leicestershire Senior Div.2 1969-70. Prem 70-71, 71-72, 73-74, 74-75, 75-76, 76-77, 77-78. Ep'th: Leics Senior Div.1 02-03. Merged: Leics Sen. Prem 05-06.

10 YEAR RECORD

99-00	00-01	01-02	02-03	03-04	04-05	05-06	06-07	07-08	08-09
LeicS 8	LeicS 14	LeicS 2	LeicS 17	LeicS 3	LeicS 9	LeicS 1	MidAl 15	MidAl 16	MidAl 15

HIGHGATE UNITED

Founded: 1948 Nickname: Red or Gate

Chairman: Anthony Clancy
Secretary: Jimmy Merry
20 Madams Hill Road
Shirley
Solihull
B90 4QQ
Tel: 07545 317 203
Manager:
Prog Editor:

Ground: The Coppice, Tythe Barn Lane, Shirley Solihull B90 1PH. Tel: 0121 744 4194.
Capacity: **Seats:** **Covered:**
Midweek Matchday: **Clubhouse:** **Shop:**
Colours(change): All red. (White/white/black).
Previous Names: None.
Previous Lges: Worcestershire/Midland Combination.
Records:
Senior Honours: Midland Combination Premier 1972-73, 73-74, 74-75.

10 YEAR RECORD

99-00	00-01	01-02	02-03	03-04	04-05	05-06	06-07	07-08	08-09
MCmP 18	MCmP 18	MCmP 13	MCmP 9	MCmP 12	MCmP 18	MCmP 14	MCmP 3	MCmP 2	MidAl 13

KIRKBY MUXLOE

Founded: 1910 Nickname:

Chairman: Les Warren
Secretary: Philip Moloney
c/o Kirkby Muxloe F.C.

Tel: 07775 992 778
Manager: Gaz Keenan
Prog Editor:

Ground: Kirby Muxloe Sports Club, Ratby Lane, LE9 2AQ. Tel: 0116 239 3201.
Capacity: **Seats:** **Covered:**
Midweek Matchday: **Clubhouse:** Yes **Shop:**
Colours(change): All royal blue. (All white).
Previous Names:
Previous Lges: Leicester Mutual. Leicester City. Leicestershire Senior. East Midlands Co.
Records:
Senior Honours: Leicestershire Co. Cup 2006-07. Leicestershire Senior Champions 07-08. East Midlands Counties Champions 2008-09.

10 YEAR RECORD

99-00	00-01	01-02	02-03	03-04	04-05	05-06	06-07	07-08	08-09
LeicS 5	LeicS 13	LeicS 5	LeicS 7	LeicS 2	LeicS 4	LeicS 8	LeicS 2	LeicS 1	EMC 1

LOUGHBOROUGH UNIVERSITY

Founded: 1920 Nickname:

Chairman: James Ellis
Secretary: Margaret Folwell
Sports Development Centre
Loughborough University
Leicestershire
LE11 3TU
Tel: 01509226127(Office Hrs)
Manager: Tom Curtis
Prog Editor:

Ground: Nanpantan Sports Ground, Nanpantan Road LE11 3YE. Tel: 01509 237 148.
Capacity: **Seats:** **Covered:**
Midweek Matchday: **Clubhouse:** **Shop:**
Colours(change): All maroon. (All pale blue).
Previous Names: None
Previous Lges: Leicestershire Senior. Midland Combination.
Records:
Senior Honours: Midland Combination Champions 2008-09.

10 YEAR RECORD

99-00	00-01	01-02	02-03	03-04	04-05	05-06	06-07	07-08	08-09
								MCmP 4	MCmP 1

MALVERN TOWN

Founded: 1947 Nickname:

Chairman: Paul Pallett
Secretary: Marg Scott
c/o Malvern Town F.C.

Tel: 07944 110 402
Manager: Joe Rawle
Prog Editor: See Secretary

Ground: Langland Stadium, Langland Ave., Malvern, WR14 2GQ. Tel: 01684 364 068.
Capacity: 2,500 **Seats:** 150 **Covered:** 310
Midweek Matchday: Tuesday **Clubhouse:** Yes **Shop:** No
Colours(change): Sky blue/claret/claret. (Claret/sky blue/sky blue).
Previous Names: None
Previous Lges: Worcestershire/Midland Combination. West Mids. Mid. Alliance. Southern.
Records: **Att:** 1,221 v Worcester City F.A. Cup. **Goals:** Graham Buffery.
Apps: Nick Clayton.
Senior Honours: Worcestershire Senior Urn (x7). Midland Combination Div.1 1955-56.

10 YEAR RECORD

99-00	00-01	01-02	02-03	03-04	04-05	05-06	06-07	07-08	08-09
WMP 9	WMP 7	WMP 9	WMP 6	WMP 1	MidAl 5	MidAl 3	SthM 17	SthM 20	SthM 22

OADBY TOWN

Founded: 1937 Nickname: The Poachers

Chairman:
Secretary: Richard Hill
General Manager
c/o Oadby Town F.C.

Tel: 07733 882 719
Manager: Matt Elliot
Prog Editor: Kelly Marie

Ground: Topps Park, Wigston Road, Oadby LE2 5QG. Tel: 0116 271 5728.
Capacity: 5,000 **Seats:** 224 **Covered:** 224
Midweek Matchday: Tuesday **Clubhouse:** Yes **Shop:** Yes
Colours(change): All white. (All red).
Previous Names: Oadby Imperial > 1951.
Previous Lges: Leicestershire Senior.
Records:
Senior Honours: Leicestershire Senior Div.2 1951-52. Prem 63-64, 67-68, 68-69, 72-73, 94-95, 96-97, 97-98, 98-99. Midland Alliance 99-00.

10 YEAR RECORD

99-00	00-01	01-02	02-03	03-04	04-05	05-06	06-07	07-08	08-09
MidAl 1	MidAl 4	MidAl 6	MidAl 4	MidAl 6	MidAl 7	MidAl 18	MidAl 11	MidAl 17	MidAl 19

2009-10

ROCESTER

Founded: 1876 Nickname: Romans

Chairman: David Price
Secretary: Barry Smith
c/o Rocester FC

Tel: 07770 762 825
Manager: Alan Beaman
Prog Editor: Barry Smith

Ground: Hillsfield, Mill Street, Rocester, Uttoxeter ST14 5JX. Tel: 01889 590 463.
Capacity: 4,000 **Seats:** 230 **Covered:** 500
Midweek Matchday: Tuesday **Clubhouse:** Yes **Shop:** Yes
Colours(change): Amber & black/black/black. (All white).
Previous Names: None.
Previous Lges: Staffs Sen. (Founder Member). W.Mids (Reg). Mid.All (FM) Southern. NPL
Records: Apps: Peter Swanwick 1962-82.

Senior Honours: Staffordshire Senior 1985-86, 86-87. West Mids (Regional) Div.1 87-88. Midland Alliance 98-99, 03-04.

10 YEAR RECORD

99-00	00-01	01-02	02-03	03-04	04-05	05-06	06-07	07-08	08-09
SthW 16	SthW 10	SthW 21	SthW 21	MidAl 1	NPL 1 22	MidAl 22	MidAl 12	MidAl 5	MidAl 20

SHIFNAL TOWN

Founded: 1964 Nickname:

Chairman: Glyn Davies
Secretary: Derek Groucott
4 Idsall Crescent
Shifnal
Shropshire
TF11 8ES
Tel: 01952 402 255
Manager: Delwyn Humphries
Prog Editor:

Ground: Phoenix Park, Coppice Lane, Shifnal TF11 8PB. Tel: 01952 463 667.
Capacity: **Seats:** Yes **Covered:** Yes
Midweek Matchday: Tuesday **Clubhouse:** Yes **Shop:** Yes
Colours(change): Red & white stripes/black/red. (Sky blue & white stripes/sky/sky)
Previous Names: None.
Previous Lges: West Midlands (Regional). Midland Combination.
Records:

Senior Honours: West Midlands (Regional) Premier 2006-07.

10 YEAR RECORD

99-00	00-01	01-02	02-03	03-04	04-05	05-06	06-07	07-08	08-09
MidAl 8	MidAl 16	MidAl 19	MidAl 20	MCmP 16	MCmP 17	MCmP 7	WMP 1	MidAl 15	MidAl 8

STRATFORD TOWN

Founded: 1944 Nickname: The Town

Chairman: Craig Hughes
Secretary: Brian Rose
1 Hastings Road
Wllesbourne

CV35 9PP
Tel: 07833 776 834
Manager: Rod Brown
Prog Editor: Alan Hawkins

Ground: Knights Lane, Tiddington, Stratford Upon Avon CV37 7BZ. Tel: 01789 269 336.
Capacity: **Seats:** Yes **Covered:** Yes
Midweek Matchday: Tuesday **Clubhouse:** Yes **Shop:** Yes
Colours(change): All blue. (All tangerine).
Previous Names: Stratford Town Amateurs 1964-70.
Previous Lges: Worcestershire/Midland Comb. Birmingham & Dist. W.Mid (Reg). Hellenic.
Records: Att: 1,078 v Aston Villa, Birmingham Senior Cup, Oct. 1996.

Senior Honours: Worcestershire/Midland Combination 1956-57, 86-87. Birmingham Senior Cup 62-63. Midland Alliance Cup 02-03, 03-04.

10 YEAR RECORD

99-00	00-01	01-02	02-03	03-04	04-05	05-06	06-07	07-08	08-09
MidAl 2	MidAl 6	MidAl 4	MidAl 3	MidAl 3	MidAl 11	MidAl 15	MidAl 4	MidAl 7	MidAl 6

STUDLEY

Founded: 1971 Nickname: Bees

Chairman: Barry Cromwell
Secretary: Mark Sealey
c/o Studley FC

Tel: 07818 490 137
Manager: Lee Adams
Prog Editor:

Ground: The Beehive, Abbeyfields Drive, Studley B80 7BE. Tel: 01527 853 087.
Capacity: 1,500 **Seats:** 200 **Covered:** Yes
Midweek Matchday: Tuesday **Clubhouse:** Yes **Shop:** Yes
Colours(change): Sky blue/navy/navy. (All white).
Previous Names: Studley BKL > 2002.
Previous Lges: Redditch & Sth Warwicks Sunday Combination. Midland Combination.
Records: Att: 810 v Leamington 2003-04. **Goalscorer:** Brian Powell.
Apps: Lee Adams - 523.
Senior Honours: Midland Combination Div.1 1991-92. Worcestershire FA Senior Urn 00-01,01-02, 02-03.

10 YEAR RECORD

99-00	00-01	01-02	02-03	03-04	04-05	05-06	06-07	07-08	08-09
MCmP 3	MCmP 2	MidAl 9	MidAl 7	MidAl 5	MidAl 18	MidAl 16	MidAl 20	MidAl 13	MidAl 14

TIPTON TOWN

Founded: 1948 Nickname:

Chairman: Bill Williams
Secretary: Angela Boden
6 Jackson Close
Burberry Grange
Tipton
DY4 0BH
Tel: 07921 167 173
Manager: John Hill
Prog Editor:

Ground: Tipton Sports Acad., Wednesbury Oak Rd, Tipton DY4 0BS. Tel: 0121 502 5534
Capacity: 1,000 **Seats:** 200 **Covered:** 400
Midweek Matchday: Wednesday **Clubhouse:** Yes **Shop:** No
Colours(change): Black & white stripes/black/red. (Orange/white/orange).
Previous Names: None.
Previous Lges: West Midlands (Regional).
Records: **Att:** 1,100 v Wolves, 01.08.88.

Senior Honours: Wednesbury Senior Cup 1975-76, 76-77, 80-81, 95-96.
West Midlands (Regional) Div.1 83-84. Prem 04-05.

10 YEAR RECORD

99-00	00-01	01-02	02-03	03-04	04-05	05-06	06-07	07-08	08-09
WestP 14	WestP 23	WestP 11	WestP 3	WestP 2	WestP 1	MidAl 11	MidAl 5	MidAl 9	MidAl 5

WESTFIELDS

Founded: 1966 Nickname: The Fields

Chairman: John Morgan
Secretary: Andrew Morris
17 Fayre Oaks Green
Kings Acre
Hereford
HR4 0QT
Tel: 07860 410 548
Manager: Sean Edwards
Prog Editor:

Ground: Allpay Park, Widemarsh Common, Hereford HR4 9NA. Tel: 07860 410 548.
Capacity: 2,000 **Seats:** 150 **Covered:** 150
Midweek Matchday: Tuesday **Clubhouse:** Yes **Shop:** Yes
Colours(change): All Maroon & sky blue. (Yellow/royal/yellow).
Previous Names: None.
Previous Lges: Herefordshire Sunday. Worcester & Dist. West Midlands (Regional).
Records: **Att:** 518 v Rushden & Daimonds, FA Cup, 1996.
Goalscorer: Paul Burton. **Apps:** Jon Pugh.
Senior Honours: Hereford Senior Cup 1985-86, 88-89, 91-92, 95-96, 01-02, 02-03, 04-05, 05-06, 07-08. West Midlands (Regional) Premier 2002-03.

10 YEAR RECORD

99-00	00-01	01-02	02-03	03-04	04-05	05-06	06-07	07-08	08-09
WestP 20	WestP 14	WestP 5	WestP 1	MidAl 13	MidAl 6	MidAl 20	MidAl 16	MidAl 11	MidAl 17

Market Drayton's championship winning side. Photo: Arthur Evans.

NORTH WEST COUNTIES LEAGUE

www.nwcfl.co.uk

Sponsored by:

Vodkat

Founded: 1982

Recent champions:

2004: Clitheroe

2005: Fleetwood Town

2006: Cammell Laird

2007: FC United of Manchester

2008: Trafford

Premier Division		P	W	D	L	F	A	Pts
AFC Fylde		42	33	5	4	122	35	104
New Mills		42	34	2	6	92	33	104
Newcastle Town		42	26	9	7	91	33	87
Congleton Town		42	26	8	8	85	44	86
Glossop North End		42	25	7	10	83	49	82
Ashton Athletic		42	18	7	17	67	68	61
Alsager Town		42	18	5	19	66	72	59
Bacup Borough		42	16	10	16	71	71	58
Silsden		42	16	10	16	62	67	58
Squires Gate		42	14	15	13	56	56	57
Runcorn Linnets		42	16	7	19	64	84	55
Atherton LR		42	12	15	15	70	77	51
Maine Road		42	14	9	19	60	74	51
Ramsbottom United	*-1*	42	13	12	17	56	72	50
Formby		42	15	3	24	57	67	48
St Helens Town		42	14	4	24	64	97	46
Nelson		42	11	12	19	68	86	45
Colne		42	11	10	21	64	75	43
Winsford United		42	10	9	23	52	82	39
Abbey Hey		42	11	5	26	60	89	38
Flixton		42	9	14	19	58	86	37
Atherton Collieries		42	7	8	27	42	93	29

Reserve Division One		P	W	D	L	F	A	Pt
Glossop North End Res.	*-1*	30	22	5	3	84	37	70
Bootle Res.	*-6*	30	21	7	2	79	38	64
New Mills Res.	*-3*	30	19	8	3	87	35	62
AFC Fylde Res.		30	16	6	8	73	37	54
Ashton Athletic Res.		30	12	12	6	65	49	48
Padiham Res.		30	13	8	9	73	53	47
Colne Res.		30	12	5	13	64	63	41
Atherton Collieries Res.		30	10	10	10	58	52	40
Irlam Res.		30	11	7	12	55	50	40
AFC Liverpool Res.	*-7*	30	13	6	11	55	52	38
Wigan Robin Park Res.	*-3*	30	7	5	18	48	64	23
Ashton Town Res.		30	5	5	20	34	89	20
Chadderton Res.	*-15*	30	9	7	14	53	69	19
Daisy Hill Res.	*-12*	30	8	6	16	33	79	18
Cheadle Town Res.	*-7*	30	6	4	20	54	91	15
Atherton LR Res.	*-3*	30	4	3	23	30	87	12

RESERVES CUP

FINAL *(May 14th at Ashton Athletic)*

Glossop North End Res. 3 Ashton Athletic Res. 1

	AFC Fylde	Abbey Hey	Alsager T.	Ashton Ath.	Atherton C.	Ath'ton LR	Bacup Boro.	Colne	Congleton	Flixton	Formby	Glossop NE	Maine Road	Nelson	New Mills	Newcastle	R'bottom U.	Runcorn L.	Silsden	Squires G.	St Helens	Winsford U.
AFC Fylde		6-1	2-0	6-0	4-0	4-0	1-1	4-1	3-3	1-1	2-1	2-0	4-3	4-1	5-0	0-0	1-1	1-0	3-0	4-0	3-1	5-1
Abbey Hey	0-3		3-4	1-0	2-2	0-5	1-3	0-1	2-2	3-1	1-1	0-1	0-1	2-3	1-2	1-4	0-1	0-4	1-1	0-1	2-2	1-4
Alsager Town	1-2	2-1		2-0	2-4	1-1	1-2	1-1	1-2	4-3	0-1	1-3	1-3	4-1	4-1	0-4	2-1	2-0	1-1	1-0	2-3	2-1
Ashton Athletic	0-3	3-1	3-4	***P***	1-2	4-1	3-2	3-1	1-1	0-1	2-1	2-0	1-1	2-1	0-1	0-4	2-1	2-2	2-1	0-1	5-0	2-2
Atherton Collieries	2-4	0-2	0-1	3-2	***R***	0-0	4-3	1-1	2-1	2-2	0-3	0-1	0-1	0-0	0-0	1-0	0-1	1-2	0-1	0-0	0-3	0-4
Atherton LR	1-2	3-0	0-2	2-1	1-0	***E***	1-1	2-2	0-2	6-0	1-3	1-1	2-5	3-1	1-2	0-3	2-2	4-0	2-2	0-1	4-0	2-2
Bacup Borough	0-2	2-3	1-1	4-2	4-1	2-2	***M***	1-1	1-1	1-0	0-1	1-2	0-2	0-4	1-2	0-4	6-3	2-4	2-2	3-1	3-0	0-2
Colne	1-3	1-3	2-3	3-1	5-4	4-0	2-0	***I***	1-2	1-2	5-0	0-5	0-1	0-2	2-2	1-3	2-0	2-0	3-0	1-1	1-3	3-2
Congleton Town	1-0	0-2	2-1	5-0	1-0	3-0	6-3	0-0	***E***	2-1	3-1	2-3	5-2	3-2	3-4	0-1	2-0	1-0	0-1	2-0	1-0	4-1
Flixton	1-3	3-2	3-1	2-2	3-5	3-4	0-0	2-1	0-3	***R***	1-4	0-1	2-3	2-2	0-3	1-1	1-1	1-1	1-0	3-3	3-0	2-1
Formby	1-5	1-3	0-2	0-0	4-0	0-2	0-1	2-1	2-3	1-0		0-1	2-0	3-4	0-1	0-2	0-1	0-1	2-5	0-1	5-1	0-1
Glossop North End	0-1	3-1	1-0	2-1	2-1	1-2	2-0	4-3	2-1	2-2	3-4	***D***	2-2	3-0	2-1	1-1	0-0	2-1	2-3	2-2	1-3	4-0
Maine Road	2-1	2-0	1-0	0-3	1-0	2-2	1-1	2-1	1-2	1-1	3-2	2-3	***I***	2-3	0-1	0-2	0-2	0-1	1-1	3-3	1-2	2-2
Nelson	1-3	1-4	2-3	1-4	5-0	1-1	1-2	2-1	1-3	0-0	2-1	2-2	1-3	***V***	0-1	1-4	1-3	2-2	2-2	1-1	1-1	2-2
New Mills	1-0	3-0	5-0	1-0	5-2	5-0	1-0	2-0	1-0	2-0	2-1	2-1	3-0	6-0	***I***	0-1	4-0	0-2	2-0	3-0	7-1	3-0
Newcastle Town	2-3	2-1	3-1	2-2	5-0	4-0	0-2	2-0	1-1	0-0	2-1	1-4	4-1	0-1	1-2	***S***	4-0	4-0	2-0	1-1	1-0	2-0
Ramsbottom United	1-3	1-4	2-1	0-1	3-0	0-0	2-4	1-0	0-0	1-1	0-0	1-3	3-1	1-1	0-3	1-1	***I***	1-3	3-4	2-1	6-3	1-2
Runcorn Linnets	0-6	2-4	2-1	1-3	3-0	2-2	1-4	1-5	1-5	6-3	1-2	1-0	3-1	4-1	1-2	0-4	2-2	***O***	3-1	1-2	1-0	0-2
Silsden	4-2	2-1	1-3	0-2	3-1	3-1	0-2	0-0	0-1	5-2	2-3	0-2	3-2	2-1	0-1	3-1	1-2	1-1	***N***	2-2	2-1	1-0
Squires Gate	1-3	1-0	3-1	0-1	3-1	1-1	1-2	3-3	0-0	2-0	1-2	2-0	3-1	2-2	1-2	1-1	3-0	2-2	0-0		1-3	1-0
St Helens Town	0-3	5-4	0-1	1-2	1-1	3-6	3-4	4-0	1-2	0-2	1-0	0-6	0-0	0-3	2-1	1-4	1-3	5-0	4-1	1-3		2-1
Winsford United	0-5	0-2	1-1	1-2	3-2	2-2	0-0	1-1	1-4	5-2	0-2	0-3	2-0	0-5	1-2	1-3	2-2	1-2	0-1	1-0	0-2	

Division One	P	W	D	L	F	A	Pts
Bootle	34	25	5	4	78	27	80
Padiham	34	22	7	5	93	41	73
Stone Dominoes	34	23	2	9	85	51	71
AFC Liverpool	34	22	3	9	82	39	69
Wigan Robin Park	34	18	5	11	61	49	59
Oldham Town	34	16	5	13	60	54	53
Cheadle Town	34	16	4	14	54	44	52
Irlam	34	13	13	8	51	43	52
Holker Old Boys	34	14	8	12	59	61	50
Chadderton	34	14	6	14	60	54	48
Eccleshall	34	14	5	15	44	44	47
Norton United	34	12	6	16	63	60	42
Darwen	34	11	7	16	51	74	40
Leek CSOB	34	7	10	17	51	72	31
AFC Blackpool	34	7	8	19	34	59	29
Rochdale Town	34	6	6	22	55	91	24
Daisy Hill	34	6	4	24	39	101	22
Ashton Town	34	4	8	22	35	91	20

DIVISION ONE TROPHY

FIRST ROUND
Daisy Hill 0 **Chadderton** 5
Eccleshall 1 **AFC Liverpool** 4

SECOND ROUND
Ashton Town 1 **Oldham Town** 4
Chadderton 2 Bootle 1
Cheadle Town 1 **Holker Old Boys** 2
Irlam 0 **AFC Blackpool** 1
Norton United 3 Wigan Robin Park 2
Padiham 2 Leek CSOB 0
Rochdale Town 0 **AFC Liverpool** 1
Stone Doms 1 Darwen 2
(Darwen expelled)

QUARTER-FINALS
AFC Blackpool 1 **Norton United** 2
AFC Liverpool 3 Chadderton 2
Oldham Town 5 Stone 0
Padiham 4 Holker OB 0

SEMI-FINALS
(played over two legs)
Oldham Town 1 Padiham 1, **Padiham** 3 Oldham Town 1
AFC Liverpool 2 Norton United 1, Norton United 0 **AFC Liverpool** 2

FINAL
(April 16th at Ashton Athletic)
AFC Liverpool 1 Padiham 0

CHALLENGE CUP

FIRST ROUND
AFC Blackpool 0 **Bootle** 2
Cheadle Town 1 **Stone Dominoes** 3
Daisy Hill 1 **Oldham Town** 6
Darwen 4 Rochdale Town 1
Holker Old Boys 0 **AFC Liverpool** 4
Irlam 1 Chadderton 0
Nelson 2 **Ashton Athletic** 3 *aet*
Padiham 4 Eccleshall 1

SECOND ROUND
Ashton Athletic 2 **Abbey Hey** 3 *aet*
Ashton Town 0 **Alsager Town** 1
Atherton Collieries 0 **AFC Fylde** 5
Atherton LR 2 Darwen 1
Bootle 3 Maine Road 3 *aet*
Replay: Maine Road 0 **Bootle** 2
Congleton Town 1 **Colne** 3
Flixton 4 Glossop North End 2
Formby 2 Squires Gate 1
Leek CSOB 0 **Oldham Town** 2
New Mills 2 AFC Liverpool 0
Norton United 0 **Stone Dominoes** 1
Padiham 2 Ramsbottom United 1
Silsden 4 Newcastle Town 1 *aet*
St Helens Town 1 **Runcorn Linnets** 2
Wigan Robin Park 3 Bacup Borough 3 *aet*
Replay: **Bacup Borough** 6 Wigan Robin Park 1
Winsford United 2 **Irlam** 4

THIRD ROUND
AFC Fylde 4 Bacup Borough 1
Alsager Town 0 **Runcorn Linnets** 2
Colne 0 **New Mills** 4
Flixton 0 **Formby** 1
Irlam 1 **Bootle** 3
Padiham 3 Atherton LR 0
Silsden 3 Abbey Hey 0
Stone Dominoes 4 Oldham Town 3 *aet*

QUARTER-FINALS
New Mills 2 Bootle 0
Runcorn Linnets 3 AFC Fylde 1 *aet (at AFC Fylde)*
Silsden 1 Formby 0
Stone Dominoes 1 **Padiham** 2

SEMI-FINALS
(played over two legs)
Padiham 0 New Mills 5, **New Mills** 1 Padiham 0
Runcorn 1 Silsden 2, Silsden 0 **Runcorn Linnets** 2

FINAL
(May 11th at Curzon Ashton)
New Mills 2 Runcorn Linnets 0

	AFCB	AFCL	Ashton	Bootle	Chadd	Chead	Daisy	Darw	Ecc	Holker	Irlam	Leek	Norton	Oldh	Pad	Roch	Stone	Wig
AFC Blackpool		3-6	0-0	1-3	0-1	0-2	3-0	1-1	2-0	2-0	1-1	1-1	0-0	0-3	2-2	1-0	3-4	0-1
AFC Liverpool	5-0		4-1	0-1	1-1	2-1	4-0	5-0	0-1	0-1	0-2	2-1	3-0	5-0	0-3	3-1	4-1	1-2
Ashton Town	4-1	0-3		1-1	1-2	2-3	2-2	1-3	0-2	0-3	0-5	1-5	2-3	2-0	1-1	0-0	3-1	0-2
Bootle	2-0	3-4	5-1	***D***	2-0	1-0	4-0	4-0	2-0	4-2	1-2	1-0	2-1	2-1	0-0	3-0	4-1	2-1
Chadderton	3-0	1-3	6-0	1-1	***I***	4-1	2-1	4-3	2-3	3-1	0-0	4-0	2-2	0-0	0-2	3-1	2-5	4-0
Cheadle Town	2-0	0-1	1-2	0-4	1-1	***V***	5-2	0-1	0-0	5-0	1-2	1-0	2-0	2-1	1-2	2-0	0-2	2-0
Daisy Hill	0-5	3-2	2-1	1-2	5-1	1-2	***I***	2-6	1-0	1-3	1-1	4-2	0-4	1-5	0-4	1-2	1-4	0-4
Darwen	0-1	1-2	3-2	0-6	3-1	0-4	4-0	***S***	0-1	1-2	1-1	4-3	4-3	2-2	0-2	2-2	2-1	0-3
Eccleshall	2-1	0-1	2-2	1-1	2-1	4-2	0-1	2-0	***I***	1-1	1-2	0-1	0-1	2-0	0-2	3-2	0-1	1-2
Holker Old Boys	1-0	0-2	0-0	3-1	1-2	2-2	2-0	0-0	2-0	***O***	2-1	5-3	2-2	7-3	1-4	4-3	1-2	1-6
Irlam	1-0	0-3	2-0	2-2	5-0	1-0	2-1	2-2	1-0	2-2	***N***	0-0	0-0	2-1	1-1	0-0	3-4	3-0
Leek CSOB	3-2	2-1	1-1	0-1	0-2	0-2	2-2	2-2	1-2	1-3	1-1		4-4	0-1	2-2	2-2	1-1	2-0
Norton United	0-0	2-3	2-0	0-4	2-1	1-2	3-1	6-1	0-1	3-2	6-0	2-3	***O***	2-0	1-3	2-3	2-1	1-2
Oldham Town	2-0	2-1	6-0	0-1	1-0	3-1	0-0	0-1	2-1	0-0	3-1	5-1	2-0	***N***	4-3	2-2	1-0	0-1
Padiham	2-1	1-1	5-1	0-2	3-1	4-2	6-0	4-1	3-5	3-3	3-2	4-0	2-3	6-0	***E***	3-1	1-2	3-0
Rochdale Town	0-1	4-5	5-2	1-3	1-4	0-2	7-2	2-1	2-4	1-2	1-1	1-4	3-2	2-7	2-5		2-4	0-3
Stone Dominoes	6-1	0-4	4-1	3-0	2-1	0-2	3-1	2-0	3-1	2-0	2-1	6-2	1-0	5-1	1-2	5-1		2-2
Wigan Robin Park	1-1	1-1	6-1	0-3	1-0	1-1	4-2	1-2	2-2	1-0	3-1	2-1	4-3	1-2	0-2	3-1	1-4	

PREMIER DIVISION - 2009-10

ABBEY HEY

Founded: 1902 Nickname:

Chairman: James Whittaker
Secretary: Tony McAllister
c/o Abbey Hey F.C.
Abbey Stadium
Goredale Avenue, Gorton
M18 7HD
Tel: 0161 231 7147
Manager: Neil Brown
Prog Editor: Gordon Lester

Ground: Abbey Stadium, Goredale Ave., Gorton M18 7HD. Tel: 0161 231 7147.
Capacity: 1,000 **Seats:** 100 **Covered:** 300
Midweek Matchday: Tuesday **Clubhouse:** Yes **Shop:** Yes
Colours(change): Red/black/red. (All blue).
Previous Names: None.
Previous Lges: Manchester Amateur. South East Lancs. Manchester.
Records: **Att:** 400 v Manchester City XI, October 1999.
985 v FC Utd of Manchester 17.03.06, played at Hyde United
Senior Honours: Manchester League 1981-82, 88-89, 88-89, 91-92, 93-94, 94-95.

10 YEAR RECORD

99-00	00-01	01-02	02-03	03-04	04-05	05-06	06-07	07-08	08-09
NWC1 14	NWC1 14	NWC1 18	NWC1 13	NWC1 21	NWC1 14	NWC1 11	NWC1 17	NWC1 17	NWCP 20

ALSAGER TOWN

Founded: 1968 Nickname: The Bullets

Chairman: Peter Clegg
Secretary: Alan Simpson
c/o Alsager Town F.C.
Town Ground, Woodland Court,
Alsager
ST7 2DP
Tel: 01270 882 336
Manager: Neil Gill
Prog Editor: Peter Clegg

Ground: Town Ground, Woodland Court, Alsager ST7 2DP. Tel: 01270 882 336.
Capacity: 3,000 **Seats:** 250 **Covered:** 1,000
Midweek Matchday: Tuesday **Clubhouse:** Yes **Shop:** Yes
Colours(change): Black & white/black/black. (All red).
Previous Names: Alsager FC (Merger of Alsager Institute & Alsager Utd) in 1965.
Previous Lges: Crewe. Mid Cheshire. Northern Premier.
Records: **Att:** 450 v Crewe Alexandra, friendly, 2004. **Goalscorer:** Gareth Rowe.
Apps: Wayne Brotherton.
Senior Honours:

10 YEAR RECORD

99-00	00-01	01-02	02-03	03-04	04-05	05-06	06-07	07-08	08-09
NWC2 12	NWC2 7	NWC2 2	NWC1 11	NWC1 9	NWC1 7	NWC1 3	NP1S 16	NP1S 14	NWCP 7

ASHTON ATHLETIC

Founded: 1968 Nickname:

Chairman: Steve Halliwell
Secretary: Alan Greenhalgh
c/o Ashton Athletic
Brocstedes Park
Downall Green, Ashton in Makerfield
WN4 0NR
Tel: 01942 716 360
Manager: David Powell
Prog Editor: See chairman

Ground: Brockstedes Park, Downall Green, Ashton in Markerfield, Wigan 01942 716360
Capacity: 500-600 **Seats:** 100 **Covered:** 300
Midweek Matchday: Tuesday **Clubhouse:** Yes **Shop:** No
Colours(change): All yellow. (Sky Blue/navy/sky blue).
Previous Names: None.
Previous Lges: Lancashire Combination, Manchester Amateur League
Records: **Att:** 165 v Runcorn Linnets 2006-07. **Apps:** Steve Rothwell - 50+
Senior Honours:

10 YEAR RECORD

99-00	00-01	01-02	02-03	03-04	04-05	05-06	06-07	07-08	08-09
Manc 13	Manc 12	Manc 5	Manc 5	Manc 10	Manc 10	Manc 4	NWC2 16	NWC2 3	NWCP 6

ATHERTON L.R.

Founded: 1954 Nickname: The Panthers

Chairman: Jane Wilcock
Secretary: Kylie Wilcock
c/o Atherton L.R.
Crilly Park
Spa Road, Atherton
M46 9XG
Tel: 01942 883 950
Manager: Dave Hughes
Prog Editor: Jeff Gorse

Ground: Crilly Park, Spa Road, Atherton, Manchester M46 9XG. Tel: 01942 883 950
Capacity: 3,000 **Seats:** 250 **Covered:** 3 sides
Midweek Matchday: Tuesday **Clubhouse:** Yes **Shop:** No
Colours(change): Yellow & blue/royal blue/yellow. (Sky blue/black/black).
Previous Names: Laburnum Rovers
Previous Lges: Bolton Comb, Cheshire County 80-82, NWCL 82-94 and NPL 94-97
Records: **Att:** 2,300 v Aldershot Town F.A. Vase Q-Final replay 93-94
Goalscorer: Shaun Parker **App:** Jim Evans
Senior Honours: NWCo Champions 1992-93, 93-94. Champs Trophy 1992-93, 93-94.

10 YEAR RECORD

99-00	00-01	01-02	02-03	03-04	04-05	05-06	06-07	07-08	08-09
NWC1 22	NWC2 2	NWC1 20	NWC1 14	NWC1 12	NWC1 15	NWC1 20	NWC1 16	NWC1 19	NWCP 12

BACUP BOROUGH

Founded: 1878 Nickname: The Boro

Chairman: Paul Fitton
Secretary: Brent Peters
Piercy Meadow
Waterfoot
Lancashire
BB4 9JH
Tel: 0780 559 3791
Manager: Brent Peters
Prog Editor: Michael Carr

Ground: Brian Boys Stadium, Cowtoot Lane, Blackthorn, Bacup, OL13 8EE 01706 878 655
Capacity: 3,000 **Seats:** 500 **Covered:** 1,000
Midweek Matchday: Wednesday **Clubhouse:** Yes **Shop:** No
Colours(change): White/black/black. (Tangerine/claret/tangerine).
Previous Names: Bacup FC
Previous Lges: Lancashire Combination 1903-82
Records: **Att:** 4,980 v Nelson 1947 **Goalscorer: Jimmy Clarke**
Senior Honours: North West Counties Division Two 2002-03.

10 YEAR RECORD

99-00	00-01	01-02	02-03	03-04	04-05	05-06	06-07	07-08	08-09
NWC2 5	NWC2 14	NWC2 12	NWC2 1	NWC1 14	NWC1 9	NWC1 17	NWC1 15	NWC1 18	NWCP 8

BOOTLE

Founded: 1953 Nickname:

Chairman: Frank Doran
Secretary: Joe Doran
16 Orchard Hey
Old Roan
Liverpool
L30 8RY
Tel: 0151 531 0665
Manager: Chris O'Bien
Prog Editor: Ian Porter

Ground: Delta Taxi Stadium, Vestey Rd, Off Bridle Road, Bootle L30 4UN 07852 742 790
Capacity: **Seats:** **Covered:**
Midweek Matchday: Tuesday **Clubhouse:** Yes **Shop:**
Colours(change): All Royal blue. (Yellow/black/black).
Previous Names: Langton Dock 1953 - 1973.
Previous Lges: Liverpool Shipping. Lancs Comb. Cheshire. Liverpool County Comb.
Records: **Att:** 750 v Casharlton Athletic, FA Trophy 1981.
Senior Honours: Liverpool County Champions 1964-65, 65-66, 67-68, 68-69, 69-70, 70-71, 71-72, 72-73, 73-74. North West Counties Div.1 Champions 2008-09

10 YEAR RECORD

99-00	00-01	01-02	02-03	03-04	04-05	05-06	06-07	07-08	08-09
NWC1 21	NWC2 16	NWC2 6	Liv 5	Liv 17	Liv 12	Liv 3	NWC2 10	NWC2 6	NWC1 1

COLNE

Founded: 1996 Nickname:

Chairman: Malcolm Young
Secretary: Edward Lambert
c/o Colne F.C.
Holt House Stadium
Colne
BB8 9SL
Tel: 01282 862 545
Manager: Nigel Coates
Prog Editor: Ray Davies

Ground: Holt House Stadium, Colne, Lancs BB8 9SL Tel: 01282 862 545
Capacity: 1,800 **Seats:** 160 **Covered:** 1,000
Midweek Matchday: Wednesday **Clubhouse:** Yes **Shop:** Yes
Colours(change): All Red. (Sky Blue/Navy/Navy).
Previous Names: None
Previous Lges: None
Records: **Att:** 1,742 v AFC Sudbury F.A. Vase SF 2004 **Goalscorer:** Geoff Payton
2,762 v FC Utd of Manchester 13.11.05, at Accrington Stan. **App:**Richard Walton
Senior Honours: BEP Cup Winners 96-97 N.W. Co Div 2 Champions 03-04

10 YEAR RECORD

99-00	00-01	01-02	02-03	03-04	04-05	05-06	06-07	07-08	08-09
NWC2 13	NWC2 19	NWC2 14	NWC2 10	NWC2 1	NWC1 10	NWC1 9	NWC1 11	NWC1 5	NWCP 18

CONGLETON TOWN

Founded: 1901 Nickname: Bears

Chairman: Peter Evans
Secretary: Ken Mead
45 Bollin Drive
Congleton
Cheshire
CW12 3RR
Tel: 01260 278 152
Manager: Anthony Buckle & Darren Twigg
Prog Editor: See secretary

Ground: Booth Street , Crescent Road, Congleton, Cheshire Tel: 01260 274 460
Capacity: 5,000 **Seats:** 250 **Covered:** 1,200
Midweek Matchday: Tuesday **Clubhouse:** Yes **Shop:** Yes
Colours(change): Black & white stripes/black/black. (All yellow).
Previous Names: Congleton Hornets
Previous Lges: Crew &District, North Staffs, Macclesfield, Cheshire , Mid Cheshire, NW Co, NPL
Records: **Att:** 6,800 v Macclesfield, Cheshire League1953-54
Goalscorer: Mick Bidde 150 + **App:** Ray Clack 600 + Graham Harrison 600 +
Senior Honours: Cheshire Senior Cup 1920-21, 37-38.

10 YEAR RECORD

99-00	00-01	01-02	02-03	03-04	04-05	05-06	06-07	07-08	08-09
NP 1 12	NP 1 22	NWC1 16	NWC1 8	NWC1 11	NWC1 19	NWC1 12	NWC1 10	NWC1 9	NWCP 4

INS & OUTS
IN: Bootle (P), Padiham (P)
OUT: AFC Fylde (P – Northern Premier League Division One North), Atherton Collieries (R)

FLIXTON

Founded: 1960 Nickname: Valiants

Chairman: Phil Greenhalgh
Secretary: Fintan Doran
c/o Flixton F.C.
Valley Road
Flixton
M41 8RQ
Tel: 0161 748 2903
Manager: Lloyd Morrison
Prog Editor: Alison Wallace

Ground: Valley Road, Flixton, Manchester M41 8RQ Tel: 0161 748 2903
Capacity: 2,000 **Seats:** 250 **Covered:** 650
Midweek Matchday: Wednesday **Clubhouse:** Yes **Shop:** No
Colours(change): Blue & white Stripes, blue/blue. (All Red).
Previous Names:
Previous Lges: S. Manc & Wythenshawe 60-63, Lancs & Che 63-73, Manc73-86, NWC 86-96, NPL 97-00
Records: **Att:** 2,050 v FC Utd of Manchester NWC Div.2, 26.12.05.
Senior Honours: NWC Div 2 Champions 1994-95. Div 11995-96.

10 YEAR RECORD

99-00	00-01	01-02	02-03	03-04	04-05	05-06	06-07	07-08	08-09
NP 1 21	NWC1 20	NWC1 21	NWC1 21	NWC2 5	NWC2 18	NWC2 2	NWC1 13	NWC1 8	NWCP 20

FORMBY

Founded: 1919 Nickname: squirrels

Chairman: Dave Webster
Secretary: Leslie Pierce
c/o Formby F.C.
Altcar Road
Formby
L37 8DL
Tel: 01704 833 615
Manager: Tony Martin
Prog Editor: See secretary

Ground: Altcar Road, Formby, Merseyside L37 4EL Tel: 01704 833 615.
Capacity: 2,000 **Seats:** 220 **Covered:** 500
Midweek Matchday: Tuesday **Clubhouse:** No **Shop:** Yes
Colours(change): Navy & yellow/navy & yellow/navy. (Green & white/green & white/gr'n)
Previous Names:
Previous Lges: Liverpool Co. Comb, 1919-68, Lancs Comb. 68-71, Cheshire Co. 71-82
Records: **Att:** 603 v Southport Liverpool Sen. Cup 2003-04
671 v FC Utd of Manchester, NWC Div.1, 21.03.07, at Skelmersdale Utd.
Senior Honours: Lancs Co. Am. Cup 1934-35

10 YEAR RECORD

99-00	00-01	01-02	02-03	03-04	04-05	05-06	06-07	07-08	08-09
NWC2 11	NWC2 12	NWC2 5	Liv 9	NWC2 3	NWC1 20	NWC1 22	NWC1 21	NWC1 13	NWCP 15

GLOSSOP NORTH END

Founded: 1886 Nickname: Hillmen

Chairman: David Atkinson
Secretary: Peter Hammond
15 Longmoor Road
Simmondley
Glossop, Derbys
SK13 9NH
Tel: 01457 863852
Manager: Steve Young
Prog Editor: Neil Rimmer

Ground: Surrey Street, Glossop, Derbys SK13 7AJ. Tel: 01457 855 469
Capacity: 2,374 **Seats:** 209 **Covered:** 509
Midweek Matchday: Wednesday **Clubhouse:** Yes **Shop:** Yes
Colours(change): All Royal Blue. (All white).
Previous Names: Glossop North End1886-1896 and Glossop FC 1898-1992
Previous Lges: The Football League. Cheshire County. Manchester. Lancashire Comb.
Records: **Att:** 10,736 v P.N.E. F.A. Cup 1913-1914
Senior Honours: Manchester Champions 1927-28. Derbyshire Senior Cup 2000-01

10 YEAR RECORD

99-00	00-01	01-02	02-03	03-04	04-05	05-06	06-07	07-08	08-09
NWC1 17	NWC1 18	NWC1 19	NWC1 20	NWC1 18	NWC1 13	NWC1 16	NWC1 9	NWC1 7	NWCP 5

MAINE ROAD

Founded: 1955 Nickname: Blues

Chairman: Ron Meredith
Secretary: Derek Barber
Flat 4, Maple Court
259 Wellington Road
Heaton Moor Stockport
SK4 5BS
Tel: 0161 431 8243
Manager: Ian Walker
Prog Editor: See secretary

Ground: Brantingham Road, Chorlton-cum-Hardy, M21 0TT Tel: 0161 861 0344
Capacity: 2,000 **Seats:** 200 **Covered:** 700
Midweek Matchday: Tuesday **Clubhouse:** Yes **Shop:** No
Colours(change): All sky blue. (Yellow/green/green).
Previous Names:
Previous Lges: Rusholme Sunday 55-66, Manchester Amateur Sunday 66-72 & Manchester 72-87
Records: **Att:** 3,125 v FC United Manchester, NWC Div.1, 04.11.06, at Stalybridge Celtic.
Senior Honours: Manchester County Champions 1982-83, 83-84, 84-85, 85-86.
NWC Div.2 Champions 1989-90. NWC Challenge Cup 2007-08.

10 YEAR RECORD

99-00	00-01	01-02	02-03	03-04	04-05	05-06	06-07	07-08	08-09
NWC1 19	NWC1 15	NWC1 22	NWC2 3	NWC2 2	NWC1 8	NWC1 10	NWC1 6	NWC1 4	NWCP 13

NELSON

Founded: 1881 Nickname: Blues

Chairman: Alan Pickering
Secretary: Gary Broughton
c/o Nelson F.C.
Victoria Park, Lomeshaye Way,
Nelson
BB9 7BN
Tel: 01282 613 820
Manager: Alex Mugan
Prog Editor: Alan Maidment

Ground: Victoria Park, Lomeshaye Way, Nelson, Lancs BB9 7BN. Tel: 01282 613 820
Capacity: 1500 **Seats:** 150 **Covered:** 200
Midweek Matchday: Wednesday **Clubhouse:** Yes **Shop:** Yes
Colours(change): All royal blue. (All white).
Previous Names:
Previous Lges: Lancs1889-98,1900-01.F Lge 1898-1900.Lancs C01-16,46-82.NWC 82-88.W.Lancs88-92
Records: Att: 14,143 v Bradford Park Avenue, Div.3 North, 10.04.26.
Senior Honours: Lancashire Champions 1895-96. N.E. Lancashire Champions 1906-07. Football League Div.3N 1922-23.

10 YEAR RECORD

99-00	00-01	01-02	02-03	03-04	04-05	05-06	06-07	07-08	08-09
NWC2 3	NWC2 4	NWC2 9	NWC2 7	NWC2 10	NWC2 6	NWC2 3	NWC1 20	NWC1 20	NWCP 17

NEW MILLS

Founded: pre1890 Nickname: The Millers

Chairman: Ray Coverley
Secretary: Sue Hyde
c/o New Mills A.F.C.
Church Lane
New Mills
SK22 4NP
Tel: 01663 747 435
Manager: Tony Hancock
Prog Editor: Glyn Jones

Ground: Church Lane, New Mills, SK22 4NP Tel: 01663 747 435
Capacity: 1,650 **Seats:** 120 **Covered:** 400
Midweek Matchday: Monday **Clubhouse:** Yes **Shop:**
Colours(change): Amber & black/amber & black/amber. (All sky & navy).
Previous Names: New Mills St Georges until 1919
Previous Lges: Manchester, North West Counties, Cheshire
Records: Att: 4,500 v Hyde United, September 1921
Senior Honours: Manchester Lge Premier Division 1924, 26, 56, 63, 65, 66, 67, 68, 70, 71 North West Counties Division Two 2007-08. Challenge Cup 2008-09.

10 YEAR RECORD

99-00	00-01	01-02	02-03	03-04	04-05	05-06	06-07	07-08	08-09
Manc1 8	Manc1 2	MancP 5	MancP 10	MancP 14	NWC2 9	NWC2 12	NWC2	NWC2 1	NWCP 2

NEWCASTLE TOWN

Founded: 1964 Nickname: Castle

Chairman: Paul Ratcliffe
Secretary: Ray Tatton
20 Glencastle Way,
Trentham
Stoke on Trent, Staffs
ST14 8QE
Tel: 01782 644916
Manager: Greg Clowes
Prog Editor: Les Morris

Ground: Lyme Valley Parkway St'm, Buckmaster Ave, Clayton, ST5 3BX T:01782 662351
Capacity: 4,000 **Seats:** 300 **Covered:** 1,000
Midweek Matchday: Tuesday **Clubhouse:** Yes **Shop:** Yes
Colours(change): All blue. (All white).
Previous Names: Parkway Hanley, Clayton Park & Parkway Clayton. Merged as NTFC 86
Previous Lges: Newcatle & District, Staffs Co & Mid Cheshire
Records: Att: 3,948 v Notts Co FA Cup 96 **Goalscorer:** Andy Bott 149
App: Dean Gillick 632
Senior Honours: Mid Cheshire Champions 1985-86. Walsall Senior Cup 1993-94, 94-95.

10 YEAR RECORD

99-00	00-01	01-02	02-03	03-04	04-05	05-06	06-07	07-08	08-09
NWC1 2	NWC1 9	NWC1 5	NWC1 4	NWC1 6	NWC1 2	NWC1 6	NWC1 12	NWC1 3	NWCP 3

PADIHAM

Founded: 1878 Nickname: Caldersiders

Chairman: Frank Heys
Secretary: Alan Smith
242 Burnley Road,
Padiham
Lancs
BB12 8SS
Tel: 0777 571 7698
Manager: Graham Howarth
Prog Editor: See secretary

Ground: Arbories Memories Sports Grd, Well Street, Padiham, BB12 8LE 01282 773 742
Capacity: 1,688 **Seats:** 159 **Covered:** Yes
Midweek Matchday: Wednesday **Clubhouse:** Yes **Shop:**
Colours(change): Blue/white/white. (Red/white/black).
Previous Names: None
Previous Lges: Lancs Comb. NWC. W.Lancs,.NE Lancs. NE Lancs Comb. E.Lancs Am.
Records: Att: 9,000 v Burnley, Dec.1884 (at Calderside Ground).
1,905 v FC Utd of Manchester, April 2006 (at Boundray Park).
Senior Honours: West Lancashire Champions 1999-00.

10 YEAR RECORD

99-00	00-01	01-02	02-03	03-04	04-05	05-06	06-07	07-08	08-09
WLa1 1	NWC2 8	NWC2 13	NWC2 4	NWC2 12	NWC2 4	NWC2 5	NWC2 3	NWC2 12	NWC1 2

RAMSBOTTOM UNITED

Founded: 1966 Nickname: The Rams

Chairman: Harry Williams
Secretary: Malcolm Holt
23 Newcombe Road
Holcombe Brook
Ramsbotton Lancs
BL0 9UU
Tel: 01204 883085
Manager: A. Johnson & B. Morley
Prog Editor: Richard Isaacs

Ground: Riverside Ground, Acre Bottom, Ramsbottom BL0 0BS.
Capacity: **Seats:** Yes **Covered:** Yes
Midweek Matchday: Tuesday **Clubhouse:** Yes **Shop:** No
Colours(change): All blue. (Red/black/red)
Previous Names:
Previous Lges: Bury Amateur, Bolton Combination & Manchester League
Records: **Att:**1,653 v FC United of Manchester 07.04.2007.
Goalscorer: Russell Brierley - 176 (1996-2003).
Senior Honours: North West Counties Division Two 1996-97

10 YEAR RECORD

99-00	00-01	01-02	02-03	03-04	04-05	05-06	06-07	07-08	08-09
NWC1 3	NWC1 3	NWC1 12	NWC1 15	NWC1 17	NWC1 5	NWC1 18	NWC1 8	NWC1 16	NWCP 14

RUNCORN LINNETS

Founded: 2006 Nickname: Linnets

Chairman: Derek Greenwood
Secretary: Lynn Johnston
Runcorn Linnets FC
PO Box 268
Runcorn
WA7 5WQ
Tel: 01606 43008
Manager: Steve Wilkes
Prog Editor: See chairman

Ground: Wincham Park, Chapel Street, Wincham, Northwich CW9 6DA Tel: 01606 43008
Capacity: **Seats:** **Covered:**
Midweek Matchday: Tuesday **Clubhouse:** Yes **Shop:**
Colours(change): Yellow & green/green/yellow & green. (Blue & white/blue/bl&wh)
Previous Names: None
Previous Lges: None.
Records: 308 v Winsford United, 2006-07.
Senior Honours: None

10 YEAR RECORD

99-00	00-01	01-02	02-03	03-04	04-05	05-06	06-07	07-08	08-09
							NWC2 2	NWC1 12	NWCP 11

SILSDEN

Founded: 1904 Nickname:

Chairman: Sean McNulty
Secretary: John Barclay
Belton House
51 Hainsworth Road
Silsden, West Yorks
BD20 0LY
Tel: 01535 656213
Manager: Paul Schofield
Prog Editor: Peter Hanson

Ground: Cougar Park, Royd Ings Ave, Keighley BD21 4BZ Tel: 01535 213 111
Capacity: **Seats:** Yes **Covered:** Yes
Midweek Matchday: Wednesday **Clubhouse:** Yes **Shop:**
Colours(change): Red/black/red (Yellow/green/yellow).
Previous Names: Reformed in 1980.
Previous Lges: Craven & District. West Riding County Amateur.
Records: **Att:**1,564 v FC United of Manchester- March 2007
Senior Honours:

10 YEAR RECORD

99-00	00-01	01-02	02-03	03-04	04-05	05-06	06-07	07-08	08-09
					NWC2 2	NWC1 14	NWC1 14	NWC1 11	NWCP 9

SQUIRES GATE

Founded: 1948 Nickname:

Chairman: Stuart Hopwood
Secretary: John Maguire
40 Stadium Avenue
Blackpool

FY4 3BQ
Tel: 01253 348 512
Manager: Russ McKenna
Prog Editor:

Ground: School Road, Marton, Blackpool, Lancs FY4 5DS Tel: 01253 798 584
Capacity: 1,000 **Seats:** 100 **Covered:** one side
Midweek Matchday: Tuesday **Clubhouse:** Yes **Shop:** No
Colours(change): All blue. (All Red)
Previous Names: Squires Gate British Legion FC >1953.
Previous Lges: Blackpool & District Amateur 1958-61. West Lancashire 1961-91.
Records: **Att:** 600 v Everton friendly 1995.
1,650 v FC Utd of Manchester at Curzon Ashton 10.03.2007.
Senior Honours:

10 YEAR RECORD

99-00	00-01	01-02	02-03	03-04	04-05	05-06	06-07	07-08	08-09
NWC2 6	NWC2 5	NWC2 3	NWC1 12	NWC1 20	NWC1 17	NWC1 13	NWC1 18	NWC1 6	NWCP 10

PREMIER DIVISION - 2009-10

ST HELENS TOWN

Founded: 1946 Nickname: Town

Chairman: John McKiernan
Secretary: Jeff Voller
105 Rathbone Road
Wavertree
Liverpool
L15 4HG
Tel: 0151 222 2963
Manager: Gary Bickerstaff
Prog Editor: See secretary

Ground: Knowsley Road, St Helens, Merseyside WA10 4AD Tel: 08707 565 252
Capacity: 19,100 **Seats:** 2,362 **Covered:** 12,408
Midweek Matchday: Tuesday **Clubhouse:** Pub **Shop:** Yes
Colours(change): Red & white stripes/red/red. (All blue).
Previous Names: St Helen's Town formed in 1903 folded in 1923.
Previous Lges: Liverpool Co Comb 1946-49 Lancs Comb 49-75, Chesh Co. 75-82
Records: **Att:** 4,000 v Manchester City 1950. **Goalscorer:** S. Pennington
App: Alan Wellens
Senior Honours: Lancs Comb Champions 1971-72 . FA Vase Winners 1986-87.

10 YEAR RECORD

99-00	00-01	01-02	02-03	03-04	04-05	05-06	06-07	07-08	08-09
NWC1 9	NWC1 4	NWC1 4	NWC1 7	NWC1 19	NWC1 3	NWC1 8	NWC1 19	NWC1 14	NWCP 16

WINSFORD UNITED

Founded: 1883 Nickname: Blues

Chairman: Mark Loveless
Secretary: Robert Astles
c/o Winsford United F.C.
Barton Stadium, Kingsway,
Winsford
CW7 3EU
Tel: 01606 558 447
Manager: Terry Murphy
Prog Editor: See secretary

Ground: Barton Stadium, Kingsway, Winsford, Cheshire CW7 3AE Tel: 01606 558 447
Capacity: 6,000 **Seats:** 250 **Covered:** 5,000
Midweek Matchday: Tuesday **Clubhouse:** Yes **Shop:** Yes
Colours(change): All royal blue. (Tangerine/black/black).
Previous Names:
Previous Lges: The Combination 1902-04. Cheshire Co. 1919-40, 47-82. N.P.L. 1987-01
Records: **Att:** 8,000 v Witton Albion, 1947. **Goalscorer:** Graham Smith 66
Apps: Edward Harrop 400
Senior Honours: Cheshire Champions 192021, 76-77.
Cheshire Senior Cup 1958-59, 79-80, 92-93. NWC Div.2 Champions 2006-07.

10 YEAR RECORD

99-00	00-01	01-02	02-03	03-04	04-05	05-06	06-07	07-08	08-09
NP P 23	NWC1 21	NWC1 7	NWC1 22	NWC2 8	NWC2 3	NWC2 4	NWC2 1	NWC1 10	NWCP 19

DIVISION ONE INS & OUTS
IN: Atherton Collieries (R), Barnoldswick Town (P – West Lancs League Premier Division).
OUT: Bootle (P), Darwen (now AFC Darwen) (R – West Lancs League Premier Division), Padiham (P)

AFC BLACKPOOL

Chairman: Henry Baldwin.
Secretary: William Singleton. c/o AFC Blackpool F.C.
Ground: Mechanics Ground, Jepson Way, Common Edge Rd, Blackpool, Lancs FY4 5DY Tel: 01253 761721.
Directions: M6 to M55,Exit Jct 4 follow Airport signs. Left at r'bout along A583 across round about to lights, right into Whitehill Rd along to roundabout.Take Lytham St Annes to T junction and traffic lights.Across main road into Jepson Way and ground..Rail to Blackpool North - then bus 11c from Talbot Rd bus station (next to rail station) to Shovels Hotel, Common Edge Rd.
Capacity: 2,000 **Seats**: 250 **Cover**: 1,700 **Floodlights**: Yes
Clubhouse: Match days, training nights. Dancehall. Matchday, hot food.
Club Shop: Manager Andrew Sneddon (01253 729962). Ties, sweaters, old programmes, badges.
HONOURS Lancs Comb Bridge Shield 72-73; NW Co's. Lg Div 3 85-86; W Lancs Lg 60-61 62-63; Lancs County FA Shield 57-58 60-61.
PREVIOUS **Leagues:** Blackpool & Fylde Comb., West Lancs, Lancs Comb. 62-68.
Grounds: Stanley Pk 47-49. **Names:** Blackpool Metal Mechanics.
RECORD **Gate:** 4,300 v FC United of Manchester - February 2006 at Blackpool FC.

FACT FILE
Formed: 1947
Club colours:
Tangerine/white/tangerine
Change colours:
White/tangerine/white
Midweek matchday: Tuesday

AFC LIVERPOOL

Chairman: Chris Stirrup
Secretary: Pat Cushion. c/o AFC Liverpool.
Ground: Valerie Park, Eaton Street, Prescot, Merseyside L34 6ND.
Tel: 0151 430 0507.
Directions: From North: M6 to Junction 26, onto M58 to Junction 3. Follow A570 to junction with A580 (East Lancs Road). (Approach junction in right hand lane of the two lanes going straight on). Cross A580 and take first road on right (Bleak Hill Road). Follow this road through to Prescot (2 miles). At traffic lights turn right, straight on at large roundabout (do not follow route onto Prescot by-pass) and right at next lights. 100 yards turn right at Hope andAnchor pub into Hope Street. Club will be in sight at bottom of road. From South: M6 to Junction 21a (M62 junction 10). Follow M62 towards Liverpool, to junction 7. Follow A57 to Rainhill and Prescot. Through traffic lights at Fusilier pub, 100 yards turn right at Hope and Anchor pub (as above). From East: Follow M62 as described in 'From South' or A580 East Lancs Road to Junction with A570 (Rainford by-pass), turn left and take first right. Follow route as 'From North'.
HONOURS NWC Div.1 Trophy 2008-09.
RECORD **Attendance:** 604 v Wigan Robin Park, 6th September 2008.

FACT FILE
Founded: 2008
Colours: All red
Change: White/black/white
Midweek matchday: Wednesday

ASHTON TOWN

FACT FILE
Founded: 1962 as Ashton Town
Colours: Red/black/black.
Change: All blue
Midweek Matches: Tuesday

Chairman:
Secretary: Steve Barrett. c/o Ashton Town F.C.
Ground: Edge Green Street, Ashton-in-Makerfield, Wigan WN4 8SL Tel: 01942 701483.
Directions: M6 Jct 23, A49 to Ashton-in-M. Right at lights onto A58 towards Bolton.
After 3/4 mile turn right at `Rams Head' P.H. into Golbourne Rd. After 200 yds right into Edge Green Street.
Ground at end.
Floodlights: No

HONOURS Warrington League Guardian Cup.

PREVIOUS **Names:** Makerfield Hill formed 1953.
Leagues: St Helens Combination. Warrington & District. Lancashire Combination 1971-78. Cheshire County 1978-82. Manchester.

RECORD **Attendance:** 1,865 v F.C. Utd of Manchester, 2007.

ATHERTON COLLIERIES

Founded: 1916
Nickname: The Colts

Chairman: Paul Gregory.
Secretary: Emil Anderson, 109 Douglas St., Atherton M46 9EB. **Tel:** 0161 288 6288 (W).
GROUND ADDRESS: Alder Street, Atherton, Greater Manchester M46 9EY. Tel: 07968 548 056.
Capacity: 2,500 **Seats:** 300 **Covered:** 1,000 **Floodlights**: Yes
Simple Directions: M61 Jct 5 towards Westhoughton, left onto A6 and right onto A579 into Atherton. Left into High St.at first light and 2nd left into Alder St and ground. **Club Shop:** No, but badges & progs on sale
Midweek Home Matchday: Monday **Clubhouse:** Mon-Fri evenings and at week end from lunch time
RECORD Attendance: 3,300 in Lancashire Combination 1920's
Previous Leagues: Bolton Combination 1920-50, 52-71, Lancs. Combination 1950-52, 71-78. Cheshire County 1978-82.
Club Colours: Black & white stripes/black/black. **Change Colours:** All blue.
RECORD Attendance: 3,300 in Lancashire Combination in 1920's
Senior Honours: North West Counties Div.3 Champions 1986-87.

BARNOLDSWICK TOWN

FACT FILE
Founded: 1972
Colours: Yellow & royal blue/royal blue/yellow
Change: All red
Midweek Matches: Tuesday

Chairman: Awerley Ashworth.
Secretary: Lynn James. c/o Barnswick Town F.C.
Ground: Silentnight Stadium, West Close Road, Barnoldswick, Colne BB18 5EW.
Tel: 01282 815 817.
Directions: Travelling from Blackburn to Colne on M65 to end, straight on at roundabout onto Vivary Way onto North Valley Road. Through two sets of traffic lights to roundabout, turn left to Barnoldswick. Straight on till you come to roundabout in Kelbrook turn left to Barnoldswick.On entering Barnoldswick straight ahead at traffic lights, straight ahead at mini roundabout. Travel through built up area past Fosters Arms pub on left set back. Take first right onto Greenberfield Lane, travel 50 yards take middle single track (signposted) travel to bottom of track and bare right to car park at rear of ground.
Travelling from Barrow on A59 from Gisburn towards Skipton turn right at Barnoldswick signpost. Travel approx 2 miles taking 1st left onto Grenberfield Lane, travel 50 yards take middle single track (signposted) travel to bottom of track bare right to car park at rear of ground.

HONOURS West Lancashire Div.1 Champions 1998-99.

PREVIOUS **Leagues**: Craven. East Lancashire. West Lancashire.

CHADDERTON

FACT FILE
Founded: 1947
Nickname: Chaddy
Colours: All Red
Change: Orange/black/orange
Midweek Matches: Monday

Chairman: Harry Mayall.
Secretary: Paul Jones. c/o of Chadderton F.C.
Ground: Andrew Street, Chadderton, Oldham, Greater Manchester OL9 0JT.
Tel: 0161 624 9733.
Directions: **From M62 Jct 20** take A627(M) to Manchester. Motorway becomes dual carriageway.
Left at first major traffic lights A669 Middleton Rd, then first left into Butterworth Street. Andrew Street is second right. Oldham Werneth (BR) 1 mile or Mills Hill (BR) I mile. **From M60 Jct 21** onto A663 to A699. Right at lights. Second left (Burnley St) and second left again (Andrew St).
Buses 24,181,182 to Middleton Rd from Lever Street of Piccadilly Gardens.
Capacity: 2,500 **Seats:** 200 **Cover**: 600 **Floodlights**: Yes
Clubhouse: Matchdays only. Hot & cold snack during & after games **Club Shop:** No

HONOURS Gilgryst Cup 1969-70.

PREVIOUS **Leagues:** Manchester. Lancashire Combination.

RECORD **Attendance:** 2,352 v FC United 2006. **Appearances:** Billy Elwell 750+ (64-90)

CHEADLE TOWN

FACT FILE
Founded: 1961
Colours: White/black/white
Change Colours:
Sky & white stripes/navy/sky & white
Midweek Matches: Wednesday

Chairman: Chris Davies.
Secretary: Brian Lindon. c/o Cheadle Town F.C.
Ground: Park Road Stadium, Park Road, Cheadle, Cheshire SK8 2AN Tel: 0161 428 2510.
Directions: M60 Jct 2, follow signs towards Cheadle (A560), first left after lights into Park Road, ground at end. 1 mile from Gatley (BR), Buses from Stockport.11,170, 310,312 and 371
Capacity: 2,500 **Seats:** 150 **Cover:** 300 **Floodlights:** Yes
Clubhouse: Open every night. Food available **Club Shop:** No
HONOURS Manchester Div.1 Champions 1979-80.
PREVIOUS **Leagues:** Manchester (pre 1987)
RECORD **Attendance :** 1,700 v Stockport County, August 1994. 3,300 v FC Utd of Manchester, 2006 (at Stockport County FC)
Scorer: Peter Tilley **Appearances:** John McArdle

DAISY HILL

FACT FILE
Founded: 1894(first known records)
Reformed: 1952
Colours: All royal blue
Change: All red
Midweek Matches: Wednesday

Chairman: Graham Follows
Secretary: Bob Naylor, 8 Bailey Fold, Westhoughton, Bolton, Lancs BL5 3HH
Tel: (H) 01942 813 720.
Ground: New Sirs, St James Street, Westhoughton, Bolton, Lancs BL5 2EB.
Tel: 01942 818 544
Directions: M61 Jct 5, A58 (Snydale Way/Park Road) for 1.5 miles, left into Leigh Road (B5235) for 1 mile, right into village then left between Church and School into St James Street. Ground 250 yds on the left. Half mile from Daisy Hill (BR)
Capacity: 2,000 **Seats:** 200 **Cover:** 250 **Floodlights:** Yes **Club Shop:** No
Clubhouse: Open normal licensing hours during any football activity. Snacks on matchdays
HONOURS Bolton Combination Premier Division Champions 1962-63, 72-73, 75-76, 77-78.
PREVIOUS **Leagues:** Westhoughton; Bolton Combination. Lancashire Combination 1978-82.
Name: Westhoughton Town **Record Goals & Apps:** Alan Roscoe 300gls 450apps.
RECORD **Attendance:** 2,000 v Horwich RMI,Westhoughton Charity Cup Final 1979-80.

ECCLESHALL

FACT FILE
Formed: 1971
Colours:
Blue & black stripes/black/black
Change: All yellow
Midwek Matchday: Wednesday

Chairman: Andy Mapperson.
Secretary: Richard Marsh, 58 Leawood Road,Trent Vale, Stoke- on -Trent Staffs. ST4 6LA
Tel: (H) 01782 524 400.
Ground Pershall Park, Chester Rd, Eccleshall, Staffordshire (All post to Secretary please)
Tel: 01785 851 351 (matchdays).
Directions: From M6 jcts 14 or 15 find way to Eccleshall High Street (B5026) drive towards Loggerheads. Pass church, cricket and tennis clubs for a mile, to the sign for Pershall. Ground is 100 yards past sign on right.
HONOURS Midland League Champions 1990, 2002-2003.
PREVIOUS **Leagues:** Stafford & District, Stafforshire Alliance.Staffordshire County North. Midland League
RECORDS **Attendance:** 2,011 v FC United of Manchester - November 2005.

HOLKER OLD BOYS

FACT FILE
Founded: 1936
Nickname: Cobs
Colours:
Green & white/green/green & white
Change: All red
Midweek Matches: Tuesday

Chairman: Dick John.
Secretary: John Adams, 20 Middlefield,Barrow in Furness, Cumbria. LA14 4AU.
Tel: 01229 431 121 (H)
Ground: Rakesmoor Lane, Hawcoat, Barrow-in-Furness, Cumbria LA14 4QB
Tel No:01229 828176
Directions: M6 Jct 36, A590 to Barrow-in-Furness, on entering Barrow, continue on A590 past Kimberley Clark Paper Mill. Take Bank Lane, first left into Hawcoat. At top of hill turn left into Rakesmoor Lane. Ground 200yds on right.
Capacity: 1,750 **Seats:** 220 **Cover:** 500 **Floodlights:** Yes
Clubhouse: Tue,Thur & Fri 8-1am, Sat noon-1am, Sun 8-12pm. Pies & peas on matchdays **Club Shop:** No
HONOURS West Lancashire Champions 1986-87.
PREVIOUS **Leagues:** North Western. Furness Premier. West Lancashire 1970-91.
Record **Attendance:** 2,303 v F.C.United F.A.Cup at Craven Park 2005-2006 **Top Scorer:** Dave Conlin

IRLAM

FACT FILE
Founded: 1969

Colours: Blue & white/blue/blue.
Change: Red/black/black

Midweek Matchday: Tuesday

Chairman: Ron Parker.

Secretary: Warren Dodd. c/o Irlan F.C.

Ground: Silver Street, Irlam, Manchester M44 6JL.
Tel: 07718 756 402 / 07969 946 277

Directions: From Junction 11 of the M60, follow the signs for Irlam onto Liverpool Road (A57). Follow road to first traffic island, and bear right onto Liverpool Road (B5320). Take the seventh road on the right onto Silver Street, and follow for approximately a quarter of a mile, where ground is on the right.

PREVIOUS **Names:** Mitchell Shackleton. **Leagues:** Manchester Amateur. Manchester League.
RECORDS **Attendance:** 950 v Manchester United Youth, August 2003.

LEEK C.S.O.B.

FACT FILE
Founded: 1945
Colours:
Red & white stripes/black/white
Change: Sky blue & white stripes/navy/navy
Midweek Matchday: Tuesday

Chairman: Chris McMullen

Secretary: Stan Lockett. c/o Leek C.S.O.B.

Ground: Harrison Park, Macclesfield Road, Leek, Staffs, Tel: 01538 383 734

Directions: M6 south Junc 17, A534 to Congleton - follow signs for Leek (A54), carry on to junction with A523, right onto A523, this road is direct to Leek, ground 8 miles on right just into Leek.

Capacity: 3,600 **Seating**: 625 **Covered Terracing**: 2,675 **Floodlights**: Yes

PREVIOUS **Leagues:** Leek & Moorland. Staffordshire County North. Midland.

Record **Attendance:** 2,590 v FC United of Manchester August 2005

HONOURS Midland League Champions 1995-96.

NORTON UNITED

FACT FILE
Founded: 1989
Colours:
Black & white/black/black
Change: All claret
Midweek Matchday: Tuesday

Chairman: Stephen Beaumont.

Secretary: Dennis Vickers, 86 Ford Green Road, Smallthorne, Stoke-on-Trent ST6 1NX
Tel: 01782 822 727 (H) 01785 354 200 (B)

Ground: Norton CC & MWI, Community Drive, Smallthorne, Stoke-on-Trent
Tel: 01782 838290

Directions: M6 J16, A500 to Burslem/Tunstall, turn off on A527, bear right at traffic island to Burslem, through lights to Smallthorne, take 3rd exit on mini r'about, turn right by pedestrian crossing into Community Drive, ground 200 metres on left.
Nearest Station: Stoke-on-Trent (mainline) Longport (local).

PREVIOUS **League:** Staffordshire Senior. Midland League > 2001

Record **Attendance:** 1,382 v FC United of Manchester 9th April 2006.

HONOURS Midland League Champions 1996-97, 98-99, 2000-01.
Staffordshire FA Senior Vase 1998-99, 2003-04.

OLDHAM TOWN

FACT FILE
Founded: 1964
Colours:
Blue/blue/white
Change: Red/white/red
Midweek Matches: Tuesday

Chairman: Ken Hughes.

Secretary: David Shepherd, 24 Hilary Avenue, Bardsley, OLdham, Lancs. OL8 2TD
Tel No: 0161 665 1375 (H)

Ground: Whitebank Stadium, Whitebank Road, Oldham, Greater Manchester OL8 3JH
Tel: 0161 624 2689

Directions: M62 jct 18, M66 to Heaton Park, right on to A576, left at 2nd lights on to A6104, follow Victoria Ave. on to Hollinwood Ave. under bridge to roundabout take 2nd exit onto Hollins Road, follow Hollins Rd for one & a half miles to Fire Station, left on through gate leading onto Elm Rd and follow to next left, Whitebank Rd on left.

Capacity: 1,000 **Seats:** 101 **Cover:** Yes **Floodlights:** Yes

Clubhouse: Open evenings and matchdays

HONOURS North West Counties Div.2 Champions 1997-98.

PREVIOUS **Leagues:** Manchester Amateur. Lancashire Combination 1981-82.

RECORD **Attendance:** 1,767 v FC United of Manchester - 2006.

ROCHDALE TOWN

FACT FILE
Founded: 1924
Colours: Black & white/black/black
Change: Yellow & green/green/yellow
Midweek matchday: Tuesday

Chairman: Mark Canning.
Secretary: Jim Picken. c/o Rochdale Town F.C.
Ground: Mayfield Sports Centre, Keswick Street, off Heywood Rd., Castleton, Rochdale OL11 3BY. Tel: 01706 527 103.
Directions: M62 Jct 20, A6272M to r'bout. Left towards Castleton (A664Edinburgh Way) to next r'bout, keeping Tesco Superstore to the left, take 1st exit to next r'bout, take 2nd exit into Manchester Rd (A664), after just under mile turn right at `Top House' P.H. into Heywood Rd., to end & ground on right.
Capacity: 1,500 **Seats**: 400 **Cover**: 650 **Floodlights**: Yes
Clubhouse: Open seven nights a night and all day Saturday. Pie & peas and sandwiches available matchdays (pie & peas only at Reserve matches). **Club Shop:** No
HONOURS Manchester Div.1 Champions 1986-87.
PREVIOUS **Leagues:** Rochdale Alliance 1924-84. Manchester 1984-89.
Names: St Gabriels (pre-1960s). Castle Gabriels >2008. **Ground:** Park pitches; Springfield Park 60-81.
Record **Attendance:** 640 v Rochdale, pre-season friendly 1991.

STONE DOMINOES

Founded: 1987
Nickname: The Doms

Chairman: Phil Bath.
Secretary: Pauline Matthews. c/o Stone Dominoes.
GROUND ADDRESS: Motiva Park, Yarnfield Lane, Yarnfield, Stone, Staffordshire ST15 0NF. Tel: 01785 761 891.
Directions: From M6 junction 15, straight on at first roundabout following A500 to Stoke, come to first slip road)before flyover) and turn right at roundabout heading to Stone A34 (5 miles), straight on at next roundabout (Trentham Gardens on your right), through village of Tittensor (take care: cameras - 40mph), at next roundabout straight on (pub in the middle, Darlaston Inn) still on A34, 2 more roundabouts *BP garage on left) get in right hand lane and turn right into Yarnfield Lane (pub on corner called the Wayfarer) football ground is about 1 mile on left before village of Yarnfield.
Midweek Home Matchday: Wednesday **Clubhouse:** Yes
Previous League: Midland League
Club Colours: Red/white/black. **Change Colours:** All blue.
RECORD Attendance: 375 v Port Vale - July 2000.
Senior Honours: Midland League Champions 1999-00. North West Counties Div 2 Champions 2002-03.

WIGAN ROBIN PARK

FACT FILE
Founded: 2005
Colours: Red & white hoops/black & red/black &red.
Change: Orange hoops/navy/navy
Midweek Matchday: Tuesday

Chairman: John Neafcy.

Secretary: Taffy Roberts. Tel: 0780 272 0794.

Ground: Robin Park Arena, Loire Drive, Robin Park, Wigan WN5 0UH.
Tel: 01942 404 950

Directions: M6 J25 take road into Wigan and follow signs for the JJB Stadium (Wigan Athletic). Ground is next to the stadium.

SENIOR HONOURS: Manchester Premier Champions 2007-08.

PREVIOUS
Leagues: Manchester 2005-08.

NORTHERN COUNTIES EAST LEAGUE

www.ncel.org.uk

Sponsored by:
KoolSport

Founded: 1982

Recent champions:
2004: Ossett Albion
2005: Goole
2006: Buxton
2007: Retford United
2008: Winterton Rangers

Premier Division		P	W	D	L	F	A	Pts
Mickleover Sports		38	28	4	6	108	47	88
Long Eaton United		38	25	6	7	76	40	81
Selby Town		38	25	5	8	89	40	80
Bridlington Town		38	23	7	8	105	51	76
Winterton Rangers		38	19	7	12	74	49	64
Arnold Town		38	17	13	8	58	46	64
Thackley		38	20	2	16	87	62	62
Dinnington Town		38	19	5	14	73	60	62
Pickering Town		38	17	7	14	81	64	58
Hallam		38	17	5	16	78	69	56
Parkgate		38	15	6	17	67	79	51
Maltby Main	*-3*	38	15	7	16	63	67	49
Nostell Miners Welfare		38	12	13	13	45	51	49
Liversedge	*-3*	38	14	7	17	60	64	46
Armthorpe Welfare		38	14	3	21	61	58	45
Hall Road Rangers		38	11	6	21	53	94	39
Shirebrook Town		38	9	4	25	47	85	31
Lincoln Moorlands Rail.		38	9	3	26	45	93	30
Brodsworth Miners Welf.		38	5	8	25	46	92	23
Eccleshill United		38	6	2	30	48	153	20

PRESIDENT'S CUP

(Top eight finishers from Premier and Division One)

FIRST ROUND

Barton Town Old Boys 5 Armthorpe Welfare 2
Bottesford Town 1 **Scarborough Athletic** 7
Dinnington Town 1 **Nostell Miners Welfare** 3
Hall Road Rangers 1 Staveley Miners Welfare 1 *aet* (4-3p)
Liversedge 1 Rainworth Miners Welfare 1 *aet* (4-3p)
Parkgate 4 Leeds Carnegie 1
Pickering Town 5 Selby Town 2
Winterton Rangers 2 **Hallam** 3

QUARTER-FINALS

Barton Town Old Boys 5 **Hallam** 5 *aet* (1-3p)
Hall Road Rangers 4 Parkgate 1
Liversedge 3 **Nostell Miners Welfare** 4
Scarborough Athletic 7 Pickering Town 1

SEMI-FINALS

Hallam 0 **Nostell Miners Welfare** 0 *aet* (1-3p)
Scarborough Athletic 5 Hall Road Rangers 1

FINAL

(played over two legs)
(April 16th)
Nostell Miners Welfare 1 Scarborough Athletic 1
(April 28th)
Scarborough Athletic 1 **Nostell Miners Welfare** 2

	Armthorpe Welfare	Arnold Town	Bridlington Town	Brodsworth Miners W.	Dinnington Town	Eccleshill United	Hall Road Rangers	Hallam	Lincoln Moorlands R.	Liversedge	Long Eaton United	Maltby Main	Mickleover Sports	Nostell Miners Welf.	Parkgate	Pickering Town	Selby Town	Shirebrook Town	Thackley	Winterton Rangers
Armthorpe Welfare		1-2	1-2	0-1	1-3	9-0	1-2	3-0	3-0	6-0	0-1	1-0	0-1	0-2	3-2	1-2	2-3	2-0	0-2	0-3
Arnold Town	1-1		1-1	1-1	5-2	1-0	3-1	1-0	1-0	0-0	1-1	0-1	4-0	3-0	4-1	2-1	2-1	1-2	3-2	1-1
Bridlington Town	0-0	6-0	***P***	4-1	5-3	5-2	4-0	6-1	4-0	3-0	8-1	2-3	1-3	1-1	4-0	1-4	1-5	3-0	1-1	1-0
Brodsworth Miners Welfare	0-2	0-1	0-3	***R***	0-2	2-2	4-1	3-2	2-2	2-1	0-2	1-3	1-3	1-1	3-4	0-2	0-0	1-2	0-5	2-1
Dinnington Town	0-1	2-0	3-3	4-1	***E***	2-4	4-2	0-1	3-0	0-4	0-1	2-0	1-2	3-0	3-0	4-2	0-2	1-1	1-2	2-0
Eccleshill United	0-3	0-6	0-2	4-4	4-1	***M***	0-3	1-6	0-6	1-4	0-2	2-4	1-2	1-2	3-2	0-4	2-7	0-3	0-9	0-2
Hall Road Rangers	7-2	2-2	1-3	3-3	2-1	2-5	***I***	1-6	1-3	3-2	0-1	2-1	0-5	1-0	1-1	1-1	2-4	2-0	0-2	0-3
Hallam	3-1	1-1	4-1	3-0	2-4	3-2	2-0	***E***	6-1	3-0	0-1	1-1	1-4	1-5	4-1	1-3	0-5	3-1	1-2	1-1
Lincoln Moorlands Railway	0-2	1-2	2-4	2-0	1-2	8-0	1-3	0-4	***R***	1-4	0-1	3-1	1-5	2-0	0-4	0-2	0-5	0-1	0-3	2-3
Liversedge	0-0	0-1	2-1	2-2	2-2	4-1	4-1	2-1	0-0		1-3	0-1	1-3	1-1	2-3	2-1	1-2	4-1	3-1	0-6
Long Eaton United	4-0	1-1	0-2	2-1	1-0	6-0	4-0	2-1	5-0	2-0	***D***	3-0	4-2	1-1	0-1	2-2	5-1	1-1	4-1	1-0
Maltby Main	4-2	1-1	0-1	3-1	1-1	6-3	1-1	0-1	1-2	1-1	3-3	***I***	0-5	1-0	2-2	2-3	0-3	4-2	0-3	6-1
Mickleover Sports	1-5	1-0	4-1	3-0	3-2	6-0	6-1	5-0	0-1	3-1	4-2	2-1	***V***	0-0	2-0	2-1	3-4	2-1	4-1	1-1
Nostell Miners Welfare	1-0	1-1	2-2	3-1	1-2	1-2	2-0	2-1	2-0	0-3	1-0	0-1	1-1	***I***	2-3	0-1	2-1	1-0	2-7	0-2
Parkgate	1-0	2-0	0-5	6-2	1-1	6-0	1-4	1-1	3-2	3-1	0-2	4-2	1-6	1-1	***S***	0-0	0-3	1-0	1-2	5-1
Pickering Town	3-1	1-1	2-3	1-0	2-3	6-4	5-0	0-3	1-1	2-3	3-0	2-3	2-3	1-1	1-3	***I***	3-2	4-2	2-3	1-1
Selby Town	1-0	3-0	1-1	2-1	1-2	3-0	0-0	1-2	6-1	1-0	3-0	3-0	1-0	2-2	2-1	3-4	***O***	0-0	1-0	2-0
Shirebrook Town	1-3	0-2	0-4	3-2	2-3	5-1	4-0	2-6	0-1	0-3	0-2	3-1	2-6	1-1	2-0	1-5	0-3	***N***	1-2	0-2
Thackley	0-2	7-2	2-1	3-0	0-2	2-3	2-3	1-1	6-1	2-1	2-4	0-2	1-3	1-2	3-1	2-0	1-2	3-2		0-1
Winterton Rangers	5-2	0-0	1-5	4-3	0-2	4-0	1-0	4-1	3-0	0-1	0-1	0-2	2-2	1-1	5-1	3-1	2-0	5-1	5-1	

Division One	P	W	D	L	F	A	Pts
Scarborough Athletic	36	29	5	2	121	24	92
Rainworth Miners Welfare	36	23	9	4	90	42	78
Askern Villa	36	21	9	6	65	34	72
Staveley Miners Welfare	36	20	8	8	77	43	68
Barton Town Old Boys	36	20	7	9	76	53	67
Bottesford Town	36	20	2	14	77	62	62
Leeds Carnegie	36	17	10	9	79	41	61
AFC Emley	36	17	9	10	59	48	60
Pontefract Collieries	36	16	5	15	62	56	53
Hemsworth Miners Welfare	36	13	11	12	57	52	50
Rossington Main	36	12	7	17	53	67	43
Appleby Frodingham	36	11	9	16	58	79	42
Grimsby Borough	36	11	7	18	52	68	40
Teversal	36	12	3	21	59	86	39
Brighouse Town	36	9	8	19	55	73	35
Worsbrough Bridge MW	36	9	5	22	45	86	32
Tadcaster Albion	36	9	4	23	47	94	31
Yorkshire Amateur	36	7	8	21	42	77	29
Glasshoughton Welfare	36	0	6	30	29	118	6

WILKINSON SWORD SHIELD

FIRST ROUND

AFC Emley 0 **Tadcaster** 2
Appleby Frodingham 3 Leeds Carnegie 2
Askern 1 **Scarborough A.** 2

SECOND ROUND

Appleby Frodingham 2 **Barton Town Old Boys** 3
Brighouse Town 5 Grimsby Borough 0
Glasshoughton Welfare 1 **Pontefract Collieries** 2
Hemsworth 0 **Teversal** 2
Rainworth Miners Welf. 4 Rossington Main 3 *aet*
Tadcaster 3 **Staveley** 4
Worsbrough Bridge MW 2 **Bottesford Town** 3
Yorkshire Amateur 2 Scarborough Athletic 0

QUARTER-FINALS

Barton Town Old Boys 1 **Staveley Miners Welfare** 2
Bottesford 3 Brighouse 2
Rainworth 2 Teversal 1
Yorkshire Amateur 0 **Pontefract Collieries** 1

SEMI-FINALS

Staveley Miners Welfare 5 Bottesford Town 0
Pontefract Collieries 3 Rainworth Miners Welfare 0

FINAL

(played over two legs)
(April 14)
Pontefract Collieries 1 Staveley Miners Welfare 1
(April 28)
Staveley Miners Welfare 2 Pontefract Collieries 1

LEAGUE CUP

FIRST ROUND

AFC Emley 1 **Grimsby Borough** 2
Bottesford Town 5 Glasshoughton Welfare 1
Scarborough Athletic 2 Leeds Carnegie 1
Staveley Miners Welfare 2 **Rainworth Miners Welfare** 3
Tadcaster Albion 1 **Hemsworth MW** 1 *aet* (3-4p)
Teversal 2 **Worsbrough Bridge MW** 3
Yorkshire Amateur 0 **Pontefract Collieries** 2

SECOND ROUND

Arnold Town 0 **Pickering Town** 3
Askern Villa 2 Scarborough Athletic 1
Barton Town Old Boys 0 **Selby Town** 1
Bottesford Town 5 **Long Eaton United** 6
Bridlington Town 1 **Winterton Rangers** 3
Brighouse Town 0 **Nostell Miners Welfare** 3
Brodsworth Miners Welfare 0 **Armthorpe Welfare** 2
Grimsby Borough 1 **Pontefract Collieries** 2
Hallam 3 Rossington Main 1
Hemsworth Miners Welfare 2 Dinnington Town 1
Liversedge 2 Shirebrook Town 1
Maltby Main 1 **Lincoln Moorlands Railway** 2
Mickleover Sports 4 Parkgate 1
Rainworth Miners Welfare 2 Appleby Frodingham 0
Thackley 2 Eccleshill United 1
Worsbrough Bridge MW 1 **Hall Road Rangers** 6

THIRD ROUND

Askern Villa 1 Armthorpe Welfare 0 *aet*
Hall Road Rangers 3 Pontefract Collieries 2
Hallam 4 Thackley 0
Lincoln Moorlands Railway 0 **Long Eaton United** 2
Liversedge 1 **Winterton Rangers** 3
Mickleover Sports 3 Hemsworth Miners Welfare 0
Rainworth Miners Welfare 0 **Pickering Town** 3
Selby Town 3 Nostell Miners Welfare 2

QUARTER-FINALS

Askern Villa 0 **Mickleover Sports** 2
Long Eaton United 3 Hall Road Rangers 0
Selby Town 4 Hallam 1
Winterton Rangers 4 Pickering Town 1

SEMI-FINALS

Mickleover Sports 1 **Long Eaton United** 5
Winterton Rangers 3 **Selby Town** 4

FINAL

(May 4th at Staveley Miners Welfare)
Long Eaton United 3 Selby Town 0

	AFC Emley	Appleby F.	Askern V.	Barton	Bottesford	Brighouse	G'houghton	Grimsby B.	Hemsworth	Leeds C.	Pontefract	Rainworth	Rossington	Scarboro.	Staveley	Tadcaster	Teversal	Worsbro.	Yorks Am
AFC Emley		3-1	0-0	1-0	1-0	2-4	7-1	3-0	1-1	1-1	1-2	1-0	4-1	1-6	0-4	4-1	4-2	0-0	1-0
Appleby Frodingham	2-2		0-1	1-1	0-3	1-1	2-1	4-1	1-1	0-6	0-4	1-1	0-2	0-2	3-4	4-0	2-1	3-3	4-2
Askern Villa	2-3	1-1		2-2	5-0	1-0	2-0	2-0	0-1	2-0	1-0	1-1	2-2	0-3	1-0	2-2	2-0	2-4	2-0
Barton Town Old Boys	2-0	2-1	0-1	***D***	1-3	2-1	4-1	3-1	3-3	3-2	2-1	2-0	3-1	2-1	0-2	2-3	4-0	2-1	2-2
Bottesford Town	2-1	0-2	2-3	2-0	***I***	3-0	8-0	1-1	1-2	2-2	2-1	2-3	0-2	1-3	0-4	3-2	3-0	7-1	4-2
Brighouse Town	1-2	4-4	2-5	1-4	3-2	***V***	4-0	1-2	1-1	0-2	2-2	1-4	1-2	1-4	3-4	3-1	4-2	4-0	1-2
Glasshoughton Welfare	0-3	2-3	0-2	1-4	1-4	0-1	***I***	1-1	0-4	0-4	1-4	1-1	2-4	0-2	2-5	0-1	2-2	1-2	1-1
Grimsby Borough	0-0	0-3	1-0	2-3	2-3	3-1	1-1	***S***	1-1	0-5	2-4	2-0	0-6	2-2	1-1	2-0	1-2	4-0	3-0
Hemsworth Miners Welf.	0-1	2-3	1-2	2-2	0-2	1-0	2-0	2-1	***I***	1-1	2-1	1-3	3-1	1-3	1-1	2-2	1-1	1-2	3-2
Leeds Carnegie	2-3	3-0	1-1	1-0	1-2	4-0	6-2	2-1	2-1	***O***	2-3	2-2	0-0	1-2	0-0	5-1	3-3	4-0	0-0
Pontefract Collieries	1-0	4-1	0-1	2-4	2-1	3-2	2-2	3-1	1-0	0-2	***N***	1-4	0-1	0-1	1-3	1-3	0-2	2-2	3-0
Rainworth Miners Welfare	1-1	1-0	1-1	3-2	3-0	1-1	5-0	2-1	4-1	4-2	1-1		5-1	1-0	2-1	7-2	4-1	3-2	4-1
Rossington Main	0-0	1-1	0-3	2-2	4-2	0-2	1-0	1-5	1-4	0-6	0-2	2-4		1-4	0-1	3-1	4-0	1-1	2-0
Scarborough Athletic	4-0	6-1	2-2	6-1	6-0	3-0	5-3	5-0	2-2	0-0	2-0	1-0	1-0	***O***	2-2	7-0	6-0	5-0	6-0
Staveley Miners Welfare	0-1	4-0	3-1	2-2	1-2	0-0	3-1	2-1	0-2	0-3	3-4	1-1	3-0	0-4	***N***	2-0	3-0	5-1	5-1
Tadcaster Albion	1-0	0-1	1-2	0-3	1-4	0-0	4-0	0-2	1-3	2-0	0-1	3-5	0-6	0-4	1-3	***E***	2-3	2-3	2-2
Teversal	2-4	4-3	0-6	0-1	0-2	0-2	8-1	3-1	2-1	5-1	1-3	1-2	2-0	1-2	1-3	4-5		2-3	2-1
Worsbrough Bridge MW	3-2	1-5	1-2	0-3	2-3	4-1	4-0	0-3	0-2	0-2	1-1	0-3	2-0	0-3	0-1	1-2	0-1		0-2
Yorkshire Amateur	1-1	5-0	0-2	1-3	0-1	2-2	2-1	1-3	3-1	0-1	3-2	1-4	1-1	1-6	1-1	0-1	0-1	2-1	

PREMIER DIVISION - 2009-10

ARMTHORPE WELFARE

Founded: 1926 Nickname: Wellie

Chairman: Stephen Taylor
Secretary: Tony Ingram
78 Grange Avenue
Hatfield
Doncaster
DN7 6RD
Tel: 01302 842 795
Manager: Des Bennett
Prog Editor: Tony Ingram

Ground: Church Street, Armthorpe, Doncaster DN3 3AG 01302 842 795(Match days only)
Capacity: 2,500 **Seats:** 250 **Covered:** 400
Midweek Matchday: Tuesday **Clubhouse:** No **Shop:** No
Colours(change): Blue & white quarters/white/white. (Black & grey hoops/blk/blk)
Previous Names:
Previous Lges: Doncaster Senior
Records: Att: 2,000 v Doncaster R Charity Match 1985-86. **Goalscorer:** Martin Johnson **App:** Gary Leighton
Senior Honours: West Riding Challenge Cup 81-82, 82-83.
Northern Counties East Div.1 Central 84-85.

10 YEAR RECORD

99-00	00-01	01-02	02-03	03-04	04-05	05-06	06-07	07-08	08-09
NCEP 11	NCEP 19	NCEP 6	NCEP 18	NCEP 14	NCEP 18	NCEP 10	NCEP 13	NCEP 9	NCEP 15

ARNOLD TOWN

Founded: 1989 Nickname: Eagles

Chairman: Roy Francis
Secretary: Roy Francis
3 Arnot Hill Road
Arnold
Nottingham
NG5 6LJ
Tel: 0115 952 2634
Manager: Andy Muldoon
Prog Editor: Paul Spencer

Ground: Eagle Valley, Oxton Road, Arnold, Nottingham NG5 8PS. Tel: 0115 965 6000.
Capacity: **Seats:** **Covered:**
Midweek Matchday: Tuesday **Clubhouse:** **Shop:**
Colours(change): All maroon. (Yellow & blue)
Previous Names: Arnold F.C. (f'nded '28 as Arnold St. Marys) merged with Arnold Kingswell ('62) in '89.
Previous Lges: Central Midland 89-93
Records: Att: 3,390 v Bristol Rovers FAC 1-Dec 1967 **Goalscorer:** Peter Fletcher - 100. **App:** Pete Davey - 346.
Senior Honours: Northern Counties East 1985-86. Central Midlands 92-93.
Northern Counties Div.1 93-94.

10 YEAR RECORD

99-00	00-01	01-02	02-03	03-04	04-05	05-06	06-07	07-08	08-09
NCEP 8	NCEP 6	NCEP 10	NCEP 15	NCEP 18	NCEP 16	NCEP 5	NCEP 15	NCEP 10	NCEP 6

BRIDLINGTON TOWN

Founded: 1920 Nickname: Seasiders

Chairman: Peter Smurthwaite
Secretary: Gavin Branton
4 Constable Way
Flamborough
East Yorks
YO15 1LZ
Tel: 07870 865 438
Manager: Gary Allanson
Prog Editor: Dom Taylor

Ground: Queensgate Lane Rental Stadium, Queensgate, YO16 7LN. Tel: 01262 606 879.
Capacity: 3,000 **Seats:** 500 **Covered:** 500
Midweek Matchday: Tuesday **Clubhouse:** Yes **Shop:** Yes
Colours(change): All red. (White/white/blue).
Previous Names: Original Bridlington Town folded in 1994. Greyhound FC changed to Bridlington Town.
Previous Lges: Driffield & Dist. East Riding Amateur. Northern Premier.
Records: Att: 1,006 v FC Utd of Manchester, NPLD1N, 03.11.07. **Goalscorer:** Neil Grimson. **Apps:** Neil Grimson - 200+ (1987-97).
Senior Honours: FA Vase 1993. Northern Counties East 89-90, 02-03. Div.1 92-93.
ERCFA Senior Cup 1921,22,23,31,53,57,61,65,67,70,72,89,93,05

10 YEAR RECORD

99-00	00-01	01-02	02-03	03-04	04-05	05-06	06-07	07-08	08-09
NCE1 5	NCE1 4	NCE1 2	NCEP 1	NP 1 11	NP P 20	NP 1 11	NP 1 24	NP1N 18	NCEP 4

BRODSWORTH WELFARE

Founded: 1912 Nickname: Broddy

Chairman: Gordon Jennings
Secretary: Robert Laws
92 Markham Avenue
Carcroft
Doncaster
DN6 8DZ
Tel: 07858 257 888
Manager: Colin Bishop & Alan Radford
Prog Editor: Tony Richardson

Ground: Welfare Ground, Woodlands, Nr Doncaster DN6 7PP 01302 728 380
Capacity: 3,000 **Seats:** 228 **Covered:** 400
Midweek Matchday: Wednesday **Clubhouse:** Yes **Shop:** No
Colours(change): All Blue. (All green).
Previous Names: Brodsworth Main > 1963. Brodsworth Miners Welfare 63-06.
Previous Lges: Doncaster Senior, Sheffield. Yorkshire.
Records:
Senior Honours: Northern Counties East Div.1 1998-99.

10 YEAR RECORD

99-00	00-01	01-02	02-03	03-04	04-05	05-06	06-07	07-08	08-09
NCEP 6	NCEP 18	NCEP 15	NCEP 14	NCEP 20	NCEP 17	NCEP 20	NCEP 20	NCEP 13	NCEP 19

DINNINGTON TOWN

Founded: 2000 Nickname: Dinno

Chairman: MD: Mark Ramsden
Secretary: Chris Dearns
14 Cockshutts Lane
Oughtbridge
Sheffield
S35 0FX
Tel: 0114 286 4696
Manager: Steve Toyne
Prog Editor: Paul Morris

Ground: 131 Laughton Road, Dinnington, Nr Sheffield S25 2PP 01909 518 555
Capacity: 2000 **Seats:** 80 **Covered:** 200
Midweek Matchday: Tuesday **Clubhouse:** Yes **Shop:** Yes
Colours(change): Yellow & black/black/yellow. (All white).
Previous Names:
Previous Lges: Central Midlands League 2000-06
Records:

Senior Honours: Central Midlands League Cup 2002-03, 05-06.
Northern Counties East Div.1 2007-08.

10 YEAR RECORD

99-00	00-01	01-02	02-03	03-04	04-05	05-06	06-07	07-08	08-09
	CM P 6	CM P 3	CM Su 6	CM Su 2	CM Su 2	CM Su 2	NCE1 9	NCE1 1	NCEP 8

HALL ROAD RANGERS

Founded: 1959 Nickname: Rangers

Chairman: Robert Smailes
Secretary: Alan Chaplin
33 Lee Street
Holderness Road
Hull
HU8 8NH
Tel: 01482 703 775
Manager: Jamie Barnwell
Prog Editor: Paul Maunoury

Ground: Dene Park, Dene Close, Beverley Road, Dunswell HU6 0AA Tel: 01482 850 101
Capacity: 1,200 **Seats:** 250 **Covered:** 750
Midweek Matchday: Wednesday **Clubhouse:** Yes **Shop:** Yes
Colours(change): Blue & white/blue/blue. (All red & black)
Previous Names:
Previous Lges: East Riding Co., Yorks 68-82
Records: **App:**1,200 v Manchester City Aug 93 **Goalscorer:** G James **App:** G James

Senior Honours: East Riding Senior Cup 1972-73, 93-94. N.C.E. Div 2 90-91.

10 YEAR RECORD

99-00	00-01	01-02	02-03	03-04	04-05	05-06	06-07	07-08	08-09
NCE1 8	NCE1 6	NCE1 9	NCE1 9	NCE1 14	NCE1 11	NCE1 14	NCE1 10	NCE1 2	NCEP 16

HALLAM (SECOND OLDEST CLUB IN THE WORLD)

Founded: 1860 Nickname: Countrymen

Chairman: Peter Hogan
Secretary: Mark Radford
34 Fairview Road
Sheffield

S5 7TB
Tel: 0114 249 7287
Manager: Wilf Race
Prog Editor: See secretary

Ground: Sandygate Road, Crosspool, Sheffield S10 5SE. Tel: 0114 230 9484.
Capacity: 1,000 **Seats:** 250 **Covered:** 400
Midweek Matchday: Tuesday **Clubhouse:** Yes **Shop:** Yes
Colours(change): All red. (Red & black).
Previous Names:
Previous Lges: Yorkshire 1952-82.
Records: **Att:** 2,000 v Hendon F.A. Amateur Cup & 13,855 v Dulwich at Hillsborough F.A. Am Cup 1955 **Goalscorer:** Anthony Wilson 46. **App:** P. Ellis 500 +
Senior Honours: Sheffield & Hallamshire Senior Cup 1950-51, 61-62, 64-65, 67-68.
Northern Counties East League Cup 2003-04.

10 YEAR RECORD

99-00	00-01	01-02	02-03	03-04	04-05	05-06	06-07	07-08	08-09
NCEP 12	NCEP 5	NCEP 3	NCEP 17	NCEP 15	NCEP 15	NCEP 17	NCEP 14	NCEP 6	NCEP 10

LINCOLN MOORLANDS RAILWAY

Founded: 1989 Nickname: The Moors

Chairman: Nicholas Robinson
Secretary: Ken Rooney
c/o Lincoln Moorlands Railway FC

Tel: 01522 874 111
Manager: Darren Dye
Prog Editor: See secretary

Ground: Moorland Sports Ground, Newark Road, Lincoln LN6 0XJ Tel: 01522 874 111
Capacity: 200 **Seats:** 200 **Covered:**
Midweek Matchday: Wednesday **Clubhouse:** Yes **Shop:** No
Colours(change): Claret & blue/claret/claret. (Royal blue & yellow/royal/royal).
Previous Names:
Previous Lges: Central Midlands.
Records:

Senior Honours: Central Midlands Supreme 1999-00.
Lincolnshire Senior Cup 2006-07.

10 YEAR RECORD

99-00	00-01	01-02	02-03	03-04	04-05	05-06	06-07	07-08	08-09
CM Su 1	CM Su 2	NCE1 4	NCE1 7	NCE1 8	NCE1 4	NCE1 7	NCE1 5	NCEP 19	NCEP 18

INS & OUTS
IN: Rainworth Miners Welfare (P), Scarborough Athletic (P)
OUT: Eccleshill United (R), Mickleover Sports (P – Northern Premier League Division One South)

PREMIER DIVISION - 2009-10

LIVERSEDGE

Founded: 1910 Nickname: sedge

Chairman: Alan Durrans
Secretary: Bryan Oakes
16 Moorlands,
Birkenshaw
Bradford
BD11 2BS
Tel: 01274 683 327
Manager: Sean Regan
Prog Editor: Alan Dearden

Ground: Clayborn Ground, Quaker Lane, Hightown Road, Cleckheaton WF15 8DF Tel: 01274 682 108
Capacity: 2,000 **Seats:** 250 **Covered:** 750
Midweek Matchday: Tuesday **Clubhouse:** Yes **Shop:** Yes
Colours(change): Sky blue/navy/sky blue. (All red).
Previous Names:
Previous Lges: Spen Valley, West Riding Co. Amateur 22-72, Yorkshire 72-82
Records: Att: 986 v Thackley **Goalscorer:** Denis Charlesworth **App:** Barry Palmer

Senior Honours: Northern Counties East League Cup 2005-06.

10 YEAR RECORD

99-00	00-01	01-02	02-03	03-04	04-05	05-06	06-07	07-08	08-09
NCEP 4	NCEP 15	NCEP 11	NCEP 9	NCEP 9	NCEP 6	NCEP 2	NCEP 12	NCEP 4	NCEP 14

LONG EATON UNITED

Founded: 1956 Nickname: Blues

Chairman: Jim Fairley
Secretary: Jim Fairley
56 Derby Road
Bramcote
Nottingham
NG9 3FY
Tel: 07971 416 444
Manager: Mark Harvey & Andy Worrall
Prog Editor: See chairman

Ground: Grange Park, Station Rd, Long Eaton, Derbys NG10 2EF Tel: 0115 973 5700
Capacity: 1,500 **Seats:** 150 **Covered:** 500
Midweek Matchday: Tuesday **Clubhouse:** Yes **Shop:** No
Colours(change): All blue. (All yellow).
Previous Names:
Previous Lges: Central Alliance 56-61, Mid Co Football Lge 61-82, NCE 82-89, Central Midlands 89-02
Records: Att: 2,019 v Burton Albion FA Cup 1973

Senior Honours: Derbyshire Senior Cup 1964-65, 75-76.
Northern Counties East Div1S 1984-85. League Cup 08-09.

10 YEAR RECORD

99-00	00-01	01-02	02-03	03-04	04-05	05-06	06-07	07-08	08-09
CM Su 17	CM Su 7	CM Su 3	NCE1 3	NCE1 2	NCEP 12	NCEP 19	NCEP 11	NCEP 12	NCEP 2

MALTBY MAIN

Founded: 1916 Nickname: Miners

Chairman: Graham McCormick
Secretary: John Mills
11 Norwood Avenue
Maltby
Rotherham
S66 8JG
Tel: 01709 813 609
Manager: Steve Adams
Prog Editor: Nick Dunhill

Ground: Muglet Lane, Maltby, Rotherham S66 7JQ. Tel: 07795 693 683.
Capacity: 2,000 **Seats:** 150 **Covered:** 300
Midweek Matchday: Wednesday **Clubhouse:** No **Shop:** No
Colours(change): Red/black/black
Previous Names: Maltby Miners Welfare 1970-96
Previous Lges: Sheffield Co Senior. Yorkshire League 1973-84
Records: Att: 1,500 v Sheffield Weds (friendly) 1991-2

Senior Honours: Sheffield & Hallamshire Senior Cup1977-78

10 YEAR RECORD

99-00	00-01	01-02	02-03	03-04	04-05	05-06	06-07	07-08	08-09
NCEP 17	NCE1 9	NCE1 6	NCE1 15	NCE1 3	NCEP 19	NCEP 18	NCEP 10	NCEP 18	NCEP 12

NOSTELL MINERS WELFARE

Founded: 1928 Nickname: The Welfare

Chairman: Granville Marshall
Secretary: Granville Marshall
82 Springhall Avenue
Crofton
Wakefield
WF4 1HD
Tel: 01924 864 462
Manager: Alan Colquhoun
Prog Editor: Jeff Dawson

Ground: The Welfare Ground, Crofton Co. Centre, Middle Lane, New Crofton, WF4 1LB Tel:01924 866010
Capacity: 1500 **Seats:** 100 **Covered:** 200
Midweek Matchday: Tuesday **Clubhouse:** Yes **Shop:** No
Colours(change): Yellow/black/yellow. (All blue).
Previous Names:
Previous Lges: Wakefield 1950-66, West Yorkshire 1966-68, Wakefield 1969-82
Records:

Senior Honours: West Yorkshire Premier Division 2004-05

10 YEAR RECORD

99-00	00-01	01-02	02-03	03-04	04-05	05-06	06-07	07-08	08-09
WYkP 3	WYkP 7	WYkP 8	WYkP 3	WYkP 5	WYkP 1	WYkP 3	NCE1 4	NCE1 5	NCEP 13

PARKGATE

Founded: 1969 Nickname: The Steelmen

Chairman: Albert Dudill
Secretary: Bruce Bickerdike
2 Cardew Close
Rawmarsh
Rotherham
S62 6LB
Tel: 01709 522 305
Manager: Sean Hutchinson
Prog Editor: Stephen Roberts

Ground: Roundwood Sports Complex, Green Lane, Rawmarsh, S62 6LA T:01709 826600
Capacity: 1,000 **Seats:** 300 **Covered:** 300
Midweek Matchday: Tuesday **Clubhouse:** Yes **Shop:** No
Colours(change): All Red & White. (All orange).
Previous Names: BSC Parkgate (1982-86) RES Parkgate (pre 1994)
Previous Lges: BIR County Senior. Yorkshire 1974-82.
Records: Att: v Worksop 1982
Senior Honours: N.C.E. Div 1 Champions 2006-07.

10 YEAR RECORD

99-00	00-01	01-02	02-03	03-04	04-05	05-06	06-07	07-08	08-09
NCE1 12	NCE1 7	NCE1 14	NCE1 8	NCE1 10	NCE1 12	NCE1 6	NCE1 1	NCEP 8	NCEP 11

PICKERING TOWN

Founded: 1888 Nickname: Pikes

Chairman: Anthony Dunning
Secretary: Keith Usher
c/o Pickering Town F.C.
Tel: 01751 473 317
Manager: Mark Wood
Prog Editor: Alasdair Dinnewell

Ground: Rec. Club, off Mill Lane, Malton Road, Pickering YO18 7DB Tel: 01751 473 317
Capacity: 2,000 **Seats:** 200 **Covered:** 500
Midweek Matchday: Tuesday **Clubhouse:** Yes **Shop:** No
Colours(change): All blue. (All yellow).
Previous Names:
Previous Lges: Beckett, York & District, Scarborough & District, Yorkshire 1972-1982
Records: Att: 1,412 v Notts County (friendly) in August 1991
Senior Honours: N.C.E. Div 2 1987-88. North Riding Cup 1990-91.
Wilkinson Sword Trophy 2000-01

10 YEAR RECORD

99-00	00-01	01-02	02-03	03-04	04-05	05-06	06-07	07-08	08-09
NCE1 11	NCE1 2	NCEP 4	NCEP 13	NCEP 5	NCEP 5	NCEP 6	NCEP 9	NCEP 3	NCEP 9

RAINWORTH MINERS WELFARE

Founded: 1922 Nickname: The Wrens

Chairman: Derek Blow
Secretary: Leslie Lee
18 The Hollies
Rainworth
Mansfield, Notts
NG21 0FZ
Tel: 01623 490 053
Manager: Rudy Funk
Prog Editor: Gordon Foster

Ground: Welfare Ground, Kirklington Road, Rainworth, Mansfield NG21 0JY
Capacity: 2000 **Seats:** 221 **Covered:** 350
Midweek Matchday: Tuesday **Clubhouse:** Yes **Shop:** No
Colours(change): All White (All Royal Blue).
Previous Names: None
Previous Lges: Notts Alliance 1922-03, Central Midlands League 2003-07
Records: Att: 5,071 v Barton Rovers FA Vase SF 2nd Leg, 1982.
Senior Honours: Notts Senior Cup Winners 1981/82.

10 YEAR RECORD

99-00	00-01	01-02	02-03	03-04	04-05	05-06	06-07	07-08	08-09
NottS 10	NottS 2	NottS 8	NottS 5	CM P 3	CM Su 20	CM Su 9	CM Su 3	NCE1 4	NCE1 2

SCARBOROUGH ATHLETIC

Founded: 2007 Nickname: The Seadogs

Chairman: Simon Cope
Secretary: John Clarke
31 Dale Edge
Eastfield
Scarborough
YO11 3EP
Tel: 01723 585 150
Manager: Brian France
Prog Editor: James Hunter

Ground: Queensgate Stadium, Bridlington, East Yorkshire YO11 3EP. Tel: 01262 606 879
Capacity: 3000 **Seats:** 500 **Covered:** 1,200
Midweek Matchday: Tuesday **Clubhouse:** Yes **Shop:** No
Colours(change): All Red (All white).
Previous Names: Formed after Scarborough F.C. folded in 2007.
Previous Lges: N/A
Records: Att: 791 v Leeds Carnegie N.C.E. Div.1 - 25.04.09.
Senior Honours: N.C.E. Div.1 Champions 2008-09.

10 YEAR RECORD

99-00	00-01	01-02	02-03	03-04	04-05	05-06	06-07	07-08	08-09
								NCE1 5	NCE1 1

SELBY TOWN

Founded: 1919 Nickname: The Robins

Chairman: Ralph Pearse
Secretary: Thomas Arkley
176 Abbots Rd
Selby
N. Yorks
YO8 8AZ
Tel: 01757 700 356
Manager: Bob Lyon
Prog Editor: See secretary

Ground: Selby Times Stadium, Richard St, Scott Rd, Selby YO8 0DB Tel: 01757 210 900
Capacity: 5,000 **Seats:** 220 **Covered:** 350
Midweek Matchday: Tuesday **Clubhouse:** Yes **Shop:** Yes
Colours(change): All red. (All blue).
Previous Names:
Previous Lges: Yorkshire 1920-82
Records: Att: 7,000 v Bradford PA FA Cup1st Round 1953-54
Senior Honours: Yorkshire League 1934-35, 35-36, 52-53, 53-54. NCE Div.1 95-96.

10 YEAR RECORD

99-00	00-01	01-02	02-03	03-04	04-05	05-06	06-07	07-08	08-09
NCEP 9	NCEP 9	NCEP 7	NCEP 16	NCEP 8	NCEP 2	NCEP 8	NCEP 5	NCEP 7	NCEP 3

SHIREBROOK TOWN

Founded: 1985 Nickname: None

Chairman: Steve Brown
Secretary: Aimee Radford
c/o Shirebrook Town F.C.
Tel: 01623 742 535
Manager: Darren Price
Prog Editor: Graham Howarth

Ground: Shirebrook Staff & Sp.S.Club, Langwith Rd, Shirebrook Mansfield NG20 8TF. Tel: 01623 742 535
Capacity: 2,000 **Seats:** 300 **Covered:** 400
Midweek Matchday: Wednesday **Clubhouse:** Yes **Shop:** No
Colours(change): Red/ black/red. (All white).
Previous Names: Shirebrook Colliery > 93.
Previous Lges: Central Midlands 1985-02
Records: App: Craig Charlesworth 345
Senior Honours: Central Midlands Supreme Champions 2000-01, 01-02
N. Co. E Div 1 2003-04

10 YEAR RECORD

99-00	00-01	01-02	02-03	03-04	04-05	05-06	06-07	07-08	08-09
CM Su 2	CM Su 1	CM Su 1	NCE1 2	NCE1 1	NCEP 10	NCEP 15	NCEP 19	NCEP 15	NCEP 17

THACKLEY

Founded: 1930 Nickname: The Reds

Chairman: Mike Smith
Secretary: Chris Frank
2 Belle Vue Close
Thackley
Bradford
BD10 8PF
Tel: 01274 615 590
Manager: Billy Fox
Prog Editor: John McCreery

Ground: Dennyfield, Ainsbury Avenue, Thackley, Bradford BD10 0TL Tel: 01274 615 571
Capacity: 3000 **Seats:** 300 **Covered:** 600
Midweek Matchday: Tuesday **Clubhouse:** Yes **Shop:** Yes
Colours(change): Red/white/red. (White/black/white).
Previous Names: Thackley Wesleyians 1930-39
Previous Lges: Bradford Am, W. Riding Co. Am., West Yorks, Yorks 67-82
Records: Att: 1,500 v Leeds United 1983
Senior Honours: W. Riding County Cup 1963-64, 66-67, 73-74, 74-75.
Bradford & District Senior Cup (x13).

10 YEAR RECORD

99-00	00-01	01-02	02-03	03-04	04-05	05-06	06-07	07-08	08-09
NCEP 20	NCEP 8	NCEP 8	NCEP 6	NCEP 11	NCEP 8	NCEP 9	NCEP 18	NCEP 16	NCEP 7

WINTERTON RANGERS

Founded: 1930 Nickname: The Reds

Chairman: David Crowder
Secretary: Mark Fowler
18 Bennett Drive
Winterton
Scunthorpe
DN15 9SG
Tel: 01724 733 383
Manager: Richard Sennett & Mark Turner
Prog Editor: Brian Crowder

Ground: West Street, Winterton, Scunthorpe DN15 9QF. Tel: 01724 732 628.
Capacity: 3,000 **Seats:** 245 **Covered:** 200
Midweek Matchday: Wednesday **Clubhouse:** Yes **Shop:** No
Colours(change): All royal blue. (All red).
Previous Names:
Previous Lges: Scunthorpe & Dist. 1945-65. Lincs 65-70. Yorkshire 70-82.
Records: Att: 1,200 v Sheffield United, flood lights switch on, October 1978.
Senior Honours: Yorkshire League 1971-72, 76-77, 78-79. NCE Div.2 1989-90.
NCE Premier 07-08.

10 YEAR RECORD

99-00	00-01	01-02	02-03	03-04	04-05	05-06	06-07	07-08	08-09
NCE1 6	NCE1 14	NCE1 7	NCE1 10	NCE1 11	NCE1 10	NCE1 5	NCE1 2	NCEP 1	NCEP 5

DIVISION ONE INS & OUTS IN: Eccleshill United (R)
OUT: Rainworth Miners Welfare (P), Scarborough Athletic (P)

AFC EMLEY

Secretary: Richard Poulain, 14 Cheviot Avenue, Meltham, Holmfirth, HD9 4DW
Tel Nos: (H) 01484 859 975. (M) 07702 712 287

Ground: The Welfare Ground, Off Upper Lane, Emley, nr Huddersfield,
West Yorkshire HD8 9RE. Tel: 01924 849 392 or 07702 712 287

Directions: From M1 Junction 38: Travel on road signposted to Huddersfield through the village of Bretton to the first roundabout. Take first exit off this roundabout signposted Denby Dale. After approximately one mile turn right at road signposted Emley. After 2 miles enter the village of Emley. Entrance to ground is opposite a white bollard in centre of road. (Narrow entrance). From M1 Junction 39: Travel on road signposted toward Denby Dale. Travel for approximately 3 miles up hill to first roundabout. Take 2nd exit and follow directions as above.

Capacity: 2000 **Seats:** 330 **Cover:** 1000

Clubhouse: Yes

Previous League: West Yorkshire League 2005-06

FACT FILE

Founded: 2005

Nickname: Pewits

Colours:

Maroon & sky blue/sky blue/maroon

Midweek Matchday: Wednesday

CLUB PERSONNEL

Chairman: Graham Roys

Programme Editor: Secretary

APPLEBY FRODINGHAM

Secretary: Steve Lumley-Holmes. Kingswood, Church Street, Scawby, Brigg, North Lincolnshire DN20 9AE.
Tel: 01652 654 044

Ground: Brumby Hall Sports Ground, Ashby Avenue, Scunthorpe DN16 1AA.
Tel: 01724 402 134. 01724 843 024 (Clubhouse)

Directions: From the M18 take J5 onto the M180. From M180 take J3 onto the M181 which is Scunthorpe (West), at the roundabout turn right onto A18, straight on at the mini roundabout (McDonalds). At the next large roundabout take the 3rd exit (A18) up the hill to the next roundabout. Turn left and the entrance to the ground is 500 yards on the left.

Previous Leagues: Central Midlands League

FACT FILE

Founded: 1990

Colours: Red/black/black.

Midweek Matches: Tuesday

CLUB PERSONNEL

Chairman: As secretary.

Programme Editor: Dick Drury

ASKERN VILLA

Secretary: Lisa Williams. Rose Cottage, Doncaster Road, Barnburgh, Doncaster DN5 7BE. Tel: 07908 160 786.

Ground: Askern Welfare Sports Ground, Doncaster Road, Askern, DN6 0AJ.
Tel No: Clubhouse: 01302 700 957.

Directions: Leave the A1 at Junction A639. Follow signs Askern/Campsall at T-Junction turn right. Take 2nd right at "Anne Arms". Ground 2nd on right (Manor Way). Car park available at the rear of Miners Welfare Club .

Previous Leagues: Central Midlands League.

Honours: Central Midlands League 2007-08

FACT FILE

Founded: 1924

Colours: Black & white/white/white.

Midweek Matches: Tuesday

CLUB PERSONNEL

Chairman: Ted Ellis.

Programme Editor: As secretary.

BARTON TOWN OLD BOYS

Secretary: Peter Mitchell. 56 Brigg Road, Barton-upon-Humber, N.Lincs DN18 5DR.
Tel: 01652 632 382 (H).

Ground: The Euronics Ground, Marsh Lane, Barton-on-Humber. Tel: 01652 635 838

Directions: Approaching from the South on A15, Barton is the last exit before the Humber Bridge. Follow the A1077 into the town. Turn right at the mini roundabout at the bottom of the hill into Holydyke. Take second left onto George Street and then into King Street. Marsh Lane is opposite the junction of King Street and High Street. The ground is at the end of Marsh Lane, on the right, immediately after the cricket ground.

Capacity: 3000 **Seats:** 240 **Cover:** 540

Clubhouse: Yes with full range of hot/cold drinks and food.

Previous League: Central Midlands League.

FACT FILE

Founded: 1995

Nickname: The Swans

Colours: Sky blue/white/sky

Midweek Matchday: Tuesday

CLUB PERSONNEL

Chairman: Paul Vickers

Manager: Carl Stead

Programme Editor: Phil Hastings

BOTTESFORD TOWN

Secretary: Victor Jubber. 16 Silica Crescent, Scunthorpe, N.Lincs DN17 2XA
Tel: 01724 340 225.

Ground: Birch Park, Ontario Road, Bottesford, Scunthorpe, DN17 2TQ.
Tel: (01724) 871883

Directions: M180 via M181-Scunthorpe. At circle (Berkeley Hotel), turn right into Scotter Road. At circle (Asda) straight ahead, 2nd left into South Park road then on to Sunningdale Road, turn right into Goodwood Road, Birch Park at end (right turn). Please note that Goodwood Road is not suitable for large vehicles. Instead, take 2nd right off Sunningdale Road which is Quebec Road, then 3rd right which is Ontario Road down to the bottom and ground is on the left.

Capacity: 1000 **Seats:** 90 **Cover:** 300 **Clubhouse:** Yes

Previous League: Lincolnshire League 1974-00. Central Midlands League 2000-07.

Honours: Lincolnshire League 1989-90, 90-91, 91-92. Central Midlands League Supreme Division 2006-07.

FACT FILE

Founded: 1974

Nickname: The Poachers

Colours: All blue and yellow

Midweek Matchday: Tuesday

CLUB PERSONNEL

Chairman: Tony Reeve

Manager: Ralph Clayton

Programme Editor: Liz Gray

BRIGHOUSE TOWN

Secretary: Malcolm Taylor. 50 Garden Road, Brighouse, West Yorks HD6 2ES.
Tel: 01484 380 088.

Ground: St. Giles Road, Brighouse HD6 2PL.
Tel: 01484 380 088

Directions: M1 to M62 travel westwards to J26 then come off motorway and go on to A58 Halifax to third set of traffic lights at Hipperholme. At lights, turn left onto A644 to Brighouse. Travel approx. one mile passing the Dusty Miller pub, take next left and, within 30-40 metres, turn left on to Spouthouse Lane. Follow this road for approximately 1/4 of a mile until road swings left at this point. Turn right in to car park. Be careful of oncoming traffic on bend.

Previous Leagues: Huddersfield Works League 1963-1975; West Riding County Amateur League 1975-2008

FACT FILE

Founded: 1963

Colours: Orange/black/orange.

Midweek Matches: Tuesday

CLUB PERSONNEL

Chairman: Chris Lister.

Programme Editor: As secretary.

ECCLESHILL UNITED

Founded: 1948
Nickname: The Eagles

Chairman: John Offless **Manager:** Steve Watson
Secretary: Mark Holstead
Programme Editor: Secretary
GROUND ADDRESS: Plumpton Park, Kingsway, Wrose, Bradford BD2 1PN **Ground Tel No:** 01274 615 739
Capacity: 2,225 **Seats:** 225 **Covered:** 415 **Floodlights:** Yes
Simple Directions: From A 650 Bradford Inner Ring road onto Canal Road and branch right at Staples (Dixons Car showrooms on right) fork left after 30mph sign to junction with Wrose Road (across junction) continuation of Kings Road. First left onto KIngsway and ground is 200 yards on right. Bradford BR - 2miles. Buses: 624 or 627
Midweek Home Matchday: Tuesday **Clubhouse:** Normal licensing hours **Club Shop:** Yes
Previous Name: Eccleshill F.C. **Previous Leagues:** Bradford Amateur and West Riding Amateur
Club Colours: Royal blue & white/royal blue/royal blue
BEST PERFORMANCE - League: 8th N.Co. E. 2003-04
RECORD Attendance: 715 v Bradford C 96-7 **Victory:** 10-1 v Blackpool Mech's FAC. **Defeat:** 0-6 v Rossendale (a) Lge Cup
Goalscorer: Stuart Taylor
Senior Honours: NCE Div 1 96-7, Bradford F.A. Senior Cup 85-86 Wet Riding Cup R-Up 99-00

GLASSHOUGHTON WELFARE

Founded: 1964

Chairman: Mick Jacobson.
Secretary: Ray Gowan. 16 Ashwood, Leeds LS14 2HA. Tel: 07973 132 183.
Programme Editor: Nigel Lea.
GROUND ADDRESS: Diggerland Stadium, Glasshoughton Centre, Leeds Road, Glasshoughton, Castleford WF10 4PF.
Tel: 01977 511 234.
Capacity: 2,000 **Seats:** None **Covered:** 250 **Floodlights:** Yes
Simple Directions: Leave M62 at exit 31 or 32. Travel towards Castleford from exit 32 the road comes into Glasshoughton. From exit 31 turn right at roundabout at Whitwood Tech. College. Ground is on Leeds Road.
Midweek Home Matchday: Tuesday **Clubhouse:** Bar with refreshments **Club Shop:** No
Previous Name(s): Anson Sports 1964-76 **Previous League:** West Yorkshire
Club Colours: Royal blue & white/royal blue/royal blue.
RECORD Attendance: 300 v Bradford City 1990 **Victory:** 8-1v Garforth T. Co Cup 00-01 **Defeat:**0-8 V Hucknall T NCE 97-8
Senior Honours: West Riding County Cup 93-94.

GRIMSBY BOROUGH

Secretary: Nigel Fanthorpe. 11 Ravendale Road, Cleethorpes DN35 0HW.
Tel: 01472 605 177.

Ground: The Hawthorns, Hawthorn Avenue, Brigg.
Tel: 01652 652 767.

Directions: From M180 junction 4 Scunthorpe East, take A18 through Brigg turning left at the War Memorial onto Wrawby Road, take the first left after East Parade/Woodbine Avenue junction, signposted Football Ground. Brigg (BR) 1 mile.

Previous Leagues: Lincolnshire League: 2003-04; Central Midlands League: 2004-08

FACT FILE

Founded: 1963

Colours: Royal blue/white/royal blue.

Midweek Matches: Wednesday

CLUB PERSONNEL

Chairman: Sean Hall.

Programme Editor: Darren Williams.

HEMSWORTH MINERS WELFARE

Secretary: Mark Crapper. 33 Newstead Terrace, Fitzwilliam, Pontefract EF9 5DH.
Tel: 01977 614 723.

Ground: Fitzwilliam Stadium, Wakefield Road, Fitzwilliam, Pontefract, WF9 5AJ

Directions: From East/West: M62 to J32 towards Pontefract then follow A628 towards Hemsworth. At Ackworth roundabout (Stoneacre Suzuki Garage), take a right on to the A638 Wakefield Road. Travel half a mile to next roundabout then take first exit. Travel one mile to crossroads and turn left into Fitzwilliam. Pass a row of shops on your right and turn left after the bus shelter before an iron bridge. To ground. From North: A1 South to M62 then follow above directions. From South: A1(M) North to A638 Wakefield Road. Travel to Ackworth Roundabout (Stoneacre Suzuki Garage) and go straight across and follow the A638 to the next roundabout. Take first exit then to crossroads. Turn left into Fitzwilliam and pass row of shops on your right. Turn left after bus shelter before iron bridge and carry on to the ground. Alternative: M1 to J32 then take M18 to A1(M).

Previous Leagues: Bentley League 1981-83; Doncaster & District Senior League 1983-1995; West Riding County Amateur League 1995-2008

FACT FILE

Founded: 1981

Colours: All royal blue.

Midweek Matches: Tuesday

CLUB PERSONNEL

Chairman: Chris Lister.

Programme Editor: As secretary.

LEEDS CARNEGIE

Secretary: James Earl. Leeds Metro Univ., A.U.Office, Headlingley Campus, Leeds LS6 3QS. Tel: 07872 029 121.

Ground: Throstle Nest, Farsley Celtic FC, Newlands, Farsley, Leeds, LS28 5BE. Tel: (0113) 255 7292 (Matchday), (0113) 8125119 (Other Times). Fax: (0113) 812 7430;

Directions: M62 East to Junction 27, then exit onto M621 towards Leeds. Exit at Junction 1 and join Leeds Ring Road North A6110 towards Pudsey. Stay on ring road until exit for Bradford A647. Exit to roundabout and take third exit onto the B6157 to Stanningley. Continue for 800 yards passing Police and Fire Station on left to Tradex Warehouse. Follow signpost to Farsley Celtic by turning left down New Street to Newlands (400 yards). Turn right on Newlands, ground is at far end. Ground is 1 mile away from New Pudsey Railway Station.

Previous Leagues: Yorkshire League 1970-79. Northern Universities Lge 1980-04. West York 2004-07.

Honours Yorkshire League: Div 2 - 1970/71; West Yorkshire League: Prem Div - 2005/06, Div 1 - 2004/05; Northern Universities League - 1980/81 1981/82 1982/83 1988/89 1991/92 1994/95 2000/01 2002/03 2003/04, League Cup - 1999/2000 2002/03.

FACT FILE

Founded: 1970

Colours: All green.

Midweek Matches: Monday

CLUB PERSONNEL

Chairman: Michael Rossiter

Programme Editor: Joe Rossiter

PONTEFRACT COLLIERIES

Secretary: Karl Blackburn. 9 Westerman Close, Fatherstone WF7 6HJ
Tel: 07971 002 126 (M)

Ground: Beechunt Lane, Pontefract WF8 4QE. Tel: 01977 600 818.

Directions: M62 jct 32 towards Pontefract. Left at lights after roundabout for park entrance and retail park. Traffic thro town should follow racecouse signs thro lights to roundabout and back to lights. Monkhill (BR) 1/2 mile. Baghill (BR) 1 mile. Tanshelf (BR) 1/2 mile .All Leeds and Castleford buses pass ground.

Capacity: 1,200 **Seats:** 300 **Cover:** 400 **Floodlights:** Yes

Clubhouse: Fully licensed. Hot & cold snacks. Open matchdays.

Previous Leagues: West Yorkshire 1958-79; Yorkshire 1979-82

Record Attendance: 1,000 v Hull City, floodlight opening 1987.

Honours N.C.E. Lg Div 1 83-84 95-96 (Div 2 R-up 82-83); Lg Cup, R-up: 96-97 Floodlit Comp 87-88 88-89; Yorks Lg Div 3 81-82; W. Riding Co. Cup R-up 87-88, 90-91;Embleton Cup (4) Castleford FA Cup (5) Wilkinson Sword 95-96 R-Up: 99-00. 02-03.

FACT FILE

Founded: 1958 Nickname: Colls

Colours: All royal blue

Midweek Matches: Tuesday

CLUB PERSONNEL

Chairman: Trevor Waddington

Programme Editor: As secretary

ROSSINGTON MAIN

Secretary: Gerald Parsons, School Bungalow, Hayfield Lane, Auckley, Doncaster DN8 3NB. Tel: 01302 770 249 (H) 07941 811 217 (M)

Ground: Welfare Ground, Oxford Street, Rossington, Doncaster DN11 0TE. Tel: 01302 865 524

Directions: Enter Rossington and go over the railway crossings. Pass the Welfare Club on right, Oxford Street is next right - ground is at bottom.8miles from Doncaster (BR)

Capacity: 2,000 Seats: 250 Cover: 500 Floodlights: Yes

Clubhouse: Evenings & matchdays, Sandwiches, rolls, satellite TV, pool.**Club Shop:** No

Previous Leagues: Doncaster Sen, Yorkshire Lge, Sheffield County Sen, Cent Mids.

Record Attendance: 1,200 v Leeds United 06.08.91.

Goalscorer: Mark Illman **Appearances:** Darren Phipps

Honours Cen. Mids. Prem Div. 84-85, Lg. Cup 83-84 84-85; Doncaster Sen Lge 1944-45, Lg. Cup 1944-45; DDSAL Shield 1990-91 R-up 1989-90.

FACT FILE
Founded: 1919
Nickname: The Colliery
Colours: All blue
Midweek matches: Tuesday

CLUB PERSONNEL
Chairman: Carl Stokes
Programme Editor: Peter Murden

STAVELEY MINERS WELFARE

Secretary: Carl McLean. c/o Baris, Nunn Brook Road, Huthwaite, Notts NG17 2HU. Tel: 07976 700 459.

Ground: Inkersall Road, Staveley, Chesterfield, Derbyshire S43 3JL. Tel: 01246 471 441

Directions: M1 jct 30, follow A619 Chesterfield - Staveley is 3 miles from jct30. Turn left at GK Garage in Staveley town centre into Inkersall Rd - ground 200yds on right at side of Speedwell Rooms. Frequent buses (47, 70, 72, 75, 77) from Chest'ld stop in Staveley centre 3 mins walk.

Capacity: 5,000 **Cover:** 400 **Seats:** 220 **Floodlights:** Yes

Clubhouse: The Staveley Miners Welfare, 500 yds from ground, open before and after games. **Club Shop:** Yes.

Previous Leagues: Chesterfield & D. Amat 1989-91; County Sen 1991-93.

Record Attendance: 280 v Stocksbridge, Sheffield Senior Cup 22/1/94

Goalscorer: Mick Godber **Appearances:** Shane Turner

Honours County Sen Lg Div 2 92-93, Div 3 91-92, Chesterfield & D. Amat Lg R-up 89-90 90-91, Byron (Lge) Cup 89-90, R-up 90-91.NCE Div 1 R-up 97-98

FACT FILE
Founded: 1989
Nickname: The Welfare
Colours: All Royal Blue
Midweek matches: Wednesday

CLUB PERSONNEL
Chairman: Terry Damms
Programme Editor: As chairman

TADCASTER ALBION

Secretary: Howard Clarke. 53 Kelcbar Close, Tadcaster, N.Yorks LS24 9NY. Tel: 01937 835 017.

Ground: The Park, Ings Lane, Tadcaster, LS24 9AY. Tel: 01937 834 119.

Directions: From West Riding and South Yorks, turn right off A659 at John Smith's Brewery Clock. From East Riding turn left off A659 after passing over river bridge and pelican crossing (New Street). Bus station over Bridge. Services 740 & 743.

Capacity: 1,500 **Seats**: 150 **Cover:** 400 **Floodlights**:Yes

Clubhouse: Yes **Club Shop:** No

Record Attendance: 1,200 v Winterton F.A.Vase 4th Rd 1996-7

Victory: 13-0 v Blidworth MW, NCE 97-98 (Lg Record) **Defeat**: 2-10 v Thackley

Previous Leagues: York, Harrogate, Yorkshire (73-82)

FACT FILE
Founded: 1892
Nickname: The Brewers
Colours:
Yellow & blue/royal blue/blue & yellow
Midweek Matchday:Tuesday

CLUB PERSONNEL
Chairman: Kevin Derry
Programme Editor: Robin Derry

TEVERSAL

Founded: 1923
Nickname: Tevie Boys

Chairman: Robert Thompson

Secretary: Kevin Newton, 8 Vere Avenue, Sutton-in-Ashfield, Notts.NG17 2DS. **Tel No**: 01623 461 145(H) 07711 358 060 (M)

Programme Editor: Secretary

GROUND ADDRESS: Teversal Grange Sports ans Social Centre, Carnarvon Sttreet, Teversal, Sutton-in-Ashfield .Notts. NG17 3HJ **Tel No**: 01623 555 944

Simple Directions: From A6075 Stanton Hill to Teversal road. At roundabout take B6014 and take second turning into Coppywood Close in Teversal and drive to the top, follow road round with ground at top.

Midweek Home Matchday: Tuesday **Clubhouse:** Yes.

Previous League(s): Central Midlands League

Club Colours: Red & black/black/red.

HONOURS: Central Midlands League 2004/05.

WORSBROUGH M.W. & ATHLETIC

Secretary: Charlie Wyatt, 4 Springfield Road, Hoyland Common, Barnsley,S.Yorks. S74 0BE. Tel & FAX: 01226 747 774 (H) 07977 947 760 (M)
Ground: Park Road, Worsbrough Bridge, Barnsley S70 5LJ. Tel: 01226 284 452
Directions: On the A61 Barnsley-Sheffield road two miles south of Barnsley, 2miles from M1 jnt 36 opposite Blackburns Bridge. Two and a half miles from Barnsley (BR). Yorkshire Traction run buses every 10 mins thru Worsbrough Bridge.
Capacity: 2,000 **Seats:** 175 **Cover:** 175 **Floodlights:** Yes
Clubhouse: Yes **Club Shop:** No
Previous Leagues: Barnsley 1952-61; Sheffield County Snr 1962-71; Yorkshire 1971-82.
Record Attendance: 1,603 v Blyth Spartans, FA Amateur Cup 1971
Appearances: Billy Pickering. **Goalscorer:** Frank Briscoe.

Honours Northern Co's East Div 1 R-up 90-91 (Div 3 R-up 85-86); Sheffield SnrCup R-up 72-73; County Snr Lg 65-66 69-70 (R-up 62-63, Lg Cup 65-66); Barnsley Lg 52-53 58-59 59-60, Lg Cup 56-57 58-59 (R-up 53-54), Beckett Cup 57-58.

FACT FILE
Founded: 1923
Reformed: 1947
Colours: Red/black/red
Midweek Matchday: Tuesday

PERSONNEL
Chairman: John Cooper
Programme Editor: Secretary

YORKSHIRE AMATEUR

Secretary: Ann Packham. 30 Roxholme Avenue, Leeds LS7 4JF.
Tel: 0113 262 0758
Ground: The Bracken Edge, Sycamore Avenue, Leeds LS8 4DZ Tel: 0113 262 4093
Directions: From South M1 to Leeds, then A58 Wetherby Road to Fforde Green Hotel, left at lights and proceed to Sycamore Ave. (on right). From East A1 to Boot & Shoe Inn then to Shaftesbury Hotel, turn right into Harehills Lane, then to Sycamore Avenue. 2.5miles from Leeds (BR). Buses 2, 3 & 20 from Briggate toHarehills Ave.
Capacity: 1,550 Seats: 200 Cover: 160 Floodlights: Yes
Clubhouse: Bar, tea bar, games, lounge. Tues-Fri 6-11pm, Sat 12-11pm, Sun 12-6pm.
Club Shop: Yes
Previous League: Yorks 20-24 30-82. **Ground:** Elland Road 1919-20
Record Attendance: 4,000 v Wimbledon, FA Amateur Cup QF 1932.
Players progressing: Gary Strodder & Stuart Naylor (W.B.A.), Peter Swan (Leeds U) Brian Deane (Doncaster R).
Honours FA Amtr Cup SF 31-32; West Riding Co. Cup (3); Yorks Lg 31-32, Div 2 58-59 (R-up 52-53 71-72), Div 3 77-78, Lg Cup 32-33; Leeds & Dist. Snr Cup.

FACT FILE

Founded: 1919

Nickname: Ammers

Colours: White/navy/red

Midweek Matches: Tuesday

CLUB PERSONNEL

Acting Chairman: William Ellis

Programme Editor: David Packham

NORTHERN LEAGUE

www.northernleague.org

Sponsored by: Skilltrainingltd

Founded: 1889

Recent champions:

2004: Dunston Federation Brewery

2005: Dunston Federation Brewery

2006: Newcastle Blue Star

2007: Whitley Bay

2008: Durham City

Division One	P	W	D	L	F	A	Pts
Newcastle Benfield	42	25	9	8	78	42	84
Consett	42	25	8	9	91	51	83
Whitley Bay	42	25	7	10	108	58	82
Spennymoor Town	42	24	10	8	78	49	82
Sunderland Nissan	42	23	9	10	93	57	78
Dunston Federation	42	20	13	9	77	48	73
Penrith Town	42	21	8	13	90	62	71
Shildon	42	18	15	9	84	58	69
West Allotment Celtic	42	19	11	12	66	60	68
Ryton	42	18	8	16	81	77	62
Tow Law Town	42	17	11	14	73	69	62
Morpeth Town	42	19	4	19	64	68	61
Chester-le-Street Town	42	17	7	18	74	72	58
Bedlington Terriers	42	15	9	18	66	76	54
Billingham Synthonia	42	12	11	19	68	75	47
Ashington	42	13	8	21	63	83	47
Billingham Town	42	11	8	23	64	96	41
Bishop Auckland	42	9	11	22	56	85	38
South Shields	42	9	10	23	52	79	37
West Auckland Town	42	8	7	27	50	99	31
Seaham Red Star	42	8	7	27	42	94	31
Northallerton Town	42	8	5	29	50	110	29

J R CLEATOR CUP

(League champions v League Cup holders)

(August 2nd at Durham City)

Durham City 2

Billingham Town 1

	Ashington	Bedlington Terriers	Billingham Synthonia	Billingham Town	Bishop Auckland	Chester-le-Street Town	Consett	Dunston Federation	Morpeth Town	Newcastle Benfield	Northallerton Town	Penrith Town	Ryton	Seaham Red Star	Shildon	South Shields	Spennymoor Town	Sunderland Nissan	Tow Law Town	West Allotment Celtic	West Auckland Town	Whitley Bay
Ashington		1-1	0-3	3-1	1-0	1-2	1-1	1-2	2-0	1-2	3-1	3-2	0-2	2-3	0-0	0-3	1-1	0-1	4-1	1-1	4-1	0-5
Bedlington Terriers	3-1		2-1	4-1	3-0	1-3	2-5	1-2	1-0	0-0	3-2	1-1	4-2	0-1	2-1	2-2	1-3	1-2	0-3	1-0	4-2	0-3
Billingham Synthonia	2-1	2-2		1-2	3-3	3-1	0-4	1-1	0-3	0-2	4-0	3-4	0-0	2-0	1-3	2-2	0-1	1-1	5-1	1-1	5-2	4-1
Billingham Town	3-3	3-1	2-1		1-3	3-4	2-4	1-4	4-1	0-2	1-1	1-1	3-2	1-2	2-2	1-2	3-1	0-3	1-1	0-1	2-6	1-1
Bishop Auckland	4-0	0-1	1-2	3-1		2-2	1-1	1-4	1-2	0-4	1-0	1-0	2-4	1-0	1-1	2-2	0-2	0-2	2-2	1-2	3-4	2-6
Chester-le-Street Town	2-3	2-3	1-0	2-1	5-2	***D***	4-2	0-2	0-1	4-2	3-1	3-2	1-0	4-0	0-1	1-1	0-2	1-2	2-3	0-3	0-0	4-3
Consett	3-0	1-0	3-2	2-1	0-2	1-0	***I***	2-2	2-3	1-0	2-0	3-1	5-2	2-2	1-1	4-1	3-2	0-2	3-1	1-1	4-0	4-1
Dunston Federation	2-2	3-1	0-2	2-1	2-1	3-3	2-0	***V***	0-0	2-0	3-0	2-1	1-1	4-2	2-2	2-2	3-0	1-2	2-0	0-0	5-1	1-0
Morpeth Town	3-1	3-4	3-1	5-1	0-1	1-2	1-1	0-2	***I***	0-2	1-2	3-3	1-0	2-1	5-0	0-2	0-2	0-3	2-1	1-0	1-0	2-1
Newcastle Benfield	2-2	3-1	2-1	1-2	2-1	1-0	1-3	2-1	3-4	***S***	6-1	2-2	2-1	3-0	1-1	3-1	2-0	2-1	3-0	5-1	2-0	0-0
Northallerton Town	1-5	0-3	1-1	0-1	1-5	1-1	2-0	0-4	2-1	0-2	***I***	1-2	4-5	1-1	1-1	3-1	3-2	2-4	4-2	1-2	0-3	0-2
Penrith Town	4-0	5-0	4-1	2-2	2-0	0-2	1-0	2-0	1-0	0-1	3-0	***O***	2-1	3-0	3-2	6-0	1-2	1-2	2-0	2-0	8-1	3-2
Ryton	1-3	1-0	2-1	1-2	2-2	3-2	3-2	1-1	4-1	2-4	5-2	2-0	***N***	1-0	2-2	1-0	2-4	2-3	5-3	1-1	0-2	0-1
Seaham Red Star	1-3	1-0	0-5	2-4	1-1	2-1	0-4	2-1	1-2	1-1	0-2	0-1	1-2		1-2	2-3	2-2	1-7	2-1	0-1	1-0	0-3
Shildon	4-0	1-0	1-1	3-2	4-0	2-2	2-4	3-0	2-2	2-0	5-1	2-2	4-2	3-0	***O***	3-2	1-1	3-2	1-2	1-0	2-3	1-1
South Shields	0-2	1-3	0-1	1-1	2-0	3-0	0-1	3-0	0-2	2-2	3-2	1-4	0-4	0-0	1-3	***N***	1-2	0-0	1-4	0-2	4-1	0-1
Spennymoor Town	3-2	3-2	4-0	2-0	2-0	2-2	0-0	2-0	2-1	0-0	3-1	2-1	0-1	4-2	2-1	1-0	***E***	3-3	0-0	3-2	3-1	2-3
Sunderland Nissan	4-0	1-1	2-2	3-1	3-2	2-3	1-3	2-1	3-0	0-0	6-1	6-0	0-1	3-1	3-1	3-2	0-4		1-2	1-1	1-1	3-1
Tow Law Town	3-2	2-2	3-0	1-0	0-0	3-2	0-1	2-2	3-1	1-2	1-0	2-3	3-3	3-3	1-1	4-1	0-0	2-1		0-0	2-0	2-1
West Allotment Celtic	3-2	1-1	5-2	3-2	3-3	2-0	1-3	0-5	1-2	1-2	3-1	2-2	4-2	1-0	0-3	2-1	2-2	3-0	1-0		4-1	1-5
West Auckland Town	0-2	2-2	3-0	1-3	1-1	0-2	0-3	0-0	1-2	0-2	0-1	2-2	2-3	3-2	0-5	1-1	0-2	4-2	0-3	0-1		0-1
Whitley Bay	2-0	5-2	1-1	8-0	5-0	2-1	3-2	1-1	5-2	2-0	6-3	4-1	2-2	5-1	2-1	1-0	2-0	2-2	3-5	1-3	4-1	

Division Two		P	W	D	L	F	A	Pts
Horden Colliery Welfare		38	24	8	6	92	44	80
Norton & Stockton Anc.		38	24	8	6	79	36	80
Esh Winning		38	23	8	7	89	59	77
Sunderland Ryhope CA		38	21	8	9	88	46	71
Marske United		38	18	8	12	63	59	62
Brandon United		38	18	7	13	85	67	61
Guisborough Town		38	18	7	13	71	53	61
Birtley Town		38	18	7	13	73	62	61
Crook Town		38	17	7	14	68	71	58
Hebburn Town		38	15	10	13	71	83	55
Whitehaven Amateurs		38	15	8	15	57	52	53
Team Northumbria		38	13	12	13	75	66	51
Stokesley Sports Club		38	14	7	17	63	67	49
Whickham		38	14	7	17	55	73	49
North Shields		38	13	6	19	53	76	45
Jarrow Roofing BCA		38	11	4	23	50	78	37
Washington	*-3*	38	10	6	22	44	61	33
Darlington Railway Ath.		38	10	2	26	45	80	32
Prudhoe Town		38	5	11	22	47	88	26
Thornaby		38	5	7	26	50	97	22

ERNEST ARMSTRONG MEMORIAL CUP

FIRST ROUND
Crook Town 2 **Team Northumbria** 4 *aet*
Guisborough 2 **Prudhoe** 3
Jarrow Roofing Boldon CA 5 Whickham 1
Marske 2 North Shields 1
SECOND ROUND
Birtley 3 Norton 2 *aet (at Norton & Stockton)*
Darl'gton RA 2 **Brandon** 3
Hebburn Town 2 Esh 0
Horden Colliery Welf. 5 Team Northumbria 0 *(at Team Northumbria)*
Stokesley Sports Club 1 Marske 1 *aet* (3-1p)
Sunderland Ryhope CA 2 Prudhoe Town 1
Thornaby 1 Washington 0
Whitehaven Amateurs 3 Jarrow Roofing BCA 2
QUARTER-FINALS
Birtley 0 **Brandon United** 1
Horden Colliery Welfare 0 Hebburn Town 0 *aet* (4-3p)
Stokesley Sports Club 0 **Whitehaven Amateurs** 1
Sunderland Ryhope CA 2 Thornaby 1
SEMI-FINALS
Sunderland Ryhope CA 3 Brandon United 0
Whitehaven 0 **Horden** 2
FINAL
(May 6th at Chester-le-St)
Horden Colliery Welf. 2 Sunderland Ryhope CA 1

BROOKS MILESON CUP

FIRST ROUND
Ashington 1 **Dunston Federation** 2
Billingham Synthonia 3 Crook Town 1
Brandon United 2 West Auckland Town 1
Darlington RA 0 **Norton & Stockton Ancients** 1
North Shields 0 **Morpeth Town** 6
Northallerton Town 4 Sunderland Ryhope CA 2
Penrith Town 3 Consett 0
Spennymoor Town 0 **Newcastle Benfield** 3
Stokesley Sports Club 2 **Sunderland Nissan** 6
Team Northumbria 0 **West Allotment Celtic** 1
SECOND ROUND
Bedlington Terriers 2 **Northallerton Town** 5
Bishop Auckland 2 **Seaham Red Star** 4 *(at Seaham)*
Chester-le-Street Town 0 **Brandon United** 1
Dunston 3 Marske 0 *aet*, **Esh Winning** 2 Whitehaven 1
Horden Colliery Welfare 0 **Tow Law Town** 2
Jarrow Roofing Boldon CA 2 **Guisborough Town** 3 *aet*
Norton & Stockton Ancients 1 **Newcastle Benfield** 3
Penrith Town 6 Hebburn 1, Prudhoe 1 **Morpeth Town** 2
Ryton 3 Birtley 0, **Shildon** 4 Billingham Town 1
Thornaby 1 **Billingham Synthonia** 7
West Allotment Celtic 1 South Shields 0
Whickham 6 Washington 1
Whitley Bay 2 Sunderland Nissan 0
THIRD ROUND
Billingham Synthonia 2 West Allotment Celtic 1
Brandon United 1 **Esh Winning** 3 *aet*
Morpeth Town 2 Guisborough Town 0
Northallerton Town 1 **Dunston Federation** 5
Penrith Town 3 Shildon 1, Ryton 2 **Tow Law Town** 3
Seaham Red Star 0 **Newcastle Benfield** 4
Whitley Bay 5 Whickham 1
QUARTER-FINALS
Billingham Synthonia 2 **Whitley Bay** 4
Dunston Federation 1 **Newcastle Benfield** 2 *aet*
Morpeth 3 Esh Winning 0, **Penrith Town** 2 Tow Law 1
SEMI-FINALS
Morpeth Town 2 **Newcastle Benfield** 3
Whitley Bay 0 **Penrith Town** 0 *aet* (3-4p)
FINAL
(May 15th at West Allotment Celtic)
Newcastle Benfield 2 Penrith Town 0

	Birtley	Brand.	Crook	Darl. R	Esh W	Guis.	Hebb.	Hord.	Jarrow	Mars.	N Shds	N&SA	Prud.	Stoke.	Sund.	Team	Thorn.	Wash.	Whick.	White.
Birtley Town		2-2	2-1	2-1	2-3	1-0	2-2	1-1	0-1	2-3	1-0	1-1	0-1	1-1	2-1	2-1	3-2	2-0	5-1	3-1
Brandon United	4-2		1-5	5-0	0-1	0-2	2-0	5-4	3-1	2-3	4-1	1-3	6-0	4-2	1-5	2-3	0-3	2-2	1-3	0-1
Crook Town	1-6	0-2		2-0	1-0	2-2	4-4	1-4	2-0	1-2	0-2	1-3	2-2	0-1	0-6	2-1	3-1	1-0	0-1	1-5
Darlington Railway Athletic	1-2	0-1	2-3		1-4	2-0	4-1	0-1	1-0	0-2	0-1	0-4	5-2	0-3	1-0	0-1	4-2	1-3	1-0	4-3
Esh Winning	2-1	3-2	1-1	2-1	***D***	2-1	1-2	0-0	3-1	2-2	6-2	0-0	5-3	2-2	1-3	3-2	2-1	4-1	4-1	3-1
Guisborough Town	5-1	2-1	1-1	1-1	3-5	***I***	1-3	0-1	1-2	2-0	3-1	0-1	5-4	3-0	2-0	2-2	2-0	2-0	1-1	3-0
Hebburn Town	1-4	2-2	2-3	2-3	5-4	1-0	***V***	0-3	2-0	4-2	0-2	1-0	2-2	1-7	4-3	3-3	2-4	1-1	2-0	1-1
Horden Colliery Welfare	2-2	1-1	3-1	1-0	3-1	3-2	5-1	***I***	3-2	6-0	4-1	3-0	3-0	5-3	1-1	2-3	5-2	4-0	3-2	1-1
Jarrow Roofing Boldon CA	0-2	1-5	0-2	1-0	1-2	3-5	3-3	0-2	***S***	0-3	1-0	1-3	3-2	3-1	0-4	0-2	1-1	1-2	6-1	2-1
Marske United	2-1	0-1	1-1	2-5	4-0	3-1	1-2	3-2	3-2	***I***	0-3	2-1	1-0	4-0	2-2	3-3	0-0	1-3	2-1	1-0
North Shields	2-2	3-3	2-3	2-0	2-2	0-0	0-1	2-3	3-1	1-0	***O***	0-5	1-3	1-3	0-8	2-0	0-0	2-1	2-1	2-5
Norton & Stockton Ancients	2-0	3-1	0-0	2-0	0-0	4-1	3-1	3-1	1-0	1-1	1-0	***N***	8-1	1-0	0-3	2-1	4-1	1-3	4-1	4-1
Prudhoe Town	2-3	0-5	2-5	1-1	1-2	1-2	1-3	0-1	1-1	2-0	2-2	2-3		2-3	0-4	0-0	2-2	1-2	0-0	1-1
Stokesley Sports Club	2-1	0-2	3-4	1-0	2-4	0-3	5-2	0-2	1-0	3-0	0-1	1-2	0-2	***T***	3-3	4-0	2-1	0-0	2-2	1-1
Sunderland Ryhope CA	3-1	0-0	1-2	4-2	1-1	4-0	0-1	0-5	0-0	0-1	4-2	1-1	1-0	2-1	***W***	3-2	5-1	2-0	3-0	1-0
Team Northumbria	3-4	4-4	6-3	4-1	1-3	0-2	3-3	1-1	8-2	0-0	1-0	0-0	1-1	4-1	1-2	***O***	3-2	1-0	0-1	0-0
Thornaby	1-2	2-3	0-4	4-0	1-4	0-5	3-2	0-2	1-4	2-4	1-4	2-5	0-1	1-2	2-2	1-4		1-1	1-3	0-3
Washington	1-2	2-3	0-2	5-1	0-3	0-1	1-3	1-1	3-0	0-0	3-1	0-1	1-0	1-2	1-2	3-0	1-2		1-2	0-1
Whickham	4-3	1-2	2-1	4-2	2-1	2-4	0-0	2-0	0-3	3-2	4-2	1-1	2-2	1-1	0-1	1-5	2-1	2-0		0-1
Whitehaven Amateurs	1-0	0-2	0-2	2-0	2-3	1-1	0-1	2-0	1-3	0-3	0-1	3-1	2-0	1-0	5-3	1-1	1-1	5-1	3-1	

ASHINGTON

Founded: 1883 Nickname: The Colliers

Chairman: Ian Lavery
Secretary: Brian Robinson
80 Milburn Road
Ashington
Northumberland
NE63 0PG
Tel: 01670 852832
Manager: Gary Middleton
Prog Editor: Mark Fitton

Ground: Woodhorn Lane, Ashington NE63 9HF. Tel: 01670 811 991
Capacity: **Seats:** **Covered:**
Midweek Matchday: Tuesday **Clubhouse:** Yes **Shop:** Yes
Colours(change): Black & White stripes/black/black.
Previous Names:
Previous Lges: N. Alliance. Football lge . N. Eastern. Midland. N. Counties . Wearside. N.P.L.
Records: **Att:** 13,199 v Rochdale FA Cup 2nd round 1950
Senior Honours: Northern League Div.2 Champions 2000-01, 03-04.

10 YEAR RECORD

99-00	00-01	01-02	02-03	03-04	04-05	05-06	06-07	07-08	08-09
NL 2 9	NL 2 1	NL 1 19	NL 2 5	NL 2 1	NL 1 10	NL 1 16	NL 1 19	NL 1 17	NL 1 16

BEDLINGTON TERRIERS

Founded: 1949 Nickname: Terriers

Chairman: David Holmes
Secretary: David Collop
62 Kingsway
Blyth
Northumberland
NE24 2RS
Tel: 07853 052 450
Manager: Tony Lowery/Keith Perry
Prog Editor: Neil Douglas

Ground: Welfare Park, Park Road, Bedlington, NE22 5DA. Tel: 07988 298 094
Capacity: 3,000 **Seats:** 300 **Covered:** 500
Midweek Matchday: Wednesday **Clubhouse:** Yes **Shop:**
Colours(change): Red with white trim/red/red.
Previous Names: Bedlington Mechanics 1949-53 Bedlington United 1961-65
Previous Lges: Northern Alliance
Records: **Att:** 2,400 v Colchester United FA Cup 1st round **Goalscorer:** John Milner
Senior Honours: Northern Lge Div 1: 97-98, 98-99, 99-00, 00-01, 01-02.
Northumberland Senior Cup 1996-97, 97-98, 2001-02,03-04.

10 YEAR RECORD

99-00	00-01	01-02	02-03	03-04	04-05	05-06	06-07	07-08	08-09
NL 1 1	NL 1 1	NL 1 1	NL 1 2	NL 1 3	NL 1 3	NL 1 2	NL 1 20	NL 1 15	NL 1 14

BILLINGHAM SYNTHONIA

Founded: 1923 Nickname: Synners

Chairman: Stuart Coleby
Secretary: Graham Craggs
10 Embleton Grove
Wynard
Stockton on Tees
TS22 5SY
Tel: 01740 645 367
Manager:
Prog Editor: David Lealman

Ground: The Stadium, Central Ave, Billingham, Cleveland TS23 1LU Tel: 01642 532 348
Capacity: 1,970 **Seats:** 370 **Covered:** 370
Midweek Matchday: Wednesday **Clubhouse:** Yes **Shop:** Yes
Colours(change): Green & white quarters/white/white
Previous Names: Billingham Synthonia Recreation
Previous Lges: Teeside 1923-the war
Records: **Att:** 4,200 v Bishop Auckland 1958 **Goalscorer:** Tony Hetherington
App: Andy Harbron
Senior Honours: Northern Lge 1956-57, 88-89, 89-90, 95-96. Div.2 86-87.

10 YEAR RECORD

99-00	00-01	01-02	02-03	03-04	04-05	05-06	06-07	07-08	08-09
NL 1 6	NL 1 8	NL 1 11	NL 1 4	NL 1 9	NL 1 2	NL 1 7	NL 1 14	NL 1 9	NL 1 15

BILLINGHAM TOWN

Founded: 1967 Nickname: Billy Town

Chairman: Tommy Donnelly
Secretary: Glenn Youngman
55 Greens Lane
Hartburn, Stockton on Tees
Cleveland
TS18 5JA
Tel: 01642 862 058
Manager:
Prog Editor: Peter Martin

Ground: Bedford Terrace, Billingham, Cleveland TS23 4AF Tel: 01642 560 043
Capacity: 3,000 **Seats:** 176 **Covered:** 600
Midweek Matchday: Tuesday **Clubhouse:** Yes **Shop:** No
Colours(change): Blue/blue/white
Previous Names: Billingham Social Club.>1892
Previous Lges: Stockton & District 1968-74 Teeside 1974-82
Records: **Att:** 1,500 v Man City FA Youth Cup 1985 **Goalscorer:** Paul Rowntree 396
App: Paul Rowntree 505
Senior Honours: Durham Cup 76-77, 77-8, 03-04

10 YEAR RECORD

99-00	00-01	01-02	02-03	03-04	04-05	05-06	06-07	07-08	08-09
NL 1 11	NL 1 9	NL 1 10	NL 1 3	NL 1 5	NL 1 7	NL 1 4	NL 1 2	NL 1 10	NL 1 17

BISHOP AUCKLAND

Founded: 1886 Nickname:

Chairman: Terry Jackson
Secretary: Tony Duffy
90 Escomb Road
Bishop Auckland
Co. Durham
DL14 6TZ
Tel: 01388 602 809
Manager: Colin Myers
Prog Editor: Dave Strong

Ground: West Auckland FC, Darlington Rd, W.Auckland DL14 9HU. Tel: 07974 286 812.
Capacity: 3,000 **Seats:** 250 **Covered:** 250
Midweek Matchday: Wednesday **Clubhouse:** Yes **Shop:** No
Colours(change): Light & dark blue/2 blue/2 blue.
Previous Names: Auckland Town 1889-1893
Previous Lges: Northern Alliance 1890-91, Northern League 1893-1988 Northern Premier 1988-2006
Records: Att: 17,000 v Coventry City FA Cup 2nd round 1952 **App:** Bob Hardisty
Senior Honours: Post War: Nth Lge 1949-50, 50-51, 51-52, 53-54, 54-55, 55-56, 66-67, 84-85, 85-86 (18th Nth Lge title).

10 YEAR RECORD

99-00	00-01	01-02	02-03	03-04	04-05	05-06	06-07	07-08	08-09
NP P 8	NP P 3	NP P 21	NP 1 15	NP 1 13	NP P 19	NP 1 22	NL 1 16	NL 1 20	NL 1 18

CHESTER-LE-STREET TOWN

Founded: 1972 Nickname: Cestrians

Chairman: Joe Burlison
Secretary: Lenny Lauchlan
48 Beaumont Drive
Washington
Tyne & Wear
NE38 7RA
Tel: 07749 924 318
Manager: Stewart Sherwodd
Prog Editor: Keith Greener

Ground: Moor Park, Chester Moor, Chester -le-Street, DH2 3RW Tel: 07972 419 275
Capacity: 3,500 **Seats:** 150 **Covered:** 1,500
Midweek Matchday: Tuesday **Clubhouse:** Yes **Shop:** No
Colours(change): Blue & white hoops/white/white
Previous Names: Garden Farm 1972-78
Previous Lges: Newcastle City Am. 1972-75, Washington 1975-77, Wearside 1977-83
Records: Att: 893 v Fleetwood FA Vase 1985 **App:** Colin Wake 361
Senior Honours: Washington League 1975-6 Wearside League1980-81 Northern League Div 2 1983-84, 97-98

10 YEAR RECORD

99-00	00-01	01-02	02-03	03-04	04-05	05-06	06-07	07-08	08-09
NL 1 13	NL 1 15	NL 1 14	NL 1 14	NL 1 17	NL 1 8	NL 1 8	NL 1 17	NL 1 18	NL 1 13

CONSETT

Founded: 1899 Nickname: Steelman

Chairman: John Hurst
Secretary: David Pyke
17 Beverley Terrace
Consett
Co. Durham
DH8 5NA
Tel: 01207 508 920
Manager:
Prog Editor: Gary Welford

Ground: Belle Vue Park, Ashdale Road, Consett, DH8 6LZ Tel: 01207 503 788
Capacity: 4,000 **Seats:** 400 **Covered:** 1000
Midweek Matchday: Wednesday **Clubhouse:** Yes **Shop:** No
Colours(change): All Red
Previous Names: None
Previous Lges: N.All 19-26, 35-37N.E.C. 26-35, 37-58, 62-64,Midland 58-60,N.Co. 60-62,Wearside 64-70
Records: Att: 7000 v Sunderland Reserves, first match at Belle Vue 1950
Senior Honours: Norh Eastern Lg 39-40 Div 2 26-27, Northern Counties Lg 61-62, Northern Leageu Div.2 1988-89, 05-06.

10 YEAR RECORD

99-00	00-01	01-02	02-03	03-04	04-05	05-06	06-07	07-08	08-09
NL 1 9	NL 1 10	NL 1 17	NL 1 20	NL 2 3	NL 1 19	NL 2 1	NL 1 4	NL 1 2	NL 1 2

DUNSTON UTS

Founded: 1975 Nickname: The Fed

Chairman: Malcolm James
Secretary: Bill Montague
12 Dundee Close
Chapel House
Newcastle-upon-Tyne
NE5 1JJ
Tel: 0191 2672 250
Manager: WilliamIrwin
Prog Editor: See secretary

Ground: UTS Stadium, Wellington Rd, Dunston, Gateshead NE11 9LJ Tel: 0191 493 2935
Capacity: 2,000 **Seats:** 120 **Covered:** 400
Midweek Matchday: Tuesday **Clubhouse:** Yes **Shop:** No
Colours(change): All Blue with white trim/blue/blue.
Previous Names: Dunston Federation Brewery > 2007. Dunston Federation > 2009.
Previous Lges: Northern Amateur & Wearside league
Records: Att: 1,550 v Sunderland Shipowners Cup Final 01.04.88 **Goalscorer:** Paul King **App:** Paul Dixon
Senior Honours: Wearside League 1988-89, 89-90. Northern League Div.2 92-93. Div.1 2003-04, 04-05.

10 YEAR RECORD

99-00	00-01	01-02	02-03	03-04	04-05	05-06	06-07	07-08	08-09
NL 1 3	NL 1 2	NL 1 3	NL 1 8	NL 1 1	NL 1 1	NL 1 3	NL 1 7	NL 1 6	NL 1 6

INS & OUTS
IN: Esh Winning (P), Horden Colliery Welfare (P), Norton & Stockton Ancients (P)
OUT: Northallerton Town (R), Seaham Red Star (R), Sunderland Nissan (W). Dunston Federation become Dunston UTS.

DIVISION ONE - 2009-10

ESH WINNING
Founded: 1885 Nickname: Stags

Chairman: Charles Ryan
Secretary: Allan Morton
20 Durham Road
Esh Winning
Co. Durham
DH7 9NP
Tel: 07929 747 885
Manager: Geoff Young
Prog Editor: Lee Stewart

Ground: West Terrace, Waterhouse, Durham DH7 9BQ Tel: 0191 373 3872
Capacity: 3,500 **Seats:** 160 **Covered:** 500
Midweek Matchday: Tuesday **Clubhouse:** Yes **Shop:** No
Colours(change): Yellow & green/green/green.
Previous Names: Esh Albion, Esh Rangers, Esh Pineapple (pre 1982)
Previous Lges: Northern 1912-35. Durham & Dist. Sunday 1968-81, N. Alliance 1981-82.
Records: Att: 5,000 v Newcastle United Reserves 1910 & Bishop Auckland 1921
Goalscorer: Alan Dodsworth 250+ **App:** Neil McLeary - 194
Senior Honours: Northern League Champions 1912-13.

10 YEAR RECORD

99-00	00-01	01-02	02-03	03-04	04-05	05-06	06-07	07-08	08-09
NL 2 15	NL 2 5	NL 2 3	NL 1 17	NL 1 15	NL 1 14	NL 1 20	NL 2 16	NL 2 13	NL 2 3

HORDEN COLLIERY WELFARE
Founded: 1908 Nickname: Colliers

Chairman: Norman Stephens
Secretary: Nicola Stephens
6 Lithgo Close
Seaton Carew
Hartlepool
TS25 1XF
Tel: 07875 229 993
Manager: Simon Corbett
Prog Editor: See secretary

Ground: Welfare Park, Seventh Street, Horden, Peterlee SR8 4LX. Tel: 0191 587 3549
Capacity: 3,000 **Seats:** 200 **Covered:** 370
Midweek Matchday: Tuesday **Clubhouse:** Yes **Shop:** Yes
Colours(change): Red & white/black/red.
Previous Names: Horden Athletic
Previous Lges: Wearside 1907-35, 63-75. North Eastern 1935-58, 62-64.
Records: Att: 8,000 FA Cup 1937
Senior Honours: Wearside Champions 1911-12, 12-13, 13-14, 33-34, 64-65, 67-68, 69-70, 70-71, 71-72, 72-73. Northern Division 2 Champions 2008-09.

10 YEAR RECORD

99-00	00-01	01-02	02-03	03-04	04-05	05-06	06-07	07-08	08-09
NL 2 12	NL 2 4	NL 2 6	NL 2 2	NL 1 18	NL 1 9	NL 1 18	NL 1 21	NL 2 5	NL 2 1

MORPETH TOWN
Founded: 1909 Nickname: Highwaymen

Chairman: Ken Beattie
Secretary: Ken Waterhouse
38 Fallowfield Way
Ashington
Northumberland
NE63 8LD
Tel: 07749 942 697
Manager:
Prog Editor: See secretary

Ground: Welfare Park, Park Road, Bedlington NE22 5DA. Tel: 01670 825 485
Capacity: 3,000 **Seats:** 300 **Covered:** 500
Midweek Matchday: Tuesday **Clubhouse:** Yes **Shop:** No
Colours(change): Yellow/black/yellow.
Previous Names: None
Previous Lges: Northern Alliance pre 1994
Records:
Senior Honours: Northern Alliance 1983-84, 93-94. Northern Lge Div 2 1995-96. Northumberland Senior Cup 2006-07.

10 YEAR RECORD

99-00	00-01	01-02	02-03	03-04	04-05	05-06	06-07	07-08	08-09
NL 1 8	NL 1 18	NL 1 18	NL 1 11	NL 1 11	NL 1 13	NL 1 6	NL 1 10	NL 1 8	NL 1 12

NEWCASTLE BENFIELD
Founded: 1988 Nickname: The Lions

Chairman: Jimmy Rowe
Secretary: Mark Hedley
50 Northumbrian Way
Royal Quays
North Shields
NE29 6XQ
Tel: 07973 699 506
Manager:
Prog Editor: Jim Clark

Ground: Sam Smiths Park, Benfield Road, Walkergate, NE6 4NU. Tel: 0191 265 9357
Capacity: 2,000 **Seats:** 150 **Covered:** 250
Midweek Matchday: Wednesday **Clubhouse:** Yes **Shop:** No
Colours(change): Purple/black/purple.
Previous Names: Heaton Corner House. Newcastle Benfield Saints.
Previous Lges: Northern Alliance 1988-2003
Records:
Senior Honours: Northern Alliance Div 2 Champions 1989-90, Div 1 1994-95, 02-03 Northern League Cup 2006-07. Northern League Champions 2008-09.

10 YEAR RECORD

99-00	00-01	01-02	02-03	03-04	04-05	05-06	06-07	07-08	08-09
NAI P 8	NAI P 7	NAI P 3	NAI P 1	NL 2 2	NL 1 4	NL 1 9	NL 1 5	NL 1 4	NL 1 1

NORTON & STOCKTON ANCIENTS

Founded: 1959 Nickname: Ancients

Chairman: Michael Mulligan
Secretary: Steven Lawson
48 Lightfoot Road
Newton Aycliffe
CO. Durham
DL5 4EP
Tel: 07871 206 474
Manager: Conrad Hillerby
Prog Editor: See secretary

Ground: Norton (Teeside) Sports Complex, Station Rd, Norton, TS20 1PE. 01642 530 203
Capacity: 2,000 **Seats:** 200 **Covered:** yes
Midweek Matchday: Wednesday **Clubhouse:** **Shop:**
Colours(change): Amber & black/black/black.
Previous Names: Norton & Stockton Cricket Club Trust
Previous Lges: Teeside (pre-1982)
Records: Att: 1,430 v Middlesborough, Friendly1988.
Senior Honours: Northern League Cup 1982-83.

10 YEAR RECORD

99-00	00-01	01-02	02-03	03-04	04-05	05-06	06-07	07-08	08-09
NL 2 8	NL 2 8	NL 2 12	NL 2 18	NL 2 18	NL 2 6	NL 2 7	NL 2 6	NL 2 10	NL 2 2

PENRITH

Founded: 1894 Nickname: Blues

Chairman: David Noble
Secretary: Walter Brogden
47 Folly Lane
Penrith
Cumbria
CA11 8BU
Tel: 01768 862 551
Manager:
Prog Editor: B Kirkbride

Ground: Frenchfield Park, Frenchfield, Penrith CA11 8UE. Tel: 01768 895 990
Capacity: 4,000 **Seats:** 200 **Covered:** 1,000
Midweek Matchday: Tuesday **Clubhouse:** Yes **Shop:** No
Colours(change): Blue/white/blue.
Previous Names: Penrith FC. Penrith Town.
Previous Lges: Carlisle & Dist. Northern 1942-82. NWC 1982-87, 90-97. NPL 1987-90.
Records: Att: 2,100 v Chester 1981 **Goalscorer:** C Short **App:** Lee Armstrong
Senior Honours: Northern League Division 2 Champions 2002-03, 07-08.

10 YEAR RECORD

99-00	00-01	01-02	02-03	03-04	04-05	05-06	06-07	07-08	08-09
NL 2 10	NL 2 7	NL 2 4	NL 2 1	NL 1 21	NL 2 8	NL 2 4	NL 2 7	NL 2 1	NL 1 7

RYTON

Founded: 1970 Nickname:

Chairman: Richard Hands
Secretary: Ken Rodger
25 Mangrove Close
St. Johns
North Walbottle
NE5 1YA
Tel: 07906 138 571
Manager: Barry Fleming
Prog Editor: See secretary

Ground: Kingsley Park, Stannerford Rd, Crawcrook, NE40 3SN Tel: 0191 413 4448
Capacity: 2,000 **Seats:** **Covered:**
Midweek Matchday: Tuesday **Clubhouse:** Yes **Shop:** No
Colours(change): Blue & black stripes/black/blue
Previous Names:
Previous Lges: Northern Combination. Northern Alliance
Records: Att: 1,100 v Newcastle United 1998
Senior Honours: Northern Alliance Division 1 Champions 1996-97.

10 YEAR RECORD

99-00	00-01	01-02	02-03	03-04	04-05	05-06	06-07	07-08	08-09
NAl P 5	NAl P 14	NAl P 13	NAl P 9	NAl P 3	NAl P 2	NAl P 11	NAl P 12	NAl P 3	NL 1 10

SHILDON

Founded: 1890 Nickname: Railwaymen

Chairman: Brian Burn
Secretary: Gareth Howe
Dean House
32/34 Dean Street
Shildon Co. Durham
DL4 1HA
Tel: 01388 722 473
Manager: Gary Forrest
Prog Editor: Bob Wake

Ground: Dean Street, Shildon, Co. Durham DL4 1HA Tel: 01388 773 877
Capacity: 4,000 **Seats:** 480 **Covered:** 1000
Midweek Matchday: Wednesday **Clubhouse:** Yes **Shop:** No
Colours(change): All blue.
Previous Names: Shildon Athletic > 1923.
Previous Lges: Auckland & Dist 1892-86, Wear Valley 1896-97, Northern 1903-07, North Eastern 1907-32
Records: Att: 11,000 v Ferryhill Athletic, Durham Senior Cup 1922
Goalscorer: Jack Downing 61 (1936-7) **App:** Bryan Dale
Senior Honours: Durham Amateur Cup 1901-02, 02-03, Durham Challenge Cup 1907-08, 25-26, 71-72, Northern League Champions 1933-34, 34-35, 35-36,36-37, 39-40, Div 2 2001-02,

10 YEAR RECORD

99-00	00-01	01-02	02-03	03-04	04-05	05-06	06-07	07-08	08-09
NL 2 5	NL 2 13	NL 2 1	NL 1 6	NL 1 4	NL 1 11	NL 1 18	NL 1 9	NL 1 5	NL 1 8

SOUTH SHIELDS

Founded: 1974 Nickname: Mariners

Chairman: Gary Crutwell
Secretary: Philip Reay
114 Basil Way
South Shields
Tyne & Wear
NE34 8UF
Tel: 0191 536 9159
Manager: Gary Steadman
Prog Editor: See secretary

Ground: Mariners Club, Filtrona Park, Shaftesbury Ave, Jarrow, NE32 3UP Tel: 0191 427 9839
Capacity: 2,500 **Seats:** 150 **Covered:** 400
Midweek Matchday: Wednesday **Clubhouse:** Yes **Shop:** Yes
Colours(change): Claret & sky blue/white/white.
Previous Names: South Shields Mariners.
Previous Lges: Northern Alliance 1974-76, Wearside 1976-95.
Records: Att:1,500 v Spennymoor, Durham Challenge Cup Final 1994-95.

Senior Honours: Northern Alliance 74-75, 75-76, Wearside lge 76-77, 92-93, 94-95, Monkwearmouth Charity Cup 1986-87.

10 YEAR RECORD

99-00	00-01	01-02	02-03	03-04	04-05	05-06	06-07	07-08	08-09
NL 1 20	NL 2 11	NL 2 8	NL 2 8	NL 2 12	NL 2 13	NL 2 18	NL 2 4	NL 2 2	NL 1 19

SPENNYMOOR TOWN

Founded: 1890 Nickname: Moors

Chairman: Bradley Groves
Secretary: David Leitch
35 North Crescent
Easington Village
Peterlee
SR8 3EG
Tel: 0191 527 3627
Manager:
Prog Editor: Garry Nunn

Ground: Brewery Field, Durham Road, Spennymoor, DL16 6JN Tel: 07748 308 247.
Capacity: 7,500 **Seats:** 300 **Covered:** 2,000
Midweek Matchday: Wednesday **Clubhouse:** Yes **Shop:** Yes
Colours(change): Black & White stripes/black/white
Previous Names: Amalgamation of Evenwood Town & Spennymoor Utd in 2005-06.
Previous Lges: None
Records:

Senior Honours: Northern League Division 2 Champions 2006-07.

10 YEAR RECORD

99-00	00-01	01-02	02-03	03-04	04-05	05-06	06-07	07-08	08-09
						NL 2 8	NL 2 1	NL 1 12	NL 1 4

TOW LAW TOWN

Founded: 1890 Nickname: Lawyers

Chairman: Sandra Gordon
Secretary: Steve Moralee
4 Fellside Close
Tow Law
Co Durham
DL13 4DD
Tel: 01388 730 865
Manager:
Prog Editor: John Dixon

Ground: Ironworks Ground, Tow Law, Bishop's Auckland DL13 4EQ Tel: 01388 731 443
Capacity: 6,000 **Seats:** 200 **Covered:** 300
Midweek Matchday: Tuesday **Clubhouse:** Yes **Shop:** Yes
Colours(change): Black & white stripes/black/black.
Previous Names: Tow Law.
Previous Lges: Northern League 1894-1900, South Durham Alliance 1900-05, Crook & District 1905-12
Records: Att: 5,500 v Mansfield Town FA Cup 1967.

Senior Honours: Northern League Champions 1923-24, 24-25, 94-95. League Cup 73-74.

10 YEAR RECORD

99-00	00-01	01-02	02-03	03-04	04-05	05-06	06-07	07-08	08-09
NL 1 10	NL 1 7	NL 1 2	NL 1 15	NL 1 16	NL 1 16	NL 1 12	NL 1 12	NL 1 7	NL 1 11

WEST ALLOTMENT CELTIC

Founded: 1928 Nickname:

Chairman: Roland Mather
Secretary: Ted Ilderton
3 Waterloo Road
Wellfield
Whitley Bay
NE25 9JF
Tel: 0191 251 8825
Manager:
Prog Editor: Steve Allott

Ground: Whitley Park, Whitley Road, Benton, NE12 9FA Tel: 0191 270 0885
Capacity: **Seats:** **Covered:**
Midweek Matchday: Monday **Clubhouse:** **Shop:**
Colours(change): Green & white hoops/green/green & white.
Previous Names:
Previous Lges: Tynemouth & District. Northern Amateur. Northern Alliance.
Records: Att: 510 v Cray Wanderers FA Vase 2004

Senior Honours: Northern Am. 1956-57, 57-58, 58-59, 59-60, 81-82, 82-83, Div 2: 38-39. Northern Alliance:1986-87, 90-91, 91-92, 97-98, 98-99, 99-2000, 01-02, 03-04. Northern League Div 2 2004-05

10 YEAR RECORD

99-00	00-01	01-02	02-03	03-04	04-05	05-06	06-07	07-08	08-09
NAl P 1	NAl P 2	NAl P 1	NAl P 3	NAl P 1	NL 2 1	NL 1 13	NL 1 18	NL 1 13	NL 1 9

WEST AUCKLAND TOWN

Founded: 1893 Nickname: West

Chairman: Jim Palfreyman
Secretary: Allen Bayles
11 Edith Terrace
West Auckland
Co. Durham
DL14 9JT
Tel: 01388 833 783
Manager:
Prog Editor: Michael Bainbridge

Ground: Darlington Road, West Auckland, Co. Durham DL14 9HU Tel: 07800 796 630
Capacity: 3,000 **Seats:** 250 **Covered:** 250
Midweek Matchday: Tuesday **Clubhouse:** Yes **Shop:** No
Colours(change): White with yellow dash/white/white.
Previous Names: Auckland St Helens. St Helens. West Auckland.
Previous Lges: Auckland & Dist 1893-96. Wear Valley 96-1900. Sth Durham All 00-05. Mid Durham05-08. Nth Lge 19-20. Palantine 20-24. Sth Duham 27-28. Gaunless Valley 33-34.
Records: Att: 6,000 v Dulwich Hamlet FA Amateur Cup 1958-59

Senior Honours: Sir Thomas Lipton Trophy 1909, 1911, Northern Lge 1959-60, 60-61. Div 2 1990-91. League Cup 1958-59, 62-63, Durham Challenge Cup 1964-65

10 YEAR RECORD

99-00	00-01	01-02	02-03	03-04	04-05	05-06	06-07	07-08	08-09
NL 1 5	NL 1 12	NL 1 7	NL 1 13	NL 1 13	NL 1 17	NL 1 5	NL 1 6	NL 1 16	NL 1 20

WHITLEY BAY

Founded: 1897 Nickname: The Bay

Chairman: Paul McIlduff
Secretary: Derek Breakwell
55 Thorntree Drive
West Monkseaton
Whitley Bay
NE26 3BD
Tel: 07889 888 187
Manager: Ian Chandler
Prog Editor: David McMeekan

Ground: Hillheads Park, Rink Way, Whitley Bay, NE25 8HR Tel: 0191 291 3637
Capacity: 4,500 **Seats:** 450 **Covered:** 650
Midweek Matchday: Tuesday **Clubhouse:** Yes **Shop:** Yes
Colours(change): Blue & white stripes/blue/blue.
Previous Names: Whitley Bay Athletic 1950-58
Previous Lges: Tyneside 1909-10, Northern All. 50-55, N. Eastern 55-58, Northern 58-88 N.P.L. 88-00
Records: 7,301 v Hendon, FA Amateur Cup 1965.

Senior Honours: Northern Alliance 1952-53, 53-54.
Northern League 1964-65, 65-66, 06-07. NPL Div 1 1990-91, FA Vase 2001-02, 08-09.

10 YEAR RECORD

99-00	00-01	01-02	02-03	03-04	04-05	05-06	06-07	07-08	08-09
NP 1 22	NL 1 11	NL 1 5	NL 1 10	NL 1 10	NL 1 5	NL 1 10	NL 1 1	NL 1 3	NL 1 3

DIVISION TWO INS & OUTS

IN: Gillford Park (P – Northern Alliance Premier Division), Newton Aycliffe (P – Wearside League), Northallerton Town (R), Seaham Red Star (R). OUT: Esh Winning (P), Horden Colliery Welfare (P), Norton & Stockton Ancients (P), Prudhoe Town (F). Stokesley Sports Club become Stokesley.

BIRTLEY TOWN

FACT FILE
Founded: 1993
Nickname: The Hoops
Colours:
Green & white hoops/white/green & white

Chairman: John Heslington.
Secretary: Trevor Armstrong. 40 Dunvegan, Birtley, Co.Durham. DH3 2JH
Tel: (H) 0191 4109 219
Ground: Birtley Sports Complex, Durham Road, Birtley DH3 2JH.
Tel: 0795 854 0389
Directions: (From Durham) Off A1 (M) for Chester le Street, take 2nd turning off roundabout and then last turn off next roundabout(both signed to Birtley). Take first left after AEI cables and ground is at rear of sports complex.
Midweek Home Matchday: Tuesday.
Previous League: Wearside 1993-07.
Honours
Wearside League 2002-03, 06-07. Division 2 1994-95. League Cup 1998, 02, 06.

BRANDON UNITED

Founded: 1968
Nickname: United

Chairman: Bill Fisher.
Secretary: Barry Ross. 5 White Cedars, Brandon, Durham DH7 8AQ.
Tel: (H) 0191 3789620 (M) 07717 673090.
Programme: Yes.
Ground: Welfare Ground, rear of Commercial Street, Brandon, Durham DH7 8PL. Tel: 07717 673 090.
Capacity: 3,000 **Seats:** 200 **Covered:** 300 **Floodlights:**Yes **Shop:** No
Simple Directions: A690 - 3 miles west of Durham City Bus 50 from Durham.
Midweek Home Matchday: Wednesday **Clubhouse:** Open every day lunch and evening. Week end entertainment
Previous Leagues: Durham & District Sunday 68-77, Northern Alliance 1977-80, Northern Amateur 80-81 & Wearside 81-83
Club Colours: All Red.
RECORD Att.: 2,500 F.A.Sunday Cup SF. **Goalscorer:** Tommy Holden **Apps:** Derek Charlton 1977-86
Honours: F.A.Sunday Cup 1975-76. Northern Alliance Div. 2 1977-78, 78-79.
Northern League Champions 2002-03. Div 2 1984-85, 99-00.

CROOK TOWN

FACT FILE
Formed: 1889
Nickname: Black & Ambers
Colours: Amber/black/black
Programme: Yes

Chairman: Stephen Buddle.
Secretary: Kieron Bennett, 4 Cloverhill,Chester le Street, Co.Durham. DH2 2LZ
Tel No: 07838 387335
Ground: Millfield Ground, West Road, Crook, County Durham DL15 9PW.
Tel: 01388 762 959.
Directions: 400 yds west of town centre on Wolsingham Road (A689). Nearest BR station is Bishop Auckland (5 miles). Buses 1A & 1B from Bishop Auckland or X46& X47 from Durham.
Midweek Home Matchday: Wednesday.
Capacity: 3,500 **Seats:** 400 **Cover:** 300 **Floodlights:** Yes
Clubhouse: Lic Bar open matchdays. Hot & Cold Food available from Shop
Club Shop: Yes
Previous Names: Crook C.W.
Leagues: Auckland & Dist. 1894-96; Northern 1896-28 29-30; Durham Central 28-29; North Eastern 30-36; Wartime Durham & North'rland 40-41;Durham Cen.41-45.
Honours FA Amateur Cup Winners 1900-01 53-54 58-59 61-62 63-64.
Northern League (5) (R-up 4) League Cup (3), (R-up 4); Durham Challenge Cup (4); Durham Benefit Bowl (6); Ernest Armstrong Memorial Trophy 1997.

DARLINGTON RAILWAY ATHLETIC

Founded: 1993

Chairman: Doug Hawman

Secretary: Rob Poynter. 18 Edward Street, Darlington, Co. Durham DL1 2RUP Tel: 07884 355513

Ground: Railway Social Club, Brinkburn Road,Darlington, Co.Durham DL3 9LF. Tel: 01325 468 125.

Capacity: 2,500 **Seats:** 175 **Covered:** 250 **Floodlights:** Yes

Simple Directions: Take A68 off A1 towards Darlington.Turn left opp.pub on right into Brinkburn Rd. Ground is 400 yds on left.

Midweek Home Matchday: Wednesday **Clubhouse:** Yes it serves all sports at the complex.

Club Colours: All red.

Previous League(s): Northern League 1919-1925, Teesside League, Darlington & District League 1993-99,

Auckland District League 1999-2001, Wearside 2001-2005.

Honours: Auckland & District League 2000-01. Wearside League 2004-05.

GILLFORD PARK

Founded: 2005

Chairman: Donald Cameron
Secretary: Mike Linden. 1 Boston Avenue, Currock, Carlisle, Cumbria, CA2 4DR
Tel: (H) 05600702490. (M) 07717 103666.
Programme: Yes.
GROUND ADDRESS: Gillford Park Stadium, Gillford Park Railway Club, Off Pettrill Bank Road, Carlisle, Cumbria CA1 3AF Tel: 01228 526 449
Capacity: 4,000 **Seats:** 800 **Covered:** 800+ **Floodlights:** Yes
Simple Directions: North and South: Exit the M6 at Junction 42, (the most Southerly of the 3 exits) and take the second (from South) or fifth (from North) exit onto the A6 toward Carlisle. Follow this road into Carlisle and after 1.7 miles turn into the second left, Petterill Bank Road. After half-a-mile and once past the shops, turn right just before the Railway Bridge into the small track that leads down to the ground. From the East: Travelling on the A69, you can join the M6 on the edge of Carlisle and follow the directions for North and South.
Midweek Home Matchday: Wednesday **Clubhouse:** Yes
Previous Names: Gifford Park Spartans.
Previous Leagues: Northern Alliance 2005-09.
Club Colours: White/white/white.
Senior Honours: Northern Alliance Division 1 Champions 2006-07. Northern Alliance Combination Cup Winners 2006-07. Premier Division Champions 2008-09. Northern Alliance Challenge Cup Winners 2008-09.

GUISBOROUGH TOWN

Founded: 1973
Nickname: Priorymen

Chairman: Sandy MacKenzie.
Secretary: Daniel Clark. 15 Scarteen Close, Guisborough, Cleveland TS14 7PB
Tel: (H) 01287 281293 (M) 07961819168.
Programme: Yes
Ground: King George V Ground, Howlbeck Rd, Guisborough, Cleveland TS14 6LA
Tel: 01287 636 925
Directions: From west: bear left at 2nd set of lights, left into Howlbeck Rd after quarter mile, ground at end. Buses from Middlesbrough
Capacity: 3,500 **Seats:** 150 **Cover:** 400 **Floodlights:** Yes **Club Shop:** Yes
Clubhouse: Open evenings & weekends. Hot & cold snacks & drinks from kitchen on matchdays
Honours FA Vase R-up 79-80; Northern Lg Cup 87-88 (Div 2 R-up 86-87),
Northern Alliance 79-80 (R-up 78-79, Lg Cup 78-79);
N. Riding Sen. Cup 89-90 90-91 91-92 92-93 94-95.
Previous Leagues: Middlesbrough & District; South Bank; Northern Alliance 77-80; Midland Counties 80-82; Northern Counties (East) 82-85.
Club Colours: White/black/red.
Record: Attendance: 3,112 v Hungerford, FA Vase SF, 1980. (at Middlesbrough FC - 5,990 v Bury, FA Cup 1st Rd 1988) **Goalscorer:** Mark Davis 341 **Appearances:** Mark Davis 587 **Win:** 6-0 v Ferryhill & v Easington **Defeat:** 0-4 v Billingham Syn.

HEBBURN TOWN

Founded: 1912
Nickname: Hornets

Chairman: Bill Laffey.
Secretary: Tom Derrick, 63 Staneway, Felling, Gateshead, NE10 8LS.Tel: 0191 442 1563 (H).
Programme: Yes
Ground: Hebburn Sports & Social Ground, Victoria Road West, Hebburn NE31 1UN Tel: 0191 483 5101
Directions: On the main road through the town about 1 mile from railway station. Hebburn lies on the Metroline - excellent bus service from Heworth Metro.
Capacity: 2,000 **Seats**:153 **Cover:**420 **Flood Lights**:Yes **Clubhouse:** Yes. **Midweek Home Matchday:** Wednesday
Previous Leagues: Jarrow & Dist. Jnr 1912-14; S Shields Comb. 1919-22. Tyneside Comb. 1922-27. Tyneside 1927-39. Northern Comb. 1941-44 45-59; North Eastern 1944-45, 59-60. Wearside 1960-89.
Names: Reyrolles. Hebburn Reyrolles (pre-1988). Hebburn 1988-00.
Club Colours: Yellow and navy stripes/navy/yellow.
Honours Shields Gazette Cup 91-92, Wearside Lg 66-67 (Monkwearmouth Charity Cup 68-69), Durham Challenge Cup 42-43 91-92, Tyneside Lg 38-39, Northern Comb. 43-44, Gateshead Charity Cup 35-36 37-38, Palmer Hospital Cup 27-28, Hebburn Aged Miners Cup 35-36, Heddon Homes Cup 42-43, Hebburn Infirmary Cup 35-36 36-37 37-38 38-39, Craven Cup 99-00.
Record Attendance: 503 v Darwen, FA Cup Prel. Rd replay 7/9/91 **Win:** 10-1 **Defeat** 3-10

JARROW ROOFING BOLDON C.A.

Founded: 1987
Nickname: Roofing

Chairman: Richard McLoughlin
Secretary: Mark Groves. 10 Scotts Avenue, Crawcrook, Tyne & Wear NE40 4DX
Programme: Yes.
Ground: Boldon Sports Ground, New Road, Boldon Colliery NE35 9DZ. Tel: 0191 519 1391
Capacity: 3,500 **Seats:**150 **Covered:** 800 **Floodlights:** Yes
Simple Directions: A 19 to junction with A184 (Sunderlamd/Newcastle). Follow signs for Boldon Asda then to North Road Social Club. Ground is behind club. East Boldon BR 800 yards.
Clubhouse: Open evenings and w/e lunchtimes. Hot food. **Club Shop:** Yes
Midweek Home Matchday: Tuesday
Previous Leagues: South Tynside Senior 1987-88. Tyneside Amateur 1988-91. Wearside 1991-96.
Club Colours: Blue with yellow trim/blue with yellow trim/blue with yellow trim.
RECORD Attendance: 1,100 v Didcot Town, FA Vase 26.03.2005)
Goalscorer: Mick Hales **Appearances:** Paul Chow
Senior Honours: Monkwearmouth Cup Winners 1994-95. Craven Cup Winners 1996-97.

MARSKE UNITED

Founded: 1956
Nickname: The Seasiders

Chairman: Billy Park.
Secretary: Les Holtby. 21 Howard Drive, Marske by Sea, Redcar, Cleveland TS11 7JE
Tel: (H) 01642 475612. (M) 0759 354 2436.
Ground: Mount Pleasant, Mount Pleasant Ave., Marske, Redcar, Cleveland. Tel: 01642 471 091
Directions: From A19 take A174 exit marked Yarm, Teesport, Redcar, Whitby and head east towards Saltburn until Quarry Lane r/about. Take 1st left (A1085) into Marske, 1st right (Meadow Rd) then 1st left (Southfield Rd),then 1st left again Mount Pleasant Ave directly into car park. By train: Darlington to Saltburn, Marske station 300 yds from ground.
Capacity: 2,500 **Seats:** 169 **Cover:** 300 **Floodlights:** Yes
Clubhouse: Open every night and weekend lunchtimes. Food served after all games. **Midweek Home Matchday:** Wednesday.
Club Colours: Yellow/blue/blue.
Honours N Riding Sen Cup 94-95; N Riding County Cup 80-81 85-86; Teesside Lg 80-81 84-85; Wearside Lg 95-96, R-up 93-94 94-95 96-97, Cup 92-93 94-95 95-96; M/mouth Charity Cup 93-94 95-96; Sunderland Ship. Cup 95-96 96-97.N.Lg Cup R-up: 00-01
Previous Leagues: Cleveland & South Bank 56-76, Teesside 76-85, Wearside 85-97.
Record Attendance: 1,359 v Bedlington Terriers (F.A.Vase) **Win:** 16-0 v North Shields. **Defeat:** 3-9
Goalscorer: Chris Morgan 169 **Appearances:** Mike Kinnair 583

NEWTON AYCLIFFE

Founded: 1965
Nickname: Aycliffe

Chairman: Gary Farley
Secretary: Stephen Cunliffe. 30 Stanfield Road, Newton Aycliffe, Co. Durham DL5 5QU
Tel: (H) 01325 320656 (M) 07872985501.
Programme: Yes.
Ground: Moore Lane Park, Newton Aycliffe Sports Club, Moore Lane, Newton Aycliffe, Co. Durham DL5 5AG
Seats: 50 (proposed for 03.2010) **Covered:** 200 (by March 03.2010)
Simple Directions: Pick up A167 either from Darlington or Rushyford, turn into Central Avenue at traffic lights near school, turn left at St Mary's Church (near Tesco), approximately 400 yards turn left into Creighton Road, 100 yards turn right into Moore Lane.
Midweek Home Matchday: Wednesday **Clubhouse:** Yes
Previous League(s): Darlington & District. Durham Alliance. Wearside.
Club Colours: Blue & black/black/black.
Record Attendance: 520 v Teesside Athletic (Sundrland Shipowners Final) 2008-09.
Senior Honours: Durham Alliance League Champions 2007-08. Wearside League Champions 2008-09.

NORTH SHIELDS

Founded: 1992
Nickname: Robins

Chairman: Alan Matthews.

Secretary: Dave Thompson, 38 Barnstable Road, North Shields NE29 8QF. Tel: 0191 259 0249

Programme: Yes.

Ground: Ralph Gardner Park, West Percy Rd., N.Shields, Tyne & Wear, NE29 OES. Tel: 07969 239 476.

Directions: South: Through Tyne Tunnel, follow signs to North Shields. Travel along Howden Rd (A187) past N.Shields sports centre on left. Continue to next r'about and take 2nd left onto Coach Lane (sign posted Tynemouth) then take 4th left into West Percy Rd. Ground on left, entrance next left. West: From Newcastle take A1058 Coast Rd. At Billy Mill r-about turn right, signed N.Shields, continue over min r-about towards Town Centre. At next r'about (Collingwood Arms) turn right, then second left, ground on left.

Clubhouse: Yes

Midweek Home Matchday: Tuesday

Club Clours: Red/red/red.

Honours: FA Amateur Cup 1968-69, Northern Lge 68-69, N.C.E. Prem. Div. 91-92,
R-up 89-90, 90-91, Lge. Cup 90-91,Wearside Lge 98-99, 01-02 03-04. R-up 00-1. Sunderland Shipowners Cup 98-99.03-04
Presidents Cup 91-92. Monkwearmouth Charity Cup 00-01. Northumberland Senior Bowl 98-99, 00-01.

NORTHALLERTON TOWN

Founded: 1994
Nickname: Town

Chairman: Dave Watson.

Secretary: Ken Lomer. 28 Aysgarth Grove, Ainderby, Romanby, Northallerton DL7 8HY. Tel: (H) 01609 779 686

Programme: Yes.

Ground: Regency Stadium, Ainderby Road, Romanby, Northallerton DL7 8HA. Tel: 01609 772418

Midweek Home Matchday: Wednesday

Previous Names: Heaton Corner House, Benfield Park, 1999 - Amalgamation between Benfield Park/North Shields St. Columbus to form Newcastle Benfield Saints.

Previous Names: Northallerton FC 1994. **Previous Leagues:** Allertonshire, Vale of Mowbray, Ripon & District, Teesside, North Yorkshire, Darlington & District, Harrogate & District .

Club Colours: Black & white/black/black.

Record Attendance: 695 v Farnborough Town, FA Trophy 3rd Round - 20.02.1993.

SeniorHonours: Northern League Cup 1993-94. Northern League Division 2 Champions 1996-97.

SEAHAM RED STAR

Founded: 1973
Nickname: The Star

Chairman: John McBeth.
Secretary: John Smith, 33A Frederick Street, Seaham, Co.Durham SR7 7HX Tel: (H) 0191 5810 423.
Programme: Yes.
Ground: Seaham Town Park, Stockton Road, Seaham, Co. Durham SR7 0HY. Tel: 0191 581 1347.
Directions: From Tyne Tunnel: A19 Teeside approx 8 miles; B1404 Seaham slip road, left at top of slip road. Right at traffic lights & first left past school into ground.
Capacity: 4,000 **Seats:** 60 **Cover:** 200 **Floodlights:** Yes **Club Shop:** No
Midweek Home Matchday: Tuesday. **Clubhouse:** Yes
Previous Name: Seaham Colliery Welfare Red Star 1978-87.
Leagues: Sunday Football; Houghton & Dist. 1973-74; Northern Alliance 1974-79; Wearside 1979-83.
Colours: Red & white stripes/black/black.
Record Gate: 1,500 v Guisborough, Wearside League & v Sunderland, floodlight opener 1979
Scorer: Tom Henderson **Appearances:** Michael Whitfield
Honours: Wearside League Champions 1981-82. League Cup Winners 1981-82.
Northern League Cup Winners 1992-93.

STOKESLEY

Founded: 1920

Chairman: John Passman.
Secretary: Trevor Wing. 6 Lockton Close, Hemlington , Middlesbrough TS8 9RH
Tel: (H) 01642 599 655. (B) 01642 717 773. (M) 07860780446.
Programme: Yes.
Ground: Stokesley Sports Club, Broughton Road, Stokesley TS9 5JQ. Tel: 01642 710 051.

Midweek Home Matchday: Wednesday.

Colours: Black and red stripes/black/black.

Previous Leagues: Langbaurgh League, South Bank League, Stokesley & District League. Teeside League 1994-99.
Wearside League 1999-2006.

HONOURS: Langbaurgh League Champions 1927-28. Stokesley & District League Champions 1975-76.
North Riding County Cup Winners 2001-02, 03-04, 05-06. Wearside League Cup Winners 2003-04, 04-05.
Monkwearmouth Cup Winners 2004-05.

SUNDERLAND RYHOPE C.A.

Founded: 1961

Chairman: Owen Haley.
Secretary: Colin Wilson. 3 Rock Lodge Road, Roker, Sunderland SR6 9NX. Tel: (H) 0191 548 6413.
Programme: Yes.
Ground: Meadow Park,Beachbrooke, Stockton Road, Ryhope, Sunderland SR2 0NZ. Tel No: 0191 523 6555.
Directions: Ground on Waterworks Road near Ryhope & Cherry Knowle Hospitals. From Sunderland follow signs for A19 South
Capacity: 2,000 **Seats:** 150 **Cover:** 200 **Floodlights:** Yes
Midweek Home Matchday: Wednesday.
Club Colours: Red and white halves/black/red.
Record **Attendance:** 1,000+ v Newcastle United 1985.
Honours Northern Alliance League Cup Winners 1981.
Previous
Names: Ryhope Youth Club. Ryhope Community Association F.C. amalgamated with Kennek Roker from Wearside League in 1999-2000 to form Kennek Ryhope CA 2000-06.
Leagues: Wearside. Seaham & District, Houghton & District. Northern Alliance 1978-82.

TEAM NORTHUMBRIA

Chairman: Ian Elvin.
Secretary: Gaz Lee. 6 North Street East, Northumbria University, City Campus, Newcastle upon Tyne NE1 8ST
Tel: 07970478723
Programme: Yes.
Ground: Coach Lane Sports Ground, Coach Lane, Benton, Newcastle Upon Tyne NE7 7XA. Tel: 0191 215 6575.
Midweek Home Matchday: Tuesday.
Colours: White/black/black/red.
Previous
Names: Northumbria University >2003.
Leagues: Northern Alliance 1999-2006.
HONOURS
Northern Alliance League Premier Division Champions 2005-06.

THORNABY

Founded: 1980

Chairman: Lol Lyons
Secretary: Peter Morris, 20 Wheatear Road, Ingleby Barwick, Stockton-on-Tees, Clevelend TS17 0TB.
Tel. No.: 01642 760 779.
Programme: Yes.
Ground: Teesdale Park, Acklam Road,Thornaby, Stockton-on-Tees TS17 7JE. Tel: 07833 524 659.
Capacity: 5,000 **Seats:** 150 **Covered:** 350 **Floodlights**: Yes
Simple Directions: A19 to Thornaby turn off, ground half mile on right. One mile from Thornaby BR
Midweek Home Matchday: Tuesday **Clubhouse:** Open daily with full social facilities for hire.
Previous Names: Stockton Cricket Club 1965-80 Stockton 1980-99 and Thornaby- on-Tees 1999-2000.
Previous League(s): Stockton & District 1980-81. Wearside 1981-85.
Club Colours: Blue with white flash down side/blue/blue.
RECORD Attendance: 3,000 v Middlesbrough friendly August 1986. **Appearances:** Michael Watson
Victory: 11-0 v Horden C.W. (Buchanan Cup) 1994-95
Senior Honours: North Riding County Cup : 1985-86. Northern League Div.2 1987-88, 91-92.

WASHINGTON

Founded: 1949
Nickname: Mechanics

Chairman: Derek Armstrong.
Secretary: Barry Spendley, 16 Raglan Oxclose, Washington, Tyne & Wear NE38 0LE
Tel: (H) 0191 415 5980 (B) 07810 536 964.
Programme: Yes.
Ground: Albany Park, Spout Lane, Concord, Washington, Tyne & Wear NE37 2AB. Tel: 07761 325 797 / 07810536964
Directions: Ground situated opposite bus station.
Capacity: 3,000 Seats: 25 Cover: Yes Floodlights: Yes Club Shop: No
Midweek Home Matchday: Wednesday.
Clubhouse: Open normal licensing hours, with live entertainment, pool etc
Previous Leagues: Gateshead & District, Washington Amateur, Northern Alliance: 1967-68, Wearside: 1968-88.
Names: Washington Mechanics, Washington Ikeda Hoover. **Ground:** Usworth Welfare Park.
Colours: All red.
Record **Attendance:** 3,800 v Bradford Park Avenue, FA Cup 1970.
Honours: Washington Amateur: 1956-57, 57-58, 58-59, 59-60, 61-62, 62-63. League Cup: 1955-56, 58-59, 60-61, 64-65

WHICKHAM

Founded: 1944

Chairman: Brian McCartney.
Secretary: Paul Nicholson. 14 South View, Burnhope, Co.Durham DH7 0AB Tel: (H) 01207 521 624
Programme: Yes.
Ground: Glebe Ground, Rectory Lane, Whickham NE16 4NA. Tel: 0191 420 0186.
Directions: A692 (Consett) from A69. Left at r'bout signed Consett/Whickham. Uphill and right at mini-r'bout. Turn left into Rectory Lane (by Lloyds Bank) for 500 yds, club house on right.
Capacity: 4,000 Seats: 100 Cover: Yes Floodlights: Yes
Midweek Matchday: Tuesday. **Clubhouse:** Mon-Fri. 12-3 & 7-11, Sat.11-11, Sun. 12-2, 7.30-11.
Colours: Black & white stripes/black/black.
Honours: Northern Combination Champions 1969-70, 72-73, 73-74.Monkwearmouth Charity Cup Winners 1976-77.
Wearside League Champions 1977-78, 87-88. League Cup Winners 1986-87.
Sunderland Shipowners Cup Winners 1977-78, 80-81. FA Vase Winners 1980-81.
Previous Names: Axwell Park Colliery Welfare. **Leagues:** Derwent Valley > 1955. Northern Comb. 1955-57, 59-74.
Tyneside Amateur 1957-59. Wearside 1974-88. **Ground:** Rectory Recreation Field.
Record **Attendance**: 3,165 v Windsor & Eton, F.A. Vase SF 1981

WHITEHAVEN AMATEURS

Founded: 1994

Chairman: S Hocking.
Secretary: Craig Routledge. 41 Main Road, Seaton, Workington CA14 1HU Tel: 0759 5276080
Ground: Focus Scaffolding Sports Complex, Coach Road, Whitehaven CA28 9DB.
Tel: 01946 692 211
Seats: 50 **Cover:** 100 **Floodlights:** Yes **Clubhouse:** Yes
Club Colours: Yellow/blue/blue.
RECORDS
Attendance: 207 v Workington Reds, Cumberland County Cup 13.12.2007.
Previous
Leagues: Wearside 1994-2008.
HONOURS
Wearside League Division 2 Champions 1994-95. Wearside League Champions 2005-06.
Monkwearmouth Charity Cup 2006-07.

SOUTH WEST PENINSULA LEAGUE

www.swpleague.co.uk

Sponsored by:

Carlsberg

Founded: 2007

Recent champions:

2008: Bodmin Town

CHARITY BOWL

(League champions v League Cup holders)

(August 3rd at Buckland Athletic)
Bodmin Town 0
Saltash United 2

CHARITY VASE

(Division One East champions v Division One West champions)

(August 3rd at Buckland Athletic)
Budleigh Salterton 2
Wadebridge Town 3

Premier Division		P	W	D	L	F	A	Pts
Bodmin Town		36	27	5	4	88	25	86
Plymouth Parkway		36	22	7	7	99	46	73
Buckland Athletic		36	21	9	6	79	39	72
Ivybridge Town		36	21	8	7	88	61	71
Saltash United		36	20	8	8	98	53	68
Tavistock	*-2*	36	20	5	11	70	58	63
Dartmouth		36	18	5	13	72	70	59
Cullompton Rangers		36	18	2	16	80	70	56
Torpoint Athletic		36	16	5	15	75	79	53
Launceston		36	14	6	16	72	70	48
Witheridge		36	13	8	15	64	54	47
St Blazey		36	11	10	15	64	74	43
Wadebridge Town		36	11	8	17	54	71	41
Falmouth Town		36	10	6	20	48	73	36
Holsworthy		36	9	6	21	48	103	33
Liskeard Athletic		36	9	5	22	39	69	32
Clyst Rovers		36	9	4	23	58	104	31
Elburton Villa		36	7	6	23	55	88	27
Newton Abbot Spurs		36	7	5	24	36	80	26

Newton Abbot - record expunged

	Bodmin Town	Buckland Athletic	Clyst Rovers	Cullompton Rangers	Dartmouth	Elburton Villa	Falmouth Town	Holsworthy	Ivybridge Town	Launceston	Liskeard Athletic	Newton Abbot	Newton Abbot Spurs	Plymouth Parkway	Saltash United	St Blazey	Tavistock	Torpoint Athletic	Wadebridge Town	Witheridge
Bodmin Town		3-0	4-1	4-1	6-0	3-0	2-0	4-0	1-1	3-1	4-1	n/a	1-0	0-0	3-2	1-0	0-1	0-2	2-0	1-0
Buckland Athletic	0-2		3-0	2-0	1-2	4-1	2-1	5-0	3-3	0-0	2-0	n/a	4-0	3-3	0-0	1-1	0-3	2-1	5-0	1-0
Clyst Rovers	1-5	3-3	***P***	3-4	3-3	2-1	2-1	3-3	1-2	6-2	3-2	5-1	0-1	1-0	1-3	1-3	2-7	2-3	1-3	2-1
Cullompton Rangers	2-3	0-3	1-5	***R***	2-5	4-1	1-1	4-1	3-1	2-4	1-2	2-3	2-0	3-1	1-3	1-1	7-1	4-1	0-3	2-1
Dartmouth	1-2	2-1	2-0	3-2	***E***	3-1	1-0	4-3	3-2	3-3	2-1	n/a	3-0	1-2	2-1	4-1	3-0	0-3	3-0	2-6
Elburton Villa	1-3	2-5	5-0	0-1	0-0	***M***	2-3	1-2	2-3	3-1	3-3	3-0	3-3	2-1	1-3	1-4	4-2	3-1	1-2	0-1
Falmouth Town	0-0	3-3	3-2	0-1	3-2	0-1	***I***	1-3	1-0	2-4	1-1	n/a	3-1	1-6	0-2	0-4	0-2	2-4	1-2	1-4
Holsworthy	2-0	0-1	4-1	3-0	0-5	1-1	2-1	***E***	1-1	1-4	0-1	n/a	0-0	1-6	0-4	3-4	1-3	1-1	3-4	2-1
Ivybridge Town	1-1	0-4	6-2	2-1	10-3	5-0	3-2	5-1	***R***	1-0	5-1	4-1	2-1	0-6	3-2	3-2	3-2	3-0	1-0	3-1
Launceston	0-3	2-3	5-2	2-4	1-0	7-1	1-2	1-1	1-3		2-0	n/a	3-0	2-3	2-2	3-0	1-2	4-2	2-0	1-4
Liskeard Athletic	1-2	1-3	1-1	1-2	2-1	2-0	1-1	1-2	1-3	2-0	***D***	n/a	3-2	1-2	0-1	1-2	0-4	1-0	3-2	0-1
Newton Abbot	n/a	n/a	n/a	n/a	n/a	n/a	n/a	n/a	n/a	n/a	3-1	***I***	n/a	n/a	n/a	1-2	n/a	1-2	n/a	n/a
Newton Abbot Spurs	0-2	1-3	2-1	2-3	1-2	0-3	1-2	4-1	0-2	0-3	3-0	n/a	***V***	0-4	0-9	2-2	1-0	2-3	0-2	1-1
Plymouth Parkway	3-2	1-1	7-1	3-0	4-0	2-1	1-3	4-1	3-0	1-1	1-0	n/a	2-0	***I***	4-2	1-1	3-1	1-2	2-2	3-3
Saltash United	2-2	1-3	4-0	1-0	2-0	3-1	3-0	10-0	3-3	3-1	2-1	n/a	6-2	3-1	***S***	2-2	2-2	3-5	2-2	3-2
St Blazey	0-4	0-4	1-2	2-3	2-1	3-1	3-3	3-1	2-2	2-3	4-1	n/a	0-0	3-1	4-2	***I***	1-3	1-7	1-3	1-1
Tavistock	0-3	0-2	2-0	4-3	1-0	2-2	2-1	3-1	2-0	3-0	4-1	n/a	2-1	2-6	1-0	1-0	***O***	1-0	2-4	1-1
Torpoint Athletic	0-6	2-0	5-1	0-6	2-4	3-1	3-1	6-1	2-3	2-2	2-0	n/a	1-3	1-3	2-2	5-3	1-1	***N***	1-0	1-1
Wadebridge Town	1-2	1-1	2-1	0-6	1-1	2-2	0-2	1-2	2-2	4-2	0-1	n/a	1-2	0-5	2-3	0-0	1-1	4-1		1-4
Witheridge	0-4	0-1	0-1	1-3	1-1	4-3	1-2	5-0	1-1	0-1	1-1	n/a	1-0	1-3	0-2	2-1	3-2	7-0	3-2	

THROGMORTON CUP

FIRST ROUND

Alphington 3 **Clyst Rovers** 5 *aet*
Appledore 2 **Dobwalls** 3 *aet*
Axminster Town 5 Exmouth Town 0 *aet*
Bovey Tracey 3 **Tavistock** 4
Buckfastleigh Rangers 2 Plymstock United 1
Crediton United 1 **Royal Marines** 2
Exeter Civil Service 1 **Witheridge** 2
Foxhole Stars 1 **Callington Town** 3
Galmpton Utd & Torbay Gents 2 Okehampton Argyle 0
Godolphin Atlantic 3 Porthleven 1
Ivybridge Town 3 Newton Abbot Spurs 1
Liskeard Athletic 4 Truro City Res. 4 *aet* (3-1p)
Liverton United 2 **Elburton Villa** 6
Newquay 4 Mousehole 2
Newton Abbot 2 **St Austell** 3
Ottery St Mary 0 **Budleigh Salterton** 2
Penryn Athletic (w/o) v Goonhavern Athletic (scr.)
Stoke Gabriel 6 Camelford 1
Teignmouth 3 Millbrook 2
Totnes & Dartington SC 0 **Buckland Athletic** 3
University of Exeter 2 **Cullompton Rangers** 4
Vospers Oak Villa 2 **Holsworthy** 3
Wadebridge Town 1 Hayle 0
Wendron United 0 **Penzance** 3

SECOND ROUND

Axminster Town 1 **Budleigh Salterton** 3
Buckland Athletic 0 **Ivybridge Town** 2
Callington Town 0 **Saltash United** 2
Clyst Rovers 5 Royal Marines 1
Cullompton Rangers 0 **Plymouth Parkway** 6
Dartmouth 1 Witheridge 1 *aet* (5-3p)
Dobwalls 2 **Bodmin Town** 2 *aet* (2-4p)
Elburton Villa 3 Holsworthy 2
Falmouth Town 2 St Blazey 1
Galmpton Utd & Torbay Gents 3 Torpoint Athletic 2
Liskeard Athletic 1 **Penzance** 3
Newquay 1 **Penryn Athletic** 4
St Austell 5 Buckfastleigh Rangers 1
Tavistock 3 Launceston 1
Teignmouth 2 **Stoke Gabriel** 7
Wadebridge Town 2 Godolphin Atlantic 1

THIRD ROUND

Budleigh Salterton 4 Stoke Gabriel 3
Dartmouth 2 **Ivybridge Town** 4
Elburton Villa 1 **Bodmin Town** 4
Galmpton Utd & Torbaby Gents 2 **Penzance** 3
Plymouth Parkway 8 Falmouth Town 0
St Austell 1 Clyst Rovers 0
Tavistock 0 **Penryn Athletic** 2
Wadebridge Town 1 **Saltash United** 2

QUARTER-FINALS

Bodmin Town 3 St Austell 1 *aet*
Budleigh Salterton 1 **Penryn Athletic** 2
Plymouth Parkway 2 Penzance 1 *aet*
Saltash United 1 **Ivybridge Town** 2

SEMI-FINALS

Bodmin Town 3 Penryn Athletic 1 *(at St Blazey)*
Ivybridge Town 4 Plymouth Parkway 2 *(at Liskeard)*

FINAL

(May 4th at Saltash United)
Bodmin Town 2 Ivybridge Town 1 *aet*

Division One East	P	W	D	L	F	A	Pts
Exeter Civil Service	32	22	6	4	80	39	72
Bovey Tracey	32	23	2	7	86	37	71
Stoke Gabriel	32	21	2	9	89	41	65
Appledore	32	20	4	8	76	40	64
Galmpton Utd/Torbay Gents	32	18	3	11	71	57	57
University of Exeter	32	16	6	10	65	58	54
Royal Marines	32	15	4	13	94	59	49
Axminster Town	32	15	4	13	68	67	49
Budleigh Salterton	32	14	6	12	68	58	48
Teignmouth	32	15	1	16	66	60	46
Alphington	32	13	3	16	61	70	42
Totnes & Dartington SC	32	10	8	14	62	72	38
Crediton United	32	10	5	17	48	58	35
Okehampton Argyle	32	7	8	17	51	97	29
Exmouth Town	32	8	4	20	46	95	28
Liverton United	32	7	3	22	47	82	24
Ottery St Mary	32	2	3	27	25	113	9

Buckfastleigh Rangers - record expunged

	Alph	Apple	Axm	Bovey	Buck	Bud	Cred	Exetr	Exmth	Galm	Liver	Oke	Ottery	Royal	Stoke	Teign	Totnes	Univ
Alphington		2-0	1-4	0-3	n/a	2-4	4-2	4-0	6-2	1-3	2-2	2-3	2-1	2-3	1-2	0-6	3-1	5-0
Appledore	2-1	***D***	2-0	2-4	n/a	2-0	3-1	1-1	5-0	3-1	4-1	1-2	2-1	2-1	5-2	1-3	2-2	4-0
Axminster Town	3-0	0-2	***I***	0-2	n/a	1-4	2-1	2-2	0-3	3-1	2-1	5-2	4-1	2-3	0-5	0-3	4-1	3-1
Bovey Tracey	0-3	1-0	5-2	***V***	0-5	5-1	2-1	2-2	3-0	2-1	0-0	2-1	5-0	2-1	0-1	1-0	5-1	2-3
Buckfastleigh Rgrs	1-1	3-3	2-0	n/a	***I***	1-2	n/a	n/a	n/a	1-3	n/a	1-8	n/a	3-3	n/a	2-1	1-4	n/a
Budleigh Salterton	2-1	1-1	2-2	3-1	n/a	***S***	3-1	0-2	2-3	2-0	5-2	3-3	6-0	1-2	1-2	2-3	3-3	0-4
Crediton United	0-4	1-3	1-3	1-3	2-2	2-4	***I***	0-3	1-1	2-3	1-1	3-0	3-0	5-2	1-0	0-2	1-1	0-0
Exeter Civil Service	1-0	4-0	2-4	2-1	3-3	1-1	4-1	***O***	1-1	5-0	4-0	6-0	2-1	3-2	5-2	2-1	0-1	0-2
Exmouth Town	0-1	2-3	1-4	1-7	0-1	1-1	3-1	1-3	***N***	4-2	3-1	4-4	4-1	0-9	0-1	1-5	2-0	0-4
Galmpton Utd & TG	1-1	3-0	2-2	1-2	n/a	3-1	3-2	1-2	2-1		3-0	7-0	4-1	5-3	2-1	2-0	2-1	2-0
Liverton United	2-3	0-5	1-2	0-2	2-0	0-2	2-6	1-2	1-2	6-0	***O***	3-6	2-0	1-3	2-1	1-2	1-0	0-3
Okehampton Argyle	1-1	0-1	3-4	0-5	n/a	1-2	1-2	2-4	3-0	3-3	2-6	***N***	2-1	0-0	1-1	1-0	2-2	1-1
Ottery St Mary	0-3	1-4	2-1	0-4	2-2	1-4	0-4	3-3	2-0	2-4	1-3	0-3	***E***	0-4	0-5	0-1	2-2	1-1
Royal Marines	7-0	2-1	1-1	4-7	n/a	1-3	0-2	1-2	7-0	2-1	0-2	7-0	11-0		1-2	2-1	3-1	6-1
Stoke Gabriel	2-3	0-0	6-1	0-2	1-0	2-1	1-0	0-5	4-0	1-2	9-1	7-0	5-2	2-0	***E***	4-2	4-0	2-1
Teignmouth	6-0	0-3	0-5	3-2	3-1	3-2	0-1	1-2	3-2	1-2	2-1	5-1	4-1	3-3	1-5	***A***	3-6	0-2
Totnes & Dartington	5-3	2-7	3-1	2-1	3-3	0-1	0-1	1-2	4-2	0-3	3-2	5-1	6-0	2-2	0-4	3-1	***S***	3-3
University of Exeter	2-0	1-5	3-1	1-3	n/a	3-1	0-0	2-3	4-2	3-2	2-1	4-2	5-0	5-1	1-6	2-1	1-1	***T***

Division One West	P	W	D	L	F	A	Pts
Penzance	32	24	3	5	107	39	75
Newquay	32	23	2	7	98	46	71
St Austell	32	21	7	4	90	40	70
Penryn Athletic	32	20	2	10	72	50	62
Callington Town	32	19	4	9	75	46	61
Porthleven	32	19	2	11	95	59	59
Dobwalls	32	15	4	13	63	51	49
Camelford	32	13	6	13	59	66	45
Foxhole Stars	32	12	8	12	69	66	44
Truro City Res.	32	13	5	14	56	68	44
Godolphin Atlantic	32	13	4	15	56	63	43
Mousehole	32	11	3	18	55	79	36
Hayle	32	9	7	16	65	72	34
Plymstock United	32	7	5	20	45	77	26
Vospers Oak Villa	32	6	4	22	44	93	22
Wendron United	32	5	5	22	31	97	20
Millbrook	32	5	3	24	40	108	18

	Callington Town	Camelford	Dobwalls	Foxhole Stars	Godolphin Atlantic	Hayle	Millbrook	Mousehole	Newquay	Penryn Athletic	Penzance	Plymstock United	Porthleven	St Austell	Truro City Res.	Vospers Oak Villa	Wendron United
Callington Town	***D***	1-2	1-0	1-1	0-2	2-1	5-0	2-0	1-3	1-4	0-2	3-2	3-3	1-0	1-1	2-1	5-0
Camelford	1-4	***I***	0-3	2-1	3-1	1-1	1-1	3-0	1-2	1-1	2-3	1-1	3-7	2-3	3-5	1-2	3-1
Dobwalls	1-2	0-2	***V***	0-2	4-2	1-0	1-1	0-2	0-4	2-1	1-3	4-0	5-2	0-3	0-0	8-0	4-0
Foxhole Stars	3-6	1-3	0-2	***I***	0-0	5-3	3-1	2-3	2-6	1-1	1-1	3-1	3-4	1-1	4-3	3-1	8-1
Godolphin Atlantic	2-4	2-2	1-3	3-3	***S***	1-3	1-2	3-1	0-5	0-4	2-1	3-0	2-1	0-2	1-0	0-2	1-2
Hayle	2-1	2-3	1-1	0-1	2-5	***I***	5-2	1-2	6-6	2-3	2-2	2-3	3-1	0-0	0-3	5-2	1-3
Millbrook	1-4	2-3	2-4	2-5	0-1	2-6	***O***	0-2	1-6	4-2	1-4	0-2	1-7	0-7	1-3	5-4	0-2
Mousehole	3-6	1-2	1-5	4-1	1-4	1-1	4-0	***N***	0-1	2-3	0-4	1-2	0-7	2-3	1-1	4-3	3-2
Newquay	1-4	5-0	2-1	2-1	3-5	0-2	6-0	5-2		2-1	4-2	3-1	4-1	1-4	0-2	1-0	8-0
Penryn Athletic	1-0	4-2	4-0	2-1	2-1	3-1	2-3	3-0	1-4	***O***	3-2	1-0	2-3	1-2	4-1	4-1	2-1
Penzance	3-2	3-1	3-2	1-0	2-0	4-0	5-1	5-0	0-2	4-0	***N***	4-2	5-2	3-4	5-1	5-0	6-0
Plymstock United	2-1	1-4	0-1	2-2	0-2	2-2	2-1	4-2	2-2	0-3	2-6	***E***	0-2	3-3	1-2	2-4	3-1
Porthleven	0-3	5-1	1-4	1-2	5-2	1-0	1-1	1-0	0-1	3-1	1-2	4-1		3-4	5-1	7-1	4-1
St Austell	1-1	0-3	7-2	5-1	1-1	6-1	3-2	4-4	3-1	3-1	1-1	2-0	0-1	***W***	2-0	4-1	3-0
Truro City Res.	0-3	2-1	2-1	2-4	3-1	2-5	5-0	0-3	2-0	1-2	1-4	2-1	1-6	2-1	***E***	0-1	4-4
Vospers Oak Villa	1-2	1-1	1-2	2-2	2-5	2-1	1-3	1-3	1-5	1-2	0-4	4-2	1-3	0-3	2-3	***S***	1-1
Wendron United	2-3	0-1	1-1	0-2	0-2	1-4	1-0	0-3	0-3	1-4	1-8	2-1	1-3	1-5	1-1	0-0	***T***

PREMIER DIVISION INS & OUTS
IN: Bovey Tracey (P – Division One East), Penzance (P – Division One West)
OUT: Newton Abbot (WS), Newton Abbot Spurs (R – Division One East)

BODMIN TOWN

Formed: 1889

Secretary: Nick Giles. 4 Sandra Way, Bodmin Cornwall PL31 2PP. Tel: 01208 757 94 (H).
Manager: Darren Gilbert.
Ground: Priory Park, Bodmin, Cornwall PL31 2AE. Tel: 01208 781 65.
Seats: Yes. **Covered Standing:** No. **Floodlights:** Yes.
Simple Directions: Situated in Priory Park through main car park. Use football car park on Saturdays.
Clubhouse: Yes.
Club Colours: Yellow & black. **Change Colours:** All white.
Previous League: South Western.
Honours: South Western League Champions 1990-91, 93-94, 05-06.
South West Peninsula Premier 2007-08, 08-09.

BOVEY TRACEY

Formed: 1950
Nickname: Moorlanders

Secretary: Steve Cooney. c-moon@btinternet.com
Manager: Paul Feasby.
Ground: Western Counties Roofing (Mill Marsh Park), Ashburton Road, Bovey Tracey TQ13 9FF.
Tel: 01626 832 780.
Seats: No. **Covered Standing:** No. **Floodlights:** No.
Clubhouse: Yes. **Club Colours:** All red. **Change Colours:** All white.
Previous League(s): South Devon.
Previous Name: Bovey Town and Bovey St Johns merged to form Bovey Tracey in 1950.
Honours: Herald Cup 1960-61. South Devon Champions 2007-08.

BUCKLAND ATHLETIC

Formed: 1977
Nickname: The Bucks

Secretary: Christine Holmes. 65 The Avenue, Newton Abbot TQ12 2DB. Tel: 01626 361 020.
Manager: Phil Bayliss & Jamie Carwardine.
Ground: Homers Heath, South Quarry, Kingskerswell Road, Newton Abbot TQ12 5JU. Tel: 01626 361 020.
Seats: Yes. **Covered Standing:** No. **Floodlights:** No.
Simple Directions: From all areas head for Penn Inn roundabout then take the Newton Abbot turn-off. Keep in left-hand lane and filter left at first set of traffic lights. Go past Sainsbury's and follow road past the Keyberry Hotel. Carry straight on until you see the CLS Laundry then turn right into ground.
Clubhouse: Yes.
Club Colours: Yellow. **Change Colours:** Sky blue and white.
Previous League: Devon County 2000-07.

CLYST ROVERS

Formed: 1926 Reformed: 1951
Nickname: The Rovers

Secretary: James Chamerlain. c/o Geroge Tancocks Garage, Unit 16-17 Kestrel Business Park, Sowton Ind. Est, Exeter EX2 7JS. Tel: 01392 445 242.
Manager: Graham Bedford and Alan Lewis.
Ground: Waterslade Park, Clyst Honiton EX5 2BA. Tel: 01392 873 498.
Capacity: 3,000 **Seats:** 130 **Covered:** 350 **Floodlights:** Yes
Simple Directions: Exit M5, junction 29(S) head for Sowton Industrial Estate. At roundabout exit right to A30 Honiton. Pass under motorway bridge, branch left onto Rockbeare Road, through Clyst Honiton and take first right after Honiton turning (200 metres). 3 miles from motorway.
Clubhouse: Yes.
Club Colours: All Yellow. **Change Colours:** Blue & black.
Previous League(s): South Western 1981-92. Western League 1992-07.

CULLOMPTON RANGERS

Formed: 1945
Nickname: The Cully

Secretary: Marcus Scott. 13 Chestnut Avenue, Cullompton EX15 1ES. Tel: 01884 32662.
Manager: Lee Annunziata.
Ground: Speeds Meadow, Cullompton EX15 1DW. Tel: 01884 33090.
Seats: No. **Covered Standing:** Yes. **Floodlights:** Yes.
Simple Directions: Leave M5 at junction 28, left at Town Centre, at Meadow Lane turn left past Sports Centre, at end of road turn right, then in 100 yards turn left into ground at end of lane.
Clubhouse: Yes.
Club Colours: Red & black. **Change Colours:** Yellow & blue.
Previous League: Devon County 1992-2007.

DARTMOUTH

Formed: 1908
Nickname: The Darts

Secretary: Kathy Greeno. Tel: 01803 832 720.
Manager: Jamie Bennellick.
Ground: Longross, Dartmouth TQ5 9LW. Tel: 01803 832 902.
Seats: Yes. **Covered Standing:** No. **Floodlights:** Yes.
Simple Directions: From Totnes the ground is on the road into Dartmouth - on the right is a BP garage - take next right (Milton Lane) then first right into ground.
Clubhouse: Yes.
Club Colours: Red & black. **Change Colours:** All white.
Previous League: Devon County 1999-2007.
Honours: Devon County League Champions 2001-02, 02-03, 06-07.

ELBURTON VILLA

Formed: 1982
Nickname: The Villa

Secretary: Peter Snopek. uconn55@googlemail.com
Manager: Scott Bamford.
Ground: Haye Road, Elburton, Plymouth PL9 8NS. Tel: 01752 480 025.
Seats: No. **Covered Standing:** No. **Floodlights:** No.
Simple Directions: From Plymouth City Centre take A379 Kingsbridge Road. At third roundabout turn left into Haye Road (signposted Saltram House). Ground 50 yards on left.
Clubhouse: Yes.
Club Colours: Red & white stripes/black. **Change Colours:** White & red.
Previous League: Devon County 1992-2007.

FALMOUTH TOWN

Formed: 1949
Nickname: The Ambers

Secretary: Mike Williams. pidgeon1981@hotmail.com
Manager: Alan Carey.
Ground: Bickland Park, Bickland Water Road, Falmouth TR11 4PB. Tel: 01326 375 156.
Seats: Yes. **Covered Standing:** Yes. **Floodlights:** Yes.
Simple Directions: Take Penryn by-pass from Asda roundabout. Leave by-pass at Hillhead roundabout, take first right and follow industrial estate signs. Ground 1/2 mile on the left.
Clubhouse: Yes.
Club Colours: Amber & black. **Change Colours:** Blue & white.
Previous League(s): South Western 1951-74. Western League 1974-83. Cornwall Combination 1983-84. South Western 1984-2007.
Honours: South Western Lge Champions 1961-62, 65-66, 67-68, 70-71, 71-72, 72-73,73-74, 85-86, 86-87, 88-89, 89-90, 91-92, 96-97, 99-00. Cornwall Combination Champions 1983-84.

HOLSWORTHY

Formed: 1891
Nickname: The Magpies

Secretary: Ivor Phillips. ivor@holsafc.wanadoo.co.uk
Manager: Mickey Clarke & Keith Rickard.
Ground: Upcott Field, Holsworthy EX22 6HF. Tel: 01409 254 295.
Seats: Yes. **Covered Standing:** Yes. **Floodlights:** Yes.
Simple Directions: Leaving Town Centre on A338, towards Bideford, 100 metres beyond mini roundabout on left-hand side.
Clubhouse: Yes.
Club Colours: Black & white stripes/black. **Change Colours:** Yellow & green.
Previous League(s): South Western 1971-2003. Devon County 2003-07.

IVYBRIDGE TOWN

Formed: 1925
Nickname: The Ivys

Secretary: Paul Cocks. secretary@ivybridgefc.com
Manager: James Lynch and Brian Howard.
Ground: Erme Valley, Ermington Road, Ivybridge. Tel: 01752 896 686.
Seats: No. **Covered Standing:** No. **Floodlights:** No.
Simple Directions: From Plymouth - leave A38 at Ivybridge and follow signs towards Ermington. Ground is immediately next to South Devon Tennis Centre. From Exeter - leave A38 at Ivybridge. Ground is in front of you at the end of the slip road.
Clubhouse: Yes.
Club Colours: Green & black. **Change Colours:** Blue & white.
Previous League: Devon County.
Honours: Devon County League Champions 2005-06.

LAUNCESTON

Formed: 1891
Nickname: The Clarets

Secretary: Keith Ellacott. launcestonfc@aol.com
Manager: Darren Garner.
Ground: Pennygillam, Pennygillam Ind. Est., Launceston PL15 7ED. Tel: 01566 773 279.
Seats: Yes. **Covered Standing:** No. **Floodlights:** Yes.
Simple Directions: Leave A30 onto Pennygillam roundabout, turn into Pennygillam Industrial Estate. Ground is 400 yards on the left.
Clubhouse: Yes.
Club Colours: All claret. **Change Colours:** Sky blue & black.
Previous League: South Western.
Honours: South Western League Champions 1995-96.

LISKEARD ATHLETIC

Formed: 1889
Nickname: The Blues

Secretary: Brian Olver. Windrush, Tremeddan Lane, Liskeard PL14 3DS. Tel: 01579 342 869.
Manager: Leigh Cooper.
Ground: Lux Park Sport Association, Coldstyle Road, Lux Park, Liskeard PL14 2HZ. Tel: 01579 342 665.
Seats: Yes. **Covered Standing:** Yes. **Floodlights:** Yes.
Simple Directions: From the Parade (middle of town) turn left at the monument, then first right following signs for Leisure Centre at Lux Park.
Clubhouse: Yes.
Club Colours: All blue. **Change Colours:** All yellow.
Previous League(s): South Western 1966-79. Western League 1979-95. South Western 1995-2007.
Honours: South Western League Champions 1976-77, 78-79. Western League Champions 1987-88.

PENZANCE

Formed: 1818
Nickname: The Magpies

Secretary: John Mead. jamead@supanet.com
Manager: Trevor Mewton.
Ground: Penlee Park, Alexandra Place, Penzance TR18 4NE. Tel: 01736 361 964.
Seats: Yes. **Covered Standing:** No. **Floodlights:** Yes.
Simple Directions: Follow road along harbour and promenade. Turn right at mini r'about into Alexandra Rd. Take either 1st (Mennaye Rd) 2nd (Alexandra Place) right.
Clubhouse: Yes. **Club Colours:** White & Black. **Change Colours:** Blue & white
Previous League(s): South Western 1951-2007.
Honours: South Western Champions 1955-56, 56-57, 74-75. South West Peninsula Div.1 West 08-09.

PLYMOUTH PARKWAY

Formed: 1988
Nickname: The Parkway

Secretary: Duncan Hedges. duncan@dhedges.fsworld.co.uk
Manager: Dave Leonard.
Ground: Bolitho Park, St Peters Road, Manadon, Plymouth PL5 3OZ.
Seats: Yes. **Covered Standing:** Yes. **Floodlights:** Yes.
Simple Directions: From Cornwall/Exeter exit at the Manadon/Tavistock junction off the Plymouth Parkway (A38), off roundabout into St Peters Road. Entrance is one mile on the right.
Clubhouse: Yes.
Club Colours: Yellow & blue. **Change Colours:** Blue & white.
Previous League(s): Devon County 1993-98. South Western 1998-2007.
Previous Name: Ex-Air Flyers Plymouth.

SALTASH UNITED

Formed: 1945
Nickname: The Ashes

Secretary: Luke Ranford. lukeranford@blueyonder.co.uk
Manager: Kevin Hendy.
Ground: Kimberley Stadium, Callington Road, Saltash PL12 6DX. Tel: 01752 845 746.
Seats: Yes. **Covered Standing:** No. **Floodlights:** Yes.
Simple Directions: At the top of Town Centre fork right at mini-roundabout. Ground is situated 400m ahead on the left-hand side next to Leisure Centre and Police Station.
Clubhouse: Yes.
Club Colours: Red & white stripes & black. **Change Colours:** White & black.
Previous League(s): South Western 1951-59. 62-76. 95-04. 06-07. Western League 1976-95. 04-06.
Honours: South Western League Champions 1953-54, 75-76.
Western League Division One Champions 1976-77. Premier Division Champions 84-85, 86-87, 88-89.

ST BLAZEY

Formed: 1896
Nickname: The Green & Blacks

Secretary: Simon Tonkins. simontonkin7@aol.com
Manager: Glynn Hooper.
Ground: Blaise Park, Station Road, St Blazey PL24 2ND. Tel: 01725 814 110.
Seats: Yes. **Covered Standing:** Yes. **Floodlights:** Yes.
Simple Directions: A390 from Lostwithiel to St Austell. At village of St Blazey turn left at traffic lights by Church/Cornish Arms pub into Station Road. Ground is 200 yards on the left.
Clubhouse: Yes.
Club Colours: Green & black. **Change Colours:** Blue & white.
Previous League: South Western 1951-2007.
Honours: South Western League Champions 1954-55, 57-58, 62-63, 63-64, 80-81, 82-83, 98-99, 00-01, 01-02, 02-03, 03-04, 04-05, 06-07.

TAVISTOCK

Formed: 1888
Nickname: The Lambs

Secretary: Phil Lowe. Tel: 01822 613 715.
Manager: Ian Southcott.
Ground: Langsford Park, Red & Black Club, Crowndale Road, Tavistock PL19 8DD. Tel: 01822 614 447.
Seats: Yes. **Covered Standing:** No. **Floodlights:** Yes.
Simple Directions: From Launceston/Okehampton, stay on A386 trhough town signposted Plymouth, past Drake's statue. Over canal turn right, signposted football ground/recycle centre. Ground is 100 metres past Tavistock college. From Plymouth, stay on A386 pass Morrisons and Texaco garage, over River Tavy, turn left signposted football ground/recycle centre. Then as above.
Clubhouse: Yes.
Club Colours: Red & black. **Change Colours:** All blue.
Previous League: South Western 1952-61, 68-07.

TORPOINT ATHLETIC

Formed: 1887
Nickname: The Point

Secretary: Victor Grimwood. 43 Henerdon Heights, Plympton, Plymouth PL7 2EY. Tel: 01752 344 263.
Manager: Stuart Dudley.
Ground: The Mill, Mill Lane, Carbeile Road, Torpoint PL11 2NA. Tel: 01752 812 889.
Seats: Yes. **Covered Standing:** Yes. **Floodlights:** Yes.
Simple Directions: Take turning at Carbeile Inn onto Carbeille Road and first turning on the right into Mill Lane.
Clubhouse: Yes.
Club Colours: Yellow & black. **Change Colours:** Red & white.
Previous League: South Western 1962-2007.
Honours: South Western League Champions 1964-65, 66-67.

WADEBRIDGE TOWN

Formed: 1894
Nickname: The Bridgers

Secretary: Bob Steggles. bob@steggles.com.
Manager: Mike Beckett.
Ground: Bodieve Park, Bodieve Road, Wadebridge PL27 7AJ. Tel: 01208 812 537.
Seats: Yes. **Covered Standing:** No. **Floodlights:** Yes.
Simple Directions: At the island junction of the A39 & Wadebridge by-pass turn to go into Wadebridge. 200 yards turn right into Bodieve Rd and then 1st right into ground.
Clubhouse: Yes.
Club Colours: All red. **Change Colours:** All blue.
Previous League(s): South Western 1952-07. **Honours:** South West Peninsula Div.1 West 2007-08

WITHERIDGE

Formed: 1920
Nickname: The Withy

Secretary: Chris Cole. chriscole128@hitmail.com
Manager: Chris Vinnicombe.
Ground: Edge Down Park, Fore Street, Witheridge EX16 8AH. Tel: 01884 861 511.
Seats: Yes. **Covered Standing:** Yes. **Floodlights:** No.
Simple Directions: B3137 Tiverton to Witheridge, on entering the village football pitch is on the right-hand side before the Fire Station and School.
Clubhouse: Yes.
Club Colours: Blue with yellow trim. **Change Colours:** All claret.
Previous League(s): Devon & Exeter >2006. Devon County 2006-07.

DIVISION 1 EAST INS & OUTS IN: Bickleigh (P – Devon & Exeter League Premier Division), Newton Abbot Spurs (R).
OUT: Bovey Tracey (P), Buckfastleigh Rangers (WS). University of Exeter become Exeter University

ALPHINGTON
Formed: 1946
Secretary: Norman Lyne-Lye. 118 Rivermead Road, Exeter EX2 4RL. Tel: 01392 661 008.
Ground: The Chronicles, Church Road, Alphington EX2 8SW. Tel: 01392 279 556.
Directions: From M5/A30/A38 follow signs for Marsh Barton Trading Estate. Ground entrance in Church Road, opposite Bridge Motor Cycles at junction to Marsh Barton.
Previous League(s): Devon County 1992-07.

APPLEDORE
Formed: 1912
Secretary: Michelle Copp. pallister06@aol.com
Ground: Marshford EX39 1PA. Tel: 01237 477 099.
Directions: From Bideford the ground is on the A386.
Previous League(s): Devon County 1998-2007.
Previous Name: Appledore & BAAC.

AXMINSTER TOWN
Formed: 1903
Secretary: Dave Lawrence. davelawrence@talktalk.net
Ground: Sector Lane EX13 5SD. Tel: 01297 35161.
Directions: From Exeter, A30 to Honiton then A35 to Axminster. Take turning to Axminster, through town, branch left past Roman Catholic Church (Sector Lane), pitch is second on the left.
Previous League(s): Devon & Exeter District.
Honours: Devon & Exeter District League Prem. Div. 2006-07.

BICKLEIGH
Secretary: Craig Mogford. craigmogford@hotmail.co.uk
Ground: Happy Meadow, Bickleigh, Tiverton
Previous League(s): Devon & Exeter.

BUDLEIGH SALTERTON
Formed: 1908
Secretary: Nick Pannell. nick@dpannell.freeserve.co.uk
Ground: Greenway Lane EX9 6SG. Tel: 01395 443 850.
Directions: Immediately before Budleigh turn left to Knowle Village, second right (Bedlands Lane), left at School then right into Greenway Lane.
Previous League(s): Devon County 1995-07.
Honours: Devon County League Champions 1995-96, 99-00.
South West Penisula Div.1 East 2007-08

CREDITON UNITED
Formed: 1910
Secretary: Mary Avery. 21 Blagdon Rise, Crediton EX17 1EN. Tel: 01363 773 912.
Ground: Lords Meadow EX17 1ES. Tel: 01363 774 671.
Directions: A377 from Exeter, turn right in front of "potters' (towards Tiverton), take next left, follow around right bend, turn right (signed Sports Centre) and follow road to phone box, turn left into sports centre car park.
Previous League(s): Western League 1990-98.
Devon League 1998-07.

EXETER CIVIL SERVICE
Formed: 1958
Secretary: Mark Willey. mw018c7335@blueyonder.co.uk
Ground: Foxhayes, Exwick EX4 2BQ. Tel: 01392 273 976
Previous League(s): Devon & Exeter League.
Honours: South West Peninulsar Div.1 East 2008-09.

EXETER UNIVERSITY
Formed: 1978
Secretary: Charlotte Edwards. The Athletic Union, Streatham Sports Centre, Stocker Road, Exeter EX4 6NG. Tel: 01392 263 505.
Ground: Topsham Road (Not Topsham Town FC), Topsham EX3 0LY. Tel: 01392 879 542.
Directions: Exit M5, junc 30, continue on A379 to the Countess Wear r'about. Take 1st exit (left) to Topsham. Stay on this road, proceed under M5 entrance to ground is immediately on left.
Previous League(s): Devon County 2002-07.

EXMOUTH TOWN
Formed: 1933
Secretary: David Richardson. davidrich43@hotmail.com
Ground: King George V Playing Field, Southern Road, Exmouth EX8 3EE Tel: 01395 263 348.
Directions: From M5 Sandy Gate Junction follow A376 to Exmouth. On entering Town club is on the right just before railway station.
Previous League(s): Western League 1973-06.
Honours: Western League Champions 1983-84, 85-86.

GALMPTON UNITED & TORBAY GENTLEMEN
Formed: 2008
Secretary: Abby Deakin. aflirty21@aol.com.
Ground: Galmpton Memorial Ground, Greenway Road TQ5 0LP.
Directions: From Totnes follow signs to Brixham when on Brixham Road turn right into Greenway Road, immediately after Churston Golf Club on your left.
Previous League(s): South Devon.

LIVERTON UNITED
Formed: 1902
Secretary: Susan Stephens. sstephens3@sky.com
Ground: Halford, Liverton TQ12 6JF.
Directions: Take Liverton turning off A38, Dumbridges (Trago) roundabout and head for old Liverton. Pass Star Inn and after approx. 1/4 mile turn left at crossroads, heading for Rora House. Turn left into ground opposite terrace of cottages on your right.
Previous League(s): South Devon.

NEWTON ABBOT SPURS
Formed: 1938
Secretary: Ashley Dawes. ashleydawes@aol.com
Ground: Recreation Ground TQ12 2AR. Tel: 01626 365 343.
Directions: At fire station roundabout enter 'The Avenue', 150 yards turn right at signpost 'Rec Trust'. Ground is on the right.
Previous League(s): South Western 1951-53, 59-71.Devon County.

OKEHAMPTON ARGYLE
Formed: 1926
Secretary: Charlie Bond. bond.charlie@googlemail.com
Ground: Simmons Park, Okehampton EX20 1EL. Tel: 01837 53997.
Directions: Turn off A30 at BP garage signposted Okehampton, turn right at junction, follow road into Okehampton. At second set of lights turn left into Mill Road, 300 yards on turn left into Simmons Way and follow signs for 'All weather pitch'.
Previous League(s): South Western. Devon & Exeter.

OTTERY ST MARY
Formed: 1911
Secretary: Alison Gannon. allisongannon@tiscali.co.uk
Ground: Washbrook Meadows EX11 1EL. Tel: 01404 813 539.
Directions: From Broad Street (Town Square) go left past the Church down over North Street, at the bottom turn right and the ground is on your left.
Previous League(s): South Western 1974-76. Western 1976-94, Devon County 1994-07.

ROYAL MARINES
Formed: 2008
Secretary: Ian Mullholland. rmfa-secretary@hotmail.co.uk.
Ground: Endurance Park, Lympstone EX8 5AR.
Tel: 01392 414 300 Ex: 4038 matchdays only

STOKE GABRIEL
Formed: 1905
Secretary: Andrew Horn. andy.horn@palmerharvey.co.uk
Ground: G J Churchward Memorial Ground, Broadley Lane TQ9 6RR. Tel: 01803 782 223.
Directions: Paignton to Brixham Road, turn right at Tweenaway junction (traffic lights) for Totnes. Approx 1/4 mile turn left at 'Parkers Arms' to Stoke Gabriel village. Approx 1 mile ground signposted on the right.
Previous League(s): Devon County 1992-07.
Honours: Devon County League Champions 1994-95, 96-97.

TEIGNMOUTH
Formed: 1946
Secretary: Nick Pearce. nicholas@nicholas94.orangehome.co.uk
Ground: Combe Valley TQ14 9EX. Tel: 01626 776 688.
Directions: From Exeter continue to lights down Exeter Hill. Turn right and take 2nd right past petrol station and turn right, continue to far end of Fouth Ave. Turn right at crossroads past the school and 1st left into club car park.
Previous League(s): South Western 1982-88.
Devon County 1992-99, 04-07. South Devon 1999-04.

TOTNES & DARTINGTON S.C.
Formed: 2005
Secretary: Ken Phillips. kenjoanphillips@hotmail.com
Ground: Foxhole Sports Ground TQ9 6EB. Tel: 01803 868 032
Directions: Leave A384 Totnes to Buckfastleigh Road at Dartington Church. Follow road/lane for 400 yards and turn right. Follow signs to lower car park. No road parking.
Previous League(s): Devon County 2005-07.

IN: Perranporth (P – Cornwall Combination)
OUT: Penzance (P)

CALLINGTON TOWN
Formed: 1989
Secretary: Nick Smith. pennyasmith@tiscali.co.uk
Ground: Ginsters Marshfield Parc, Callington Community College, Launceston Road PL17 7DR. Tel: 01579 382 647.
Directions: From A388 follow Launceston Road. Callington Community College is 1/4 mile from Town Centre on the right. Inside College park in first car park.
Previous League(s): East Cornwall >1999. South Western 99-07.
Honours: East Cornwall League Champions 1997-98, 98-99.

CAMELFORD
Formed: 1893
Secretary: Hilary Kent. hilarykent@camelfordfc.fsnet.co.uk
Ground: Trefew Park PL32 9TS. Tel: 07798 918 360.
Directions: From South, drive into Camelford up Victoria Road for 300 yards, turn left into Victoria Gardens. Follow road around for approx. 300 yards. Entrance is on the right up the lane. From North, turn right inot Victoria Gardens as you enter Camelford.
Previous League(s): South Western 1955-63.
East Cornwall 1990-07.

DOBWALLS
Formed: 1939
Secretary: John Blake. johnblake@jefferys.uk.com
Ground: Lantoom Park PL14 4LR. Tel: 01626 776 688.
Previous League(s): East Cornwall 2002-07.

FOXHOLE STARS
Formed: 1910
Secretary: Richard Tucker. Tel: 01726 67297.
Ground: Goverseth Park PL26 7UP. Tel: 01726 824 615.
Directions: In village turn into Goverseth Refinery entrance. Turn left into appraoch road and follow to ground, pitch on your right.
Previous League(s): East Cornwall >2007.
Honours: East Cornwall Champions 2002-03, 04-05, 06-07.

GODOLPHIN ATLANTIC AFC
Formed: 1980
Secretary: Margaret Ashwood. godolphin.arms@btconnect.com
Ground: Godolphin Way, Newquay TR7 3BU.
Previous League(s): East Cornwall.

HAYLE
Formed: 1906
Secretary: Bella Richards. bellarichards@hotmail.co.uk
Ground: Trevassack Park TR27 5HT. Tel: 01736 757 157.
Directions: Approach Hayle on the A30 from Camborne. At the r'about to the town (McDonalds) take the 4th exit. With Lidl on the right-hand side you come to mini r'about. Turn left towards Fraddam, follow this road for 3/4 mile, under railway viaduct and turn immediately right onto Viaduct Hill. Follow for 1/2 to 1st set of crossroads, ground is on your left.
Previous League(s): Cornwall Combination.

MILLBROOK
Formed: 1888
Secretary: Murray Hyslop. Tel: 01752 823 271.
Ground: Mill Park, Millbrook PL11 1EN. Tel: 01752 822 113.
Directions: Through village, turn left signposted Southdown Road. Follow road through. Ground at far end beside lake.
Previous League(s): South Western 1980-07.

MOUSEHOLE
Secretary: Christine Tonkin. christine.a.tonkin@btinternet.com
Ground: Trungle Park, Paul TR19 6XB. Tel: 01736 731 518.
Directions: Come to Penzance. Take seafront road to Newlyn. At Newlyn crossroads go straight across and up hill. Housing estate on both sides. Continue along road until you come to a t-junction (signposted Paul, Moushole). Take left turn for 1/2 mile. Before you come to the Church turn right at telephone box and continue to the end of lane arriving at ground.
Previous League(s): Cornwall Combination 1960-07.

NEWQUAY
Formed: 1890
Secretary: Derek Cherry. derek.cherry1@btinternet.com
Ground: Mount Wise, Clevedon Road, Newquay TR7 2BU.
Tel: 01637 872 935.
Directions: From Grannel Link Road turn right onto Mount Wise just past lights turn right into Clevedon Road.
Previous League(s): South Western 1951-07.
Honours: South Western Champions 1958-59, 59-60, 77-78, 79-80, 81-82, 83-84, 87-88.

PENRYN ATHLETIC
Formed: 1963
Secretary: Mike Young. Upalong, 1 Dunregan Road, Penryn, Cornwall TR10 8HJ. Tel: 01326 374 098.
Ground: Kernick, Kernick Road, Penryn TR10 8QF.
Tel: 01326 375 182.
Directions: At Treluswell r'about, follow signs for Kernick Ind. Est. Turn left at the Asda, ground 200 yards on the right.
Previous League(s): Cornwall Combination 1977-85, 86-87. South Western 1985-86, 00-01.
Honours: Cornwall Combination Champions 1981-82, 82-83, 84-85, 86-87, 89-90, 92-93, 93-94, 95-96, 99-00.

PERRANPORTH
Formed: 1904
Secretary: Helen Edwards. helen.edwards15@btinternet.com
Ground: Ponsmere Valley, Budnick Estate, Perranporth TR6 0DB.
Previous League(s): Cornwall Combination.
Honours: Cornwall Combination 2008-09.

PLYMSTOCK UNITED
Formed: 1946
Secretary: Dave Baskwill. david.baskwill@btinternet.com
Ground: Dean Cross PL9 7AZ. tel: 01752 406 776.
Directions: From Devon, A38 take A374 (Embankment Road) at lights turn left onto A379 at roundabout take 2nd exit (Pomphlett Road), at lights turn right into Dean Cross Road. From Cornwall, Tamar Bridge take A38 to Marsh Mills roundabout. Take third exit (City Centre) on to A374 then as above.
Previous League(s): Devon County 1992-07.

PORTHLEVEN
Formed: 1896
Secretary: Vidal James. 6 Wheal Ager, Pool, Redruth, Cornwall TR15 3QL. Tel: 01209 313 768.
Ground: Gala Parc, Mill Lane, Porthleven TR13 9LQ.
Tel: 01326 574 754.
Directions: A394 Helston - Penzance Road turn left at Porthleven signpost at bottom of hill. Ground on left as you enter village. Park opposite the ground.
Previous League(s): Cornwall Combination 1959-67, 77-89. South Western 1967-77, 89-07.
Honours: Cornwall Combination Champions 1959-60, 63-64, 65-66, 66-67, 78-79, 88-89.

ST AUSTELL
Formed: 1890
Secretary: Peter Beard. 24 Alexander Road, St Austell PL25 4QP. Tel: 01726 64138.
Ground: Poltair Park, Trevarthian Road, St Austell PL25 4LY. Tel: 01726 66099
Directions: Near Poltair School and St Austell Brewery (5 mins from St Austell Rail Station).
Previous League(s): South Western 1951-07.

TRURO CITY RESERVES
Secretary: Ian Anear. ian.anear@gmail.com
Ground: Treyew Road. 01872 225 400.
Previous League(s): Cornwall Combination.

VOPSERS OAK VILLA
Formed: 1912
Secretary: Ian Thomas. thomas-14@sky.com
Ground: The Mill, Ferndale Road, Weston Mill PL2 2EL.
Tel: 01752 363 352.
Directions: From Tamar Bridge take Deonport turning off the A38, take 2nd exit off r'about and at 1st set of lights turn left into Ferndale Road, ground 100 yards on the left.
Previous League(s): Devon County 1992-07. (as Weston Mill Oak Villa until 1998).

WENDRON UNITED
Formed: 1986
Secretary: Nick Scoley. nick.scoley@virgin.net
Ground: Underlane, Carnkie, Helston TR13 0EH.
Tel: 01209 860 946.
Previous League(s): Cornwall Combination 1998-07.

SPARTAN SOUTH MIDLANDS LEAGUE

www.ssmfl.org

Sponsored by: Molten

Founded: 1998

Recent champions:
2004: Beaconsfield SYCOB
2005: Potters Bar Town
2006: Oxford City
2007: Edgware Town
2008: Beaconsfield SYCOB

Premier Division		P	W	D	L	F	A	Pts
Biggleswade Town		40	27	4	9	100	41	85
Harefield United		40	26	7	7	103	45	85
Chalfont St Peter		40	23	9	8	99	56	78
Broxbourne Borough V & E		40	20	8	12	76	63	68
Kingsbury London Tigers		40	18	12	10	68	52	66
Leverstock Green		40	18	10	12	90	60	64
Hanwell Town		40	17	11	12	81	53	62
Tring Athletic		40	18	8	14	81	67	62
Welwyn Garden City		40	18	7	15	69	75	61
Hertford Town		40	15	13	12	61	46	58
Langford		40	16	9	15	81	82	57
Colney Heath		40	16	8	16	67	71	56
Oxhey Jets		40	15	10	15	77	82	55
St Margaretsbury		40	15	8	17	54	62	53
Aylesbury Vale		40	14	7	19	56	74	49
Biggleswade United		40	13	6	21	52	82	45
Brimsdown Rovers		40	10	11	19	59	77	41
Haringey Borough		40	10	7	23	50	83	37
Cockfosters		40	9	6	25	62	101	33
Holmer Green		40	6	10	24	36	80	28
Kentish Town	*-11*	40	7	7	26	58	128	17

Berkhamsted Town - record expunged

PREMIER DIVISION CUP

FIRST ROUND
Aylesbury Vale 4 Oxhey Jets 1
Berkhamsted Town 5 Colney Heath 4 *aet*
Chalfont St Peter 1 **Harefield United** 3
Hanwell Town 0 **Broxbourne Borough V & E** 2
Langford 3 Biggleswade Town 1 *aet*
Welwyn Garden City 2 **Haringey Borough** 3

SECOND ROUND
Aylesbury Vale 2 Haringey Borough 0
Biggleswade United 3 Berkhamsted Town 1
Brimsdown Rovers 1 **Tring Athletic** 2
Broxbourne Borough V & E 0 **St Margaretsbury** 1
Cockfosters 2 Holmer Green 1
Harefield United 4 Leverstock Green 2
Kingsbury London Tigers 2 Kentish Town 0
Langford 1 **Hertford Town** 3

QUARTER-FINALS
Aylesbury Vale 3 Hertford Town 0
Biggleswade United 3 Cockfosters 0
Kingsbury London Tigers 1 **St Margaretsbury** 2 *aet*
Tring Athletic 3 Harefield United 0

SEMI-FINALS
Aylesbury Vale 1 **St Margaretsbury** 3
Tring Athletic 3 Biggleswade United 1

FINAL
(May 5th at Colney Heath)
Tring Athletic 2 St Margaretsbury 0

	Aylesb'y V.	Berk'ted T.	Big'wade T.	Big'wade U.	Brimsdown	Broxbourne	Chalfont	Cockfosters	Colney Hth	Hanwell T.	Harefield	Haringey B.	Hertford T.	Holmer G.	Kentish T.	Kingsbury	Langford	Leverstock	Oxhey Jets	St Marg'bury	Tring Ath.	Welwyn GC
Aylesbury Vale		2-3	0-4	3-1	4-0	1-3	4-2	2-1	2-1	1-2	2-3	2-1	0-3	1-1	2-2	2-1	1-2	2-2	3-0	2-1	0-3	3-2
Berkhamsted Town	n/a		n/a	1-3	1-0	n/a	n/a	n/a	4-2	0-2	0-3	5-1	n/a	n/a	n/a	n/a	1-5	n/a	0-3	1-3	n/a	n/a
Biggleswade Town	1-2	5-2		6-0	1-0	1-2	3-2	7-1	4-0	1-0	3-0	4-0	1-0	0-2	2-0	4-4	3-0	1-0	3-1	6-1	0-4	1-0
Biggleswade United	1-1	1-1	1-0	***P***	1-0	1-0	1-7	3-2	0-1	2-1	1-2	1-3	3-2	0-0	4-1	0-0	2-2	1-3	3-1	2-1	1-2	0-2
Brimsdown Rovers	4-1	2-0	0-3	0-1	***R***	1-2	2-1	2-2	1-3	0-3	1-2	3-0	2-0	1-1	4-0	0-1	6-0	1-4	2-2	1-1	3-3	0-3
Broxbourne Borough V&E	2-0	3-2	2-2	1-1	1-3	***E***	2-2	1-1	3-0	1-2	1-3	3-0	3-1	1-0	4-6	2-1	3-3	3-2	1-1	2-1	2-1	5-2
Chalfont St Peter	1-1	7-2	1-2	2-0	2-0	5-0	***M***	4-1	0-3	1-1	1-3	2-1	2-0	2-0	3-1	2-1	3-2	2-1	3-1	2-3	4-2	3-0
Cockfosters	3-0	0-3	0-2	3-2	2-3	0-2	2-3	***I***	1-2	2-0	1-1	4-3	2-1	2-3	2-6	2-3	1-2	0-2	2-4	3-0	1-1	3-3
Colney Heath	1-0	n/a	2-1	3-2	0-2	5-0	1-2	2-3	***E***	2-1	0-1	2-2	3-3	2-0	2-1	1-1	1-4	3-3	0-2	1-1	3-1	2-1
Hanwell Town	3-4	n/a	0-2	4-1	1-1	1-3	2-2	5-2	5-1	***R***	1-1	1-1	1-1	1-0	0-0	2-3	5-1	4-1	4-3	1-1	2-1	7-0
Harefield United	3-1	n/a	3-1	4-2	5-3	4-0	2-3	5-0	1-1	0-0		8-1	1-2	2-0	8-2	1-0	2-0	1-2	4-0	2-1	3-1	0-1
Haringey Borough	4-2	n/a	0-2	2-0	2-2	2-0	1-4	1-0	1-1	1-1	0-5	***D***	3-2	1-1	0-4	0-1	0-1	0-2	2-2	0-1	0-3	1-2
Hertford Town	2-0	4-3	2-2	3-0	0-0	0-0	1-2	1-1	0-4	1-0	0-1	2-1	***I***	3-0	2-2	1-1	0-1	1-1	3-0	1-0	1-1	2-1
Holmer Green	0-2	2-5	1-2	0-2	2-2	0-0	0-0	2-1	3-4	1-3	0-2	2-0	0-3	***V***	1-3	2-2	0-2	0-8	1-3	2-1	1-3	0-2
Kentish Town	2-1	4-3	0-7	3-4	1-1	0-4	1-10	2-3	2-4	0-5	1-5	2-4	0-2	1-1	***I***	0-1	2-4	0-5	1-1	0-3	0-6	1-4
Kingsbury London Tigers	2-0	2-3	1-0	3-1	1-3	3-1	0-3	3-0	1-0	1-0	0-3	2-0	0-0	2-1	2-0	***S***	3-3	1-2	2-2	5-1	3-1	1-1
Langford	5-2	n/a	2-4	2-1	3-1	0-4	2-3	6-4	2-2	3-1	1-1	3-2	1-1	6-1	1-2	1-1	***I***	1-1	0-0	1-2	2-3	3-1
Leverstock Green	0-1	3-0	3-3	0-0	4-0	3-0	3-3	5-0	3-2	2-2	3-3	2-1	1-3	2-1	6-0	3-2	3-2	***O***	1-3	0-2	1-3	0-2
Oxhey Jets	0-0	n/a	1-3	3-4	5-0	1-4	1-0	2-1	5-1	0-2	3-2	1-2	3-3	3-2	4-3	3-1	4-2	3-3	***N***	2-1	3-4	0-3
St Margaretsbury	1-1	n/a	3-0	3-1	1-1	0-1	1-1	2-0	1-0	1-2	0-3	2-1	2-1	3-1	1-3	0-4	2-1	2-1	1-2		1-2	3-1
Tring Athletic	1-0	n/a	0-1	5-1	5-1	0-5	3-3	2-1	2-1	1-3	3-1	0-3	0-2	1-1	3-1	2-2	1-3	0-2	1-1	1-1		3-0
Welwyn Garden City	3-0	4-0	0-7	1-0	3-2	3-2	1-1	1-2	3-0	3-2	2-2	1-3	0-5	1-2	2-2	2-2	3-1	1-0	4-1	1-1	3-2	

Division One		P	W	D	L	F	A	Pts
Royston Town		40	33	4	3	138	30	103
Kings Langley		40	26	9	5	93	34	87
Hatfield Town		40	26	4	10	97	55	82
Bedford Town Res.		40	20	12	8	68	39	72
Hoddesdon Town		40	21	8	11	73	41	71
New Bradwell St Peter		40	20	10	10	80	56	70
Amersham Town		40	20	10	10	88	66	70
Harpenden Town		40	20	7	13	95	60	67
London Colney		40	19	8	13	94	57	65
Cranfield United		40	20	4	16	84	65	64
Tokyngton Manor		40	17	7	16	71	84	58
Winslow United		40	16	8	16	71	88	56
Stony Stratford Town		40	15	6	19	83	91	51
Bedford		40	12	8	20	61	95	44
Ampthill Town		40	12	6	22	63	74	42
Crawley Green		40	10	9	21	60	70	39
Arlesey Athletic		40	10	6	24	57	114	36
Sport London E Benfica		40	9	8	23	64	99	35
Buckingham Athletic		40	7	6	27	45	78	27
Sun Postal Sports	*-3*	40	7	7	26	51	106	25
Brache Sparta		40	5	3	32	48	182	18

DIVISION ONE CUP

FIRST ROUND

Bedford Town Res. 4 Stony Stratford Town 2
Harpenden Town 3 Cranfield United 0
Hatfield Town 2 **Royston Town** 3
Kings Langley 5 Sport London E Benfica 2
London Colney 3 Buckingham Athletic 2

SECOND ROUND

Ampthill Town 3 Brache Sparta 0
Arlesey Athletic 1 **New Bradwell St Peter** 2
Bedford 2 **Royston Town** 6
Bedford Town Res. 2 London Colney 0
Crawley Green 2 Harpenden Town 1
Hoddesdon Town 2 **Winslow United** 4
Kings Langley 4 Amersham Town 1
Sun Postal Sports 2 **Tokyngton Manor** 3

QUARTER-FINALS

Ampthill Town 4 Tokyngton Manor 2
Bedford Town Res. 2 **Crawley Green** 2 *aet* (2-4p)
Kings Langley 2 New Bradwell St Peter 0
Royston Town 2 Winslow United 0

SEMI-FINALS

Crawley Green 1 **Ampthill Town** 2
Royston Town 2 Kings Langley 0

FINAL

(May 2nd at Biggleswade Town)
Royston Town 2 Ampthill Town 0

	Amersham Town	Ampthill Town	Arlesey Athletic	Bedford	Bedford Town Res.	Brache Sparta	Buckingham Athletic	Cranfield United	Crawley Green	Harpenden Town	Hatfield Town	Hoddesdon Town	Kings Langley	London Colney	New Bradwell St Ptr	Royston Town	Sport London E Ben.	Stony Stratford Town	Sun Postal Sports	Tokyngton Manor	Winslow United
Amersham Town		2-1	2-1	4-1	1-1	3-1	2-2	0-1	3-2	3-1	3-2	0-2	1-0	1-1	4-3	1-1	3-5	4-2	1-1	3-2	6-0
Ampthill Town	2-0		0-3	1-3	1-1	6-2	1-1	0-3	1-2	1-4	4-1	2-3	0-1	1-5	1-3	0-3	3-0	4-1	4-1	2-2	2-3
Arlesey Athletic	2-2	2-0		1-2	2-1	4-2	3-1	0-7	0-0	3-3	1-2	0-4	0-3	1-6	0-3	0-5	1-1	0-4	3-6	1-3	0-1
Bedford	1-2	3-0	1-2		0-1	4-0	1-2	0-1	4-3	2-2	2-1	1-3	1-2	1-4	3-1	2-4	1-1	3-2	3-3	2-3	2-1
Bedford Town Res.	0-3	0-0	3-1	1-2	***D***	3-1	2-0	3-0	1-0	2-0	2-0	5-3	3-0	2-1	1-1	0-1	0-2	2-0	6-0	5-2	2-2
Brache Sparta	3-2	2-1	3-5	1-1	1-1	***I***	3-1	0-7	1-3	0-3	2-5	0-6	0-10	2-1	1-2	0-4	2-2	4-3	3-5	1-4	1-4
Buckingham Athletic	0-3	1-1	0-1	2-4	0-1	10-0	***V***	3-2	3-1	1-2	1-1	1-2	0-1	0-2	1-2	0-3	0-1	0-2	2-1	2-1	0-1
Cranfield United	2-2	0-3	1-0	2-1	1-1	6-4	1-0	***I***	1-0	0-1	4-2	1-2	2-2	0-3	0-1	0-4	2-1	1-3	4-1	7-0	2-4
Crawley Green	2-2	0-2	2-2	2-2	1-1	8-4	3-0	1-4	***S***	2-1	0-1	0-3	0-2	0-2	1-1	1-2	0-2	2-3	3-2	1-2	2-0
Harpenden Town	1-4	2-1	5-1	10-1	0-2	11-0	1-1	2-4	3-2	***I***	1-3	1-4	0-2	3-2	1-1	1-0	2-0	1-0	3-0	3-0	3-0
Hatfield Town	4-2	4-2	4-0	5-0	1-0	5-0	2-0	3-0	4-2	3-1	***O***	0-0	3-1	1-1	2-1	0-4	3-0	3-2	2-0	2-0	4-0
Hoddesdon Town	0-2	0-0	4-0	3-1	0-0	1-0	2-0	3-0	0-0	2-1	1-1	***N***	1-1	1-0	1-1	1-4	3-1	3-0	1-3	0-1	0-1
Kings Langley	2-0	1-0	2-0	0-0	1-1	9-1	3-1	3-4	1-0	2-1	2-0	2-0		3-0	2-1	1-2	3-0	3-1	2-0	5-2	2-1
London Colney	3-3	2-1	1-3	7-1	2-3	8-0	5-1	3-1	2-1	2-2	0-2	0-1	1-1		4-1	1-2	4-0	6-2	4-1	1-2	3-2
New Bradwell St Peter	1-2	3-1	5-2	3-0	2-0	3-0	4-3	0-2	0-0	1-1	4-2	2-1	0-4	5-0	***O***	2-5	5-2	3-0	3-1	1-1	1-1
Royston Town	3-1	4-0	7-1	5-0	3-1	13-0	3-1	1-0	2-0	4-0	2-0	3-2	0-0	2-2	1-1	***N***	5-0	1-3	8-0	2-1	3-1
Sport London E Benfica	3-1	1-3	3-3	1-1	2-2	7-0	2-3	0-4	2-3	0-3	0-4	1-3	1-4	1-2	1-2	1-6	***E***	2-2	4-0	1-3	5-4
Stony Stratford Town	1-0	1-4	6-1	5-1	1-1	3-2	3-0	2-2	2-2	0-2	7-6	2-0	1-5	1-2	1-1	1-4	3-1		4-0	4-3	1-4
Sun Postal Sports	0-3	0-3	2-0	1-2	0-1	2-0	1-1	2-3	0-1	0-4	3-5	1-1	0-0	0-0	1-2	0-6	1-1	3-1		3-1	1-2
Tokyngton Manor	3-4	1-2	5-2	0-0	0-2	3-0	3-0	3-2	0-7	3-3	0-2	0-5	2-2	1-0	1-0	2-1	4-2	2-0	4-3		0-0
Winslow United	3-3	3-2	2-5	3-1	1-4	3-1	1-0	1-0	2-0	1-6	0-2	2-1	3-3	1-1	1-4	2-5	1-4	3-3	5-2	1-1	

Res. Division One		P	W	D	L	F	A	Pt
Oxhey Jets Res.		30	22	3	5	92	39	69
Lev'stock G. Res.		30	18	6	6	79	41	60
Tring Athletic Res.		30	13	5	12	52	59	44
Cockfosters Res.		30	12	7	11	63	54	43
Holmer G. Res.		30	13	3	14	58	58	42
London Col. Res.		30	9	11	10	46	60	38
St Marg'bury Res.		30	10	7	13	59	69	37
Colney Heath Res		30	10	5	15	51	60	35
Broxbourne Res.		30	10	5	15	57	73	35
Harpenden Res.	*-1*	30	9	8	13	47	66	34
Hoddesdon Res.		30	4	10	16	45	70	22

Res. Div. Two East	P	W	D	L	F	A	Pt
Royston T. Res.	24	20	3	1	103	24	63
Hadley Res.	24	14	4	6	53	34	46
Bigg'wade U. Res.	24	14	1	9	63	41	43
Bigg'wade T. Res.	24	12	4	8	61	47	40
Crawley G. Res.	24	12	4	8	42	38	40
Langford Res.	24	12	3	9	58	46	39
The 61 FC Res.	24	11	5	8	50	44	38
Hatfield T. Res.	24	10	6	8	62	44	36
Wodson Park Res.	24	8	6	10	44	39	30
Ampthill Town Res.	24	9	2	13	55	56	29
Kent Athletic Res.	24	6	1	17	25	84	19
Caddington Res.	24	4	1	19	24	82	13
Sawbridgew'th Res.	24	2	4	18	30	91	10

Res. Div. Two West	P	W	D	L	F	A	Pt
K. Langley Res.	24	16	6	2	61	29	54
Ay'bury Vale Res.	24	16	5	3	60	30	53
AFC D'stable Res.	24	15	5	4	87	31	50
Tring Cor. Res.	24	15	3	6	61	43	48
Buck'ham A. Res.	24	14	2	8	52	33	44
Risborough Res.	24	11	4	9	46	40	37
Sun Postal Res.	24	10	4	10	37	31	34
Cranfield Utd Res.	24	8	4	12	32	41	28
N. Bradwell Res.	24	7	2	15	48	59	23
S. Stratford Res.	24	6	5	13	39	54	23
Totternhoe Res.	24	6	3	15	42	70	21
Winslow Utd Res.	24	4	3	17	31	67	15
Old Bradwell Res.	24	3	4	17	29	97	13

Division Two		P	W	D	L	F	A	Pts
The 61 FC (Luton)		32	25	6	1	89	25	81
Hadley		32	25	5	2	90	22	80
AFC Dunstable		32	21	5	6	102	50	68
Tring Corinthians		32	18	5	9	84	57	59
Padbury United		32	19	2	11	71	55	59
Wodson Park		32	16	5	11	65	40	53
Bucks Students Union		32	15	4	13	72	54	49
Mursley United		32	13	8	11	56	67	47
Pitstone & Ivinghoe		32	13	4	15	73	67	43
Risborough Rangers		32	13	3	16	48	58	42
Markyate		32	12	3	17	55	64	39
Caddington		32	9	3	20	62	82	30
Totternhoe		32	7	8	17	45	75	29
Kent Athletic		32	7	6	19	43	79	27
Aston Clinton	*-3*	32	8	5	19	44	83	26
Old Bradwell United		32	4	7	21	33	79	19
Bletchley Town		32	3	9	20	46	121	18

MK Wanderers - record expunged

DIVISION TWO CUP

FIRST ROUND
Kent Ath 0 **Bucks SU** 2
Padbury 1 **Wodson Pk** 4

SECOND ROUND
Aston Clinton 2 **Bucks Students U.** 2 *aet* (2-4p)
MK Wanderers (scr.) v **Totternhoe** (w/o)
Markyate 1 **AFC Dunstable** 3
Pitstone 4 **Caddington** 5
Risborough 0 **Mursley** 1
The 61 FC 1 **Hadley** 2
Tring Corinthians 2 Bletchley Town 1
Wodson Park 3 Old Bradwell United 0

QUARTER-FINALS
Hadley 0 Wodson Park 0 *aet* (5-4p)
Mursley 6 Caddington 1
Totternhoe 1 AFC Dunstable 0
Tring Corinthians 1 Bucks Student Union 0 *aet (at Hemel Hempstead Town)*

SEMI-FINALS
Hadley 2 Mursley United 0
Tring Cor. 0 **Totternhoe** 3

FINAL
(May 6th at London Colney)
Hadley 0 Totternhoe 0 *aet* (5-4p)

RESERVES CHALLENGE TROPHY

FINAL *(April 30th at Broxbourne Borough V & E)*
Royston Town Res. 3 St Margaretsbury Res. 2

CHALLENGE TROPHY

FIRST ROUND
Amersham Town 5 AFC Dunstable 0
Ampthill Town 1 **Cranfield United** 4
Arlesey Athletic 1 **Biggleswade Town** 5
Aylesbury Vale 0 **Winslow United** 2
Bedford Town Res. 0 **Tring Athletic** 1 *aet*
Berkhamsted Town 0 **Brimsdown Rovers** 2
Biggleswade United 1 Tokyngton Manor 0
Brache Sparta 1 **Hoddesdon Town** 3
Broxbourne Borough V & E 4 Tring Corinthians 1
Buckingham Athletic 2 **Colney Heath** 4 *aet*
Crawley Green 1 Welwyn Garden City 0
Hadley 4 Totternhoe 1
Hanwell Town 6 Bucks Students Union 3
Hatfield Town 0 **Cockfosters** 2
Kent Athletic 4 Pitstone & Ivinghoe 3
Kentish Town 5 Caddington 1
Kings Langley 2 Leverstock Green 1
Kingsbury London Tigers 3 Holmer Green 2 *aet*
Langford 3 Bletchley Town 0
Markyate 1 **St Margaretsbury** 6
MK Wanderers (scr.) v **Royston Town** (w/o)
Mursley United 2 Sun Postal Sports 0
New Bradwell St Peter 6 Bedford 2
Oxhey Jets 3 Harpenden Town 1
Padbury United 3 **Chalfont St Peter** 5
Risborough Rangers 1 Aston Clinton 0
Sport London E Benfica 1 **Hertford Town** 3 *aet*
The 61 FC (Luton) 3 Harefield United 0
Wodson Park 0 **London Colney** 1

SECOND ROUND
Biggleswade Town 2 Mursley United 1
Brimsdown Rovers 3 Kings Langley 0
Chalfont St Peter 3 Kingsbury London Tigers 2
Colney Heath 2 Hanwell Town 0
Cranfield United 1 **Hoddesdon Town** 3
Crawley Green 1 **Cockfosters** 2
Haringey Borough 1 **Broxbourne Borough V & E** 2
Kentish Town 2 St Margaretsbury 1
Langford 2 London Colney 0
New Bradwell St Peter 6 Winslow United 3
Oxhey Jets 5 Kent Athletic 0
Risborough Rangers 0 **Amersham Town** 6
Royston Town 1 Old Bradwell United 0
Stony Stratford Town 1 **Hadley** 3
The 61 FC (Luton) 3 Hertford Town 1
Tring Athletic 2 Biggleswade United 0

THIRD ROUND
Amersham Town 0 **The 61 FC (Luton)** 2
Biggleswade Town 4 Hoddesdon Town 0
Brimsdown Rovers 1 **Hadley** 3
Broxbourne Borough V & E 4 **Cockfosters** 5
Chalfont St Peter 4 New Bradwell St Peter 0
Kentish Town 3 Royston Town 2
Langford 3 Colney Heath 0
Tring Athletic 2 Oxhey Jets 0

QUARTER-FINALS
Biggleswade Town 3 Kentish Town 2
Chalfont St Peter 2 The 61 FC (Luton) 1
Hadley 1 **Tring Athletic** 3
Langford 3 **Cockfosters** 4

SEMI-FINALS
Biggeswade Town 3 **Tring Athletic** 4
Cockfosters 2 **Chalfont St Peter** 5

FINAL
(April 28th at Harefield United)
Chalfont St Peter 2 **Tring Athletic** 3

	AFCD	Aston	Blet.	Buck.	Cadd.	Had.	Kent	MKW	Mark.	Murs.	Old B.	Pad.	Pit.	Ris.	61FC	Tott.	Trin.	Wod.
AFC Dunstable		7-1	2-0	3-0	3-1	3-3	5-2	n/a	3-4	5-1	2-0	4-2	3-0	2-2	1-3	5-0	4-2	3-2
Aston Clinton	2-5		1-1	0-4	2-4	2-7	2-0	n/a	0-1	1-1	1-0	3-4	4-1	2-0	0-1	1-4	1-0	0-4
Bletchley Town	2-5	3-3		3-3	1-5	0-4	1-1	n/a	3-2	3-3	2-2	1-2	0-5	4-5	0-4	1-5	2-5	1-1
Bucks Stdnts Union	4-4	1-1	4-2	***D***	4-0	0-2	2-3	n/a	4-0	5-1	5-0	3-0	3-5	1-2	1-3	2-0	0-1	3-2
Caddington	3-3	4-5	6-0	2-1	***I***	1-1	3-5	n/a	2-5	2-3	1-5	3-1	4-0	1-2	2-4	1-1	0-3	2-0
Hadley	4-0	4-0	9-1	1-0	3-1	***V***	1-0	n/a	3-1	3-1	2-0	3-1	1-1	1-0	0-0	3-1	1-1	1-2
Kent Athletic	0-6	1-3	1-1	2-3	3-1	1-5	***I***	2-0	2-0	1-1	2-1	0-1	2-2	0-2	1-3	1-1	0-3	1-6
MK Wanderers	n/a	n/a	n/a	n/a	n/a	n/a	n/a	***S***	n/a	n/a	n/a	n/a	n/a	n/a	n/a	n/a	n/a	n/a
Markyate	1-4	3-2	9-2	0-2	1-0	0-2	0-4	n/a	***I***	0-3	3-2	4-0	5-2	2-0	0-3	2-2	3-3	1-0
Mursley United	0-4	3-1	2-0	1-2	2-0	0-6	3-2	n/a	2-1	***O***	3-3	1-0	3-2	3-1	1-2	4-2	2-2	0-0
Old Bradwell United	0-4	3-1	1-1	3-6	2-1	0-1	0-2	2-1	0-3	1-1	***N***	0-3	1-2	1-2	0-6	1-0	0-5	0-2
Padbury United	1-3	1-1	6-2	2-1	7-1	3-1	4-2	n/a	2-0	2-0	4-1		1-0	1-2	1-5	3-0	2-3	3-1
Pitstone & Ivinghoe	2-1	4-0	6-1	3-1	2-0	0-3	6-0	7-2	1-0	3-3	1-1	4-5	***T***	0-2	0-2	6-2	5-0	0-2
Risborough Rangers	0-3	5-0	1-2	0-2	2-3	0-3	1-0	10-1	1-0	0-3	4-1	0-2	7-3	***W***	0-4	0-0	1-0	2-5
The 61 FC (Luton)	3-1	2-1	5-1	4-0	2-1	1-2	3-0	7-4	4-1	5-1	1-1	1-1	2-1	3-3	***O***	2-0	3-1	0-0
Totternhoe	1-1	1-3	5-1	2-1	2-4	0-4	1-1	n/a	1-1	1-2	3-1	1-3	2-0	2-0	0-2		1-6	1-5
Tring Corinthians	3-1	3-0	1-4	2-2	3-2	1-5	5-3	n/a	4-2	3-0	3-0	2-3	3-1	3-1	3-3	7-2		2-3
Wodson Park	1-2	1-0	7-0	0-2	4-1	0-1	3-0	n/a	1-0	4-2	2-2	2-0	3-5	1-0	0-3	1-1	0-1	

AYLESBURY

Founded: 1930 Nickname: The Moles

Chairman: Roger Dance
Secretary: Ian Brown
18 Picasso Place
Aylesbury
Bucks
HP19 8SY
Tel: 07947 338 462
Manager: Mark Eaton
Prog Editor: Bev Kilmartin

Ground: Haywod Sports & S.Club, Haywards Way, Aylesbury, HP19 8SY 07947 338 462
Capacity: 1,000 **Seats:** 50 **Covered:** 50
Midweek Matchday: Tuesday **Clubhouse:** Yes **Shop:** No
Colours(change): Red & black halves/black/red. (White/maroon or sky/maroon or sky).
Previous Names: Negretti & Zambra. Stocklake. Belgrave. Haywood Utd. Aylesbury Vale.
Previous Lges: Chiltonian
Records: Att: 250 v Aylesbury United **App:** Ben Stevens
Senior Honours: Spartan South Midlands Div.1 2003-04.

10 YEAR RECORD

99-00	00-01	01-02	02-03	03-04	04-05	05-06	06-07	07-08	08-09
	SSM1 9	SSM2 2	SSM1 9	SSM1 1	SSM P 3	SSM P 5	SSM P 9	SSM P 13	SSM P 15

BIGGLESWADE UNITED

Founded: 1929 Nickname:

Chairman: Steve Rowland
Secretary: Tracey James
17 Havelock Road
Biggleswade
Beds
SG18 0DB
Tel: 07714 661 827
Manager: David Elkin
Prog Editor: See secretary

Ground: Second Meadow, Fairfield Rd, Biggleswade, Beds SG18 0AA Tel: 01767 600408
Capacity: 2,000 **Seats:** 30 **Covered:** 130
Midweek Matchday: Wednesday **Clubhouse:** Yes **Shop:** No
Colours(change): Red/navy/red (Yellow/royal blue/ royal blue)
Previous Names:
Previous Lges: Beds & District and Midland. Herts County.
Records: Att: 250 v Biggleswade Town
Senior Honours: Spartan South Midlands Div.1 1996-97.
Hunts FA Premier Cup 98-99 and Beds Senior Trophy 03-04, Beds Senior Cup 2001-02

10 YEAR RECORD

99-00	00-01	01-02	02-03	03-04	04-05	05-06	06-07	07-08	08-09
SSM S 4	SSM S 3	SSM1 4	SSM1 8	SSM1 8	SSM1 3	SSM P 9	SSM P 14	SSM P 18	SSM P 1

BRIMSDOWN ROVERS

Founded: 1947 Nickname:

Chairman: Alec Holloway
Secretary: Peter Wade
5 Goldsdown Close
Enfield

EN3 7RR
Tel: 07954 994 201
Manager: Justin Moseley
Prog Editor: See secretary

Ground: Brimsdown Sports & S.C, Goldsdown Rd, Enfield, EN3 7RP Tel: 0208 804 5491
Capacity: 2,300 **Seats:** 150 **Covered:** 300
Midweek Matchday: Wednesday **Clubhouse:** Yes **Shop:** No
Colours(change): Black & white stripes/black/black. (Red & white stripes/red/red)
Previous Names: Durham Rovers, Brimsdown FC
Previous Lges: Northern Suburban
Records: Att: 412 v Chesham United FA Cup 3rd Qual Round 91
Senior Honours: Spartan Champions 92-93, Spartan Lge Cup 95-96,
SSML Div 1 Cup 2005-06, SSML Div 1 Champions 06-07

10 YEAR RECORD

99-00	00-01	01-02	02-03	03-04	04-05	05-06	06-07	07-08	08-09
SSM S 8	SSM S 14	SSM1 17	SSM1 11	SSM1 10	SSM1 11	SSM1 5	SSM1 1	SSM P 8	SSM P 17

BROXBOURNE BOROUGH V & E

Founded: 1959 Nickname:

Chairman: Peter Harris
Secretary: John Venables
156 Crossbrook Street
Cheshunt
Herts
EN8 8JY
Tel: 07746 239 938
Manager: Tony Faulkner
Prog Editor: See chairman

Ground: Broxbourne Borougn V & E Club, Goffs Lane,Cheshunt, Herts EN7 5QN Tel: 01992 624 281
Capacity: 500 **Seats:** 300 **Covered:** yes
Midweek Matchday: Tuesday **Clubhouse:** Yes **Shop:** No
Colours(change): All Blue. (All Red)
Previous Names: Somerset Ambury V & E
Previous Lges: Herts Senior
Records: Att: 120 **Goalscorer:** Wayne Morris **App:** Brian Boehmer
Senior Honours:

10 YEAR RECORD

99-00	00-01	01-02	02-03	03-04	04-05	05-06	06-07	07-08	08-09
SSM P 20	SSM P 5	SSM P 11	SSM P 13	SSM P 16	SSM P 9	SSM P 11	SSM P 8	SSM P 12	SSM P 4

INS & OUTS
IN: Dunstable Town (R – Southern League Division One Midlands), Hatfield Town (P), Hillingdon Borough (R – Isthmian League Division One North), Royston Town (P)
OUT: Berkhamsted Town (WS), Biggleswade Town (P – Southern League Division One Midlands), Cockfosters (R), Holmer Green (R)

CHALFONT ST PETER

Founded: 1926 Nickname: Saints

Chairman: Dennis Mair
Secretary: John Carroll
30 Pembroke Road
Greenford
Middlesex
UB6 9QP
Tel: 07950 981 008
Manager: Danny Edwards
Prog Editor: Benny Goodman/Ian Doorbar

Ground: Mill Meadow, Amersham Road, Chalfont St Peter SL9 9QX Tel: 01753 885 797
Capacity: 4,500 **Seats:** 220 **Covered:** 120
Midweek Matchday: Tuesday **Clubhouse:** Yes **Shop:** Yes
Colours(change): Red/green/red. (Yellow/blue/yellow).
Previous Names:
Previous Lges: G W Comb. Parthernon. London. Spartan. L Spartan. Athenian. Isthmian.
Records: **Att:** 2,550 v Watford benefit match 1985 **App:** Colin Davies
Senior Honours: Isthmian Lge Div 2 87-88, Berks & Bucks Intermediate Cup 52-53

10 YEAR RECORD

99-00	00-01	01-02	02-03	03-04	04-05	05-06	06-07	07-08	08-09
Isth2 22	Isth3 22	Isth3 14	Isth2 15	Isth2 14	Isth2 11	Isth2 8	SSM P 6	SSM P 2	SSM P 3

COLNEY HEATH

Founded: 1907 Nickname: Magpies

Chairman: Martin Marlborough
Secretary: Martin Marlborough
124 Rosestock Lane
Colney Heath
St Albans, Herts
AL4 0QN
Tel: 07960 155 463
Manager: Scott Lacey
Prog Editor: See secretary

Ground: The Recreation Ground, High St, Colney Heath AL4 0NS. Tel: 01727 826 188
Capacity: **Seats:** **Covered:**
Midweek Matchday: **Clubhouse:** Yes **Shop:**
Colours(change): Black & white stripes/black/black & white. (Red/white/red)
Previous Names:
Previous Lges: Herts Senior County League 1953-2000
Records:
Senior Honours: Herts County League Div 2 Champions 1953-54 Div 1 A 55-56, Prem 58-99, 99-00, Div 1 88-89, Spartan South Midlands Div 1 2005-06 , SSML Cup 05-06

10 YEAR RECORD

99-00	00-01	01-02	02-03	03-04	04-05	05-06	06-07	07-08	08-09
HertP 1	SSM S 5	SSM1 3	SSM1 5	SSM1 6	SSM1 5	SSM1 1	SSM P 16	SSM P 15	SSM P 12

DUNSTABLE TOWN

Founded: 1998 Nickname: The Blues

Chairman: Peter Burgoyne
Secretary: Richard Scott
145 Victoria Street
Dunstable
Bedfordshire
LU6 3BB
Tel: 07843 930 189
Manager: Darren Feighery
Prog Editor: See secretary

Ground: Creasey Park Stadium, Brewers Hill Rd, Dunstable LU6 1BB. Tel: 01582 667 555.
Capacity: 3,500 **Seats:** 350 **Covered:** 1000
Midweek Matchday: Tuesday **Clubhouse:** Yes **Shop:** Yes
Colours(change): All royal blue. (Red & black/black/black)
Previous Names:
Previous Lges: Spartan South Midlands 1998-2000. Isthmian 2003. Southern 2004-09.
Records:
Senior Honours: Spartan Sth. Midlands Div.1 1999-00. Premier 02-03. Bedfordshire Senior Cup 03-04, 08-09.

10 YEAR RECORD

99-00	00-01	01-02	02-03	03-04	04-05	05-06	06-07	07-08	08-09
SSM1 1	SSM S 2	SSM P 7	SSM P 1	Isth1N 5	SthP 20	SthW 21	SthM 11	SthM 13	SthM 21

HANWELL TOWN

Founded: 1948 Nickname: Magpies

Chairman: Bob Fisher
Secretary: Bob Fisher
22 Fairfield Avenue
Edgware
Middlesex
HA8 9AQ
Tel: 07730 822 216
Manager: Keith Rowlands/James Wise
Prog Editor: See chairman

Ground: Reynolds Field, Preivale Lane, Perivale, Greenford, UB6 8TL. Tel: 0208 998 1701
Capacity: 1,250 **Seats:** 175 **Covered:** 600
Midweek Matchday: Tuesday **Clubhouse:** Yes **Shop:** No
Colours(change): Black & white stripes/black/black & white (Yellow/blue/white)
Previous Names:
Previous Lges: Dauntless. Wembley & Dist. Middlesex. London Spartan. Southern.
Records: **Att:** 600 v Spurs **Goalscorer:** Keith Rowlands
App: Phil Player 617 (20 seasons)
Senior Honours: London Spartan Senior Div. 83-84. London Senior Cup 1991-92, 92-93.

10 YEAR RECORD

99-00	00-01	01-02	02-03	03-04	04-05	05-06	06-07	07-08	08-09
SSM P 10	SSM P 7	SSM P 3	SSM P 8	SSM P 6	SSM P 2	SSM P 3	SthS 21	SSM P 9	SSM P 7

HAREFIELD UNITED

Founded: 1868 Nickname: Hares

Chairman: Keith Ronald
Secretary: Ray Green
12 Priory Cottages
Harvil Road
Harefield
UB9 6AS
Tel: 07834 771 212
Manager: Glenn Bellis
Prog Editor: See chairman

Ground: Preston Park, Breakespeare Road North, Harefield, UB9 6NE Tel: 01895 833 474
Capacity: 1,200 **Seats:** 150 **Covered:** yes
Midweek Matchday: Tuesday **Clubhouse:** Yes **Shop:** No
Colours(change): Red/black/black. (White/red/red)
Previous Names:
Previous Lges: Uxbridge & Dist, Gt Western Comb, Panthernon, Middlesex, Athenian & Isthmian.
Records: Att: 430 v Bashley FA Vase
Senior Honours: Middx Prem Cup 85-86, SSM Div 1 Winners 03, 04

10 YEAR RECORD

99-00	00-01	01-02	02-03	03-04	04-05	05-06	06-07	07-08	08-09
SSM S 15	SSM S 5	SSM1 2	SSM P 4	SSM P 5	SSM P 5	SSM P 4	SSM P 2	SSM P 5	SSM P 2

HARINGEY BOROUGH

Founded: 1907 Nickname: Borough

Chairman: Aki Achillea
Secretary: John Bacon
7 Everett Close,
West Cheshunt
Herts
EN7 6XD
Tel: 07979 050 190
Manager: Tom Loizu
Prog Editor: See secretary

Ground: Coles Park, White Hart Lane, London N17 7JP . Tel: 0208 889 1415 (Matchday)
Capacity: 2,500 **Seats:** 280 **Covered:** yes
Midweek Matchday: **Clubhouse:** Yes **Shop:** No
Colours(change): Yellow/green/yellow (Green/black/green)
Previous Names: Tufnell Park 1907
Previous Lges: London. Isthmian. Spartan. Delphian. Athenian.
Records: Att: 400
Senior Honours: London Senior Cup 1912-13, 90-91, Athenian League 1913-14

10 YEAR RECORD

99-00	00-01	01-02	02-03	03-04	04-05	05-06	06-07	07-08	08-09
SSM P 18	SSM P 18	SSM P 12	SSM P 15	SSM P 18	SSM P 18	SSM P 19	SSM P 21	SSM1 2	SSM P 18

HATFIELD TOWN

Founded: 1886 Nickname:

Chairman: Ted Collie
Secretary: Phil Knott
64 Briars Lane
Hatfield
Herts
AL10 8ET
Tel: 07768 924 395
Manager: Trevor Lloyd
Prog Editor: TBA

Ground: Welwyn Garden City FC, Herns Way, Panshanger AL7 1TA. Tel: 01707 328 470
Capacity: 1,500 **Seats:** 40 **Covered:** 120
Midweek Matchday: **Clubhouse:** Yes **Shop:** Yes
Colours(change): All royal blue. (Tangerine/white/black or red).
Previous Names: Hatfield FC > 1906. Hatfield Utd > 1922. Hatfield Utd Ath. > 1948
Previous Lges: Mid. Hertfordshire. Herts County. Parthenon. London. Metropolitan.
Records:
Senior Honours: Herts Senior Champions 2007-08

10 YEAR RECORD

99-00	00-01	01-02	02-03	03-04	04-05	05-06	06-07	07-08	08-09
HertP 15	Hert1 1	HertP 14	Hert1 1	HertP 7	HertP 3	HertP 2	HertP 5	HertP 1	SSM1 3

HERTFORD TOWN

Founded: 1908 Nickname: The Blues

Chairman: Mick Clarke
Secretary: Michael Persighetti
37 Brookside
Hertford
Herts
SG13 7LJ
Tel: 07530 056 401
Manager: Pablo Ardiles
Prog Editor: Peter Boyer

Ground: Hertingfordbury Park, West Street, Hertford, SG13 8EZ Tel: 01992 583 716
Capacity: 6,500 **Seats:** 200 **Covered:** 1,500
Midweek Matchday: Tuesday **Clubhouse:** Yes **Shop:** Yes
Colours(change): All Blue (All Red)
Previous Names:
Previous Lges: Herts Co. Spartan. Delphian 59-63. Athenian 63-72. Eastern Co 72-73.
Records: Att: 5,000 v Kingstonian FA Am Cup 2nd Round 55-56 **App:** Robbie Burns
Senior Honours: Herts Senior Cup 66-67 East Anglian Cup 62-63, 69-70

10 YEAR RECORD

99-00	00-01	01-02	02-03	03-04	04-05	05-06	06-07	07-08	08-09
Isth3 14	Isth3 19	Isth3 11	Isth1N 24	Isth2 3	Isth2 4	Isth2 13	SSM P 3	SSM P 4	SSM P 10

HILLINGDON BOROUGH

Founded: 19190 Nickname: Boro

Chairman: Gamdoor Dhaliwal
Secretary: Alan Taylor
53 Hitherbroom Road
Hayes
Middlesex
UB3 3AF
Tel: 07808 275 665
Manager: Steve Hale
Prog Editor: See secretary

Ground: Middlesex Stadium, Breakspear Rd, Ruislip HA4 7SB. Tel: 01895 639 544.
Capacity: 1,500 **Seats:** 150 **Covered:** 150
Midweek Matchday: **Clubhouse:** Yes **Shop:**
Colours(change): White/royal blue/royal. (Orange/black/black.
Previous Names: Yiewsley. Bromley Park Rangers.
Previous Lges: Southern 1964-84, 2006-08. South Midlands 1990-2006. Isthmian 2008-09
Records:
Senior Honours: South Midlands Cup 1996-97.

10 YEAR RECORD

99-00	00-01	01-02	02-03	03-04	04-05	05-06	06-07	07-08	08-09
SSM P 14	SSM P 8	SSM P 16	SSM P 12	SSM P 12	SSM P 6	SSM P 2	SthW 16	SthW 13	Isth1N 22

KENTISH TOWN

Founded: 1994 Nickname: Townies

Chairman: Catherine Dye
Secretary: James Thompson
Flat 4
Dartingdon, Plender Street
London
NW1 0DE
Tel: 07866 437 211
Manager: Rakatahr Hudson
Prog Editor: See chairman

Ground: Copthall Stad., Greenland Lane, Hendon, London NW4 1RL Tel: 0208 202 6478
Capacity: **Seats:** **Covered:**
Midweek Matchday: **Clubhouse:** **Shop:**
Colours(change): Light blue/navy/navy. (Red & white/red/red)
Previous Names: None
Previous Lges: Camden & Islington Youth Midweek Lge. Enfield & District Youth.
Records:
Senior Honours: Spartan South Midlands Division One 2007-08.

10 YEAR RECORD

99-00	00-01	01-02	02-03	03-04	04-05	05-06	06-07	07-08	08-09
				SSM2 10	SSM1 9	SSM1 11	SSM1 6	SSM1 1	SSM P 21

KINGSBURY LONDON TIGERS

Founded: 2006 Nickname: Tigers

Chairman: Mesba Ahmed
Secretary: Valdas Dambrauskas
London Tigers
1st Floor Office, Wech C.Centre
Athens Gardens , Elgin Ave
W9 3RS
Tel: 0207 289 3995
Manager: See secretary
Prog Editor: Jawar Ali

Ground: Silver Jubilee Park, Townsend Lane, London NW9 7NE Tel: 0208 205 1645
Capacity: **Seats:** **Covered:**
Midweek Matchday: **Clubhouse:** **Shop:**
Colours(change): Orange/black/black (Yellow/blue/blue)
Previous Names: Kingsbury Town and LondonTigers merged in 2006.
Previous Lges:
Records:
Senior Honours:

10 YEAR RECORD

99-00	00-01	01-02	02-03	03-04	04-05	05-06	06-07	07-08	08-09
							SSM P 13	SSM P 14	SSM P 5

LANGFORD

Founded: 1908 Nickname: Reds

Chairman: Ian Chessum
Secretary: Frank Woodward
4 View View
Langford
Biggleswade Beds
SG18 9RT
Tel: 07837 849 950
Manager: Hendy Manning/Roy Ryall
Prog Editor: Grant Beckwith

Ground: Forde Park, Langford Road, Henlow, Beds SG16 6AF. Tel: 01462 816 106
Capacity: 2,000 **Seats:** 109 **Covered:** 100
Midweek Matchday: Tuesday **Clubhouse:** Yes **Shop:**
Colours(change): Red & white/white/red. (All blue).
Previous Names:
Previous Lges:
Records: Att: 450 v QPR 75th Anniversary 85
Senior Honours: South Midlands League Champions 1988-89.

10 YEAR RECORD

99-00	00-01	01-02	02-03	03-04	04-05	05-06	06-07	07-08	08-09
SSM S 11	SSM S 7	SSM1 6	SSM1 13	SSM1 2	SSM P 17	SSM P 17	SSM P 17	SSM P 6	SSM P 11

LEVERSTOCK GREEN

Founded: 1895 Nickname: The Green

Chairman: Kate Binns
Secretary: Brian Barter
11 Curlew Close
Berkhamsted
Herts
HP4 2HZ
Tel: 07982 072 783
Manager: Colin Jones
Prog Editor: See secretary

Ground: Pancake Lane, Leverstock Green, H. Hempstead, HP2 4BN Tel: 01442 246 280
Capacity: 1,500 **Seats:** 50 **Covered:** 100
Midweek Matchday: Tuesday **Clubhouse:** Yes **Shop:** No
Colours(change): White/green/green. (Yellow & blue/blue)
Previous Names: None
Previous Lges: West Herts (pre 1950) & Herts County 50-91
Records: Att: 1,000 **App:** Jonnie Wallace
Senior Honours: South Midlands Senior Division 1996-97.

10 YEAR RECORD

99-00	00-01	01-02	02-03	03-04	04-05	05-06	06-07	07-08	08-09
SSM S 12	SSM S 10	SSM1 8	SSM1 4	SSM P 9	SSM P 14	SSM P 6	SSM P 5	SSM P 7	SSM P 6

OXHEY JETS

Founded: Nickname: Jets

Chairman: Phil Andrews
Secretary: David Fuller
4 Sage Close
Biggleswade
Beds
SG18 8WH
Tel: 07786 627 659
Manager: Benny Higham
Prog Editor: See secretary

Ground: Boundary Stadium, Atham Way, Watford WD19 6FW Tel: 0208 421 6277
Capacity: 1,000 **Seats:** 100 **Covered:** 100
Midweek Matchday: Wednesday **Clubhouse:** Yes **Shop:** No
Colours(change): All royal blue. (All yellow)
Previous Names:
Previous Lges: Herts Senior County
Records: Att: 257 v Barnet Herts Senior Cup 05-06 **App:**Ian Holdon
Senior Honours: Herts Senior County Premier 2000-01, 01-02, 02-03.
SSML Div 1 Champions 2004-2005, Herts Senior Centenary Trophy 2004-2005

10 YEAR RECORD

99-00	00-01	01-02	02-03	03-04	04-05	05-06	06-07	07-08	08-09
HertP 7	HertP 1	HertP 1	HertP 1	HertP 2	SSM1 1	SSM P 13	SSM P 7	SSM P 19	SSM P 13

ROYSTON TOWN

Founded: 1872 Nickname:

Chairman: Steve Jackson
Secretary: Dave Chappell
19 Windsor Road
Royston
Herts
SG8 9JF
Tel: 07787 426 613
Manager: Paul Attfield
Prog Editor: Alan Barlow

Ground: Garden Walk, Royston, Herts, SG8 7HP Tel: 01763 241 204
Capacity: **Seats:** **Covered:**
Midweek Matchday: **Clubhouse:** **Shop:**
Colours(change): White/black/white. (All red).
Previous Names: None
Previous Lges: Cambridgeshire & Herts Co. Isthmian
Records: Att: 876 v Aldershot Town, 1993-94.
Senior Honours: Herts County Champions 1976-77. South Midlands Div.1 1978-79, 08-09.

10 YEAR RECORD

99-00	00-01	01-02	02-03	03-04	04-05	05-06	06-07	07-08	08-09
SSM P 11	SSM P 17	SSM P 8	SSM P 16	SSM P 13	SSM P 16	SSM P 18	SSM P 20	SSM1 5	SSM1 1

ST MARGARETSBURY

Founded: 1894 Nickname: Athletic

Chairman: Gary Stock
Secretary: Philip Hayward
2 Meridan Way
Amwell Lane
Stansted Abbotts
SG12 8DW
Tel: 07721 415 579
Manager: Lee Judges
Prog Editor: Dave Barker

Ground: Recreation Grd, Station Road, St Margarets, SG12 8EH Tel: 01920 870 473
Capacity: 1,000 **Seats:** 60 **Covered:** 60
Midweek Matchday: Tuesday **Clubhouse:** Yes **Shop:** No
Colours(change): Red & black stripes/black/black (White & red/red/red)
Previous Names: Stanstead Abbots > 1962
Previous Lges: East Herts, Hertford & District, Waltham & District, 47-48 Herts Co. 48-92
Records: Att: 450 v Stafford Rangers FA Cup 2001-02
Senior Honours: Spartan Lg 95-96 Herts Senior Centenary Trophy 92-93,
Herts Charity Shield 97-98

10 YEAR RECORD

99-00	00-01	01-02	02-03	03-04	04-05	05-06	06-07	07-08	08-09
SSM P 16	SSM P 13	SSM P 5	SSM P 5	SSM P 3	SSM P 7	SSM P 12	SSM P 15	SSM P 11	SSM P 14

PREMIER DIVISION - 2009-10

TRING ATHLETIC

Founded: 1958 Nickname: Athletic

Chairman: Alan Foskett
Secretary: Bob Winter
21 Bunyan Close
Tring
Herts
HP23 5PS
Tel: 07979 816 528
Manager: Phil Casserley
Prog Editor: Barry Simmons

Ground: The Grass Roots Stadium, Pendley Sp. Centre, Cow Lane,Tring, HP23 5NS Tel: 01442 891 144
Capacity: 1,233 **Seats:** 150 **Covered:** 100+
Midweek Matchday: Tuesday **Clubhouse:** Yes **Shop:** Yes
Colours(change): Red/black/black (Yellow/green/green)
Previous Names: None
Previous Lges: West Herts 58-88
Records: Goalscorer: Andy Humphreys - 209 **App:** Mark Boniface - 642
Senior Honours: Spartan South Midlands Senior Division 1999-00

10 YEAR RECORD

99-00	00-01	01-02	02-03	03-04	04-05	05-06	06-07	07-08	08-09
SSM S 1	SSM S 4	SSM1 5	SSM1 3	SSM1 4	SSM P 4	SSM P 10	SSM P 11	SSM P 10	SSM P 8

WELWYN GARDEN CITY

Founded: 1921 Nickname: Citizens

Chairman: Gary Bevan
Secretary: Richard Dunning
38 Cowper Road
Welwyn Garden City
Herts
AL7 3LS
Tel: 07940 125 082
Manager: Paul Faulkner
Prog Editor: Paul Gregory

Ground: Herns Lane, Welwyn Garden City, Herts AL7 1TA Tel: 01707 328 470
Capacity: 1,500 **Seats:** 40 **Covered:** 120
Midweek Matchday: Tuesday **Clubhouse:** Yes **Shop:** Yes
Colours(change): Sky blue/claret/sky blue (White/red/red)
Previous Names: None
Previous Lges: Spartan, Metropolitan & Greater London
Records:
Senior Honours: South Midlands Champions 1973-74. Div.1 81-82.

10 YEAR RECORD

99-00	00-01	01-02	02-03	03-04	04-05	05-06	06-07	07-08	08-09
SSM P 19	SSM P 19	SSM1 16	SSM1 6	SSM1 3	SSM P 8	SSM P 8	SSM P 4	SSM P 16	SSM P 9

DIVISION ONE INS & OUTS
IN: AFC Dunstable (P), Hadley (P), Hatfield Town (P), Royston Town (P)
OUT: Arlesey Athletic (W), Cockfosters (R), Holmer Green (R), Winslow United (F)

AFC DUNSTABLE

Chairman: Simon Bullard.
Secretary: Craig Renfrew, 75B, Princes Street, Dunstable, Beds, LU6 3AS.
Tel (H) 01582 471794 (B & M) 07976 192530 Fax:- (H) 01582 471794
Email: renfrewcraig@aol.com
Programme Editor: Craig Renfrew.
Manager: Alex Butler.
Ground: Creasey Park, Creasey Park Drive, Brewers Hill Road Dunstable LU6 1BB
Tel 01582 667555
Colours: Royal blue/royal/white.
Alternate colours: White/red/red.
Directions: From Dunstable Town Centre take A5 North and at the first main roundabout turn left into Bewers Hill Road. Go past the fire station on the left to the first mini roundabout and turn Right immediately after the roundabout into Creasey Park Drive and the ground is at the End of the road on the left.

AMERSHAM TOWN

Chairman: Lawrence Lipka.
Secretary: Stephen Cogdell, 44, Dane Close, Amersham, Bucks HP7 9LZ
Tel (H) 01494 580544 (B) 07919 273508 Email stephencogdell@hotmail.com
Programme Editor: Michael Gahagan.
Manager: Simon Damery.
Ground: Spratleys Meadow, School Lane, Amersham, Bucks. HP7 0EL. Tel 01494 727428
Colours: Black & white quarters/black/black.
Alternate colours: Yellow & black quarters/black/yellow.
Directions: From London, take the A413 towards Aylesbury. At bottom of Amersham old town, turn right into Mill Lane. At junction at top of Mill Lane, turn left into School Lane. Ground is 100 yards on the left.

AMPTHILL TOWN

Chairman: Steve Roach.
Secretary: Eric Turner, 5, Arthur Street, Ampthill, Beds. MK45 2QG.
Tel (H) 01525 403128 (M) 07908 374118
Email: ericturner789@btinternet.com
Programme Editor: Eric Turner
Manager: Steve Goodridge.
Ground: Ampthill Park, Woburn Road, Ampthill MK45 2HX Tel: 01525 404440.
Colours: Yellow/blue/yellow. **Alternate colours**: All red.
Directions: From South leave M1 at Junction 12 Toddington.Turn right as sign posted until you meet the junction with the Ampthill by pass. Go straight across until you meet a mini roundabout at the town centre. Turn left into Woburn Street. The ground is about half a mile on the right just past a layby. From the North, leave the M1 at junction 13 and turn left. At first set of traffic lights turn right onto A507 Ridgmont bypass. Continue until you see the right hand turning signposted for Ampthill, ground is about a mile on the left opposite the Rugby ground

BEDFORD FC

Chairman: Lui La Mura.
Secretary: Paolo Riccio, 15, Linisfarne Priory, Bedford, Beds. MK41 0RE
Tel (M) 07950 755771 Email:- paolo.riccio@ntlworld.com
Programme Editor: Geoffrey Seagrave.
Manager: Luke Capon.
Ground: McMullen Park, Meadow Lane, Cardington, Bedford, MK44 3SB. Tel: 01234 831024.
Colours: Black & white stripes/black/black. **Alternate colours**: All blue.
Directions: From the M1 Junction 13 take the A421 on to the Bedford Bypass, take the third exit on to the A603, the ground is 250 yards on the left. From the A1 at Sandy take A603 to Bedford, the ground is on the right just before you reach the Bedford Bypass.

BEDFORD TOWN RESERVES

Chairman: David Howell.
Secretary: Patrick Allen, 37, Harter Road, Kempston, Beds. MK42 7EY
Tel: (H) 01234 857513 (M) 07961 558184 (H Fax) 01234 857513
Email:- pat.allen1@hotmail.co.uk
Programme Editor: Carl Allen.
Manager: Steve Rigby.
Ground: The New Eyrie, Meadow Lane, Cardington, Bedford, Beds. MK44 3SB Tel:- 01234 831558
Colours: All blue. **Alternate Colours**:- Yellow/navy blue/yellow.
Directions: From A1, take the A603 to Sandy & Bedford. Go through Willington and ground is 1.5 miles on the right & signposted Meadow Lane. From M1 junction 13, take the A421 to Bedford bypass. Exit at the Sandy turn off onto the A603. Ground is first turning on the left about 300yards from by pass.

BRACHE SPARTA COMMUNITY FC

(Formerly Brache Sparta)
Chairman: Zulfqar Ahmed.
Secretary: Christpher Juraszek, Bat & barrel, 104 – 106, Park Street, Luton. LU1 3EY
Tel (H) 01582 651110 (B) 01582 651111 (M) 07737 408121
Email: chris.juraszek@ntlworld.com
Programme Editor: As for Secretary
Manager: Mark Teeling.
Ground: Foxdell Recreation Ground, Dallow Road, Luton, Beds. LU1 1TG Tel: 01582 720751.
Colours: White/black/black & white hoops. **Alternate Colours**: Yellow/blue/blue.
Directions: From M1 Junction 11 take A505 towards Luton. At first roundabout turn right (3rd exit) car showrooms will be on the left. Straight ahead at A505 by pass roundabout, over mini-roundabout by B & Q store on the left, into Dallow Road. Entry to ground is approximately 50 yards on the right adjacent to Foxdell Junior School. From Luton use A505 by pass and turn left at large roundabout – Aldi store on your left.

BUCKINGHAM ATHLETIC

Chairman: John Webb.
Secretary: Charles Bassano, 62, Moreton Road, Buckingham, MK18 1PE.
Tel (H) 01280 817801 (M) 07810 755193 Email: charles.bassano@sky.com
Programme Editor: Colin Howkins
Email: john.webb4@tesco.net.
Manager: Don Watts.
Ground: Stratford Fields, Stratford Road, Buckingham. MK18 1NY Tel: 01280 816945.
Colours: Sky & navy quarters/sky/sky. **Alternate colours**: All red.
Directions: From Oxford, Aylesbury or Bletchley, take the Buckingham ring road to the A422 Stony Stratford roundabout, turn left, towards town centre. The ground is situated at the bottom of the hill on the left. From Milton Keynes (A422) straight across the Stony Stratford roundabout. At the Buckingham ring road roundabout, go straight across towards the town centre and the ground is at the bottom of the hill on the left at about half a mile.

COCKFOSTERS

Chairman: Colin Bell.
Secretary: Graham Bint, 15, Chigwell Park, Chigwell, Essex, IG7 5BE.
Tel (H) 0208 500 7369. (B) 0208 500 7369. (M) 07729 709926 Fax: (H & B) 0208500 7369.
Email: graham.bint@ntlworld.com
Programme Editor: Alan Simmons.
Email thebellfamily24@btunternet.com
Manager: Neil Ewing.
Ground: Cockfosters Sports Ground, Chalk Lane, Cockfosters, Herts, EN4 9JG. Tel: 0208 449 5833.
Colours: All red. **Alternate colours**: Yellow/blue/blue.
Directions: Leaving the M25 motorway at junction 24 (Potters Bar) take the A111 signposted to Cockfosters. The ground is situated approximately 2 miles from the motorway on the right immediately before Cockfosters underground station.
VEHICLE DRIVERS PLEASE BE AWARE THAT THE YELLOW LINES & PARKING RESTRICTIONS IN CHALK LANE ARE STRICTLY ENFORCED ON SATURDAYS.

CRANFIELD UNITED

Chairman: Geoff Crook.
Secretary: Larry Corkrey Chapel Cottage, Cranfield Road, Moulsoe, Bucks. MK16 0HB
Tel (H) 01908 618371 (M) 07854 936405 (H Fax) 01908 618371
Email: larrycor@btinternet.com
Programme Editor: See Secretary
Manager: Craig Connell.
Ground: Crawley Road, Cranfield, Beds MK43 0AA . Tel: 01234 751 444.
Colours: All red. **Alternate colours**: White/black/white.
Directions: After entering the village of Cranfield take the North Crawley/Newport Pagnell road. The ground is on the left hand side just before leaving the speed limit signs.

CRAWLEY GREEN

Chairman: Alan Clark.
Secretary: Eddie Downey, 9, Keymer Close, Luton, Beds LU2 8JS
Tel (H) 01582 451202 (M) 07956 107477
Email eddied@thamesideltd.co.uk
Programme Editor: Alan Clark.
Email alan.clark@mwkl.co.uk
Manager: Neil Tattersall.
Ground: Barton Rovers FC Sharpenhoe Road, Barton Le Clay, Beds. MK45 4SD
Tel 01582 882398.
Colours: All maroon. **Alternate colours**: Yellow/blue/yellow.
Directions: From M1 junction 12, turn right from South, turn left from the North, onto the A5120. After approximately 1.5 miles take the second turning on the right signposted Harlington and Barton. Follow the road through Sharpenhoe to Barton, at mini roundabout turn right and after about 400 yards turn right to the ground. Ground entrance is in Luton Road. Other directions are on the Barton Rovers FC Website.

HADLEY FC

Chairman: Guy Slee.
Secretary: Bob Henderson, 25, Potters Road, New Barnet, Herts. EN5 5HS
Tel (H) 0208 441 0164 Email: matchsecretary@hadleyfc.com
Programme Editor: Mark Bunn.
Manager: Ian Gray.
Ground: Potters Bar Town FC, Parkfield Stadium, Watkins Rise (Off The Walk), Potters Bar, Herts. EN6 1QB Tel 01707 654833
Colours: Red/black/black. **Alternate Colours:** Blue/black/white.
Directions: From M25, exit at junction 24 towards Potters Bar along Southgate Road A111. Turn right at first set of traffic lights into the High Street A1000. After the petrol station on the left and the pedestrian crossing, take the first left into The Walk. After 200 yards turn right into Watkins Rise and the ground is at the end on the right. Nearest BR station is Potters Bar.
PLEASE NOTE: DO NOT PARK IN THE MAYFAIR LODGE HOME CAR PARK OPPOSITE THE GROUND OR YOU WILL BE CLAMPED

HARPENDEN TOWN

Chairman: Kelvin Gregory.: Les Crabtree, 11, Wensley Close, Harpenden, Herts. AL5 1RZ
Tel 01582 622669 (B) 0208 424 3287 (M) 07968 120032 Fax 0208 424 3321
Email: l.crabtree@colart.co.uk or les-crabtree@lineone.net
Programme Editor: See Secretary
Manager: Christian Garzarolli.
Ground: Rothamsted Park, Amenbury Lane, Harpenden. AL5 2EF. Tel: 07968 120032
Colours: Yellow/royal blue/royal blue. **Alternate Colours**: Red/red/black.
Directions: A1081 into Harpenden town centre cross mini roundabout at Station Road. At next mini roundabout turn right into Leyton Road then turn left into Amenbury Lane, car park 50 yards on left. Ground entrance through car park to right hand corner to right of the swimming pool.
PLEASE NOTE, PARK IN PUBLIC PAY & DISPLAY CAR PARK.

HODDESDON TOWN

Chairman: Roger Merton.
Secretary: Jane Sinden, 22, Hatley Road, Wrestlingsworth, Sandy, Beds SG19 2EH
Tel (H) 01767 631297 (B) 01707 391477 Fax (H) 01767 631562
Email: janedsinden@fsmail.net
Programme Editor: See Secretary
Manager: Geoff O'Vell.
Ground: The Stewart Edwards Stadium, Lowfield ,Park View, Hoddesdon, Herts, EN11 8PX.
Tel: 01992 463133.
Colours: White/black/black. **Alternate colours**: Blue/blue/yellow.
Directions: From A10 take Hoddesdon turn off, A1170. Follow slip road to roundabout then turn right into Amwell Street. Take the first right at church into Pauls Lane. Follow road round to left (Taveners Way). At mini roundabout opposite Iceland store, Turn right into Brocket Road. At T junction turn left into Park View and the ground is 200 yards on the left
NOTE – PLEASE NOTE THERE ARE SATURDAY PARKING RESTRICTIONS IN OPERATION IN PARK VIEW.

HOLMER GREEN

Chairman:. Frank Francies.
Secretary: Mike Andrews, 134, Marys Mead, Hazlemere, High Wycombe, Bucks. HP15 7DZ
Tel (H) 01494 715687 (B) 01494 715480 (M) 07885 181186 (Fax) (H) 01494 715480
Email:- mikeandrews@btinternet.com
Programme Editor: John Anderson.
Manager: Chris Allen.
Ground: HGSA Watchet Lane, Holmer Green, High Wycombe, Bucks HP15 6UF. Tel: 01494 711485.
Colours: Green/white/green. **Alternate colours**: Yellow/white/white.
Directions: From Amersham on A404 High Wycombe Road. After approximately 2 miles turn right into Sheepcote Dell Road. Continue until end of road by Bat & Ball Public House. Turn right then immediately left. Continue approximately 1/2 mile until two mini-roundabouts, turn left in front of the Mandarin Duck into Watchet Lane. Ground 150 yards on right.

KINGS LANGLEY

Chairman: Derry Edgar.
Secretary: Andy Mackness, 79, Weymouth Street, Apsley, Hemel Hempstead, Herts HP3 9SJ.
Tel (H) 01442 398186 (M) 07976 692801.
Email: andymackness@yahoo.co.uk
Programme Editor: Roy Mitchard
Manager: Steve Heath.
Ground: Gaywood Park, Hempstead Road, Kings Langley.WD4 8BS Tel: 07976 692801.
Colours: Red & white/blue/red. **Alternate colours**: Black & white/black/black.
Directions: From M25 leave at junction 20. Take A4251 to Kings Langley. Through the village. The ground is approximately 1/2 mile on the right.

LONDON COLNEY

Chairman: Tony Clafton.
Secretary: Dave Brock, 50, Seymour Road, St.Albans AL3 5HW.
Tel (H) 01727 761644 (Fax) 01727 761644 (M) 07508 035835
Email: davebrock42@hotmail.com
Programme Editor: See chairman.
Manager: Julian Robertson.
Ground: Cotlandswick Playing Fields, London Colney, Herts AL2 1DW. Tel: 01727 822132.
Colours: All royal blue. **Alternate colours**: Red & black stripes/black.black.
Directions: From M25 junction 22 follow A1081to St Albans. At London Colney roundabout take A414 signposted Hemel Hempstead/Watford. Hidden turn into ground after approximately 500 metres (just after lay-by) signposted "Sports Ground". Follow road around past the rugby club to ground entrance.

NEW BRADWELL ST PETER

Manager: Steve Tucker.
Chairman: John Haynes.
Secretary: Ian Rollins, 16, Masefield Grove, Bletchley, Milton Keynes, Bucks MK3 5AR
Tel (H) 01908 643783 (M) 07912 076473
Email HonSecretary@Newbradwellstpeter.co.uk
Programme Editor: Adrian Haynes.
Ground: The Recreation Ground, Bradwell Road, Bradville, Milton Keynes. Tel: 01908 313835.
Colours: All maroon. **Alternate colours**: Yellow/blue/white.
Directions: From M1 junction 14, go towards Newport Pagnell, turn left at first roundabout into H3 (A422 Monks Way). Go six roundabouts then turn right into V6 (Grafton Street). At first roundabout drive all the way around and then take the first left. At 1st mini-roundabout turn left. Straight across next mini-roundabout. Ground is then immediately on the left.

SPORT LONDON E BENFICA

Chairman: John Vitorino.
Secretary: Ninette Fernandes, 106, Victoria Road, London NW6 6QB
Tel (H) 0207 625 5486 (M) 07969 036246,
Email info@sportlondonebenficafc.co.uk or ninettefernandes@vida-nova.com
Programme Editor: Jose Viana.
Manager: Jose Viana
Ground: Haringey Borough, Coles Park, White Hart Lane, London N17 7JP Tel 0208 889 1415
Colours: Red/white/red. **Alternate Colours**: White/red/black.
Directions: From Junction 25 of the M25 (or from the Great Cambridge roundabout on the A406 North Circular Road) turn south onto the A10 and follow it until traffic lights with a slip lane on right before turning into White Hart Lane. This will be the second main set of traffic lights after the Great Cambridge roundabout where it meets the North Circular Road. After turning into White Hart Lane, the ground is about 500 yards on the left after a petrol station.

STONY STRATFORD TOWN

Chairman: Christopher Wise.
Secretary: Steven Sartain, 29, Magdalen Close, Stony Stratford, Milton Keynes, MK11 1PW.
Tel (H & Fax) 01908 265306 after 6pm. (M) 07901 664000
Email: steve.sartain456@btinternet.com or secretary@stonystratfordtownfc.co.uk
Programme Editor: Paul Grimsley.
Manager: James Stoyles.
Ground: Ostlers Lane, Stony Stratford, Milton Keynes. MK11 1AR Tel: 07914 012709.
Colours: Sky & navy blue/navy/navy. **Alternate colours**: Yellow/black.black.
Directions: From Dunstable A5. On approaching Bletchley continue on A5 trunk road (Hinckley) to end of dual carriageway. At A5/A508 roundabout take first exit, through traffic lights. Ostlers Lane second exit on right. From Buckingham A422 to A5/A508 roundabout, take last exit, through traffic lights, over bridge. Ostlers Lane second exit on the right.

SUN POSTAL SPORTS

Chairman: Andrew Toon.
Secretary: Maurice Tibbles, 4, Lambert Court, Bushy Grove Road, Watford, Herts. WD23 2HF
Tel: (H) 01923 468069 (M) 07895 066075
Email: tibbles.joe@live.com
Programme Editor: See chairman.
Manager: Mark Simmonds.
Ground: Sun Postal Sports Club Bellmountwood Avenue, Watford.WD17 3BN Tel: 01923 227453
Colours: Yellow/blue/blue. **Alternate colours**: All red.
Directions: From Watford town centre take the A411 (Hempstead Road) away from the Town Hall towards Hemel Hempstead. At 2nd set of traffic lights turn left into Langley Way. At the next roundabout, where there is a parade of shops on the left and the “Essex Arms” on the right, take the third exit into Cassiobury Drive. Then take the first turn left into Bellmount Wood Avenue then at the left hand bend turn right into the Club entrance.

TOKYNGTON MANOR

Chairman: Terry Spinger.
Secretary: Dave McArdle, 26, Longhale, Pitstone, Bucks. LU7 9GF
Tel (H) 01525 244700 (M) 07912 574224
Email: djmtmfc@live.co.uk
Programme Editor: Sabrah Armah.
Manager: Matt Oliver.
Ground: Hanwell Town FC, Reynolds Field, Perivale Lane Greenford, Middlesex UB6 8TL
Tel 0208 998 1701
Colours: Black & white/black/black. **Alternate colours**: Yellow & blue/blue/blue.
Directions: Exit junction16 of the M25 onto the A40(M) towards London. Go over the Greenford fly-over and get into the nearside lane signposted Ealing & Perivale exit. At top of slip road turn right across the A40 and the ground is immediately on the left. Turn first left into Perivale Lane and the entrance is 200 yards on the left. The nearest station is Perivale – London Central line Underground.

DIVISION TWO INS & OUTS	IN: Berkhamsted (N) OUT: AFC Dunstable (P), Hadley (P), Markyate (W)

ASTON CLINTON
Secretary: Mark Foster, 17, New Road, Aston Clinton, Bucks HP22 5JD
Tel (H) 01296 630884 (B) 07831 765738 (M) 07831765738
Ground: Aston Clinton Park, London Road, Aston Clinton, Bucks. HP22 5HL Tel. 01296 631818
Directions: The ground is situated in Aston Clinton village off the main road (old A41) The ground is opposite the Duck Inn pub. Aston Clinton can be approached on the B489 from Dunstable or via the A418 from Leighton Buzzard.through Aylesbury following the signs for the A41 to Aston Clinton.

BERKHAMSTED FC
Secretary: Ben Terry, 21B Cookham Road, Maidenhead, Berks SL6 7EF. Tel (H) 01628 780332 (M) 07779 352562
Ground: Broadwater, Lower Kings Road, Berkhamsted, Herts HP4 2AA Tel 01442 862815
Directions: Exit A41 onto the A416 and go straight over the town centre traffic lights into Lower Kings Road. Go over the canal bridge and take the first left into Broadwater. Follow the road left parallel to the canal. The ground is on the right hand side between the canal and the railway.

BLETCHLEY TOWN
Secretary: Michelle Snead, 13, Colston Bassett, Emerson Valley, Milton Keynes, Bucks MK4 2BU
Tel (H) 01908 505046 (M) 07895 256905
Ground: Scots Club, Selbourne Avenue, Bletchley, Milton Keynes. MK3 5BX Tel 01908 368881
Directions: From Bletchley town centre, take the Buckingham road at the Three Trees pub and turn left at the roundabout into Newton Road. Bear right and take the second turning left into Selbourne Avenue. Turn left onto a private road and go through the narrow railway arch, the ground is 300 yards on the left. Full directions are available from the club website.

BUCKS STUDENTS UNION
Secretary: Jack Edmeads, Bucks Stiudents Union, Queen Alexandra Road, High Wycombe, Bucks HP11 2JZ
Tel (H) 01494 601600 (M) 07877 498346 Email
Ground: Amersham Town FC, Spratleys Meadow, School Lane, Amersham, Bucks. HP7 0EL. Tel 01494 727428
Directions: From London, take the A413 towards Aylesbury. At the bottom of Amersham Old Town, turn right into Mill Lane. At the junction at the top of Mill Lane, turn left into School Lane and the ground is 100 yards on the left.

CADDINGTON
Secretary: Mick Gregory, Pipers Farm, Mancroft Road, Aley Green, Luton LU1 4DR. Tel (H) 01582 841386
(B) 01582 841386 (M) 07778 010066 Fax 01582 841386
Ground: Caddington Recreation Club, Manor Road, Caddington. Luton LU1 4HH. Tel 01582 505151.
Directions: From M1 junction 10A roundabout turn right on A1081 towards Harpenden. Take the first right (Newlands Road). After 500 yards at the end of Newlands Road (T-junction), turn left into Caddington village. At end of village green turn left into Manor Road (adjacent shops). Proceed 800 metres. Clubhouse and ground on left next to Catholic Church.

KENT ATHLETIC
Secretary: George Trott, 45, Gooseberry Hill, Luton, Beds LU3 2JZ. Tel (H) 01582 619230 (M) 07854 674586
Ground: Kent Social Club, Tenby Drive, Luton, LU4 9BN
Tel: 01582 582723.
Directions: From M1 Junction 11 take A505 towards Luton. Take the first turning on the left (Stoneygate Road), straight over at the roundabout and turn right at traffic lights into Beechwood Road. Take the first road on the left (Pembroke Avenue) and then the first right into Tenby Drive. Ground and car park 100 yards on left.

MK WANDERERS
Secretary: Neill Davy, 79, Stokenchurch Place, Bradwell Common, Milton Keynes. Bucks. MK13 8AZ
Tel (H) 01908 606802 (B) 01604 665563 (M) 07818 057070
Ground: Kents Hill Pavilion, Frithwood Crescent, Kents Hill, Milton Keynes. MK7 6HQ
Directions: From M1 Junction 13 take the A421 towards Milton Keynes. After approx 3 miles at the first roundabout go straight across onto the dual carriageway. At the next roundabout go straight over onto Standing Way. Take the first exit on the left into Groveway and across three roundabouts. Turn slight left into Firthwood Crescent and then turn right to stay on Firthwood Crescent. The ground is on the right. For other directions consult the website.

MURSLEY UNITED
Secretary: Bob Dixon, 40, Tweedale Close, Mursley, Bucks. MK17 0SB. Tel (H) 01296 720187 (M) 07852 229126
Ground: The Playing Field, Station Road, Mursley. MK17 0SU
Directions: From Milton Keynes take A421, (H8 Standing Way) towards Buckingham.. After leaving Milton Keynes take first exit at roundabout, signposted Mursley. At traffic island in village turn right into Station Road. Ground is on the right hand side on leaving the village.

OLD BRADWELL UNITED
Secretary: Laura Bird, 78, Harrowden, Bradwille, Milton Keynes, Bucks. MK13 7DB.
Tel (H) 01908 311598 (M) 07941 053125
Ground: Abbey Road, Bradwell Village, Milton Keynes, MK13 9AR Tel 01908 312355.
Directions: From M1 Junction 14, go towards Newport Pagnell. Turn left at first roundabout into H3 Monks Way. Follow H3 and at the sixth roundabout (Bancroft Roundabout) turn left into Grafton Street. Take the first right fork into Bradwell (Rawlings Road). At the mini roundabout turn left into Loughton Road. Take the next right into Primrose Road and bear right to the ground at the bottom of Primrose Road.

PADBURY UNITED
Secretary: Graham Chaplin, 14, The Sidings, Stourbridge DY8 2XT. Tel (M) 07710 471237
Ground: Springfields Playing Field, Padbury Buckingham, Bucks MK18 2AQ.
Directions: From Buckingham follow ring road with signs to Aylesbury (A413). From Aylesbury follow signs to Buckingham (A413). Padbury is 2 miles south of Buckingham on A413 and 3 Miles north of Winslow on A413. Turn off A413 opposite bus shelter on Springfields Estate and follow road forward. Playing field gates are in front of you.

PITSTONE & I VINGHOE
Secretary: Stuart Plenty, 62 Station Road, Ivinghoe, Leighton Buzzard, Beds. LU7 9EB. Tel (M) 07732 309520
Ground: Pitstone Recreation Ground, Vicarage Road, Pitstone LU7 9RY. Tel 01296 661271 (match days only).
Directions: From Dunstable, take B489 Tring Road, turn right into Ivinghoe, follow road through to Pitstone roundabout, turn left, ground on the right. From Aylesbury, take A41M, and exit at B488 sign posted Dunstable. Go straight over two roundabouts and take the first turn left into Vicarage Road. The ground is on the left opposite the Village Farm Museum.

RISBOROUGH RANGERS
Secretary: Nick Bishop, 28, Stratton Road, Princes Risborough, Bucks, HP27 9AX. Tel (H) 01844 342934 (B) 01844 276173 (M) 07855 958236 (B Fax) (B) 01844 274199
Ground: " Windsors" Horsenden Lane, Princes Risborough. Bucks HP27 9NE. Tel 07745 478647 (Match days only)
Directions: On entering Prices Risborough from Aylesbury, turn left at first roundabout. At the second roundabout turn right. Go pass Esso petrol station on left hand side. After approximately 400 yards take the right fork. Take second turn on left (Picts Lane). At junction turn right over the railway bridge and then immediately right again. Ground is approximately 200 yards on the right hand side.

THE 61 F.C. (LUTON)
Secretary: Richard Everitt, 44, Somersby Close, Luton, LU13XB.
Tel (H) 01582 485095 (M) 07729 858553
Ground: Kingsway Ground, Beverley Road, Luton. LU4 8EU
Tel: 01582 485095
Directions: From M1 Junction 11, follow signs to Luton Town Centre. At PC World roundabout turn right into
Chaul End Lane . Then first left into Cannaught Road, then third left into Beverley Road the ground
is 50yards on the right.

TOTTERNHOE
Secretary: Jim Basterfield, 41, Park Avenue, Totternhoe, Dunstable, Beds, LU6 1QF. Tel (H) 01582 667941. (B) 01582 605353. (M) 07870 284499 (B Fax) 01582 660103
Ground: Totternhoe Recreation Ground, Dunstable Road, Totternhoe LU6 1RG. Tel: 01582 606738.
Directions: From Dunstable Town Centre take the B489 towards Tring. At the fourth roundabout turn right, signposted Totternhoe. Go down the hill out of Dunstable into Totternhoe and the ground is on the right just past Dunstable Town Cricket Club.

TRING CORINTHIANS
Secretary: Gary Mendham, 72, Mill View Road, Tring, Herts. HP23 4EW Tel. (H) 01442 823589 (M) 07886 528214,
Ground: Icknield Way, Tring, Herts HP23 5HJ
Tel 07886 528214
Directions: At M25 join A41(M) and after 11 miles join the B488 Icknield Way and sign posted Dunstable. After approximately one & half miles, the ground is on the left opposite the Lakeside housing estate. From Aylesbuty, take the A41(M) towards London and take the turning sign posted B488 Dunstable and then follow the directions above.

WODSON PARK
Secretary: Ian Bush, 42, Burnet Square, Hertford, Herts SG14 2HD. Tel (H) 01992 587334 (B) 01920 863136
(M) 07958 799552 Fax 01992 306773
Ground: Ware FC, Wadesmill Road, Ware Herts SG12 0UQ
Tel 01920 463247
Directions: From the South, leave the M25 at junction 25 and take the A10 north pastCheshunt and Hertford. Leave the A10 at junction of A602 and B1001. Take the last right into Watton Road into Ware. Go past the cemetery on the right and turn left at the roundabout into Wadesmill Road (A1170). Ground at the top of the hill, turn right into the Wodson Sports Centre. From the North, leave the A1 (M) at junction 7 and take the A602 to Ware. At the roundabout take the second exit onto Watton Road into Ware and then proceed as above.

SUSSEX COUNTY LEAGUE

www.scfl.org.uk

Sponsored by:
No Sponsor

Founded: 1920

Recent champions:

2004: Chichester City United

2005: Horsham YMCA

2006: Horsham YMCA

2007: Eastbourne Town

2008: Crowborough Athletic

Division One		P	W	D	L	F	A	Pts
Eastbourne Utd Ass.		38	23	6	9	79	37	75
Arundel		38	21	10	7	96	53	73
Horsham YMCA		38	23	4	11	72	53	73
Wick		38	21	8	9	77	60	71
Three Bridges		38	20	7	11	75	51	67
Shoreham		38	18	11	9	63	45	65
Chichester City Utd		38	19	5	14	74	70	62
Redhill		38	16	13	9	70	43	61
Lingfield		38	14	15	9	62	51	57
Ringmer	*-10*	38	19	5	14	86	60	52
Selsey		38	14	9	15	59	48	51
Pagham		38	13	9	16	51	59	48
St Francis Rangers		38	13	8	17	64	65	47
Whitehawk		38	13	8	17	62	64	47
Hailsham Town		38	12	7	19	54	92	43
Hassocks		38	10	10	18	49	61	40
East Grinstead Town		38	8	9	21	54	84	33
East Preston		38	9	5	24	53	85	32
Oakwood		38	8	5	25	43	97	29
Worthing United		38	4	10	24	42	107	22

JOHN O'HARA CUP

(Division One and Division Two teams)

FIRST ROUND

Hailsham Town 2 Sidley United 2 *aet*

Replay: Sidley United 0 **Hailsham Town** 2

Lancing 3 East Preston 1

Loxwood 1 Selsey 1 *aet*

Replay: **Selsey** 2 Loxwood 0

Oakwood 3 Littlehampton Town 0

Ringmer 3 **Peacehaven & Telscombe** 4

Rustington 2 Hassocks 1

SECOND ROUND

Bexhill United 0 **East Grinstead Town** 2

Chichester City United 1 **Selsey** 2

Crawley Green 1 **Arundel** 3

Eastbourne United Association 3 Westfield 3 *aet*

Replay: Westfield 2 **Eastbourne United Association** 4

Lingfield 5 Lancing 3

Mile Oak 0 **St Francis Rangers** 3

Oakwood 2 Worthing United 0

Pagham 2 Seaford Town 1

Peacehaven & Telscombe 2 Midhurst & Easebourne Utd 1

Redhill 2 Wealden 1

Rye United 3 Hailsham Town 1

Sidlesham 1 **Shoreham** 3

Southwick 0 **Whitehawk** 4

Steyning Town 1 **Three Bridges** 2

Storrington 0 **Horsham YMCA** 8

Wick 2 Rustington 0

THIRD ROUND

Arundel 5 Pagham 2

Horsham YMCA 1 Eastbourne United Association 0

Oakwood 2 Shoreham 0 *aet*

Redhill 3 Wick 1

Rye United 2 Three Bridges 2 *aet*

Replay: **Three Bridges** 1 Rye United 0

Selsey 1 East Grinstead Town 0

St Francis Rangers 1 **Peacehaven & Telscombe** 2

Whitehawk 3 Lingfield 1

QUARTER-FINALS

Oakwood 0 **Three Bridges** 1 *aet*

Peacehaven & Telscombe 2 **Arundel** 3

Redhill 4 Horsham YMCA 4 *aet*

Replay: **Horsham YMCA** 2 Redhill 1 *aet*

Selsey 1 **Whitehawk** 2 *aet*

SEMI-FINALS

Arundel 1 **Whitehawk** 1 *aet* (1-4p) *(at Shoreham)*

Horsham YMCA 2 Three Bridges 1 *(at Hassocks)*

FINAL

(April 10th at Lancing)

Whitehawk 2 Horsham YMCA 1

	Arun.	Chic.	EG	EP	E'bn	Hail.	Has.	Hor.	Ling.	Oak.	Pag.	Red.	Ring.	Sel.	Sho.	St F.	Thre.	Whit.	Wick	Wor.
Arundel		3-1	6-0	1-0	3-1	8-1	4-1	3-4	1-1	3-0	1-1	2-1	5-2	4-0	2-5	2-0	4-2	4-0	1-1	4-3
Chichester City United	2-5		1-0	2-0	2-1	4-3	2-1	2-0	3-4	7-1	2-3	1-1	2-0	4-0	0-2	0-2	1-4	1-1	5-1	0-0
East Grinstead Town	1-1	2-3		2-1	2-3	0-4	1-2	2-5	0-1	2-3	2-1	1-2	0-1	0-2	0-3	1-1	1-1	3-5	3-5	1-2
East Preston	1-1	0-2	0-2		4-1	1-2	1-2	0-2	3-0	2-3	3-1	0-6	3-2	1-1	1-4	3-2	1-2	6-0	0-0	2-1
Eastbourne United Assoc.	0-1	5-0	0-1	4-0	***D***	1-1	0-0	1-1	1-2	2-0	2-0	2-0	1-2	2-0	1-0	2-2	3-2	5-1	3-0	4-0
Hailsham Town	1-3	1-3	1-1	2-1	2-0	***I***	1-1	1-4	0-0	4-1	0-3	0-2	1-7	2-1	1-4	3-2	0-2	1-0	0-5	7-5
Hassocks	0-3	4-0	3-0	1-2	0-0	0-0	***V***	0-2	2-2	3-1	3-2	1-1	2-3	4-1	0-1	1-1	0-3	2-1	3-3	3-0
Horsham YMCA	2-2	1-2	3-2	3-1	0-2	4-1	1-0	***I***	3-0	1-0	2-3	2-1	2-1	1-0	3-0	1-2	1-0	2-1	2-2	2-1
Lingfield	4-1	1-2	2-2	4-2	0-0	2-0	2-0	0-1	***S***	7-0	1-0	2-0	1-1	2-1	2-1	2-3	2-4	2-0	1-3	2-2
Oakwood	2-3	6-3	1-5	0-4	0-5	5-1	1-0	0-2	1-2	***I***	0-2	1-1	1-2	1-1	0-0	0-4	0-3	1-4	1-2	2-1
Pagham	2-0	0-1	2-2	4-1	2-3	0-1	3-1	1-0	2-0	0-0	***O***	1-1	2-0	0-4	0-3	1-1	0-4	1-1	1-3	4-0
Redhill	2-2	3-3	3-3	4-1	2-1	3-1	3-2	3-4	1-1	2-1	0-1	***N***	2-1	2-0	0-1	2-3	4-1	0-0	3-0	2-0
Ringmer	2-1	5-1	6-3	6-0	0-3	2-3	2-1	1-4	4-3	4-1	2-3	1-1		2-0	1-0	2-4	1-2	0-2	2-0	1-0
Selsey	1-3	4-0	0-2	2-0	1-2	3-1	0-0	2-1	0-0	0-0	2-0	0-0	0-0	***O***	2-2	5-1	3-0	5-0	2-1	8-0
Shoreham	1-0	1-1	1-1	2-1	1-2	0-0	2-0	2-2	1-1	3-0	2-0	0-0	1-1	1-1	***N***	1-0	3-3	1-3	2-4	2-1
St Francis Rangers	0-2	0-3	4-1	3-1	1-3	2-1	2-3	3-0	2-2	1-4	2-2	0-2	1-1	0-1	1-2	***E***	0-1	2-1	2-2	5-0
Three Bridges	2-2	2-1	0-0	3-1	1-2	3-4	3-1	1-2	0-0	3-0	4-1	1-1	2-0	1-4	5-1	3-1		1-1	1-3	2-0
Whitehawk	2-2	1-3	0-2	1-1	0-2	6-1	4-0	5-0	1-1	2-3	3-0	0-2	1-2	5-1	1-3	2-0	1-2		1-0	3-2
Wick	2-1	2-0	3-0	5-2	2-6	2-0	3-2	3-1	1-1	2-1	1-1	2-1	0-2	1-0	4-3	2-0	1-0	0-2		4-4
Worthing United	2-2	0-4	2-3	2-2	1-3	1-1	0-0	2-1	2-2	4-1	1-1	0-6	1-14	2-1	0-1	0-4	0-1	0-0	0-2	

NORMAN WINGATE TROPHY
(Division One champions v John O'Hara Cup holders)

(July 29th at Crowborough Athletic)

Crowborough Athletic 1 Shoreham 0

ROY HAYDEN TROPHY
(Division One champions v Sussex Senior Cup holders)

(August 6th at Crowborough Athletic)

Crowborough Athletic 1 Brighton & Hove Albion 0

ivision Two		P	W	D	L	F	A	Pts
eacehaven & Telscombe		**34**	**25**	**5**	**4**	**104**	**31**	**80**
ile Oak		**34**	**24**	**3**	**7**	**92**	**35**	**75**
rawley Down		**34**	**19**	**10**	**5**	**77**	**33**	**67**
ustington		**34**	**20**	**4**	**10**	**66**	**39**	**64**
Vestfield		**34**	**17**	**8**	**9**	**57**	**46**	**59**
ye United		**34**	**16**	**8**	**10**	**66**	**45**	**56**
eaford Town	*+3*	**34**	**16**	**5**	**13**	**61**	**56**	**56**
idley United		**34**	**12**	**9**	**13**	**49**	**57**	**45**
ancing		**34**	**12**	**6**	**16**	**55**	**65**	**42**
oxwood		**34**	**11**	**8**	**15**	**44**	**49**	**41**
outhwick		**34**	**12**	**5**	**17**	**58**	**71**	**41**
torrington		**34**	**12**	**5**	**17**	**43**	**58**	**41**
teyning Town	*-3*	**34**	**12**	**6**	**16**	**42**	**67**	**39**
ittlehampton Town		**34**	**9**	**10**	**15**	**65**	**82**	**37**
Vealden		**34**	**10**	**6**	**18**	**57**	**69**	**36**
idhurst & Easebourne		**34**	**9**	**6**	**19**	**46**	**74**	**33**
exhill United		**34**	**8**	**6**	**20**	**45**	**67**	**30**
idlesham		**34**	**3**	**8**	**23**	**27**	**110**	**17**

DIVISION TWO CUP

FIRST ROUND
Bexhill United 0 **Steyning Town** 2

Crawley Down 5 Westfield 3

SECOND ROUND
Littlehampton Town 4 **Crawley Down** 6

Midhurst & Easebourne United 4 Sidlesham 0

Mile Oak 2 Loxwood 0

Peacehaven & Telscombe 9 Wealden 0

Rye United 2 Steyning Town 1

Sidley United 2 **Lancing** 4

Southwick 0 **Seaford Town** 2

Storrington 1 **Rustington** 3

QUARTER-FINALS
Midhurst & Easebourne Utd 1 **Peacehaven & Telscombe** 5

Mile Oak 1 Lancing 1 *aet*

Replay: **Lancing** 3 Mile Oak 1

Rustington 7 Crawley Down 5 *aet*

Seaford Town 3 Rye United 1

SEMI-FINALS
Peacehaven & Telscombe 5 Lancing 1 *(at Ringmer)*

Seaford Town 1 Rustington 0 *(at Shoreham)*

FINAL
(April 10th at Shoreham)

Seaford Town 0 **Peacehaven & Telscombe** 1

	Bexhill United	Crawley Down	Lancing	Littlehampton Town	Loxwood	Midhurst & Easebourne United	Mile Oak	Peacehaven & Telscombe	Rustington	Rye United	Seaford Town	Sidlesham	Sidley United	Southwick	Steyning Town	Storrington	Wealden	Westfield
Bexhill United		0-3	2-3	0-0	0-2	2-0	3-2	3-5	2-6	0-3	0-2	1-0	1-0	2-3	2-3	3-0	2-2	1-1
Crawley Down	0-2		1-1	6-0	4-0	3-0	2-0	1-2	2-0	3-0	1-1	9-0	3-1	1-1	2-2	2-0	2-2	2-0
Lancing	1-1	3-3		4-1	3-0	2-1	1-4	0-2	0-2	2-4	3-2	3-0	1-2	2-2	1-2	1-0	1-0	1-1
Littlehampton Town	5-3	3-1	1-6	***D***	2-2	2-2	0-1	0-2	0-2	4-4	4-2	6-0	2-1	4-3	1-1	1-2	1-2	0-2
Loxwood	0-0	1-3	2-1	1-1	***I***	1-0	0-1	0-6	0-0	2-1	1-1	3-0	4-0	2-1	1-2	0-1	1-4	1-1
Midhurst & Ease.	3-2	2-2	2-0	1-4	1-5	***V***	3-1	1-2	0-2	1-2	2-0	2-2	1-1	4-1	2-2	2-2	3-2	0-3
Mile Oak	3-0	2-3	4-1	6-3	2-0	7-0	***I***	2-0	2-0	1-1	2-0	7-0	2-1	3-1	6-0	2-0	4-1	4-1
Peacehaven & Tel.	3-0	1-1	6-0	3-2	1-1	6-0	4-0	***S***	3-4	4-2	5-1	5-1	3-0	4-0	4-0	5-1	4-0	0-0
Rustington	1-0	1-2	0-1	3-0	3-1	2-1	1-2	1-0	***I***	2-2	3-1	7-0	2-0	7-1	0-3	0-4	2-1	3-0
Rye United	2-1	2-0	4-3	1-1	0-2	0-1	3-1	0-3	0-0	***O***	5-2	6-0	3-1	0-0	3-1	5-1	1-0	1-2
Seaford Town	2-1	1-1	1-2	7-2	1-0	4-1	1-1	0-4	0-2	1-0	***N***	2-0	4-1	5-2	2-1	0-2	3-2	3-1
Sidlesham	1-1	0-4	0-4	2-5	2-1	0-2	0-7	3-3	1-1	2-2	0-1		2-2	1-3	0-4	0-1	2-3	3-3
Sidley United	3-2	3-0	4-1	2-2	1-0	3-1	0-1	2-2	3-1	2-1	2-2	4-1	***T***	3-2	0-0	3-3	1-1	0-5
Southwick	3-1	0-1	5-1	2-2	1-4	2-1	0-3	1-2	2-1	1-0	0-2	4-0	0-1	***W***	2-3	2-4	2-1	4-2
Steyning Town	2-1	0-1	2-1	1-4	0-4	2-1	1-1	0-3	0-3	0-5	1-0	0-1	2-0	0-3	***O***	1-4	2-3	1-2
Storrington	1-2	1-1	0-0	2-0	1-0	0-2	0-3	0-2	1-2	0-1	1-2	2-0	0-1	4-2	0-0		0-4	1-0
Wealden	0-3	1-3	3-1	2-2	3-1	4-3	2-4	0-3	3-0	1-2	0-4	1-2	1-1	0-0	1-2	5-1		0-3
Westfield	2-1	0-4	1-0	3-0	1-1	1-0	2-1	4-2	1-2	0-0	3-1	1-1	1-0	0-2	3-1	4-3	3-2	

Division Three	P	W	D	L	F	A	Pts
Clymping	**26**	**19**	**3**	**4**	**70**	**29**	**60**
Little Common	**26**	**18**	**3**	**5**	**66**	**37**	**57**
Haywards Heath Town	**26**	**17**	**4**	**5**	**57**	**20**	**55**
Newhaven	**26**	**15**	**6**	**5**	**64**	**39**	**51**
Dorking Wanderers	**26**	**15**	**2**	**9**	**70**	**45**	**47**
Forest	**26**	**11**	**7**	**8**	**40**	**33**	**40**
Saltdean United	**26**	**10**	**6**	**10**	**32**	**42**	**36**
Uckfield Town	**26**	**10**	**4**	**12**	**47**	**48**	**34**
Broadbridge Heath	**26**	**8**	**3**	**15**	**41**	**57**	**27**
Bosham	**26**	**7**	**5**	**14**	**35**	**53**	**26**
Rottingdean Village	**26**	**5**	**10**	**11**	**31**	**48**	**25**
Ifield Edwards	**26**	**6**	**6**	**14**	**39**	**54**	**24**
Hurstpierpoint	**26**	**4**	**4**	**18**	**34**	**75**	**16**
Pease Pottage Village	**26**	**4**	**3**	**19**	**30**	**76**	**15**

TOM STABLER MEMORIAL TROPHY

(March 4th at Sevenoaks Town)

Kent County League 2

Sussex County League Division Three 3

DIVISION THREE CUP

FIRST ROUND

Broadbridge Heath 2 Uckfield Town 0

Dorking Wanderers 4 Little Common 0

Ifield Edwards 1 **Clymping** 2

Newhaven 2 **Pease Pottage Village** 3

Rottingdean Village 1 Hurstpierpoint 1 *aet*

Replay: **Hurstpierpoint** 2 Rottingdean Village 0

Saltdean United 4 Forest 1

QUARTER-FINALS

Dorking Wanderers 2 Pease Pottage Village 1

Haywards Heath Town 3 Broadbridge Heath 1 *aet*

Hurstpierpoint 0 **Bosham** 3

Saltdean United 3 Clymping 2

SEMI-FINALS

Dorking Wanderers 4 Bosham 2 *(at Arundel)*

Haywards Heath Town 2 Saltdean United 1 *(at Ringmer)*

FINAL

(April 10th at Wick)

Dorking Wanderers 0 **Haywards Heath Town** 2

	Bosham	Broadbridge Heath	Clymping	Dorking Wanderers	Forest	Haywards Heath Town	Hurstpierpoint	Ifield Edwards	Little Common	Newhaven	Pease Pottage Village	Rottingdean Village	Saltdean United	Uckfield Town
Bosham		0-1	1-3	0-1	3-0	1-3	2-2	2-0	2-3	2-2	7-0	0-2	3-3	0-5
Broadbridge Heath	7-0		0-4	3-4	1-1	0-5	4-2	2-2	0-3	1-2	0-0	1-4	0-1	0-4
Clymping	0-0	2-3	***D***	3-0	3-1	2-1	6-1	2-0	1-2	1-5	5-0	6-1	4-1	1-0
Dorking Wanderers	2-3	4-2	1-3	***I***	2-2	1-2	6-3	4-0	0-3	3-1	7-1	4-0	1-2	2-1
Forest	1-2	2-1	1-2	1-3	***V***	1-1	1-1	2-1	2-0	2-3	3-0	2-0	2-0	1-1
Haywards Heath Town	0-0	2-0	0-2	0-3	2-2		8-0	1-0	5-1	1-1	4-0	1-0	2-1	1-0
Hurstpierpoint	0-3	3-1	3-5	1-5	0-2	0-4		2-3	1-4	2-4	4-2	1-1	1-0	0-1
Ifield Edwards	4-0	2-1	1-4	3-3	1-4	0-1	2-2	***T***	2-4	2-3	3-4	1-1	2-0	1-2
Little Common	2-1	2-3	1-3	1-0	1-0	1-3	2-1	5-2	***H***	2-0	4-2	1-1	2-2	3-0
Newhaven	5-0	5-2	2-3	1-2	1-1	0-3	3-1	2-1	2-2	***R***	1-1	2-0	4-1	3-0
Pease Pottage Village	3-0	2-5	0-2	2-5	0-1	1-0	1-2	0-2	2-4	1-3	***E***	4-1	0-1	1-4
Rottingdean Village	0-2	0-2	2-2	3-1	1-2	0-1	1-0	2-2	1-5	2-2	1-1	***E***	1-1	1-1
Saltdean United	2-0	1-0	0-0	0-3	1-0	2-1	1-0	1-1	1-5	2-3	2-0	0-2		3-2
Uckfield Town	2-1	0-1	2-1	4-3	2-3	1-5	3-1	0-1	0-3	1-4	5-2	3-3	3-3	

Res. Premier Div.	P	W	D	L	F	A	Pt
E'bne Town Res.	26	17	5	4	60	23	56
Hastings Utd Res.	26	16	4	6	66	32	52
Shoreham Res.	26	15	2	9	57	43	47
Hassocks Res.	26	13	5	8	53	49	44
Pagham Res.	26	12	6	8	39	29	42
Selsey Res.	26	12	6	8	41	37	42
Crawley D. Res.	26	11	7	8	45	41	40
Whitehawk Res.	26	11	3	12	39	43	36
Arundel Res.	26	11	3	12	41	48	36
E'bne Utd A. Res.	26	9	5	12	57	51	32
St Francis R. Res.	26	8	8	10	35	34	32
Hailsham T. Res.	26	8	7	11	50	48	31
Ringmer Res.	26	4	1	21	22	73	13
Southwick Res.	26	2	4	20	23	77	10

Res. Division East	P	W	D	L	F	A	Pt
Mile Oak Res.	26	19	5	2	75	25	62
Lingfield Res.	26	19	2	5	80	43	59
Ltle Common Res.	26	18	4	4	69	33	58
Westfield Res.	26	18	3	5	66	30	57
Peacehaven Res.	26	16	2	8	76	33	50
Sidley Utd Res.	26	13	5	8	70	48	44
Redhill Res.	26	14	0	12	74	63	42
Seaford T. Res.	26	12	2	12	39	47	38
Rye United Res.	26	10	3	13	40	52	33
Saltdean Utd Res.	26	9	2	15	48	66	29
Pease Pott. Res.	26	8	1	17	38	71	25
Newhaven Res.	26	7	1	18	33	63	22
Bexhill Utd Res.	26	3	2	21	31	93	11
Wealden Res.	26	0	0	26	21	93	0

Res. Division West	P	W	D	L	F	A	Pt
Steyning T. Res.	26	16	4	6	71	38	52
Wick Res.	26	14	5	7	69	43	47
Midhurst & E. Res.	26	14	4	8	67	40	46
Rustington Res.	26	14	4	8	66	46	46
Lancing Res.	26	14	4	8	48	32	46
East Preston Res.	26	13	4	9	54	47	43
Chichester Res.	26	13	2	11	51	44	41
Worthing Utd Res.	26	10	2	14	51	54	32
Littlehampton Res.	26	8	7	11	53	49	31
Sidlesham Res.	26	9	3	14	42	78	30
Broadbdge H. Res.	26	8	5	13	38	58	29
Dorking Wdrs Res.	26	8	3	15	53	72	27
Storrington Res.	26	7	5	14	42	76	26
Loxwood Res.	26	6	4	16	38	66	22

Forest Res. - record expunged

RESERVES CUP

FINAL *(March 16th at Ringmer)*

Eastbourne Town Res. 1 Little Common Res. 0

ARUNDEL

Founded: 1889 Nickname: Mulletts

Chairman: Bob Marchant
Secretary: Kathy Wilson
5 Pearson Road
Arundel
West Sussex
BN18 9HP
Tel: 07778 783 294
Manager: Richard Towers
Prog Editor: See secretary

Ground: Mill Road, Arundel, W. Sussex BN18 9QQ. Tel: 01903 882 548
Capacity: 2,200 **Seats:** 100 **Covered:** 200
Midweek Matchday: Tuesday **Clubhouse:** Yes **Shop:** No
Colours(change): Red/white/red (All Blue)
Previous Names:
Previous Lges: West Sussex
Records: **Att:** 2,200 v Chichester League 67-68 **Goalscorer:** Paul J Bennett **App:** 537 Paul Bennett (Goalkeeper)
Senior Honours: Sussex County Champions 1957-58,5 8-59, 86-87.

10 YEAR RECORD

99-00	00-01	01-02	02-03	03-04	04-05	05-06	06-07	07-08	08-09
SxC2 2	SxC1 13	SxC1 9	SxC1 17	SxC1 6	SxC1 9	SxC1 7	SxC1 3	SxC1 3	SxC1 2

CHICHESTER CITY UNITED

Founded: 2000 Nickname:

Chairman: John Hutter
Secretary: Michael Maiden
31 The Avenue
Hambrook
Chichester
PO18 8TZ
Tel: 07971 818 761
Manager: Ade Girdler
Prog Editor: Chester Brownton

Ground: Oaklands Way, Chichester, W Sussex PO19 6AR Tel: 07836 775 003
Capacity: 2,000 **Seats:** none **Covered:** 200
Midweek Matchday: Tuesday **Clubhouse:** Yes **Shop:** Yes
Colours(change): White/green/green. (Yellow/blue/blue)
Previous Names: Chichester FC (pre 1948) Chichester City 48-2000 amalgamated with Portfield in 2000
Previous Lges:
Records:
Senior Honours: Sussex County Division One 2003-04.

10 YEAR RECORD

99-00	00-01	01-02	02-03	03-04	04-05	05-06	06-07	07-08	08-09
SxC1 17	SxC1 7	SxC1 3	SxC1 4	SxC1 1	SxC1 16	SxC1 8	SxC1 11	SxC1 16	SxC1 7

CRAWLEY DOWN

Founded: 1993 Nickname:

Chairman: Brian Suckling
Secretary: Jane Suckling
15 Buckley Place
Crawley Down
West Sussex
RH10 4JG
Tel: 07917 460 405
Manager: Darren Guirey
Prog Editor:

Ground: The Haven Sportsfield, Hophurst Lane, Crawley Dn RH10 4LJ Tel: 01342 717 140
Capacity: 1,000 **Seats:** **Covered:** 50
Midweek Matchday: **Clubhouse:** **Shop:**
Colours(change): All Red (White/black/black)
Previous Names: Crawley Down United > 1993. Crawley Down Village > 1999.
Previous Lges: Mid Sussex
Records: **Att:**404 v East Grinstead Town 96
Senior Honours:

10 YEAR RECORD

99-00	00-01	01-02	02-03	03-04	04-05	05-06	06-07	07-08	08-09
SxC2 4	SxC2 16	SxC2 11	SxC2 15	SxC2 11	SxC2 10	SxC2 5	SxC2 16	SxC2 6	SxC2 3

CROWBOROUGH ATHLETIC

Founded: 1894 Nickname: The Crows

Chairman: Ken Saunders
Secretary: Karen Scott
Llandilo
Old Lane
Crowborough
TN6 2AF
Tel: 07983 676 210
Manager: Stuart Nowell
Prog Editor: See secretary

Ground: Crowborough Co. Stadium, Alderbrook Rec, Fermor Rd, TN6 3DJ. 01892661893.
Capacity: 2,000 **Seats:** **Covered:** 150
Midweek Matchday: **Clubhouse:** **Shop:**
Colours(change): All blue. (All red).
Previous Names:
Previous Lges: Sussex County 1974 - 2008. Isthmian 2008-09
Records:
Senior Honours: Sussex County Div. 1 Champions 2007-08. League Cup 2006-07.

10 YEAR RECORD

99-00	00-01	01-02	02-03	03-04	04-05	05-06	06-07	07-08	08-09
SxC3 4	SxC2 17	SxC3 4	SxC3 3	SxC3 1	SxC2 1	SxC1 6	SxC1 4	SxC1 1	Isth1S 22

INS & OUTS

IN: Crawley Down (P), Crowborough Athletic (R – Isthmian League Division One South), Mile Oak (P), Peacehaven & Telscombe (P)
OUT: East Preston (R), Horsham YMCA (P – Isthmian League Division One South), Oakwood (R), Worthing United (R)

EAST GRINSTEAD TOWN

Founded: 1890 Nickname: The Wasps

Chairman: Richard Tramontin
Secretary: Brian McCorquodale
72 Milton Crescent
East Grinstead

RH19 1TN
Tel: 07802 528 513
Manager: Steve Johnson
Prog Editor: Lee Quinn

Ground: East Court, College Lane, East Grinstead RH19 3LS Tel: 01342 325 885
Capacity: 3,000 **Seats:** none **Covered:** 400
Midweek Matchday: **Clubhouse:** Yes **Shop:** No
Colours(change): Amber & black stripes/black/black. (Sky & navy stripes/navy/navy)
Previous Names: East Grinstead > 1997.
Previous Lges: Mid Sussex, Sussex County, Souhern Amateur
Records: **Att:** 2,006 v Lancing F A Am Cup **App:** Guy Hill

Senior Honours: Sussex County League Division Two 2007-08.

10 YEAR RECORD

99-00	00-01	01-02	02-03	03-04	04-05	05-06	06-07	07-08	08-09
SxC2 6	SxC2 4	SxC2 5	SxC2 3	SxC1 9	SxC1 18	SxC2 7	SxC2 11	SxC2 1	SxC1 17

EASTBOURNE UNITED ASSOCIATION

Founded: 1894 Nickname: The U's

Chairman: Les Aisbitt
Secretary: Brian Dowling
79 Harebeating Drive
Hailsham
East Sussex
BN27 1JE
Tel: 01323 442 488
Manager: Brian Dennis
Prog Editor: See secretary

Ground: The Oval, Channel View Road, Eastbourne, BN22 7LN Tel: 01323 726 989
Capacity: 3,000 **Seats:** 160 **Covered:** 160
Midweek Matchday: Tuesday **Clubhouse:** Yes **Shop:** Yes
Colours(change): Black & white halves/black/white. (Sky blue/sky/yellow).
Previous Names: Eastbourne Old Comrades, Eastbourne United merged with Shinewater Assoc in 2000
Previous Lges: Metropolitan 56-64, Athenian 64-77 & Isthmian 77-92
Records: **Att:** 11,000 at Lynchmore

Senior Honours: Sussex County Champions 1954-55, 08-09, Sussex Senior Cup (5).

10 YEAR RECORD

99-00	00-01	01-02	02-03	03-04	04-05	05-06	06-07	07-08	08-09
SxC1 15	SxC1 11	SxC1 19	SxC2 8	SxC2 3	SxC1 5	SxC1 14	SxC1 7	SxC1 11	SxC1 1

HAILSHAM TOWN

Founded: 1885 Nickname: The Stringers

Chairman: Mervyn Walker
Secretary: Sue Williams
Horse Eye Cottage
Magham Down
Hailsham East Sussex
BN27 1PY
Tel: 07719 590 268
Manager: Dave Shearing
Prog Editor: Lee Mewett

Ground: The Beaconsfield, Western Road, Hailsham BN27 3DN. Tel: 01323 840 446
Capacity: 2,0000 **Seats:** none **Covered:** 100
Midweek Matchday: Tuesday **Clubhouse:** Yes **Shop:**
Colours(change): Yellow/green/yellow (All light blue)
Previous Names: Hailsham.
Previous Lges: East Sussex, Southern Combination
Records: **Att:** 1350 v Hungerford T. FA Vase Feb 89 **Goalscorer:** Howard Stephens 51 **App:** Phil Comber 713
Senior Honours:

10 YEAR RECORD

99-00	00-01	01-02	02-03	03-04	04-05	05-06	06-07	07-08	08-09
SxC2 7	SxC2 3	SxC1 6	SxC1 15	SxC1 12	SxC1 12	SxC1 10	SxC1 6	SxC1 13	SxC1 15

HASSOCKS

Founded: 1902 Nickname: The Robins

Chairman: Derek Hurley
Secretary: Dave Knight
21 Farnham Avenue
Hassocks
West Sussex
BN6 8NR
Tel: 01273 842 023
Manager: Dave John
Prog Editor: Paul Elphick

Ground: The Beacon, Brighton Road, Hassocks BN6 9LY Tel: 01273 846 040
Capacity: 1,800 **Seats:** 270 **Covered:** 100
Midweek Matchday: Tuesday **Clubhouse:** Yes **Shop:** No
Colours(change): All Red. (Yellow/black/black)
Previous Names:
Previous Lges: Mid Sussex, Brighton & Hove & Dist and Southern Counties Comb
Records: **Att:** 610 v Burgess Hill Town **Goalscorer:** Pat Harding 43

Senior Honours:

10 YEAR RECORD

99-00	00-01	01-02	02-03	03-04	04-05	05-06	06-07	07-08	08-09
SxC1 7	SxC1 12	SxC1 11	SxC1 8	SxC1 7	SxC1 8	SxC1 9	SxC1 5	SxC1 7	SxC1 16

LINGFIELD

Founded: 1893 Nickname:

Chairman: Gus O'Keefe
Secretary: Pamela Tomsett
61 Drivers Mead
Lingfield
Surrey
RH7 6EX
Tel: 07903 428 228
Manager: Tony Beckingham
Prog Editor: See secretary

Ground: Sports Pavillion, Godstone Road, Lingfield, Surrey RH7 6BT Tel: 01342 834 269
Capacity: 1,000+ **Seats:** Soon **Covered:** Yes
Midweek Matchday: Tuesday **Clubhouse:** Yes **Shop:** No
Colours(change): Red & Yellow stripes/black/yellow.(Blue & white stripes/white /blue)
Previous Names: None.
Previous Lges: Redhill. Surrey Intermediate. Combined Counties. Mid Sussex.
Records:
Senior Honours:

10 YEAR RECORD

99-00	00-01	01-02	02-03	03-04	04-05	05-06	06-07	07-08	08-09
SxC2 18	SxC2 18	SxC3 16	SxC3 9	SxC3 8	SxC3 3	SxC3 2	SxC2 10	SxC2 2	SxC1 8

MILE OAK

Founded: 1960 Nickname: The Oak

Chairman: Les Hamilton
Secretary: Colin Brown
19 The Crescent
Southwick
West Sussex
BN42 4LB
Tel: 07774 754 468
Manager: Anthony Whittington
Prog Editor:

Ground: Mile Oak Rec. Chalky Road, Portslade, Brighton BN41 2YU 01273 423 854
Capacity: **Seats:** **Covered:**
Midweek Matchday: **Clubhouse:** **Shop:**
Colours(change): Tangerine/black/black & tangerine. (All Green)
Previous Names:
Previous Lges: Southern Counties Combination, Brighton & Hove District
Records: Att: 186
Senior Honours: Brighton Hove & District Champions 1980-81.
Sussex County Div 2 Champions.

10 YEAR RECORD

99-00	00-01	01-02	02-03	03-04	04-05	05-06	06-07	07-08	08-09
SxC2 11	SxC2 15	SxC2 14	SxC2 16	SxC2 7	SxC2 11	SxC2 8	SxC2 9	SxC2 5	SxC2 2

PAGHAM

Founded: 1903 Nickname: The Lions

Chairman: Brent Williams
Secretary: Marc Hilton
6 East Avenue
Middleton-On-Sea

PO22 6EG
Tel: 07771 810 757
Manager: Dave Berkowitz
Prog Editor: admin@paghamfc.org.uk

Ground: Nyetimber Lane, Pagham, W Sussex PO21 3JY Tel: 01243 266 112
Capacity: 2,000 **Seats:** 200 **Covered:** 200
Midweek Matchday: **Clubhouse:** Yes **Shop:** No
Colours(change): White/black/black & white. (Green/white/green & white)
Previous Names: None
Previous Lges: Chichester 1903-50, West Sussex 50-69
Records: Att: 1,200 v Bognor 1971 **Goalscorer:** Dick De Luca **App:** Graham Peach
Senior Honours: Sussex County Division Two 1978-79, 86-87, 06-07.
Division One 80-81, 87-88, 88-89.

10 YEAR RECORD

99-00	00-01	01-02	02-03	03-04	04-05	05-06	06-07	07-08	08-09
SxC1 16	SxC1 6	SxC1 8	SxC1 9	SxC1 17	SxC1 19	SxC2 13	SxC2 1	SxC1 9	SxC1 11

PEACEHAVEN & TELSCOMBE

Founded: 1923 Nickname:

Chairman: Jim Edwards
Secretary: Margaret Edwards
2 Tuscan Court
The Esplanade
Telscombe Cliffs, E Sussex
BN10 7HF
Tel: 01273 582 471
Manager: Darren Guirey
Prog Editor:

Ground: The Sports Park, Piddinghoe Ave, Peacehaven, BN10 8RJ Tel: 01273 582 471
Capacity: **Seats:** **Covered:**
Midweek Matchday: **Clubhouse:** **Shop:**
Colours(change): Black & white stripes/black/white (All Yellow & blue)
Previous Names: Formed when Peacehaven Rangers and Telscombe Tye merged.
Previous Lges:
Records:
Senior Honours: Sussex County Div.3 2005-06. Div.2 2008-09

10 YEAR RECORD

99-00	00-01	01-02	02-03	03-04	04-05	05-06	06-07	07-08	08-09
SxC2 14	SxC2 2	SxC1 12	SxC1 18	SxC2 12	SxC2 17	SxC3 1	SxC2 5	SxC2 4	SxC2 1

REDHILL

Founded: 1894 Nickname: Reds/Lobsters

Chairman: Andy Wheeler
Secretary: Phil Whatling
44 Knighton Road
Redhill

RH1 6EQ
Tel: 07929 742 081
Manager: Dean Forbes
Prog Editor:

Ground: Kiln Brow, Three Arch Road, Redhill, Surrey RH1 5AE Tel: 01737 762 129
Capacity: 2,000 **Seats:** 150 **Covered:** 150
Midweek Matchday: Tuesday **Clubhouse:** Yes **Shop:** Yes
Colours(change): Red & white/red/red. (White/black/white).
Previous Names:
Previous Lges: E & W Surrey. Spartan. Southern Sub. London. Athenian.
Records: Att: 8,000 v Hastings U FA Cup 1956 **Goalscorer:** Steve Turner 119 **App:** Brian Medlicott 766
Senior Honours: Athenian League (2) Surrey Senior cup 28-29, 65-66

10 YEAR RECORD

99-00	00-01	01-02	02-03	03-04	04-05	05-06	06-07	07-08	08-09
SxC1 12	SxC1 14	SxC1 15	SxC1 12	SxC1 11	SxC1 13	SxC1 18	SxC1 15	SxC1 8	SxC1 7

RINGMER

Founded: 1906 Nickname: Blues

Chairman: David Ruffles
Secretary: David Ruffles
29 Sadlers Way
Ringmer

BN8 5HG
Tel: 01273 813 224
Manager: Bob Munnery
Prog Editor: See secretary

Ground: Caburn Ground, Anchor Field, Ringmer BN8 5QN. Tel: 01273 812 738.
Capacity: 1,000 **Seats:** 100 **Covered:** Yes
Midweek Matchday: Tuesday **Clubhouse:** Yes **Shop:** Yes
Colours(change): Navy & light blue/navy/navy. (All white).
Previous Names: None.
Previous Lges: Brighton.
Records: 1,350 v Southwick, Sussex County League, 1970-71.

Senior Honours: Sussex County Division Two 1968-69. Division One 1970-71. Sussex Senior Cup 1972-73.

10 YEAR RECORD

99-00	00-01	01-02	02-03	03-04	04-05	05-06	06-07	07-08	08-09
SxC1 19	SxC1 10	SxC1 2	SxC1 7	SxC1 10	SxC1 6	SxC1 2	SxC1 9	SxC1 10	SxC1 9

SELSEY

Founded: 1903 Nickname: Blues

Chairman: David Lee
Secretary: Tony Ford
77 Drift Road
Selsey

PO20 0PN
Tel: 07778 628 547
Manager: Danny Hinshelwood
Prog Editor: See secretary

Ground: High Street Ground, Selsey, Chichester, PO20 0QG Tel: 01243 603 420
Capacity: 1,000 **Seats:** 25 **Covered:** 98
Midweek Matchday: Tuesday **Clubhouse:** Yes **Shop:** No
Colours(change): All Blue. (All Yellow).
Previous Names:
Previous Lges: Chichester & District, West Sussex.
Records: Att: 750-800 v Chichester or Portfield 1950's

Senior Honours: Sussex County Division Two 1963-64, 75-76.

10 YEAR RECORD

99-00	00-01	01-02	02-03	03-04	04-05	05-06	06-07	07-08	08-09
SxC1 10	SxC1 4	SxC1 4	SxC1 11	SxC1 18	SxC2 14	SxC2 2	SxC1 8	SxC1 15	SxC1 10

SHOREHAM

Founded: 1892 Nickname: Musselmen

Chairman: Matthew Major
Secretary: Gary Millis
21 Glover Avenue
Lancing
W Sussex
BN15 9RG
Tel: 07801 477 979
Manager: Mark Burt/Darren Donnelly
Prog Editor: See secretary

Ground: Middle Road, Shoreham-by-Sea, W Sussex, BN43 6LT Tel: 01273 454 261
Capacity: 1,500 **Seats:** 150 **Covered:** 700
Midweek Matchday: **Clubhouse:** Yes **Shop:** No
Colours(change): All Blue. (All orange).
Previous Names: None.
Previous Lges: W Sussex.
Records: Att: 1,342 v Wimbledon

Senior Honours: Sussex County Division One 1951-52, 52-53, 77-78. Division Two 61-62, 76-77, 93-94. John O'Hara League Cup 2007-08.

10 YEAR RECORD

99-00	00-01	01-02	02-03	03-04	04-05	05-06	06-07	07-08	08-09
SxC1 20	SxC2 13	SxC2 2	SxC1 16	SxC1 19	SxC2 3	SxC1 13	SxC1 13	SxC1 12	SxC1 6

ST. FRANCIS RANGERS

Founded: 2002 Nickname: Saints/Rangers

Chairman: John Goss
Secretary: Mrs Clare Cannon
20 Priory Road
Burgess Hill
West Sussex
RH15 9HB
Tel: 01444 246 723
Manager: John Goss
Prog Editor: Colin Mansbridge

Ground: Princess Royal Hospital, Lewes Rd, Haywards Hth RH16 4EX Tel:01444 441881
Capacity: 1,000 **Seats:** None **Covered:** 100
Midweek Matchday: Tuesday **Clubhouse:** Yes **Shop:** No
Colours(change): Black & white/white/white (white/orange/orange)
Previous Names: Formed when Ansty Rangers & St Francis merged 2002.
Previous Lges:
Records:
Senior Honours:

10 YEAR RECORD

99-00	00-01	01-02	02-03	03-04	04-05	05-06	06-07	07-08	08-09
			SxC3 6	SxC3 2	SxC2 4	SxC2 3	SxC2 2	SxC1 14	SxC1 12

THREE BRIDGES

Founded: 1901 Nickname: Bridges

Chairman: Alan Bell
Secretary: Martin Clarke
18 Mannings Close
Pound Hill
Crawley
RH10 3TX
Tel: 01293 883 726
Manager: Paul Falli
Prog Editor: Alf Blackler

Ground: Jubilee Field, Three Bridges Rd, Crawley, RH10 3TX Tel: 01293 442 000
Capacity: 3,500 **Seats:** 120 **Covered:** 600
Midweek Matchday: **Clubhouse:** Yes **Shop:**
Colours(change): Amber & black stripes/black/black.(Blue & white stripes /blue/blue)
Previous Names: Three Bridges Worth 1936-52, Three Bridges Utd 53-64
Previous Lges: Mid Sussex, E Grinstead, Redhill & Dist 36-52
Records: **Att;** 2,000 v Horsham 1948 **App:** John Malthouse
Senior Honours: Sussex RUR Cup 82-83

10 YEAR RECORD

99-00	00-01	01-02	02-03	03-04	04-05	05-06	06-07	07-08	08-09
SxC1 14	SxC1 8	SxC1 7	SxC1 14	SxC1 4	SxC1 7	SxC1 15	SxC1 12	SxC1 6	SxC1 5

WHITEHAWK

Founded: 1945 Nickname: Hawks

Chairman: Wally Sweetman
Secretary: John Rosenblatt
25 Arundel Street
Kemp Town
Brighton
BN2 5TH
Tel: 07724 519 370
Manager: George Parris
Prog Editor: Fred Moore

Ground: Enclosed Ground, East Brighton Park, Brighton BN2 5TS Tel: 01273 609 736
Capacity: 3,000 **Seats:** none **Covered:** 500
Midweek Matchday: **Clubhouse:** Yes **Shop:** No
Colours(change): All Red (All Blue)
Previous Names: Whitehawk & Manor Farm Old Boys untill 1958
Previous Lges: Bighton & Hove District
Records: **Att;** 2,100 v Bognor regis Town FA Cup 88-89. **Goalscorer;** Billy Ford
App: Ken Powell 1,103
Senior Honours: Sussex County League Div.1 1961-62, 63-64, 83-84. Div.2 67-68, 80-81. Sussex Senior Cup 50-51, 61-62 Sussex RUR Charity Cup (3)

10 YEAR RECORD

99-00	00-01	01-02	02-03	03-04	04-05	05-06	06-07	07-08	08-09
SxC1 11	SxC1 17	SxC1 13	SxC1 2	SxC1 8	SxC1 3	SxC1 3	SxC1 2	SxC1 2	SxC1 13

WICK

Founded: 1892 Nickname: Wickers

Chairman: Carl Stabler
Secretary: Allan Luckin
12 Lammas Close
Littlehampton
West Sussex
BN17 6HU
Tel: 07816 954 349
Manager: Vic Short
Prog Editor:

Ground: Coomes Way, Wick, Littlehampton, W Sussex BN17 7LS Tel: 01903 713 535
Capacity: 1,000 **Seats:** 100 **Covered:** Yes
Midweek Matchday: **Clubhouse:** Yes **Shop:** No
Colours(change): Red & black stripes/black with white stripe/black with white stripe (Black/black/black).
Previous Names: Lyminster FC.
Previous Lges: West Sussex
Records: **Att:** 900
Senior Honours: Sussex County Division One 1989-90, 93-94. Div.2 81-82, 85-86. Sussex Senior Cup 92-93.

10 YEAR RECORD

99-00	00-01	01-02	02-03	03-04	04-05	05-06	06-07	07-08	08-09
SxC1 18	SxC1 3	SxC1 14	SxC1 19	SxC1 4	SxC1 2	SxC1 12	SxC1 16	SxC1 5	SxC1 4

EASTBOURNE UNITED ASSOCIATION F.C.
Division One champions 2008-09.
Photo: Roger Turner.

HAILSHAM TOWN
Photo: Roger Turner.

DIVISION TWO INS & OUTS	IN: Clymping (P). East Preston (R), Little Common (P), Oakwood (R), Worthing United (R) OUT: Bexhill United (R), Crawley Down (P), Mile Oak (P), Peacehaven & Telscombe (P), Sidlesham (R)

CLYMPING

Formed: 1947

Chairman: Frank Sumner
Secretary: Ian Campbell. 207 Timberleys, Littlehampton BN17 6DQ. Tel: 07738 156 359.
Manager: Dom Di Paola.
Ground: Clymping Village Hall, Clymping, Littelhampton BN17 5GW. Tel: 07951 196 784.
Directions: Follow A259 west of Littlehampton. Just over the Bridge, on the right hand side before the small roundabout.
Clubhouse: Yes.
Club Colours: All blue. **Change Colours:** Red/white/red.
Previous League(s): Littlehampton & District 1947-49. West Sussex 1949-2008.
Previous Name: None
Honours: Sussex County Division 3 Champions 2008-09.

EAST PRESTON

Formed: 1966

Chairman: Michael Barnes
Secretary: Keith Freeman. 41 Ambersham Crescent, East Preston, Sussex BN16 1AJ. Tel: 01903 771 158 (H).
Manager: Trevor Waller
Ground: Roundstone Recreation Ground, Lashmar Road, East Preston, Sussex BN16 1ESTel: 01903 776 026
Directions: From Worthing proceed west for 6 miles on A259. At Roundstone Brwers Fayre pub turn south, over level crossing turn left for 50 yards then first right into Roundstone Drive.
Clubhouse: Yes
Club Colours: Black & white stripes/black/black. **Change Colours:** All blue.
Previous Name: East Grinstead > 1997.
Previous League(s): Mid Sussex. Sussex County. Southern Amateur
Honours: Sussex County Division 2 Champions 2007-08

LANCING

Formed: 1941

Chairman: Peter Hind
Secretary: Mick Clark. Owls Haven, 11 St Lukes Close, BN15 8SQ. Tel: 01903 762 781 (H)
Manager: Martin Gander
Ground: Culver Road, Lancing, West Sussex BN15 9AX. Tel: 01903 767 285.
Directions: From A27 turn south at Lancing Manor r'about into Grinstead Lane, 3rd turning on right North Farm Rd. Turn left then immed. right into Culver Rd. From railway station take 3rd turning on left heading north.
Clubhouse: Yes
Club Colours: Yellow/blue/yellow. **Change Colours:** All red.
Previous Name: Lancing Athletic.
Previous League(s): Brighton Hove & District.
Honours: Brighton League 1946-47, 47-48.

LITTLE COMMON

Formed: 1966

Chairman: Ken Cherry
Secretary: Mrs Margaret Cherry. 11 Bidwell Avenue, Bexhill-on-sea, East Sussex TN39 4DB. Tel: 01424 217 191
Manager: Mark Linch
Ground: Little Common Sports Pavilion, Little Common Recreation Ground, Green Lane, Bexhill-on-Sea, East Sussex TN39 4PH. Tel: 01424 845 861.
Directions: From the west take the A259, at Little Common roundabout take second exit into Peartree Lane and then left into Little Common Recreation Ground car park.
Clubhouse: Yes
Club Colours: Claret & blue/claret/claret. **Change Colours:** Yellow/navy/navy.
Previous Name: Albion United > 1986.
Previous League(s): Hastings. East Sussex. Sussex County 1978-94. East Sussex 1994-2005.
Honours: East Sussex League Champions 1975-76, 76-77, 04-05.

LITTLEHAMPTON TOWN

Formed: 1896

Chairman: Neil Taylor

Secretary: Alan Barnes, 10 Emmabrook Court, Sea Road, Littlehampton, W.Sussex BN16 2NG
Tel: 01903 721219 and 07882 460 357 (M)

Manager: Gary Young & John Suter.

Ground: The Sportsfield, St Flora's Road, Littlehampton BN17 6BD. Tel: 01903 716 390

Directions: Leave A259 at Waterford Business Park and turn into Horsham Road. After Shell Garage turn left into St. Floras Road. Ground is at the end of road on the left.

Clubhouse: Yes

Club Colours: Yellow/black/black. **Change Colours:** All white.

Honours: Sussex County Champions 1958-59(shared) 75-76 84-85 90-91 96-97. Sussex Senior Cup 1949 1970

NOTE OF INTEREST: Lost in the F.A.Cup Preliminary Round v Tunbridge Wells 15-16 on penalties after 40 kicks had been taken. A European record and only one short of the world record.

LOXWOOD

Chairman: Derek Waterman.

Secretary: George Read. 2 Grove Road, Petworth GU28 0BT. Tel: 01798 343 839 (H). 07791 766 857 (M).

Manager: Barry Hunter.

Ground: Loxwood Sports Association, Plaistow Road, Loxwood RH14 0SX. Tel: 01404 753 185

Directions: Leave A272 between Billinghurst and Wisborough Green and join the B2133 for 3.4 miles. On entering Loxwood Village take 1st left into Plaistow Road, ground situed 100 yards on the left.

Clubhouse: Yes.

Club Colours: Black & white/black/white. **Change Colours:** Red/white/red.

Previous League(s): West Sussex.

Honours: Sussex County Division 3 Champions 2007-08.

MIDHURST & EASEBOURNE

Chairman: Darren Chiverton.

Secretary: Ted Dummer MBE. 14 Nine Acres, June Lane, Midhurst, West Sussex GU29 9EP. Tel: 01730 813 887.

Manager: Tony Minoldo.

Ground: Rotherfield, Dodsley Lane, Easebourne, Midhurst, W. Sussex GU29 9BE. Tel: 01730 816 557.

Directions: Ground one mile out of Midhurst on London Road (A286) opposite Texaco Garage.
Ample car parking.

Clubhouse: Yes.

Club Colours: Royal blue with black trim/Black/Royal. **Change Colours:** All red.

Previous Names: Post WW2 Midhurst FC and Easeboune FC amalgated to form Midhurst & Easebourne United.

Previous League(s): West Sussex 1999-2002.

Honours: Sussex County Division Two League Cup 1988-1989.
Sussex County Division Three League Cup 2002-2003

OAKWOOD

Formed: 1962

Chairman: Stuart Lovegrove.

Secretary: Kelly Whittaker. 10 Hunstanton Close, Ifield, Crawley, West Sussex RH11 0UG. Tel: 07973 752 761.

Manager: John Mist.

Ground: Tinsley Lane, Three Bridges, Crawley RH10 8AJ. Tel: 01293 515 742.

Directions: From the South on M23, take junction 10 exit left onto A2011, next roundabout take fourth exit right, next roundabout second exit, take first right into Tinsley Lane. Ground entrance 100 metres on left.

Clubhouse: Yes.

Club Colours: Red & black stripes/black/black. **Change Colours:** All blue.

Previous League(s): Crawley & District 1966 - 1980. Southern Counties Combination 1980 - 1984.

Honours: Sussex County Div.2 League Cup 1989-90.

RUSTINGTON

Chairman: John Virgoe.
Secretary: Paul Cox. 28 The Gilberts, Sea Road, Rustington BN16 2LY. Tel: 07771 623 224.
Manager: Peter Matthews.
Ground: Recreation Ground, Jubilee Avenue, Rustington, West Sussex BN16 3NB. Tel: 01903 770 495.
Directions: From the East follow A259 past Sainsburys. Left at next roundabout on to B2187 over Windmill Bridge. Straight on at roundabout, first right, then first left into Woodlands Avenue. Car park is 80 yards on your right, next to the Village hall. From the West proceed to Watersmead roundabout with Bodyshop on your left. Take B2187 half a mile, past BP garage, take third right into Albert Road, then first right into Woodlands Avenue.
Clubhouse: Yes.
Club Colours: Royal blue/royal/white. **Change Colours:** Red & black/black/red.
Honours: Sussex County Division Three Champions 2006-07.

RYE UNITED

Formed: 1938

Chairman: Clive Taylor.
Secretary: Roger Bond. 12 Gregory Walk, Sedlescombe, East Sussex TN33 0QZ. Tel: 07738 154 685.
Manager: Scott Price.
Ground: Sydney Allnut Pavillion, Rye Football & Cricket Salts, Fishmarket Road, Rye TN31 7NU.
Tel: 01797 223 855
Directions: Outskirts of Rye on the A268 joins A259 opposite Skinners Rover garage.
Clubhouse: Yes.
Club Colours: Red & black/black/black. **Change Colours:** All green.
Previous Names: Rye United and Iden FC amalgamated to form Rye & Iden United in 2001. Changed back to Rye United 2006.
Previous League(s): Sussex County 1952-84. Kent County 1984 - 2000.
Honours: Sussex County Division Two Champions 2001-02, 02-03. League Cup 2001-02,02-03, 04-05.

SEAFORD TOWN

Chairman: Mick Webster.
Secretary: John Smith. 24 Heathfield Road,Seaford BN25 1TJ. Tel: 07919 993 751.
Manager: Bob Laundon.
Ground: The Crouch, Bramber Road, Seaford BN25 1AG. Tel: 01323 892 221.
Directions: A259 to Seaford. At mini r'about by station, turn left (coming from Newhaven) or RIGHT (from Eastbourne). At end of Church Street, across junction, then left at end. After 500m turn left up Ashurst Road Bramber Road is at the top.
Club Colours: All red. **Change Colours:** White/black/black.
Honours: Sussex Division Two Champions 2005-2006.

SIDLEY UNITED

Formed: 1906

Chairman: Michael Day.
Secretary: Robin Powell. Flat 4, 14 Park Road, Bexhill On Sea TN39 3HY. Tel: 07785 703 636.
Manager: John Lambert & Wayne Farrier.
Ground: Gullivers Sports Ground, Glovers Lane, Sidley, Bexhill on Sea TN39 5BL. Tel: 01424 217 078
Directions: From Brighton: On A259 turn left at Little Common roundabout into Pear Tree Lane. Turn right into Turkey Road. Turn right onto A269 from Ninfield. Turn left at Glovers Lane and first left into North Road.
Clubhouse: Yes.
Club Colours: All navy. **Change Colours:** Yellow & black/black/yellow.
Honours: Sussex Division One Champions 2000-2001.

SOUTHWICK

Formed: 1882

Chairman: Steve Wotherspoon.
Secretary: Paul Symes. 55 Downsway, Southwick BN42 4WE. Tel: 07908 289 758
Manager: Dominic Shepherd.
Ground: Old Barn Way, off Manor Hall Way, Southwick, Brighton BN42 4NT. Tel: 01273 701 010
Directions: A27 from Brighton take first left after Southwick sign to Leisure Centre. Ground adjacent. Five minutes walk from Fishergate or Southwick stations.
Clubhouse: Yes.
Club Colours: Red & black stripes/black/black. **Change Colours:** Yellow/red/yellow.
Previous League(s): West Sussex 1896-1920. Sussex Co., 1920-52, 54-84. Metropolitan 1952-54. Combined Counties 1984-85. Isthmian 1985-92.
Honours: Sussex County League Champions (6) Sussex Senior Cup Winners (10)

STEYNING TOWN

Chairman: Mrs Gina Barnes.
Secretary: Mrs. Gina Barnes, 36 Shooting Field, Steyning W. Sussex BN44 3RQ. Tel: 07742 305 847.
Manager: Mark Dalgleish.
Ground: The Shooting Field, Steyning, W. Sussex BN44 3RP. Tel: 01903 812 228.
Directions: Entering Steyning from the west. Take 1st left in the High St (Tanyard Lane) Follow into Shooting Field estate, ground is 4th turn on the left. Entering Steyning from the east. From the High St., turn right into Church St.. Turn left by Church into Shooting Field estate. NB Coaches MUST park in Church Street Car Park.
Clubhouse: Yes.
Club Colours: All red. **Change Colours:** Yellow/black/yellow.
Previous League(s): West Sussex 1896-1920. Sussex Co., 1920-52, 54-84. Metropolitan 1952-54. Combined Counties 1984-85. Isthmian 1985-92.
Honours: Sussex County Div 2 Champions 1977-78. Div.1 1984-5,85-86. League Cup 1978-9,83-84, 85-86.

STORRINGTON

Formed: 1920

Chairman: Malcolm McMichael.
Secretary: Keith Dalmon, 4 End Cottages, Turnpike Road, Amberley, Arundel, BN18 9LX. Tel: 07889 367 956.
Manager: Rick Hamilton.
Ground: Recreation Ground, Pulborough Road, Storrington RH20 4HJ. Tel: 01903 745 860.
Directions: A24 right at roundabout at Washington. Four miles to Storrington through village. Third exit at roundabout and second right into Spearbridge Road.
Clubhouse: Yes.
Club Colours: Blue/blue/white. **Change Colours:** White/black/white.
Honours: Sussex Division Two Cup Winners 1979. Division Three Cup Winners 1998. Vernon Wentworth Cup Winners 1998, 2003. Sussex Division Three Champions 2005.

WEALDEN

Formed: 1988

Chairman: Tom Parker.
Secretary: Derek York. 59 Anglesey Avenue, Hailsham BN27 3BQ. Tel: 01323 848 024.
Manager: Simon Rowland.
Ground: The Oaks, Old Eastbourne Road, Uckfield, East Sussex TN22 5QL. Tel: 01825 890 905
Directions: Next to the Rajdutt Restaurant on the Old Eastbourne Road, south of Uckfield town centre.
Clubhouse: Yes.
Club Colours: Sky blue/navy/sky. **Change Colours:** All orange.
Honours: Sussex County Div 2 League Cup Winners 2004-05.

WESTFIELD

Formed: 1927

Chairman: Graham Drinkwinter.

Secretary: Gill Jordan. 54 New Moor Street, Westfield, Nr Hastings TN35 4OP. Tel: 07928 176 658.

Manager: Duncan Jones.

Ground: The Parish Field, Main Road, Westfield TN35 4SB. Tel: 01483 751 011.

Directions: From Hastings take the A21, turning right onto the A28 towards Ashford. Travel through Westfield, and the ground is located off Westfield Lane on the left.

Clubhouse: Yes.

Club Colours: Yellow & green/green/green. **Change Colours:** All blue.

Previous League(s): Hastings League. East Sussex 1971-1997.

Honours: East Sussex Champions 1977-78. League Cup 1977-78. Hastings Senior Cup 2007-08.

WORTHING UNITED

Formed: 1952

Chairman: Brian Harwood.

Secretary: Malcolm Gamlen. 1 Westbourne Avenue, Worthing BN14 8DE. Tel: 07743 322 571.

Manager: Jason Rutherford.

Ground: The Robert Albion Memorial Ground, Lyons Way, Worthing BN14 9JF. 01903 234 466.

Directions: From the West past Hill Barn roundabout to second set of traffic lights, turn left into Lyons Way. From East first set of traffic lights at end of Sompting bypass, turn right into Lyons Way.

Clubhouse: Yes.

Club Colours: Sky blue & white stripes/navy/navy. **Change Colours:** Red & white/red/red.

Previous Name(s): Wigmore Athletic 1952-88. Amalgamated with Southdown to form Worthing United in 1988.

Honours: Sussex County Div.2 Champions 1973-74. Div.3 1989-90.

WORTHING UNITED FC
Photo: Roger Turner.

DIVISION THREE INS & OUTS	IN: Bexhill United (R), Sidlesham (R), TD Shipley (P – West Sussex League Premier Division) OUT: Clymping (P), Little Common (P)

BEXHILL UNITED
Secretary: Dane Martin. 33 Reginald Road, Bexhill-on-sea TN39 3PH. Tel: 07815 425 682
Ground: The Polegrove, Brockley Road, Bexhill-on-Sea, East Sussex TN39 3EX. Tel: 07815 425 682.
Directions: A27 to Little Common then fourth exit off roundabout to Cooden Beach. Left and follow to end, turn right into Brockby Road. Ground at bottom of hill on the right.
Colours: White/black/black.
Change: Yellow/blue/yellow.

BOSHAM
Secretary: Ian Sumnall. St. Aubins, Birdham Road, Chichester PO20 7BX. Tel: 07733 125 678.
Ground: Bosham Recreation Ground, Walton Lane, Bosham, Chichester PO18 8QF. Tel: 01243 574 011.
Directions: From Chichester take the A259 towards Portsmouth. On reaching Bosham turn left at the Swan P.H. roundabout. 1/2 mile to T junction, turn left & car park 50 yds on left.
Honours: Sussex County Lge Div. 3 99-00
Colours: All red. Change Colours: All blue.

BROADBRIDGE HEATH
Founded: 1919
Secretary: Andrew Crisp. 19 Church Road, Broadbridge Heath RH12 3LD Tel: 07966 118 480.
Ground: Wickhurst Lane, Broadbridge Heath, Horsham RH12 3YS. Tel: 01403 211 311
Directions: Alongside A24, Horsham north/south bypass. From the A24 Horsham Bypass, at the large roundabout/underpass take the Broadbridge Heath Bypass towards Guildford and then at the first roundabout turn left into Wickhurst Lane.
Colours: All royal blue. Change Colours: All red.

DORKING WANDERERS
Formed: 1999
Secretary: Mrs Penny Gregg. 16 Walford Road, North Holmwood Dorking RH5 4JA. Tel: 07706 359 987.
Ground: West Humble Playing Fields, London Road, Dorking.
Directions: Take A24 to Dorking at roundabout stay on A24 to Leatherhead. Go past Denbies Vineyard on left. At end of vineyard take 2nd turning on the left straight into the playing field.
Honours: West Sussex League Champions 06-07.
Colours: Blue & black/black/black. Change: All yellow.

FOREST
Secretary: Peter Farley, 7 Spinney Close, Horsham RH12 4PL Tel: 07850 041 243.
Ground: Roffey Sports & Social Club, Spooners Road, Roffey RH12 4DY. Tel: 01403 210 223.
Directions: Spooners Rd. is off the main Crawley road, 100 yds from the `Star' PH, towards Crawley
Colours: All orange. Change: Light blue/navy/navy.

HAYWARDS HEATH TOWN
Secretary: Antony Sim. 59 Wickens Court, Middle Village, Bolnore Village, Haywards Heath RH16 4GL. Tel: 01444 453 754.
Ground: Hanbury Park Stadium, Haywards Heath RH16 3PX. Tel: 01444 412 837.
Directions: A272 to Haywards Heath town centre. At Sussex roundabout, north on B2708 (Hazelgrove Road) take first right into New England Road, then the 4th right (Allen Road) leads to ground.
Colours: Blue/blue/blue & white. Change: All yellow.

HURSTPIERPOINT
Secretary: Mrs Janet Williamson. 55 Western Road Hurstpierpoint BN6 9SX. Tel: 07706 554327.
Ground: Fairfield Rec. Ground, Cuckfield Road, BN6 9SD. Tel: 01273 834 783.
Directions: At Hurstpierpoint crossroads, go north into Cuckfield Road (B2117) for 1km. Ground entrance between houses nos.158 & 160.
Colours: All blue. Change: Green & white/white/green.

IFIELD EDWARDS
Secretary: Rob Anderson, 1 Old Orchards, Church Rd, Worth, Crawley. RH10 7QA. Tel: 07988 843 357.
Ground: Edwards Sports & Social Club, Ifield Green, Rusper Road, Crawley. Tel: 01293 420 598.
Directions: From A23 Crawley by-pass going north, left at r'about signed Charlwood. Third left into Ifield Green, first right past Royal Oak (PH) into Rusper Road.
Colours: Red & black/black/black. Change: All yellow.

NEWHAVEN
Secretary: John Carpenter. 7 Jackson Mews, Harpers Road Newhaven BN9 9QZ
Tel: 07733 370 398.
Ground: Fort Road Recreation Ground, Newhaven, East Sussex BN9 9EE. Tel: 01273 513 940.
Directions: A259, follow one-way system around town, left at Police Station into South Road, which becomes Fort Road.
Colours: Red & white/red/red. Change: All white.

PEASE POTTAGE VILLAGE
Secretary: Mrs Lorraine Bonner. 11 Gabriel Road Maidenbower, Crawley RH10 7LG
Tel: 07701 011 513
Ground: Finches Field, Old Brighton Road Pease Pottage RH11 9AH. Tel: 01293 538 651
Directions: Off M23/A23 towards Brighton turn off at Pease Pottage. Past service station to roundabout, take 3rd exit over bridge sharp left, follow signs to Finches Field. Approx. 300 yards past Grapes Public House on the right.
Colours: All royal blue.
Change: White & green/green/green.

ROTTINGDEAN VILLAGE
Secretary: David Carruthers
115 Sutton Avenue No, Peacehaven BN10 7QJ.
Tel: 07831 582 072.
Ground: Rottingdean Sports Centre, Falmer Road, Rottingdean BN2 7DA. Tel: 01273 306 436
Directions: After leaving the Rottingdean Village one way system go past Bazehill Road and the entrance to the ground is next on the right.
Colours: Red/red/black.
Change: Royal blue/black/royal.

SALTDEAN UNITED
Secretary: Iain Fielding. 40 Rowan Way, Rottingdean BN2 7FP. Tel: 07880 870 886.
Ground: Hill Park, Coombe Vale, Saltdean, Brighton BN2 8HJ. Tel: 01273 309 898.
Directions: A259 coast road east from Brighton to Saltdean Lido, left into Arundel Drive West, and Saltdean Vale to bridle path at beginning of Combe Vale. Club 200yds along track.
Colours: Red & black stripes/black/black.
Change: Green & white/green/green.

SIDLESHAM
Secretary: Stephen Carson. 20 Hunnisett Close, Selsey PO20 0FH. Tel: 07827 243 331
Ground: Recreation Ground, Selsey Road, Sidlesham, Nr Chichester PO20 7RD. Tel: 01243 641 538.
Directions: From Chichester bypass take the B2145 (Hunston/Selsey). Head towards Selsey. Upon entering Sidlesham, ground on right hand side (between houses).
Colours: Yellow/green/yellow. Change: Red/black/red.

TD SHIPLEY
Secretary: Eddie Howe. 23 Ivanhoe Close, Langley Green, Crawley RH11 7UF. Tel: 07988 728 729.
Ground: The Pavilion, Dragons Lane, Shipley RH13 8GB. Tel: 07804 325 228.
Directions: Exit the A24 onto the A272 at the Buckbarn crossroads signposted Billinghurst. The ground is 1.5 miles on the right.
Colours: All red. Change: Yellow/blue/yellow.

UCKFIELD TOWN
Secretary: Chris Goodby. The Millstones, Five Ash Down, Uckfield TN22 3AP. Tel: 07905 517 314.
Ground: Victoria Pleasure Ground, Uckfield TN22 5DJ. Tel: 01825 769 400.
Directions: Take Eastbourne road (old A22) south of Uckfield town centre. Entrance to ground is 1/2 mile on the right (just after the Police station).
Colours: Red/black/black. Change: All blue.

UNITED COUNTIES LEAGUE

www.ebucl.com

Sponsored by: Hereward Teamwear

Founded: 1895

Recent champions:
2004: Spalding United
2005: Cogenhoe United
2006: Woodford United
2007: Deeping Rangers
2008: Stotfold

Reserve Division One	P	W	D	L	F	A	Pts
Stotfold Res.	32	23	3	6	90	34	72
Stewarts/Lloyds Corby Res.	32	21	5	6	81	36	68
N'pton Sileby Rangers Res.	32	17	9	6	73	49	60
Desborough Town Res.	32	17	5	10	76	48	56
Bourne Town Res.	32	16	4	12	66	60	52
St Neots Town Res.	32	14	9	9	77	60	51
Whitworths Res.	32	16	3	13	56	60	51
Blackstones Res.	32	12	12	8	48	43	48
Woodford United Res.	32	11	11	10	62	62	44
Wellingborough Town Res.	32	14	2	16	59	74	44
Northampton Spencer Res.	32	11	5	16	57	75	38
Cogenhoe United Res.	32	9	8	15	49	68	35
Raunds Town Res.	32	10	4	18	49	59	34
Huntingdon Town Res.	32	8	9	15	45	67	33
Bugbrooke St Michaels Res.	32	8	6	18	55	74	30
Yaxley Res.	32	7	4	21	51	90	25
Olney Town Res.	32	7	3	22	44	79	24

Premier Division		P	W	D	L	F	A	Pts
Stewarts & Lloyds Corby		**40**	**27**	**7**	**6**	**95**	**40**	**88**
Stotfold		**40**	**27**	**3**	**10**	**106**	**63**	**84**
Newport Pagnell Town		**40**	**24**	**10**	**6**	**84**	**40**	**82**
Deeping Rangers		**40**	**24**	**8**	**8**	**96**	**50**	**80**
Boston Town		**40**	**23**	**11**	**6**	**79**	**51**	**80**
St Ives Town	*-3*	**40**	**24**	**7**	**9**	**76**	**44**	**76**
Daventry Town	*-3*	**40**	**22**	**7**	**11**	**83**	**51**	**70**
Long Buckby		**40**	**20**	**7**	**13**	**78**	**52**	**67**
Cogenhoe United		**40**	**15**	**13**	**12**	**58**	**55**	**58**
Raunds Town		**40**	**16**	**8**	**16**	**60**	**68**	**56**
Desborough Town		**40**	**15**	**6**	**19**	**62**	**68**	**51**
Northampton Spencer		**40**	**14**	**9**	**17**	**64**	**71**	**51**
Blackstones		**40**	**13**	**11**	**16**	**60**	**63**	**50**
Yaxley		**40**	**14**	**7**	**19**	**47**	**55**	**49**
Sleaford Town		**40**	**13**	**9**	**18**	**57**	**74**	**48**
Holbeach United		**40**	**12**	**11**	**17**	**56**	**60**	**47**
St Neots Town		**40**	**12**	**7**	**21**	**66**	**75**	**43**
Wellingborough Town		**40**	**7**	**8**	**25**	**30**	**66**	**29**
Bourne Town		**40**	**6**	**9**	**25**	**47**	**99**	**27**
Potton United		**40**	**4**	**7**	**29**	**38**	**116**	**19**
Rothwell Corinthians		**40**	**3**	**5**	**32**	**36**	**117**	**14**

	Blackstones	Boston Town	Bourne Town	Cogenhoe United	Daventry Town	Deeping Rangers	Desborough Town	Holbeach United	Long Buckby	Newport Pagnell Town	Northampton Spencer	Potton United	Raunds Town	Rothwell Corinthians	Sleaford Town	St Ives Town	St Neots Town	Stewarts & Lloyds Corby	Stotfold	Wellingborough Town	Yaxley
Blackstones		0-1	0-0	1-1	3-3	0-3	3-2	2-2	0-2	2-0	0-3	4-0	1-1	3-2	2-3	1-2	4-1	2-1	1-6	1-2	3-0
Boston Town	3-0		4-2	2-2	2-1	1-3	3-1	2-1	4-0	2-2	2-1	3-1	1-1	6-1	4-2	0-2	2-1	1-0	2-2	2-0	2-1
Bourne Town	0-4	1-4	***P***	0-1	1-2	0-2	2-4	0-5	1-0	0-1	2-2	4-1	3-3	2-2	2-0	2-8	2-2	1-1	2-7	0-0	1-0
Cogenhoe United	1-2	2-2	2-1	***R***	2-3	1-0	2-2	2-1	3-2	0-1	1-1	4-0	1-2	1-0	1-1	0-1	0-2	1-2	1-0	4-2	2-0
Daventry Town	1-2	3-1	4-0	1-0	***E***	4-3	1-1	1-1	2-2	0-1	1-2	7-1	2-1	2-1	2-0	1-2	3-0	0-1	5-0	3-2	2-1
Deeping Rangers	1-3	5-2	1-1	4-1	2-5	***M***	6-1	1-0	1-1	1-3	2-0	6-1	2-0	5-2	1-1	3-1	4-1	0-2	2-1	2-1	0-0
Desborough Town	0-0	1-2	2-1	0-2	1-2	0-1	***I***	5-3	2-0	1-2	4-0	5-2	1-3	2-1	1-2	1-0	4-2	2-4	0-3	2-1	0-0
Holbeach United	1-1	0-2	2-0	0-1	0-1	1-1	2-0	***E***	2-2	1-1	2-3	2-2	0-3	1-0	2-2	2-0	2-2	3-2	0-1	1-0	0-1
Long Buckby	2-0	0-0	1-1	1-1	4-1	2-3	2-1	3-1	***R***	3-2	3-1	2-0	4-1	5-0	1-0	1-2	1-0	0-0	3-1	5-0	1-0
Newport Pagnell Town	0-0	0-1	4-0	2-2	1-0	1-1	1-1	2-0	3-2		0-2	3-0	3-1	4-0	3-0	2-2	2-0	1-0	4-1	3-1	1-0
Northampton Spencer	1-1	1-1	3-2	1-1	2-0	1-3	1-2	3-4	0-3	2-2		2-1	1-1	1-0	2-2	0-2	0-2	0-2	2-3	3-1	1-1
Potton United	2-0	1-4	3-1	1-2	0-2	2-3	1-5	0-0	0-4	1-1	1-5	***D***	0-1	3-0	0-5	0-4	0-0	0-1	2-3	1-0	1-3
Raunds Town	2-2	1-2	2-1	0-1	1-1	2-2	1-0	1-0	2-1	0-4	1-4	2-1	***I***	3-1	2-1	0-1	3-2	0-2	0-2	1-0	1-2
Rothwell Corinthians	2-0	1-2	0-3	4-2	2-4	0-5	0-1	0-1	2-3	1-6	2-5	4-4	0-2	***V***	1-5	0-4	3-5	0-4	0-7	0-0	1-0
Sleaford Town	0-1	2-2	2-0	2-2	0-4	0-5	2-0	2-4	0-4	3-2	0-2	4-0	1-3	2-0	***I***	1-0	2-0	0-3	1-1	1-0	2-0
St Ives Town	1-1	2-2	4-3	1-2	1-1	0-3	1-0	2-0	2-1	1-2	2-0	3-1	1-3	4-0	2-2	***S***	2-1	1-0	2-1	0-1	3-1
St Neots Town	2-1	0-1	3-4	3-0	1-3	2-1	3-3	2-2	4-0	3-0	3-2	2-2	4-2	2-2	2-1	0-1	***I***	1-2	0-1	0-2	1-3
Stewarts & Lloyds Corby	4-3	3-0	4-1	2-2	2-2	3-3	2-0	2-1	2-1	3-3	4-0	10-1	4-1	1-0	6-1	1-1	4-3	***O***	1-0	2-0	1-0
Stotfold	3-2	3-1	2-0	3-2	2-0	2-1	3-1	2-1	4-2	2-4	4-1	2-0	6-4	5-0	4-2	3-3	1-4	1-3	***N***	3-1	6-2
Wellingborough Town	0-3	0-0	5-0	1-1	0-2	0-1	0-1	1-2	1-0	0-5	0-3	1-1	2-2	1-0	0-0	0-3	1-0	1-3	1-2		0-2
Yaxley	2-1	1-1	2-0	1-1	2-1	1-3	1-2	2-3	2-4	0-2	3-0	2-0	1-0	1-1	3-0	1-2	2-0	2-1	0-3	1-1	

Division One		P	W	D	L	F	A	Pts
P'borough Northern Star		**30**	**24**	**2**	**4**	**94**	**24**	**74**
Daventry United		**30**	**19**	**5**	**6**	**81**	**40**	**62**
N'pton Sileby Rangers		**30**	**16**	**4**	**10**	**67**	**47**	**52**
N'pton ON Chenecks		**30**	**16**	**3**	**11**	**63**	**52**	**51**
AFC Kempston Rovers		**30**	**13**	**8**	**9**	**66**	**64**	**47**
Rushden & Higham Utd		**30**	**11**	**13**	**6**	**50**	**37**	**46**
Whitworths		**30**	**12**	**9**	**9**	**56**	**47**	**45**
Buckingham Town		**30**	**14**	**3**	**13**	**56**	**60**	**45**
Eynesbury Rovers	*-6*	**30**	**13**	**10**	**7**	**59**	**48**	**43**
Bugbrooke St Michaels		**30**	**10**	**9**	**11**	**61**	**53**	**39**
Thrapston Town	*-3*	**30**	**12**	**5**	**13**	**54**	**58**	**38**
Wootton Blue Cross		**30**	**8**	**5**	**17**	**49**	**71**	**29**
Burton Park Wanderers		**30**	**7**	**6**	**17**	**41**	**71**	**27**
Huntingdon Town		**30**	**6**	**8**	**16**	**37**	**62**	**26**
Olney Town		**30**	**8**	**1**	**21**	**41**	**69**	**25**
Irchester United		**30**	**3**	**5**	**22**	**33**	**105**	**14**

Reserve Division Two		P	W	D	L	F	A	Pts
P'boro Northern Star Res.		28	22	1	5	82	30	67
Deeping Rangers Res.	-3	28	21	3	4	81	33	63
N'pton ON Chenecks Res.		28	16	5	7	78	44	53
AFC Kempston Rovers Res.		28	16	4	8	60	45	52
Daventry Town Res.		28	14	7	7	83	47	49
Eynesbury Rovers Res.		28	13	4	11	43	37	43
Rothwell Corinthians Res.		28	11	7	10	52	58	40
Long Buckby Res.		28	11	5	12	62	61	38
Irchester United Res.		28	9	7	12	55	66	34
Rushden & Higham Res.		28	9	6	13	33	43	33
Burton Park Wanderers Res.		28	8	9	11	50	64	33
Thrapston Town Res.		28	9	4	15	42	60	31
Buckingham Town Res.		28	8	1	19	50	83	25
St Ives Town Res.		28	5	5	18	41	79	20
Wootton Blue Cross Res.		28	3	2	23	32	94	11

RESERVES CUP

FINAL *(April 29th at Rothwell Corinthians)*

Blackstones Res. 1 Northampton Spencer Res. 0

LEAGUE CUP

PRELIMIINARY ROUND

AFC Kempston Rovers 0 **Wellingborough Town** 4
Daventry United 1 **Daventry Town** 2
Deeping Rgrs 4 **Northampton Sileby Rgrs** 4 *aet* (3-4p)
Huntingdon Town 1 **Stewarts & Lloyds Corby** 2
St Ives Town 1 Sleaford Town 0
Whitworths 0 **Desborough Town** 3

FIRST ROUND

Bourne Town 0 **Eynesbury Rovers** 2
Buckingham Town 1 Rushden & Higham United 0
Daventry Town 0 **Cogenhoe United** 2
Harborough Town (scr.) v **N'pton ON Chenecks** (w/o)
Holbeach United 4 Bugbrooke St Michaels 1
Long Buckby 0 **Stewarts & Lloyds Corby** 2
Newport Pagnell Town 3 Wellingborough Town 0
Northampton Sileby Rgrs 2 **Boston Town** 2 *aet* (1-4p)
Northampton Spencer 3 Desborough Town 2 *aet*
Olney Town 1 **Blackstones** 2
Peterborough Northern Star 5 Rothwell Corinthians 0
Potton United 5 Yaxley 0
Raunds Town 4 Wootton Blue Cross 0
St Ives Town 4 St Neots Town 3 *aet*
Stotfold 6 Irchester United 0
Thrapston Town 2 Burton Park Wanderers 1 *aet*

SECOND ROUND

Blackstones 1 Buckingham Town 0
Cogenhoe United 0 **Stotfold** 2
Holbeach United 2 Boston Town 2 *aet* (6-5p)
Newport Pagnell Town 2 Eynesbury Rovers 1
N'pton ON Chenecks 0 **Peterborough Northern Star** 4
Potton Utd 2 **Northampton Spencer** 1 *(Potton expelled)*
St Ives Town 5 Raunds Town 1 *aet*
Thrapston Town 1 **Stewarts & Lloyds Corby** 2

QUARTER-FINALS

Peterborough Northern Star 0 **Blackstones** 5
St Ives Town 5 Holbeach United 0
Stewarts & Lloyds Corby 1 Northampton Spencer 0
Stotfold 3 Newport Pagnell Town 1

SEMI-FINALS

Stewarts & Lloyds Corby 3 Blackstones 0
Stotfold 1 St Ives Town 0

FINAL

(April 22nd at Raunds Town)
Stewarts & Lloyds Corby 0 **Stotfold** 1

	AFC Kempston	Buckingham T.	Bugbrooke SM	Burton Pk W.	Daventry Utd	Eynesbury R.	Huntingdon T.	Irchester Utd	N'ton ON Chen	N'pton Sileby	Olney Town	P'boro. NS	Rushden/HU	Thrapston T.	Whitworths	Wootton BC
AFC Kempston Rovers		2-0	3-2	2-2	1-1	1-1	0-0	6-2	6-0	3-2	3-1	0-6	2-1	7-2	3-4	4-1
Buckingham Town	1-4		6-5	2-1	0-3	1-1	1-2	3-0	3-1	1-6	5-2	0-1	1-2	3-2	4-1	4-1
Bugbrooke St Michaels	5-1	2-2	***D***	4-1	2-1	2-2	1-0	6-2	0-1	2-2	3-1	0-2	0-0	0-2	1-1	0-0
Burton Park Wanderers	4-2	1-2	1-4	***I***	1-4	1-4	2-2	1-1	2-5	3-1	0-1	0-4	0-5	2-1	4-1	2-1
Daventry United	6-0	3-0	2-2	2-0	***V***	2-2	2-0	8-1	1-2	3-0	4-1	4-1	1-2	3-2	1-0	4-0
Eynesbury Rovers	2-2	4-2	1-5	2-1	4-1	***I***	2-2	2-2	2-1	1-3	3-1	0-1	0-2	3-3	2-2	3-1
Huntingdon Town	1-1	1-2	2-1	2-0	0-1	1-2	***S***	2-2	1-3	1-2	2-2	1-3	0-2	2-4	2-2	1-5
Irchester United	0-1	2-0	2-2	1-3	2-6	0-4	3-4	***I***	0-7	3-2	1-3	1-7	1-2	0-2	0-5	2-1
Northampton ON Chenecks	2-3	3-4	3-1	4-4	2-4	1-0	1-3	3-0	***O***	1-1	3-1	1-1	2-1	1-0	2-3	5-2
Northampton Sileby Rangers	3-0	0-1	3-2	1-1	4-1	0-2	7-0	2-1	2-0	***N***	4-3	1-3	1-1	2-1	3-1	1-2
Olney Town	0-4	0-2	0-5	2-0	0-2	0-1	1-2	4-1	1-2	0-5		2-0	0-2	0-2	3-0	0-2
Peterborough Northern Star	7-1	2-1	5-0	3-1	3-0	1-3	3-1	8-1	3-0	4-0	3-0	***O***	2-0	5-0	1-1	4-1
Rushden & Higham United	3-3	3-0	3-1	1-0	2-2	1-1	1-1	1-1	1-3	0-1	2-3	2-1	***N***	1-1	1-1	2-2
Thrapston Town	1-0	2-3	3-1	1-1	2-3	2-3	3-1	4-1	2-1	3-0	0-5	0-2	2-2	***E***	2-1	1-1
Whitworths	3-0	1-1	1-1	5-0	2-2	3-1	1-0	2-0	0-2	1-2	3-2	1-4	0-0	3-0		2-1
Wootton Blue Cross	1-1	2-1	0-1	1-2	2-4	3-1	2-0	4-0	0-1	2-6	3-2	1-4	4-4	1-4	2-5	

IN: Daventry United (P)
OUT: Potton United (R)

BLACKSTONES

Founded: 1920 Nickname: Stones

Chairman: Kevan Doyle
Secretary: Ian MacGillivray
20 New Road
Ryhall
Stamford, Lincs
PE9 4HL
Tel: 01780 762 263
Manager: David Bird
Prog Editor: Kevin Boor

Ground: Lincoln Road, Stamford, Lincs PE9 1SH Tel: 01780 757 835
Capacity: 1,000 **Seats:** 100 **Covered:** yes
Midweek Matchday: Tuesday **Clubhouse:** Yes **Shop:** No
Colours(change): Green/black/green. (Orange/black/orange)
Previous Names: Rutland Ironworks & Blackstone (until 1975)
Previous Lges: Peterborough Works, Peterborough,Stamford & District
Records: **Att:** 700 v Glinton
Senior Honours: Lincs Senior CupA 92-93, 03-04

10 YEAR RECORD

99-00	00-01	01-02	02-03	03-04	04-05	05-06	06-07	07-08	08-09
UCL P 6	UCL P 12	UCL P 12	UCL P 16	UCL P 11	UCL P 15	UCL P 10	UCL P 8	UCL P 4	UCL P 13

BOSTON TOWN

Founded: 1964 Nickname: Poachers

Chairman: Mick Vines
Secretary: Ron Bennett
172 Woodville Road
Boston
Lincs
PE21 8BU
Tel: 01205 354 252
Manager: Bob-Don Duncan
Prog Editor: Pat Meggeson

Ground: Tattershall Road, Boston, Lincs PE21 9LR Tel: 01205 365 470
Capacity: 6,000 **Seats:** 450 **Covered:** 950
Midweek Matchday: Tuesday **Clubhouse:** Yes **Shop:**
Colours(change): All Blue (Yellow/black/black)
Previous Names: Boston > 1994
Previous Lges: Lincs, Central Alliance, Eastern co, Midland N. Co. E, C. Mids
Records: **Att:** 2,700 v Boston United FA Cup 1970.
Goalscorer: Gary Bull 57 during 2006-07 season.
Senior Honours: Midland League 1974-75, 78-79, 80-81. Central Midlands 88-89
United Counties League 1994-95, 00-01.

10 YEAR RECORD

99-00	00-01	01-02	02-03	03-04	04-05	05-06	06-07	07-08	08-09
UCL P 3	UCL P 1	UCL P 8	UCL P 8	UCL P 5	UCL P 11	UCL P 6	UCL P 2	UCL P 6	UCL P 5

BOURNE TOWN

Founded: 1883 Nickname: Wakes

Chairman: Andy Stubley
Secretary: Pete Stanton
77 Station Street
Rippingale
Bourne
PE10 0SX
Tel: 07921 298 591
Manager: Martin Lakin
Prog Editor: See chairman

Ground: Abbey Lawn, Abbey Road, Bourne, Lincs PE10 9EN. Tel: 01778 422 292
Capacity: 3,000 **Seats:** 300 **Covered:** 750
Midweek Matchday: Wednesday **Clubhouse:** Yes **Shop:**
Colours(change): Claret & sky blue stripes/navy/navy. (Yellow/blue/blue).
Previous Names:
Previous Lges: Peterborough, UCL 47-56, Central Alliance 58-61 & Midland Co 61-63
Records: **Att:** FA Trophy 1970 **Goalscorer:** David Scotney
Senior Honours: U.C.L. Champions 68-69,69-70, 71-72,90-91,
Lincs Senior A Cup 1971-72, 2005-2006

10 YEAR RECORD

99-00	00-01	01-02	02-03	03-04	04-05	05-06	06-07	07-08	08-09
UCL P 12	UCL P 13	UCL P 13	UCL P 19	UCL P 15	UCL P 19	UCL P 13	UCL P 18	UCL P 18	UCL P 19

COGENHOE UNITED

Founded: 1958 Nickname: Cooks

Chairman: Derek Wright
Secretary: Lewis Sander
23 Wheatfield Road
Abington
Northampton
NN3 2NE
Tel: 01604 408 285
Manager: Darren Collins
Prog Editor: Phil Wright

Ground: Compton Park, Brafield Road, Cogenhoe NN7 1ND Tel: 01604 890 521
Capacity: 5,000 **Seats:** 100 **Covered:** 200
Midweek Matchday: Tuesday **Clubhouse:** Yes **Shop:** No
Colours(change): All Blue (Red/black/black)
Previous Names:
Previous Lges: Central Northants Comb, prem 67-84
Records: **Att:** 1,000 Charity game 90 **Goalscorer & Appearances:** Tony Smith
Senior Honours: United Counties League 2004-05.

10 YEAR RECORD

99-00	00-01	01-02	02-03	03-04	04-05	05-06	06-07	07-08	08-09
UCL P 2	UCL P 2	UCL P 3	UCL P 9	UCL P 6	UCL P 1	UCL P 5	UCL P 5	UCL P 9	UCL P 9

DAVENTRY TOWN

Founded: 1886 Nickname:

Chairman: Iain Humphrey
Secretary: Matt Hogsden
2 Lamport Court
Heartland, Daventry
Northants
NN11 8UF
Tel: 01327 310 557
Manager:
Prog Editor: Harvey Potter

Ground: Comm. Park, Browns Rd, Daventry, Northants NN11 4NS Tel: 07530 081 987
Capacity: 2,000 **Seats:** 250 **Covered:** 250
Midweek Matchday: Tuesday **Clubhouse:** Yes **Shop:**
Colours(change): All purple. (All yellow).
Previous Names:
Previous Lges: Northampton Town (pre-1987) & Central Northways Comb 87-89
Records: **Att:** 850 v Utrecht (Holland) 1989
Senior Honours: United Counties League Div.1 1989-90, 90-91, 00-01, 07-08.

10 YEAR RECORD

99-00	00-01	01-02	02-03	03-04	04-05	05-06	06-07	07-08	08-09
UCL 1 5	UCL 1 1	UCL P 15	UCL P 10	UCL P 22	UCL P 22	UCL 1 6	UCL 1 4	UCL 1 1	UCL P 7

DAVENTRY UNITED

Founded: 1968 Nickname: Motormen

Chairman: Dave Hirons
Secretary: Nigel Foster
29 Dryden Avenue
Daventry
Northants
NN11 9DJ
Tel: 07876 133 308
Manager: Darren Foster
Prog Editor: See secretary

Ground: Royal Oak Way, Southing, Daventry, Northants NN11 8PQ 01327 704914
Capacity: 1,000 **Seats:** yes **Covered:** yes
Midweek Matchday: Tuesday **Clubhouse:** Yes **Shop:** No
Colours(change): Blue & Yellow/blue/blue. (All red)
Previous Names: Ford Sports Daventry > 2007
Previous Lges: Central Northants Combination 1968 - 1977.
Records:
Senior Honours: UCL Div.1 Champions 1992-93, 95-96. Premier 1999-00, 01-02.

10 YEAR RECORD

99-00	00-01	01-02	02-03	03-04	04-05	05-06	06-07	07-08	08-09
UCL P 1	UCL P 4	UCL P 1	UCL P 11	UCL P 9	UCL P 6	UCL P 19	UCL P 20	UCL 1 5	UCL 1 2

DEEPING RANGERS

Founded: 1964 Nickname: Rangers

Chairman: Kevin Davenport
Secretary: Haydon Whitman
14 Courtfields
Market Deeping
Peterborough
PE6 8GD
Tel: 01778 380 455
Manager: Tunkay Korkmaz
Prog Editor: Robin Crowson

Ground: Deeping Sp. Club, Outgang Rd, Market Deeping, PE6 8LQ Tel: 01778 344 701.
Capacity: 1,000 **Seats:** 180 **Covered:** 250
Midweek Matchday: Tuesday **Clubhouse:** Yes **Shop:**
Colours(change): All claret & blue. (White/sky blue/sky blue)
Previous Names: None
Previous Lges: Peterborough & District 1966 - 1999.
Records:
Senior Honours: Lincs Sen Cup, B Cup, Peterborough FA Cup (3),
UCL Premier Champions 2006-07

10 YEAR RECORD

99-00	00-01	01-02	02-03	03-04	04-05	05-06	06-07	07-08	08-09
UCL 1 3	UCL 1 2	UCL P 10	UCL P 5	UCL P 17	UCL P 12	UCL P 20	UCL P 1	UCL P 7	UCL P 4

DESBOROUGH TOWN

Founded: 1896 Nickname: Ar Tam

Chairman: Kevin O'Brien
Secretary: John Lee
85 Breakleys Road
Desborough
Northants
NN14 2PT
Tel: 01536 760 002
Manager: Dave Williams
Prog Editor: John Lee

Ground: Waterworks Field, Braybrooke Rd, Desborough NN14 2LJ Tel: 01536 761 350
Capacity: 8,000 **Seats:** 250 **Covered:** 500
Midweek Matchday: Tuesday **Clubhouse:** Yes **Shop:**
Colours(change): All Blue. (All yellow)
Previous Names: None
Previous Lges: None
Records: **Att:** 8,000 v Kettering Town
Senior Honours: N'hants/Utd Co. Champs 1900-01, 01-02, 06-07, 20-21, 23-24, 24-25 27-28, 48-49, 66-67. Lge C 77-78, 00-01, 07-08. N'hants Sen C 1910-11, 13-14, 28-29, 51-52.

10 YEAR RECORD

99-00	00-01	01-02	02-03	03-04	04-05	05-06	06-07	07-08	08-09
UCL P 8	UCL P 7	UCL P 5	UCL P 18	UCL P 16	UCL P 10	UCL P 18	UCL P 14	UCL P 3	UCL P 11

HOLBEACH UNITED

Founded: 1929 Nickname: Tigers

Chairman: Dave Dougill
Secretary: Jamie Hiller
40 Cornfields
Holbeach
Lincs
PE12 7QR
Tel: 07989 646 834
Manager: Shaun Keeble & Dick Creasey
Prog Editor: Mike Palmer

Ground: Carters Park, Park Road, Holbeach, Lincs PE12 7EE Tel: 01406 424 761
Capacity: 4,000 **Seats:** 200 **Covered:** 450
Midweek Matchday: Tuesday **Clubhouse:** Yes **Shop:** No
Colours(change): Gold & black/black/gold & black.(Blue & white/blue/blue & white)
Previous Names:
Previous Lges: Peterborough U Co L 46-55, Eastern 55-62, Midland Co 62-63
Records: **Att:** 4,094 v Wisbech 1954
Senior Honours: United Counties League 1989-90, 02-03.
Lincs Sen A Cup (4), Senior Cup B 57-58

10 YEAR RECORD

99-00	00-01	01-02	02-03	03-04	04-05	05-06	06-07	07-08	08-09
UCL P 16	UCL P 14	UCL P 2	UCL P 1	UCL P 7	UCL P 3	UCL P 17	UCL P 11	UCL P 11	UCL P 16

LONG BUCKBY

Founded: 1937 Nickname: Bucks

Chairman: Guy Loveland
Secretary: Dave Austin
8 Pytchley Drive
Long Buckby
Northants
NN6 7PL
Tel: 01327 842 788
Manager: Adam Sandy
Prog Editor: John Crockett

Ground: Station Road, Long Buckby NN6 7QA Tel: 01327 842 682
Capacity: 1,000 **Seats:** 200 **Covered:** 200
Midweek Matchday: Tuesday **Clubhouse:** Yes **Shop:** No
Colours(change): Claret & blue/claret/sky blue. (All orange).
Previous Names: Long Buckby Nomads
Previous Lges: Rugby & District Central, Northants Combination pre 68
Records: **Att:** 750 v Kettering Town
Senior Honours: United Counties League Div.2 1970-71, 71-72.
Northants Senior Cup 2008-09.

10 YEAR RECORD

99-00	00-01	01-02	02-03	03-04	04-05	05-06	06-07	07-08	08-09
UCL P 20	UCL P 19	UCL P 18	UCL P 20	UCL P 21	UCL P 8	UCL P 21	UCL P 12	UCL P 2	UCL P 8

NEWPORT PAGNELL TOWN

Founded: 1963 Nickname: Swans

Chairman: Geoff Cardno
Secretary: Stephen Handley
31 Maulden Gardens
Giffard Park
Milton Keynes
MK14 5JJ
Tel: 01908 614 745
Manager: Terry Shrieves
Prog Editor: Danny Goodwin

Ground: Willen Road, Newport Pagnell MK16 0DF Tel: 01908 611 993
Capacity: 2,000 **Seats:** 100 **Covered:** 100
Midweek Matchday: Tuesday **Clubhouse:** Yes **Shop:** No
Colours(change): White & Green/black/green & black (All Navy Blue)
Previous Names: Newport Pagnell Wanderers > 1972.
Previous Lges: North Bucks 1963-71. South Midlands 1971-73.
Records:
Senior Honours: United Counties League Div.1 1981-82, 01-02.
Bucks & Berks Intermediate Cup 2001-02

10 YEAR RECORD

99-00	00-01	01-02	02-03	03-04	04-05	05-06	06-07	07-08	08-09
UCL 1 7	UCL 1 6	UCL 1 1	UCL P 2	UCL P 13	UCL P 18	UCL P 15	UCL P 7	UCL P 15	UCL P 3

NORTHAMPTON SPENCER

Founded: 1936 Nickname: Millers

Chairman: Graham Wrighting
Secretary: Nick Hillery
18 Countess Road
Northmpton

NN5 7DY
Tel: 01604 756 580
Manager: Andy Peaks
Prog Editor: Andy Goldsmith

Ground: Kingsthorpe Mill, Studand Road, Northampton NN5 6NE Tel: 01604 718 898
Capacity: 2,000 **Seats:** 100 **Covered:** 350
Midweek Matchday: Tuesday **Clubhouse:** Yes **Shop:** No
Colours(change): Green/green/white. (All royal blue).
Previous Names: Spencer School Old Boys
Previous Lges:
Records: **Att:** 800 v Nttm Forest 1993 **App;** P. Jelley 622 1984-2002
Senior Honours: United Counties League Div.1 1984-85. Premier 1991-92.
Northants Senior Cup Winners 2005-06

10 YEAR RECORD

99-00	00-01	01-02	02-03	03-04	04-05	05-06	06-07	07-08	08-09
UCL P 5	UCL P 8	UCL P 17	UCL P 12	UCL P 18	UCL P 16	UCL P 3	UCL P 6	UCL P 13	UCL P 12

PREMIER DIVISION - 2009-10

RAUNDS TOWN

Founded: 1946 Nickname: Shopmates

Chairman: David Tyrrell
Secretary: Michael Latimer
19 Crome Close
Wellingborough
Northants
NN8 4SW
Tel: 01933 677 704
Manager: Lee Howard
Prog Editor: Barrie Tomkins

Ground: Kiln Park, London Rd, Raunds, Northants NN9 6EQ Tel: 01933 623 351
Capacity: 3,000 **Seats:** 250 **Covered:** 600
Midweek Matchday: Tuesday **Clubhouse:** Yes **Shop:** Yes
Colours(change): Red & black/black/black. (White/red/red).
Previous Names:
Previous Lges: Rushden & Dist, Cent. Northants Comb, U.C.L. , Southern 96-00
Records: **Att:** 1500 v Crystal Palace 1991 **Goalscorer:** Shaun Keeble **App:** Martin Lewis - 355
Senior Honours: United Counties League Div.1 1982-83. Premier 95-96. Northants Senior Cup 90-91

10 YEAR RECORD

99-00	00-01	01-02	02-03	03-04	04-05	05-06	06-07	07-08	08-09
SthE 21	UCL P 3	UCL P 4	UCL P 15	UCL P 20	UCL P 20	UCL P 8	UCL P 13	UCL P 17	UCL P 10

ROTHWELL CORINTHIANS

Founded: 1934 Nickname: Corinthians

Chairman: Mark Budworth
Secretary: Mark Budworth
5 Jackson Way
Kettering
Northants
NN15 7DL
Tel: 01536 521 973
Manager: Lee Duffy
Prog Editor: Mark Budworth

Ground: Sergeants Lawn, Desborough Road, Rothwell, NN14 6JQ Tel: 01536 418 688
Capacity: **Seats:** 50 **Covered:** 200
Midweek Matchday: **Clubhouse:** Yes **Shop:** No
Colours(change): Red/black/red. (All blue).
Previous Names: None
Previous Lges: Kettering & District Amateur/East Midlands Alliance 1934 - 1995.
Records:
Senior Honours: East Midlands Alliance Champions 1989-90, 94-95.

10 YEAR RECORD

99-00	00-01	01-02	02-03	03-04	04-05	05-06	06-07	07-08	08-09
UCL 1 13	UCL 1 7	UCL 1 14	UCL 1 8	UCL 1 12	UCL 1 8	UCL 1 10	UCL 1 7	UCL 1 3	UCL P 21

SLEAFORD TOWN

Founded: 1968 Nickname: Town

Chairman: Tony Farrow
Secretary: Steve Thomas
15 Pavillion Gardens
Sleaford
Lincs
NG34 8GH
Tel: 07929 008 856
Manager: Brian Rowland
Prog Editor: Paul Stafford

Ground: Estaforde Park, Boston Road, Sleaford, Lincs NG34 7GH. Tel: 01529 415 951
Capacity: **Seats:** 88 **Covered:** 88
Midweek Matchday: **Clubhouse:** Yes **Shop:**
Colours(change): Green/black/green. (All red).
Previous Names:
Previous Lges: Lincolnshire
Records:
Senior Honours: United Counties League Div.1 2005-06.

10 YEAR RECORD

99-00	00-01	01-02	02-03	03-04	04-05	05-06	06-07	07-08	08-09
Lincs 12	Lincs 6	Lincs 5	Lincs 2	Lincs 1	UCL 1 6	UCL 1 1	UCL 1 2	UCL P 14	UCL P 15

ST. IVES TOWN

Founded: 1887 Nickname: Saints

Chairman: Neville Nania
Secretary: Chris George
16 Canberra Drive
St. Ives

PE27 3UR
Tel: 01480 382 257
Manager: Warren Everdell & Jez Hall
Prog Editor: Jezz Hall

Ground: Westwood Road, St. Ives PE27 6WU Tel: 01480 463 207
Capacity: **Seats:** Yes **Covered:** Yes
Midweek Matchday: Tuesday **Clubhouse:** Yes **Shop:** No
Colours(change): White & black/black/black & white. (All white)
Previous Names: None
Previous Lges: Cambs, Central Amateur, Hunts, Peterborough & District
Records:
Senior Honours: Hunts Senior Cup, Hunts Premier Cup, Hinchingbrooke Cup 2006-07

10 YEAR RECORD

99-00	00-01	01-02	02-03	03-04	04-05	05-06	06-07	07-08	08-09
UCL 1 6	UCL 1 13	UCL 1 16	UCL 1 9	UCL 1 10	UCL 1 3	UCL P 9	UCL P 10	UCL P 5	UCL P 6

ST. NEOTS TOWN
Founded: 1879 Nickname: Saints

Chairman: John Delaney
Secretary: Peter Naylor
6 Philip Gardens
Eynesbury
St Neots, Cambs
PE19 2QH
Tel: 07894 133 200
Manager: Steve Lomas
Prog Editor: TBC

Ground: Rowley Park, Cambridge Road, St Neots, Cambs PE19 6SN Tel: 01480 470 012
Capacity: 3,000 **Seats:** 250 **Covered:** 850
Midweek Matchday: Tuesday **Clubhouse:** Yes **Shop:** No
Colours(change): Sky & navy blue quarters/navy/navy. (Gold/black/black)
Previous Names: St. Neots & District > 1951.
Previous Lges: S Midlands, Cent. Alliance, UCL, Eastern Co., Hunts
Records: **Att:** 2,000 v Wisbech 1966

Senior Honours: United Counties League 1967-68. Div.1 94-95.
Hunts Sen. Cup (34), & Hunts Prem Cup 2001-02

10 YEAR RECORD

99-00	00-01	01-02	02-03	03-04	04-05	05-06	06-07	07-08	08-09
UCL P 13	UCL P 5	UCL P 6	UCL P 13	UCL P 4	UCL P 14	UCL P 4	UCL P 17	UCL P 8	UCL P 17

STEWARTS & LLOYDS CORBY
Founded: 1935 Nickname: The Foundrymen

Chairman: TBC
Secretary: John Davies
6 Manitoba Close
Corby
Northants
NN18 9HX
Tel: 07588 018 397
Manager: TBC
Prog Editor: TBC

Ground: Recreation Ground, Occupation Road, Corby NN17 1EH Tel: 01536 401 497
Capacity: 1,500 **Seats:** 100 **Covered:** 200
Midweek Matchday: Tuesday **Clubhouse:** Yes **Shop:** No
Colours(change): Maroon & amber/maroon/maroon. (All navy blue).
Previous Names: Hamlet S & L 1989-92.
Previous Lges: Kettering Amateur
Records: **Goalscorer:** Joey Martin 46

Senior Honours: United Counties League Div.1 1973-74, 74-75. Premier 85-86, 08-09.

10 YEAR RECORD

99-00	00-01	01-02	02-03	03-04	04-05	05-06	06-07	07-08	08-09
UCL P 9	UCL P 11	UCL P 14	UCL P 6	UCL P 19	UCL P 21	UCL P 16	UCL P 16	UCL P 12	UCL P 1

STOTFOLD
Founded: 1946 Nickname: The Eagles

Chairman: Phil Pateman
Secretary: Julie Longhurst
49 Astwick Road
Stotfold
Hitchin, Herts
SG5 4AU
Tel: 01462 731 167
Manager: Gordon Bickerstaff
Prog Editor: Phil Pateman

Ground: Roker Park, The Green, Stotfold, Hitchin, Herts SG5 4AN Tel: 01462 730 765
Capacity: 5,000 **Seats:** 300 **Covered:** 300
Midweek Matchday: Tuesday **Clubhouse:** Yes **Shop:**
Colours(change): Amber/black/black. (Blue & white hoops/blue/blue).
Previous Names:
Previous Lges: Biggleswade & Dist, Norths Herts & South Midlands
Records: **Att:**1,000 **Goalscorer:** Roy Boon **Apps:** Roy Boon & Dave Chellew

Senior Honours: S. MIdlands Lg 80-81, Beds Senior Cup 64-5, 93-94,
Beds Prem Cup 81-82, 98-99. United Counties League 2007-08

10 YEAR RECORD

99-00	00-01	01-02	02-03	03-04	04-05	05-06	06-07	07-08	08-09
UCL P 4	UCL P 15	UCL P 9	UCL P 17	UCL P 10	UCL P 9	UCL P 11	UCL P 19	UCL P 1	UCL P 2

WELLINGBOROUGH TOWN
Founded: 2004 Nickname: Doughboys

Chairman: Martin Potton
Secretary: Mick Walden
2 Woodstock Close
Wellingborough
Northants
NN8 5YQ
Tel: 01933 400 063
Manager: Rob Gould
Prog Editor: See secretary

Ground: The Dog & Duck, London Road, Wellingborough NN8 2DP Tel: 01933 441 388
Capacity: **Seats:** Yes **Covered:** Yes
Midweek Matchday: Tuesday **Clubhouse:** Yes **Shop:**
Colours(change): Yellow/royal blue/yellow. (All white)
Previous Names: Original team (Formed 1867) folded in 2002 reforming in 2004
Previous Lges: Metropolitan. Southern.
Records:

Senior Honours: United Counties League 1964-65.

10 YEAR RECORD

99-00	00-01	01-02	02-03	03-04	04-05	05-06	06-07	07-08	08-09
UCL P 15	UCL P 18	UCL P 21				UCL 1 2	UCL P 3	UCL P 10	UCL P 18

PREMIER - 2009-10

YAXLEY

Founded: 1900 Nickname: The Cuckoos

Chairman: Alan Andrews
Secretary: Mrs Sandra Cole
22 Hillcrest Avenue
Yaxley
Peterborough
PE7 3LS
Tel: 07982 924 123
Manager: Gary Clipston
Prog Editor: Mrs Carole Green

Ground: Leading Drove, Holme Road, Yaxley, Peterborough PE7 3NA Tel: 01733 244 928
Capacity: 1,000 **Seats:** 150 **Covered:** yes
Midweek Matchday: Tuesday **Clubhouse:** Yes **Shop:** Yes
Colours(change): All blue. (All red).
Previous Names: Yaxley Rovers.
Previous Lges: Peterborough & Dist., Hunts & West Anglia
Records: **Goalscorer:** Ricky Hailstone 16

Senior Honours: United Counties League Div.1 1996-97.
Hunts Senior Cup (7), UCL Cup 2005-2006

10 YEAR RECORD

99-00	00-01	01-02	02-03	03-04	04-05	05-06	06-07	07-08	08-09
UCL P 14	UCL P 10	UCL P 11	UCL P 7	UCL P 8	UCL P 4	UCL P 7	UCL P 15	UCL P 16	UCL P 14

DIVISION ONE INS & OUTS IN: Potton United (R)
OUT: Daventry United (P)

A.F.C. KEMPSTON ROVERS

Founded: 1884
Nickname: Walnut Boys

Chairman: Russell Shreeves
Secretary: Kevin Howlett,53 Silverdale Street, Kempston, Bedford MK42 8BE. **Tel No:** 01234 852 056 (H)
Prog Editor: Mark Kennett. Tel: 01234 400 835.
Ground: Hillgrounds Leisure, Hillgrounds Rd, Kempston, Bedford MK42 8SZ. Tel: 01234 852 346.
Capacity: 2,000 **Seats:** 100 **Cover:** 250 **Floodlights:** Yes
Directions: M1 jct 13, A421 to Kempston, Hillgrounds Rd is off the B531 main Kempston-Bedford road. Entrance to Hillgrounds Road is opposite Sainsburys onthe B531 - ground can be found just over twi miles from Sainsburys entrance.British Rail to Bedford Thameslink/Midland then bus No.103 from Bedford town centre stops outside ground
Club Shop: No, but old programmes available from clubhouse.
Clubhouse: Open 7-11pm Tues - Sun. & w/e lunch 12-3pm. Sky TV, pool, hot pies & pasties. **Midweek Home matchday:** Tuesday.
Colours: Red & white stripes/black/black. **Change:** Blue & black stripes/blue/bue
PREVIOUS: League: South Midlands 27-53.
HONOURS U.C.L. Prem. 73-74 R-up 56-57 59-60, Div 1 57-58 85-86, Div 2 55-56 R-up 67-68, KO Cup 55-56 57-58 59-60 74-75 76-77; Beds Senior Cup 08-09 37-38 76-77 91-92 R-up 92-93.

BUCKINGHAM TOWN

Founded: 1883
Nickname: Robins

Chairman: Tony Rosenberg
Secretary: Robin Taylor. c/o Buckingham Town FC. Tel: 07860 539 106.
Programme Editor: Carl Waine. Tel: 01280 817 194.
GROUND ADDRESS: Ford Meadow, Ford Street, Buckingham MK18 1AG. **Ground Tel. No:** 01280 816 257
Capacity: 2,500 **Seats:** 200 **Covered:** 200 **Floodlights:** Yes
Simple Directions: From Town Centre take A413 (Aylesbury) and turn right at Phillips Ford Garage after 400 yards.
Midweek Home Matchday: Wednesday **Clubhouse:** Open evenings **Club Shop:** Yes
Previous Leagues: Aylesbury & Dist., North Bucks, Hellenic 53-57, S.Mids 57-74, U.Co. L. 74-86 and Southern 86-97
Club Colours: All Red **Change Colours:** All White
RECORD Attendance: 2,451 v Orient F.A.Cup 84-85
Fee Paid: £7,000 to Wealdstone for Steve Jenkins 1992 **Received:** £1,000 from Kettering Town for Terry Shrieves.
Senior Honours: Southern Lg. Southern Div. 90-91 U.C.L. 83-84 85-86 Berks & Bucks Sen. Cup 83-84

BUGBROOKE ST MICHAELS

Founded: 1929
Nickname: Badgers

Chairman: Glen Moore
Secretary: Debbie Preston. 6 Witham Green, Northampton NN5 7JQ. Tel: 07940 453 838.
Programme Editor: Debbie Preston
Ground: Birds Close, Gayton Road, Bugbrooke NN7 3PH. Tel: 01604 830 707
Capacity: 2,500 **Seats:** 120 **Cover:** Yes **Floodlights:** Yes
Clubhouse: Yes - normal licensing
Directions: M1.Jct 16 Take A45 to Northampton. At 1st roundabout follow signs to Bugrooke. Through village and club is immediately past last house on left.
Club Colours: Yellow & blue/royal blue/blue. **Change Colours:** Black & white stripes/black/black.
HONOURS: Northants Junior Cup 89-90, Central Northants Comb. (6) UCL Res Div 2 R-up 94-95 U.C.L. Div One Champions 98-99
PREVIOUS League : Central Northants Combination 1952-87 **Ground:** School Close
RECORD Attendance: 1,156 **Scorer:** Vince Thomas **Appearances:** Jimmy Nord
Players progressing: Kevin Slinn (Watford), Craig Adams (Northampton)

BURTON PARK WANDERERS

Chairman: Sue Neill

Secretary: Sam Gordon. 186 Station Road, Burton Latimer, Northants NN15 5NU. Tel: 07980 013 506.

Ground: Rothwell Town FC, Home Close, Cecil Street, Rothwell, Northants NN14 2EZ Tel: 01536 710 694.

Capacity: 3,500 **Seats:** 264 **Cover:** 1,264 **Floodlights:** Yes

Directions: A14/A6 to Rothwell. At town centre r'about turn into Bridge Street (right if northbound, left if southbound), take 3rd left into Tresham St., ground is at top on left. 3 miles from Kettering (BR); Rothwell is served by Kettering to Market Harborough buses.

HONOURS UCL Div 1 R-up, Benevolent Cup R-up

PREVIOUS **League**: Kettering Amateur

RECORD **Attendance**: 253 v Rothwell, May 1989

Players progressing : Shaun Wills (Peterborough), Laurie Dudfield (Leicester City)

FACT FILE
Founded: 1961
Nickname: The Wanderers
Colours: Azure/black/black
Change Colours: Red/white/red
Prog Ed: See chairman

EYNESBURY ROVERS

Chairman: Brian Abraham.

Secretary: Deryck Irons, 12 Hadleigh Close, Bedford MK41 8JW. Tel: 01234 268111
Email Address: deryckirons@aol.com **Website**: www.eynesburyrovers.org.uk

Ground: Alfred Hall Memorial Ground, Hall Road, Eynesbury, St Neots PE19 2SF. Tel: 01480 477 449

Capacity: 2,000 **Seats:** 200 **Cover:** 500 **Floodlights:** Yes Club Shop: No

Directions: Two miles from A1, on South side of St Neots urban area, near St Neots Community College.

Clubhouse: Large bar, committee room.Available for private hire

HONOURS UCL Div 1 76-77; Hunts Snr Cup (11), Hunts Premier Cup 50-51 90-91 95-96; Hinchingbrooke Cup (7) 46-4748-52 57-58 66-67; Cambs Invitation Cup 61-62; E Anglian Cup R-up 90-91 91-92;Hunts Scott Gatty Cup(4) (R-up 93-94 res); Hunts Jnr Cup 21-22 26-27 UCL

PREVIOUS **Leagues:** Sth Mids 34-39; UCL 46-52; Eastern Co's 52-63

RECORD **Gate:** 5,000 v Fulham 1953 (Stanley Matthews guested for Eynesbury)

Players progressing: Chris Turner (Peterborough), Denis Emery (Peterborough)

FACT FILE
Founded: 1897 Nickname: Rovers
Colours: Royal & white stripes/royal/royal
Change Colours: All yellow
Midweek matchday: Tuesday
Prog Ed: Graham Mills (01480 385 425)

HUNTINGDON TOWN

Chairman: Hans Reif

Secretary: Russell Yezek,39 Thongsley,Huntingdon, Cambs. PE29 1NU
Tel Nos: 01480 394903 (H) 07974 664818 (M)
e-mail: russell.jezek@ntlworld.com

Ground: Jubilee Park, Kings Ripton Road,, Huntingdon, Cambridgeshire PE28 2NT. Tel: 07929 651 226

Capacity: 1,000 **Seats:** None **Cover:** 100 **Floodights:** Yes

Directions From A1/A14 junction follow A14 towards Huntingdon. Go across first round about onto A141 and then over three further roundabouts before turning left towards Kings Ripton. Ground is situated half a mile on left.

Clubhouse: Yes **Club Shop:** No

PREVIOUS **League:** Cambridgeshire League 'A' 2003

HONOURS: Cambridge League Div.1B Champions 1999-00 Hunts. Jumior Cup: 1999-00' 2000-021 01-02 Hunts Scott Gatty Cup: 2001-02

FACT FILE
Founded: 1995
Colours: Red & Black /Red/Red
Change: Sky & Navy/navy/navy
Programme Editor: Russell Yezek

IRCHESTER UNITED

Chairman: Geoff Cotter

Secretary: Glynn Cotter, 3 Bank Hill View, Littlree Harrowden, Wellingborough, Northants NN9 5AR Tel Nos: 01933 402 514 (H) 07802 728736 (M)

Ground: Alfred Street, Irchester NN29 7DR Tel: 01933 312 877

Capacity: 1,000 **Seats:** None **Cover:**Yes **Floodlights:** Yes

Directions: Off Rushden Road to Wollaston Road, next to recreation ground

Clubhouse: Yes

HONOURS Northants League Div 2 30-31 31-32, Rushden & District League (9) Northants Jnr.Cup 29-30,33-34,48-49 75-6,

PREVIOUS **Leagues:** Rushden & District 1936-69

FACT FILE
Founded: 1883
Colours: All Red
Change: White/black/black
Programme Editor: Geoff Cotter
Tel: 01933 314 997

NORTHAMPTON O.N. CHENECKS

Chairman: Eddie Slinn
Secretary: Trevor Cadden, 26 Greenfield Road, Spinney Hill, NNorthampton NN3 2LH
Tel Nos: 01604 407070 (H) 07894 425 823 (M)

Ground: Old Northamptonians Sports Ground,Billing Road,Northampton NN1 5RX

Tel. No.: 01604 634 045

Capacity: 1,350 **Seats:** Yes **Cover:** Yes **Floodlights:** No

Directions: South ring road, exit A43 Kettering. Turn left at the lights, to the top of hill and the ground is 200 yds on right. **Clubhouse:** Yes

HONOURS UCL Div 1 77-78 79-80, Northants Jnr Cup R-up 93-94

PREVIOUS **Leagues:** Northampton Town League (pre-1969)

FACT FILE
Founded: 1946
Colours: White /navy/white
Change colours: All red
Programme Editor: Simon Abbott
Tel: 07814 552 322

NORTHAMPTON SILEBY RANGERS

Chairman: Robert Clarke
Secretary: Dave Battams, 15 Vincent Close, St Giles Park, Duston, Northampton NN5 6YA. Tel: 01604 590 085.
Ground: Fernie Fields Sports Ground, Moulton, Northampton NN3 7BD Tel: 01604 670366
Capacity: 700 **Seats:** 100 **Cover:** Yes **Floodlights:** No
Directions: Approach from A43 Kettering - follow signs to Northampton as far as the large roundabout with traffic lights (Round Spinney roundabout). Take the 5th exit signposted to Moulton Park and after a quarter of a mile turn left in the ground. Approach from A45 - leave A45 at the exit signposted to A43 Ring Road/Kettering/Corby and take the dual carriageway for around 2 miles to the second roundabout. Take the 2nd exit signposted to Moulton Park and after a quarter of a mile turn left into the ground.
Clubhouse: Large bar with food
HONOURS UCL Div 1 93-94,02-03 Benevolent Cup R-up 93-94; Northants Jnr Cup 93-94 96-97 97-98; 02-03 Northampton Town Lg 88-89 89-90
PREVIOUS **League:** Northampton Town (pre-1993)
Name: Northampton Vanaid >00 Northampton Sileby Rangers 2000-2004
RECORD **Attendance:** 78

FACT FILE
Founded: 1968
Nickname: Sileby
Colours: All red
Change colours: White/royal//white
Programme Editor: Dave Battams

OLNEY TOWN

Chairman: Paul Tough
Secretary: Mrs Karen Keeping. 7 Court Corner, Olney, Bucks MK46 5QH.
Tel: 07808 776 715.

Ground: Recreation Ground, East St., Olney, Bucks MK46 4DW. Tel: 01234 712 227
Capacity: 2,000 **Seats:** None **Cover:** Yes **Floodlights:** No
Clubhouse: Yes

Directions: Enter Olney on A509 from Wellingborough, 100yds on left enter East St, the ground is 200 yds on left

HONOURS UCL Div 1 72-73, Berks & Bucks I'mediate Cup 92-93

PREVIOUS **Leagues:** Nth Bucks, Rushden & District

FACT FILE
Founded: 1903
Colours: Green & white stripes/green/green
Change colours: Yellow & green/yellow/yellow
Programme Editor: Paul Tough
Tel: 01908 617 685

PETERBOROUGH NORTHERN STAR

Chairman: Vince Elliott
Secretary: Graham Phillips. 54 Amberley Slope, Peterborough PE4 6QQ.
Tel: 07973 253 529.
Ground: Chestnut Avenue, Dogsthorpe, Eye, Peterborough, Cambs PE1 4PE.
Tel: 01733 564 894
Directions From A1 turn onto A1139 Fleton Parkway Jct 7 (near Perkins Engines) at Traffic Lights left into Eastfield Rd. Turn right at Barclays Bank then right again into Eastern Avenue. Second left is Chestnut Avenue.
Capacity: 1,500 **Seats:** Yes **Cover:** Yes **Floodlights** Yes
PREVIOUS **League** Peterborough League >2003
Name: Eye United >2005
HONOURS Peterborough League 2002-03. United Counties Div.1 2008-09.

FACT FILE
Founded : Early 1900
Colours: White/black/black
Change: Red & white/black/red
Midweek Matchday: Wednesday
Programme Editor: Rodney Payne
Tel: 07803 718 163

POTTON UNITED

Chairman: Alan Riley

Secretary: Mrs Bev Strong. 20 Berwick Way, Sandy, Beds SG19 1TR.
Tel: 07703 442 565

Ground: The Hollow, Bigglewade Road, Potton, Beds SG19 2LU.
Tel: 01767 261 100

Directions: Outskirts of Potton on Biggleswade Road (B1040) Sandy BR 3.5 miles.
Buses from Biggleswade.
Capacity: 2,000 **Seats:** 200 **Covered:** 250 **Floodlights:** Yes **Clubhouse:** Yes
Previous Leagues: South Midlands 1946-55 Centarl Alliance 56-61
Previous Ground: Recreation Ground pre 1947
RECORD Attendance: 470 v Hastings Town F.A.Vase 1989
Senior Honours: Utd Co Champions 86-87 88-89, Div1 03-04, Beds Senior Cup(5), Hunts Prem Cup (4).
E.Anglian Cup 96-97

FACT FILE
Formed: 1943
Nickname: Royals
Colours: All blue
Change colours: Red/black/black
Programme Editor: Secretary

RUSHDEN & HIGHAM UNITED

Chairman: Philip Palmer

Secretary: Chris Ruff, 23 Queensway, Higham Ferrers, Northants. NN10 8BU.
Tel: 01933 358 862

Ground: Hayden Road, Rushden, Northants NN10 0HX.
Tel: 01933 410 036.

Directions: From A6/A45 junction take Higham/Rushden bypass. At third roundabout turn right, then turn right immediately after the school. From Bedford (A6) take bypass and turn left at first roundabout then turn right immediately after the school.

FACT FILE
Formed: 2007
(After the merger of Rushden Rangers & Higham Town)
Colours: Orange/orange/orange & black
Change colours: All blue
Programme Editor: Secretary

THRAPSTON TOWN

Chairman: Mark Brown

Secretary: Mark Brown, 3 Drayton Place, Irthlingborough, Northants. NN9 5TD
01933 388 671 (H) 07885 640 947 (M) email: mark@datsprint.co.uk

Ground: Chancery Lane, Thrapston, Northants NN14 4JL. Tel: 01832 732 470
Capacity: 1,000 **Seats:** Yes **Cover:** Yes **Floodlights:** Yes

Directions: Chancery Lane off A605 in town centre

Clubhouse: Yes

HONOURS Northants Junior Cup 87-88, 98-99, 03-04
Kettering Am Lg 70-71 72-73 73-74 77-78
UCL Div1 Runners -Up 99-00

PREVIOUS **League:** Kettering Amateur (pre-1978)

FACT FILE
Founded: 1960 Nickname: Venturas
Colours: All royal blue
Change colours: Purple/black/black
Programme Editor: Mrs Cathy Stevens

WELLINGBOROUGH WHITWORTH

Chairman: Brian Higgins

Secretary: Julian Souster. 3 Wilbye Grange, Wellingborough, NN8 3PS.
Tel: 01933 381 302 (H)

Ground: London Road, Wellingborough, Northants NN8 2DP. Tel: 01933 227 324
Capacity: 1000 Seats: None **Cover:** Yes **Floodlights:** Soon

Directions: Off London Road at Dog & Duck public house

Clubhouse: Yes

Club Shop: No

PREVIOUS **Names:** Whitworths
Leagues: Rushden & District; East Midlands Aliance (pre-1985)

HONOURS Rushden & District Lg 76-77; Northants Jun Cup 96. UCL Division One Champions 2006-07.

FACT FILE
Formed: 1973
Nickname: Flourmen
Colours: Red/black/red
Change colours: All blue
Programme Editor: Julian Souster

WOOTTON BLUE CROSS

Founded: 187
Nickname: Blue Cross

Chairman: Bryan Keens

Secretary: Mrs Dawn Frear, 21 Ridge Road, Kempston, Beds. MK43 9BP. **Tel:** 01234 854 583.

Programme Editor: Secretary.

GROUND ADDRESS: Weston Park, Bedford Rd., Wootton MK43 9JT. **Ground Tel. No.:** 01234 767 662

Capacity: 2,000 **Seats:** 50 **Covered:** 250 **Floodlights:** Yes

Simple Directions: Four miles south of Bedford on main road through village at rear od Post Office.

Midweek Home Matchday: Tuesday **Clubhouse:** Open every evening and w.e lunchtimes. **Club Shop:**No

Previous Grounds: Rec. Ground, Fishers Field, Rose & Crown & Cockfield.

Previous League(s): Bedford & Dist. S.Midlands 46-55

Club Colours: Blue & white/blue/blue **Change Colours:** Red & black stripes/black/red & black.

RECORD Attendance: 838 v Luton Beds Prem Cup 1988 **Senior Honours**: Beds Senior Cup 70-71 2001-02

STWARTS AND LLOYDS CORBY FC
Bac Row (L-R): Michael Byrne, Tom Mills, Paul Caswell, Paul Malone, Paul Djeneralovic, Chris Logan (Capt), Paul Doherty, Richard Lavin. **Front:** Dominic Johnson, Stuart McClarty, Ryan Cottingham, Michael Stanton, Mark Forbes, Matthew Garscadden. Photo: Arthur Evans.

ALTON TOWN F.C. - WESSEX PREMIER LEAGUE
Photo: Eric Marsh.

WESSEX LEAGUE

www.wessexleague.co.uk

Sponsored by: Sydenhams

Founded: 1986

Recent champions:

2004: Winchester City

2005: Lymington & New Milton

2006: Winchester City

2007: Gosport Borough

2008: AFC Totton

Premier Division	**P**	**W**	**D**	**L**	**F**	**A**	**Pts**
Poole Town	**42**	**38**	**2**	**2**	**144**	**34**	**116**
VTFC	**42**	**31**	**8**	**3**	**141**	**35**	**101**
Moneyfields	**42**	**29**	**4**	**9**	**99**	**44**	**91**
Wimborne Town	**42**	**26**	**9**	**7**	**115**	**41**	**87**
Brockenhurst	**42**	**24**	**10**	**8**	**71**	**41**	**82**
Newport IOW	**42**	**24**	**5**	**13**	**87**	**64**	**77**
Christchurch	**42**	**22**	**8**	**12**	**77**	**48**	**74**
Hamworthy United	**42**	**21**	**5**	**16**	**77**	**73**	**68**
New Milton Town	**42**	**18**	**10**	**14**	**72**	**55**	**64**
Fareham Town	**42**	**16**	**13**	**13**	**64**	**53**	**61**
Romsey Town	**42**	**16**	**12**	**14**	**65**	**75**	**60**
Bemerton Heath Harl.	**42**	**16**	**5**	**21**	**56**	**67**	**53**
Cowes Sports	**42**	**13**	**11**	**18**	**65**	**78**	**50**
Brading Town	**42**	**13**	**8**	**21**	**62**	**70**	**47**
Bournemouth	**42**	**12**	**8**	**22**	**60**	**89**	**44**
Hayling United	**42**	**11**	**8**	**23**	**66**	**96**	**41**
Alresford Town	**42**	**11**	**7**	**24**	**53**	**88**	**40**
Lymington Town	**42**	**10**	**8**	**24**	**58**	**104**	**38**
Alton Town	**42**	**9**	**9**	**24**	**56**	**105**	**36**
Laverstock & Ford	**42**	**8**	**7**	**27**	**49**	**106**	**31**
Hamble ASSC	**42**	**5**	**6**	**31**	**30**	**121**	**21**
Horndean	**42**	**5**	**5**	**32**	**45**	**125**	**20**

LEAGUE CUP

FIRST ROUND

Alresford Town 6 Verwood 0, **Brading Town** 3 Fareham 1
Christchurch 3 Hythe & Dibden 1 *aet*
Downton 0 **New Milton** 2, **Hamble ASSC** 1 East Cowes 0
Horndean 4 AFC Portchester 1
Ringwood Town 4 Blackfield & Langley 1
Stockbridge 0 **Bemerton Heath Harlequins** 2
Tadley Calleva 2 Whitchurch United 1
United Services Portsmouth 1 **Moneyfields** 4
Wimborne Town 5 Fawley 0

SECOND ROUND

Alresford 2 Alton Town 1, **Bemerton Heath** 3 Fleet Spurs 0
Bournemouth 3 Brockenhurst 1, **Christchurch** 3 Amesbury 2
Farnborough North End 7 AFC Aldermaston 2
Hamble ASSC 1 **Andover New Street** 2
Hamworthy United 2 Ringwood Town 0
Hayling United 4 Petersfield 2, Horndean 1 **Cowes Sports** 3
Newport IOW 1 **Brading** 2, **Poole Town** 3 Lymington Town 0
Romsey 0 **New Milton** 4, Shaftesbury 1 **Warminster Town** 2
Tadley Calleva 0 **VTFC** 5, Totton & Eling 0 **Moneyfields** 1
Wimborne Town 4 Laverstock & Ford 1

THIRD ROUND

Alresford Town 0 **Hamworthy United** 1
Bemerton Heath Harlequins 1 **Hayling United** 3 *aet*
Christchurch 7 Bournemouth 1, Cowes 1 **Moneyfields** 6
Farnborough North End 2 Warminster Town 1
New Milton Town 3 **VTFC** 5
Poole Town 3 Brading Town 0
Wimborne Town 5 Andover New Street 0

QUARTER-FINALS

Farnborough North End 0 **Moneyfields** 3
Hayling United 0 **Hamworthy United** 1
VTFC 6 Christchurch 0, Wimborne Town 0 **Poole Town** 4

SEMI-FINALS

(played over two legs)
Hamworthy Utd 1 Poole Town 0, Poole 2 **Hamworthy United** 2
VTFC 2 Moneyfields 0, Moneyfields 0 **VTFC** 3

FINAL

(May 4th at New Milton Town)
VTFC 2 Hamworthy United 1

	Alre.	Alton	Bem.	Bour	Bra.	Broc.	Chri.	Cow.	Fare.	Hmb	Hmw	Hayl.	Hor.	Lav.	Lym.	Mon.	NwM	Nwp.	Pool.	Rom	VT	Wim
Alresford Town		3-3	0-2	2-0	1-0	1-1	1-0	1-2	3-2	1-0	1-1	3-2	3-2	1-2	3-1	1-3	1-2	1-3	1-4	0-1	1-3	1-5
Alton Town	0-2		0-3	2-2	0-1	3-2	3-2	1-1	2-1	2-1	2-2	1-4	0-1	2-0	0-4	2-3	0-2	1-2	1-5	1-1	1-1	1-6
Bemerton Hth Harlequins	4-1	4-3		2-0	2-1	2-0	1-2	2-2	0-2	3-0	3-4	2-2	1-0	1-0	0-2	2-1	0-1	1-2	0-2	0-1	1-7	0-1
Bournemouth	2-2	2-1	2-1	***P***	1-0	0-3	2-2	1-4	1-1	4-1	0-1	3-0	2-1	0-1	1-1	0-2	0-0	3-1	1-2	3-3	0-5	1-4
Brading Town	2-2	0-0	2-1	2-3	***R***	0-1	0-2	1-3	1-1	6-0	0-4	6-0	6-2	2-3	2-0	1-2	0-2	1-1	2-4	2-1	0-0	0-1
Brockenhurst	1-0	3-0	2-0	2-1	0-0	***E***	1-1	1-1	3-1	2-0	3-1	2-0	3-0	1-1	2-1	0-3	2-1	6-1	3-0	1-1	0-4	1-3
Christchurch	1-2	2-0	1-1	3-1	1-1	0-0	***M***	3-1	3-1	1-0	1-0	2-1	6-0	6-1	2-1	0-3	0-0	3-1	1-3	3-1	3-2	0-1
Cowes Sports	1-0	3-4	0-2	3-2	2-0	0-2	1-1	***I***	3-3	0-1	2-3	3-0	0-4	8-3	6-2	1-3	0-1	1-1	3-4	3-1	0-0	1-3
Fareham Town	3-2	4-1	1-1	0-2	1-1	1-3	3-1	4-2	***E***	2-0	3-0	1-1	4-0	0-0	3-0	1-2	1-1	1-0	0-3	0-0	0-0	2-1
Hamble ASSC	0-1	0-0	1-2	0-3	2-4	1-2	1-0	0-0	1-5	***R***	0-2	2-2	2-2	1-3	3-2	0-7	0-2	2-1	0-5	0-1	1-6	0-5
Hamworthy United	3-2	1-1	3-0	3-1	2-1	3-0	1-0	4-0	1-2	4-1		3-1	3-2	2-1	0-2	2-2	0-1	1-2	0-1	2-4	0-8	0-1
Hayling United	2-1	2-1	3-1	2-1	6-1	0-2	0-0	0-1	3-1	8-0	2-5	***D***	2-1	0-2	2-2	0-3	1-3	2-3	0-7	1-3	1-2	2-2
Horndean	2-0	2-5	1-2	4-4	0-1	0-0	0-3	0-3	0-1	2-0	2-3	2-2	***I***	1-2	1-3	1-4	2-2	0-3	0-3	1-3	1-3	1-4
Laverstock & Ford	1-1	1-3	0-2	0-1	0-1	1-2	1-4	4-0	0-3	2-2	2-3	0-3	6-3	***V***	2-2	0-2	1-2	0-6	0-4	1-3	0-3	0-5
Lymington Town	0-0	4-2	2-4	2-1	1-2	1-3	0-3	0-0	1-2	0-2	1-1	1-2	4-3	2-1	***I***	1-4	0-6	4-1	1-4	0-0	0-3	0-4
Moneyfields	2-1	3-0	2-1	3-1	3-1	1-2	0-2	4-0	3-0	2-2	3-0	5-1	3-0	4-0	3-4	***S***	2-0	1-2	0-3	1-1	0-4	0-1
New Milton Town	8-1	2-3	0-0	2-4	1-4	1-2	1-2	0-0	1-0	6-1	1-3	2-1	5-0	4-2	2-2	0-0	***I***	0-1	0-3	3-0	0-4	1-2
Newport IOW	2-0	4-1	2-1	3-2	4-2	1-1	3-1	1-1	2-1	7-0	2-0	2-1	0-1	2-1	4-0	1-2	2-3	***O***	0-1	3-1	2-4	1-1
Poole Town	3-1	7-1	2-0	6-0	4-1	1-0	3-0	3-0	2-0	3-0	4-1	3-0	10-0	4-0	4-3	3-0	2-0	6-3	***N***	4-0	1-1	1-5
Romsey Town	4-3	4-0	3-0	3-2	2-0	0-5	0-6	1-3	0-0	3-2	2-1	2-2	1-0	2-2	4-0	1-5	1-1	2-3	2-3		0-2	0-0
VTFC	2-1	6-1	2-0	8-0	2-1	3-0	4-1	3-0	2-2	4-0	4-1	4-1	4-0	7-1	6-1	0-1	2-2	3-1	1-5	4-0		5-1
Wimborne Town	6-0	2-1	4-1	1-0	2-3	1-1	1-2	4-0	0-0	4-0	2-3	5-1	9-0	1-1	6-0	1-2	3-0	0-1	2-2	2-2	3-3	

Division One		P	W	D	L	F	A	Pts
Totton & Eling	-1	40	31	8	1	124	34	100
Blackfield & Langley		40	28	7	5	102	35	91
Utd Services Portsmouth		40	23	8	9	119	66	77
Petersfield Town		40	22	10	8	86	56	76
Warminster Town		40	22	8	10	98	47	74
Whitchurch United		40	21	10	9	102	62	73
Hythe & Dibden		40	19	10	11	101	78	67
Farnborough North End		40	18	12	10	66	49	66
Fawley		40	18	8	14	84	59	62
Stockbridge		40	16	12	12	68	66	60
Ringwood Town		40	17	6	17	86	80	57
Amesbury Town		40	15	8	17	83	90	53
Verwood Town		40	14	9	17	65	75	51
AFC Aldermaston		40	12	6	22	64	91	42
Shaftesbury		40	11	9	20	61	92	42
Tadley Calleva		40	11	6	23	66	102	39
Downton		40	9	10	21	56	91	37
East Cowes Victoria Ath.		40	8	8	24	48	109	32
AFC Portchester		40	6	11	23	49	106	29
Andover New Street		40	7	6	27	58	111	27
Fleet Spurs		40	3	6	31	36	123	15

COMBINATION CUP

FINAL *(May 1st at Totton & Eling)*
Christchurch Res. 5 Bashley Res. 0

Combination One		P	W	D	L	F	A	Pts
VTFC Res.		30	26	2	2	123	20	80
Christchurch Res.		30	19	4	7	77	42	61
Moneyfields Res.		30	19	3	8	76	37	60
AFC Totton Res.		30	17	3	10	60	49	54
Bemerton Heath H Res.		30	16	5	9	73	51	53
Gosport Borough Res.		30	15	5	10	75	50	50
Laverstock & Ford Res.		30	13	6	11	43	64	45
Lymington Town Res.		30	13	5	12	48	64	44
Hayling United Res.		30	12	4	14	48	59	40
Hamble ASSC		30	10	9	11	55	61	39
Cowes Sports Res.		30	11	3	16	60	71	36
Alton Town Res.		30	10	4	16	56	71	34
Ringwood Town Res.		30	7	3	20	42	79	24
Bashley Res.		30	7	3	20	55	96	24
Brockenhurst Res.		30	6	4	20	46	83	22
Horndean Res.		30	5	5	20	54	94	20

Combination Two		P	W	D	L	F	A	Pts
Brading Town Res.		24	19	1	4	65	26	58
Petersfield Town Res.		24	17	2	5	61	29	53
Alresford Town Res.		24	16	3	5	77	28	51
U. Services P'smth Res.		24	15	1	8	62	41	46
Blackfield/Langley Res.		24	13	5	6	57	44	44
Totton & Eling Res.		24	12	4	8	60	31	40
Fareham Town Res.	-1	24	10	4	10	55	48	33
Fawley Res.		24	8	3	13	31	68	27
Romsey Town Res.		24	4	11	9	36	44	23
AFC Portchester Res.		24	7	2	15	42	72	23
Whitchurch United Res.		24	4	7	13	25	62	19
Fleet Spurs Res.		24	4	3	17	29	61	15
Aldermaston Res.	-1	24	2	4	18	30	76	9

	AFC Aldermaston	AFC Portchester	Amesbury Town	Andover New Street	Blackfield & Langley	Downton	East Cowes Victoria Athletic	Farnborough North End	Fawley	Fleet Spurs	Hythe & Dibden	Petersfield Town	Ringwood Town	Shaftesbury	Stockbridge	Tadley Calleva	Totton & Eling	United Services Portsmouth	Verwood Town	Warminster Town	Whitchurch United
AFC Aldermaston		3-0	1-3	3-2	0-3	3-2	5-0	0-1	0-3	0-3	2-4	2-4	2-3	0-1	1-1	3-2	2-2	0-3	0-0	0-5	0-3
AFC Portchester	1-1		0-2	2-1	1-3	0-2	2-5	2-1	0-3	0-0	1-1	2-2	3-4	1-2	2-2	2-5	1-3	1-1	1-1	2-1	0-4
Amesbury Town	2-7	5-0		2-0	1-4	4-3	4-4	3-1	3-0	4-0	2-2	2-2	4-5	3-0	3-4	1-1	2-3	1-1	0-3	0-2	1-1
Andover New Street	1-3	1-1	3-3		0-2	2-2	3-1	1-3	3-3	3-0	2-3	0-1	5-4	4-2	0-1	4-2	0-4	1-3	1-6	0-4	2-6
Blackfield & Langley	2-1	3-1	1-2	1-0	***D***	5-1	3-0	0-2	2-1	0-0	2-1	1-3	2-0	2-1	4-1	7-0	1-1	3-2	1-1	4-1	3-0
Downton	1-0	2-4	2-0	1-0	0-5	***I***	0-2	0-2	0-3	1-1	2-4	0-4	3-1	1-2	1-5	3-0	1-3	2-3	2-3	1-1	1-4
East Cowes Victoria Ath.	4-1	2-0	1-2	1-2	0-4	1-1	***V***	0-3	0-4	5-1	0-3	0-2	1-1	3-2	1-3	1-1	0-7	1-3	2-0	2-2	0-2
Farnborough North End	1-0	2-4	4-0	1-0	0-0	1-1	1-1	***I***	0-0	4-4	4-1	1-2	3-2	2-2	2-1	4-0	0-3	0-0	1-0	1-1	0-3
Fawley	2-1	4-0	2-1	5-0	1-2	1-1	3-0	1-2	***S***	6-1	1-2	3-3	1-2	4-0	3-2	3-2	0-3	1-4	3-1	3-5	2-2
Fleet Spurs	0-2	2-2	0-1	2-1	0-4	1-4	1-1	0-4	0-1	***I***	3-4	1-2	1-2	1-2	1-2	0-4	1-4	1-3	1-2	0-6	1-2
Hythe & Dibden	3-2	2-2	4-0	5-2	1-1	2-2	3-3	2-0	1-1	3-0	***O***	1-0	3-4	3-0	5-3	7-1	2-2	3-4	3-1	0-3	3-1
Petersfield Town	2-2	2-1	2-1	7-1	2-2	7-1	2-1	0-1	2-1	3-0	1-0	***N***	1-0	1-1	3-1	2-2	2-3	2-2	1-5	1-1	4-0
Ringwood Town	2-3	4-1	3-2	2-0	1-1	0-1	8-0	4-2	1-3	5-2	4-3	2-3		1-1	0-0	0-1	0-3	2-3	1-1	1-2	3-1
Shaftesbury	1-3	1-1	5-6	2-0	2-5	3-3	1-0	2-2	2-1	3-1	4-4	2-3	4-2		1-2	0-3	0-2	3-2	3-1	0-5	1-1
Stockbridge	3-1	2-3	1-1	1-1	0-3	1-1	5-1	1-1	2-2	5-1	2-0	1-0	2-4	1-0	***O***	3-2	0-0	2-2	1-1	0-4	1-1
Tadley Calleva	0-4	4-1	2-4	2-1	0-2	2-2	4-0	2-2	0-2	1-3	1-3	3-2	3-2	2-0	1-2	***N***	0-4	1-7	3-1	0-3	1-3
Totton & Eling	6-0	5-0	3-1	2-2	3-1	3-1	6-0	2-0	1-3	8-1	4-2	3-1	5-0	5-1	4-0	3-1	***E***	3-1	0-0	2-1	2-1
Utd Services Portsmouth	3-1	7-0	5-2	9-1	0-2	3-1	5-1	2-1	4-3	9-0	4-1	0-3	1-2	0-0	1-2	3-3	2-3		3-2	2-0	4-4
Verwood Town	2-4	3-2	3-4	3-2	0-5	1-0	0-3	0-2	1-0	4-0	4-3	1-1	0-2	1-0	1-2	3-2	1-2	2-5		1-0	4-4
Warminster Town	9-0	5-2	2-0	4-0	2-1	2-3	2-0	1-1	1-1	5-1	1-2	0-1	2-1	4-3	1-0	3-1	1-1	1-2	0-0		3-2
Whitchurch United	1-1	3-0	3-1	2-6	2-5	2-0	7-0	1-3	2-0	1-0	2-2	5-0	1-1	6-1	2-0	2-1	1-1	4-1	5-1	5-2	

INS & OUTS
IN: Blackfield & Langley (P), Totton & Eling (P), Winchester City (R – Southern League Division One South & West)
OUT: Hamble ASSC (R), Horndean (R), VTFC (P - Southern League Division One South & West)

ALRESFORD TOWN

Founded: 1898 Nickname:

Chairman: Trevor Ingram
Secretary: Keith Curtis
26 Cranbury Road
Eastleigh
Hampshire
SO50 5HA
Tel: 02380 328 813
Manager: Tim Cole
Prog Editor: Gregory Boughton

Ground: Alresbury Park, The Avenue, Alresford, Hants SO24 9EP. Tel: 01962 735 100
Capacity: **Seats:** Yes **Covered:** Yes
Midweek Matchday: Tuesday **Clubhouse:** Yes **Shop:**
Colours(change): Black & white stripes/black/black & white. (All yellow)
Previous Names:
Previous Lges: Winchester League, North Hants league, Hampshire League
Records:
Senior Honours: Winchester Lge Div 2 & Div 1

10 YEAR RECORD

99-00	00-01	01-02	02-03	03-04	04-05	05-06	06-07	07-08	08-09
	Hant2 3	Hant2 2	Hant1 11	Hant1 8	Wex2 10	Wex2 20	Wex1 2	WexP 21	WexP 18

ALTON TOWN

Founded: 1919 Nickname:

Chairman: Jim McKell
Secretary: Jim McKell
Scotch Corner
Huntsmead
Alton
GU34 2SF
Tel: 07740 099 374
Manager: Steve Lynch & Clive Ventham
Prog Editor: Imageprint

Ground: Alton (Bass) Sports Ground, Anstey Road, Alton, Hants GU34 2RL
Capacity: 2,000 **Seats:** 200 **Covered:** 250
Midweek Matchday: Tuesday **Clubhouse:** Yes **Shop:** No
Colours(change): White/black/black (Yellow/green/yellow)
Previous Names: Present club formed in 1990 when Alton Town and Bass Alton merged.
Previous Lges: Hampshire League >2002
Records:
Senior Honours: Hants Senior Cup 1958, 1969, 1972 & 1978.
Hampshire Champions 2001-02.

10 YEAR RECORD

99-00	00-01	01-02	02-03	03-04	04-05	05-06	06-07	07-08	08-09
HantP 20	HantP 7	HantP 1	Wex1 17	Wex1 18	Wex1 19	Wex1 20	WexP 17	WexP 14	WexP 19

BEMERTON HEATH HARLEQUINS

Founded: 1989 Nickname: Quins

Chairman: Steve Slade
Secretary: Andy Hardwick
20 Herbert Road
Salisbury
Wilts
SP2 9LF
Tel: 01722 502 684
Manager: I Chalke & B Boutellier
Prog Editor: Steve Brooks

Ground: The Clubhouse, Western Way, Bemerton Heath, Salisbury, SP2 9DP Tel: 01722 331 925
Capacity: 2,100 **Seats:** 250 **Covered:** 350
Midweek Matchday: Tuesday **Clubhouse:** Yes **Shop:** No
Colours(change): Black & white 1/4s/black/black & white (Amber/white/amber or white)
Previous Names: Bemerton Athletic, Moon FC & Bemerton Boys merged in 1989
Previous Lges: Salisbury & Wilts Comb, Salisbury & Andover Sunday
Records: **Att:**1,118 v Aldershot Town **App:** Keith Richardson
Senior Honours: Wiltshire Senior Cup 1992-3

10 YEAR RECORD

99-00	00-01	01-02	02-03	03-04	04-05	05-06	06-07	07-08	08-09
Wex 10	Wex 11	Wex 11	Wex 18	Wex 12	Wex1 14	Wex1 14	WexP 11	WexP 13	WexP 12

BLACKFIELD & LANGLEY

Founded: 1935 Nickname:

Chairman: Doug Sangster
Secretary: See chairman
3 Fir Tree Grove
Butts Ash Lane, Hythe
Southampton
SO45 3RA
Tel: 07899 927 165
Manager: John Gittens
Prog Editor: Ian Hoare

Ground: Gang Warily Rec., Newlands Rd, Southampton, SO45 1GA Tel: 07881 991013 Md
Capacity: 2,500 **Seats:** 180 **Covered:** nil
Midweek Matchday: Tuesday **Clubhouse:** Yes **Shop:**
Colours(change): White/green/white. (White & green stripes/green/green).
Previous Names:
Previous Lges: Southampton Senior. Hampshire.
Records: **Att:** 240
Senior Honours: Hants Div 97-88, Div 2 84-85, Southampton Senior Cup (4)

10 YEAR RECORD

99-00	00-01	01-02	02-03	03-04	04-05	05-06	06-07	07-08	08-09
HantP 3	Wex 21	Wex 17	Wex 21	Wex 21	Wex2 7	Wex2 14	Wex1 16	Wex1 10	Wex1 2

BOURNEMOUTH

Founded: 1875 Nickname: Poppies

Chairman: Bob Corbin
Secretary: Mike Robins
7 Wesley Road
Poole
Dorset
BH12 3BE
Tel: 07947 687 808
Manager: Danny Neville
Prog Editor: See secretary

Ground: Victoria Park, Namu Road, Winton, Bournemouth, BH9 2RA Tel: 01202 515 123
Capacity: 3,000 **Seats:** 205 **Covered:** 205
Midweek Matchday: Tuesday **Clubhouse:** Yes **Shop:** Yes
Colours(change): All Red (all blue)
Previous Names: Bournemouth Rovers, Bournemouth Dean Park
Previous Lges: Hampshire
Records: Goalscorer: Brian Chike
Senior Honours: Hampshire League

10 YEAR RECORD

99-00	00-01	01-02	02-03	03-04	04-05	05-06	06-07	07-08	08-09
Wex 19	Wex 14	Wex 18	Wex 14	Wex 20	Wex1 11	Wex1 7	WexP 5	WexP 5	WexP 15

BRADING TOWN

Founded: 1871 Nickname:

Chairman: Keith Newbery MBE
Secretary: Bob Blezzard
105 Perowne Way
Sandown
Isle of Wight
PO36 6DR
Tel: 07923 404 075
Manager: Steve Brougham
Prog Editor: Sam Turner

Ground: The Peter Henry Ground, Vicarage Lane, I.o.W. PO36 0AR Tel: 01983 405 217
Capacity: **Seats:** **Covered:**
Midweek Matchday: Wednesday **Clubhouse:** **Shop:**
Colours(change): White with red trim/red/red. (Blue/white/blue)
Previous Names:
Previous Lges: Isle of Wight. Hampshire.
Records:
Senior Honours:

10 YEAR RECORD

99-00	00-01	01-02	02-03	03-04	04-05	05-06	06-07	07-08	08-09
HantP 5	HantP 6	HantP 8	HantP 17	HantP 18	Wex2 16	Wex2 3	WexP 10	WexP 15	WexP 14

BROCKENHURST

Founded: 1898 Nickname: The Badgers

Chairman: Dave Stansbridge
Secretary: Paul Christopher
31 Wedgewood Close
Holbury
Southampton, Hampshire
SO45 3QF
Tel: 07837 587 657
Manager: John Pyatt
Prog Editor: Dave Stansbridge

Ground: Grigg Lane, Brockenhurst, Hants SO42 7RE Tel: 01590 623 544
Capacity: 2,000 **Seats:** 200 **Covered:** 300
Midweek Matchday: Tuesday **Clubhouse:** Yes **Shop:**
Colours(change): Blue & white quarters/blue/blue. (Green/black/green).
Previous Names:
Previous Lges: Hampshire
Records: Att: 1,104 v St Albans City
Senior Honours: Hants Int Cup 61-62, Bournemouth Sen Cup 60-61, Hampshire Lg 75-76

10 YEAR RECORD

99-00	00-01	01-02	02-03	03-04	04-05	05-06	06-07	07-08	08-09
Wex 18	Wex 9	Wex 6	Wex 20	Wex 9	Wex1 18	Wex1 21	WexP 13	WexP 6	WexP 5

CHRISTCHURCH

Founded: 1885 Nickname: Priory

Chairman: Mick Ryan
Secretary: Ian Harley
3 Egmont Close
Avon Castle
Ringwood
BH24 2DJ
Tel: 07900 133 954
Manager: Graham Kemp
Prog Editor: Dennis Miller

Ground: Hurn Bridge S.C, Avon Causeway, Christchurch BH23 6DY Tel: 01202 473 792
Capacity: 1,200 **Seats:** 215 **Covered:** 265
Midweek Matchday: Tuesday **Clubhouse:** Yes **Shop:**
Colours(change): All Blue (All Red)
Previous Names:
Previous Lges: Hampshire
Records: App: John Haynes
Senior Honours: Hants Jnr Cup (3), Hants Intermediate Cup 86-87, Bournemouth Senior Cup (5)

10 YEAR RECORD

99-00	00-01	01-02	02-03	03-04	04-05	05-06	06-07	07-08	08-09
Wex 12	Wex 17	Wex 15	Wex 13	Wex 11	Wex1 17	Wex1 10	WexP 14	WexP 16	WexP 7

COWES SPORTS

Founded: 1881 Nickname: Yachtsmen

Chairman: Ian Lee
Secretary: Glynn M Skinner
66 Yarborough Road
East Cowes
Isle of Wight
PO32 6SB
Tel: 07854 889 446
Manager: Kevin Winchcombe
Prog Editor: Peter Jeffery

Ground: Westwwod Park, Reynolds Close, off Park Rd, Isle of Wight PO13 7NT Tel: 01983 293 793
Capacity: 1,850 **Seats:** 450 **Covered:** 450
Midweek Matchday: Tuesday **Clubhouse:** Yes **Shop:** No
Colours(change): Blue & white stripes/black/blue (Red/white/red)
Previous Names: Club formed after the merger of Cowes and White Sports during 80s.
Previous Lges: Hampshire (pre 1994)
Records:

Senior Honours: Hampshire League 1993-94.

10 YEAR RECORD

99-00	00-01	01-02	02-03	03-04	04-05	05-06	06-07	07-08	08-09
Wex 9	Wex 10	Wex 16	Wex 15	Wex 14	Wex1 13	Wex1 16	WexP 9	WexP 9	WexP 13

FAREHAM TOWN

Founded: 1946 Nickname: The Robins

Chairman: Nick Ralls
Secretary: Ian Tewson
16 Martin Avenue
Stubbington
Fareham
PO14 2RT
Tel: 07930 853 235
Manager: Matt Parr
Prog Editor: Paul Proctor

Ground: Cams Alders, Palmerston Drive, Fareham, Hants PO14 1BJ Tel: 07810 844 466
Capacity: 2,000 **Seats:** 450 **Covered:** 500
Midweek Matchday: Tuesday **Clubhouse:** Yes **Shop:** Yes
Colours(change): Red/black/red. (White/white/black)
Previous Names:
Previous Lges: Portsmouth, Hampshire & Southern
Records: Att: 2,015 v Spurs (friendly 1985)

Senior Honours: Hampshire Senior Cup 1957, 1963, 1968, 1993,
Hampshire League Champions.

10 YEAR RECORD

99-00	00-01	01-02	02-03	03-04	04-05	05-06	06-07	07-08	08-09
Wex 11	Wex 15	Wex 10	Wex 5	Wex 7	Wex1 16	Wex1 9	WexP 8	WexP 8	WexP 10

HAMWORTHY UNITED

Founded: 1926 Nickname:

Chairman: Bruce Scammell
Secretary: Peter Gallop
51a Symes Road
Hamworthy
Poole, Dorset
BH15 4PR
Tel: 07846 974 263
Manager: Phil Simkin
Prog Editor:

Ground: The County Ground, Blandford Close, Hamworthy, Poole, BH15 4PR Tel: 01202 674 974
Capacity: 2,000 **Seats:** **Covered:**
Midweek Matchday: Wednesday **Clubhouse:** Yes **Shop:** No
Colours(change): Maroon & sky blue/sky blue/maroon. (Orange/black/black)
Previous Names: Hamworthy St. Michael merged with Trinidad Old Boys 1926
Previous Lges: Dorset Premier
Records:

Senior Honours: Dorset Premier League 2002-03, 03-04.

10 YEAR RECORD

99-00	00-01	01-02	02-03	03-04	04-05	05-06	06-07	07-08	08-09
Dor P 8	Dor P 5	Dor P 5	Dor P 1	Dor P 1	Wex1 15	Wex1 6	WexP 15	WexP 10	WexP 8

HAYLING UNITED

Founded: 1884 Nickname:

Chairman: Michael Thornton
Secretary: Shirley Westfield
14 Harold Road
Hayling Island
Hampshire
PO11 9LT
Tel: 07724 540 916
Manager: Mark Poulton
Prog Editor: Steve Hayward

Ground: Hayling College, Church Road, Hayling Island, Hampshire PO11 0NU
Capacity: **Seats:** **Covered:**
Midweek Matchday: Tuesday **Clubhouse:** Yes **Shop:** No
Colours(change): Black & white stripes/black/black. (All light blue).
Previous Names:
Previous Lges: Waterlooville & District > 1952 , Portsmouth Lge 1952-91, Hampshire Lge 1991-2004
Records:

Senior Honours: Hampshire Lge Div 1 Champions 2002-03, Wessex Div 1 2006-07

10 YEAR RECORD

99-00	00-01	01-02	02-03	03-04	04-05	05-06	06-07	07-08	08-09
HantP 9	Hant1 4	Hant1 3	Hant1 1	Hant1 5	Wex3 2	Wex2 2	Wex1 1	WexP 12	WexP 16

LAVERSTOCK & FORD

Founded: 1956 Nickname:

Chairman: Gino Nardiello
Secretary: Brian Ford
11 Chantry Road
Wilton
Salisbury
SP2 0LT
Tel: 07743 538 984
Manager: Ady Burford
Prog Editor: Michael Eyers

Ground: The Dell, Church Rd, Laverstock, Salisbury, Wilts SP1 1TQ Tel: 01722 327 401
Capacity: **Seats:** **Covered:**
Midweek Matchday: Tuesday **Clubhouse:** **Shop:**
Colours(change): Green & white hoops/green/green & white. (Yellow/blue/white).
Previous Names:
Previous Lges: Salisbury & District. Hampshire.
Records:
Senior Honours:

10 YEAR RECORD

99-00	00-01	01-02	02-03	03-04	04-05	05-06	06-07	07-08	08-09
Hant2 4	Hant2 4	Hant2 3	Hant2 1	Hant1 11	Wex3 11	Wex3 2	Wex1 12	Wex1 2	WexP 20

LYMINGTON TOWN

Founded: 1876 Nickname:

Chairman: Richard Maton
Secretary: See chairman
11 Wryneck Close
Lordswood
Southampton
SO16 8FJ
Tel: 07927 900 404
Manager: Wayne Lockey
Prog Editor: Derek Webb

Ground: The Sports Ground, Southampton Road, Lymington, SO41 9ZG 01590 671 305
Capacity: 3,000 **Seats:** 200 **Covered:** 300
Midweek Matchday: Tuesday **Clubhouse:** **Shop:**
Colours(change): Red/white/black. (Blue/blue/black or white)
Previous Names:
Previous Lges: Hampshire.
Records:
Senior Honours: Wessex Lge Cup 2006-07

10 YEAR RECORD

99-00	00-01	01-02	02-03	03-04	04-05	05-06	06-07	07-08	08-09
HantP 13	HantP 17	HantP 14	HantP 15	HantP 7	Wex2 1	Wex1 17	WexP 12	WexP 20	WexP 18

MONEYFIELDS

Founded: 1987 Nickname: Moneys

Chairman: Paul Lipscombe
Secretary: Wayne Dalton
128 Wymering Road
North End
Portsmouth
PO2 7HY
Tel: 07766 411 346
Manager: Bob De Sroix/Miles Rutherford
Prog Editor: David Hayter

Ground: Moneyfields Sp. Centre, Moneyfields Ave, Copnor, Portsmouth PO3 6LB Tel: 02392 665 260
Capacity: 1,500 **Seats:** 150 **Covered:** 150
Midweek Matchday: Tuesday **Clubhouse:** Yes **Shop:** Yes
Colours(change): Yellow & navy/navy/yellow. (White with blue/blue/white).
Previous Names: Portsmouth Civil Service
Previous Lges: Portsmouth. Hampshire.
Records: **Att:** 250 v Fareham, Wessex Div.1 2005-06. **Goalscorer:** Lee Mould 86
App: Matt Lafferty - 229 **Victory:** 9-0v Blackfield & Langley 01-02.
Senior Honours: Portsmouth Premier Champions 1990-91, 91-92. Senior Cup 1990-91. Hampshire Champions 1996-97.

10 YEAR RECORD

99-00	00-01	01-02	02-03	03-04	04-05	05-06	06-07	07-08	08-09
Wex 6	Wex 16	Wex 9	Wex 10	Wex 17	Wex1 10	Wex1 11	WexP 7	WexP 7	WexP 3

NEW MILTON TOWN

Founded: 2007 Nickname: The Linnets

Chairman: Peter Baker
Secretary: Richard Phippard
198 Butts Road
Sholing
Southampton
SO19 1BP
Tel: 07515 775 442
Manager:
Prog Editor: Rick Ashton

Ground: Fawcett Fields, Christchurch Road, New Milton, BH25 6QB Tel: 01425 628 191
Capacity: 3,000 **Seats:** 262 **Covered:** 262
Midweek Matchday: Tuesday **Clubhouse:** **Shop:**
Colours(change): All maroon & sky blue. (Yellow & green/green/yellow & green)
Previous Names: Lymington Town > 1988, AFC Lymington 1988-98, Lymington & New Milton 1998-07
Previous Lges: Isthmian. Southern.
Records:
Senior Honours: Wessex League 1998-99, 04-05.

10 YEAR RECORD

99-00	00-01	01-02	02-03	03-04	04-05	05-06	06-07	07-08	08-09
Wex 2	Wex 2	Wex 5	Wex 6	Wex 4	Wex1 1	Isth1 16	SthS 17	WexP 19	WexP 9

NEWPORT I.O.W.

Founded: 1888 Nickname: The Port

Chairman: Paul Phelps
Secretary: Dave Bartlett
8 Solent Village
Thorness Bay Holiday Park
Cowes, Isle of Wight
PO31 8NQ
Tel: 07717 251 839
Manager: Derek Ohren
Prog Editor: Peter Westhorpe

Ground: St George's Park, St George's Way, Newport, PO30 2QH. Tel: 01983 525 027
Capacity: 5,000 **Seats:** 300 **Covered:** 1,000
Midweek Matchday: Wednesday **Clubhouse:** Yes **Shop:** Yes
Colours(change): Yellow/blue/yellow. (All green)
Previous Names:
Previous Lges: I.O.W. 1896-28. Hants 28-86. Wessex 86-90.
Records: **Att:** 2,270 v Portsmouth (friendly) 07.07.2001.
Goalscorer: Roy Grilfillan - 220 1951-57. **Apps:** Jeff Austin - 540 1969-87.
Senior Honours: Southern League Eastern Division 2000-01. Hants Senior Cup (x8). I.O.W. Cup (34)

10 YEAR RECORD

99-00	00-01	01-02	02-03	03-04	04-05	05-06	06-07	07-08	08-09
SthE 3	SthE 1	SthP 19	SthE 16	SthE 19	Isth1 18	Isth1 22	SthS 20	SthS 22	WexP 6

POOLE TOWN

Founded: 1880 Nickname: The Dolphins

Chairman: Clive Robbins
Secretary: Bill Reid
15 Addison Close
Romsey
Hampshire
SO51 7TL
Tel: 01794 517 991
Manager: Tommy Killick
Prog Editor: Ian Claxton

Ground: Tatnam Grd, Oakdale School, School Lane, Poole, BH15 3JR Tel: 07771604289
Capacity: 2,000 **Seats:** 154 **Covered:** 120
Midweek Matchday: Tuesday **Clubhouse:** Yes **Shop:**
Colours(change): Red & white halves/red/red & white. (Sky blue with navy trim).
Previous Names: Poole Hornets and Poole Rovers amalgamated on 20.09.1890.
Previous Lges: Western 22-26, Southern 26-30, Western 30-57, Southern 57-96, Hampshire 96-04
Records: Not known.
Senior Honours: Western League 1956-57. Dorset Senior Cup (12), Wessex League Champions 2008-09.

10 YEAR RECORD

99-00	00-01	01-02	02-03	03-04	04-05	05-06	06-07	07-08	08-09
Hant1 1	HantP 2	HantP 5	HantP 4	HantP 3	Wex2 2	Wex1 8	WexP 4	WexP 4	WexP 1

ROMSEY TOWN

Founded: 1886 Nickname:

Chairman: Ken Jacobs
Secretary: Lee Harrison
39 The Foxgloves
Hedge End
Southampton
SO30 OUG
Tel: 07838 719 988
Manager: Glenn Burnett
Prog Editor: See secretary

Ground: The Bypass Ground, South Front, Romsey, SO51 8GJ Tel: 01794 513 685
Capacity: **Seats:** **Covered:**
Midweek Matchday: Tuesday **Clubhouse:** Yes **Shop:**
Colours(change): White/black/black. (All yellow).
Previous Names: None
Previous Lges: Hampshire.
Records:
Senior Honours: Wessex League Champions 1989-90.

10 YEAR RECORD

99-00	00-01	01-02	02-03	03-04	04-05	05-06	06-07	07-08	08-09
HantP 22	Hant1 16	Hant1 15	Hant2 13	Hant2 2	Wex2 4	Wex2 13	Wex1 3	WexP 18	WexP 11

TOTTON & ELING

Founded: 1925 Nickname:

Chairman: Philip Gates
Secretary: Mike Clarke
54 Irving Road
Maybush
Southampton
SO16 4EN
Tel: 02380 789 652
Manager: Kev Dawtry
Prog Editor: TBC

Ground: Totton & Eling S.C., Southern Gdns, Totton, SO40 8RW Tel: 02380 862 143
Capacity: **Seats:** Yes **Covered:** Yes
Midweek Matchday: Tuesday **Clubhouse:** **Shop:**
Colours(change): Red/black/black. (Claret/blue/blue).
Previous Names: BAT Sports > 2007
Previous Lges: Hampshire.
Records: 2,763 v AFC Wimbledon, FA Vase (game switched to AFC Wimbedon).
Senior Honours: Hampshire Champions 1987-88, 88-89. Wessex Division 1 2008-09.

10 YEAR RECORD

99-00	00-01	01-02	02-03	03-04	04-05	05-06	06-07	07-08	08-09
Wex 5	Wex 13	Wex 19	Wex 11	Wex 15	Wex1 9	Wex1 18	Wex2 5	Wex1 5	Wex1 1

WIMBORNE TOWN

Founded: 1878 Nickname: Magpies

Chairman: Ken Stewart
Secretary: Peter Barham
Chelmer
17 Margards Lane
Verwood, Dorset
BH31 6LP
Tel: 07956 833 316
Manager: Alex Browne
Prog Editor: Ken Fergus

Ground: The Cuthbury, Cowgrove Road, Wimborne, Dorset, BH21 4EL Tel: 01202 884 821
Capacity: 3,250 **Seats:** 275 **Covered:** 425
Midweek Matchday: Tuesday **Clubhouse:** Yes **Shop:** Yes
Colours(change): Black & white stripes/black/black. (All Yellow)
Previous Names:
Previous Lges: Dorset Lge, Dorset Comb, Western Lge 81-86
Records: **Att:** 3,250 v Bamber Bridge **Goalscorer:** Jason Lovell **App:** James Sturgess
Senior Honours: FA Vase Winners 1991-2, Wessex Lge 91-92,93-94, 99-00, Dorset Senior Am Cup 36-37, 63-64

10 YEAR RECORD

99-00	00-01	01-02	02-03	03-04	04-05	05-06	06-07	07-08	08-09
Wex 1	Wex 3	Wex 8	Wex 4	Wex 2	Wex1 7	Wex1 12	WexP 6	WexP 3	WexP 4

WINCHESTER CITY

Founded: Nickname:

Chairman: James Mann
Secretary: Andy Spreadbury
19 Symes Road
Romsey
Hampshire
SO51 5BD
Tel: 07528 687 689
Manager: Shaun Brooks
Prog Editor: John Moody

Ground: Denplan City Ground, Hillier Way, Winchester SO23 7SR. Tel: 01962 810 200.
Capacity: 2,500 **Seats:** 200 **Covered:** 275
Midweek Matchday: Tuesday **Clubhouse:** Yes **Shop:** Yes
Colours(change): Red & black stripes/blk/blk. (Yellow with blue trim/blue/blue).
Previous Names: None
Previous Lges: Hampshire 1898-71, 73-03. Southern 71-73, 06-09. Wessex 03-06.
Records: **Att:** 1,818 v Bideford, FA Vase Semi-final. **Goalscorer:** Andy Forbes. **Apps:** Ian Mancey.
Senior Honours: Hants Senior Cup 1932, 2005. Southampton Senior Cup 2000-01. Hants Lge Champions 02-03. Wessex Lge 03-04, 05-06. F.A. Vase 2004.

10 YEAR RECORD

99-00	00-01	01-02	02-03	03-04	04-05	05-06	06-07	07-08	08-09
Hant1 4	Hant1 1	HantP 3	HantP 1	Wex 1	Wex1 2	Wex1 1	SthW 13	SthW 17	SthW 22

DIVISION ONE INS & OUTS
IN: Hamble ASSC (R), Horndean (R)
OUT: Blackfield & Langley (P), Totton & Eling (P)

AFC ALDERMASTON

Chairman: Martin Desay
Secretary: Gareth Dew. 58 Portway, Baughurst, Tadley, Hampshire RG26 5PE.
Tel: 07544 591 383.
Programme Editor: Matt Desay. Tel: 01189 817 071.
Ground: AWE Recreational Society, Aldermaston, Nr Tadley, Berkshire RG7 4PR. Tel: 01189 827 614.
Directions: From M3 Junction 6, take A340 to Tadley travelling through the village towards Kingsclere. Turn right at signpost for AWE West Gate Stores delivery. The ground is situated on the west side of AWE Aldermaston & has a large car park.
Midweek Matchday: Wednesday.
Colours: All red. **Change colours:** All blue.

AFC PORTCHESTER

Chairman: Steve Woods.
Secretary: Paul Kelly. 100 Southampton Road, Portsmouth, Hampshire PO6 4XR.
Tel: 07955 016 033.
Ground: Wicor Recreation Ground, Cranleigh Road, Portchester, Fareham, Hampshire PO16 9DP.
Tel: 07955 016 033.
Directions: From M3 Junction 11, follow signs to Portchester into Portchester Road. After approx 1 mile at roundabout take 2nd exit into Cornaway Road. At T junction turn right into Cranleigh Road & follow road to the end.
Midweek Matchday: Tuesday. **Floodlights:** No.
Colours: All tangerine. **Change colours:** Black & white stripes/black/black.

AMESBURY TOWN

Formed: 1904

Chairman: Jason Cameron.

Secretary: Tony Hinchliffe, 12 Lanes Close, Amesbury, Wiltshire SP4 7RW. Tel: 07731 792 800.

Programme Editor: Secretary.

Ground: Bonnymead Park, Recreation Road, Amesbury, Wiltshire SP4 7BB. Tel: 01980 623 489.

Capacity: 2,000 **Seats:** 120 **Cover:** Yes **Floodlights:** Yes **Clubhouse:** Yes

Directions: From A303 Countess Road Roundabout, towards town centre through lights and turn right by bus station. Left at end of road at T junction bt Lloyds Bank go over bridge and left into 'Recreation Road on sharp right bend.

Midweek Home Matches: Tuesday.

PREVIOUS Leagues: Salisbury & District, Wiltshire County, Western, Hampshire.

Name: Amesbury F.C.

RECORD Attendance: 625 v Taunton Town 1997

Colours: All blue. **Change Colours**: All Yellow.

ANDOVER NEW STREET

Formed: 1895

Chairman: Graham Waters

Secretary: Trevor Knight. Unit 18, Focus 303 Business Park, Andover, Hampshire SP10 5NY.
Tel: 07786 921 202.

Programme Editor: Jimmy Wilson.

Ground: Foxcotte Park, Charlton, Andover SP11 0HS Tel No: 01264 358 358 (Weekends from midday, evenings from 7pm)

Directions: Follow ring road to Charlton.Turn right at the Royal Oak Pub. Carry on for about 3/4 mile then take last exit from roundabout signposted to Sports Centre.

Midweek home matchdays: Thursday. **Floodlights:** Yes.

Clubhouse: Open all day Saturdays and Sundays and from 1900 hours on week days.

Colours: Green & black/black/black. **Changes:** White/blue/white.

PREVIOUS Leagues: Andover & District, North Hants, Hampshire Premier. **Name:** New Street

HONOURS Hampshire Premier Runners-Up 2003-004. Trophyman Cup Winners 2003-4

RECORD Attendance: 240

DOWNTON

Founded: 1905 **Nickname:**The Robins

Chairman: Ian Drinkwater

Secretary: Jim Blake, 35 Orchard Rd., Morgans Vale, Redlynch, Salisbury, Wilts. SP5 2JA

Tel No: 07712 180 548.

Programme Editor: Pat Drinkwater.

GROUND ADDRESS: Brian Whitehead Sports Ground, Wick Lane, Downton SP5 3NF. Tel No: 01725 512 162

Capcity: 1,600 **Seats:** 250 **Cover:** 400 (incl 4 for wheelchairs) **Floodlights**: Yes

Simple Directions: The ground is situated 6 miles south of Salisbury on the A338 to Bournemouth. In the village – sign to Sports Centre (to west) – this is Wick Lane – football pitch and Club approx 1/4 mile on the left.

Midweek Home Matchday: Tuesday **Clubhouse:** Bar with kitchen facilities **Club Shop:** No

Previous Leagues: Bournemouth, Hants (pre 1993)

Club Colours: Red/white/red **Change Colours:** Yellow/blue/yellow

RECORD Attendance: 55 v AFC Bournemouth (Friendly)

Senior Honours: Wilts Senior Cup: 79-80 80-81 R-up (3) Wilts Junior Cup 49-50 Wessex Lg Cup 95-96

EAST COWES VICTORIA ATHLETIC

Chairman: Jackie Millroy.

Secretary: Darren Dyer, 5 Acorn Gardens, East Cowes, Isle of Wight PO32 6TD.

Tel: 07725 128 701.

Programme Editor: See secretary.

Ground: Beatrice Avenue Ground, Whippingham, East Cowes, I.O.W. PO32 6PA Tel: 01938 297 165.

Directions: From East Cowes ferry terminal follow Well Road into York Avenue until reaching Prince of Wells PH, turn at the next right into Crossways Road then turn left into Beatrice Avenue, from Fishbourne follow signs to East Cowes and Whippingham Church, ground is 200 yards from the church on Beatrice Avenue.

Midweek Matchday: Tuesday. **Floodlights:** Yes.

Colours: Red & white stripes/black/black. **Change colours:** All Green.

FARNBOROUGH NORTH END

Chairman: Paul Xiberras

Secretary: Paul Xiberras. 5 Cricket Way, Weybridge, Surrey KT13 9LP. Tel: 07733 385 849.

Programme Editor: TBC

GROUND ADDRESS: Cody Sports & Social Club, Old Ively Road, Pyestock, Farnborough, Hampshire GU14 0LS.

Tel. No.: 01252 543 009 (matchdays only).

Capacity: 1,000 **Clubhouse:** Yes **Club Shop:** No

Simple Directions: Off M3 Jct 4 take A327 towards Farnborough, into Kennels Lane opposite Nokia building and turn right at roundabout. then left at next roundabout into old Aveley Road. Ground in front of clubhouse.

Midweek Home Matchday: Tuesday **Floodlights:** Yes

Previous Name: Covies **Previous Leagues:** Hampshire and Surrey Intermediate

Club Colours: Red/black/black **Change Colours:** Blue/white/blue

Record Goalscorer: Paul Griffitrhs 320 **Appearances**: Andy Dermott 516

FAWLEY

Formed: 1923

Chairman: Colin Stewart.

Secretary: Sandie Earl. 81 The Warren Holbury Southampton, Hampshire SO45 2QD. Tel: 07759 956 257.

Programme Editor: Tom Hardiman.

Ground: Waterside Sports & Social Club, 179 Long Lane, Holbury, Southampton, SO45 2QD Tel: 02380 893750(club) or 896621(office).

Directions: Leave the M27 at Junction 2 and follow the A326 to Fawley/Beaulieu. Head south for approx 7 miles. The Club is situated on the right hand side 2/3 mile after crossing the Hardley roundabout. The Club is positioned directly behind the service road on the right hand side.

Midweek Home Matchday: Wednesday. **Floodlights:** Yes.

Colours: All blue. **Change:** All yellow.

PREVIOUS **Leagues:** Hants Premier. **Names:** Esso F.C.

FLEET SPURS

Chairman: Robert Taylor.

Secretary: Paul Hampshire. 65 Turgis Road, Fleet, Hampshire GU51 1EL.

Tel: 07850 810 133.

Ground: Kennels Lane Southwood Farnborough Hampshire GU14 0NJ .

Directions: From the M3 Junction 4A take the A327 towards Farnborough/Cove. Left at the roundabout, over the railway line, left at the next roundabout Kennels Lane is on the right opposite the Nokia building, entrance is 100 yards on the left.

Midweek Matchday: Tuesday. **Floodlights:** Yes.

Colours: All blue & red. **Change colours:** Yellow/black/yellow.

HAMBLE ASSC

Founded: 1938

Chairman: Jenny Headington.

Secretary: Ward Puddle. 81 Wakefield Road, Midanbury, Southampton SO18 2DG. Tel: 07801 305 392.

Programme Editor: See secretary.

Ground: Folland Park, Kings Avenue, Hamble-Le-Rice, Southampton SO31 4NF. Tel: 02380 452 173.

Capacity: 1,000 **Seats**:150 **Covered**: 150 **Floodlights**: Yes

Directions: From M27, junction 8 follow signs for Southampton East. At Windhover roundabout take exit for Hamble (B3397) Hamble Lane. Proceed for 3 miles. On entering Hamble, the ground is on the right off Kings Avenue (opposite the Harrier P.H.)

Clubhouse: Yes.

Midweek Home Matchday: Tuesday.

Colours: Sky blue/maroon/sky blue. **Change:** White/red/red.

Honours: Southampton Senior Cup 1984-85, 86-87, 91-92.

HORNDEAN

Founded: 1887
Chairman: David Sagar.
Secretary: Michael Austin. 22 Abbas Green, Havant, Hampshire PO9 4EP. Tel: 07946 071 966.
Programme Editor: Ian Sheppard.
Ground: Five Heads Park, Five Heads Road, Horndean, Hampshire PO8 9NZ. Tel: 02392 591 363.
Capacity: 3,500 **Seats**:500 **Covered**: 1,250 **Floodlights**: Yes
Directions: Leave A3(M) at junction 2 & follow signs for Cowplain/Clanfield A3, taking slip road passing Morrisons store on the right, crossing over the mini roundabout. Turn right at next roundabout taking last exit signed Horndean/Petersfield A3 onto Portsmouth Road. Continue for approx 300m. Five Heads Road is on the left and the ground is 800m on the left.
Clubhouse: Yes.
Midweek Home Matchday: Tuesday.
Colours: All red. **Change:** All blue.
Previous Leagues: Waterlooville & District 1989-49. Portsmouth 1949-72. Hampshire 1972-2004.
Records: Attendance: 1,560 v Waterlooville, Victory Cup, April 1971.
Goalscorer: Frank Bryson - 348 (including 83 during the 1931-32 season).

HYTHE & DIBDEN

Chairman: Robert Parsons
Secretary: Nicky Oakley. 47 Hobart Drive, Hythe, Southampton, Hampshire SO45 6FT. Tel: 07538 770 644.
Programme Editor: Vanessa Cox.
Ground: Ewart Recreation Ground, Jones Lane, Hythe, Southampton SO45 6AA.
Tel: 02380 845 264 (matchdays only).
Directions: Travel along the A326 then at the Dibden roundabout take the first left into Southampton Road. Continue for approx. 1 mile and then turn left into Jones Lane just before the Shell Filling Station and the ground is 200 yards on your left. Car parking is available in the Dibden Parish Hall car park at the bottom end of the ground.
Midweek Matchday: Wednesday **Floodlights:** Yes.
Colours: Green & white/white/white. **Change colours:** All blue.

PETERSFIELD TOWN

Chairman: Ian Essai
Secretary: Mark Nicholl, 49 Durford Road, Petersfield, Hants GU31 4ER
Tel: 07949 328 240.
Programme Editor: See secretary.
Ground: Love Lane, Petersfield, Hampshire GU31 4BW Tel: 01730 233 416.
Directions: Off A3 circulatory system in Petersfield town centre (well signposted) or 10 min. Walk from Petersfield railway station.
Midweek Matches: Tuesday. **Floodlights:** Yes.
Colours: Red & black stripes/black/black. **Change colours:** Yellow/blue/blue.

RINGWOOD TOWN

Founded: 1879
Chairman: Steve Simpson.
Secretary: Aubrey Hodder. 6 Fromond Close, Lymington, Hampshire SO41 9LQ. Tel: 01590 679 156.
Ground: The Canotec Stadium, Long Lane, Ringwood, Hampshire BH24 3BX. Tel.No.: 01425 473 448
Directions: To Ringwood on A31 (M27). From town centretravel one mile. Right into Moorhouse Lane at petrol station and turn into Long Lane after 200 yards. Ground 250 yards on left
Midweek Matches: Tuesday
Colours: All red. **Change colours:** All blue.

SHAFTESBURY

Chairman: Peter Stacey

Secretary: Chris Woods. 16 Crookhays, Shaftesbury, Dorest SP7 8DX. Tel: (H) 01747 853 602.

Programme Editor: Beverley Dyckes.

Ground: Cockrams, Coppice Street, Shaftesbury SP7 8PF. Tel: 01747 853 990.

Cover: Yes **Floodlights:** Yes **Clubhouse**: Yes

Directions: From the North (A350) at the Ivy Cross roundabout take 2nd exit (Salisbury/Blandford) after 300 yards turn right into Coppice Street and after 200 yards turn right into car park and ground is on the right. From East (A30) at Royal Chase roundabout take 3rd exit (Sherborne/Yeovil) and take 3rd left into Coppice Street and follow as above. Parking s not permitted in the Tesco Car Park.

Midweek Matches: Wednesday.

Colours: All red. **Change colours**: Green & white/green/green.

STOCKBRIDGE

Chairman: Paul Barker.

Secretary: Robin Smith. Curlews Farm, Quarley, Andover, Hants. SP11 8PT

Tel: 07988 884 478.

Programme Editor: Mavis Savage.

Ground: Stockbridge Recreation Ground, High Street, Stockbridge, Hants, SO20 6EU.

Tel: 07963 453 162.

Directions: Off Stockbridge High Street. 1st right at the BT sub-station into the Recreation Ground.

Midweek Matches: Tuesday. **Floodlights:** Yes.

Colours: All red. **Change colours:** Blue & yellow/blue/blue & yellow.

TADLEY CALLEVA

Chairman: G. White.

Secretary: Carli Doyle. 24 gravelly Close, Tadley, Hampshire RG26 3PE.

Tel: 07789 387 166.

Ground: Barlows Park, Silchester Road, Tadley RG26 3PX .

Programme Editor: Secretary.

Directions: From M3 Basingstoke Junction 6 take the A340 to Tadley, travel through Tadley and at the main traffic lights turn right into Silchester Road and proceed for 0.5 miles then turn left into the car park.

Midweek Matches: Wednesday. **Floodlights:** Yes.

Colours: Yellow & black/black/yellow. **Change colours:** Claret & blue/claret/claret & blue.

UNITED SERVICES PORTSMOUTH

Chairman: Richard Stephenson Lt. RN.

Secretary: Bob Brady, 3 Brook Close, Sarisbury Green, Southampton, Hants. SO31 7DW

Tel: 07887 541 782.

Programme Editor: See secretary.

Ground: Victory Stadium, HMS Temeraire, Burnaby Road, Portsmouth PO1 2EJ

Tel: (Office) 02392 725 315. (Clubhouse) 02392 724 235.

Directions: Leave the M27 at Junction 12 and join the M275 to Portsmouth. Follow the signs to Gunwharf, turn right at the traffic lights into Park Road then left at the next set of lights into Burnaby Road and the entrance is at the end of this road via HMS Temeraire. For parking - turn right into Burnaby Road, under the rail bridge then immediately right into the macadam car park and follow the parking signs.

Midweek Matches: Tuesday **Floodlights:** Yes.

Colours: All royal blue. **Change colours:** Red & white/red/red.

Previous Name: Portsmouth Royal Navy

VERWOOD TOWN

Chairman: Michael Fry

Secretary: Roy Mortimer. 1 Burley Close, Verwood, Dorset BH31 6TQ. Tel: 07801 713 462.

Programme Editor: Dan Eldridge.

Ground: Potterne Park, Potterne Way, Verwood, Dorset BH21 6RS. Tel: 01202 814 007.

Directions Leave the A31 at Ringwood and take the B3081 towards Verwood (approx 5 miles) Pass through Ebblake Industrial Estate traffic lights and proceed to Woodlinken Drive and turn left. Continue down Woodlinken Drive into Lake Road. At 'T' junction turn left into Newtown Road. At next 'T' junction, Manor Road, turn left and then continue for approx 100 yards then turn let into Potterne Way and the ground is at the end of the road.

Midweek Home Matches: Wednesday. **Floodlights:** Yes.

Colours: Red/black/black. **Change:** Yellow /blue/yellow.

WARMINSTER TOWN

Chairman: N McGuckian.

Secretary: Ashley Wain. 1 Southleigh View, Warminster, Wiltshire BA12 9LJ. Tel: 07734 959 648.

Programme Editor: Jan Loftus.

Ground: 73 Weymouth Street, Warminster, Wiltshire BA12 9NS. Tel No: 01985 217 828.

Directions: A36 from Salisbury, head for town centre, turn left at traffic lights in town centre signposted A350 Shaftesbury. Club is situated approx. 400 yards on left hand side at top of Weymouth Street.

Midweek Home Matchday: Wednesday. **Floodlights:** Yes.

Colours: Red & black stripes/black/red. **Change:** Blue/navy/blue.

WHITCHURCH UNITED

Chairman: Gary Shaughnessy.

Secretary: Paul Driver. 31 Micheldever Road Whitchurch Hampshire RG28 7JE

Tel: 07921 548 222.

Programme Editor: John Rutledge

Ground: Longmeadow Winchester Road, Whitchurch, Hampshire RG28 3RD. Tel: 01256 892 493.

Directions: From the A34 take the B3400 to Overton and Longmeadow is on your right.

Midweek Home Matchday: Tuesday. **Floodlights:** Yes.

Colours: All red. **Change:** All blue.

WEST MIDLANDS (REGIONAL) LEAGUE

Sponsored by:

No sponsor

Founded: 1889

Recent champions:

2004: Malvern Town

2005: Tipton Town

2006: Market Drayton Town

2007: Shifnal Town

2008: Bridgnorth Town

Premier Division		P	W	D	L	F	A	Pts
AFC Wulfrunians		40	28	3	9	89	47	87
Bloxwich United		40	27	4	9	123	50	85
Bewdley Town		40	26	7	7	107	52	85
Ellesmere Rangers		40	25	7	8	105	45	82
Dudley Town		40	24	7	9	91	55	79
Wellington		40	21	6	13	76	62	69
Darlaston Town		40	20	6	14	67	58	66
Heath Town Rangers	*-1*	40	19	4	17	68	68	60
Wednesfield		40	16	11	13	68	59	59
Shawbury United		40	16	9	15	59	66	57
Lye Town		40	16	7	17	69	62	55
Dudley Sports		40	15	10	15	53	55	55
Tividale		40	15	8	17	63	64	53
Bromyard Town		40	14	8	18	61	67	50
Gornal Athletic		40	13	10	17	56	60	49
Goodrich		40	10	11	19	58	88	41
Ludlow Town		40	12	5	23	66	99	41
Pelsall Villa		40	7	13	20	53	72	34
Wolverhampton Casuals		40	10	2	28	60	113	32
Ledbury Town		40	8	7	25	68	128	31
Bustleholme	*-3*	40	4	3	33	39	129	12

PREMIER DIVISION CUP

FIRST ROUND

Bewdley Town 6 Wolverhampton Casuals 3

Bloxwich United 0 **AFC Wulfrunians** 2

Bromyard Town 1 **Pelsall Villa** 2

Goodrich 1 Ellesmere Rangers 0

Heath Town Rangers 3 Shawbury United 0

SECOND ROUND

AFC Wulfrunians 3 Dudley Town 1

Bustleholme 1 **Bewdley Town** 5

Darlaston Town 0 **Wednesfield** 1

Goodrich 0 **Heath Town Rangers** 2

Ledbury Town 2 Lye Town 0

Ludlow Town 2 **Gornal Athletic** 3

Pelsall Villa 2 Dudley Sports 1

Tividale 2 Wellington 2 *aet* (3-2p)

QUARTER-FINALS

Bewdley Town 3 Ledbury Town 2

Heath Town Rangers 2 Gornal Athletic 2 *aet* (11-10p)

Pelsall Villa 0 **Tividale** 2

Wednesfield 2 AFC Wulfrunians 0

SEMI-FINALS *(played over two legs)*

Tividale 0 Heath Town Rangers 0, **Heath Town Rgrs** 3 Tividale 3 *aet* (3-1p)

Wednesfield 1 Bewdley 3, **Bewdley** 3 Wednesfield 1

FINAL

Not played

	AFC Wulfs	Bewdley	Bloxwich	Bromyard	Bust'holme	Darlaston	Dudley S.	Dudley T.	Ellesmere	Goodrich	Gornal Ath.	Heath TR.	Ledbury T.	Ludlow T.	Lye Town	Pelsall Villa	Shawbury	Tividale	Wednesf'ld	Wellington	W'pton C.
AFC Wulfrunians		2-2	0-2	3-1	3-0	1-4	0-2	1-1	1-1	5-0	2-1	4-0	2-1	2-1	0-1	3-0	3-0	3-0	4-0	2-5	3-2
Bewdley Town	5-2		6-0	1-1	1-0	6-1	1-2	3-1	3-3	4-1	1-3	1-0	4-2	3-1	3-1	2-1	3-0	2-2	2-2	3-4	4-2
Bloxwich United	3-0	4-2	***P***	2-3	8-0	1-2	3-1	2-1	2-0	5-1	3-1	4-2	6-2	4-0	3-1	4-2	0-0	1-2	2-1	2-0	11-1
Bromyard Town	0-1	1-2	1-0	***R***	3-1	0-2	0-2	1-2	2-4	1-4	2-1	1-1	3-3	4-1	2-1	2-2	2-3	3-1	2-0	0-1	1-4
Bustleholme	0-3	2-2	0-6	2-1	***E***	0-5	1-3	2-4	2-5	1-1	0-3	1-2	1-1	1-4	1-5	0-5	1-2	2-1	0-2	2-4	2-3
Darlaston Town	2-3	0-1	0-0	1-2	3-1	***M***	2-0	2-3	1-2	1-1	2-1	0-0	3-1	3-0	4-1	1-0	1-4	1-1	1-0	0-1	2-1
Dudley Sports	0-1	1-4	2-0	2-2	4-1	0-1	***I***	0-1	0-2	1-2	1-1	2-1	3-1	3-0	0-4	1-1	0-2	2-1	0-0	2-2	2-0
Dudley Town	2-1	2-3	4-3	2-1	3-0	1-0	0-3	***E***	1-1	1-1	0-1	4-1	3-1	4-0	5-1	4-1	4-0	1-0	1-2	5-0	1-1
Ellesmere Rangers	1-2	1-0	2-1	2-1	7-0	6-4	4-1	1-2	***R***	1-0	3-0	1-1	10-1	4-0	0-1	1-0	1-1	1-1	2-1	2-0	4-2
Goodrich	0-5	0-5	2-5	0-1	1-3	2-2	0-0	3-1	1-4		1-1	2-3	3-2	5-3	1-1	4-3	1-1	1-2	1-1	0-2	2-1
Gornal Athletic	1-2	1-2	0-2	0-1	2-0	1-4	0-2	3-5	2-1	2-2		2-0	3-1	1-1	1-1	3-1	1-2	1-1	1-2	2-3	3-1
Heath Town Rangers	1-4	1-0	3-4	3-1	3-1	4-1	4-1	1-4	0-2	3-2	3-1	***D***	6-0	1-0	0-2	1-0	2-1	5-1	1-3	2-1	0-1
Ledbury Town	1-2	0-5	2-2	2-0	1-0	2-4	4-1	3-3	1-6	4-3	1-1	1-2	***I***	6-2	1-5	2-2	2-1	1-6	5-1	2-5	5-1
Ludlow Town	1-4	0-6	1-7	2-2	5-2	5-0	1-1	2-3	4-3	1-1	1-2	1-2	5-0	***V***	0-3	3-1	1-0	0-3	4-4	2-1	1-2
Lye Town	0-3	0-1	0-4	0-1	2-0	1-2	2-2	1-1	0-5	0-1	0-2	3-0	4-2	1-2	***I***	0-0	5-0	3-0	1-2	1-1	3-0
Pelsall Villa	0-2	1-1	2-0	1-1	5-2	1-2	1-3	2-1	1-0	0-2	0-2	1-1	1-1	1-3	2-2	***S***	1-1	0-1	2-2	1-4	1-3
Shawbury United	2-0	1-0	0-4	2-1	2-1	0-0	0-1	0-2	0-4	4-1	1-1	1-2	6-1	1-0	3-5	3-3	***I***	3-1	1-1	2-2	1-3
Tividale	1-3	1-4	2-4	1-2	4-1	2-1	0-0	0-1	0-1	2-1	2-2	2-1	5-0	1-0	2-1	2-0	2-4	***O***	1-1	3-1	0-2
Wednesfield	0-1	2-3	0-0	2-2	3-1	0-1	3-1	4-2	3-1	1-2	1-1	2-1	3-1	0-2	2-1	1-2	1-2	1-1	***N***	1-0	3-0
Wellington	1-2	0-1	1-5	1-0	1-3	2-0	2-1	2-2	0-0	2-0	2-0	4-2	4-1	5-2	0-1	1-1	1-0	3-1	2-4		2-1
Wolverhampton Casuals	2-4	3-5	0-4	2-6	6-1	0-1	0-0	1-3	2-6	3-2	0-1	1-2	1-0	2-4	3-4	0-4	1-2	0-4	1-6	1-3	

PREMIER DIVISION CONSTITUTION 2009-10

AFC WULFRUNIANS
Formed: 2005
Ground: Castlecroft Stadium, Castlecroft Road, Wolverhampton, West Midlands WV3 8NA.
Tel: 01902 761 410.

BEWDLEY TOWN
Formed:1978
Ground: Ribbesford Meadows, Ribbesford, Bewdley, Worcs DY12 1JN.
Tel: 07733 264 893.

BLOXWICH UNITED AFC
Ground: Grosvenor Park, (Old Red Lion Ground), Somerfield Road, Bloxwich WS3 2EJ.
Tel: 07771 717 349.

BROMYARD TOWN
Formed: 1893
Ground: Delahay Meadow, Stourport Road, Bromyard, Herfordshire HR7 4NT.
Tel: 07885 849 948.

BUSTLEHOLME
Formed: 1975
Ground: Tipton Town FC. Wednesbury Oak Road, Tipton B71 1PJ.
Tel: 07836 265 300.

DARLASTON TOWN
Formed: 1874
Ground: City Ground, Waverley Road, Darlaston WS10 8ED.

DUDLEY SPORTS
Formed: 1978
Ground: Dudley Emplyees S & S, Hillcrest Avenue, Brierley Hill, West Mids. DY5 3QH
Tel: 07739 099 385.

DUDLEY TOWN
Formed: 1893
Ground: Dell Stadium, Bryce Road, Brierley Hill, West Mids DY5 4NE.
Tel: 07960 181 530.

ELLESMERE RANGERS
Formed: 1969
Ground: Beech Grove Playing Fields, Ellesmere, Shrops. SY12 0BT.
Tel: 07947 864 357.

GOODRICH
Formed: 1995
Ground: Goodrich Sports Ground, Stafford Road, Fordhouse, Wolverhampton WV10 7EH.
Tel: 07813 467 220

GORNAL ATHLETIC
Formed: 1945
Ground: Garden Walk Stadium, Garden Walk, Lower Gornal DY3 2NR.
Tel: 07762 585 149.

HEATH TOWN RANGERS
Ground: Wednesfield FC. Cottage Ground, Amos Lane, Wednesfield WV11 1ND.
Tel: 07980 501 331.

LEDBURY TOWN
Formed: 1893
Ground: New Street, Ledbury, Herefordshire HR8 2EL.
Tel: 07929 268 947.

LUDLOW TOWN
Formed: 1876
Ground: The SBS Stadium, Bromfield Road, Ludlow. SY8 2BY
Tel: 01584 876 000.

LYE TOWN
Formed: 1930
Ground: Sports Ground, Stourbridge Road, Lye, Stourbridge DY9 7DH.
Tel: 01384 422 672.

OLDBURY ATHLETIC
Formed: 1981
Ground: Halesowen Town FC, Old Hawne Lane, Halesowen, West Midlands B63 3TB.
Tel: 0121 550 9433.

SHAWBURY UNITED
Formed: 1992
Ground: Butler Sports Centre, Bowens Field, Wem SY4 5AP.
Tel: 07905 443 209.

TIVIDALE
Formed: 1954
Ground: The Beeches, Packwood Road, Tividale, Warley, W. Midlands B69 1UL
Tel: 07876 197 758.

WEDNESFIELD
Ground: Cottage Ground, Amos Lane, Wednesfield WV11 1ND.
Tel: 07980 501 331.

WELLINGTON
Formed: 1968
Ground: Wellington Playing Fields, Wellington, Hereford, Heredfordshire HR4 8AZ.
Tel: 07974 447 817

WOLVERHAMPTON CASUALS
Founded: 1899
Ground: Brinsford Stadium, Brinsford Lane, Coven Heath, Wolverhampton WS10 7PR.
Tel: 07870 737 229.

INS & OUTS
In: Oldbury Athletic (S –Midland Combination League Premier Division)
Out: Pelsall Villa (S –Midland Combination League Premier Division)

Division One	P	W	D	L	F	A	Pts
Wellington Amateurs	32	24	3	5	86	20	75
Bilbrook	32	22	4	6	83	34	70
Bridgnorth Town Res.	32	19	8	5	73	37	65
Stafford Town	32	17	4	11	95	62	55
Bilston Town	32	15	8	9	55	52	53
AFC Wombourne Utd	32	16	4	12	65	49	52
Penn Croft	32	15	2	15	63	58	47
Dudley United	32	13	5	14	50	50	44
Warstone Wanderers	32	12	7	13	58	64	43
Warley Development	32	13	3	16	71	66	42
Blackheath Town	32	10	12	10	47	45	42
Riverway	32	12	6	14	56	67	42
Malvern Town Res.	32	10	8	14	58	76	38
Wolverhampton Utd	32	8	4	20	43	75	28
Shenstone Pathfinder	32	8	4	20	51	92	28
Wednesbury Town	32	8	3	21	43	93	27
Sporting Khalsa	32	6	3	23	39	96	21

DIVISION ONE CUP

FIRST ROUND

Bilston Town 5 Malvern Town Res. 3

SECOND ROUND

AFC Wombourne United 2 Wellington Amateurs 0
Bilbrook 1 Warstones Wanderers 0
Bilston Town 2 Blackheath Town 0
Penn Croft 2 Shenstone Pathfinder 1 *aet*
Riverway 0 **Dudley United** 1
Sporting Khalsa 1 **Stafford Town** 4
Warley Development 1 **Wednesbury Town** 2
Wolverhampton United 2 Bridgnorth Town Res. 1

QUARTER-FINALS

AFC Wombourne United 2 Bilbrook 1
Bilston Town 3 Stafford Town 1
Penn Croft 3 Wolverhampton United 0
Wednesbury Town (scr.) v **Dudley United** (w/o)

SEMI-FINALS *(played over two legs)*

AFC Wombourne United 2 Dudley United 0,
Dudley United 2 **AFC Wombourne United** 2
Penn Croft 3 Bilston 4, Bilston Town 1 **Penn Croft** 4

FINAL

(May 16th at Wolverhampton Casuals)
AFC Wombourne United 3 Penn Croft 1

	AFC Wombourne Utd	Bilbrook	Bilston Town	Blackheath Town	Bridgnorth Town Res.	Dudley United	Malvern Town Res.	Penn Croft	Riverway	Shenstone Pathfinder	Sporting Khalsa	Stafford Town	Warley Development	Warstone Wanderers	Wednesbury Town	Wellington Amateurs	Wolverhampton United
AFC Wombourne United		0-2	0-1	2-0	0-2	1-1	2-3	2-1	1-0	2-1	6-1	1-0	4-2	3-2	2-1	1-0	4-0
Bilbrook	2-1		4-0	2-2	2-1	3-0	2-3	2-1	2-4	3-2	1-2	1-0	3-0	1-1	7-2	1-0	2-2
Bilston Town	3-3	1-0	***D***	3-0	3-2	3-1	3-0	0-4	2-1	3-1	3-4	1-1	2-1	0-0	3-0	1-1	4-3
Blackheath Town	2-2	1-3	1-2	***I***	0-0	3-1	2-2	2-1	1-0	5-0	0-0	3-3	1-3	2-2	2-2	0-1	1-1
Bridgnorth Town Res.	2-0	0-4	5-0	2-1	***V***	2-1	3-3	2-2	2-2	2-1	5-0	4-1	5-2	3-1	0-0	0-2	5-0
Dudley United	2-1	1-2	2-2	1-1	1-2	***I***	2-3	4-1	3-1	2-0	3-0	4-3	0-1	2-1	1-3	1-0	1-1
Malvern Town Res.	2-3	0-6	2-1	0-0	1-1	1-4	***S***	2-1	1-1	7-3	1-0	0-3	4-0	3-3	1-2	2-3	3-0
Penn Croft	2-2	1-0	3-4	2-3	1-3	1-0	3-2	***I***	1-2	3-0	4-3	1-4	2-1	0-1	4-2	0-2	0-1
Riverway	4-3	0-4	0-0	1-1	0-2	0-1	3-2	1-3	***O***	2-3	4-1	5-4	4-0	2-4	5-0	2-1	0-3
Shenstone Pathfinder	2-0	1-3	1-2	0-1	3-1	4-4	4-1	1-2	2-2	***N***	2-0	3-7	1-1	0-1	1-1	0-4	2-0
Sporting Khalsa	0-4	1-3	1-1	2-1	3-4	1-0	1-2	2-3	1-1	3-6		2-4	1-3	1-4	0-1	0-5	3-1
Stafford Town	4-2	0-4	2-1	0-2	1-2	3-1	3-3	1-0	5-0	8-1	5-1		5-3	0-1	6-1	1-6	6-2
Warley Development	1-6	2-1	2-2	2-1	0-1	0-1	6-0	1-2	6-2	6-1	9-1	1-4	***D***	5-1	3-1	0-1	2-0
Warstone Wanderers	1-3	1-4	3-0	0-2	0-0	1-2	2-0	3-4	1-3	6-0	5-1	2-2	2-2	***I***	3-2	0-6	1-3
Wednesbury Town	0-2	2-6	3-1	1-3	0-6	0-3	3-2	1-5	1-2	2-0	0-2	1-6	1-4	2-3	***V***	3-2	2-5
Wellington Amateurs	3-1	2-2	1-0	3-0	2-2	4-0	4-0	4-1	5-0	5-1	2-0	1-0	2-1	5-0	2-0		1-0
Wolverhampton United	2-1	0-1	0-3	1-3	0-2	1-0	2-2	0-4	1-2	3-4	3-1	2-3	4-1	1-2	1-3	0-6	

WEST MIDLANDS (REGIONAL) LEAGUE DIVISION ONE CONSTITUTION 2009-10

AFC WOMBOURNE UNITED . . . Mile Flat Sports Ground, Mile Flat, Wall Heath, Kingswinford DY6 0AU 01384 37758
BILBROOK . . . . Pendeford Lane, Wolverhampton WV9 5HQ . . . . Non
BILSTON TOWN . . . . Queen Street, Bilston, Wolverhampton WV14 7EX 01902 49149
BLACKHEATH TOWN . . . . York Road Sports & Social, York Road, Oldbury, Rowley Regis B65 0RR 0121 559 556
BRIDGNORTH TOWN RESERVES . . . . . Crown Meadow, Innage Lane, Bridgnorth WV16 4HS 01746 76274
DUDLEY UNITED . . . . Mile Flat Sports Ground, Mile Flat, Wall Heath, Kingswinford DY6 0AU 01384 37758
HANWOOD UNITED. . . . . Hanwood Recreation Ground, Hanwood, Shrewsbury. . . . . Non
MALVERN TOWN RESERVES. . . . . . . Langland Stadium, Langland Avenue, Malvern WR14 2EQ 01684 57429
PENN CROFT . . . . Aldersley Leisure Village, Aldersley Road, Wolverhampton WV6 9NW. 01902 55620
RIVERWAY . . . . Long Lane Park, Long Lane, Essington WV11 2AA 01922 40660
SHENSTONE PATHFINDER Shenstone PF (Pavilion Club), Birmingham Road, Shenstone, Lichfield WS14 0LR 01543 48165
SPORTING KHALSA . . . . Abbey Park, Glastonbury Crescent, Mossley, Bloxwich, Walsall WS3 2RQ 01922 47764
STAFFORD TOWN . . . . Rowley Park Stadium, Averill Road, West Road, Stafford ST17 9XX. 01785 25106
TRYSULL. . . . . Wolverhampton Casuals FC, Brinsford Lane, Coven Heath, Wolverhampton WV10 7PR 01902 78321
WARLEY DEVELOPMENT . . . . York Road Sports & Social, York Road, Oldbury, Rowley Regis B65 0RR. Non
WARSTONE WANDERERS . . . Cradley Town FC, Beeches View Avenue., Cradley, Halesowen B63 2HB 01384 56965
WELLINGTON AMATEURS . . . . School Grove Oakengates Telford TF2 6BQ . . . . Non
WOLVERHAMPTON UNITED . . . . Prestwood Road West, Wednesfield, Wolverhampton WV11 1HL. 01902 73088

IN: Hanwood United (P), Trysull (P)
OUT: Wednesbury Town (R)

ivision Two		P	W	D	L	F	A	Pts
anwood United		26	21	4	1	70	23	67
rysull		26	17	3	6	63	23	54
tone Old Alleynians	*-3*	26	16	5	5	56	29	50
rens Nest		26	14	5	7	57	35	47
lack Country Rangers		26	12	8	6	55	42	44
entley		26	12	5	9	61	52	41
arlaston Town Res.		26	11	6	9	44	42	39
enkridge Town		26	9	8	9	42	37	35
yrley Juniors		26	9	6	11	45	42	33
eath Town Rangers Res.		26	10	2	14	40	51	32
ahal		26	6	4	16	51	65	22
ye Town Res.		26	6	1	19	33	70	19
enbury United		26	2	7	17	42	75	13
ttingshall Park Farm		26	3	4	19	24	97	13

Warstone Wanderers Res. - record expunged

DIVISION TWO CUP

FIRST ROUND

Bentley 2 **Stone Old Alleynians** 3
Black Country Rangers (w/o) v Warstone Wanderers Res. (scr.)
Darlaston Town Res. 5 Tenbury United 1
Hanwood United 7 Penkridge Town 2
Heath Town Rangers Res. 2 Lye Town Res. 1
Trysull 5 Wyrley Juniors 0
Wrens Nest 10 Mahal 3

QUARTER-FINALS

Black Country Rangers 4 Hanwood United 0
Darlaston Town Res. 1 **Stone Old Alleynians** 1 *aet* (2-3p)
Trysull 5 Ettingshall Park Farm 0
Wrens Nest 5 Heath Town Rangers Res. 2

SEMI-FINALS

(played over two legs)

Black Country Rangers 1 Stone Old Alleynians 3, Stone Old Alleynians 2 **Black Country Rangers** 4 *aet* (4-5p)
Trysull 0 Wrens Nest 2, **Wrens Nest** 2 Trysull 2

FINAL

(May 16th at Tividale)

Black Country Rangers 5 Wrens Nest 2

	Bentley	Black Country Rangers	Darlaston Town Res.	Ettingshall Park Farm	Hanwood United	Heath Town Rgrs Res.	Lye Town Res.	Mahal	Penkridge Town	Stone Old Alleynians	Tenbury United	Trysull	Warstone Wders Res.	Wrens Nest	Wyrley Juniors
Bentley		4-2	3-2	3-0	1-2	2-1	2-3	2-2	4-2	2-3	2-2	0-1	1-0	1-4	3-4
Black Country Rangers	1-2	***D***	2-1	6-0	2-5	2-1	3-1	3-2	4-1	1-1	1-0	0-0	1-4	2-2	0-1
Darlaston Town Res.	4-3	0-3	***I***	1-1	0-2	1-3	2-0	2-0	0-0	3-3	2-0	3-2	4-2	3-1	2-2
Ettingshall Park Farm	2-5	2-4	3-7	***V***	1-5	2-2	0-1	2-4	3-2	0-4	2-2	0-6	2-6	1-4	0-5
Hanwood United	3-3	4-0	4-0	3-0	***I***	3-2	4-0	2-0	0-0	2-0	4-1	2-1	7-0	1-0	0-0
Heath Town Rangers Res.	0-3	2-0	3-0	0-1	3-4	***S***	1-0	3-1	1-2	0-4	4-3	0-1	n/a	0-0	2-4
Lye Town Res.	0-2	1-4	0-4	0-1	1-4	2-3	***I***	1-3	0-0	0-1	3-4	1-0	n/a	1-5	2-5
Mahal	1-2	2-3	2-3	10-0	1-4	0-1	3-5	***O***	1-1	1-4	4-4	1-5	1-3	1-3	2-2
Penkridge Town	3-1	1-1	0-0	5-0	0-2	3-1	2-1	1-2	***N***	2-3	6-1	0-2	2-0	3-1	1-1
Stone Old Alleynians	1-1	2-2	1-0	6-0	0-2	2-1	7-1	2-1	2-2		1-0	1-0	2-0	1-2	2-1
Tenbury United	2-2	2-4	1-2	1-1	2-5	2-1	2-5	2-3	1-3	0-1		3-7	1-3	2-2	1-1
Trysull	4-1	1-1	0-0	5-0	4-1	1-2	4-0	4-0	3-0	2-1	3-2	***T***	5-2	3-2	2-0
Warstone Wanderers Res.	n/a	n/a	2-5	n/a	0-3	3-2	2-5	3-0	0-2	n/a	n/a	1-7	***W***	n/a	n/a
Wrens Nest	0-3	3-3	3-1	3-1	0-0	6-0	3-2	3-1	1-2	1-2	2-1	2-0	n/a	***O***	3-0
Wyrley Juniors	3-4	1-1	0-1	3-1	1-2	2-3	1-2	1-3	1-0	2-1	4-1	0-2	4-0	0-1	

WEST MIDLANDS (REGIONAL) LEAGUE DIVISION TWO CONSTITUTION 2009-10

ENTLEY. . . . . Bentley Road South, Darlaston WS10 8LN 07737 29675
LACK COUNTRY RANGERS . . . Cradley Town FC, The Beeches, Packwood Road, Tividale B69 1UL 01384 211743
ARLASTON TOWN RESERVES . . . . City Ground, Waverley Road, Darlaston WS10 8ED . . . . None
TTINGSHALL PARK FARM . . . . Stafford Road, Fordhouses, Wolverhampton . . . . None
EATH TOWN RANGERS RESERVES Bilbrook FC, Pendeford Lane, Wolverhampton WV9 5HQ . . . . None
AHAL. . . . . Hadley Stadium, Wilson Road, Smethwick, Warley B68 9JW 0121 434 4848
ALVERN RANGERS. . . . . Victoria Playing Fields, Pickersleigh Road, Malvern WR14 2QN . . . . None
ENKRIDGE TOWN . . . . Monkton Recreation Centre, Pinfold Lane, Penkridge, Stafford ST19 5QP . . . . None
ENSNETT PANTHERS . . . . Dudley Town FC, The Dell Stadium, Bryce Road, Brierley Hill DY5 4NE 01384 812943
TONE OLD ALLEYNIANS. . . . . Springbank Park, Yarnfield Road, Yarnfield, Stone ST15 0NF 01785 761891
ENBURY UNITED . . . . Palmers Meadow, Burford, Tenbury Wells WR15 8AP . . . . None
EM TOWN. . . . . Butler Sports Centre, Bowens Field, Wem SY4 5AW. 01939 233287
RENS NEST . . . . Gornal Athletic FC, Garden Walk, Lower Gornal, Dudley DY3 2NH 01384 358398
YRLEY JUNIORS . . . . . Brereton Social FC, Red Lion Ground, Armitage Lane, Brereton, Rugeley WS15 1ED. 01889 585526

: Malvern Rangers (N), Pensnett Panthers (P - Sunday football), Wem Town (P - Shropshire County League Premier Division)

UT: Hanwood United (P), Lye Town Res. (W), Trysull (P), Warstone Wanderers Res. (WS)

WESTERN LEAGUE

www.toolstationleague.com

Sponsored by:

Toolstation

Founded: 1892

Recent champions:

2004: Bideford

2005: Bideford

2006: Bideford

2007: Corsham Town

2008: Truro City

Premier Division	**P**	**W**	**D**	**L**	**F**	**A**	**Pts**
Bitton	**40**	**26**	**6**	**8**	**85**	**32**	**84**
Frome Town	**40**	**23**	**7**	**10**	**74**	**44**	**76**
Willand Rovers	**40**	**20**	**13**	**7**	**72**	**49**	**73**
Dawlish Town	**40**	**23**	**3**	**14**	**93**	**52**	**72**
Bristol Manor Farm	**40**	**22**	**6**	**12**	**75**	**53**	**72**
Bideford	**40**	**20**	**9**	**11**	**68**	**43**	**69**
Wellington Town	**40**	**20**	**7**	**13**	**87**	**53**	**67**
Welton Rovers	**40**	**19**	**9**	**12**	**64**	**52**	**66**
Hallen	**40**	**19**	**8**	**13**	**57**	**40**	**65**
Brislington	**40**	**18**	**6**	**16**	**62**	**54**	**60**
Melksham Town	**40**	**15**	**14**	**11**	**59**	**53**	**59**
Sherborne Town	**40**	**17**	**8**	**15**	**55**	**59**	**59**
Street	**40**	**13**	**7**	**20**	**55**	**65**	**46**
Ilfracombe Town	**40**	**11**	**11**	**18**	**48**	**70**	**44**
Bishop Sutton	**40**	**9**	**16**	**15**	**48**	**48**	**43**
Calne Town	**40**	**11**	**10**	**19**	**70**	**78**	**43**
Radstock Town	**40**	**12**	**6**	**22**	**56**	**95**	**42**
Barnstaple Town	**40**	**10**	**9**	**21**	**49**	**82**	**39**
Corsham Town	**40**	**10**	**8**	**22**	**37**	**80**	**38**
Chard Town	**40**	**9**	**5**	**26**	**30**	**77**	**32**
Devizes Town	**40**	**5**	**8**	**27**	**41**	**106**	**23**

	Barnstaple Town	Bideford	Bishop Sutton	Bitton	Brislington	Bristol Manor Farm	Calne Town	Chard Town	Corsham Town	Dawlish Town	Devizes Town	Frome Town	Hallen	Ilfracombe Town	Melksham Town	Radstock Town	Sherborne Town	Street	Wellington Town	Welton Rovers	Willand Rovers
Barnstaple Town		1-3	0-2	4-0	0-2	3-3	2-4	0-2	3-3	1-4	2-1	2-1	1-0	1-1	0-3	2-0	1-2	1-2	1-5	1-6	2-2
Bideford	1-1		2-2	1-2	1-0	0-1	4-2	0-1	3-0	2-1	1-1	0-4	1-0	0-1	1-1	2-3	3-0	1-1	1-2	1-0	2-0
Bishop Sutton	0-1	1-4	***P***	0-1	0-0	4-2	1-1	1-2	4-1	0-1	1-1	1-2	4-0	2-0	1-1	2-2	2-1	1-4	1-2	1-1	1-1
Bitton	5-0	1-1	1-4	***R***	3-0	0-0	2-1	1-0	2-0	2-2	8-0	2-1	4-1	2-0	0-0	3-0	0-1	2-0	1-0	0-1	3-0
Brislington	1-0	0-3	1-0	0-3	***E***	1-0	5-2	3-0	4-0	0-4	7-0	2-2	0-1	4-0	0-1	2-1	0-3	3-1	2-3	2-1	0-0
Bristol Manor Farm	3-0	0-0	1-1	0-3	0-2	***M***	2-1	3-2	4-1	0-1	1-2	2-1	0-1	4-1	5-0	2-4	2-1	2-1	2-0	3-0	2-3
Calne Town	2-3	0-3	2-1	2-2	3-3	4-4	***I***	1-0	7-0	1-7	3-0	0-1	0-2	0-1	0-2	2-1	0-4	1-1	1-1	1-2	4-1
Chard Town	1-0	0-4	1-1	0-2	2-1	1-2	0-2	***E***	1-0	0-2	2-2	0-1	1-4	0-3	0-3	0-3	0-2	2-5	0-2	1-1	0-3
Corsham Town	0-1	1-5	1-0	0-5	0-2	1-0	0-0	1-0	***R***	1-0	2-0	4-4	0-5	5-1	0-0	4-0	1-3	1-1	1-7	0-2	1-1
Dawlish Town	4-0	4-2	0-3	3-0	1-0	0-2	3-1	4-0	0-1		6-0	1-2	2-1	3-1	1-0	7-0	3-2	5-2	1-4	1-2	0-3
Devizes Town	1-2	2-3	3-1	0-4	0-1	1-1	1-2	1-1	0-0	3-4		1-4	1-0	1-2	0-4	2-3	1-1	2-2	0-5	2-1	1-2
Frome Town	1-0	1-1	1-0	2-0	6-0	0-1	3-1	3-1	1-0	0-3	2-1	***D***	1-1	2-2	2-2	0-3	5-0	3-0	1-0	1-1	1-2
Hallen	2-0	1-0	2-0	0-1	0-1	1-2	1-0	2-2	2-0	2-1	2-1	1-0	***I***	3-1	1-0	4-0	4-0	0-0	1-3	1-1	2-2
Ilfracombe Town	1-2	1-2	0-0	0-4	2-1	2-4	2-2	1-0	2-0	4-4	1-3	1-3	1-1	***V***	0-3	2-0	1-1	4-1	1-1	1-2	0-0
Melksham Town	1-1	1-0	2-2	1-1	2-1	0-3	3-3	0-2	1-1	1-5	3-0	1-2	2-0	1-1	***I***	1-3	4-2	2-1	4-1	1-4	3-3
Radstock Town	2-1	1-2	0-0	0-3	0-4	0-3	0-5	1-0	1-0	0-0	7-1	2-4	1-3	2-3	1-2	***S***	1-2	0-0	4-4	4-3	0-4
Sherborne Town	2-2	0-1	0-0	0-6	1-3	0-1	1-1	1-2	2-0	2-1	4-1	1-0	1-0	2-1	2-0	2-2	***I***	1-0	1-0	1-2	2-0
Street	3-2	0-1	0-1	2-1	0-0	0-2	1-5	3-0	3-2	0-2	4-2	0-1	2-1	2-0	0-1	5-1	3-1	***O***	0-2	0-1	2-4
Wellington Town	2-1	2-5	0-0	0-1	2-1	7-2	3-2	4-1	1-2	3-1	1-0	1-3	1-2	1-2	1-1	4-0	1-1	1-2	***N***	5-0	1-1
Welton Rovers	1-1	1-1	2-1	4-2	1-1	1-3	2-0	4-0	0-2	3-1	2-0	3-0	1-1	1-0	0-0	1-2	2-0	2-1	1-4		1-3
Willand Rovers	3-3	2-0	1-1	1-2	5-2	2-1	3-1	0-2	2-0	1-0	4-2	0-2	1-1	0-0	2-1	4-1	2-2	1-0	1-0	2-0	

Division One		P	W	D	L	F	A	Pts
Larkhall Athletic		38	30	5	3	127	27	95
Longwell Green Sports		38	27	4	7	78	40	85
Bradford Town		38	22	6	10	106	55	72
Cadbury Heath	*-3*	38	21	8	9	84	54	68
Keynsham Town		38	19	9	10	62	46	66
Hengrove Athletic		38	19	4	15	57	52	61
Oldland Abbotonians		38	17	8	13	65	60	59
Shrewton United	*-1*	38	18	4	16	73	66	57
Westbury United	*-1*	38	16	8	14	71	50	55
Wells City		38	14	10	14	54	70	52
Portishead Town		38	14	9	15	56	59	51
Gillingham Town		38	14	8	16	71	72	50
Bridport		38	14	7	17	51	65	49
Elmore		38	12	7	19	72	104	43
Clevedon United		38	11	7	20	60	78	40
Roman Glass St George		38	8	15	15	58	77	39
Shepton Mallet		38	10	6	22	51	88	36
Almondsbury		38	8	11	19	70	91	35
Odd Down		38	7	9	22	51	80	30
Minehead Town		38	5	3	30	33	116	18

LES PHILLIPS CUP

PRELIMINARY ROUND

Barnstaple Town 2 **Gillingham Town** 6
Bideford 0 **Melksham Town** 1
Bishop Sutton 2 Minehead Town 0
Bridport 2 **Portishead Town** 2 *aet* (5-6p)
Brislington 3 Sherborne Town 0
Corsham Town 3 Wells City 1
Longwell Green Sports 2 Hallen 0
Odd Down 0 **Chard Town** 1 *aet*
Roman Glass St George 1 **Dawlish Town** 5 *aet*
Wellington Town 3 Radstock Town 1 *aet*

FIRST ROUND

Almondsbury 1 **Corsham Town** 2
Bitton 2 Longwell Green Sports 1
Bradford Town 2 Dawlish Town 1
Cadbury Heath 1 **Melksham Town** 2
Calne Town 4 Brislington 1
Chard Town 1 **Bristol Manor Farm** 3
Clevedon United 1 **Wellington Town** 2
Devizes Town 0 **Keynsham Town** 1
Elmore 1 **Bishop Sutton** 4
Hengrove Athletic 0 **Street** 3
Ilfracombe Town 3 **Gillingham Town** 4
Larkhall Athletic 1 **Welton Rovers** 2 *aet*
Oldland Abbotonians 3 Shrewton United 1
Portishead Town 0 **Willand Rovers** 1
Westbury United 0 **Frome Town** 2
Weston St Johns (scr.) v **Shepton Mallet** (w/o)

SECOND ROUND

Bitton 3 **Street** 5
Gillingham Town 3 **Calne Town** 4
Melksham Town 1 **Bristol Manor Farm** 1 *aet* (6-7p)
Oldland Abbotonians 3 Corsham Town 2 *aet*
Shepton Mallet 1 **Bishop Sutton** 4 *aet*
Wellington Town 4 **Bradford Town** 5 *aet*
Welton Rovers 3 Keynsham Town 0
Willand Rovers 1 **Frome Town** 2

QUARTER-FINALS

Calne Town 2 Welton Rovers 2 *aet* (4-3p)
Frome Town 1 **Bristol Manor Farm** 2
Oldland Abbotonians 3 Bradford Town 1
Street 2 Bishop Sutton 1 *aet*

SEMI-FINALS

Bristol Manor Farm 0 **Oldland Abbotonians** 1
Calne Town 5 Street 1

FINAL *(May 9th at Welton Rovers)*

Calne Town 1 **Oldland Abbotonians** 2

	Alm	Bra.	Bri.	Cad	Cle.	Elm	Gil	Hen	Key	Lar	Lon	Min	Odd	Old	Por	Rom	She	Shr	Wel	Wes
Almondsbury		1-1	1-4	0-4	3-3	2-6	1-2	1-1	1-3	0-0	2-2	9-1	2-1	2-3	4-1	1-3	4-2	3-4	1-2	2-2
Bradford Town	2-2		5-1	0-3	3-3	2-1	7-1	4-1	5-1	0-1	1-3	7-0	3-3	2-0	0-0	5-0	4-2	2-3	2-0	2-0
Bridport	3-2	2-4		0-1	4-1	0-2	3-1	2-0	2-1	0-5	1-0	2-1	3-1	0-2	2-1	1-1	3-2	2-4	0-2	1-2
Cadbury Heath	3-0	3-0	1-1		3-1	8-1	4-1	2-5	1-0	0-3	2-3	1-0	3-2	0-2	1-5	3-2	2-0	1-0	3-0	2-1
Clevedon United	2-5	1-5	0-1	2-2	***D***	0-2	1-3	0-1	0-1	1-3	4-1	1-0	2-2	1-5	1-0	2-2	3-1	1-2	0-1	2-3
Elmore	4-4	4-3	1-3	3-3	2-4	***I***	5-4	0-3	0-2	0-2	2-5	5-0	3-2	2-2	1-3	2-3	4-1	2-1	2-2	2-6
Gillingham Town	4-2	1-3	2-0	2-2	2-2	0-2	***V***	1-2	1-1	0-0	0-2	2-1	4-2	1-1	7-0	3-2	4-0	1-3	2-1	1-5
Hengrove Athletic	0-0	0-1	2-0	1-0	0-4	3-1	1-0	***I***	0-1	2-2	0-1	3-1	1-1	2-1	2-1	3-0	2-0	0-5	0-2	2-1
Keynsham Town	1-1	1-3	3-1	0-1	2-1	5-2	2-0	3-2	***S***	0-2	0-1	6-1	4-2	1-1	2-0	1-1	2-1	2-0	3-0	2-2
Larkhall Athletic	4-0	2-2	5-0	5-1	6-0	6-0	1-1	0-2	4-0	***I***	3-2	5-2	3-0	8-0	5-0	5-1	4-1	6-0	6-1	4-2
Longwell Green Sports	1-0	2-1	1-0	3-2	2-1	5-1	1-0	1-2	1-2	2-1	***O***	2-1	1-1	4-2	3-0	3-0	2-0	3-1	1-3	1-0
Minehead Town	2-2	0-7	1-0	0-0	1-2	2-1	0-3	0-3	1-0	1-6	1-3	***N***	3-0	3-2	2-4	1-2	0-2	0-1	1-2	0-3
Odd Down	0-1	2-3	2-1	2-4	1-3	1-1	2-5	1-0	2-2	0-2	0-1	5-2		0-1	3-1	1-1	1-1	4-3	0-1	0-2
Oldland Abbotonians	5-2	0-1	0-0	1-4	2-3	0-1	0-3	3-2	1-1	0-1	3-2	4-0	1-0	***O***	2-1	0-0	5-1	2-0	3-0	2-1
Portishead Town	5-1	4-0	2-2	2-0	0-1	2-2	3-0	2-0	1-0	1-3	0-0	0-0	0-2	1-3	***N***	2-1	3-1	2-1	1-1	1-0
Roman Glass St George	2-0	0-4	3-3	3-3	2-2	1-3	1-4	1-3	2-3	0-1	0-3	7-2	1-0	0-0	1-1	***E***	5-0	0-3	2-2	1-1
Shepton Mallet	0-1	3-2	0-0	0-7	2-1	1-1	3-1	1-2	0-0	3-1	2-5	2-1	2-4	1-1	1-3	1-1		3-2	4-0	2-1
Shrewton United	3-4	1-4	2-1	1-1	2-0	3-0	3-1	2-1	2-3	0-3	0-2	5-0	3-0	3-1	1-1	1-1	3-2		3-3	2-0
Wells City	2-1	2-6	1-1	1-1	1-0	7-1	1-1	3-2	0-1	1-6	1-3	3-1	1-1	0-2	2-1	2-2	2-3	1-0		0-3
Westbury United	3-2	1-0	0-1	1-2	0-4	3-0	2-2	3-1	0-0	1-3	0-0	4-0	5-0	6-2	1-1	2-3	1-0	3-0	0-0	

PREMIER DIVISION - 2009-10

BARNSTAPLE TOWN

Founded: 1906 Nickname: Barum

Chairman: Steve James
Secretary: David Cooke
51 Walnut Way
Barnstaple
Devon
EX32 7RF
Tel: 07939 217 084
Manager: Owen Pickard
Prog Editor:

Ground: Mill Road, Barnstaple, North Devon, EX31 1JQ Tel: 01271 343 469/345 455
Capacity: 5,000 **Seats:** 250 **Covered:** 1,000
Midweek Matchday: Tuesday **Clubhouse:** Yes **Shop:** Yes
Colours(change): All red. (All blue)
Previous Names: Pilton Yeo Vale
Previous Lges: North Devon, Devon & Exeter, South Western
Records: Att: 6,200 v Bournemouth FA Cup 1st `round 51-52 **App:** Ian Pope
Senior Honours: Western Champions 1952-53, 79-80, Devon Pro Cup (12), Devon Sen Cup 92-93. Western League Div.1 93-94.

10 YEAR RECORD

99-00	00-01	01-02	02-03	03-04	04-05	05-06	06-07	07-08	08-09
WestP 15	WestP 4	WestP 12	WestP 15	WestP 10	WestP 12	WestP 13	WestP 7	WestP 12	WestP 18

BIDEFORD

Founded: 1949 Nickname: The Robins

Chairman: Roy Portch
Secretary: Kevin Tyrrell
69 Laurel Avenue
Bideford
North Devon
EX39 3AZ
Tel: 07929 078 613
Manager: Sean Joyce
Prog Editor:

Ground: The Sports Ground, Kingsley Road, Bideford EX39 2NG. Tel: 01237 474 974
Capacity: 6,000 **Seats:** 375 **Covered:** 1,000
Midweek Matchday: Tuesday **Clubhouse:** Yes **Shop:**
Colours(change): All Red (All blue)
Previous Names: Bideford Town
Previous Lges: Devon & Exeter 47-49, Western 49-72, Southern 72-75,
Records: Att: 6,000 v Gloucester C FA Cup 4th Qual round.
Goalscorer: Tommy Robinson 259 **App:** Derek May 527
Senior Honours: Western Lge 1963-64, 70-71, 71-72, 81-82, 82-83, 01-02, 03-04, 04-05, 05-06. Div 1 51-52, Div 3 49-50. Devon Sen. Cup 79-80

10 YEAR RECORD

99-00	00-01	01-02	02-03	03-04	04-05	05-06	06-07	07-08	08-09
WestP 13	WestP 5	WestP 1	WestP 3	WestP 1	WestP 1	WestP 1	WestP 4	WestP 6	WestP 6

BISHOP SUTTON

Founded: 1977 Nickname: Bishops

Chairman: George Williams
Secretary: Steve Hillier
9 Greyfield Common
High Littleton
Bristol
BS39 6YL
Tel: 07713 681 235
Manager: Lee Lashenko
Prog Editor:

Ground: Lakeview, Wick Road, Bishops Sutton, Bristol BS39 5XN. Tel: 01275 333 097
Capacity: 1,500 **Seats:** 100 **Covered:** 200
Midweek Matchday: Wednesday **Clubhouse:** Yes **Shop:** No
Colours(change): All Blue (all yellow)
Previous Names:
Previous Lges: Weston & District (youth), Bristol & Avon, Somerset Senior >1991
Records: Att: 400 v Bristol City
Senior Honours: Somerset Junior Cup 1980-81. Western League Div.1 97-98.

10 YEAR RECORD

99-00	00-01	01-02	02-03	03-04	04-05	05-06	06-07	07-08	08-09
WestP 12	WestP 16	WestP 15	WestP 12	WestP 16	WestP 18	WestP 16	WestP 21	WestP 19	WestP 15

BITTON

Founded: 1922 Nickname:

Chairman: John Langdon
Secretary: Mrs Becky Jones
High View
Keynsham Road
Willsbridge, Bristol
BS30 6EQ
Tel: 07590 123 982
Manager: Andy Black
Prog Editor:

Ground: Recreation Ground, Bath Road, Bitton, Bristol BS30 6HX. Tel: 0117 932 3222
Capacity: 1,000 **Seats:** 48 **Covered:** 200
Midweek Matchday: Wednesday **Clubhouse:** Yes **Shop:** No
Colours(change): Red & white/black/black (Yellow/green/yellow)
Previous Names:
Previous Lges: Avon Premier Combination, Gloucestershire County
Records: Goalscorer: A. Cole
Senior Honours: Somerset Senior Cup 92-93. Les Phillips Cup 07-08. Western League Champions 2008-09.

10 YEAR RECORD

99-00	00-01	01-02	02-03	03-04	04-05	05-06	06-07	07-08	08-09
West1 6	West1 5	West1 6	West1 8	West1 2	WestP 8	WestP 8	WestP 8	WestP 7	WestP 1

IN: Larkhall Athletic (P), Longwell Green Sports (P)
OUT: Chard Town (R), Devizes Town (R), Frome Town (P – Southern League Division One South & West)

BRISLINGTON

Founded: 1956 Nickname: Bris

Chairman: Fred Hardwell
Secretary: Kevin Jacobs
179 Bishopsworth Road
Bedminster Down
Bristol
BS13 7LG
Tel: 07976 724 202
Manager: Jeff Meacham
Prog Editor:

Ground: Ironmould Lane, Brislington, Bristol BS4 4TZ Tel: 0117 977 4030
Capacity: 2,000 **Seats:** 144 **Covered:** 1,500
Midweek Matchday: Tuesday **Clubhouse:** Yes **Shop:** No
Colours(change): Red & black/black/red. (Yellow & black/yellow/yellow)
Previous Names:
Previous Lges: Somerset Senior until 1991
Records:

Senior Honours: Somerset Senior League 1988-89. Somerset Premier Cup 1992-93. Western Lge Div.1 1994-95.

10 YEAR RECORD

99-00	00-01	01-02	02-03	03-04	04-05	05-06	06-07	07-08	08-09
WestP 3	WestP 8	WestP 3	WestP 2	WestP 7	WestP 10	WestP 10	WestP 17	WestP 13	WestP 10

BRISTOL MANOR FARM

Founded: 1964 Nickname: The Farm

Chairman: Geoff Sellek
Secretary: Andy Radford
16 Westward Road
Bishopsworth
Bristol
BS13 8DA
Tel: 07747 038 423
Manager: John Black
Prog Editor:

Ground: The Creek, Portway, Sea Mills, Bristol, BS9 2HS Tel: 0117 968 3571
Capacity: 2,000 **Seats:** 98 **Covered:** 350
Midweek Matchday: Tuesday **Clubhouse:** Yes **Shop:** No
Colours(change): Red/black/black (All yellow)
Previous Names:
Previous Lges: Bristol Suburban 64-69, Somerset Senior 69-77
Records: Att; 500 v Portway **App:** M. Baird

Senior Honours: Glos Trophy 1987-88, Glos Am. Cup 1989-90. Western Lge Div.1 82-83.

10 YEAR RECORD

99-00	00-01	01-02	02-03	03-04	04-05	05-06	06-07	07-08	08-09
WestP 17	WestP 18	WestP 19	WestP 11	WestP 3	WestP 7	WestP 3	WestP 12	WestP 16	WestP 5

CALNE TOWN

Founded: 1886 Nickname: Lilywhites

Chairman: Mark Barrett
Secretary: Mark Barrett
1 Market Hill
Calne
Wiltshire
SN11 0NT
Tel: 07770924923
Manager: Kelvin Highmore
Prog Editor:

Ground: Bremhill View, Calne SN11 9EE Tel: 01249 819 186
Capacity: 2,500 **Seats:** 78 **Covered:** 250
Midweek Matchday: Wednesday **Clubhouse:** Yes **Shop:** No
Colours(change): White/black/black (All blue)
Previous Names: None.
Previous Lges: Wiltshire.
Records: Att: 1,100 v Swindon friendly 87 **Goalscorer:** Robbie Lardner
App: Gary Swallow 259
Senior Honours: Wiltshire Senior Cup (x3)

10 YEAR RECORD

99-00	00-01	01-02	02-03	03-04	04-05	05-06	06-07	07-08	08-09
West1 13	West1 19	West1 19	West1 5	West1 9	West1 2	WestP 5	WestP 13	WestP 14	WestP 16

CORSHAM TOWN

Founded: 1884 Nickname:

Chairman: Ken Baldwin
Secretary: Richard Taylor
7 Cresswells
Corsham
Wiltshire
SN13 9NJ
Tel: 07944 183 973
Manager: Mel Gingell
Prog Editor:

Ground: Southbank Ground, Lacock Road, Corsham, SN13 9HS Tel: 01249 715 609
Capacity: 1,500 **Seats:** no **Covered:** yes
Midweek Matchday: Wednesday **Clubhouse:** Yes **Shop:** Yes
Colours(change): Red & white/red/red. (Yellow & blue/blue/blue)
Previous Names: None.
Previous Lges: Wiltshire County
Records: Att: 550 v Newport Co. FA Cup **App:** Craig Chaplin

Senior Honours: Wiltshire Senior Cup 1975-76, 96-97, 04-05. Western League 2006-07.

10 YEAR RECORD

99-00	00-01	01-02	02-03	03-04	04-05	05-06	06-07	07-08	08-09
West1 16	West1 9	West1 9	West1 6	West1 5	WestP 2	WestP 2	WestP 1	WestP 5	WestP 19

PREMIER DIVISION - 2009-10

DAWLISH TOWN

Founded: 1889 Nickname: Seasiders

Chairman: Dave Fenner
Secretary: Sandra Walmsley
2 Lodge Court
Elm Grove Road
Dawlish
EX7 0EB
Tel: 07966 585 213
Manager: Jeff Evans
Prog Editor:

Ground: Playing Fields, Sandy Lane, Exeter Rd, Dawlish EX7 0AF Tel: 01626 863 110
Capacity: 2,000 **Seats:** 200 **Covered:** 200
Midweek Matchday: Tuesday **Clubhouse:** Yes **Shop:**
Colours(change): Green & white/green/green (All blue)
Previous Names: Dawlish > 1983
Previous Lges: Devon & Exeter
Records: Att: 1,500 v Heavitee Utd
Senior Honours: Western Lge Div 1 Champions 05-06, Lg Cup 80-81, 83-84, 2007-08
Devon Premier Cup 69-70, 72-73, 80-81, Devon Snr Cup 57-58, 67-68, Devon St Lukes Cup 82-83, 2007-08

10 YEAR RECORD

99-00	00-01	01-02	02-03	03-04	04-05	05-06	06-07	07-08	08-09
WestP 9	WestP 11	WestP 6	WestP 13	WestP 17	West1 4	West1 1	WestP 10	WestP 2	WestP 4

HALLEN

Founded: 1949 Nickname:

Chairman: Barrie Phillips
Secretary: Charmaine Phillips
145a Station Road
Henbury
Bristol
BS10 7LZ
Tel: 07753 435 738
Manager: Gary Domone
Prog Editor:

Ground: Hallen Centre, Moorhouse Lane, Hallen Bristol BS10 7RU Tel: 0117 950 5559
Capacity: 2,000 **Seats:** 200 **Covered:** 200
Midweek Matchday: Wednesday **Clubhouse:** Yes **Shop:**
Colours(change): Royal blue & black/black/royal blue. (All yellow)
Previous Names: Lawrence Weston Ath, Lawrence Weston Hallen
Previous Lges: Glous Co lg, Hellenic
Records: Att: 803 v Bristol Rovers 1997
Senior Honours: Gloucestershire Co. Lge 1988-89, 92-93. Western Lge Div.1 03-04.

10 YEAR RECORD

99-00	00-01	01-02	02-03	03-04	04-05	05-06	06-07	07-08	08-09
Hel P 13	West1 4	West1 10	West1 4	West1 1	WestP 4	WestP 9	WestP 9	WestP 15	WestP 9

ILFRACOMBE TOWN

Founded: 1902 Nickname: Bluebirds

Chairman: Allan day
Secretary: Tony Alcock
2 Worth Road
Ilfracombe
Devon
EX34 9JA
Tel: 07973 469 673
Manager: Barry Yeo
Prog Editor:

Ground: Marlborough Park, Ilfracombe, Devon EX34 8PD Tel: 01271 865 939
Capacity: 2,000 **Seats:** 60 **Covered:** 450
Midweek Matchday: Tuesday **Clubhouse:** Yes **Shop:**
Colours(change): Blue & white/blue/blue. (Yellow/red/red)
Previous Names:
Previous Lges: North Devon, E Devon Premier, Exeter & Dist., Western,
Records: Att: 3,000 v Bristol City **Goalscorer:**Kevin Squire **App;** Bob Hancock 459
Senior Honours: E Devon Premier Lge, N. Devon Sen Lge, N. Devon Prem Lge.

10 YEAR RECORD

99-00	00-01	01-02	02-03	03-04	04-05	05-06	06-07	07-08	08-09
West1 11	West1 16	West1 14	West1 18	West1 16	West1 8	West1 4	West1 3	WestP 8	WestP 14

LARKHALL ATHLETIC

Founded: 1914 Nickname: Larks

Chairman: Jim McClay
Secretary: Garry Davy
84 London Road West
Bath
Somerset
BA1 7DA
Tel: 07942 445 498
Manager: Neil Kirkpatrick
Prog Editor:

Ground: Plain Ham, Charlcombe Lane, Larkhall, Bath BA1 8DJ Tel: 01225 334 952
Capacity: 1,000 **Seats:** Yes **Covered:** 50
Midweek Matchday: Wednesday **Clubhouse:** Yes **Shop:**
Colours(change): All Blue (All red)
Previous Names: None
Previous Lges: Somerset Senior
Records:
Senior Honours: Somerset Senior Cup 1975-76, Somerset Senior Champions.
Western Div 1 Champions 1988-89, 93-94, 94-95, 08-09.

10 YEAR RECORD

99-00	00-01	01-02	02-03	03-04	04-05	05-06	06-07	07-08	08-09
West1 9	West1 15	West1 12	West1 13	West1 8	West1 5	West1 7	West1 5	West1 3	West1 1

LONGWELL GREEN SPORTS

Founded: 1966 Nickname: The Green

Chairman: Chris Wyrill
Secretary: David Heal
4 Harptree Court
Longwell Green
Bristol
BS30 7AG
Tel: 07771 900 413
Manager: Julian Harmer
Prog Editor:

Ground: Longwell Green Com. Centre, Shellards Rd, BS30 9DW Tel: 0117 932 3722
Capacity: 1,000 **Seats:** Yes **Covered:** 100
Midweek Matchday: Tuesday **Clubhouse:** Yes **Shop:** Yes
Colours(change): Blue & white/black/black (All green)
Previous Names: None
Previous Lges: Gloucestershire County.
Records: Att: 500 v Mangotsfield 2005
Senior Honours:

10 YEAR RECORD

99-00	00-01	01-02	02-03	03-04	04-05	05-06	06-07	07-08	08-09
					GlCo 2	West1 12	West1 8	West1 8	West1 2

MELKSHAM TOWN

Founded: 1876 Nickname:

Chairman: Michael Perrin
Secretary: David Phillips
37 Duxford Close
Bowerhill
Melksham, Wilts
SN12 6XN
Tel: 07870 746 107
Manager: Wayne Thorne
Prog Editor:

Ground: The Conigre, Market Place, Melksham, SN12 6ES. Tel: 01225 702 843
Capacity: 1,500 **Seats:** 150 **Covered:** 600
Midweek Matchday: Monday **Clubhouse:** Yes **Shop:**
Colours(change): Yellow/black/black. (White/navy/navy)
Previous Names: None
Previous Lges: Wiltshire 1894-1974, 93-94, Western 74-93
Records: Att: 2,821 v Trowbridge Town FA Cup 57-58
Senior Honours: Wiltshire Shield (6) Western League Div 1 79-80,96-97, Wiltshire Senior Cup (4)

10 YEAR RECORD

99-00	00-01	01-02	02-03	03-04	04-05	05-06	06-07	07-08	08-09
WestP 6	WestP 9	WestP 10	WestP 8	WestP 14	WestP 14	WestP 14	WestP 5	WestP 11	WestP 11

RADSTOCK TOWN

Founded: 1895 Nickname:

Chairman: Paul Lewis
Secretary: Simon Wilkinson
46 Manor Park
Writhlington
Radstock
BA3 3NB
Tel: 07917 001 499
Manager: Nigel Bryant
Prog Editor:

Ground: Southfields Recreation Grd, Southfields, Radstock BA3 2NZ Tel: 01761 435 004
Capacity: 1,500 **Seats:** 80 **Covered:** yes
Midweek Matchday: Tuesday **Clubhouse:** Yes **Shop:** No
Colours(change): Red/black/red. (All Yellow)
Previous Names: Radstock.
Previous Lges: Somerset Senior League.
Records:
Senior Honours:

10 YEAR RECORD

99-00	00-01	01-02	02-03	03-04	04-05	05-06	06-07	07-08	08-09
SomP 10	SomP 5	SomP 7	SomP 10	SomP 3	West1 3	WestP 12	WestP 16	WestP 17	WestP 17

SHERBORNE TOWN

Founded: 1894 Nickname:

Chairman: Steve Paradise
Secretary: Colin Goodland
235 Larkhill Road
Yeovil
Somerset
BA21 3LL
Tel: 07929 090 612
Manager: Kevin Leigh
Prog Editor:

Ground: Raleigh Grove, Terrace Playing Field, Sherborne, DT9 5NS Tel: 01935 816 110
Capacity: **Seats:** Yes **Covered:** Yes
Midweek Matchday: Wednesday **Clubhouse:** Yes **Shop:**
Colours(change): Black & white/black/black. (Yellow/white/white).
Previous Names:
Previous Lges: Dorset Prem Lge
Records: Att: 1,000 v Eastleigh, Andy Shephard Memorial match 27.07.03.
Senior Honours: Dorset Prem Lge 81-82, Dorset Senior Cup 2003-04

10 YEAR RECORD

99-00	00-01	01-02	02-03	03-04	04-05	05-06	06-07	07-08	08-09
Dor P 16	Dor P 12	Dor P 2	Dor P 6	Dor P 5	Dor P 6	Dor P 2	West1 4	West1 2	WestP 12

STREET

Founded: 1880 Nickname: The Cobblers

Chairman: Mark Clarke
Secretary: Ms Melanie Dowden
6 Eileen Close
Street
Somerset
BA16 0SW
Tel: 07743 080 192
Manager: David Pople
Prog Editor:

Ground: The Tannery Ground, Middlebrooks, Street, BA16 0TA Tel: 01458 445 987
Capacity: 2,000 **Seats:** 120 **Covered:** 25
Midweek Matchday: Tuesday **Clubhouse:** Yes **Shop:**
Colours(change): White/green/white. (Red & white/red/red)
Previous Names: None
Previous Lges: Somerset Senior.
Records: Att; 4,300 v Yeovil Town FA Cup 47
Senior Honours: Somerset Senior League 1996-97.

10 YEAR RECORD

99-00	00-01	01-02	02-03	03-04	04-05	05-06	06-07	07-08	08-09
West1 8	West1 13	West1 8	West1 15	West1 12	West1 7	West1 3	WLaP 19	WestP 18	WestP 13

WELLINGTON TOWN

Founded: 1892 Nickname: Wellie

Chairman: Ken Bird
Secretary: Ken Pearson
6 Gables
Otterford
Chard
TA20 3QS
Tel: 07789 055 942
Manager: Warren Patmore
Prog Editor:

Ground: Wellington Playing Field, North St, Wellington, TA21 8NA Tel: 01749 679 971
Capacity: 3,000 **Seats:** none **Covered:** 200
Midweek Matchday: Wednesday **Clubhouse:** Yes **Shop:** No
Colours(change): Tangerine/black/tangerine (All blue)
Previous Names: None
Previous Lges: Taunton Saturday, Somerset Senior.
Records: Goalscorer: Ken Jones
Senior Honours: Western League Div.1 Champions 2007-08.

10 YEAR RECORD

99-00	00-01	01-02	02-03	03-04	04-05	05-06	06-07	07-08	08-09
West1 10	West1 14	West1 17	West1 12	West1 10	West1 14	West1 17	West1 7	West1 1	WestP 7

WELTON ROVERS

Founded: 1887 Nickname: Rovers

Chairman: Maurice Down
Secretary: Malcolm Price
18 Hayes Park Road
Midsomer Norton
Bath
BA3 2EW
Tel: 07970 791 644
Manager: Mark Harrington
Prog Editor:

Ground: West Clewes, North Road, Midsomer Norton BA3 2QD Tel: 01761 412 097
Capacity: 2,400 **Seats:** 300 **Covered:** 300
Midweek Matchday: Tuesday **Clubhouse:** Yes **Shop:** No
Colours(change): All green. (Yellow/blue/yellow).
Previous Names: None
Previous Lges: None
Records: Att: 2,000 v Bromley FA Am Cup 1963 **Goalscorer:** Ian Henderson 51
Senior Honours: Western Lge 1911-12, 64-65, 65-66, 66-67, 73-74. Div.1 59-60, 87-88.
Somerset Senior Cup (10)

10 YEAR RECORD

99-00	00-01	01-02	02-03	03-04	04-05	05-06	06-07	07-08	08-09
West1 2	WestP 10	WestP 18	WestP 16	WestP 8	WestP 17	WestP 4	WestP 15	WestP 9	WestP 8

WILLAND ROVERS

Founded: 1946 Nickname: Rovers

Chairman: Mike Mitchell
Secretary: Tony Baker
2 Burn Rew Farm
Dean Hill Road
Willand
EX15 3XD
Tel: 07788 758 711
Manager: Clive Jones
Prog Editor:

Ground: Silver Street, Willand, Collumpton, Devon EX15 2RG Tel: 01884 33885
Capacity: 2,000 **Seats:** 75 **Covered:** 150
Midweek Matchday: Tuesday **Clubhouse:** Yes **Shop:**
Colours(change): All White (Yellow/blue/yellow)
Previous Names: None.
Previous Lges: Devon County.
Records: Att: 650 v Newton Abbot 1992-3 **Goalscorer:** Paul Foreman
Senior Honours: Devon Co Lge 1998-99,00-01, Western Lge Div 1 2004-05,
Les Phillips Cup 2006-07

10 YEAR RECORD

99-00	00-01	01-02	02-03	03-04	04-05	05-06	06-07	07-08	08-09
Devon 7	Devon 1	West1 15	West1 7	West1 6	West1 1	WestP 6	WestP 6	WestP 3	WestP 3

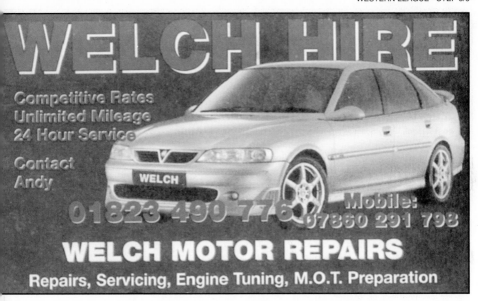

DIVISION ONE INS & OUTS	IN: Chard Town (R), Devizes Town (R) OUT: Larkhall Athletic (P), Longwell Green Sports (P)

ALMONDSBURY U.W.E.

Secretary: Douglas Coles. 156 Rodway Road, Patchway, Bristol BS34 5ED.
Tel: 07748 655 399.

Ground: The Field, Almondsbury, BS34 4AA.
Tel: 01454 612 240.

Directions: Exit M5 at Junction 16. Arriving from the south take the left exit lane. Turn left at lights and ground is 150m on right hand side. Arriving from east take right hand lane on slip road. Take 3rd exit nd ground is 150m on right hand side.

Clubhouse: Yes.

FACT FILE

Colours: White & green/white & green/white.

Change colours: All gold.

Midweek Matches: Tuesday

CLUB PERSONNEL

Chairman: Mike Blessing

Manager: Danny Phillips

BRADFORD TOWN

Chairman: Les Stevens. **Manager:** Paul Shanley.

Secretary: Nikki Akers. 26 Churches, Bradford-on-Avon, Wiltshire BA15 1RD. Tel: 07866 693 167.

GROUND ADDRESS: Bradford Sports Club, Trowbridge Road, Bradford on Avon Wiltshire BA15 1EW. Tel: 01225 866 649.

Simple Directions: On entering Bradford on Avon follow signs for A363 to Trowbridge. The ground is after a mini roundabout and behind a stone wall on the right.

Midweek Home Matchday: Tuesday.

Previous League: Wiltshire Senior.

Club Colours: Navy & sky blue/navy/navy & sky. **Change Colours:** Yellow/black/yellow.

BRIDPORT

Founded: 1885 **Nickname:** Bees

Chairman: Adrian Scadding. **Manager:** Ian Hutchinson

Secretary: Chris Tozer. 162 South Street, Bridport, Dorset DT6 3NP. Tel: 07500 064 317.

GROUND ADDRESS: The Beehive, St Mary's Field, Bridport, Dorset DT6 5LN. Tel: 01308 423 834.

Capacity: 2,000 **Seats:** 200 **Covered:** 400 **Floodlights:**Yes

Simple Directions: Take West Bay road from town centre and turn right judt before Palmers Brewery

Midweek Home Matchday: Tuesday **Clubhouse:** Matchdays and functions **Club Shop:** No

Previous League: Perry Street, Western 61-84 Dorset Combination 84-89

Club Colours: Red & black/black/red **Change Colours:** All blue.

RECORD Attendance: 1,150 v Exeter City 1981 **Goalscorer: (in season)** Ellis Hoole 36

Fee Paid: £1,000 for Steve Crabb **Fee Received:** £2,000 for Tommy Henderson.

Senior Honours: Dorset Senior Cup (8) Dorset Sènior Amateur Cup (6)

CADBURY HEATH

Secretary: Martin Painter, 44 Chesterfield Road, Downend, Bristol BS16 5RQ
Tel No: 0117 949 2844

Ground: Springfield, Cadbury Hearg Road, Bristol BS30 8BX
Tel No: 0117 967 5731 (Social Club)

Directions: M5 & M4 to M32 Exit 1 to Ring Road. Left to Cadbury Heath at roudabout. Then right into Tower Road North and left at mini roundabout. Turn right into Cadbury Heath Road after 150 metres. Ground is on right via Cadbury Heath Social Club Car park.

Clubhouse: Yes

PREVIOUS **League:** Gloucestershire County Lge.

HONOURS Glos. County Lge 98-99, R-up 99-00.

FACT FILE
Colours: All red.
Change colours: Yellow/blue/blue.
Midweek Matches: Wednesday

CLUB PERSONNEL
Chairman: Steve Plenty
Manager: Lee Knighton

CHARD TOWN

Chairman: Brian Beer. **Manager:** Ian Burns.

Secretary: Michael Hawes, 18 Norrington Way, Chard, Somerset TA20 2JP. Tel: 07906 904 138 (M)

Programme: Yes.

Ground: Dening Sports Field, Zembard Lane, Chard TA20 1JL Tel: 01460 61402

Capacity: 1,500 Seats: 60 Cover: 200 Floodlights: Yes

Directions: Follow sports centre signs off main A30 High Street along Helliers Road. Right into Upper Combe Street and left into Zembard Lane. BR 7miles Axminster or 8 miles Crewkerne.

Midweek Home Matchday: Tuesday. **Clubhouse:** Matchdays & most evenings. Snacks served.

Colours: Red/white/white. **Change:** White/blue/blue.

PREVIOUS Leagues: Somerset Senior 1920-24, 48-75; Perry Street 1925-48. **Grounds:** None

HONOURS: Som. Snr Lg 49-50 53-54 59-60 67-68 69-70 (Lg Cup 61-62 71-72 76-77); Western Lg Div 1 R-up 83-84 87-88 95-96 05-06, (Merit Cup 82-83, Comb. Cup(Res) 91-92 (R-up 92-93)); Som. Snr Cup 52-53 66-67; S W Co's Cup 88-89; Western Com Lge 96-97, Cup 96-97.

CLEVEDON UNITED

Secretary: Colin Clarke. 49 Hillside Road Portishead Nr BRISTOL N Somerset BS20 8JW
Tel: 07768 525 670

GROUND The Hand Stadium, Clevedon, North Somerset BS20 6TG
Tel: 01275 871 600.

Directions: Junction 20 M5. At bottom roundabout turn right at Tesco roundabout turn left. Continue along road and cross river bridge, turn left into Davis Lane. Continue along Davis Lane for approximately 3/4 mile, ground is on right.

Capacity: 3,650 Seats: 300 Cover: 1,600 Floodlights: Yes

Clubhouse: Yes in which clubs mementoes are also sold.

PREVIOUS **League:** Somerset County League >2003

RECORD **Attendance:** 420

HONOURS Somerset County Lge Prem. Div 98-99

FACTFILE
Founded: 1970
Colours: Red/black/red.
Change: Yellow/blue/yellow.
Midweek Matchday: Wednesday

CLUB PERSONNEL
Chairman: Colin Clarke
Managers: Alan Smith

DEVIZES TOWN

Chairman: Shaun Moffat. **Manager:** Kev Whitbread

Secretary: Andy Muckle. 3 Siwian Cottages, Old Road, Studley, Calne, Wiltshire SN11 9ND. Tel: 07505 007 498.

Programme: Price £1.00 **Editor:** Andy Muckle & Becky Marshall.

GROUND ADDRESS: Nursteed Road, Devizes SN10 3DX. Tel: 01380 722 817.

Capcity: 2,500 **Seats:** 370 **Covered:** 400 **Floodlights:** Yes

Simple Directions: Off Nursteed Road (A 342 signposted Andover) town ground on right opposite Eastleigh Road.

Midweek Home Matchday: Tuesday **Clubhouse:** Open daily with function room and Sky TV Club **Shop:** In club

Previous Name: Southbroom (until early 1900s) **Previous League(s):** Wilts Combination and Wilts Premier

Club Colours: Red & white/black/red. **Change Colours:** Blue & white/blue/blue.

BEST PERFORMANCE - League: 5th Western Premier 2002-01.

Senior Honours: Western Div 1 1999-00. Wiltshire Senior Cup (14).

ELMORE

Secretary: Neville Crocker, Rivercroft,4 Little Silver, Tiverton, Devon EX16 4PH Tel: 07814 923 708.

Ground: Horsdon Park, Tiverton, Devon EX16 4DB Tel: 01884 252 341

Directions: M5 Jct 27, A373 towards Tiverton, leave at first sign for Tiverton & Business Park. Ground is 500yds on right.

Capacity: 2,000 **Seats**: 200 **Cover:** 200 **Floodlights:** Yes

Clubhouse: 11am-11pm Mon-Sat. Full canteen service - hot & cold meals & snacks

Club Shop: Yes

HONOURS East Devon Snr Cup 72-73 75-76, Western Lge R-up 94-95. Lge Cup 90-91 94-95, Div 1 R-up 90-91, Prem Div Merit Cup R-up 91-92, Div 1 Merit Cup 86-87 89-90 90-91, Devon St Lukes Cup R-up 90-91, Devon Snr Cup 87-88, Devon Intermediate Cup 60-61, Football Express Cup 60-61, Devon & Exeter Div 2A 73-74 86-87(res)(Div 1A 76-77(res)), Devon Yth Cup 77-78.

PREVIOUS **Leagues:** Devon & Exeter 47-74; South Western 74-78 Grounds: None

RECORD **Attendance:** 1,713 v Tiverton Town Fri.April 14th 95
Appearances: P Webber **Win:** 17-0 **Defeat:** 2-7

FACT FILE
Founded: 1947
Nickname: Eagles
Colours: All Green
Change colours: Red & white/red/red
Midweek matches: Wednesday

CLUB PERSONNEL
Chairman: Alan J Cockram
Manager: Simon Harder & Mike Taylor

GILLINGHAM TOWN

Chairman: David Graham.

Secretary: Terry Lucas. 43 Fern Brook Lane, Gillingham, Dorset SP8 4FL. Tel: 07873 587 455

Manager: Adrian Foster.

Ground: Hardings Lane, Gillingham SP8 4HX. Tel: 01747 823 673

Directions: Proceed to middle of town to the High Street. Hardings Lane is a turning off of the High Street, at the Shaftesbury or Southern end of the High Street.

PREVIOUS **Leagues:** Dorset Premier.

FACT FILE
Colours: All tangerine
Change colours: Navy &sky/navy/sky
Midweek matches: Tuesday

HENGROVE ATHLETIC

Chairman: Paul Hynam.

Secretary: Graham Whittaker. 18 Hengrove Avenue, Hengrove, Bristol BS14 9TB. Tel: 07970 848 285.

Manager: Jamie Hillman.

Ground: Norton Lane, Whitchurch, Bristol BS14 0BT. Tel: 01275 832 894

Directions: Take A37 from Bristol through Whitchurch village past Maes Knoll pub, over hump bridge taking next turning on right, which is Norton Lane. Ground is immediately after Garden Centre.

HONOURS Somerset County Premier Division 2005-06.
Somserset Senior Cup 1979-80.

PREVIOUS **Leagues:** Bristol Suburban League 1948-74, Somerset County League 74-06.

FACT FILE
Founded: 1948
Colours: Green & white/black/black
Change colours: Yellow/green/green
Midweek matches: Tuesday

KEYNSHAM TOWN

Founded: 1895
Nickname: K's

Chairman: Steve Nicholls **Manager:** Stuart Nethercott

Secretary: John Peake, 27 Orwell Drive, Keynsham, Bristol BS31 1QB. Tel: 07704 340 170.

GROUND ADDRESS: Crown Fields, Bristol Road, Keynsham, Bristol BS31 2DZ. **Ground Tel.No:** 01179 986 5876.

Capacity: 2,000 **Seats:** 72 **Covered:** 170 **Floodlights:** Yes **Club Shop:** No

Simple Directions: Ground is on A4175 off Bristol to Bath A4. On left immediately after 30mph sign.

Midweek Home Matchday: Tuesday **Clubhouse:** Matchdays and some evenings

Previous Leagues: Bristol & District, Bristol Comb., Bristol Premier and Somerset Senior.

Club Colours: Gold/black/gold. **Change Colours:** White/blue/white.

Senior Honours: Somerset Senior Cup 51-52 57-58 02-03

MINEHEAD TOWN

Secretary: Trish Hill, 10 Warden Road, Minehead, Somerset TA24 5DS. Tel No: 07790 299 760.
Ground: The Recreation Ground, Irnham Road, Minehead, Somerset TA24 5DP.
Tel: 07816 923 171.
Directions: Entering town from east on A39 turn right into King Edward Road at Police station, first left into Alexandra Rd and follow signs to car park;ground entrance within. Regular buses to Minehead from Taunton, the nearestrailhead. (Steam train 'holiday route' Taunton to Minehead)
Capacity: 3,500 Seats: 350 Cover: 400 Floodlights: Yes
Clubhouse: Yes **Club Shop:** No
HONOURS Southern Lg R-up 76-77, Div 1 Sth 75-76, Merit Cup 75-76; Western Lg R-up 66-67 71-72, Div 1 90-91 98-99, Alan Young Cup 67-68 (jt with Glastonbury),Somerset Premier Cup 60-61 73-74 76-77.
PREVIOUS **Leagues:** Somerset Senior; Southern 72-83.
RECORD **Attendance:** 3,600 v Exeter City, FA Cup 2nd Rd, 77
BEST SEASON FA Cup: 2nd Rd 76-77, 1-2 v Portsmouth (A); 77-78, 0-3 v Exeter City (H)

FACT FILE
Founded: 1889
Colours: All Blue
Change colours: All Yellow
Midweek Matches: Wednesday
Programme: Yes

CLUB PERSONNEL
Chairman: Brian Walder
Manager: Robert Boyd & Gary Hillard

ODD DOWN

Founded: 1901

Chairman: Dave Loxton. **Manager:** Lee Burns.

Secretary: Lorraine Brown. 18 Albert Avenue, Peasedown St John, Bath, BA2 8JB. Tel: 07734 924 435.

Programme: Yes

GROUND ADDRESS: Lew Hill Memorial Ground, Combe Hay Lane, Odd Down BA2 8AP. Tel: 01225 832 491.

Capacity: 1.000 **Seats:** 160 **Covered:** 250 **Floodlights:** Yes

Simple Directions: Ground is behind the Park & Ride car park on main A367 in Odd Down.

Midweek Home Matchday: Tuesday **Clubhouse:** Open Matchdays. **Club Shop:** No

Previous Leagues: Wilts Premier. Bath & District and Somerset Senior

Club Colours: Blue & black/black/black. **Change Colours:** White & blue/blue/yellow.

RECORD Appearances: Steve Fuller 475 **Goalscorer:** Joe Matano 104.

Victory: 11-1 v Minehead (H) Western Prem 19.03.94.

OLDLAND ABBOTONIANS

Chairman: Andrew Thresher. **Manager**: Spencer Thomas.

Secretary: Derek Jones. 161 Talbot Road, Brislington, Bristol BS4 2NZ. Tel: 07836 648 327.

GROUND ADDRESS: Aitchison Playing Field, Castle Road, Oldland Common BS30 9PP. Tel: 0117 932 8263.

Simple Directions: Exit M4 at Jct19 to M32. Exit M32 at Jct 1after 400 yds and take 1st exit from roundabout for A4174. Straight over traffic lights to next roundabout continuing on A4174. Go over five roundabouts for approximately 4.8 miles. At next roundabout take 1st exit to Deanery Road (A420) and continue for 0.9 miles to Griffin Public house and turn right into Bath Road (A4175) . Continue for 1.3 miles to Oldland Common High Street and look for Dolphin Public House.
Turning for Castle Street is next left between Chinese Chip Shop and Post Office. Ground is at the end of Castle Road.

Midweek Home Matchday: Wednesday.

Previous Leagues: Somerset County.

Club Colours: Blue & white/blue/blue. **Change Colours:** All yellow.

Honours: Les Phillips Cup 2008-09.

PORTISHEAD TOWN

Founded: 1910
Nickname: Posset

Chairman: Bob Parsons. **Manager**: Dave Willis.

Secretary: Brian Hobbs, 13 St Peters Road, Portsihead, Bristol BS20 6QY. Tel: 07791 412 724.

Programme: Yes.

GROUND ADDRESS: Bristol Road, Portishead, Bristol BS20 6QG. Tel: 01275 817 600.

Capacity: 1,000 **Seats:** None **Covered:**150 **Floodlights:** No

Simple Directions: Follow A369 to Portishead and at outskirts of town take first exit left at roundabout. Ground is about 150 yards on left.

Midweek Home Matchday: Tuesday. **Clubhouse:** Yes.

Previous Names: Portishead. **Leagues:** Somerset County

Club Colours: White/black/black. **Change Colours:** All Blue.

Honours: Champions Somerset County League 2004-05.

ROMAN GLASS ST GEORGE

Chairman: Roger Hudd. **Manager**: Roger Hudd.

Secretary: Mrs Emily Baldwin. 21 Brook Road Mangotsfield Bristol BS16 9DX Tel: 07708 277 592.

GROUND ADDRESS: Whiteway Road, St George, Bristol BS5 7RP. Tel: 0117 983 7707.

Simple Directions: Leave M32 at Jct 2, turn left to mini-roundabout, left into Fishponds Road. At traffic lights turn right into Royate Hill, under viaduct and rail bridge to end of road, turn left at lights into Whitehall Road, straight on at mini-roundabout and take next right into Plummers Hill. At end of road turn left into Clouds Hill Road, take third turning left approximately 1/4 mile (Worlds End pub on corner), up hill until road levels out, turn right into lane between houses No 168 - 170. Ground at end of lane.

Midweek Home Matchday: Tuesday .

Club Colours: White/black/white. **Change Colours:** All red.

Previous Leagues: Gloucestershire County.

Honours: Gloucestershire County League Champions 2006-07.

SHEPTON MALLET

Secretary: Gary Banfield. 50 Barrington Place, Shepton Mallet, Somerset BA4 5GH. Tel: 07762 880 705.

Ground: The Playing Fields, Old Wells Rd., West Shepton, Shepton Mallett, Somerset BA4 5XN Tel: 01749 344 609

Capacity: 2500 **Covered Seating:** 120 **Floodlights:** Yes

Directions: Take the Glastonbury road from Shepton Mallett town centre then turn right at the

junction with Old Wells Rd (approx. 1/2 mile, near the "King William" P.H.) - the ground is 300 yards on the left.

Clubhouse: Yes, open match days

Previous League: Somerset Senior.

HONOURS Somerset Senior League 2000-01

CLUB RECORDS Attendance: 274 v Chippenham Town F.A.Cup 2000-01.

FACT FILE
Founded: 1986
Colours: Black & white/black/red
Change colours: Claret/white/yellow
Midweek matchday: Tuesday
Programme : Yes

CLUB PERSONNEL
Chairman: John Hugill.
Manager: Keith Brown.

SHREWTON UNITED

Secretary: Paul Robinson. 4 Brocks Orchard Shrewton Salisbury, SP3 4JG Tel: 07786 802 688.

Ground: Recreation Ground, Mill Lane, Shrewton, Wiltshire SP3 4JY. Tel: 07786 802 688.

Directions: From A303 left at Winterbourne Stoke and left at The Royal Oak. Then turn right at mini roundabout on outskirts of village, and then turn left at the George Inn and follow Football Club signs. From Devizes A360 turn leftt at mini roundabout on outskirts of village, and then turn left at the George Inn and follow Football Club signs.

PREVIOUS **League:** Wiltshire League >2003

HONOURS Wiltshire Lge Prem Div. 2001-02 02-03, R-up 00-01, Lge Senior Cup 01-02 02-03

FACT FILE
Colours: Maroon & royal/navy/navy
Change Colours: Maroon & sky/sky/sky
Midweek Matchday: Tuesday
Programme: Yes

CLUB PERSONNEL
Chairman: Dougy Hill.
Manager: Stuart Withers.

WELLS CITY

Secretary: Steve Vowles. 47 Keward Avenue WELLS Someset BA5 1TS

Tel: 07727 091 317.

Ground: Athletic Ground, Rowdens Road, Wells, Someset BA5 1TU

Tel: 01749 679971

Directions: From North & Southwest - Follow A39 to Strawberry Way to roundabout, follow A371 East Somerset Way and take right turn into Rowdens Road. Ground is on left. From East - Follow A371 from Shepton Mallet. After approximately 5 miles on East Somerset Way take left turn into Rowdens Road. Ground is on left.

PREVIOUS **Leagues:** Somerset County.

FACT FILE
Colours: Blue/blue/white
Change Colours: All white
Midweek Matches: Tuesday

CLUB PERSONNEL
Chairman: Stephen Loxton.
Manager: Tim Moxey.

WESTBURY UNITED

Secretary: Roger Arnold. 4 Bramble Drive, Westbury, Wilts BA13 3UY. Tel: 07919 380 911.
Ground: Meadow Lane, Westbury BA13 3AF. Tel: 01373 823 409.
Directions: In town centre, A350, follow signs for BR station, Meadow Lane on right (club signposted). Ten mins walk from railway station (on main London-South West and South Coast-Bristol lines).
Capacity: 3,500 Seats: 150 Cover: 150 Floodlights: Yes
Clubhouse: Evenings 7-11pm, Fri, Sat & Sun lunchtimes 12-3pm Club Shop: No
HONOURS Western Lg Div 1 91-92, Wilts Senior Cup 31-32 32-33 47-48 51-52, Wilts Combination, Wilts Lg 34-35 37-38 38-39 49-50 50-51 55-56, Wilts Premier Shield R-up 92-93
PREVIOUS **Leagues:** Wilts Comb.; Wilts Co. (pre-1984)
Ground: Redland Lane (pre-1935)
RECORD Gate: 4,000 - v Llanelli, FA Cup 1st Rd 37 & v Walthamstow Ave. FA Cup 37
Players progressing: John Atyeo (Bristol City)

FACT FILE
Formed: 1921
Nickname: White Horsemen
Colours: Green& white/green/green
Change Colours: Navy & gold/navy/navy
Midweek Matches: Tuesday
Programme: Yes

CLUB PERSONNEL
Chairman: Phillip Alford.
Manager: Paul Brickley.

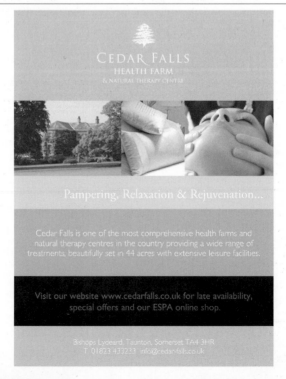

ANGLIAN COMBINATION LEAGUE

www.angliancombination.org.uk

Sponsored by:

Dolphin Autos

Founded: 1964

Recent champions:

2004: Cromer Town

2005: Blofield United

2006: Cromer Town

2007: Blofield United

2008: Wroxham Res.

Premier Division		**P**	**W**	**D**	**L**	**F**	**A**	**Pts**
Sheringham		**30**	**20**	**4**	**6**	**70**	**36**	**64**
Blofield United		**30**	**18**	**6**	**6**	**82**	**49**	**60**
Acle United		**30**	**15**	**10**	**5**	**65**	**37**	**55**
Cromer Town		**30**	**17**	**4**	**9**	**57**	**38**	**55**
Loddon United		**30**	**14**	**9**	**7**	**48**	**37**	**51**
Hempnall		**30**	**13**	**7**	**10**	**40**	**41**	**46**
North Walsham Town		**30**	**13**	**4**	**13**	**62**	**54**	**43**
Brandon Town		**30**	**11**	**7**	**12**	**56**	**52**	**40**
Beccles Town		**30**	**11**	**6**	**13**	**43**	**44**	**39**
Dersingham Rovers		**30**	**12**	**3**	**15**	**52**	**60**	**39**
Sprowston Athletic		**30**	**10**	**8**	**12**	**37**	**44**	**38**
AFC Norwich		**30**	**10**	**6**	**14**	**48**	**55**	**36**
Wroxham Res.	***-1***	**30**	**9**	**7**	**14**	**36**	**50**	**33**
Watton United		**30**	**8**	**5**	**17**	**50**	**70**	**29**
Hindringham		**30**	**8**	**2**	**20**	**51**	**90**	**26**
Holt United		**30**	**4**	**6**	**20**	**28**	**68**	**18**

	AFC Norwich	Acle United	Beccles Town	Blofield United	Brandon Town	Cromer Town	Dersingham R.	Hempnall	Hindringham	Holt United	Loddon United	North Walsham	Sheringham	Sprowston Ath.	Watton United	Wroxham Res.
AFC Norwich	***P***	2-4	2-1	2-1	2-8	0-2	2-1	1-3	6-3	1-0	1-3	3-4	1-3	1-1	5-4	3-0
Acle United	1-0	***R***	3-4	1-2	2-1	2-2	3-1	1-1	4-1	1-1	0-0	4-0	0-0	1-0	1-1	4-0
Beccles Town	0-0	1-2	***E***	1-2	3-0	0-1	0-0	1-0	4-2	2-0	1-1	4-1	2-3	4-1	2-4	0-1
Blofield United	1-1	2-6	2-3	***M***	3-0	4-1	2-1	2-0	2-4	8-0	3-3	3-2	3-3	5-2	2-1	5-0
Brandon Town	3-2	3-3	2-0	3-3	***I***	3-1	1-2	0-2	8-4	3-1	1-1	1-0	0-4	0-1	2-2	2-0
Cromer Town	3-1	2-0	1-1	3-3	1-0	***E***	4-1	1-1	2-0	5-1	0-1	2-0	0-4	2-0	1-3	2-1
Dersingham Rovers	2-0	1-2	2-0	0-3	0-4	2-0	***R***	2-0	3-4	3-4	1-4	2-3	2-4	2-0	6-2	W-L
Hempnall	1-0	1-3	4-1	1-0	3-2	0-5	1-2		2-2	3-0	0-0	1-0	1-2	2-2	2-1	3-0
Hindringham	0-4	0-4	2-3	0-3	1-2	1-2	4-2	0-2	***D***	3-1	2-4	0-5	1-3	1-3	4-3	3-0
Holt United	0-2	0-3	0-1	0-3	2-2	1-3	1-1	0-2	0-3	***I***	4-1	1-2	2-0	1-1	0-3	1-2
Loddon United	0-0	4-1	2-1	2-0	0-2	0-4	2-0	3-0	4-1	0-0	***V***	4-0	2-3	2-1	2-0	0-0
North Walsham Town	1-0	3-3	2-0	0-1	1-1	3-1	2-4	2-0	5-2	3-0	6-0	***I***	2-2	0-1	6-1	2-2
Sheringham	2-1	3-1	0-1	1-4	4-0	0-1	3-4	6-1	2-0	2-1	0-0	2-3	***S***	2-1	3-1	1-0
Sprowston Athletic	0-0	1-1	2-0	1-1	1-0	1-5	3-2	0-0	0-1	1-1	1-2	4-1	1-3	***I***	0-3	2-0
Watton United	1-3	0-4	1-1	4-5	2-2	2-0	1-2	1-2	2-2	1-4	1-0	1-0	0-4	0-2	***O***	1-2
Wroxham Res.	2-2	0-0	1-1	3-4	1-0	2-0	1-1	1-1	5-0	3-1	3-1	4-3	0-1	1-3	1-3	***N***

ANGLIAN COMBINATION PREMIER DIVISION CONSTITUTION 2009-10

CLE UNITED . . . . Bridewell Lane, Acle, Norwich NR13 3RA 01493 752989
ECCLES TOWN . . . . College Meadow, Common Lane, Beccles NR34 7FA 07729 782817
LOFIELD UNITED . . . . Old Yarmouth Road, Blofield, Norwich NR13 4LE 07748 863203
RANDON TOWN . . . . Remembrance Playing Field, Church Road, Brandon IP27 0JB 01842 813177
ROMER TOWN . . . . Cabbell Park, Mill Road, Cromer NR27 0AD 01263 512185
ERSINGHAM ROVERS . . . . . Behind Feathers Hotel, Manor Road, Dersingham, King's Lynn PE31 6LN 01485 542707
EMPNALL . . . . Bungay Road, Hempnall, Norwich NR15 2NG 01508 498086
ODDON UNITED . . . . George Lane Playing Field, Loddon, Norwich NR14 6NB 01508 528497
ATTISHALL . . . . Mattishall Playing Fields, South Green, Mattishall, Norwich NR20 3JY 01362 850246
ORTH WALSHAM TOWN . . . . Sports Centre, Greens Road, North Walsham NR28 0HW 01692 406888
HERINGHAM . . . . Recreation Ground, Weybourne Road, Sheringham NR26 8WD 01263 824804
PIXWORTH UNITED . . . . Spixworth Village Hall, Crostick Lane, Spixworth, Norwich NR10 3NQ 01603 898092
PROWSTON ATHLETIC . . Sprowston Sports & Social Club, Blue Boar Lane, Sprowston, Norwich NR7 8RJ 01603 427688
T ANDREWS . . . . Thorpe Recreation Ground, Laundry Lane, Thorpe St Andrew, Thorpe NR7 0XQ 01603 300316
ATTON UNITED . . . . Watton Playing Field, Dereham Road, Watton, Thetford IP25 6EZ 01953 881281
ROXHAM RESERVES . . . . Trafford Park, Skinners Lane, Wroxham NR12 8SJ 01603 783538

I: Mattishall (P), St Andrews (P)
UT: Hindringham (R), Holt United (R)
FC Norwich become Spixworth United

DON FROST MEMORIAL CUP

(Premier Division champions v Mummery Cup holders)

(August 15th at Bungay Town)

Wroxham Res. 0 **Hempnall** 3

Division One		P	W	D	L	F	A	Pts
St Andrews		28	20	0	8	61	38	60
Mattishall		28	17	7	4	89	47	58
Kirkley & Pakefield Res.		28	17	4	7	79	33	55
Corton		28	16	4	8	56	31	52
Horsford United		28	16	3	9	79	55	51
Bungay Town		28	13	6	9	44	32	45
Wymondham Town		28	13	5	10	53	51	44
Caister		28	11	5	12	50	57	38
Stalham Town		28	10	6	12	42	62	36
Wells Town		28	7	8	13	28	45	29
Sole Bay		28	8	4	16	38	70	28
Scole United		28	7	6	15	44	68	27
Long Stratton		28	8	2	18	49	63	26
Gayton United	*-2*	28	7	6	15	41	69	25
Attleborough Town		28	5	4	19	42	74	19

MUMMERY CUP

(Premier Division and Division One teams)

FIRST ROUND

Acle United 4 Scole Utd 0
(at Scole United)

Attleborough Town 0 **Loddon United** 4

Blofield 4 Wells Town 1

Brandon 2 **Sheringham** 7

Bungay Town 3 **Dersingham Rovers** 4

Cromer Town 0 **Stalham Town** 0 *aet* (2-4p)

Gayton Utd 6 Mattishall 2

Hempnall 1 **Corton** 4

Hindringham 0 **North Walsham Town** 2

Horsford United 5 Wroxham Res. 2

Long Stratton 1 **Kirkley & Pakefield Res.** 2

Sole Bay 0 **Holt United** 6

Sprowston Ath 3 Caister 2

St Andrews 1 **Beccles T.** 3

Wymondham Town 2 AFC Norwich 1

SECOND ROUND

Acle United 0 **Loddon United** 0 *aet* (3-4p)

Beccles Town 2 Horsford United 0

Blofield 3 Holt United 0

Gayton 0 **Stalham Town** 2

Kirkley Res. 0 **Corton** 2

Sheringham 4 North Walsham Town 1

Sprowston Athletic 1 **Wymondham Town** 1 *aet* (4-5p)

Watton United 2 **Dersingham Rovers** 4

QUARTER-FINALS

Beccles Town 3 Stalham 1

Blofield 2 Loddon United 0

Dersingham Rovers 2 Sheringham 1

Wymondham Town 1 **Corton** 2

SEMI-FINALS

Beccles Town 2 Corton 0

Dersingham Rovers 0 **Blofield United** 4

FINAL

(May 4th at Wroxham)

Blofield United 4 Beccles Town 0

	Attleborough Town	Bungay Town	Caister	Corton	Gayton United	Horsford United	Kirkley/Pakefield Res.	Long Stratton	Mattishall	Scole United	Sole Bay	St Andrews	Stalham Town	Wells Town	Wymondham Town
Attleborough Town		1-2	0-4	0-3	1-3	1-2	1-5	3-2	1-1	1-5	0-0	2-3	3-4	2-1	7-0
Bungay Town	3-2	***D***	2-0	1-0	2-2	2-2	0-1	2-3	2-1	0-1	1-1	2-1	0-0	0-1	1-2
Caister	1-1	0-3	***I***	0-2	W-L	1-3	0-5	3-2	3-6	3-2	2-1	0-1	2-2	0-1	1-2
Corton	1-3	1-0	0-1	***V***	2-0	2-0	0-0	2-0	1-3	2-0	4-2	1-2	4-1	4-0	1-2
Gayton United	3-1	1-5	0-3	4-4	***I***	1-4	1-5	2-1	0-5	1-1	9-3	0-3	0-3	2-2	2-1
Horsford United	5-4	0-2	4-4	4-0	5-0	***S***	2-5	3-2	4-1	2-2	5-0	3-6	6-3	1-0	7-3
Kirkley & Pakefield Res.	6-0	2-0	2-4	1-1	11-0	5-0	***I***	4-0	1-4	8-4	1-2	1-0	4-0	2-0	2-0
Long Stratton	4-0	2-1	1-1	0-5	1-2	1-6	0-0	***O***	1-5	4-1	4-2	6-2	2-4	1-2	0-2
Mattishall	1-0	2-4	2-2	5-1	2-2	1-0	4-1	2-0	***N***	5-1	6-1	5-4	4-0	6-2	2-2
Scole United	2-4	1-2	2-1	0-2	W-L	0-2	2-1	0-3	5-5		5-2	2-4	1-2	1-0	0-4
Sole Bay	3-2	1-2	1-4	0-5	W-L	2-1	3-1	0-5	2-2	2-2		0-3	2-0	0-1	1-0
St Andrews	3-0	1-0	5-1	1-4	1-0	0-1	0-1	1-0	0-3	2-0	2-1	***O***	4-2	3-1	2-1
Stalham Town	2-0	0-0	1-3	0-2	0-4	4-2	2-0	2-1	2-3	2-2	0-6	0-4	***N***	0-0	1-1
Wells Town	3-0	1-1	0-4	0-0	2-2	0-3	1-2	4-2	1-1	1-1	2-0	1-2	0-1	***E***	1-1
Wymondham Town	2-2	2-4	6-2	1-2	1-0	3-2	2-2	2-1	4-2	3-1	1-0	0-1	2-4	3-0	

ANGLIAN COMBINATION DIVISION ONE CONSTITUTION 2009-10

BUNGAY TOWN.................... Maltings Meadow, Ditchingham, Bungay NR35 2RU...................... 01986 8940
CAISTER .... Caister Playing Fields, off Allendale Road, Caister-on-Sea NR30 5ES.................. Nor
CORTON............................ The Street, Corton, Lowestoft NR32 5HE .... Nor
HINDRINGHAM............... Sports & Social Club, Wells Rd, Hindringham, Fakenham NR21 0PN 01328 8786
HOLT UNITED .... Sports Centre, Kelling Road, Holt NR25 7DU......................... 01263 7112
HORSFORD UNITED.................. Village Hall, Holt Road, Horsford NR10 3DN.................. 01603 8933
KIRKLEY & PAKEFIELD RESERVES Kirkley & Pakefield Comm Centre, Walmer Road, Lowestoft NR33 7LE 01502 5135
LONG STRATTON............... Manor Road Playing Fields, Long Stratton, Norwich NR15 2XR .... Nor
NORWICH ST JOHNS......... Cringleford Recreation Ground, Oakfields Road, Cringleford NR4 6XE......... Nor
PORINGLAND WANDERERS . Poringland Memorial Field, The Footpath, Poringland, Norwich NR14 7RF.............. 01508 4951
REEPHAM TOWN .... Stimpson's Piece Rec Ground, Bartle Court, Reepham, Norwich NR10 4LL.......... Nor
SCOLE UNITED...................... Ransome Avenue Playing Field, Scole, Diss IP21 4EA...................... 01379 7412
SOLE BAY UNITED .... Reydon High School, Wangford Road, Reydon, Southwold IP18 6QA........... Nor
STALHAM TOWN .... Rivers Park, Stepping Stone Lane, Stalham, Norwich NR12 9EP............... Nor
WELLS TOWN .... Beach Road, Wells-next-the-Sea NR23 1DR........................ 01328 7109
WYMONDHAM TOWN .... Kings Head Meadow, Back Lane, Wymondham NR18 0LB 01953 6073

IN: Hindringham (R), Holt United (R), Norwich St Johns (P), Poringland Wanderers (P), Reepham Town (P)
OUT: Attleborough Town (R), Gayton United (R), Mattishall (P), St Andrews (P)

ivision Two		P	W	D	L	F	A	Pts
orwich St Johns		28	24	1	3	99	27	73
eepham Town		28	23	1	4	79	28	70
oringland Wanderers		28	17	2	9	70	48	53
ellesdon		28	16	3	9	72	43	51
orwich CEYMS		28	15	3	10	72	53	48
reat Yarmouth Town Res.		28	14	3	11	66	63	45
nglian Windows		28	12	4	12	59	76	40
/est Lynn SSC		28	11	6	11	56	65	39
eccles Caxton		28	11	3	14	68	56	36
cle United Res.	-1	28	10	6	12	51	59	35
orwich United Res.		28	9	2	17	63	74	29
/ortwell		28	8	3	17	33	64	27
ownham Town Res.	-1	28	5	7	16	37	65	21
prowston Wanderers		28	5	5	18	52	94	20
akenham Town Res.		28	4	3	21	41	103	15

Oulton Broad & Notleys - record expunged

C S MORLEY CUP

(Anglian Combination club reserve teams)

FINAL

(March 25th at Holt United)

Acle United Res. 1 Sprowston Athletic Res. 1 *aet* (4-3p)

	Acle United Res.	Anglian Windows	Beccles Caxton	Downham Town Res.	Fakenham Town Res.	Great Yarmouth Town Res.	Hellesdon	Norwich CEYMS	Norwich St Johns	Norwich United Res.	Oulton Broad & Notleys	Poringland Wanderers	Reepham Town	Sprowston Wanderers	West Lynn SSC	Wortwell
Acle United Res.		3-0	1-1	5-3	8-1	0-3	2-2	2-2	2-4	5-3	n/a	6-0	1-3	2-0	0-0	1-1
Anglian Windows	3-3		3-2	7-1	3-2	3-3	0-4	1-2	0-7	3-0	8-3	1-3	3-2	1-0	1-1	2-1
Beccles Caxton	4-0	2-4	***D***	4-0	7-1	4-1	0-1	1-3	0-1	5-6	3-1	2-0	2-3	2-2	9-2	0-1
Downham Town Res.	0-1	2-0	0-0	***I***	3-2	2-3	0-1	2-2	1-0	0-4	0-0	0-2	1-3	2-2	3-3	5-0
Fakenham Town Res.	2-3	4-4	1-2	0-0	***V***	2-3	2-5	5-3	0-4	1-4	1-2	1-3	2-1	2-3	1-8	0-1
Great Yarmouth Town Res.	1-2	5-1	1-3	3-0	4-0	***I***	0-2	1-7	1-4	2-1	3-2	3-1	2-1	6-0	3-1	4-1
Hellesdon	6-0	3-0	5-2	3-2	5-2	1-4	***S***	1-2	1-3	4-1	n/a	2-0	1-1	4-4	2-3	1-0
Norwich CEYMS	3-0	3-1	1-0	6-2	5-2	6-1	0-3	***I***	0-2	2-1	n/a	3-1	1-2	5-1	1-1	5-1
Norwich St Johns	3-0	6-0	4-2	2-0	11-1	3-0	3-0	2-1	***O***	3-1	4-0	2-2	0-3	4-1	2-0	4-1
Norwich United Res.	2-0	6-2	0-2	2-2	5-0	4-2	3-1	5-0	1-2	***N***	n/a	2-3	0-5	3-4	1-2	2-4
Oulton Broad & Notleys	n/a	n/a	0-4	n/a	3-1	3-1	3-2	1-4	n/a	1-3		1-3	n/a	3-1	1-1	3-1
Poringland Wanderers	3-1	2-4	7-1	W-L	2-0	6-0	4-2	2-1	1-4	8-1	11-0	***T***	1-2	3-3	2-0	2-1
Reepham Town	5-0	4-0	3-2	4-0	2-3	1-0	2-0	4-1	3-2	6-1	11-0	3-2	***W***	4-1	3-0	1-0
Sprowston Wanderers	2-3	2-7	1-2	3-4	1-2	3-3	0-4	2-3	2-5	3-2	n/a	1-4	2-6	***O***	3-2	2-3
West Lynn SSC	W-L	2-3	3-2	2-1	2-1	3-3	3-2	6-4	2-7	1-1	n/a	2-3	0-1	4-1		2-1
Wortwell	2-0	1-2	1-5	1-1	1-1	1-4	0-6	1-0	1-5	2-1	1-0	0-3	0-1	2-3	4-1	

ANGLIAN COMBINATION DIVISION TWO CONSTITUTION 2009-10

CLE UNITED RESERVES . . . . Bridewell Lane, Acle, Norwich NR13 3RA 01493 752989
NGLIAN WINDOWS . . . . Horsford Manor, Cromer Road, Norwich NR5 8AP 01603 404723
TTLEBOROUGH TOWN. . . . . Recreation Ground, Station Road, Attleborough NR17 2AS 01953 455365
ECCLES CAXTON . . . . Caxton Meadow, Adjacent Beccles Station, Beccles NR34 9QH 01502 712829
RADENHAM WANDERERS. . . . . Hale Road, Bradenham, Thetford IP25 7RA . . . . None
OWNHAM TOWN RESERVES . . . Memorial Playing Field, Lynn Road, Downham Market PE38 9QE 01366 388424
AYTON UNITED . . . . Lime Kiln Road, Gayton, King's Lynn PE32 1QB . . . . None
ELLESDON . . . . Hellesdon Community Centre, Wood View Road, Hellesdon, Norwich NR6 5QB. 01603 427675
UNDFORD . . . . The Glebe, Mundford, Thetford IP26 5EJ . . . . None
ORWICH CEYMS . . . . Hilltops Sports Centre, Main Road, Swardeston, Norwich NR14 8DU 01508 578826
PROWSTON ATHLETIC RESERVES . . . . . Blue Boar Lane, Sprowston, Norwich NR7 8RJ. 01603 427688
PROWSTON WANDERERS . . . Sprowston Cricket Club, Barkers Lane, Sprowston, Norwich NR7 8QZ. 01603 404042
HETFORD ROVERS. . . . . Euston Park, Euston, near Thetford IP24 2QP . . . . None
HORPE VILLAGE . . . . Thorpe Recreation Ground, Laundry Lane, Thorpe St Andrew, Norwich NR7 0XQ 01603 300316
/EST LYNN SSC . . . . West Lynn Sports & Social Club, St Peters Road, West Lynn PE34 3LB 01553 761646
/ORTWELL . . . . Wortwell Playing Field, opposite Bell PH, High Road, Wortwell, Harleston IP20 0HH . . . . None

V: Attleborough Town (R), Bradenham Wanderers (P), Gayton United (R), Mundford (P), Sprowston Athletic Res. (P), Thetford Rovers (P), horpe Village (P)

UT: Great Yarmouth Town Res. (S - Eastern Counties League Reserve Division North), Fakenham Town Res. (R), Norwich St Johns (P), orwich United Res. (S - Eastern Counties League Reserve Division North), Oulton Broad & Notleys (WS), Poringland Wanderers (P), eepham Town (P)

Division Three		P	W	D	L	F	A	Pts
Mundford		28	21	6	1	99	28	69
Thetford Rovers		28	19	3	6	101	46	60
Bradenham Wanderers		28	17	3	8	86	58	54
Sprowston Athletic Res.		28	16	3	9	73	63	51
Thorpe Village		28	15	5	8	75	56	50
Beccles Town Res.		28	15	5	8	76	59	50
East Harling		28	14	1	13	73	68	43
Hempnall Res.		28	12	5	11	53	58	41
Loddon United Res.		28	9	8	11	53	57	35
Cromer Town Res.	*-1*	28	9	5	14	49	60	31
Aylsham		28	8	7	13	47	58	31
Caister Res.		28	9	4	15	55	82	31
Martham		28	8	2	18	46	81	26
Thorpe Rovers		28	4	3	21	26	74	15
Swaffham Town Res.		28	2	4	22	35	99	10

CYRIL BALLYN CUP

(Division Two, Three, Four, Five and Six first teams and external league reserve sides)

FIRST ROUND
Bradenham Wanderers 0
Thetford Rovers 1
City of Norwich SOBU 1
Norwich St Johns 11
Easton 0 **Sprowston W.** 2
Harleston Town 6
Fakenham Town Res. 1
Hellesdon 1 Hemsby 0
Thorpe Vill. 4 Redgrave 2
Waveney 4 Buxton 1
SECOND ROUND
Anglian Windows 2
Hoveton Wherrymen 1
(at Hoveton Wherrymen)
Great Yarmouth Res. 2
Poringland 2 *aet* (3-2p)
Harleston Town 2
Hellesdon 2 *aet* (4-3p)
Marlingford 1 Waveney 1
aet (4-3p)
Martham 0 **Freethorpe** 3
Necton 3 East Harling 2
Newton Flot. 2 Thorpe R. 1
Norwich CEYMS 2
Downham Town Res. 1
Norwich SJ 2 Thorpe V. 1
Norwich United Res. 5
South Walsham 1
Oulton Broad & Notleys 1
Beccles Caxton 4
Swaffham Town Res. 2
Reepham Town 4
Thetford Rovers 3
Foulsham 2
UEA 9 Sprowston W 0
West Lynn 0 **Mundford** 4
Wortwell 2 Aylsham 1
THIRD ROUND
Anglian Windows 1
Reepham Town 5
Harleston 5 Necton SSC 2
Marlingford 1 **Mundford** 2
Newton Flotman 2 **Norwich CEYMS** 3
Norwich SJ 3 Beccles C. 0
Thetford Rovers 3 **Great Yarmouth Town Res.** 6
UEA 1 **Norwich U. Res.** 4
Wortwell 3 Freethorpe 2
QUARTER-FINALS
Gt Yarmouth Town Res. 0
Reepham Town 1
Norwich SJ 4 Harleston 1
Norwich United Res. 4
Mundford 5 *aet*
Wortwell 0 **Norwich CEYMS** 1 *aet*
SEMI-FINALS
Norwich CEYMS 2
Mundford 2 *aet* (5-4p)
Norwich SJ 0 **Reepham** 4
FINAL
(May 8th at Wroxham)
Reepham Town 3
Norwich CEYMS 2

	Aylsham	Beccles T.	Brad'ham	Caister	Cromer T.	East Harl.	Hempnall	Loddon	Martham	Mundford	Sprow. A.	Swaffham	Thetford R.	Thorpe R.	Thorpe V.
Aylsham	***D***	3-0	3-3	2-1	5-0	0-1	1-3	2-2	0-2	0-5	1-1	2-2	0-5	3-0	1-3
Beccles Town Res.	1-3	***I***	3-1	2-2	1-2	2-6	5-2	1-0	5-1	1-6	7-3	1-0	2-1	1-0	4-2
Bradenham Wanderers	4-0	1-5	***V***	5-1	2-3	0-6	1-0	3-0	7-1	1-7	1-2	2-1	2-0	3-1	4-3
Caister Res.	1-1	2-1	1-4	***I***	3-3	2-1	0-2	3-2	1-7	1-3	1-3	6-1	3-3	5-0	1-2
Cromer Town Res.	0-1	1-4	2-2	1-2	***S***	1-3	4-1	0-1	5-1	2-2	4-5	2-1	0-1	2-0	0-0
East Harling	1-4	6-5	2-5	9-2	0-2	***I***	2-3	4-1	3-1	0-4	2-5	3-2	2-6	2-0	1-3
Hempnall Res.	2-1	4-3	5-3	1-3	2-2	2-0	***O***	0-0	5-0	1-3	0-0	2-1	1-5	2-0	1-4
Loddon United Res.	2-2	1-1	0-2	4-3	1-4	3-3	2-2	***N***	2-1	1-1	5-2	7-1	0-3	3-1	2-1
Martham	1-0	1-2	1-5	2-3	W-L	1-4	1-1	3-2		0-3	3-1	6-1	2-2	1-3	2-4
Mundford	3-0	2-2	2-3	4-1	5-1	5-1	5-1	3-0	2-0		4-1	6-0	3-0	5-1	1-1
Sprowston Athletic Res.	4-1	1-1	1-7	3-1	3-2	2-1	3-1	6-2	7-0	2-4	***T***	2-4	1-3	1-0	1-0
Swaffham Town Res.	2-2	3-4	2-5	0-3	3-2	1-2	1-3	0-4	3-6	2-2	1-5	***H***	1-4	1-1	1-4
Thetford Rovers	5-2	3-3	4-3	8-1	7-0	2-4	3-2	3-1	3-1	1-3	4-0	6-0	***R***	8-1	4-2
Thorpe Rovers	0-5	0-3	0-5	2-0	0-2	2-3	0-3	2-5	3-1	0-0	2-3	5-0	0-3	***E***	0-2
Thorpe Village	4-2	2-6	2-2	6-2	4-2	2-1	5-1	0-0	4-0	4-6	1-5	2-0	6-4	2-2	***E***

ANGLIAN COMBINATION DIVISION THREE CONSTITUTION 2009-10

AYLSHAM .... Sir Williams Lane, Aylsham, Norwich NR11 6AN .... Nor
BECCLES TOWN RESERVES .... College Meadow, Common Lane, Beccles NR34 7FA 07729 78281
CAISTER RESERVES .... Caister Playing Fields, off Allendale Road, Caister-on-Sea NR30 5ES .... Non
CROMER TOWN RESERVES .... Cabbell Park, Mill Road, Cromer NR27 0AD 01263 51218
EAST HARLING .... Memorial Fields, Church Street, East Harling NR16 2NA 01953 71825
EASTON.......................... Easton College, Bawburgh Road, Norwich NR9 5DX 01603 73120
FAKENHAM TOWN RESERVES .... Clipbush Park, Clipbush Lane, Fakenham NR21 8SW 01328 855445/85585
FOULSHAM .... Playing Field, Guist Road, Foulsham, Dereham NR20 5RZ .... Non
FREETHORPE .... School Road, Freethorpe, Norwich NR13 3NZ 01493 70153
HARLESTON TOWN.......... Rec & Memorial Leisure Centre, Wilderness Lane, Harleston IP20 9DD 01379 8545
HEMPNALL RESERVES................. Bungay Road, Hempnall, Norwich NR15 2NG 01508 49808
LODDON UNITED RESERVES .... George Lane Playing Field, Loddon, Norwich NR14 6NB.................... 01508 52849
MARLINGFORD .... Bayer Social Club, Marlpit Lane, Norwich NR5 8YT 01603 78766
MARTHAM............ Coronation Recreation Ground, Rollesby Road, Martham, Great Yarmouth NR29 4SP 01493 74025
NEWTON FLOTMAN ..... Newton Flotman Village Centre, Grove Way, Newton Flotman, Norwich NR15 1PU................ Non
NORTH WALSHAM TOWN RESERVES ...... Greens Road, North Walsham NR28 0HW 01692 40688

IN: Easton (P), Fakenham Town Res. (R), Foulsham (P), Freethorpe (P), Harleston Town (P), Marlingford (P), Newton Flotman (P), Nor Walsham Town Res. (P)

OUT: Bradenham Wanderers (P), Morley Village (WS), Mundford (P), Sprowston Athletic Res. (P), Swaffham Town Res. (R), Thetfo Rovers (P), Thorpe Rovers (R), Thorpe Village (P)

ivision Four		P	W	D	L	F	A	Pts
orth Walsham Town Res.		30	23	5	2	86	30	74
oulsham		30	22	1	7	107	52	67
arleston Town		30	21	3	6	105	45	66
reethorpe		30	19	4	7	79	44	61
aston		30	19	2	9	81	45	59
ewton Flotman	*-1*	30	17	4	9	60	32	54
arlingford		30	15	4	11	57	47	49
lofield United Res.		30	15	2	13	77	57	47
outh Walsham		30	12	6	12	52	64	42
Vymondham Town Res.		30	9	7	14	60	71	34
t Andrews Res.		30	9	4	17	49	80	31
FC Norwich Res.		30	8	4	18	56	72	28
lattishall Res.	*-1*	30	8	5	17	47	65	28
Vells Town Res.	*-1*	30	5	7	18	48	88	21
randon Town Res.	*-2*	30	5	1	24	42	125	14
lindringham Res.	*-3*	30	1	5	24	32	121	5

Division Five		P	W	D	L	F	A	Pt
Sheringham Res.		28	20	6	2	106	49	66
Bungay Town Res.		28	19	7	2	88	34	64
Necton SSC		28	19	2	7	99	61	59
Hoveton Wherrymen		28	18	1	9	86	50	55
UEA	*-1*	28	16	3	9	63	36	50
Watton United Res.		28	15	1	12	70	50	46
Long Stratton Res.		28	14	2	12	49	45	44
Stalham Town Res.		28	13	3	12	59	50	42
Mundford Res.		28	11	3	14	51	64	36
Sprowston Wanderers Res.		28	9	5	14	50	76	32
Norwich CEYMS Res.		28	9	2	17	48	87	29
Attleborough Town Res.		28	7	4	17	48	72	25
Poringland Wanderers Res.	*-1*	28	7	4	17	52	82	24
Aylsham Res.	*-1*	28	8	1	19	39	79	24
City of Norwich SOBU		28	1	4	23	29	102	7

Division Six		P	W	D	L	F	A	Pt
Dersingham Rovers Res.		26	18	5	3	83	38	59
Redgrave Rangers		26	18	3	5	86	33	57
Waveney		26	17	5	4	80	33	56
Buxton FC		26	17	4	5	108	48	55
Hellesdon Res.		26	16	2	8	83	44	50
Hemsby		26	16	2	8	81	47	50
Corton Res.		26	11	3	12	57	46	36
Horsford United Res.	*-1*	26	9	4	13	42	61	30
Thorpe Village Res.		26	9	3	14	49	72	30
Holt United Res.		26	6	5	15	36	77	23
Scole United Res.	*-1*	26	7	2	17	53	77	22
Martham Res.		26	6	4	16	45	100	22
Reepham Town Res.	*-1*	26	4	4	18	37	88	15
Easton Res.		26	3	4	19	27	103	13

	AFC Nor. Res.	Blofield Res.	Brandon Res.	Easton	Foulsham	Freethorpe	Harleston T.	Hin'ham Res.	Marlingford	Ma'ishall Res.	N. Flotman	N W'ham Res.	Sth Walsham	St And. Res.	Wells T. Res.	Wy'ham Res.
AFC Norwich Res.		1-3	5-1	1-3	1-4	1-4	0-2	7-0	1-0	2-3	1-2	1-6	2-2	4-2	6-4	0-1
Blofield United Res.	2-3	***D***	5-0	1-0	5-4	1-4	0-3	W-L	0-0	4-1	3-2	1-2	1-2	0-5	3-0	5-1
Brandon Town Res.	0-2	2-12	***I***	2-6	0-11	1-7	2-3	11-0	2-5	3-2	0-2	0-4	2-5	2-2	3-2	1-3
Easton	5-0	4-2	W-L	***V***	1-4	0-3	3-0	2-2	2-0	5-1	5-0	1-3	3-0	5-1	5-1	3-1
Foulsham	6-3	5-2	6-1	1-4	***I***	4-0	1-2	5-3	5-2	4-0	1-0	2-4	3-2	6-2	2-2	6-1
Freethorpe	2-1	2-0	8-0	2-1	1-4	***S***	2-6	3-0	5-2	1-1	2-1	1-2	2-1	5-0	W-L	2-1
Harleston Town	3-2	4-1	5-0	3-2	5-1	5-0	***I***	13-1	1-0	3-0	2-3	3-4	1-2	9-0	2-0	1-0
Hindringham Res.	3-2	0-5	2-6	1-3	L-W	1-9	0-2	***O***	1-2	2-3	2-9	1-2	1-1	2-4	2-2	2-2
Marlingford	2-0	3-2	W-L	2-3	0-2	1-5	2-2	3-1	***N***	W-L	3-2	1-1	5-0	2-2	7-0	3-0
Mattishall Res.	0-2	2-4	L-W	2-3	0-2	1-1	1-6	1-1	0-4		0-3	3-1	1-2	4-0	5-1	4-0
Newton Flotman	1-0	1-1	7-0	5-1	2-1	3-0	4-1	W-L	1-0	1-4		1-1	L-W	2-0	0-0	2-1
North Walsham Town Res.	3-3	1-0	W-L	1-0	3-1	0-0	4-1	5-0	6-2	2-0	1-0	***F***	3-1	1-2	8-0	3-3
South Walsham	3-1	2-1	1-0	0-4	2-4	2-2	3-3	4-3	2-0	2-2	0-4	1-3	***O***	1-2	2-1	4-5
St Andrews Res.	3-2	0-6	5-1	2-2	1-6	2-1	2-3	2-0	0-2	0-1	0-1	0-1	1-2	***U***	1-4	0-2
Wells Town Res.	1-1	2-4	8-0	2-1	1-2	1-3	1-7	6-1	0-2	3-3	2-1	0-6	2-2	0-5	***R***	0-2
Wymondham Town Res.	1-1	1-3	7-2	2-4	2-4	1-2	4-4	7-0	1-2	3-2	0-0	1-5	2-1	3-3	2-2	

ANGLIAN COMBINATION DIVISION FOUR CONSTITUTION 2009-10

LOFIELD UNITED RESERVES . . . . Old Yarmouth Road, Blofield, Norwich NR13 4LE 07748 863203
UNGAY TOWN RESERVES . . . . Maltings Meadow, Ditchingham, Bungay NR35 2RU 01986 894028
OVETON WHERRYMEN . . . . Playing Field, Stalham Road, Hoveton, Wroxham NR12 8DG . . . . None
ONG STRATTON RESERVES . . . . Manor Road Playing Fields, Long Stratton, Norwich NR15 2XR . . . . None
IATTISHALL RESERVES . . . . . . Mattishall Playing Fields, South Green, Mattishall, Norwich NR20 3JY 01362 850246
ECTON SSC . . . . Tuns Road, Necton, Swaffham PE37 8EH 01760 723864
HERINGHAM RESERVES . . . . Recreation Ground, Weybourne Road, Sheringham NR26 8WD 01263 824804
OUTH WALSHAM . . . . The Playing Field, South Walsham . . . . None
PIXWORTH UNITED RESERVES Spixworth Village Hall, Crostick Lane, Spixworth, Norwich NR10 3NQ 01603 898092
T ANDREWS RESERVES. Thorpe Recreation Ground, Laundry Lane, Thorpe St Andrew, Thorpe NR7 0XQ 01603 300316
WAFFHAM TOWN RESERVES . . . . . . Shoemakers Lane, off Cley Road, Swaffham PE37 7NT 01760 722700
HORPE ROVERS . . . . Dussindale Park, Pound Lane, Thorpe, Norwich NR7 0SR . . . . None
EA. . . . . UEA Sports Ground, Colney Lane, Norwich NR4 7RG . . . . None
VATTON UNITED RESERVES. . . . Watton Playing Field, Dereham Road, Watton, Thetford IP25 6EZ 01953 881281
VELLS TOWN RESERVES. Beach Road, Wells-next-the-Sea NR23 1DR. 01328 710907
VYMONDHAM TOWN RESERVES . . . Kings Head Meadow, Back Lane, Wymondham NR18 0LB 01953 607326

N: Bungay Town Res. (P), Hoveton Wherrymen (P), Long Stratton Res. (P), Necton SSC (P), Sheringham Res. (P), Swaffham Town Res. R), Thorpe Rovers (R), UEA (P), Watton United Res. (P)

UT: Brandon Town Res. (R), Easton (P), Foulsham (P), Freethorpe (P), Harleston Town (P), Hindringham Res. (R), Marlingford (P), lewton Flotman (P), North Walsham Town Res. (P)

FC Norwich Res. become Spixworth United Res.

BEDFORDSHIRE COUNTY LEAGUE

Sponsored by:
No Sponsor

Founded: 1904

Recent champions:

2004: Elstow Abbey

2005: Caldecote

2006: Caldecote

2007: Westoning Recreation Club

2008: Campton

	AFC Kemp.	Bedford SA	Blunham	Caldecote	Campton	Dunton	Henlow	Ickwell/OW	Meltis Cor.	Oakley Sp.	Renhold	Riseley	Sandy	Sharnbrook	Wilsham.
AFC Kempston Town		5-1	0-1	3-1	2-4	3-1	4-0	3-5	2-2	3-1	2-2	4-1	n/a	1-1	3-1
Bedford Sports Athletic	1-1		1-4	1-4	0-8	0-3	0-4	1-2	1-1	3-1	0-0	3-4	n/a	1-3	0-1
Blunham	5-2	3-1	***P***	2-1	1-2	0-3	6-1	4-1	1-3	0-0	1-1	9-2	n/a	5-2	1-1
Caldecote	2-0	9-0	2-0	***R***	3-2	4-1	6-0	4-1	1-1	W-L	1-1	6-1	n/a	1-0	6-3
Campton	3-2	5-0	0-1	1-3	***E***	4-1	3-0	1-0	0-0	3-3	2-2	5-0	n/a	4-1	3-1
Dunton	2-3	1-1	1-5	1-4	0-3	***M***	6-0	0-5	2-1	3-2	1-3	2-4	n/a	2-2	0-2
Henlow	2-2	0-0	1-4	0-1	0-1	1-4	***I***	0-0	0-2	2-2	1-0	0-5	n/a	0-1	0-5
Ickwell & Old Warden	1-1	2-4	2-1	1-4	3-3	3-0	1-4	***E***	3-3	2-1	1-0	3-1	n/a	0-0	3-5
Meltis Corinthians	1-1	6-1	1-1	0-2	1-1	2-0	3-0	2-3	***R***	3-2	0-1	4-0	2-0	3-0	9-0
Oakley Sports	2-0	4-1	2-1	2-4	2-4	1-3	6-1	4-4	1-2		3-5	5-2	4-1	3-1	0-5
Renhold United	0-3	9-2	3-2	4-2	2-3	1-2	3-0	2-2	2-2	2-2	***D***	2-2	n/a	3-3	2-1
Riseley Sports	1-4	1-7	2-1	0-1	1-3	3-2	1-2	8-5	2-4	0-5	4-1	***I***	n/a	1-0	3-1
Sandy	n/a	n/a	n/a	n/a	n/a	n/a	n/a	1-5	n/a	n/a	2-4	3-3	***V***	n/a	n/a
Sharnbrook	3-0	4-0	1-2	2-3	0-5	0-3	0-1	2-2	1-2	1-0	7-0	3-0	6-2		0-3
Wilshamstead	2-3	7-1	0-2	3-5	1-5	1-5	3-2	0-4	1-3	0-3	2-4	1-5	n/a	4-2	

Premier Division	**P**	**W**	**D**	**L**	**F**	**A**	**Pts**
Caldecote	**26**	**21**	**2**	**3**	**80**	**30**	**65**
Campton	**26**	**18**	**5**	**3**	**78**	**30**	**59**
Meltis Corinthians	**26**	**13**	**9**	**4**	**61**	**29**	**48**
Blunham	**26**	**14**	**4**	**8**	**63**	**36**	**46**
AFC Kempston Town	**26**	**11**	**7**	**8**	**57**	**46**	**40**
Ickwell & Old Warden	**26**	**10**	**8**	**8**	**59**	**58**	**38**
Renhold United	**26**	**9**	**10**	**7**	**55**	**51**	**37**
Dunton	**26**	**10**	**2**	**14**	**49**	**58**	**32**
Riseley Sports	**26**	**10**	**1**	**15**	**54**	**83**	**31**
Oakley Sports	**26**	**8**	**5**	**13**	**57**	**55**	**29**
Wilshamstead	**26**	**9**	**1**	**16**	**54**	**74**	**28**
Sharnbrook	**26**	**7**	**5**	**14**	**40**	**49**	**26**
Henlow	**26**	**5**	**4**	**17**	**22**	**69**	**19**
Bedford Spts Athletic	**26**	**3**	**5**	**18**	**31**	**92**	**14**

Sandy - record expunged

BRITANNIA CUP

FIRST ROUND

Bedford Sports Athletic 3 Ickwell & Old Warden 1

Caldecote 6 Dunton 1

Campton 4 AFC Kempston 3

Henlow 2 Wilshamstead 0

Meltis Corries 2 Oakley 1

Renhold Utd 3 Sharnbrook 1

QUARTER-FINALS

Blunham 3 Riseley Sports 1

Campton 0 **Bedford SA** 2

Henlow 0 **Caldecote** 2

Meltis Corinthians 1 **Renhold** 2

SEMI-FINALS

Bedford Sports Athletic 0 **Caldecote** 4

Renhold United 1 **Blunham** 2

FINAL

(May 9th at Biggleswade United)

Caldecote 3 Blunham 1

BEDFORDSHIRE LEAGUE PREMIER DIVISION CONSTITUTION 2009-10

AFC KEMPSTON TOWN . . . . Hillgrounds Road, Kempston, Bedford MK42 8SZ. 01234 85234
BIGGLESWADE UNITED RESERVES . Second Meadow, Fairfield Road, Biggleswade SG18 0AA 01767 60040
BLUNHAM . . . . The Playing Fields, Blunham Road, Moggerhanger, Sandy MK44 3RG. Non
CALDECOTE . . . . Harvey Close, Upper Caldecote, Biggleswade SG18 9BQ. . . . . Non
CAMPTON . . . . The Recreation Ground, Church Road, Campton SG17 5BN. . . . . Non
DUNTON . . . . Horseshoe Close, Dunton SG18 8RY. . . . . Non
ICKWELL & OLD WARDEN . . . . Ickwell Green, Ickwell, Biggleswade SG18 9EF . . . . Non
MELTIS CORINTHIANS . . . . Meltis Sports Club, Miller Road, Bedford MK42 9NY. 01234 35287
OAKLEY SPORTS. . . . . Oakley Village Sports Centre, Oakley, Bedford MK43 7RG . . . . Non
RENHOLD UNITED . . . . Renhold Playing Fields, Renhold, Bedford . . . . Non
RISELEY SPORTS. . . . . Gold Street, Riseley MK44 1EG . . . . Non
SHARNBROOK . . . . Playing Fields, Lodge Road, Sharnbrook MK44 1JP . . . . Non
SOUTHILL ALEXANDER . . Biggleswade Town FC, Carlsberg Stadium, Langford Rd, Biggleswade SG18 9JT 07879 80210
WESTONING RECREATION CLUB . . Recreation Ground, Greenfield Road, Westoning MK45 5JB. . . . . Non
WILSHAMSTEAD . . . . Jubilee Playing Fields, Bedford Road, Wilshamstead MK45 3HN . . . . Non
WOBURN. . . . . Crawley Road, Woburn MK17 9QD . . . . Non

IN: Biggleswade United Res. (P - Spartan South Midlands League Reserve Division Two East), Southill Alexander (N), Westonin Recreation Club (P), Woburn (P)

OUT: Bedford Sports Athletic (R), Henlow (R), Sandy (WS)

Division One	P	W	D	L	F	A	Pt
Westoning Rec. Club	28	23	1	4	115	34	70
Woburn	28	20	2	6	89	51	62
Meltis Albion	28	19	2	7	89	39	59
Kempston	28	17	2	9	66	52	53
Flitwick Town	28	15	3	10	63	46	48
Ickwell & Old Wdn Res.	28	13	6	9	67	62	45
Stevington	28	11	3	14	69	66	36
Campton Res.	28	10	5	13	51	58	35
Marston Social	28	9	7	12	57	62	34
AFC Kempston T. Res.	28	8	9	11	59	68	33
Caldecote Res.	28	9	4	15	56	64	31
Sandy Res.	28	9	3	16	49	92	30
Kemp. Hammers Sports	28	8	3	17	49	78	27
Royal Oak Kempston	28	7	3	18	42	82	24
Elstow Abbey	28	3	5	20	39	106	14

CENTENARY CUP

Final *(May 4th at Biggleswade United)*

Royal Oak Kempston 3 Woburn 1

Division Two	P	W	D	L	F	A	Pt
Blunham Res.	26	18	6	2	59	24	60
Meppershall Jurassic	26	16	4	6	85	67	52
Great Barford	26	12	8	6	62	51	44
Clifton	26	12	7	7	56	50	43
Marabese Ceramics	26	13	3	10	68	38	42
Potton Wdrs	*-2*25	14	1	10	75	47	41
Kings AFC	26	10	7	9	62	51	37
Marston Shelton R.	26	11	4	11	62	70	37
Oakley Sports Res.	26	12	0	14	60	61	36
Meltis Corries Res.	26	10	5	11	51	63	35
Saffron	*-2*25	7	3	15	50	55	22
Mulberry Bush	26	6	3	17	42	76	21
Blue Chip	26	5	5	16	50	77	20
Lidlington Utd Spts	26	5	4	17	39	91	19

JUBILEE CUP

Final *(May 4th at Caldecote)*

Meppershall Jurassic 4 Great Barford 2

Division Three	P	W	D	L	F	A	P
Leighton United	26	21	3	2	121	20	6
T. Tuns Galacticos	26	17	5	4	81	32	5
Meppershall	26	14	6	6	88	64	4
Dunton Res.	26	13	8	5	81	56	4
Marsh Leys	26	14	2	10	84	69	4
Caldecote A	26	12	5	9	76	66	4
Westoning RC Res.	26	13	2	11	71	61	4
Renhold Village	26	12	2	12	73	68	3
Sandy A	26	11	1	14	54	68	3
Riseley Sports Res.	26	8	4	14	61	79	2
Wilshamstead Res.	26	7	6	13	45	77	2
Flitwick Town Res.	26	6	3	17	36	67	2
Stewartby Village	26	4	3	19	39	110	1
Kempston Athletic	26	2	6	18	37	110	1

WATSON SHIELD

Final *(May 1st at Biggleswade United)*

Leighton United 1 Three Tuns Galacticos 0 *aet*

CAMBRIDGESHIRE COUNTY LEAGUE

Sponsored by:
Kershaw and BIS

Founded: 1891

Recent champions:
2004: Fulbourn Institute
2005: Fulbourn Institute
2006: Sawston United
2007: Great Shelford
2008: Waterbeach

	Camb. UP	Cottenham	Eaton Soc.	Ely City R.	Fordham	Fulbourn	Gt Shelford	Histon A	Hundon	Lakenheath	Littleport	N'dingworth	Newmarket	Over Sports	Waterbeach
Cambridge University Press		5-1	1-2	3-0	5-0	3-2	2-0	1-1	4-0	5-2	4-1	8-0	2-0	3-2	2-2
Cottenham United	2-0		4-1	1-2	0-2	5-3	2-3	3-2	3-1	0-2	3-5	6-1	12-2	1-3	1-0
Eaton Socon	2-1	0-4	***P***	2-0	1-3	2-2	0-1	1-1	2-4	1-7	1-3	4-1	2-1	0-0	0-5
Ely City Res.	2-4	4-0	1-3	***R***	0-0	0-2	2-4	1-1	0-1	2-6	0-1	5-3	0-0	1-3	0-3
Fordham	0-4	3-4	2-1	4-1	***E***	1-2	0-3	2-2	2-1	1-5	2-5	6-1	1-0	1-3	1-2
Fulbourn Institute	1-0	3-1	3-1	1-1	4-0	***M***	1-1	2-1	1-2	3-0	2-2	3-1	4-0	1-0	3-0
Great Shelford	1-1	1-0	3-1	2-1	4-2	2-4	***I***	3-0	2-1	1-4	3-1	4-0	1-0	1-0	1-4
Histon A	2-2	1-4	2-1	1-1	1-2	1-2	0-1	***E***	3-1	6-4	0-0	4-1	3-0	2-3	0-1
Hundon	3-3	3-2	1-2	3-1	3-1	0-4	3-2	1-5	***R***	0-5	0-0	2-1	2-3	2-2	1-2
Lakenheath	0-0	4-0	2-2	2-8	7-1	3-3	2-1	2-1	4-0		1-1	4-0	6-1	2-1	3-2
Littleport Town	0-1	2-2	3-1	2-0	4-1	1-2	3-3	4-1	1-0	3-3	***D***	2-0	1-2	3-1	2-1
Needingworth United	0-8	0-1	1-3	1-3	1-1	0-5	2-0	1-1	0-3	0-4	1-5	***I***	1-1	0-1	2-2
Newmarket Town Res.	0-2	1-3	0-7	2-5	4-0	0-3	1-2	1-4	4-5	2-4	1-4	2-2	***V***	2-1	2-4
Over Sports	0-2	1-2	2-1	1-1	2-0	2-2	1-1	0-3	2-0	2-2	2-1	3-2	1-1		1-0
Waterbeach	3-2	2-2	1-2	3-1	1-4	2-3	2-3	1-3	1-4	0-4	6-0	4-3	5-1	1-1	

Premier Division		P	W	D	L	F	A	Pts
Fulbourn Institute		28	19	6	3	71	32	63
Lakenheath		28	18	6	4	94	47	60
Cambridge Univ. Press		28	17	6	5	78	29	57
Great Shelford		28	17	4	7	54	40	55
Littleport Town		28	14	7	7	60	44	49
Cottenham United	*-3*	28	14	2	12	69	57	41
Over Sports		28	11	8	9	41	38	41
Waterbeach		28	12	4	12	60	52	40
Hundon		28	11	3	14	47	62	36
Histon A		28	9	8	11	52	46	35
Eaton Socon		28	10	4	14	46	59	34
Fordham		28	9	3	16	43	71	30
Ely City Res.		28	6	6	16	43	59	24
Newmarket Town Res.		28	4	4	20	34	87	16
Needingworth United		28	1	5	22	26	95	8

PREMIER DIVISION CUP

FIRST ROUND
Cambridge UP 4 Newmarket Res. 0
Eaton Socon (w/o) v Wickhambrook (scr.)
Ely City Res. 3 **Fulbourn Institute** 4
Fordham 1 **Great Shelford** 7
Histon A 2 Cottenham United 0
Hundon 1 **Waterbeach** 4
Littleport Town 2 **Lakenheath** 4
Needingworth United 0 **Over Sports** 1

QUARTER-FINALS
Cambridge University Press 1 **Great Shelford** 4
Eaton Socon 1 **Histon A** 7
Fulbourn Institute 3 Over Sports 0
Waterbeach 0 **Lakenheath** 3

SEMI-FINALS
Great Shelford 0 **Histon A** 3
Lakenheath 2 **Fulbourn Institute** 3

FINAL
(May 12th at Cambridge City)
Fulbourn Institute 2 Histon A 1

CAMBRIDGESHIRE COUNTY LEAGUE PREMIER DIVISION CONSTITUTION 2009-10

CAMBRIDGE UNIVERSITY PRESS . CUP Sports Ground, Shaftesbury Road, Cambridge CB2 2BS . . . . None
COTTENHAM UNITED . . . . . . King George V Playing Field, Lamb Lane, Cottenham, Cambridge CB4 8TB 01954 250873
EATON SOCON . . . . River Road, Eaton Ford, St Neots PE19 3AU . . . . None
ELY CITY RESERVES . . . . The Unwin Ground, Downham Road, Ely CB6 2SH 01353 662035
FORDHAM . . . . Recreational Ground, Carter Street, Fordham, Ely CB7 5NJ . . . . None
FOXTON . . . . Hardman Road, off High Street, Foxton CB22 6RP . . . . None
FULBOURN INSTITUTE . . . . Fulbourn Recreation, Home End, Fulbourn CB1 5BS. . . . . None
GREAT SHELFORD . . . . Recreation Ground, Woollards Lane, Great Shelford CB2 5LZ. 01223 842590
HISTON A . . . . The Glass World Stadium, Bridge Road, Impington, Cambridge CB4 9PH 01223 237373
HUNDON . . . . Upper North Street, Hundon CO10 8EE. . . . . None
LAKENHEATH . . . . The Nest, Wings Road, Lakenheath IP27 9HW . . . . None
LITTLEPORT TOWN . . . . Sports Centre, Camel Road, Littleport, Ely CB6 1PU. 01353 860600
NEEDINGWORTH UNITED . . . . Mill Field, Holywell Road, Needingworth PE27 8TE . . . . None
NEWMARKET TOWN RESERVES Sherbourn Stadium, Cricket Field Rd, off New Cheveley Rd, Newmarket CB8 8BT 01638 663637
OVER SPORTS . . . . Over Recreation Ground, The Dole, Over, Cambridge CB4 5NW . . . . None
WATERBEACH. . . . . Waterbeach Reacreation Ground, Cambridge Road, Waterbeach CB5 9NJ . . . . None
WEST WRATTING. . . . . Recreation Ground, Bull Lane, West Wratting CB1 5NJ. . . . . None
WHITTLESFORD UNITED . . . . The Lawn, Whittlesford CB2 4NG . . . . None

IN: Foxton (P), West Wratting (P), Whittlesford United (P)
OUT: Wickhambrook (WN)

Senior Division A		P	W	D	L	F	A	Pts
West Wratting		30	25	2	3	87	42	77
Foxton		30	19	6	5	71	42	63
Whittlesford United		30	19	5	6	86	45	62
Girton United		30	18	6	6	61	37	60
Hardwick		30	15	9	6	56	43	54
Brampton		30	13	7	10	63	65	46
Soham Town Rgrs Res.		30	13	5	12	55	54	44
Mildenhall Town Res.	*-3*	30	14	2	14	68	72	41
Somersham Town		30	11	5	14	60	54	38
Debden		30	12	1	17	44	57	37
Cherry Hinton		30	8	6	16	43	60	30
Great Paxton	*-5*	30	9	5	16	57	72	27
Wisbech Town Res.	*-3*	30	8	6	16	54	73	27
Castle Camps		30	6	7	17	51	80	25
Hemingfords United		30	4	10	16	46	63	22
Comberton United		30	0	10	20	34	77	10

WILLIAM COCKELL CUP

FIRST ROUND

Comberton United 0 **Cherry Hinton** 1
Debden 1 **Brampton** 3
Great Paxton 1 **Castle Camps** 4
Hardwick 2 **Foxton** 4
Mildenhall Res. 1 **Hemingfords United** 1 *aet* (3-4p)
Soham Town Rangers Res. 1 **Girton United** 3
Whittlesford United 2 West Wratting 1
Wisbech Town Res. 2 Somersham Town 1

QUARTER-FINALS

Cherry Hinton 2 Castle Camps 1
Brampton 0 **Girton United** 2
Whittlesford United 5 Foxton 0
Wisbech Town Res. 0 **Hemingfords United** 2 *aet*

SEMI-FINALS

Cherry Hinton 2 **Girton United** 3
Whittlesford United 7 Hemingfords United 2

FINAL

(May 4th at Cambridge City)
Whittlesford United 1 **Girton United** 1 *aet* (2-3p)

	Brampton	Castle Camps	Cherry Hinton	Comberton United	Debden	Foxton	Girton United	Great Paxton	Hardwick	Hemingfords Utd	Mildenhall T. Res.	Soham Town Res.	Somersham Town	West Wratting	Whittlesford United	Wisbech Town Res.
Brampton		4-1	3-2	2-0	3-1	2-3	0-3	1-1	0-4	0-0	1-0	4-1	1-5	3-1	3-1	3-0
Castle Camps	1-1		2-5	3-2	2-4	2-2	0-1	3-4	1-3	0-5	4-5	3-0	2-3	2-3	1-1	1-1
Cherry Hinton	3-3	1-3	***S***	3-2	0-5	1-2	0-0	2-1	0-0	0-2	5-1	1-1	2-1	0-1	4-2	3-2
Comberton United	3-3	1-1	2-2	***E***	1-2	1-1	2-3	0-3	0-1	1-4	1-2	1-1	2-2	1-4	1-5	2-2
Debden	0-2	1-0	2-0	2-1	***N***	2-4	0-2	4-0	0-2	1-0	0-5	1-2	2-5	2-4	0-5	2-3
Foxton	3-2	4-2	1-0	4-1	0-1	***I***	1-1	3-1	3-1	4-1	3-0	2-1	3-2	2-4	2-3	4-1
Girton United	3-1	1-1	1-0	2-2	2-1	0-3	***O***	10-3	1-0	3-2	0-1	1-0	1-1	3-4	2-1	4-1
Great Paxton	1-2	0-0	0-0	7-0	1-3	2-3	1-3	***R***	1-2	3-2	6-0	1-1	2-4	0-3	4-2	2-3
Hardwick	3-3	2-0	3-2	1-0	1-0	1-1	2-1	1-5		2-2	5-2	1-1	2-2	3-4	0-3	1-0
Hemingfords United	2-2	1-2	1-2	2-2	3-0	1-3	0-1	1-1	2-2	***D***	1-2	2-4	0-2	2-2	1-2	1-1
Mildenhall Town Res.	2-6	6-4	4-2	2-1	2-1	1-1	0-4	6-1	2-5	6-0	***I***	1-2	2-0	3-4	1-2	3-0
Soham Town Rgrs Res.	5-1	3-1	2-1	2-0	2-0	1-4	2-4	3-1	3-2	4-2	1-4	***V***	3-1	1-2	0-1	1-3
Somersham Town	1-2	5-1	5-2	2-0	0-3	3-2	3-0	1-4	1-2	1-1	4-0	2-2		0-1	1-3	1-2
West Wratting	6-3	0-1	3-0	3-0	2-0	0-1	3-1	3-0	1-1	6-2	3-1	2-0	2-1	***A***	3-2	2-1
Whittlesford United	4-0	7-2	3-0	4-2	2-2	3-1	1-1	6-0	1-1	2-1	2-2	5-0	1-0	3-5		4-2
Wisbech Town Res.	5-2	4-5	2-0	2-2	1-2	1-1	1-2	0-1	1-2	2-2	3-2	0-6	4-1	3-6	3-5	

CAMBRIDGESHIRE COUNTY LEAGUE SENIOR DIVISION A CONSTITUTION 2009-10

BRAMPTON . . . . Thrapston Road Playing Fields, Brampton, Huntingdon PE28 4TB . . . . None
CASTLE CAMPS . . . . Recreation Ground, Bumpstead Road, Castle Camps, Cambridge CB1 6SN . . . . None
CHATTERIS TOWN . . . . West Street, Chatteris PE16 6HW 01354 692139
CHERRY HINTON . . . . Recreation Ground, High Street, Cherry Hinton, Cambridge . . . . None
DEBDEN . . . . Recreation Ground, High Street, Debden, Saffron Walden CB11 3LB . . . . None
GIRTON UNITED . . . . Girton Recreation Ground, Cambridge Road, Girton CB3 0FH . . . . None
GREAT PAXTON . . . . Recreation Ground, High Street, Great Paxton, St Neots PE19 6RG. . . . . None
HARDWICK. . . . . Egremont Road, Hardwick, Cambridge CB3 7XR . . . . None
HEMINGFORDS UNITED . Peace Mem. Playing Fields, Manor Rd, Hemingford Grey, Huntingdon PE28 9BX . . . . None
MILDENHALL TOWN RESERVES. . . . . Recreation Way, Mildenhall, Bury St Edmunds IP28 7HG. 01638 713449
MILTON . . . . Milton Recreation Ground, The Sycamores, Milton, Cambridge CB4 6ZN. . . . . None
RHS UNITED . . . . Eternit Sports Ground, Whaddon Road, Meldreth SG8 5RL 01763 260250
SAWSTON UNITED. . . . . Spicers Sports Ground, New Road, Sawston CB2 4BW. . . . . None
SOHAM TOWN RANGERS RESERVES . . . . . . Julius Martin Lane, Soham, Ely CB7 5EQ 01353 720732/722139
SOMERSHAM TOWN . . . . West End Ground, St Ives Road, Somersham, Huntingdon PE27 3EN. 01487 843384
WISBECH TOWN RESERVES . . . Barton Road Recreation Ground, Barton Road, Wisbech PE13 1LE. . . . . None

IN: Chatteris Town (P), Milton (P), RHS United (P) Sawston United (P)
OUT: Comberton United (R), Foxton (P), West Wratting (P), Whittlesford United (P)

ienior Division B		P	W	D	L	F	A	Pts
;awston United		32	24	3	5	112	41	75
/lilton		32	24	2	6	96	47	74
:hatteris Town		32	20	6	6	76	33	66
RHS United		32	20	3	9	109	64	63
;oham United		32	19	3	10	108	60	60
laddenham Rovers		32	17	8	7	93	64	59
Vest Row Gunners		32	16	7	9	98	58	55
ìreat Chesterford		32	14	4	14	64	76	46
.inton Granta		32	13	5	14	72	62	44
/larch T. Utd Res.	*-3*	32	13	7	12	70	67	43
)utwell Swifts		32	10	6	16	57	74	36
:ottenham Utd Res.		32	10	6	16	55	72	36
luntisham Rangers		32	10	3	19	61	81	33
;wavesey Institute		32	8	5	19	53	83	29
;affron Crocus		32	8	4	20	54	109	28
lelions Bumpstead		32	6	2	24	48	140	20
.ittleport T. Res.	*-3*	32	2	2	28	39	134	5

PERCY OLDHAM CUP

FIRST ROUND
Great Chesterford 3 Saffron Crocus 2

SECOND ROUND
Bluntisham Rangers 2 Helions Bumpstead 0
Cottenham United Res. 1 **Soham United** 3
Great Chesterford 4 West Row Gunners 2
Linton Granta (w/o) v Littleport Town Res.
March Town United Res. 3 **Sawston United** 4
Milton 4 Haddenham Rovers 1
Outwell Swifts 2 Swavesey Institute 0
RHS United 2 Chatteris Town 1

QUARTER-FINALS
Bluntisham Rangers 0 **Sawston United** 4
Great Chesterford 1 Outwell Swifts 0
RHS United 2 **Milton** 4
Soham United 4 Linton Granta 1

SEMI-FINALS
Soham United 1 **Sawston United** 2
Milton 3 Great Chesterford 1

FINAL *(May 6th at Histon)*
Milton 1 Sawston United 0

	Blu	Cha	Cot	GtC	Had	Hel	Lin	Litt	Mar	Mil	Out	RHS	Saff	Saw	Soh	Swa	Wes
Bluntisham Rangers		2-2	3-1	4-0	1-4	3-4	2-1	4-1	1-4	1-4	2-0	3-4	1-1	2-3	0-2	0-2	3-2
Chatteris Town	4-0		3-2	4-0	1-1	7-1	2-1	2-0	4-0	4-2	1-2	3-0	5-1	2-2	1-0	1-0	1-1
Cottenham United Res.	1-1	3-1		1-3	1-1	3-1	0-4	4-2	3-0	1-7	3-1	1-5	6-0	1-3	3-1	1-2	2-3
Great Chesterford	3-2	1-3	2-1	***S***	1-3	4-1	2-2	5-3	1-0	3-2	0-2	1-0	6-1	0-5	3-1	2-2	0-2
Haddenham Rovers	1-0	1-1	0-0	4-2	***E***	4-1	1-0	7-1	2-3	2-3	5-3	5-3	9-1	1-4	3-4	3-3	3-2
Helions Bumpstead	0-4	2-4	1-2	1-3	3-7	***N***	4-2	4-4	1-4	0-1	5-2	1-8	2-4	0-3	0-4	1-4	0-6
Linton Granta	4-1	2-0	6-2	2-0	2-4	0-1	***I***	2-0	3-3	1-4	3-2	2-4	5-0	4-4	1-2	3-0	1-1
Littleport Town Res.	1-2	0-4	3-3	1-2	2-3	0-3	0-4	***O***	1-8	1-3	0-4	1-3	0-1	2-4	1-10	2-5	1-6
March Town United Res.	3-2	0-0	1-1	5-2	3-2	3-0	2-3	4-1	***R***	1-2	0-3	3-3	5-0	0-3	2-2	2-1	1-1
Milton	1-0	1-0	1-0	2-0	0-3	3-2	3-0	2-3	2-1		5-1	4-1	7-1	3-2	2-0	5-2	1-1
Outwell Swifts	3-2	1-4	1-1	3-1	3-3	3-3	2-3	1-2	0-1	1-3	***D***	1-3	5-2	1-1	2-2	3-1	0-0
RHS United	5-2	0-1	0-3	7-4	2-2	3-2	4-1	6-1	8-0	2-2	1-2	***I***	4-1	2-0	6-4	4-1	3-4
Saffron Crocus	2-4	3-0	7-2	2-2	2-2	1-2	2-1	6-3	1-2	3-5	1-0	2-6	***V***	0-2	2-3	2-2	0-6
Sawston United	9-1	3-0	3-0	2-3	4-2	14-0	3-1	2-0	3-2	3-1	8-1	2-4	2-1		2-1	4-0	4-2
Soham United	3-1	1-4	3-2	2-2	6-1	9-0	3-2	13-0	5-3	1-7	5-1	2-3	6-0	2-1	***B***	3-0	3-4
Swavesey Institute	4-3	0-4	0-1	2-6	0-1	7-2	1-1	4-2	3-1	1-5	0-1	0-4	1-2	1-4	0-3		2-2
West Row Gunners	2-4	0-3	3-0	4-0	2-3	14-0	3-5	3-0	3-3	5-3	3-2	3-1	3-2	1-3	1-2	5-2	

CAMBRIDGESHIRE COUNTY LEAGUE SENIOR DIVISION B CONSTITUTION 2009-10

LUNTISHAM RANGERS . . . . Mill Lane, Bluntisham, Huntingdon PE28 3LP. . . . . None
:OMBERTON UNITED . . . . Recreation Ground, Hines Lane, Comberton CB3 7BZ . . . . None
:OTTENHAM UNITED RESERVES . King George V Playing Field, Lamb Lane, Cottenham CB4 8TB 01954 250873
LY CITY A . . . . The Unwin Ground, Downham Road, Ely CB6 2SH 01353 662035
OWLMERE . . . . Chrishall Road, Fowlmere, Royston SG8 7RE . . . . None
;REAT CHESTERFORD. . . Great Chesterford Rec Ground, Newmarket Road, Great Chesterford CB10 1NS. . . . . None
IADDENHAM ROVERS . . . . Hop Row, Haddenham, Ely CB6 3SR. . . . . None
INTON GRANTA . . . . Recreation Ground, Meadow Lane, Linton, Cambridge CB21 6HX . . . . None
IARCH TOWN UNITED RESERVES GER Sports Ground, Robin Goodfellow Lane, March PE15 8HS 01354 653073
UTWELL SWIFTS . . . . The Nest, Wisbech Road, Outwell, Wisbech PE14 8PA. . . . . None
;AFFRON CROCUS . . . . Ickleton Recreation Ground, Frogge Street, Ickleton CB10 1NS . . . . None
OHAM UNITED . . . . Qua Fen Common, Soham, Ely CB7 5DQ . . . . None
WAVESEY INSTITUTE. . . . . The Green, High Street, Swavesey CB24 4QU . . . . None
/EST ROW GUNNERS . . . . Beeches Road, West Row, Bury St Edmunds IP28 8NY . . . . None
/EST WRATTING RESERVES. . . . . Recreation Ground, Bull Lane, West Wratting CB1 5NJ. . . . . None
/ISBECH ST MARY . . . . Station Road, Wisbech St Mary, Wisbech PE13 4RT. . . . . None

/: Comberton United (R), Ely City A (P- Division 1B), Fowlmere (P - Division 1A), West Wratting Res. (P - Division 1A), Wisbech St Mary P - Division 1B)
)UT: Chatteris Town (P), Helions Bumpstead (R - Division 1A), Littleport Town Res. (R - Division 1B)
/lilton (P), RHS United (P) Sawston United (P)

BIS LEAGUE FINALS

IVISION ONE PLAY-OFF *(May 14th at Wisbech St Mary)* **Wisbech St Mary** 3 West Wratting Res. 1
IVISION TWO PLAY-OFF *(May 9th at Lakenheath)* **Lakenheath Res.** 3 Hardwick Res. 1
:REAKE CHARITY SHIELD ***(Div One/Two teams)*** **FINAL** *(May 5th at Cambridge City)* **Melbourn** 3 Sutton United 0
IVISION THREE PLAY-OFF *(May 9th at Huntingdon United RGE)* **Ashdon Villa** 3 Huntingdon United RGE 2
OHN ABLETT CUP ***(Div Three teams)*** **FINAL** *(May 5th at Cambridge City)* **Melbourn** 3 Sutton United 0
IVISION FOUR PLAY-OFF *(May 13th at Exning Athletic)* **Sawston United Res.** 2 Exning Athletic 1
IVISION FIVE PLAY-OFF *(May 16h at Emneth Spartans)* **Cherry Hinton Res.** 3 Emneth Spartans 1
IAIGH/PECK CUP ***(Div Four/Five teams)*** **FINAL** *(May 8th at Histon)* **Cherry Hinton Res.** 4 Gransden Cheq. Res. 0

Division One A	**P**	**W**	**D**	**L**	**F**	**A**	**Pts**
West Wratting Res.	24	16	4	4	73	40	52
Fowlmere	24	15	6	3	69	36	51
Cambdge Univ. Press Res.	24	14	8	2	72	35	50
Fulbourn Institute Res.	24	13	5	6	59	46	44
Duxford United	24	12	5	7	58	35	41
Barrington	24	11	6	7	54	44	39
Steeple Bumpstead	24	10	4	10	62	56	34
Girton United Res.	24	7	6	11	36	48	27
Gamlingay United *-3*	24	9	2	13	56	55	26
Sawston Rovers	24	6	5	13	42	65	23
Cambourne Rovers	24	6	3	15	48	62	21
Camden United	24	3	6	15	35	67	15
Comberton United Res.	24	3	2	19	25	100	1

Division One B	**P**	**W**	**D**	**L**	**F**	**A**	**Pts**
Wisbech St Mary	24	19	2	3	84	31	59
Ely City A	24	16	4	4	69	38	52
Newmarket White Lion	24	14	2	8	82	43	44
Fenstanton	24	13	2	9	69	54	41
Longstanton	24	12	3	9	65	49	39
Eaton Socon Res.	24	11	4	9	67	65	37
Bottisham Sports	24	11	3	10	42	43	36
Hemingfords Utd Res.	24	10	4	10	45	46	34
Waterbeach Res.	24	6	6	12	51	70	24
Gransden Chequers	24	7	3	14	36	59	24
St Ives Rangers	24	6	4	14	31	66	22
Buckden	24	5	6	13	42	68	21
Barton Mills	24	4	1	19	24	75	13

Division Two A	**P**	**W**	**D**	**L**	**F**	**A**	**Pts**
Hardwick Res.	26	22	3	1	93	29	69
Melbourn	26	20	3	3	98	37	63
Elsworth Sports	26	19	1	6	83	38	58
Cambridge Univ. Press A	26	15	3	8	78	41	48
Fulbourn Spts & Soc. Club	26	15	1	10	83	68	46
Great Shelford Res.	26	15	1	10	67	53	46
Thaxted Rangers	26	13	3	10	76	64	42
Balsham	26	12	3	11	66	58	39
Wilbraham	26	10	4	12	56	55	34
Bassingbourn	26	6	5	15	51	73	23
Papworth	26	6	3	17	50	69	21
Whittlesford United Res.	26	6	3	17	37	95	21
Great Chishill	26	4	2	20	34	81	14
Linton Granta Res.	26	0	3	23	22	133	3

Division Two B	**P**	**W**	**D**	**L**	**F**	**A**	**Pts**
Lakenheath Res.	26	22	3	1	108	37	69
Somersham Town Res.	26	16	5	5	66	38	53
Sutton United	26	16	3	7	80	56	51
Godmanchester Res.	26	14	5	7	59	31	47
The Vine	26	11	5	10	53	54	38
March Rangers	26	11	4	11	57	62	37
Pymoor	26	11	2	13	84	79	35
Over Sports Res.	26	11	2	13	62	63	35
Newmarket Town A *-3*	26	10	4	12	68	68	31
Witchford	26	8	5	13	65	76	29
Needingworth Utd Res.	26	7	8	11	36	54	29
Wisbech St Mary Res.	26	6	7	13	60	77	25
Milton Res.	26	5	4	17	24	80	19
Stretham Hotspurs	26	2	7	17	53	100	13

Division Three A	**P**	**W**	**D**	**L**	**F**	**A**	**Pts**
Ashdon Villa	26	20	1	5	84	37	61
Dullingham	26	18	4	4	73	40	58
Steeple Morden	26	18	2	6	113	39	56
RHS United Res.	26	17	4	5	101	42	55
Hundon Res.	26	15	3	8	93	47	48
Harston	26	15	1	10	76	50	46
Great Shelford A	26	12	2	12	64	67	38
Abington United	26	11	3	12	64	55	36
Lode	26	11	3	12	57	63	36
Great Chesterford Res.	26	9	5	12	60	72	32
Eaton Socon A	26	8	2	16	75	86	26
Foxton Res.	26	5	3	18	43	100	18
Camden United Res.	26	4	0	22	33	141	12
Mott MacDonald	26	2	1	23	32	129	7

Division Three B	**P**	**W**	**D**	**L**	**F**	**A**	**Pts**
Huntingdon United RGE	26	20	4	2	104	30	64
Burwell Swifts	26	20	2	4	84	33	62
Chatteris Town Res.	26	16	4	6	70	46	52
Mepal Sports	26	15	4	7	62	38	49
Little Downham Swifts	26	12	8	6	62	38	44
Bluntisham Rgrs Res.	26	14	2	10	51	35	44
Isleham United	26	13	4	9	62	59	43
Ely Crusaders	26	10	3	13	46	61	33
Brampton Res.	26	10	2	14	57	58	32
Wisbech St Mary A	26	10	2	14	69	78	32
Fordham Res.	26	8	6	12	56	64	30
Hemingfords United A	26	5	6	15	43	71	21
Cottenham United A	26	2	4	20	46	116	10
Soham United Res.	26	1	1	24	30	115	4

Division Four A	**P**	**W**	**D**	**L**	**F**	**A**	**Pts**
Sawston United Res.	24	18	4	2	84	28	58
Fulbourn Institute A	24	15	6	3	97	34	51
City Life	24	13	6	5	65	38	45
Steeple Bumpstead Res.	24	12	2	10	53	44	38
Figleaves	24	11	3	10	56	63	36
Barton *-3*	24	10	3	11	53	63	30
Hempstead United	24	8	6	10	46	60	30
Saffron Rangers	24	9	3	12	39	53	30
Orwell	24	8	6	10	42	59	30
Duxford United Res.	24	8	4	12	53	64	28
Litlington Athletic	24	6	7	11	57	70	25
Sawston Rovers Res.	24	5	7	12	41	69	22
Saffron Crocus Res.	24	2	5	17	38	79	11

(Dalehead United - record expunged)

Division Four B	**P**	**W**	**D**	**L**	**F**	**A**	**Pts**
Exning Athletic	24	18	2	4	85	47	56
Estover Park	24	14	5	5	77	38	47
Earith United	24	13	4	7	63	36	43
Fenstanton Res.	24	12	4	8	46	46	40
Tydd United	24	12	4	8	59	61	40
Milton A	24	10	3	11	38	42	33
Haddenham Rov. Res.	24	10	1	13	68	68	31
Wicken Amateurs	24	8	6	10	51	63	30
W. Row Gunners Res.	24	9	3	12	50	64	30
Barton Mills Res. *-3*	24	10	1	13	43	47	28
Cambdge Com. Church	24	7	6	11	45	51	27
The Vine Res.	24	5	4	15	44	80	19
Outwell Swifts Res.	24	4	5	15	42	68	17

Division Five A	P	W	D	L	F	A	Pt
Fowlmere Res.	24	19	4	1	78	25	61
Debden Res.	24	18	1	5	86	29	55
Hardwick A	24	17	3	4	69	22	54
West Wratting A	24	16	2	6	77	32	50
Hundon A	24	13	4	7	75	39	43
Cambourne Res.	24	9	6	9	58	51	33
Gt Chishill Res.	24	10	3	11	50	55	33
Melbourn Res.	24	10	2	12	75	65	32
Haslingfield	24	9	2	13	57	71	29
St. Morden Res.	24	7	3	14	45	72	24
Barrington Res.	24	6	1	17	40	85	19
Comberton A *-3*	24	4	3	17	36	59	12
Newport Veterans	24	1	0	23	21	162	3

Division Five B	P	W	D	L	F	A	Pt
Cherry Hin. Res.	24	19	1	4	117	29	58
Burwell Sw. Res.	24	18	2	4	72	34	56
Gransden C. Res.	24	16	5	3	94	53	53
Swavesey I. Res.	24	16	3	5	76	45	51
Longstanton Res.	24	13	4	7	64	49	43
Cbg Ambassadors	24	11	2	11	49	48	35
Papworth Res.	24	9	4	11	42	54	31
City Life Res.	24	7	3	14	40	68	24
Isleham Utd Res.	24	7	2	15	49	71	23
Lode Res.	24	6	4	14	35	59	22
Elsworth Sp. Res.	24	6	3	15	49	59	21
Bottisham S. Res.	24	6	1	17	36	93	19
Cambridge Ath.	24	5	0	19	38	99	15

Division Five C	P	W	D	L	F	A	Pt
Emneth Spartans	24	20	2	2	120	29	62
Chatteris Town A	24	19	4	1	142	22	61
W'bech Fen Stars	24	15	4	5	82	32	49
Walsoken United	24	14	3	7	118	65	45
Estover Park Res.	24	12	3	9	69	54	39
March Rgrs Res.	24	11	1	12	66	53	34
Chatt. Fen Tigers	24	9	4	11	56	63	31
Witchford Res.	24	10	1	13	59	72	31
L. Down.Sw. Res.	24	9	3	12	65	78	30
Wisbech St M. B	24	8	5	11	76	71	29
Coldham United	24	9	2	13	67	73	29
Supercue	24	4	0	20	34	177	12
Outwell Sw. A *-3*	24	0	0	24	13	178	-3

CENTRAL MIDLANDS LEAGUE

Sponsored by: Abacus Lighting

Founded: 1971
Recent champions:
2004: Retford United
2005: Dunkirk
2006: Barton Town Old Boys
2007: Bottesford Town
2008: Askern Welfare

	Blid	Calv	Clip	Fore	Harr	Harw	Hatf	Kimb	Kins	Nett	New	Oll	Pinx	Radc	Roll	Sou	Sutt	York
Blidworth Welfare	***S***	0-3	1-2	0-5	3-2	0-2	0-4	6-1	1-2	3-1	1-2	1-3	5-0	1-2	3-1	0-2	0-4	1-1
Calverton Miners Welfare	4-2	***U***	5-1	0-2	8-1	4-0	10-3	6-0	5-0	4-0	0-2	3-0	0-1	3-2	6-0	4-0	1-2	4-1
Clipstone Welfare	2-0	0-3	***P***	0-2	3-1	1-2	3-0	1-2	1-2	2-3	3-0	1-2	1-0	4-3	3-1	3-0	3-2	1-1
Forest Town	1-0	0-0	3-0	***R***	3-1	0-1	2-5	4-0	4-0	3-1	1-1	2-0	1-0	3-2	3-1	1-0	1-3	3-0
Harrowby United	2-1	0-5	1-2	1-3	***E***	1-4	2-1	1-0	0-2	3-2	1-2	2-4	0-2	1-7	3-6	0-0	0-7	1-4
Harworth Colliery Institute	0-4	0-4	0-1	1-2	6-1	***M***	4-2	4-2	1-0	4-2	2-3	1-0	1-1	2-1	5-3	3-1	3-1	1-1
Hatfield Main	3-2	0-9	1-0	0-1	1-1	0-3	***E***	7-2	2-3	3-3	2-1	1-2	0-2	3-1	4-1	1-2	2-2	3-3
Kimberley Town	0-0	1-7	1-2	2-8	3-3	1-0	2-4		0-2	3-2	1-2	2-4	2-3	1-3	5-2	0-2	4-0	1-4
Kinsley Boys	3-1	1-1	0-0	2-3	7-1	2-2	4-1	3-3		2-0	0-1	0-3	0-0	0-1	1-0	1-1	4-1	3-0
Nettleham	0-5	1-3	2-1	0-3	5-0	2-2	1-3	2-2	1-0		2-4	1-1	0-1	2-3	1-0	2-2	0-3	1-2
Newark Town	1-2	3-1	0-3	2-2	3-0	5-0	1-1	4-0	4-1	3-1	***D***	1-0	0-1	1-5	7-1	2-2	3-0	5-0
Ollerton Town	2-0	1-3	2-0	3-0	9-0	3-2	2-0	3-1	1-0	2-0	0-0	***I***	3-0	3-1	8-3	2-0	1-1	1-2
Pinxton	1-0	0-4	5-0	2-2	1-3	2-0	7-0	7-0	1-0	2-1	1-2	0-1	***V***	1-3	3-0	1-0	1-4	0-2
Radcliffe Olympic	3-0	3-0	5-1	1-0	6-1	2-1	4-0	7-1	5-2	1-1	4-1	0-0	4-0	***I***	2-1	5-2	1-1	3-0
Rolls Royce Leisure	1-3	3-6	0-1	0-8	1-4	2-3	3-3	2-2	1-1	0-4	1-3	3-4	0-9	1-3	***S***	0-2	6-4	3-5
Southwell City	1-1	2-2	2-3	2-4	1-0	0-1	4-2	0-1	3-1	2-1	0-3	1-1	3-6	0-1	3-1	***I***	2-3	1-5
Sutton Town	2-2	3-0	0-3	2-1	3-1	2-1	5-1	0-0	5-0	5-1	6-2	1-1	1-0	1-2	5-0	4-1	***O***	4-3
Yorkshire Main	5-5	1-2	1-4	2-4	4-1	1-3	2-0	4-1	1-1	2-2	1-2	3-1	0-4	1-3	9-1	3-0	2-0	***N***

Supreme Division		P	W	D	L	F	A	Pts
Radcliffe Olympic		34	25	3	6	99	40	78
Forest Town		34	24	4	6	85	35	76
Calverton Miners Welf.		34	24	3	7	120	36	75
Ollerton Town		34	21	6	7	73	36	69
Newark Town		34	21	5	8	76	46	68
Sutton Town		34	19	6	9	87	53	63
Harworth Colliery Inst.		34	18	4	12	65	57	58
Pinxton		34	18	3	13	65	43	57
Clipstone Welfare		34	18	2	14	56	53	56
Yorkshire Main		34	14	7	13	76	70	49
Kinsley Boys		34	12	8	14	50	55	44
Southwell City		34	9	7	18	44	68	34
Hatfield Main	*-3*	34	10	6	18	63	94	33
Blidworth Welfare		34	9	5	20	54	68	32
Kimberley Town	*+3*	34	6	6	22	47	109	27
Nettleham		34	6	7	21	48	79	25
Harrowby United		34	6	3	25	40	119	21
Rolls Royce Leisure		34	2	3	29	49	136	9

Premier Division	P	W	D	L	F	A	Pts
Louth Town	28	25	1	2	87	28	76
Westella & Willerby	28	21	4	3	77	23	67
Kirkby Town	28	21	3	4	96	30	66
Parramore Sports	28	16	7	5	74	38	55
Parkhouse	28	14	3	11	69	58	45
Newark Flowserve	28	13	4	11	49	50	43
Hutton Cranswick Utd	28	12	6	10	59	48	42
Church Warsop Welf.	28	9	7	12	57	54	34
Kiveton Park	28	8	6	14	45	61	30
Bentley Colliery	28	9	3	16	40	75	30
Phoenix Spts & Social	28	7	6	15	39	55	27
Thoresby Coll. Welfare	28	8	3	17	37	60	27
Bulwell Town	28	6	3	19	29	69	21
Welbeck Welfare	28	6	3	19	42	88	21
Thorne Colliery	28	4	3	21	36	99	15

Bolsover Town - record expunged

CENTRAL MIDLANDS LEAGUE SUPREME DIVISION CONSTITUTION 2009-10

BLIDWORTH WELFARE .... Blidworth Recreation Centre, Mansfield Road, Blidworth, Mansfield NG21 0LR 01623 793361
CALVERTON MINERS WELFARE . Calverton Miners Welfare, Hollinwood Lane, Calverton NG14 6NR................ 0115 965 4390
CLIPSTONE WELFARE......... Lido Ground, Clipstone Road East, Clipstone, Mansfield NG21 9AZ.............. 01623 477978
FOREST TOWN .... Forest Town Academy, Clipstone Road West, Forest Town, Mansfield NG19 0EE 01623 624678
GRANTHAM RANGERS .... Dickens Road, Grantham NG31 9QY.......................... 01476 590822
HARWORTH COLLIERY INSTITUTE....... Scrooby Road, Bircotes, Doncaster DN11 8JT 01302 750614
HATFIELD MAIN .... Dunscroft Welfare Ground, Broadway, Dunscroft, Doncaster DN7 4HD 01302 841326
KIMBERLEY TOWN .... The Stag Ground, Nottingham Road, Kimberley NG16 2ND 0115 938 2788
KINSLEY BOYS.................... Kinsley Playing Fields, Wakefield Road, Kinsley WF9 5EH 07883 373232
KIRKBY TOWN.................. Summit Centre, Lowmoor Road, Kirkby-in-Ashfield NG17 7LL.................. 01623 751822
LOUTH TOWN.................................. Park Avenue, Louth LN11 8BY 07712 653791
NETTLEHAM .... Mulsanne Park, Field Close, Nettleham, Lincoln LN2 2RX 01522 750007
NEWARK TOWN.................... Collingham FC, Station Road, Collingham NG23 7RA 01636 892303
OLLERTON TOWN .... The Lane, Walesby Lane, New Ollerton, Newark NG22 9UX.............................. None
PARRAMORE SPORTS .... Davy Sports & Social Club, Prince of Wales Road, Sheffield S9 4ER .... None
PINXTON .... Welfare Ground, Wharf Road, Pinxton NG16 6NY........................ 07989 324249
SOUTHWELL CITY........... War Memorial Recreation Ground, Bishops Drive, Southwell NG25 0JP 01636 814386
SUTTON TOWN .... The Fieldings, Huthwaite Road, Sutton-in-Ashfield NG17 2HB.................. 01623 552376
WESTELLA & WILLERBY .... Hill Top Sports & Social Club, Willerby Low Road, Willerby, Hull HU16 5JD............... 01482 671306

IN: Kirkby Town (P), Louth Town (P), Parramore Sports (P), Westella & Willerby (P)
OUT: Radcliffe Olympic (P - East Midlands Counties League), Rolls Royce Leisure (W), Yorkshire Main (R)
Harrowby United become Grantham Rangers

QUARTET CATERING LEAGUE CUP

PRELIMINARY ROUND
Bentley Colliery 0 **Newark Town** 2
Blidworth Welfare 0 **Southwell City** 3
Welbeck Welfare 3 Rolls Royce 2
FIRST ROUND
Calverton MW 4 Harrowby Utd 0
Church Warsop 0 **Louth Town** 3
Clipstone 3 Hutton Cranswick 1
Kimberley Town 2 Bulwell Town 0
Kinsley Boys 3 Pinxton 0
Kirkby Town 0 Radcliffe Olympic 0
Replay: **Radcliffe** 3 Kirkby Town 1
Newark T. (w/o) v Mablethorpe (scr).
Nettleham 3 Hatfield Main 3
Replay: **Hatfield Main** 3 Nettleham 1
Ollerton Town 3 Kiveton Park 0
Parramore Sports 3 Parkhouse 2
Phoenix S&S 1 Newark Flowserve 0
Sutton Town (w/o) v Bolsover (scr.)
Thoresby CW 1 Welbeck Welfare 1
Replay: **Welbeck** 4 Thoresby CW 2
Thorne Colliery 0 **Forest Town** 2
Westella & Willerby 2 Harworth CI 1
Yorkshire Main 5 Southwell City 4
SECOND ROUND
Kimberley Town 0 **Welbeck Welfare** 3
Kinsley Boys 0 **Sutton Town** 2
Yorkshire Main 2 **Parramore Sports** 3
Newark Town 4 Hatfield Main 0
Forest Town 1 Radcliffe Olympic 1
Replay: Radcliffe 1 **Forest** 1 *aet* (3-4p)
Clipstone 1 **Westella & Willerby** 2
Phoenix S&S 3 Calverton MW 1
Louth Town 2 Ollerton Town 1
QUARTER-FINALS
Parramore Sports 3 Phoenix 0
Welbeck Welfare 1 **Louth Town** 2
Sutton Town 1 Forest Town 0
Westella/Willerby 3 Newark Town 1
SEMI-FINALS
Parramore Sports 0 **Westella & Willerby 1** *(at Harworth Colliery Inst.)*
Sutton T. 1 Louth T. 0 *(at Harrowby)*
FINAL *(May 4th at Alfreton Town)*
Westella & Willerby 0 **Sutton Town** 2

	Ben	Bol	Bul	Chu	Hut	Kir	Kiv	Lou	New	Par	Par	Pho	Tho	Thrn	Wel	Wes
Bentley Colliery		3-0	2-2	2-1	0-3	1-5	3-1	1-2	0-2	0-3	0-5	2-2	2-0	0-4	5-4	0-3
Bolsover Town	n/a		1-3	n/a	1-4	0-2	n/a	2-6	n/a	n/a	1-5	n/a	4-0	4-2	n/a	0-5
Bulwell Town	2-0	4-3	***P***	3-4	1-2	0-6	0-3	1-4	0-1	0-2	0-3	2-4	1-1	5-0	1-0	0-4
Church Warsop	1-2	4-2	1-3	***R***	1-2	0-0	2-2	2-6	1-1	5-1	1-3	5-1	4-0	4-2	9-0	0-1
Hutton C'swick	1-0	3-1	2-0	1-2	***E***	1-2	6-1	2-2	0-3	6-1	2-2	2-1	2-0	5-2	2-2	1-2
Kirkby Town	6-1	n/a	1-1	1-0	3-3	***M***	5-0	0-1	5-1	3-2	1-3	4-0	8-1	8-0	5-0	1-2
Kiveton Park	2-2	n/a	1-0	2-1	1-5	1-2	***I***	0-5	2-2	3-2	1-1	2-0	2-3	1-3	4-1	1-2
Louth Town	2-1	n/a	4-2	4-0	3-1	1-4	3-0	***E***	6-1	5-2	6-1	3-2	3-1	4-0	2-1	1-2
Newark F'serve	8-0	n/a	1-0	2-2	3-1	3-4	1-0	0-3	***R***	1-5	0-4	1-0	1-2	1-1	3-0	0-1
Parkhouse	2-4	n/a	3-0	3-1	3-0	2-7	2-1	0-3	3-5		0-0	2-1	3-1	6-0	3-0	1-3
Parramore Spts	2-0	n/a	3-1	2-2	2-1	1-2	2-2	0-2	1-0	0-2		1-0	5-2	8-1	4-4	2-2
Phoenix Spts/S.	2-3	3-1	4-0	1-1	1-1	1-4	3-1	0-1	0-2	2-2	1-2	***D***	2-0	5-0	1-7	1-0
Thoresby CW	2-3	n/a	5-0	1-1	2-1	1-3	2-3	1-2	3-0	2-1	0-3	0-0	***I***	3-1	2-0	0-1
Thorne Colliery	1-3	n/a	0-2	0-2	3-4	1-4	0-0	2-6	1-4	0-4	2-4	1-1	3-2	***V***	2-3	0-4
Welbeck Welfare	2-0	n/a	1-2	1-4	3-0	0-2	1-7	0-1	0-2	3-7	0-8	4-0	1-0	4-6		0-6
Westella & W.	5-3	n/a	7-0	7-0	2-2	2-0	2-1	1-2	5-0	2-2	3-2	2-3	4-0	2-0	0-0	

Reserve Supreme		P	W	D	L	F	A	Pt
Carlton Town Res.	*-3*	28	21	5	2	108	31	65
Staveley MW Res.		28	18	6	4	96	41	60
Heanor Town Res.		28	16	4	8	80	53	52
Teversal Res.		28	15	4	9	58	53	49
Belper Town Res.		28	15	3	10	65	50	48
Mickleover Sports Res.		28	15	2	11	79	47	47
Dunkirk Res.		28	15	2	11	68	61	47
Rainworth MW Res.		28	10	5	13	52	55	35
Holbrook MW Res.	*-1*	28	9	9	10	54	62	35
Blidworth Welfare Res.		28	10	5	13	44	68	35
Shirebrook Town Res.		28	9	3	16	61	71	30
Forest Town Res.		28	9	2	17	43	77	29
Graham Street P. Res.		28	8	4	16	32	67	28
Radford Res.		28	6	2	20	41	97	20
Sutton Town Res.		28	3	6	19	40	88	15

Reserve Premier		P	W	D	L	F	A	Pt
Yorks Main Res.	*-12*	22	18	1	3	103	24	52
Kiveton Park Res.		22	16	2	4	69	21	50
Southwell City Res.		22	14	4	4	46	20	46
Radcliffe Olym. Res.		22	12	3	7	57	46	39
Clipstone W. Res.		22	10	8	4	40	29	38
Calverton MW Res.		22	8	6	8	46	38	30
Ollerton Town Res.		22	8	4	10	35	43	28
Nettleham Res.		22	7	3	12	41	59	24
Pinxton Res.		22	5	2	15	51	67	17
Church Warsop Res.		22	4	5	13	29	52	17
Bulwell Town Res.		22	4	3	15	34	83	15
Newark Town Res.		22	4	3	15	28	97	15

PHOENIX TROPHIES FLOODLIGHT CUP

PRELIMINARY ROUND
Clipstone 3 **Forest Town** 6
FIRST ROUND
Blidworth 4 Rolls Royce 0
Calverton MW 3 Southwell 0
Forest T. 0 **Sutton Town** 1 *aet*
Hatfield Main 1 **Harworth CI** 2
Nettleham 0 **Newark Town** 1
Ollerton Town 0 **Parramore** 2
Pinxton 8 Kimberley Town 0
Radcliffe O. 4 Harrowby Utd 0
QUARTER-FINALS
Radcliffe 3 Calverton MW 2
Pinxton 4 Blidworth Welfare 1
Sutton Town 3 Newark T. 2
Harworth 7 Parramore 2
SEMI-FINALS
Sutton Town 2 Harworth1
Pinxton 3 Radcliffe Olympic 1
FINAL
(April 29th at Sth Normanton)
Sutton Town 0 **Pinxton** 4

PHOENIX TROPHIES RESERVES CUP
FINAL *(April 1st at Radford)*
Holbrook Res. 1 **Carlton T. Res.** 2 *aet*

CENTRAL MIDLANDS LEAGUE PREMIER DIVISION CONSTITUTION 2009-10

BENTLEY COLLIERY .... Bentley Miners Welfare, The Avenue, Bentley, Doncaster DN5 0NP................ 01302 87442
BULWELL TOWN ...... Goosedale Sports Ground, Goosedale Lane, Bestwood Village, Nottingham NG15 8FG 0115 963 018
CHURCH WARSOP WELFARE Church Warsop MW, Wood Lane, Church Warsop, Mansfield NG20 0SR 01623 84202
DRONFIELD TOWN............. Gosforth Fields, Bubnell Road, Stubley Drive, Dronfield S18 8NP.................. Nor
EASINGTON UNITED................ Low Farm, Beck Street, Easington, Hull HU12 0TT .... Nor
FC BRIMINGTON .... Babbage Way, off Sandy Lane, Worksop S80 1TN.............................. Nor
FC05...................... Bilsthorpe Sports Field, Eakring Road, Bilsthorpe, Newark NG22 8SX.................. Nor
HUTTON CRANSWICK UNITED........ Rotsea Lane, Hutton Cranswick, Driffield YO25 9QG.......................... Nor
KIVETON PARK................ Kiveton Park MW, Hard Lane, Kiveton Park, Sheffield S26 6NB 07763 46797
PARKHOUSE .... Mill Lane Ground, Mill Lane, Clay Cross, Chesterfield 07816 75877
PHOENIX SPORTS & SOCIAL . Phoenix Sports Complex, Bawtry Road, Brinsworth, Rotherham S60 5PA 01709 36386
SOUTH NORMANTON ...... ExChem Sports Ground, Lees Lane, South Normanton, Alfreton DE55 2AD 01773 58149
THORESBY COLLIERY WELFARE Thoresby Colliery Spts Ground, Fourth Avenue, Edwinstowe NG21 9NS............. 07802 41798
THORNE COLLIERY .... Moorends Welfare, Grange Road, Moorends, Thorne, Doncaster DN8 4LU............. 07855 54522
WELBECK WELFARE........ Colliery Ground, Elkesley Rd, Meden Vale, Warsop, Mansfield NG20 9PS 07863 56857
YORKSHIRE MAIN.................... Edlington Lane, Edlington, Doncaster DN12 1DA........................ 07775 71455

IN: Dronfield Town (P - Midland Regional Alliance Premier Division), Easington United (P - Humber Premier League Premier Division FC05 (P - Midland Amateur Alliance Premier Division), FC Brimington (P - Sunday football),South Normanton (N), Yorkshire Main (R)
OUT: Bolsover Town (WS), Kirkby Town (P), Mablethorpe Athletic (WN), Newark Flowserve (W - Notts Senior League Senior Division Louth Town (P), Parramore Sports (P), Westella & Willerby (P)

CHESHIRE LEAGUE

www.mcfl.co.uk

Sponsored by: Cheshire Building Society

Founded: 1919

Recent champions:
2004: Middlewich Town
2005: Barnton
2006: Middlewich Town
2007: Middlewich Town
2008: Styal

	Bar	Bill	CAZ	Cro	Cur	Gam	Gar	Gre	Knu	Lin	Mid	Pil	SC	Sty	Tra	Woo
Barnton		1-2	0-1	1-1	3-1	1-4	1-2	2-5	3-4	2-3	0-1	1-0	3-4	0-3	1-2	0-8
Billinge	2-0		0-0	1-2	2-6	2-2	0-3	0-3	3-2	1-0	1-5	2-1	0-1	2-2	4-3	1-3
Club AZ	4-3	1-0	***D***	1-0	3-1	0-0	0-1	2-0	5-0	8-0	1-2	0-1	1-2	4-0	0-0	1-0
Crosfields-Rylands	3-2	1-1	2-0	***I***	2-1	3-1	4-0	2-5	2-0	5-1	2-1	3-3	5-0	2-1	2-2	0-2
Curzon Ashton Res.	2-1	1-0	0-3	0-2	***V***	1-3	2-1	5-0	4-3	2-0	0-2	0-2	1-4	0-1	0-2	1-4
Gamesley	5-1	0-2	0-3	0-1	0-1	***I***	1-1	1-1	2-2	1-1	0-3	0-1	1-5	3-1	1-0	1-1
Garswood United	1-3	1-1	0-0	0-1	0-1	1-0	***S***	3-3	2-2	1-1	1-4	3-2	1-3	0-2	0-4	3-4
Greenalls Padgate St Os.	1-2	2-2	0-2	3-0	2-1	4-1	1-2	***I***	3-3	2-1	1-3	1-2	0-1	1-0	2-0	1-1
Knutsford	4-3	0-4	0-4	0-3	2-4	1-0	0-2	1-3	***O***	1-0	1-2	2-5	1-1	1-2	2-1	2-3
Linotype & Cheadle HN	1-1	1-1	2-3	0-2	0-1	3-3	1-0	2-0	2-0	***N***	2-1	0-2	1-2	3-1	2-1	1-4
Middlewich Town	2-0	1-0	3-3	3-2	0-1	3-0	2-0	5-0	3-0	8-0		3-1	2-0	4-0	1-1	2-1
Pilkington	6-1	0-1	0-3	2-4	2-1	3-1	1-3	4-2	4-3	8-2	2-1	***O***	5-0	2-2	1-1	2-5
Stalybridge Celtic Res.	6-0	4-0	2-3	2-2	2-1	2-2	0-1	5-0	5-0	1-1	2-2	5-1	***N***	2-0	1-2	1-1
Styal	4-1	3-2	2-0	3-1	2-3	4-1	2-1	1-2	2-2	2-1	1-1	2-2	4-1	***E***	3-2	1-3
Trafford Res.	2-1	5-1	1-3	2-0	4-1	1-2	3-0	3-3	1-1	1-0	0-0	2-0	3-1	0-1		2-5
Woodley	3-1	4-1	2-2	6-2	5-0	2-0	2-1	0-2	4-0	2-2	4-1	8-1	2-0	8-0	2-0	

ivision One	P	W	D	L	F	A	Pts
Voodley	30	22	5	3	99	32	71
liddlewich Town	30	20	5	5	71	27	65
lub AZ	30	18	6	6	61	24	60
rosfields-Rylands	30	17	5	8	61	44	56
talybridge Celtic Res.	30	15	6	9	65	46	51
tyal	30	14	5	11	52	55	47
ilkington	30	14	4	12	66	62	46
rafford Res.	30	12	7	11	51	41	43
reenalls Padgate St Oswalds	30	12	6	12	53	57	42
urzon Ashton Res.	30	13	0	17	43	57	39
illinge	30	9	7	14	39	58	34
arswood United	30	9	6	15	35	51	33
inotype & Cheadle HN	30	7	7	16	34	67	28
amesley	30	6	9	15	36	55	27
nutsford	30	5	6	19	40	82	21
arnton	30	4	2	24	39	87	14

Reserve Division	P	W	D	L	F	A	Pt
Pilkington Res.	28	21	4	3	56	22	67
Linotype & Cheadle HN Res.	28	19	0	9	92	53	57
Styal Res.	28	18	3	7	80	46	57
Greenalls Padgate SO Res.	28	17	2	9	84	52	53
Crosfields-Rylands Res.	28	17	2	9	68	46	53
Golborne Sports Res.	28	14	3	11	54	52	45
Eagle Sports Res.	28	14	2	12	65	57	44
Middlewich Town Res.	28	13	3	12	68	56	42
Daten Res.	28	10	3	15	49	66	33
Poynton Res.	28	10	2	16	53	67	32
Gamesley Res.	28	8	4	16	50	70	28
Billinge Res.	28	8	3	17	53	58	27
Garswood United Res.	28	7	6	15	39	58	27
Crewe Res.	28	7	3	18	51	110	24
Denton Town Res.	28	6	2	20	56	105	20

Broadheath Central - record expunged

RESERVES CUP

FINAL *(April 8th at Trafford)*

Greenalls PSO Res. 3 Crosfields/Rylands Res. 2

PRESIDENT'S CUP

(First Round losers from divisional cups)

PRELIMINARY ROUND

Eagle Sports 5 Poynton Res. 0

Pilkington Res. 3 Golborne Sports Res. 0

Competition abandoned due to inclement weather

CHESHIRE LEAGUE DIVISION ONE CONSTITUTION 2009-10

ILLINGE .... John Eddleston Sports Ground, Rainford Road, Billinge WN5 7PF 07742 418591
LUB AZ .... Mulberries Sports Centre, Astra Zeneca (off A34), Macclesfield SK10 4TF 01625 514040
ROSFIELDS-RYLANDS .... Rylands Recreation Club, Gorsey Lane, Warrington WA2 7RZ 01925 625700
AGLE SPORTS .... Eagle Sports Club, Thornton Road, Great Sankey, Warrington WA5 1RB 01925 632926
AMESLEY .... Melandra Park, Melandra Castle Road, Gamesley, Glossop SK13 6UQ .... None
ARSWOOD UNITED The Wooders, Simms Lane End, Garswood Rd, Garswood, Ashton-in-Makerfield WN4 0XF 01744 892258
OLBORNE SPORTS .... Simpson Playing Fields, Stone Cross Road, Lowton WA3 2FL 01942 510161
REENALLS PADGATE ST OSWALDS .... Walkers Club, Long Lane, Warrington WA2 8PU 01925 634971
NUTSFORD .... Manchester Road, Knutsford WA16 0NU .... None
INOTYPE & CHEADLE HN .... The Heath, Norbreck Avenue, Cheadle, Stockport SK8 2ET 0161 282 6574
IIDDLEWICH TOWN .... Seddon Street, Middlewich CW10 9DT 01606 835842
ILKINGTON .... Ruskin Drive, Dentons Green, St Helens WA10 6RP 01744 22893
TALYBRIDGE CELTIC RESERVES ..... Bower Fold, Mottram Road, Stalybridge SK15 2RT 0161 338 2828/8443
TYAL .... Altrincham Road, Styal, Wilmslow SK9 4JE 01625 529303
RAFFORD RESERVES .... Shawe View, Pennybridge Lane, Flixton, Urmston M41 5DL 0161 747 1727/749 8217
VOODLEY .... 86 Witton Street, Northwich CW9 5AE .... None

V: Eagle Sports (P), Golborne Sports (P)
UT: Barnton (R), Curzon Ashton Res. (S - Lancashire League West Division)

J B PARKER DIVISION ONE CUP

FIRST ROUND

Barnton 1 **Middlewich Town** 3
Crosfields-Rylands 4 Woodley 0
Garswood United 1 **Trafford Res.** 2
Greenalls Padgate St Oswalds 4 Billinge 0
Curzon Ashton Res. 3 **Club AZ** 4
Gamesley 2 **Pilkington** 3
Linotype & Cheadle HN 2 Styal 1
Stalybridge Celtic Res. 5 Knutsford 2

QUARTER-FINALS

Club AZ 0 **Crosfields** 1, **Middlewich Town** 3 Pilkington 0
Stalybridge Celtic Res. 6 Linotype & Cheadle HN 0
Trafford Res. 0 **Greenalls Padgate St Oswalds** 1

SEMI-FINALS

Crosfields-Rylands 1 Stalybridge Celtic Res. 0
Middlewich Town 2 Greenalls Padgate St Oswalds 0

FINAL *(March 25th at Trafford)*

Middlewich Town 1 Crosfields-Rylands 0

Division Two	P	W	D	L	F	A	Pts
Golborne Sports	32	22	4	6	84	35	70
Eagle Sports	32	20	5	7	97	52	65
Moore United	32	19	7	6	69	36	64
Lostock Gralam	32	19	6	7	81	42	63
Tarporley Victoria	32	17	8	7	72	36	59
Warrington Town Res.	32	17	8	7	55	33	59
Whitchurch Alport	32	13	9	10	59	46	48
Grappenhall Sports	32	14	5	13	69	57	47
Poynton	32	13	8	11	59	50	47
Daten	32	14	3	15	59	57	45
Crewe	32	13	6	13	58	57	45
Denton Town	32	10	3	19	59	107	33
Monk Sports	32	8	5	19	52	73	29
Congleton Town Res.	32	7	7	18	50	91	28
Maine Road Res.	32	9	0	23	46	71	27
Malpas	32	8	3	21	46	98	27
Broadheath Central	32	4	3	25	34	108	15

DIVISION TWO CUP

PRELIMINARY ROUND

Moore United 1 **Daten** 4

FIRST ROUND

Broadheath Central 3 Maine Road Res. 1
Daten 2 Eagle Sports 1 *aet*
Grappenhall Sports 2 Tarporley Victoria 1
Lostock Gralam 1 **Denton** 3
Malpas 2 **Crewe** 3
Monk Sports 5 Congleton Town Res. 3
Warrington Town Res. 1 **Golborne Sports** 2
Whitchurch Alport 3 Poynton 2

QUARTER-FINALS

Broadheath Central 1 **Whitchurch Alport** 3
Crewe 1 Golborne Sports 0
Daten 1 Grappenhall Spts 0
Monk 5 Denton Town 1

SEMI-FINALS

Whitchurch Alpt 0 **Daten** 1
Crewe 3 Monk Sports 2

FINAL

(April 22nd at Northwich V.)

Crewe 0 **Daten** 1

	Broad.	Congle.	Crewe	Daten	Denton	Eagle	Golb'ne	Grappen	Lostock.	Maine R	Malpas	Monk	Moore	Poynton	Tarp'ley	Warring.	Whit.
Broadheath Central		3-2	1-4	1-3	2-4	0-8	0-3	0-5	1-3	2-4	0-2	2-3	0-2	1-3	0-4	0-0	2-4
Congleton Town Res.	5-0		0-5	3-1	2-1	4-3	2-6	1-4	2-2	2-1	1-6	2-0	0-6	1-1	2-4	3-3	0-2
Crewe	2-1	2-0	***D***	0-3	3-0	1-2	2-3	1-3	1-4	3-0	5-1	5-4	1-1	2-2	0-1	0-2	1-1
Daten	5-1	2-3	1-2	***I***	1-3	3-1	1-1	2-1	1-0	4-1	4-0	1-3	0-2	3-3	0-3	2-3	2-1
Denton Town	2-0	8-4	3-0	0-1	***V***	1-4	0-7	4-3	2-5	0-2	2-3	1-3	1-3	1-4	5-3	2-2	1-1
Eagle Sports	5-0	9-1	2-2	3-0	5-1	***I***	3-3	1-2	4-3	2-0	4-3	5-0	2-1	1-3	0-2	3-2	4-3
Golborne Sports	2-2	3-0	0-1	4-0	7-0	1-2	***S***	2-3	2-0	3-1	5-3	1-0	2-0	1-1	1-0	2-0	3-1
Grappenhall Sports	2-3	2-0	0-3	5-2	6-0	2-2	1-3	***I***	1-3	4-1	5-1	3-2	1-2	1-0	1-1	0-2	0-2
Lostock Gralam	9-0	0-0	5-1	2-2	9-4	4-2	0-3	0-2	***O***	6-1	4-0	2-1	1-0	2-1	3-2	1-0	0-0
Maine Road Res.	2-0	3-2	0-2	2-4	2-3	2-4	1-3	6-2	1-3	***N***	0-1	0-3	0-1	2-1	0-1	0-1	1-2
Malpas	2-3	3-2	0-3	0-6	3-4	0-2	1-5	0-0	3-3	1-5		3-2	1-5	2-0	1-3	0-3	0-3
Monk Sports	1-2	2-1	3-3	0-3	1-4	1-3	0-2	3-3	1-3	2-0	1-3		1-2	3-1	2-2	1-2	0-2
Moore United	5-1	1-0	5-2	2-0	3-0	1-2	3-0	1-1	2-1	1-2	2-1	2-2	***T***	6-2	0-0	2-1	4-3
Poynton	4-1	2-2	3-0	2-1	1-1	0-4	3-0	3-1	1-0	1-0	7-1	1-5	2-2	***W***	0-1	0-2	3-0
Tarporley Victoria	3-1	0-0	4-0	4-0	5-1	3-2	2-3	1-0	1-1	4-1	7-1	4-1	1-1	1-1	***O***	1-2	2-2
Warrington Town Res.	2-1	2-2	1-0	0-1	7-0	1-1	2-1	2-3	0-1	3-1	2-0	1-1	0-0	2-1	2-1		1-1
Whitchurch Alport	3-3	4-1	1-1	1-0	5-0	2-2	0-2	3-2	0-1	0-4	0-0	4-0	5-1	0-2	2-1	1-2	

CHESHIRE LEAGUE DIVISION TWO CONSTITUTION 2009-10

BARNTON . . . . Townfield, Townfield Lane, Barnton, Northwich CW8 4LH . . . . Non
CONGLETON TOWN RESERVES . . Booth Street Ground, off Crescent Road, Congleton CW12 4DG 01260 27446
CREWE . . . . Cumberland Arena, Thomas Street, Crewe CW1 2BD 01270 53791
DATEN . . . . Culcheth Sports Club, Charnock Road, Culcheth, Warrington WA3 5SH 01925 76309
DENTON TOWN . . . . Whittles Park, Heather Lea, Denton M34 6EJ . . . . Non
GRAPPENHALL SPORTS . . . Grappenhall Sports Club, Stockton Lane, Grappenhall, Warrington WA4 3HQ . . . . Non
LOSTOCK GRALAM . . . . The Park Stadium, Manchester Road, Lostock Gralam CW9 7PJ 01606 4214
MAINE ROAD RESERVES . Manchester County FA Ground, Branthingham Rd, Chorlton-cum-Hardy M21 0TT 0161 604 762
MALPAS . . . . Malpas & District Sports Club, Oxheys, Wrexham Road, Malpas SY14 7EJ 01948 86066
MONK SPORTS . . . . Hillock Lane, Woolston, Warrington WA1 4QL 01925 81232
MOORE UNITED . . . . Carlsberg Tetley Club, Long Lane, Warrington WA2 8PU 01925 63497
NEW MILLS RESERVES . . . . Church Lane, Church Road, New Mills SK22 4NP 01663 74743
POYNTON . . . . London Road North, Poynton, Stockport SK12 1AG 01625 87576
TARPORLEY VICTORIA . . . . Tattenhall Recreation Club, Field Lane, Tattenhall CH3 9QF 01829 77071
WARRINGTON TOWN RESERVES . . . . . Cantilever Park, Common Lane, Warrington WA4 2RS 01925 63193
WHITCHURCH ALPORT . . . . Yockings Park, Blackpark Road, Whitchurch SY13 1PG 01948 66741

IN: Barnton (R), New Mills Res. (S - North West Counties League Reserve Division)
OUT: Broadheath Central (W), Eagle Sports (P), Golborne Sports (P)

DORSET PREMIER LEAGUE

www.the-dpl.co.uk

Sponsored by:
No sponsor

Founded: 1957

Recent champions:
2004: Hamworthy United
2005: Hamworthy Recreation
2006:Holt United
2007: Westland Sports
2008: Portland United

	Bla	Bri	Chi	Cob	Cra	HR	HU	Hol	PB	Por	SM	SU	Swa	Wes	Win
Blandford United		3-1	1-4	2-1	2-2	0-3	0-2	1-3	2-3	0-3	4-2	3-1	0-2	0-7	0-6
Bridport Res.	2-1		2-8	2-0	0-0	3-2	1-2	1-4	0-5	1-4	1-1	0-3	1-5	0-2	0-5
Chickerell United	6-0	3-1		3-1	1-0	0-1	6-0	2-3	0-0	2-0	4-1	4-1	1-0	1-1	0-2
Cobham Sports	6-2	1-2	2-2		0-2	2-3	1-2	2-4	2-7	4-6	4-3	0-1	0-0	2-2	2-4
Cranborne	2-0	0-1	0-4	2-3		0-5	5-2	1-3	0-2	1-4	4-3	1-2	1-2	1-1	1-3
Hamworthy Recreation	5-0	5-0	2-0	5-1	3-1		3-2	2-3	0-0	1-1	2-3	0-0	0-4	1-0	5-2
Hamworthy United Res.	1-2	1-2	1-5	1-0	2-0	1-3		1-4	1-1	0-6	1-1	3-0	0-3	0-1	1-3
Holt United	10-0	3-0	1-1	2-3	3-0	2-2	5-2		1-2	0-3	5-1	1-0	6-3	3-0	4-1
Poole Borough	4-0	3-0	1-1	7-0	2-2	2-1	4-2	4-1		1-1	1-1	1-0	3-2	2-1	2-2
Portland United	2-0	6-1	1-0	5-1	4-0	0-3	6-0	3-0	1-0		1-0	2-0	1-2	2-1	1-7
Sturminster Marshall	1-3	3-4	2-3	3-1	0-1	1-2	5-1	0-5	0-1	2-3		2-1	1-2	2-4	2-1
Sturminster Newton Utd	1-1	0-1	2-2	1-0	2-2	0-5	1-0	1-0	2-3	0-5	1-0		2-1	0-1	2-0
Swanage Town & Herston	1-1	1-2	0-3	4-1	3-0	1-1	4-1	2-1	3-0	2-2	3-1	4-0		1-3	2-4
Westland Sports	6-1	3-0	1-3	3-0	3-0	1-1	9-0	1-1	4-1	2-2	4-2	2-0	1-1		3-1
Wincanton Town	2-0	7-2	1-1	0-3	1-1	1-1	4-1	1-2	0-2	3-2	4-0	1-0	0-4	2-2	

	P	W	D	L	F	A	Pts
ortland United	28	19	4	5	77	34	61
oole Borough	28	17	8	3	64	30	59
olt United	28	18	3	7	80	40	57
hickerell United	28	16	7	5	70	28	55
amworthy Rec.	28	16	7	5	67	31	55
Vestland Sports	28	15	8	5	69	30	53
wanage Town & H.	28	15	5	8	62	37	50
Vincanton Town	28	14	5	9	68	46	47
turminser Newton	28	9	4	15	24	45	31
ridport Res.	28	9	2	17	31	81	29
ranborne	28	5	6	17	30	61	21
landford United	28	6	3	19	29	89	21
amworthy Utd Res.	28	6	2	20	31	85	20
turminster Marshall	28	5	3	20	43	71	18
obham Sports	28	5	3	20	43	80	12

LEAGUE CUP

FIRST ROUND
(ties played over two legs)
Hamworthy Rec 2 Bridport Res. 1, Bridport Res. 1 **Hamworthy Rec** 5
Portland 0 Wincanton 2, Wincanton 1 **Portland** 6
Stur. Nwton 1 Swanage 4, **Swanage** 2 Stur. Newtn 1
Cranborne 1 Chickerell 4, **Chickerell** 4 Cranborne 0
Hamworthy United Res. 1 Sturminster Marshall 2, **Sturminster Marshall** 3 Hamworthy United Res. 0
Holt United 5 Blandford 1, Blandford 3 **Holt United** 4
Cobham S. 0 Westland 4, **Westland** 5 Cobham S. 2

QUARTER-FINALS
(ties played over two legs)
Chickerell United 2 Sturminster Marshall 0, Sturminster Marshall 2 **Chickerell United** 3
Hamworthy Recreation 1 Westland Sports 0, Westland Sports 0 **Hamworthy Recreation** 1
Holt United 1 Portland 7, **Portland United** 0 Holt 0
Swanage 1 Poole Boro. 0, **Poole B.** 5 Swanage 2

SEMI-FINALS
Poole Boro. 0 **Portland** 3
Chickerell United 0 Hamworthy Recreation 0

FINAL
(May 12th at Weymouth)
Portland United 2 Chickerell Utd 2 *aet* (4-2p)

DORSET PREMIER LEAGUE CONSTITUTION 2009-10

LANDFORD UNITED . . . . Recreation Ground, Park Road, Blandford Forum DT11 7BX . . . . None
RIDPORT RESERVES . . . . St Marys Field, Skilling Hill Road, Bridport DT6 5LN 01308 423834
HICKERELL UNITED . . . . Weymouth College, Cranford Avenue, Weymouth DT4 7LQ 01305 208892
OBHAM SPORTS . . . . Cobham Sports & Social Club, Merley House Lane, Wimborne BH21 3AA 01202 885773
RANBORNE . . . . Recreation Ground, Penny's Lane, Cranborne, Wimborne BH21 5QE . . . . None
AMWORTHY RECREATION. Hamworthy Rec Club, Magna Road, Canford Magna, Wimborne BH21 3AP 01202 881922
AMWORTHY UNITED RESERVES . County Grnd, Blandford Close, Hamworthy, Poole BH15 4BF 01202 674974
OLT UNITED . . . . Gaunts Common, Holt, Wimborne BH21 4JR 01258 840379
ARLEY SPORTS . . . . Parley Sports Club, Christchurch Road, West Parley BH22 8SQ 01202 573345
OOLE BOROUGH . . . . Turlin Moor Recreation Ground, Blandford Moor, Hamworthy, Poole BH21 5XX . . . . None
ORTLAND UNITED . . . . New Grove Corner, Grove Road, Portland DT5 1DP 01305 861489
HERBORNE TOWN RESERVES. . Raleigh Grove, The Terrace Playing Fields, Sherborne DT9 5NS 01935 816110
TURMINSTER MARSHALL . . . . Churchill Close, Sturminster Marshall BH21 4BQ . . . . None
TURMINSTER NEWTON UTD . . . Barnetts Field, Honeymead Lane, Sturminster Newton DT10 7EW 01258 471406
WANAGE TOWN & HERSTON . . . . . . Day's Park, off De Moulham Road, Swanage BH19 2JW 01929 424673
VESTLAND SPORTS . . . . Alvington Lane, Yeovil BA22 8UX . . . . None
VEYMOUTH RESERVES . . . . Wessex Stadium, Radipole Lane, Weymouth DT4 9XJ 01305 785558
VINCANTON TOWN . . . . Wincanton Sports Ground, Moor Lane, Wincanton BA9 9EJ 01963 31815

N: Parley Sports (P - Dorset County League Senior Division), Sherborne Town Res. (P - Dorset County League Reserve Division), Veymouth Res. (N)

EDGAR MAIDMENT CHARITY SHIELD

(League Champions v League Cup holders)

(December 27th at Portland United)
Portland United 1 Hamworthy Recreation 0

SUPPLEMENTARY CUP

(League Cup First Round losers)

FIRST ROUND *(played over two legs)*
Cranborne 5 Cobham Sports 0, Cobham Sports 0 **Cranborne** 0
Poole Borough (scr.) v **Hamworthy United Res.** (w/o)
Sturminster Newton 2 Blandford Utd 0, Blandford 0 **Sturminster Newton Utd** 0
Wincanton Town 5 Bridport Res. 0, Bridport Res. 0 **Wincanton Town** 1

SEMI-FINALS
Cranborne 1 **Hamworthy United Res.** 2
Sturminster Newton 2 Wincanton 2 *aet*
Replay: **Wincanton** 3 Sturminster N. 0

FINAL *(May 5th at Shaftesbury)*
Wincanton Town 1 Hamworthy Utd Res. 0

ESSEX & SUFFOLK BORDER LEAGUE

www.essexsuffolkborderleague.freeserve.co.uk

Sponsored by:

Kent Blaxill

Founded: N/A

Recent champions:

2004: Little Oakley

2005: Gas Recreation

2006: Gas Recreation

2007: Gas Recreation

2008: Gas Recreation

	Alr	Brig	Cog	Ded	Earl	Gas	Gt B	Hat	Litt	Mer	TB	Tip	Uni	Wee	WB	WN
Alresford Colne Rgrs	***P***	4-3	4-3	2-0	3-3	0-1	2-1	0-1	1-0	1-4	1-2	1-1	1-4	2-9	0-3	0-0
Brightlingsea Regent	1-6	***R***	2-0	0-1	2-1	2-6	2-2	1-0	2-2	3-2	1-2	3-1	0-8	1-2	1-2	2-1
Coggeshall Town	1-1	1-2	***E***	0-0	1-1	4-4	0-1	1-2	0-2	1-0	0-2	0-0	1-1	1-4	0-4	1-2
Dedham Old Boys	2-1	3-1	1-1	***M***	2-2	0-3	2-1	L-W	0-0	1-3	3-2	0-0	1-3	1-0	1-1	2-0
Earls Colne	6-1	0-4	3-1	1-1	***I***	3-1	4-1	3-3	2-4	0-5	0-6	4-2	2-3	0-1	3-2	3-3
Gas Recreation	2-0	5-5	6-1	4-1	6-1	***E***	2-3	1-5	2-9	3-2	3-4	0-3	2-1	2-2	1-3	1-2
Great Bentley	6-0	0-1	2-1	5-1	0-2	3-0	***R***	3-3	1-3	2-2	0-1	2-1	1-0	0-1	0-5	0-1
Hatfield Peverel	1-1	2-0	1-1	1-1	1-1	1-4	2-3		1-4	2-0	1-5	0-2	1-1	1-0	0-2	0-5
Little Oakley	2-0	1-1	0-0	2-2	2-0	4-3	0-0	1-5	***D***	3-1	1-2	2-3	2-1	0-2	3-1	3-0
Mersea Island	0-3	2-0	3-3	0-2	3-5	2-0	3-1	2-3	3-4	***I***	2-3	1-0	1-4	0-3	0-3	3-6
Team Bury	0-0	5-0	5-0	2-0	4-1	2-2	7-0	5-0	2-1	5-2	***V***	6-0	2-0	2-0	0-2	0-0
Tiptree Heath	3-2	0-1	1-3	4-0	1-1	1-4	4-0	0-1	4-1	3-3	0-2	***I***	0-1	0-1	1-1	2-2
University of Essex	2-0	4-6	2-2	2-4	5-1	2-0	3-1	1-3	1-2	5-3	3-3	5-2	***S***	7-0	0-1	3-0
Weeley Athletic	3-2	0-1	3-0	3-0	0-1	3-1	1-1	1-0	1-0	2-1	2-1	1-2	2-2	***I***	0-2	1-0
West Bergholt	4-0	5-0	4-0	1-0	0-1	1-2	5-0	3-0	5-0	1-1	3-0	1-0	1-0	4-1	***O***	2-0
White Notley	5-0	5-0	3-0	5-2	3-1	0-1	3-2	4-1	1-5	1-1	6-3	1-2	2-2	1-0	0-4	***N***

Premier Division		P	W	D	L	F	A	Pts
West Bergholt		**30**	**23**	**3**	**4**	**76**	**15**	**72**
Team Bury		**30**	**21**	**4**	**5**	**85**	**34**	**67**
Weeley Athletic		**30**	**17**	**3**	**10**	**49**	**36**	**54**
Little Oakley		**30**	**15**	**6**	**9**	**63**	**47**	**51**
University of Essex		**30**	**14**	**6**	**10**	**76**	**47**	**48**
White Notley		**30**	**14**	**6**	**10**	**62**	**47**	**48**
Gas Recreation		**30**	**13**	**4**	**13**	**72**	**70**	**43**
Earls Colne	*+2*	**30**	**10**	**8**	**12**	**56**	**71**	**40**
Brightlingsea Regent		**30**	**12**	**4**	**14**	**48**	**73**	**40**
Hatfield Peverel	*-2*	**30**	**11**	**7**	**12**	**42**	**56**	**38**
Dedham Old Boys		**30**	**9**	**9**	**12**	**34**	**50**	**36**
Tiptree Heath		**30**	**9**	**7**	**14**	**43**	**50**	**34**
Great Bentley	*+2*	**30**	**9**	**5**	**16**	**42**	**62**	**34**
Alresford Colne Rangers		**30**	**7**	**6**	**17**	**39**	**73**	**27**
Mersea Island		**30**	**7**	**5**	**18**	**55**	**73**	**26**
Coggeshall Town		**30**	**2**	**11**	**17**	**28**	**66**	**17**

A V LEE MEMORIAL TROPHY

(Premier Division champions v League Cup holders)

(August 25th at Gas Recreation)

Gas Recreation 1 **Hatfield Peverel** 2

Reserve Premier Division	P	W	D	L	F	A	Pt
Gas Recreation Res.	26	21	3	2	109	32	66
White Notley Res.	26	18	5	3	85	37	59
Great Bentley Res.	26	16	2	8	86	41	50
University of Essex Res.	26	16	1	9	73	33	49
Clare Town Res.	26	14	2	10	71	66	44
Little Oakley Res.	26	13	4	9	56	56	43
West Bergholt Res.	26	11	6	9	68	51	39
Brightlingsea Regent Res	26	11	4	11	77	61	37
Earls Colne Res.	26	10	6	10	64	65	36
Alresford Colne Rgrs Res.	26	10	3	13	46	59	33
Coggeshall Town Res.	26	9	3	14	43	73	30
Mistley United Res.	26	5	4	17	39	77	19
Bures United Res.	26	3	3	20	29	87	12
Weeley Athletic Res.	26	1	2	23	26	134	5

Reserve Division Two	P	W	D	L	F	A	Pt
Holland Res.	26	17	6	3	72	28	57
Dedham Old Boys Res.	26	16	5	5	81	28	53
Glemsford/Cavendish Res.	26	15	5	6	58	50	50
Sudbury Athletic Res.	26	12	9	5	44	39	45
Great Bradfords Res.	26	11	8	7	41	34	41
Boxted Lodgers Res.	26	9	7	10	51	54	34
Foxash Social Res.	26	8	9	9	50	54	33
Mersea Island Res.	25	9	6	10	35	43	33
Tiptree Heath Res.	26	9	5	12	50	45	32
Gosfield United Res.	26	6	10	10	38	51	28
Lawford Lads Res.	25	7	5	13	47	68	26
Bradfield Rovers Res	26	6	8	12	36	59	26
Hatfield Peverel Res.	26	6	7	13	32	54	25
Hedinghams United Res.	26	2	6	18	33	61	12

ESSEX & SUFFOLK BORDER LEAGUE PREMIER DIVISION CONSTITUTION 2009-10

ALRESFORD COLNE RANGERS. . . . . Ford Lane, Alresford, Colchester CO7 8AY 07796 03646
BRIGHTLINGSEA REGENT . . . . North Road, Brightlingsea, Colchester CO7 0PL 01206 30419
DEDHAM OLD BOYS. . . . . The Playing Field, The Drift, Dedham, Colchester CO7 6AH . . . . Non
EARLS COLNE . . . . Earls Colne Recreation Club, Halstead Road, Earls Colne, Colchester CO6 2NG 01787 22358
GAS RECREATION . . . . Bromley Road, Colchester CO4 3JF 01206 86038
GREAT BENTLEY . . . . The Green, Great Bentley, Colchester CO7 8LX 01206 25153
HATFIELD PEVEREL . . . . Strutt Memorial Field, Maldon Road, Hatfield Peverel CM3 2JP. . . . . Non
HEDINGHAMS UNITED . . . . Lawn Meadow, Yeldham Road, Sible Hedingham, Halstead CO9 3QJ . . . . Non
HOLLAND. . . . . Eastcliff Sports Ground, Dulwich Road, Holland-on-Sea CO15 5HR. 01255 81487
LITTLE OAKLEY . . . . War Memorial Club Ground, Harwich Road, Little Oakley, Harwich CO12 5EB. 01255 88037
MERSEA ISLAND . . . . The Glebe, Colchester Road, West Mersea CO5 8JZ 01206 38521
TIPTREE JOBSERVE . . . . Warriors Rest, Maypole Road, Tiptree CO5 0EJ. . . . . Non
UNIVERSITY OF ESSEX. . . . . . University of Essex Sports Centre, Wivenhoe Park, Colchester CO4 3SQ 01206 87325
WEELEY ATHLETIC. . . . . Clacton Leisure Centre, Vista Road, Clacton-on-Sea CO15 6DB 01255 42964
WEST BERGHOLT. . . . . Lorkin Daniel Field, Lexden Road, West Bergholt, Colchester CO6 3BW. 01206 24152
WHITE NOTLEY . . . . Oak Farm, Faulkbourne, Witham CM8 1ST 01376 51986

IN: Hedinghams United (P), Holland (P)
OUT: Coggeshall Town (R), Team Bury (P - Eastern Counties League Division One)
Tiptree Heath become Tiptree Jobserve

Division One		P	W	D	L	F	A	Pts
Holland		26	18	5	3	61	19	59
Hedinghams United		26	17	4	5	75	34	55
Sudbury Athletic		26	17	2	7	62	33	53
Lawford Lads	*+3*	26	13	3	10	54	44	45
Rowhedge		26	12	8	6	62	44	44
Clacton United		26	11	6	9	56	51	39
Mistley United		26	12	2	12	55	49	38
Boxted Lodgers	*-3*	26	9	5	12	46	62	29
Foxash Social		26	7	8	11	40	61	29
Bures United		26	7	7	12	33	51	28
Glemsford & Cavedish U.		26	7	6	13	42	52	27
Great Bradfords		26	6	7	13	48	66	25
Bradfield Rovers		26	7	4	15	42	74	25
Gosfield United		26	3	5	18	24	60	14

St Osyth - record expunged

LEAGUE CUP

FIRST ROUND

Bradfield 1 **Hatfield P.** 8
Bures 1 **Great Bradfords** 4
Clacton United 2 Boxted 0
Earls Colne 5 Uni. Essex 2
Gas Rec 1 **Coggeshall** 2
Gosfield 0 **Dedham OB** 2
Gt Bentley 5 Glemsford 0
Holland 0 **Alresford CR** 2
Kelvedon Social v **Brightlingsea Regent** (w/o)
Lawford 2 Mersea Is. 1 *aet*
Little Oakley 3 Hedinghams 0
Rowhedge 2 **Foxash** 4
Sudbury Ath. 3 Mistley 1
Tiptree Hth 3 **Team Bury** 5
Weeley 0 **White Notley** 1
West Bergholt (w/o) v St Osyth (scr.)

SECOND ROUND

Alresford Colne Rgrs 3 White Notley 2
Clacton Utd 3 Foxash 1
Coggeshall 0 **Earls Colne** 1
Great Bentley 0 **Dedham** 2
Great Bradfords 2 **Brightlingsea Regent** 3
Hatfield Pev. 2 Lawford 0
Ltle Oakley 1 Team Bury 0
West Bergholt 2 Sudbury Athletic 0

QUARTER-FINALS

Little Oakley 0 **Hatfield Peverel** 3
Brightlingsea Regent 3 Earls Colne 2 *aet*
Alresford Colne Rangers 0 **West Bergholt** 4
Clacton Utd 1 **Dedham** 3

SEMI-FINALS

Hatfield Peverel 3 Brightlingsea Regent 0
West Bergholt 2 Dedham Old Boys 0

FINAL

(April 29th at AFC Sudbury)

Hatfield Peverel 2 **West Bergholt 4** *aet*

	Boxted	Bradf'd	Bures	Clacton	Foxash	Glem.	Gosf'ld	Gt Brad	Heding.	Holland	Lawford	Mistley	Row.	S Osyth	Sud. A
Boxted Lodgers		1-3	W-L	1-4	1-3	1-6	4-1	2-2	1-1	2-2	2-5	0-3	1-5	2-4	0-4
Bradfield Rovers	3-2	***D***	0-0	0-4	2-4	2-0	2-0	4-6	4-2	0-3	0-1	2-3	2-5	6-0	2-1
Bures United	1-1	1-0	***I***	6-0	1-1	2-1	5-3	0-3	0-3	1-4	2-1	0-7	4-1	n/a	0-2
Clacton United	3-2	3-3	1-0	***V***	5-0	0-2	2-0	1-1	1-4	0-2	3-4	4-4	4-1	n/a	1-1
Foxash Social	2-4	2-3	1-1	0-5	***I***	1-1	3-1	1-1	4-1	0-3	1-1	2-1	2-4	n/a	1-8
Glemsford & Cavendish	1-3	5-1	2-3	1-2	1-1	***S***	5-0	1-1	0-5	1-0	1-1	0-3	2-2	n/a	2-3
Gosfield United	0-1	1-1	0-0	2-2	2-1	2-2	***I***	0-1	0-3	2-1	2-4	2-3	1-1	5-2	1-2
Great Bradfords	1-4	7-3	2-2	1-3	1-1	0-2	2-1	***O***	1-5	1-2	1-0	0-2	3-4	n/a	2-4
Hedinghams United	3-3	7-1	2-0	4-1	5-0	5-1	4-1	5-4	***N***	0-0	1-0	1-1	2-1	n/a	2-1
Holland	4-0	2-0	2-2	4-1	3-1	4-0	1-0	5-1	3-2		4-1	3-1	1-1	6-1	0-1
Lawford Lads	0-5	3-1	4-0	3-1	1-3	6-1	0-1	3-1	2-0	0-4		4-0	1-0	n/a	1-2
Mistley United	1-2	7-1	4-1	0-3	0-1	3-1	3-1	6-1	0-4	0-2	0-2	***O***	0-5	n/a	2-1
Rowhedge	4-2	2-2	3-0	1-1	2-2	0-3	4-0	3-2	4-1	1-1	2-2	2-1	***N***	6-2	3-2
St Osyth	n/a	n/a	2-1	n/a	0-4	0-1	n/a	n/a	n/a	n/a	n/a	1-2	n/a	***E***	n/a
Sudbury Athletic	0-1	2-0	3-1	4-1	3-2	1-0	3-0	2-2	0-3	0-1	6-4	4-0	2-1	7-1	

ESSEX & SUFFOLK BORDER LEAGUE DIVISION ONE CONSTITUTION 2009-10

BOXTED LODGERS . . . . The Playing Field, Cage Lane, Boxted, Colchester CO4 5RE 01206 271969
BRADFIELD ROVERS . . . . The Playing Field, The Street, Bradfield, Manningtree CO11 2UU . . . . None
BURES UNITED . . . . Recreation Ground, Nayland Road, Bures CO8 5BX . . . . None
CLACTON UNITED . . . . Clacton Leisure Centre, Vista Road, Clacton-on-Sea CO15 6DB 01255 429647
CLARE TOWN . . . . Playing Field, Harp Lane, Clare CO2 8NP . . . . None
COGGESHALL TOWN . . . . The Crops, West Street, Coggeshall CO6 1NS 01376 562843
FOXASH SOCIAL . . . . Foxash Playing Field, Harwich Road, Lawford, Manningtree CO11 2LP 01206 231309
GLEMSFORD & CAVENDISH UNITED . . . Memorial Hall, Melford Road, Cavendish CO10 8AA . . . . None
GOSFIELD UNITED . . . . The Playing Field, Church Lane, Gosfield, Halstead CO9 1UD . . . . None
GREAT BRADFORDS . . . . The Bell, Kynaston Road, Panfield, Braintree CM7 5AQ . . . . None
KIRBY ATHLETIC . . . . Kirby Playing Field, Halstead Road, Kirby Cross CO13 0LW . . . . None
LAWFORD LADS . . . . School Lane, Lawford, Manningtree CO11 2JA 01206 397211
ROWHEDGE . . . . Rectory Road, Rowhedge CO5 7HP 01206 728022
SUDBURY ATHLETIC . . . . Delphi Sports Club, Newton Road, Sudbury CO10 2RR 01787 372331
WEST CLACTON ALLIANCE . . . . FC Clacton, Rush Green Road, Clacton-on-Sea CO16 7BQ 01255 432590
WORMINGFORD WANDERERS . . . Wormingford PF, Main Road, Wormingford, Colchester CO6 3AX . . . . None

IN: Clare Town (P - Halstead & District League), Coggeshall Town (R), Kirby Athletic (P - Colchester & East Essex League Premier Division), West Clacton Alliance (N), Wormingford Wanderers (P - Colchester & East Essex League Premier Division)

OUT: Hedinghams United (P), Holland (P), Kelvedon Social (WN - Colchester & East Essex League Division Three), Mistley United (W)

TOMMY THOMPSON CUP

FINAL *(May 4th at Little Oakley)*

White Notley Res. 4 Gas Recreation Res. 1

RESERVES CUP

FINAL *(April 22nd at Stanway Rovers)*

Clare Town Res. 1 Gas Rec Res. 1 *aet* (3-2p)

ESSEX OLYMPIAN LEAGUE

www.eofl.co.uk

Sponsored by: LFC Insurance Group

Founded: 1966

Recent champions:

2004: White Ensign

2005: White Ensign

2006: Harold Wood Athletic

2007: White Ensign

2008: White Ensign

	Benfleet	Canning T.	Epping	Faces	Frenford Snr	Galleywood	Harold Wood	Kelvedon H.	M & B Club	Manford Way	Mountnessing	Ongar Town	Potter Street	White Ensign
Benfleet		0-2	5-2	5-4	2-4	2-2	0-4	5-3	1-2	4-2	1-1	4-2	2-1	4-0
Canning Town	0-2	***P***	2-0	1-4	0-0	3-0	1-1	1-0	0-1	0-0	3-4	0-0	1-2	0-2
Epping	1-2	0-3	***R***	3-4	0-1	1-4	1-1	2-4	1-4	1-0	2-3	1-3	4-0	2-2
Faces	2-2	2-5	2-1	***E***	1-2	1-3	2-7	0-6	3-2	0-2	0-2	5-2	3-1	2-3
Frenford Senior	1-0	2-1	3-2	4-1	***M***	1-0	3-1	1-3	3-0	3-0	1-2	2-1	4-0	2-2
Galleywood	1-3	3-1	1-1	4-1	0-1	***I***	1-1	1-4	3-1	0-2	2-2	2-3	0-1	1-0
Harold Wood Athletic	4-1	2-0	1-2	W-L	3-2	2-0	***E***	2-1	2-1	2-1	1-3	4-2	4-1	2-2
Kelvedon Hatch	8-1	3-1	4-0	4-1	2-2	4-0	1-3	***R***	1-4	2-3	6-2	4-3	4-2	5-0
M & B Club	1-1	1-0	0-2	4-1	2-0	1-0	2-5	0-2		1-1	3-3	1-6	3-2	3-3
Manford Way	3-0	2-1	2-0	1-0	1-0	1-3	0-3	2-2	1-1		0-1	2-2	1-0	2-0
Mountnessing Boca	2-2	0-2	8-3	3-1	3-1	2-2	1-1	2-1	2-4	4-2	***D***	4-3	3-1	5-2
Ongar Town	2-3	0-3	2-0	5-2	3-5	4-2	0-4	0-2	2-3	2-2	4-1	***I***	1-5	1-2
Potter Street	6-2	4-2	0-1	3-0	2-3	5-0	1-1	0-4	3-0	1-3	2-2	2-0	***V***	L-W
White Ensign	2-3	1-3	4-0	0-3	0-1	0-3	1-6	1-1	2-4	2-1	1-1	1-3	4-1	

Premier Division		P	W	D	L	F	A	Pts
Harold Wood Athletic		26	17	6	3	67	30	57
Frenford Senior		26	17	3	6	52	32	54
Kelvedon Hatch		26	16	3	7	81	39	51
Mountnessing Boca		26	14	8	4	66	51	47
M & B Club		26	12	5	9	49	50	41
Benfleet		26	12	5	9	57	62	41
Manford Way		26	11	6	9	37	35	39
Canning Town		26	9	4	13	36	36	31
Potter Street		26	9	2	15	46	52	29
Galleywood		26	8	5	13	38	48	29
Ongar Town		26	8	3	15	56	66	27
White Ensign		26	7	6	13	37	59	27
Faces	*-3*	26	7	1	18	45	75	22
Epping	*+3*	26	5	3	18	33	65	21

Reserve Division One		P	W	D	L	F	A	Pts
Harold Wood Athletic Res.		24	18	3	3	44	20	57
M & B Club Res.		24	18	2	4	65	16	56
Shell Club Corringham) Res.		24	18	0	6	52	27	54
Frenford Senior Res.		24	13	6	5	58	32	45
Manford Way Res.		24	12	4	8	56	35	40
Rayleigh Town Res.	*-1*	24	12	3	9	46	34	38
Canning Town Res.	*+3*	24	7	5	12	39	52	29
White Ensign Res.	*+2*	24	7	5	12	40	50	28
Mountnessing Boca Res.		24	8	4	12	33	60	28
Epping Res.	*-3*	24	8	4	12	34	42	25
Bishop's Stortford Swifts Res.		24	6	5	13	19	47	23
Old Chelmsfordians Res.		24	4	2	18	38	67	14
Galleywood Res.		24	2	3	19	27	69	9

Reserve Division Two		P	W	D	L	F	A	Pts
Kelvedon Hatch Res.		20	15	2	3	72	26	47
Faces Res.		20	12	3	5	58	35	39
Benfleet Res.		20	12	2	6	49	30	38
Runwell Hospital Res.		20	11	3	6	69	32	36
Hutton Res.		20	11	3	6	54	36	36
Leigh Ramblers Res.		20	10	3	7	27	28	33
Ramsden Res.	-3	20	7	3	10	37	41	21
Barnston Res.		20	7	0	13	29	69	21
Hannakins Farm Res.	+3	20	5	1	14	28	61	19
Ryan Res.		20	6	1	13	29	66	19
Basildon Town Res.		20	2	3	15	33	61	[illegible]

ESSEX OLYMPIAN LEAGUE PREMIER DIVISION CONSTITUTION 2009-10

BENFLEET .... The Club House, Woodside Extension, Manor Road, Benfleet, Rayleigh SS7 4BG 01268 74395

CANNING TOWN . . Terence McMillan Stadium, Newham Leisure Centre, 281 Prince Regents Lane, London E13 8SD 020 7511 447

EPPING .... Stonards Hill Rec Ground, Tidy's Lane, Epping CM16 6SP 07932 53269

FACES................. Ford Sports & Social Club, Aldbrough Road South, Newbury Park, Ilford IG3 8HG 020 8590 379

FRENFORD SENIOR............. Oakfields Sports Ground, Forest Road, Barkingside IG6 2JL................ 020 8500 199

GALLEYWOOD................ Clarkes Field, Slades Lane, Galleywood, Chelmsford CM2 8RW................. 01245 35297

HAROLD WOOD ATHLETIC ..... Harold Wood Recreation Park, Harold View, Harold Wood RM3 0LX 01708 34882

KELVEDON HATCH .... New Hall, School Road, Kelvedon Hatch, Brentwood CM15 0DH................ 07768 27453

MANFORD WAY .... London Marathon Sports Ground, Forest Road, Hainault IG6 3HJ 020 8500 348

MOUNTNESSING BOCA .... The Football Academy, Sports Pavilion, Langston Road, Loughton IG10 3TQ............ 0870 084 211

ONGAR TOWN.................... Sports Ground, Love Lane, High Street, Ongar CM5 9BL.................... 01277 36383

RAYLEIGH TOWN .... Rayleigh Town Sports/Soc. Club, London Road, Rayleigh SS6 9DT............. 01268 78400

WESTHAMIANS .... London Playing Fields, Forest Road, Fairlop IG6 3AS.................. 020 8500 377

WHITE ENSIGN .... Borough Football Comb. HQ, Eastwoodbury Lane, Southend-on-Sea SS2 6XG 01702 52048

IN: Rayleigh Town (P), Westhamians (P)

OUT: Beaumont Athletic (WN), M & B Club (R), Potter Street (W)

	Bishop's Stortford Swifts	Buckhurst Hill	Burnham Ramblers Res.	Hannakins Farm	Herongate Athletic	Hutton	Leigh Ramblers	Leytonstone United	Linford Wanderers	Old Chelmsfordians	Rayleigh Town	Roydon	Ryan	Sandon Royals	Shell Club Corringham	Westhamians
Bishop's Stortford Swifts		4-1	W-L	1-1	4-2	1-6	3-1	5-1	3-1	2-3	2-2	6-0	2-0	1-3	2-1	0-3
Buckhurst Hill	0-5		7-4	3-1	8-1	5-5	4-1	1-1	5-0	2-2	2-1	5-0	6-1	4-0	0-1	1-2
Burnham Ramblers Res.	1-2	0-4	***D***	1-2	4-2	1-0	7-1	8-3	2-5	2-4	3-3	7-1	2-4	2-3	0-4	2-4
Hannakins Farm	0-2	3-4	7-0	***I***	3-0	2-1	0-0	6-3	1-2	0-3	3-7	2-2	4-1	0-1	2-1	0-0
Herongate Athletic	2-2	1-3	5-1	1-1	***V***	0-4	1-0	4-0	1-0	3-3	1-2	3-2	W-L	0-1	4-2	0-3
Hutton	3-1	2-3	10-2	4-0	6-0	***I***	4-0	4-3	5-1	5-0	3-8	5-0	2-4	4-2	2-2	6-2
Leigh Ramblers	0-4	1-0	2-2	1-5	6-1	1-2	***S***	3-2	2-2	3-3	1-4	0-0	4-0	2-3	2-1	0-3
Leytonstone United	4-4	2-2	1-3	4-2	2-4	1-7	2-3	***I***	0-4	1-4	1-9	2-1	1-0	3-7	2-1	0-2
Linford Wanderers	1-2	2-1	3-2	0-1	2-0	1-4	3-3	5-2	***O***	0-0	2-1	5-1	2-5	0-4	1-4	0-2
Old Chelmsfordians	0-2	2-3	8-1	1-1	1-0	0-2	1-1	3-4	1-2	***N***	0-3	4-2	0-1	3-4	1-1	0-1
Rayleigh Town	2-1	1-3	4-1	2-0	6-1	3-2	4-1	14-0	0-0	5-0		7-1	4-0	5-1	1-2	0-1
Roydon	2-4	0-2	2-4	3-3	4-2	0-6	0-1	2-2	2-1	2-0	0-4	***O***	2-5	0-1	4-5	1-2
Ryan	1-2	1-3	6-2	0-3	5-3	1-2	3-1	3-2	1-3	1-2	1-2	0-1	***N***	2-1	1-3	1-5
Sandon Royals	1-1	3-2	2-2	0-2	3-0	1-4	2-2	3-0	0-1	3-0	6-2	3-2	0-1	***E***	3-3	0-2
Shell Club Corringham	3-0	0-3	1-1	5-0	5-1	2-2	5-1	5-0	2-1	3-0	2-4	0-0	1-2	3-1		3-2
Westhamians	3-2	2-2	W-L	4-0	9-1	1-2	3-3	5-1	0-0	10-2	1-2	1-1	1-0	6-1	2-1	

Reserve Division Three		P	W	D	L	F	A	Pt
Westhamians Res.		24	18	3	3	64	27	57
Buckhurst Hill Res.	*-3*	24	18	2	4	86	31	53
Herongate Athletic Res.		24	14	5	5	53	35	47
Linford Wanderers Res.		24	12	7	5	86	42	43
Potter Street Res.		24	12	4	8	63	35	40
Sungate Res.		24	10	5	9	43	38	35
Sandon Royals Res.		24	10	3	11	59	52	33
Writtle Res.	*-3*	24	10	3	11	45	59	30
Upminster Res.		24	8	5	11	45	55	29
Broomfield Res.	*+3*	24	7	5	12	35	54	29
Shenfield Assoc. Res.	*+3*	24	6	3	15	30	61	24
Leytonstone United Res.		24	3	4	17	35	104	13
Springfield Res.		24	3	1	20	29	80	10

Division One	**P**	**W**	**D**	**L**	**F**	**A**	**Pts**
Westhamians	**30**	**21**	**5**	**4**	**82**	**32**	**68**
Rayleigh Town	**30**	**21**	**3**	**6**	**112**	**42**	**66**
Hutton	**30**	**21**	**3**	**6**	**114**	**48**	**66**
Buckhurst Hill	**30**	**18**	**5**	**7**	**89**	**49**	**59**
Bish. Stortford Swifts	**30**	**17**	**5**	**8**	**70**	**48**	**56**
Shell Corringham	**30**	**15**	**6**	**9**	**72**	**45**	**51**
Sandon Royals	**30**	**15**	**4**	**11**	**63**	**59**	**49**
Hannakins Farm	**30**	**11**	**7**	**12**	**55**	**57**	**40**
Linford Wanderers	**30**	**12**	**5**	**13**	**50**	**57**	**40**
Ryan	**30**	**12**	**0**	**18**	**51**	**66**	**36**
Leigh Ramblers	**30**	**7**	**9**	**14**	**47**	**74**	**32**
Old Chelmsfordians	**30**	**8**	**7**	**15**	**51**	**70**	**31**
Herongate Athletic	**30**	**8**	**3**	**19**	**44**	**92**	**27**
Burnham Ramblers Res.	**30**	**7**	**4**	**19**	**67**	**100**	**25**
Leytonstone United	**30**	**5**	**4**	**21**	**50**	**124**	**19**
Roydon	**30**	**4**	**6**	**20**	**38**	**92**	**18**

ESSEX OLYMPIAN LEAGUE DIVISION ONE CONSTITUTION 2009-10

BISHOP'S STORTFORD SWIFTS . Silver Leys, Hadham Road (A1250), Bishop's Stortford CM23 2QE 01279 658941
BUCKHURST HILL. . . . . Roding Lane, Buckhurst Hill IG9 6BJ 020 8504 1189
HANNAKINS FARM . . . . Hannakins Farm Community Centre, Rosebay Avenue, Billericay CM12 0SY 01277 630851
HUTTON. . . . . East Thurrock United FC, Rookery Hill, Corringham SS17 9LB. 01375 644166
LAKESIDE . . . . Lakeside Pitches, Lakeside Retail Park, Thurrock RM20 2ZL 01375 379352
LEIGH RAMBLERS . . . . Belfairs Park, Eastwood Road North, Leigh-on-Sea SS9 4LR 01702 421077
M & B CLUB . . . . Sanofi-Aventis Sports & Social Club, Dagenham Road, Dagenham RM7 0QX 020 8919 2156
RYAN . . . . Town Mead Leisure Park, Brooker Road, Waltham Abbey EN9 1JH. 01992 714949
SANDON ROYALS . . . . Sandon Sports Club, Woodhill Road, Sandon, Chelmsford CM2 7AQ 01245 476626
SHELL CLUB CORRINGHAM . . . . . . The Springhouse, Springhouse Road, Corringham SS17 7QT 01375 673100
SOUTHMINSTER ST LEONARDS King George V Playing Fields, Station Road, Southminster CM0 7EW 07718 869883
SUNGATE . . . . Ford Sports & Social Club, Aldborough Road South, Newbury Park, Ilford IG3 8HG 020 8590 3797

IN: M & B Club (R), Southminster St Leonards (P), Sungate (P)

OUT: Burnham Ramblers Res. (R), Herongate Athletic (R), Leytonstone United (R), Old Chelmsfordians (R), Rayleigh Town (P), Roydon (R), Westhamians (P)

Linford Wanderers become Lakeside

	Barnston	Basildon Town	Broomfield	Debden Sports Res.	Maldon St Marys	Metpol Chigwell NE	Newham United	Ramsden	Runwell Hospital	Shenfield Association	Southminster St Leonards	Springfield	Stambridge United	Sungate	Takeley Res.	Upminster	Writtle
Barnston		1-4	1-6	1-6	2-2	3-1	0-6	1-5	0-2	2-2	0-2	0-5	n/a	1-4	2-1	1-3	0-1
Basildon Town	1-0		0-2	3-0	0-4	n/a	0-1	1-1	0-1	5-1	0-0	1-1	2-1	0-5	0-5	0-1	1-2
Broomfield	1-0	2-0	*D*	0-1	2-4	4-2	2-3	2-0	1-0	7-0	3-1	2-1	n/a	0-1	1-1	0-2	0-1
Debden Sports Res.	2-2	2-0	1-2	*I*	1-2	n/a	1-1	3-3	0-4	3-3	4-1	0-2	n/a	1-3	1-1	3-1	2-2
Maldon St Marys	6-0	2-2	1-1	2-2	*V*	n/a	0-0	1-3	0-1	5-1	3-1	1-1	n/a	1-3	3-1	2-1	0-1
Metpol Chigwell NE	n/a	0-0	1-1	0-1	n/a	*I*	3-3	n/a	2-3	0-3	3-0	1-2	n/a	2-4	n/a	1-2	n/a
Newham United	7-1	2-2	3-3	1-1	2-2	n/a	*S*	3-2	2-2	6-1	1-2	3-3	n/a	4-5	3-2	1-1	4-3
Ramsden	4-0	4-1	4-1	2-1	1-0	n/a	3-2	*I*	1-0	3-2	1-3	0-0	7-0	1-4	2-3	1-2	0-1
Runwell Hospital	3-0	1-0	3-2	1-3	0-2	n/a	4-2	3-2	*O*	2-2	0-0	3-2	n/a	1-1	1-2	4-1	4-0
Shenfield Association	4-0	1-1	1-1	0-2	1-3	n/a	0-0	0-2	1-3	*N*	0-2	4-0	6-2	1-3	1-2	1-1	2-3
Southminster St Leonards	4-1	2-1	4-0	1-1	1-1	n/a	3-2	0-0	6-0	5-0		1-1	n/a	3-1	1-1	2-0	2-1
Springfield	4-0	0-2	1-5	2-5	1-0	n/a	0-3	3-1	1-0	0-5	2-4		n/a	2-4	4-1	2-1	2-2
Stambridge United	3-1	n/a	n/a	2-5	3-6	n/a	n/a	n/a	n/a	n/a	n/a	n/a	*T*	n/a	n/a	1-4	n/a
Sungate	12-0	4-2	2-1	0-1	2-3	n/a	0-1	2-0	1-1	1-1	3-3	4-0	n/a	*W*	3-3	5-1	6-2
Takeley Res.	3-0	6-0	1-3	1-1	1-0	n/a	2-1	1-2	0-0	7-0	1-2	3-0	n/a	1-1	*O*	3-1	3-3
Upminster	4-3	8-0	3-4	1-2	0-1	n/a	2-0	0-2	0-1	1-0	3-2	2-0	n/a	3-2	2-1		1-2
Writtle	4-3	0-2	0-1	2-2	2-7	n/a	2-1	1-2	1-3	0-2	1-2	0-0	n/a	1-5	2-3	1-1	

Division Two		**P**	**W**	**D**	**L**	**F**	**A**	**Pts**
Sungate		**28**	**17**	**6**	**5**	**87**	**39**	**57**
Southminster St Leonards		**28**	**16**	**8**	**4**	**60**	**32**	**56**
Runwell Hospital		**28**	**15**	**6**	**7**	**48**	**33**	**51**
Maldon St Marys		**28**	**13**	**8**	**7**	**58**	**34**	**47**
Broomfield		**28**	**14**	**4**	**10**	**55**	**40**	**46**
Takeley Res.		**28**	**12**	**8**	**8**	**60**	**40**	**44**
Ramsden	*-1*	**28**	**14**	**4**	**10**	**52**	**41**	**43**
Debden Sports Res.		**28**	**10**	**11**	**7**	**52**	**44**	**41**
Newham United		**28**	**10**	**10**	**8**	**65**	**49**	**40**
Upminster		**28**	**12**	**3**	**13**	**47**	**46**	**39**
Writtle		**28**	**9**	**6**	**13**	**41**	**61**	**33**
Springfield		**28**	**8**	**7**	**13**	**40**	**57**	**31**
Basildon Town		**28**	**6**	**6**	**16**	**29**	**59**	**24**
Shenfield Association		**28**	**4**	**8**	**16**	**37**	**70**	**20**
Barnston	*+3*	**28**	**1**	**3**	**24**	**22**	**108**	**9**

Stambridge United - record expunged

Metpol Chigwell NE - record expunged

ESSEX OLYMPIAN LEAGUE DIVISION TWO CONSTITUTION 2009-10

BROOMFIELD . . . . The Angel Meadow, Main Road, Broomfield, Chelmsford CM1 7AH. 01245 44381

BURNHAM RAMBLERS RESERVES. Leslie Field, Springfield Road, Burnham-on-Crouch CM0 8TE 01621 78438

HERONGATE ATHLETIC . . . . Adjacent to 77 Billericay Road, Herongate, Brentwood CM13 3PU 01277 81071

LEYTONSTONE UNITED. . . . . Ilford Wanderers RFC, Forest Road, Hainault IG6 3HJ 020 8500 462

MALDON ST MARYS . . . . Maldon Promenade, Park Drive, Maldon CM9 5UR 01621 85616

OLD CHELMSFORDIANS . . . . Lawford Lane, Roxwell Road, Chelmsford CM1 2NS 01245 42044

ROMFORD RESERVES . . . . Aveley Sports & Social Club, Purfleet Road, Aveley RM15 4DT 01708 86361

ROYDON. . . . . Roydon Playing Fields, Harlow Road, Roydon, Harlow CM19 5HE 07967 02271

RUNWELL HOSPITAL . . . . Runwell Hospital, Runwell Chase, Wickford SS11 7QE. 07966 71880

SAWBRIDGEWORTH TOWN RESERVES Crofters End, West Road, Sawbridgeworth CM21 0DE 01279 72203

STANSTED RESERVES . . . . Hargrave Park, Cambridge Road, Stansted CM24 8DL. 01279 81289

TAKELEY RESERVES . . . . . . Station Road (adjacent to rail bridge), Takeley, Bishop's Stortford CM22 6SG 01279 87040

IN: Burnham Ramblers Res. (R), Herongate Athletic (R), Leytonstone United (R), Old Chelmsfordians (R), Romford Res. (N), Roydon (R Sawbridgeworth Town Res. (S - Spartan South Midlands League Reserve Division Two), Stansted Res. (Essex & Herts Borde Combination)

OUT: Barnston (R), Basildon Town (R), Debden Sports Res. (R), Metpol Chigwell NE (WS), Newham United (R), Ramsden (R), Shenfie Association (R), Springfield (R), Southminster St Leonards (P), Stambridge United (WS), Sungate (P), Upminster (R), Writtle (R)

ESSEX OLYMPIAN LEAGUE DIVISION THREE CONSTITUTION 2009-10

BARNSTON . . . . High Easter Road, Barnston, Dunmow CM6 1LZ 07712 129459
BASILDON TOWN . . . . Selex Sports Ground, Gardiners Lane South, Gardiners Way, Basildon SS14 3AP 01268 883128
CATHOLIC UNITED . . . . SE Essex College Sports Ground, Wellstead Gardens, Westcliff-on-Sea SS0 0AY 01702 348786
CRANES UNITED . . . . Clapton FC, The Old Spotted Dog, 212 Upton Lane, Forest Gate E7 9NP 020 8472 0822
DEBDEN SPORTS RESERVES . . . . Chigwell Lane, Loughton, Ilford IG10 3TP 020 8508 9392
NEWHAM UNITED . . . . Cave Road, Plaistow E13 9DX 07939 788048
RAMSDEN . . . . Nursery Sports Ground, Downham Road, Ramsden Heath, Billericay CM11 1PU 01268 711502
SHENFIELD ASSOCIATION . . . . The Drive, Warley, Brentwood CM13 3BH 01277 226816
SPRINGFIELD . . . . Springfield Hall Park, Arun Close, Springfield, Chelmsford CM1 7QE 01245 492441
UPMINSTER . . . . Hall Lane Playing Fields, Hall Lane, Upminster, Romford RM14 1AU 01708 220320
WADHAM LODGE . . . . Wadham Lodge Sports Ground, Kitchener Road, Walthamstow E17 4JP 020 8527 2444
WRITTLE . . . . Paradise Road Playing Fields, Writtle, Chelmsford CM1 3HW 01245 420332

IN: Barnston (R), Basildon Town (R), Catholic United (P - Southend Borough Combination Premier Division), Cranes United (P - Ilford & District League Premier Division), Debden Sports Res. (R), Newham United (R), Ramsden (R), Shenfield Association (R), Springfield (R), Upminster (R), Wadham Lodge (P - Essex Business Houses League Premier Division), Writtle (R)

SENIOR CUP

FIRST ROUND

Bishop's Stortford Swifts 2 Old Chelmsfordians 0
Burnham Ramblers Res. 0 **Leigh Ramblers** 2
Debden Sports Res. 6 White Ensign 1
Faces 3 Frenford Senior 2 *aet*
Harold Wood Athletic 2 Upminster 0
Herongate Athletic (w/o) v Beaumont Athletic
Kelvedon Hatch 1 **Sungate** 5
Linford Wanderers 5 Basildon Town 1
Manford Way 4 Sandon Royals 2
Mountnessing 0 **Metpol Chigwell NE** 2
Newham United 2 Runwell Hospital 1
Rayleigh Town 0 **Hannakins Farm** 2
Shell Club Corringham 2 Barnston 1 *aet*
Southminster St Leonards 1 **Potter Street 5** *aet*
Westhamians 4 **Hutton** 4 *aet* (1-3p)
Writtle 0 **Buckhurst Hill** 1 *aet*

SECOND ROUND

Benfleet 0 **Harold Wood Athletic** 1
Broomfield 0 **Faces** 3
Buckhurst Hill 4 Takeley Res. 2
Canning Town 5 Roydon 1
Debden Sports Res. 1 **Sungate** 5
Epping 1 Herongate Athletic 0
Hannakins Farm 1 **Bishop's Stortford Swifts** 3
Leytonstone United 2 Ramsden 0
M & B Club 3 Potter Street 1
Manford Way 5 Linford Wanderers 0
Metpol Chigwell NE 2 Leigh Ramblers 0
Newham United 2 **Shell Club Corringham** 5
Ongar Town 2 **Galleywood** 2 *aet* (1-4p)
Ryan 1 **Hutton** 5
Springfield 5 Shenfield Association 4 *aet*
Stambridge United 1 **Maldon St Marys** 2

THIRD ROUND

Bishop's Stortford Swifts 2 Maldon St Marys 0
Buckhurst Hill 4 Leytonstone United 1
Canning Town 1 **Epping** 2
Galleywood 2 Hutton 1
Harold Wood Athletic 1 **Manford Way** 2
Shell Club Corringham 1 **M & B Club** 2
Springfield 0 **Metpol Chigwell NE** 3
Sungate 5 Faces 2

QUARTER-FINALS

Buckhurst Hill 4 **Galleywood** 5
Epping 0 **Bishop's Stortford Swifts** 5
Metpol Chigwell NE (scr.) v **Manford Way** (w/o)
Sungate 0 **M & B Club** 2

SEMI-FINALS

M & B Club 4 Bishop's Stortford Swifts 3
Manford Way 3 Galleywood 2 *aet*

FINAL

(May 13th at Billericay Town)
Manford Way 4 M & B Club 2 *aet*

DENNY KING MEMORIAL CUP
(Senior Cup First and Second Round losers)

FIRST ROUND

Debden Sports 3 White Ensign 2
Frenford Senior 5 Southminster St Leonards 1
Ongar Town 2 Herongate Athletic 1
Ramsden 3 **Rayleigh Town** 6
Roydon 0 **Kelvedon Hatch** 6
Runwell Hospital 1 **Upminster** 1 *aet* (4-5p)
Shenfield Association 3 **Mountnessing Boca** 5
Stambridge United (scr.) v **Sandon Royals** (w/o)
Writtle 0 **Takeley Res.** 6
Competition abandoned due to inclement weather

RESERVES CUP

FINAL *(May 6th at Billericay Town)*
M & B Club Res. 2 Rayleigh Town Res. 0

SENIOR CHALLENGE CUP
(Prem Div champions v Senior Cup holders)

(August 23rd at White Ensign)
White Ensign 2 **Kelvedon Hatch** 5

JUNIOR CHALLENGE CUP
(Res Div One champions v Reserves Cup holders)

(August 23rd at Harold Wood Athletic)
Harold Wood Athletic Res. 3 Shell Club Res. 2

GLOUCESTERSHIRE COUNTY LEAGUE

www.countyleague.co.uk

Sponsored by: Surridge

Founded: 1968

Recent champions:
2004: Almondsbury
2005: Highridge Utd
2006: Lydney Town
2007: Roman Glass St George
2008: Hardwicke

	AXA	B & W	Berk.	Bish. C.	Chip. S.	DRG	Ellwood	Hanham	Henb'y	H'ridge	Kings S.	Patc.	Slimb.	Tavern.	Thornb'y	Tuffley	Yate Res
AXA		3-3	3-1	1-2	3-2	2-0	2-4	3-2	2-2	1-0	3-1	3-2	1-1	3-0	2-1	3-4	2-5
B & W Avonside	3-1		5-1	1-1	1-2	0-1	0-1	3-3	2-3	1-2	0-0	1-1	1-0	1-2	3-1	2-2	3-5
Berkeley Town	2-2	2-3		2-1	2-1	0-4	1-2	0-0	0-1	1-1	0-3	3-1	1-6	0-0	1-1	1-3	3-2
Bishops Cleeve Res.	2-2	0-2	3-1		7-0	5-4	3-2	3-2	3-0	2-0	0-2	3-0	2-2	0-1	2-2	2-3	2-0
Chipping Sodbury Town	1-1	0-2	0-2	1-3		0-2	2-1	1-3	0-2	1-3	0-3	3-2	0-3	3-0	1-2	1-4	1-4
DRG Stapleton	1-4	1-0	1-2	1-3	0-1		3-4	1-4	2-3	2-0	0-4	0-4	2-2	0-2	0-2	3-2	2-2
Ellwood	1-0	0-2	5-0	0-1	5-1	0-0		7-1	1-3	2-1	1-0	2-0	1-1	2-0	5-1	3-1	3-2
Hanham Athletic	2-3	4-2	3-5	0-3	1-0	2-2	0-1		0-4	1-3	0-3	1-2	2-3	0-2	1-0	1-1	3-3
Henbury	6-1	4-0	4-0	2-1	4-1	3-5	2-1	1-1		2-0	2-2	1-1	2-0	0-1	1-1	2-3	3-0
Highridge United	2-2	2-0	1-3	1-3	3-1	2-0	0-4	1-1	2-4		0-3	3-1	0-1	2-0	0-1	0-2	2-2
Kings Stanley	3-4	3-1	5-0	0-1	4-2	2-2	2-0	3-0	1-0	4-1		3-0	1-4	1-0	3-0	5-1	2-1
Patchway Town	2-2	1-0	0-1	3-0	3-1	2-7	0-1	2-1	1-1	2-0	3-5		0-1	0-2	0-2	2-1	0-3
Slimbridge	4-1	1-2	2-0	7-0	2-0	5-0	1-0	1-0	2-0	2-1	5-0	2-0		0-2	3-1	4-0	4-2
Taverners	2-2	1-2	3-0	1-1	2-0	0-0	1-1	0-2	3-5	6-1	0-2	0-0	0-3		0-0	3-3	0-1
Thornbury Town	4-0	1-2	1-3	1-3	2-2	4-0	0-3	2-2	4-2	0-0	1-2	2-2	2-3	0-1		3-2	4-1
Tuffley Rovers	2-3	5-3	0-1	0-1	2-1	10-0	0-4	1-2	1-0	0-4	1-2	4-4	0-2	2-0	0-2		0-4
Yate Town Res.	0-0	1-1	4-0	2-0	1-0	9-0	5-2	3-1	4-0	0-2	4-2	1-2	0-2	1-1	0-2	2-4	

		P	W	D	L	F	A	Pts
Slimbridge		32	24	4	4	79	24	76
Kings Stanley		32	22	3	7	76	37	69
Ellwood		32	20	3	9	69	36	63
Bishops Cleeve Res.		32	18	5	9	63	46	59
Henbury		32	17	6	9	69	46	57
AXA		32	13	10	9	65	67	49
Yate Town Res.		32	14	6	12	74	53	48
Taverners		32	11	9	12	36	38	42
Thornbury Town		32	11	8	13	50	50	41
B & W Avonside		32	11	7	14	52	55	40
Tuffley Rovers		32	12	4	16	64	70	40
Berkeley Town		32	11	5	16	39	71	38
Highridge United		32	10	5	17	40	55	35
Patchway Town		32	9	7	16	43	60	34
Hanham Athletic		32	7	8	17	46	69	29
DRG Stapleton	*-3*	32	8	6	18	46	85	27
Chipping Sodbury	*-3*	32	5	2	25	30	79	14

LES JAMES LEAGUE CUP

PRELIMINARY

Chipping Sodbury Town 0 **Slimbridge** 3

FIRST ROUND

B & W Avonside 3 AXA 1
DRG Stapleton 2 **Yate Town Res.** 3
Hanham Athletic 0 **Kings Stanley** 3
Henbury 4 Ellwood 1
Patchway Town 2 Berkeley Town 1
Taverners 1 Highridge United 1 (4-3p)
Thornbury Town 4 Slimbridge 3
Tuffley Rovers 0 **Bishops Cleeve Res.** 2

QUARTER-FINALS

B & W Avonside 1 **Kings Stanley** 5
Henbury (w/o) v Taverners (scr.)
Patchway Town 2 Bishops Cleeve Res. 2 (5-3p)
Thornbury Town 0 **Yate Town Res.** 1

SEMI-FINALS

Henbury 4 Patchway Town 0 *(at Yate Town)*
Kings Stanley 2 Yate Town Res. 1 *(at Slimbridge)*

FINAL *(May 16th at Slimbridge)*

Henbury 1 **Kings Stanley** 1 (3-4p)

GLOUCESTERSHIRE COUNTY LEAGUE CONSTITUTION 2009-10

AXA . . . . AXA Sports Ground, Station Road, Henbury, Bristol BS10 7TB 0117 950 230
BERKELEY TOWN . . . . Station Road, Berkeley GL13 9AJ 07831 23210
BISHOPS CLEEVE . . . . Kayte Lane, Bishops Cleeve, Cheltenham GL52 3PD 01242 67616
BRIMSCOMBE & THRUPP . . . . The Meadow, London Road, Brimscombe, Stroud GL5 2QE 07828 42711
CHIPPING SODBURY TOWN . . . . . The Ridings, Wickwar Road, Chipping Sodbury, Bristol BS37 6BQ 07787 52210
DRG STAPLETON . . . . Frenchay Park Road, Frenchay, Bristol BS16 1LG 07783 70247
ELLWOOD . . . . Bromley Road, Ellwood, Coleford GL16 7LY 01594 83296
HANHAM ATHLETIC . . . . The Playing Fields Pavilion, 16 Vicarage Road, Hanham, Bristol BS15 3AH 07900 26290
HENBURY . . . . Arnell Drive Playing Field, Henbury, Bristol BS10 7AS 0117 959 047
HIGHRIDGE UNITED . . . . Bristol Manor Farm FC, The Creek, The Portway, Sea Mills, Bristol BS9 2HY 0117 968 357
KINGS STANLEY . . . . Marling Close, Broad Street, Kings Stanley, Stonehouse GL10 3PN 01453 82897
KINGSWOOD . . . . Kingswood PF, Wickwar Road, Kingswood, Wotton-under-Edge GL12 8RZ 07971 68209
PATCHWAY TOWN . . . . Scott Park, Coniston Road, Patchway, Bristol BS34 5JR 0117 949 395
ROCKLEAZE AVONSIDE . . . . Coombe Dingle Sport Complex, Coombe Dingle, Bristol BS9 2BJ 0117 962 671
TAVERNERS . . . . Nailsworth Primary School, Forest Green, Nailsworth, Stroud GL6 0ET 01453 83486
THORNBURY TOWN . . . . Mundy Playing Fields, Kington Lane, Thornbury BS35 1NA 01454 41364
TUFFLEY ROVERS . . . . Glevum Park, Lower Tuffley Lane, Gloucester GL2 5DT 01452 42340
YATE TOWN RESERVES . . . . Lodge Road, Yate, Bristol BS37 7LE 01454 22810

IN: Brimscombe & Thrupp (P - Gloucestershire Northern Senior League Division One), Kingswood (P - Gloucestershire Northern Senic League Division One)
OUT: Slimbridge (P - Hellenic League Division One West)
B & W Avonside become Rockleaze Avonside

Slimbridge League Champions 2008-09
Back - L to R: Jamie Martin, Ryan Chandler, Thomas Cole, Lewis Wilton, William Wellon, Marc Roffe, Ian Preece, James Inch.
Front - L to R: Craig Cole, Marvyn Roberts, Leon Sterling, James Cole, Edward Ward.

Kings Stanley Les James League Cup Winners 2008-09
Back - L to R: Roger Bassett (Secretary), Russell Tritton (Manager), Adam Smith, Steve Potter, Gavin Dean, Ben Newman, Aidan Mercer, Jon Peacock, Matt Casey, Bob Hartfield (Assist. Manager), Alan Simmonds (Physio).
Front - L to R: Mike Beckingham, Luke Barstow, Sam Prior, Martin Mc Dermott (Capt),Tony Francis, Jon Embling, Dave Legg, Paul Webster.

HAMPSHIRE PREMIER LEAGUE

www.hpfl.co.uk

Sponsored by: Puma Engineering

Founded: 2007

Recent champions: 2008: AFC Stoneham

	AFCS	B'mth	Clanf	Cold	Fleet.	Hamb	Head	Liss	Lock	Ludw	Lynd	Otter	Over	Paul	QKS	Sport	Team	Winch
AFC Stoneham		2-0	2-1	1-4	6-1	4-1	3-0	3-1	3-0	n/a	5-3	2-0	1-2	2-1	3-2	1-0	1-3	1-1
Bournemouth University	1-7	***S***	2-4	2-3	0-1	5-3	5-0	7-0	2-1	n/a	1-3	3-3	4-3	3-0	2-1	3-0	1-3	1-1
Clanfield	4-3	4-1	***E***	2-3	7-2	9-2	2-2	2-2	2-3	n/a	5-0	3-2	0-3	3-2	0-0	2-0	3-2	6-2
Colden Common	1-0	3-4	4-2	***N***	1-0	6-2	6-2	6-1	3-1	n/a	2-2	3-1	3-2	3-2	2-1	1-1	0-3	3-2
Fleetlands	0-2	1-1	3-1	0-2	***I***	3-1	4-3	5-2	1-1	n/a	3-1	0-2	6-1	1-1	4-1	1-1	0-6	1-0
Hamble Club	0-2	0-8	0-3	1-2	4-4	***O***	0-2	2-4	1-2	6-4	2-2	1-5	1-2	1-6	0-3	2-6	4-3	0-3
Headley United	5-1	3-2	2-3	1-2	0-4	0-2	***R***	3-2	9-1	1-1	1-2	1-1	4-3	0-2	1-6	2-3	3-5	0-4
Liss Athletic	0-0	2-2	3-6	3-13	6-2	3-0	0-5		1-1	4-1	1-3	2-4	5-2	0-6	1-3	4-4	1-5	0-0
Locks Heath	1-6	6-0	0-5	4-2	3-1	5-1	3-1	5-0		3-1	2-0	0-2	5-2	2-1	1-1	5-0	6-3	2-0
Ludwig Leisure B'stoke	0-6	n/a	n/a	0-7	n/a	n/a	n/a	n/a	3-3	***D***	2-5	n/a	n/a	1-2	n/a	n/a	n/a	n/a
Lyndhurst	1-2	5-1	0-2	1-5	0-2	5-0	4-1	3-1	2-1	n/a	***I***	0-0	3-4	3-5	1-0	1-1	5-3	1-2
Otterbourne	3-2	4-3	1-3	1-1	3-0	10-0	4-0	5-2	1-1	2-3	0-1	***V***	4-1	1-2	0-4	2-1	3-1	0-2
Overton United	2-2	1-2	2-5	1-7	3-3	2-2	2-3	3-2	1-1	n/a	4-1	2-1	***I***	1-4	1-0	1-0	1-4	4-0
Paulsgrove	2-1	1-2	3-1	1-1	3-0	9-1	7-0	3-3	4-0	n/a	5-1	4-1	1-3	***S***	5-1	2-0	2-4	2-0
QK Southampton	0-3	4-0	1-1	1-4	1-1	3-0	2-2	2-2	0-4	n/a	2-6	2-4	0-5	3-2	***I***	2-1	1-6	1-0
Sporting BTC	1-3	2-1	0-1	3-5	1-5	2-0	2-2	1-4	2-2	0-1	3-4	1-4	3-2	0-4	0-1	***O***	0-2	1-3
Team Solent	2-2	1-1	1-5	2-3	5-3	2-0	2-0	7-1	2-1	n/a	2-1	4-1	5-1	1-6	2-3	5-2	***N***	4-0
Winchester Castle	1-3	1-4	0-2	2-5	1-4	2-2	2-1	0-3	1-2	2-2	4-3	0-2	0-6	2-2	2-1	1-1	1-3	

LEAGUE CUP

PRELIMINARY ROUND
AFC Stoneham 2 Team Solent 1.
QK Southampton 0 **Sporting BTC** 2

FIRST ROUND
Bournemouth Univ. 1 AFC Stoneham 0
Clanfield 2 Fleetlands 1 *aet*
Colden Common 5 Ludwig Leisure 3
Liss 6 Hamble 0, **Locks H.** 3 Lyndhurst 1
Otterbourne 2 **Paulsgrove** 4
Overton United 5 Headley 3
Win. Castle 1 **Spting BTC** 1 *aet* (3-5p)

QUARTER-FINALS
Liss Athletic 1 **Colden Common** 4
Locks Heath 3 Clanfield 1
Overton 2 B'mouth University 1 *aet*
Sptg BTC 1 **Paulsgrove** 1 *aet* (4-5p)

SEMI-FINALS
Colden Common 3 Locks Heath 2
Paulsgrove 3 Overton United 1

FINAL *(May 4th at Fareham Town)*
Paulsgrove 2 Colden Common 1

Senior Division	P	W	D	L	F	A	Pts
Colden Common	32	25	4	3	109	52	79
Clanfield	32	21	4	7	99	53	67
Team Solent	32	21	2	9	103	62	65
AFC Stoneham	32	20	4	8	79	44	64
Paulsgrove	32	19	4	9	100	45	61
Locks Heath	32	16	6	10	72	60	54
Otterbourne	32	16	5	11	75	52	53
Fleetlands	32	13	7	12	66	70	46
Bournemouth University	32	13	5	14	74	73	44
Lyndhurst	32	13	4	15	68	72	43
Overton United	32	13	4	15	73	82	43
QK Southampton	32	11	6	15	53	66	39
Winchester Castle	32	8	6	18	40	71	30
Headley United	32	8	4	20	59	91	28
Liss Athletic	32	6	8	18	62	113	26
Sporting BTC	32	5	7	20	43	78	22
Hamble Club	32	2	4	26	36	127	10

Ludwig Leisure Basingstoke - record expunged

Combination	P	W	D	L	F	A	P
Paulsgrove Res.	24	22	1	1	101	22	67
Locks Heath Res.	24	17	3	4	83	36	54
Colden Common Res.	24	12	4	8	66	41	40
Winchester Castle Res.	24	13	0	11	47	46	39
Clanfield Res.	24	11	5	8	66	47	38
Fleetlands Res.	24	11	5	8	46	39	38
Otterbourne Res.	24	10	5	9	45	43	35
Team Solent Res.	24	9	3	12	51	63	30
AFC Stoneham Res.	24	9	3	12	46	63	30
Sporting BTC Res.	24	6	6	12	36	51	24
QK Southampton Res.	24	7	3	14	37	57	24
Overton United Res.	24	7	1	16	44	71	22
Hamble Club Res.	24	2	1	21	30	119	7

COMBINATION CUP

FINAL *(May 4th at Fareham Town)*
Locks Heath Res. 3 Clanfield Res. 1

HAMPSHIRE PREMIER LEAGUE SENIOR DIVISION CONSTITUTION 2009-10

AFC STONEHAM . . . . Stoneham Park, Stoneham Lane, Eastleigh, Southampton SO50 9HQ. 07765 04642
BOURNEMOUTH UNIVERSITY. . Bournemouth SC, Chapel Gate, East Parley, Christchurch BH23 6BD. 01202 58193
CLANFIELD. . . . . Peel Park, Chalton Lane, Clanfield, Waterlooville PO8 0RJ 07765 23823
COLDEN COMMON . . . . Colden Common Rec., Main Road, Colden Common, Winchester SO21 1RP. 01962 71236
FLEETLANDS . . . . Vector Aerospace, Fleetlands, Lederle Lane, Gosport PO13 0AA. 01329 23972
HAMBLE CLUB . . . . Shell Mex Ground, Hamble Lane, Hamble-le-Rice, Southampton SO31 4QJ 07818 20440
HEADLEY UNITED . . . . Headley Pavilion, Mill Lane, Headley GU35 0PD . . . . Non
LIPHOOK UNITED . . . . Recreation Ground, London Road, Liphook GU30 7AN. . . . . Non
LISS ATHLETIC . . . . Newman Collard Ground, Hill Brow Road, Liss GU33 7LH 01730 89402
LOCKS HEATH . . . . Locksheath Rec, 419 Warsash Road, Titchfield Common, Fareham PO14 4JX 01489 60093
LYNDHURST . . . . Wellands Road, Lyndhurst SO43 7AB . . . . Non
OTTERBOURNE. . . . . Oakwood Park, Oakwood Avenue, Otterbourne SO21 2ED 01962 71468
OVERTON UNITED . . . . Overton Recreation Centre, Bridge Street, Overton RG25 3LZ. 01256 77056
PAULSGROVE. . . . . Paulsgrove Social Club, Marsden Road, off Allaway Avenue, Paulsgrove, Portsmouth PO6 4JB 023 9232 410
QK SOUTHAMPTON. . . . . Lordshill Recreation Centre, Redbridge Lane, Lordshill, Southampton SO16 0XN 07801 55033
SPORTING BISHOPS WALTHAM . . . . . Priory Park, Elizabeth Way, Bishop Waltham SO32 1SQ . . . . Non
TEAM SOLENT. . . . . Hardmoor Sports Ground, Stoneham Lane, Eastleigh, Southampton SO50 9HT 023 8061 757
WINCHESTER CASTLE Hants Co. Council Sports Ground, Petersfield Road (A31), Chilcombe, Winchester SO23 8ZB 01962 86698

IN: Liphook United (S - Surrey Elite Intermediate League Intermediate Division)
OUT: Ludwig Leisure Basingstoke (WS)
Sporting BTC become Sporting Bishops Waltham

HERTS SENIOR COUNTY LEAGUE

www.hsc.leaguemanager.biz

Sponsored by:

No sponsor

Founded: 1898

Recent champions:

2004: Hadley

2005: Hadley

2006: Whitewebbs

2007: Whitewebbs

2008: Hatfield Town

	Baldock	Bedmd	Bov'don	Buntfd	Codic.	Evergn	Her. Hth	Knebwth	Lemsfd	L.Lions	M Police	Mill End	Park St	Sand.	Standon	Worm.
Baldock Town Letchworth	***P***	19-0	1-3	3-2	2-3	2-0	2-0	4-1	2-2	1-1	1-0	4-1	3-0	3-2	3-0	3-4
Bedmond Sports & Social	0-8	***R***	1-4	0-3	0-12	1-4	0-11	4-2	0-7	2-14	0-11	1-7	1-2	0-9	0-3	1-5
Bovingdon	0-3	10-2	***E***	11-1	2-2	3-2	5-2	2-0	3-0	1-4	0-2	2-3	3-6	0-3	7-1	1-2
Buntingford Town	5-0	6-2	2-4	***M***	4-5	0-5	4-2	1-0	2-3	1-4	3-7	1-1	1-3	3-3	0-9	4-2
Codicote	1-4	10-0	1-2	7-0	***I***	1-3	2-1	4-1	3-3	0-1	1-2	4-1	2-2	5-2	3-1	3-2
Evergreen	0-3	6-0	3-2	2-1	1-1	***E***	1-2	2-3	2-2	0-2	1-4	1-2	1-3	1-1	5-2	4-1
Hertford Heath	1-4	2-0	1-2	5-1	1-6	1-1	***R***	2-0	2-0	0-6	4-0	1-2	1-1	3-1	0-3	0-2
Knebworth	0-2	4-0	2-4	2-5	0-5	1-3	1-3		0-5	1-2	0-4	0-5	0-5	0-3	2-4	3-3
Lemsford	1-2	6-1	1-2	8-0	4-1	1-3	4-1	6-1	***D***	1-2	2-2	1-3	2-0	3-1	1-2	2-4
London Lions	4-1	10-0	10-0	7-1	2-2	2-0	2-3	0-0	1-2	***I***	2-0	3-1	1-2	4-2	4-2	4-0
Met. Police Bushey	0-1	21-1	6-0	13-1	2-0	6-2	4-1	4-0	2-2	3-1	***V***	3-2	3-0	7-1	5-1	1-0
Mill End Sports	1-0	5-2	1-4	6-0	1-2	0-6	2-3	0-0	2-3	1-1	1-3	***I***	2-2	0-2	5-2	0-1
Park Street Village	4-1	6-0	1-0	2-2	0-1	1-1	1-0	5-0	4-1	3-0	1-1	1-1	***S***	2-0	0-1	7-1
Sandridge Rovers	1-0	5-1	0-0	6-0	2-2	1-0	1-1	4-1	1-4	2-0	0-2	1-4	2-3	***I***	3-3	0-1
Standon & Puckeridge	0-4	8-0	2-3	4-3	2-0	0-1	3-0	5-0	2-1	1-1	3-3	2-0	2-1	1-1	***O***	1-2
Wormley Rovers	1-1	6-1	1-2	0-1	2-3	1-2	1-1	3-0	1-3	1-3	2-4	3-2	0-2	1-3	0-1	***N***

Premier Division		**P**	**W**	**D**	**L**	**F**	**A**	**Pts**
Metropolitan Police Bushey		**30**	**22**	**4**	**4**	**125**	**34**	**70**
London Lions		**30**	**19**	**5**	**6**	**98**	**34**	**62**
Baldock T. Letchchworth		**30**	**19**	**3**	**8**	**87**	**38**	**60**
Park Street Village		**30**	**17**	**7**	**6**	**70**	**34**	**58**
Codicote		**30**	**16**	**6**	**8**	**92**	**50**	**54**
Bovingdon		**30**	**17**	**2**	**11**	**82**	**66**	**53**
Standon & Puckeridge		**30**	**15**	**4**	**11**	**71**	**58**	**49**
Lemsford		**30**	**14**	**5**	**11**	**81**	**52**	**47**
Evergreen		**30**	**13**	**5**	**12**	**63**	**50**	**44**
Mill End Sports	*+3*	**30**	**11**	**5**	**14**	**62**	**59**	**41**
Sandridge Rovers		**30**	**11**	**7**	**12**	**63**	**55**	**40**
Hertford Heath		**30**	**11**	**4**	**15**	**55**	**62**	**37**
Wormley Rovers	*-3*	**30**	**11**	**3**	**16**	**53**	**63**	**33**
Buntingford Town		**30**	**8**	**3**	**19**	**58**	**126**	**27**
Knebworth		**30**	**2**	**3**	**25**	**25**	**99**	**9**
Bedmond Sports & Social		**30**	**1**	**0**	**29**	**21**	**226**	**3**

RESERVES CHALLENGE CUP

FINAL

(May 2nd at Bovingdon)

Hinton Res. 0 Codicote Res. 0 *aet* (5-4p)

Reserve Division One	P	W	D	L	F	A	Pt
Codicote Res.	24	20	0	4	64	22	60
Baldock Town Letch. Res.	24	18	3	3	83	28	57
Park Street Village Res.	24	17	2	5	72	30	53
London Lions Res.	24	13	2	9	70	43	41
Evergreen Res.	24	12	5	7	71	55	41
Met. Police Bushey Res.	24	11	6	7	61	42	39
Sarratt Res.	24	9	5	10	48	55	32
Bovingdon Res.	24	9	4	11	57	49	31
Hinton Res.	24	7	7	10	53	62	28
Sandridge Rovers Res.	24	9	1	14	48	61	28
Buntingford Town Res.	24	5	3	16	28	68	18
Lemsford Res.	24	3	3	18	30	79	12
Knebworth Res.	24	1	3	20	19	110	6

Reserve Division Two	P	W	D	L	F	A	Pt
Wormley Rovers Res.	22	14	5	3	59	30	47
Hertford Heath Res.	22	14	4	4	72	44	46
Cuffley Res.	22	13	1	8	62	52	40
Harpenden Rovers Res.	22	12	3	7	62	45	39
Standon & Puckeridge Res.	22	12	1	9	63	49	37
Letchworth GC Eagles Res.	22	10	2	10	56	44	32
Croxley Guild Res.	22	9	4	9	50	54	31
Bedmond Spts/Social Res.	22	9	2	11	61	63	29
Chipperfield Corinthians Res.	22	7	4	11	49	60	25
Old Parmiterians Res.	22	7	1	14	48	70	22
Mill End Sports Res.	22	6	2	14	42	61	20
Bushey Rangers Res.	22	4	1	17	45	97	13

HERTS SENIOR COUNTY LEAGUE PREMIER DIVISION CONSTITUTION 2009-10

BALDOCK TOWN LETCHWORTH ..... Herts County FA, Baldock Road, Letchworth SG6 2EN 01462 677622
BOVINGDON .... Green Lane, Bovingdon, Hemel Hempstead HP3 0LA 01442 832628
CHIPPERFIELD CORINTHIANS .... Queens Street, Chipperfield, Kings Langley WD4 9BT 07958 744441
CODICOTE .... Hertford Town FC, Hertingfordbury Park, West Street, Hertford SG13 8EZ 01992 583716
CROXLEY GUILD............. Croxley Guild of Sport, The Green, Croxley Green, Watford WD3 3JX.............. 01923 770534
CUFFLEY.................... King George's Playing Fields, Northaw Road East, Cuffley EN6 4LU 07815 174434
EVERGREEN .... South Way, Kings Langley, Abbots Langley WD4 8PN 01923 267812
HERTFORD HEATH .... The Playing Field, Trinity Road, Hertford Heath SG13 7QS .... None
LEMSFORD .... Welwyn Playing Fields, Ottway Walk, Welwyn AL6 9AT............................ None
LONDON LIONS................... Rowley Lane Sports Ground, Arkley, Barnet EN5 3HW 020 8441 6051
METROPOLITAN POLICE BUSHEY .... Aldenham Road, Bushey, Watford WD2 3TR......................... 01923 243947
MILL END SPORTS .... King George V Playing Fields, Penn Road, Mill End, Rickmansworth WD3 8QX 01923 776392
PARK STREET VILLAGE.......... William Bird Playing Fields, Toulmin Drive, St Albans AL3 6DR 01727 852401
SANDRIDGE ROVERS .... Spencer Recreation Ground, Sandridge, St Albans AL4 9DD 01727 835506
STANDON & PUCKERIDGE .... Station Road, Standon, Ware SG11 1QT 01920 823460
WORMLEY ROVERS............... Wormley Sports Club, Church Lane, Wormley EN10 7QF.................. 01992 460650

IN: Chipperfield Corinthians (P), Croxley Guild (P), Cuffley (P)

OUT: Bedmond Sports & Social (R), Buntingford Town (R), Knebworth (R)

	AFC Hatfield	Allenburys	Bedwell	Bushey	Chipperfield	Croxley Guild	Cuffley	Debden Spts	Harpenden R.	Hinton	Hitchin TA	Kimpton Rov.	Letch. GCE	O Parmiter.	Sarratt	St Peters
AFC Hatfield Town		0-2	1-3	1-1	0-1	2-3	2-4	1-3	0-3	0-1	0-7	3-0	1-0	2-2	1-3	5-2
Allenburys Sports	4-1	***D***	6-2	2-1	0-3	1-3	0-8	2-3	3-4	1-1	5-1	2-2	1-4	3-2	4-6	5-3
Bedwell Rangers	0-3	2-8	***I***	2-6	0-3	1-2	0-5	1-10	L-W	5-4	1-3	1-5	1-6	1-1	2-2	1-5
Bushey Rangers	2-0	2-3	4-1	***V***	1-4	1-1	2-5	2-3	0-5	2-1	2-3	3-0	1-1	5-3	2-0	4-1
Chipperfield Corinthians	6-0	2-1	10-0	3-2	***I***	0-2	4-1	2-1	3-2	3-2	2-0	3-1	0-1	2-0	2-1	9-0
Croxley Guild	3-3	2-1	5-0	1-1	2-3	***S***	0-0	1-1	4-1	0-1	4-1	2-1	3-2	1-1	1-1	3-1
Cuffley	4-1	2-1	7-0	4-0	2-0	9-0	***I***	3-1	3-1	2-0	2-1	4-2	1-0	3-4	1-0	5-1
Debden Sports	8-2	6-2	3-1	2-5	0-1	1-2	0-3	***O***	9-0	3-0	3-2	4-0	5-4	4-1	1-2	7-1
Harpenden Rovers	10-1	1-6	6-1	0-2	0-5	2-1	0-2	3-2	***N***	4-3	1-4	2-2	2-5	1-3	0-4	2-2
Hinton	3-4	4-1	7-0	2-1	0-5	3-2	1-1	4-3	2-5		1-2	1-3	W-L	1-3	4-0	W-L
Hitchin Town Arena	9-3	5-0	5-0	2-0	1-1	3-3	0-3	3-1	0-3	0-0		1-2	6-0	4-1	3-1	4-2
Kimpton Rovers	5-1	1-0	5-0	2-1	2-1	5-1	1-5	2-1	3-1	2-2	1-6		2-2	0-2	5-1	3-2
Letchworth GC Eagles	7-0	2-3	7-2	0-4	1-2	4-1	0-2	0-6	3-2	1-2	0-8	3-2	***O***	0-0	2-1	2-0
Old Parmiterians	4-1	1-1	6-1	3-1	0-3	0-1	0-4	0-3	2-1	0-2	L-W	1-2	L-W	***N***	1-0	W-L
Sarratt	4-1	0-1	4-1	0-3	0-1	3-1	1-2	1-1	4-2	1-0	0-2	3-0	4-2	2-2	***E***	3-0
St Peters	0-4	0-2	6-1	6-2	0-2	1-2	2-1	0-2	0-6	0-2	0-7	0-4	2-1	3-0	1-0	

Division One	**P**	**W**	**D**	**L**	**F**	**A**	**Pts**
Cuffley	**30**	**25**	**2**	**3**	**98**	**25**	**77**
Chipperfield Corries	**30**	**25**	**1**	**4**	**86**	**23**	**76**
Hitchin Town Arena	**30**	**19**	**3**	**8**	**93**	**42**	**60**
Debden Sports	**30**	**17**	**2**	**11**	**97**	**51**	**53**
Croxley Guild	**30**	**14**	**8**	**8**	**57**	**54**	**50**
Kimpton Rovers	**30**	**15**	**4**	**11**	**65**	**59**	**49**
Hinton	**30**	**13**	**4**	**13**	**54**	**54**	**43**
Allenburys Sports	**30**	**13**	**3**	**14**	**71**	**74**	**42**
Sarratt	**30**	**12**	**4**	**14**	**52**	**49**	**40**
Bushey Rangers	**30**	**12**	**4**	**14**	**63**	**61**	**40**
Letchw'th GC Eagles	**30**	**12**	**3**	**15**	**60**	**64**	**39**
Harpenden Rovers	**30**	**12**	**2**	**16**	**70**	**79**	**38**
Old Parmiterians	**30**	**10**	**6**	**14**	**43**	**52**	**36**
St Peters	**30**	**7**	**1**	**22**	**41**	**89**	**22**
AFC Hatfield Town	**30**	**6**	**3**	**21**	**44**	**104**	**21**
Bedwell Rangers	**30**	**2**	**2**	**26**	**31**	**90**	**8**

AUBREY CUP

FIRST ROUND

Kimpton Rovers 2 Letchworth GC Eagles 1

SECOND ROUND

Allenburys 4 **Debden Sps** 6
Bushey Rgrs 1 St Peters 0
Codicote 5 **Baldock TL** 6
Croxley Guild 5 Bedwell 3
Evergreen 5 AFC Hatfield 1 Hertford Heath 0
Chipperfield Cor. 1 *aet*
Hitchin Town Arena 8 Bedmond Sports & Social 0
Kimpton Rovers 2 **Buntingford Town** 3 *aet*
Knebworth 3 Wormley 2
Lemsford 2 London Lions 1
Met. Police Bushey 3 Sandridge Rovers 1
Mill End Sports 2 Harpenden Rovers 0
Old Parmiterians 0 **Sarratt** 5
Park St Village 3 Cuffley 1 *aet*
Standon & P. 6 Hinton 1

THIRD ROUND

Baldock T. Letchworth 2 Hitchin Town Arena 0
Bovingdon 5 Standon & Puckeridge 3
Buntingford 2 Sarratt 0
Bushey Rgrs 3 Croxley 0
Debden Spts 3 Knebworth 1
Evergreen 1 **Chipperfield Corinthians** 2 *aet*
Metropolitan Police Bushey 0 **Park Street Village** 3
Mill End 4 Lemsford 2 *aet*

QUARTER-FINALS

Bovingdon 3 Baldock 1
Chipperfield 5 Buntingford 0
Debden Sports 2 **Mill End** 3
Park Street 2 Bushey 1

SEMI-FINALS

Chipperfield 2 **Mill End** 3
Park Street 2 Bovingdon 1

FINAL

(May 4th at HCFA, Letchworth)
Mill End 3 Park Street 1

HERTS SENIOR COUNTY LEAGUE DIVISION ONE CONSTITUTION 2009-10

AFC HATFIELD TOWN .... Birchwood Leisure Centre, Birchwood, Longmead, Hatfield AL10 0AN. 01707 270772
ALLENBURYS SPORTS .... Glaxo Smith Kline, Westfield Park Road, Ware SG12 0DP .... None
BEDMOND SPORTS & SOCIAL .. Toms Lane Rec, Toms Lane, Bedmond, Abbots Langley WD5 0RB 01923 267991
BELSTONE .... The Medburn Ground, Watling Street, Radlett WD6 3AB. 020 8207 2395
BUNTINGFORD TOWN......... Sainsburys Distribution Centre, London Road, Buntingford SG9 9JR 01763 271522
BUSHEY RANGERS .... Moatfield, Bournehall Lane, Bushey WD23 3JU 020 8386 1875
DEBDEN SPORTS .... Chigwell Lane, Loughton, Ilford IG10 3TP 020 8508 9392
HARPENDEN ROVERS .... Acres Corner, Cravells Road, Harpenden Common AL5 1BQ .... None
HINTON .... Holtwhites Sports & Social, Kirkland Drive, Enfield EN2 0RU 020 8363 4449
KIMPTON ROVERS .... Kimpton Recreation Ground, High Street, Kimpton, Hitchin SG4 8RA .... None
KNEBWORTH .... The Recreation Ground, Watton Road, Knebworth, Stevenage SG3 6AH....................... None
LETCHWORTH GARDEN CITY EAGLES Pixmore Playing Fields, Ledgers Lane, Baldock Road, Letchworth SG6 2EN .... None
OLD PARMITERIANS............. Thomas Parmiter Sports Centre, Garston, Watford WD25 0JU............... 01923 682805
SARRATT.................... King George V Playing Fields, Georges V Way, Sarratt WD3 6AU. .... None
ST PETERS .... Lemsford Village Hall, Brocket Road, Lemsford AL8 7TT 01707 333548
WALKERN RANGERS............. Jubilee Pavilion, High Street, Walkern, Stevenage SG2 7PD.............................. None
WHITWELL VILLAGE............ King George V Recreation Ground, Bradway, Whitwell SG4 8BE .... None

IN: Bedmond Sports & Social (R), Belstone (P - Sunday football), Buntingford Town (R), Knebworth (R), Whitwell (formerly Whitwell Village) (P - North & Mid-Herts League Premier Division)
OUT: Chipperfield Corinthians (P), Croxley Guild (P), Cuffley (P), Hitchin Town Arena (W), North Mymms (WN)
Bedwell Rangers become Walkern Rangers

KENT COUNTY LEAGUE

www.kentcountyfootballleague.co.uk

Sponsored by:

Vandanel

Founded: 1922

Recent champions:

2004: Crockenhill

2005: Cray Valley Paper Mills

2006: Lewisham Borough (Community)

2007: Holmesdale

2008: Norton Sports

Premier Division		P	W	D	L	F	A	Pts
Hollands & Blair		28	20	6	2	76	31	66
Fleet Leisure	*-1*	28	21	1	6	69	31	63
Stansfeld O & B Club		28	18	5	5	71	34	59
Orpington	*-1*	28	17	1	10	56	36	51
Cray Valley Paper Mills		28	13	5	10	50	44	44
Bearsted		28	12	6	10	50	47	42
Coney Hall	*-1*	28	12	7	9	40	48	42
Phoenix Sports		28	11	7	10	59	50	40
Lewisham Boro. (Com.)	*-3*	28	13	2	13	43	47	38
Bly Spartans	*-1*	28	12	1	15	50	63	36
Rusthall		28	10	5	13	40	47	35
Snodland		28	4	7	17	37	63	19
Milton & Fulston United	*-1*	28	6	2	20	52	88	19
Bromley Green		28	5	4	19	33	69	19
Sheerness East		28	5	3	20	41	69	18

	Bearsted	Bly Spartans	Bromley G.	Coney Hall	Cray Valley	Fleet Leisure	Hollands & B.	Lewisham B.	Milton/Fulston	Orpington	Phoenix Spts	Rusthall	Sheerness E.	Snodland	Stansfeld O&B
Bearsted		6-0	2-1	1-1	0-1	2-2	1-1	2-0	2-1	1-3	0-0	1-3	4-1	2-1	1-0
Bly Spartans	2-2		2-0	4-1	2-0	2-3	1-2	0-2	4-1	0-6	3-2	1-0	3-2	3-1	2-3
Bromley Green	1-3	2-1	***P***	0-2	1-2	0-4	0-1	3-1	2-2	2-3	0-2	2-1	3-1	0-0	3-3
Coney Hall	4-2	2-1	1-0	***R***	3-3	0-3	1-1	0-2	3-5	3-0	3-3	0-0	1-0	2-0	0-5
Cray Valley Paper Mills	0-0	2-1	8-1	0-1	***E***	2-0	1-1	1-2	8-1	2-1	1-0	2-1	2-1	2-2	1-3
Fleet Leisure	1-0	1-0	8-1	4-1	3-1	***M***	0-2	2-0	2-1	1-3	4-1	3-0	3-2	2-0	4-2
Hollands & Blair	4-1	6-2	3-1	2-0	5-0	4-1	***I***	1-2	3-1	2-1	3-2	4-0	2-1	4-1	1-1
Lewisham Boro. (Comm.)	1-2	1-2	3-3	2-2	2-0	0-1	3-4	***E***	3-2	1-2	2-1	2-1	1-2	2-1	1-3
Milton & Fulston United	3-4	6-1	2-4	0-1	2-3	0-3	0-7	1-2	***R***	2-6	1-2	6-2	3-2	1-4	1-5
Orpington	4-1	1-0	2-1	1-2	1-0	2-1	1-3	2-3	2-0		0-1	1-0	4-0	2-2	2-1
Phoenix Sports	3-2	2-3	3-1	3-0	3-3	1-2	1-1	4-1	4-0	0-1	***D***	2-2	7-3	3-2	2-2
Rusthall	4-0	W-L	2-1	2-2	1-3	1-2	1-3	2-0	1-1	3-1	3-4	***I***	1-0	2-1	2-1
Sheerness East	1-2	4-5	3-0	1-2	1-2	0-6	1-1	1-2	2-4	W-L	3-1	1-3	***V***	3-1	1-1
Snodland	2-5	1-5	1-0	1-2	2-0	0-3	2-4	0-2	1-3	2-0	2-2	1-1	3-3		1-1
Stansfeld O & B Club	2-1	4-0	3-0	2-0	3-0	3-0	4-1	2-0	5-2	2-4	2-0	2-1	2-1	4-2	

KENT COUNTY LEAGUE PREMIER DIVISION CONSTITUTION 2009-10

BEARSTED . . . . Otham Sports Ground, Honey Lane, Otham, Maidstone ME15 8RG. 07860 360280
BLY SPARTANS . . . . Bly Spartans Sports Ground, Rede Court Road, Strood ME2 3TU. 01634 710577
CANTERBURY CITY . . . . Bridge Recreation Ground, Patrixbourne Road, Bridge, Canterbury CT4 5BL . . . . None
CONEY HALL . . . . Tiepigs Lane, Coney Hall, West Wickham BR4 9BT 020 8462 9103
CRAY VALLEY PAPER MILLS . . . . . Badgers Sports Ground, Middle Park Avenue, Eltham SE9 5HT. 020 8850 4273
FLEET LEISURE . . . . Beauwater Leisure Sports Club, Nelson Road, Northfleet DA11 7EE 01474 359222
HOLLANDS & BLAIR. . . . . . Rochagas Sports & Social, Star Meadow, Dartford Avenue, Gillingham ME7 3AN 01634 573839
LEWISHAM BOROUGH (COMMUNITY) . . . Ladywell Arena, Doggett Road, Catford SE6 4QX 020 8314 1986
MILTON & FULSTON UNITED. . . UK Paper Sports Ground, Gore Court Road, Sittingbourne ME10 1QN 01795 564213
ORPINGTON. . . . . Westcombe Park & Orpington SC, Goddington Lane, Orpington BR6 9SH 01689 834902
PHOENIX SPORTS. . . . . Phoenix Sports Club, Mayplace Road East, Bexleyheath DA7 6JT 01322 526159
RUSTHALL. . . . . Jockey Farm, Nellington Lane, Rusthall, Tunbridge Wells TN4 8SH. 07940 277138
SNODLAND . . . . Potyn's Field, Paddlesworth Road, Snodland ME6 5DL 01634 243961
STANSFELD O & B CLUB . . . . Cray Wanderers FC, Oxford Road, Sidcup DA14 6LW 020 8300 2987
SUTTON ATHLETIC . . . . The Roaches, Parsonage Lane, Sutton-at-Hone, Dartford DA4 9HD 01322 280507
TONBRIDGE INVICTA. . . . Swanmead Sports Ground, Swanwead Way, off Cannon Lane, Tonbridge TN9 1PP 01732 350473

IN: Canterbury City (P - Division One East), Sutton Athletic (P - Division One West), Tonbridge Invicta (P - Division One West)

OUT: Bromley Green (R - Division One East), Sheerness East (R - Division One East)

GR ROOFING CHAMPIONS TROPHY

(Premier Division champions v Inter-Regional Challenge Cup holders)

(September 3rd at Faversham Town)

Norton Sports 2

Fleet Leisure 2 *aet* (7-6p)

Division One East		P	W	D	L	F	A	Pts
Canterbury City		20	15	5	0	75	23	50
AFC Sheppey		20	12	3	5	39	28	39
University of Kent	*-1*	20	12	3	5	79	37	38
Otford United		20	7	6	7	39	34	27
APM Mears		20	7	5	8	35	37	26
Kennington		20	7	5	8	41	48	26
New Romney		20	7	4	9	37	44	25
Staplehurst/Mon.		20	6	5	9	31	44	23
Guru Nanak	*-1*	20	7	3	10	25	54	23
Oakwood		20	5	7	8	27	37	22
Lydd Town	*-6*	20	1	2	17	17	59	-1

Betteshanger Welfare - record expunged

BILL MANKELOW INTER REGIONAL CHALLENGE CUP

(Premier and Division One teams)

FIRST ROUND EAST

Lydd Town 1 **Guru Nanak** 2

Otford 3 APM Mears 1

FIRST ROUND WEST

Belvedere 2 **Metrogas** 3

Bromleians Sports 2 Bridon Ropes 0

Farnborough OB Guild 1 Crockenhill 0

Greenways 2 Westerham 0

Hawkhurst United 2 Tonbridge Invicta 0

Sutton Ath. 3 Tudor Spts 1

SECOND ROUND EAST

Bearsted (w/o) v Betteshanger Welfare

Canterbury City 1 **Hollands & Blair** 2

Kennington 3 Sheppey 0

New Romney 2 **Bly Spartans** 11

Otford 1 **Bromley Green** 2

Sheerness East 1 **Milton & Fulston United** 3

Staplehurst & Monarchs United 1 **Guru Nanak** 2

University of Kent 3 **Oakwood** 5

SECOND ROUND WEST

Coney Hall 2 Chipstead 0

Cray Valley Paper Mills 4 Bromleians Sports 0

Farnborough OB Guild 1 **Rusthall** 3

Greenways 0 **Fleet Leis.** 1

Metrogas 4 Sutton Ath. 0

Orpington 3 Hawkhurst 0

Phoenix Spts 1 Stansfeld 0

Snodland 1 **Lewisham Borough (Community)** 6

THIRD ROUND EAST

Bearsted 7 Guru Nanak 2

Bly 6 Kennington 3

Hollands & Blair 3 Bromley Green 0

Milton & FU 3 Oakwood 2

THIRD ROUND WEST

Coney Hall 2 **Rusthall** 4

Cray Valley Paper Mills 1 **Orpington** 2

Metrogas 0 **Lewisham Borough (Community)** 1

Phoenix Spts 2 **Fleet Leisure** 2 *aet* (4-5p)

QUARTER-FINALS

Bly Spartans 0 **Milton & Fulston Utd** 3

Fleet Leisure 0 **Rusthall** 2

Hollands & Blair 1 Bearsted 0 aet

Orpington 2 Lewisham Borough (Community) 1

SEMI-FINALS

Milton & Fulston United 0 **Hollands & Blair** 5

Rusthall 0 **Orpington** 1

FINAL

(May 7th at Chatham Town)

Hollands & Blairs 2 Orpington 1 *aet*

	AFC	APM	Bett	Cant	Guru	Kenn	Lydd	New	Oak	Off	Stap	Uni
AFC Sheppey	***D***	5-1	n/a	0-1	1-1	4-1	2-1	2-1	2-1	2-0	1-0	0-2
APM Mears	2-3	***I***	n/a	0-2	2-1	1-4	3-1	1-1	0-0	3-1	4-0	1-4
Betteshanger Welfare	n/a	n/a	***V***	n/a	2-0	n/a	n/a	n/a	n/a	n/a	3-3	n/a
Canterbury City	6-1	1-1	3-2		7-0	5-2	9-1	3-1	2-2	3-2	4-1	5-1
Guru Nanak	0-1	0-3	n/a	0-4	***O***	3-1	1-0	5-3	3-1	0-4	3-3	0-9
Kennington	1-2	1-0	n/a	3-3	1-3	***N***	3-0	3-3	1-1	0-3	2-1	3-3
Lydd Town	1-4	0-7	n/a	2-3	0-0	4-2	***E***	1-2	1-4	0-0	0-3	1-5
New Romney	1-1	2-3	n/a	2-2	4-0	5-1	3-1		1-0	0-2	0-1	1-8
Oakwood	4-3	1-1	n/a	0-4	1-3	1-3	3-0	0-2	***E***	1-0	0-0	1-6
Otford United	1-1	1-1	n/a	1-4	2-1	3-4	3-2	2-4	1-1	***A***	6-2	4-2
Staplehurst & Monarchs United	0-3	3-1	n/a	1-1	0-1	2-2	2-1	5-0	1-2	1-1	***S***	2-11
University of Kent	3-1	6-0	n/a	2-6	7-0	1-3	W-L	3-1	3-3	2-2	1-3	***T***

KENT COUNTY DIVISION ONE EAST CONSTITUTION 2009-10

AFC SHEPPEY . . . . Medway Ports Authority Ground, Holm Place, Halfway, Sheerness ME12 3AT. 01795 66805
APM MEARS . . . . Cobdown Sports & Social Club, Ditton Corner, Station Road, Aylesford ME20 6AU. 01622 71682
BROMLEY GREEN. . . . . The Swan Centre, Cudworth Road, South Willesborough, Ashford TN24 0BB. 01233 64598
KENNINGTON . . . . Kennington Cricket Club, Ulley Road, Kennington, Ashford TN24 9HY. 07887 99521
LARKFIELD & NEW HYTHE WANDERERS New Hythe Lane, Larkfield, Aylesford ME20 6PU 01732 87331
NEW ROMNEY. . . . . The Maud Pavilion, Station Road, New Romney TN28 8SR. 01797 36485
OAKWOOD. . . . . Honey Lane, Otham, Maidstone ME15 8RG 07745 38332
OTFORD UNITED . . . . Otford Recreation Ground, High Street, Otford, Sevenoaks TN14 5PG. 01959 52440
PREMIER. . . . . Hersden Recreation Ground, Hersden, Canterbury CT3 4HY 07825 70450
SHEERNESS EAST . . . . . . Sheerness East WMC, 47 Queensborough Road, Halfway, Sheerness ME12 3BZ. 01795 66204
STAPLEHURST & MONARCHS UNITED The Old County Ground, Norman Road, West Malling ME19 6RL. Non
UNIVERSITY OF KENT. The Oast House, Park Wood Road, Giles Lane, University of Kent, Canterbury CT2 7SY 01227 82743
WOODSTOCK PARK . . . . Sittingbourne Research Centre, Broadoak Road, Sittingbourne ME9 8AG 07774 65491

IN: Bromley Green (R), Larkfield & New Hythe Wanderers (P - Division Two East), Premier (P - Division Two East), Sheerness East (P Woodstock Park (P - Division Two East)

OUT: Betteshanger Colliery Welfare (WS), Canterbury City (P - Division One East), Guruk Nanak (S - Division One West), Lydd Town (R Division Two East)

Division One West	P	W	D	L	F	A	Pts
Tonbridge Invicta	24	16	4	4	51	18	52
Sutton Athletic	24	16	4	4	55	30	52
Bridon Ropes	24	14	5	5	44	28	47
Belvedere	24	14	4	6	57	31	46
Farnborough OBG	24	10	5	9	49	44	35
Tudor Sports	24	8	9	7	37	32	33
Greenways	24	9	6	9	38	43	33
Metrogas	24	9	5	10	41	38	32
Bromleians Sports	24	9	3	12	30	38	30
Crockenhill	24	7	4	13	33	49	25
Hawkhurst United	24	4	9	11	32	52	21
Chipstead	24	5	2	17	26	56	17
Westerham	24	3	4	17	22	56	13

WEST KENT CHALLENGE SHIELD

(Western region clubs from outside the Premier Division)

FIRST ROUND

Blackheath United 4 **Metrogas** 7

Bridon Ropes 4 Hawkhurst United 1

Bromleians Sports 2 Charlton Athletic Community 2 *aet* (7-6p)

Chipstead 0 **Belvedere** 4

Farnborough Old Boys Guild 3 Borough United 3 *aet* (5-3p)

Greenways 1 **Wickham Park** 2

Halls 0 **Eltham Palace** 3

Old Bexleians 2 **Sutton Athletic** 7

Tudor Sports 3 Erith '147 0

SECOND ROUND

Bromleians Sports 3 **Bridon Ropes** 5 *aet*

Chislehurst 1 **Tonbridge Invicta** 2

Eltham Palace 0 **Fleetdown United** 1

Meridian Sports 1 **Forest Hill Park** 4

OPK 0 **Belvedere** 2

Sutton Athletic 3 Metrogas 1

Tudor Sports 4 Wickham Park 2

Westerham 2 Farnborough Old Boys Guild 2 *aet* (4-2p)

QUARTER-FINALS

Sutton Athletic 2 Fleetdown United 1

Tonbridge Invicta 4 Bridon Ropes 3 *aet*

Tudor Sports 2 Forest Hill Park 1

Westerham 0 **Belvedere** 3

SEMI-FINALS

Belvedere 0 **Tudor Sports** 1

Sutton Athletic 1 **Tonbridge Invicta** 2

FINAL

(April 15th at Sevenoaks Town)

Tudor Sports 1 Tonbridge Invicta 0

	Belvedere	Bridon Ropes	Bromleians Sports	Chipstead	Crockenhill	Farnborough OB Guild	Greenways	Hawkhurst United	Metrogas	Sutton Athletic	Tonbridge Invicta	Tudor Sports	Westerham
Belvedere	***D***	2-0	1-0	0-2	2-1	6-2	3-1	4-1	0-1	2-1	1-1	2-2	11-1
Bridon Ropes	0-2	***I***	3-2	3-1	2-2	2-1	2-0	2-0	2-0	2-4	1-0	0-3	3-0
Bromleians Sports	1-5	2-3	***V***	1-0	2-0	1-2	2-0	1-0	3-0	0-3	1-0	1-2	1-3
Chipstead	0-5	1-2	1-3		2-0	0-7	3-1	1-3	1-2	1-2	0-0	1-4	1-2
Crockenhill	1-3	2-1	1-1	1-5	***O***	1-0	2-4	1-1	2-1	0-1	1-2	4-2	1-0
Farnborough Old Boys Guild	1-1	0-3	4-1	3-1	3-1	***N***	4-3	1-1	2-3	2-2	1-2	1-1	3-2
Greenways	0-1	0-4	0-0	2-1	7-3	1-1	***E***	2-0	1-1	0-2	0-4	2-1	3-1
Hawkhurst United	4-0	0-1	1-1	2-2	3-3	0-1	1-2		3-2	3-3	0-3	1-1	2-1
Metrogas	5-2	1-1	1-4	2-1	0-1	5-2	1-2	6-0	***W***	2-3	2-3	1-1	2-0
Sutton Athletic	1-1	2-2	1-0	3-0	3-2	4-2	1-2	5-3	3-1	***E***	0-1	3-0	2-1
Tonbridge Invicta	1-0	2-2	5-0	5-0	2-1	2-1	2-2	6-0	0-1	1-2	***S***	2-0	2-1
Tudor Sports	3-1	0-0	0-1	3-0	1-0	1-4	3-3	0-0	1-1	2-0	1-2	***T***	1-1
Westerham	1-2	1-3	2-1	0-1	1-2	0-1	0-0	3-3	0-0	0-4	0-3	1-4	

KENT COUNTY LEAGUE DIVISION ONE WEST CONSTITUTION 2009-10

BELVEDERE.................. Memorial Ground, 101a Woolwich Road, Abbey Wood SE2 0DY................. 01322 436724

BRIDON ROPES .... Meridian Sports Club, Charlton Park Road, Charlton SE7 8QS 020 8856 1923

CHARLTON ATHLETIC COMMUNITY Samuel Montagu Youth Centre, 122 Broadwalk, Kidbrooke SE3 8ND 020 8856 1126/9680

CHIPSTEAD .... Chipstead Rec, Chevening Road, Chipstead, Sevenoaks TN13 2RZ 07753 603944

CROCKENHILL.................. Wested, Eynsford Road, Crockenhill, Swanley BR8 8EH.................... 01322 662067

FARNBOROUGH OLD BOYS GUILD Farnborough (Kent) Sports Club, High Street, Farnborough BR6 7BA 01689 826949

GREENWAYS.................. Fleet Leisure & Sports Club, Nelson Road, Northfleet DA11 7EE................. 01474 359222

GURU NANAK.................. AEI Henley Sports Club, Dunkirk Close, Gravesend DA12 5NN.......................... None

METROGAS .... Marathon Playing Fields, Forty Foot Way, New Eltham SE9 2HL 020 8859 1579

OLD BEXLEIANS .... Seven Acre Sports Club, Church Manor Avenue, Abbey Wood SE2 0HY........................ None

TUDOR SPORTS........................ 31 Eltham Road, Lee Green SE12 8ES.. None

WICKHAM PARK ...... Wickham Park Sports Club, 228-230 Pickhurst Rise, West Wickham, Bromley BR4 0AQ........ 020 8777 2550

IN: Charlton Athletic Community (P - Division Two West), Guru Nanak (S - Division One East), Old Bexleians (P - Division Two West), Wickham Park (P - Division Two West)

OUT: Bromleians Sports (W), Hawkchurch United (W), Sutton Athletic (P), Tonbridge Invicta (P), Westerham (R - Division Two West)

PROMOTION PLAY-OFF

(Division One West v Division One East runners-up)

(May 16th at Sutton Athletic)

Sutton Athletic 3 AFC Sheppey 0

Division Two East		P	W	D	L	F	A	Pts
Premier		24	19	3	2	75	29	60
Woodstock Park		24	16	4	4	66	33	52
Larkfield & New Hythe		24	15	3	6	69	45	48
Swale United		24	11	4	9	56	52	37
Bredhurst Juniors	*-3*	24	12	2	10	62	56	35
AFC Sevenoaks		24	10	4	10	67	63	34
Lanes End		24	9	5	10	49	58	32
Borden Village		24	7	7	10	46	56	28
Malgo		24	7	6	11	60	68	27
Platt United		24	6	4	14	49	69	22
Saga Sports & Social		24	6	4	14	45	67	22
Tenterden Town	*-1*	24	5	5	14	44	79	19
Pembury	*-3*	24	5	5	14	32	45	17

LES LECKIE CUP

(Eastern region clubs from outside the Premier Division)

FIRST ROUND

AFC Sheppey 7 Saga Sports & Social 0

APM Mears 5 Kennington 3

Borden Village 7 Tenterden Town 2

Guru Nanak (w/o) v Betteshanger Welfare

Lanes End 3 N. Romney 1

Larkfield1 **Swale United** 3

Malgo 2 **Premier** 11

Platt United 3 **Bredhurst Juniors** 7

Woodstock Park 1 **Canterbury City** 6

SECOND ROUND

AFC Sevenoaks 2 AFC Sheppey 1

APM Mears 1 **Oakwood** 4

Guru Nanak 3 Bredhurst Juniors 1

Lanes End 3 Premier 1 *aet*

Lydd 1 **Canterbury City** 9

Pembury 1 **Staplehurst** 2

Swale Utd 1 **Otford Utd** 2

University of Kent 2 Borden Village 1

QUARTER-FINALS

AFC Sevenoaks 1 **Lanes End** 2

Canterbury City 5 Staplehurst & Monarchs 0

Guru Nanak 0 **University of Kent** 3

Otford United 2 **Oakwood** 3

SEMI-FINALS

Canterbury City 2 Oakwood 0

Lanes End (scr.) v University of Kent (w/o)

FINAL

(April 30th at Faversham)

Canterbury City 3 University of Kent 2

	AFC Sevenoaks	Borden Village	Bredhurst Jnrs	Lanes End	Larkfield/NHW	Malgo	Pembury	Platt United	Premier	Saga Spts & S.	Swale United	Tenterden Town	Woodstock Pk
AFC Sevenoaks	***D***	0-2	4-2	1-3	4-1	6-3	2-1	5-5	3-4	3-4	3-0	9-2	0-1
Borden Village	3-3	***I***	2-3	1-1	0-2	1-2	2-1	4-0	1-4	1-1	2-2	3-3	3-1
Bredhurst Juniors	3-5	1-1	***V***	7-2	4-2	4-2	1-5	3-1	3-1	2-5	0-3	3-0	1-5
Lanes End	3-2	2-3	1-3		0-8	4-0	2-0	4-3	0-2	3-0	1-4	3-3	1-3
Larkfield & New Hythe Wdrs	1-1	4-2	1-7	2-1	***T***	4-2	5-2	4-0	2-2	0-2	4-0	2-1	1-1
Malgo	5-5	5-1	5-4	1-1	3-5	***W***	3-3	1-3	1-3	2-2	4-6	1-2	4-2
Pembury	1-2	1-1	1-2	2-2	1-2	0-5	***O***	1-2	1-2	1-0	3-0	2-2	1-1
Platt United	2-1	1-2	2-3	2-4	2-5	2-2	0-2		3-1	2-0	1-2	3-1	3-4
Premier	3-0	7-1	2-0	6-3	3-2	1-1	3-1	3-1	***E***	3-0	4-1	8-0	0-0
Saga Sports & Social	2-3	5-4	2-1	1-4	3-5	1-4	2-0	2-2	1-3	***A***	0-2	4-5	1-4
Swale United	6-1	1-2	1-3	1-1	2-3	2-1	1-0	3-3	2-4	4-4	***S***	5-0	3-2
Tenterden Town	1-3	3-2	2-2	2-3	0-3	1-2	0-1	6-5	0-3	4-2	3-4	***T***	2-2
Woodstock Park	5-1	3-2	1-0	1-0	2-1	5-1	3-1	6-1	2-3	5-1	3-1	4-1	

KENT COUNTY DIVISION TWO EAST CONSTITUTION 2009-10

AFC SEVENOAKS. . . . . Sevenoaks Town FC, Greatness Park, Seal Road, Sevenoaks TN14 5BL 01732 74198
BORDEN VILLAGE . . . . Borden Playstool, Wises Lane, Borden, Sittingbourne ME9 8LP 07903 01679
BREDHURST JUNIORS . . . . 44 Two Sports Ground, Featherby Road, Gillingham ME8 6AN. 01634 23335
CHARTHAM SPORTS CLUB. . . . . . . Memorial Field, Station Road, Chartham, Canterbury CT4 7HX. . . . . Non
HAMSTREET. . . . . Hamstreet FC, Hamstreet, Ashford . . . . Non
HAWKENBURY . . . . Hawkenbury Recreation Ground, Hawkenbury Road, Tunbridge Wells TN2 5BW. . . . . Non
LANES END. . . . . Waller Park, Wood Lane, Darenth, Dartford DA2 7LR 01322 22100
LYDD TOWN. . . . . The Lindsey Field, Dengemarsh Road, Lydd, Romney Marsh TN29 9JH 01797 32190
MALGO . . . . The Old County Ground, Norman Road, West Malling ME19 6RL. . . . . Non
PEMBURY. . . . . Woodside Recreation Ground, Henwoods Mount, Woodside Road, Pembury TN2 4BH 07970 02662
PLATT UNITED. . . . . Stonehouse Field, Longmill Lane (off A25), Platt TN15 8QS. 07702 63434
SAGA SPORTS & SOCIAL . . . . . . Canteen Meadow, The Street, Bishopsbourne, Canterbury CT4 5HX . . . . Non
SWALE UNITED. . . . . UK Paper Sports Ground, Gore Court Road, Sittingbourne ME10 1QN 01795 47704
TENTERDEN TOWN . . . . Recreation Ground Road, High Street, Tenterden TN30 6RA 07786 93215

IN: Chartham Sports Club (P - Canterbury & District League Premier Division), Hamstreet (P - Ashford & District League Premier Divisiion Hawkenbury (P - Tonbridge & District League Premier Division), Lydd Town (R - Division One East)

OUT: Larkfield & New Hythe Wanderers (P - Division One East), Premier (P - Division One East), Woodstock Park (P - Division One East,

FLOODLIGHT CUP

(All Eastern teams from Premier Division and selected teams from Division One East)

(Not contested in 2008-09)

Division Two West	P	W	D	L	F	A	Pts
Old Bexleians	24	15	5	4	73	36	50
Wickham Park	24	15	4	5	59	39	49
Charlton Ath. Community	24	14	5	5	72	39	47
Forest Hill Park	24	12	8	4	71	41	44
Borough United	24	13	5	6	58	42	44
Eltham Palace	24	12	5	7	56	47	41
Fleetdown United	24	10	9	5	48	34	39
OPK	24	10	4	10	51	48	34
Erith '147	24	8	3	13	52	65	27
Blackheath United	24	6	5	13	47	60	23
Halls	24	4	4	16	31	81	16
Meridian Sports	24	3	3	18	27	78	12
Chislehurst	24	2	4	18	40	75	10

RESERVES CUP

FINAL

(April 9th at Lordswood)

Greenways Res. 3 Bly Spartans Res. 1

Reserve Division East		P	W	D	L	F	A	Pt
Otford United Res.		24	19	3	2	64	22	60
New Romney Res.	*-1*	24	17	2	5	62	26	52
Borden Village Res.		24	13	5	6	66	40	44
Bearsted Res.		24	11	9	4	50	32	42
University of Kent Res.	*-1*	24	10	6	8	46	45	35
Oakwood Res.	*-3*	24	11	3	10	72	52	33
APM Mears Res.		24	9	4	11	44	52	31
Bromley Green Res.		24	9	3	12	43	50	30
Staplehurst & Monarchs Res.		24	8	3	13	54	61	27
Platt United Res.		24	7	3	14	48	59	24
Kennington Res.	*-3*	24	6	5	13	36	59	20
Larkfield & New HW Res.		24	5	4	15	37	70	19
Lydd Town Res.	*-3*	24	5	2	17	26	80	14

Reserve Division West		P	W	D	L	F	A	Pt
Orpington Res.		24	19	1	4	86	31	58
Bly Spartans Res.		24	18	3	3	74	39	57
Belvedere Res.		24	13	5	6	68	42	44
Coney Hall Res.	*-3*	24	15	1	8	70	50	43
Stansfeld O & B Club Res.		24	11	3	10	57	47	36
Greenways Res.		24	10	5	9	52	42	35
Crockenhill Res.		24	9	7	8	58	54	34
Fleet Leisure Res.		24	11	1	12	58	58	34
Chipstead Res.		24	10	3	11	64	59	33
Fleetdown United Res.		24	8	4	12	45	60	28
Rusthall Res.		24	3	7	14	37	62	16
Borough United Res.		24	5	0	19	34	99	15
Westerham Res.	*-3*	24	1	6	17	40	100	6

	Blackheath United	Borough United	Charlton Athletic Community	Chislehurst	Eltham Palace	Erith '147	Fleetdown United	Forest Hill Park	Halls	Meridian Sports	OPK	Old Bexleians	Wickham Park
Blackheath United	***D***	1-3	0-3	7-2	2-2	3-4	0-0	2-4	1-1	1-2	3-2	2-5	2-7
Borough United	3-1	***I***	1-3	6-1	2-1	4-2	1-1	4-3	3-3	1-0	2-0	2-3	2-1
Charlton Athletic Community	4-1	2-3	***V***	5-4	10-2	4-0	3-1	1-0	4-1	7-4	4-1	3-3	5-1
Chislehurst	1-2	5-5	1-1		0-2	1-1	1-3	0-4	6-1	4-3	1-2	3-4	1-4
Eltham Palace	2-1	1-4	1-1	3-0	***T***	5-1	2-2	3-6	2-0	5-0	2-0	4-3	2-0
Erith '147	3-0	2-0	2-2	3-1	4-3	***W***	0-3	0-3	7-3	1-2	1-3	2-6	0-3
Fleetdown United	2-3	4-1	0-2	1-1	2-1	2-3	***O***	2-2	4-3	1-0	4-1	3-1	0-1
Forest Hill Park	3-2	1-1	3-5	3-1	2-2	2-2	1-1		5-0	5-0	0-1	3-3	3-0
Halls	1-6	0-5	3-1	3-2	1-2	2-1	0-0	2-6	***W***	1-1	1-2	0-7	2-6
Meridian Sports	0-2	0-2	1-1	2-1	1-3	1-8	1-5	1-3	0-2	***E***	2-9	0-4	0-4
OPK	2-2	3-1	2-0	4-1	1-1	4-2	1-2	4-4	5-0	3-3	***S***	0-4	0-1
Old Bexleians	2-2	2-0	2-0	2-0	4-2	3-0	2-2	1-2	3-0	3-2	4-1	***T***	1-1
Wickham Park	2-1	2-2	2-1	4-2	0-3	5-3	3-3	3-3	2-1	2-1	3-0	2-1	

KENT COUNTY LEAGUE DIVISION TWO WEST CONSTITUTION 2009-10

BEXLEIANS . . . . Seven Acre Sports Club, Church Manor Avenue, Abbey Wood SE2 0HY . . . . None
BLACKHEATH UNITED. . . . Bellingham Leisure & Lifestyle Centre, Randlesdown Road, Bellingham SE6 3BT. 0208 697 0043
BOROUGH UNITED. . . . . Princes Golf & Leisure Club, Darenth Road, Dartford DA1 1LZ. 01322 276565
CHISLEHURST. . . . . Coldharbour Leisure Centre, Chaple Farm Road, New Eltham SE9 3LX 020 8851 8692
CROFTON ALBION . . . . Crofton Albion Sports & Social Club, Weigall Road, Lee SE12 8HF 020 8856 8385
ELTHAM PALACE. . . . . Beaverwood Lodge, Beaverwood Road, Chislehurst BR7 6HF 020 8300 1385
ERITH '147 SPORTS . . . . STC Sports Ground, Ivor Grove, New Eltham SE9 2AJ . . . . None
FLEETDOWN UNITED . . . . Heath Lane Open Space, Heath Lane (Lower), Dartford DA1 2QD 01322 273848
FOREST HILL PARK. . . . . Ladywell Arena, Doggetts Road, Catford SE6 4QX. 0208 314 1986
HALLS . . . . Bexley Park Sports & Social Club, Calvert Drive, Bexley DA2 7GU . . . . None
MERIDIAN SPORTS . . . . Meridian Sports & Social, 110 Charlton Park Lane, Charlton SE7 8QS 020 8856 1923
OPK . . . . Meridian Sports & Social Club, 110 Charlton Park Lane, Charlton SE7 8QS 020 8856 1923
SEVEN ACRE SPORTS. . . . . . . Seven Acre Sports Club, Church Manor Avenue, Abbey Wood SE2 0HY . . . . None
WESTERHAM . . . . . . Westerham Sports Association, King George V PF, Costells Meadow, Westerham TN16 1BL. 01959 561106

IN: Bexleians (P - South London Alliance Premier Division), Crofton Albion (P - South London Alliance Premier Division), Seven Acre Sports (P - South London Alliance Premier Division), Westerham (R - Division One West)

OUT: Charlton Athletic Community (P - Division One West), Crofton Albion (P - Division One West), Old Bexleians (P - Division One West), Wickham Park (P - Division One West)

Canterbury City FC
Winners: Division One East
Les Leckie Cup

Fleet Leisure FC
Premier Division - Runners-Up

Vandanel
Kent County Football League
Representative Squad 2008-2009

Vandanel Kent County League
Premier Division Champions 2008-09
Bill Manklow Inter-Regional Cup Winners 2008-2009

Hollands & Blair FC
Winners: Premier Division
Bill Manklow Inter-Regional
Challenge Cup
Kent CFA Intermadiate
Challenge Shield

Mick Moran - Hollands & Blair FC
Kent County Football League
Personality of the Year
(Presentation by Eddie Diplock,
President KCFL)
Aford Awards Manager of the Year

Stansfeld O&B Club FC
Premier Division

Premier FC
Winners: Division Two East

Scott Kennett - PremierFC
Winner of four Aford Awards Manager of the Month awards.
(Presentation by Cyril Windiate, Chairman KCFL)

Tonbridge Invicta FC
Winners: Division One West
Finalist: Barry Bundock West Kent Challenge Shield

Tonbridge Invicta FC
Winners: Division One West
Finalist: Barry Bundock West Kent Challenge Shield

LEICESTERSHIRE SENIOR LEAGUE

Sponsored by:
Everards Brewery

Founded: 1896

Recent champions:
2004: Loughborough Dynamo
2005: Thurnby Rangers
2006: Friar Lane & Epworth
2007: Stapenhill
2008: Kirby Muxloe SC

	Anstey N.	Asfordby A.	Ashby Ivan.	Aylestone P.	Birstall Utd	Blaby & W.	Cottesmore	Highfield R.	Leics Const.	Ratby Spts	Rothley I.	Saffron D.	Thurmaston	Thurnby R.
Anstey Nomads		12-0	9-3	3-0	3-0	6-1	5-1	4-1	0-0	1-0	1-0	2-2	2-0	4-0
Asfordby Amateurs	1-13	***P***	0-8	0-1	1-5	0-9	0-2	0-2	0-2	0-2	1-6	1-2	0-3	1-5
Ashby Ivanhoe	2-1	9-0	***R***	3-2	5-1	1-4	7-0	2-0	2-2	1-0	2-1	4-4	1-0	5-4
Aylestone Park	0-2	2-0	2-5	***E***	0-3	1-4	8-1	4-1	3-1	3-4	2-6	3-2	4-4	2-3
Birstall United	0-1	3-0	0-1	3-2	***M***	0-1	1-1	0-3	0-1	2-0	2-3	1-4	1-0	2-3
Blaby & Whetstone Ath.	0-0	8-0	1-1	7-0	2-0	***I***	1-0	2-0	4-2	1-0	5-1	4-1	4-0	2-0
Cottesmore Amateurs	0-9	1-0	2-1	0-1	1-4	1-2	***E***	1-0	0-1	0-4	2-2	0-2	3-1	0-1
Highfield Rangers	0-2	0-0	3-5	2-1	1-2	1-1	3-2	***R***	3-0	2-0	2-0	6-2	3-2	1-2
Leics Constabulary	2-0	4-1	3-0	2-3	1-3	1-1	5-0	3-0		3-1	0-1	4-1	5-2	2-2
Ratby Sports	1-4	3-1	0-4	0-2	1-0	3-1	4-0	0-2	2-3		2-2	4-2	3-1	1-2
Rothley Imperial	2-3	13-1	1-3	2-1	2-2	2-1	0-0	1-2	1-0	1-1	***D***	3-0	5-0	3-1
Saffron Dynamo	0-3	7-2	1-5	3-0	3-2	0-2	4-2	3-0	1-1	0-5	0-2	***I***	3-1	1-8
Thurmaston Town	0-4	2-1	3-4	2-2	2-4	0-5	1-2	0-2	0-4	0-4	2-4	2-2	***V***	1-6
Thurnby Rangers	0-1	3-2	1-1	2-1	1-0	0-0	1-0	1-1	0-0	1-1	1-2	0-1	3-1	

Premier Division		**P**	**W**	**D**	**L**	**F**	**A**	**Pts**
Anstey Nomads		**26**	**21**	**3**	**2**	**95**	**16**	**66**
Blaby/Whetstone Athletic		**26**	**18**	**5**	**3**	**73**	**21**	**59**
Ashby Ivanhoe		**26**	**18**	**4**	**4**	**85**	**45**	**58**
Rothley Imperial		**26**	**14**	**5**	**7**	**66**	**37**	**47**
Leics Constabulary		**26**	**13**	**6**	**7**	**52**	**31**	**45**
Thurnby Rangers	*-3*	**26**	**13**	**6**	**7**	**51**	**36**	**42**
Highfield Rangers		**26**	**12**	**3**	**11**	**41**	**40**	**39**
Ratby Sports		**26**	**11**	**3**	**12**	**46**	**39**	**36**
Saffron Dynamo		**26**	**10**	**4**	**12**	**51**	**67**	**34**
Birstall United		**26**	**10**	**2**	**14**	**41**	**43**	**32**
Aylestone Park	*-3*	**26**	**9**	**2**	**15**	**50**	**65**	**23**
Cottesmore Amateurs		**26**	**6**	**3**	**17**	**22**	**68**	**21**
Thurmaston Town		**26**	**2**	**3**	**21**	**30**	**81**	**9**
Asfordby Amateurs		**26**	**0**	**1**	**25**	**13**	**127**	**1**

LEICESTER FENCING TROPHY

FINAL *(May 7th at Friar Lane & Epworth)*
Holwell Sports Res. 2 Barrow Town Res. 0

Combination Division One		P	W	D	L	F	A	Pt
Kirby Muxloe SC Res.		30	20	5	5	94	36	65
Leics Constabulary Res.		30	20	1	9	70	44	61
Holwell Sports Res.		30	18	4	8	80	38	58
Ibstock United Res.		30	17	6	7	64	46	57
Blaby & Whetstone Ath. Res.		30	15	5	10	57	44	50
Birstall United Res.		30	15	4	11	54	56	49
Ellistown Res.		30	14	3	13	80	72	45
Rothley Imperial Res.		30	14	3	13	52	56	45
St Andrews SC Res.		30	13	4	13	63	54	43
Earl Shilton Albion Res.	*-1*	30	12	2	16	59	93	37
Anstey Town Res.		30	10	4	16	53	69	34
Ratby Sports Res.		30	8	8	14	53	57	32
Sileby Town Res.		30	9	5	16	60	65	32
Barrow Town Res.	*-1*	30	9	4	17	60	87	30
Lutterworth Athletic Res.		30	6	7	17	42	73	25
Thurmaston Town Res.		30	5	5	20	43	94	20

Combination Division Two		P	W	D	L	F	A	Pt
Anstey Nomads Res.		22	14	4	4	62	30	46
Saffron Dynamo Res.		22	14	2	6	52	23	44
Ravenstone Res.	*-1*	22	14	3	5	44	21	44
Ashby Ivanhoe Res.		22	14	2	6	56	35	44
Hathern Res.		22	13	2	7	45	34	41
Barlestone St Giles Res.		22	9	3	10	36	37	30
Narboro. & Littlethorpe Res.		22	9	3	10	29	31	30
Cottesmore Amateurs Res.		22	8	5	9	38	40	29
Highfield Rangers Res.		22	7	1	14	24	55	22
Dunton & Broughton R. Res.		22	4	6	12	25	34	18
Lutterworth Town Res.		22	4	3	15	26	53	15
FC Khalsa Res.		22	3	4	15	23	67	13

LEICESTERSHIRE SENIOR LEAGUE PREMIER DIVISION CONSTITUTION 2009-10

ASFORDBY AMATEURS.... Hoby Road Sports Ground, Hoby Road, Asfordby, Melton Mowbray LE14 3TL 01664 43454
ASHBY IVANHOE .... Hood Park, North Street, Ashby-de-la-Zouch LE65 1HU 01530 41218
AYLESTONE PARK .... Dorset Avenue, Wigston, Leicester LE18 4WD 0116 277 530
BIRSTALL UNITED.......................... Meadow Lane, Birstall LE4 4FN 0116 267 123
BLABY & WHETSTONE ATHLETIC .. Blaby & Whetstone BC, Warwick Road, Whetstone LE8 6LW.............. 0116 286 485
COTTESMORE AMATEURS .... Rogues Park, Main Street, Cottesmore, Oakham LE15 4DH.............. 01572 81348
HIGHFIELD RANGERS .... 443 Gleneagles Avenue, Rushey Mead, Leicester LE4 7YJ 0116 266 000
LEICS CONSTABULARY.................. Police Headquarters, St Johns, Enderby .... 0116 248 2198(matchdays only
LUTTERWORTH ATHLETIC................. Dunley Way, Lutterworth LE17 4NA 01455 55665
RATBY SPORTS .... Desford Lane, Ratby, Leicester LE6 0LF.............. 0116 239 247
ROTHLEY IMPERIAL............... Loughborough Road, Mountsorrell, Leicester LE7 7NH 0116 292 053
SAFFRON DYNAMO .... Cambridge Road, Whetstone LE8 3LG 0116 284 969
SILEBY TOWN................ Memorial Park, Seagrave Road, Sileby, Loughborough LE12 7TP 07708 231563/07860 84204
STAPENHILL .... Maple Grove, Stapenhill, Burton-on-Trent DE15 9NN 01283 56247
THURMASTON TOWN .... Elizabeth Park, Checkland Road, Thurmaston, Leicester LE4 8FN.............. 0116 260 251
THURNBY NIRVANA .... Dakyn Road, Thurnby Lodge Estate, Leicester LE5 2ED.............. 0116 243 369

IN: Lutterworth Athletic (P), Sileby Town (P), Stapenhill (N)
OUT: Anstey Nomads (P - East Midlands Counties League)
Thurnby Nirvana are a merger of Thurnby Rangers and Leicester Nirvana (youth football)

Division One	P	W	D	L	F	A	Pts
Sileby Town	26	22	1	3	66	24	67
Lutterworth Athletic	26	18	6	2	69	26	60
Barlestone St Giles	26	18	3	5	73	28	57
Friar Lane & Epworth Res.	26	12	6	8	57	45	42
Narborough/Littlethorpe	26	11	8	7	53	38	41
Hathern	26	12	5	9	51	48	41
FC Dynamo	26	11	4	11	65	53	37
Anstey Town	26	11	3	12	55	50	36
Ravenstone	26	10	6	10	43	41	36
Dunton & Broughton Rgrs	26	8	6	12	38	40	30
FC Khalsa	26	6	5	15	47	72	23
Evington	26	4	7	15	34	68	19
Lutterworth Town	26	3	3	20	24	82	12
Earl Shilton Albion	26	1	7	18	26	86	10

BEACON BITTER CUP

PREMIER DIVISION SECTION FIRST ROUND

Cottesmore Amateurs 4 Saffron Dynamo 2
Highfield Rangers 2 Asfordby Amateurs 0
Ratby Sports 2 Birstall United 1
Rothley Imperial 1 **Leics Constabulary** 2
Thurmaston Town 2 **Ashby Ivanhoe** 12
Thurnby Rangers 0 **Anstey Nomads** 4

PREMIER DIVISION SECTION SECOND ROUND

Anstey Nomads 2 Ashby Ivanhoe 1
Blaby & Whetstone Athletic 1 **Aylestone Park** 3
Cottesmore Amateurs 2 Highfield Rangers 1
Ratby Sports 2 Leics Constabulary 1

DIVISION ONE SECTION FIRST ROUND

Barlestone St Giles 0 Dunton & Broughton 0 (4-2p)
Evington 2 FC Khalsa 2 (4-3p)
Friar Lane & Epworth Res. 1 Ravenstone 0
Lutterworth Town 0 **Hathern** 0 (5-6p)
Narborough & Littlethorpe 0 **Anstey Town** 1
Sileby Town 1 **FC Dynamo** 2

DIVISION ONE SECTION SECOND ROUND

Barlestone St Giles 4 FC Dynamo 1
Earl Shilton Albion 1 **Anstey Town** 4
Hathern 1 Evington 0
Lutterworth Athletic 1 **Friar Lane & Epworth Res.** 4

QUARTER-FINALS

Aylestone Park 1 **Barlestone St Giles** 8
Cottesmore Amateurs 0 **Anstey Nomads** 3
Friar Lane & Epworth Res. 8 Hathern 0
Ratby Sports 1 Anstey Town 1 *aet* (4-2p)

SEMI-FINALS

Anstey Nomads 4 Barlestone St Giles 2
Ratby Sports 2 **Friar Lane & Epworth Res.** 3

FINAL *(May 12th at Barrow Town)*

Friar Lane & Epworth Res. 2 **Anstey Nomads** 3

	Anstey T.	Barlestone	Dunton&B	E. Shilton	Evington	FC Dynamo	FC Khalsa	Friar Lane	Hathern	L'worth Ath.	L'rworth T.	Narboro.	Ravenstone	Sileby Town
Anstey Town		1-1	3-1	1-1	5-1	2-3	1-2	1-3	3-0	1-4	2-1	1-3	2-0	1-4
Barlestone St Giles	2-1	***D***	2-0	6-0	1-1	3-0	5-1	4-2	3-0	0-1	5-2	2-0	1-0	2-3
Dunton/Broughton	1-3	0-4	***I***	0-1	1-0	2-0	3-0	7-0	5-3	2-2	5-1	1-4	1-1	1-0
Earl Shilton Albion	2-4	0-4	0-3	***V***	3-3	0-6	1-5	2-2	1-2	0-5	1-2	2-2	1-3	1-2
Evington	1-2	1-4	0-0	2-2	***I***	1-5	1-1	1-1	1-3	1-7	4-0	3-3	1-6	1-2
FC Dynamo	2-2	4-1	1-1	6-0	2-0	***S***	2-3	1-2	4-1	1-3	3-0	0-1	1-3	3-8
FC Khalsa	0-3	0-3	3-1	4-4	2-1	3-5	***I***	2-5	2-3	1-3	3-2	1-3	2-2	2-4
Friar Lane/E. Res.	0-1	2-4	4-1	6-0	1-2	4-4	3-0	***O***	0-0	1-1	3-1	1-1	2-0	4-2
Hathern	6-4	2-2	2-0	3-1	0-3	4-1	6-3	2-1	***N***	0-2	6-1	2-2	1-0	0-2
Lutterworth Ath.	3-1	1-4	2-1	3-0	4-0	4-0	3-3	3-1	3-0		4-0	2-2	1-0	0-0
Lutterworth Town	0-8	1-7	0-0	1-1	1-2	2-4	1-0	1-3	0-4	2-2	***O***	1-2	1-4	0-1
Narborough & L.	6-1	1-2	1-1	3-0	5-0	0-5	2-1	2-1	1-1	1-2	1-2	***N***	5-0	0-2
Ravenstone	1-0	2-1	2-0	3-2	3-1	1-1	2-2	2-4	0-0	2-4	3-1	1-1	***E***	2-3
Sileby Town	2-1	2-0	1-0	5-0	4-2	2-1	3-1	0-1	3-0	2-0	4-0	3-1	2-0	

LEICESTERSHIRE SENIOR LEAGUE DIVISION ONE CONSTITUTION 2009-10

ɜARLESTONE ST GILES . . . . Barton, Barlestone CV13 0EP 01455 291392
ↄOALVILLE TOWN RESERVES . . . . Owen Street Sports Ground, Owen Street, Coalville LE67 3DA. 01530 833365
)ESFORD . . . . Sport in Desford, Peckleton Lane, Desford, Leicester LE9 9JU. 01455 828786
)UNTON & BROUGHTON RANGERS . . . . Station Road, Dunton Bassett LE17 5LF 07802 647846
ΞARL SHILTON ALBION . . . . Stoneycroft Park, New Street, Earl Shilton LE9 7FR. 01455 844277
ΞVINGTON . . . . Aylestone Park FC, Dorset Avenue, Wigston, Leicester LE18 4WB. 0116 277 5307
ꟻC DYNAMO. . . . . Nanpantan Sports Ground, Nanpantan Road, Loughborough LE11 3YD 01509 237148
ꟻC KHALSA . . . . Judgemeadow Community College, Marydene Drive, Evington, Leicester LE5 6HP. 0116 2417580
ꟻRIAR LANE & EPWORTH. . . . . Knighton Lane East, Aylestone Park, Leicester LE2 6FT. 0116 283 3629
ꟷATHERN. . . . . Pasture Lane, Hathern, Loughborough LE12 5LJ 07952 113090
ꓘIRBY MUXLOE SC RESERVES. . . . . Ratby Lane, Kirby Muxloe, Leicester LE9 9AQ. 0116 239 3201
.UTTERWORTH TOWN. . . . . Hall Lane, Bitteswell, Lutterworth LE17 4LN 01455 554046
ꟽELTON MOWBRAY BS. . . . . All England Sports Ground, Melton Mowbray LE13 1BP . . . . None
ꟽARBOROUGH & LITTLETHORPE . . . . Leicester Road, Narborough LE19 2DG 0116 275 1855
ꓤAVENSTONE. . . . . Ravenslea, Ravenstone, Coalville LE67 2AW 07856 179485

N: Coalville Town Res. (N), Desford (P - Leicester & District League Premier Division), Kirby Muxloe SC Res. (P - Combination Division One), Melton Mowbray BS (P - North Leicestershire League Premier Division)
OUT: Anstey Town (R - North Leicestershire League Premier Division), Lutterworth Athletic (P), Sileby Town (P)

LIVERPOOL COUNTY PREMIER LEAGUE

www.liverpoolcountypremierleague.com

Sponsored by:

Frank Armitt

Founded: 2006

Recent champions:

2007: Waterloo Dock

2008: Waterloo Dock

	Aigburth PH	Birchfield	Cheshire Lines	East Villa	Ford Motors	Lucas Sports	NELTC	Old Xavrians	Page Celtic	Red Rum	Roma	South Liverpool	South Sefton B.	Speke	St Aloysius	Waterloo Dock
Aigburth People's Hall	***P***	4-1	1-2	2-2	1-0	4-0	2-0	1-0	2-0	1-2	4-3	0-1	0-0	n/a	2-2	2-1
Birchfield	1-1	***R***	2-1	3-3	0-2	1-0	2-2	1-3	0-2	3-3	4-1	1-2	3-4	n/a	3-0	0-4
Cheshire Lines	1-3	2-1	***E***	3-2	1-2	1-0	0-2	2-3	3-5	1-1	4-1	0-5	1-1	n/a	2-0	1-2
East Villa	3-1	1-1	4-0	***M***	1-2	2-3	2-2	2-5	1-2	3-0	5-0	2-1	1-1	n/a	0-0	0-1
Ford Motors	0-3	1-0	0-1	1-2	***I***	1-4	3-1	1-3	1-1	1-1	6-0	0-0	1-0	n/a	1-2	1-1
Lucas Sports	3-0	2-0	1-2	3-3	2-1	***E***	3-2	0-4	1-1	5-2	3-1	2-2	1-0	n/a	2-2	0-8
NELTC	0-3	0-1	1-2	0-4	1-2	3-3	***R***	1-0	1-3	1-4	0-1	3-0	1-2	n/a	2-2	0-3
Old Xaverians	1-1	2-2	1-1	0-2	7-1	1-1	4-0		3-0	1-1	5-0	3-2	2-0	n/a	3-3	0-2
Page Celtic	3-1	3-0	1-1	1-3	4-0	0-3	2-2	1-2	***D***	1-0	1-2	2-2	1-1	n/a	1-1	0-2
Red Rum	0-1	1-3	0-4	4-0	1-4	2-2	3-1	3-3	0-1	***I***	4-1	2-1	2-3	4-1	3-2	1-3
Roma	0-3	0-1	2-3	0-1	0-5	4-3	0-1	0-2	1-2	1-2	***V***	3-1	0-0	n/a	1-2	0-4
South Liverpool	2-3	4-0	3-1	4-1	3-1	1-2	3-3	4-0	3-0	4-0	5-1	***I***	2-1	n/a	0-2	0-2
South Sefton Borough	2-3	4-1	1-3	0-0	2-3	1-0	3-0	1-4	2-1	5-5	3-4	0-2	***S***	2-3	2-3	1-6
Speke	1-4	n/a	n/a	n/a	n/a	n/a	4-7	n/a	n/a	n/a	1-9	n/a	0-3	***I***	n/a	n/a
St Aloysius	2-5	1-3	3-4	3-2	1-1	4-0	2-3	2-4	1-1	5-1	4-1	2-2	3-0	n/a	***O***	1-5
Waterloo Dock	1-2	3-1	2-0	3-2	4-1	5-1	5-3	0-0	3-1	5-2	4-3	5-1	6-0	4-1	3-2	***N***

Premier Division		P	W	D	L	F	A	Pts
Waterloo Dock		28	24	2	2	93	26	74
Aigburth People's Hall		28	17	5	6	56	33	56
Old Xaverians		28	15	8	5	66	35	53
South Liverpool	*+2*	28	13	5	10	60	42	46
Cheshire Lines		28	13	4	11	47	50	43
Lucas Sports	*+3*	28	11	7	10	50	58	43
East Villa		28	10	8	10	54	46	38
Page Celtic		28	10	8	10	41	42	38
Ford Motors		28	11	5	12	43	47	38
St Aloysius	*-4*	28	9	9	10	57	57	32
Red Rum		28	8	7	13	50	66	31
Birchfield		28	8	6	14	39	56	30
South Sefton Borough		28	7	7	14	40	59	28
NELTC		28	5	6	17	36	64	21
Roma		28	5	1	22	31	82	16

Speke - record expunged

R A BRICKWORK PREMIER DIVISION CUP

FIRST ROUND

Birchfield 2 **Aigburth People's Hall** 6
Cheshire Lines 2 **Ford Motors** 6
East Villa 3 Page Celtic 1
Red Rum 2 Lucas Sports 1 *aet*
Roma 1 **St Aloysius** 4
South Liverpool (w/o) v Speke
South Sefton Borough 3 Old Xaverians 2 *aet*
Waterloo Dock 2 NELTC 0

QUARTER-FINALS

Aigburth People's Hall 2 East Villa 0
St Aloysius 1 **South Sefton Borough** 2
South Liverpool 2 Ford Motors 2 *aet* (4-2p)
Waterloo Dock 1 Red Rum 1 *aet* (6-5p)

SEMI-FINALS

South Liverpool 3 Aigburth People's Hall 0
South Sefton Borough 1 **Waterloo Dock** 2

FINAL

(May 14th at LCFA, Wavertree)
South Liverpool 1 **Waterloo Dock** 2

LIVERPOOL COUNTY PREMIER LEAGUE PREMIER DIVISION CONSTITUTION 2009-10

AIGBURTH PEOPLE'S HALL . . . . . Cheshire Lines FC, Southmead Road, Allerton, Liverpool L19 5NB 0151 427 717
ALBANY ATHLETIC. . . . . Springfield Park, adjacent Alder Hey Hospital, West Derby, Liverpool L13 0BQ . . . . None
BIRCHFIELD. . . . . Edge Hill College, St Helens Road, Ormskirk L39 4QP. 01695 58474
CHESHIRE LINES . . . . Southmead Road, Allerton, Liverpool L19 5NB 0151 427 717
EAST VILLA . . . . Litherland Sports Park, Boundary Road, Litherland, Liverpool L21 7NW. 0151 288 633
FORD MOTORS. . . . . Ford Sports & Social Club, Cronton Lane, Widnes WA8 5AJ 0151 424 707
KINGSLEY UNITED . . . . Quarry Bank School Playing Fields, Greenhill Road, Allerton, Liverpool L18 6HF. . . . . Non
LUCAS SPORTS. . . . . William Collins Memorial Ground, Commercial Road, Liverpool. . . . . Non
OLD XAVERIANS . . . . St Francis Xaviers College, Beconsfield Road, Liverpool L25 6EG. 0151 288 100
PAGE CELTIC . . . . King George V Sports Complex, Long View Lane, Huyton, Liverpool L36 7UN 0151 443 571
RED RUM . . . . Croxteth Commnity Comprehensive School, Parkstile Lane, Liverpool L11 0PB. 0151 546 416
SACRE COEUR FORMER PUPILS . . . Scargreen PF, Scargreen Avenue, Norris Green L11 3BE . . . . Non
SOUTH LIVERPOOL. . . . . Jericho Lane, Aigburth, Liverpool L17 5AR. . . . . Non
SOUTH SEFTON BOROUGH . . . . Mill Dam Field, Bridges Lane, Sefton Village.. . . . . Non
ST ALOYSIUS . . . . King George V Sports Complex, Long View Lane, Huyton, Liverpool L36 7UN 0151 443 571
WATERLOO DOCK. . . . . Edinburgh Park, Townsend Lane, Liverpool L6 0BB 0151 263 526

IN: Albany Athletic (P), Kingsley United (P), Sacre Coeur Former Pupils (P)
OUT: NELTC (R), Roma (R), Speke (WS)

LORD MAYOR'S CHARITY SHIELD

(Prem champs v Peter Coyne/George Mahon Cup holders)

(August 14th at LCFA, Walton Hall Avenue)

Waterloo Dock 2 **Aighburth People's Hall** 4

Division One		P	W	D	L	F	A	Pts
Albany Athletic	*-3*	30	23	3	4	79	42	69
Kingsley United	*+3*	30	19	3	8	77	57	63
Sacre Coeur F'mer Pup.		30	19	4	7	64	37	61
REMYCA United		30	18	6	6	60	87	60
Stoneycroft		30	13	5	12	65	70	44
Copperas Hill		30	12	6	12	76	63	42
Edge Hill BCOB		30	12	6	12	73	64	42
BRNESC		30	12	6	12	60	63	42
Mackets Grenadier		30	12	6	12	54	62	42
Angus Village		30	11	5	14	57	65	38
Collegiate Old Boys		30	10	6	14	67	63	36
Warbreck		30	10	6	14	56	68	36
Leyfield		30	9	3	18	54	81	30
Essemay Old Boys		30	7	7	16	49	68	28
Alder		30	7	3	20	51	75	24
Bankfield		30	6	5	19	44	71	23

ROY WADE MEMORIAL CUP

FIRST ROUND

Angus Village 0 **Collegiate Old Boys** 5
Edge Hill BCOB 3 BRNESC 1 *aet*
Kingsley United 5 Copperas Hill 2
Mackets Grenadier 1 **Albany Athletic** 2
REMYCA United 2 Leyfield 1
Sacre Coeur Former P. 4 Bankfield 4 *aet* (2-1p)
Stoneycroft 1 **Essemay Old Boys** 2
Warbreck 1 **Alder** 2

QUARTER-FINALS

Albany Athletic 4 Alder 4 *aet* (7-6p)
Collegiate OB 1 **Sacre Coeur Former Pupils** 2
Kingsley United 3 **Essemay Old Boys** 5
REMYCA United 4 Edge Hill BCOB 2

SEMI-FINALS

Albany Athletic 4 REMYCA United 1
Sacre Coeur Former Pupils 3 **Essemay Old Boys** 4

FINAL

(April 22nd at Litherland Sports Park)
Albany Athletic 4 Essemay Old Boys 2

	Albany Athletic	Alder	Angus Village	BRNESC	Bankfield	Collegiate Old B.	Copperas Hill	Edge Hill BCOB	Essemay Old B.	Kingsley United	Leyfield	Mackets Gren.	REMYCA United	Sacre Coeur FP	Stoneycroft	Warbreck
Albany Athletic		4-3	5-0	3-4	W-L	3-2	4-3	5-4	1-0	6-3	4-1	6-2	4-1	1-0	2-5	W-L
Alder	0-1		2-3	0-4	2-1	0-4	2-2	2-4	5-2	1-2	2-0	1-3	0-2	2-3	2-3	4-0
Angus Village	1-0	5-4	***D***	1-0	2-2	4-3	3-6	1-1	0-1	1-2	4-1	0-1	1-2	1-0	0-5	4-1
BRNESC	1-4	2-3	1-3	***I***	0-4	2-0	0-10	3-6	3-1	4-0	3-1	0-2	1-2	2-2	0-2	0-1
Bankfield	2-2	1-4	0-4	1-2	***V***	2-2	2-4	0-5	2-2	1-4	3-0	1-2	1-2	0-1	2-3	1-2
Collegiate Old Boys	2-2	2-0	3-0	1-1	5-1	***I***	2-5	2-4	1-1	1-1	8-3	4-1	1-2	0-1	2-3	2-1
Copperas Hill	1-3	4-1	2-2	1-5	2-0	2-3	***S***	2-1	2-4	2-2	1-1	1-3	0-2	1-4	7-1	1-2
Edge Hill BCOB	0-1	3-0	1-3	1-5	1-2	3-2	2-5	***I***	1-1	3-1	1-2	2-2	1-1	6-2	3-1	5-0
Essemay Old Boys	1-3	2-0	3-3	1-5	4-1	1-2	0-1	5-0	***O***	1-6	1-1	2-1	1-1	1-2	3-1	1-4
Kingsley United	1-2	3-1	2-1	3-3	2-4	2-1	3-0	3-0	5-2	***N***	3-1	3-2	0-5	1-0	3-1	3-2
Leyfield	2-5	3-5	5-4	5-1	2-0	2-0	1-5	2-4	4-2	0-2		3-1	1-1	1-2	1-4	4-3
Mackets Grenadier	0-2	0-0	3-1	2-2	4-4	0-2	3-3	4-3	2-1	0-4	2-4	***O***	1-0	1-0	3-1	3-1
REMYCA United	1-2	2-1	4-2	1-2	L-W	2-1	2-0	2-2	1-0	5-1	3-2	2-0	***N***	5-4	2-1	2-2
Sacre Coeur Former Pupils	2-1	3-0	0-0	0-2	3-1	6-2	3-0	2-1	5-2	3-0	4-0	2-1	1-1	***E***	1-0	1-1
Stoneycroft	0-3	2-2	2-1	1-1	3-2	5-5	1-1	0-2	1-1	1-8	2-1	4-2	3-1	2-4		5-2
Warbreck	0-0	5-2	3-2	1-1	2-3	3-2	1-2	3-3	4-2	3-4	1-0	3-3	1-3	1-3	3-2	

LIVERPOOL COUNTY PREMIER LEAGUE DIVISION ONE CONSTITUTION 2009-10

ANGUS VILLAGE............ Joe Stone Memorial Ground, Lower Lane, Fazakerley, Liverpool L9 7AD.................... None
BRNESC.............................. Melling Road, Aintree, Liverpool L9 0LQ.............................. None
COLLEGIATE OLD BOYS....... Alder Road Sports Club, Alder Road, West Derby, Liverpool L12 2BA.................. None
COPPERAS HILL.............................. Breckside Park, Liverpool .... None
EAST VILLA RESERVES ...... Litherland Sports Park, Boundary Road, Litherland, Liverpool L21 7NW................ 0151 288 6338
EDGE HILL BCOB .... William Collins Mem. Ground, Commercial Road, Liverpool .... None
ESSEMAY OLD BOYS .... Jericho Lane Playing Field, Jericho Lane, Liverpool L17 5AR .... None
HALEWOOD TOWN .... Hollies Road Playing Fields, Hollies Road, Halewood, Liverpool L26 0TH................. None
LEYFIELD........................ Thomas Lane Playing Fields, Thomas Lane, Liverpool .... None
MACKETS VILLAGE............... Great Lakes, Lower Road, Halebank, Widnes WA8 8NT .... None
NELTC.............................. Edinburgh Park, Townsend Lane, Liverpool L6 0BB .... None
OLD HOLTS .... Simpson Ground, Hillfoot Road, Liverpool L25 0ND 0151 486 3166
REMYCA UNITED .... Playfootball.com, Drummond Road, Thornton L20 6DX.......................... None
ROMA .... Kirkby Sports Centre, Valley Road, Kirkby L20 9PQ 0151 443 4404
STONEYCROFT................. Maiden Lane Playing Fields, Maiden Lane, Liverpool L13 9AN........................ None
WARBRECK........................ Playfootball.com, Drummond Road, Thornton L20 6DX.......................... None

IN: East Villa Res. (P), Halewood Town (P), NELTC (R), Old Holts (P), Roma (R)
OUT: Albany Athletic (P), Alder (R - Division Two South), Bankfield (W), Kingsley United (P), Sacre Coeur Former Pupils (P)
Mackets Grenadier become Mackets Village

Division Two	P	W	D	L	F	A	Pts
Halewood Town	**28**	**23**	**2**	**3**	**88**	**30**	**71**
Old Holts	**28**	**21**	**2**	**5**	**106**	**37**	**65**
East Villa Res.	**28**	**20**	**3**	**5**	**96**	**45**	**63**
Clubmoor Farmers	**28**	**20**	**2**	**6**	**106**	**60**	**62**
Pinewoods	**28**	**16**	**4**	**8**	**88**	**51**	**52**
NELTC Res.	**28**	**15**	**6**	**7**	**66**	**48**	**51**
South Liverpool Res.	**28**	**16**	**2**	**10**	**76**	**43**	**50**
Old Xaverians Res.	**28**	**15**	**3**	**10**	**70**	**62**	**48**
Warbreck Res.	**28**	**12**	**4**	**12**	**80**	**66**	**40**
Blueline	**28**	**8**	**3**	**17**	**59**	**66**	**27**
Liobians	**28**	**8**	**1**	**19**	**47**	**78**	**25**
Eli Lilly	**28**	**6**	**6**	**16**	**62**	**91**	**24**
Redgate Rovers	**28**	**5**	**2**	**21**	**35**	**98**	**17**
Leisure Sports Orchard	**28**	**2**	**4**	**22**	**32**	**111**	**10**
Rockville Wallasey	**28**	**1**	**0**	**27**	**30**	**155**	**3**

St Dominics - record expunged

PETER COYNE / GEORGE MAHON CUP

(All first teams in league)

FIRST ROUND

Alder 1 **Collegiate Old Boys** 4
Angus V. 4 Copperas Hill 3
Clubmoor Farmers 4 Albany 2
Edge Hill BCOB 2 **Blueline** 3
Eli Lilly 4 Rockville Wallasey 3
Essemmay OB 2 **Old Holts** 3
Halewood Town 1 **BRNESC** 2
Leyfield 0 **Warbreck** 4
(at Warbreck)
Mackets 1 **REMYCA** 2 *aet*
Redgate 0 **Pinewoods** 2
St Dominics (scr.) v **Sacre Coeur Former Pupils** (w/o)

SECOND ROUND

Angus Village 1 **Aigburth** 4
Bankfield 2 Leisure Sports 1
Cheshire Lines 0 **Sacre Coeur FPs** 0 *aet* (3-4p)
Clubmoor F. 1 **Waterloo Dk** 4
Collegiate OB 4 REMYCA 2
East Villa 5 Ford Motors 1
Eli Lilly 1 **Lucas Sports** 5
Kingsley 0 **South Sefton** 4
Liobians 1 **Stoneycroft** 6
NELTC 2 **Roma** 3 *aet*
Pinewoods 1 **Page Celtic** 3
Red Rum 1 **Birchfield** 1 *aet* (1-3p)
Sth Liverpool 3 BRNESC 2
St Aloysius 3 Old Xavs 1
St Dominics 0 **Old Holts** 4
Warbreck 4 Blueline 3
(at Blueline)

THIRD ROUND

Bankfield 2 **Old Holts** 5
Sacre Coeur FP 1 Roma 0
Collegiate 2 Birchfield 1
East Villa 3 **St Aloysius** 3 *aet* (3-4p)
South Sefton Borough 1 **Aigburth PH** 1 *aet* (0-3p)
Lucas Sports 5 Stoneycroft 0
Warbreck 1 **Sth Liverpool** 4
Waterloo Dock 1 Page 0

QUARTER-FINALS

Waterloo Dock 1 **South Liverpool** 1 *aet* (5-6p)
St Aloysius 4 Collegiate 0
Lucas 4 Sacre Coeur Pupils 1
Aigburth PH 4 Old Holts 1

SEMI-FINALS

Sth Liverpool 2 St Aloysius 1
Lucas Sports 1 Aigburth People's Hall 1 *aet* (5-4p)

FINAL

(May 24th at Everton)
South Liverpool 1 Lucas 0

	Blueline	Clubmoor	East V. Res.	Eli Lilly	Halewood	Leisure S.	Liobians	NELTC Res.	Old Holts	Old Xav Res.	Pinewoods	Redgate R.	Rockville W.	Sth Liv. Res.	St Dominics	W'breck Res.
Blueline		2-3	3-3	2-0	1-2	0-0	1-0	2-3	2-1	2-5	2-5	2-3	3-1	0-2	W-L	0-5
Clubmoor Farmers	4-2		6-2	4-2	1-2	6-2	5-0	3-2	2-3	3-1	2-3	2-1	3-2	2-0	2-2	5-4
East Villa Res.	3-2	1-2	***D***	3-3	2-1	8-0	8-1	3-0	2-2	4-3	3-2	8-1	10-1	2-0	n/a	W-L
Eli Lilly	0-0	2-11	2-3	***I***	4-7	5-1	1-2	2-5	3-4	3-5	1-1	5-1	4-1	0-3	n/a	5-6
Halewood Town	4-2	2-3	0-1	1-1	***V***	5-0	6-1	0-0	2-1	3-2	3-2	1-0	W-L	4-0	5-2	3-0
Leisure Spts Orchard	2-5	1-8	0-4	2-4	1-5	***I***	1-2	1-2	1-3	0-1	0-2	2-2	7-4	1-9	n/a	2-6
Liobians	3-4	0-6	2-3	2-2	1-5	4-1	***S***	1-2	0-6	4-1	2-3	0-2	6-0	2-4	1-1	3-5
NELTC Res.	2-1	1-1	4-0	5-1	1-2	2-2	2-3	***I***	3-5	1-1	4-2	2-1	6-1	2-1	1-0	1-1
Old Holts	4-2	10-0	1-2	6-0	1-2	9-1	3-1	1-3	***O***	3-0	1-0	5-2	2-0	2-0	n/a	4-1
Old Xaverians Res.	1-0	2-2	1-4	3-2	1-5	3-0	3-1	3-2	4-6	***N***	2-1	3-2	6-0	0-2	n/a	1-1
Pinewoods	4-2	4-3	3-2	4-1	1-2	6-0	2-1	5-5	0-1	5-1		6-2	10-2	2-1	3-0	2-2
Redgate Rovers	0-5	1-4	0-4	2-2	0-7	2-1	0-2	1-2	0-5	1-2	1-0	***T***	3-2	1-6	2-5	2-5
Rockville Wallasey	0-9	1-7	0-5	2-3	1-5	0-2	0-3	0-2	1-11	1-6	3-8	5-4	***W***	0-7	1-6	0-10
South Liverpool Res.	2-1	3-5	4-2	3-1	1-2	4-1	1-0	4-0	3-3	1-4	1-1	4-0	7-0	***O***	3-1	1-4
St Dominics	n/a	3-3	2-7	n/a	2-1	n/a	2-2	1-2	1-7	n/a	0-3	4-2	5-3	n/a		n/a
Warbreck Res.	4-2	4-3	1-4	2-3	1-7	0-0	1-0	0-2	0-3	3-5	1-4	6-0	6-2	1-2	4-1	

LORD WAVERTREE CUP

FIRST ROUND

Clubmoor F. 1 **Halewood** 2 *aet*
Eli Lilly 1 **Blueline** 4
Liobians 7 Leisure Sports 1
(at Leisure Sports)
Old Xavs Res. 1 **NELTC Res.** 2
Pinewoods 3 Warbreck Res. 2
Redgate 0 **East Villa Res.** 3
Rockville Wallasey 5 South Liverpool Res. 4 *aet*
St Dominics 2 **Old Holts** 4

QUARTER-FINALS

Blueline 0 **East Villa Res.** 3
Halewood Town 3 Rockville 1
NELTC Res. 1 **Old Holts** 2
Pinewoods 3 Liobians 0

SEMI-FINALS

Old Holts 0 **East Villa Res.** 4
Pinewoods 1 Halewood 0

FINAL

(May 6th at Litherland Sports Park)
East Villa Res. 1 Pinewoods 0

LIVERPOOL COUNTY PREMIER LEAGUE DIVISION TWO NORTH CONSTITUTION 2009-10

BLUELINE . . . . Buckley Hill Playing Fields, Buckley Hill Lane, Netherton, Bootle L29 1YB . . . . Nor
BOOTLE A. . . . . Litherland Sports Park, Boundary Road, Litherland, Liverpool L21 7NW. 0151 288 63
CLUBMOOR FARMERS . . . . Clubmoor Recreation Playing Fields, Townsend Avenue, Clubmoor, Liverpool. . . . . Nor
CROXTETH. . . . . MYA, Long Lane, Aintree, Liverpool L9 7AA . . . . Nor
PINEWOODS . . . . Carr Lane Playing Fields, Carr Lane, Ainsdale, Southport . . . . Nor
REDGATE ROVERS . . . . Clarence House School, West Lane, Freshfield, Formby, Liverpool L37 7AZ 01704 821
ST HELENS TOWN RESERVES. . . . . . . St Helens College, Bobbies Lane, Eccleston, St Helens 01744 6133
WALTON PLAYERS . . . . Lower Breck Road, Anfield, Liverpool L6 0AG. . . . . No
WARBRECK RESERVES . . . . Playfootball.com, Drummond Road, Thornton L20 6DX. . . . . No

IN: Blueline (S - Division Two), Bootle A (N), Clubmoor Farmers (S - Division Two), Croxteth (N), Pinewoods (S - Division Two), Redga Rovers (S - Division Two), St Helens Town Res. (N), Walton Players (N), Warbreck Res. (S - Division Two)

LIVERPOOL COUNTY PREMIER LEAGUE DIVISION TWO SOUTH CONSTITUTION 2009-10

ALDER . . . . Alder Road Sports Club, Alder Road, West Derby, Liverpool L12 2BA . . . . No
ALUMNI. . . . . Jericho Lane, Liverpool L17 5AR . . . . No
ELI LILLY. . . . . Thomas Lane Playing Fields, Thomas Lane, Liverpool L14 5NR . . . . No
HALEBANK . . . . Halebank Playing Field, Blackburn Avenue, Halebank, Widnes WA8 8UJ. . . . . No
LIOBIANS . . . . Mersey Road, Aigburth, Liverpool L17 6AG . . . . Nor
NELTC RESERVES. Edinburgh Park, Townsend Lane, Liverpool L13 9DY. . . . . Nor
OLD XAVERIANS RESERVES . . . . St Francis Xaviers College, Beconsfield Road, Liverpool L25 6EG. 0151 288 10
SOUTH LIVERPOOL RESERVES. . . . . Jericho Lane, Aigburth, Liverpool L17 5AR. . . . . No
UNITY . . . . Wavertree Playground, Wellington Road, Wavertree, Liverpool L15 4LE . . . . No

IN: Alder (R), Alumni (P - Liverpool Old Boys League Division One), Eli Lilly (S - Division Two), Halebank (P - Warrington & District Leag Premier Division), Liobians (S - Division Two), NELTC Res. (S - Division Two), Old Xaverians Res. (S - Division Two), South Liverpool Re (S - Division Two)

MANCHESTER LEAGUE

Sponsored by: Bridgewater Office Supplies

Founded: 1893

Recent champions: 2004: Royton Town 2005: Prestwich Heys 2006: Prestwich Heys 2007: Prestwich Heys 2008: Wigan Robin Park

	AVRO	Ath T	Brei	Chap	EM	Elton	Greg	Hind	Holl	Leigh	Penn	Pres	Roch	Roy	Sprin	Stoc	Wals	Wyth
AVRO		2-1	3-1	1-3	2-1	5-1	0-1	1-0	2-4	2-2	0-0	1-3	4-0	3-2	1-2	5-2	1-3	0-1
Atherton Town	2-4	***P***	2-0	1-0	1-2	4-0	1-1	0-2	2-1	3-2	2-0	4-2	2-3	1-2	1-2	4-2	1-2	0-2
Breightmet United	0-6	1-5	***R***	0-4	0-7	2-2	0-5	1-5	2-3	1-1	1-2	3-4	2-1	2-2	2-4	1-2	0-1	1-6
Chapel Town	0-4	1-1	3-1	***E***	3-1	1-0	1-2	1-0	1-2	6-0	3-3	0-2	3-0	2-1	1-0	0-4	1-3	1-3
East Manchester	1-3	1-0	4-0	1-1	***M***	4-1	1-2	5-0	4-2	2-1	4-1	1-1	1-2	1-1	3-2	2-4	2-1	3-0
Elton Vale	0-3	0-2	8-1	3-3	1-0	***I***	2-3	1-2	1-3	2-2	4-1	3-1	3-2	3-0	2-6	1-0	3-0	3-3
Gregorians	2-2	4-1	1-1	2-1	2-2	2-0	***E***	4-0	5-0	2-0	6-0	2-1	4-0	2-1	0-1	0-0	1-1	2-0
Hindsford	3-1	1-1	6-1	3-2	0-0	0-2	2-3	***R***	0-1	1-1	5-3	3-1	3-1	1-3	0-3	1-2	1-3	2-3
Hollinwood	1-5	5-3	2-0	2-0	4-2	5-3	2-2	13-2		4-4	6-3	1-2	4-2	2-2	1-1	1-1	1-0	2-3
Leigh Athletic	0-3	3-2	4-3	3-3	2-2	2-2	2-1	2-1	4-6	***D***	5-1	2-1	0-0	0-3	2-2	7-0	1-2	3-1
Pennington	3-5	1-6	3-1	0-2	2-2	0-3	1-0	1-0	3-1	1-2	***I***	1-5	0-2	4-3	0-1	1-1	2-3	2-6
Prestwich Heys	0-3	0-2	2-2	2-1	1-2	4-4	1-2	5-2	1-1	1-0	6-1	***V***	1-1	3-3	1-3	1-0	1-2	3-2
Rochdale Sacred Heart	1-5	2-1	4-2	1-3	2-1	2-5	0-4	0-2	1-2	4-2	6-4	3-3	***I***	0-3	1-1	1-3	1-3	3-2
Royton Town	2-2	1-4	3-0	3-1	1-1	3-1	0-0	2-2	1-3	2-3	3-1	0-0	3-1	***S***	1-2	4-0	3-2	1-2
Springhead	1-2	3-1	2-0	3-3	4-0	1-0	0-3	2-1	3-1	2-1	4-0	5-1	4-1	2-5	***I***	1-1	0-1	1-2
Stockport Georgians	0-0	1-1	4-1	1-1	0-0	1-1	3-2	3-0	2-0	1-0	3-0	0-3	4-1	0-1	1-1	***O***	3-0	2-2
Walshaw Sports Club	3-2	2-1	2-0	1-1	4-3	2-1	0-3	2-1	1-2	0-0	4-1	4-0	4-2	1-2	1-5	2-4	***N***	2-0
Wythenshawe Amateur	4-2	0-2	2-1	0-0	6-1	2-2	0-2	1-0	4-0	3-1	2-0	3-3	0-0	4-1	3-1	1-2	3-3	

Premier Division		P	W	D	L	F	A	Pts
Gregorians		34	22	8	4	77	27	74
Springhead		34	20	6	8	75	44	66
Walshaw Sports Club		34	20	4	10	65	53	64
Wythenshawe Amateur		34	18	7	9	76	52	61
Hollinwood		34	18	6	10	88	72	60
AVRO	*-3*	34	19	5	10	85	50	59
Stockport Georgians		34	15	11	8	57	47	56
Royton Town		34	14	9	11	68	56	51
East Manchester		34	13	9	12	67	57	48
Atherton Town		34	14	4	16	65	55	46
Chapel Town		34	12	9	13	57	54	45
Prestwich Heys		34	12	9	13	66	67	45
Elton Vale		34	11	8	15	68	72	41
Leigh Athletic		34	10	11	13	64	70	41
Hindsford		34	10	4	20	52	75	34
Rochdale Sacred Heart		34	9	5	20	51	88	32
Pennington		34	6	4	24	46	107	22
Breightmet United		34	1	5	28	34	115	8

GILGRYST CUP

FIRST ROUND

AVRO 2 Pennington 0
Springhead 1 **Rochdale Sacred Heart** 4

SECOND ROUND

Atherton Town 0 **Royton Town** 2
Breightmet United 2 **Stockport Georgians** 3
Chapel Town 1 **Leigh Athletic** 2
East Manchester 1 **Prestwich Heys** 1 *aet* (4-5p)
Elton Vale 0 **Walshaw Sports Club** 3
Gregorians 4 Hindsford 3
Hollinwood 2 AVRO 1
Wythenshawe Amateur 7 Rochdale Sacred Heart 0

QUARTER-FINALS

Leigh Athletic 0 **Wythenshawe Amateur** 2
Prestwich Heys 2 **Hollinwood** 3
Walshaw Sports Club 5 Gregorians 0
Royton Town 1 **Stockport Georgians** 2

SEMI-FINALS

Hollinwood 1 **Stockport Georgians** 4
Walshaw Sports Club 2 **Wythenshawe Amateur** 3

FINAL

(May 14th at Trafford)
Wythenshawe Amateur 3 Stockport Georgians 1

MANCHESTER LEAGUE PREMIER DIVISION CONSTITUTION 2009-10

AVRO . . . . . Lancaster Club, Broadway, Failsworth, Oldham M35 0DX 0161 681 3083
ATHERTON TOWN . . . . . Eckersley Fold Lane, Leigh Road, Atherton M46 0QQ 01942 884882
CHAPEL TOWN . . . . . Rowton Park, Willow Drive, Chapel-en-le-Frith, High Peak SK23 0ND . . . . . None
DUKINFIELD TOWN . . . . . Woodhams Park, Birch Lane, Dukinfield SK16 5AP 0161 343 4529
EAST MANCHESTER . . . . . Wright Robinson Sports College, Abbey Hey Lane, Gorton M18 8RL 0161 370 5121
ELTON VALE . . . . . Elton Sports Club, Elton Vale Road, Bury BL8 2RZ 0161 762 0666
HINDSFORD . . . . . Squires Lane, Tyldesley M29 8JF . . . . . None
HOLLINWOOD . . . . . Chapel Road Playing Fields, Grammar School Road, Hollinwood, Oldham OL8 4QY 0161 911 5017
LEIGH ATHLETIC . . . . . Leigh Sports Village, Madley Park, Charles Street, Leigh WN7 4GX 01942 673500
MANCHESTER GREGORIANS . . . MCFC, Platt Lane Complex, Yew Tree Road, Fallowfield M14 7UU . . . . . None
OLD ALTRINCHAMIANS . . . . . Crossford Bridge Sports Ground, Danefield Road, Sale M33 7WR 0161 767 9233
PRESTWICH HEYS . . . . . Sandgate Road, Whitefield M45 6WG 0161 773 8888
ROCHDALE SACRED HEART . . . . . Fox Park, Belfield Mill Lane, Rochdale OL16 2UB . . . . . None
ROYTON TOWN . . . . . Crompton Cricket Club Complex, Christine Street, Shaw, Oldham OL2 7SF 01706 847421
SPRINGHEAD . . . . . Ashfield Crescent, St John Street, Lees, Oldham OL4 4DG 0161 627 0260
STOCKPORT GEORGIANS . . . . . Cromley Road, Woodsmoor, Stockport SK2 7DT 0161 483 6581
WALSHAW SPORTS CLUB . . . . . Walshaw Sports Club, Sycamore Road, Tottington, Bury BL8 3EG 01204 882448
WYTHENSHAWE AMATEUR . . . . . Longley Lane, Northenden, Wythenshawe M22 4LA 0161 998 7268

IN: Dukinfield Town (P), Old Altrinchamians (P)
OUT: Breightmet United (R), Pennington (R)
Gregorians become Manchester Gregorians

	Bee	Bur	Duk	Fiv	Hey	Man	Mon	Old	Sal	SA	Sta	Wes	Whi	Wil	Wyt
Beechfield United		2-5	1-1	6-0	7-0	3-2	3-1	1-1	6-1	1-2	2-3	3-1	2-0	3-0	2-1
Bury Amateurs	4-2	***D***	2-2	1-0	6-1	10-0	0-2	1-6	5-1	1-0	0-1	2-1	2-0	2-1	0-2
Dukinfield Town	2-1	6-1	***I***	7-0	3-2	5-1	4-2	0-1	9-0	4-1	9-2	3-1	n/a	7-0	3-4
Fives Athletic	0-4	0-1	3-11	***V***	0-3	1-2	2-3	0-1	0-2	0-1	1-3	0-1	6-0	3-3	2-4
Heywood St James	3-3	1-3	1-4	2-1	***I***	0-4	1-5	1-2	2-4	4-5	3-2	1-2	n/a	3-2	2-4
Manchester Juniors	L-W	1-3	0-3	1-2	0-1	***S***	0-4	0-7	4-3	2-2	2-4	1-3	4-8	1-2	1-4
Monton Amateurs	3-2	4-1	0-3	5-0	2-2	6-1	***I***	1-3	1-0	0-2	2-2	0-3	W-L	5-1	4-0
Old Altrinchamians	1-3	3-2	3-3	5-0	0-0	4-1	1-1	***O***	3-1	1-0	4-1	1-1	8-2	3-0	3-1
Salford Victoria	1-4	1-0	0-6	2-3	2-6	4-2	1-6	0-7	***N***	0-5	2-3	1-3	7-1	3-4	0-1
Stand Athletic	1-1	1-2	1-3	4-2	2-1	2-1	0-0	4-0	6-2		2-4	3-5	n/a	4-1	2-0
Standians	2-2	1-4	2-3	3-2	3-1	10-4	3-3	0-6	3-3	1-6		2-3	n/a	1-3	4-7
West Didsbury & Chorlton	0-2	2-4	2-3	2-1	3-1	2-0	1-0	3-0	3-0	1-2	3-3	***O***	n/a	4-1	2-2
Whitworth Valley	1-4	0-1	0-15	3-3	2-4	2-3	0-2	1-5	3-5	1-2	2-3	0-8	***N***	n/a	1-6
Wilmslow Albion	2-4	0-4	1-5	0-1	1-1	0-3	1-4	1-0	1-3	2-2	2-2	1-2	n/a	***E***	0-5
Wythenshawe Town	3-2	0-2	0-3	14-0	3-1	5-2	2-4	0-4	6-4	3-4	4-2	1-1	6-1	6-0	

Division One	P	W	D	L	F	A	Pts
Dukinfield Town	**26**	**21**	**3**	**2**	**112**	**32**	**66**
Old Altrinchamians	**26**	**17**	**5**	**4**	**70**	**26**	**56**
Bury Amateurs	**26**	**17**	**1**	**8**	**66**	**41**	**52**
Stand Athletic	**26**	**15**	**4**	**7**	**64**	**42**	**49**
West Didsbury & Chorlton	**26**	**15**	**4**	**7**	**55**	**38**	**49**
Beechfield United	**26**	**14**	**5**	**7**	**70**	**40**	**47**
Monton Amateurs	**26**	**14**	**5**	**7**	**68**	**39**	**47**
Wythenshawe Town	**26**	**15**	**2**	**9**	**82**	**54**	**47**
Standians	**26**	**9**	**6**	**11**	**67**	**83**	**33**
Heywood St James	**26**	**6**	**4**	**16**	**44**	**73**	**22**
Wilmslow Albion	**26**	**4**	**4**	**18**	**30**	**81**	**16**
Salford Victoria	**26**	**5**	**1**	**20**	**41**	**99**	**16**
Manchester Juniors	**26**	**4**	**1**	**21**	**36**	**90**	**13**
Fives Athletic	**26**	**3**	**1**	**22**	**24**	**91**	**10**

Whitworth Valley - record expunged

MURRAY SHIELD

FIRST ROUND

Beechfield United 5 Manchester Juniors 0

Fives 1 **Bury Amateurs** 5 *(at Bury Amateurs)*

Monton Amateurs 0 **Old Altrinchamians** 3

Stand Athletic (w/o) v Dukinfield Town

Standians 1 **Salford V.** 3

West Didsbury & C. (w/o) v AFC Blackley

Wilmslow Albion 2 Whitworth Valley 1

Wythenshawe Town 9 Heywood St James 4

QUARTER-FINALS

Stand Ath 3 Wilmslow 1

Old Alts 5 Salford Vics 0

Bury Ams 2 **Beechfield** 4

Wythenshawe Town (scr.) **West Didsbury & Chorlton** (w/o)

SEMI-FINALS

Old Altrinchamians 2 Beechfield United 1

Stand Athletic 0 **West Didsbury & Chorlton** 1

FINAL

(April 1st at Trafford)

Old Altrinchamians 1 West Didsbury/Chorlton 0

MANCHESTER LEAGUE DIVISION ONE CONSTITUTION 2009-10

BEECHFIELD UNITED . . . . Salford Sports Village, Littleton Road, Salford M7 3NQ 0161 604 760
BREIGHTMET UNITED . . . . Moss Park, Bury Road, Breightmet, Bolton BL2 6NY 01204 53393
BURY AMATEURS . . . . Cams Lane, Radcliffe, Manchester M26 3SW . . . . Non
FIVES ATHLETIC . . . . Harriet Street, Walkden, Worsley M28 3QA . . . . Non
HEYWOOD ST JAMES . . . . Phoenix Ground, Shepherd Street, Heywood OL10 1JW . . . . Non
MANCHESTER JUNIORS . . . . Ford Lane Playing Fields, Church Road, Northenden M22 4WE . . . . Non
MONTON AMATEURS . . . . Granary Lane, Worsley M28 4PH . . . . Non
PENNINGTON . . . . Jubilee Park, Leigh Road, Atherton M46 0PJ . . . . Non
SALFORD VICTORIA . . . . Salford Sports Village, Lower Kersal, Littleton Road, Salford M7 3NQ 0161 604 760
STANDIANS . . . . Ringley Road, Whitefield M45 7LN . . . . Non
WEST DIDSBURY & CHORLTON . . . . Brookburn Road, Chorlton-cum-Hardy M21 8EH . . . . Non
WILMSLOW ALBION . . . . Oakwood Farm, Styal Road, Wilmslow SK9 4HP 01625 53582
WYTHENSHAWE TOWN . . . . Ericstan Park, Timpson Road, Baguley M23 9RT 0161 998 507

IN: Breightmet United (R), Pennington (R)

OUT: AFC Blackley (WN), Dukinfield Town (P), Old Altrinchamians (P), Stand Athletic (W), Whitworth Valley (WS - Rochdale Alliance)

Division Two		P	W	D	L	F	A	Pt
Dukinfield Res.	*-3*	30	21	5	4	89	41	65
Elton Vale Res.		30	18	3	9	78	57	57
E. M'chester Res.		30	16	5	9	65	37	53
Monton Ams Res.		30	15	8	7	76	58	53
AVRO Res.		30	13	9	8	73	56	48
Gregorians Res.		30	14	6	10	59	52	48
Leigh Ath. Res.		30	13	7	10	67	55	46
W'shawe A. Res.	*-3*	30	13	7	10	68	63	43
Prestwich H. Res.		30	12	5	13	51	59	41
Rochdale SH Res.		30	11	6	13	54	62	39
S. Georgians Res.		30	10	8	12	57	56	38
Springhead Res.		30	11	4	15	57	71	37
Walshaw S. Res.		30	9	4	17	47	59	31
Hindsford Res.		30	8	4	18	58	75	28
W. Didsbury Res.		30	7	1	22	51	95	22
Bury Ams Res.	*-3*	30	6	4	20	45	99	19

Division Three		P	W	D	L	F	A	Pt
Old Alts Res.		26	17	6	3	102	40	57
Stand Ath. Res.		26	17	5	4	86	56	56
Beechfield Res.		26	17	4	5	88	59	55
Hollinwood Res.		26	17	0	9	106	61	51
Atherton T. Res.		26	13	5	8	73	53	44
Chapel Town Res.		26	13	4	9	76	56	43
Gregorians A		26	13	4	9	64	50	43
W'shawe T. Res.		26	12	2	12	59	73	38
Royton Town Res.		26	8	8	10	44	53	32
Breightmet Res.		26	9	2	15	49	83	29
Bury Amateurs A		26	8	2	16	50	63	26
S. Georgians A	*-7*	26	6	4	16	42	67	15
Walshaw Spts A		26	4	3	19	34	100	15
Hollinwood A		26	1	5	20	39	98	8

Division Four		P	W	D	L	F	A	Pt
Dukinfield A	*-6*	20	18	0	2	83	25	48
Fives Ath. Res.		20	11	3	6	66	48	36
Gregorians B		20	12	0	8	38	39	36
Wilmslow Res.		20	11	1	8	33	32	34
Pennington Res.		20	8	3	9	32	37	27
Standians Res.		20	9	0	11	41	49	27
Leigh Athletic A		20	7	4	9	35	41	25
Salford Vics Res.		20	7	3	10	41	51	24
Beechfield A		20	7	2	11	45	52	23
West Didsbury A		20	6	3	11	47	60	21
Bury Amateurs B		20	4	1	15	25	52	13

OPEN TROPHY

FINAL *(May 13th at Flixton)*

Elton Vale Res. 2 East Manchester Res. 1

LEAGUE CUP

FINAL *(May 18th at New Mills)*

Old Altrichamias Res. 5 Gregorians A 0

MIDDLESEX COUNTY LEAGUE

www.mcfl.org.uk

Sponsored by:
Cherry Red

Founded: 1984

Recent champions:

2004: Wraysbury

2005: Hanworth Villa

2006: Battersea Ironsides

2007: Sport London E Benfica

2008: Indian Gymkhana

	Bedfont Spts	Bethnal Green	Broadfields U.	FC Dep. Galicia	Hayes Gate	Hayes United	Indian Gymkhana	Kodak (Harrow)	Marsh Rangers	Newham BSECP	Park View	Southall	Will. Constantine
Bedfont Sports		0-1	1-1	3-0	1-0	1-2	0-2	0-1	3-1	1-2	4-1	2-2	3-4
Bethnal Green United	2-5	***P***	1-0	5-0	6-2	1-1	0-1	3-1	3-0	1-0	n/a	1-0	4-3
Broadfields United	1-1	0-4	***R***	4-2	1-1	2-3	3-1	3-5	2-2	L-W	1-7	1-4	5-0
FC Deportivo Galicia	0-4	2-6	1-5	***E***	1-4	1-3	0-12	1-2	0-3	0-4	W-L	0-0	1-4
Hayes Gate	0-6	1-5	1-2	3-0	***M***	L-W	1-1	3-1	4-1	2-3	n/a	2-0	4-1
Hayes United	2-3	3-2	3-1	3-0	8-0	***I***	0-1	3-0	4-0	L-W	W-L	3-2	3-0
Indian Gymkhana	2-3	0-2	3-2	2-4	2-2	1-2	***E***	2-2	1-1	0-3	n/a	2-1	2-1
Kodak (Harrow)	1-5	1-5	2-3	1-1	5-1	0-2	1-1	***R***	2-5	1-1	n/a	2-5	2-2
Marsh Rangers	0-4	1-3	1-2	6-0	0-2	1-1	0-1	1-1		5-5	W-L	W-L	1-1
Newham Borough (SECP)	1-6	1-3	4-1	1-1	1-1	0-1	2-0	0-4	L-W	***D***	W-L	2-2	1-1
Park View	n/a	2-1	n/a	5-0	7-0	4-3	2-1	3-1	n/a	L-W	***I***	5-0	2-0
Southall	0-2	1-4	4-0	3-0	4-1	1-1	3-0	5-4	3-0	W-L	n/a	***V***	2-2
Willesden Constantine	1-4	0-4	2-2	W-L	1-0	0-2	0-9	0-2	0-1	1-4	2-3	3-3	

Premier Division		**P**	**W**	**D**	**L**	**F**	**A**	**Pts**
Bethnal Green United		**22**	**18**	**1**	**3**	**66**	**23**	**55**
Hayes United		**22**	**16**	**3**	**3**	**50**	**17**	**51**
Bedfont Sports		**22**	**13**	**3**	**6**	**58**	**26**	**42**
Indian Gymkhana		**22**	**9**	**5**	**8**	**46**	**33**	**32**
Southall	***-3***	**22**	**9**	**6**	**7**	**45**	**32**	**30**
Newham Boro. (SECP)	***-6***	**22**	**9**	**6**	**7**	**35**	**31**	**27**
Kodak (Harrow)		**22**	**6**	**6**	**10**	**41**	**52**	**24**
Marsh Rangers		**22**	**6**	**6**	**10**	**30**	**42**	**24**
Broadfields United	***-3***	**22**	**7**	**5**	**10**	**41**	**46**	**23**
Hayes Gate	***-6***	**22**	**7**	**4**	**11**	**35**	**50**	**19**
Willesden Constantine		**22**	**4**	**6**	**12**	**27**	**59**	**18**
FC Deportivo Galicia		**22**	**1**	**3**	**18**	**15**	**78**	**3**

Park View - record expunged

ALEC SMITH CUP

PRELIMINARY ROUND

Broadfields 3 **Hayes Gate** 4

FIRST ROUND

Bedfont Sports 1 **Indian Gymkhana** 2 *aet*
FC Deportivo Galicia 1 **Kodak (Harrow)** 5
Hayes Gate 0 **Hayes United** 1
Newham Borough (SECP) 2 Park View 1

QUARTER-FINALS

Hayes United 2 Indian Gymkhana 2 *aet* (4-3p)
Kodak (Harrow) 1 **Bethnal Green United** 3
Southall 2 Marsh Rangers 1
Willesden Constantine (w/o) v Newham Borough (SECP) (scr.)

SEMI-FINALS

Southall 1 **Bethnal Green United** 3
Willesden Constantine 0 **Hayes United** 1

FINAL

(April 18th at Yeading)
Bethnal Green United 1 **Hayes United** 2 *aet*

MIDDLESEX COUNTY LEAGUE PREMIER DIVISION CONSTITUTION 2009-10

BETHNAL GREEN UNITED RESERVES Mile End Stadim, Rhodeswell Rd, Burdett Rd, Poplar E14 7TW 020 8980 1885
BROADFIELDS UNITED . . . Broadfields Country Club, Broadfields, Headstone Lane, North Harrow HA2 6NN 020 8421 4739/5260
COPLAND . . . . Stonebridge Recreation Ground, Hillside, London NW10 8LW . . . . None
FC DEPORTIVO GALICIA . . . . Osterley Sports Club, Tentelow Lane, Osterley, Southall UB2 4LW 020 8574 3774
HAYES GATE . . . . Springfield Road, Hayes UB4 0JS 020 8573 1203
HOUNSLOW WANDERERS . . . . Conquest Club, Wood Lane, Isleworth TW7 5EJ 020 8560 2892
INDIAN GYMKHANA . . . . Indian Gymkhana Club, Thornbury Avenue, Osterley TW7 4NQ 020 8568 4009
KODAK (HARROW) . . . . Zoom Leisure Centre, Kodak Sports Ground, Harrow View, Harrow HA2 6QQ 020 8427 1957
MARSH RANGERS . . . . Rosedale College, Wood End Green Road, Hayes UB3 2SE 020 8573 2097/7103
NORTH KENSINGTON . . . . Birkbeck Sports Ground, Birkbeck Avenue, Greenford UB6 8LS 020 8578 1930
SINGH SABHA . . . . Broadfields Country Club, Broadfields, Headstone Lane, North Harrow HA2 6NN 020 8421 4739/5260
SLOANE . . . . Royal Hospital South Grounds, Chelsea Embankment, London SW3 4SR . . . . None
SNARESBROOK INTERWOOD . . . Peter May Sports Centre, Wadham Road, Walthamstow E17 4HR 020 8531 9358
SOUTHALL . . . . Osterley Sports Club, Tentelow Lane, Osterley, Southall UB2 4LW 020 8574 3774
STONEWALL . . . . Broadfields Country Club, Broadfields, Headstone Lane, North Harrow HA2 6NN 020 8421 4739/5260
VALLANCE . . . . Meath Gardens Playing Fields, Smart Street, London E2 0QB . . . . None
WILLESDEN CONSTANTINE . . . . Alperton Sports Ground, Alperton Lane, Wembley HA0 1JH 020 8997 9909

IN: Bethnal Green United Res. (N), Copland (P - Division One Central & East), Hounslow Wanderers (P - Division One West), North Kensington (P - Division One West), Singh Sabha (formerly Singh Sabha Barking) (P - Essex & Business Houses League Division One), Sloane (P - Division One Central & East), Snaresbrook Interwood (P - youth football), Stonewall (P - Division One Central & East), Vallance (formerly Beaumont Athletic (S - Essex Olympian League Premier Division)

OUT: Bedfont Sports (P - Combined Counties League Division One), Bethnal Green United (P - Essex Senior League), Park View (WS), Hayes United (W), Newham Borough (SECP) (W)

SENIOR OPEN CUP

FIRST ROUND

Hounslow Wanderers 3 The Wilberforce Wanderers 2
Imperial College Old Boys 1 **Blue Marlin** 3
My Generation Sports 5 Kodak (Harrow) 4
North Kensington 2 **Indian Gymkhana** 3
St Johns Arsenal Deaf 4 Uxbridge Town 3 *aet*

SECOND ROUND

Bedfont Sports 4 Broadfields United 1
Bethnal Green United 1 London United Football Academy 1 *aet* (6-5p)
FC Deportivo Galicia 1 FC Team 0
Hayes Gate 1 **Stedfast United** 5
Hendon A (w/o) v FC Baresi
Hillingdon Abbots Seniors 4 CB Hounslow Social 2
Hounslow Wanderers 2 **FC Assyria** 4
Indian Gymkhana 3 Grosvenor House 0
My Generation Sports 4 Brentham 1
North Greenford United Social 1 **Marsh Rangers** 7
Park View 4 Galatasaray 1
Sloane 1 **Hayes United** 2 *aet*
South Acton 4 Newham Borough (SECP) 4 *aet* (3-1p)
Southall 5 Willesden Constantine 1
St Johns Arsenal Deaf 3 Blue Marlin 2
Stonewall 2 **Harrow St Mary's** 4

THIRD ROUND

FC Deportivo Galicia 2 **Hayes United** 3
Harrow St Mary's 1 **Bedfont Sports** 2
Hendon A 1 **FC Assyria** 5
Hillingdon Abbots Seniors 5 South Acton 3
Indian Gymkhana 6 My Generation Sports 4
Marsh Rangers 2 **Bethnal Green United** 3
St Johns Arsenal Deaf (w/o) v Park View (scr.)
Stedfast United 1 **Southall** 5

QUARTER-FINALS

Bedfont Sports 6 St Johns Arsenal Deaf 0
Bethnal Green United 3 FC Assyria 1
Hillingdon Abbots Seniors 2 **Southall** 4
Indian Gymkhana 2 Hayes United 0

SEMI-FINALS

Bedfont Sports 0 **Bethnal Green United** 2
Southall 0 **Indian Gymkhana** 1

FINAL *(May 9th at Yeading)*

Indian Gymkhana 2 **Bethnal Green United** 4

Division One Central & East		P	W	D	L	F	A	Pt
Copland		20	14	2	4	64	26	44
Stonewall		20	12	3	5	41	31	39
Sloane		20	10	4	6	43	33	34
St Johns Arsenal Deaf		20	10	3	7	51	35	33
Hendon A		20	7	5	8	40	41	26
The Wilberforce Wdrs		20	7	5	8	38	42	26
FC Assyria	*-3*	20	7	5	8	41	48	23
London Utd F'ball Ac.	*-6*	20	8	3	9	28	29	21
FC Team	*-3*	20	7	3	10	28	47	21
Blue Marlin		20	6	2	12	38	48	20
Uxbridge Town		20	2	5	13	22	54	11

Division Two		P	W	D	L	F	A	Pt
LPOSSA		20	15	1	4	68	27	46
Hillingdon		20	15	1	4	68	39	46
Greens United		20	14	3	3	71	33	45
Barn Elms		20	10	4	6	50	39	34
Bedfont Town		20	9	3	8	69	67	30
Warren		20	9	2	9	53	55	29
Junior All Stars	*-3*	20	8	7	5	48	34	28
Hilltop		20	8	3	9	50	46	27
Maiwand	*-3*	20	5	1	14	30	58	13
CB Hounslow Utd Social		20	2	4	14	35	72	10
The Wanderers		20	0	1	19	22	94	1

Division Three Hounslow & District		P	W	D	L	F	A	Pt
Hanworth Villa A		20	15	2	3	72	25	47
Grange Park		20	14	2	4	75	28	44
Kensington Dragons		20	14	2	4	66	26	44
Sandgate		20	12	5	3	76	26	41
West London Saracens	*-3*	20	8	4	8	55	30	25
Eutectic	*-3*	20	9	1	10	43	48	25
Hanworth		20	8	1	11	63	73	25
Horseed	*-6*	20	7	2	11	45	44	17
West Side Rangers		20	5	2	13	28	98	17
AFC Heathrow		20	3	1	16	25	102	10
AMU	*-3*	20	4	0	16	28	76	9

Division One West		P	W	D	L	F	A	Pt
North Kensington		20	13	4	3	55	28	43
Hounslow Wanderers		20	12	3	5	49	29	39
Stedfast United		20	11	2	7	73	50	35
Nth Greenford Utd Social		20	11	2	7	50	37	35
Grosvenor House		20	10	2	8	47	42	32
South Acton		20	8	3	9	34	49	27
Hillingdon Abbots Seniors		20	6	5	9	34	44	23
Harrow St Mary's		20	6	4	10	30	41	22
My Generation Sports	*-3*	20	7	4	9	40	56	22
Brentham		20	5	3	12	34	50	18
Imperial College Old Boys		20	4	2	14	30	50	14

Senior Reserve Division		P	W	D	L	F	A	P
Hayes Gate Res.		20	17	3	0	80	18	54
Brentham Res.		20	15	2	3	71	37	47
Indian Gymkhana Res.		20	12	3	5	54	39	39
Kodak (Harrow) Res.		20	11	3	6	78	41	36
CB Hounslow US Res.		20	9	3	8	51	34	30
Feltham Res.	*-6*	20	9	4	7	43	41	25
Hillingdon Res.		20	7	2	11	35	42	23
Kensington Dragons Res.		20	5	3	12	41	79	18
North Kensington Res.		20	6	0	14	37	81	18
Sloane Res.		20	5	1	14	38	67	16
Imperial College OB Res.	*-3*	20	2	0	18	23	72	3

JIM ROGERS DIVISION ONE PRESIDENT'S CUP

FINAL *(April 4th at Yeading)*

Stedfast United 5 North Greenford United Social 0

SIR JOHN SALMOND DIVISION TWO CUP FINAL

(March 28th at Yeading)

Junior All Stars 3 Greens United 0

JEFF NARDIN SENIOR RESERVE DIVISION TROPHY

FINAL *(May 2nd at Yeading)*

Hayes Gate Res. 7 Kensington Dragons Res. 1

P D MARDON DIVISION THREE CUP FINAL

(April 25th at Yeading)

Sandgate 3 Hanworth Villa A 2

NORTH BERKS LEAGUE

www.nbfl.co.uk

Sponsored by:
No sponsor

Founded: 1908

Recent champions:

2004: Kintbury Rangers
2005: Drayton
2006: Lambourn Sports
2007: Ardington & Lockinge
2008: Lambourn Sports

	AFC Wallingford	Ardington & Lockinge	Blewbury	Crowmarsh Gifford	Drayton	Faringdon Town	Harwell International	Harwell Village	Lambourn Sports	Saxton Rovers	Steventon	Wootton & Dry Sandford
AFC Wallingford	***D***	5-2	1-1	1-1	0-0	0-0	0-1	1-3	1-3	1-4	4-1	1-0
Ardington & Lockinge	1-0	***I***	4-3	3-2	3-5	0-3	3-2	0-2	1-1	0-0	0-2	0-1
Blewbury	4-3	4-0	***V***	1-0	2-3	0-1	1-4	5-0	0-3	1-2	2-0	0-2
Crowmarsh Gifford	7-2	1-3	0-3	***I***	3-2	2-1	5-2	4-2	4-1	0-3	4-0	0-3
Drayton	4-3	4-0	1-1	0-6	***S***	0-2	1-1	3-5	2-4	2-3	2-2	3-4
Faringdon Town	1-0	3-1	3-3	1-1	1-2	***I***	4-0	2-4	1-1	1-2	5-0	0-1
Harwell International	1-4	0-1	1-3	1-3	1-3	2-5	***O***	0-2	1-0	0-6	0-2	2-2
Harwell Village	5-1	1-4	2-6	3-1	2-1	0-2	5-1	***N***	4-2	0-2	1-2	0-1
Lambourn Sports	0-0	2-0	1-2	3-4	0-1	4-2	3-2	2-5		2-1	2-2	7-3
Saxton Rovers	4-0	1-1	1-1	5-2	6-0	0-0	7-0	8-1	3-3	***O***	1-0	3-1
Steventon	2-4	1-0	3-2	0-5	1-2	2-3	0-2	1-2	2-4	1-3	***N***	1-3
Wootton & Dry Sandford	4-0	1-1	2-3	2-0	1-5	1-4	1-2	3-1	2-2	0-2	5-0	***E***

Division One	P	W	D	L	F	A	Pts
Saxton Rovers	22	16	5	1	67	17	53
Faringdon Town	22	11	5	6	45	26	38
Wootton & Dry Sandford	22	11	3	8	43	37	36
Harwell Village	22	12	0	10	50	52	36
Crowmarsh Gifford	22	11	2	9	55	42	35
Blewbury	22	10	4	8	48	37	34
Lambourn Sports	22	9	6	7	50	43	33
Drayton	22	9	4	9	46	51	31
Ardington & Lockinge	22	7	4	11	28	44	25
AFC Wallingford	22	5	5	12	32	49	20
Steventon	22	5	2	15	25	56	17
Harwell International	22	5	2	15	26	61	17

Division Two	P	W	D	L	F	A	Pt
Didcot Casuals	20	14	4	2	65	26	46
Warborough & Shillingford	20	14	3	3	62	33	45
Marcham	20	14	2	4	57	30	44
Benson	20	10	6	4	54	27	36
Saxton Rovers Res.	20	8	6	6	52	42	30
Lambourn Sports Res.	20	9	0	11	49	45	27
Coleshill United	20	6	6	8	50	46	24
East Hendred	20	4	6	10	36	52	18
Grove Rangers	20	5	3	12	32	63	18
Faringdon Town Res.	20	5	2	13	35	55	17
Sutton Courtenay	20	1	2	17	28	101	5

Division Three	P	W	D	L	F	A	Pt
Childrey	24	19	2	3	81	34	59
Long Wittenham Athletic	24	17	4	3	78	36	55
Botley	24	16	3	5	79	33	51
Shrivenham A	24	15	2	7	61	36	47
Drayton Res.	24	14	4	6	65	45	46
Coleshill United Res.	24	10	4	10	64	53	34
Benson Lions	24	11	0	13	53	56	33
Blewbury Res.	24	8	4	12	38	54	28
Wootton/Dry Sandford Res.	24	8	1	15	52	75	25
Harwell International Res.	24	7	3	14	50	77	24
Harwell Village Res.	24	7	2	15	32	70	23
Ardington & Lockinge Res.	24	5	2	17	31	68	17
Grove Rangers Res.	24	2	3	19	41	88	9

NORTH BERKS LEAGUE DIVISION ONE CONSTITUTION 2009-10

AFC WALLINGFORD .... Wallingford Sports Park, Hithercroft Road, Wallingford OX10 9RB 01491 835044
ARDINGTON & LOCKINGE.............. White Road, Ardington, Wantage OX12 8QB.......................... None
BLEWBURY .... Bohams Road, Blewbury, Didcot OX11 9HB.......................... None
CROWMARSH GIFFORD .... Crowmarsh Recreation Ground, Crowmarsh Gifford, Wallingford OX10 8EB 07951 959090
DIDCOT CASUALS .... Didcot Town Training Pitch, Ladygrove, Didcot OX11 7GA.......................... None
DRAYTON .... Recreation Ground, Lockway, Drayton, Abingdon OX14 4LF.......................... None
FARINGDON TOWN .... Tucker Park, Park Road, Faringdon SN7 7DP 01367 241759
HARWELL VILLAGE .... Westfields Recreation Ground, Harwell, Didcot OX11 0LG.......................... None
LAMBOURN SPORTS.............. Bockhampton Road, Lambourn, Hungerford RG17 7PS 01488 72214
SAXTON ROVERS .... Recreation Ground, Caldecott Road, Abingdon OX14 5HR .... None
WARBOROUGH & SHILLINGFORD .... Village Green, Warborough OX10 7DN .... None
WOOTTON & DRY SANDFORD..... Community Centre, Besseleigh Road, Wootton OX13 6DN .... None

IN: Didcot Casuals (P), Warborough & Shillingford (P)
OUT: Harwell International (R), Steventon (R)

Division Four	P	W	D	L	F	A	Pt
Hanney United	20	17	1	2	79	26	52
Benson Res.	20	14	1	5	54	40	43
Stanford-in-the-Vale	20	12	3	5	65	37	39
Faringdon Town A	20	9	2	9	33	40	29
Uffington United	20	8	2	10	50	66	26
Marcham Res.	20	8	1	11	40	43	25
East Hendred Res.	20	6	4	10	22	24	22
Challow United	20	6	3	11	39	42	21
Hagbourne United	20	6	3	11	33	49	21
Didcot Casuals Res.	20	6	3	11	36	67	21
Steventon Res.	20	5	3	12	38	55	18

Division Five	P	W	D	L	F	A	Pt
Coleshill United A	20	16	1	3	76	22	49
Uffington United Res.	20	15	2	3	67	25	47
Stanford-in-the-Vale Res.	20	12	1	7	68	39	37
Benson Lions Res.	20	11	2	7	45	25	35
Long Wittenham Athletic Res.	20	10	4	6	52	38	34
Kennington United Res.	19	8	4	7	30	41	28
Hanney United Res.	20	7	1	12	43	48	22
Sutton Courtenay Res.	20	4	5	11	35	47	17
Didcot Casuals A	20	5	2	13	29	63	17
Challow United Res.	20	5	0	15	24	86	15
Hagbourne United Res.	19	4	2	13	27	62	14

(Hagbourne Res. v Kennington Utd Res. not played)

CHARITY SHIELD

FIRST ROUND

Ardington & Lockinge 1 **Stanford-in-the-Vale** 3
Benson Lions 2 Coleshill United 0
Botley United 4 **Crowmarsh Gifford** 4 *aet* (2-3p)
Challow United 2 **Blewbury** 5
Didcot Casuals 4 Kingsclere 2
Drayton 6 Childrey 1
Faringdon Town 7 Wootton & Dry Sandford 2
Grove Rangers 4 Harwell International 2
Harwell Village 3 Hanney United 1
Marcham 1 **Benson** 2
Sutton Courtenay 2 **Long Wittenham Athletic** 4
Uffington United 2 **East Hendred** 4
Warborough & Shillingford 1 **Saxton Rovers** 3

SECOND ROUND

Benson 2 **Saxton Rovers** 4
Benson Lions 2 **Lambourn Sports** 3
Blewbury 1 **Drayton** 3
Crowmarsh Gifford 8 E. Hendred 0
Faringdon Town 2 AFC Wallingford 1
Long Wittenham Athletic 0 **Harwell Village** 1
Stanford-in-the-Vale 1 Grove Rangers 0
Steventon 0 **Didcot Casuals** 2

QUARTER-FINALS

Drayton 1 Didcot Casuals 0
Faringdon Town 7 Stanford-in-the-Vale 1
Lambourn Sports 1 **Harwell Village** 2
Saxton Rovers 3 Crowmarsh Gifford 0

SEMI-FINALS

Faringdon Town 3 Harwell Village 2 *(at Crowmarsh Gifford)*
Drayton 1 **Saxton Rovers** 6 *(at Faringdon Town)*

FINAL

(May 2nd at Abingdon United)
Saxton Rovers 3 Faringdon Town 0 *aet*

NORTH BERKS CUP

FIRST ROUND

AFC Wallingford 10 Benson Lions 1
Blewbury 3 Harwell Village 2
Botley United 8 Challow United 0
Coleshill United 1 **Long Wittenham Athletic** 2
Drayton 3 Stanford-in-the-Vale 1
Faringdon Town (w/o) v Kingsclere
Grove Rangers 0 **Crowmarsh Gifford** 5
Harwell International 2 **Ardington & Lockinge** 4
Marcham 6 Hanney United 1
Steventon 0 **Didcot Casuals** 2
Sutton Courtenay 0 **Benson** 2
Warborough & Shillingford 1 **Wootton & Dry Sandford** 5

SECOND ROUND

Ardington & Lockinge 2 Botley United 1
Blewbury (w/o) v East Hendred
Drayton 1 **Didcot Casuals** 2
Faringdon Town 3 Benson 0
Lambourn Sports 2 Crowmarsh Gifford 1
Long Wittenham 6 Uffington United 3
Marcham 0 **Saxton Rovers** 4
Wootton & Dry Sandford 0 **AFC Wallingford** 2

QUARTER-FINALS

Lambourn Sports 1 **AFC Wallingford** 2
Saxton Rovers 6 Ardington & Lockinge 2
Long Wittenham Athletic 1 **Faringdon Town** 2
Blewbury 3 Didcot Casuals 2

SEMI-FINALS

Faringdon Town 1 **Saxton Rovers** 2
Blewbury 4 AFC Wallingford 2

FINAL

(May 9th at Abingdon United)
Saxton Rovers 1 Blewbury 0

WAR MEMORIAL CUP

FINAL *(April 24th at Wantage Town)*
Botley United 4 Stanford-in-the-Vale 3

A G KINGHAM CUP

FINAL *(May 9th at Abingdon United)*
Saxton Rovers Res. 2 Drayton Res. 1

LEAGUE CUP

FINAL *(April 25th at AFC Wallingford)*
Coleshill United A 3 Marcham Res. 1

NAIRNE PAUL CUP

FINAL *(May 2nd at Abingdon United)*
Shrivenham A 2 Saxton Rovers Res. 1

NORTHANTS COMBINATION LEAGUE

www.northantscombination.co.uk

Sponsored by:
MDH Teamwear

Founded: N/K

Recent champions:
2004: Moulton
2005: Caledonian Strip Mills
2006: Corby Hellenic Fisher
2007: Harpole
2008: Harpole

	Brixworth AS	Corby M'sons	Corby Peg.	Harborough	Harpole	Heyford Ath.	Kislingbury	Medbourne	Milton	Moulton	Roade	Stanion Utd	Weldon Utd	Whitefield
Brixworth All Saints		6-2	2-1	0-3	1-2	4-0	2-0	7-0	4-1	2-1	5-0	5-1	1-0	1-1
Corby Madisons	5-1	***P***	2-1	1-2	3-9	2-3	0-1	1-3	4-1	1-3	1-5	3-1	1-1	6-2
Corby Pegasus	0-1	1-4	***R***	0-1	0-2	6-1	1-1	1-2	2-1	1-1	3-1	3-0	0-0	2-0
Harborough Town	0-2	2-0	6-1	***E***	0-5	4-3	1-1	2-2	1-1	5-0	1-0	4-0	1-0	2-3
Harpole	2-0	1-0	6-0	2-1	***M***	1-1	1-1	4-0	3-1	7-1	2-0	3-0	5-1	3-0
Heyford Athletic	1-3	2-2	2-1	0-4	0-3	***I***	0-2	2-0	0-3	3-2	1-5	2-2	1-1	2-5
Kislingbury	3-0	1-0	3-2	3-0	1-2	3-1	***E***	3-1	3-0	2-0	4-2	2-0	2-1	5-4
Medbourne	0-6	5-1	4-2	1-4	1-5	1-1	1-4	***R***	5-0	2-2	3-3	9-2	0-2	1-0
Milton	1-2	5-0	3-3	1-5	0-1	2-3	1-1	0-5		1-4	0-2	2-1	3-2	3-1
Moulton	1-2	3-1	4-0	2-3	1-2	2-1	1-5	7-1	2-0		1-4	2-0	4-3	6-1
Roade	0-4	2-1	1-1	1-2	1-3	4-1	1-3	3-3	1-1	1-1	***D***	5-0	3-0	1-1
Stanion United	2-2	5-2	2-3	0-8	2-9	2-2	2-5	1-6	2-1	2-3	1-4	***I***	0-1	3-7
Weldon United	0-0	2-1	1-1	1-2	2-3	2-2	1-4	1-2	3-3	3-0	3-3	2-5	***V***	4-1
Whitefield Norpol	0-3	1-1	4-1	3-2	0-3	1-2	3-4	1-7	3-2	2-2	6-3	5-0	4-3	

Premier Division	P	W	D	L	F	A	Pts
Harpole	26	24	2	0	89	18	74
Kislingbury	26	20	4	2	67	28	64
Brixworth All Saints	26	18	3	5	66	27	57
Harborough Town	26	17	3	6	66	33	54
Medbourne	26	11	5	10	65	65	38
Moulton	26	11	4	11	56	55	37
Roade	26	9	7	10	56	52	34
Whitefield Norpol	26	9	4	13	59	72	31
Heyford Athletic	26	6	7	13	37	67	25
Corby Pegasus	26	6	6	14	37	55	24
Weldon United	26	5	8	13	40	52	23
Corby Madisons	26	6	3	17	45	69	21
Milton	26	5	5	16	37	63	20
Stanion United	26	3	3	20	36	100	12

NORTHANTS COMB./ NORTHAMPTON TOWN LEAGUE CHAMPIONS CUP

(15th October at Northampton Spencer)

Harpole 1 Northampton Harlequins 0

PREMIER DIVISION CUP

FIRST ROUND

Moulton 2 **Kislingbury** 2 *aet* (1-3p)
Corby Madisons 3 **Weldon United** 5
Medbourne 7 Heyford Athletic 1
Whitefield Norpol 1 **Brixworth All Saints** 3
Stanion United 1 **Harpole** 6
Corby Pegasus 0 **Roade** 3

QUARTER-FINALS

Milton 3 **Roade** 4
Brixworth All Saints 3 Harborough Town 0
Weldon United 0 **Medbourne** 3
Kislingbury 2 Harpole 2 *aet* (3-1p)

SEMI-FINALS

Medbourne 0 **Brixworth All Saints** 3
Kislingbury 8 Roade 1

FINAL

(April 30th at Northampton Town)

Brixworth All Saints 2 **Kislingbury** 2 *aet* (1-3p)

NORTHANTS COMBINATION PREMIER DIVISION CONSTITUTION 2009-10

BRIXWORTH ALL SAINTS .... St Davids Close, off Froxhill Crescent, Brixworth NN6 9EA 01604 880073
CORBY KHALSA .... Corby Rugby Club, Rockingham Road, Corby NN17 1AE .... None
CORBY PEGASUS............. West Glebe South Pavilion, Cottingham Road, Corby NN17 1EL.................. 01536 402041
HARBOROUGH TOWN .... Leisure Centre, Northampton Road, Market Harborough LE16 9HE............... 01858 465934
HARPOLE .... Playing Field, Larkhall Lane, Harpole NN7 4DP.......................... None
HEYFORD ATHLETIC .... Nether Heyford Playing Field, Nether Heyford NN7 3LL........................ None
KISLINGBURY .... Playing Fields, Beech Lane, Kislingbury, Northampton NN7 4AL 01604 831225
MEDBOURNE .... Medbourne Sports & Social Club, Hallaton Road, Medbourne LE16 8DR.................. None
MILTON .... Collingtree Road, Milton Malsor, Northampton NN7 3AU .... None
MOULTON......................... Brunting Road, Moulton, Northampton NN3 7QF 01604 492675
QUEEN ELEANOR GREAT HOUGHTON . Leys Lane, Great Houghton, Northampton NN4 7AL....................... 01908 542675
ROADE............................. Connolly Way, Hyde Road, Roade NN7 2LU 01604 862814
WELDON UNITED.......................... Oundle Road, Weldon NN17 3JT .... None
WHITEFIELD NORPOL......... Sports Ground, Wootton Hall PHQ, Mereway, Northampton NN4 0JF .... None

IN: Queen Eleanor Great Houghton (P)
OUT: Stanion United (R)
Corby Madisons become Corby Khalsa

Division One		P	W	D	L	F	A	Pts
Queen Eleanor Gt Houghton		24	19	2	3	65	25	59
Corby Kingfisher Athletic		24	15	5	4	64	37	50
Wootton St George		24	12	6	6	57	32	42
Cold Ashby Rovers		24	13	3	8	57	42	42
Earls Barton United		24	11	6	7	48	33	39
Kettering Nomads		24	10	4	10	43	40	34
Punjab United		24	9	6	9	44	48	33
Welford Victoria		24	8	4	12	40	40	28
James King Blisworth		24	8	4	12	51	56	28
Stanwick Rovers		24	7	4	13	49	59	25
Corby Phoenix		24	6	4	14	40	65	22
Spratton		24	7	1	16	37	75	22
Bective Wanderers		24	5	3	16	39	82	18

DIVISION ONE CUP FINAL *(April 14th at Raunds Town)*
Earls Barton United 2 Corby Kingfisher 0

Division Two		P	W	D	L	F	A	Pts
Finedon Volta		24	21	1	2	80	21	64
Daventry Drayton Grange		24	15	4	5	65	33	49
Ringstead Rangers		24	14	6	4	70	38	48
Ristee Towers		24	9	10	5	52	41	37
Gretton	*+2*	24	10	5	9	55	55	37
Corby Danesholme Vikings		24	9	7	8	47	36	34
Wollaston Victoria		24	9	3	12	54	55	30
Wellingboro. Ranelagh	*-3*	24	9	4	11	37	51	28
Burton United		24	7	4	13	50	55	25
Clipston		24	7	3	14	24	40	24
Weedon	*-1*	24	7	4	13	33	58	24
Islip United	*-3*	24	6	6	12	37	72	21
Crick Athletic		24	4	1	19	34	83	13

DIV. TWO CUP FINAL *(April 7th at Wellingborough T.)*
Corby Danesholme Vikings 3 Ringstead Rangers 2

Division Three		P	W	D	L	F	A	Pts
Wellingboro. Old Grammians		26	21	2	3	85	34	65
Great Doddington		26	20	2	4	88	29	62
Corby Strip Mills	*-3*	26	20	3	3	111	28	60
Kettering Orchard Park		26	17	2	7	83	36	53
Wellingborough Saxons		26	13	5	8	91	69	44
Weavers Old Boys		26	12	6	8	81	68	42
Corby Eagles		26	12	1	13	58	54	37
Corby Locomotives		26	11	4	11	62	60	37
Staverton Park Rangers	*-3*	26	11	1	14	46	64	31
Dainite Sports		26	6	3	17	43	83	21
Hillmorton	*-3*	26	7	1	18	56	82	19
Wilby		26	6	0	20	34	107	18
Wilbarston	*-3*	26	5	3	18	36	88	15
Wellingborough Raffertys		26	4	1	21	39	111	13

DIVISION THREE CUP FINAL *(April 2nd at Cogenhoe)*
Wellingborough Old Grammarians 4 Corby Strip Mills 0

Division Four		P	W	D	L	F	A	Pts
Kettering Ise Lodge	*+2*	26	21	4	1	92	24	69
Wellingborough Rising Sun		26	15	4	7	84	52	49
Wellingborough WMC		26	15	3	8	83	60	48
Corby Everards	*-4*	26	16	3	7	82	42	47
Kettering Town Galaxy		26	14	4	8	83	47	46
AFC Wymington		26	14	4	8	79	70	46
CSV United		26	14	2	10	71	60	44
West Haddon		26	12	6	8	58	45	42
Yardley United	*+2*	26	7	1	18	46	90	24
Corby Talisman		26	7	2	17	65	87	23
Kettering Park Rovers		26	6	4	16	48	88	22
Corby Hearth	*-1*	26	5	7	14	50	79	21
Walgrave Amber	*-3*	26	5	7	14	52	83	19
Thrapston	*-6*	26	4	3	19	38	104	9

DIV. FOUR CUP FINAL *(April 9th at Wellingborough)*
Ketting Ise Lodge 4 Kettering Town Galaxy 2 *aet*

Reserve Premier Division		P	W	D	L	F	A	Pts
Moulton Res.		26	18	1	7	72	40	55
Roade Res.		26	15	4	7	65	36	49
Kettering Nomads Res.		26	13	5	8	54	43	44
Whitefield Norpol Res.		26	13	4	9	66	55	43
Harpole Res.		26	14	1	11	47	36	43
Weldon United Res.		26	12	4	10	73	51	40
Milton Res.		26	10	5	11	51	53	35
Kislingbury Res.		26	9	7	10	55	49	34
Northampton ON Chenecks A		26	10	4	12	54	55	34
Corby Madisons Res.		26	11	1	14	58	75	34
Corby Pegasus Res.	*+2*	26	7	9	10	46	47	32
Bugbrooke St Michaels A		26	9	4	13	58	73	31
James King Blisworth Res.	*-7*	26	7	4	15	38	75	18
Heyford Athletic Res.	-3	26	5	5	16	21	70	17

Reserve Division One		P	W	D	L	F	A	Pts
Harborough Town Res.		26	20	3	3	91	24	63
Gretton Res.		26	18	3	5	78	38	57
Stanion United Res.		26	16	3	7	63	45	51
Kettering Orchard Pk Res.		26	16	1	9	89	54	49
Wootton St George Res.		26	13	6	7	48	33	45
Weldon United A		26	12	6	8	56	47	42
Bugbrooke St Michaels B	*-3*	26	13	4	9	58	37	40
Queen Eleanor Gt H. Res.		26	11	5	10	71	65	38
Medbourne Res.		26	9	7	10	55	64	34
Ringstead Rangers Res.		26	9	2	15	49	76	29
Finedon Volta Res.		26	8	3	15	59	72	27
Wollaston Victoria Res.		26	4	8	14	52	81	20
Harpole A		26	3	4	19	36	106	13
Spratton Res.		26	1	3	22	34	97	6

Reserve Division Two		P	W	D	L	F	A	Pts
Brixworth All Saints Res.		26	25	1	0	115	21	76
Corby Locomotives Res.		26	21	1	4	142	41	64
Welford Victoria Res.		26	19	2	5	118	33	59
Dav. Drayton Grange Res.	*+2*	26	15	6	5	99	50	53
Earls Barton United Res.		26	15	2	9	86	43	47
Wellingborough Old G. Res.	*+4*	26	12	4	10	70	58	44
Islip United Res.	*-4*	26	13	2	11	94	57	37
Bective Wanderers Res.	*-3*	26	10	3	13	57	79	30
Stanwick Rovers Res.		26	9	0	17	55	71	27
Crick Athletic Res.	*+2*	26	7	4	15	46	119	27
Weedon Res.	*-5*	26	9	3	14	65	73	25
Wilby Res.	*-1*	26	3	4	19	33	135	12
SV United Res.	*-9*	26	4	1	21	36	113	4
Dainite Sports Res.	*-6*	26	2	3	21	31	154	3

RESERVE PREMIER DIVISION CUP FINAL
(April 21st at Bugbrooke St Michaels)
Corby Pegasus Res. 2 Whitefield Norpol Res. 1

RESERVE DIVISION ONE CUP FINAL
(April 16th at Wellingborough Town)
Gretton Res. 3 Bugbrooke St Michaels B 0

RESERVE DIVISION TWO CUP FINAL
(April 28th at Wellingborough Town)
Corby Locomotives Res. 4
Brixworth All Saints Res. 2

NORTHERN ALLIANCE LEAGUE

Sponsored: Pin Point Recruitment

Founded: 1890

Recent champions:
2004: West Allotment Celtic
2005: Shankhouse
2006: Team Northumbria
2007: Harraby Catholic Club
2008: Walker Central

	Alnwick	Ashington C.	Blyth Town	Carlisle City	Cramlington	Gillford Park	Harraby CC	Heaton Stan.	Heddon	Murton	Newc. Univ.	Peterlee T.	Ponteland	Seaton Del.	Shankhouse	Walker Cent.	Wark
Alnwick Town	***P***	2-3	3-3	0-2	2-0	1-3	0-1	3-1	2-0	4-0	3-1	2-1	1-4	3-2	2-0	1-1	3-3
Ashington Colliers	2-0	***R***	1-3	2-0	1-4	0-2	1-5	0-3	1-1	2-3	2-2	3-0	1-1	1-3	2-2	0-1	8-2
Blyth Town	3-0	3-1	***E***	0-5	4-2	1-2	1-1	2-6	2-2	4-2	1-1	3-5	3-3	1-2	1-3	1-4	3-1
Carlisle City	2-2	2-2	3-1	***M***	2-1	1-1	0-0	3-0	1-1	4-1	2-2	6-4	0-0	2-5	2-6	1-1	3-3
Cramlington Town	2-3	2-0	1-2	1-6	***I***	0-1	2-1	1-1	2-2	1-2	1-2	4-1	2-1	1-2	2-1	1-3	4-3
Gillford Park	1-1	3-0	2-3	2-1	2-2	***E***	3-0	2-2	2-1	0-0	3-2	3-2	1-0	1-1	2-2	2-3	3-1
Harraby Catholic Club	2-1	1-0	2-1	1-1	3-0	0-0	***R***	3-0	3-2	5-0	3-0	2-1	4-0	0-0	1-0	0-1	0-0
Heaton Stannington	0-3	2-1	3-0	2-2	3-2	0-2	0-1		2-2	4-0	2-1	2-1	1-3	5-3	5-4	0-0	6-0
Heddon	3-1	1-1	2-2	1-1	2-1	0-1	0-3	1-1		3-2	1-2	6-3	3-3	2-0	0-1	1-1	0-4
Murton	2-3	0-4	4-3	5-1	1-1	0-2	1-1	2-3	1-2	***D***	1-2	4-1	2-0	1-3	3-0	1-3	4-1
Newcastle University	0-3	1-2	2-3	2-1	3-4	1-4	2-4	4-3	0-1	4-1	***I***	0-0	0-1	3-1	4-2	3-6	3-4
Peterlee Town	1-1	5-1	2-4	2-2	1-2	0-1	1-2	1-2	0-1	3-2	6-2	***V***	0-6	1-2	1-1	4-2	0-3
Ponteland United	0-2	2-0	2-2	4-1	1-0	0-2	1-1	3-3	1-0	1-0	0-0	0-1	***I***	3-3	2-5	1-6	2-2
Seaton Delaval Amateurs	1-1	1-2	2-2	1-3	2-1	1-1	5-0	3-0	3-1	7-2	3-0	3-0	3-2	***S***	1-2	2-4	2-0
Shankhouse	2-1	7-0	3-1	0-1	2-1	3-3	1-1	1-1	0-0	1-2	1-0	2-1	2-2	1-4	***I***	1-1	2-4
Walker Central	2-1	3-1	3-0	6-1	3-3	2-1	2-1	3-0	1-1	4-2	2-0	8-1	3-2	1-1	4-2	***O***	7-2
Wark	3-2	1-1	2-4	2-3	5-2	1-3	0-2	2-2	2-0	1-0	1-3	6-0	6-5	1-4	4-5	0-8	***N***

Premier Division		P	W	D	L	F	A	Pts
Walker Central		32	23	8	1	99	38	77
Gillford Park		32	19	10	3	61	32	67
Harraby Catholic Club		32	18	9	5	54	27	63
Seaton Delaval Amateurs		32	17	7	8	76	48	58
Alnwick Town		32	13	7	12	57	51	46
Carlisle City		32	11	13	8	65	61	46
Heaton Stannington	*-3*	32	13	9	10	65	59	45
Shankhouse		32	12	9	11	65	59	45
Blyth Town		32	11	8	13	67	77	41
Ponteland United		32	9	11	12	56	60	38
Heddon		32	8	13	11	43	50	37
Wark		32	10	6	16	70	94	36
Cramlington Town		32	9	5	18	53	68	32
Newcastle University		32	9	5	18	52	72	32
Ashington Colliers		32	8	7	17	46	68	31
Murton	*-6*	32	9	3	20	51	78	24
Peterlee Town		32	6	4	22	50	88	22

BOSCH POWER TOOLS CUP

PRELIMINARY ROUND
Seaton Delaval Amateurs 3 Wark 2 *aet*

FIRST ROUND
Blyth Town 2 Cramlington Town 0
Gillford Park 3 Peterlee Town 2
Harraby Catholic Club 3 Carlisle City 0
Murton 2 Alnwick Town 1
Ponteland United 1 **Newcastle University** 4
Seaton Delaval Amateurs 3 Ashington Colliers 1
Shankhouse 3 **Heaton Stannington** 4
Walker Central 2 **Heddon** 5

QUARTER-FINALS
Gillford Park 2 Harraby Catholic Club 2 *aet* (3-1p)
Newcastle University 0 **Heddon** 4
Seaton Delaval Amateurs 3 Murton 1
Heaton Stannington 3 **Blyth Town** 4

SEMI-FINALS
Heddon 3 Seaton Delaval Amateurs 2
Gillford Park 4 Blyth Town 2 *aet*

FINAL
(April 13th at Prudhoe Town)
Heddon 1 **Gillford Park** 2

NORTHERN ALLIANCE PREMIER DIVISION CONSTITUTION 2009-10

ALNWICK TOWN . . . . . St James's Park, Weavers Way, Alnwick NE66 1BG 01665 603162
ASHINGTON COLLIERS . . . . . Hirst Welfare, Woodhorn Lane, Ashington NE63 9HF 07517 764653
BLYTH TOWN . . . . . South Newsham Playing Fields, Blyth . . . . . None
CARLISLE CITY . . . . . Sheepmount Sports Complex, Sheepmount, Carlisle CA3 8XL 01228 625599
CRAMLINGTON TOWN . . . . . Sporting Club of Cramlington, Highburn, Cramlington NE23 6YB 01670 591970
HARRABY CATHOLIC CLUB . . . . . Harraby Community Centre, Edgehill Road, Carlisle CA1 3SL . . . . . None
HEATON STANNINGTON . . . Grounsell Park, Newton Road, High Heaton, Newcastle-upon-Tyne NE7 7HP . . . . . None
HEDDON . . . . . Bullockstead Sports Complex, Ponteland Road, Kenton Bank Foot, Newcastle-upon-Tyne NE13 8AH . . . 0191 271 1153
KILLINGWORTH SPORTING . . . . Miller's Dene, Fossway, Walkerdene, Newcastle-upon-Tyne NE6 4YA . . . . . None
MURTON . . . . . Recreation Park, Church Lane, Murton, Seaham SR7 9RD . . . . . None
NEWCASTLE UNIVERSITY . . . . . Cochrane Park, Etherstone Avenue, Newcastle-upon-Tyne NE7 7JX . . . . . None
PONTELAND UNITED . The Leisure Centre Ground, Callerton Lane, Ponteland, Newcastle-upon-Tyne NE20 9EG 01661 825441
SEATON DELAVAL AMATEURS . . . . . Wheatridge Park, Seaton Delaval, Whitley Bay NE25 0QH . . . . . None
SHANKHOUSE . . . . . Northburn Sports Complex, Crawhall Lane, Cramlington NE23 3YP 01670 714154
STOCKSFIELD . . . . . Kimberley Park, Broomhouse Road, Prudhoe NE42 5EH 01661 835900
WALKER CENTRAL . . . . . Monkchester Green, Walker, Newcastle-upon-Tyne NE6 5LJ 0191 265 7270
WARK . . . . . Wark Sports Club, Wark, Hexham NE48 3NP 01434 230259

IN: Killingworth Sporting (formerly Killingworth YPC) (P), Stocksfield (P)
OUT: Gillford Park (P - Northern League Division Two), Peterlee Town (R)

LONGHORN HARDWARE LEAGUE CUP

PRELIMINARY ROUND
Berwick United (w/o) v Penrith A (scr.)
Gosforth Bohemian 2 **Percy Main** 3
FIRST ROUND
Blyth Town 0 **Stocksfield** 1
Cullercoats 5 Berwick United 1
Gateshead Rutherford 3 Gillford Pk 1
Percy Main Ams 1 **Cramlington Town** 2
Harraby CC 3 Ashington Colliers 1
Heaton Stan. (w/o) v Westerhope (scr.)
Hebburn Reyrolle 0 **Shankhouse** 1
Heddon 2 Murton 1 *aet*
Newcastle EE Rail 1 **Seaton Delaval** 4
Newcastle University 3 Alnwick Town 0
Northbank Carlisle 2 Killingworth 1
Peterlee Town 7 Seaton Burn 0
Ponteland United 0 **Walker Central** 2
Red Row Welfare 0 **Wark** 5
Wallington 3 Carlisle City 2
Whitley Bay A 4 **Chopwell** 5
SECOND ROUND
Forest Hall 2 **Stobswood Welfare** 3 *aet*
G'head Rutherford 2 **Wallsend Town** 3
Cramlington Town 1 **Hexham** 2 *aet*
Harraby CC 7 Northbank Carlisle 1
Heddon 5 Newcastle British Telecom 0
Newcastle Univ. 2 Benfield Chemfica 0
Peterlee Town 2 Wideopen 1 *aet*
Walker Central 3 North Shields Ath. 0
Wark 3 Amble 0
South Shields United 3 Chopwell 0
Tynemouth United 0 **Amble United** 6
Wallington 0 **Stocksfield** 3
Wallsend BC 1 **Heaton Stannington** 4
Whitley Bay Town 3 **Cullercoats** 4
Willington Quay Saints 0 **Seaton Delaval Amateurs** 0 *aet* (1-3p)
Shankhouse (w/o) v Haydon Bdge (scr.)
THIRD ROUND
Amble United 1 **Wark** 4
Harraby CC 3 Wallsend Town 1
Peterlee Town 1 **Shankhouse** 2
Seaton Delaval 2 Newcastle Univ. 1
South Shields United 1 **Hexham** 2
Stobswood Welfare 2 Heddon 1
Walker Central 1 **Cullercoats** 3
Heaton Stan. 6 Stocksfield 6 *aet* (7-6p)
QUARTER-FINALS
Harraby Catholic Club 4 Stocksfield 1
Seaton Delaval Ams 2 **Cullercoats** 3
Shankhouse 1 **Hexham** 2
Wark 3 Stobswood Welfare 2
SEMI-FINALS
Cullercoats 3 Hexham 2
Wark 0 **Harraby Catholic Club** 3
FINAL *(May 4th at Prudhoe Town)*
Harraby Cath. Club 1 **Cullercoats** 2

Division One		P	W	D	L	F	A	Pts
Killingworth YPC		28	19	2	7	72	44	59
Stocksfield		28	18	4	6	70	42	58
Whitley Bay A		28	18	3	7	85	43	57
Cullercoats		28	17	4	7	96	43	55
Percy Main Amateurs		28	17	2	9	58	42	53
Newc. EE Rail Club		28	14	3	11	64	49	45
Gateshead Rutherf'd		28	11	6	11	62	58	39
Chopwell Officials	*-3*	28	13	3	12	50	52	39
Northbank Carlisle		28	9	8	11	58	58	35
Hebburn Reyrolle	*-3*	28	10	5	13	46	53	32
Wallington	*-6*	28	10	5	13	56	65	29
Gos. Boh. Garnett	*-6*	28	9	6	13	51	64	27
Berwick United		28	6	5	17	31	79	23
Seaton Burn		28	4	4	20	29	66	16
Red Row Welfare		28	3	4	21	29	99	13

Penrith A, Westerhope JG - record expunged

PIN POINT PERSONNEL COMBINATION CUP

PRELIMINARY ROUND
Northbank 1 **Berwick United** 2
FIRST ROUND
Ghd Rutherford 0 **Wallington** 2
Hebburn R. 1 **Gosforth BG** 2
Killingworth YPC 2 **Cullercoats** 3
Newc. EE R. 1 **Westerhope** 3
Berwick U. 3 Seaton B. 2 *aet*
Penrith A (scr.) v **R. Row** (w/o)
Stocksfield 3 Percy Main 1
Whitley Bay A 3 Chopwell Officials Club 2 *aet*
QUARTER-FINALS
Cullercoats 4 Gosforth Bohemian Garnett 2
Wallington 2 Berwick United 1
Red Row Welfare (w/o) Westerhope JG (scr.)
Whitley Bay A 7 Stocksfield 3
SEMI-FINALS
Cullercoats 2 **Whitley Bay A** 3
Red Row Welf. 2 Wallington 1
FINAL *(May 19th at Ashington)*
Whitley Bay A 2 Red Row Welfare 0

	Ber	Cho	Cul	Gat	Gos	Heb	Kil	New	Nor	Pen	Per	Red	Sea	Sto	Wal	Wes	Whi
Berwick United		0-2	1-6	1-2	3-1	3-2	0-3	2-7	2-2	n/a	2-1	1-1	2-2	2-0	1-1	n/a	0-2
Chopwell Officials Club	0-1		2-1	2-2	3-2	0-1	1-2	1-3	2-1	n/a	2-1	5-1	3-0	1-1	3-1	n/a	3-3
Cullercoats	4-2	10-0	***D***	4-2	5-0	1-1	7-1	3-0	3-1	n/a	4-0	12-1	2-1	0-2	4-4	n/a	4-2
Gateshead Rutherford	7-0	2-1	0-5	***I***	1-2	1-3	5-1	2-1	1-5	n/a	2-0	3-0	7-1	0-2	2-1	6-1	2-2
Gosf. Bohemian Garnett	2-1	0-2	6-2	2-2	***V***	1-1	2-2	1-0	2-2	n/a	0-2	3-2	1-1	1-2	6-2	n/a	1-3
Hebburn Reyrolle	5-1	0-2	0-1	0-0	1-0	***I***	1-4	2-1	1-1	7-3	3-1	1-0	2-3	0-0	4-1	n/a	2-4
Killingworth YPC	8-0	2-1	3-4	2-1	4-1	4-3	***S***	4-1	6-1	n/a	1-3	2-0	3-0	2-4	1-0	n/a	1-0
Newcastle East End Rail	2-1	3-0	2-1	4-4	1-0	6-1	1-0	***I***	2-3	n/a	1-2	3-1	2-3	2-6	4-0	n/a	3-0
Northbank Carlisle	4-0	0-2	0-5	1-1	1-2	3-2	2-2	2-2	***O***	n/a	1-4	12-1	2-1	2-3	2-1	n/a	4-1
Penrith A	n/a	n/a	n/a	n/a	n/a	n/a	4-1	n/a	n/a	***N***	n/a	n/a	n/a	n/a	n/a	n/a	n/a
Percy Main Amateurs	2-0	3-2	3-2	3-1	2-2	2-1	4-1	3-1	3-0	n/a		6-0	0-0	1-2	3-2	3-6	0-3
Red Row Welfare	0-0	1-2	0-0	1-3	2-1	1-2	0-5	2-4	3-0	n/a	0-4		0-2	2-7	2-4	n/a	1-6
Seaton Burn	0-1	1-3	0-3	2-4	1-3	2-4	0-1	1-1	1-2	n/a	1-2	1-2	***O***	0-1	0-1	n/a	1-4
Stocksfield	4-0	6-3	1-1	2-1	3-4	5-2	1-2	1-0	2-1	3-2	1-2	5-2	1-2	***N***	3-2	4-1	4-0
Wallington	3-2	2-1	6-1	5-1	5-4	3-1	0-2	2-5	1-1	n/a	1-0	2-2	5-2	1-1	***E***	n/a	0-2
Westerhope JG	n/a	n/a	1-1	n/a	n/a	n/a	n/a	2-6	n/a	n/a	n/a	1-2	n/a	n/a	n/a		1-2
Whitley Bay A	6-2	2-1	2-1	5-3	8-1	2-0	1-3	1-2	2-2	n/a	6-1	3-1	4-0	6-0	5-0	n/a	

NORTHERN ALLIANCE DIVISION ONE CONSTITUTION 2009-10

AMBLE UNITED . . . . Running Track Pitch, Coquet High School, Acklington Road, Amble NE65 0NG 01665 71063
BERWICK UNITED . . . . Rampart Sports Ground, Newfields, Berwick-on-Tweed TD15 1SN . . . . Non
CHOPWELL OFFICIALS CLUB. . . . . . . Welfare Park, Chopwell, Newcastle-upon-Tyne NE17 7BZ . . . . Non
CULLERCOATS. . . . . Links Avenue, Farringdon Road, Cullercoats NE30 3EY . . . . Non
GATESHEAD RUTHERFORD Farnacres, Beggarswood Park, Coach Lane, Lobley Hill, Gateshead NE11 8HJ . . . . Non
GOSFORTH BOHEMIANS . . . . Benson Park, Gosforth, Newcastle-upon-Tyne . . . . Non
HEBBURN REYROLLE . . . . Hebburn Sports Ground, 16 South Drive, Hebburn NE31 1UN 0191 483 510
MORPETH SPORTING CLUB . . . Morpeth Town FC, Craik Park, Morpeth Common, Morpeth NE61 2YX. 01670 51378
NEWCASTLE EAST END RAIL CLUB Swan Hunter Rec, Stotts Rd, Walkergate, Newcastle-upon-Tyne NE6 4UD . . . . Non
NORTHBANK CARLISLE. . . . . Sheepmount Sports Complex, Sheepmount, Carlisle CA3 8XL. 01228 62559
PERCY MAIN AMATEURS . . . . . . Purvis Park, St John's Green, Percy Main, North Shields NE29 6HE 0191 257 483
PETERLEE TOWN . . . . Eden Lane Playing Fields, Peterlee SR8 5DS. 0191 586 300
SEATON BURN. . . . . Seaton Burn Welfare, Seaton Burn, Newcastle-upon-Tyne. . . . . Non
SOUTH SHIELDS UNITED. . . . . The Dell, Quarry Lane, South Shields NE34 7NL . . . . Non
WALLINGTON . . . . Oakford Park, Scots Gap, Morpeth NE61 4EJ . . . . Non
WHITLEY BAY A . . . . Hillheads Park, Rink Way, off Hillheads Road, Whitley Bay NE25 8HR 0191 291 363

IN: Amble United (P), Peterlee Town (R), South Shields United (P)
OUT: Killingworth Sporting (formerly Killingworth YPC) (P), Penrith Town A (WS), Stocksfield (P), Westerhope JG (WS)
Gosforth Bohemian Garnett become Gosforth Bohemians, Red Row Welfare become Morpeth Sporting Club

Division Two	P	W	D	L	F	A	Pts
Amble United	28	22	3	3	90	19	69
South Shields United	28	19	4	5	59	36	61
Stobswood Welfare	28	16	5	7	70	36	53
Forest Hall	28	14	5	9	55	40	47
Willington Quay Saints	28	12	8	8	74	58	44
Wideopen & District	28	13	5	10	60	56	44
North Shields Athletic	28	12	7	9	63	55	43
Benfield Chemfica	28	12	4	12	42	45	40
Wallsend Town	28	12	3	13	65	56	39
Wallsend Boys Club	28	10	8	10	50	47	38
Hexham	28	11	3	14	48	57	36
Amble	28	11	3	14	49	61	36
Whitley Bay Town	28	6	5	17	37	77	23
Newc. British Telecom	28	4	3	21	30	102	15
Tynemouth United	28	1	4	23	28	75	7

PIN POINT PERSONNEL AMATEUR CUP

FIRST ROUND
Amble 8 Newcastle BT 1
Amble United 4 Whitley Bay Town 1
Benfield Chemfica 5 South Shields United 0
Forest Hall 3 Tynemouth United 2
Wallsend Boys Club 4 North Shields Athletic 3
Wallsend Town 2 **Hexham** 4
Wideopen & District 0 **Stobswood Welfare** 3
Willington Quay Saints (w/o) v Haydon Bridge United (scr.)

QUARTER-FINALS
Forest Hall 2 Willington Quay Saints 1
Hexham 1 **Amble United** 2
Stobswood Welfare 1 **Amble** 2
Wallsend Boys Club 1 **Benfield Chemfica** 4

SEMI-FINALS
Amble United 2 Amble 1
Forest Hall 2 Benfield Chemfica 1

FINAL
(April 7th at Whitley Bay)
Amble United 2 **Forest Hall** 3

	Amble	Amble Utd	Ben. Chemica	Forest Hall	Hexham	Newcastle BT	N Shields Ath.	S. Shields Utd	Stobswood	Tynemouth	Wallsend BC	Wallsend Town	W. Bay Town	Wideopen	Willington Q.
Amble		0-4	0-1	2-1	2-0	0-1	4-2	2-2	1-4	4-2	3-4	2-0	2-1	5-2	4-2
Amble United	4-0	***D***	4-0	2-2	6-0	3-0	2-1	3-0	2-0	1-0	2-0	4-2	10-0	1-0	2-1
Benfield Chemfica	2-1	1-2	***I***	1-0	1-1	1-1	0-3	3-0	2-1	2-0	3-4	2-5	2-0	1-2	3-3
Forest Hall	1-0	2-1	0-2	***V***	3-2	6-0	1-3	1-4	1-0	4-2	2-1	2-1	0-2	1-1	0-1
Hexham	5-0	2-3	1-2	1-1	***I***	3-2	3-1	0-1	1-0	3-0	1-4	3-1	1-4	6-2	5-2
Newcastle British Telecom	2-8	0-10	2-4	0-7	1-2	***S***	2-4	0-3	1-4	2-1	1-1	0-1	0-1	0-4	2-1
North Shields Athletic	2-2	1-1	2-1	0-4	3-0	5-1	***I***	1-2	2-0	4-2	4-1	2-5	2-1	2-0	1-1
South Shields United	3-1	2-6	2-1	2-0	1-0	6-1	2-0	***O***	2-1	2-2	2-0	1-0	4-0	2-3	2-1
Stobswood Welfare	3-0	1-0	3-1	3-3	3-1	7-1	2-2	2-0	***N***	1-1	2-1	4-2	4-3	3-1	3-0
Tynemouth United	0-1	0-2	0-2	0-1	0-2	2-2	3-8	0-2	0-4		3-5	3-5	0-1	1-5	0-3
Wallsend Boys Club	3-0	1-1	1-1	1-1	4-0	3-1	3-3	1-2	2-1	0-0		1-4	1-0	0-0	2-4
Wallsend Town	3-0	2-1	1-2	1-3	3-0	4-0	2-2	0-1	2-2	2-1	2-1	***O***	4-1	1-3	4-5
Whitley Bay Town	3-4	0-6	3-0	1-3	0-2	3-1	1-1	0-2	1-2	1-4	0-0	4-4	***N***	2-2	2-2
Wideopen & District	3-0	1-2	1-0	2-4	4-0	6-3	3-2	3-3	1-8	2-0	0-2	3-2	5-1	***E***	1-1
Willington Quay Saints	1-1	0-5	2-1	4-1	3-3	2-3	6-0	4-4	2-2	4-1	4-3	3-2	9-1	3-0	

NORTHERN ALLIANCE DIVISION TWO CONSTITUTION 2009-10

AMBLE . . . . Amble Welfare Ground, Acklington Road, Amble NE65 0NG. . . . . None
CRAMLINGTON BLUE STAR Shankhouse FC, Northburn Sports Complex, Crawhall Lane, Cramlington NE23 3YP 01670 714154
CULLERCOATS CUSTOM PLANET. . Burradon Welfare Ground, Front Street, Burradon NE23 7NG . . . . None
FOREST HALL . . . . Palmersville Community Centre, Great Lime Road, Forest Hall NE12 9HW . . . . None
HEXHAM . . . . Wentworth Leisure Centre, Wentworth Park, Hexham NE46 3PD. 01434 607080
NEWCASTLE BRITISH TELECOM . . . . Dudley Recreation Ground, Dudley NE23 7HS . . . . None
NEWCASTLE CHEMFICA . . . . Heaton Sports Ground, Heaton, Newcastle-upon-Tyne NE6 5NY . . . . None
NORTH SHIELDS ATHLETIC. . . . . Collingwood View PF, West Percy Road, North Shields NE29 7RQ . . . . None
STOBSWOOD WELFARE. . . . . Stobswood Welfare Ground, Stobswood, Morpeth NE61 3AZ . . . . None
SWALWELL . . . . Spa Well Road, Derwenthaugh, Blaydon-on-Tyne NE21 6JA. . . . . None
TYNEMOUTH UNITED . . . . Coach Lane Campus, Benton, Newcastle-upon-Tyne NE7 7XA 0191 215 6800
WALLSEND BOYS CLUB . . . . St Peter's Road, Wallsend NE28 7LQ. . . . . None
WALLSEND TOWN . . . . Langdale School Ground, Mitford Gardens, Wallsend NE28 0HG . . . . None
WHITLEY BAY TOWN. . . . . Burradon Welfare Ground, Front Street, Burradon NE23 7NG . . . . None
WIDEOPEN & DISTRICT. . . . Lockey Park, Great North Road, Wideopen, Newcastle-upon-Tyne NE13 6LN. . . . . None
WILLINGTON QUAY SAINTS . . . Wallsend Rising Sun Ground, King's North Road, Wallsend NE28 9JQ. None

IN: Cramlington Blue Star (P - North East Amateur League), Cullercoats Custom Planet (P - Tyneside Amateur League Division One), Swalwell (P - youth football)
OUT: Amble United (P), South Shields United (P)
Benfield Chemfica become Newcastle Chemfica

CHARITY CUP
(League Cup First Round losers)

PRELIMINARY ROUND
Ponteland United 2 Murton 1

FIRST ROUND
Blyth Town 5 Seaton Burn 3
Hebburn Reyrolle 1 **Red Row Welfare** 3
Whitley Bay A 3 Percy Main Amateurs 1
Newcastle East End Rail Club 4 Ashington Colliers 2
Carlisle City (w/o) v Berwick Utd (scr.)
Heaton Stann. (w/o) v Gillford Park (scr.)
Ponteland 6 Gosforth Boh. Garnett 1
Killingworth YPC 0 **Alnwick Town** 3

QUARTER-FINALS
Carlisle City 3 **Newcastle EE Rail** 4
Ponteland United 0 **Alnwick Town** 1
Blyth Town 3 Whitley Bay A 2
Red Row Welfare (w/o) Heaton Stannington (scr.)

SEMI-FINALS
Newcastle East End Rail Club 3 Blyth Town 1
Red Row Welfare (scr.) v **Alnwick Town** (w/o)

FINAL
(May 16th at Pin Point Sports Ground)
Newcastle East End Rail Club 0 **Alnwick Town** 2

OXFORDSHIRE SENIOR LEAGUE

Sponsored by:
No sponsor

Founded: N/A

Recent champions:

2004: Eynsham Association
2005: Berinsfield CA
2006: Oxford University Press
2007: Garsington
2008: Rover Cowley

	Adderbury	Bletch'ton	Chadlington	Enstone S.	Eynsham	Garsington	Horspath	Kennington	Marston	Oxford UP	Rover C.	Stonesfield
Adderbury Park	***P***	1-5	0-2	3-4	6-2	2-3	2-2	2-0	1-1	3-0	1-2	1-1
Bletchington	3-3	***R***	2-2	4-2	0-1	1-1	4-2	3-1	2-0	1-3	2-0	3-4
Chadlington	3-4	1-1	***E***	2-6	3-0	0-5	1-2	4-1	4-2	1-3	2-3	3-0
Enstone Sports	1-1	0-6	4-0	***M***	2-0	1-3	2-5	1-2	2-2	1-0	4-3	3-0
Eynsham Association	3-1	1-3	3-0	1-1	***I***	0-1	0-6	2-1	1-1	2-0	0-1	0-2
Garsington	5-4	3-1	1-1	2-0	2-0	***E***	3-9	3-4	2-0	2-2	6-6	6-1
Horspath	2-2	4-1	1-1	2-3	5-1	1-4	***R***	3-0	2-2	0-1	2-3	6-2
Kennington United	0-1	0-4	1-3	1-7	0-1	0-1	1-3		4-2	3-2	0-2	1-0
Marston Saints	2-1	0-6	1-2	2-1	1-1	1-5	1-5	4-3		0-3	1-1	5-3
Oxford University Press	2-2	2-4	3-1	2-0	1-1	1-4	0-2	2-2	3-3	***D***	3-2	0-1
Rover Cowley	1-3	4-2	3-1	2-0	2-0	1-2	2-5	2-1	0-0	1-1	***I***	2-1
Stonesfield Sports	1-1	1-3	2-0	1-0	4-2	2-1	1-1	0-3	4-1	2-3	3-3	***V***

Premier Division	P	W	D	L	F	A	Pts
Garsington	22	15	4	3	65	38	49
Horspath	22	12	5	5	70	37	41
Bletchington	22	12	4	6	61	36	40
Rover Cowley	22	11	5	6	46	40	38
Enstone Sports	22	9	3	10	45	44	30
Oxford University Press	22	8	6	8	37	38	30
Stonesfield Sports	22	8	4	10	36	48	28
Adderbury Park	22	6	8	8	45	45	26
Chadlington	22	7	4	11	37	48	25
Eynsham Association	22	6	4	12	22	43	22
Marston Saints	22	4	8	10	32	56	20
Kennington United	22	6	1	15	29	52	19

BEN TURNER CUP

(President's Cup First Round losers)

FIRST ROUND
Enstone 5 Eynsham 1
Horspath 4 **Rover Cowley** 8
Kennington 1 **M. Cheney** 3
N. Oxford 1 **Kidlington OB** 5
Oakley 2 BCS Bardwell 1
Watlington 1 **Marston Sts** 2
QUARTER-FINALS
Adderbury Pk 3 Marston 2
M Cheney 3 Kidlington OB 2
Oakley 1 **Rover Cowley** 3
Yarnton 1 **Enstone Sports** 5
SEMI-FINALS
Middleton Cheney 0
Adderbury Park 0 *aet* (2-3p)
Rover Cowley 3 Enstone 2
FINAL
(April 13th at OUP)
Rover Cowley 3
Adderbury Park 5

PRESIDENT'S CUP

FIRST ROUND
Broughton & North Newington 5 Enstone Sports 0
Chadlington 3 Adderbury Park 1
Garsington 3 Rover Cowley 1 **aet**
Horspath 1 **Wheatley '04** 5
Kennington United 1 **Charlton United** 2
Kidlington Old Boys 2 **Freeland** 4
Long Crendon 2 BCS Bardwell 1
Mansfield Road 5 Watlington Town 0
Marston Saints 2 **Hinksey** 3
Oxford University Press 4 North Oxford 2
Slade Farm 3 Eynsham Association 3 *aet* (3-1p)
Yarnton 0 **Bletchington** 2
Middleton Cheney 1 **Fritwell** 4
Stonesfield Sports 5 Oakley United 1
Charlton Utd 2 **Broughton & North Newington** 3
SECOND ROUND
Garsington 5 Oxford University Press 0
Hinksey 3 Freeland 2
Long Crendon 1 **Mansfield Road** 3
Slade Farm 0 **Chadlington** 1
Stonesfield Sports 0 **Bletchingdon** 1
QUARTER-FINALS
Bletchingdon 6 Wheatley '04 2
Broughton & North Newington 1 **Hinksey** 3
Chadlington 3 Garsington 1
Fritwell 3 Mansfield Road 2
SEMI-FINALS
Fritwell 0 **Chadlington** 1
Bletchingdon 4 Hinksey 3
FINAL
(May 4th at Kidlington)
Chadlington 1 Bletchingdon 0

OXFORDSHIRE SENIOR LEAGUE PREMIER DIVISION CONSTITUTION 2009-10

ADDERBURY PARK .... Adderbury Park Playing Fields, Round Close Road, Adderbury, Banbury OX17 .... Non
BCS BARDWELL .... Chaffinch Way, Mallards Way Estate, Bicester .... Non
BLETCHINGTON .... Bletchingdon Sports & Social Club, Oxford Road, Kidlington OX5 3BU 01869 35003
CHADLINGTON .... Chadlington Sports & Social, Chapel Road, Chadlington, Chipping Norton OX7 3NX 01608 67672
ENSTONE SPORTS .... Charlbury Road, Enstone OX7 4LN 01608 67782
EYNSHAM ASSOCIATION .... Oxford Road, Eynsham, Witney OX29 4DA .... Non
FRITWELL .... Playing Field, Fewcott Road, Fritwell OX27 7QA .... Non
GARSINGTON .... Garsington Sports Club, Denton Lane, Garsington, Oxford OX44 9EL 01865 36172
HORSPATH .... Rover Cowley Cricket Ground, Romanway, Cowley, Oxford OX4 6NL .... Non
KENNINGTON UNITED .... Playfield Road, Kennington, Oxford OX1 5RS .... Non
MARSTON SAINTS .... Boults Lane, Old Marston, Oxford OX3 0PW 01865 20397
OXFORD UNIVERSITY PRESS .... Jordan Hill, Banbury Road, Oxford OX2 8EF .... Non
ROVER COWLEY .... Rover Cowley Football Ground, Romanway, Cowley, Oxford, OX4 6NL .... Non
STONESFIELD SPORTS ...... Stonesfield Playing Field, Field Close, Longmore, Stonesfield OX29 8HA .... Non

IN: BCS Bardwell (P), Fritwell (P)

CLARENDON CUP FINAL

FINAL

(April 13th at Oxford University Press)

Garsington Res. 3 Bletchington Res. 3 *aet* (4-2p)

IVOR GUBBINS CUP FINAL

FINAL

(May 4th at Kidlington)

Slade Farm Res. 2 Enstone Sports

Division One	P	W	D	L	F	A	Pts
Garsington Res.	22	16	4	2	62	31	52
Fritwell	22	14	5	3	67	35	47
BCS Bardwell	22	12	5	5	59	37	41
Middleton Cheney	22	10	7	5	41	29	37
Wheatley '04	22	10	4	8	73	44	34
Oakley United	22	10	3	9	51	52	33
Kidlington Old Boys	22	10	2	10	47	44	32
Charlton United	22	7	5	10	42	54	26
North Oxford	22	5	8	9	34	49	23
Watlington Town	22	5	5	12	33	49	20
Eynsham Association Res.	22	4	2	16	30	73	14
Yarnton	22	2	4	16	38	80	10

Division Two	P	W	D	L	F	A	Pt
Slade Farm United	20	16	3	1	45	15	51
Freeland	20	15	2	3	72	22	47
Mansfield Road	20	14	3	3	69	36	45
Bletchington Res.	20	12	3	5	39	25	39
Broughton & North Newington	20	11	3	6	51	26	36
Hinksey	20	9	2	9	63	44	29
Yarnton Res.	20	6	2	12	39	65	20
Horspath Res.	20	4	3	13	41	63	15
Long Crendon	20	4	3	13	31	73	15
Chadlington Res.	20	2	3	15	22	59	9
Oxford University Press Res.	20	1	5	14	18	62	8

Division Three	P	W	D	L	F	A	Pt
Freeland Res.	22	15	4	3	83	37	49
Fritwell Res.	22	15	1	6	61	40	46
Broughton & North N'ton Res.	22	14	3	5	49	31	45
Marston Saints Res.	22	13	5	4	55	32	44
Adderbury Park Res.	22	14	1	7	67	28	43
Slade Farm Res.	22	8	5	9	55	54	29
Oakley Res.	22	8	2	12	59	56	26
Stonesfield Sports Res.	22	7	5	10	41	44	26
Long Crendon Res.	22	8	2	12	43	61	26
BCS Bardwell Res.	22	7	2	13	45	48	23
Charlton United Res.	22	3	4	15	18	84	13
Enstone Sports Res.	22	2	2	18	17	78	8

	BCS Bardwell	Charlton United	Eynsham Association Res.	Fritwell	Garsington Res.	Kidlington Old Boys	Middleton Cheney	North Oxford	Oakley United	Watlington Town	Wheatley '04	Yarnton
BCS Bardwell	***D***	3-1	2-0	2-3	0-5	4-1	2-1	5-0	2-2	3-2	3-1	5-3
Charlton United	3-3	***I***	3-4	0-3	4-2	L-W	1-1	1-1	0-3	0-4	4-3	6-4
Eynsham Association Res.	0-5	3-0	***V***	1-4	0-3	1-3	1-3	0-0	2-0	4-3	1-7	2-3
Fritwell	3-1	4-1	7-2	***I***	1-1	3-2	2-1	1-1	1-1	4-1	3-3	6-1
Garsington Res.	4-2	5-2	6-1	3-2	***S***	4-3	4-1	1-0	4-0	W-L	2-2	2-2
Kidlington Old Boys	2-1	2-4	6-2	1-3	2-3	***I***	1-4	2-0	4-0	1-1	4-3	2-1
Middleton Cheney	0-0	1-1	W-L	2-1	1-1	2-0	***O***	1-1	2-0	5-0	3-1	2-2
North Oxford	2-2	2-2	5-0	0-6	1-2	2-6	3-0	***N***	4-2	2-2	2-2	2-1
Oakley United	2-8	1-3	3-1	7-1	2-0	1-1	5-4	4-1		1-0	2-7	8-1
Watlington Town	0-3	0-2	4-2	2-2	3-5	0-2	1-1	2-1	0-2	***O***	3-2	0-0
Wheatley '04	0-0	5-1	3-0	1-2	2-3	3-1	1-3	4-0	4-2	6-0	***N***	5-1
Yarnton	2-3	0-3	3-3	1-5	0-2	2-1	1-3	3-4	2-3	1-5	4-8	***E***

OXFORDSHIRE SENIOR LEAGUE DIVISION ONE CONSTITUTION 2009-10

BROUGHTON & NORTH NEWINGTON. . Shutford Road, North Newington, Banbury OX16 9AT . . . . None
CHARLTON UNITED . . . . Charlton PF, Oddington Road, Charlton-on-Otmoor, Kidlington OX5 2TJ . . . . None
EYNSHAM ASSOCIATION . . . . Oxford Road, Eynsham, Witney OX29 4DA . . . . None
FREELAND. . . . . The Simon Hole Memorial Ground, Wroslyn Road, Freeland, Witney OX29 8HL . . . . None
GARSINGTON RESERVES . . . . . Garsington Sports Club, Denton Lane, Garsington, Oxford OX44 9EL. 01865 361720
HINKSEY . . . . Brasenose College Sports Ground, Abingdon Road, Oxford OX1 4PN. 01865 243478
KIDLINGTON OLD BOYS . . . . Exeter Close, Crown Road, Kidlington OX5 1AP . . . . None
MANSFIELD ROAD . . . . The University Club, Mansfield Road, Oxford OX1 3SZ. 01865 271044
MIDDLETON CHENEY . . . . Astrop Road, Middleton Cheney, Banbury OX17 2PG . . . . None
NORTH OXFORD. . . . . Rover Cowley Cricket Ground, Romanway, Cowley, Oxford OX4 6NL . . . . None
OAKLEY UNITED. . . . . Playfield Fields, Oxford Road, Oakley, Aylesbury HP18 9RE. . . . . None
SLADE FARM UNITED. . . . . Bicester Community College, Queens Avenue, Bicester OX26 2NS. 01869 243331
WATLINGTON TOWN . . . . Shirburn Road, Watlington OX49 5BZ . . . . None
YARNTON . . . . Green Lane, Yarnton OX5 1TE 01865 842037

IN: Broughton & North Newington (P), Freeland (P), Hinksey (P), Mansfield Road (P), Slade Farm United (P)
OUT: BCS Bardwell (P), Fritwell (P), Wheatley '04 (W)

PETERBOROUGH & DISTRICT LEAGUE

www.pdfl.org

Sponsored by:
Marshalls

Founded: 1902

Recent champions:
2005: Whittlesey United
2006: Ortonians
2007: Peterborough Sports
2008: Perkins Sports

	AFC Fletton	Alconbury	Crowland Town	Deeping Sports	Leverington Spts	Moulton Harrox	Oundle Town	Parson Drove	Peterborough Spts	Pinchbeck United	Ramsey Town	Rutland Rangers	Stamford B'dere	Uppingham Town	Whittlesey United	Wimblington
AFC Fletton	***P***	3-4	9-0	3-2	1-2	0-2	6-0	5-2	11-1	4-1	1-1	3-1	7-1	1-1	1-4	6-1
Alconbury	0-2	***R***	0-2	1-0	6-1	3-3	5-4	3-1	3-1	2-1	0-5	1-2	2-1	5-0	1-0	3-3
Crowland Town	0-3	2-1	***E***	3-5	2-2	1-4	5-1	1-0	4-0	2-4	0-7	0-5	2-3	0-3	0-4	0-2
Deeping Sports	0-0	0-1	4-4	***M***	1-1	2-1	3-0	4-1	3-1	3-6	0-1	2-4	5-1	3-2	2-2	6-0
Leverington Sports	2-2	1-0	5-0	1-2	***I***	3-2	3-2	1-1	0-0	1-1	2-4	1-6	1-1	6-3	0-4	0-3
Moulton Harrox	1-3	2-1	4-2	2-1	5-1	***E***	3-2	3-0	2-0	2-0	2-1	2-0	4-1	3-2	2-5	3-3
Oundle Town	1-1	6-8	3-1	1-5	1-1	2-3	***R***	2-2	0-0	3-6	0-3	0-6	3-1	0-2	1-4	1-3
Parson Drove	1-2	2-3	0-0	0-3	6-1	1-1	2-0		3-0	0-0	0-2	0-0	3-0	3-0	0-3	2-1
Peterborough Sports	2-4	2-5	0-2	1-3	1-5	0-4	1-1	3-3	***D***	1-5	0-7	0-8	2-1	1-7	1-5	2-4
Pinchbeck United	1-4	2-2	3-1	1-1	1-2	0-0	2-2	2-1	n/p	***I***	0-4	2-1	3-0	5-3	4-1	4-2
Ramsey Town	1-2	5-1	4-1	5-0	2-2	0-0	7-0	5-0	4-2	1-1	***V***	0-4	7-0	7-1	1-0	7-0
Rutland Rangers	2-3	5-1	3-1	5-2	4-1	1-1	4-1	1-1	9-1	4-0	0-0	***I***	4-2	3-0	2-2	4-1
Stamford Belvedere	1-5	1-3	2-3	0-6	0-2	1-9	4-2	0-3	0-0	1-2	0-9	0-3	***S***	3-4	1-6	2-3
Uppingham Town	1-3	0-2	3-1	0-3	2-3	1-3	1-1	1-1	6-3	1-1	1-1	0-2	4-2	***I***	0-4	2-4
Whittlesey United	0-1	2-3	7-0	4-2	1-2	3-0	11-0	3-0	6-1	5-0	0-1	3-0	2-2	2-0	***O***	8-1
Wimblington	1-4	4-3	1-2	3-3	4-4	1-6	1-0	1-4	2-2	1-3	1-2	1-4	2-3	1-0	0-3	***N***

Premier Division		P	W	D	L	F	A	Pts
Ramsey Town		30	21	6	3	104	21	69
AFC Fletton		30	21	5	4	100	37	68
Rutland Rangers		30	20	5	5	97	32	65
Whittlesey United		30	20	3	7	104	29	63
Moulton Harrox		30	19	6	5	79	41	63
Alconbury		30	17	3	10	73	63	54
Deeping Sports	*-1*	30	14	6	10	76	55	47
Pinchbeck United	*-2*	29	13	8	8	61	55	45
Leverington Sports	*-1*	30	11	10	9	57	68	42
Parson Drove		30	8	9	13	43	51	33
Wimblington		30	9	5	16	55	93	32
Crowland Town		30	8	3	19	42	92	27
Uppingham Town		30	7	5	18	51	77	26
Oundle Town		30	2	7	21	40	104	13
Stamford Belvedere		30	3	3	24	35	111	12
Peterborough Sports		29	1	6	22	29	117	9

Pinchbeck United v Peterborough Sports - not played

JACK HOGG CHARITY SHIELD

(League champions v Peterborough Senior Cup holders)

(August 9th at PFA, Chestnut Avenue)

Moulton Harrox 2 Parson Drove 2

Shield shared

PETERBOROUGH & DISTRICT LEAGUE PREMIER DIVISION CONSTITUTION 2009-10

AFC FLETTON . . . . Celta Road, Peterborough PE2 9JD 01733 55610
ALCONBURY. . . . . Great North Road, Alconbury, Huntingdon PE28 4EX 01480 89131
COATES ATHLETIC . . . . Manor Leisure Centre, Station Road, Whittesey, Peterborough PE17 1UA 01733 20229
CROWLAND TOWN . . . . Snowden Field, Thorney Road, Crowland PE6 0AL 01733 21154
DEEPING SPORTS. . . . . Outgang Road, Towngate East, Market Deeping PE6 8LQ 01778 34470
LEVERINGTON SPORTS . . . . Church Road, Leverington, Wisbech PE13 5DE 01945 46508
MOULTON HARROX . . . . Broad Lane, Moulton, Spalding PE12 6PN. 01406 37199
OUNDLE TOWN . . . . Station Road, Oundle, Peterborough PE8 4DE 01832 27418
PARSON DROVE . . . . Main Road, Parson Drove, Wisbech PE13 4LF . . . . Non
PINCHBECK UNITED . . . . Glebe Playing Fields, Knight Street, Pinchbeck, Spalding PE11 3RB 01775 76205
RAMSEY TOWN . . . . Cricketfield Lane, Ramsey, Huntingdon PE26 1BG 01487 81421
RUTLAND RANGERS . . . . Greetham Community Centre, Great Lane, Greetham, Oakham LE15 7NG. 01572 81254
STAMFORD BELVEDERE . . . . Queen Eleanor School, Green Lane, Stamford PE9 1HE 01780 75101
UPPINGHAM TOWN. . . . . North Street East, Uppingham LE15 9QJ 01572 82144
WHITTLESEY UNITED . . . . Manor Leisure Centre, Station Road, Whittlesey, Peterborough PE7 1UA 01733 20229
WIMBLINGTON . . . . Parkfield Sports & Social Club, Chapel Lane, Wimblington, March PE15 0QX. 01354 74155

IN: Coates Athletic (P)
OUT: Peterborough Sports (W)

PETERBOROUGH SENIOR CUP

(Premier Division teams and top eight Division One first teams)

FIRST ROUND

Whittlesey United 9 Peterborough Sports 0
Long Sutton Athletic 0 **AFC Fletton** 6
Ramsey Town 2 Kings Cliffe United 1
Netherton United 3 **Moulton Harrox** 4
Deeping Sports 0 **Parson Drove** 0 *aet* (6-7p)
Stamford Belvedere 4 Wimblington 2
Crowland Town 2 **Uppingham Town** 6
Oundle Town 1 **Werrington Town** 3

SECOND ROUND

Werrington Town 1 **Ketton** 3
Alconbury 1 Ramsey Town 0
Stamford Belvedere 0 **Moulton Harrox** 3
Coates Athletic 3 AFC Fletton 2
Guyhirn 2 **Leverington Sports** 4
Rutland Rangers 3 Pinchbeck United 1
Whittlesey United 2 Thorney 0
Parson Drove 5 Uppingham Town 2

QUARTER FINALS

Moulton Harrox 2 Parson Drove 0
Rutland Rangers 2 Leverington Sports 1
Coates Athletic 3 Alconbury 1 *aet*
Whittlesey United 5 Ketton 1

SEMI-FINALS

Rutland Rangers 2 Coates Athletic 0
Whittlesey United 2 **Moulton Harrox** 4 *aet*

FINAL

(May 4th at Peterborough United)
Rutland Rangers 6 Moulton Harrox 1

Division One	P	W	D	L	F	A	Pt
Coates Athletic	22	20	1	1	81	17	61
Eye Sports & Social	22	17	4	1	69	20	55
Netherton United	22	15	2	5	76	27	47
Kings Cliffe United	22	9	3	10	51	47	30
Ketton	22	9	2	11	31	45	29
Stilton United	22	8	4	10	47	48	28
Guyhirn	22	7	5	10	41	74	26
Warboys Town	22	6	7	9	34	48	25
Long Sutton Athletic	22	7	3	12	33	49	24
Sutton Bridge United	22	7	2	13	44	61	23
Thorney	22	7	1	14	36	52	22
Werrington Town	22	2	2	18	33	88	8

Division Two		P	W	D	L	F	A	Pt
Manea United		20	15	3	2	65	24	48
Powerleague		20	15	2	3	81	29	47
Sawtry		20	12	3	5	69	30	39
SSPIO		20	11	4	5	64	26	37
Castor & Ailsworth		20	11	2	7	53	36	35
Langtoft United		20	10	4	6	43	39	34
Peterborough Rovers	*-2*	20	10	2	8	49	43	30
Doddington United		20	6	0	14	41	52	18
Gedney Hill		20	4	2	14	28	66	14
Parkside		20	2	4	14	30	92	10
Benwick Athletic		20	0	2	18	17	103	2

Combination One		P	W	D	L	F	A	Pt
Whittlesey United Res.		24	17	4	3	67	27	55
Holbeach United Res.		24	15	1	8	69	37	46
Oundle Town Res.		24	14	4	6	71	40	46
Deeping Sports Res.	*-2*	24	13	4	7	52	43	41
Moulton Harrox Res.	*-1*	24	11	8	5	57	32	40
Ramsey Town Res.		24	12	2	10	53	44	38
Parson Drove Res.		24	12	2	10	36	42	38
Wimblington Res.		24	10	6	8	37	36	36
AFC Fletton Res.	*-1*	24	10	2	12	39	55	31
Long Sutton Athletic Res.		24	4	9	11	38	61	21
Langtoft United Res.		24	5	4	15	32	51	19
Leverington Sports Res.	*-1*	24	3	5	16	29	71	13
Alconbury Res.		24	2	5	17	28	69	11

PETERBOROUGH CHALLENGE CUP

FINAL *(May 1st at PFA, Chestnut Avenue)*
Eye Sports & Social 4 SSPIO 0

PETERBOROUGH JUNIOR CUP

FINAL *(May 6th at PFA, Chestnut Avenue)*
Deeping Sports Res. 1 Whittlesey United Res. 0 *aet*

PETERBOROUGH MINOR CUP

FINAL *(April 18th at PFA, Chestnut Avenue)*
Netherton United A 2 Wimblington A 1

Combination Two		P	W	D	L	F	A	Pt
Netherton United Res.		22	17	4	1	80	28	55
Ramsey Town A	*-1*	22	17	2	3	82	37	52
Pinchbeck United Res.		22	14	3	5	65	27	45
Ketton Res.		22	12	4	6	52	45	40
Eye Sports & Social Res.	*-1*	22	11	2	9	45	57	34
Coates Athletic Res.		22	10	3	9	45	35	33
Stamford Belvedere Res.		22	9	3	10	43	48	30
Crowland Town Res.	*-1*	22	7	2	13	46	68	22
Kings Cliffe United Res.		22	5	6	11	42	45	21
Werrington Town Res.		22	6	3	13	41	64	21
Doddington United Res.	*-1*	22	2	5	15	29	70	10
Uppingham Town Res.		22	3	1	18	30	76	10

Combination Three		P	W	D	L	F	A	Pt
Peterborough Rovers Res.		26	17	5	4	90	42	56
Rutland Rangers Res.		26	17	5	4	71	26	56
Netherton United A		26	16	5	5	66	36	53
Warboys Town Res.	*-1*	26	16	5	5	64	31	52
SSPIO Res.	*-3*	26	12	7	7	61	48	40
Wimblington A		26	11	5	10	49	44	38
Manea United Res.		26	10	6	10	64	56	36
Leverington Sports A	*-2*	26	11	5	10	53	57	36
Stilton United Res.		26	10	2	14	72	70	32
Thorney Res.		26	9	3	14	40	72	30
Sawtry Res.	*-1*	26	9	2	15	49	63	28
Stamford Belvedere A	*-3*	26	7	4	15	44	68	22
Crowland Town A	*-1*	26	5	1	20	35	86	15
Sutton Bridge United Res.		26	4	1	21	45	104	13

READING LEAGUE

www.rdgleague.co.uk

Sponsored by:

No sponsor

Founded: 1989

Recent champions:

2004: Highmoor/IBIS

2005: Marlow United

2006: Cookham Dean

2007: Ascot United

2008: Westwood United

	Berks County Sports	Cookham Dean	Highmoor/IBIS	Mortimer	Rabson Rovers	Reading YMCA	Royal Mail	Sandhurst Devels	Taplow United	Westwood United	Woodcote & Stoke Row	Woodley Town
Berks County Sports	***S***	0-1	0-0	3-1	0-3	0-1	3-1	1-3	1-1	3-6	1-1	2-3
Cookham Dean	1-2	***E***	0-0	3-0	0-0	3-1	5-1	2-2	2-2	3-3	4-1	2-4
Highmoor/IBIS	1-1	W-L	***N***	3-1	3-2	1-2	4-1	2-1	3-1	0-1	2-1	1-0
Mortimer	2-1	1-2	3-5	***I***	1-2	1-1	0-0	0-4	6-3	2-5	2-2	0-6
Rabson Rovers	0-1	2-1	2-3	2-2	***O***	0-2	2-0	2-0	1-1	0-3	5-1	0-3
Reading YMCA	2-1	3-1	1-2	2-1	4-1	***R***	2-3	0-3	4-0	2-2	1-0	1-3
Royal Mail	3-0	4-2	3-2	7-3	4-1	1-5		4-3	4-2	4-3	2-1	2-3
Sandhurst Devels	3-1	4-2	4-1	7-0	4-3	1-2	1-1		4-1	1-2	3-1	1-2
Taplow United	3-2	1-2	0-6	3-1	1-3	0-5	4-3	2-0		1-1	2-1	2-5
Westwood United	1-1	1-2	4-1	4-2	1-4	2-2	5-1	0-0	2-1	***D***	0-2	4-4
Woodcote & Stoke Row	0-2	2-2	1-3	4-1	2-0	2-2	2-2	2-0	2-2	3-2	***I***	0-3
Woodley Town	2-2	1-2	1-2	5-1	6-1	1-1	1-2	3-0	5-1	1-0	3-2	***V***

Senior Division		**P**	**W**	**D**	**L**	**F**	**A**	**Pts**
Woodley Town		22	15	3	4	65	29	48
Highmoor/IBIS	*-3*	22	14	3	5	45	30	42
Reading YMCA		22	12	5	5	46	29	41
Westwood United		22	9	7	6	52	40	34
Sandhurst Devels		22	10	3	9	49	34	33
Cookham Dean		22	9	6	7	42	35	33
Royal Mail	*-3*	22	11	3	8	53	54	33
Rabson Rovers	*-1*	22	8	3	11	36	43	26
Woodcote/Stoke Row		22	5	6	11	33	44	21
Berks County Sports		22	5	6	11	28	39	21
Taplow United		22	5	5	12	34	63	20
Mortimer		22	2	4	16	31	74	10

Premier Division	**P**	**W**	**D**	**L**	**F**	**A**	**Pts**
Frilsham & Yattendon	20	16	2	2	66	29	50
Highmoor/IBIS Res.	20	13	2	5	65	36	41
Unity	20	13	2	5	45	28	41
Wok'gham/Embrook A	20	10	5	5	58	33	35
Park United	20	8	5	7	45	30	29
REME Arborfield	20	9	0	11	39	60	27
AFC Corinthians	20	7	5	8	37	37	26
Marlow United Res.	20	6	4	10	34	45	22
Ashridge Park	20	6	1	13	42	71	19
Cookham Dean Res.	20	4	3	13	32	54	15
Hurst	20	2	3	15	32	72	9

READING LEAGUE SENIOR DIVISION CONSTITUTION 2009-10

BERKS COUNTY SPORTS . Berks County Sports & Social Club, Sonning Lane, Sonning, Reading RG4 6ST . . . . Non

COOKHAM DEAN. . . . . Alfred Major Recreation Ground, Hillcrest Avenue, Cookham Rise, Maidenhead SL6 9NB 01628 81942

FRILSHAM & YATTENDON . . . . . Frilsham Playing Field, Frilsham Common, Frilsham, near Hermitage 01635 20184

HIGHMOOR/IBIS . . . . Prudential IBIS Sports Club, Scours Lane, Reading RG3 6AY. 0118 942 413

MORTIMER. . . . . Alfred Palmer Memorial PF, West End Road, Mortimer, Reading RG7 3TJ . . . . Non

RABSON ROVERS . . . . Lower Whitley Rec, Basingstoke Road, Reading RG2 0JA . . . . Non

READING YMCA . . . . Reading Town FC, Scours Lane, Tilehurst, Reading RG30 6AY 0118 945 355

SANDHURST DEVELS. . . . . Sandhurst Memorial Ground, York Town Road, Sandhurst GU47 9BJ . . . . Non

TAPLOW UNITED . . . . Stanley Jones Field, Berry Hill, Taplow SL6 0DA 01628 62174

THEALE ROYAL MAIL . . . . Theale Recreation Ground, Englefield Rd, Theale, Reading RG7 5AS . . . . Non

WESTWOOD UNITED. . . . . Cotswold Sports Centre, Downs Way, Tilehurst, Reading RG31 6LX. . . . . Non

WOODCOTE & STOKE ROW . . . . . . Woodcote Recreation Ground, Woodcote, Reading RG8 0QY . . . . Non

IN: Frisham & Yattendon (P)

OUT: Woodley Town (P – Hellenic League Division One East)

Royal Mail have merged with Theale to become Theale Royal Mail

BERKS TROPHY CENTRE INTERMEDIATE CUP

FINAL *(May 9th at Reading Town)*
Highmoor/IBIS Res. 2 Woodley Town Res. 0

BERKS TROPHY CENTRE JUNIOR CUP

FINAL *(May 8th at Reading Town)*
Reading YMCA Res. 1 Woodley Town A 0 *aet*

BERKS TROPHY CENTRE SENIOR CUP

(Senior and Premier Division teams)

FIRST ROUND

Ashbridge Park 1 **Reading YMCA** 2
Frilsham & Yattendon 4 Hurst 0 *aet*
Park United 2 **Westwood United** 6
Taplow United 1 **Sandhurst Devels** 3

SECOND ROUND

AFC Corinthians 0 **Reading YMCA** 2
Berks County Sports 0 **Woodcote & Stoke Row** 3
Frilsham & Yattendon 2 **Sandhurst Devels** 4 *aet*
Marlow United Res. 1 **Mortimer** 2
Rabson Rovers 1 **Royal Mail** 3
Unity 1 **Cookham Dean** 2
Westwood United 5 Wokingham & Emmbrook A 4
Woodley Town 4 Highmoor/IBIS 3

QUARTER-FINALS

Mortimer 1 **Sandhurst Devels** 2
Reading YMCA 2 Royal Mail 1
Westwood United 0 **Woodley Town** 3
Woodcote & Stoke Row 1 **Cookham Dean** 2

SEMI-FINALS

Sandhurst Devels 1 Reading YMCA 1 *aet* (5-4p)
Cookham Dean 1 **Woodley Town** 2

FINAL

(May 20th at Reading FC)

Woodley Town 1
Sandhurst Devels 0

	AFC Corinthians	Ashridge Park	Cookham Dean Res.	Frilsham & Yattendon	Highmoor/IBIS Res.	Hurst	Marlow United Res.	Park United	REME Arborfield	Unity	Wokingham & Em. A
AFC Corinthians	***P***	1-3	5-2	3-3	0-4	6-2	2-2	1-1	2-0	0-1	1-1
Ashridge Park	0-1	***R***	5-2	3-8	2-7	3-7	4-2	0-1	5-1	0-1	2-3
Cookham Dean Res.	0-0	0-0	***E***	0-7	3-1	8-0	2-3	0-0	3-4	2-4	0-4
Frilsham & Yattendon	3-2	5-2	5-0	***M***	0-2	1-1	3-0	2-1	4-0	2-0	3-1
Highmoor/IBIS Res.	3-2	6-2	5-3	5-1	***I***	4-3	4-2	1-2	2-1	1-2	1-1
Hurst	3-1	1-3	1-2	1-2	1-3	***E***	1-1	0-5	3-4	3-3	1-7
Marlow United Res.	1-2	1-3	3-1	1-4	3-1	1-0	***R***	2-2	1-2	1-2	4-2
Park United	1-2	8-1	2-0	2-3	0-1	7-2	2-2		2-0	1-4	2-0
REME Arborfield	3-2	7-3	1-3	1-4	0-8	3-1	1-4	3-2	***D***	0-2	4-1
Unity	1-2	4-1	W-L	3-4	3-1	2-0	6-0	5-3	0-3	***I***	2-2
Wokingham & Emmbrook A	3-2	5-0	4-1	1-2	5-5	6-1	1-0	1-1	8-1	2-0	***V***

READING LEAGUE PREMIER DIVISION CONSTITUTION 2009-10

AFC CORINTHIANS . . . . Civil Service Club, James Lane, Burghfield, Reading RG30 3RS 0118 983 3423
ASHRIDGE PARK . . . . Cantley Park, Twyford Road, Wokingham RG40 5QT . . . . None
COOKHAM DEAN RESERVES. . Alfred Major Rec, Hillcrest Ave., Cookham Rise, Maidenhead SL6 9NB 01628 819423
HIGHMOOR/IBIS RESERVES . . . . . . Prudential IBIS Sports Club, Scours Lane, Reading RG3 6AY. 0118 942 4130
MARLOW UNITED RESERVES . . . . Gossmore Park, Gossmore Lane, Marlow SL7 1QF . . . . None
PARK UNITED. . . . . Bishopswood Sports Ground, Horsepond Road, Sonning Common, Reading RG4 9BT . . . . None
REME ARBORFIELD. . . . . . Sports Pavilion, Biggs Lane, Hazelbrook Barracks,Arborfield, Reading RG2 9NH. . . . . None
SPENCERS WOOD . . . . . Reading University, Bulmershe Court, Woodlands Ave, Woodley, Reading RG1 1HY . . . . None
UNITY. . . . . Cintra Park, Cintra Avenue, Reading RG2 7AU 0118 954 7275
WEST READING. . . . . Victoria Recreation Ground, Kentwood Hill, Tilehurst, Reading RG31 6HH . . . . None
WESTWOOD UNITED RESERVES. . . . Cotswold SC, Downs Way, Tilehurst, Reading RG31 6LX . . . . None
WOKINGHAM & EMMBROOK A . . . . Lowther Rd, Emmbrook, Wokingham RG41 1JB. 0118 978 0209

IN: Spencers Wood (P), West Reading (P), Westwood United Res. (P)

OUT: Frilsham & Yattendon (P), Hurst (R), Shinfield (WN)

Division One		P	W	D	L	F	A	Pt
West Reading		18	12	4	2	51	26	40
Spencers Wd	*-2*	18	11	5	2	33	14	36
Westwood Res.	*-3*	18	12	2	4	36	28	35
Berinsfield CA		18	7	4	7	33	28	25
SRCC		18	7	2	9	44	41	23
Woodley T. Res.		18	5	7	6	24	26	22
Berks CS Res.		18	5	2	11	24	34	17
Goring United		18	5	2	11	29	41	17
Theale		18	5	2	11	26	47	17
Newtown Henley		18	4	4	10	22	37	16

Division Two	P	W	D	L	F	A	Pt
S'hurst Dev. Res.	26	18	7	1	81	28	61
Barton Rovers FC	26	18	3	5	99	48	57
Sonning	26	17	4	5	80	41	55
Finchampstead A	26	15	5	6	70	44	50
Twyford/Ruscmbe	26	14	5	7	62	43	47
Mortimer Res.	26	13	2	11	42	43	41
Wokingham/E. B	26	11	4	11	58	60	37
Woodley Town A	26	9	3	14	40	51	30
Highmoor/Ibis A	26	9	3	14	44	62	30
Linear United	26	8	4	14	62	79	28
Taplow Utd Res.	26	8	3	15	36	60	27
Woodcote Res.	26	8	2	16	50	76	26
Hurst Res.	26	6	1	19	38	80	19
Radstock	26	4	2	20	25	72	14

Division Three		P	W	D	L	F	A	Pt
Turnpike Sports		26	24	0	2	137	24	72
Rdg YMCA Res.		26	21	1	4	102	25	64
Wrightchoice CSA		26	20	2	4	73	30	62
Wargrave		26	18	3	5	90	46	57
Sonning Sports		26	14	2	10	70	52	44
AFC C'thians Res.		26	12	3	11	54	61	39
Crowthorne S.	*-6*	26	13	1	12	85	73	34
Berinsfield Res.		26	9	3	14	56	68	30
Goring Utd Res.		26	8	5	13	56	71	29
Sonning Res.		26	9	1	16	59	71	28
Winnershe Rgrs		26	7	2	17	53	105	23
Compton FC		26	5	3	18	45	96	18
Taplow United A		26	4	1	21	40	111	13
The Hop Leaf		26	4	1	21	21	108	13

SOMERSET COUNTY LEAGUE

full-time.thefa.com

Sponsored by:

Errea

Founded: 1986

Recent champions:

2004: Team Bath Res.

2005: Mangotsfield United Res.

2006: Hengrove Athletic

2007: Burnham United

2008: Nailsea United

Premier Division		P	W	D	L	F	A	Pts
Bridgwater Town Res.		34	26	5	3	89	39	83
Shirehampton		34	23	4	7	102	55	73
Frome Town Res.		34	18	4	12	83	56	58
Bishops Lydeard		34	16	10	8	63	51	58
Taunton Blackbrook	*-1*	34	18	5	11	63	53	58
Cutters Friday		34	17	5	12	73	55	56
Watchet Town		34	15	8	11	47	41	53
Cheddar		34	15	7	12	84	64	52
Mangotsfield United Res.		34	14	5	15	63	58	47
Glastonbury Town		34	13	7	14	61	52	46
Backwell United		34	13	6	15	47	57	45
Castle Cary		34	13	6	15	55	68	45
Nailsea United		34	13	4	17	54	66	43
Winscombe		34	13	3	18	56	80	42
Timsbury Athletic		34	10	5	19	45	71	35
Cleeve West Town		34	9	3	22	44	68	30
Burnham United		34	6	5	23	31	76	23
Odd Down Res.	*-1*	34	5	6	23	42	92	20

	Bac	Bis	Bri	Bur	Cas	Che	Cle	Cut	Fro	Gla	Man	Nai	Odd	Shi	Tau	Tim	Wat	Win
Backwell United		0-2	4-1	1-0	0-0	2-1	2-1	0-0	0-2	2-1	1-1	0-2	2-0	3-3	3-3	1-0	1-2	0-4
Bishops Lydeard	1-1	***P***	2-4	0-0	1-2	2-1	1-0	3-2	3-2	2-2	2-1	2-2	3-1	3-4	1-3	2-0	2-4	3-0
Bridgwater Town Res.	3-0	2-0	***R***	1-1	5-0	5-3	1-0	1-0	2-1	1-1	4-3	2-1	4-0	4-3	3-1	3-0	0-0	5-1
Burnham United	0-3	2-3	0-3	***E***	1-2	3-3	0-1	2-2	0-1	1-0	2-1	3-0	4-0	1-3	0-2	0-1	0-1	1-2
Castle Cary	4-2	0-2	1-2	5-1	***M***	0-3	3-1	4-5	2-2	2-0	1-1	2-1	2-2	0-3	2-1	2-1	2-3	1-3
Cheddar	6-0	1-1	4-1	2-0	3-1	***I***	3-0	2-1	1-4	3-3	1-2	2-2	3-2	3-6	5-2	4-1	1-1	2-0
Cleeve West Town	2-0	1-3	2-4	0-1	0-1	0-4	***E***	0-2	1-3	0-0	4-2	4-0	4-1	3-2	0-1	1-2	2-2	2-4
Cutters Friday	1-0	3-3	2-3	3-0	3-1	3-2	5-2	***R***	0-1	0-2	3-2	3-2	6-1	3-5	1-0	4-1	3-0	2-2
Frome Town Res.	0-4	2-3	1-1	7-0	8-2	5-3	1-2	4-1		3-1	4-1	2-3	4-1	1-2	2-1	1-2	3-0	1-2
Glastonbury Town	5-0	0-0	4-2	1-1	2-0	4-3	2-3	3-1	1-1	***D***	2-4	4-2	7-2	1-3	2-0	0-1	2-3	1-4
Mangotsfield United Res.	0-2	0-1	0-4	8-0	0-2	1-3	3-1	1-0	2-3	1-0	***I***	3-1	1-1	2-4	1-2	5-0	0-1	3-2
Nailsea United	3-1	2-5	0-3	5-0	1-1	1-2	2-0	2-1	4-2	0-3	2-4	***V***	1-1	1-4	1-2	2-1	2-1	2-0
Odd Down Res.	1-4	1-1	1-5	3-0	1-3	2-0	2-4	0-3	1-4	0-1	2-3	0-2	***I***	1-1	2-0	1-4	2-0	2-3
Shirehampton	4-1	2-3	1-2	1-0	3-1	2-2	4-2	3-1	1-2	2-1	0-1	2-1	5-1	***S***	6-1	5-0	1-2	6-0
Taunton Blackbrook	1-0	2-2	0-3	4-1	3-2	4-4	1-0	1-1	3-1	2-0	0-1	1-0	3-1	1-2	***I***	2-1	2-1	6-1
Timsbury Athletic	1-4	1-0	1-1	1-3	1-2	2-1	4-0	1-3	2-2	1-3	1-1	1-2	1-1	2-3	3-4	***O***	2-1	3-1
Watchet Town	1-0	1-1	0-1	3-1	1-1	1-0	0-0	0-2	2-0	2-0	0-0	1-2	3-1	2-3	0-0	5-1	***N***	2-1
Winscombe	1-3	2-0	1-3	3-2	2-1	0-3	2-1	1-3	2-3	0-2	2-4	3-0	1-4	3-3	0-4	1-1	2-1	

SOMERSET COUNTY LEAGUE PREMIER DIVISION CONSTITUTION 2009-10

BACKWELL UNITED . . . . The Playing Fields, West Town Road, Backwell, Bristol BS48 3HG 01275 46261

BISHOPS LYDEARD. . . . . Darby Way, Bishops Lydeard TA4 3BE . . . . Non

BRIDGWATER TOWN RESERVES . . . Fairfax Park, College Way, Bath Road, Bridgwater TA6 4TZ. 01278 44689

BRISLINGTON RESERVES . . . . Ironmould Lane, Brislington, Bristol BS4 5SA 0117 977 403

CASTLE CARY . . . . Donald Pither Memorial PF, Catherines Close, Castle Cary BA7 7HP 01963 35153

CHEDDAR. . . . . Bowdens Park, Draycott Road, Cheddar BS27 3RL 01934 74373

CUTTERS FRIDAY . . . . The Cutters Club, Stockwood Lane, Stockwood, Bristol BS14 8SJ 01275 83983

FROME TOWN RESERVES. . . . . Badgers Hill, Berkley Road, Frome BA11 2EH 01373 46408

GLASTONBURY TOWN. . . . . Abbey Moor Stadium, Godney Road, Glastonbury BA6 9AF. 01458 83146

MANGOTSFIELD UNITED RESERVES. . . . Cossham Street, Mangotsfield, Bristol BS17 3EN. 0117 956 01

NAILSEA UNITED . . . . Grove Sports Ground, Old Church, Nailsea BS48 4ND. 01275 85689

PAULTON ROVERS RESERVES . . . . Athletic Ground, Winterfield Road, Paulton BS39 7RF 01761 41290

SHIREHAMPTON . . . . Recreation Ground, Penpole Lane, Shirehampton, Bristol BS11 0EA. 0117 923 546

ST GEORGE EASTON-IN-GORDANO . . . . Court Hay, Easton-in-Gordano, Bristol BS20 0PY 01275 37423

TAUNTON BLACKBROOK . . . . Taunton Town FC, Wordsworth Drive, Taunton TA1 2HG 01823 27819

TIMSBURY ATHLETIC . . . . Recreation Ground, North Road, Timsbury, Bath BA2 0JH 01761 47252

WATCHET TOWN. . . . . Memorial Ground, Doniford Road, Watchet TA23 0TG 01984 63104

WINSCOMBE. . . . . Recreation Ground, The Lynch, Winscombe BS25 1AP . . . . 01934 842720(cricket clu

IN: Brislington Res. (P), Paulton Rovers Res. (P), St George Easton-in-Gordano (P)

OUT: Burnham United (R), Cleeve West Town (R), Odd Down Res. (R)

Division One		P	W	D	L	F	A	Pts
St George EG		34	22	5	7	86	38	71
Brislington Res.	*-2*	34	22	5	7	75	49	69
Paulton Rov. Res.		34	18	8	8	75	47	62
Fry Club		34	18	6	10	64	46	60
Langford Rovers		34	17	5	12	76	77	56
Larkhall A. Res.	*-1*	34	17	3	14	77	51	53
Nailsea Town		34	15	8	11	51	36	53
Ilminster Town		34	13	11	10	68	49	50
Keynsham T. Res.		34	14	6	14	72	55	48
Stockwood GR		34	14	6	14	54	50	48
Street Res.		34	14	5	15	67	72	47
Portishead T. Res.		34	13	7	14	62	62	46
Saltford		34	10	9	15	42	57	39
Worle		34	10	7	17	69	78	37
Churchill Club		34	10	5	19	48	66	35
Peasedown A.	*-12*	34	12	8	14	57	78	32
Westland United		34	6	11	17	54	75	29
Burnham Utd Res.		34	2	3	29	29	140	9

PREMIER / DIVISION ONE CUP

FIRST ROUND
Castle Cary 2 B. Lydeard 1
Fry Club 3 **Winscombe** 4
Westland 1 **Frome Res.** 2
SECOND ROUND
Bridgwater Town Res. 3 **Larkhall Athletic Res.** 4
Burnham United 0 **Mangotsfield United Res.** 7
Cheddar 3 Portishead Res. 1
Churchill 4 Keynsham Res. 3
Cleeve West Town 2 **Ilminster Town** 3
Glastonbury Town 3 Brislington Res. 0
Langford R. 1 **Castle Cary** 2
Nailsea Town 2 Paulton Rovers Res. 0
Nailsea United 4 Worle 0
Peasedown 2 Backwell 0
Saltford 1 Frome Res. 0
Shirehampton 3 Winscombe 0
St George Easton-in-G. 3 Odd Down Res. 2
Stockwood Green 3 Cutters Friday 1
Taunton Blackbrook 2 Watchet Town 0
Timsbury 0 **Street Res.** 2
THIRD ROUND
Churchill 0 **Nailsea Town** 2
Castle Cary 2 Saltford 0
Taunton Blackbrook 1 St George Easton-in-Gordano 0
Glastonbury Town 1 **Shirehampton** 3
Larkhall Athletic Res. 4 **Cheddar** 4 *aet* (2-4p)
Mangotsfield United Res. 2 Stockwood Green 0
Ilminster 2 **Nailsea United** 3
Street Res. 3 Peasedown 2
QUARTER-FINALS
Mangotsfield United Res. 2 **Nailsea United** 3
Shirehampton 4 Castle Cary 1 *aet*
Taunton Blackbrook 4 Street Res. 0
Nailsea Town 1 **Cheddar** 2
SEMI-FINALS
Cheddar 0 **T. Blackbrook** 3
Shirehampton 1 Nailsea U 0
FINAL
(*May 14th at Portishead*)
Shirehampton 5 Taunton Blackbrook 3 *aet*

	Bri	Bur	Chu	Fry	Ilm	Key	Lan	Lar	Nai	Pau	Pea	Por	Sal	StG	Sto	Str	Wes	Wor
Brislington Res.		1-1	2-3	0-3	5-1	3-1	2-2	2-0	1-1	1-4	3-0	3-2	3-2	1-0	1-2	3-4	1-0	3-3
Burnham United Res.	0-2		0-3	0-2	0-3	2-1	1-4	2-7	2-4	0-3	1-3	1-7	1-4	1-5	2-1	0-4	2-3	0-8
Churchill Club	2-2	1-0		1-2	1-4	4-2	4-2	2-0	0-1	3-6	1-2	0-1	1-2	0-4	1-3	1-2	2-0	3-1
Fry Club	2-3	4-1	2-0	***D***	2-2	2-3	1-2	3-1	1-1	3-1	4-3	5-2	1-0	1-2	1-3	2-0	2-0	4-0
Ilminster Town	3-4	4-0	1-1	3-0	***I***	0-1	0-1	0-0	1-1	5-2	7-1	3-1	3-0	0-1	0-2	4-0	1-0	4-4
Keynsham Town Res.	0-1	9-1	4-0	1-2	1-1	***V***	4-1	2-1	1-0	1-3	2-0	5-2	6-0	0-1	0-2	6-1	1-1	2-2
Langford Rovers	1-5	11-2	1-0	3-1	2-1	5-3	***I***	1-3	1-0	0-4	2-2	3-2	1-1	1-0	3-9	2-3	8-5	3-1
Larkhall Athletic Res.	0-2	7-0	3-2	4-0	3-1	0-2	4-0	***S***	3-0	1-1	1-2	2-2	2-0	6-2	1-2	5-3	4-3	3-0
Nailsea Town	2-4	0-0	1-0	0-2	4-1	1-0	1-3	0-1	***I***	0-3	7-1	0-0	1-1	1-3	1-0	2-1	5-0	2-1
Paulton Rovers Res.	2-1	9-0	2-1	0-1	0-2	0-3	5-2	0-3	0-0	***O***	2-0	1-1	0-0	3-0	1-0	2-3	2-2	2-0
Peasedown Athletic	1-3	4-3	3-3	1-1	0-0	2-2	2-1	3-1	0-2	2-2	***N***	3-4	2-0	1-1	3-2	4-2	5-2	0-2
Portishead Town Res.	1-3	2-1	1-1	1-0	0-4	1-3	0-0	4-2	0-1	3-4	3-1		1-1	2-0	2-0	1-1	4-0	0-2
Saltford	0-1	2-1	3-0	1-1	0-0	3-0	1-0	2-1	0-6	1-2	0-1	3-1	***O***	1-5	1-1	0-1	2-2	4-3
St George Easton-in-Gordano	4-1	5-0	1-1	3-1	2-2	3-0	6-0	2-1	3-0	0-1	4-0	1-0	4-1	***N***	6-1	3-0	2-1	6-0
Stockwood Green Robinsons	0-2	4-1	1-2	1-1	1-1	4-1	0-1	0-2	1-0	3-3	1-3	0-2	1-0	0-2	***E***	2-1	0-0	3-1
Street Res.	1-2	4-0	4-1	2-4	2-2	3-3	1-3	2-1	0-3	2-1	3-0	3-2	0-3	2-2	0-2		3-3	7-1
Westland United	0-2	2-2	0-1	1-1	5-1	3-2	0-3	1-4	1-1	2-3	5-1	2-3	1-1	2-2	1-1	0-1		4-1
Worle	1-2	7-1	3-2	0-2	2-3	0-0	3-3	3-0	0-2	1-1	1-1	3-4	3-2	6-1	3-1	2-1	1-2	

SOMERSET COUNTY LEAGUE DIVISION ONE CONSTITUTION 2009-10

SHOP SUTTON RESERVES . . . . Lake View, Wick Road, Bishop Sutton, Bristol BS39 5XP 01275 333097
JRNHAM UNITED. . . . . Burnham Road Playing Fields, Cassis Close, Burnham-on-Sea TA8 1NN 01278 794615
.EEVE WEST TOWN. . . . . King George V Playing Fields, Meeting House Lane, Cleeve BS49 4PD 01934 832173
.EVEDON UNITED RESERVES. Coleridge Vale Playing Fields, Southley Road, Clevedon BS21 6PF. 01275 871878
?Y CLUB . . . . Fry Club, Somerdale, Keynsham, Bristol BS31 2AU 0117 937 6500/6501
.MINSTER TOWN . . . . Recreation Ground, Ilminster TA19 0EF. . . . . None
:YNSHAM TOWN RESERVES . . . . . . Crown Field, Bristol Road, Keynsham, Bristol BS31 2BE. 0117 986 5876
NGFORD ROVERS . . . . Westland United FC, Winterstoke Road, Weston-super-Mare BS24 9AA. 01934 632037
RKHALL ATHLETIC RESERVES. . . . . Plain Ham, Charlcombe Lane, Larkhall, Bath BA1 8DJ. 01225 334952
ILSEA TOWN . . . . Fryth Way, Pound Lane, Nailsea BS48 2AS . . . . None
ILSEA UNITED RESERVES . . . . Grove Sports Ground, Old Church, Nailsea BS48 4ND. 01275 856892
)D DOWN RESERVES . . . . . Lew Hill Memorial Ground, Combe Hay Lane, Odd Down, Bath BA2 8PH 01225 832491
)RTISHEAD TOWN RESERVES. . . . Bristol Road Playing Fields, Portishead, Bristol BS20 6QB 01275 847136
ADSTOCK TOWN RESERVES . . . . Southfield Recreation Ground, Frome Hill, Radstock BA3 3NZ. 01761 435004
.LTFORD. . . . . Playing Fields, Norman Road, Saltford BS31 0BQ 01225 873725
OCKWOOD GREEN ROBINSONS. Hursley Lane, Woolard Lane, Whitchurch, Bristol BS14 0QY 01275 891300
REET RESERVES . . . . The Tannery Ground, Middlebrooks, Street BA16 0TA 01458 444987
ORLE. . . . . Worle Recreation Ground, Station Road, Worle, Weston-super-Mare BS22 6AU . . . . None

: Bishop Sutton Res. (P - Division Two East), Burnham United (R), Cleeve West Town (R), Clevedon United Res. (P - Division Two est), Nailsea United Res. (P - Division Two West), Odd Down Res. (R), Radstock Town Res. (P - Division Two East)

JT: Brislington Res. (P), Burnham United Res. (R - Division Two West), Churchill Club (R - Division Two West), Paulton Rovers Res. (P), ›asedown Athletic (R - Division Two East), St George Easton-in-Gordano (P), Westland United (R - Division Two West)

	Bishop Sutton Res.	Clutton	Cutters Friday Res.	Dundry Athletic	Frome Collegians	Fry Club Res.	Hengrove Athletic Res.	Imperial	Radstock Town Res.	Shepton Mallet Res.	Stockwood Green Robs Res.	Timsbury Athletic Res.	Tunley Athletic	Welton Rovers Res.	Westfield
Bishop Sutton Res.		2-1	2-1	3-0	0-1	1-1	3-0	4-0	0-1	4-1	5-0	2-0	5-0	5-0	3-4
Clutton	0-5	***D***	4-1	1-3	3-1	0-2	1-1	6-2	1-2	2-2	1-3	9-1	0-0	1-3	4-2
Cutters Friday Res.	2-2	4-2	***I***	1-3	0-2	1-0	0-1	1-1	2-4	7-1	3-2	5-1	2-0	1-2	0-3
Dundry Athletic	2-1	2-2	3-1	***V***	3-3	1-6	3-2	0-0	0-2	2-1	3-1	3-1	3-0	2-1	0-0
Frome Collegians	0-4	1-4	1-2	3-0		1-1	2-3	3-0	2-1	5-1	6-2	1-1	1-1	1-2	4-0
Fry Club Res.	4-2	3-1	1-3	2-4	2-2	***T***	0-3	2-0	0-2	2-1	2-1	2-3	2-1	1-1	2-1
Hengrove Athletic Res.	3-3	3-2	3-3	2-2	6-0	4-1	***W***	1-1	1-0	4-2	1-1	3-0	6-1	1-1	1-1
Imperial	0-2	0-1	0-0	2-1	3-2	1-4	1-0	***O***	0-2	0-0	2-0	5-1	1-4	1-5	3-2
Radstock Town Res.	0-2	2-1	2-1	1-2	1-0	7-0	3-1	1-0		2-0	6-0	4-2	0-0	0-4	1-0
Shepton Mallet Res.	0-2	4-4	0-3	1-4	3-1	4-2	1-3	1-1	2-2	***E***	1-4	2-2	2-3	0-4	1-3
Stockwood Green R. Res.	1-2	0-3	1-0	1-4	1-2	3-2	5-2	0-3	1-2	4-0	***A***	3-2	0-1	1-0	0-3
Timsbury Athletic Res.	0-4	3-1	2-5	1-0	2-5	1-3	0-3	1-1	0-4	1-3	0-2	***S***	1-3	0-5	1-2
Tunley Athletic	0-5	2-2	0-0	2-2	1-2	2-2	1-1	4-3	3-1	2-0	0-1	0-0	***T***	0-0	3-1
Welton Rovers Res.	1-1	2-0	3-0	1-1	1-2	2-2	1-2	5-0	0-2	4-0	1-1	2-1	1-1		3-1
Westfield	0-1	2-3	5-3	5-0	2-0	4-1	1-4	0-1	2-2	6-0	0-3	2-1	2-1	1-2	

Division Two East		P	W	D	L	F	A	Pts
Bishop Sutton Res.		**28**	**19**	**4**	**5**	**75**	**23**	**61**
Radstock Town Res.		**28**	**19**	**3**	**6**	**57**	**27**	**60**
Hengrove Athletic Res.		**28**	**14**	**9**	**5**	**65**	**40**	**51**
Welton Rovers Res.		**28**	**14**	**8**	**6**	**57**	**29**	**50**
Dundry Athletic	*-1*	**28**	**14**	**7**	**7**	**53**	**47**	**48**
Frome Collegians		**28**	**12**	**5**	**11**	**54**	**50**	**41**
Westfield		**28**	**12**	**3**	**13**	**55**	**48**	**39**
Fry Club Res.		**28**	**11**	**6**	**11**	**52**	**57**	**39**
Cutters Friday Res.		**28**	**10**	**5**	**13**	**52**	**51**	**35**
Tunley Athletic		**28**	**8**	**11**	**9**	**36**	**46**	**35**
Stockwood Green Res.		**28**	**11**	**2**	**15**	**42**	**57**	**35**
Clutton		**28**	**9**	**6**	**13**	**60**	**58**	**33**
Imperial	*-3*	**28**	**8**	**7**	**13**	**32**	**53**	**28**
Shepton Mallet Res.		**28**	**3**	**6**	**19**	**34**	**83**	**15**
Timsbury Athletic Res.	*-3*	**28**	**3**	**4**	**21**	**29**	**84**	**10**

SOMERSET COUNTY LEAGUE DIVISION TWO EAST CONSTITUTION 2009-10

CLUTTON. . . . . Warwick Fields, Upper Bristol Road, Clutton, Bristol BS39 5TA. . . . . Non

CUTTERS FRIDAY RESERVES . . . The Cutters Club, Stockwood Lane, Stockwood, Bristol BS14 8SJ 01275 83983

DUNDRY ATHLETIC. . . . . Dundry Playing Field, Crabtree Lane, Dundry, Bristol BS41 8LN. 0117 964 553

FROME COLLEGIANS. . . . . Selwood School, Berkley Road, Frome BA11 2EF. . . . . Non

FRY CLUB RESERVES . . . . Fry Club, Somerdale, Keynsham, Bristol BS31 2AU 0117 937 6500/650

HENGROVE ATHLETIC RESERVES . . . . Norton Lane, Whitchurch, Bristol BS14 0BT 01275 83289

IMPERIAL. . . . . Bristol Imperial Sports Club, West Town Lane, Whitchurch, Brislington BS4 5DT. 01275 54600

PEASEDOWN ATHLETIC . . . . . Miners Welfare Park, Church Road, Peasedown St John, Bath BA2 8AF. 01761 43731

PURNELLS SPORTS . . . . High Littleton Miners Welfare Ground, Timsbury Road, High Littleton, Bristol . . . . Non

SHEPTON MALLET RESERVES West Shepton Playing Fields, Old Wells Road, Shepton Mallet BA4 5XN. 01749 34460

STOCKWOOD GREEN ROBINSONS RESERVES Hursley Lane, Woolard Lane, Whitchurch, Bristol BS14 0QY 01275 89130

TIMSBURY ATHLETIC RESERVES . . . Recreation Ground, North Road, Timsbury, Bath BA2 0JH 01761 47252

TUNLEY ATHLETIC. . . . . The Recreation Centre, Bath Road, Tunley BA2 0EB. . . . . Non

WELTON ROVERS RESERVES . . . . West Clewes, North Road, Midsomer Norton BA3 2QD 01761 41209

WESTFIELD . . . . Fosseway Playing Fields, Charlton Lane, Midsomer Norton BA3 4BD . . . . Non

IN: Peasedown Athletic (R), Purnells Sports (P - Mid-Somerset League Premier Division)

OUT: Bishop Sutton Res. (P), Radstock Town Res. (P)

Division Two West		P	W	D	L	F	A	Pts
Clevedon Utd Res.		26	19	6	1	82	33	63
Nailsea United Res.		26	19	3	4	94	37	60
Berrow		26	18	6	2	86	34	60
Yatton Athletic		26	14	4	8	78	52	46
Creech St Michael		26	11	7	8	56	42	40
Congresbury		26	11	6	9	66	54	39
Wells City Res.		26	10	6	10	49	53	36
Combe St Nicholas		26	8	8	10	48	50	32
Cheddar Res.		26	8	7	11	36	43	31
Banwell	*-1*	26	7	4	15	54	58	24
Weston St J. Res.		26	7	3	16	50	82	24
Long Ashton	*-5*	26	8	3	15	38	64	22
Wrington-Redhill		26	7	1	18	36	89	22
Backwell U. Res.	*-7*	26	2	2	22	18	100	1

DIVISION TWO CUP

FIRST ROUND

Clutton 1 **Nailsea United Res.** 2

Combe St Nicholas 2 Stockwood Green Res. 0

Weston St Johns Res. 4 Radstock Town Res. 2

Cutters Res. 3 Lg Ashton 2

Hengrove Athletic Res. 1 Timsbury Athletic Res. 0

Imperial 2 **Yatton Athletic** 4

Clevedon United Res. 2 **Bishop Sutton Res.** 4

Creech St Michael 2 **Westfield** 3

Fry Club Res. 7 Banwell 0

Welton Rovers Res. 2 Wrington-Redhill 1 *aet*

Backwell United Res. 2 Tunley Athletic 2 *aet* (5-4p)

Dundry Athletic 3 **Congresbury** 3 *aet* (3-4p)

Berrow 2 Wells City Res. 0

SECOND ROUND

Weston St Johns Res. 3 Hengrove Athletic Res. 1

Frome Collegians 2 Cutters Friday Res. 1

Shepton Mallet Res. 3 **Fry Club Res.** 5

Congresbury 4 Combe St Nicholas 3 *aet*

Nailsea United Res. 3 Backwell United Res. 1

Cheddar Res. 2 **Yatton** 3

Westfield 4 B. Sutton Res. 2

Welton Rovers Res. 2 **Berrow** 4 *aet*

QUARTER-FINALS

Congresbury 1 **Westfield** 2

Fry Club Res. 1 Weston St Johns Res. 0

Nailsea United Res. 3 **Berrow** 4 *aet*

Yatton Athletic 2 Frome Collegians 1

SEMI-FINALS

Yatton Athletic 3 Westfield 2

Fry Club Res. 1 **Berrow** 2

FINAL

(May 12th at Cheddar)

Berrow 3 Yatton Athletic 0

	Backwell U. Res.	Banwell	Berrow	Cheddar Res.	Clevedon U Res.	Combe St Nich.	Congresbury	Creech St Mich.	Long Ashton	Nailsea Utd Res.	Wells City Res.	Weston SJ Res.	Wrington-Redhill	Yatton Athletic
Backwell United Res.		1-1	0-4	1-4	0-3	0-3	0-1	0-4	0-0	2-5	0-1	0-3	0-1	2-3
Banwell	6-4	***D***	5-5	2-1	0-2	0-2	3-3	0-1	1-2	0-1	5-2	1-2	8-0	4-5
Berrow	8-0	2-1	***I***	4-3	0-2	1-1	3-2	2-0	6-1	4-1	4-0	3-1	2-0	1-0
Cheddar Res.	1-2	1-0	0-2	***V***	1-1	2-1	1-1	0-4	0-1	0-0	2-1	1-2	3-1	0-0
Clevedon United Res.	4-1	5-1	2-2	4-3		1-1	5-2	0-3	2-1	2-0	4-4	7-2	5-0	3-1
Combe St Nicholas	6-0	3-4	2-2	1-1	1-2	***T***	2-4	1-0	3-0	0-3	1-3	1-1	4-1	1-5
Congresbury	5-0	1-0	2-5	3-3	0-1	2-2	***W***	0-1	3-1	2-3	6-2	2-2	3-0	0-1
Creech St Michael	7-1	2-2	1-1	2-0	1-1	1-1	4-3	***O***	1-2	2-4	1-1	4-2	1-2	4-1
Long Ashton	4-0	1-2	1-5	0-2	2-4	2-3	1-4	2-2		2-2	2-1	2-0	3-1	2-4
Nailsea United Res.	6-0	4-0	4-3	6-0	2-3	4-2	4-3	6-3	4-1	***W***	1-1	5-1	9-0	6-2
Wells City Res.	6-0	2-1	0-2	1-1	2-2	3-1	1-2	4-2	0-1	0-3	***E***	3-1	4-3	1-0
Weston St Johns Res.	1-2	4-3	1-5	1-2	3-6	2-4	2-4	2-3	5-2	0-4	2-2	***S***	2-1	0-6
Wrington-Redhill	4-0	1-0	1-7	0-3	0-7	1-1	2-3	2-0	4-2	0-4	3-4	4-8	***T***	2-1
Yatton Athletic	9-2	1-4	3-3	2-1	0-4	5-0	5-5	2-2	5-0	4-3	3-0	5-0	5-2	

SOMERSET COUNTY LEAGUE DIVISION TWO WEST CONSTITUTION 2009-10

BACKWELL UNITED RESERVES . . The Playing Fields, West Town Rd, Backwell , Bristol BS48 3HG 01275 462612
BANWELL . . . . Riverside Ground, Riverside, Banwell BS29 6EE 01934 820773
BERROW . . . . Red Road Playing Fields, Berrow, Burnham-on-Sea TA8 2LY . . . . None
BURNHAM UNITED RESERVES. . . . . Burnham Rd PF, Cassis Close, Burnham-on-Sea TA8 1NN. 01278 794615
CHEDDAR RESERVES . . . . Bowdens Park, Draycott Road, Cheddar BS27 3RL 01934 743736
CHURCHILL CLUB . . . . Ladymead Lane, Churchill, Winscombe BS25 5NH 01934 852739
COMBE ST NICHOLAS. . . . . Slades Cross, Combe St Nicholas TA20 3HQ 01460 234743
CONGRESBURY . . . . Broadstones Playing Fields, Stonewell Lane, Congresbury BS49 5DL. 01934 832150
CREECH ST MICHAEL. . . . . . . Creech St Michael Rec, Hyde Lane, Creech St Michael, Taunton TA3 5QJ . . . . None
LONG ASHTON . . . . Long Ashton Recreation Ground, Keedwell Hill, Long Ashton BS41 9DP . . . . None
WELLS CITY RESERVES. . . . . The Athletic Ground, Rowdens Road, Wells BA5 1TU 01749 679971
WESTLAND UNITED . . . . Westland Sports Club, Winterstoke Road, Weston-super-Mare BS24 9AA 01934 632037
WESTON ST JOHNS . . . . Coleridge Road, Bournville Estate, Weston-super-Mare BS23 3UP 01934 612862
WRINGTON-REDHILL . . . . Recreation Ground, Silver Street, Wrington BS40 5QE . . . . None
YATTON ATHLETIC. . . . . Hangstones Playing Fields, Stowey Road, Yatton BS49 4HY. . . . . None

IN: Burnham United Res. (R), Churchill Club (R), Westland United (R)

OUT: Clevedon United Res. (P), Nailsea United Res. (P)

Weston St Johns Res. become Weston St Johns

STAFFORDSHIRE COUNTY SENIOR LEAGUE

www.leaguewebsite.co.uk/staffordshirecountyseniorleague

Sponsored by:

No sponsor

Founded: 1957

Recent champions:

2004: Holditch Miners

2005: Fegg Hayes

2006: Hanley Town

2007: Wolstanton United

2008: Wolstanton United

Premier Division	P	W	D	L	F	A	Pts
Foley	34	23	5	6	84	34	74
Wolstanton United	34	22	7	5	95	33	73
Hanley Town	34	21	7	6	76	36	70
Stretton Eagles	34	20	10	4	64	28	70
Redgate Clayton	34	21	6	7	84	38	69
Congleton Vale	34	18	8	8	60	36	62
Ball Haye Green	34	18	4	12	82	43	58
Florence	34	16	7	11	56	37	55
Abbey Hulton United	34	15	7	12	58	59	52
Newcastle Town Res.	34	11	11	12	50	45	44
Goldenhill Wanderers	34	11	4	19	51	67	37
Sandbach United	34	10	6	18	40	64	36
Eccleshall AFC	34	10	5	19	47	65	35
Norton	34	10	5	19	43	70	35
Alsager Town Res.	34	8	7	19	40	79	31
Barlaston	34	7	6	21	33	64	27
Audley & District	34	5	4	25	33	118	19
Rocester Res.	34	3	5	26	33	113	14

	Abb	Als	Aud	Ball	Barl	Cong	Ecc	Flor	Foley	Gold	Han	New	Nort.	Redg	Roc	Sand	Stret	Wols
Abbey Hulton United		1-4	2-1	0-1	5-1	2-1	3-2	0-0	0-3	2-0	3-2	1-1	0-2	1-2	1-0	1-2	1-4	2-1
Alsager Town Res.	0-0	***P***	1-1	1-4	1-2	2-3	0-0	2-3	0-4	3-1	0-2	2-2	2-0	0-5	3-1	1-2	0-1	1-1
Audley & District	2-4	3-0	***R***	1-4	1-1	0-6	0-5	0-6	0-4	2-5	0-10	0-3	3-1	1-6	3-2	2-3	0-3	0-4
Ball Haye Green	0-1	4-0	4-0	***E***	6-1	2-2	3-0	0-2	0-1	3-2	1-2	3-1	1-1	0-4	11-0	0-0	2-0	2-3
Barlaston	2-3	0-1	4-0	0-3	***M***	1-3	0-1	1-2	0-1	3-2	0-2	1-1	0-0	0-5	2-1	0-2	0-2	1-2
Congleton Vale	2-2	1-0	5-1	1-0	1-0	***I***	2-0	1-1	1-2	2-0	1-0	1-3	1-1	3-0	3-0	1-0	1-2	2-2
Eccleshall AFC	1-3	0-0	2-0	1-2	2-1	0-2	***E***	1-3	4-2	1-3	3-5	0-4	2-1	2-3	7-1	0-3	0-1	1-5
Florence	2-2	4-0	3-1	0-1	3-1	0-0	1-2	***R***	1-1	1-0	0-1	1-0	0-2	1-2	3-1	4-1	0-1	0-4
Foley	2-2	5-1	4-0	3-2	0-2	3-0	3-0	0-2		1-2	2-2	2-1	8-2	1-2	2-1	9-0	0-0	4-2
Goldenhill Wanderers	2-3	4-1	6-0	0-4	2-4	1-5	1-3	2-1	1-2	***D***	1-2	2-1	3-1	1-2	1-0	1-2	0-4	2-2
Hanley Town	2-1	4-0	1-1	1-3	1-0	0-1	4-0	1-1	3-2	1-3	***I***	3-0	3-0	1-0	2-1	2-1	1-1	2-1
Newcastle Town Res.	2-2	3-0	2-2	2-0	1-1	2-0	1-0	0-2	0-0	1-1	1-1	***V***	3-1	2-2	1-1	2-0	0-2	0-4
Norton	1-0	3-4	0-1	0-3	3-0	2-2	2-3	2-1	0-2	2-0	1-3	1-3	***I***	0-4	0-2	1-0	1-5	0-6
Redgate Clayton	4-1	2-2	4-0	3-2	3-0	3-1	1-0	1-1	1-2	5-0	1-1	1-3	1-2	***S***	3-1	0-2	4-0	1-3
Rocester Res.	2-6	0-5	2-6	0-5	1-1	1-3	1-1	0-4	0-2	0-1	1-6	2-1	1-6	2-6	***I***	3-1	1-1	0-7
Sandbach United	2-3	2-3	1-0	2-2	0-2	0-1	2-2	0-2	0-2	1-1	2-2	2-1	0-2	2-3	2-1	***O***	0-3	2-2
Stretton Eagles	2-0	5-0	2-1	3-1	1-1	1-1	1-1	4-1	1-3	0-0	1-3	2-1	1-1	0-0	5-1	2-0	***N***	2-1
Wolstanton United	4-0	6-0	8-0	5-3	2-0	2-0	1-0	2-0	1-2	2-0	2-0	2-1	2-1	0-0	2-2	3-1	1-1	

STAFFORDSHIRE COUNTY LEAGUE PREMIER DIVISION CONSTITUTION 2009-10

ABBEY HULTON UNITED.......... Birches Head Road, Abbey Hulton, Stoke-on-Trent ST2 8DD 01782 54423

BALL HAYE GREEN .... Ball Haye Green WMC, Ball Haye Green, Leek ST13 6BH 01538 37192

BARLASTON .... Motiva Park, Yarnfield Lane, Yarnfield, ST15 0NF.............................. 01782 76189

CONGLETON VALE . . Biddulph Victoria FC, Knypersley S&S, Tunstall Road, Knypersley, Stoke-on-Trent ST8 7AQ....... 01782 52273

ECCLESHALL AFC................... Pershall Park, Chester Road, Eccleshall ST21 6NE............................ 01785 85135

FLORENCE .... Florence Sports & Social, Lightwood Road, Longton, Stoke-on-Trent ST3 4JS............. 01782 31288

FOLEY .... Whitcombe Road, Meir, Stoke-on-Trent ST3 6NU.............................. 01782 59527

GOLDENHILL WANDERERS . . Sandyford Cricket Club, Shelford Rd, Sandyford, Stoke-on-Trent ST6 5LA 01782 83900

HANLEY TOWN................. Abbey Lane, Abbey Hulton, Bucknall, Stoke-on-Trent ST2 8AU 01782 26723

HOLT JCB .... Rocester FC, Hillsfield, Mill Street, Rocester, Rocester, Uttoxeter ST14 5TX 01889 59046

KIDSGROVE ATHLETIC RESERVES. . The Seddon Stadium, Hollinwood Rd, Kidsgrove ST7 1DH 01782 78241

MANOR INNE .... Alsager Town FC, The Town Ground, Wood Park, Alsager ST7 2DP 01270 88233

NEWCASTLE TOWN RESERVES Lyme Valley Parkway, Buckmaster Ave, Clayton, Newcastle-u-Lyme ST5 3BF. . . 01782 662351/62235

NORTON.............. Norton CC & MW Institute, Community Drive, Smallthorne, Stoke-on-Trent ST6 1QF.......... 01782 83829

REDGATE CLAYTON.............. Northwood Lane, Clayton, Newcastle-under-Lyme ST5 4BN 01782 71740

SANDBACH UNITED....... Winsford United FC, The Barton Stadium, Wharton Road, Winsford CW7 3AE 01606 55844

STRETTON EAGLES .... Shobnall Sports Ground, Shobnall Road, Burton-on-Trent DE14 2BB 01283 56799

WOLSTANTON UNITED . Bradwell Comm. Centre, Riceyman Road, Bradwell, Newcastle-under-Lyme ST5 8LF 01782 66081

IN: Holt JCB (P), Kidsgrove Athletic Res. (N), Manor Inne (P)

OUT: Alsager Town Res. (R), Audley & District (R - Division Two), Rocester Res. (F)

Division One	P	W	D	L	F	A	Pts
Manor Inne	26	19	3	4	85	34	60
Holt JCB	26	17	3	6	64	41	54
Hanley Town Res.	26	15	7	4	66	39	52
Barton United	26	13	7	6	60	38	46
Northwood Town	26	14	2	10	51	42	44
Chesterton	26	10	9	7	61	52	39
Congleton Athletic	26	10	7	9	53	58	37
Featherstone	26	10	6	10	66	66	36
Kidsgrove Carpets	26	9	7	10	42	43	34
Redgate Clayton Res.	26	8	6	12	48	44	30
Longton Harriers	26	6	8	12	38	57	26
Ashbourne United	26	5	6	15	48	77	21
Hawkins Sports	26	4	4	18	38	74	16
Stafford Town u-21s	26	3	3	20	36	91	12

Brereton Town - record expunged

LEAGUE CUP

(Premier and Division One teams)

FIRST ROUND

Abbey Hulton 4 Norton 0
Ashbourne United 0 **Redgate Clayton** 6
Ball Haye Green 10 Audley 1
Barlaston 0 **Foley** 5
Barton 1 Rocester Res. 0
Brereton Town 1 **Eccleshall AFC** 3 *aet*
Congleton Ath 3 Hanley 2
Florence 5 Chesterton 2
Goldenhill Wdrs 2 **Holt JCB** 0 *(Goldenhill expelled)*
Hanley Town Res. 2 **Kidsgrove Carpets** 4
Hawkins Sports 1 **Newcastle Town Res.** 5
Longton Harriers 3 Northwood Town 2
Manor Inne 0 **Stretton E.** 4
Redgate Clayton Res. 3 Congleton Vale 1
Stafford Town u-21s 2 **Sandbach United** 3
Wolstanton 1 Alsager Res. 0

SECOND ROUND

Abbey Hulton United 2 Stretton Eagles 1
Florence 0 **Redgate** 2 *aet*
Sandbach United 3 **Wolstanton United** 4 **aet**
Eccleshall AFC 2 Newcastle Town Res. 1
Longton 1 **Kidsgrove C.** 3
Congleton Athletic 1 **Ball Haye Green** 3
Foley 4 Redgate Clay. Res. 0
Holt JCB 2 **Barton United** 3

QUARTER-FINALS

Foley 1 **Abbey Hulton Utd** 5
Eccleshall AFC 2 **Wolstanton United** 3
Redgate Clayton 3 **Ball Haye Green** 5
Kidsgrove Carpets 0 **Barton United** 2

SEMI-FINALS

Wolstanton 4 Barton United 0
Abbey Hulton United 1 **Ball Haye Green** 2

FINAL

(April 27th at Norton United)
Ball Haye Green 3 Wolstanton Utd 3 *aet* (4-2p)

	Ashbourne United	Barton United	Brereton Town	Chesterton	Congleton Athletic	Featherstone	Hanley Town Res.	Hawkins Sports	Holt JCB	Kidsgrove Carpets	Longton Harriers	Manor Inne	Northwood Town	Redgate Clayton Res.	Stafford Town u-21s
Ashbourne United		1-3	15-1	7-2	4-3	5-2	0-3	4-3	3-5	1-5	1-1	0-4	3-3	0-2	2-2
Barton United	3-0	***D***	n/a	1-1	5-1	3-3	3-3	1-0	0-1	3-1	5-0	1-0	4-0	2-1	1-1
Brereton Town	n/a	1-6	***I***	n/a	n/a	n/a	0-2	0-2	3-3	1-3	n/a	n/a	n/a	n/a	n/a
Chesterton	1-0	3-3	n/a	***V***	2-2	1-2	4-1	5-0	4-5	0-0	3-3	6-4	1-0	0-0	2-1
Congleton Athletic	4-3	1-0	n/a	0-5	***I***	1-2	2-3	4-1	2-2	1-1	1-1	0-2	3-3	0-0	5-4
Featherstone	2-2	5-5	n/a	7-2	2-5	***S***	0-2	3-1	2-3	3-4	3-1	1-4	2-3	4-2	2-4
Hanley Town Res.	6-2	3-1	n/a	4-3	4-0	1-1	***I***	0-1	1-0	2-1	3-1	1-4	4-2	1-1	4-0
Hawkins Sports	1-1	2-5	n/a	2-2	1-2	1-3	1-1	***O***	0-3	0-1	5-2	0-6	1-4	4-3	6-1
Holt JCB	2-0	2-1	n/a	4-4	2-5	2-3	0-1	4-2	***N***	3-1	2-1	2-1	1-0	2-0	7-0
Kidsgrove Carpets	2-1	1-1	n/a	0-0	1-3	1-1	2-2	3-1	0-1		2-2	1-4	0-1	3-2	2-0
Longton Harriers	1-1	3-2	3-1	1-3	2-0	5-0	1-5	0-0	0-2	2-5		1-5	1-2	1-1	4-2
Manor Inne	5-0	3-0	n/a	3-1	2-2	2-2	4-4	6-2	4-1	2-1	2-0	***O***	3-2	1-0	5-1
Northwood Town	3-2	0-1	n/a	0-2	5-2	1-3	2-0	5-2	1-0	3-0	0-1	3-2	***N***	1-0	4-2
Redgate Clayton Res.	7-1	2-3	n/a	2-0	1-2	3-2	2-6	2-1	3-3	0-1	0-0	2-3	2-1	***E***	4-1
Stafford Town u-21s	2-4	0-3	n/a	0-4	0-2	2-6	1-1	3-0	2-5	4-3	2-3	0-4	0-2	1-6	

STAFFORDSHIRE COUNTY LEAGUE DIVISION ONE CONSTITUTION 2009-10

ALSAGER TOWN RESERVES .... The Town Ground, Wood Park, Alsager ST7 2DP 01270 882336
ASHBOURNE.................. Rocester FC, Hillsfield, Mill Street, Rocester, Uttoxeter ST14 5TX 01889 590463
BARTON UNITED .... Holland SC, Efflinch Lane, Barton-under-Needwood, Burton-upon-Trent DE13 8ET 01283 713972
CHEADLE TOWN OLD BOYS .... South Moorlands Leisure Centre, Allen Street, Cheadle ST10 1HJ 01538 753883
CHESTERTON .... Red Street Community Centre, Talke Road, Chesterton, Newcastle-under-Lyme ST5 7AH .... None
CONGLETON ATHLETIC .... Back Lane Playing Fields, Back Lane, Congleton CW12 4RB .... None
HANLEY TOWN RESERVES....... Abbey Lane, Abbey Hulton, Bucknall, Stoke-on-Trent ST8 8AJ.................. 01782 267234
HAWKINS SPORTS .... Hawkins Sports Club, Coppice Lane, Cheslyn Hay, Walsall WS6 7EY.............. 01922 417286
KEELE UNIVERSITY .... Sports Centre, Keele University, Keele ST5 5BG 01782 733368
LONGTON HARRIERS .... Malthouse, Leek Road, Cellarhead ST3 5DF........................... None
NORTHWOOD TOWN .... Northwood Stadium, Keeling Road, Hanley, Stoke-on-Trent ST1 6PA 01782 234400
REDGATE CLAYTON RESERVES ... Northwood Lane, Clayton, Newcastle-under-Lyme ST5 4BN 01782 717409
STONE DOMINOES RESERVES ...... Motiva Park, Yarnfield Lane, Yarnfield, Stone ST15 0NF 01782 761891
TALBOT ATHLETIC .... Bradeley Sports Centre, Chell Heath Road, Bradeley ST6 7LH......................... None
WOLSTANTON UNITED RESERVES Bradwell CC, Riceyman Rd, Bradwell, Newcastle-u-Lyme ST5 8LF............... 01782 660818

IN: Alsager Town Res. (R), Cheadle Town Old Boys (P), Keele University (N), Stone Dominoes Res. (N), Talbot Athletic (P), Wolstanton United Res. (P)

OUT: Brereton Town (WS), Featherstone (W), Holt JCB (P), Kidsgrove Athletic (W), Manor Inne (P), Stafford Town u-21s (W)

Ashbourne are a merger of Ashbourne United and Ashbourne Town (East Midlands Senior League Premier Division)

Division Two	P	W	D	L	F	A	Pts
Talbot Athletic	22	16	2	4	64	33	50
Wolstanton Utd Res.	22	15	5	2	60	31	50
Cheadle Town OB	22	15	4	3	80	27	49
Ball Green Y & A	22	12	6	4	74	39	42
Foley Res.	22	12	4	6	67	32	40
Abbey Hulton Utd Res.	22	10	3	9	65	30	33
Sandbach Utd u-19s	22	9	3	10	60	46	30
Waterhayes	22	9	2	11	55	52	29
Stone Old Alleyn. Res.	22	9	1	12	46	47	28
Florence Res.	22	6	4	12	37	51	22
Rugeley Rangers	22	2	0	20	36	90	6
Tunstall Town	22	0	0	22	7	173	0

SFC - record expunged

PRESIDENT'S TROPHY

(Division One and Division Two teams)

FIRST ROUND
Waterhayes 1 **Chesterton** 10
Ashbourne United 2 **Kidsgrove Carpets** 2 *aet* (3-4p)
Ball Green Y & A 1 Abbey Hulton United Res. 0
Cheadle 3 Northwood Town 1
Congleton A. 4 Foley Res. 1
Hawkins Sports 1 **Redgate Clayton Res.** 3 *aet*
Manor Inne 6 Longton H. 4
Rugeley Rangers 1 **Stone Alleynians Res.** 7
SFC 2 **Brereton Town** 3 *aet*
Sandbach u-19s 3 Holt JCB 1
Stafford Town u-21s 1 **Wolstanton United Res.** 2
Talbot Athletic (w/o) v Florence Res. (scr.)

SECOND ROUND
Ball GY& A 4 Hanley Res. 2
Chesterton 2 **Wolstanton United Res.** 3
Congleton Athletic (w/o) v Brereton Town (scr.)
Manor I. 4 Stone OA Res. 3
Talbot 1 **Sandbach u-19s** 3
Kidsgrove C. 8 Tunstall 1
Cheadle 4 Barton United 0
Redgate Clayton Res. (w/o) v Ball Haye Green Res. (scr.)

QUARTER-FINALS
Congleton A. 3 Kidsgrove C. 2
Cheadle Town Old Boys 1 **Ball Green Y & A** 2
Sandbach u-19s 0 **Manor I.** 3
Wolstanton United Res. 1 Redgate Clayton Res. 0 *aet*

SEMI-FINALS
Ball GY&A 2 Congleton Ath. 1
Wolstanton United Res. 2 **Manor Inne** 2 *aet* (4-5p)

FINAL
(April 20th at Norton United)
Ball Green Y & A 0 **Manor Inne** 2

	A Hulton	Ball G.	Cheadle	Florence	Foley	Rugeley	SFC	S'bach	Stone O	Talbot A.	Tunstall	W'hayes	Wolstan
Abbey Hulton United Res.	***D***	2-2	1-1	0-2	1-3	3-1	2-2	1-2	1-0	1-2	12-0	4-0	1-3
Ball Green Y & A	2-2	***I***	1-7	4-1	3-2	5-0	5-1	4-3	3-2	3-3	10-1	4-1	2-3
Cheadle Town Old Boys	1-0	2-2	***V***	0-0	1-1	4-2	n/a	4-1	6-0	4-0	8-0	2-1	2-3
Florence Res.	0-4	0-3	1-5	***I***	2-2	3-2	3-3	2-9	3-0	0-1	6-0	1-2	1-4
Foley Res.	5-2	1-1	2-6	2-1	***S***	7-1	n/a	0-0	2-0	4-1	8-0	2-0	2-0
Rugeley Rangers	0-5	3-4	2-7	1-4	1-6	***I***	2-6	1-3	3-4	0-6	8-0	0-2	1-5
SFC	n/a	2-3	n/a	4-2	n/a	10-2	***O***	2-1	n/a	n/a	7-2	n/a	n/a
Sandbach United u-19s	0-3	0-1	2-6	1-1	2-3	3-0	n/a	***N***	2-1	1-5	5-0	3-1	3-4
Stone Old Alleynians Res.	0-6	1-0	0-2	2-0	5-3	5-1	n/a	1-4		0-1	6-0	3-1	2-2
Talbot Athletic	0-4	3-1	5-1	3-2	3-1	4-0	3-0	3-1	3-1		6-0	4-2	0-4
Tunstall Town	0-9	0-14	0-7	0-3	0-11	1-5	n/a	0-11	1-9	0-5	***T***	0-9	1-7
Waterhayes	4-2	1-4	1-3	5-3	1-0	6-3	n/a	4-3	1-3	2-2	9-0	***W***	1-5
Wolstanton United Res.	2-1	1-1	2-1	1-1	1-0	3-1	n/a	1-1	2-1	1-4	5-3	1-1	***O***

STAFFORDSHIRE COUNTY LEAGUE DIVISION TWO CONSTITUTION 2009-10

AFC WATERHAYES. . . . . Holditch Miners Welfare, London Road, Chesterton, Newcastle-under-Lyme ST5 7PT 01782 56440
ABBEY HULTON UNITED RESERVES Birches Head Rd, Abbey Hulton, Stoke-on-Trent ST2 8DD 01782 54423
AUDLEY . . . . Town Fields, Old Road, Bignall, Stoke-on-Trent ST7 8QH. 01782 72348
CHEADLE SMU. . . . . South Moorlands Leisure Centre, Allen Street, Cheadle ST10 1HJ 01538 75388
FLORENCE RESERVES . . . . Florence Sports & Social, Lightwood Road, Longton, Stoke-on-Trent ST3 4JS. 01782 31288
FOLEY RESERVES . . . . Whitcombe Road, Meir, Stoke-on-Trent ST3 6NU 01782 59527
KEELE UNIVERSITY RESERVES . . . . Sports Centre, Keele University, Keele ST5 5BG 01782 73336
KIDSGROVE ATHLETIC YOUTH . . . . . . Alsager Leisure Club, Hassal Road, Alsager ST7 2HP 01270 52950
NORTON Y & A. . . . . Ball Green High School, Wilding Road, Ball Green, Stoke-on-Trent ST6 8BA . . . . Non
RUGELEY RANGERS . . . . Green Lane Playing Fields, Rugeley. . . . . Non
SANDBACH UNITED RESERVES . Legends Club, Bentley Works, Sunnybank Rd, Crewe CW2 8WD 01270 65686
STONE OLD ALLEYNIANS RESERVES . Motiva Park, Yarnfield Rd, Yarnfield, Stone ST15 0NF 01785 76189
STRETTON EAGLES RESERVES. . Shobnall Spts Ground, Shobnall Rd, Burton-on-Trent DE14 2BB 01283 56799
TUNSTALL TOWN . . . . Alsager Leisure Club, Hassal Road, Alsager ST7 2HP 01270 52950

IN: Audley (formerly Audley & District) (R - Premier Division), Cheadle SMU (N), Keele University Res. (N) , Kidsgrove Athletic Youth (N), Stretton Eagles Res. (P - Burton & District League Premier Division)
OUT: Ball Haye Green Res. (WN), Cheadle Town Old Boys (P), SFC (WS), Talbot Athletic (P), Wolstanton United Res. (P)
Ball Green Y & A become Norton Y & A, Sandbach United u-19s become Sandbach United Res.

LEEK & MOORLAND CUP

(Staffordshire County Senior League sides affiliated to Leek & District FA)

FIRST ROUND
Alsager Res. 1 **Newcastle T. Res.** 2
Eccleshall AFC 0 **Abbey Hulton** 4
Manor Inne 1 Florence 0
Stretton Eagles 5 Goldenhill Wdrs 1

SECOND ROUND
Abbey Hulton United 3 Norton 1
Audley & District 2 **Congleton Vale** 3
Barlaston 1 **Redgate Clayton** 2
Brereton Town (scr.) v **Northwood Town** (w/o)
Chesterton 1 **Ball Haye Green** 2
Manor Inne 2 Stretton Eagles 1
Sandbach United 1 **Hanley Town** 3
Wolstanton United 4 Newcastle Town Res. 2

QUARTER-FINALS
Abbey Hulton Utd 1 **Wolstanton Utd** 6
Ball Haye Green 2 **Congleton Vale** 3
Manor Inne 7 Northwood Town 0
Redgate Clayton 3 Hanley 2 *aet*

SEMI-FINALS
Redgate Clayton 3 Congleton Vale 2
Wolstanton United 2 **Manor Inne** 3

FINAL
(March 27th at Ball Haye Green)
Redgate Clayton 0 **Manor Inne** 2

SUFFOLK & IPSWICH LEAGUE

www.suffolkandipswichleague.co.uk

Sponsored by: Kingsley Healthcare

Founded: 1896

Recent champions:

2004: East Bergholt United

2005: East Bergholt United

2006: East Bergholt United

2007: Grundisburgh

2008: Brantham Athletic

	Capel Plough	Coplestonians	Crane Sports	East Bergholt	Felixstowe U.	Framlingham	Grundisburgh	Ipswich Ath.	Leiston St M.	Melton St A.	Ransomes	St Johns	Stonham A.	Stowupland	Westerfield	Woodbridge
Capel Plough	***S***	2-1	1-0	0-0	2-1	2-2	0-2	2-0	4-0	0-0	6-2	4-2	3-1	1-1	3-0	2-2
Coplestonians	0-6	***E***	0-1	3-2	0-6	0-1	2-1	2-3	1-0	1-2	0-2	4-3	0-2	0-1	0-0	1-2
Crane Sports	2-2	1-1	***N***	2-2	1-0	5-2	2-3	1-2	1-1	1-2	1-0	5-2	7-0	1-1	1-0	1-0
East Bergholt Utd	0-0	3-2	2-2	***I***	1-1	7-1	2-3	3-1	2-2	2-2	0-2	2-1	4-3	2-0	0-1	0-4
Felixstowe United	1-1	3-1	0-2	1-1	***O***	2-2	2-3	1-4	4-1	1-5	0-4	0-4	5-1	1-0	2-2	0-0
Framlingham Town	1-2	2-0	2-2	3-1	2-1	***R***	1-2	3-1	2-1	3-2	1-4	4-1	3-2	0-0	0-1	3-0
Grundisburgh	3-1	2-2	4-3	3-1	6-2	4-3		1-1	2-2	6-3	2-0	8-2	4-2	3-2	5-0	1-1
Ipswich Athletic	1-2	1-0	1-2	3-2	2-1	2-1	0-2		2-1	1-2	3-0	2-1	3-3	3-2	3-2	3-0
Leiston St Margarets	0-2	0-0	1-2	1-3	2-1	6-1	1-3	0-3	***D***	1-0	0-0	1-1	0-1	3-0	3-0	1-0
Melton St Audrys	0-0	2-3	1-2	3-0	3-2	3-3	1-1	1-5	2-0	***I***	0-2	3-1	2-1	2-0	4-2	1-2
Ransomes Sports	1-1	3-0	1-1	4-2	1-1	1-3	4-1	3-2	1-0	1-1	***V***	3-3	2-0	3-1	0-1	0-4
St Johns	2-3	5-0	1-4	2-4	5-0	6-2	1-2	4-1	1-2	1-3	2-1	***I***	3-3	1-3	3-4	1-1
Stonham Aspal	0-5	2-2	2-3	0-0	0-3	1-1	0-3	2-6	3-3	2-2	1-2	3-1	***S***	0-4	0-0	0-1
Stowupland Falcons	1-4	0-1	3-3	3-1	1-4	1-1	3-2	3-4	0-1	1-2	2-2	2-2	7-1	***I***	6-1	0-0
Westerfield United	0-2	1-3	0-4	5-0	3-1	0-1	0-1	1-0	1-2	1-0	1-3	4-0	2-3	1-4	***O***	1-2
Woodbridge Athletic	2-2	1-2	3-3	5-2	0-2	1-3	2-0	1-1	1-1	1-2	0-1	3-1	2-0	4-0	3-1	***N***

enior Division	P	W	D	L	F	A	Pts
rundisburgh	**30**	**21**	**5**	**4**	**83**	**46**	**68**
apel Plough	**30**	**17**	**11**	**2**	**65**	**28**	**62**
rane Sports	**30**	**15**	**10**	**5**	**66**	**40**	**55**
pswich Athletic	**30**	**17**	**3**	**10**	**64**	**49**	**54**
ansomes Sports	**30**	**15**	**7**	**8**	**53**	**40**	**52**
elton St Audrys	**30**	**14**	**7**	**9**	**56**	**47**	**49**
ramlingham Town	**30**	**13**	**7**	**10**	**57**	**61**	**46**
Voodbridge Athletic	**30**	**12**	**9**	**9**	**48**	**36**	**45**
eiston St Margarets	**30**	**9**	**8**	**13**	**37**	**44**	**35**
ast Bergholt United	**30**	**8**	**9**	**13**	**51**	**63**	**33**
towupland Falcons	**30**	**8**	**8**	**14**	**52**	**54**	**32**
elixstowe United	**30**	**8**	**7**	**15**	**49**	**60**	**31**
Vesterfield United	**30**	**9**	**3**	**18**	**36**	**59**	**30**
oplestonians	**30**	**8**	**5**	**17**	**32**	**60**	**29**
t Johns	**30**	**6**	**5**	**19**	**63**	**81**	**23**
tonham Aspal	**30**	**4**	**8**	**18**	**39**	**83**	**20**

Division One		P	W	D	L	F	A	Pts
Old Newton United		**26**	**18**	**3**	**5**	**76**	**39**	**57**
Achilles		**26**	**16**	**5**	**5**	**75**	**36**	**53**
Mendlesham		**26**	**15**	**4**	**7**	**70**	**43**	**49**
Wenhaston United		**26**	**15**	**1**	**10**	**62**	**49**	**46**
Stanton	**-6**	**26**	**16**	**3**	**7**	**63**	**37**	**45**
St Edmunds 65		**26**	**14**	**3**	**9**	**55**	**47**	**45**
Wickham Market		**26**	**12**	**6**	**8**	**57**	**42**	**42**
Cockfield United		**26**	**12**	**1**	**13**	**43**	**56**	**37**
Haughley United		**26**	**10**	**3**	**13**	**50**	**48**	**33**
Thurston		**26**	**9**	**3**	**14**	**63**	**71**	**30**
Bramford Road OB		**26**	**8**	**2**	**16**	**39**	**56**	**26**
BT Trimley	**-3**	**26**	**8**	**0**	**18**	**32**	**74**	**21**
Claydon		**26**	**5**	**2**	**19**	**32**	**69**	**17**
Willis		**26**	**5**	**2**	**19**	**36**	**86**	**17**

SUFFOLK & IPSWICH LEAGUE SENIOR DIVISION CONSTITUTION 2009-10

CHILLES . . . . Pauls Social Club, Selmet Close, Ipswich IP2 9BA 01473 604874
APEL PLOUGH . . . . Friars, Capel St Mary, Ipswich IP9 2XS . . . . None
OPLESTONIANS . . . . Copleston High School, Copleston Road, Ipswich IP4 5HD 01473 244178
RANE SPORTS. . . . . King George V Playing Field, Old Norwich Road, Ipswich IP1 6LE 01473 464030
AST BERGHOLT UNITED . . . . Gandish Road, East Bergholt, Colchester CO7 6TP. 01473 728581
ELIXSTOWE UNITED . . . . Trimley Sports & Social Club, High Road, Trimley St Martin, Felixstowe IP11 0RJ 01394 275240
RAMLINGHAM TOWN . . . . Sports Field, Badlingham Road, Framlingham, Woodbridge IP13 9HS. 01728 724038
RUNDISBURGH . . . . The Playing Field, Ipswich Road, Grundisburgh, Woodbridge IP13 6TJ 07974 047221
PSWICH ATHLETIC . . . . Bourne Vale Social Ground, Halifax Road, Ipswich IP2 8RE. 01473 687685
EISTON ST MARGARETS . . . . Junction Meadow, Abbey Road, Leiston IP16 4RD 01728 831239
IELTON ST AUDRYS . . . . St Audrys Sports & Social Club, Lodge Farm Lane, Melton, Woodbridge IP12 1LX . . . . None
LD NEWTON UNITED. . . . . Church Road, Old Newton, Stowmarket IP14 4ED 01449 770035
ANSOMES SPORTS. . . . . Ransomes Sports & Social Club, Sidegate Avenue, Ipswich IP4 4JJ 01473 726134
TOWUPLAND FALCONS. . . . . The Village Hall, Church Road, Stowupland IP14 4BQ. 01449 771010
VESTERFIELD UNITED . . . . . Rushmere Sports Club, The Street, Rushmere St Andrew, Ipswich IP5 1DE. 01473 272525
VOODBRIDGE ATHLETIC RAF Woodbridge, Rock Barracks, Otley Road, Sutton Heath Estate, Woodbridge IP2 3LU. . . . . None

N: Achilles (P), Old Newton United (P)

UT: St Johns (R), Stonham Aspal (R)

CLUB COLOURS JUNIOR CUP

FINAL *(April 25th at Framlingham Town)*

Stonham Aspal A 2 East Bergholt United A 1

J R TRAVEL RESERVES CUP

FINAL *(May 1st at Needham Market)*

Crane Sports Res. 3 Leiston St Margarets Res. 1

OMNICO CUP

FIRST ROUND

AFC Titans 0 **Stanton** 8
Aldeburgh Town 6 Sizewell 2
Bacton United 3 Elmswell 2
Benhall St Mary 1 **BT Trimley** 2 *aet*
Bildeston Rgrs 2 **Woolverstone** 9
Cockfield Utd 4 Sproughton Sports 0
Halesworth Town 6 Bramford 2
Haughley United 1 Henley Athletic 0
Ipswich Exiles 4 AFC Hoxne 1
John Bull United 0 **Albion Mills** 3
Needham Market Vets (w/o)
Martlesham Athletic (scr.)
Old Newton 6 St Clements Hospital 0
Shotley 0 **Trimley Red Devils** 9
Sporting '87 2 Sal. Army 2 *aet* (7-6p)
St Edmunds '65 8 Tacket Street 0
Thurston 5 Great Blakenham 0
Walsham-le-W. A 2 Ipswich Postals 1
Waterside 5 Stradbroke United 4 *aet*
Wenhaston Utd 4 Saxmundham 1
Willis 4 Ufford Sports 0

SECOND ROUND

Albion Mills 0 **Mendlesham** 3
Aldeburgh Town 2 **Ipswich United** 4
Bramford Rd 1 Bacton 1 *aet* (7-6p)
Claydon 3 Dennington United 0
Coddenham 0 **Achilles** 4
Halesworth 5 Tattingstone United 1
Old Newton United 3 Sporting '87 0
Parkside Utd (scr.) **BT Trimley** (w/o)
St Edmunds '65 2 Cockfield United 1
Stanton 6 AFC Crowley 4 *aet*
Walsham-le-Willows A 0 **Thurston** 3
Waterside 3 Somersham 1
Willis 3 Wenhaston United 1
Woolverstone 2 **Trimley Red Devils** 3
Needham Mkt Vets 1 **Wickham Mkt** 3
Ipswich Exiles 1 **Haughley United** 2

THIRD ROUND

Achilles 4 Ipswich United 2
Bramford Road Old Boys 1
Westerfield United 2
East Bergholt United 1
Coplestonians 2
Felixstowe United 6 Willis 1
Halesworth Town 2 **St Johns** 5
Ipswich Ath. 2 **Grundisburgh** 4 *aet*
Leiston St Margarets 6 Waterside 0
Melton St A 0 **Crane Sports** 1 *aet*
Old Newton Utd 0 **Ransomes Spts** 5
BT Trimley 0 **Claydon** 1
Stonham Aspal 1 **Capel Plough** 3
Stowupland F. 0 **St Edmunds '65** 2
Trimley Red Devils 2 Mendlesham 0
Wickham Market 1 Framlingham 0
Woodbridge Athletic 6 Stanton 2
Haughley United 4 Thurston 2 *aet*

FOURTH ROUND

Achilles 1 **Coplestonians** 1 *aet* (3-4p)
Felixstowe United 1 Trimley RD 0
Leiston St Margarets 2 Haughley 1
Ransomes 2 Capel P. 2 *aet* (4-1p)
St Edmunds 2 Woodbridge Ath. 1 *ae*
St Johns 0 **Crane Sports** 2
Westerfield 3 Wickham Market 1
Claydon 1 **Grundisburgh** 2

QUARTER-FINALS

Crane Sports 3 Leiston St Marg. 0
St Edmunds '65 0 **Grundisburgh** 2
Westerfield United 0 **Ransomes Sports** 4 *(at Ransomes Sports)*
Coplestonians 2 **Felixstowe United** 4

SEMI-FINALS

Ransomes Sports 3 Crane Sports 2
(at Bourne Vale Sports Club)
Grundisburgh 2 Felixstowe United 0
(at Melton St Audrys)

FINAL

(May 5th at Woodbridge Town)
Grundisburgh 0 **Ransomes Sports** 1

Intermediate Division A		P	W	D	L	F	A	Pt
Grundisburgh Res.		26	18	2	6	59	37	56
Old Newton United Res.		26	16	2	8	62	49	50
Melton St Audrys Res.		26	14	6	6	71	28	48
Ipswich Athletic Res.		26	15	3	8	65	42	48
East Bergholt United Res.		26	14	4	8	60	48	46
Crane Sports Res.		26	12	2	12	41	42	38
Coplestonians Res.		26	11	3	12	55	59	36
Achilles Res.		26	10	5	11	42	51	35
Capel Plough Res.		26	9	5	12	47	52	32
Stanton Res.		26	10	2	14	52	58	32
Ransomes Sports Res.		26	9	5	12	52	59	32
Felixstowe United Res.		26	8	4	14	40	52	28
Stowupland Falcons Res.		26	8	4	14	43	79	28
Stonham Aspal Res.		26	3	3	20	28	61	12

Intermediate Division B		P	W	D	L	F	A	Pt
Woodbridge Athletic Res.		24	19	0	5	92	28	5[illegible]
Westerfield United Res.		24	17	2	5	67	32	5[illegible]
St Johns Res.		24	16	2	6	89	46	5[illegible]
Cockfield United Res.	*-1*	23	14	1	8	65	47	4[illegible]
Framlingham Town Res.		23	12	2	9	61	56	3[illegible]
Leiston St Margarets Res.	*-1*	23	10	4	9	49	41	3[illegible]
Claydon Res.	*-1*	24	9	7	8	57	55	3[illegible]
Wickham Market Res.	*-1*	24	9	3	12	52	63	2[illegible]
Thurston Res.		24	9	2	13	46	60	2[illegible]
Wenhaston United Res.		24	8	2	14	50	62	2[illegible]
St Edmunds '65 Res.	*-2*	23	7	2	14	42	75	2[illegible]
Mendlesham Res.	*-1*	24	5	4	15	49	81	1[illegible]
BT Trimley Res.		24	2	3	19	32	105	[illegible]

Division Two		P	W	D	L	F	A	Pt
Halesworth Town		24	17	1	6	59	42	52
Saxmundham S.		24	15	6	3	65	24	51
Bacton United		24	13	5	6	69	40	44
Sporting 87		24	12	5	7	53	40	41
Ipswich Exiles		24	10	6	8	50	46	36
Parkside United		24	10	3	11	66	49	33
Elmswell		24	9	5	10	48	47	32
AFC Hoxne	*-3*	24	10	4	10	41	46	31
Salvation Army		24	10	0	14	49	62	30
Stradbroke United		24	7	5	12	51	58	26
Bramford United		24	8	2	14	53	69	26
Bildeston Rgrs	*-1*	24	5	7	12	43	67	21
Sizewell Ass.		24	4	3	17	27	84	15

Division Three		P	W	D	L	F	A	Pt
Trimley Red Dev.		22	19	3	0	76	20	60
Somersham		22	12	6	4	54	30	42
Henley Athletic		22	12	5	5	56	31	41
AFC Crowley		22	11	3	8	56	43	36
Ipswich United		22	11	2	9	55	45	35
Albion Mills		22	10	4	8	44	37	34
Waterside		22	9	3	10	52	54	30
John Bull United		22	9	3	10	47	56	30
Woolverstone Utd		22	8	3	11	49	63	27
Coplestonians A		22	6	3	13	54	64	21
St Clements Hosp		22	5	2	15	44	77	17
Ipswich Postals	*-1*	22	1	1	20	28	95	3

Division Four		P	W	D	L	F	A	Pt
Great Blakenham		24	15	6	3	59	32	51
Tacket St BBOB		24	14	5	5	60	41	47
Saxm'ham Res.	*-1*	24	13	6	5	55	37	44
Benhall St Mary		24	12	5	7	54	39	41
Ips. Exiles Res.		24	10	8	6	52	42	38
Sproughton Spts		24	10	6	8	48	33	36
Ufford Sports		24	10	5	9	50	39	35
Coddenham	*-6*	24	9	8	7	64	60	29
S'ham Aspal A		24	8	4	12	60	56	28
Walsham-le-W. A		24	7	4	13	44	57	25
Albion Mills Res.		24	6	6	12	36	47	24
Bramford Res.		24	5	3	16	40	67	18
Sizewell Res.	*-3*	24	3	2	19	29	101	8

Division Five		P	W	D	L	F	A	Pt
Tattingstone Utd		24	19	2	3	98	36	59
Aldeburgh Town		24	19	1	4	101	39	58
Bacton Utd Res.		23	17	3	3	74	36	54
Henley Ath. Res.		24	17	2	5	76	38	53
Sporting 87 Res.		24	13	0	11	55	50	39
Bramford Rd Res.		23	10	5	8	68	44	35
Woolverstone Res.		24	11	2	11	87	67	35
Salv. Army Res.		24	8	3	13	31	59	27
Stowupland F. A		24	7	3	14	44	72	24
AFC Hoxne Res.		24	5	4	15	45	85	19
Bildeston R. Res.		24	6	0	18	49	104	18
Stradbroke Res.	*-1*	24	4	2	18	45	96	13
Halesworth Res.	*-4*	24	3	5	16	33	80	10

Division Six		P	W	D	L	F	A	Pt
Elmswell Res.		22	18	2	2	81	31	56
East Bergholt A		22	14	5	3	85	33	47
AFC Titans		22	12	4	6	56	45	40
Old Newton U. A		22	11	4	7	59	45	37
Somersham Res.		22	11	3	8	52	47	36
Dennington Utd		22	10	1	11	58	64	31
St Clements Res.		22	8	6	8	50	47	30
Coddenham Res.		22	8	4	10	51	49	28
Benhall St M. Res.		22	6	3	13	43	72	21
Need. M. Vets	*-4*	22	6	5	11	26	36	19
Sproughton Res.		22	3	4	15	30	59	13
Shotley		22	4	1	17	26	89	13

SURREY ELITE INTERMEDIATE LEAGUE

Sponsored by:
No sponsor

Founded: 2008

	Bat	Cro	Elm	EpA	EpE	Esh	Eve	Hol	Hor	Lip	Mil	Old	Rei	Ton	Woo	Wra
Battersea Ironsides		3-1	3-1	2-3	0-0	7-0	0-1	4-2	0-0	0-3	1-0	0-0	3-1	11-0	5-0	2-2
Croydon Greenside	1-3		1-3	2-1	2-4	4-1	2-3	2-2	0-2	0-3	0-0	2-2	8-2	7-0	4-1	1-0
Elm Grove	0-1	0-4		3-3	0-2	3-1	2-4	n/a	0-2	0-3	2-0	3-3	3-1	7-4	5-1	0-1
Epsom Athletic	1-2	6-0	3-3		2-4	1-1	0-3	5-2	3-4	1-2	3-0	3-1	4-0	4-1	5-1	2-0
Epsom Eagles	1-3	3-1	4-1	3-3		W-L	2-1	n/a	4-0	3-2	4-2	4-2	3-5	3-0	5-1	W-L
Esher Athletic	L-W	1-0	2-4	0-1	0-3		1-8	n/a	1-2	1-2	1-3	0-1	3-2	7-1	4-2	0-2
Eversley	2-1	3-1	2-1	2-1	1-1	3-1		n/a	1-0	0-0	1-2	6-2	2-1	4-0	4-0	3-2
Holland Sports	n/a	2-6	0-3	1-1	0-1	1-3	0-4		n/a	n/a	n/a	n/a	n/a	n/a	n/a	n/a
Horsley	1-2	4-2	3-1	3-0	0-5	W-L	2-2	5-0		3-2	1-1	2-1	1-3	W-L	5-2	3-1
Liphook United	1-3	3-0	2-0	2-0	3-1	W-L	2-1	n/a	1-0		6-0	3-0	4-1	2-0	2-0	W-L
Milford & Witley	2-2	1-3	3-2	0-2	2-5	1-2	1-2	4-0	2-5	2-3		1-0	5-2	7-1	10-0	W-L
Old Rutlishians	1-2	1-1	2-1	2-3	1-3	3-3	1-2	n/a	1-3	2-1	1-2		2-0	6-0	2-1	1-3
Reigate Priory	1-2	0-3	0-3	0-5	0-4	2-1	0-3	3-0	1-3	0-5	3-0	1-3		6-2	2-3	W-L
Tongham	1-10	3-5	3-1	1-7	1-10	3-2	0-10	4-1	1-12	0-3	0-5	1-6	1-1		0-2	1-12
Woodmansterne Hyde	1-4	3-5	4-1	1-0	0-8	2-0	0-7	n/a	1-5	0-3	1-2	4-3	0-1	2-4		W-L
Wraysbury	2-4	2-0	0-0	2-2	3-1	9-0	1-1	n/a	1-0	1-0	L-W	L-W	3-1	9-0	11-1	

LEAGUE CUP

FIRST ROUND

Elm Grove 1 **Croydon Greenside** 2, Esher 0 **Liphook** 7
Eversley 5 Epsom Athletic 2
Holland Sports (scr.) **Epsom Eagles** (w/o)
Horsley 1 Battersea I'sides 0, **Milford** 7 Reigate Priory 0
Tongham 2 **Old Rutlishians** 6
Woodmansterne Hyde 2 **Wraysbury** 4

QUARTER-FINALS

Liphook United 2 Old Rutlishians 0
Horsley 4 **Croydon Greenside** 4 *aet* (3-5p)
Milford & Witley 0 **Eversley** 1
Wraysbury 5 **Epsom Eagles** 5 *aet* (4-5p)

SEMI-FINALS

Epsom Eagles 2 Croydon Greenside 0
Liphook United 0 **Eversley** 1

FINAL

(May 9th at Ashford Town (Middx))
Eversley 4 Epsom Eagles 1

Intermediate Division	P	W	D	L	F	A	Pts
Eversley	28	21	4	3	82	27	67
Liphook United	28	22	1	5	63	19	67
Epsom Eagles	28	21	3	4	90	36	66
Battersea Ironsides	28	19	5	4	76	27	62
Horsley	28	18	3	7	66	39	57
Epsom Athletic	28	13	5	10	69	45	44
Wraysbury	28	12	4	12	67	23	40
Milford & Witley	28	12	3	13	54	53	39
Croydon Greenside	28	11	3	14	60	58	36
Old Rutlishians	28	9	5	14	50	55	32
Elm Grove	28	8	4	16	50	62	28
Reigate Priory	28	7	1	20	37	79	22
Woodmansterne Hyde	28	7	0	21	34	107	21
Esher Athletic	28	5	2	21	33	69	17
Tongham	28	3	1	24	29	161	10

Holland Sports - record expunged

Reserve Division		P	W	D	L	F	A	Pt
Elm Grove Res.	*+2*	18	12	4	2	63	31	42
Battersea Ironsides Res.		18	11	4	3	56	20	37
Liphook United Res.		18	10	3	5	49	35	33
Eversley Res.	*+2*	18	7	9	2	37	20	32
Bedfont Sports Res.	*-1*	18	7	4	7	47	46	24
Horsley Res.		18	6	4	8	29	41	22
Reigate Priory Res.		18	6	3	9	30	58	21
Milford & Witley Res.	*+3*	18	4	2	12	26	44	17
Croydon Greenside Res.	*-4*	18	5	2	11	35	45	13
Epsom Eagles Res.		18	3	3	12	31	63	12

Tongham Res. - record expunged
Woodmansterne Hyde Res. – record expunged

RESERVES CUP FINAL

(May 7th at Chessington & Hook United)
Eversley Res. 3 Liphook Res. 3 *aet* (4-2p)

SUBSIDIARY CUP FINAL

(May 2nd at Horsley)
Eversley Res. 2 Croydon Greenside Res. 1

SURREY ELITE INTERMEDIATE LEAGUE INTERMEDIATE DIVISION CONSTITUTION 2009-10

BATTERSEA IRONSIDES . . . . Battersea Ironsides S&S Club, Openview, Earlsfield SW17 0AW 020 8874 9913
BLETCHINGLEY . . . . Grange Meadow, Godstone RH9 8LN 01883 742844
CROYDON GREENSIDE . . . . Cumnor House Sports Ground, Pampisford Road, Purley CR2 6DH 020 8665 5368
ELM GROVE . . . . Combe Lane, Whiteley Village, Walton-on-Thames KT12 4EL 01932 844671
EPSOM ATHLETIC . . . . Esher FC, Strenue Sports Ground, Lynwood Road, Thames Ditton KT7 0DN . . . . None
EPSOM EAGLES . . . . King Georges Field, Auriol Pk, Salisbury Road, Worcester Park KT4 7DG . . . . None
ESHER . . . . Strenue Sports Club, Lynwood Road, Thames Ditton KT7 0DN. . . . . None
HORSLEY . . . . Toms Field, Long Reach, West Horsley KT24 6NE 01483 282516
OLD RUTLISHIANS . . . . Old Rutlishians Association, Poplar Road, Merton Park SW19 3JS 020 8542 3678
OXTED & DISTRICT. . . . . Master Park, Church Lane, Oxted RH8 9LD 01883 716001
REIGATE PRIORY . . . . Reigate Priory Cricket Club, off Park Lane, Reigate RH2 8JX 01737 240872
RIPLEY VILLAGE . . . . The Green, Ripley, Woking GU23 6AR 01483 225484
SPELTHORNE SPORTS. . . . . Spelthorne Sports Club, 296 Staines Road West, Ashford TW15 1RY 01932 783625
TONGHAM . . . . Recreation Ground, Poyle Road, Tongham GU10 1BS. 01252 782893
WANDGAS SPORTS . . . . Wandgas Sports & Social, Grafton Road, Worcester Park KT4 7JW 020 8337 3666
WOODMANSTERNE HYDE. . . . . The Park, Woodmansterne Street, Woodmansterne 01737 350109

IN: Bletchingley (P - Crawley & District League Premier Division), Oxted & District (P - Surrey South Eastern Combination Intermediate Division One), Ripley Village (P - Surrey Intermediate League (West) Premier Division), Spelthorne Sports (P - Surrey Intermediate League (West) Premier Division), Wandgas Sports (P - Surrey South Eastern Combination Intermediate Division One)
OUT: Eversley (P - Combined Counties League Division One), Holland Sports (WS), Liphook United (S - Hampshire Premier League), Milford & Witley (R - Surrey Intermediate League (West) Premier Division), Wraysbury (R - East Berkshire League Premier Division)
Esher Athletic become Esher

WEARSIDE LEAGUE

www.wearside-football-league.org.uk

Sponsored by: No sponsor

Founded: 1892

Recent champions:

2004: North Shields

2005: Darlington Railway Athletic

2006: Whitehaven Amateurs

2007: Birtley Town

2008: New Marske Sports Club

	P	W	D	L	F	A	Pts
Newton Aycliffe	36	29	3	4	121	28	90
New Marske Sports Club	36	26	7	3	93	43	85
Easington Colliery	36	22	8	6	82	43	74
Teesside Athletic	36	21	11	4	77	40	74
Jarrow	36	21	5	10	72	38	68
Coxhoe Athletic	36	18	6	12	79	61	60
Ryhope Colliery Welfare	36	15	8	13	49	44	53
Annfield Plain	36	14	9	13	78	73	51
Ashbrooke Belford House	36	15	5	16	71	76	50
Kirkbymoorside	36	15	4	17	61	59	49
Cleator Moor Celtic	36	14	4	18	68	63	46
Hartlepool	36	14	4	18	54	61	46
Wolviston	36	10	10	16	55	69	40
Silksworth CC	36	11	6	19	50	75	39
Boldon Community Assoc.	36	11	6	19	49	94	39
Windscale	36	10	6	20	44	71	36
Guisborough Town HC	36	7	2	27	46	97	23
East Durham United	36	6	5	25	39	93	23
Willington	36	6	5	25	51	111	23

South Shields Harton & Westoe - record expunged

WEARSIDE LEAGUE CONSTITUTION 2009-10

ANNFIELD PLAIN .... Derwent Park, West Road, Annfield Plain DH9 8PZ .... Non
ASHBROOKE BELFORD HOUSE .... Silksworth Welfare, Silksworth, Sunderland .... Non
BOLDON COMMUNITY ASSOCIATION . Boldon Welfare, New Road, Boldon Colliery NE35 9DS .... 0191 536 4180 (Cricket Club
CLEATOR MOOR CELTIC .... Celtic Club, Birks Road, Cleator Moor CA25 5HR.......................... 01946 81247
COXHOE ATHLETIC .... Beechfield Park, Coxhoe DH6 4SD.................................. Non
EASINGTON COLLIERY .... Welfare Park Ground, Easington Colliery, Peterlee SR8 3JZ 0191 489 693
GUISBOROUGH TOWN HC .... King George Ground, Howlbeck Road, Guisborough TS14 6LA 01287 63692
HARTLEPOOL....................... Grayfields Enclose, Jesmond Gardens, Hartlepool.................................. Non
HOUGHTON TOWN .... Houghton Sports Complex, Leyburn Drive, Houghton-le-Spring DH4 5AH 01915 53646
JARROW.................... Perth Green Community Assoc., Inverness Road, Jarrow NE32 4AQ................ 0191 489 374
KIRKBYMOORSIDE .... Kirkby Mills, Kirkbymoorside, York YO62 6NS .... Non
NEW MARSKE SPORTS CLUB .... Gurney Street, New Marske, Redcar TS11 8EG 01642 47980
RYHOPE COLLIERY WELFARE. . Ryhope Recreation Park, Ryhope St, Ryhope, Sunderland SR2 0AB................ 0191 521 284
SCARBOROUGH TOWN . George Pindar Comm. Spts College, Moor Lane, Eastfield, Scarborough YO11 3LW 01723 58219
SILKSWORTH CC .... Silksworth Welfare Park, Silksworth, Sunderland .... Non
TEESSIDE ATHLETIC .... Green Lane, Redcar TS10 3RW.................................. Non
WILLINGTON..................... Hall Lane Ground, Hall Lane Estate, Willington DL15 0QF 01388 74622
WINDSCALE......................... Falcon Field, Smithfield, Egremont CA22 2QN 01946 82042
WOLVISTON.................. Metcalfe Park, Wynyard Road, Wolviston, Billingham TS22 5NE 07768 32165

IN: Houghton Town (formerly Sunderland South) (P - Durham Alliance), Scarborough Town (Teesside League Division Two)
OUT: East Durham United (W), Newton Aycliffe (P - Northern League Division Two), South Shields Harton & Westoe Colliery Welfare (WS

MONKWEARMOUTH CHARITY CUP

PRELIMINARY ROUND

Coxhoe Athletic 1 **Easington Colliery** 2
East Durham United 3 Belford House 2 *aet*
Guisborough Town HC 3 Hartlepool 1
Silksworth CC 0 **Newton Aycliffe** 2

FIRST ROUND

Boldon Community Association 0 **Cleator Moor Celtic** 6
Easington Colliery 0 **Jarrow** 4
Newton Aycliffe 2 **Kirkbymoorside** 3
Ryhope Colliery Welfare 0 **New Marske Sports Club** 3
Teesside Athletic 1 **Annfield Plain** 3
Willington 0 **East Durham United** 1
Windscale (w/o) v Guisborough Town HC (scr.)
Wolviston (w/o) v South Shields Harton & Westoe (scr.)

QUARTER-FINALS

Kirkbymoorside 2 **Annfield Plain** 3 *aet*
New Marske Sports Club 4 East Durham United 0
Windscale 0 **Jarrow** 2
Wolviston 2 Cleator Moor Celtic 0

SEMI-FINALS

Annfield Plain 1 Wolviston 0
New Marske Sports Club 0 **Jarrow** 4

FINAL

(April 10th at Jarrow)
Jarrow 1 **Annfield Plain** 4

	Annfield Plain	Belford House	Boldon Community Association	Cleator Moor Celtic	Coxhoe Athletic	Easington Colliery	East Durham United	Guisborough Town HC	Hartlepool	Jarrow	Kirkbymoorside	New Marske Sports Club	Newton Aycliffe	Ryhope Colliery Welfare	Silksworth CC	South Shields Harton & Westoe	Teesside Athletic	Willington	Windscale	Wolviston
Annfield Plain		4-4	6-1	0-3	3-0	3-1	2-1	1-0	1-0	1-3	1-1	2-4	0-3	6-0	1-2	n/a	1-1	4-4	2-0	0-3
Belford House	2-2		0-1	2-1	5-3	0-1	4-3	2-1	4-0	1-3	2-6	4-4	1-2	0-2	1-0	n/a	1-2	0-2	1-1	2-4
Boldon Community Assoc.	3-3	2-2		3-1	1-7	0-2	2-0	3-1	3-1	2-1	0-2	1-4	1-8	0-2	4-3	n/a	2-5	4-4	1-4	4-3
Cleator Moor Celtic	5-4	2-4	6-2		2-1	0-2	2-0	6-1	1-0	1-3	5-1	1-3	0-3	1-2	2-3	n/a	0-1	3-3	2-4	8-2
Coxhoe Athletic	2-2	3-0	4-1	1-0		6-1	3-2	2-0	2-1	1-3	7-1	0-3	1-1	1-0	4-1	n/a	3-4	5-2	2-2	3-0
Easington Colliery	1-0	7-1	2-1	2-2	6-1		2-0	8-1	4-1	2-0	3-1	1-2	1-0	1-4	1-0	4-1	2-0	1-1	6-0	2-2
East Durham United	2-2	0-5	0-0	0-2	1-0	0-3		1-2	1-2	0-3	0-2	1-8	0-2	0-2	4-2	n/a	3-4	5-1	2-0	1-6
Guisborough Town HC	1-5	1-3	0-1	0-1	1-1	1-2	2-4		0-2	3-4	4-3	2-3	1-2	1-2	2-1	n/a	1-1	5-2	3-0	1-2
Hartlepool	0-3	3-1	1-0	2-1	3-4	1-1	2-1	0-2		0-4	1-3	2-2	1-4	1-0	4-1	2-1	0-2	4-0	2-1	4-2
Jarrow	1-3	1-3	3-0	2-0	4-0	1-1	6-1	4-2	1-0		0-1	1-1	2-0	1-0	0-0	n/a	3-1	5-1	2-1	0-0
Kirkbymoorside	2-1	0-1	4-1	2-0	0-2	3-4	1-2	2-1	1-2	1-0		0-3	2-3	1-1	1-1	n/a	1-1	2-1	5-1	3-0
New Marske Sports Club	5-1	2-1	1-1	2-1	0-1	1-3	5-1	2-0	1-0	3-0	3-2		2-1	2-0	3-2	n/a	0-0	7-1	1-0	0-0
Newton Aycliffe	7-3	4-1	3-0	2-0	2-2	2-0	6-0	6-1	3-2	2-0	2-0	5-0		6-1	8-0	n/a	0-2	5-0	5-0	3-1
Ryhope Colliery Welfare	1-0	0-2	1-1	0-0	3-1	1-1	0-0	5-0	2-1	1-2	2-1	1-2	0-1		1-2	2-0	0-0	2-2	3-0	2-0
Silksworth CC	1-2	1-3	0-1	3-0	3-0	2-3	0-0	2-3	1-1	3-2	2-1	1-3	1-7	0-2		n/a	1-1	1-0	3-1	2-0
S. Shields Harton & Westoe	n/a	n/a	n/a	n/a	n/a	n/a	n/a	n/a	n/a	n/a	n/a	n/a	n/a	n/a	n/a		n/a	n/a	n/a	n/a
Teesside Athletic	5-2	4-0	1-2	0-0	1-0	0-0	1-1	4-1	3-2	0-0	1-0	2-2	1-5	3-0	5-1	n/a		3-1	4-1	3-2
Willington	1-2	1-5	1-0	1-4	0-2	3-4	3-2	5-1	0-4	1-4	0-2	1-2	1-5	1-4	1-2	1-3	0-3		2-3	0-4
Windscale	0-2	0-2	6-0	1-2	2-2	0-0	4-0	3-0	0-3	1-0	1-0	1-3	0-3	1-0	2-1	1-1	2-5	0-1		1-1
Wolviston	3-3	3-1	2-0	1-3	0-2	2-1	2-0	2-0	1-1	0-3	0-3	2-4	0-0	2-2	1-1	n/a	0-3	2-3	0-0	

SUNDERLAND SHIPOWNERS CUP

PRELIMINARY ROUND

Belford House 0 **East Durham United** 2
New Marske Sports Club 3 **Silksworth CC** 3 *aet* (3-5p)
Newton Aycliffe 3 Kirkbymoorside 2
Wolviston 3 Ryhope Colliery Welfare 2 *aet*

FIRST ROUND

Cleator Moor Celtic 8 Boldon Community Association 0
Coxhoe Athletic 5 Hartlepool 0
Easington Colliery 6 Windsale 2
East Durham United 1 **Wolviston** 6
Jarrow 2 Willington 0
Newton Aycliffe 1 Guisborough Town HC 0
South Shields Harton & Westoe 3 **Annfield Plain** 4 *aet*
Teesside Athletic 4 Silksworth CC 1

QUARTER-FINALS

Cleator Moor Celtic 1 **Newton Aycliffe** 1 *aet* (3-4p)
Coxhoe Athletic 1 **Teesside Athletic** 2
Easington Colliery 2 Wolviston 1
Jarrow 2 Annfield Plain 2 *aet* (5-4p)

SEMI-FINALS

Newton Aycliffe 4 Jarrow 2
Teesside Athletic 2 Easington Colliery 1

FINAL

(May 22nd at Newton Aycliffe)
Newton Aycliffe 0 **Teesside Athletic** 1

LEAGUE CUP

Not contested in 2008-09

WEST CHESHIRE LEAGUE

www.west-cheshire.org.uk

Sponsored by: Carlsberg

Founded: 1892

Recent champions:
2004: Newton
2005: Heswall
2006: Poulton Victoria
2007: West Kirby
2008: West Kirby

	Aintree	Blacon	CL Res.	Castrol	Christ.	E'mere	Halton	Heswall	Maghull	Marine.	N Bright.	Newton	Poulton	Runc.	Upton	Vauxhall	W Kirby
Aintree Villa		6-0	0-2	0-3	3-3	3-1	3-0	3-1	3-1	1-1	1-0	n/a	n/a	2-5	1-2	n/a	n/a
Blacon Youth Club	n/a		1-5	0-2	1-3	0-4	5-3	0-2	1-3	0-3	n/a	0-1	2-6	0-7	1-2	1-2	1-4
Cammell Laird Res.	n/a	3-1	***D***	2-0	3-0	0-3	5-0	0-0	2-1	3-0	n/a	1-3	1-1	0-2	1-3	2-4	1-1
Castrol Social	2-2	3-0	0-3	***I***	1-2	1-2	2-1	2-2	3-0	3-0	5-0	4-3	0-0	1-0	0-1	2-1	0-1
Christleton	n/a	5-1	0-3	2-2	***V***	3-1	0-3	0-2	1-3	0-0	n/a	0-1	0-3	2-3	1-1	2-2	0-4
Ellesmere Port	0-3	4-1	0-5	0-2	1-2	***I***	4-1	3-3	0-2	1-1	n/a	2-2	0-2	0-0	1-2	2-0	1-4
Halton	1-6	1-1	3-2	1-2	0-1	1-2	***S***	0-2	1-1	0-1	n/a	0-2	3-1	1-3	1-2	1-1	3-8
Heswall	0-1	2-2	1-6	2-0	2-1	1-3	3-1	***I***	0-2	0-1	n/a	2-5	0-3	0-2	2-4	3-2	2-1
Maghull	n/a	3-1	3-1	1-2	2-0	0-2	3-1	3-0	***O***	3-3	2-0	2-2	0-2	4-4	2-3	4-1	1-5
Marine Res.	2-2	4-1	2-3	1-2	2-1	5-4	3-1	1-1	1-3	***N***	n/a	1-2	0-1	0-7	0-2	4-1	1-2
New Brighton	n/a	n/a	n/a	n/a	n/a	n/a	n/a	n/a	n/a	n/a		n/a	0-4	n/a	n/a	n/a	n/a
Newton	2-1	3-1	4-2	0-1	2-1	1-1	0-1	6-1	3-1	0-0	n/a		0-3	3-1	1-2	1-1	3-2
Poulton Victoria	8-2	1-0	2-1	6-2	2-1	1-2	3-0	5-1	1-1	1-2	n/a	0-1	***O***	0-0	2-0	0-0	1-1
Runcorn Town	2-1	0-0	2-2	1-2	3-1	3-2	4-2	1-1	6-0	1-4	n/a	2-1	3-0	***N***	2-3	4-0	0-4
Upton Athletic Association	2-4	2-1	0-3	1-0	2-1	0-2	4-2	0-3	3-0	3-1	n/a	4-3	0-2	2-2	***E***	0-1	2-2
Vauxhall Motors Res.	1-1	4-2	0-5	0-1	4-3	2-1	3-1	4-3	1-2	1-1	n/a	4-1	0-5	0-6	1-1		1-2
West Kirby	4-0	6-0	3-2	5-1	2-2	1-0	5-0	4-1	3-1	1-5	n/a	1-2	2-1	0-0	2-2	1-0	

Division One		P	W	D	L	F	A	Pts
West Kirby		**28**	**18**	**6**	**4**	**77**	**34**	**60**
Upton Athletic Assoc.		**28**	**17**	**5**	**6**	**51**	**40**	**56**
Poulton Victoria		**28**	**16**	**6**	**6**	**55**	**23**	**54**
Runcorn Town		**28**	**14**	**8**	**6**	**69**	**35**	**50**
Newton		**28**	**15**	**5**	**8**	**56**	**41**	**50**
Castrol Social		**28**	**15**	**3**	**10**	**41**	**38**	**48**
Cammell Laird Res.		**28**	**14**	**4**	**10**	**67**	**40**	**46**
Maghull		**28**	**12**	**5**	**11**	**51**	**53**	**41**
Marine Res.		**28**	**11**	**6**	**11**	**47**	**48**	**39**
Ellesmere Port		**28**	**11**	**5**	**12**	**48**	**46**	**38**
Heswall		**28**	**9**	**6**	**13**	**42**	**62**	**33**
Vauxhall Mtrs Res.	*-3*	**28**	**9**	**6**	**13**	**41**	**61**	**30**
Christleton		**28**	**6**	**5**	**17**	**35**	**56**	**23**
Halton	*-3*	**28**	**4**	**3**	**21**	**33**	**73**	**12**
Blacon Youth Club		**28**	**1**	**3**	**24**	**25**	**88**	**6**

Aintree Villa - record expnged

New Brighton - record expunged

PYKE CUP

FIRST ROUND

Aintree Villa 0 **Maghull** 2

SECOND ROUND

Maghull 2 **Poulton Victoria** 4
Blacon Youth Club 1 **Castrol Social** 6
Christleton 1 **Ellesmere Port** 2
Halton 0 **Marine Res.** 2
Heswall 1 Cammell Laird Res. 0
New Brighton (scr.) v **Runcorn Town** (w/o)
Newton 2 West Kirby 4 *(West Kirby expelled)*
Vauxhall Motors Res. 2 Upton Athletic Association 1

QUARTER-FINALS

Marine Res. 2 **Ellesmere Port** 3 *aet*
Poulton Victoria 0 **Castrol Social** 1
Runcorn Town 0 **Heswall** 1
Vauxhall Motors Res. 1 **Newton** 2

SEMI-FINALS

Newton 2 Castrol Social 0
Ellesmere Port 1 **Heswall** 2

FINAL

(April 10th at Vauxhall Motors)
Heswall 0 **Newton** 3

WEST CHESHIRE LEAGUE DIVISION ONE CONSTITUTION 2009-10

BLACON YOUTH CLUB . . . . Cairns Crescent Playing Fields, Blacon, Chester CH1 5JF . . . . Non
CAMMELL LAIRD RESERVES . . . . . Kirklands, St Peters Road, Rock Ferry, Birkenhead CH42 1PY 0151 645 312
CASTROL SOCIAL. . . . . Castrol Sports & Social Club, Chester Road, Whitby, Ellesmere Port CH66 2NX 0151 357 371
CHRISTLETON. . . . . Little Heath Road, Christleton, Chester CH3 7AH. 01244 33658
ELLESMERE PORT . . . . Whitby Sports & Social Club, Chester Road, Whitby, Ellesmere Port CH66 2NX. 0151 200 7080/705
HALTON. . . . . Pavilions Club, Sandy Lane, Weston Point, Runcorn WA7 4EX 01928 590 50
HELSBY. . . . . Helsby Community Sports Club, Chester Road, Helsby WA6 0DL 01928 72226
HESWALL. . . . . Gayton Park, Brimstage Road, Heswall CH60 1XG. 0151 342 817
MAGHULL . . . . Old Hall Field, Hall Lane, Maghull L31 7BB. 0151 526 732
MARINE RESERVES. . . . . Arriva Stadium, College Road, Crosby, Liverpool L23 3AS 0151 924 1743/404
NEWTON . . . . Millcroft, Frankby Road, Greasby CH47 0NB 0151 677 828
RUNCORN TOWN. . . . . Pavilions Club, Sandy Lane, Weston Point, Runcorn WA7 4EX 01928 59050
UPTON ATHLETIC ASSOCIATION . . Cheshire Co. S&S Club, Plas Newton Lane, Chester CH2 1PR 01244 31816
VAUXHALL MOTORS RESERVES Vauxhall Spts Ground, Rivacre Rd, Hooton, Ellesmere Pt CH66 1NJ. 0151 328 1114/327 229
WEST KIRBY . . . . Marine Park, Greenbank Road, West Kirby CH48 5HL . . . . Non
WILLASTON. . . . . Johnston Recreation Ground, Neston Road, Willaston CH64 2TL. . . . . Non

IN: Helsby (P), Willaston (P)

OUT: Aintree Villa (WS), New Brighton (WS), Poulton Victoria (F)

COOPER SMITH TROPHY

(May 2nd at Cammell Laird)

West Cheshire League 5 Cheshire County League 0

Division Two	P	W	D	L	F	A	Pts
Helsby	30	22	5	3	78	29	71
Willaston	30	16	10	4	78	43	58
Ashville	30	17	6	7	77	48	57
Mossley Hill Athletic	30	17	4	9	57	34	55
Maghull Res.	30	14	9	7	49	40	51
Southport Trinity	30	12	9	9	54	45	45
Poulton Victoria Res.	30	13	5	12	42	45	44
Mallaby	30	12	6	12	52	59	42
West Kirby Res.	30	12	5	13	70	51	41
Capenhurst Villa	30	12	5	13	60	59	41
AFC Bebington Athletic	30	10	9	11	52	63	39
Chester Nomads	30	9	5	16	48	58	32
New Brighton Res.	30	8	8	14	42	64	32
Bronze Social	30	9	4	17	44	61	31
Grange Athletic	30	5	7	18	44	79	22
Heswall Res.	30	2	3	25	24	93	9

WEST CHESHIRE BOWL

FIRST ROUND

AFC Bebington Athletic 3 Heswall Res. 2
Bronze Social 1 **Grange Athletic** 4
Chester Nomads 1 **Capenhurst Villa** 4
Helsby 4 Willaston 1
Mossley Hill Athletic 4 Ashville 2
Poulton Victoria Res. 2 Maghull Res. 1 *aet*
Southport Trinity 4 New Brighton Res. 2
West Kirby Res. 0 **Mallaby** 5

QUARTER-FINALS

Helsby 5 Capenhurst Villa 4
Mallaby 5 Mossley Hill Athletic 2
Poulton Victoria Res. 2 Grange Athletic 0
Southport Trinity 0 **AFC Bebington Athletic** 2

SEMI-FINALS

Mallaby 1 Poulton Victoria Res. 0
Helsby 4 AFC Bebington Athletic 3

FINAL

(April 30th at Cammell Laird)

Mallaby 3 **Helsby** 7

	AFC Bebington	Ashville	Bronze Social	Capenhurst	Chester Nmds	Grange Athletic	Helsby	Heswall Res.	Maghull Res.	Mallaby	Mossley Hill A.	N B'ton Res.	Poulton V. Res.	Southport Trin.	W. Kirby Res.	Willaston
AFC Bebington Athletic		3-2	2-3	2-2	1-1	2-2	1-5	5-3	2-3	1-0	1-5	1-1	1-3	1-1	2-2	1-3
Ashville	2-0		4-3	5-1	2-0	4-0	2-1	0-1	1-3	7-0	1-1	1-2	3-3	2-2	1-4	1-1
Bronze Social	0-2	2-3	***D***	0-5	2-0	2-1	1-2	3-1	0-4	4-0	1-0	3-2	1-2	1-1	0-3	3-1
Capenhurst Villa	1-3	2-4	1-0	***I***	2-1	5-1	1-3	4-1	6-2	4-1	1-3	1-0	0-2	0-1	1-0	1-1
Chester Nomads	2-4	1-4	1-0	1-6	***V***	2-3	3-4	7-1	2-1	1-3	3-1	3-2	0-1	3-1	1-0	0-1
Grange Athletic	2-3	0-2	3-1	4-3	3-3	***I***	1-3	3-0	0-0	3-3	1-6	2-3	1-1	0-2	1-1	2-1
Helsby	5-0	2-2	4-1	2-0	2-0	3-1	***S***	2-0	0-0	3-3	2-0	4-1	3-0	2-1	2-1	1-1
Heswall Res.	2-2	1-3	1-1	1-2	0-3	1-0	0-4	***I***	1-4	0-2	1-3	1-4	1-2	0-0	0-8	0-4
Maghull Res.	0-2	4-4	2-1	1-1	2-2	3-1	0-4	3-2	***O***	2-0	0-1	1-1	3-0	0-2	1-1	2-1
Mallaby	1-1	0-1	3-1	3-1	0-3	6-1	1-4	5-1	2-1	***N***	0-0	1-1	1-1	0-3	3-1	2-4
Mossley Hill Athletic	0-1	0-1	1-1	5-2	3-1	1-0	2-0	2-0	0-1	3-1		2-0	1-3	3-0	4-3	2-0
New Brighton Res.	1-3	2-6	2-0	0-0	1-0	3-3	0-2	2-0	0-1	1-3	0-2	***T***	3-1	4-4	0-4	1-1
Poulton Victoria Res.	1-0	3-4	0-3	3-2	2-0	3-1	0-1	2-0	1-1	1-2	0-1	1-2	***W***	1-0	1-0	3-3
Southport Trinity	3-1	3-1	5-2	0-0	0-0	2-1	2-1	4-3	2-3	1-2	2-1	1-1	4-1	***O***	1-2	1-3
West Kirby Res.	5-2	1-3	3-3	2-3	3-1	4-2	1-4	2-0	0-1	2-3	1-1	7-2	2-0	4-3		2-3
Willaston	2-2	2-1	2-1	7-2	3-3	6-1	3-3	7-1	0-0	2-1	6-3	5-0	1-0	2-2	2-1	

WEST CHESHIRE LEAGUE DIVISION TWO CONSTITUTION 2009-10

AFC BEBINGTON ATHLETIC .... Unilever Sports Ground, Bromborough CH62 3PU.............................. None
ASHVILLE..................... Villa Park, Cross Lane, Wallasey Village, Wallasey CH45 8RH 0151 638 2127
BRONZE SOCIAL .... Unilever Sports Ground, Bromborough CH62 3PU.............................. None
CAPENHURST VILLA.......... Capenhurst Sports Ground, Capenhurst Lane, Capenhurst CH1 6ER .... None
CHESTER NOMADS .... Garrison Ground, Eaton Road, Chester, CH4 7ER.............................. None
FC PENSBY .... Ridgewood Park, Fishers Lane, Pensby CH61 5XF .... None
GRANGE ATHLETIC................ Netherpool Sports Ground, Ellesmere Port CH66 2TH .... None
HESWALL RESERVES............... Gayton Park, Brimstage Road, Heswall CH60 1XG.................... 0151 342 8172
MAGHULL RESERVES.................. Old Hall Field, Hall Lane, Maghull L31 7BB...................... 0151 526 7320
MALLABY......................... Unilever Sports Ground, Bromborough CH62 3PU.............................. None
MARSHALLS .... IM Marsh Campus, Barkhill Road, Aigburth, Liverpool L17 6BD............... 0151 231 5233
MOSSLEY HILL ATHLETIC .... Mossley Hill Athletic Club, Mossley Hill Road, Liverpool L18 8DX 0151 724 4377
NEW BRIGHTON .... Harrison Drive, Wallasey Village, Wallasey CH45 3HL .... None
SOUTHPORT TRINITY............... Police Club, Fairfield, Prescot Road, Liverpool L7 0JD 0151 228 2352
WEST KIRBY RESERVES .... Marine Park, Greenbank Road, West Kirby CH48 5HL .... None

IN: FC Pensby (P), Marshalls (P)

OUT: Helsby (P), Poulton Victoria Res. (F), Willaston (P)

New Brighton Res. become New Brighton

Division Three		P	W	D	L	F	A	Pts
FC Pensby		**30**	**22**	**4**	**4**	**64**	**28**	**70**
Marshalls		**30**	**18**	**5**	**7**	**98**	**42**	**59**
Runcorn Town Res.		**30**	**16**	**7**	**7**	**74**	**49**	**55**
Christleton Res.		**30**	**14**	**10**	**6**	**62**	**39**	**52**
Richmond Raith R. Jacobs		**30**	**13**	**11**	**6**	**56**	**38**	**50**
Hale		**30**	**14**	**7**	**9**	**74**	**46**	**49**
Upton Athletic Ass. Res.		**30**	**14**	**5**	**11**	**62**	**58**	**47**
Ashville Res.		**30**	**11**	**11**	**8**	**57**	**49**	**44**
Capenhurst Villa Res.		**30**	**12**	**7**	**11**	**57**	**50**	**43**
Mersey Royal		**30**	**11**	**6**	**13**	**62**	**60**	**39**
Manor Athletic	*-3*	**30**	**11**	**5**	**14**	**65**	**64**	**35**
Ellesmere Port Res.		**30**	**8**	**9**	**13**	**56**	**74**	**33**
Southport Trinity Res.		**30**	**8**	**5**	**17**	**42**	**78**	**29**
FOCUS	*-3*	**30**	**8**	**5**	**17**	**53**	**94**	**26**
St Werburghs	*-3*	**30**	**5**	**6**	**19**	**53**	**97**	**18**
Blacon Youth Club Res.		**30**	**2**	**3**	**25**	**32**	**101**	**9**

WEST CHESHIRE SHIELD

FIRST ROUND

Ashville Res. 1 Runcorn Town Res. 2
(Runcorn Town Res. expelled)
Blacon Youth Club Res. 2 Southport Trinity Res. 3
(Southport Trinity Res. expelled)
Capenhurst Villa Res. 5 Hale 3
Ellesmere Port Res. 2 **Manor Athletic** 4
Marshalls 2 **St Werburghs** 5
Mersey Royal 2 FOCUS 0
Richmond Raith Rovers Jacobs 2 Christleton Res. 0
Upton AA Res. 1 FC Pensby 4 *(Upton Res. expelled)*

QUARTER-FINALS

Capenhurst Villa Res. 1 **Ashville Res.** 2 *aet*
St Werburghs 1 **Manor Athletic** 2
Richmond Raith Rovers Jacobs 3 **Upton AA Res.** 4
Mersey Royal (scr.) v **Blacon Youth Club Res.** (w/o)

SEMI-FINALS

Ashville Res. 4 Blacon Youth Club Res. 1 *aet*
Upton AA Res. 4 Manor Athletic 4 *aet* (3-1p)

FINAL *(May 1st at Vauxhall Motors)*

Upton AA Res. 3 Ashville Res. 0

	Ash	Bla	Cap	Chr	Ell	FCP	Foc	Hale	Man	Mar	Mer	Ric	Run	Sou	StW	Upt
Ashville Res.		5-2	0-0	1-1	1-2	2-1	2-1	1-3	3-2	2-0	1-1	1-1	3-2	0-0	3-1	1-3
Blacon Youth Club Res.	1-5	***D***	1-5	1-7	1-3	0-6	3-3	2-4	0-4	1-7	1-5	2-2	1-2	2-3	3-0	1-2
Capenhurst Villa Res.	2-2	1-0	***I***	2-1	5-2	1-2	1-2	0-1	2-3	0-3	3-2	2-1	0-2	3-2	3-0	2-0
Christleton Res.	0-2	1-0	2-1	***V***	1-1	0-1	4-2	3-3	3-3	1-1	5-2	0-0	4-3	5-1	0-1	1-0
Ellesmere Port Res.	4-4	6-1	2-2	0-5	***I***	1-1	4-1	2-1	1-1	0-4	0-3	0-0	2-6	1-0	3-2	3-4
FC Pensby	2-0	4-2	2-0	1-3	2-1	***S***	6-1	3-1	1-0	0-2	3-2	2-0	3-1	1-1	2-0	1-0
FOCUS	2-1	3-1	1-1	1-2	3-2	1-6	***I***	2-6	3-2	0-6	2-7	2-3	2-3	1-1	0-0	1-2
Hale	2-0	0-4	1-1	4-0	1-1	1-2	5-0	***O***	2-2	1-1	3-2	1-2	1-2	6-1	2-2	2-1
Manor Athletic	4-3	1-0	2-1	0-1	2-1	1-2	1-2	0-4	***N***	2-0	2-3	2-2	3-3	2-3	3-0	9-2
Marshalls	2-1	6-0	4-4	2-5	3-1	1-1	8-0	1-0	4-3		2-1	2-3	3-0	9-1	7-3	4-0
Mersey Royal	2-2	2-0	2-1	2-0	1-3	0-1	1-4	2-4	2-1	1-2	***T***	1-1	0-5	2-0	7-1	0-2
Richmond Raith Rov. Jacobs	2-2	3-0	4-2	1-1	7-0	1-2	2-1	3-1	2-0	3-2	1-1	***H***	0-1	4-1	1-1	1-0
Runcorn Town Res.	1-1	4-0	1-3	1-1	3-2	1-1	2-1	2-2	6-0	3-2	1-1	2-2	***R***	6-2	2-1	1-4
Southport Trinity Res.	0-2	2-0	2-3	0-0	2-1	0-1	4-5	1-2	3-4	1-0	3-3	2-0	0-4	***E***	3-2	3-2
St Werburghs	2-2	2-2	2-5	0-3	5-5	2-3	4-2	1-10	2-1	3-9	3-4	1-4	2-3	3-0	***E***	4-1
Upton AA Res.	3-4	3-0	1-1	2-2	2-2	2-1	4-4	2-0	3-5	1-1	3-0	3-0	2-1	4-0	4-3	

WEST CHESHIRE LEAGUE DIVISION THREE CONSTITUTION 2009-10

ASHVILLE RESERVES . . . . Villa Park, Cross Lane, Wallasey Village, Wallasey CH45 8RH 0151 638 2127
BLACON YOUTH CLUB RESERVES . . Cairns Crescent Playing Fields, Blacon, Chester CH1 5JF . . . . None
CAPENHURST VILLA RESERVES . Capenhurst Sp. Grnd, Capenhurst Lane, Capenhurst CH1 6ER . . . . None
CHRISTLETON RESERVES . . . . Little Heath Road, Christleton, Chester CH3 7AH. 01244 336589
ELLESMERE PORT RESERVES . Whitby S & S Club, Chester Rd, Whitby, Ellesmere Port CH66 2NX. 0151 200 7080/7050
HALE . . . . Hale Park, The High Street, Hale Village, Liverpool L24 4AF. . . . . None
MANOR ATHLETIC. . . . . OC Sports & Leisure Club, 28 Bridle Road, Bromborough CH62 6AR. 0151 356 6159
MERSEY ROYAL. Unilever Sports Ground, Bromborough CH62 3PU. . . . . None
MOSSLEY HILL ATHLETIC RESERVES Mossley Hill Athletic Club, Mossley Hill Road, Liverpool L18 8DX. 0151 724 4377
PRESCOT CABLES RESERVES. . . . Sutton Leisure Centre, Elton Head Road, St Helens WA9 5AU. 01744 677375
RICHMOND RAITH ROVERS . . . . Childwall Sports College, Queens Drive, Fiveways L15 6XZ 0151 722 1561
RUNCORN TOWN RESERVES . . . . Pavilions Club, Sandy Lane, Weston Point, Runcorn WA7 4EX 01928 590508
SOUTHPORT TRINITY RESERVES . . . . Police Club, Fairfield, Prescot Road, Liverpool L7 0JD 0151 228 2352
ST WERBURGHS . . . . Kings School, Wrexham Road (A483), Chester CH4 7QL. 01244 689500
UPTON ATHLETIC ASSOCIATION RESERVES Cheshire County S & S Club, Plas Newton Lane, Chester CH2 1PR 01244 318167

IN: Mossley Hill Athletic Res. (P - I-Zingari Combination Division One), Prescot Cables Res. (P - Warrington & District League Division Two)
OUT: FC Pensby (P), FOCUS (W), Marshalls (P)
Richmond Raith Rovers Jacobs become Richmond Raith Rovers

BILL WEIGHT MEMORIAL CUP

(Divisional champions and Pyke Cup holders)

SEMI-FINALS

Poulton Victoria 0 **West Kirby** 0 *aet* (4-5p)
Mossley Hill Athletic 2 **Castrol Social** 2 *aet* (4-5p)

FINAL

(September 24th at Ashville)

West Kirby 1 Castrol Social 1 *aet* (4-2p)

WEST LANCASHIRE LEAGUE

www.westlancashirefootball.co.uk

Sponsored by: Sports 360

Founded: 1904

Recent champions:
2004: Kirkham & Wesham
2005: Kirkham & Wesham
2006: Kirkham & Wesham
2007: Kirkham & Wesham
2008: Garstang

	Barnold.	Blackpl	Burnley	Charn.	Coppull	Dalton	Eagley	Euxton	Freckle.	Fulwood	Garstang	Hasl'den	Poulton	Stonec	Turton	Vickers.
Barnoldswick Town	***P***	3-1	3-1	2-3	0-0	7-0	0-1	4-2	0-0	0-3	1-0	0-0	3-1	11-0	5-0	2-2
Blackpool Wren Rovers	1-3	***R***	1-3	2-1	2-4	4-1	2-3	2-2	0-2	0-3	0-0	2-2	8-2	7-0	4-1	1-0
Burnley United	0-1	0-4	***E***	3-3	0-2	3-1	2-4	n/a	0-2	0-3	2-0	3-3	3-1	7-4	5-1	0-1
Charnock Richard	1-2	6-0	3-3	***M***	2-4	1-1	0-3	5-2	3-4	1-2	3-0	3-1	4-0	4-1	5-1	2-0
Coppull United	1-3	3-1	4-1	3-3	***I***	W-L	2-1	n/a	4-0	3-2	4-2	4-2	3-5	3-0	5-1	W-L
Dalton United	L-W	1-0	2-4	0-1	0-3	***E***	1-8	n/a	1-2	1-2	1-3	0-1	3-2	7-1	4-2	0-2
Eagley	2-1	3-1	2-1	2-1	1-1	3-1	***R***	n/a	1-0	0-0	1-2	6-2	2-1	4-0	4-0	3-2
Euxton Villa	n/a	2-6	0-3	1-1	0-1	1-3	0-4		n/a	n/a	n/a	n/a	n/a	n/a	n/a	n/a
Freckleton	1-2	4-2	3-1	3-0	0-5	W-L	2-2	5-0	***D***	3-2	1-1	2-1	1-3	W-L	5-2	3-1
Fulwood Amateurs	1-3	3-0	2-0	2-0	3-1	W-L	2-1	n/a	1-0	***I***	6-0	3-0	4-1	2-0	2-0	W-L
Garstang	2-2	1-3	3-2	0-2	2-5	1-2	1-2	4-0	2-5	2-3	***V***	1-0	5-2	7-1	10-0	W-L
Haslingden St Mary's	1-2	1-1	2-1	2-3	1-3	3-3	1-2	n/a	1-3	2-1	1-2	***I***	2-0	6-0	2-1	1-3
Poulton Town	1-2	0-3	0-3	0-5	0-4	2-1	0-3	3-0	1-3	0-5	3-0	1-3	***S***	6-2	2-3	W-L
Stoneclough	1-10	3-5	3-1	1-7	1-10	3-2	0-10	4-1	1-12	0-3	0-5	1-6	1-1	***I***	0-2	1-12
Turton	1-4	3-5	4-1	1-0	0-8	2-0	0-7	n/a	1-5	0-3	1-2	4-3	0-1	2-4	***O***	W-L
Vickerstown CC	2-4	2-0	0-0	2-2	3-1	9-0	1-1	n/a	1-0	1-0	L-W	L-W	3-1	9-0	11-1	***N***

Premier Division		P	W	D	L	F	A	Pts
Charnock Richard		30	19	9	2	72	35	66
Blackpool Wren Rovers		30	20	4	6	70	26	64
Garstang		30	16	7	7	55	44	55
Dalton United		30	15	9	6	63	39	54
Freckleton		30	15	7	8	47	33	52
Barnoldswick Town		30	12	6	12	55	53	42
Euxton Villa		30	10	10	10	44	48	40
Turton		30	10	8	12	44	49	38
Fulwood Amateurs		30	12	2	16	54	60	38
Vickerstown CC		30	9	10	11	64	69	37
Haslingden St Mary's	*-3*	30	10	9	11	49	60	36
Poulton Town		30	9	7	14	57	55	34
Stoneclough		30	7	8	15	38	52	29
Coppull United	*-6*	30	9	5	16	37	50	26
Eagley		30	6	8	16	61	80	26
Burnley United		30	5	3	22	35	92	18

RICHARDSON CUP

FIRST ROUND
Charnock Richard 3 Barnoldswick Town 0
Euxton Villa 0 **Coppull United** 1
Freckleton 2 Poulton Town 1
Fulwood Amateurs 0 **Blackpool Wren Rovers** 2
Garstang 3 **Vickerstown CC** 3 *aet* (3-4p)
Haslingden St Mary's 3 Burnley United 2
Stoneclough 0 **Dalton United** 3
Turton 2 Eagley 1

QUARTER-FINALS
Blackpool Wren Rovers 1 Charnock Richard 0
Dalton United 4 Freckleton 3
Vickerstown CC 1 **Turton** 2
Haslingden St Mary's 2 Coppull United 1

SEMI-FINALS
Turton 1 Haslingden St Mary's 0 *aet*
(at Barnoldswick Town)
Dalton United 1 Blackpool Wren Rovers 1 *aet* (4-2p) *(at Kendal Town)*

FINAL
(April 30th at LCFA, Leyland)
Turton 1 **Dalton United** 2

WEST LANCASHIRE LEAGUE PREMIER DIVISION CONSTITUTION 2009-10

AFC DARWEN .... Anchor Ground, Anchor Road BB3 0BB 01254 705677
BLACKPOOL WREN ROVERS .... Bruce Park, School Road, Marton, Blackpool FY4 5EL.................... 01253 760570
CHARNOCK RICHARD .... Charter Lane, Charnock Richard, Chorley PR7 5LY 01257 794288
COPPULL UNITED .... Springfield Road, Coppull PR7 5FJ 01257 795190
DALTON UNITED .... Railway Meadow, Beckside Road, Dalton-in-Furness LA15 8DP 07743 271736
EAGLEY........................ Eagley Sports Complex, Dunscar Bridge, Bolton BL7 9PQ 01204 306830
EUXTON VILLA .... Runshaw Hall Lane, Euxton, Chorley PR7 6HH.............................. None
FRECKLETON............... Hodgson Memorial Ground, Bush Lane, Freckleton, Preston PR1 1SB 01772 679174
FULWOOD AMATEURS .... Lightfoot Lane, Fulwood, Preston PR2 3LP 01772 861827
GARSTANG .... Riverside Community Centre, High Street, Garstang PR3 1AF.................. 01995 601586
HASLINGDEN ST MARY'S .... South Shore Street, Haslingden, Rossendale BB4 5DX 01706 221814
LOSTOCK ST GERARDS .... Wateringpool Lane, Lostock Hall PR5 5UA.................................. None
POULTON TOWN .... Cottam Hall Playing Fields, Blackpool Old Road, Poulton-le-Fylde FY6 7RH 01253 896150
STONECLOUGH .... Brook Street, opposite Europa Business Park, Stoneclough, Kearsley, Bolton .... None
TEMPEST UNITED............... Tempest Road, Chew Moor Village, Lostock, Bolton BL6 4HP 01942 811938
TURTON .... Thomasson Fold, Turton, Edgworth, Bolton BL7 0PD 07929 965160
VICKERSTOWN CC............... Park Vale, Mill Lane, Walney, Barrow-in-Furness LA14 3ND .... None

IN: AFC Darwen (formerly Darwen) (R - North West Counties League Division One), Lostock St Gerards (P), Tempest United (P)
OUT: Barnoldswick Town (P - North West Counties League Division One), Burnley United (R)

WILF CARR MEMORIAL TROPHY

(Premier Division champions v Richardson Cup holders)

(August 2nd at Garstang)

Garstang 2

Haslingden St Mary's 0

Division One	P	W	D	L	F	A	Pts
Tempest United	26	18	2	6	63	41	56
Lostock St Gerards	26	16	5	5	63	34	53
Hawcoat Park	26	13	5	8	62	40	44
Fleetwood Hesketh	26	12	7	7	58	43	43
Trimpell-Slyne	26	11	5	10	40	36	38
Millom	26	12	2	12	47	65	38
Norcross & Warbreck	26	10	5	11	58	49	35
Milnthorpe Corinthians	26	10	4	12	55	52	34
Hesketh Bank	26	8	9	9	45	49	33
Crooklands Casuals	26	10	2	14	49	55	32
Croston Sports	26	8	7	11	41	58	31
Wyre Villa	26	8	5	13	44	55	29
Crosshills	26	7	6	13	45	68	27
Furness Rovers	26	5	4	17	32	57	19

PRESIDENT'S CUP

FIRST ROUND

Fleetwood Hesketh 1 **Millom** 2

Hawcoat Park 2 Croston Sports 1

Hesketh Bank 0 **Lostock St Gerards** 3

Tempest United 4 Crosshills 0

Trimpell-Slyne 4 Milnthorpe Corinthians 2

Wyre Villa 0 **Norcross & Warbreck** 5

QUARTER-FINALS

Crooklands Casuals 5 **Furness Rovers** 0

(Crooklands Casuals expelled)

Lostock St Gerards 2 **Norcross & Warbreck** 3

Tempest United 2 **Millom** 4

Hawcoat Park 5 Trimpell-Slyne 2

SEMI-FINALS

Furness Rovers 2 Hawcoat Park 1 *(at Barrow)*

Norcross & Warbreck 2 **Millom** 2 *aet* (2-4p)

(at Milnthorpe Corinthians)

FINAL *(April 8th at Barrow)*

Furness Rovers 1 **Millom** 2

	Crooklands Casuals	Crosshills	Croston Sports	Fleetwood Hesketh	Furness Rovers	Hawcoat Park	Hesketh Bank	Lostock St Gerards	Millom	Milnthorpe Corries	Norcross/Warbreck	Tempest United	Trimpell-Slyne	Wyre Villa
Crooklands Casuals		6-0	5-1	2-0	1-2	2-2	2-6	0-2	4-1	1-2	1-0	1-3	0-3	4-3
Crosshills	3-1	***D***	0-1	1-3	2-3	2-2	1-4	0-4	2-3	3-2	1-6	1-1	2-2	4-4
Croston Sports	0-2	2-4	***I***	3-3	1-1	2-1	2-3	1-4	1-4	4-4	2-1	4-3	1-1	3-2
Fleetwood Hesketh	1-4	3-3	3-1	***V***	3-1	6-1	2-2	5-2	1-3	1-2	4-2	2-3	1-1	4-0
Furness Rovers	2-1	1-2	0-2	2-2	***I***	0-1	2-2	0-2	1-3	0-0	2-1	1-3	3-0	2-3
Hawcoat Park	2-0	5-3	0-0	1-3	5-1	***S***	5-1	3-1	9-0	6-1	0-2	0-1	2-1	2-2
Hesketh Bank	4-1	1-1	2-1	0-1	2-1	1-3	***I***	1-1	2-1	1-0	1-1	1-2	1-3	1-1
Lostock St Gerards	1-2	3-2	4-0	0-0	3-0	2-1	1-1	***O***	5-1	6-3	2-1	2-4	3-0	4-0
Millom	5-1	2-0	3-1	0-1	3-2	1-3	3-3	3-2	***N***	0-6	0-4	1-4	0-1	3-2
Milnthorpe Corinthians	1-1	0-1	2-2	2-3	3-0	2-4	6-0	0-1	1-2		4-1	4-3	1-2	0-2
Norcross & Warbreck	5-2	3-4	1-1	2-1	6-2	2-1	1-1	2-2	2-3	2-3	***O***	1-3	2-1	4-2
Tempest United	3-2	1-0	4-2	3-1	2-1	1-1	3-2	1-2	3-0	2-3	1-3	***N***	1-2	3-1
Trimpell-Slyne	2-0	4-1	0-1	0-2	2-1	2-0	3-2	3-3	1-1	0-1	2-0	3-4	***E***	0-1
Wyre Villa	1-3	1-2	1-2	2-2	2-1	1-2	1-0	0-1	3-1	4-2	3-3	0-1	2-1	

WEST LANCASHIRE LEAGUE DIVISION ONE CONSTITUTION 2009-10

BURNLEY UNITED................ Barden Sports Ground, Barden Lane, Burnley BB10 1JQ .... Non

CROOKLANDS CASUALS .... Longlands Park, Greystone Lane, Dalton-in-Furness LA15 8PX 01229 46501

CROSSHILLS .... Holmes Lane, Crosshills, Keighley BD20 8BN .... Non

CROSTON SPORTS .... Old Emmanuel School, Westhead Road, Croston, Leyland PR26 9RR.................. 01772 60026

FLEETWOOD HESKETH .... Fylde Road, Southport PR9 9XH 01704 22796

HAWCOAT PARK .... Hawcoat Park Sports Ground, Hawcoat Lane, Barrow-in-Furness LA14 4HF 01229 82529

HESKETH BANK............... Centenary Sports Ground, Station Road, Hesketh Bank PR4 6SR.......................... Non

MILL HILL ST PETERS .... Opposite Mill Hill Hotel, Bridge Street, Buncer Lane, Blackburn BB2 2QY 01254 67555

MILLOM......................... Millom RL Club, Devonshire Road, Millom LA18 4PG 01229 77203

MILNTHORPE CORINTHIANS .... Strands Lane, Milnthorpe LA7 7AE 01539 56213

NORCROSS & WARBRECK .... Anchorsholme Lane, Thornton Cleveleys, Blackpool FY5 1LX 01253 85983

THORNTON CLEVELEYS............ Bourne Road, Cleveleys, Thornton Cleveleys FY5 4QA 01253 86966

TRIMPELL-SLYNE................... Bottomdale Road, Slyne, Lancaster LA2 6BG .... Non

WYRE VILLA.................... Hallgate Park, Stalmine Village, Poulton-le-Fylde FY6 0LB 01253 70146

IN: Burnley United (R), Mill Hill St Peters (P), Thornton Cleveleys (P)

OUT: Furness Rovers (R), Lostock St Gerards (P), Tempest United (P)

ivision Two		P	W	D	L	F	A	Pts
hornton Cleveleys		24	17	3	4	48	16	54
ill Hill St Peters		24	15	5	4	71	23	50
urness Cavaliers		24	15	4	5	70	35	49
AC/EE Springfield	*-3*	24	15	5	4	78	56	47
ytham Town		24	13	6	5	73	47	45
urnley Belvedere		24	12	4	8	56	31	40
olton County		24	11	6	7	59	45	39
odmorden Borough		24	10	4	10	39	46	34
hinney Hill		24	7	3	14	42	86	24
skam United		24	7	2	15	36	53	23
ancs Constabulary		24	3	5	16	31	73	14
alney Island		24	3	1	20	22	65	10
SK Ulverston Rangers		24	2	4	18	26	75	10

CHALLENGE CUP

FIRST ROUND

Askam United 3 Bolton County 1
Burnley Belvedere 3 Whinney Hill 0
Furness Cavaliers 5 Lancs Constabulary 1
GSK Ulverston Rangers 1 **Thornton Cleveleys** 2
Todmorden Borough 2 **Walney Island** 3

QUARTER-FINALS

BAC/EE Springfields 5 Lytham Town 2
Burnley Belvedere 5 Askam United 5 *aet* (17-16p)
Thornton Cleveleys 3 Mill Hill St Peters 0
Walney Island 2 Furness Cavaliers 0

SEMI-FINALS

BAC/EE Springfields 1 Walney Island 0
(at Milnthorpe Corinthians)
Thornton Cleveleys 1 Burnley Belvedere 0
(at Blackpool Wren Rovers)

FINAL

(April 22nd at Lancaster City)
BAC/EE Springfield 0 **Thornton Cleveleys** 2

	Askam	BAC/EE	Bolton Co.	Burnley B.	Furn. Cav.	GSK Ulv.	Lancs Con.	Lytham T.	Mill Hill SP	Thornton	Todmorden	Walney Is.	Whinney H
Askam United	***D***	3-6	3-2	0-1	0-5	5-0	2-0	0-7	1-3	1-2	0-1	4-1	2-2
BAC/EE Springfield	1-3	***I***	7-5	2-0	6-4	6-2	4-2	3-3	3-2	2-1	6-3	2-1	1-0
Bolton County	6-1	2-2	***V***	3-1	1-4	4-0	4-1	1-3	2-2	1-1	3-2	1-0	1-0
Burnley Belvedere	2-1	7-1	1-4	***I***	0-1	3-0	5-0	0-6	1-1	2-1	2-1	4-1	7-0
Furness Cavaliers	2-0	1-1	4-2	1-1	***S***	5-3	2-2	8-0	2-1	0-1	1-0	2-1	14-0
GSK Ulverston Rangers	0-5	1-3	1-4	1-1	0-1	***I***	5-1	1-3	0-7	0-1	0-1	0-2	0-0
Lancashire Constabulary	0-0	2-6	2-2	0-1	0-3	1-1	***O***	1-7	0-2	1-3	3-2	1-0	4-7
Lytham Town	4-2	2-2	1-0	0-1	3-2	3-3	3-2	***N***	2-2	1-3	5-1	5-2	4-0
Mill Hill St Peters	1-0	3-3	1-1	1-0	7-1	7-1	5-0	4-0		0-2	3-0	5-0	7-2
Thornton Cleveleys	1-0	5-0	1-2	3-2	4-0	3-0	3-0	2-2	1-0		0-1	2-0	2-0
Todmorden Borough	2-0	4-2	1-1	2-1	1-1	5-3	3-2	2-2	0-1	1-1	***T***	3-1	3-2
Walney Island	1-3	0-4	0-3	1-1	1-3	2-1	2-5	1-4	0-4	0-1	1-0	***W***	2-3
Whinney Hill	3-0	0-5	6-4	0-12	0-3	2-3	1-1	4-3	1-2	0-4	5-0	4-2	***O***

WEST LANCASHIRE LEAGUE DIVISION TWO CONSTITUTION 2009-10

SKAM UNITED . . . . Duddon Road, James Street, Askam-in-Furness LA16 7AH 01229 464576
AC/EE SPRINGFIELD. . . . . BAC Sports Ground, South Meadow Lane, Preston PR1 8JP 01772 464351
OLTON COUNTY . . . . Radcliffe Road, Darcy Lever, Bolton BL3 1AN 07745 456378
URNESS CAVALIERS . . . . Rampside Road, Barrow-in-Furness LA13 0HN. . . . . None
URNESS ROVERS . . . . Wilkie Road, Barrow-in-Furness LA14 5UQ . . . . None
SK ULVERSTON RANGERS . . . . off North Lonsdale Road, Ulverston LA12 9DZ 01229 582261
ANCASHIRE CONSTABULARY . . . . Police HQ, Saunders Lane, Hutton, Preston PR4 5SG 01772 412970
ONGRIDGE TOWN . . . . Inglewhite Road, Longridge, Preston PR3 2DB . . . . None
YTHAM TOWN . . . . Lytham Academy, Ballam Road, Lytham St Annes FY8 4LE 01253 733873
ODMORDEN BOROUGH . . . . Bellholme, Warland, Rochdale Road, Todmorden OL14 6UH . . . . None
ALNEY ISLAND. . . . . Tummerhill Play Flos, Ocean Road, Walney, Barrow-in-Furness LA14 3HN . . . . None
HINNEY HILL . . . . Clayton-le-Moors, Accrington BB5 5NF . . . . None

N: Furness Rovers (R), Longridge Town (P - Preston & District League Premier Division)
UT: Burnley Belvedere (W), Mill Hill St Peters (P), Thornton Cleveleys (P)

eserve Div. One		P	W	D	L	F	A	Pt
oulton Town Res.		28	21	0	7	63	40	63
uxton Villa Res.		28	19	2	7	68	42	59
arnoldswick T. Res.		28	19	1	8	96	44	58
ulwood Amateurs Res.		28	16	5	7	57	38	53
hornton Clev. Res.		28	13	5	10	59	46	44
arstang Res.		28	12	4	12	52	37	40
harnock Richard Res.		28	13	1	14	61	48	40
agley Res.		28	12	4	12	56	48	40
empest United Res.		28	12	2	14	58	68	38
urnley Belvedere Res.		28	10	6	12	60	52	36
'pl Wren Rovers Res.		28	9	4	15	39	63	31
urton Res.		28	9	2	17	57	79	29
orcross & W. Res.	*-6*	28	10	3	15	38	66	27
reckleton Res.		28	5	6	17	45	91	21
AC/EE S'fields Res.		28	5	5	18	57	104	20

Reserve Div. Two		P	W	D	L	F	A	Pt
Hasl'den SM Res.	*-6*	26	22	2	2	86	22	62
Fleet. Hesketh Res.		26	19	2	5	105	30	59
Coppull United Res.		26	13	8	5	66	28	47
Todmorden B. Res.		26	14	5	7	69	59	47
Burnley United Res.		26	13	6	7	61	51	45
Milnthorpe C. Res.		26	12	7	7	70	47	43
Wyre Villa Res.		26	11	4	11	48	57	37
Bolton County Res.		26	10	3	13	45	56	33
Lytham Town Res.	*-4*	26	10	5	11	56	68	31
Whinney Hill Res.		26	8	6	12	49	70	30
Stoneclough Res.		26	7	6	13	32	54	27
Crosshills Res.		26	4	4	18	32	79	16
Hesketh Bank Res.		26	4	3	19	28	79	15
Mill Hill St Ptrs Res.		26	3	3	20	17	64	12

HOUSTON CUP

FINAL

(May 4th at Padiham)
BAC/EE Springfield Res. 2
Barnoldswick Town Res. 1

WILTSHIRE LEAGUE

www.wiltshirefootballleague.com

Sponsored by: Plaister Autos

Founded: 1976

Recent champions:
2004: Trowbridge Town
2005: Corsham Town Res.
2006: Corsham Town Res.
2007: Corsham Town Res.
2008: Wroughton

	Bdf	Bro	Cal	Cor	Dev	FC	Mar	Mel	New	Pew	Pur	Shr	Tro	War	Wby	Wes	Wro
Bradford Town Res.	***P***	2-1	0-1	4-0	1-0	3-0	3-0	0-6	2-4	5-1	2-1	4-2	1-5	2-0	4-2	5-1	0-2
Bromham	0-3	***R***	1-3	2-1	3-2	1-2	2-1	0-1	2-1	8-1	0-2	1-1	4-0	1-1	1-3	9-0	2-1
Calne Town Res.	2-1	1-0	***E***	3-0	2-0	3-0	1-1	3-0	2-3	5-0	0-1	4-0	1-0	5-0	2-0	7-0	1-1
Corsham Town Res.	2-1	1-1	0-2	***M***	2-2	1-0	0-4	1-4	0-10	5-0	1-7	0-4	0-4	1-1	0-3	2-3	1-3
Devizes Town Res.	4-3	1-1	2-2	4-1	***I***	2-3	1-1	1-2	0-5	1-1	3-5	0-0	2-4	4-0	0-0	6-2	0-1
FC Chippenham Youth	0-3	6-1	0-3	2-1	1-2	***E***	1-0	0-1	2-2	5-2	0-2	0-3	2-1	2-3	1-3	5-1	3-1
Marlborough Town	0-3	1-1	2-1	1-1	2-2	1-2	***R***	0-2	1-2	2-0	2-4	5-0	1-4	5-2	0-2	1-2	1-2
Melksham Town Res.	3-0	3-1	1-0	1-0	2-0	1-0	1-0		2-3	2-4	2-1	3-1	3-1	7-0	1-1	6-0	2-0
New College Swindon	2-1	4-1	5-2	7-0	4-2	6-2	4-0	2-0		4-2	0-2	3-0	3-2	5-1	4-0	7-0	3-2
Pewsey Vale Res.	3-5	0-0	0-2	3-2	2-0	2-5	0-0	1-2	0-5	***D***	1-4	2-2	2-1	0-3	2-3	0-0	2-2
Purton Res.	2-1	6-1	1-1	3-1	3-1	5-1	5-0	1-2	2-1	6-0	***I***	2-0	2-3	4-1	0-3	6-0	1-2
Shrewton United Res.	0-2	5-3	0-5	3-1	4-4	3-3	3-0	0-2	2-2	4-1	1-2	***V***	1-0	2-0	4-1	3-0	1-2
Trowbridge Town Res.	3-1	2-1	1-2	1-2	2-0	3-0	0-2	0-4	1-2	1-2	2-1	0-0	***I***	4-0	1-0	0-2	0-1
Warminster Town Res.	1-1	0-5	3-2	1-0	0-3	2-1	1-1	2-3	3-2	2-3	2-2	2-1	1-5	***S***	1-2	2-4	0-6
Westbury United Res.	2-1	3-0	1-2	1-1	2-2	0-1	0-2	1-4	0-1	9-0	0-1	3-2	3-0	3-2	***I***	1-1	2-1
Westside	2-2	2-0	2-2	1-0	1-2	4-1	0-1	0-1	0-1	3-1	1-4	4-4	2-3	4-1	1-5	***O***	1-5
Wroughton	4-0	1-2	1-0	1-0	6-1	4-0	1-4	2-1	0-3	8-1	3-6	6-1	1-2	3-0	1-0	1-0	***N***

Premier Division		P	W	D	L	F	A	Pts
New College Swindon		**32**	**26**	**2**	**4**	**110**	**36**	**80**
Melksham Town Res.		**32**	**26**	**1**	**5**	**75**	**26**	**79**
Purton Res.		**32**	**23**	**2**	**7**	**94**	**38**	**71**
Calne Town Res.		**32**	**20**	**5**	**7**	**72**	**27**	**65**
Wroughton		**32**	**20**	**2**	**10**	**75**	**41**	**62**
Westbury United Res.		**32**	**15**	**5**	**12**	**59**	**44**	**50**
Bradford T. Res.	***-1***	**32**	**16**	**2**	**14**	**66**	**56**	**49**
Trowbridge T. Res.		**32**	**15**	**1**	**16**	**56**	**49**	**46**
FC Chippenham Yth		**32**	**12**	**2**	**18**	**51**	**70**	**38**
Shrewton Utd Res.	***-1***	**32**	**10**	**8**	**14**	**57**	**67**	**37**
Bromham		**32**	**10**	**6**	**16**	**56**	**61**	**36**
Marlborough Town		**32**	**9**	**7**	**16**	**42**	**53**	**34**
Westside	***-1***	**32**	**9**	**5**	**18**	**44**	**94**	**31**
Devizes Town Res.	***-1***	**32**	**7**	**10**	**15**	**54**	**68**	**30**
Warminster T. Res.		**32**	**7**	**5**	**20**	**38**	**93**	**26**
Pewsey Vale Res.		**32**	**6**	**6**	**20**	**39**	**106**	**24**
Corsham Town Res.		**32**	**4**	**5**	**23**	**28**	**87**	**17**

CORSHAM PRINT SENIOR CUP

FIRST ROUND

New College 17 Pewsey Res. 0

SECOND ROUND

Calne Res. 5 Devizes Res. 0
Marlborough 0 **Bromham** 3
Melksham Town Res. 1 New College Swindon 0
Purton Res. 5 Trowbridge Town Res. 2 *aet*
Warminster Town Res. 0 **FC Chippenham Youth** 8
Westbury United Res. 1 **Shrewton United Res.** 4
Westside 3 **Bradford Res.** 5
Wroughton 3 **Corsham Res.** 1
(Wroughton expelled)

QUARTER-FINALS

Bradford Res. 2 Purton Res. 0
Calne Town Res. 1 **Melksham Town Res.** 2 *aet*
Corsham Town Res. 4 Shrewton United Res. 3
FC Chipp'ham 4 Bromham 0

SEMI-FINALS

Corsham Town Res. 1 **Bradford Town Res.** 3
FC Chippenham Youth 1 **Melksham Town Res.** 2

FINAL

(April 25th at Corsham Town)
Bradford Town Res. 1 **Melksham Town Res.** 3

Division One		P	W	D	L	F	A	Pt
Minety		24	17	3	4	80	30	54
AFC Castrol		24	16	6	2	81	38	54
KC		24	15	6	3	78	40	51
SKS Blyskawica	*-3*	24	16	5	3	80	36	50
Intel	-1	24	12	5	7	49	40	40
Chalke Valley		24	11	4	9	64	45	37
Malmesbury V. Res.	*-4*	24	12	4	8	69	43	36
Swindon NALGO	*-1*	24	9	7	8	48	59	33
AFC Abbey Rodb'ne	*-1*	24	7	3	14	42	66	23
Castle Combe		24	5	5	14	42	54	20
Lower Stratton	*-1*	24	3	3	18	37	79	11
Blunsdon United	*-1*	24	4	0	20	31	99	11
Wroughton Res.	*-3*	24	3	1	20	27	99	7

Division Two		P	W	D	L	F	A	Pt
Greenmeadow		24	20	2	2	87	18	62
Byrons Wanderers		24	15	3	6	74	47	48
Swindon Irons		24	14	3	7	67	40	45
Moredon Cheney		24	14	3	7	71	47	45
KMLC	*-4*	24	12	5	7	74	47	37
Marlborough Res.		24	12	1	11	45	51	37
Ramsbury	*-1*	24	7	10	7	55	56	30
Wilton Town		24	9	2	13	44	65	29
Blunsdon U. Res.	*-1*	24	8	5	11	35	49	28
FC Chip'ham Y. Res.		24	8	2	14	48	57	26
Pembroke		24	6	3	15	39	70	21
Chiseldon		24	4	6	14	35	65	18
Castle C'be Res.	*-1*	24	4	1	19	33	95	12

FOUNTAIN TROPHIES JUNIOR CUP

FINAL

(April 25th at Corsham Town)
Chalke Valley 1 Greenmeadow 0
aet

WILTSHIRE LEAGUE PREMIER DIVISION CONSTITUTION 2009-10

BRADFORD TOWN RESERVES . Avon Sports Ground, Trowbridge Road, Bradford-on-Avon BA15 1EE 01225 86664
CALNE TOWN RESERVES . . . . Lickhill Road, Bremhill View, Calne SN11 8AE 01249 81918
CORSHAM TOWN RESERVES . . . . Southbank Ground, Lacock Road, Corsham SN13 9HS 01249 71560
DEVIZES TOWN RESERVES. . . . . Nursteed Road, Devizes SN10 3EJ 01380 72281
FC CHIPPENHAM YOUTH . . . . Stanley Park, Chippenham . . . . Non
KC. . . . . Ermin Street, Stratton, Swindon SN3 4RH. 01793 83448
MARLBOROUGH TOWN. Elcot Lane, Marlborough SN8 2BG 01672 51334
MELKSHAM TOWN RESERVES. . . . . The Conigre, Market Place, Melksham SN12 6ES. 01225 70284
NEW COLLEGE SWINDON . Swindon Supermarine FC, Highworth Road, South Marston, Swindon SN3 4SF. 01793 82877
PEWSEY VALE. . . . . Recreation Ground, Kings Corner, Ball Road, Pewsey SN9 5BS 01672 56299
PURTON RESERVES . . . . The Red House, Church Street, Purton SN5 4DY. 01793 77026
SHREWTON UNITED RESERVES . . . Recreation Ground, Mill Lane, Shrewton, Salisbury SP3 4JU 07796 09812
TROWBRIDGE TOWN RESERVES . . . . . . Woodmarsh, North Bradley, Trowbridge BA14 0SB . . . . Non
WARMINSTER TOWN RESERVES. . . . . 73 Weymouth Street, Warminster BA12 9NS. 01985 21782
WESTBURY UNITED RESERVES . . . . Meadow Lane, Westbury BA13 3AF 01373 82340
WESTSIDE . . . . Southbrook Recreation Ground, Pinehurst Road, Swindon . . . . Non
WROUGHTON . . . . The Weir Field, Wroughton WMC, Devizes Road, Wroughton SN4 0SA 01793 81231

IN: KC (P), Pewsey Vale (R - Hellenic League Division One West)
OUT: Bromham (W), Pewsey Vale Res. (R)

CORNWALL COMBINATION

www.comboleaguearchive.110mb.com

Sponsored by: Jollys

Founded: 1959

Recent champions:

2004: Penryn Athletic Res.

2005: Goonhavern

2006: Truro City Res.

2007: Illogan RBL

2008: Truro City Res.

		P	W	D	L	F	A	Pts
Perranporth		38	33	4	1	174	20	103
Perranwell		38	28	7	3	141	36	91
Illogan RBL		38	24	9	5	95	35	81
Helston Athletic		38	19	8	11	95	65	65
St Just		38	18	6	14	69	76	60
St Ives Town		38	16	11	11	76	57	59
Penzance Res.		38	17	7	14	94	76	58
Porthleven Res.	*-3*	38	16	12	10	79	63	57
St Agnes		38	16	8	14	79	86	56
Penryn Athletic Res.		38	15	9	14	62	63	54
Newquay Res.		38	15	7	16	74	63	52
Falmouth Town Res.		38	13	12	13	95	75	51
Holmans Sports Club		38	15	4	19	79	92	49
RNAS Culdrose	*-3*	38	13	10	15	87	86	48
St Day		38	12	6	20	68	90	42
Hayle Res.	*-3*	38	10	9	19	65	102	36
Mullion		38	10	5	23	71	120	35
Portreath		38	8	8	22	54	83	32
Wendron United Res.		38	8	5	25	53	126	29
Ludgvan		38	0	1	37	16	212	1

SUPPLEMENTARY CUP

(Combination Cup Preliminary and First Round losers)

PRELIMINARY ROUND

Hayle Res. 1 **St Agnes** 4

Penryn Athletic Res. 0 **Holmans Sports Club** 1

Portreath 2 Ludgvan 1

Wendron United Res. 3 **RNAS Culdrose** 5

QUARTER-FINALS

Holmans Sports Club 1 Illogan RBL 0

RNAS Culdrose 0 **Falmouth Town Res.** 3

St Agnes 0 **Portreath** 3

St Day 1 **Helston Athletic** 7

SEMI-FINALS

Helston Athletic 2 **Falmouth Town Res.** 3

(at Porthleven)

Portreath 2 Holmans Sports Club 1

(at Illogan RBL)

FINAL *(May 24th at Wendron United)*

Falmouth Town Res. 4 Portreath 0

GEORGE EVELY CUP

(Cornwall Combination Cup winners v East Cornwall League Cup winners)

(May 3rd at Penryn Athletic)

Perranporth 2

Launceston Res. 0

	Falmouth Res.	Hayle Res.	Helston Athletic	Holmans SC	Illogan RBL	Ludgvan	Mullion	Newquay Res.	Penryn Res.	Penzance Res.	Perranporth	Perranwell	Porthleven Res.	Portreath	RNAS Culdrose	St Agnes	St Day	St Ives Town	St Just	Wendron Res.
Falmouth T. Res.		1-1	0-3	1-2	1-1	12-0	3-2	6-2	1-3	3-3	2-2	3-3	1-1	2-2	1-1	4-1	3-1	1-3	2-3	9-0
Hayle Res.	4-0		1-2	4-2	1-3	2-0	4-2	1-0	2-2	2-6	1-7	1-4	1-7	4-0	3-3	1-1	0-3	1-1	1-2	1-1
Helston Athletic	3-1	3-1		4-7	0-2	4-0	5-0	2-2	1-2	3-2	0-2	2-4	2-4	2-0	3-2	2-2	1-0	1-1	4-2	2-0
Holmans Spts Club	1-2	2-2	2-4		0-3	2-1	0-2	4-1	3-2	0-4	1-4	0-2	0-1	3-0	0-6	2-0	2-3	5-2	1-2	4-1
Illogan RBL	3-2	5-0	1-0	0-0		7-0	10-1	2-0	3-0	2-4	1-1	2-2	2-0	1-0	3-0	1-1	2-0	0-0	2-0	3-0
Ludgvan	0-8	0-2	0-8	0-5	1-6		4-4	1-2	0-2	0-6	0-13	0-15	0-5	1-4	1-5	0-6	0-3	0-5	1-4	1-8
Mullion	4-2	3-1	3-1	0-1	2-3	5-0		1-5	6-2	2-10	0-4	0-6	0-4	2-2	0-5	4-4	1-2	3-1	1-1	8-0
Newquay Res.	1-0	0-1	1-3	2-3	0-1	4-0	1-2		1-0	2-2	2-2	1-0	0-1	1-1	1-4	3-1	3-1	1-1	3-1	6-0
Penryn Athletic Res.	1-1	1-0	3-3	1-2	3-4	4-0	2-0	0-3		1-1	1-4	2-4	3-2	3-2	1-1	1-0	1-2	2-1	4-2	1-1
Penzance Res.	1-1	3-3	1-2	2-1	5-3	6-0	8-2	3-2	0-2		0-3	0-3	3-0	2-0	4-3	0-0	1-3	0-1	1-3	2-2
Perranporth	7-0	8-0	3-0	9-1	3-0	9-0	6-0	3-0	2-0	8-0		1-2	5-2	4-0	4-1	5-0	3-1	1-1	6-0	5-0
Perranwell	1-1	9-1	2-1	3-0	2-1	9-0	5-0	6-2	0-0	5-0	1-2		4-0	4-0	2-0	7-0	1-1	4-2	5-2	5-1
Porthleven Res.	1-1	3-1	1-1	3-3	2-1	4-0	1-0	2-2	1-3	1-2	0-4	0-2		5-4	3-2	1-1	2-1	2-2	L-W	3-0
Portreath	2-3	2-1	3-3	3-4	0-1	4-0	2-0	2-2	2-1	1-2	0-5	0-2	2-2		1-3	2-3	1-2	4-3	1-0	2-1
RNAS Culdrose	0-3	4-4	2-7	1-1	1-4	3-0	3-1	3-2	0-1	1-0	0-6	2-2	2-2	0-0		1-3	6-1	3-4	5-1	3-3
St Agnes	2-3	3-1	0-6	4-2	0-6	6-1	2-0	0-5	1-0	3-4	2-6	2-2	1-1	2-1	7-2		3-0	0-2	2-0	6-2
St Day	2-4	3-8	2-2	4-7	0-0	6-0	0-2	0-4	1-2	3-0	0-6	3-6	1-1	3-1	1-4	3-4		0-1	1-1	4-5
St Ives Town	4-0	0-1	3-1	3-2	1-1	6-1	4-3	2-0	1-1	1-0	0-1	2-3	4-4	2-2	4-1	1-2	0-0		1-0	4-0
St Just	4-3	3-1	2-2	2-1	2-2	3-1	3-2	1-2	3-3	4-3	1-3	1-0	1-2	2-0	2-2	2-1	2-5	2-1		4-1
Wendron Utd Res.	0-4	3-1	1-2	4-3	0-3	5-2	3-3	0-5	2-1	0-3	0-7	0-4	1-5	2-1	0-2	2-3	0-2	4-1	0-1	

CORNWALL COMBINATION CUP

PRELIMINARY ROUND

Falmouth Town Res. 3 Penryn Athletic Res. 2
Perranporth 9 Wendron Res. 0
Portreath 3 Holmans Sports Club 2
St Agnes 0 Porthleven Res. 0
Replay: **Porthleven Res.** 4 St Agnes 1

FIRST ROUND

Illogan RBL 0 **St Just** 1
Ludgvan 1 **Penzance Res.** 6
Newquay Res. 2 St Day 1
Perranporth 5 Falmouth Town Res. 4
Perranwell 8 Helston Athletic 0
Porthleven Res. 3 Hayle Res. 0
Portreath 2 **Mullion** 5
St Ives Town 5 RNAS Culdrose 0

QUARTER-FINALS

Mullion 2 **Penzance Res.** 3
Perranporth 3 Newquay Res. 1
Perranwell 2 Porthleven Res. 2
Replay: Porthleven Res. 0 **Perranwell** 6
St Just 2 St Ives Town 1

SEMI-FINALS

Perranporth 3 St Just 1
(at Falmouth Town)
Perranwell 2 Penzance Res. 0
(at Hayle)

FINAL

(April 12th at St Day)
Perranporth 3 Perranwell 0

CORNWALL COMBINATION CONSTITUTION 2009-10

FALMOUTH TOWN RESERVES	Bickland Park, Bickland Water Road, Falmouth TR11 4PB	01326 37515
HAYLE RESERVES	Trevassack Park, Viaduct Hill, Hayle TR27 5HT	01736 75715
HELSTON ATHLETIC	Kellaway Parc, Clodgy Lane, Helston TR13 8BN	01326 57374
HOLMANS SPORTS CLUB	Blaythorne Mem. Sports Ground, Pendarves, Camborne TR14 7QG	01209 71363
ILLOGAN RBL	Oxland Park, Richards Lane, Illogan, Redruth TR16 4HA	01209 21648
LUDGVAN	Ludgvan Community Centre, Fairfield, Ludgvan TR20 8ES	01736 74077
MULLION	Clifden Parc, Clifden Close, Mullion, Helston TR12 7EQ	01326 24067
NEWQUAY RESERVES	Mount Wise, Clevedon Road, Newquay TR7 2BU	01637 87293
PENRYN ATHLETIC RESERVES	Kernick, Kernick Road, Penryn TR10 8QF	01326 37518
PENZANCE RESERVES	Penlee Park, Alexandra Place, Penzance TR18 4NE	01736 36196
PERRANWELL	King George V Playing Field, School Hill, Perranwell Station TR3 7LA	01872 87020
PORTHLEVEN RESERVES	Gala Parc, Mill Lane, Porthleven TR13 9LQ	01326 57475
PORTREATH	Clijah Croft, Wheal Trefusis, Redruth TR15 2NQ	01209 21658
RNAS CULDROSE	Sports Field, RNAS Culdrose, Helston TR12 7RH	01326 574121x716
ST AGNES	Enys Park, West Polperro, St Agnes TR5 0SS	01872 55367
ST DAY	Vogue, St Day, Redruth TR16 5NP	Non
ST IVES TOWN	The Saltings, Lelant TR6 3DL	Non
ST JUST	Lafrowda Park, St Just, Penzance TR19 7RY	01736 78850
TROON	Grouter Park, Croft Common, Troon, Camborne TR14 9HT	Non
WENDRON UNITED RESERVES	Underlane, Carnkie, Wendron, Helston TR13 0EH	01209 86094

IN: Troon (P - Mining League Premier Division)
OUT: Perranporth (P - South West Peninsula League Division One West)

DORSET COUNTY LEAGUE

Sponsored by:

No sponsor

Founded: N/K

Recent champions:

2004: Cranborne

2005: Chickerell United.

2006: Sturminster Marshall

2007: Wincanton Town

2008: Chickerell United

Senior Division		P	W	D	L	F	A	Pts
Parley Sports		**22**	**19**	**1**	**2**	**63**	**19**	**58**
Weymouth Sports		**22**	**14**	**3**	**5**	**57**	**33**	**45**
Easton United		**22**	**12**	**2**	**8**	**53**	**38**	**38**
Okeford United		**22**	**10**	**5**	**7**	**38**	**35**	**35**
AC Matravers		**22**	**9**	**5**	**8**	**38**	**47**	**32**
Stourpaine		**22**	**8**	**3**	**11**	**34**	**47**	**27**
Witchampton United		**22**	**6**	**8**	**8**	**33**	**44**	**26**
Wareham Rangers	*-7*	**22**	**9**	**3**	**10**	**35**	**33**	**23**
Tintinhull		**22**	**6**	**4**	**12**	**30**	**37**	**22**
Moreton	*-1*	**22**	**7**	**2**	**13**	**34**	**44**	**22**
Bishop's Caundle		**22**	**4**	**8**	**10**	**27**	**40**	**20**
Kangaroos		**22**	**4**	**4**	**14**	**31**	**56**	**16**

FC Polonia - record expunged

	AC Matravers	Bishop's Caundle	Easton United	FC Polonia	Kangaroos	Moreton	Okeford United	Parley Sports	Stourpaine	Tintinhull	Wareham Rangers	Weymouth Sports	Witchampton United
AC Matravers	***S***	2-2	2-0	n/a	3-3	5-1	2-1	2-6	2-6	1-0	1-0	2-3	0-0
Bishop's Caundle	1-2	***E***	0-3	4-1	6-2	2-0	1-1	2-4	2-2	0-3	0-2	0-0	0-1
Easton United	4-4	2-1	***N***	3-1	2-0	0-1	2-1	1-2	5-1	4-0	0-1	2-3	1-1
FC Polonia	3-2	n/a	0-2	***I***	n/a	n/a	0-1	2-0	2-0	3-3	n/a	n/a	1-2
Kangaroos	0-3	3-1	2-6	n/a	***O***	0-3	1-1	0-4	4-1	1-3	0-2	2-4	2-3
Moreton	0-1	2-2	2-5	0-0	4-2	***R***	3-6	0-1	1-2	3-1	3-1	2-3	3-0
Okeford United	1-1	0-1	0-1	1-2	4-2	3-2		0-3	0-3	3-1	3-1	1-0	1-0
Parley Sports	7-0	3-0	3-0	2-1	1-0	1-0	5-2		2-0	2-1	3-2	5-3	4-1
Stourpaine	2-1	0-2	1-3	n/a	0-0	1-2	2-3	1-0		1-0	2-5	3-2	0-5
Tintinhull	1-2	1-1	5-2	n/a	0-2	1-0	1-3	0-3	1-1		0-1	2-2	4-0
Wareham Rangers	2-1	1-1	3-4	2-2	1-2	2-0	0-0	2-1	1-3	3-0	***D***	1-2	0-1
Weymouth Sports	4-0	4-0	5-1	n/a	1-0	3-0	1-2	1-2	2-0	2-2	5-3	***I***	3-0
Witchampton United	3-1	2-2	0-5	n/a	3-3	2-2	2-2	1-1	4-2	0-3	1-1	3-4	***V***

Reserve Division		P	W	D	L	F	A	Pt
Sherborne T. Res.		24	19	3	2	79	23	60
Poole Boro Res.		24	17	6	1	56	17	57
Shaftesbury Res.		24	14	3	7	54	32	45
Gill'gham T. Res.		24	12	5	7	42	31	41
Holt United Res.		24	11	4	9	49	34	37
Wincanton Res.		24	10	2	12	41	49	32
Portland Res.	*-1*	24	10	2	12	49	50	31
Stur. Newton Res.		24	10	1	13	30	35	31
Chickerell Res.		24	9	3	12	37	45	30
Swanage Res.	*-3*	24	9	3	12	50	48	27
Blandford U. Res.		24	6	5	13	23	41	23
Wareham R. Res.		24	4	3	17	26	78	15
Cranborne Res.		24	4	2	18	20	73	14

Division One		P	W	D	L	F	A	Pt
Upwey/Broadwey		26	22	3	1	115	36	69
Chickerell U. A	*-3*	26	19	1	6	92	37	55
Wool RBL		26	18	1	7	73	50	55
AFC Bluebridge		26	17	2	7	68	36	53
The Balti House		26	14	3	9	70	53	45
Crossways	*-12*	26	15	3	8	81	67	36
Bere Regis	*-1*	26	11	3	12	60	80	35
Ferndown Sports		26	9	6	11	55	55	33
Stalbridge		26	9	2	15	62	79	29
Corfe Castle		26	9	1	16	56	81	28
Piddletrenthide	*-1*	26	8	1	17	41	58	24
Child Okeford		26	7	3	16	47	89	24
Mere Town		26	4	7	15	53	89	19
Lytchett Red Tri.		26	1	2	23	49	112	5

DORSET COUNTY LEAGUE SENIOR DIVISION CONSTITUTION 2009-10

AC MATRAVERS . . . . Lytchett Matravers Recreation Ground, High Street, Lytchett Matravers . . . . None
AFC WEST MOORS . . . . . . Fryers Field Recreation Ground, Station Road, West Moor, Ferndown BH22 0LJ . . . . None
BISHOP'S CAUNDLE . . . . Bishop's Caundle Recreation Ground, Bishop's Caundle . . . . None
EASTON UNITED . . . . Grove Road Playing Field, Easton, Portland DT5 1DA . . . . None
KANGAROOS . . . . Dorchester Recreation Ground, Weymouth Avenue, Dorchester DT1 1JN . . . . None
MORETON . . . . Puddletown Recreation Ground, Three Lanes End, Puddletown DT2 8RR . . . . None
OKEFORD UNITED . . . . Recreation Ground, Castle Lane, Okeford Fitzpaine, Blandford Forum DT11 0RL . . . . None
STOURPAINE . . . . Dick Draper Memorial Fields, Stourpaine, Blandford Forum . . . . None
TINTINHULL . . . . Montacute Road, Tintinhull, Yeovil BA22 8QD . . . . None
UPWEY & BROADWEY . . . . Dorchester Road, Upwey, Weymouth DT3 5BX . . . . None
WAREHAM RANGERS . . . . Purbeck Sports Centre, Worgret Road, Wareham BH20 4PH 01929 556454
WEYMOUTH SPORTS . . . . Weymouth College, Cranford Avenue, Weymouth DT4 7LQ 01305 208892
WITCHAMPTON UNITED . . . . Crichel Park, Witchampton. 01258 840986
WOOL RBL . . . . Wool Recreation Ground, Colliers Lane, Wool, Wareham BH20 6DJ. . . . . None

IN: AFC West Moors (formerly AFC Bluebridge) (P), Upwey & Broadwey (P), Wool RBL (P)

OUT: Allendale (WN), Broadmayne (WN), FC Polonia (WS), Parley Sports (P - Dorset Premier League)

Division Two		P	W	D	L	F	A	Pt
Kingston Lacy		24	23	0	1	108	24	69
Poundbury		24	17	1	6	115	44	52
FC Windowman		24	16	3	5	97	48	51
Sturm. Mars. Res.		24	14	4	6	105	53	46
Horse & Groom	*-3*	24	15	0	9	91	62	42
Harbour View Dev.		24	13	2	9	66	57	41
Witchampton Res.		24	10	4	10	60	70	34
AC Mat. Res.	*-1*	24	9	2	13	57	71	28
Piddlehinton Utd		24	8	1	15	57	74	25
M Newton/C'istock		24	6	3	15	42	74	21
Wyke Regis SC	*-1*	24	4	5	15	31	79	16
Puddletown	-3	24	5	3	16	44	100	15
Handley Sports		24	1	2	21	21	138	5

Division Three		P	W	D	L	F	A	Pt
Dorchester Sports		26	21	3	2	112	39	66
Milborne Sports		26	16	4	6	86	49	52
Stickland United		26	13	3	10	72	50	42
Granby Rovers	*-3*	26	13	3	10	71	41	39
Catterick	*-2*	26	12	5	9	81	74	39
Stourpaine Res.		26	12	2	12	58	62	38
Shaftesbury		26	10	6	10	73	67	36
Westover Spartans		26	10	5	11	62	64	35
Swanage A	*-4*	26	10	7	9	50	57	33
Okeford Utd Res.		26	8	7	11	55	64	31
Pid'trenthide Res.		26	9	4	13	68	97	31
Donhead United		26	9	4	13	50	90	31
Sturminster N. A		26	5	4	17	51	88	19
Wool RBL Res.		26	4	3	19	45	92	15

Division Four		P	W	D	L	F	A	Pt
FC Windowman Res.		18	14	3	1	61	30	45
Athletico D'chester		18	14	2	2	82	26	44
Bridport A		18	14	1	3	95	20	43
Gillingham Town A		18	9	2	7	67	33	29
Flight Refuelling		18	7	3	8	45	41	24
Bish. Caundle Res.		18	7	3	8	46	67	24
Dorch. Town Rov.		18	5	2	11	51	71	17
Stalbridge Res.		18	4	4	10	37	87	16
Owermoigne		18	1	5	12	20	75	8
Weym'th Wdrs	*-1*	18	2	1	15	33	87	6

EAST CORNWALL LEAGUE

Sponsored by:
Cornish Guardian

Founded: 1960

Recent champions:
2004: Liskeard Athletic Res.
2005: Foxhole Stars
2006: Saltash United Res.
2007: Foxhole Stars
2008: Torpoint Athletic Res.

	Bere Alston United	Biscovey	Bodmin Town Res.	Lanreath	Launceston Res.	Liskeard Athletic Res.	Morwenstow	Padstow United	Probus	Saltash United Res.	St Stephen	Sticker	Tavistock Res.	Torpoint Athletic Res.	Wadebridge T. Res.
Bere Alston United		5-2	2-1	4-3	0-1	3-2	4-0	n/a	2-1	2-2	2-1	3-3	0-1	2-3	0-1
Biscovey	1-1		0-3	4-1	2-2	3-2	4-3	n/a	2-1	2-4	3-4	0-4	0-3	0-5	2-3
Bodmin Town Res.	2-3	1-2	***P***	0-1	3-0	0-0	1-0	4-0	5-2	1-3	3-5	2-2	3-2	0-3	2-0
Lanreath	3-4	1-0	3-4	***R***	1-2	1-0	1-5	n/a	3-1	1-1	4-4	1-2	2-3	1-1	1-3
Launceston Res.	1-0	3-0	3-2	3-1	***E***	1-0	2-0	n/a	0-1	3-1	4-3	0-1	1-1	1-3	4-3
Liskeard Athletic Res.	1-3	6-1	3-1	0-3	1-4	***M***	2-2	n/a	2-2	2-2	2-3	2-2	2-4	0-3	5-1
Morwenstow	1-2	5-2	3-0	2-4	1-4	2-4	***I***	n/a	5-1	1-2	2-2	1-1	3-3	1-3	1-1
Padstow United	n/a	n/a	n/a	n/a	n/a	n/a	n/a	***E***	2-1	1-15	0-6	n/a	n/a	n/a	n/a
Probus	1-2	0-1	1-4	1-1	2-3	2-3	3-2	n/a	***R***	1-2	0-1	4-1	0-1	2-3	1-1
Saltash United Res.	7-1	5-2	7-0	5-2	0-0	1-0	5-1	n/a	5-2		1-0	3-1	2-1	3-2	2-0
St Stephen	1-1	3-0	0-1	1-0	1-1	2-1	1-4	5-1	4-1	1-0	***D***	3-0	1-0	0-3	1-1
Sticker	5-1	2-2	5-1	4-2	1-1	0-0	1-0	9-0	2-1	0-1	1-0	***I***	4-1	1-6	0-0
Tavistock Res.	2-1	5-1	2-1	6-2	0-2	2-1	5-0	n/a	3-3	2-4	1-3	0-1	***V***	0-2	1-1
Torpoint Athletic Res.	2-1	6-1	4-2	6-1	1-1	4-3	8-1	14-0	4-1	2-1	2-1	6-2	2-1		4-0
Wadebridge Town Res.	0-5	4-0	0-1	2-1	4-1	2-0	2-0	2-0	0-1	0-7	3-1	1-2	0-0	3-4	

Premier Division	P	W	D	L	F	A	Pts
Torpoint Athletic Res.	26	23	2	1	92	30	71
Saltash United Res.	26	19	4	3	76	30	61
Launceston Res.	26	15	6	5	48	33	51
Sticker	26	12	8	6	48	42	44
Bere Alston United	26	13	4	9	54	48	43
St Stephen	26	12	5	9	47	41	41
Tavistock Res.	26	11	5	10	50	42	38
Wadebridge Town Res.	26	9	6	11	36	47	33
Bodmin Town Res.	26	10	2	14	44	56	32
Lanreath	26	6	4	16	45	68	22
Liskeard Athletic Res.	26	5	6	15	44	54	21
Biscovey	26	6	3	17	37	82	21
Morwenstow	26	5	5	16	46	68	20
Probus	26	4	4	18	36	62	16

Padstow United - record expunged

SUPPLEMENTARY CUP
(League Cup First Round losers)

FIRST ROUND
Bude Town 3 Lifton 1
Nanpean Rovers 0 **Plymouth Parkway Res.** 16
Saltash United Res. 5 Camelford Res. 2
St Stephens Borough (w/o) v Padstow United (scr.)
Tavistock Res. 2 Polperro 0
Wadebridge Town Res. 4 St Stephen 0
QUARTER-FINALS
Bude Town 3 Wadebridge Town Res. 1
Plymouth Parkway Res. 4 St Blazey 0
Saltash United Res. 5 Tavistock Res. 0
St Stephens Borough 5 Plymstock United Res. 2
SEMI-FINALS *(played over two legs)*
Bude Town 1 Plymouth Parkway Res. 1, **Plymouth Parkway Res.** 6 Bude Town 1
St Stephens Borough 0 Saltash United Res. 1, **Saltash United Res.** 5 St Stephens Borough 1
FINAL *(May 7th at Torpoint Athletic)*
Plymouth Parkway Res. 1 **Saltash United Res.** 3

EAST CORNWALL LEAGUE PREMIER DIVISION CONSTITUTION 2009-10

BERE ALSTON UNITED .... Recreation Field, The Down, Bere Alston PL20 7HG .... None
BISCOVEY .... Par Athletics Track, Moorland Road, Par, St Austell PL24 2PB .... None
BODMIN TOWN RESERVES .... Priory Park, Bodmin PL31 2AE 01208 7816
BUDE TOWN .... Broadclose, Bude EX23 8DR .... None
LANREATH .... Rally Park, Lanreath Village Hall, Lanreath. .... None
LAUNCESTON RESERVES...... Pennygillam, Pennygillam Industrial Estate, Launceston PL15 7ED.............. 01566 77327
LISKEARD ATHLETIC RESERVES .... Lux Park, Coldstyle Lane, Liskeard PL14 3HY 01579 34266
MORWENSTOW.................... Playing Field, Shop, Morwenstow, Bude EX23 9SQ .... None
PLYMOUTH PARKWAY RESERVES. . Bolitho Park, St Peters Road, Manadon, Plymouth PL5 3QZ.............. None
PROBUS .... Recreation Ground, Probus TR2 4JS .... None
SALTASH UNITED RESERVES .... Kimberley Stadium, Callington Road, Saltash PL12 6DX 01752 84574
ST STEPHEN .... Trethosa Road, St Stephen, St Austell PL26 7PZ .... None
STICKER .... Burngallow Park, Burngallow Lane, Sticker, St Austell PL26 7EN.............. 01726 7100
TAVISTOCK RESERVES............ Langsford Park, Crowndale Road, Tavistock PL19 8DD 01822 61444
TORPOINT ATHLETIC RESERVES .... The Mill, Mill Lane, Torpoint PL11 2NA 01752 81288
WADEBRIDGE TOWN RESERVES ..... Bodieve Park, Bodieve Road, Wadebridge PL27 7AJ 01208 81253

IN: Bude Town (P), Plymouth Parkway Res. (P)
OUT: Padstow United (WS)

Division One	P	W	D	L	F	A	Pts
Plymouth Parkway Res.	28	25	1	2	122	32	76
Bude Town	28	17	6	5	103	40	57
Elburton Villa Res.	28	17	5	6	79	38	56
St Stephens Borough	28	17	4	7	80	55	55
Roche	28	15	4	9	61	41	49
Callington Town Res.	28	12	7	9	72	55	43
St Blazey Res.	28	12	6	10	65	55	42
St Dominick	28	12	4	12	54	69	40
Camelford Res.	28	11	5	12	53	67	38
Lifton	28	11	3	14	61	52	36
Polperro	28	10	3	15	44	70	33
Holsworthy Res.	28	8	6	14	50	75	30
Plymstock United Res.	28	5	5	18	49	100	20
Nanpean Rovers	28	2	5	21	35	117	11
St Columb Major	28	2	3	23	33	99	9

St Newlyn East - record expunged

LEAGUE CUP

FIRST ROUND

Bodmin Town Res. 4 Plymouth Parkway Res. 2

Bude 1 **Morwenstow** 3

Camelford Res. 1 **Probus** 1 *aet* (4-5p)

Holsworthy Res. 3 Nanpean Rovers 2

Lanreath 2 St Stephens Borough1

Launceston Res. 2 St Blazey Res. 0

Lifton 1 **Elburton Res.** 2

Padstow United v **St Dominick** (w/o)

Roche 3 Plymstock Res. 0

Saltash United Res. 2 **Liskeard Atheltic Res.** 3

St Columb Major (w/o) v St Newlyn East

St Stephen 1 **Callington Town Res.** 3

Sticker 4 Wadebridge Town Res. 1

Tavistock Res. 1 **Bere Alston United** 2

Torpoint Res. 1 Polperro 0

SECOND ROUND

Callington Town Res. 2 Biscovey 1

Elburton Villa Res. 2 Bodmin Town Res. 0

Lanreath 3 Morwenstow 2

Launceston Res. 2 St Columb Major 0

Liskeard Res. 2 **Sticker** 3

Probus 5 **St Dominick** 5 *aet* (4-5p)

Roche 2 Holsworthy Res. 1

Torpoint Athletic Res. 4 Bere Alston United 1

QUARTER-FINALS

Callington Town Res. 1 **Roche** 3

Elburton Villa Res. 0 **Launceton Res.** 2

Sticker 1 **Lanreath** 2

Torpoint Athletic Res. 1 **St Dominick** 2

SEMI-FINALS

(played over two legs)

Launceston Res. 0 Roche 0, Roche 0 **Launceston Res.** 0 *aet* (3-4p)

Lanreath 5 St Dominick 1, St Dominick 1 **Lanreath** 1

FINAL

(April 12th at Liskeard)

Lanreath 1 **Launceston Res.** 2

	Bude Town	Callington	Camelford	Elburton	Holsworthy	Lifton	Nanpean R.	Plym. Parkway	Plymstock	Polperro	Roche	St Blazey Res.	St Columb	St Dominick	St Newlyn East	St Stephens B.
Bude Town		5-0	1-1	2-2	5-1	1-0	3-0	2-0	8-1	7-1	1-1	2-4	5-1	9-1	11-1	1-1
Callington Town Res.	0-0		0-1	2-3	1-1	2-2	8-1	2-3	4-0	2-4	1-2	2-6	5-1	2-0	n/a	4-3
Camelford Res.	3-3	1-6	***D***	1-4	4-1	0-5	3-0	1-7	2-3	6-1	1-2	1-4	0-0	3-0	n/a	3-5
Elburton Villa Res.	3-2	0-2	2-2	***I***	5-0	3-2	W-L	2-4	4-0	4-1	2-1	1-1	5-0	3-2	n/a	4-0
Holsworthy Res.	2-4	2-4	2-3	0-2	***V***	4-2	1-0	1-2	4-2	3-1	1-1	3-3	W-L	4-3	n/a	2-0
Lifton	3-1	1-5	0-1	2-1	0-0	***I***	5-1	1-2	3-1	4-1	2-3	1-2	3-0	4-0	n/a	4-2
Nanpean Rovers	0-9	3-3	0-2	1-11	2-2	0-3	***S***	0-5	2-2	2-2	0-5	1-5	2-1	3-4	5-3	2-5
Plymouth Parkway Res.	6-2	2-1	6-1	4-1	7-0	4-1	11-0	***I***	4-2	1-1	4-1	6-2	6-1	4-0	n/a	2-0
Plymstock United Res.	2-7	2-2	4-1	1-3	4-4	2-2	3-3	2-4	***O***	0-1	1-7	2-1	4-1	1-7	n/a	2-5
Polperro	1-3	0-0	0-2	1-4	3-1	2-3	2-1	2-6	4-2	***N***	0-1	0-5	4-1	0-1	n/a	2-0
Roche	1-4	2-3	0-1	2-1	5-0	2-1	7-2	3-2	2-0	1-2		0-1	2-0	1-0	3-1	2-3
St Blazey Res.	0-3	2-3	3-1	1-1	1-4	2-1	6-3	1-2	7-0	0-4	2-2	***O***	1-1	0-3	n/a	0-2
St Columb Major	0-6	2-4	2-3	0-6	3-2	3-2	2-3	1-4	2-4	4-4	3-4	2-3	***N***	1-5	n/a	0-2
St Dominick	1-5	2-2	2-2	1-1	4-2	3-2	5-2	0-8	3-2	0-2	2-0	3-1	W-L	***E***	n/a	1-1
St Newlyn East	n/a	n/a	n/a	n/a	n/a	n/a	n/a	n/a	n/a	n/a	n/a	n/a	3-1	n/a		n/a
St Stephens Borough	4-2	4-2	4-3	3-1	4-3	4-2	2-1	1-6	3-0	6-2	1-1	1-1	10-1	4-1	n/a	

EAST CORNWALL LEAGUE DIVISION ONE CONSTITUTION 2009-10

CALLINGTON TOWN RESERVES	Callington Com. College, Launceston Rd, Callington PL17 7DR	01579 382647
CAMELFORD RESERVES	Trefew Park, Trefew, Camelford PL32 9TS	None
EDGCUMBE	Horsan Field, Antony Road, Torpoint	None
ELBURTON VILLA RESERVES	Haye Road, Elburton, Plymouth PL9 8HS	01752 480025
HOLSWORTHY RESERVES	Upcott Field, North Road, Holsworthy EX22 6HF	01409 254295
LIFTON	Recreation Ground, Lifton	None
MILLBROOK RESERVES	Mill Park, off Southdown Road, Millbrook, Torpoint PL11 1EN	01752 822113
NANPEAN ROVERS	Victoria Park, Victoria Bottoms, Nanpean PL26 7YE	01726 823435
PLYMSTOCK UNITED RESERVES	Dean Cross, Dean Cross Road, Plymstock PL9 7AZ	01752 406776
POLPERRO	Killigarth, Polperro, Looe	None
ROCHE	Trezaise Road, Roche, St Austell PL26 8HD	01726 890718
ST BLAZEY RESERVES	Blaise Park, Station Road, St Blazey PL24 2ND	01726 814110
ST COLUMB MAJOR	Recreation Ground, West Street, St Columb Major TR9 6RP	None
ST DENNIS	Boscawen Park, St Dennis PL26 8AP	01726 822635
ST DOMINICK	Lovells Park, St Dominick	None
ST STEPHENS BOROUGH	Saltmill Park, Saltmill Lane, Saltash PL12 6LG	None

IN: Edgcumbe (P - Duchy League Premier Division), Millbrook Res. (N), St Dennis (P - Duchy League Premier Division)

OUT: Bude Town (P), Plymouth Parkway Res. (P), St Newlyn East (WS)

HAMPSHIRE LEAGUE 2004

www.hampshireleague2004.com

Sponsored by:
Zenith Coach Travel

Founded: 2004

Recent champions:

2005: Sporting BTC

2006: Mottisfont.

2007: Mottisfont

2008: Mottisfont

	Andover Res.	Botley Village	Broughton	Crusaders	Denmead & Pur.	Durley	East Lodge	Fair Oak	Four Marks	Hedge End Rgrs	Ludgershall Spts	Michelmersh& T.	Mottisfont	Netley Cent Spts.	Twyford
Andover Res.		2-4	1-2	1-4	0-4	2-3	2-3	3-2	3-2	0-1	2-1	2-3	1-1	1-0	1-2
Botley Village	3-1		3-1	1-1	0-1	1-0	2-3	4-3	1-0	2-4	W-L	2-1	0-2	0-1	3-1
Broughton	3-2	1-0		4-2	2-3	3-3	2-1	0-0	2-0	2-3	2-1	2-0	3-3	1-6	3-1
Crusaders	3-1	1-3	5-1		2-3	3-2	1-6	2-1	4-1	1-3	2-2	1-2	1-0	0-4	2-3
Denmead & Purbrook	2-0	1-2	2-2	3-2		5-0	1-3	4-3	W-L	0-0	4-1	4-1	0-2	2-2	0-1
Durley	4-3	1-2	1-0	6-1	1-1		1-3	1-3	3-2	0-2	3-0	0-5	0-3	0-5	1-1
East Lodge	3-3	0-1	1-2	2-3	1-1	1-4		3-0	3-2	4-4	L-W	4-1	0-1	3-2	3-0
Fair Oak	2-3	0-6	0-6	1-2	0-2	2-1	1-2		2-2	1-2	1-3	3-3	0-1	2-9	W-L
Four Marks	0-3	2-4	2-2	3-3	1-0	1-2	1-0	2-0		0-2	4-1	0-0	0-1	0-6	2-2
Hedge End Rangers	0-3	1-1	0-2	1-3	3-1	2-1	2-2	6-1	0-2		0-3	8-0	3-0	2-0	1-0
Ludgershall Sports	4-1	1-1	3-1	2-1	0-3	3-0	0-3	0-1	1-1	1-2		2-9	3-2	1-2	5-2
Michelmersh & Timsbury	1-3	1-1	7-0	6-0	1-2	1-2	0-3	0-1	5-2	1-4	2-1		0-2	0-1	2-1
Mottisfont	2-0	2-4	1-3	1-0	0-1	5-3	0-5	5-0	1-0	1-4	0-0	2-3		2-4	4-2
Netley Central Sports	3-1	1-0	3-1	5-0	1-2	9-0	3-2	7-0	2-0	2-1	4-0	4-2	W-L		3-2
Twyford	3-3	3-2	1-7	2-3	0-1	3-2	1-1	5-1	2-2	2-3	3-0	0-3	1-6	1-10	

	P	W	D	L	F	A	Pts
Netley Central Sports	28	23	1	4	99	26	70
Hedge End Rangers	28	18	4	6	64	36	58
Denmead & Purbrook	28	17	5	6	53	31	56
Botley Village	28	16	4	8	53	36	52
East Lodge	28	14	5	9	65	41	47
Broughton	28	14	5	9	60	55	47
Mottisfont	28	14	3	11	50	41	45
Michelmersh & Timsbury	28	11	3	14	60	57	36
Crusaders	28	11	3	14	53	70	36
Ludgershall Sports	28	9	4	15	39	56	31
Durley	28	9	3	16	45	72	30
Andover Res.	28	8	3	17	48	65	27
Twyford	28	7	5	16	45	74	26
Four Marks	28	5	7	16	34	55	22
Fair Oak	28	5	3	20	31	84	18

LEAGUE CUP

FIRST ROUND

Broughton 1 **Fair Oak** 3
Crusaders 4 Botley Villaage 3
Denmead & Purbrook 3 Four Marks 2
Durley 1 **Hedge End Rangers** 2
East Lodge 1 **Andover Res.** 2
Netley Central Sports 5 Mottisfont 0
Twyford 1 **Ludgershall Sports** 2

QUARTER-FINALS

Andover Res. 3 Fair Oak 2
Crusaders 1 **Netley Central Sports** 2 *aet*
Hedge End Rgrs 1 Denmead/Purbrook 1 *aet* (7-6p)
Ludgershall Sports 1 **Michelmersh & Timsbury** 3

SEMI-FINALS

Michelmersh & Timsbury 1 Hedge End Rangers 1 *aet* (3-1p)
Netley Central Sports 3 Andover Res. 1

FINAL

(April 15th at Hamble ASSC)

Netley Central Sports 1 Michelmersh & Timsbury 0 *aet*

HAMPSHIRE LEAGUE 2004 CONSTITUTION 2009-10

ANDOVER RESERVES . . . . . . The Portway Stadium, West Portway Industrial Estate, Andover SP10 3LF 01264 35130
BOTLEY VILLAGE . . . . Botley Recreation Ground, High Street, Botley, Southampton SO30 2EA. 01489 78044
BROUGHTON . . . . The Sportsfield, Buckholt Road, Broughton, Stockbridge SO20 8DA. 01794 30115
CRUSADERS . . . . Worthies Sports & Social Club, Eversley Park, Kings Worthy, Winchester SO23 7NJ 01962 88045
DURLEY. . . . . Kytes Lane, Durley, Southampton SO32 2AE. . . . . Non
FAIR OAK . . . . Lapstone Park, Pavilion Close, Botley Road, Fair Oak, Eastleigh SO50 7AN . . . . Non
FOUR MARKS. . . . . The Recreation Ground, Upland Lane, Four Marks, Alton GU34 5AF . . . . Non
HEDGE END RANGERS . . . Norman Rodaway Rec, Heathouse Lane, Hedge End, Southampton SO30 0LE . . . . Non
HORNDEAN UNITED . . . . . King George V Playing Field, Southwick Rd, Denmead, Waterlooville PO7 6XT . . . . Non
INFINITY. . . . . Taunton's College, Hill Lane, Southampton SO15 5RL 023 8051 181
MICHELMERSH & TIMSBURY . . Timsbury Rec Trust, Mannyngham Way, Timsbury, Romsey SO51 0NJ 01794 36895
MOTTISFONT. . . . . Bengers Lane, Mottisfont, Romsey SO51 0LR . . . . Non
NETLEY CENTRAL SPORTS . . . . . Netley Rec, Station Road, Netley Abbey, Southampton SO21 5AF. 023 8045 226
PORTSMOUTH ROYAL NAVY . . Victory Stadium, HMS Temeraire, Burnaby Road, Portsmouth PO1 2EJ 023 9272 5315/423
TWYFORD. . . . . Hunters Park, Park Lane, Twyford, Winchester SO21 1QT . . . . Non

IN: Infinity (P - Winchester & District League), Portsmouth Royal Navy (N)
OUT: East Lodge (F), Ludgershall Sports (W - Andover & District League)
Denmead & Purbrook become Horndean United

HUMBER PREMIER LEAGUE

www.humberprem.com

Sponsored by:

No Sponsor

Founded: 2000

Recent champions:

2004: Hutton Cranswick United

2005: Reckitts

2006: Reckitts

2007: Sculcoates Amateurs

2008: Sculcoates Amateurs

Premier Division		P	W	D	L	F	A	Pts
Chalk Lane		28	22	3	3	107	25	69
Reckitts		28	21	3	4	80	31	66
Sculcoates Amateurs		28	19	1	8	73	46	58
Easington United		28	15	6	7	71	55	51
St Andrews Police Club		28	15	4	9	66	64	49
Beverley Town		28	15	3	10	45	33	48
Hedon Rangers		28	12	3	13	53	52	39
Pocklington Town		28	10	6	12	39	47	36
Cleethorpes Town	*-3*	28	11	5	12	46	61	35
Hornsea Town		28	8	5	15	48	64	29
North Ferriby United Res.		28	7	6	15	36	53	27
Westella & Willerby Res.		28	8	3	17	35	63	27
Malet Lambert YC		28	5	7	16	33	66	22
Barton Town OB Res.		28	6	2	20	27	59	20
Hessle Rangers		28	5	5	18	36	76	20

	Barton Town O. Boys Res.	Beverley Town	Chalk Lane	Cleethorpes Town	Easington United	Hedon Rangers	Hessle Rangers	Hornsea Town	Malet Lambert YC	North Ferriby United Res.	Pocklington Town	Reckitts	Sculcoates Amateurs	St Andrews Police Club	Westella & Willerby Res.
Barton Town Old Boys Res.		1-0	1-2	0-2	3-2	2-1	0-1	0-1	0-1	0-2	4-2	0-1	0-2	1-2	1-2
Beverley Town	2-1		0-1	2-1	3-1	4-0	1-1	2-1	0-1	0-0	2-1	1-3	1-0	3-0	2-0
Chalk Lane	10-0	3-0	***P***	7-0	8-1	4-1	2-0	4-1	4-1	3-2	5-0	0-0	4-2	14-2	7-0
Cleethorpes Town	3-2	0-0	1-0	***R***	1-3	2-1	5-1	4-1	4-1	2-1	2-1	0-2	0-1	1-2	3-3
Easington United	3-0	1-2	0-1	2-0	***E***	2-2	3-3	0-3	3-1	2-1	2-0	2-1	3-2	6-2	4-1
Hedon Rangers	5-2	1-0	4-1	1-1	1-2	***M***	2-1	5-2	2-0	1-3	3-1	2-5	0-1	3-5	1-0
Hessle Rangers	3-3	1-3	1-7	3-2	4-4	1-3	***I***	1-3	3-8	2-2	0-4	0-2	2-5	1-2	0-1
Hornsea Town	1-2	1-2	1-4	6-0	1-2	2-2	3-0	***E***	1-1	4-0	0-6	0-2	2-6	1-2	2-2
Malet Lambert YC	0-0	1-4	1-3	2-2	2-2	0-4	1-3	2-4	***R***	1-1	0-1	1-6	0-1	2-1	0-2
North Ferriby United Res.	1-0	2-1	0-4	2-4	2-2	0-3	2-0	1-1	0-1		0-1	1-3	1-3	1-1	5-0
Pocklington Town	4-1	3-1	1-0	0-0	0-7	2-0	0-1	2-2	1-1	1-0	***D***	1-2	0-2	1-1	2-1
Reckitts	2-0	1-2	2-2	8-2	3-4	2-1	2-0	3-1	2-2	5-0	5-0	***I***	2-1	2-1	0-2
Sculcoates Amateurs	2-0	4-1	1-1	6-1	4-3	4-0	1-2	5-0	3-1	4-3	2-1	2-9	***V***	3-4	0-1
St Andrews Police Club	2-1	3-2	2-3	3-2	2-2	2-0	3-1	3-0	5-0	4-2	1-1	1-2	3-4		5-1
Westella & Willerby Res.	0-2	0-4	0-3	0-1	2-3	1-4	2-0	1-3	4-1	0-1	2-2	2-3	1-2	4-2	

HUMBER PREMIER LEAGUE PREMIER DIVISION CONSTITUTION 2009-10

BEVERLEY TOWN . . . . Recreation Ground, Norwood, Beverley HU17 9HW 01482 862520
CHALK LANE . . . . Hull University, Inglemire Lane, Hull HU6 7TE 01482 466000
CLEETHORPES TOWN . . . . Lucarly's Wilton Road, Humberston, Grimsby DN36 4AW 01472 812936
HALL ROAD RANGERS RESERVES . . . . Dene Park, Beverley Road, Dunswell, Hull HU6 0AB 01482 850101
HEDON RANGERS . . . . Destiny Fitness, Staithes Road, Hedon, Hull HU12 8DX 01482 896113
HESSLE RANGERS . . . . Blackburn Leisure, Prescott Avenue, Brough HU15 1BB . . . . None
HESSLE SPORTING CLUB . . . . South Hunsley School, Melton, North Ferriby HU14 3HS 01482 631208
HORNSEA TOWN . . . . Hollis Recreation Ground, Atwick Road, Hornsea HU18 1EL . . . . None
MALET LAMBERT YC . . . . Malet Lambert School, James Reckitt Avenue, Hull HU8 0JD 01482 374211
NORTH FERRIBY UNITED RESERVES . Grange Lane, Church Road, North Ferriby HU14 3AA 01482 634601
POCKLINGTON TOWN . . . . The Balk, Pocklington, York YO42 2NZ 01759 303638
RECKITTS . . . . Humberside Police Sports Ground, Inglemire Lane, Hull HU6 8JG 01482 856954
SCULCOATES AMATEURS . . . . . Hull & East Riding Spts Ground, Chanterlands Avenue, Hull HU5 4ED 01482 342156
ST ANDREWS . . . . East Mount Recreation Ground, Waveney Road, Hull HU8 9NB 01482 326111x2317
WESTELLA & WILLERBY RESERVES . . Hill Top S&S, Willerby Low Rd, Willerby, Hull HU16 5JD 01482 671306

N: Hall Road Rangers Res. (P), Hessle Sporting Club (P)

OUT: Barton Town Old Boys Res. (W), Easington United (P - Central Midlands League Premier Division), Hutton Cranswick United Res. (WS)

St Andrews Police Club become St Andrews

Division One	P	W	D	L	F	A	Pts
Hall Road Rangers Res.	22	17	1	4	74	22	52
Hessle Sporting Club	22	16	2	4	61	33	50
Bransholme Athletic	22	14	3	5	69	43	45
North Cave	22	13	1	8	59	37	40
North Ferriby Athletic	22	12	3	7	56	31	39
Scarborough Athletic Res.	22	9	3	10	61	51	30
Brandesburton	22	9	2	11	50	59	29
Kingburn Athletic	22	7	4	11	45	62	25
Bridlington Sports Club	22	8	1	13	46	56	22
Withernsea	22	6	2	14	48	77	20
Inter Charter	22	4	7	11	36	55	19
Long Riston	22	2	1	19	23	102	7

Kinnersley - record expunged

GRAYS CUP

FIRST ROUND
Barton TOB Res. 2 **Scarborough Ath. Res.** 2 *aet* (2-4p)
Brandesburton 3 **Withernsea** 5
Bransholme 3 **Hall Road Rangers Res.** 3 *aet* (2-4p)
Bridlington Sports Club 5 Inter Charter 3 *aet*
Cleethorpes Town 0 **Malet Lambert YC** 1
Hessle Rangers 5 Easington United 2.
Hornsea Town 3 Westella & Willerby Res. 3 *aet* (7-6p)
Kingburn Athletic 0 **Chalk Lane** 3
North Cave 1 **Sculcoates Amateurs** 6
North Ferriby Athletic 2 **Reckitts** 3
North Ferriby United Res. 5 Kinnersley 2
Pocklington Town 4 Long Riston 0

SECOND ROUND
Beverley Town 0 **Sculcoates Amateurs** 2
Hall Road Rangers Res. 1 **Reckitts** 4
Hedon Rangers 1 **Chalk Lane** 2
Hessle Rangers 2 Hornsea Town 0
Hessle Sporting Club 3 **Pocklington Town** 4
North Ferriby United Res. 0 **Malet Lambert YC** 4
Scarborough Athletic Res. 1 **St Andrews Police Club** 3
Withernsea 3 Bridlington Sports Club 1

QUARTER-FINALS
Chalk Lane 2 St Andrews Police Club 0
Malet Lambert YC 2 Withernsea 1
Reckitts 3 Hessle Rangers 1 *aet (at Hessle Rangers)*
Sculcoates Amateurs 1 Pocklington Town 0

SEMI-FINALS
Chalk Lane 3 Malet Lambert YC 1 *aet (at Pockington)*
Sculcoates Amateurs 3 **Reckitts** 5 *(at Hall Road)*

FINAL *(May 14th at Hall Road Rangers)*
Reckitts 1 Chalk Lane 0

	Brandesburton	Bransholme Athletic	Bridlington Sports Club	Hall Road Rangers Res.	Hessle Sporting Club	Inter Charter	Kingburn Athletic	Kinnersley	Long Riston	North Cave	Nth Ferriby Athletic	Scarboro. Athletic Res.	Withernsea
Brandesburton		1-0	0-2	1-0	0-5	4-4	3-0	0-3	3-1	1-6	0-5	4-3	3-5
Bransholme Athletic	0-0	***D***	1-2	1-2	2-2	3-0	3-2	1-6	6-2	3-2	5-3	4-3	2-2
Bridlington Sports Club	6-2	1-3	***I***	3-6	0-1	2-3	0-1	5-6	5-0	1-4	1-6	4-1	3-5
Hall Road Rangers Res.	2-1	3-2	5-0	***V***	0-1	2-1	8-0	3-1	9-0	2-0	4-1	1-1	7-1
Hessle Sporting Club	2-1	2-4	1-2	4-3		3-1	7-3	6-4	6-0	3-2	0-5	3-2	4-1
Inter Charter	1-3	3-5	1-4	1-4	0-0		2-2	6-6	2-1	3-1	1-1	1-4	3-1
Kingburn Athletic	3-1	3-6	2-1	1-4	3-4	2-2		2-1	2-1	5-4	1-4	1-3	3-1
Kinnersley	1-1	n/a	n/a	1-6	2-1	1-1	n/a		3-1	2-3	4-0	5-1	n/a
Long Riston	2-6	1-7	2-1	0-3	0-6	3-3	0-5	0-7		1-6	0-2	1-4	5-0
North Cave	2-1	4-1	3-2	3-1	1-3	3-0	1-0	6-0	5-1	***O***	0-3	3-1	6-1
North Ferriby Athletic	2-4	2-3	1-1	0-1	0-1	2-0	2-2	1-2	5-0	0-1	***N***	3-0	3-2
Scarborough Athletic Res.	5-4	2-6	7-3	0-2	3-1	1-1	0-0	1-4	11-0	3-1	1-2	***E***	4-3
Withernsea	3-7	1-2	1-2	0-5	0-2	4-3	5-4	5-1	5-2	1-1	3-4	3-2	

HUMBER PREMIER LEAGUE DIVISION ONE CONSTITUTION 2009-10

BRANDESBURTON . . . . . . Brandesburton Playing Fields , Catwick Lane, Brandesburton , Driffield YO25 8SB . . . . Non
BRANSHOLME ATHLETIC . . . . Hull University, Inglemire Lane, Hull HU6 7TE 01482 46600
BRIDLINGTON SPORTS CLUB . . Bridlington SC, Dukes Park, Moorfield Road, Bridlington YO16 4LE 01262 60601
CROWN. . . . . Fitling Road, Humbleton, Hull HU11 4NS . . . . Non
EAST RIDING RANGERS . . . . Wyke VI Form College, Grammar School Road, Hull HU5 4NX 01482 34634
INTER CHARTER . . . . East Mount Recreation Ground, Waveney Road, Hull HU8 9NB 01482 326111x231
KINGBURN ATHLETIC . . . . Springhead Lane, Anlaby, Hull . . . . Non
LONG RISTON . . . . Long Riston Playing Fields, Long Riston . . . . Non
NORTH CAVE . . . . North Cave Playing Fields, Church Street, North Cave, Brough HU15 2LJ . . . . Non
NORTH FERRIBY ATHLETIC. . . . . South Hunsley School, Melton, North Ferriby HU14 3HS 01482 63120
SCARBOROUGH ATHLETIC RESERVES Hutton Cranswick Utd FC, Rotsea Lane, Hutton Cranswick, Driffield YO25 9QG. . . . . Non
WITHERNSEA . . . . Hull Road, Withernsea HU19 2EG . . . . Non

IN: Crown (P - East Riding County Amateur League Premier Division), East Riding Rangers (P - youth football)
OUT: Hall Road Rangers Res. (P), Hessle Sporting Club (P), Kinnersley (WS), Pinefleet Wolfreton (WN)

LINCOLNSHIRE LEAGUE

Sponsored by:
Sills & Betteridge

Founded: 1948

Recent champions:
2004: Sleaford Town
2005: Wyberton
2006: Hykeham Town
2007: Skegness Town
2008: Skegness Town

	Boston T.	CGB Hum.	C'thorpes	Grantham.	Grimsby	H'castle	Hykeham	Linc. Moor.	Lincoln U.	Louth Utd	Ruston S.	Skegness	Sleaford
Boston Town Res.		0-7	6-0	3-0	W-L	5-6	0-3	2-1	4-2	2-2	1-5	0-4	2-2
CGB Humbertherm	W-L		3-0	n/a	2-0	4-0	3-1	2-1	3-0	3-1	3-2	1-1	2-0
Cleethorpes Town Res.	W-L	0-2		3-2	4-2	1-4	1-4	2-1	1-1	0-4	1-3	1-7	2-6
Grantham Town Res.	4-0	n/a	n/a		n/a	n/a	n/a	2-1	n/a	n/a	1-0	n/a	n/a
Grimsby Borough Res.	0-6	0-4	2-2	n/a		2-3	1-8	3-2	1-2	0-7	0-4	0-2	2-7
Horncastle Town	2-1	1-2	2-0	2-3	4-1		2-2	4-0	0-3	1-7	2-0	2-0	1-1
Hykeham Town	2-1	3-5	2-1	6-1	1-1	5-0		0-0	5-1	1-2	1-1	8-1	0-0
Linc. Moorlands Rail. Res.	3-4	0-2	2-0	5-2	2-1	2-2	1-1		0-1	1-1	0-4	2-2	0-2
Lincoln United Res.	1-2	5-0	5-1	n/a	7-0	1-1	3-2	2-2		1-2	0-4	3-2	1-1
Louth United	5-0	W-L	4-0	n/a	3-1	0-3	1-4	2-1	3-2		2-3	1-1	5-0
Ruston Sports	3-2	1-3	5-2	2-0	4-0	2-1	0-5	1-1	3-1	3-2		2-1	3-0
Skegness Town	6-0	5-3	2-1	0-0	5-0	2-1	1-2	3-2	1-1	1-2	0-1		3-1
Sleaford Town Res.	2-1	3-3	3-0	1-0	3-0	0-0	0-0	1-0	1-2	2-1	0-0	0-1	

	P	W	D	L	F	A	Pts
CGB Humbertherm	22	17	2	3	57	24	53
Ruston Sports	22	15	3	4	54	28	48
Louth United	22	13	3	6	57	30	42
Hykeham Town	22	11	7	4	60	26	40
Skegness Town	22	11	4	7	51	34	37
Horncastle Town	22	10	5	7	42	41	35
Lincoln United Res.	22	9	5	8	45	39	32
Sleaford Town Res.	22	8	8	6	35	29	32
Boston Town Res.	22	7	2	13	39	56	23
Linc. Moorlands Rail. Res.	22	2	7	13	24	42	13
Cleethorpes Town Res.	22	3	2	17	20	70	11
Grimsby Borough Res.	22	1	2	19	17	82	5

Grantham Town Res. - record expunged

SUPPLEMENTARY CUP

FIRST ROUND
Boston Town Res. 3 Grimsby Borough Res. 2
Cleethorpes Res. 0 **Lincoln Moorlands Rail Res.** 4
Lincoln United Res. 2 Hykeham Town 2 *aet* (4-3p)
Ruston 6 Louth United 1
Sleaford Town Res. 1 **Grantham Town Res.** 5

QUARTER-FINALS
CGB Humbertherm 6 Grantham Town Res. 3
Lincoln Moorlands Railway Res. 2 Horncastle Town 0
Lincoln United Res. 1 Ruston Sports 0
Skegness Town 0 **Boston Town Res.** 1

SEMI-FINALS
Lincoln Moorlands Railway Res. 0 **Boston Town Res.** 1
Lincoln United Res. 0 **CGB Humbertherm** 3

FINAL
(April 23rd at Lincoln Moorlands)
Boston Town Res. 2 **CGB Humbertherm** 2 *aet* (2-4p)

LEAGUE CUP

FIRST ROUND
CGB Humbertherm 1 **Louth United** 3
Cleethorpes Town Res. 1 **Boston Town Res.** 3
Grantham Town Res. 1 Grimsby Borough Res. 0
Horncastle Town 0 **Ruston Sports** 1
Lincoln United Res. 6 Skegness Town 1

QUARTER-FINALS
Hykeham Town 2 Boston Town Res. 1
Lincoln Moorlands Railway Res. 2 Louth United 1
Lincoln United Res. 1 **Sleaford Town Res.** 4
Ruston Sports 1 Grantham Town Res. 1 *aet* (4-3p)

SEMI-FINALS
Ruston Sports 1 Lincoln Moorlands Railway Res. 0
Sleaford Town Res. 0 **Hykeham Town** 3

FINAL *(April 30th at Lincoln United)*
Hykeham Town 1 **Ruston Sports** 2

LINCOLNSHIRE LEAGUE CONSTITUTION 2009-10

BOSTON TOWN RESERVES .... The Stadium, Tattershall Road, Boston PE21 9LR........................ 01205 365470
CGB HUMBERTHERM............. Fulstow Playing Field, Thoresby Road, Fulstow, near Louth .... None
CLEETHORPES TOWN RESERVES .. Lucarly's, Wilton Road, Humberston, Grimsby DN36 4AW 01472 812936
GRIMSBY BOROUGH RESERVES.. St James School Playing Field, Dudley St, Grimsby DN34 4SY 01472 503260
HARVEST.......................... Novartis Sports Ground, Pyewipe, Grimsby DN31 2SR.. None
HECKINGTON UNITED .... Heckington Sports Club, Howell Road, Heckington, Sleaford NG34 9RX............... 01529 460491
HORNCASTLE TOWN .... The Wong, Boston Road, Horncastle LN9 6EY .... None
HYKEHAM TOWN .... Memorial Hall Ground, Newark Road, North Hykeham, Lincoln LN6 9RY............... 01522 880035
LINCOLN MOORLANDS RAILWAY RESERVES ... Newark Road, Lincoln LN6 8RT 01522 520184/874111
LINCOLN UNITED RESERVES..... Sports Pavilion, Ashby Avenue, Hartsholme, Lincoln LN6 0DY 01522 696400/690674
LOUTH TOWN RESERVES .... Park Avenue, Louth LN11 8BY 07712 653791
LOUTH UNITED .... Marshlands, Main Road, Saltfleetby, Louth LN11 7SS.................... 01507 339 884
RUSTON SPORTS............... Ruston Sports & Social Club, Newark Road, Lincoln LN6 8RB 01522 882111
SKEGNESS TOWN .... Burgh Road, Skegness PE25 2RJ.. 01754 612654
SKELLINGTHORPE PFC .... Monson Park Playing Field, Skellingthorpe, Lincoln LN6 5UE .... None
SLEAFORD TOWN RESERVES......... Eslaforde Park, Boston Road, Sleaford NG34 9GH 01529 415951

IN: Harvest (formerly Harvest Pet Products) (P - Grimsby & District League Division One), Heckington United (P - Lincoln & District League), Louth Town Res. (N), Skellingthorpe PFC (formerly Plough Skellingthorpe) (P - Lincoln & District League)
OUT: Grantham Town Res. (WS)

SHROPSHIRE COUNTY LEAGUE

http://www.scpfl1950.co.uk/

Sponsored by:

Sportsjamkits.com

Founded: 1950

Recent champions:

2004: Ellesmere Rangers

2005: Broseley Juniors

2006: Hanwood United

2007: Hanwood United

2008: Hanwood United

	Broseley Juniors	Clee Hill United	Dawley Bank	Haughmond	Ludlow Town Res.	Market Drayton Town Res.	Morda United	Newport County Borough	Shifnal Town Res.	Shifnal United	St Martins	Telford Juniors	Telford Town	Wem Town
Broseley Juniors		3-0	4-0	1-1	1-0	0-0	1-0	1-1	2-2	1-1	1-0	2-1	7-0	1-5
Clee Hill United	1-7	***P***	n/a	0-5	1-3	1-0	2-2	3-1	0-1	1-3	2-2	1-5	3-0	0-8
Dawley Bank	n/a	1-1	***R***	n/a	n/a	n/a	n/a	n/a	n/a	n/a	n/a	n/a	n/a	n/a
Haughmond	2-1	3-1	n/a	***E***	4-2	3-3	1-1	3-1	1-1	1-2	2-1	2-0	3-1	1-1
Ludlow Town Res.	2-2	3-1	n/a	3-2	***M***	2-1	2-4	4-0	2-0	4-1	1-5	2-1	7-1	1-2
Market Drayton Town Res.	0-1	6-1	3-2	2-3	2-2	***I***	2-1	3-0	1-4	0-0	0-1	3-1	4-1	0-1
Morda United	1-1	3-1	n/a	0-1	3-2	1-1	***E***	2-2	1-1	1-3	1-2	1-2	1-2	1-2
Newport County Borough	0-1	5-0	n/a	2-3	4-2	3-0	1-2	***R***	4-3	2-3	1-6	3-1	0-0	0-3
Shifnal Town Res.	2-1	4-1	n/a	1-2	4-0	3-2	5-1	0-3		0-2	6-1	1-0	3-1	2-3
Shifnal United	3-1	2-0	3-0	1-2	2-4	0-0	1-3	1-2	3-1		2-1	3-1	3-1	4-2
St Martins	3-1	1-0	4-0	1-0	3-4	1-1	0-3	1-1	1-1	2-0	***D***	1-1	7-0	0-3
Telford Juniors	0-3	0-0	n/a	0-4	1-5	2-2	2-2	1-1	4-2	1-1	0-2	***I***	3-1	2-5
Telford Town	0-4	6-4	3-2	0-8	0-2	0-4	0-7	2-2	1-5	0-3	3-4	1-2	***V***	0-9
Wem Town	1-0	5-1	n/a	1-3	5-0	4-0	1-1	1-3	2-0	2-2	3-1	4-2	8-0	

Premier Division	P	W	D	L	F	A	Pts
Wem Town	24	18	3	3	81	25	57
Haughmond	24	16	5	3	60	27	53
Shifnal United	24	13	5	6	46	33	44
Ludlow Town Res.	24	13	2	9	59	50	41
Broseley Juniors	24	11	7	6	44	26	40
St Martins	24	11	5	8	47	37	38
Shifnal Town Res.	24	11	4	9	52	39	37
Newport County Borough	24	8	6	10	42	46	30
Morda United	24	7	8	9	43	38	29
Market Drayton Town Res.	24	6	8	10	37	36	26
Telford Juniors	24	5	6	13	33	52	21
Clee Hill United	24	3	3	18	25	78	12
Telford Town	24	2	2	20	21	103	8

Dawley Bank - record expunged

PREMIER DIVISION CUP

FIRST ROUND

Broseley Juniors (w/o) v Dawley Bank

Clee Hill United 1 **Telford Juniors** 6

Market Drayton Town Res. 2 **Newport County Borough** 2 *aet* (4-5p)

Shifnal Town Res. 2 Ludlow Town Res. 1

Shifnal United 2 Haughmond 1

Telford Town 3 **Morda United** 5

QUARTER-FINALS

Newport County Borough 2 Broseley Juniors 1

Shifnal United 1 Wem Town 0

St Martins 0 **Morda United** 1

Telford Juniors 4 Shifnal Town Res. 1

SEMI-FINALS

Morda United 5 Telford Juniors 0

Newport County Borough 1 **Shifnal United** 3

FINAL

(May 16th at Ellesmere Rangers)

Morda United 1 **Shifnal United** 3

SHROPSHIRE COUNTY LEAGUE PREMIER DIVISION CONSTITUTION 2009-10

BROSELEY JUNIORS .... Birchmeadow, Broseley TF12 5LP .... None
CLEE HILL UNITED .... Knowle Sports Ground, Tenbury Road, Clee Hill, Ludlow SY8 3NE .... None
ELLESMERE RANGERS RESERVES .... Beech Grove Playing Fields, Ellesmere SY12 0BT............................ None
HAUGHMOND................. Mereside Recreation Centre, Springfield, Shrewsbury SY2 6LH 01743 35779
IMPACT UNITED .... Grainger Road, Leegomery, Telford TF1 6UJ.................................. None
LUDLOW TOWN RESERVES........... SBS Stadium, Bromfield Road, Ludlow SY8 2BY 01584 87600
MORDA UNITED........................ Weston Road, Morda, Oswestry SY10 9NS 01691 65962
NEWPORT COUNTY BOROUGH .... Shukers Field, Avenue Road, Newport TF10 7EA........................ 01952 82580
SHIFNAL TOWN RESERVES.......... Phoenix Park, Coppice Green Lane, Shifal TF11 8PB 01952 46366
SHIFNAL UNITED................ Idsall Sports Centre, Coppice Green Lane, Shifnal TF11 8PD 01952 46049
ST MARTINS............... St Martins Playing Fields, Overton Road, St Martins, Oswestry SY11 3DG .... None
TELFORD JUNIORS .... Ironbridge Power Station, Buildwas Road, Ironbridge TF8 7BL.................. None

IN: Ellesmere Rangers Res. (P), Impact United (P)

OUT: Dawley Bank (WS), Market Drayton Town Res. (F), Telford Town (W), Wem Town (P - West Midlands (Regional) League Division Two)

Division One		P	W	D	L	F	A	Pts
Ellesmere R. Res.		22	15	4	3	53	18	49
Impact United	*-3*	22	15	3	4	55	21	45
Wrockwardine Wd		22	14	2	6	67	31	44
Church Stretton T.		22	13	3	6	35	31	42
FC Hodnet		22	12	5	5	42	26	41
Dawley Wanderers		22	11	5	6	57	37	38
Wroxeter Rovers		22	10	3	9	48	41	33
Whitchurch Alp. Res.		22	8	6	8	35	45	30
Brown Clee		22	4	6	12	26	41	18
Oakengates Athletic		22	5	2	15	45	63	17
Meole Brace		22	2	3	17	17	84	9
Morda United Res.		22	2	0	20	18	60	6

Craven Arms Town - record expunged

INSIGHT RON JONES CUP

(all teams in league)

FIRST ROUND

Broseley Juniors 4 Haughmond 2
Dawley Wanderers 12 Craven Arms Town 0
FC Hodnet 1 **Shifnal Town Res.** 2
Ludlow Town Res. 0 **Shifnal United** 3
Market Drayton Town Res. (w/o) v Hopesgate Utd (scr.)
Morda United 0 **Wem Town** 1
Newport County Borough 1 **Oakengates Athletic** 2
Telford Juniors 1 **Impact United** 2
Telford Town 0 **Ellesmere Rangers Res.** 3
Whitchurch Alport Res. 1 **Clee Hill United** 2
Wrockwardine Wood 2 **Church Stretton Town** 3
Wroxeter Rovers 2 **Dawley Bank** 4

SECOND ROUND

Broseley Juniors 1 **Shifnal United** 3
Brown Clee 1 **Oakengates Athletic** 1 *aet* (4-5p)
Church Stretton Town 2 **Ellesmere Rangers Res.** 6
Impact United (w/o) v Market Drayton Town Res. (scr.)
Meole Brace 0 **Wem Town** 4
Morda Utd 4 **Clee Hill United** 3 *(Morda United expelled)*
Shifnal Town Res. 2 **Dawley Wanderers** 2 *aet* (2-4p)
St Martins (w/o) v Dawley Bank (scr.)

QUARTER-FINALS

Clee Hill United 0 **Impact United** 4
Oakengates Athletic 0 **Shifnal United** 1
St Martins 3 Dawley Wanderers 2
Wem Town 1 Ellesmere Rangers Res. 0

SEMI-FINALS

Impact United 2 St Martins 0
Wem Town 1 Shifnal United 0

FINAL

(May 21st at Ellesmere Rangers)
Wem Town 1 **Impact United** 3

TURNERS FURNITURE DIVISION ONE CUP

	Bro	Chu	Crav	Daw	Elle	FCH	Imp	Meo	Mor	Oak	Whi	Wck	Wrx
Brown Clee	***D***	0-2	n/a	1-4	0-3	0-0	0-0	3-3	3-1	3-1	2-3	1-3	0-1
Church Stretton Town	3-1	***I***	n/a	0-0	1-0	1-3	1-0	2-0	1-0	1-0	1-1	2-5	4-2
Craven Arms Town	0-1	0-2	***V***	n/a	0-4	1-0	n/a	n/a	n/a	n/a	0-2	n/a	n/a
Dawley Wanderers	3-3	2-0	n/a	***I***	1-1	2-1	1-2	4-0	6-0	6-2	3-3	2-5	1-1
Ellesmere Rgrs Res.	2-0	0-1	n/a	4-1	***S***	2-1	3-0	5-0	3-0	4-1	1-1	2-0	4-2
FC Hodnet	3-1	2-0	n/a	1-0	2-2	***I***	1-1	1-1	1-0	3-2	3-0	2-3	0-3
Impact United	2-0	4-1	n/a	3-2	0-1	1-0	***O***	5-0	4-1	7-1	1-1	4-0	0-3
Meole Brace	2-0	3-3	2-0	0-1	0-5	0-4	0-7	***N***	2-5	1-8	0-3	0-6	0-6
Morda United Res.	0-4	2-4	8-0	4-2	1-3	0-3	1-2	0-1		0-1	0-2	0-4	1-2
Oakengates Athletic	2-0	0-1	n/a	1-4	3-3	1-3	0-2	6-2	3-1		4-5	2-6	2-2
Whitchurch Alport Res.	2-2	1-3	n/a	2-5	0-3	2-3	2-5	1-0	1-0	2-1	***O***	0-2	1-1
Wrockwardine Wood	1-1	3-0	n/a	2-3	0-1	3-3	0-1	7-2	4-0	2-1	4-0	***N***	2-3
Wroxeter Rovers	0-1	2-3	n/a	1-4	3-1	1-2	2-4	2-0	4-1	5-3	1-2	1-5	***E***

FIRST ROUND

Dawley Wanderers 1 **FC Hodnet** 2
Ellesmere Rgrs Res. 3 Brown Clee 0
Impact United 7 Wroxeter Rovers 0
Morda Res. (w/o) v Hopesgate (scr.)
Whitchurch Res. 2 **Meole Brace** 4
Wrock. Wood 5 Church Stretton 3

QUARTER-FINALS

Craven Arms (scr.) v **Morda Res.** (w/o)
FC Hodnet 1 **Ellesmere Res.** 3 *aet*
Impact 0 Oakengates 0 aet (4-3p)
Wrockwardine Wd 2 Meole Brace 0

SEMI-FINALS

Ellesmere Res. 4 Morda Utd Res. 0
Wrockwardine Wood 2 **Impact** 4 *aet*

FINAL

(May 14th at Morda United)
Impact United 1 **Ellesmere Rangers Res.** 1 *aet* (2-4p)

SHROPSHIRE COUNTY LEAGUE DIVISION ONE CONSTITUTION 2009-10

BROWN CLEE . . . . Hall Meadow, Cleobury North, Bridgnorth WV16 6RP . . . . None
CHURCH STRETTON TOWN . . . . Russell's Meadow, Church Stretton SY6 6AT . . . . None
FC HODNET . . . . Hodnet Sports Centre, Hodnet, Market Drayton. . . . . None
KETLEY BANK UNITED. . . . . . Ketley Bank Recreation Ground, Dukes Hill, Ketley Bank, Telford TF2 0DB . . . . None
MEOLE BRACE . . . . Church Road, Meole Brace, Shrewsbury SY3 9HF . . . . None
MORDA UNITED RESERVES . . . . Weston Road, Morda, Oswestry SY10 9NS 01691 659621
NEWPORT TOWN . . . . Shukers Field, Avenue Road, Newport TF10 7EA. 01952 825801
OAKENGATES ATHLETIC . . . . . Hadley Learning Community, Waterloo Road, Hadley, Telford TF1 5NU . . . . None
WELLINGTON AMATEURS RESERVES . . . . . School Grove Oakengates Telford TF2 6BQ . . . . None
WHITCHURCH ALPORT RESERVES . . Yockings Park, Blackpark Road, Whitchurch SY13 1PG 01948 667415
WOOFFERTON . . . . Aynall Lane, Brimfield. 01568 615398
WROCKWARDINE WOOD . . . . New Road, Wrockwardine Wood TF2 7AB 01952 613086
WROXETER ROVERS . . . . Springfield, Wroxeter . . . . None

IN: Ketley Bank United (P - Telford Combination Premier Division), Newport Town (N), Wellington Amateurs Res. (N), Woofferton (S - Herefordshire League Premier Division)

OUT: Craven Arms Town (WS), Dawley Wanderers (F), Ellesmere Rangers Res. (P), Hopesgate United (WN), Impact United (P)

TEESSIDE LEAGUE

Sponsored by: Jack Hatfields Sports

Founded: 1891

Recent champions:
2004: Hartlepool
2005: Carlin How WMC
2006: Carlin How WMC
2007: Carlin How WMC
2008: BEADS

	BEAD	B'dale	DarlC	DarlRA	DarlRy	Fishb.	Grange	Guisb.	N Orm.	Nunth	Rich M	Rich T	Stokes	Thorn
BEADS		n/a	4-0	4-2	2-2	1-0	4-5	n/a	3-4	8-2	6-2	4-1	3-2	3-2
Bedale	1-3	***D***	1-1	n/a	n/a	n/a	n/a	0-4	n/a	n/a	3-3	n/a	n/a	1-3
Darlington Cleveland Bdge	1-2	n/a	***I***	4-0	2-1	2-2	1-3	3-1	6-2	5-2	2-0	2-3	1-0	0-4
Darlington RA Res.	1-6	n/a	3-1	***V***	0-0	1-2	2-4	n/a	0-1	3-4	1-1	2-1	1-0	1-4
Darlington Rugby Club	0-3	3-2	4-0	1-1	***I***	0-1	2-2	2-2	3-2	5-1	3-1	3-1	1-2	0-1
Fishburn Park	0-2	n/a	5-2	2-1	1-0	***S***	2-1	n/a	4-0	0-0	0-2	3-0	1-1	0-1
Grangetown Boys Club	0-2	4-0	1-2	5-0	5-0	2-3	***I***	17-4	2-0	2-2	4-2	2-0	4-2	0-0
Guisborough Quoit	n/a	n/a	n/a	1-1	n/a	1-4	n/a	***O***	0-4	n/a	2-3	4-0	n/a	2-1
North Ormesby Sports	3-6	n/a	4-0	4-2	1-5	2-1	2-1	n/a	***N***	0-1	7-1	3-1	1-2	1-4
Nunthorpe Athletic	0-2	6-1	3-0	2-2	1-2	4-1	3-2	1-5	3-3		4-3	2-1	3-0	1-1
Richmond Mavericks	1-1	n/a	1-0	5-1	3-0	2-1	1-3	n/a	6-2	3-2	***O***	0-1	3-3	2-3
Richmond Town	0-4	n/a	1-3	2-0	2-4	2-5	0-3	n/a	1-2	1-3	1-0	***N***	0-2	1-1
Stokesley Spts Club Res.	0-7	n/a	3-0	3-1	1-4	2-1	2-2	0-5	0-1	1-0	2-3	2-2	***E***	4-1
Thornaby Dubliners	1-2	n/a	3-2	2-4	2-2	3-0	1-3	n/a	1-4	4-1	3-2	10-0	3-3	

Division One		P	W	D	L	F	A	Pts
BEADS		22	18	2	2	79	29	56
Grangetown Boys Club		22	12	4	6	56	33	40
Thornaby Dubliners		22	11	5	6	55	36	38
North Ormesby Sports		22	11	1	10	49	53	34
Darlington Rugby Club		22	9	5	8	42	35	32
Nunthorpe Athletic		22	9	5	8	44	49	32
Fishburn Park	*-3*	22	10	3	9	35	31	30
Stokesley SC Res.		22	8	5	9	37	43	29
Richmond Mavericks		22	8	3	11	44	50	27
Darl. Cleveland Bridge		22	8	1	13	36	51	25
Darl. Railway Athletic Res.		22	4	4	14	29	58	16
Richmond Town		22	4	2	16	22	60	14

Bedale, Guisborough Quoit - records expunged

J V MADDEN TROPHY

(League champions v McMillan Bowl holders)

(Aug 2nd at BEADS) BEADS 0 **Guisboro. Quoit** 3

LOU MOORE MEMORIAL SHIELD

(Division One teams)

GROUP ONE

Bedale 1 Fishburn Park 1
Bedale 1 Richmond Town 2
North Ormesby Sports 4 Fishburn Park 0
North Ormesby Sports 2 Richmond Town 2
Nunthorpe Athletic 4 North Ormesby Sports 0
Nunthorpe Athletic 2 Fishburn Park 0
Richmond Mavericks 4 Bedale 1
Richmond Mavericks 1 Nunthorpe Athletic 3
Thornaby Dubliners 6 North Ormesby Sports 1
Thornaby Dubliners 2 Richmond Mavericks 2

GROUP TWO

BEADS 2 Darlington Cleveland Social 2
BEADS 1 Stokesley Sports Club Res. 1
Darlington RA Res. 1 Guisborough Quoit 2
Darlington Rugby Club 1 Grangetown Boys Club 5
Darlington Rugby Club 4 Stokesley Spts Club Res. 1
Grangetown Boys Club 1 BEADS 0
Grangetown Boys Club 10 Darlington RA Res. 5
Guisborough Quoit 0 Darlington Rugby Club 3
Guisborough Quoit 0 Stokesley Sports Club Res. 4
Stokesley SC Res. 0 Darlington Cleveland Social 2
Stokesley Sports Club Res. 4 Darlington RA Res. 0
Competition abandoned due to inclement weather

R T RAINE TROPHY

(McMillan Bowl First Round losers)

FIRST ROUND

BEADS 5 Grangetown YCC 0
Fishburn Park 1 Billingham Kader 0
Teesside Athletic Res. 0 **Thornaby Dubliners** 1

QUARTER-FINALS

BEADS 2 Norton & Stockton Ancients Res. 0
Billingham Town Res. (scr.) v **Redcar RC** (w/o)
Darlington RC 1 **Thornaby Dubliners** 1 *aet* (3-4p)
South Bank St Peters 3 Fishburn Park 0

SEMI-FINALS

BEADS 3 South Bank St Peters 2
Thornaby Dubliners 4 Redcar Rugby Club 0

FINAL

(May 11th at Norton & Stockton Ancients)
BEADS 0 **Thornaby Dubliners** 3

TEESSIDE LEAGUE DIVISION ONE CONSTITUTION 2009-10

BEADS .... Beechwood & Easterside SC, Marton Road, Middlesbrough TS4 3PP 01642 311304
DARLINGTON CLEVELAND BRIDGE Eastbourne Sports Complex, Bourne Avenue, Darlington DL1 1LJ 01325 243177/243188
DARLINGTON CROFT .... Croft WMC, Hurworth Road, Hurworth Place, Darlington DL2 2DA .... None
DARLINGTON GRAMMAR SCHOOL RA Darlington Rail Athletic Club, Brinkburn Road, Darlington DL3 9LF 01325 468125
FISHBURN PARK .... Eskdale School, Broomfield Park, Whitby YO22 4HS. .... None
GRANGETOWN BOYS CLUB . . . Grangetown YCC, Trunk Road, Grangetown, Middlesbrough TS6 7HP 01642 455435
NORTH ORMESBY SPORTS ...... Unity City Academy Road, Ormesby, Middlesbrough TS3 8RE .... None
NUNTHORPE ATHLETIC .... Recreation Club, Guisborough Road, Nunthorpe TS7 0LD 01642 313251
RICHMOND MAVERICKS. . . Brompton-on-Swale Sports Ground, Brompton-on-Swale, Richmond DL10 7HT .... None
RICHMOND TOWN .... Earls Orchard Playing Fields, Sleegill, Richmond DL10 4RH. .... None
SOUTH BANK ST PETERS . . . St Peters School, Normanby Road, South Bank, Middlesbrough TS6 6SP 01642 453462
STOKESLEY RESERVES. . . . Stokesley Sports Club, Broughton Road, Stokesley, Middlesbrough TS9 5JQ 01642 710051
THORNABY DUBLINERS ...... Harold Wilson Sports Complex, Badger Avenue, Thornaby TS17 0EX .... None

IN: South Bank St Peters (P)
OUT: Bedale (WS), Guisborough Quoit (WS)
Darlington Railway Athletic Res. become Darlington Grammar School RA, Darlington Rugby Club become Darlington Croft, Stokesley Sports Club Res. become Stokesley Res.

McMILLAN BOWL

FIRST ROUND

Billingham Kader 1 **Great Ayton United** 2
Billingham Town Res. 3 **Whinney Banks YCC** 5
Coulby Newham 2 BEADS 1
Darlington Cleveland Bridge 5 Norton & SA Res 2 *aet*
Darlington Rugby Club 4 **North Ormesby Sports** 5
Fishburn Park 0 **St Mary's College** 1
Grangetown Boys Club 3 Richmond Town 0
Grangetown YCC 1 **Richmond Mavericks** 7
Nunthorpe Athletic 4 Thornaby Dubliners 4 *aet* (4-3p)
Redcar Rugby Club 0 **Stokesley Sports Club Res.** 2
Scarborough Town 3 South Bank St Peters 1
Teesside Athletic Res. 0 **Acklam Steelworks** 4

SECOND ROUND

Darlington RA Res. 4 North Ormesby Sports 2
Grangetown BC (w/o) v Coble Ennis Square (scr.)
Great Ayton United 7 Acklam Steelworks 0
Nunthorpe Athletic 8 Stokesley Sports Club Res. 3
Richmond Mavericks 10 Bedale 4
Scarborough Town 7 Guisborough Quoit 2
St Mary's College 3 Darlington Cleveland Bridge 0
Whinney Banks YCC 3 Coulby Newham 1

QUARTER-FINALS

Grangetown Boys Club 4 Great Ayton United 2
Richmond Mavericks 4 Darlington RA Res. 0
Scarborough Town 1 **Nunthorpe Athletic** 2
St Mary's College 0 **Whinney Banks YCC** 2

SEMI-FINALS

Nunthorpe Athletic 3 Richmond Mavericks 2
Whinney Banks YCC 2 Grangetown Boys Club 0

FINAL

(April 27th at Norton & Stockton Ancients)
Nunthorpe Athletic 1 Whinney Banks YCC 1 *aet* (4-2p)

Division Two		P	W	D	L	F	A	Pts
Scarborough Town		20	16	4	0	72	11	52
South Bank St Peters		20	16	1	3	71	41	49
Whinney Banks YCC		20	14	1	5	71	36	43
Coulby Newham		20	11	3	6	47	32	36
Redcar Rugby Club		20	8	4	8	44	61	28
Great Ayton United		20	7	5	8	38	35	26
Acklam Steelworks	-3	20	7	2	11	44	47	20
Norton & SA Res.		20	5	3	12	31	47	18
Teesside Athletic Res.		20	5	2	13	24	50	17
St Mary's College		20	3	3	14	25	46	12
Grangetown YCC		20	3	2	15	23	84	11

Coble Ennis Square, Billingham Town Res., Billingham Kader - records expunged

ALEX BURNESS PLATE

(Division Two teams)

GROUP ONE

Bill. Kader 2 Bill'ham T. Res. 0
Great Ayton 2 Norton Res. 2
Norton Res. 3 Bill'gham Kader 3
Norton Res. 3 St Mary's Coll. 1
Redcar RC 7 Norton Res. 1
Redcar RC 3 St Mary's Coll. 3
Scarboro. Town 2 Redcar RC 0

GROUP TWO

Acklam 1 Teesside Ath. Res. 0
Coulby Newham 2 Acklam 3
Coulby N. 2 Teesside A. Res. 2
Grangetown YCC 1 Sth Bank 9
Grangetown 0 Whinney BYCC 9
South Bank 5 Coulby New. 3
Teesside Athletic Res. 2 Grangetown YCC 0
Teesside Athletic Res. 1 South Bank St Peters 3
Whinney Banks YCC 3 Acklam Steelworks 0

Competition abandoned due to inclement weather

	Acklam	Bill. K	Bill. T	Coble	Coulby	Grange	Great	Norton	Redcar	Scarb	South	St Mary	Tees	Whiney
Acklam Steelworks		2-1	n/a	4-1	2-2	4-3	1-1	4-3	7-2	2-3	3-4	1-0	1-3	1-3
Billingham Kader	4-1	***D***	1-1	n/a	1-3	2-1	0-2	1-0	1-1	1-3	0-5	0-3	n/a	0-1
Billingham Town Res.	2-7	n/a	***I***	n/a	0-3	n/a	2-4	2-1	0-5	n/a	3-7	n/a	n/a	2-1
Coble Ennis Square	n/a	3-2	n/a	***V***	1-11	n/a	n/a	n/a	n/a	n/a	n/a	n/a	n/a	n/a
Coulby Newham	3-2	0-0	n/a	n/a	***I***	2-0	2-0	3-1	4-1	1-1	3-4	2-1	3-1	1-3
Grangetown YCC	2-9	n/a	1-7	n/a	0-6	***S***	2-2	0-1	1-6	0-7	2-4	1-1	2-0	1-11
Great Ayton United	2-3	n/a	n/a	n/a	2-2	1-0	***I***	0-1	2-1	1-1	3-4	5-1	1-0	3-2
Norton & Stockton Res.	1-0	n/a	3-2	n/a	1-4	1-2	1-6	***O***	1-1	1-2	1-2	4-3	3-0	1-4
Redcar Rugby Club	1-0	n/a	n/a	4-3	3-2	4-2	3-2	4-2	***N***	2-2	3-4	1-3	1-0	1-8
Scarborough Town	3-0	5-1	9-1	n/a	5-1	3-0	2-0	0-0	12-0		4-0	1-0	3-1	9-0
South Bank St Peters	3-2	11-1	n/a	n/a	2-1	10-1	2-1	5-3	3-3	1-3	***T***	3-1	1-0	2-3
St Mary's College	2-0	n/a	3-1	4-0	0-1	1-2	2-2	3-2	1-4	1-4	1-2	***W***	3-3	0-4
Teesside Athletic Res.	5-0	3-2	1-4	n/a	0-2	2-1	2-3	2-1	2-2	0-5	1-10	2-0	***O***	0-5
Whinney Banks YCC	1-2	4-0	5-3	n/a	3-2	9-1	3-1	2-2	3-1	0-2	2-5	2-1	3-0	

TEESSIDE LEAGUE DIVISION TWO CONSTITUTION 2009-10

ACKLAM STEELWORKS .... Acklam Steelworks Sports Club, Park Road South, Middlesbrough TS4 2RD 01642 818717
CARGO FLEET .... Thorntree Park, The Greenway, Thorntree, Middlesbrough TS3 9HR .... None
COULBY NEWHAM .... Hemlington Recreation Ground, Cass House End, Hemlington, Middlesbrough TS8 9LF ....
GRANGETOWN YCC .... Grangetown YCC, Trunk Road, Grangetown, Middlesbrough TS6 7HP 01642 455435
GREAT AYTON UNITED .... Leven Park, Easby Lane, Great Ayton, Middlesbrough DL9 6JJ .... None
GUISBOROUGH TOWN BLACK SWAN........ Howlbeck Road, Guisborough TS14 6LA 01287 636925
NORTON & STOCKTON ANCIENTS RESERVES Norton Sports Complex, Station Road, Norton, Stockton TS20 1PE 01642 530203
REDCAR NEWMARKET .... Rye Hills School, Redcar Lane, Redcar TS10 1PE. .... None
REDCAR RUGBY CLUB.............. Redcar Rugby Club, Green Lane, Redcar TS10 3RW .... None
SOUTH PARK RANGERS...... Smiths Dock Park, Skippers Lane, Normanby, Middlesbrough TS6 0JF .... None
ST MARY'S COLLEGE............. St Mary's College, Saltersgill Lane, Middlesbrough TS4 3JP.......................... 01642 814680
STOCKTON TOWN .... Bishopton Road West, Stockton-on-Tees TS19 0QD .... None
TEESSIDE ATHLETIC RESERVES.............. Green Lane, Redcar TS10 3RW.. None
WHINNEY BANKS YCC .... Hall Garth School, Hall Drive, Acklam, Middlesbrough TS5 7JX 01642 813776

IN: Cargo Fleet (P - youth football), Guisborough Town Black Swan (N), Redcar Newmarket (P - Sunday football), South Park Rangers (P - youth football), Stockton Town (P - youth football)

OUT: Coble Ennis Square (WS), Billingham Town Res. (WS), Billingham Kader (WS), Scarborough Town (P - Wearside League), South Bank St Peters (P)

WEST RIDING COUNTY AMATEUR LEAGUE

www.wrc.leaguemanager.biz

Sponsored by:

No sponsor

Founded: 1922

Recent champions:

2004: Silsden

2005: Golcar United

2006: Bay Athletic

2007: Wibsey

2008: Bay Athletic

	Ardsley Celtic	Bay Athletic	Brighouse	Campion	Golcar United	Halifax Irish	Hall Green	Hemsworth	Kirkburton	Lower Hopton	Marsden	Meltham	Ovenden	Overthorpe	Storthes Hall	Wibsey
Ardsley Celtic	***P***	3-3	0-0	2-4	0-3	1-2	2-3	2-1	3-2	0-3	6-3	0-3	2-5	2-0	1-1	1-0
Bay Athletic	3-2	***R***	1-0	3-1	5-1	3-1	4-1	12-1	3-1	2-1	1-1	2-1	2-1	9-1	4-3	5-0
Brighouse Town Res.	4-1	0-1	***E***	2-3	0-4	1-1	1-0	1-0	2-4	1-0	0-3	0-3	0-2	1-3	2-1	1-0
Campion	4-1	0-1	2-1	***M***	4-0	0-1	3-3	7-0	4-1	2-1	2-1	2-2	0-3	2-2	2-1	4-1
Golcar United	1-1	1-2	2-4	1-1	***I***	1-0	1-0	3-1	1-1	1-1	4-0	0-6	3-5	3-0	4-1	2-3
Halifax Irish Club	4-4	0-3	2-1	2-1	1-3	***E***	1-4	7-1	1-2	1-1	1-3	1-3	2-4	4-2	3-2	1-7
Hall Green United	3-1	3-4	3-2	3-4	3-3	0-4	***R***	5-0	1-1	2-0	1-0	2-2	2-0	5-3	2-2	5-0
Hemsworth Miners W. Res.	1-9	2-2	1-0	4-5	0-3	1-2	1-2		2-2	1-6	4-1	0-4	0-4	2-1	1-1	1-1
Kirkburton	3-0	3-2	1-2	2-3	1-0	3-2	1-2	1-0	***D***	1-3	5-2	3-1	1-3	7-0	0-3	4-4
Lower Hopton	3-0	1-2	1-1	2-3	0-3	1-2	4-1	5-0	3-1	***I***	3-1	1-0	0-3	2-1	2-1	2-5
Marsden	3-2	1-6	3-0	0-2	1-5	5-1	2-2	3-0	1-2	0-0	***V***	2-2	1-1	3-2	2-1	1-3
Meltham Athletic	3-1	2-6	6-4	1-2	0-2	5-0	2-1	4-0	3-1	3-1	1-0	***I***	0-3	7-1	1-1	5-2
Ovenden West Riding	1-0	0-0	3-1	1-4	3-2	4-0	5-0	7-0	2-2	4-0	3-1	3-2	***S***	6-0	0-0	4-1
Overthorpe Sports	3-2	0-8	2-1	2-3	0-4	3-4	0-5	3-1	2-6	4-2	3-1	4-1	0-12	***I***	2-3	3-2
Storthes Hall	1-1	1-2	2-1	3-2	2-3	2-0	5-2	2-2	1-1	1-0	1-2	3-0	1-2	8-0	***O***	4-1
Wibsey	2-2	0-2	2-2	3-4	2-1	3-1	2-2	3-0	3-2	1-2	4-0	9-5	1-3	5-1	1-3	***N***

Premier Division	P	W	D	L	F	A	Pts
Bay Athletic	30	25	4	1	103	33	79
Ovenden West Riding	30	23	4	3	97	28	73
Campion	30	20	4	6	80	50	64
Golcar United	30	15	5	10	65	48	50
Meltham Athletic	30	15	4	11	78	57	49
Hall Green United	30	13	7	10	68	60	46
Kirkburton	30	12	6	12	65	59	42
Storthes Hall	30	11	8	11	61	46	41
Lower Hopton	30	12	4	14	51	48	40
Wibsey	30	11	5	14	71	73	38
Halifax Irish Club	30	11	3	16	52	74	36
Marsden	30	9	5	16	47	68	32
Brighouse Town Res.	30	8	4	18	36	57	28
Ardsley Celtic	30	6	7	17	52	72	25
Overthorpe Sports	30	8	1	21	48	121	25
Hemsworth Miner W. Res.	30	3	5	22	28	108	14

PREMIER DIVISION CUP

FIRST ROUND

Campion 6 Marsden 2

Hall Green United 0 **Bay Athletic** 3

Hemsworth Miners Welfare 0 **Meltham Athletic** 8

Lower Hopton 2 Ardsley Celtic 0

Ovenden West Riding 4 Golcar United 1 *aet*

Overthorpe Sports Club 0 **Brighouse Town Res.** 9

Storthes Hall 0 **Kirkburton** 3

Wibsey 5 Halifax Irish Club 3

QUARTER-FINAL

Brighouse Town Res. 3 Campion 1

Kirkburton 2 **Bay Athletic** 3

Lower Hopton 3 Ovenden West Riding 2

Meltham Athletic 5 Wibsey 2

SEMI-FINAL

Brighouse Res. 1 **Meltham Ath.** 2 *(at Liversedge)*

Lower Hopton 1 **Bay Athletic** 6 *(at Brighouse Town)*

FINAL

(May 4th at Brighouse Town)

Meltham Athletic 5 Bay Athletic 3

WEST RIDING COUNTY AMATEUR LEAGUE PREMIER DIVISION CONSTITUTION 2009-10

ALBION SPORTS . . . . Myra Shay, Barkerend Road, Bradford BD3 0AB 07771 68500
ARDSLEY CELTIC . . . . The Crescent, East Ardsley, Wakefield WF3 2EG. 07950 13188
BAY ATHLETIC . . . . Syngenta Sports, 509 Leeds Road, Huddersfield HD2 1YJ 01484 514367
BRIGHOUSE TOWN RESERVES. . . . . St Giles Road, Hove Edge, Brighouse HD6 2PL 01484 380088
CAMPION . . . . Manningham Mills Sports Ground, Scotchman Road, Manningham, Bradford BD9 4SH 01274 546726
GOLCAR UNITED . . . . Longfield Recreation Ground, Golcar, Huddersfield HD7 4AZ 07779 700098
HALIFAX IRISH CLUB. . . . . Natty Lane, Illingworth, Halifax HX2 9DS 01422 36013
HALL GREEN UNITED . . . . . Crigglestone Sports Club, Painthorpe Lane, Crigglestone, Wakefield WF4 3JU 01924 25454
KIRKBURTON. . . . . Gregory Playing Fields, Kirkburton, Huddersfield HD8 0XH 07738 98758
LOWER HOPTON. . . . . Woodend Road, Lower Hopton, Mirfield WF14 8PP 01924 492048
MARSDEN. . . . . Fall Lane, Marsden, Huddersfield HD7 6LX 01484 84419
MELTHAM ATHLETIC . . . . Broadlands Recreation Ground, Meltham, Holmfirth HD9 5QY. 07787 96220
OVENDEN WEST RIDING . . . . Natty Lane, Illingworth, Halifax HX2 9DS 01422 24435
STORTHES HALL. . . . . Police Sports Ground, Woodfield Park, Lockwood Scar, Huddersfield HD4 6BW 07957 69118
TYERSAL . . . . Arkwright Street, off Dick Lane, Tyersal, Bradford BD4 8JL 07710 00624
WIBSEY. . . . . Westwood Park, Cooper Lane, Bradford BD6 3NN 07739 52155

IN: Albion Sports (P), Tyersal (P)

OUT: Hemsworth Miners Welfare Res. (R), Overthorpe Sports (R)

Division One	P	W	D	L	F	A	Pts
Tyersal	26	22	1	3	75	27	67
Albion Sports	26	21	2	3	108	38	65
Steeton	26	17	6	3	66	27	57
Salts	26	15	5	6	60	39	50
Ventus & Yeadon Celtic	26	14	3	9	74	42	45
Heckmondwike Town	26	13	3	10	65	57	42
Wakefield City	26	12	2	12	46	59	38
Hunsworth	26	11	1	14	52	65	34
Eastmoor	26	6	7	13	48	72	25
Littletown	26	7	3	16	39	69	24
Dudley Hill Rangers	26	6	5	15	46	59	23
South Bradford	26	6	1	19	32	87	19
Keighley Shamrocks	26	4	5	17	30	54	17
Crag Road United	26	5	2	19	36	82	17

DIVISION ONE CUP

FIRST ROUND

Albion Sports 5 Heckmondwike Town 4
Crag Road United 3 **Dudley Hill Rangers** 4
Eastmoor 3 **South Bradford** 4
Littletown 2 **Wakefield City** 4
Tyersal 2 Steeton 1
Ventus & Yeadon Celtic 2 **Salts** 3

QUARTER-FINALS

Albion Sports 11 South Bradford 0
Hunsworth 2 Dudley Hill Rangers 0
Salts 0 **Tyersal** 2
Wakefield City 2 Keighley Shamrocks 0

SEMI-FINALS

Hunsworth 3 Wakefield City 1 *(at Ardsley Celtic)*
Tyersal 4 Albion Sports 3 *(at Campion)*

FINAL

(May 20th at Littletown)
Tyersal 3 Hunsworth 1 *aet*

	Albion Sports	Crag Road United	Dudley Hill Rangers	Eastmoor	Heckmondwike Town	Hunsworth	Keighley Shamrocks	Littletown	Salts	South Bradford	Steeton	Tyersal	Ventus & Yeadon Celtic	Wakefield City
Albion Sports		6-1	4-1	7-2	2-1	6-1	4-2	5-2	3-3	7-0	2-0	0-1	2-2	3-1
Crag Road United	2-8	***D***	0-3	3-4	4-3	1-2	1-0	2-1	0-4	1-4	2-2	0-2	0-3	2-2
Dudley Hill Rangers	1-3	3-2	***I***	4-4	1-2	3-4	0-0	1-2	2-1	1-3	1-2	1-3	1-2	7-1
Eastmoor	1-4	6-1	4-0	***V***	2-2	1-2	3-2	0-0	2-2	1-0	1-7	2-3	1-3	2-5
Heckmondwike Town	1-2	6-1	4-3	4-0	***I***	2-1	2-1	3-2	0-5	5-1	1-1	1-5	2-2	5-6
Hunsworth	5-2	2-1	3-3	6-1	1-2	***S***	5-2	4-3	0-3	2-0	0-2	0-3	4-3	1-2
Keighley Shamrocks	1-2	0-4	0-0	2-2	0-1	2-0	***I***	1-0	0-2	3-1	1-1	1-3	0-4	3-1
Littletown	1-9	3-1	2-2	2-2	1-4	2-6	4-2	***O***	1-2	0-1	2-6	0-2	2-0	2-1
Salts	2-7	2-1	1-0	2-0	3-2	6-0	2-1	3-0	***N***	2-1	1-1	1-3	1-4	1-1
South Bradford	0-8	2-3	1-4	2-2	3-5	2-0	3-2	1-3	3-2		0-5	1-4	0-1	0-3
Steeton	0-3	4-2	2-1	3-1	1-0	4-1	0-0	1-0	2-2	9-0	***O***	3-2	2-1	2-0
Tyersal	2-4	4-0	4-1	5-3	2-0	3-0	2-0	4-1	3-1	4-1	2-0	***N***	3-1	3-0
Ventus & Yeadon Celtic	3-4	5-1	5-1	0-1	5-0	3-1	5-4	6-0	2-3	5-1	0-3	2-2	***E***	1-3
Wakefield City	2-1	1-0	0-1	1-0	2-7	3-1	2-0	0-3	0-3	5-1	1-3	3-1	0-6	

WEST RIDING COUNTY AMATEUR LEAGUE DIVISION ONE CONSTITUTION 2009-10

BRONTE WANDERERS .... Marley Stadium, Aireworth Road, Keighley BD21 4DB 01535 609910
DUDLEY HILL RANGERS .... Newhall Park School, Newhall Road, Bierley, Bradford BD4 6AF 07967 359883
EASTMOOR .... King George V Playing Fields, Woodhouse Road, Eastmoor, Wakefield WF1 4RD 01924 375367
HECKMONDWIKE TOWN .... Cemetery Road, Heckmondwike WF16 9ED 01924 442907
HEMSWORTH MINERS WELFARE RESERVES Fitzwilliam Stadium, Wakefield Road, Fitzwilliam, Pontefract WF9 5AJ ... 01977 610444
HUNSWORTH .... Birkenshaw Middle School, Bradford Road, Gomersal, Cleckheaton BD19 4BE 07711 197741
KEIGHLEY SHAMROCKS .... Marley Stadium, Aireworth Road, Keighley BD21 4DB 01535 609910
LITTLETOWN .... Beck Lane, Heckmondwike WF16 0JZ 07930 852796
OVERTHORPE SPORTS .... Overthorpe Park, Edge Top Road, Dewsbury WF12 0BG 01924 464164
SALTS .... Salts Playing Fields, Hirst Lane, Saltaire, Shipley BD18 4DD 01274 583427
STEETON .... Summer Hill Lane, Steeton BD20 6RX 01585 683387
TYERSAL RESERVES .... Arkwright Street, off Dick Lane, Tyersal, Bradford BD4 8JL 07710 006241
VENTUS & YEADON CELTIC .... Dam Lane, Yeadon, Leeds 07721 468967
WAKEFIELD CITY .... West Yorks Sports & Social, Walton Lane, Sandal, Wakefield WF2 6NG 01924 258760

IN: Bronte Wanderers (P), Hemsworth Miners Welfare Res. (R), Overthorpe Sports (R), Tyersal Res. (P)
OUT: Albion Sports (P), Crag Road United (R), South Bradford (E), Tyersal (P)

Division Two	P	W	D	L	F	A	Pts
Bronte Wanderers	**22**	**14**	**6**	**2**	**67**	**30**	**48**
Tyersal Res.	**22**	**14**	**4**	**4**	**61**	**39**	**46**
West Horton	**22**	**14**	**3**	**5**	**67**	**41**	**45**
Storthes Hall Res.	**22**	**12**	**3**	**7**	**54**	**31**	**39**
Kirkburton Res.	**22**	**12**	**2**	**8**	**61**	**47**	**38**
Rawdon Old Boys	**22**	**10**	**2**	**10**	**41**	**48**	**32**
Campion Res.	**22**	**9**	**4**	**9**	**41**	**32**	**31**
Dudley Hill Athletic	**22**	**5**	**7**	**10**	**40**	**64**	**22**
Steeton Res.	**22**	**6**	**3**	**13**	**53**	**62**	**21**
Golcar United Res.	**22**	**5**	**6**	**11**	**39**	**56**	**21**
Dynamoes	**22**	**5**	**3**	**14**	**44**	**80**	**18**
Morley Town	**22**	**4**	**1**	**17**	**32**	**70**	**13**

Liversedge u-19s - record expunged

Reserve Division	P	W	D	L	F	A	Pt
Bay Athletic Res.	20	14	3	3	65	22	45
Ardsley Celtic Res.	20	13	1	6	60	25	40
Ventus & Yeadon Celtic Res.	20	12	4	4	67	40	40
Salts Res.	20	12	2	6	52	24	38
Lower Hopton Res.	20	12	2	6	46	30	38
Hall Green United Res.	20	8	7	5	51	39	31
Ovenden West Riding Res.	20	8	3	9	43	39	27
Marsden Res.	20	5	6	9	37	43	21
Wakefield City Res.	20	5	2	13	32	77	17
Littletown Res.	20	4	2	14	33	66	14
Bronte Wanderers Res.	20	1	0	19	18	99	3

RESERVE DIVISION CUP

FINAL *(May 18th at Lower Hopton)*

Ardsley Celtic Res. 3 Ovenden WR Res. 1

	Bronte Wanderers	Campion Res.	Dudley Hill Athletic	Dynamoes	Golcar United Res.	Kirkburton Res.	Liversedge u-19s	Morley Town	Rawdon Old Boys	Steeton Res.	Storthes Hall Res.	Tyersal Res.	West Horton
Bronte Wanderers	***D***	3-2	6-2	3-0	4-2	3-0	n/a	10-0	3-2	2-0	2-1	3-3	3-0
Campion Res.	0-0	***I***	1-1	2-2	0-1	0-2	0-3	0-1	1-2	2-1	1-2	4-0	3-2
Dudley Hill Athletic	3-3	2-1	***V***	2-1	3-3	4-6	n/a	2-1	0-1	1-1	2-1	0-1	0-7
Dynamoes	1-6	1-6	1-2	***I***	4-3	4-11	3-3	3-1	2-4	2-9	0-3	1-2	0-4
Golcar United Res.	2-2	0-3	2-2	2-4	***S***	1-2	n/a	2-1	2-1	3-3	2-1	1-1	2-3
Kirkburton Res.	2-0	2-2	3-0	8-2	2-2	***I***	2-2	3-2	0-1	3-1	1-6	1-2	0-3
Liversedge u-19s	7-1	n/a	6-1	n/a	n/a	6-1	***O***	n/a	n/a	n/a	n/a	n/a	1-2
Morley Town	3-5	0-3	3-3	2-4	0-5	2-4	n/a	***N***	3-1	4-0	1-4	0-5	1-2
Rawdon Old Boys	3-0	3-2	2-2	1-5	2-0	1-3	3-2	3-0		2-5	2-0	3-3	0-4
Steeton Res.	0-4	4-5	7-4	2-1	4-1	1-4	1-6	0-2	3-5		2-2	3-4	4-5
Storthes Hall Res.	2-3	2-0	3-0	1-1	7-2	2-1	6-2	4-2	3-0	0-1	***T***	1-3	2-2
Tyersal Res.	1-1	1-2	3-1	2-1	2-1	6-2	n/a	5-3	4-2	4-1	0-2	***W***	7-2
West Horton	1-1	0-1	7-4	4-4	5-0	2-1	3-2	2-0	3-0	2-1	3-5	4-2	***O***

DIVISION TWO CUP

FIRST ROUND

Dudley Hill Athletic 1 **Morley Town** 3
Dynamoes 3 **Kirkburton Res.** 5
Farnley (scr.) v **Campion Res.** (w/o)
Golcar United Res. 7 West Horton 1
Rawdon Old Boys 3 Bronte Wdrs 2
Tyersal Res. 0 **Storthes Hall Res.** 3

QUARTER-FINALS

Campion Res. 1 **Golcar Res.** 1 *aet* (0-3p)
Rawdon (w/o) v Liversedge u-19s (scr)
Steeton Res. 5 Morley Town 0
Storthes H. Res. 3 Kirkburton Res. 0

SEMI-FINALS

Golcar Res. 2 **Storthes Hall Res.** 3
Rawdon OB 3 Steeton Res. 2 *aet*

FINAL *(May 15th at Campion)*

Storthes Hall Res. 2 Rawdon OB 1

WEST RIDING COUNTY AMATEUR LEAGUE DIVISION TWO CONSTITUTION 2009-10

AFC EMLEY RESERVES . . . . The Welfare Ground, off Upper Lane, Emley, Huddersfield HD8 9RE 01924 84932
ARDSLEY CELTIC RESERVES . . . . The Crescent, East Ardsley, Wakefield WF3 2EG 07950 13188
BAY ATHLETIC RESERVES . . . . Syngenta Sports, 509 Leeds Road, Huddersfield HD2 1YJ 01484 51436
CAMPION RESERVES . . Manningham Mills Sports Ground, Scotchman Road, Manningham, Bradford BD9 4SH 01274 54672
CRAG ROAD UNITED . . . . Apperley Road, Greengates, Bradford BD10 0PX 07781 80821
DUDLEY HILL ATHLETIC . . . . Hunsworth Lane, East Bierley BD4 6RN 07837 93944
GOLCAR UNITED RESERVES. . . . . . Longfield Recreation Ground, Golcar, Huddersfield HD7 4AZ 07779 70009
KIRKBURTON RESERVES . . . . Gregory Playing Fields, Kirkburton, Huddersfield HD8 0XH 07738 98758
MORLEY TOWN . . . . Glen Road, Morley, Leeds LS27 9HG 07709 72708
RAWDON OLD BOYS . . . . Hanson Field, Rawdon, Leeds 07748 82823
STEETON RESERVES. Summer Hill Lane, Steeton BD20 6RX 01585 68338
STORTHES HALL RESERVES . . . . Woodfield Park, Lockwood Scar, Huddersfield HD4 6BW 07957 69118
WEST HORTON . . . . Myra Shay, Bakerend Road, Bradford BD3 0AB 07974 17698
WESTBROOK YMCA . . . . Lawnswood YMCA, Otley Road, Leeds LS16 6HQ 0113 261 248

IN: AFC Emley Res. (N), Ardsley Celtic Res. (P - Reserve Division), Bay Athletic Res. (P - Reserve Division), Crag Road United (R) Westbrook YMCA (P - Harrogate & District League Premier Division)

OUT: Bronte Wanderers (P), Dynamoes (F), Farnley (WN), Liversedge u-19s (WS), Tyersal Res. (P)

WEST RIDING COUNTY AMATEUR LEAGUE DIVISION THREE (FORMERLY RESERVE) CONSTITUTION 2009-10

ALBION SPORTS RESERVES. . . . . Avenue Road, Bradford BD3 0AB . . . . None
BRONTE WANDERERS RESERVES. . . . Marley Stadium, Aireworth Road, Keighley BD21 4DB 01535 60991
HALL GREEN UNITED RESERVES . . . . . Painthorpe Lane, Crigglestone, Wakefield WF4 3JU 01924 25454
HECKMONDWIKE TOWN RESERVES . . . . . . Cemetary Road, Heckmondwike WF16 9ED 01924 44290
HUDDERSFIELD YMCA. New Hey Road, Huddersfield HD3 3XF 01484 65405
LITTLETOWN RESERVES . . . . Beck Lane, Heckmondwike WF16 0JZ 07930 85279
LOWER HOPTON RESERVES . . . . Woodend Road, Lower Hopton, Mirfield WF14 8PP 01924 49204
MARSDEN RESERVES . . . . Fell Lane, Marsden, Huddersfield t.b.a. 01484 84419
OVENDEN WEST RIDING RESERVES . . . . Natty Lane, Illingworth, Halifax HX2 9DS 01422 24435
SALTS RESERVES . . . . Salts Playing Fields, Hirst Lane, Saltaire, Shipley BD18 4DD 01274 58342
VENTUS & YEADON CELTIC RESERVES . . . . Dam Lane, Yeadon, Leeds. 07721 46896
WAKEFIELD CITY RESERVES . West Yorks Sports & Social, Walton Lane, Sandal, Wakefield WF2 6NG 01924 25876

IN: Albion Sports Res. (N), Heckmondwike Town Res. (N), Huddersfield YMCA (P - Huddersfield & District League)

OUT: Ardsley Celtic Res. (P), Bay Athletic Res. (P)

WEST YORKSHIRE LEAGUE

www.wya.leaguemanager.biz

Sponsored by:

No sponsor

Founded: 1928

Recent champions:

2004: Aberford Albion

2005: Nostell Miners Welfare

2006: Leeds Met Carnegie

2007: Bardsey

2008:Carlton Athletic

Premier Division	P	W	D	L	F	A	Pts
Knaresborough Town	30	20	8	2	64	21	68
Leeds City	30	21	3	6	74	41	66
Whitkirk Wanderers	30	19	4	7	72	36	61
Beeston St Anthony's	30	17	6	7	81	45	57
Carlton Athletic	30	15	4	11	60	62	49
Sherburn White Rose	30	12	9	9	53	44	45
Ripon City	30	12	5	13	46	53	41
Bardsey	30	12	4	14	62	63	40
Aberford Albion	30	11	6	13	53	55	39
Boroughbridge	30	12	2	16	52	45	38
Otley Town	30	11	3	16	46	60	36
Field Sports & Social	30	11	2	17	57	65	35
Rothwell Athletic	30	10	3	17	46	64	33
Pool	30	9	6	15	47	70	33
Howden Clough	30	6	4	20	41	86	22
Wetherby Athletic	30	5	5	20	34	78	20

	Aberford Albion	Bardsey	Beeston St Anthony's	Boroughbridge	Carlton Athletic	Field Sports & Social	Howden Clough	Knaresborough Town	Leeds City	Otley Town	Pool	Ripon City	Rothwell Athletic	Sherburn White Rose	Wetherby Athletic	Whitkirk Wanderers
Aberford Albion	***P***	3-0	1-4	2-1	1-1	0-2	0-2	0-2	1-2	2-0	2-2	4-1	1-1	5-0	1-0	0-3
Bardsey	2-0	***R***	0-3	0-3	3-1	3-1	2-2	1-3	2-3	1-2	4-2	4-1	0-1	2-1	0-0	2-3
Beeston St Anthony's	1-1	5-0	***E***	0-1	3-4	2-1	3-1	0-3	1-2	1-2	3-0	1-1	3-1	1-1	6-0	2-2
Boroughbridge	3-0	2-3	2-3	***M***	4-0	3-5	1-0	1-2	0-2	1-3	0-0	2-1	2-1	2-3	2-0	0-1
Carlton Athletic	6-3	2-6	2-6	2-1	***I***	2-1	3-0	0-0	2-5	2-1	0-2	3-1	1-1	1-4	1-0	0-3
Field Sports & Social	4-3	5-1	0-2	0-3	2-4	***E***	2-3	1-0	0-1	3-2	4-1	1-2	4-3	1-1	3-1	0-2
Howden Clough	0-2	1-7	0-4	3-2	1-2	4-0	***R***	2-3	0-1	3-3	1-3	3-3	2-6	1-6	2-1	0-3
Knaresborough Town	6-0	2-3	5-3	1-0	3-0	2-0	4-2		1-0	2-0	0-0	0-0	4-0	1-0	0-0	2-2
Leeds City	3-3	4-2	2-4	4-2	2-2	3-2	3-1	1-1	***D***	2-0	5-1	3-2	2-1	2-0	3-1	0-1
Otley Town	1-3	3-0	0-4	0-2	1-2	2-1	1-3	0-3	4-3	***I***	2-2	0-4	2-1	3-1	7-1	0-2
Pool	0-5	0-6	3-4	0-3	0-4	2-5	3-0	1-2	0-1	3-2	***V***	2-1	4-1	1-1	3-2	5-1
Ripon City	3-6	3-0	2-0	0-5	0-2	2-1	0-0	0-4	3-2	0-0	4-2	***I***	1-2	0-3	1-2	1-0
Rothwell Athletic	2-2	2-1	2-4	3-1	0-3	4-1	3-0	1-3	0-4	0-1	2-1	0-1	***S***	3-2	1-4	1-5
Sherburn White Rose	1-0	2-2	1-1	1-0	3-1	2-2	6-0	1-1	1-6	2-0	0-0	0-2	3-0	***I***	2-2	3-1
Wetherby Athletic	0-2	1-3	4-4	3-3	2-1	0-5	3-2	1-3	2-1	1-3	2-3	1-4	0-3	0-2	***O***	0-1
Whitkirk Wanderers	2-0	2-2	1-3	2-0	3-6	5-0	6-2	1-1	1-2	5-1	3-1	0-2	2-0	3-0	6-0	***N***

WEST YORKSHIRE LEAGUE PREMIER DIVISION CONSTITUTION 2009-10

ABERFORD ALBION . . . . Bunkers Hill, Main Street (South), Aberford LS25 3DE . . . . None
ALTOFTS . . . . Altofts Sports Club, Lock Lane, Altofts, Normanton WF6 2QJ 01924 892708
BARDSEY . . . . The Sportsfield, Keswick Lane, Bardsey LS17 9AQ 01937 574286
BEESTON ST ANTHONY'S . . . . Beggars Hill, Sunnyview Gdns, Beeston Road, Beeston, Leeds 0113 270 7223
BOROUGHBRIDGE . . . . Aldborough Road, Boroughbridge, York YO51 9EA 01423 324206
CARLTON ATHLETIC . . . . Carlton Cricket Club, Town Street, Carlton, Wakefield WF3 3QU 0113 282 1114
FIELD SPORTS & SOCIAL. . . . Field Sports Ground, Hollingwood Lane, Lidget Green, Bradford BD7 2RQ 01274 546726
KNARESBOROUGH TOWN. . . . . Manse Lane, Knaresborough HG5 8LF 07773 679971
LEEDS CITY . . . . Adel WMA, Church Lane, Adel, Leeds LS16 8DE 0113 293 0525
OSSETT COMMON ROVERS. . . . . Illingworth Park, Manor Road, Ossett WF5 0LH . . . . None
OTLEY TOWN . . . . Old Show Ground, Pool Road, Otley LS20 1DY 01943 451025
POOL . . . . Pool S&S Club, Arthington Lane, Pool-in-Wharfedale, Otley LS21 1LG 0113 284 3932
RIPON CITY . . . . Mallorie Park Drive, Ripon HG4 2QD 01765 600542
ROTHWELL ATHLETIC. . . . . Royds Lane, Rothwell, Leeds LS26 0BE . . . . Club HQ: 0113 282 0723
SHERBURN WHITE ROSE. . . . . . Recreation Ground, Finkle Hill, Sherburn-in-Elmet, Leeds LS25 6EB . . . . None
WHITKIRK WANDERERS . . . . . . Whitkirk Sports & Social Club, Selby Road, Whitkirk, Leeds LS15 0AA 0113 264 6623

IN: Altofts (P), Ossett Common Rovers (P)

OUT: Howden Clough (R), Wetherby Athletic (R)

Division One	P	W	D	L	F	A	Pts
Altofts	28	21	4	3	72	29	67
Ossett Cmn Rovers	28	20	1	7	60	33	61
Robin Hood Athletic	28	16	5	7	63	39	53
Pontefract Sp./Soc.	28	16	4	8	54	37	52
East End Park WMC	28	14	6	8	56	43	48
Old Centralians	28	12	6	10	58	41	42
Horbury Town	28	11	6	11	41	39	39
Nostell MW Res.	28	11	3	14	38	45	36
Old Headingley	28	10	5	13	44	37	35
Kellingley Welfare	28	10	5	13	34	52	35
Kippax Athletic	28	10	3	15	38	54	33
Hartshead	28	9	5	14	43	53	32
Ilkley Town	28	8	4	16	38	52	28
Featherstone Colliery	28	4	6	18	30	71	18
Woodhouse Hill WMC	28	5	3	20	32	76	18

Churwell Lions - record expunged

LEAGUE CUP

FIRST ROUND

Barwick 0 **Aberford** 3
Boston Spartans 2 **Field** 4
Carlton Athletic 3 Ilkley 2
Churwell 2 **Boroughbdge** 6
Hartshead 3 Woodhouse Hill WMC 2
Howden Clough 3 Tadcaster Magnet Sports 1
Hunslet 2 Sandy Lane 1
Leeds City 3 **Kippax Ath.** 1 *(Leeds City expelled)*
Old Centralians 2 Old Headingley 1
Ossett CR 4 Gt Preston 1
Pontefract Spts & Social 2 Kellingley Welfare 1
Robin Hood 0 **Beeston** 1
Stanley 2 **South Milford** 3
Whitkirk 2 **Knaresboro.** 4
Wyke Wdrs 0 **Ripon City** 1

SECOND ROUND

Aberford 9 Swillington 0
Altofts 5 Wetherby Ath. 2
Bardsey 3 **Rothwell T.** 4
Beeston 0 **Boroughbdge** 3 Brighouse Old Boys 2
Carlton Athletic 3 East End Park WMC 0
Ossett Common Rovers 1 **Featherstone** 3 Ripon 0
Field 2 Knaresborough 0
Horbury Town 3 Rothwell Athletic 1
Howden Clough 0 **Pontefract Spts & Social** 8
Kippax 2 **Mount St M.** 3
Nostell Res. 0 **Sherburn** 3
O. Centralians 5 Hunslet 0
Oxenhope 0 **Hartshead** 1
Pool 1 **Otley Town** 3
South Milford 1 **Baildon Trinity Athletic** 3

THIRD ROUND

Altofts 5 Otley Town 0
Boroughbridge 0 **Sherburn White Rose** 2
Carlton Athletic 2 Baildon Trinity Athletic 1
Featherstone Colliery 0 **Aberford Albion** 1
Field 6 Old Centralians 2
Hartshead 3 Rothwell T. 0
Mount St Mary's 2 **Pontefract Spts & Social** 3
Ossett Common Albion 0 **Horbury Town** 1

QUARTER-FINALS

Aberford 5 Hartshead 1
Altofts 1 **Field Spts & S.** 3
Carlton Ath. 1 **Sherburn** 2
Pontefract Sports & Social 3 Horbury Town 2

SEMI-FINALS

Pontefract Spts & Social 4 Aberford 1 *(at Altofts)*
Sherburn White Rose 3 Field 0 *(at Nostell MW)*

FINAL

(May 9th at Wetherby Ath.)
Pontefract Sports & Social 0 **Sherburn White Rose** 2

	Alt	Chu	Eas	Fea	Har	Hor	Ilk	Kel	Kip	Nos	OC	OH	Oss	Pon	Rob	Woo
Altofts		5-0	3-0	3-1	1-0	2-1	1-0	3-1	6-1	3-2	2-2	1-0	2-1	1-2	2-0	2-3
Churwell Lions	n/a		n/a	4-2	3-4	1-1	n/a	n/a	n/a	1-4	n/a	n/a	n/a	0-4	n/a	3-5
East End Park WMC	2-2	n/a	***D***	0-0	1-1	3-1	3-2	2-1	3-0	1-0	2-2	2-2	1-4	2-1	2-1	8-0
Featherstone Colliery	0-4	3-2	1-3	***I***	1-1	0-3	1-4	1-2	2-0	0-3	1-1	0-2	0-2	0-4	0-2	1-1
Hartshead	0-6	7-1	6-4	5-0	***V***	1-2	1-0	0-2	3-1	1-0	2-6	1-2	1-3	0-1	1-3	3-2
Horbury Town	2-4	8-0	0-1	3-2	0-2	***I***	3-1	3-0	0-0	2-2	1-0	1-1	0-1	1-3	0-1	5-2
Ilkley Town	1-1	n/a	2-5	1-0	3-3	2-2	***S***	0-1	3-2	1-2	2-1	1-1	0-1	0-2	3-1	1-0
Kellingley Welfare	2-2	2-0	1-0	3-4	1-2	0-0	0-5	***I***	0-0	2-1	4-3	0-1	1-3	2-0	1-3	2-2
Kippax Athletic	0-4	3-0	0-1	6-3	2-1	2-0	2-1	1-0	***O***	0-1	2-3	2-1	1-3	1-3	3-3	2-0
Nostell Miners Welf. Res.	1-5	2-1	0-3	1-1	2-0	0-2	2-1	2-0	0-2	***N***	2-0	1-0	1-3	0-2	1-3	6-1
Old Centralians	0-2	6-3	3-2	1-1	0-1	4-1	3-1	5-0	4-1	3-1		0-0	3-1	2-3	4-0	3-0
Old Headingley	0-1	n/a	1-1	3-5	2-1	3-1	7-1	1-2	1-0	1-2	2-0	***O***	0-2	2-4	2-3	3-0
Ossett Common Rovers	6-2	2-1	3-1	4-1	2-1	0-1	2-1	1-2	0-1	2-0	4-1	1-0	***N***	0-4	1-1	4-1
Pontefract Sports & Social	0-1	4-1	4-2	1-2	2-2	0-1	0-1	1-1	2-1	1-1	1-3	2-1	0-4	***E***	2-0	4-2
Robin Hood Athletic	1-2	5-0	2-1	4-1	3-2	2-2	4-0	4-0	4-2	2-4	1-1	2-1	5-0	1-1		5-0
Woodhouse Hill WMC	0-4	5-4	L-W	4-1	1-1	0-3	1-0	2-3	2-3	3-0	1-0	0-4	1-2	3-4	0-2	

WEST YORKSHIRE LEAGUE DIVISION ONE CONSTITUTION 2009-10

BAILDON TRINITY ATHLETIC. . . . . The Dell, Cliffe Lane, West Baildon, Shipley BD17 5LB . . . . None
EAST END PARK WMC . . . . Skelton Road, Leeds LS9 9EP . . . . None
HARTSHEAD . . . . Littletown Recreation Ground, Hartshead 01274 87336
HORBURY TOWN . . . . Slazengers Sports Complex, Engine Lane, Horbury, Wakefield WF4 5NH 01924 27422
HOWDEN CLOUGH . . . . Batley Sports Centre, Windmill Lane, Batley WF17 0QD 01924 32618
ILKLEY TOWN. . . . . Denton Road, Ilkley LS29 0AA . . . . None
KELLINGLEY WELFARE . Kellingley (Knottingley) Soc C, Marine Villa Road, Knottingley, Wakefield WF11 8ER 01977 67311
KIPPAX . . . . Rear of Swillington MW, Wakefield Road, Swillington LS26 8DT . . . . None
NOSTELL MINERS WELFARE RESERVES . Middle Lane, New Crofton, Wakefield WF4 1LB 01924 86601
OLD CENTRALIANS . . . . West Park Playing Fields, North Parade, West Park, Leeds LS16 5AY. . . . . None
OLD HEADINGLEY . . . . Collingham & Linton SA, Harewood Road, Collingham, Wetherby LS22 5BL . . . . None
OXENHOPE RECREATION. . . . . Marley Playing Fields, Keighley. . . . . None
ROBIN HOOD ATHLETIC. . . . . Behind Coach & Horses, Rothwell Haigh, Leeds LS26 0SF. 0113 282 102
WETHERBY ATHLETIC. . . . . . Wetherby Sports Association, The Ings, Boston Road, Wetherby LS22 5HA 01937 58569
WYKE WANDERERS . . The Albert Morton Mem. P. Flds, New Popplewell Lane, Scholes, Cleckheaton BD19 6NN . . . . None

IN: Baildon Trinity Athletic (P), Howden Clough (R), Oxenhope Recreation (P), Wetherby Athletic (R), Wyke Wanderers (P)
OUT: Altofts (P), Churwell Lions (WS), Featherstone Colliery (R), Ossett Common Rovers (P), Pontefract Sports & Social (W), Woodhouse Hill WMC (R)
Kippax Athletic become Kippax

Division Two	P	W	D	L	F	A	Pts
Baildon Trinity Athletic	28	20	5	3	80	28	65
Oxenhope Recreation	28	18	8	2	80	32	62
Wyke Wanderers	28	18	4	6	66	28	58
Boston Spartans	28	17	7	4	76	48	58
Brighouse Old Boys	28	15	6	7	65	46	51
Rothwell Town	28	12	6	10	66	53	42
Hunslet	28	12	5	11	54	57	41
Mount St Mary's	28	11	5	12	52	47	38
Sandy Lane	28	9	3	16	42	69	30
Barwick	28	8	5	15	44	54	29
Great Preston	28	7	5	16	47	74	26
Swillington Saints	28	7	4	17	36	72	25
Stanley United	28	6	5	17	38	65	23
South Milford	28	5	7	16	42	76	22
Tadcaster Magnet Sports	28	5	5	18	32	71	20

LEAGUE TROPHY

FINAL *(April 30th at Altofts)*

Whitkirk Wanderers Res. 3 Otley Town Res. 1

Alliance One	P	W	D	L	F	A	Pt
Beeston St Anthony's Res.	28	24	3	1	88	22	75
Whitkirk Wanderers Res.	28	19	2	7	76	34	59
Rothwell Athletic Res.	28	15	5	8	67	40	50
Knaresborough Town Res.	28	15	3	10	79	55	48
Robin Hood Athletic Res.	28	15	2	11	69	48	47
Ossett Common Rovers Res.	28	14	4	10	65	54	46
Sherburn White Rose Res.	28	13	4	11	56	46	43
Boroughbridge Res.	28	12	5	11	48	48	41
Wetherby Athletic Res.	28	11	6	11	56	70	39
Aberford Albion Res.	28	10	6	12	49	60	36
Field Sports & Social Res.	28	10	2	16	51	64	32
Horbury Town Res.	28	8	5	15	59	68	29
Ripon City Res.	28	9	2	17	51	91	29
Hartshead Res.	28	6	3	19	44	89	21
Kippax Athletic Res.	28	2	2	24	23	92	8

Alliance Two	P	W	D	L	F	A	Pt
Bardsey Res.	26	19	1	6	68	37	58
Carlton Athletic Res.	26	18	3	5	76	38	57
Leeds City Res.	26	16	6	4	64	32	54
Altofts Res.	26	15	2	9	68	49	47
Otley Town Res.	26	12	7	7	50	45	43
Brighouse Old Boys Res.	26	12	6	8	63	47	42
Old Headingley Res.	26	11	5	10	54	49	38
East End Park WMC Res.	26	10	5	11	57	64	35
Howden Clough Res.	26	10	4	12	62	65	34
Ilkley Town Res.	26	9	4	13	47	53	31
Boston Spartans Res.	26	6	6	14	61	80	24
Rothwell Town Res.	26	6	4	16	50	79	22
Baildon Trinity Athletic Res.	26	5	6	15	40	55	21
Woodhouse Hill WMC Res.	26	3	1	22	38	105	10

	Baildon TA	Barwick	Boston S.	Brighse OB	Gt Preston	Hunslet	Mount SM	Ox'hope	Rothwell T.	Sandy L.	S. Milford	Stanley	Swilli'gton	Tad. Mag.	Wyke W.
Baildon Trinity Athletic		4-0	0-0	1-0	4-2	3-0	6-1	1-1	7-1	2-0	3-1	2-0	4-0	3-1	2-1
Barwick	1-3	***D***	2-3	4-2	5-2	2-2	1-0	0-1	2-3	3-3	0-0	1-2	0-2	2-1	0-2
Boston Spartans	2-2	3-1	***I***	1-3	3-3	4-0	4-1	0-7	6-2	3-0	3-0	2-2	5-3	8-2	3-1
Brighouse Old Boys	2-6	2-4	0-3	***V***	3-1	3-0	2-2	3-0	1-0	2-1	5-3	7-2	7-1	W-L	2-2
Great Preston	0-2	2-1	0-1	1-3	***I***	2-3	0-2	3-3	3-2	2-5	2-5	1-1	2-1	4-1	1-4
Hunslet	2-9	2-4	5-0	1-1	0-1	***S***	2-2	1-10	2-1	3-1	6-0	0-1	2-0	3-1	1-1
Mount St Mary's	1-3	1-0	1-3	1-2	1-2	0-2	***I***	1-1	2-1	5-0	3-2	7-1	2-3	5-0	0-3
Oxenhope Recreation	1-1	4-1	0-3	1-1	5-3	2-0	1-1	***O***	3-2	3-2	3-0	4-0	2-0	3-0	2-1
Rothwell Town	2-3	1-0	2-2	3-0	5-1	2-1	0-3	2-2	***N***	4-0	8-0	1-1	2-2	5-0	0-3
Sandy Lane	2-0	1-3	2-1	1-4	3-3	1-3	2-1	1-2	1-5		2-2	2-1	0-2	2-1	1-8
South Milford	1-1	2-2	1-3	0-0	3-3	5-1	1-3	1-8	2-3	0-2		4-3	4-0	0-1	1-2
Stanley United	2-0	0-2	3-4	1-3	1-2	1-1	0-2	1-3	2-3	1-2	3-0	***T***	1-1	1-2	0-2
Swillington Saints	1-2	3-2	1-2	3-3	2-0	0-5	1-3	0-3	2-2	1-5	0-3	1-2	***W***	2-4	1-0
Tadcaster Magnet Sports	0-4	1-1	3-3	1-4	1-0	0-4	0-0	2-2	1-3	3-0	1-1	2-3	2-3	***O***	0-2
Wyke Wanderers	3-2	2-0	1-1	2-0	4-1	0-2	4-1	1-3	1-1	1-0	5-0	4-2	3-0	3-1	

WEST YORKSHIRE LEAGUE DIVISION TWO CONSTITUTION 2009-10

BARWICK. . . . . Back of Village Hall, Chapel Lane, Barwick-in-Elmet, Leeds LS15 4HL . . . . Club HQ: 0113 281 3065
BOSTON SPARTANS . . . . Stables Lane, Boston Spa, Wetherby LS23 6BX. . . . . None
BRIGHOUSE OLD BOYS . . . . Lightcliffe & Hipperholme School, Stoney Lane, Lightcliffe, Halifax HX3 8TL 01422 201028
FEATHERSTONE COLLIERY . Featherstone MW, Cresseys Corner, Green Lane, Featherstone WF7 6EH . . . . None
GLASSHOUGHTON WELFARE RESERVES . . . Leeds Road, Glasshoughton WF10 4PF 01977 511234
GREAT PRESTON. . . . . Berry Lane, Great Preston LS25 8AX. . . . . None
HUNSLET. . . . . Community Sports Club, Anchor Street, Hunslet Green, Leeds LS10 2AT 0113 270 6851
LEEDS GRYPHONS . . . . Gryphon Sports Centre, University of Leeds, Woodsley Road, Leeds LS2 9LZ 0113 343 6771
MOUNT ST MARY'S . . . . David Young Academy, off North Parkway, Seacroft, Leeds LS14 6NU. . . . . None
ROTHWELL TOWN . . . . off Fifth Avenue, Leeds Road, Rothwell, Leeds LS26 0HG . . . . None
SOUTH MILFORD . . . . The Maltings, South Milford, Leeds. . . . . None
STANLEY UNITED . . . . Welfare Sports Ground, Saville Road, Methley, Leeds LS26 0DT . . . . None
SWILLINGTON SAINTS . . . . Welfare Sports Ground, Wakefield Road, Swillington, Leeds LS26 8DT . . . . None
TADCASTER MAGNET SPORTS . Magnet Spts & Social Club, Queens Gardens, Tadcaster LS24 9HD 01937 833435
WOODHOUSE HILL WMC. . . . . Woodlands School Playing Field, Wakefield Road, Normanton WF6 1BB 01924 893462

IN: Featherstone Colliery (R), Glasshoughton Welfare Res. (N), Leeds Gryphons (N), Woodhouse Hill WMC (R)

OUT: Baildon Trinity Athletic (P), Oxenhope Recreation (P), Sandy Lane (W), Wyke Wanderers (P)

OTHER LEAGUES 2008-09

ACCRINGTON & DISTRICT LEAGUE
(Bracewells Transport)

Premier Division	P	W	D	L	F	A	Pt
Church Town	16	14	1	1	89	15	43
Edenfield	16	12	3	1	72	25	39
Bridge Inn -3	16	9	4	3	52	20	28
Baileys	16	7	3	6	40	33	24
Ramsbottom Town	16	5	5	6	27	37	20
O'twistle SM A -3	16	5	3	8	29	48	15
Crown Rovers -3	16	4	3	9	29	62	12
Whinney Hill A	16	3	3	10	25	58	12
Wellington	16	0	1	15	15	80	1

Accrington Loyal - record expunged

Division One	P	W	D	L	F	A	Pts
The Tavern	22	19	1	2	102	27	58
Reservado RU	22	16	4	2	74	28	52
Crown Rov. Res.	22	16	2	4	71	45	50
Hapton -3	22	12	3	7	81	43	36
Churcht'n Res. -3	22	11	3	8	80	50	33
Black Horse	22	10	3	9	59	54	33
Sydney St WMC	22	8	0	14	48	55	24
Burn. Rd Bowling	22	7	2	13	43	88	23
Rose & Crown -6	22	8	2	12	51	72	20
Accrington Town	22	6	1	15	39	80	19
Church Kirk R. -3	22	5	3	14	48	68	15
Globe Bullough P.	22	2	0	20	30	116	6

ALDERSHOT & DISTRICT LEAGUE

Premier Division	P	W	D	L	F	A	Pts
BOSC	21	17	2	2	77	23	53
Frimley Select	21	17	1	3	61	22	52
Frimley	21	11	3	7	41	29	36
Farnboro. NE Res.	21	10	2	9	33	39	32
Yateley Green	21	9	4	8	39	40	31
Hindhead Athletic	21	5	2	14	34	51	17
Crookham Krak'toa	21	4	2	15	23	43	14
Wey Valley	21	3	0	18	17	78	9

Hook Athletic - record expunged

Division One	P	W	D	L	F	A	Pts
Bagshot	18	17	0	1	60	10	51
Yateley G. Res.	18	13	2	3	45	25	41
Sandhurst Sports	18	11	2	5	39	28	35
Fleet Spurs A	18	10	2	6	32	19	32
Hale Rovers	18	10	1	7	54	34	31
Headley Utd Res.	18	5	5	8	26	38	20
Wey Valley Res.	18	6	0	12	27	38	18
Letef Select	18	4	5	9	32	40	17
Hartley Wintney A	18	5	0	13	39	56	15
Wrecclesham A	18	0	1	17	22	88	1

Division Two	P	W	D	L	F	A	Pts
Sth Farnborough	20	16	2	2	77	28	50
Eversley A	20	15	2	3	76	17	47
AFC Froyle	20	13	2	5	64	34	41
Courtmoor	20	13	1	6	65	28	40
Four Marks Res.	20	10	3	7	44	21	33
Hindhead A. Res.	20	9	2	9	46	58	29
Farnham United	20	7	2	11	38	72	23
Real Tek	20	6	1	13	35	52	19
Shalford A	20	5	1	14	40	85	16
Yateley B	20	3	2	15	34	77	11
Inter Mytchett Crus.	20	3	2	15	33	80	11

Division Three	P	W	D	L	F	A	Pts
Frensham RBL -3	18	15	2	1	117	15	44
A'shot Spartans	18	12	5	1	82	32	41
Alton United	18	12	0	6	72	39	36
Bagshot Res.	18	10	3	5	62	42	33
Fleet Spurs Vets	18	10	2	6	65	53	32
BOSC Res.	18	7	2	9	67	56	23
Normandy	18	7	2	9	33	50	23
Duke of York	18	5	1	12	34	52	16
Wey Valley A	18	3	1	14	29	107	10
Shalford B	18	0	0	18	14	129	0

Farnham United Res. - record expunged

ALTRINCHAM & DISTRICT LEAGUE

Division One	P	W	D	L	F	A	Pts
Cringlewood Ath.	24	22	1	1	79	26	67
King George	24	17	4	3	72	28	55
Knutsford A	24	11	6	7	50	34	39
Sale Rovers	24	12	1	11	51	52	37
Old York '06	24	7	6	11	40	57	27
Atlantic	24	6	6	12	52	72	24
Sale Amateurs	24	5	8	11	35	39	23
Styal A	24	6	4	14	37	66	22
Kartel Sports	24	1	6	17	29	71	9

Division Two	P	W	D	L	F	A	Pts
Old Alt'chamians A	20	17	1	2	71	33	52
Salford AFC	20	15	2	3	66	36	47
Butcher	20	12	2	6	69	45	38
Heaton Moor Pho.	20	11	1	8	56	44	34
Northenden Vics	20	10	1	9	48	41	31
Irlam A	20	9	2	9	57	44	29
Fernley	20	8	0	12	55	81	24
Timperley Wdrs	20	6	3	11	40	64	21
Egerton	20	5	3	12	45	58	18
Brooklands	20	4	4	12	40	58	16
Trafford United	20	2	3	15	29	72	9

ANDOVER & DISTRICT LEAGUE

	P	W	D	L	F	A	Pts
Borough Arms	12	8	3	1	43	21	27
ABC United	12	8	1	3	54	23	25
AFC Andover	12	7	2	3	39	19	23
Inkpen Sports	12	5	3	4	30	30	18
Whitchurch Utd A	12	3	2	7	28	32	11
Test Valley Lions	12	3	1	8	5	53	10
King's Somborne	12	1	2	9	19	40	5

AYLESBURY & DISTRICT LEAGUE

Premier Division	P	W	D	L	F	A	Pts
Hale Leys United	22	15	4	3	79	22	49
Bierton	22	15	3	4	78	33	48
Aston Park	22	15	1	6	85	34	46
Aylesb'y Dynamos	22	14	3	5	59	33	45
St Johns FC	22	11	3	8	62	46	36
Elmhurst	22	10	3	9	66	62	33
Walton Ct Wdrs	22	7	7	8	46	50	28
Bucks CC	22	8	1	13	59	60	25
Aston Clinton Res.	22	7	3	12	41	59	24
Wingrave	22	4	6	12	40	75	18
Long Marston	22	4	3	15	23	63	15
Mandeville	22	3	1	18	31	132	10

Division One	P	W	D	L	F	A	Pts
Berkhamsted Spts	24	22	1	1	103	22	67
Downley Albion	24	19	3	2	82	23	60
P & IC United	24	17	2	5	87	35	53
B'grove Dynamos	24	16	1	7	67	39	49
Bedgrove United	24	12	4	8	74	34	40
Wendover	24	11	1	12	46	55	34
Lane End	24	9	5	10	60	54	32
Thame Town	24	7	4	13	53	68	25
Tring Cor. Colts	24	7	3	14	44	76	24
Bucks CC Res.	24	6	3	15	35	80	21
Dairy Maid	24	5	3	16	35	83	18
Haddenham Utd	24	5	2	17	17	83	17
Quainton	24	1	6	17	25	76	9

Division Two	P	W	D	L	F	A	Pts
Britannia	22	20	0	2	89	27	60
P & IC Utd Res.	22	14	2	6	69	36	44
Bierton Res.	22	11	5	6	64	38	38
Haydon United	22	12	2	8	48	49	38
St Johns Res.	22	11	1	10	55	52	34
Wendover Res.	22	10	2	10	69	47	32
Great Milton	22	9	5	8	54	61	32
Lg Marston Res.	22	8	4	10	36	50	28
Rose & Crown	22	8	1	13	38	60	25
Aston Clinton A	22	7	2	13	53	63	23
Fairford Leys	22	5	2	15	40	88	17
Oving	22	3	2	17	25	69	11

Division Three	P	W	D	L	F	A	Pts
Bedgrove U. Res.	18	16	0	2	77	19	48
Lane End Res.	18	14	0	4	80	29	42
Wingrave Res.	18	12	2	4	91	43	38
Haddenham Res.	18	10	1	7	49	38	31
Stone Magnets	18	9	2	7	54	43	29
Bedgrove D. Res.	18	7	1	10	51	36	22
Sparta Royals	18	6	2	10	30	73	20
Ludgershall	18	4	3	11	38	69	15
AC Meadowcroft	18	4	1	13	26	80	13
Aylesbury Pk Rgrs	18	2	0	16	28	94	6

BANBURY & LORD JERSEY FA

Premier Division	P	W	D	L	F	A	Pts
Bodicote Sports	18	17	0	1	49	13	51
Bishops Itchington	18	13	2	3	96	26	41
Cropredy	18	11	1	6	56	42	34
Arncott	18	9	2	7	41	44	29
Steeple Aston	18	8	4	6	38	32	28
KEA	18	9	0	9	44	46	27
Hornton	18	6	0	12	41	52	18
Barford United	18	6	0	12	38	68	18
Drayton Village	18	5	2	11	35	43	17
Kings Sutton	18	0	1	17	19	91	1

Division One	P	W	D	L	F	A	Pts
ABK Sports	18	16	1	1	81	28	49
Wroxton Sports	18	15	2	1	85	22	47
Fenny Compton	18	12	0	6	68	30	36
B. Itchington Res.	18	8	5	5	55	35	29
Heyford Athletic A	18	9	1	8	51	47	28
Deddington Town	18	8	3	7	44	48	27
Heyford United	18	7	2	9	44	54	23
Glory Farm	18	6	0	12	38	64	18
Cropredy Res.	18	1	1	16	14	72	4
Souldern	18	0	1	17	14	94	1

Division Two	P	W	D	L	F	A	Pts
KEA Res.	16	13	2	1	76	26	41
Woodford Utd A	16	13	1	2	48	18	40
The Swan FC	16	11	2	3	42	30	35
Bardwell	16	7	4	5	35	26	25
FC Naranja	16	7	1	8	33	26	22
Bloxham	16	6	2	8	35	42	20
Mid. Cheney Res.	16	6	0	10	36	43	18
Abba Athletic	16	2	2	12	37	58	8
Banbury Galaxy	16	0	0	16	7	80	0

Division Three	P	W	D	L	F	A	Pts
Deddington Res.	24	19	2	3	101	39	59
Heyford Utd Res.	24	19	2	3	80	35	59
Heyford Ath. B	24	15	2	7	85	55	47
KEA. A	24	13	3	8	76	55	42
ABK Sports Res.	24	12	3	9	72	55	39
K. Sutton Res.	24	9	5	10	65	60	32
Wroxton Sp. Res.	24	10	2	12	60	73	32
Glory Farm Res.	24	8	5	11	52	60	29
Bodicote Sp. Res.	24	9	2	13	45	62	29
Drayton Vill. Res.	24	7	3	14	46	83	24
Finmere	24	5	5	14	52	83	20
Fenny Com. Res.	24	5	3	16	51	86	18
Stple Aston Res.	24	5	3	16	39	78	18

BASINGSTOKE & DISTRICT LEAGUE

Premier Division	P	W	D	L	F	A	Pts
FC Censo	16	14	1	1	67	11	43
R & B Sports	16	11	2	3	49	19	35
Rangers	16	8	2	6	33	32	26
Tad. Calleva Res.	16	7	4	5	33	36	25
Hook	16	8	0	8	40	29	24
Winterthur	16	6	3	7	42	45	21
Oakley Athletic	16	6	1	9	31	44	19
Bramley United	16	4	3	9	28	45	15
AFC Ald'maston A	16	0	0	16	11	73	0

Division One	P	W	D	L	F	A	Pts
Headley Athletic	16	12	3	1	55	17	39
Sherfield	16	12	3	1	52	20	39
Overton United A	16	10	2	4	58	27	32
Sherborne St John	16	9	3	4	45	23	30
AFC Berg	16	7	4	5	43	28	25
Ludwig Leisure A	16	6	0	10	38	60	18
FC Burghclere	16	2	3	11	33	71	9
Hook Res.	16	2	1	13	31	55	7
Bas. Labour Club	16	2	1	13	23	77	7

Division Two	P	W	D	L	F	A	Pts
Welly Old Boys	20	18	1	1	79	17	55
Old Basing	20	13	4	3	73	40	43
Headley Ath. Res.	20	13	3	4	61	32	42
Tadley Calleva A	20	11	1	8	60	42	34
Rangers Res.	20	11	0	9	69	49	33
Heathpark	20	9	2	9	73	60	29
Baughurst	20	7	5	8	37	44	26
AFC Berg Res.	20	7	4	9	59	56	25
Cromwell Inn	20	6	2	12	47	78	20
Herriard Sports	20	3	2	15	41	86	11
AFC Ald'maston B	20	0	0	20	19	114	0

BATH & DISTRICT LEAGUE
(Roper Rhodes Bathrooms)

Division One	P	W	D	L	F	A	Pts
Chew Valley Snrs	20	13	3	4	74	29	42
Civil S. Larkhall	20	13	2	5	66	24	41
Trowbridge Hse	20	13	2	5	56	37	41
Dogtown Odd D.	20	12	1	7	38	43	37
University of Bath	20	11	3	6	69	31	36
Saltford Res.	20	9	3	8	28	28	30
WESA	20	9	2	9	33	56	29
Fry Club Old B.	20	9	1	10	37	32	28
Oldfield Sports	20	7	1	12	25	52	22
Aces SSJ	20	3	2	15	34	76	11
Sportzcoach Utd	20	1	0	19	19	71	3

Division Two	P	W	D	L	F	A	Pts
Great Western FC	22	17	3	2	97	36	54
Bath Athletic	22	15	2	5	84	28	47
Bath Arsenal	22	14	3	5	79	35	45
Univ. of Bath Res.	22	14	0	8	79	38	42
Saltford A	22	13	1	8	77	50	40
Freshford Sports	22	12	2	8	58	42	38
Bath Spa Univ.	22	11	3	8	47	36	36
Oval Sports	22	9	2	11	46	56	29
Fairfield Pk Rgrs	22	8	1	13	47	69	25
Red Dwarf	22	3	2	17	31	85	11
Purnell Sports A	22	2	3	17	32	92	9
Newbridge	22	3	0	19	31	141	9

Division Three	P	W	D	L	F	A	Pts
WESA Res.	22	18	4	0	87	21	58
Stothert & Pitt	22	16	0	6	58	25	48
Cutters Friday A	22	12	4	6	54	41	40
CS Larkhall Vets	22	11	6	5	68	47	39
FC Von Essen	22	11	4	7	46	36	37
Rising Sun	22	9	7	6	44	43	34
Fry Club OB Res.	22	9	6	7	37	42	33
Bath Rangers	22	5	8	9	45	56	23
Aces SSJ Res.	22	6	3	13	53	67	21
Weston Youth	22	5	5	12	45	53	20
Timsbury Ath. A	22	2	4	16	37	77	10
Westfield	22	1	3	18	30	96	6

Peasedown Athletic Res. – record expunged

BECKETT LEAGUE
(RJF Homes)

Premier Division	P	W	D	L	F	A	Pt
Kirk'moorside Res.	20	13	6	1	39	16	45
Sinnington	20	11	7	2	53	22	40
Thornton Dale	20	11	4	5	46	27	37
Union Rovers	20	10	2	8	33	28	32
Bagby & Balk	20	8	7	5	53	42	31
Gillamoor	20	9	2	9	54	47	29
Rosedale	20	8	3	9	30	38	27
Heslerton Res.	20	7	3	10	38	47	24
Kirkdale United	20	6	4	10	40	37	22
O. Malton St M. A	20	5	3	12	27	57	18
Ryedale Res. *-3*	20	1	1	18	19	71	1

Division One	P	W	D	L	F	A	Pts
Anlaby United	20	17	1	2	85	22	52
Slingsby	20	16	2	2	84	19	50
Pro Pak	20	15	1	4	62	31	46
Thornton Dale Res.	20	7	6	7	38	35	27
Duncombe Park	20	7	6	7	41	51	27
Gillamoor Res.	20	7	4	9	47	61	25
Ampleforth	20	6	5	9	38	50	23
Amotherby	20	5	4	11	26	43	19
Amotherby Res. *-3*	20	6	2	12	51	71	17
St Clements Res.	20	4	2	14	33	85	14
Union Rov. Res.	20	2	3	15	28	64	9

BIRKENHEAD & WIRRAL LEAGUE

Premier Division	P	W	D	L	F	A	Pts
Claughton Hotel	16	10	4	2	47	28	24
Future	16	9	4	3	46	26	22
Corsair	16	10	1	5	49	37	21
The Crown	16	8	3	5	36	27	19
FC Village	16	6	4	6	39	35	16
Parkfield BA	16	4	4	8	32	41	12
Universal Windows	16	4	4	8	38	48	12
Shaftesbury	16	4	3	9	34	53	11
Moreton	16	2	3	11	28	54	7

Division One	P	W	D	L	F	A	Pts
Sheridans	20	18	0	2	87	29	36
Upton	20	12	4	4	73	47	28
Tower	20	11	3	6	54	45	25
Bee Hotel	20	10	2	8	51	43	22
Wirral Wanderers	20	7	5	8	38	45	19
Central Park	20	6	6	8	44	52	18
Neston Legion	20	6	5	9	55	75	17
Meliora Cogito	20	7	2	11	49	68	16
Bronze Soc. Res.	20	5	3	12	52	61	13
Unitor	20	5	3	12	45	63	13
Bebington Rovers	20	5	3	12	40	60	13

BIRMINGHAM AFA

Premier Division	P	W	D	L	F	A	Pts
Shirley Athletic	24	16	4	4	56	40	52
Erin Go Bragh	24	15	6	3	76	37	51
Village	24	13	4	7	45	28	43
Boldmere Falcons	24	11	7	6	58	35	40
Aston Labs	24	11	2	11	64	61	35
Sutton United	24	9	6	9	31	31	33
Cresconians	24	9	3	12	42	52	30
AFC Somers	24	9	3	12	43	64	30
Silhill	24	8	3	13	42	53	27
Flamengo	24	7	6	11	37	55	27
Handsw'th GSOB	24	7	5	12	42	54	26
Wake Green Ams	24	5	9	10	29	40	24
Ajax United	24	5	4	15	31	46	19

Division One	P	W	D	L	F	A	Pts
Aston	20	13	3	4	53	28	42
Walsall Phoenix	20	10	5	5	41	33	35
Old Wulfrunians	20	9	6	5	38	27	33
Village Res.	20	9	5	6	51	35	32
St Francis	20	8	7	5	50	34	31
Kynoch	20	8	7	5	48	43	31
Sutton Utd Res.	20	8	6	6	38	40	30
Athletic Sparkhill	20	6	7	7	35	34	25
CPA Holy Name	20	6	1	13	28	37	19
Resolution	20	6	1	13	33	51	19
Parkfield Amtrs	20	0	6	14	26	79	6

Division Two	P	W	D	L	F	A	Pts
H'wth GSOB Res.	22	16	1	5	72	38	49
Inter Vaughans	22	14	3	5	62	29	45
Wake Green Res.	22	12	4	6	52	35	40
John Rose	22	11	4	7	45	28	37
West Hagley	22	10	5	7	46	44	35
Old Nortonians	22	10	3	9	42	31	33
Silhill Res.	22	8	5	9	46	46	29
Great Barr	22	8	3	11	35	56	27
Village A	22	7	3	12	32	53	24
Old Wulfs Res.	22	6	5	11	66	56	23
W Midlands Travel	22	6	5	11	44	74	23
Cresconians Res.	22	2	3	17	31	83	9

Division Three	P	W	D	L	F	A	Pts
Crusaders	26	23	1	2	123	27	70
St Georges War.	26	14	7	5	70	43	49
Desi *-6*	26	16	6	4	86	45	48
Silhill A	26	13	4	9	64	63	43
Resolution Res.	26	14	1	11	62	61	43
Sutton United A	26	12	4	10	70	65	40
Malremo Rangers	26	12	3	11	59	54	39
Shere Punjab	26	11	5	10	56	50	38
Wake Green A	26	9	5	12	39	55	32
Britannia Old Boys	26	8	3	15	55	73	27
Acocks Green	26	7	3	16	42	67	24
Shirley Ath. Res.	26	7	3	16	45	77	24
Wal. Phoenix Res.	26	6	3	17	30	68	21
Urban Athletic	26	4	4	18	46	99	16

Division Four	P	W	D	L	F	A	Pts
Bustleholme Ath.	24	17	3	4	84	34	54
St Annes	24	14	9	1	80	32	51
Cable & Wireless	24	15	3	6	74	54	48
CPA Holy N. Res.	24	14	5	5	71	49	47
BT	24	11	5	8	60	53	38
Dosthill Boys	24	11	4	9	51	58	37
Bearwood Athletic	24	11	3	10	66	63	36
Shirley Athletic A	24	10	1	13	78	79	31
Pathfinder	24	9	4	11	53	61	31
Sportsco	24	5	6	13	50	64	21
Elmdon Heath	24	5	5	14	46	70	20
H'owen Lighthse	24	5	2	17	41	90	17
Village B	24	3	2	19	31	78	11

Division Five	P	W	D	L	F	A	Pts
Balsalorna	26	20	3	3	93	40	63
St Pauls	26	20	2	4	101	46	62
AFC Hayes Harr.	26	19	5	2	76	28	62
Sutton United B	26	15	1	10	65	59	46
Phoenix United *-3*	26	13	4	9	71	66	40
Old Wulfrunians A	26	10	5	11	55	54	35
Silhill B	26	11	2	13	65	74	35
Meriden Athletic	26	10	5	11	54	69	35
Birmigham Citadel	26	8	3	15	47	69	27
Rubery *-4*	26	9	3	14	66	84	26
Parkfield A. Res.	26	8	1	17	40	66	25
Bromsgrove T. *-4*	26	7	3	16	56	70	20
AG Athletic	26	6	2	18	47	72	20
Inter Quinton	26	5	3	18	60	99	18

Division Six	P	W	D	L	F	A	Pts
St Georges Res.	20	15	3	2	52	24	48
Shelfield Rangers	20	14	4	2	53	22	46
Wood Wanderers	20	11	4	5	42	30	37
JE Yardley	20	10	5	5	48	32	35
Bentley Heath U.	20	7	5	8	43	44	26
Coton Green A	20	7	4	9	42	41	25
Royal Heath Rgrs	20	6	7	7	37	37	25
Old Wulfrunians B	20	7	2	11	37	39	23
Harborne Athletic	20	4	3	13	29	52	15
H'worth GSOB A	20	4	3	13	26	68	15
Crusaders Res.	20	3	4	13	29	49	13

Division Seven	P	W	D	L	F	A	Pts
Crusaders A	24	17	2	5	79	53	53
Birch Cop. Bullets	24	15	4	5	68	38	49
Aston Res.	24	13	6	5	58	35	45
AFC Meadway *-6*	24	15	5	4	71	42	44
Wake Green A. B	24	11	4	9	66	53	37
Sportsco Res.	24	11	4	9	52	46	37
H'sworth GSOB B	24	10	3	11	60	64	33
Premier FC	24	8	6	10	38	37	30
Village C	24	6	6	12	42	58	24
Flamengo Res.	24	6	6	12	37	57	24
Deer Park OB	24	7	1	16	53	73	22
Walsall Phoenix A	24	6	2	16	44	88	20
Manchester Wdrs	24	5	3	16	40	64	18

Kingshurst Phoenix - record expunged

Division Eight	P	W	D	L	F	A	Pts
Aston A	24	18	2	4	94	36	56
Bournville Colts *-3*	24	16	6	2	72	27	51
Sutton United C	24	13	5	6	66	44	44
Desi Res.	24	12	4	8	62	42	40
Maypole	24	10	6	8	42	43	36
Balsalorna Res. *-3*	24	11	4	9	50	43	34
St Georges W. A	24	10	2	12	58	68	32
Real Riverside	24	9	3	12	51	54	30
Britannia OB Res.	24	9	2	13	65	86	29
Bosnian Sp. Club	24	8	4	12	54	59	28
Sporting Aztecs	24	8	3	13	51	50	27
Maple Leaf Rov.	24	7	4	13	47	70	25
Elmdon Hth Res.	24	2	1	21	33	123	7

Division Nine	P	W	D	L	F	A	Pts
Yardley Ex-Serv.	26	24	0	2	151	27	72
Shelfield R. Res.	26	17	4	5	70	33	55
Handsworth Ath.	26	17	3	6	66	39	54
Cosmopolitans	26	13	5	8	63	53	44
Wulfrun Invicta	26	12	3	11	64	65	39
Sptg Aztecs Res.	26	9	9	8	69	58	36
NWCA/Shylet Tig.	26	11	3	12	65	79	36
Old Wulfrunians C	26	9	6	11	58	50	33
Edgbaston United	26	9	4	13	54	69	31
Selly Oak Legend	26	8	7	11	45	70	31
Red Star Galaxy	26	7	5	14	60	68	26
Wake Green A. C	26	7	4	15	35	66	25
AFC Hay. H. Res.	26	6	6	14	47	82	24
Real R'side Res.	26	2	3	21	29	117	9

BISHOP'S STORTFORD, STANSTED & DISTRICT LEAGUE

Premier Division	P	W	D	L	F	A	Pts
Alemite Athletic	22	18	3	1	74	19	39
North Weald	22	18	1	3	73	31	37
Sal. Army Harlow	22	15	3	4	80	46	33
Quendon Athletic	22	13	4	5	63	21	30
Old Street	22	10	5	7	54	35	25
Loughton	22	11	3	8	48	35	25
Sheering	22	10	3	9	58	68	23
Langley Rangers	22	9	4	9	39	40	22
Hatfield Heath	22	6	0	16	53	76	12
Birchanger	22	4	1	17	35	76	9
Pelly House	22	3	1	18	44	96	7
White Roding	22	1	0	21	22	100	2

Division One	P	W	D	L	F	A	Pts
Heath Rovers	24	21	1	2	81	17	43
Hatfield Hth Res.	24	18	2	4	88	26	38
Sheering Res.	24	14	3	7	98	33	31
Thorley Park	24	14	3	7	59	47	31
North Weald Res.	24	12	6	6	66	42	30
Avondale Rgrs	24	10	4	10	49	50	24
Albury	24	11	1	12	54	57	23
Herts Rangers	24	8	4	12	47	54	20
Dunmow Rhodes	24	9	1	14	40	62	19
Potter Street A	24	7	4	13	52	91	18
Lower Street	24	6	5	13	42	79	17
Thaxted Rgrs Res.	24	5	3	16	40	93	13
Frontiers	24	2	1	21	25	90	5

BLACKBURN & DISTRICT COMBINATION

Premier Division	P	W	D	L	F	A	Pts
Clifton	20	15	2	3	92	24	47
Rhoden Inn	20	15	2	3	83	33	47
Blackburn United	20	15	2	3	56	22	47
Havelock Inn	20	10	4	6	53	34	34
Hollins Grove CC	20	8	3	9	32	48	27
Bank Top	20	7	1	12	30	64	22
Rishton United	20	6	3	11	50	53	21
Bowling Green *-3*	20	7	1	12	39	62	19
Nabs Head	20	5	2	13	38	67	17
Cabin End *-6*	20	6	2	12	42	60	14
Islington	20	3	4	13	36	84	13

Division Two	P	W	D	L	F	A	Pts
Prince of Wales	27	19	4	4	99	45	61
Alexandra Hotel	27	14	4	9	67	61	46
Rishton Utd Res.	27	13	5	9	62	60	44
Feildens Arms	27	12	7	8	73	50	43
Blackburn U. Res.	27	12	5	10	55	49	41
Blackburn Olym.	27	8	7	12	63	68	31
Worth Avenue	27	9	3	15	49	50	30
Enty	27	8	6	13	58	74	30
Blue Star	27	7	7	13	49	76	28
Sporting Athletic	27	7	4	16	46	88	25

Division Three	P	W	D	L	F	A	Pts
Mill Hill Res.	24	19	2	3	112	30	59
Belthorn Dog Inn	24	19	1	4	102	36	58
F'cowles/P. Res. *-1*	24	15	2	7	72	56	46
Rishton United A	24	13	2	9	68	52	41
Maxlocal	24	10	5	9	74	52	35
Knowles Arms	24	9	5	10	57	65	32
Hole I'Th Wall	24	6	2	16	36	82	20
Hordens *-1*	24	4	1	19	34	109	12
Witton Inn	24	2	2	20	34	107	8

BOSTON & DISTRICT LEAGUE

(Cropley's Suzuki)

Premier Division	P	W	D	L	F	A	Pts
Coningsby	20	17	2	1	68	19	53
Swineshead Inst.	20	13	3	4	72	30	42
Freiston	20	13	2	5	64	30	41
North Sea Utd *-12*	20	16	0	4	58	39	36
Wyberton	20	10	1	9	45	41	31
Billinghay Athletic	20	8	3	9	47	40	27
Skegness T. Res.	20	8	1	11	29	47	25
Spilsby Town	20	6	6	8	36	47	24
Kirton Town	20	5	1	14	35	66	16
Wrangle United	20	2	1	17	31	74	7
Westside Rangers	20	2	0	18	34	86	6

Division One	P	W	D	L	F	A	Pts
Swineshead Res.	22	18	0	4	79	37	54
Woodhall Spa U.	22	15	1	6	72	39	46
Fishtoft	22	14	2	6	52	40	44
Old Leake	22	13	1	8	58	35	40
Park Road OB	22	10	3	9	48	44	33
Wainfleet United	22	9	2	11	58	50	29
Old Doningtonians	22	8	3	11	41	49	27
Nortoft United	22	8	1	13	36	64	25
Coningsby Res.	22	8	0	14	43	61	24
Spilsby T. Res. *-1*	22	6	4	12	35	48	21
Pointon *-3*	22	6	4	12	42	68	19
Holbeach Bank	22	5	3	14	40	69	18

Division Two	P	W	D	L	F	A	Pts
Spalding Harriers	22	17	1	4	78	29	52
Wyberton Res.	22	17	1	4	66	19	52
Sutterton	22	15	2	5	63	43	47
Spalding Town	22	13	4	5	81	39	43
Boston T. Old B.	22	12	2	8	54	35	38
Mareham United	22	11	3	8	60	49	36
Tydd St Mary	22	8	4	10	42	69	28
Skegness WMC *-3*	22	9	3	10	51	53	27
Westside R. Res.	22	7	3	12	41	59	24
Friskney	22	3	2	17	27	81	11
Sportsman	22	2	4	16	42	77	10
Fosdyke	22	2	3	17	27	79	9

Wrangle United Res. - record expunged

Division Three	P	W	D	L	F	A	Pts
Fishtoft Res.	24	22	0	2	87	24	66
Spalding T. Res. *-1*	24	15	2	7	72	58	46
Billinghay Res.	24	15	0	9	82	46	45
O. D'tonians Res.	24	14	3	7	75	54	45
Pointon Res.	24	11	5	8	57	63	38
Woodhall S. Res.	24	11	4	9	59	58	37
Holbeach St Mks	24	11	3	10	63	50	36
Kirton Town Res.	24	11	1	12	65	51	34
Freiston Res.	24	8	3	13	61	66	27
Spalding H. Res.	24	6	5	13	43	61	23
Park United	24	6	5	13	48	88	23
Eastville/M'ville/NL	24	3	6	15	39	81	15
Mareham U. Res.	24	3	3	18	42	93	12

BOURNEMOUTH LEAGUE

(Hayward)

Premier Division	P	W	D	L	F	A	Pts
B'mouth Electric	22	19	2	1	67	13	59
Westover B'mouth	22	15	2	5	50	26	47
Sway	22	14	1	7	48	29	43
Hamw. Rec. Res.	22	14	1	7	49	37	43
Old Oakmeadians	22	13	2	7	48	28	41
Pennington St Mks	22	12	4	6	43	32	40
Redlynch/Woodfalls	22	9	3	10	35	33	30
Suttoners Civil	22	5	5	12	32	47	20
Verwood T. Res.	22	4	4	14	21	44	16
Mudeford Mens	22	4	3	15	24	55	15
Southbourne	22	3	5	14	19	53	14
Ferndown Town	22	3	2	17	25	64	11

Division One	P	W	D	L	F	A	Pts
Dorset Knob	22	16	3	3	65	28	51
Parley Spts Res.	22	16	3	3	57	27	51
Harrington United	22	12	3	7	65	32	39
Trinidad	22	12	3	7	63	33	39
Fordingbdge Turks	22	11	5	6	53	39	38
B'mth Electric Res.	22	11	3	8	61	55	36
St Mary's	22	11	2	9	59	65	35
Allendale Res.	22	9	4	9	52	44	31
Redhill Rangers	22	9	4	9	41	44	31
AFC Highcliffe	22	4	2	16	35	86	14
Suttoners C. Res.	22	3	0	19	21	80	9
AIB	22	1	2	19	26	65	5

Division Two	P	W	D	L	F	A	Pts
Portcastrian	22	18	3	1	77	32	57
Alderholt	22	14	3	5	52	29	45
Westover Res.	22	13	2	7	49	36	41
Twynham Rgrs	22	12	4	6	79	45	40
JP Morgan	22	12	1	9	68	53	37
Cobham Spts Res.	22	12	1	9	61	50	37
New Milton Linnets	22	9	6	7	43	40	33
Sway Res.	22	9	2	11	45	43	29
Walkford	22	7	1	14	37	59	22
Mploy *-3*	22	4	4	14	25	65	13
Universal Plastering	22	3	3	16	21	51	12
Ringwood United	22	3	2	17	36	90	11

Division Three	P	W	D	L	F	A	Pts
Bisterne United	22	18	0	4	77	32	54
Suttoners Civil A	22	14	4	4	63	50	46
Cherry Bees	22	12	6	4	57	31	42
O. Oakm. Res. *-3*	22	13	1	8	68	33	37
Parkside Wdrs	22	12	1	9	69	48	37
Stourvale	22	11	4	7	48	34	37
AFC Burton	22	11	2	9	55	43	35
Redlynch/WU Res.	22	9	2	11	54	44	29
AFC Parkstone	22	6	5	11	34	48	23
Fencing Centre	22	6	2	14	42	68	20
Parley Sports A *-1*	22	4	3	15	35	73	14
Shamrock	22	1	0	21	20	118	3

Division Four	P	W	D	L	F	A	Pts
Tuakana	22	22	0	0	106	12	66
Wallisdown Cons	22	16	1	5	60	29	49
Queens Park Ath.	22	14	3	5	74	42	45
N. Milton Eagles	22	12	4	6	51	42	40
Burley	22	9	5	8	41	50	32
B'mouth UST *-1*	22	8	6	8	46	40	29
Magpies	22	8	3	11	40	52	27
Albany Athletic FC	22	8	1	13	51	61	25
AFC Highcliffe Res.	22	7	3	12	39	49	24
FIFA Standard	22	6	3	13	36	53	21
Griffin	22	4	0	18	27	89	12
Phoenix	22	3	1	18	37	89	10

Division Five	P	W	D	L	F	A	Pts
S.Coast Demolition	22	19	3	0	129	33	60
Henleys Electric	22	16	4	2	85	39	52
Pennington Res.	22	15	6	1	99	25	51
Branksome Celtic	22	14	4	4	85	44	46
Screw-It Carpentry	22	11	2	9	56	33	35
Walker Scott	22	11	2	9	56	67	35
Twynham R. Res.	22	10	2	10	89	72	32
Rockbourne	22	7	0	15	52	87	21
Bournemouth A	22	5	4	13	33	62	19
Somerford Sports	22	6	1	15	33	92	19
Fordingbridge Res.	22	1	3	18	29	98	6
Magpies Res.	22	1	1	20	22	116	4

Division Six	P	W	D	L	F	A	Pts
Bisterne Rangers	22	19	1	2	96	21	58
Little Brit Inn *-3*	22	17	3	2	105	32	51
Queens Pk A. Res.	22	15	5	2	94	32	50
AFC Bransgore	22	12	0	10	68	45	36
Southbourne Res.	22	10	5	7	54	51	35
Alderholt Res.	22	9	5	8	43	37	32
Ringwood Athletic	22	9	2	11	47	63	29
Bransgore United	22	7	7	8	41	54	28
Portcastrian Res.	22	4	6	12	27	67	18
AFC Burton Res.	22	5	0	17	34	105	15
B'mouth Hospital	22	4	2	16	38	60	14
Fordingbridge A	22	2	2	18	28	108	8

BRIGHTON, HOVE & DISTRICT LEAGUE

Premier Division	P	W	D	L	F	A	Pts
Brighton Electricity	18	13	3	2	40	13	42
Montpelier Villa	18	11	4	3	40	19	37
Ovingdean	18	8	3	7	35	38	27
American Exp. *-3*	18	8	4	6	42	23	25
O & G United	18	6	6	6	25	31	24
Hanover	18	6	4	8	28	32	22
Brighton Nth End	18	6	4	8	34	41	22
Portslade Athletic	18	5	5	8	31	34	20
CCK	18	5	4	9	33	42	19
Real Brunswick	18	3	1	14	18	53	10

Division One	P	W	D	L	F	A	Pts
Hikers BHA	20	17	3	0	102	22	54
Southern Rgrs OB	20	16	1	3	56	26	49
AFC Stanley	20	10	3	7	37	29	33
Montpelier View *-3*	20	8	6	6	40	34	27
Ampito	20	7	6	7	37	39	27
Coversure Athletic	20	7	5	8	42	38	26
Rott'dean V. Res.	20	7	4	9	40	55	25
Teamstats.net	20	6	4	10	38	55	22
Montpelier V. Res.	20	5	4	11	38	58	19
Autopaints B'ton	20	4	4	12	32	56	16
Midway	20	1	4	15	27	77	7

Division Two	P	W	D	L	F	A	Pts
Crew Club Sports	16	12	1	3	53	21	37
BSM08	16	10	2	4	71	32	32
Ricardo	16	10	2	4	39	29	32
American E. Res.	16	8	3	5	33	29	27
Chailey *-3*	16	8	3	5	33	42	24
Legal & General	16	7	2	7	44	28	23
The Windmill	16	6	1	9	38	54	19
Rottingdean V. A	16	2	1	13	21	65	7
Seaford Town A	16	1	1	14	16	48	4

Division Three	P	W	D	L	F	A	Pts
Peacehaven GC	18	16	0	2	70	23	48
Falmer Falcons	18	14	1	3	74	23	43
B. Electricity Res.	18	12	1	5	66	35	37
Rottingdean Dyn.	18	12	1	5	52	36	37
Portslade A. Res.	18	9	1	8	50	33	28
Newhvn White H.	18	6	3	9	59	65	21
Brighton A & E	18	6	1	11	39	48	19
S'thern ROB Res.	18	6	1	11	47	72	19
Midway Res.	18	2	1	15	28	95	7
Montpelier V. Res.	18	2	0	16	34	89	6

Division Four	P	W	D	L	F	A	Pts
Orb360	14	10	4	0	48	23	34
PHS United	14	8	4	2	39	24	28
Vista	14	7	3	4	21	24	24
Boys Brigade OB	14	6	4	4	34	31	22
Stoneham Park	14	6	1	7	33	25	19
Saltdean Sharks	14	4	2	8	26	34	14
Real Southwick	14	3	2	9	25	40	11
Montpelier Villa A	14	1	2	11	14	39	5

BRISTOL PREMIER COMBINATION

Premier Division	P	W	D	L	F	A	Pts
Mendip United	26	22	1	3	75	24	67
Nicholas Wdrs	26	18	4	4	81	43	58
Wick	26	15	4	7	59	26	49
RG St George Res.	26	14	2	10	50	39	44

Pucklechurch Sp.	26	12	7	7	49	43	43
S. Bristol Central	26	12	5	9	51	48	41
St Philips Marsh AS	26	10	9	7	40	40	39
Talbot Knowle	26	9	5	12	52	60	32
Winterbourne Res.	26	9	3	14	45	58	30
Hallen Res.	26	8	5	13	44	57	29
Bitton Res.	26	7	6	13	33	45	27
Hartcliffe	26	7	6	13	37	54	27
Brimsham Green	26	5	2	19	29	56	17
Highridge Utd Res.	26	3	3	20	24	76	12

Division One	P	W	D	L	F	A	Pts
Longwell GS Res.	24	19	2	3	63	17	59
AEK Boco	24	15	2	7	70	41	47
Shaftesbury Crus.	24	14	5	5	55	40	47
Oldland Abbs Res.	24	14	1	9	64	50	43
Patchway T. Res.	24	11	5	8	40	39	38
Hillfields Old B.	24	12	2	10	52	56	38
Totterdown Utd	24	12	1	11	60	56	37
Olveston United	24	11	1	12	41	48	34
Seymour United	24	10	3	11	38	51	33
Henbury Res.	24	10	2	12	46	46	32
Frampton Athletic	24	7	1	16	43	55	22
Greyfriars Athletic	24	3	3	18	33	70	12
St Marys	24	3	2	19	35	71	11

BRISTOL & AVON LEAGUE

	P	W	D	L	F	A	Pts
Broad Walk Res.	26	25	1	0	177	18	76
De-Veys	26	21	2	3	142	35	65
Mendip Utd Res.	26	21	0	5	107	44	63
Lawrence Res. *-3*	26	20	0	6	88	44	57
Carmel United	26	15	3	8	99	48	48
Bideford Old B.	26	12	5	9	46	47	41
Crown Parkway	26	13	0	13	76	80	39
Knowle Reds	26	11	3	12	59	85	36
Long Ashton Res.	26	7	3	16	43	73	24
Redcliffe United	26	6	2	18	42	98	20
Wessex Wdrs A	26	5	3	18	35	145	18
Bradley Stoke T. A	26	5	2	19	43	89	17
Greyfriars Ath. B	26	4	2	20	25	91	14
Golden Hill Res. *-3*	26	3	2	21	30	115	8

BRISTOL & DISTRICT LEAGUE

Senior Division	P	W	D	L	F	A	Pts
Lawrence Rovers	22	18	2	2	76	21	56
Made for Ever	22	14	3	5	53	29	45
Coalpit Heath	22	13	2	7	75	48	41
Hallen A	22	11	2	9	38	34	35
Shireh'pton Res.	22	11	1	10	55	57	34
Nicholas W. Res.	22	9	6	7	54	63	33
AXA Res.	22	9	2	11	43	56	29
Wick Res.	22	7	6	9	44	54	27
Hanham A Res.	22	7	4	11	39	46	25
Crosscourt Utd	22	7	4	11	42	53	25
Chip. Sodb'y Res.	22	8	1	13	29	41	25
Hartcliffe Com. C.	22	0	3	19	30	76	3

Division One	P	W	D	L	F	A	Pts
Old Sodbury	24	20	2	2	87	21	62
Miners Rangers	24	16	3	5	74	47	51
RG St George A	24	14	3	7	57	39	45
St Pancras *-3*	24	12	4	8	50	51	37
Bitton A *+3*	24	9	5	10	45	54	35
Bendix	24	10	3	11	57	41	33
Knowle United	24	10	3	11	37	37	33
Longwell GS A	24	9	4	11	55	50	31
S Brist. Cent Res.	24	8	4	12	53	57	28
Pucklechurch Res.	24	9	1	14	36	48	28
Sea Mills Park	24	7	5	12	46	50	26
Shaftesb'y C. Res.	24	5	4	15	47	95	19
Hartcliffe CC Res.	24	4	5	15	31	85	17

Division Two	P	W	D	L	F	A	Pts
Seymour U. Res.	24	20	2	2	73	28	62
Bris'ton Cricketers	24	17	4	3	95	28	55
Rangeworthy	24	13	5	6	71	39	44
Hambrook *-3*	24	14	2	8	63	34	41
Greyfriars Res.	24	11	6	7	57	54	39
Winterbourne U A	24	12	2	10	55	57	38
Nicholas Wdrs A	24	9	5	10	44	41	32
AEK Boco Res.	24	10	2	12	55	56	32
Patchway Town A	24	9	4	11	52	58	31
Frys Club A	24	7	2	15	38	60	23
Iron Acton Res.	24	5	1	18	31	90	16
DRG Stptn Res. *-9*	24	5	5	14	32	57	11
Highridge Utd A	24	3	2	19	24	88	11

Division Three	P	W	D	L	F	A	Pts
Eden Grove *-3*	26	23	3	0	96	23	69
Warmley Saints	26	17	3	6	83	50	54
Broad Walk	26	16	4	6	115	56	52
Stockwood Wdrs	26	14	1	11	72	57	43
Hanham Ath. A	26	12	5	9	67	48	41
Tilly Rangers	26	12	3	11	62	73	39
Oakland	26	11	3	12	48	54	36
Olveston Utd Res.	26	10	5	11	36	47	35
Westerleigh Spts	26	8	3	15	52	77	27
Shirehampton A	26	8	3	15	53	93	27
Chip. Sodbury A	26	7	5	14	55	71	26
Totterdown Res.	26	7	5	14	49	68	26
Frampton A. Res.	26	5	6	15	36	64	21
Hillfields OB Res.	26	6	3	17	45	88	21

Division Four	P	W	D	L	F	A	Pts
Bradley Stoke T.	22	16	3	3	74	20	51
St Phil. MAS Res.	22	16	0	6	61	38	48
Shireway Sports	22	14	3	5	67	26	45
Impact Squad *-3*	22	15	3	4	64	33	45
Longwell G. B *-3*	22	11	3	8	56	52	33
T'bot Knowle Res.	22	10	2	10	57	48	32
Oldland Abbots A	22	9	3	10	45	51	30
AXA A	22	8	2	12	43	55	26
Fry Club B	22	7	3	12	42	58	24
Made for E. Res.	22	7	1	14	30	53	22
St Marys FC Res.	22	4	2	16	33	80	14
St Nicholas	22	2	1	19	29	87	7

Division Five	P	W	D	L	F	A	Pts
Henbury B	22	18	2	2	67	27	56
Portville Warriors	22	16	2	4	101	28	50
Inter The B'field *-3*	22	16	2	4	89	34	47
Pucklechurch A	22	10	3	9	48	54	33
Wick A	22	8	6	8	57	47	30
Soundwell Vics	22	8	2	12	46	62	26
Greyfriars Ath. A	22	7	4	11	38	65	25
Brimsham G. Res.	22	6	6	10	39	65	24
Coalpit Hth Res.	22	6	5	11	40	64	23
Bendix Res.	22	6	4	12	36	62	22
AEK Boco A	22	4	7	11	50	56	19
St Pancras Res.	22	4	3	15	34	81	15

Division Six	P	W	D	L	F	A	Pts
Southmead C. Sp.	24	21	1	2	130	23	64
St George Rgrs	24	20	1	3	135	33	61
RG St George B	24	15	3	6	82	34	48
Hambrook Res.	24	13	5	6	57	48	44
S Bristol Cent. A	24	13	1	10	69	73	40
Bradley S. T. Res.	24	13	0	11	73	51	39
Rangeworthy Res.	24	11	4	9	74	65	37
Brazil	24	10	4	10	58	72	34
Crosscourt Res.	24	7	4	13	42	81	25
Bris'ton Crick. Res.	24	6	2	16	42	74	20
AXA B	24	4	4	16	41	86	16
Seymour Utd A	24	4	4	16	36	96	16
Little Thatch	24	1	3	20	38	141	6

BRISTOL & SUBURBAN LEAGUE

Premier Div One	P	W	D	L	F	A	Pts
St Aldhelms	26	21	4	1	97	17	67
Broad Plain Hse	26	17	7	2	69	31	58
CTK Southside *-1*	26	18	3	5	83	38	56
Alm'bury T. Res.	26	16	3	7	58	42	51
Teyfant Athletic	26	15	5	6	82	54	50
S Glos (Hamb'k)	26	10	5	11	47	43	35
Stoke Gifford Utd	26	10	3	13	47	59	33
Winford PH	26	8	7	11	39	58	31
Avonmouth	26	7	7	12	38	57	28
Old Georgians	26	7	4	15	46	64	25
Ashton Utd FC *-7*	26	8	6	12	49	59	23
Glenside 5 OB *-1*	26	6	3	17	32	83	20
Fishponds OB	26	3	3	20	33	65	12
Alm'sbury Res. *-9*	26	4	4	18	37	87	7

Premier Div Two	P	W	D	L	F	A	Pts
Southmead Ath.	26	23	2	1	102	26	71
Cadbury Hth Res.	26	20	4	2	80	24	64
Ridings High	26	20	2	4	72	31	62
Lockleaze *-6*	26	13	5	8	61	37	38
Wessex Wdrs	26	10	7	9	46	53	37
Little Stoke	26	9	7	10	46	56	34
Bristol Nth West	26	10	4	12	42	53	34
St Aldhelms Res.	26	9	6	11	51	41	33
Severn Beach	26	10	3	13	49	62	33
TC Sports	26	8	6	12	39	55	30
Brist. Telephones	26	7	6	13	48	54	27
Whitchurch	26	5	2	19	40	95	17
Brislington A	26	2	8	16	36	78	14
Old Cothamians	26	3	4	19	38	85	13

Division One	P	W	D	L	F	A	Pts
Bristol Athletic	24	19	3	2	65	27	60
Lawrence Weston	24	18	0	6	52	27	54
Tytherington Res.	24	15	4	5	72	36	49
Broad Plain H Res.	24	13	3	8	63	63	42
Ashton Old Boys	24	12	3	9	58	46	39
Filton Athletic	24	11	6	7	55	46	39
B & W A'side Res.	24	10	2	12	46	45	32
Ridings High Res.	24	10	2	12	35	36	32
Fishponds OB Res.	24	8	4	12	52	59	28
Totterdown PoB	24	8	3	13	45	62	27
Bris. Phones Res.	24	6	2	16	36	63	20
Ashton Rangers	24	5	2	17	37	62	17
Hengrove Ath. A	24	3	2	19	34	78	11

Division Two	P	W	D	L	F	A	Pts
Imperial Saints	24	21	1	2	103	33	64
Avonmouth Res.	24	19	2	3	95	42	59
Keynsham T. A	24	15	3	6	84	56	48
Almondsbury A	24	15	2	7	65	49	47
Tyndalls Pk Rgrs	24	11	4	9	52	43	37
Cadbury Heath A	24	11	3	10	74	60	36
St Aldhelms A	24	11	1	12	48	58	34
Stoke Gifford Res.	24	10	3	11	59	63	33
S'thmead A. Res.	24	9	1	14	45	81	28
Little Stoke Res.	24	7	0	17	42	75	21
Corinthian Sports	24	6	3	15	38	80	21
Oldbury Crus.	24	5	3	16	40	75	18
OlCoth'mians Res.	24	3	0	21	30	60	9

Division Three	P	W	D	L	F	A	Pts
Mangotsfield A	24	18	4	2	89	31	58
Ingleside	24	16	2	6	97	41	50
TC Sports Res.	24	14	4	6	51	39	46
Thrissell Nomads	24	13	7	4	61	53	46
Eagle Hse Elite *-1*	24	15	1	8	90	51	45
O Georgians Res.	24	9	7	8	55	51	34
Glenside 5 Res.	24	10	3	11	50	52	33
Ashton Utd Res.	24	9	2	13	51	63	29
Sefton Park	24	8	4	12	56	74	28
Parson Street OB	24	8	2	14	63	63	26
Fishponds OB A	24	7	3	14	59	80	24
Teyfant Ath. Res.	24	7	3	14	45	71	24
Brandon TT Spts	24	1	0	23	21	119	3

Division Four	P	W	D	L	F	A	Pts
Lockleaze Res.	24	20	3	1	62	21	63
Bristol County	24	20	2	2	162	35	62
Sev. Beach Res.	24	13	1	10	71	55	40
Broad Plain H. A	24	11	6	7	56	55	39
Golden Hill Spts	24	10	3	11	60	67	33
Hanham A. Colts	24	9	2	13	46	74	29
Avonmouth A	24	8	4	12	59	73	28
Wessex W. Res.	24	8	3	13	55	74	27
Coupland Insul.	24	7	6	11	48	73	27
St Annes Town	24	7	5	12	42	60	26
Wanderers	24	6	7	11	48	52	25
S Glos (H.) Res.	24	7	2	15	58	82	23
Ridings High A	24	7	2	15	33	79	23

Division Five	P	W	D	L	F	A	Pts
Cartwheel Sports	26	21	3	2	138	28	66
Lebeq United	26	21	3	2	149	41	66
Lawrence W. Res.	26	19	2	5	100	45	59
Avonmouth United	26	17	1	8	103	42	52
Filton Athletic Res.	26	15	2	9	57	62	47
Oldbury Crus. Res.	26	14	3	9	82	72	45
Winford PH Res.	26	10	3	13	53	83	33
Emersons Green	26	9	5	12	62	53	32
AFC Spartans	26	8	4	14	54	88	27
Fishponds OB B	26	8	2	16	51	93	26
Stoke Gifford U. A	26	5	6	15	30	72	21
T'down PoB Res	26	5	5	16	36	116	20
Whitchurch Res	26	4	3	19	33	97	15
Parson St OB Res.	26	4	2	20	36	92	14

BROMLEY & DISTRICT LEAGUE

Premier Division	P	W	D	L	F	A	Pts
AFC Mottingham	20	15	3	2	59	23	48
Phoenix Spts Res.	20	13	3	4	65	29	42
Holmesdale A	20	12	4	4	58	39	40
Barnehurst	20	9	4	7	38	29	31
South East Ath.	20	9	3	8	45	45	30
Rotherhithe	20	7	4	9	46	42	25

Heathfield FC	20	6	5	9	32	42	23
Erith '147 Res.	20	6	2	12	23	40	20
Shelton Athletic	20	5	4	11	44	54	19
Univ. Greenwich	20	4	6	10	32	51	18
Running Horses	20	4	2	14	40	88	14

Division One	P	W	D	L	F	A	Pts
Catford Exiles	20	18	1	1	77	30	55
Highfield Rovers	20	11	3	6	49	27	36
Ilderton Athletic	20	10	5	5	40	34	35
Welling Park	20	9	3	8	50	48	30
Dulwich Town	20	9	3	8	51	50	30
Iron Tugboat City	20	8	4	8	45	44	28
Barnet Wood	20	6	4	10	41	60	22
Old Colfeians A	20	6	3	11	46	57	21
Biggin Hill	20	6	2	12	35	50	20
OPK Res.	20	5	3	12	34	48	18
Chislehurst Dyn.	20	4	5	11	33	53	17

Division Two	P	W	D	L	F	A	Pts
AFC Heathfield	16	14	1	1	77	22	43
Old Colfeians B	16	11	3	2	50	28	36
Latter-Day Saints	16	10	0	6	40	40	30
Ex-Blues	16	7	1	8	62	45	22
Charl. A Deaf Res.	16	7	1	8	52	41	22
F'borough OBG B	16	6	0	10	32	65	18
AFC Bromley	16	5	1	10	40	57	16
Swan & Mitre	16	4	1	11	32	50	13
Crofton Albion B	16	4	0	12	35	72	12

BURTON & DISTRICT LEAGUE

Pedigree Division	P	W	D	L	F	A	Pts
Stretton Spartans	24	16	4	4	75	40	52
Barton United FC	24	15	6	3	79	35	51
Willington Res.	24	15	6	3	79	39	51
The Elms	24	15	3	6	85	39	48
R. Lion Horninglow	24	13	6	5	81	40	45
The Seal Inn	24	11	6	7	58	38	39
Gresley Rovers A	24	10	5	9	55	41	35
The Dart	24	8	5	11	45	57	29
Marstons	24	7	3	14	53	72	24
Crown Inn	24	5	4	15	52	83	19
Overseal St Matt.	24	5	4	15	40	91	19
Ashbourne U. Res.	24	5	0	19	34	97	15
Lichfield City Res.	24	4	2	18	27	91	14

TAG Division	P	W	D	L	F	A	Pts
Lichfield City A	22	19	1	2	118	30	58
Real Medina	22	18	2	2	78	26	56
Kaleef	22	16	1	5	64	30	49
Barton Royal Oak	22	13	3	6	88	38	42
Grange Inn	22	12	1	9	64	45	37
Blacksmiths Arms	22	11	3	8	62	49	36
Netherseal St Ptrs	22	11	1	10	80	67	34
Bk Horse Stanton	22	8	1	13	51	50	25
Midway FC	22	6	5	11	35	60	23
Jubilee Winshill	22	3	1	18	33	60	10
Whit'gton Brenstar	22	3	1	18	47	161	10
Real Medina Yth	22	2	0	20	21	125	6

CANTERBURY & DISTRICT LEAGUE
(Barton PO & Stores)

Premier Division	P	W	D	L	F	A	Pts
Chartham Sp. Club	18	15	2	1	51	11	47
Chilham	18	15	1	2	73	22	46
Ash	18	9	5	4	42	29	32
Charing	18	9	3	6	54	33	30
Monument Eagles	18	8	1	9	38	46	25
Lesters Elite	18	6	5	7	36	34	23
Red Arrow Sports	18	6	4	8	25	50	22
Littlebourne	18	4	3	11	39	66	15
Sturry	18	3	3	12	30	52	12
The Prince Wales	18	0	3	15	19	64	3

Prince Albert Canterbury - record expunged

Division One	P	W	D	L	F	A	Pts
F'stone Lanterns	22	16	4	2	76	16	52
University Kent A	22	15	4	3	58	26	49
Canterb'y City Res.	22	12	8	2	58	32	44
Snowdown CW	22	9	6	7	55	51	33
RS Beltinge	22	10	3	9	42	41	33
Sharsted	22	10	2	10	41	49	32
Minster	22	8	4	10	41	47	28
Blean	22	7	5	10	44	56	26
Post Office	22	6	4	12	62	55	22
Chilham Res.	22	6	3	13	46	70	21
Sturry Res.	22	6	1	15	36	71	19
Woodnesborough	22	4	2	16	45	90	14

Division Two	P	W	D	L	F	A	Pts
Burgess-Hodgson	16	11	2	3	61	37	35
St Stephens	16	10	3	3	63	30	33
Europeans	16	9	5	2	78	37	32
St Margarets	16	8	3	5	52	31	27
Sentinels	16	6	4	6	41	33	22
Bekesbourne Spts	16	6	3	7	51	70	21
Gentil Knight	16	4	6	6	37	35	18
Ashford Borough	16	4	0	12	35	53	12
The Two Sawyers	16	0	2	14	17	109	2

Division Three	P	W	D	L	F	A	Pts
Betteshanger Res.	18	16	1	1	72	24	49
Ash Res.	18	12	2	4	39	32	38
Swalecliffe	18	10	2	6	45	35	32
Woodmans Hall	18	7	5	6	44	40	26
The Swan	18	8	0	10	43	29	24
Pfizer Athletic	18	7	2	9	42	42	23
Herne Bay Ath.	18	7	2	9	41	43	23
Wingham	18	6	2	10	29	51	20
Post Office Res.	18	4	2	12	34	69	14
USA	18	4	0	14	32	56	12

CAPITAL LEAGUE

Eastern Division	P	W	D	L	F	A	Pts
Aveley Res.	20	13	3	4	66	37	42
Harlow Town Res.	20	13	3	4	58	34	42
Chelmsford Res.	20	12	5	3	53	27	41
Billericay T. Res.	20	10	5	5	43	33	35
Cheshunt Res.	20	7	6	7	39	36	27
AFC H'church Res.	20	8	2	10	38	46	26
Enfield Town Res.	20	7	3	10	43	42	24
Maldon Town A	20	6	5	9	43	43	23
Bish. Stortf'd Res.	20	7	2	11	49	50	23
Brimsdown Res.	20	4	3	13	21	55	15
Ware Res.	20	4	1	15	33	83	13

Western Division	P	W	D	L	F	A	Pts
Hayes & Ydg Res.	18	15	1	2	63	16	46
Staines Town Res.	18	11	0	7	38	29	33
Maidenhead Res.	17	9	3	5	37	22	30
Wingate & F. Res.	17	9	1	7	40	33	28
Hitchin Town Res.	18	8	1	9	36	29	25
Hemel Hemp. Res.	18	6	6	6	40	30	24
St Albans City Res.	18	6	2	10	29	34	20
Potters Bar Res.	18	6	2	10	25	54	20
Harrow Boro. Res.	18	5	3	10	33	40	18
Windsor & E. Res.	18	4	1	13	8	62	13

CENTRAL & SOUTH NORFOLK LEAGUE
(Crown Fire)

Division One	P	W	D	L	F	A	Pts
Thetford Athletic	22	18	1	3	95	22	55
Saham Toney	22	18	0	4	119	28	54
Mulbarton Wdrs	22	16	3	3	67	32	51
Shipdham	22	11	4	7	49	44	37
East Harling Res.	22	10	2	10	67	62	32
Bridgham United	22	9	2	11	44	81	29
Gressenhall	22	8	2	12	47	53	26
Yaxham	22	7	3	12	61	72	24
Dereham Town A	22	6	5	11	31	62	23
Hingham Athletic	22	6	3	13	48	58	21
Rockland United	22	4	5	13	35	87	17
Toftwood Rangers	22	3	2	17	30	92	11

Dereham Posties - record expunged
North Elmham - record expunged

Division Two	P	W	D	L	F	A	Pts
Dickleburgh	24	18	2	4	86	31	56
Attleborough T. A	24	16	4	4	84	50	52
Cockers	24	16	3	5	75	39	51
Swaffham Town A	24	15	3	6	66	43	48
Watton United A	24	14	2	8	80	40	44
Tacolneston	24	12	4	8	62	45	40
Wymondham T. A	24	11	5	8	57	44	38
Morley Vill. Res.	24	10	2	12	68	65	32
Bunwell	24	10	2	12	64	63	32
Sah. Toney Res.	24	6	1	17	50	91	19
Necton SSC Res.	24	6	0	18	48	111	18
Hingham A. Res.	24	3	2	19	37	83	11
Yaxham Res.	24	2	4	18	26	98	10

Division Three	P	W	D	L	F	A	Pts
Thetford R. Res.	24	18	2	4	107	44	56
West End FC	24	17	1	6	80	37	52
Shropham United	24	15	4	5	85	30	49
Bradenham Res.	24	15	4	5	62	41	49
Swanton Morley	24	13	3	8	63	46	42
Sporle	24	13	2	9	82	51	41
Bawdeswell	24	12	3	9	68	62	39
Foulsham Res.	24	8	5	11	61	64	29
Gt Cressingham	24	8	4	12	47	56	28
Wendling	24	8	3	13	49	54	27
Gressenhall Res.	24	5	4	15	32	87	19
Shipdham Res. -3	24	3	2	19	31	90	8
Rockland U. Res.	24	2	1	21	22	127	7

Division Four	P	W	D	L	F	A	Pts
Hethersett Athletic	22	20	1	1	129	21	61
Northwold S&SC	22	15	2	5	91	43	47
Castle Acre Swifts	22	14	5	3	65	38	47
Hindolveston	22	14	3	5	66	37	45
Splitz United	22	11	2	9	66	61	35
Beetley	22	10	2	10	37	52	32
Fakenham T. A	22	10	1	11	47	60	31
Thurton & Ashby	22	10	0	12	65	58	30
Colkirk	22	8	3	11	52	56	27
Methwold Rovers	22	5	1	16	44	97	16
Breckland Wdrs	22	3	0	19	33	99	9
Shropham U. Res.	22	2	0	20	22	95	6

CHELTENHAM ASSOCIATION LEAGUE

Division One	P	W	D	L	F	A	Pts
FC Barometrics	24	19	2	3	57	20	59
Moreton Rangers	24	15	6	3	60	26	51
Newton FC	24	16	2	6	53	26	50
Finlay Rovers -3	24	14	3	7	58	45	42
Whaddon United	24	12	2	10	52	41	38
Kings	24	10	5	9	40	32	35
Endsleigh	24	8	8	8	53	40	32
Siddington	24	8	4	12	39	41	28
Woodmancote	24	8	3	13	57	49	27
Bish. Cleeve A -3	24	7	6	11	31	41	24
Prestbury Rovers	24	7	3	14	34	45	24
Andoversford	24	5	2	17	34	102	17
Shipton Oliffe	24	3	2	19	30	90	11

Division Two	P	W	D	L	F	A	Pts
Whaddon U. Res.	26	22	1	3	102	36	67
Star Res.	26	21	1	4	84	33	64
Apperley/Tewk. D.	26	15	5	6	58	31	50
Winchcombe Res.	26	14	4	8	47	47	46
Charlton Rovers	26	13	6	7	56	41	45
AC Olympia	26	12	4	10	46	41	40
Northway	26	10	5	11	57	59	35
Gala Wilton Res.	26	10	4	12	54	51	34
Bredon Res.	26	8	8	10	45	53	32
Northleach Town	26	8	5	13	49	62	29
Brockworth Res.	26	6	4	16	38	71	22
Chelt. CS Res.	26	4	6	16	35	55	18
Dowty Dyn. -3	26	4	6	16	32	65	15
Chelthm Saras A	26	4	3	19	45	103	15

Division Three	P	W	D	L	F	A	Pts
Broadway United	24	22	1	1	117	25	67
Tewkesbury Rov.	24	19	3	2	103	43	60
Falcons	24	17	1	6	86	38	52
Glouc. Elmleaze	24	15	5	4	71	33	50
Tewkesbury Town	24	10	4	10	57	54	34
Smiths Ath. Res.	24	10	4	10	39	56	34
FC Electrics	24	8	3	13	61	58	27
Belmore United -3	24	8	5	11	53	64	26
Phoenix United -3	24	9	1	14	43	63	25
Bourton Rov. Res.	24	6	4	14	31	65	22
St Marks CA	24	6	2	16	43	89	20
Chelt'ham CS A	24	4	3	17	27	71	15
Apperley/TD Res.	24	3	2	19	30	102	11

Division Four	P	W	D	L	F	A	Pts
Churchdown Pant.	24	22	1	1	101	26	67
FC B'metrics Res.	24	17	2	5	91	32	53
Elmbridge Old B.	24	16	2	6	79	53	50
Southside	24	13	4	7	68	38	43
Charlton Rov. Res.	24	12	5	7	52	35	41
Tivoli Rovers	24	12	2	10	68	47	38
Bredon A	24	9	5	10	45	62	32
Andoversf'd Res.	24	9	4	11	56	76	31
Finlay R. Res. -3	24	8	2	14	47	100	23
Brockworth Alb. A	24	6	1	17	31	78	19
Kings Res.	24	4	6	14	33	53	18
Smiths Ath. Res.	24	3	7	14	45	70	16
Chelt. Saracens B	24	2	5	17	46	92	11

Division Five	P	W	D	L	F	A	Pts
C & G	22	18	1	3	106	17	55
Falcons Res.	22	17	2	3	66	26	53

	P	W	D	L	F	A	Pts
Star A	22	14	6	2	75	34	48
Cleevonians	22	12	2	8	56	46	38
Gala Wilton A	22	11	1	10	54	40	34
Charlton Kings	22	10	1	11	52	66	31
FC Electrics Res.	22	8	3	11	48	58	27
Tewkes. T. Res. *-3*	22	9	3	10	48	55	24
Sherborne Harr.	22	6	2	14	34	64	20
Apperley/Tewk. A	22	5	4	13	32	71	19
Belmore U Res. *-3*	22	5	2	15	35	75	14
Charlton Rov. A	22	1	5	16	18	72	8

Division Six	P	W	D	L	F	A	Pts
Chelt. Saracens C	16	12	1	3	64	24	37
RSG	16	11	2	3	76	19	35
Fintan *-6*	16	12	2	2	75	20	32
FC Barometrics A	16	9	1	6	40	24	28
66 Star United *-3*	16	8	1	7	62	44	22
Cheltenham CS B	16	6	2	8	30	48	20
Leckhampton Rov.	16	6	1	9	30	39	19
Winchcombe T. A	16	3	0	13	36	70	9
Northleach T. Res.	16	0	0	16	4	129	0

CHESTER & DISTRICT LEAGUE

Premier Division	P	W	D	L	F	A	Pts
Highfield Athletic	20	14	5	1	79	38	47
Waggon & Horses	20	11	5	4	53	42	38
Chester Nm. Res.	20	11	4	5	42	36	37
Sutton Way Villa	20	9	5	6	64	54	32
Castrol Soc. Res.	20	8	5	7	45	39	29
Kelsall	20	7	6	7	42	44	27
Hoole Rangers	20	7	3	10	50	67	24
Newton Bears	20	7	2	11	48	60	23
Crossway	20	5	4	11	46	60	19
City Bar	20	3	6	11	45	57	15
Tarvin Athletic	20	4	3	13	36	53	15

Kydds Athletic - record expunged

Division One	P	W	D	L	F	A	Pts
AFC Beb'ton Res.	22	18	3	1	67	24	57
Parkgate FC	22	13	5	4	66	32	44
Helsby Res.	22	13	3	6	69	30	42
Highfield A. Res.	22	12	1	9	65	64	37
FC Woodlands	22	11	3	8	66	44	36
Duddon United	22	10	5	7	42	44	35
Robin Hood	22	8	3	11	48	48	27
Saughall Thurs.	22	7	4	11	46	70	25
Cestrian Alex	22	6	5	11	49	67	23
Frodsham United	22	5	6	11	42	69	21
Ashton Lions	22	4	4	14	39	64	16
Chester Nmds A	22	2	4	16	38	81	10

Division Two	P	W	D	L	F	A	Pts
FC Pensby Res.	16	14	1	1	77	21	43
Newton Res.	16	10	3	3	60	30	33
Chester N. B *-3*	16	12	0	4	54	38	33
Rangers Breaks	16	9	1	6	52	29	28
Barrow Athletic	16	7	4	5	37	35	25
Hoole Rgrs Res.	16	5	2	9	34	57	17
Boughton Athletic	16	3	1	12	31	54	10
Vicars X Doves	16	3	1	12	24	72	10
Moneysupermkt.com	16	2	1	13	28	60	7

MBCS - record expunged

Division Three	P	W	D	L	F	A	Pts
Willaston Nomads	18	13	3	2	84	30	42
Manor Ath. Res.	18	13	3	2	64	24	42
Kelma	18	12	2	4	65	23	38
Halfway Hse Celt.	18	10	5	3	61	39	35
West Meter	18	10	1	7	40	41	31
Saughall T. Res.	18	5	3	10	43	61	18
Lodge Bar	18	5	1	12	30	60	16
Frodsham Vets	18	5	1	12	29	65	16
Uberlube	18	4	1	13	33	68	13
Crossway Res.	18	2	2	14	30	69	8

CHESTERFIELD & DISTRICT AMATEUR LEAGUE

	P	W	D	L	F	A	Pts
Cricketers	20	18	0	2	99	19	54
Chesterfield Town	20	14	4	2	73	27	46
Nags Head	20	11	5	4	83	41	38
Duckmanton Com.	20	11	5	4	83	47	38
Clowne Miners W.	20	9	5	6	57	40	32
Whaley Thorns	20	9	2	9	70	50	29
Holmefield Arms	20	7	5	8	50	52	26
Hopflower	20	6	5	9	47	42	23
Renishaw S. Club	20	4	2	14	41	63	14
Harleys	20	4	1	15	39	90	13
North Wingfield U.	20	0	0	20	17	188	0

Clowne Rovers - record expunged

CHORLEY ALLIANCE

	P	W	D	L	F	A	Pts
International Allstars	16	12	2	2	62	16	38
Imperial	16	12	1	3	62	31	37
Whittle	16	11	1	4	57	27	34
Hop Pocket	16	8	2	6	63	37	26
Railway Vets	16	7	3	6	69	52	24
Chorley Saints	16	6	4	6	51	45	22
Spartak Chorley	16	3	2	11	23	64	11
Hardly Athletic	16	3	1	12	27	90	10
Hop Pocket Res.	16	2	0	14	33	85	6

CIRENCESTER & DISTRICT LEAGUE

Division One	P	W	D	L	F	A	Pts
Real Fairford	22	17	2	3	71	25	53
South Cerney	22	17	1	4	55	30	52
Ashton Keynes	22	15	4	3	71	29	49
Avonvale United	22	12	7	3	58	29	43
Kingshill Sports	22	13	2	7	45	39	41
Bibury	22	7	7	8	44	29	28
Oaksey	22	8	3	11	47	44	27
The Beeches	22	6	4	12	39	60	22
Poulton	22	5	4	13	37	58	19
CHQ United	22	4	5	13	61	75	17
Golden Farm	22	4	1	17	39	83	13
Down Ampney	22	3	2	17	23	89	11

Division Two	P	W	D	L	F	A	Pts
Stratton Utd FC	26	20	3	3	123	48	63
Bibury Res.	26	19	3	4	94	40	60
Tetbury Town A	26	18	3	5	74	42	57
Ash. Keynes Res.	26	15	1	10	63	62	46
Avonvale U. Res.	26	11	8	7	63	47	41
Oakridge *-10*	26	15	5	6	91	57	40
Real Fairf'd Res.	26	11	5	10	64	53	38
Oaksey Res.	26	11	3	12	54	68	36
Minety Res.	26	9	4	13	53	56	31
CHQ Utd Res. *-6*	26	9	4	13	48	72	25
Corinium Sports	26	5	7	14	45	80	22
Chalford A	26	4	4	18	34	73	16
Kingshill Sp. Res.	26	4	3	19	39	92	15
Sth Cerney Res.	26	3	3	20	30	85	12

COLCHESTER & EAST ESSEX LEAGUE
(K P Evans & Co)

Premier Division	P	W	D	L	F	A	Pts
Harwich & Park. A	18	15	2	1	69	22	47
Wormingford Wdrs	18	12	2	4	61	30	38
Colne Engaine	18	11	2	5	37	26	35
Kirby Athletic	18	8	4	6	29	28	28
Colch. Hotspurs	18	7	4	7	24	22	25
Wimpole	18	7	4	7	44	47	25
Univ. of Essex A	18	8	0	10	37	46	24
Tollesbury	18	6	4	8	29	38	22
Harwich Rangers	18	3	2	13	28	56	11
Oyster	18	0	2	16	20	63	2

Division One	P	W	D	L	F	A	Pts
Real Ravensdale	20	16	3	1	86	28	51
St Ives	20	15	1	4	75	25	46
Univ. of Essex B	20	13	3	4	51	23	42
Castle	20	10	2	8	54	41	32
Ardleigh United	20	9	2	9	52	54	29
Cinque Port	20	7	4	9	36	43	25
Colchester Ath.	20	6	5	9	31	43	23
AFC Informa	20	7	2	11	30	48	23
AXA FC	20	6	0	14	31	52	18
Stoke-by-Nayland	20	4	3	13	22	72	15
Whitehall	20	4	1	15	30	69	13

Division Two	P	W	D	L	F	A	Pts
Eastcliff	18	14	3	1	58	20	45
Brightlingsea A	18	11	3	4	56	30	36
FC Clacton A	18	10	2	6	40	43	32
Feering United	18	8	3	7	41	43	27
Wimpole Res.	18	8	2	8	57	51	26
New Field	18	7	2	9	38	53	23
Nayland Rangers	18	6	4	8	52	60	22
Great Bentley A	18	6	2	10	34	44	20
Univ. of Essex C	18	5	4	9	48	50	19
Wormingford Res.	18	2	1	15	24	54	7

Division Three	P	W	D	L	F	A	Pts
Boxford Rovers	22	18	1	3	88	33	55
FCC XI	22	15	2	5	84	34	47
Sudbury Ath. A	22	15	2	5	61	39	47
Clacton Utd Res.	22	13	3	6	80	51	42
Kirby Athletic Res.	22	11	3	8	63	50	36
Univ. of Essex D	22	8	3	11	40	48	27
Brantham Ath. A	22	7	5	10	54	50	26
Abbey Fields	22	7	3	12	65	79	24
Colch. Ath. Res.	22	6	4	12	39	55	22
Feering Utd Res.	22	5	5	12	36	77	20
Lexden Rovers	22	4	4	14	23	67	16
Stoke-by-N. Res.	22	3	5	14	28	78	14

COVENTRY ALLIANCE

Premier Division	P	W	D	L	F	A	Pts
Alvis	30	23	4	3	108	25	73
Christ The King	30	18	4	8	72	45	58
Folly Lane BBOB	30	17	6	7	57	39	57
Bedworth Ex-S.	30	15	7	8	68	47	52
Hawkes Mill Spts	30	13	9	8	61	56	48
Witherley United	30	14	5	11	73	66	47
Mount Nod H'way	30	14	4	12	75	63	46
Ambleside Sports	30	12	4	14	54	66	40
Potters Green	30	11	6	13	40	52	39
Triumph Athletic	30	11	5	14	61	71	38
Bulkington S & S	30	9	9	12	47	53	36
Dunlop	30	9	8	13	48	55	35
AEI Rugby	30	10	5	15	60	76	35
Stockton	30	9	6	15	50	65	33
Peugeot	30	9	3	18	65	77	30
Stock'ford AA Pav	30	1	5	24	23	106	8

Division One	P	W	D	L	F	A	Pts
Alvis Res.	22	14	4	4	53	37	46
Bourton/Frankton	22	13	3	6	55	40	42
Woodlands WMC	22	13	3	6	38	24	42
Coventry Univ.	22	11	5	6	41	33	38
Coundon Court	22	10	7	5	52	35	37
Nun. Griff & Coton	22	8	6	8	48	57	30
Christ The K. Res.	22	8	3	11	45	54	27
Coventry Colliery	22	8	3	11	55	49	24
Collycroft Sports	22	7	3	12	41	51	24
Stockton Res.	22	6	3	13	30	49	21
Folly Lane Res.	22	4	8	10	42	54	20
Brooklands/Jag.	22	4	4	14	41	58	16

Division Two	P	W	D	L	F	A	Pts
Copsewood (Cov)	22	17	2	3	73	22	53
Peugeot Res.	22	13	5	4	56	35	44
Kenilworth Wdns	22	14	1	7	57	35	43
Fillongley	22	14	1	7	56	51	43
Brooklands/J.Res.	22	9	6	7	61	55	33
Balsall/Berkswell	22	9	5	8	66	60	32
Hub	22	9	3	10	47	52	30
Potters G. Res.	22	8	4	10	40	39	28
Shilton	22	5	6	11	49	54	21
Dunlop Res.	22	4	8	10	42	52	20
Christ The King A	22	4	4	14	34	70	16
Sptng Club (GNP)	22	2	3	17	36	92	9

Division Three	P	W	D	L	F	A	Pts
Hartshill	22	17	1	4	68	28	52
Brinklow	22	15	4	3	68	29	49
Coundon Ct Res.	22	12	3	7	60	43	39
Whitnash	22	10	3	9	59	46	33
Cop'wd (Cov) Res.	22	9	5	8	50	50	32
Mount Nod Res.	22	9	5	8	53	55	32
Cov. Univ. Res.	22	8	3	11	43	60	27
Jaguar-Daimler	22	7	4	11	40	44	25
Folly Lane A	22	7	3	12	37	56	24
Bulkington Res.	22	7	2	13	37	64	23
Triumph Ath. Res.	22	6	3	13	38	60	21
Witherley U. Res.	22	5	4	13	32	50	19

Division Four	P	W	D	L	F	A	Pts
Church Lawford	18	13	3	2	64	32	42
Bedworth ES Res.	18	13	2	3	73	25	41
Ambleside S. Res.	18	10	1	7	40	34	31
Cherry Tree	18	7	4	7	50	48	25
AEI Rugby Res.	18	8	1	9	38	42	25
Kenilworth W Res.	18	6	4	8	39	46	22
Hawkes Mill Res.	18	4	8	6	35	45	20
Cov. Colliery Res.	18	6	1	11	34	57	19
Woodlands Res.	18	5	3	10	30	48	18
Peugeot A	18	3	3	12	27	53	12

Collycroft Sports Res. - record expunged

Division Five	P	W	D	L	F	A	Pts
Bermuda WMC	24	18	3	3	88	23	57
Massey-F. Res.	24	18	1	5	83	35	55
Attleboro. Snooker	24	17	3	4	90	34	54
Shilton Res.	24	14	5	5	64	50	47
Hartshill Res.	24	11	3	10	51	75	36
Wolston	24	9	5	10	60	54	32
Coventry Univ. A	24	9	5	10	44	54	32
Balsall/Berk. Res.	24	9	4	11	69	68	31
Rugby	24	7	5	12	50	58	26
Bilton Social	24	7	5	12	46	61	26
Bourton & F. Res.	24	5	4	15	58	72	19
Fillongley Res.	24	6	1	17	35	82	19
AEI Rugby A	24	2	4	18	29	101	10

CRAVEN & DISTRICT FA

Premier Division	P	W	D	L	F	A	Pts
Long Lee Juniors	22	17	3	2	79	24	54
Gargrave	22	15	2	5	64	38	47
Grassington Utd *-1*	22	13	6	3	77	32	44
Skipton LMS	22	13	3	6	76	36	42
Grindleton *-1*	22	8	5	9	49	53	28
Waddington	22	8	4	10	48	62	28
WFC Clitheroe	22	6	9	7	42	45	27
Cononley Sports	22	8	3	11	51	61	27
Hellifield Sports	22	8	1	13	46	76	25
Pendle Athletic	22	6	4	12	38	61	22
Oxenhope R. Res.	22	5	5	12	34	68	20
Skipton Town	22	1	3	18	33	81	6

Division One	P	W	D	L	F	A	Pts
Cowling	20	15	2	3	55	22	47
Rolls Royce	20	15	0	5	45	31	45
Trawden Celtic	20	11	7	2	42	23	40
Settle United	20	12	3	5	68	43	39
AFC Padiham	20	9	2	9	44	39	29
Gargrave Res.	20	8	2	10	33	44	26
Embsay	20	7	2	11	49	44	23
Oakworth	20	5	5	10	27	47	20
Bradley	20	4	6	10	23	40	18
Bingley Town	20	4	2	14	26	49	14
Earby Town	20	3	3	14	24	54	12

Ravenscliffe - record expunged

Division Two	P	W	D	L	F	A	Pts
Silsden White Star	26	20	1	5	113	44	61
Skipton LMS Res.	26	20	1	5	76	47	61
Chatburn -3	26	20	2	4	110	44	59
Carleton Rovers	26	17	5	4	83	35	56
Wilsden Juniors	26	15	2	9	102	56	47
Pendle Renegades	26	10	6	10	73	70	36
Grassington Res.	26	10	4	12	49	78	34
Skipton T. Res.	26	10	3	13	68	100	33
Oakworth Res. *-1*	26	8	4	14	48	60	27
Rolls Royce Res.	26	7	4	15	65	92	25
Embsay Res. *-3*	26	8	3	15	43	60	24
Cononley S. Res.	26	7	3	16	64	115	24
Horton	26	5	4	17	36	78	19
Barn'swick Barons	26	4	0	22	48	99	12

CRAWLEY & DISTRICT LEAGUE
(Crawley Car Company)

Premier Division	P	W	D	L	F	A	Pts
Bletchingley	16	11	2	3	64	21	35
St Francis Flyers	16	10	2	4	45	23	32
Ifield Edw'ds Res.	16	10	0	6	57	30	30
Merstham Newton	16	8	2	6	52	24	26
Three Bridges A	16	7	3	6	42	32	24
Phoenix Utd FC	16	6	3	7	40	30	21
Real Hydraquip	16	6	2	8	29	48	20
Maidenbower Vill.	16	5	3	8	34	52	18
Sporting Crawley	16	0	1	15	16	119	1

Division One	P	W	D	L	F	A	Pts
FG Galaxy	14	12	1	1	62	14	37
Broadfield	14	9	2	3	54	24	29
Furnace Green Rv.	14	9	2	3	58	33	29
St Francis F. Res.	14	7	2	5	58	42	23
Ifield Edwards A	14	6	2	6	36	28	20
Phoenix Utd Res.	14	4	2	8	26	38	14
Horley Wanderers	14	3	0	11	27	53	9
Stones	14	0	1	13	12	101	1

Division Two	P	W	D	L	F	A	Pts
Chagos Island	20	16	2	2	74	20	50
Wingspan	20	14	3	3	90	30	45
Maid'bwr Res. *-3*	20	14	2	4	93	38	41
Ifield Edwards B	20	12	2	6	62	44	38
Sptg Crawley Res.	20	10	3	7	57	50	33
Border Wdrs	20	9	2	9	50	60	29
Worth Pk Rgrs *+3*	20	6	1	13	71	97	22
Real H'quip Res.	20	7	0	13	44	57	21
Phoenix United A	20	5	3	12	31	59	18
Rowfant Village	20	5	2	13	38	71	17
Sporting Devils	20	1	2	17	33	117	5

Salterbeck - record expunged

CUMBERLAND COUNTY LEAGUE
(Tesco)

Premier Division	P	W	D	L	F	A	Pts
Netherhall	18	16	2	0	70	12	50
Aspatria	18	14	3	1	60	20	45
Longtown *-3*	18	10	2	6	34	27	29
Mirehouse	18	8	3	7	44	40	27
Cockermouth	18	6	6	6	35	29	24
Wigton Harriers	18	5	7	6	31	34	22
Frizington WS *-6*	18	8	3	7	52	41	21
Whitehaven MWe	18	5	0	13	30	46	15
Silloth *-6*	18	1	2	15	15	84	-1
Cleator M Res. *-12*	18	3	0	15	23	61	-3

Division One	P	W	D	L	F	A	Pts
Whitehaven AFC	16	13	2	1	75	23	41
Bransty Rangers	16	10	2	4	60	53	32
Carlisle City Res.	16	8	1	7	53	43	25
St Margaret Marys	16	6	6	4	30	30	24
Hts Liddesdale *-3*	16	6	5	5	40	44	20
Wigton Athletic	16	5	4	7	41	57	19
Parton United	16	4	5	7	37	47	17
St Bees	16	4	2	10	36	55	14
Windscale Res. *-6*	16	1	3	12	27	47	0

DEVON & EXETER LEAGUE

Premier Division	P	W	D	L	F	A	Pts
St Martins	30	22	6	2	92	41	72
Bickleigh	30	18	5	7	86	48	59
Exmouth Amtrs	30	16	5	9	66	46	53
Thorverton	30	16	2	12	74	65	50
Topsham Town	30	15	4	11	67	58	49
Univ. Exeter Res.	30	13	4	13	62	52	43
Newtown	30	12	6	12	60	65	42
Heavitree Soc. Utd	30	12	6	12	56	61	42
Hatherleigh Town	30	13	3	14	62	70	42
Sidmouth Town	30	11	8	11	51	44	41
Feniton *-1*	30	11	7	12	65	60	39
Clyst Valley	30	9	7	14	42	56	34
Otterton	30	9	5	16	53	78	32
B. Salterton Res.	30	8	6	16	44	62	30
Wellington T. Res.	30	7	9	14	56	75	30
Beer Albion	30	6	1	23	37	92	19

Senior One	P	W	D	L	F	A	Pts
Alphington Res.	26	18	6	2	68	28	60
Willand Rov. Res.	26	17	6	3	56	28	57
Bow AAC	26	15	5	6	52	43	50
Sidbury United	26	14	5	7	58	34	47
Univ. of Exeter A	26	11	5	10	58	53	38
Elmore Res.	26	11	4	11	57	48	37
Seaton Town	26	11	3	12	47	44	36
Halwill	26	10	4	12	48	56	34
Culm United	26	8	5	13	55	57	29
East Budleigh	26	8	3	15	39	48	27
Broadclyst Soc. C.	26	7	6	13	55	85	27
Cul'mpton Res. *-5*	26	8	4	14	39	62	23
Upottery	26	6	4	16	35	54	22
Westexe Rovers	26	5	6	15	42	69	21

Senior Two	P	W	D	L	F	A	Pts
Heavitree US Res.	24	19	3	2	83	29	60
Morchard Bishop	24	15	6	3	56	22	51
Beacon Knights	24	13	4	7	51	35	43
Univ. of Exeter B	24	12	4	8	58	43	40
North Tawton	24	11	2	11	44	53	35
B'staple Town Res.	24	10	3	11	59	44	33
Newtown Res.	24	8	6	10	44	54	30
Exmouth Am. Res.	24	8	4	12	46	43	28
Honiton Town	24	8	4	12	39	52	28
Exeter CS Res.	24	8	3	13	40	45	27
Dawlish T. Res. *-4*	24	9	4	11	43	67	26
Lympstone	24	5	3	16	39	73	18
Sidmouth T. Res.	24	4	6	14	24	66	18

Senior Three	P	W	D	L	F	A	Pts
Tipton St John	26	22	1	3	81	36	67
Witheridge Res.	26	17	3	6	80	40	54
Axminster T. Res.	26	16	4	6	68	37	52
Uplowman Athletic	26	13	5	8	63	54	44
Colyton	26	12	2	12	58	51	38
South Zeal United	26	12	2	12	55	67	38
Winkleigh	26	9	4	13	43	52	31
Kentisbeare	26	9	3	14	37	80	30
Clyst Valley Res.	26	8	5	13	51	55	29
Pinhoe	26	8	5	13	49	63	29
Lapford	26	8	4	14	46	57	28
Sandford	26	9	1	16	39	54	28
Bampton	26	7	5	14	29	40	26
Seaton Town Res.	26	6	8	12	44	57	26

Senior Four	P	W	D	L	F	A	Pts
Phoenix Club	26	23	2	1	105	14	71
Chard Town Res.	26	17	4	5	85	29	55
Crescent	26	14	2	10	58	49	44
Topsham T. Res.	26	12	6	8	54	49	42
Newton St Cyres	26	13	2	11	61	62	41
Oakwood	26	12	3	11	56	52	39
Crediton Utd Res.	26	12	2	12	59	56	38
St Martins Res.	26	10	9	7	61	49	37
Offwell Rangers	26	9	6	11	54	67	33
Tedburn St Mary	26	10	1	15	48	55	31
Newtown A	26	8	3	15	45	72	27
Dunkeswell Rov.	26	7	6	13	46	74	27
Westexe R. Res.	26	5	3	18	32	82	18
Woodbury	26	4	3	19	31	85	15

Senior Five	P	W	D	L	F	A	Pts
Countess Wear D.	26	19	3	4	79	32	60
Okehampton Res.	26	18	2	6	81	29	56
Dawlish United	26	16	7	3	64	33	55
Broadclyst Res. *-1*	25	15	1	9	77	40	45
Sidbury U. Res. *-4*	25	15	2	8	56	40	43
Bickleigh Res.	26	13	2	11	65	66	41
Lord's XI *-1*	26	10	7	9	69	57	36
Thorverton Res.	26	10	6	10	46	44	36
Colaton Raleigh	26	10	3	13	73	60	33
Exmouth Ams A	26	9	4	13	44	62	31
Sampfd Peverel *-1*	26	9	3	14	44	50	29
Ottery SM Res. *-1*	26	8	2	16	41	80	25
Axmouth United	26	4	3	19	38	83	15
Kent'beare Res. *-1*	26	2	1	23	29	130	6

Intermediate One	P	W	D	L	F	A	Pts
Wellington Town A	26	19	4	3	108	41	61
Cullompton A	26	15	4	7	74	58	49
Feniton Res.	26	14	6	6	72	42	48
Hemyock *-4*	25	15	5	5	82	40	46
Uplowman Res.	26	10	8	8	61	57	38
Awliscombe Utd	26	10	6	10	45	42	36
UAU Exeter *-4*	26	13	1	12	61	68	36
Beer Albion Res.	26	10	4	12	69	73	34
Exmouth T. Res.	26	9	5	12	43	56	32
Exmouth Amtrs B	26	9	4	13	61	79	31
Alphington A *-1*	26	8	7	11	62	84	30
Dawlish Town A *-3*	25	8	8	9	60	53	29
Culm Utd Res.	26	5	3	18	42	77	18
Honiton T. Res.	26	2	3	21	35	105	9

Intermediate Two	P	W	D	L	F	A	Pts
Heavitree SU A	26	21	3	2	91	43	66
Silverton	26	17	5	4	85	41	56
Cheriton Fitzpaine	26	16	3	7	71	39	51
AFC Sidford	26	14	8	4	74	51	50
East Budleigh Res.	26	13	6	7	72	46	45
Rockbeare Rkts	26	10	6	10	55	55	36
Clyst Valley A	26	8	7	11	60	66	31
Hatherleigh Res.	26	8	5	13	65	78	29
Priory	26	8	5	13	58	71	29
Langdon FC	26	9	2	15	58	81	29
Axminster T. A *-1*	26	9	2	15	60	71	28
Oak	26	7	4	15	53	74	25
Bow AAC Res. *-1*	26	7	4	15	36	57	24
Lympstone Res. *-1*	26	2	6	18	31	96	11

Intermediate Three	P	W	D	L	F	A	Pts
Beacon K. Res.	26	19	3	4	91	31	60
Okehampton A. A	26	17	4	5	79	45	55
Bampton Res. *-1*	26	16	4	6	64	29	51
Amory Argyle	26	14	4	8	74	53	46
Met Office	26	12	7	7	51	42	43
Newton SC Res. *-1*	26	12	5	9	70	45	40
Bradninch	26	9	6	11	60	68	33
North Tawton Res.	26	9	5	12	68	67	32
Halwill Res.	26	8	7	11	58	74	31
Follygate & I'leigh	26	9	3	14	59	79	30
Langdon Res. *-4*	26	9	5	12	64	74	28

	P	W	D	L	F	A	Pts
Colyton Res.	26	8	3	15	53	71	27
Winkleigh Res.	26	4	7	15	41	86	19
Exmouth Arms	26	3	3	20	34	102	12

Intermediate Four	P	W	D	L	F	A	Pts
Dawlish Utd Res.	26	24	1	1	97	26	73
Amory Argyle Res.	26	17	3	6	84	55	54
Sandford Res.	26	16	3	7	57	53	51
Hemyock Res.	26	14	4	8	68	49	46
Seaton Town A *-5*	26	14	4	8	84	55	41
Countess WD Res.	26	11	5	10	69	56	38
Otterton Res.	26	10	5	11	62	69	35
Lapford Res.	26	8	9	9	55	68	33
Tedburn SM Res.	26	10	2	14	64	59	32
Morchard B. Res.	26	8	3	15	46	53	27
Offwell Rgrs Res.	26	6	5	15	57	72	23
Feniton A	26	7	2	17	47	87	23
Cheriton F. Res. *-1*	26	5	5	16	50	87	19
Tipton St J. Res.	26	6	1	19	48	99	19

DRIFFIELD & DISTRICT LEAGUE
(Horsley & Dawson)

Premier Division	P	W	D	L	F	A	Pts
Driff. Evening Inst.	18	15	3	0	74	17	48
H. Cranswick U. A	18	12	1	5	57	30	37
Mermaid	18	10	3	5	49	30	33
Driffield Rangers	18	10	2	6	59	37	32
Brid'ton Excelsior	18	10	1	7	58	61	31
Brid. S. Club Res.	18	9	2	7	52	44	29
Nafferton	18	6	5	7	44	46	23
Foresters Athletic	18	5	1	12	33	77	16
Stirling Castle	18	2	0	16	25	77	6
FC Corn. Bar Res.	18	1	2	15	38	70	5

Division One	P	W	D	L	F	A	Pts
H. Cranswick U. B	22	18	2	2	91	23	56
Burton Agnes	22	16	5	1	52	20	53
Middleton Rovers	22	16	3	3	68	33	51
Langtoft	22	10	4	8	48	44	34
Bridlington Rov.	22	10	2	10	57	57	32
Flamborough -3	22	11	3	8	67	43	30
Bridlington SC A	22	5	8	9	36	50	23
Bridlington Tigers	22	7	2	13	34	56	23
Spiders	22	6	3	13	32	57	21
Nafferton Old B.	22	5	3	14	43	65	18
Little Driffield	22	5	3	14	36	79	18
Rose/Crown Driff.	22	2	4	16	32	69	10

Division Two	P	W	D	L	F	A	Pts
Bay Horse Kilham	20	16	0	4	75	29	48
N. Frod'ham Res.	20	15	2	3	106	41	47
Brid.n Seabirds	20	15	2	3	90	34	47
Flamborough Res.	20	9	3	8	65	43	30
Driffield Wdrs	20	10	0	10	56	48	30
Burton Ag. Res.	20	9	2	9	57	54	29
Full Measure	20	9	1	10	55	56	28
Foresters A. Res.	20	7	4	9	59	63	25
Pocklington T. B	20	7	3	10	48	56	24
North Burton	20	3	2	15	30	73	11
Driffield Star	20	0	1	19	18	162	1

DUCHY LEAGUE
(Bodmin Sports Trophies)

Premier Division	P	W	D	L	F	A	Pts
Edgcumbe	22	18	2	2	80	20	56
Torpoint Athletic A	22	18	1	3	69	33	55
St Dennis	22	17	0	5	80	29	51
St Teath	22	13	4	5	52	34	43
Gunnislake	22	12	2	8	70	58	38
Looe Town	22	12	0	10	56	35	36
Lamerton	22	7	2	13	32	44	23
Foxhole S. Res.	22	7	2	13	47	78	23
St Mawgan	22	6	1	15	31	70	19
Pensilva	22	4	5	13	27	49	17
Altarnun	22	5	2	15	35	65	17
Launceston Utd	22	2	1	19	29	93	7

Division One	P	W	D	L	F	A	Pts
St Cleer	24	19	3	2	73	27	60
Saltash United A	24	16	5	3	89	26	53
Fowey United	24	15	5	4	105	46	50
Lanivet	24	12	6	6	68	45	42
St Dominick Res.	24	13	1	10	45	38	40
Tywardreath RBL	24	11	5	8	67	47	38
Godolphin A. Res.	24	11	3	10	41	44	36
Boscastle	24	9	7	8	51	50	34
Mevagissey	24	8	5	11	45	44	29
St Merryn	24	8	5	11	46	52	29
Maker-with-Rame	24	4	4	16	43	101	16
Holywell B/Cub. *-3*	24	4	1	19	27	90	10
Dobwalls Res.	24	0	2	22	24	114	2

Division Two	P	W	D	L	F	A	Pts
Bodmin Saints	26	21	2	3	121	28	65
Probus Res.	26	19	4	3	83	34	61
Week St Mary	26	16	2	8	88	52	50
St Anns Chapel	26	15	4	7	70	55	49
Grampound *+3*	26	14	2	10	76	50	47
St.Stephen Res.	26	12	3	11	61	61	39
Calstock	26	10	7	9	75	67	37
Delabole United	26	11	3	12	71	77	36
Pelynt	26	10	3	13	64	69	33
Polperro Res. *-3*	26	9	3	14	50	73	27
St Breward	26	7	2	17	51	98	23
Camelford A *-3*	26	7	1	18	54	98	19
Biscovey Res. *-1*	26	5	5	16	43	90	19
St Minver *-1*	26	4	3	19	32	87	14

DURHAM ALLIANCE
(Carcraft)

	P	W	D	L	F	A	Pts
Simonside SC	30	24	3	3	117	40	75
Whitehill	30	23	2	5	118	43	71
Seaham KM *+3*	30	18	7	5	108	51	64
Cornforth United	30	19	1	10	87	54	58
Hartlepool Town	30	18	4	8	81	50	58
Ebchester	30	14	6	10	68	67	48
Brandon Brit. Leg.	30	13	6	11	85	86	45
Birtley Town Res.	30	12	5	13	68	66	41
Shildon Railway	30	12	4	14	70	75	40
Sunderland South	30	10	8	12	57	58	38
Brandon Utd Res.	30	9	6	15	57	83	33
Thornley	30	6	9	15	60	84	27
Consett u-21s	30	8	2	20	40	86	26
Wheatley Hill *-6*	30	8	5	17	58	89	23
H'pool St Francis	30	5	3	22	32	87	18
Durham Gdn Hse	30	3	5	22	55	142	14

EAST BERKSHIRE LEAGUE

Premier Division	P	W	D	L	F	A	Pts
Orchard Park Rgrs	22	18	4	0	72	24	58
FC Beaconsfield	22	16	1	5	73	30	49
Waltham	22	15	2	5	55	33	47
Eastcote	22	12	4	6	74	41	40
Running Horse	22	10	6	6	54	43	36
New Windsor OB	22	8	4	10	53	54	28
Maidenhead T.n	22	8	1	13	40	51	25
Chalvey (WMC) S.	22	6	5	11	42	58	23
Iver Heath Rov.	22	6	5	11	38	54	23
Windsor Great Pk	22	5	3	14	31	71	18
Old Windsor	22	3	5	14	36	66	14
Slough Heating	22	3	4	15	36	79	13

EAST CHESHIRE LEAGUE
(Trade Mark Collections)

	P	W	D	L	F	A	Pts
Boarhound	22	19	1	2	108	18	58
Wilmslow Sports	22	19	1	2	91	27	58
Club AZ Res.	22	17	0	5	88	24	51
Poynton Nomads	22	14	3	5	70	48	45
Old Alts Veterans	22	10	4	8	54	53	34
Juno United	22	7	4	11	49	60	25
Mary Dendy	22	7	3	12	53	73	24
Poynton Kings	22	6	3	13	36	56	21
High Lane	22	6	3	13	36	69	21
Old Alts Youth	22	4	8	10	44	73	20
Poynton A	22	3	6	13	39	89	15
Old Alts B	22	1	2	19	20	98	5

EAST LANCASHIRE LEAGUE

Division One	P	W	D	L	F	A	Pts
Rimington	26	20	6	0	96	34	66
Worsthorne	26	19	3	4	88	34	60
Hurst Green	26	17	5	4	90	35	56
Mill Hill	26	14	4	7	91	50	46
Langho	26	14	4	8	82	57	46
Stacksteads St Jos.	26	12	4	9	64	62	40
Canberra	26	10	4	11	75	66	37
Enfield	26	10	2	14	50	72	32
Read United	26	8	7	11	55	67	31
Borrowdale Utd	26	7	4	15	40	73	25
Colne United	26	7	3	15	50	77	24
Goodshaw United	26	5	5	16	43	81	20
Rock Rovers	26	6	5	15	46	78	19
Peel Park	26	3	2	21	39	123	11

Division Two	P	W	D	L	F	A	Pts
Oswaldtwistle St M.	24	18	4	2	70	26	58
Bacup CC	24	16	4	4	81	31	52
Burnley GSOB	24	16	3	5	77	46	51
Barrowford Celtic	24	14	8	2	71	35	50
F'cowles/Pleas'ton	24	13	2	9	68	45	41
Rawtenstall	24	12	2	10	69	60	38
Pendle Forest SC	24	11	2	11	54	57	35
Clitheroe RBL	24	10	3	11	50	58	33
Barnoldswick T. A	24	8	2	14	57	82	26
Padiham A	24	7	1	16	52	73	22
Burnley B'dere A	24	7	3	14	52	60	21
Burnley Boys Club	24	4	0	20	32	101	12
Sabden	24	2	2	20	45	104	8

Reserve Division	P	W	D	L	F	A	Pts
Langho Res.	26	20	1	5	99	49	61
Worsthorne Res.	26	18	6	2	75	30	60
Hurst Green Res.	26	16	5	5	74	38	53
Enfield FC Res.	26	13	8	5	62	44	47
Rimington Res.	26	13	6	7	74	37	45
Oswaldtwistle Res.	26	13	5	8	50	35	44
Barrowford C. Res.	26	12	5	9	64	60	41
Rock Rovers Res.	26	10	4	12	54	60	34
Burn. GSOB Res.	26	10	3	13	54	78	33
Stacksteads Res.	26	9	5	12	45	57	32
Pendle Forest Res.	26	5	5	16	48	68	20
Read United Res.	26	3	7	16	37	84	16
Colne Utd Res.	26	3	5	18	38	86	14
Peel Park Res.	26	3	3	20	37	83	12

EAST LINCS COMBINATION
(Teamsport90)

Division One	P	W	D	L	F	A	Pts
Grainthorpe	20	15	3	2	70	20	48
North Somercotes	20	15	2	3	64	20	47
Waltham Tea Gdns	20	14	3	3	68	32	45
AFC Louth	20	10	2	8	49	45	32
Sutton	20	9	3	8	50	41	30
Tetford	20	9	3	8	43	40	30
Manby	20	8	2	10	51	48	26
Alford	20	5	4	11	40	59	19
Newmarket Inn	20	4	5	11	42	58	17
North Thoresby	20	3	2	15	28	80	11
Mablethorpe	20	1	3	16	28	90	6

Division Two	P	W	D	L	F	A	Pts
Louth United Res.	18	16	1	1	71	23	49
A&G Auto Repairs	18	14	0	4	64	20	42
Holton-le-Clay	18	10	3	5	51	39	33
Louth Old Boys	18	9	2	7	57	48	29
Burgh *-4*	18	8	5	5	45	30	25
Donington	18	7	3	8	45	43	24
Sutton Res.	18	7	2	9	39	45	23
N Somercotes Res.	18	4	4	10	34	52	16
Scamblesby	18	3	4	11	31	43	13
Golden Fleece	18	0	0	18	17	111	0

Division Three	P	W	D	L	F	A	Pts
Keelby United	20	18	2	0	115	20	56
Woolpack	20	15	1	4	90	32	46
Barnoldby	20	14	2	4	90	38	44
Theddlethorpe	20	14	0	6	84	52	42
Chapel Swifts	20	13	0	7	95	48	39
Louth OB Res.	20	8	1	11	57	68	25
Mablethorpe Res.	20	8	1	11	46	79	25
Louth Mariners	20	6	0	14	37	69	18
Sutton Colts	20	4	1	15	38	101	13
Ludford	20	2	3	15	30	109	9
Marrowbone & C.	20	2	1	17	30	96	7

Division Four	P	W	D	L	F	A	Pts
Tetney Rovers	18	17	0	1	91	19	51
Healing Hotspurs	18	15	1	2	71	22	46
Woodman	18	10	0	8	55	52	30
PK Construction	18	9	2	7	58	39	29
Sutton Veterans	18	8	3	7	49	54	27
Alford Town Res.	18	5	3	10	37	65	18
Chapel Swifts Res.	18	5	1	12	40	55	16
Samuels	18	4	3	11	40	55	15
Thed'thorpe Res.	18	4	3	11	36	81	15
Holton-le-C. Res.	18	4	2	12	37	72	14

EAST MIDLANDS SENIOR LEAGUE

Premier Division	P	W	D	L	F	A	Pts
Punjab United FC	18	15	1	2	84	16	46
Derby Singh Bros	18	14	0	4	62	30	42
Stretton Village	18	12	3	3	70	27	39

	P	W	D	L	F	A	Pts
Sudbury Park	18	11	2	5	66	40	35
Ambergate	18	11	0	7	41	40	33
Allendon Sports	18	7	1	10	30	51	22
Findern Sports	18	6	1	11	40	58	19
Derby Deaf	18	4	1	13	27	65	13
Ashbourne Town	18	3	1	14	35	58	10
Stanley Common	18	2	0	16	23	93	6

EAST RIDING AMATEUR LEAGUE
(Admiral Signs)

Premier Division	P	W	D	L	F	A	Pts
Crown	20	17	1	2	65	23	52
Sutton Fields Rgrs	20	13	2	5	42	37	41
Eddie Beedle	20	12	2	6	44	30	38
Quaddy Rangers	20	10	2	8	63	42	32
P'fleet Wolf. Res.	20	9	2	9	43	40	29
SC Electrical	20	9	2	9	43	41	29
The Lair	20	6	7	7	44	49	25
AFC West Hull	20	7	3	10	39	48	24
Kingburn Ath. Res.	20	6	4	10	52	56	22
AFC Preston	20	5	4	11	34	44	19
Raine	20	1	1	18	17	76	4

Division One	P	W	D	L	F	A	Pts
AFC Hull	22	17	1	4	107	45	52
Hull Athletic	22	14	2	6	65	48	44
Swiss Cottage	22	12	2	8	68	46	38
Anlaby Park	22	11	5	6	51	40	38
Spring Bank Tigers	22	11	2	9	61	47	35
P. Wolfreton Tigers	22	10	3	9	74	56	33
AFC W. Hull Res.	22	9	5	8	42	43	32
Paull Wanderers	22	8	5	9	50	50	29
Hessle Sp. C. Res.	22	9	2	11	46	62	29
AFC Preston Res.	22	8	4	10	63	70	28
Geoff Wednesday	22	4	5	13	34	67	17
Duke of Wellington	22	1	0	21	24	111	3

Division Two	P	W	D	L	F	A	Pts
Skippers	20	20	0	0	94	17	60
Willerby H. Homes	20	14	1	5	48	24	43
AFC Piper	20	13	1	6	68	48	40
Goodwin	20	10	3	7	70	51	33
South Holderness	20	10	1	9	48	42	31
AFC Malt Shovel	20	9	3	8	39	35	30
AFC Humber	20	7	4	9	55	56	25
Kingburn Ath. A	20	7	2	11	32	45	23
Staks	20	5	5	10	41	54	20
The Courts	20	4	2	14	40	72	14
AFC West Hull A	20	0	0	20	16	107	0

EAST RIDING COUNTY LEAGUE

Premier Division	P	W	D	L	F	A	Pts
Beverley T. Res.	18	12	2	4	40	24	38
Howden Amtrs	18	12	2	4	42	31	38
Viking Raiders	18	12	0	6	57	34	36
Wawne Ferry	18	11	1	6	66	39	34
Goole Goods Off.	18	10	1	7	54	33	31
Holme Rovers	18	6	3	9	32	51	21
Reckitts Res.	18	5	4	9	33	50	19
VIP Comms	18	4	4	10	22	39	16
Sculcoates Res.	18	4	2	12	35	48	14
Easington U. Res.	18	4	1	13	35	67	13

Division One	P	W	D	L	F	A	Pts
Corner Bar	22	17	2	3	71	26	53
Hodgsons	22	16	1	5	51	28	49
North Cave Res.	22	14	3	5	68	42	45
South Cave Utd	22	14	3	5	42	33	45
Lord Nelson Bev.	22	11	0	11	47	42	33
Beverley Town J.	22	10	2	10	37	52	32
Westella & W. J.	22	8	5	9	50	51	29
Gilberdyke	22	7	2	13	46	60	23
Aldborough Utd	22	6	4	12	49	45	22
Haltemprice	22	6	4	12	29	54	22
Sutton Park	22	4	2	16	38	61	14
Brand'burton Res.	22	3	4	15	23	57	13

Division Two	P	W	D	L	F	A	Pts
Trades/Lbr Club	22	18	3	1	67	33	57
AFC Rovers	22	18	2	2	74	32	56
Park Athletic	22	17	3	2	93	20	54
FC Ridings	22	8	5	9	43	43	29
West Hull Amrs	22	9	2	11	36	37	29
Hedon United	22	8	4	10	42	40	28
Leven Mmbrs Club	22	8	3	11	43	47	27
Skidby Millers	22	7	4	11	46	64	25
Withernsea Res.	22	6	4	12	34	71	22
Howden Ams Res.	22	5	3	14	36	65	18
Long Riston Res.	22	5	2	15	40	75	17
Lewis Ashley Serv	22	4	3	15	45	72	15

Division Three	P	W	D	L	F	A	Pts
Cliffe	20	17	1	2	69	21	52
Hedon Rgrs Res.	20	16	3	1	65	24	51
Total Sign S'tions	20	15	3	2	89	36	48
Hornsea T. Res.	20	10	3	7	55	39	33
Skirlaugh	20	9	4	7	58	59	31
Molescroft Rgrs	20	8	5	7	61	52	29
Plexus Networking	20	4	4	12	42	59	16
Mkt Weighton Utd	20	2	10	8	25	50	16
Patrington Res.	20	3	3	14	31	70	12
Leven MC Res.	20	3	2	15	26	75	11
Shiptonthorpe Utd	20	2	4	14	27	63	10

Division Four	P	W	D	L	F	A	Pts
Waterloo	22	18	2	2	92	23	56
Wawne F. Res.	22	16	5	1	67	31	53
Roos	22	17	1	4	82	25	52
South Cave Res.	22	11	1	10	51	39	34
Brandesburton A	22	10	4	8	54	46	34
Viking Rdrs Res.	22	9	4	9	37	43	31
North Newbald	22	9	2	11	41	51	29
Molescroft R. Res.	22	7	3	12	42	62	24
Holme Rov. Res.	22	5	3	14	37	60	18
Eastrington Vill.	22	4	6	12	36	70	18
Howden Town	22	5	3	14	32	74	18
Easington Utd Cas	22	3	2	17	24	71	11

Division Five	P	W	D	L	F	A	Pts
Haltemprice Rgrs	18	17	0	1	82	33	51
Hedon Rgrs Jnrs	18	14	0	4	66	29	42
Gilberdyke Res.	18	13	0	5	71	35	39
M. Weighton Res.	18	12	0	6	55	45	36
Cliffe Res.	18	10	1	7	61	43	31
Withernsea A	18	7	2	9	33	52	23
Hornsea Town A	18	5	0	13	40	56	15
Skirlaugh Res.	18	4	2	12	27	51	14
Shiptonthorpe Res.	18	3	1	14	32	54	10
Brandesburton B	18	2	0	16	31	100	6

EAST SUSSEX LEAGUE
(K & P Motoring World)

Premier Division	P	W	D	L	F	A	Pts
St Leonards Social	16	10	4	2	40	19	34
Hollington United	16	9	3	4	43	29	30
Peasmarsh & Iden	16	9	2	5	35	21	29
Sedlescombe	16	7	3	6	30	25	24
Hooe Sports	16	7	2	7	36	51	23
J. Club Tackleway	16	6	2	8	36	31	20
Punnetts Town	16	6	2	8	24	32	20
Peche Hill Select	16	3	7	6	28	33	16
Rock-a-Nore	16	2	1	13	14	45	7

Division One	P	W	D	L	F	A	Pts
Q Ball	22	21	1	0	90	21	64
Polegate Town	22	17	2	3	68	28	53
Icklesham Cas.	22	10	3	9	66	55	33
Hollington U. Res.	22	10	3	9	41	45	33
Bexhill AAC	22	9	5	8	58	48	32
Athletico	22	9	5	8	60	53	32
Wheatsheaf	22	10	1	11	48	48	31
Catsfield	22	9	3	10	48	62	30
Crowhurst	22	4	8	10	54	67	20
Mountfield United	22	6	2	14	29	55	20
Ninfield United	22	5	2	15	31	64	17
Ticehurst	22	4	1	17	31	78	13

Division Two	P	W	D	L	F	A	Pts
Wadhurst United	22	16	2	4	59	20	50
White Knight	22	15	3	4	60	29	48
Robertsbridge U.	22	13	6	3	52	25	45
Herstmonceux	22	13	4	5	52	35	43
Old Town Athletic	22	9	7	6	57	43	34
Northiam	22	9	3	10	42	44	30
Hastings Rgrs *+3*	22	6	8	8	31	36	29
P'marsh/I. Res. *-3*	22	10	0	12	48	48	27
Sandhurst	22	5	5	12	21	55	20
Battle Baptists	22	4	5	13	21	42	17
Hawkhurst Res.	22	4	2	16	30	52	14
Magham Down	22	2	7	13	25	69	13

Division Three	P	W	D	L	F	A	Pts
Hurst	22	19	1	2	80	22	58
Cinque Ports	22	17	2	3	73	40	53
Red Lion	22	13	2	7	49	33	41
E'bne Dynamos	22	11	5	6	52	35	38
Beulah Baptists	22	12	2	8	55	49	38
Battle Rangers	22	12	2	8	45	47	38
Hollington Utd A	22	9	0	13	55	59	27
Mayfield	22	7	3	12	32	54	24
Hastings R. Res.	22	7	2	13	35	59	23
E'bne Fishermen	22	7	0	15	40	55	21
Pebsham Sibex	22	5	1	16	28	55	16
Ninfield Utd Res.	22	3	0	19	13	49	9

Division Four	P	W	D	L	F	A	Pts
Nelson Tigers	20	17	1	2	118	31	52
E'bourne Galaxy	20	16	0	4	70	26	48
Crowhurst Res	20	14	0	6	67	38	42
Cranbrook Town	20	10	1	9	54	41	31
Icklesham C. Res.	20	9	2	9	54	57	29
St Helens	20	8	3	9	57	57	27
Burwash	20	7	5	8	47	51	26
Bexhill AAC Res.	20	7	2	11	41	52	23
JC Tack'way Res.	20	5	2	13	39	76	17
Victoria Baptists	20	4	3	13	36	78	15
Peasmarsh/Iden A	20	2	3	15	19	95	9

The Wilton - record expunged

Division Five	P	W	D	L	F	A	Pts
Travaux	22	20	2	0	87	34	62
Punnetts T. Res.	22	15	1	6	71	39	46
Orington	22	14	2	6	75	38	44
Sedlesc'mbe Res.	22	12	4	6	55	37	40
Peche Hill S. Res.	22	10	3	9	41	36	33
Northiam Res.	22	10	2	10	68	69	32
Nelson Tgrs Res.	22	10	2	10	59	61	32
Westfield A	22	8	3	11	51	52	27
Hastings Elite	22	7	1	14	35	68	22
Heathfield Hot.	22	7	1	14	37	72	22
Mountfield U. Res.	22	5	1	16	49	53	16
JC Tackleway A	22	3	0	19	35	104	9

Division Six	P	W	D	L	F	A	Pts
Guestling Rgrs	22	17	3	2	72	26	54
Eastbourne Ath.	22	14	4	4	52	27	46
Battle Bapts Res.	22	14	1	7	52	40	43
Wadhurst Res.	22	13	3	6	51	27	42
HG Aerospace *+3*	22	9	2	11	49	60	32
White Knight Res.	22	8	2	12	50	49	26
Catsfield Res.	22	7	5	10	49	64	26
Magham D. Res.	22	8	1	13	57	54	25
Robertsbdge Res.	22	6	5	11	43	51	23
Herst'ceux Res.	22	6	5	11	31	57	23
Sandhurst Res.	22	5	6	11	37	61	21
Ltle Common A *-3*	22	4	5	13	50	77	14

ESKVALE & CLEVELAND LEAGUE
(Wilf Noble)

	P	W	D	L	F	A	Pts
Lingdale	28	22	4	2	130	29	70
Boosbeck St Aid.	28	18	6	4	105	43	60
Goldsborough	28	18	6	4	95	41	60
Loftus Athletic	28	16	6	6	102	55	54
Hollybush United	28	16	4	8	80	64	52
Stokesley SC A	28	15	4	9	80	69	49
Lealholm	28	13	4	11	71	58	43
Gt Ayton Utd Res.	28	12	5	11	76	64	41
Carlin How	28	11	4	13	64	56	37
Lingdale United	28	9	8	11	88	79	35
Brotton Rail. Arms	28	8	7	13	51	82	31
Staithes Athletic	28	9	3	16	56	78	30
Fox Inn	28	7	2	19	35	81	23
N Skelton Bulls Hd	28	2	2	24	25	143	8
Boosbeck United	28	0	3	25	19	135	3

ESSEX BUSINESS HOUSES LEAGUE

Premier Division	P	W	D	L	F	A	Pts
Loass	20	14	2	4	61	25	44
Flanders	20	13	3	4	49	32	42
Wadham Lodge	20	13	0	7	61	34	39
Brampton Park	20	12	2	6	53	32	38
Toby	20	10	4	6	44	35	34
Old Barkabbeyans	20	7	6	7	34	32	27
Rainham WMC	20	7	4	9	32	51	25
Collier Row Snrs	20	5	4	11	20	41	19
Bancroft	20	4	3	13	24	45	15
AFC Kings	20	4	3	13	22	47	15
Melbourne Sports	20	4	3	13	23	49	15

Euro Dagenham - record expunged
Newham Borough - record expunged

Division One	P	W	D	L	F	A	Pts
West Essex	22	18	1	3	59	29	55
West Green	22	15	3	4	75	40	48
Platinium	22	15	2	5	72	33	47
Ultrachem TKO	22	12	4	6	55	35	40
Barking Borough	22	10	4	8	49	42	34
Stags Head	22	10	2	10	48	45	32
Old Barks Res.	22	7	6	9	34	32	27
Asianos	22	7	5	10	29	52	26
Snaresbrook	22	5	7	10	39	48	22
Collier Row S. Res.	22	5	3	14	32	82	18
Harold Park	22	4	5	13	32	49	17
S. Sabha Barking	22	1	4	17	26	63	7

Division Two	P	W	D	L	F	A	Pts
Juva	18	12	3	3	56	40	39
Barking BS *+2*	18	8	5	5	49	38	31
Loass Res.	18	7	5	6	40	39	26
Rush Green *-1*	18	7	5	6	47	39	25
Allied Rec	18	7	1	10	37	40	22
FC Romania	18	6	3	9	30	46	21
O Barkabbeyans B	18	3	4	11	27	44	13

ESSEX & HERTS BORDER COMBINATION

	P	W	D	L	F	A	Pts
Grays Ath. Res.	24	17	2	5	73	44	53
Gt Wakering Res.	24	17	1	6	79	45	52
Heybridge S. Res.	24	15	5	4	74	32	50
Brentwood T. Res.	24	15	4	5	58	26	49
Thurrock Res.	24	14	4	6	64	34	46
Waltham A. Res.	24	13	3	8	45	37	42
Canvey Is. Res.	24	13	2	9	72	51	41
Barking Res.	24	9	2	13	48	65	29
Stansted Res.	24	8	4	12	43	56	28
Concord R. Res.	24	8	3	13	43	61	27
Clapton Res.	24	4	1	19	37	82	13
Basildon Utd Res.	24	2	4	18	37	84	10
Bowers/P'sea Res.	24	1	5	18	21	77	8

FALMOUTH-HELSTON LEAGUE

Division One	P	W	D	L	F	A	Pts
Mawnan	30	22	5	3	93	29	71
Chacewater *+3*	30	18	3	9	96	58	60
Truro City A	30	19	3	8	77	41	60
Perranwell Res.	30	17	8	5	80	54	59
Pendeeen Rovers	30	18	3	9	71	47	57
Falmouth Ath. *-3*	30	16	5	9	83	58	50
St Keverne	30	14	1	15	78	67	43
Holmans SC Res.	30	9	11	10	54	51	38
Penryn Ath. Res.	30	11	5	14	56	62	38
Mousehole Res.	30	10	7	13	56	62	37
Falmouth Town A	30	8	11	11	62	67	35
St Agnes Res. *-1*	30	8	7	15	53	72	33
St Day Res. *-1*	30	10	1	19	43	101	28
Falmouth Albion	30	7	5	18	43	83	26
Helston Ath. Res.	30	8	2	20	42	84	26
Stithians	30	6	1	23	43	94	19

Division Two	P	W	D	L	F	A	Pts
Constantine	28	20	3	5	86	37	63
Mawnan Res.	28	17	4	7	63	37	55
Camborne Park	28	14	4	10	65	56	46
Troon Res.	28	14	3	11	69	54	45
Porthleven Rgrs	28	13	5	10	66	60	44
Lizard Argyle	28	13	4	11	54	56	43
Perranporth Res.	28	13	2	13	56	55	41
Rosudgeon-Kenn.	28	11	6	11	71	69	39
RNAS C'rose Res.	28	11	4	13	62	56	37
Hayle A	28	10	7	11	55	58	37
Carharrack	28	11	4	13	55	64	37
Frogpool-Cusgarne	28	11	3	14	53	70	36
Wendron United A	28	10	4	14	52	64	34
Marazion Blues	28	7	6	15	36	59	27
Lanner	28	4	3	21	42	90	15

Mawgan - record expunged

Division Three	P	W	D	L	F	A	Pts
Trispen Res.	28	25	2	1	108	30	77
Mullion Res.	28	25	2	1	96	20	77
Wendron United B	28	20	3	5	126	42	63
Penryn Athletic B	28	17	5	6	104	54	56
Cury	28	17	4	7	108	68	55
Falm'th Ath. Res.	28	17	2	9	80	52	53
St Day A	28	13	2	13	59	91	41
Hayle B	28	11	4	13	75	69	37
Lizard Argyle Res.	28	10	3	15	55	74	33
Ruan Minor	28	9	4	15	65	64	31
Constantine Res.	28	9	3	16	57	74	30
Carharrack Res.	28	6	0	22	44	113	18
Rosudgeon-K. Res.	28	5	2	21	45	114	17
Stithians Res.	28	4	2	22	38	112	14
Frogpool-C. Res.	28	3	0	25	51	134	9

Helston Athletic A - record expunged

FURNESS PREMIER LEAGUE

Premier Division	P	W	D	L	F	A	Pts
Dalton Utd Res.	28	20	5	3	68	23	65
Vickerstown Res.	28	20	3	5	83	38	63
Hawcoat Pk Res.	28	17	2	9	72	39	53
Millom Res.	28	16	2	10	61	54	50
Kirkby United	28	16	1	11	74	52	49
Furness C. Res.	28	13	5	10	67	48	44
Holker OB Res.	28	11	9	8	45	52	42
Barrow Island *-3*	28	12	6	10	65	48	39
Bootle FC	28	11	4	13	65	59	37
Barrow Celtic	28	11	2	15	64	86	35
Haverigg United	28	9	6	13	46	50	33
Furness R. Res.	28	8	5	15	48	73	29
Askam Utd Res.	28	7	5	16	55	80	26
Walney Is. Res.	28	5	4	19	24	69	19
Furness Ath. *-6*	28	2	5	21	35	101	5

Division One	P	W	D	L	F	A	Pts
Barrow Wdrs	26	20	6	0	122	29	66
Crooklands Res.	26	20	3	3	109	38	63
SDO	26	17	2	7	100	42	53
Hawcoat Pk A	26	15	3	8	64	51	48
Vickerstown A	26	14	2	10	68	50	44
Furness Rov. A	26	12	4	10	55	62	40
Dalton United A	26	9	7	10	40	45	34
Millom A	26	10	2	14	57	66	32
GSK Ulv'ston Res.	26	8	4	14	48	77	28
Furness Cav. A	26	7	6	13	34	66	27
Askam United A	26	8	3	15	55	98	27
Haverigg U. Res.	26	7	4	15	34	70	25
Walney Island A	26	5	2	19	33	78	17
Holker Old B. A	26	5	2	19	35	82	17

GAINSBOROUGH & DISTRICT LEAGUE

Division One	P	W	D	L	F	A	Pts
AAFC Friendship	21	17	2	2	82	15	53
White Lion	21	16	2	3	87	26	50
Harworth Colliery	21	14	0	7	68	51	42
Smiffys	21	13	1	7	66	34	40
Rampton Hosp.	21	8	3	10	40	48	27
Retford T. Res.	21	4	3	14	25	70	15
Morton Amateurs	21	4	2	15	31	92	14
East Drayton	21	1	1	19	27	91	4

Division Two	P	W	D	L	F	A	Pts
Mattersey	16	14	1	1	46	17	43
Bridon	16	10	2	4	40	21	32
Saxilby Ath. *+3*	16	6	3	7	28	30	24
Sun Inn Wheatley	16	6	3	7	26	35	21
Harworth Col. Jnrs	16	5	5	6	31	32	20
Ropery Inn *-3*	16	7	1	8	35	24	19
Epworth Town A	16	5	3	8	46	32	18
Wroot	16	4	3	9	26	39	15
Marshalls Sports	16	3	3	10	20	68	12

GLOUCESTERSHIRE NORTHERN SENIOR LEAGUE

(Errea South West)

Division One	P	W	D	L	F	A	Pts
Longlevens	30	21	6	3	83	34	69
Brimscombe & T.	30	20	4	6	79	35	64
Kingswood	30	20	3	7	74	40	63
Broadwell Amats	30	18	4	8	62	33	58
Sharpness	30	17	7	6	54	25	58
Dursley Town	30	17	6	7	59	41	57
Star	30	12	5	13	46	52	41
Tetbury Town	30	12	4	14	57	53	40
Lydbrook Athletic	30	12	4	14	46	48	40
Shortwood Res.	30	11	5	14	53	52	38
Gala Wilton	30	11	3	16	59	65	36
Ramblers	30	7	9	14	40	60	30
Cheltenham CS	30	8	3	19	41	91	27
Brockworth Alb.	30	6	5	19	43	73	23
Wotton Rovers	30	6	4	20	34	76	22
Cam Bulldogs	30	3	6	21	28	80	15

Division Two	P	W	D	L	F	A	Pts
Stonehouse Town	30	23	4	3	93	30	73
Barnwood United	30	20	4	6	79	27	64
Bredon	30	19	3	8	55	32	60
Winchcombe T.	30	16	4	10	51	37	52
Harrow Hill Res.	30	15	3	12	60	47	48
Newton Hth/Stroud	30	13	7	10	56	43	46
Chalford	30	13	5	12	57	44	44
Soudley	30	12	8	10	62	65	44
Smiths Athletic *-2*	30	13	6	11	68	56	43
Longford *-3*	30	11	7	12	45	53	37
Hatherley Rgrs *-1*	30	10	6	14	51	80	35
Bourton Rovers *-3*	30	10	7	13	47	51	34
Tidenham *-3*	30	11	4	15	47	55	34
Viney St Swithins	30	8	3	19	46	59	27
Mitcheldean	30	8	2	20	37	69	26
Charfield	30	0	3	27	20	138	3

GRANTHAM & DISTRICT LEAGUE

Premier Division	P	W	D	L	F	A	Pts
Buckminster Utd	26	19	6	1	90	36	63
Greyhounders	26	19	5	2	60	25	62
Colsterworth Utd	26	19	4	3	98	41	61
Ruskington Rov.	26	18	4	4	92	41	58
RHP Newark	26	15	6	5	71	44	51
Barrowby	26	10	5	11	62	62	35
Barkston & Syston	26	9	6	11	46	67	33
Ancaster Rovers	26	9	2	15	38	61	29
Harrowby U. Res.	26	7	4	15	56	71	25
Croxton	26	6	7	13	35	58	25
Whatton United	26	7	1	18	56	77	22
Gran.Squash Club	26	6	4	16	51	76	22
Three Gab. Colts	26	6	3	17	40	59	21
Balderton Old B.	26	1	5	20	36	113	8

Division One	P	W	D	L	F	A	Pts
Bottesford Res. *-3*	20	17	0	3	91	27	48
Red Lion Bourne	20	16	0	4	85	25	48
Lord Harrowby	20	13	2	5	69	45	41
Heckington Millers	20	13	1	6	76	45	40
Caythorpe	20	9	3	8	64	61	30
Skillington	20	9	1	10	64	55	28
Sky Blues	20	8	1	11	54	72	25
Morton	20	6	6	8	49	51	24
Ancaster R. Res.	20	5	1	14	26	77	16
Baston	20	4	3	13	30	77	15
Pointon Colts *+3*	20	1	0	19	24	97	6

GRAVESEND LEAGUE

Premier Division	P	W	D	L	F	A	Pts
Craggs Farm	12	9	1	2	38	8	28
Old Prince Orange	12	8	2	2	52	13	26
Viewpoint	12	8	2	2	36	15	26
Lullingstone Castle	12	6	0	6	33	31	18
AFC Welsh Tavern	12	3	3	6	30	35	12
Swan Valley	12	3	1	8	15	48	10
Horton Kirby	12	0	1	11	6	60	1

Division One	P	W	D	L	F	A	Pts
Woodlands Ath.	16	14	0	2	70	21	42
Stone Club & Inst.	16	9	2	5	49	34	29
Meopham	16	9	2	5	40	30	29
NK Aces	16	9	1	6	42	29	28
Craggs Farm Res.	16	8	3	5	34	36	27
Bean	16	7	1	8	35	37	22
Viewpoint Res.	16	6	0	10	30	34	18
The Rising Eagles	16	3	3	10	29	59	12
Peacock Celtic	16	0	2	14	24	73	2

Division Two	P	W	D	L	F	A	Pts
Earl Grey	22	20	0	2	95	19	60
Culverstone Utd	22	16	3	3	88	32	51
Fleetdown Utd B	22	16	3	3	87	34	51
AFC Welsh T. Res.	22	12	2	8	65	46	38
Real Man of Kent	22	11	4	7	58	56	37
Ash Green	22	11	3	8	60	46	36
Fleetway Printers	22	10	1	11	63	57	31
AZ 82	22	7	2	13	66	66	23
Oakfield	22	6	5	11	50	74	23
Joydens Wood	22	4	2	16	40	110	14
FC Stone	22	3	3	16	38	80	12
Meopham Res.	22	1	2	19	33	123	5

GREAT YARMOUTH & DISTRICT LEAGUE

Division One	P	W	D	L	F	A	Pts
Catfield	18	17	1	0	98	14	52
MK United	18	15	2	1	99	22	47
Reedham	18	10	2	6	62	54	32
Arches *-6*	18	11	1	6	51	25	31
GY International	18	6	5	7	33	35	23
Gunton	18	7	1	10	45	65	22
Golfers Arms	18	6	1	11	40	72	19

Lacon Arms	18	5	2	11	49	69	17
Tramway	18	2	1	15	26	80	7
Caister A -3	18	2	2	14	28	95	5

Division Two	P	W	D	L	F	A	Pts
Albion (GY)	24	21	2	1	135	22	65
Shrublands	24	16	1	7	93	70	49
MK United Res.	24	15	2	7	66	42	47
Gt Yarm. Peelers	24	13	4	7	69	54	43
Hemsby Res.	24	13	3	8	67	47	42
Norfolk & Chance	24	11	5	8	58	60	38
South Yarmouth	24	10	3	11	70	58	33
Prostar Windows	24	9	5	10	65	65	32
Paperclip	24	9	1	14	55	73	28
Gorleston Wdrs	24	7	5	12	66	71	26
Gt Yarmouth Utd	24	7	1	16	43	86	22
Carpathians	24	4	3	17	40	92	15
Martham A	24	3	1	20	29	116	10

GRIMSBY LEAGUE

Division One	P	W	D	L	F	A	Pts
Harvest Pet Prods	12	11	1	0	53	6	34
Nunsthorpe Tav.	12	9	1	2	51	21	28
Number One Pub	12	9	0	3	39	18	27
Imm. Bluestone	12	4	0	8	10	22	12
Buddies II	12	3	0	9	23	44	9
Drywall Athletic	12	2	1	9	16	38	7
MRF	12	2	1	9	21	64	7

GUILDFORD & WOKING ALLIANCE

Premier Division	P	W	D	L	F	A	Pts
Millmead	22	16	3	3	70	36	51
AFC Bourne	22	14	2	6	54	38	44
Hambledon	22	13	2	7	38	29	41
AFC Bedfont G.	22	11	5	6	55	38	38
Emmanuel	22	9	4	9	53	47	31
Lightwater United	22	8	7	7	41	43	31
Pirbright Sports	22	8	5	9	46	47	29
Holmbury St Mary	22	7	4	11	47	51	25
Windlesham	22	7	4	11	35	47	25
Milford & Witley A	22	6	4	12	32	63	22
Hersham	22	5	3	14	41	63	18
Addlestone Town	22	3	7	12	34	44	16

Division One	P	W	D	L	F	A	Pts
Shepperton FB	18	15	3	0	62	17	48
Surrey Athletic	18	15	2	1	65	19	47
Godalming Utd	18	7	5	6	46	48	26
New Haw Wdrs	18	6	6	6	41	42	24
Univ. of Surrey A	18	6	4	8	38	43	22
W. Byfleet Albion	18	5	4	9	24	31	19
Weybrook Wdrs	18	5	3	10	27	32	18
Guild. City Wey. A	18	4	5	9	32	44	17
Dunsfold	18	3	6	9	27	57	15
Windlesham Res.	18	3	4	11	34	63	13

Division Two	P	W	D	L	F	A	Pts
AFC Woburn Arms	20	17	0	3	85	40	51
Knaphill A	20	14	1	5	60	34	43
Spelthorne Spts A	20	12	2	6	57	33	38
AFC Hersham	20	12	1	7	60	33	37
Emmanuel Res.	20	10	3	7	43	39	33
Oatlands	20	9	5	6	42	31	32
AFC Gomshall	20	9	1	10	54	55	28
Lightwater Res.	20	6	2	12	39	55	20
Mytchett Rangers	20	6	2	12	35	71	20
Staines Lam. B	20	2	3	15	35	57	9
Milford & Witley B	20	2	2	16	31	93	8

Division Three	P	W	D	L	F	A	Pts
AFC B'font G. Res.	18	13	1	4	60	26	40
Elstead	18	11	2	5	50	23	35
Cobham United	18	11	2	5	49	27	35
FC Shepperton	18	11	2	5	48	37	35
AFC Chilworth	18	11	1	6	57	33	34
New Haw W. Res.	18	9	0	9	51	43	27
Guildford Park	18	8	1	9	39	33	25
Cranleigh A	18	6	2	10	29	44	20
Shalford Youth	18	3	2	13	21	55	11
Weybrook W. Res.	18	0	1	17	14	97	1

Division Four Nth	P	W	D	L	F	A	Pts
Keens Pk Rgrs	22	19	1	2	74	26	58
Bed. Green Soc N	22	16	2	4	85	54	50
Egham Crick. C.	22	16	1	5	64	41	49
Woking/Horsell A	22	14	4	4	60	35	46
AFC Crown/Anch.	22	13	3	6	58	29	42
Ripley Village A	22	11	2	9	44	41	35
AFC Guildford	22	8	2	12	47	58	26
Christian Woking	22	8	1	13	42	55	25
Worp. Phoenix B	22	5	4	13	38	55	19
DJST	22	5	1	16	45	75	16
Surrey Ath. Res.	22	3	1	18	41	81	10
Byfleet	22	3	0	19	33	81	9

Division Four Sth	P	W	D	L	F	A	Pts
Bed. G. Social Sth	18	14	1	3	73	31	43
Holmbury SM Res.	18	13	1	4	62	28	40
Merrow A	18	10	4	4	69	37	34
Worp. Phoenix A	18	9	5	4	62	33	32
Hambledon Res.	18	6	5	7	41	44	23
AFC Bourne Res.	18	6	4	8	29	42	22
Elstead Res.	18	5	5	8	37	37	20
Milford & Witley C	18	4	5	9	32	57	17
Millmead Res.	18	3	5	10	30	60	14
Dunsfold Res.	18	1	3	14	19	85	6

HALIFAX & DISTRICT LEAGUE

(Ziggy's Spice House)

Premier Division	P	W	D	L	F	A	Pts
Luddendenfoot	22	15	3	4	66	24	48
Hebden Royd RS	22	13	4	5	60	38	43
Greetland	22	12	3	7	50	33	39
Ryburn United	22	9	7	6	38	34	34
Shelf United	22	10	3	9	39	52	33
Midgley United +3	22	8	4	10	48	48	31
Elland United	22	9	4	9	37	40	31
Warley Rangers	22	7	7	8	38	40	28
Halifax Irish Cent.	22	6	8	8	46	44	26
Siddal Athletic -3	22	7	6	9	42	49	24
Sowerby United	22	5	4	13	48	70	19
Stainland United	22	3	3	16	29	69	12

Division One	P	W	D	L	F	A	Pts
Holmfield	18	12	2	4	57	35	38
Calder	18	12	2	4	53	31	38
Hebden Royd Res.	18	10	4	4	47	36	34
Northowram -3	18	11	2	5	57	45	32
Stump Cross +3	18	9	1	8	52	37	31
Mixenden United	18	6	4	8	27	38	22
Denholme United	18	6	2	10	55	65	20
Salem	18	5	2	11	50	66	17
Martin's Nest -3	18	5	2	11	44	60	14
Brigh'se OB A +3	18	3	1	14	28	57	13

Division Two	P	W	D	L	F	A	Pts
Sowerby Bridge	20	15	2	3	80	38	47
Siddal Ath. Res.	20	11	3	6	66	38	36
Kingston	20	11	0	9	54	58	33
Elland Allstars	20	9	3	8	59	59	30
Ryburn Res. +2	20	7	4	9	52	55	27
Junction FC	20	7	4	9	48	61	25
Halifax IC Res. -4	20	7	7	6	48	44	24
Engineers	20	6	5	9	45	50	23
Copley United +3	20	6	2	12	54	86	23
Shelf United Res.	20	6	4	10	48	57	22
Warley Rgrs Res.	20	4	8	8	41	49	20

Division Three	P	W	D	L	F	A	Pts
Volunteer Arms	20	17	1	2	87	39	52
AFC Crossleys	20	15	2	3	99	50	47
Halifax Athletic	20	12	3	5	75	32	39
Sowerby B. Res.	20	12	3	5	68	40	39
Ludd'foot Res.	20	10	3	7	73	56	33
Midgley Utd Res.	20	9	2	9	41	44	29
Wadsworth Utd	20	7	3	10	49	52	24
Sowerby U. Res.	20	7	1	12	56	86	22
D'holme Res. +3	20	2	5	13	49	84	14
Calder Res. -3	20	4	1	15	26	80	10
Salem Res.	20	2	2	16	32	92	8

HARROGATE & DISTRICT LEAGUE

Premier Division	P	W	D	L	F	A	Pts
Thirsk Falcons	26	23	2	1	122	25	71
Pateley Bridge	26	20	2	4	71	37	62
Westbrook YMCA	26	14	4	8	50	48	46
Kirk Deighton Rgrs	26	12	7	7	59	48	43
Spa Athletic	26	13	3	10	63	54	42
Bedale Town	26	11	5	10	69	54	38
Kirkby Malzeard	26	10	6	10	57	55	36
Burley Trojans	26	8	5	13	55	62	29
Harlow Hill	26	8	5	13	43	69	29
Eccleshill Utd Res.	26	9	1	16	56	72	28
Sherwood	26	8	3	15	47	77	27
Otley Town A	26	7	3	16	45	62	24
Bramham	26	5	7	14	53	91	22
Pannal Sports	26	5	5	16	39	75	20

Division One	P	W	D	L	F	A	Pts
Harold Styans	24	21	0	3	97	43	63
Otley Rovers	24	17	2	5	59	28	53
Killinghall Nmds	24	15	0	9	82	60	45
Masham	24	13	2	9	62	65	41
Beckwithshaw Sts	24	12	4	8	65	49	40
Knaresboro. Celtic	24	11	5	8	73	57	38
Bramhope	24	9	4	11	63	52	31
Clifford	24	9	4	11	65	75	31
Pool Res.	24	9	3	12	58	67	30
Kirk Deighton Res.	24	8	1	15	56	83	25
Guiseley Red Lion	24	6	6	12	44	42	24
Addingham	24	5	4	15	39	80	19
Dalton Athletic	24	3	1	20	52	114	10

Silsden Res. - record expunged

Division Two	P	W	D	L	F	A	Pts
Leeds City A	22	20	1	1	89	14	61
Thirsk Falc. Res.	22	16	2	4	74	31	50
Harold Styans Res.	22	12	4	6	49	42	40
W'bk YMCA Res.	22	11	5	6	55	36	38
Harlow Hill Res.	22	10	4	8	44	54	34
Pannal Srts Res.	22	10	1	11	42	48	31
Beck'shaw Res.	22	8	4	10	36	53	28
Wigton Moor	22	6	8	8	46	51	26
Spa Athletic Res.	22	5	6	11	29	64	21
Sherwood Res.	22	5	4	13	26	29	19
Boroughbridge A	22	4	1	17	28	70	13
Burley Troj. Res.	22	2	6	14	23	49	12

Ripon City A - record expunged

Division Three	P	W	D	L	F	A	Pts
Wetherby Ath. A	26	18	3	5	119	36	57
Bramham Res.	26	15	7	4	83	44	52
Brafferton Rgrs	26	16	3	7	79	55	51
K. Malzeard Res.	26	16	3	7	76	57	51
Pool A	26	14	4	8	73	50	46
Catterick Village	26	11	5	10	57	47	38
Ripon Red Arrows	26	11	4	11	66	79	37
Helperby United	26	10	4	12	72	93	34
Otley Rovers Res.	26	11	0	15	44	73	33
Hampsthwaite Utd	26	8	6	12	59	73	30
Pannal Sports A	26	8	3	15	61	82	27
Thirsk Falcons A	26	8	2	16	57	75	26
Pateley Bdge Res.	26	7	3	16	54	93	24
Addingham Res.	26	3	5	18	49	92	14

HARTLEPOOL CHURCH & DISTRICT LEAGUE

(Hartlepool Snooker)

Premier Division	P	W	D	L	F	A	Pts
Raglan	26	23	2	1	117	29	71
Gillens Arms	26	18	7	1	116	32	61
Hartlepool Res.	26	19	2	5	108	48	59
Headland Level 6	26	16	1	9	92	67	49
Seaton -3	26	14	5	7	84	58	44
Chester -3	26	14	2	10	98	72	41
Rileys MBM	26	13	2	11	80	77	41
Sandersons Rem.	26	11	4	11	77	70	37
Owton Manor SC	26	8	8	10	59	72	32
Fens Htl Stranton	26	9	2	15	52	82	29
St James -3	26	8	3	15	64	90	24
A & N Evans -3	26	6	2	18	58	102	17
Hartlepool Coz	26	2	0	24	47	138	6
Greenw'd Rov. -3	26	0	2	24	48	163	-1

Mason & Gerald Martin - record expunged

HEREFORDSHIRE LEAGUE

(Hereford Times)

Premier Division	P	W	D	L	F	A	Pts
Westfields Res.	26	19	2	5	94	35	59
Sutton United FC	26	16	5	5	82	46	53
Ewyas Harold	26	15	7	4	72	39	52
Woofferton	26	14	5	7	66	39	47
Bromyard Res. -3	26	14	4	8	56	44	43
Wellington Res.	26	13	3	10	50	41	42
Hinton	26	9	11	6	53	45	38
H'ford Lads Club	26	8	7	11	51	51	31
Leominster Town	26	9	2	15	52	58	29
Ledbury T. Res.	26	9	2	15	37	54	29
Ross Town	26	8	4	14	51	57	28
Peg'sus J. Res. -6	26	7	4	15	38	66	19
Fownhope -3	26	6	3	17	32	98	18
Kington Town	26	3	5	18	38	99	14

Division One	P	W	D	L	F	A	Pts
Holme Lacy	22	18	3	1	78	30	57
Ewyas H. Res. *-3*	22	18	1	3	77	45	52
Weston *-6*	22	14	2	6	66	44	38
Wellington Colts	22	12	1	9	62	34	37
Hay St M. Res.	22	11	4	7	59	37	37
Stoke Prior *-3*	22	12	1	9	67	33	34
Bartestree	22	10	1	11	42	47	31
Woofferton Res. *-3*	22	9	3	10	52	49	27
Shobdon	22	6	1	15	38	59	19
Fownhope Res. *-3*	22	6	2	14	21	83	17
Lads Club Colts *-6*	22	4	2	16	37	81	8
Burghill	22	1	1	20	17	74	4

Division Two	P	W	D	L	F	A	Pts
Leintwardine	18	12	4	2	68	23	40
Hampton Pk Rgrs	18	12	4	2	49	18	40
Dore Valley	18	11	2	5	40	27	35
Toros	18	9	2	7	37	36	29
Weobley	18	8	3	7	35	26	27
Orcop Juniors	18	6	6	6	39	35	24
Pegasus Colts *-3*	18	7	4	7	39	50	22
Ledbury T. Colts	18	6	2	10	44	48	20
Kington Town Res.	18	3	3	12	27	58	12
Bartestree Res.	18	1	0	17	12	69	3

Division Three	P	W	D	L	F	A	Pts
Hinton Res.	22	18	2	2	76	23	56
Holme Lacy Res.	22	15	3	4	70	31	48
Kingstone	22	14	3	5	79	52	45
Bucknell	22	13	5	4	69	38	44
Pencombe	22	11	2	9	58	47	35
Leominster Res.	22	10	4	8	41	46	34
H'fd Civil Service	22	9	1	12	46	56	28
Holmer	22	8	2	12	46	42	26
Polska PGL	22	7	0	15	50	75	21
Presteigne Colts	22	6	0	16	33	83	18
Weston Res.	22	4	2	16	26	57	14
Orleton Colts	22	4	2	16	49	93	14

HERTFORD & DISTRICT LEAGUE

Premier Division	P	W	D	L	F	A	Pts
Westmill	22	17	3	2	60	25	37
Bengeo Trinity	22	16	3	3	55	29	35
Greenbury U.	22	15	4	3	66	28	34
Waltham Ab. A	22	11	3	8	51	43	25
Goffs Oak	22	8	4	10	38	48	20
Elizabeth Allen OB	22	8	3	11	38	48	19
Baldock Cannon	22	8	3	11	35	50	19
Hertford Heath	22	8	2	12	39	53	18
Buntingford Wdrs	22	6	5	11	35	43	17
Thundridge United	22	5	4	13	25	32	14
Harlow Link	22	6	2	14	45	68	14
Inter	22	4	4	14	33	53	12

Division One	P	W	D	L	F	A	Pts
Broxb'ne Badgers	26	21	4	1	93	17	46
Royston Town A	26	17	3	6	95	46	37
Cottered	26	16	4	6	67	39	36
Hertford Celtic	26	15	3	8	77	51	33
Waltham Abbey B	26	13	2	11	68	49	28
Much Hadham	26	13	2	11	64	59	28
Wodson Park	26	11	6	9	48	45	28
Watton-at-Stone	26	11	4	11	72	61	26
County Hall Rgrs	26	9	8	9	56	69	26
Saracens	26	8	7	11	52	52	23
Bengeo T. Res.	26	6	6	14	34	53	18
Mangrove	26	4	4	18	27	83	12
Eliz. Allen Res.	26	5	2	19	41	109	12
Westmill Res.	26	3	5	18	28	89	11

Division Two	P	W	D	L	F	A	Pts
Oracle C'ponents	26	23	1	2	120	27	47
Baldock C. Res.	26	20	2	4	81	30	42
Brox. B'gers Res.	26	17	5	4	77	39	39
Hert. Celtic Res.	26	17	5	4	74	39	39
Roydon Spartans	26	15	3	8	73	44	33
Braughing Rov.	26	13	2	11	69	46	28
Elizabeth Allen A	26	12	3	11	61	52	27
Ware Lions OB	26	10	3	13	75	68	23
Buntingf'd W. Res.	26	10	2	14	48	56	22
Thundridge Res.	26	9	3	14	54	79	21
Cottered Res.	26	7	4	15	35	56	18
Watton-at-S. Res.	26	4	5	17	47	105	13
E-Trade Deac'field	26	3	2	21	28	91	8
Mangrove Res.	26	1	2	23	18	128	4

HOPE VALLEY AMATEUR LEAGUE

Premier Division	P	W	D	L	F	A	Pts
Brampton FC	24	19	0	5	71	28	57
Whaley Bridge	24	17	4	3	73	24	55
Dove Holes	24	15	5	4	73	38	50
Harpur Hill	24	15	3	6	61	38	48
Tideswell United	24	11	5	8	41	37	38
Grindleford	24	10	7	7	51	44	37
Tintwistle Villa	24	12	4	8	46	40	37
Bradwell	24	9	7	8	47	39	34
Dronfield W'dhse	24	6	5	13	31	51	23
Dronfield Town A	24	5	6	13	42	67	21
Hunters Bar	24	5	4	15	35	64	19
Furness Vale	24	3	4	17	29	75	13
Blazing Rag	24	0	4	20	25	80	4

Division A	P	W	D	L	F	A	Pts
Hayfield	26	18	1	7	134	51	55
Totley Sports	26	16	6	4	84	55	54
Buxton Christians	26	15	6	5	70	48	51
Bakewell Town	26	16	1	9	83	48	49
Whaley Bge Res.	26	15	4	7	56	33	49
Dove Holes Res.	26	14	2	10	44	46	44
Dronfield Town B	26	11	6	9	59	58	39
Chinley	26	10	5	11	76	74	35
Buxworth	26	9	6	11	47	67	33
Dronfield W. Res.	26	9	5	12	57	63	32
Queens	26	10	0	16	46	79	30
Grindleford Res.	26	7	4	15	46	62	25
Calver	26	4	2	20	33	86	14
Edale	26	3	2	21	35	100	11

Division B	P	W	D	L	F	A	Pts
Tideswell U. Res.	22	17	2	3	67	23	53
Hathersage	22	15	4	3	54	21	49
Bradwell Res.	22	13	4	5	60	41	43
Baslow	22	11	2	9	57	43	35
Furness Vale Res.	22	9	4	9	57	55	31
Eyam	22	9	3	10	40	47	30
Red Lion FC	22	7	8	7	46	48	29
Youlgrave United	22	8	3	11	52	54	27
Peak Dale	22	5	8	9	41	42	23
Bamford	22	6	4	12	32	57	22
Stoney Middleton	22	4	5	13	34	50	17
Queens Res.	22	4	1	17	27	86	13

HUDDERSFIELD WORKS & COMBINATION LEAGUE

Division One	P	W	D	L	F	A	Pts
Bay Athletic A	18	15	3	0	77	19	48
Moldgreen Res.	18	14	3	1	76	26	45
Uppermill A	18	9	2	7	46	44	29
M'green C'vative	18	8	4	6	52	34	28
Hepworth U. Res.	18	8	2	8	47	34	26
Netherton B	18	8	1	9	45	71	25
Syngenta SC	18	8	0	10	59	58	24
Railway	18	5	2	11	56	86	17
Heywoods IC A	18	5	0	13	46	71	15
Grange Moor Res.	18	1	1	16	18	79	4

Division Two	P	W	D	L	F	A	Pts
Aimbry	18	17	1	0	91	24	52
Sovereign Sports	18	13	3	2	80	22	42
Springhead	18	11	2	5	44	17	35
Lindley Libs Res.	18	10	2	6	55	44	32
Ireti Athletic	18	6	3	9	49	83	21
Lepton H'landers A	18	5	5	8	29	50	20
Kirkheaton R. B	18	5	3	10	25	35	18
Uppermill C	18	4	3	11	35	63	15
Upperthong A	18	3	2	13	16	58	11
Berry Brow	18	2	4	12	30	58	10

HUDDERSFIELD & DISTRICT LEAGUE

Division One	P	W	D	L	F	A	Pts
Lepton H'landers	20	16	1	3	58	31	49
Britannia Sports	20	13	3	4	64	36	42
Diggle	20	10	5	5	49	35	35
Heywood Irish C.	20	10	4	6	50	43	34
Newsome WMC	20	10	3	7	47	34	33
Shepley	20	9	4	7	33	30	31
Hepworth United	20	7	4	9	40	43	25
Uppermill	20	5	3	12	30	48	18
Meltham Ath. Res.	20	4	5	11	21	43	17
Wooldale Wdrs	20	3	4	13	24	51	13
New Mill	20	2	6	12	23	45	12

Division Two	P	W	D	L	F	A	Pts
Cumberworth	24	16	4	4	48	20	52
Moldgreen	24	16	2	6	85	38	50
Netherton	24	14	6	4	83	38	48
Lamb Inn FC	24	14	4	6	64	36	46
Slaithwaite United	24	12	7	5	61	47	43
Kirkheaton Rov.	24	11	2	11	57	51	35
Westend FC	24	9	7	8	40	42	34
Berry Brow Lib	24	10	2	12	41	34	32
KKS Ashbrow	24	10	2	12	48	49	32
Scholes	24	9	4	11	46	51	31
Honley	24	9	0	15	50	80	27
Mount	24	4	2	18	23	69	14
Stag	24	0	2	22	28	119	2

Lindley Liberal - records expunged

Division Three	P	W	D	L	F	A	Pts
Scissett Res.	26	20	2	4	78	34	62
Skelmanthorpe	26	18	3	5	79	47	57
YMCA	26	17	6	3	75	28	57
Grange Moor	26	13	3	10	59	48	42
Holmbridge	26	12	5	9	64	56	41
Upperthong	26	9	8	9	52	55	35
Dalton Crusaders	26	10	3	13	62	63	33
Brook Motors	26	10	2	14	58	60	32
HV Academicals	26	9	5	12	46	51	32
Paddock Rangers	26	7	10	9	53	57	31
Shelley	26	9	4	13	46	63	31
Heyside	26	9	1	16	70	80	28
Linthwaite Ath.	26	6	2	18	45	103	20
Lindley	26	6	0	20	39	81	18

Division Four	P	W	D	L	F	A	Pts
Royal Dolphins	16	13	0	3	64	30	39
Dewsb'y Town OB	16	12	1	3	68	25	37
Fenay Bridge	16	12	0	4	39	34	36
Cartworth Moor	16	9	1	6	44	34	28
Farnley Terriers	16	8	0	8	37	28	24
Flockton	16	5	3	8	29	43	18
Coach & Horses FC	16	3	3	10	34	46	12
Hade Edge	16	4	0	12	32	54	12
Marsden A	16	2	0	14	20	73	6

Reserve Div One	P	W	D	L	F	A	Pts
Diggle Res.	20	15	0	5	57	31	45
Kirkheaton R. Res.	20	14	3	3	59	23	45
Lepton H. Res.	20	11	3	6	40	33	36
Uppermill Res.	20	10	5	5	60	38	35
Netherton Res.	20	10	4	6	49	32	34
Meltham Ath. A	20	9	3	8	41	39	30
Newsome Res.	20	7	4	9	47	44	25
Heywood IC Res.	20	6	4	10	49	62	22
Berry Brow L. Res.	20	5	3	12	41	63	18
Britannia Sp. Res.	20	4	1	15	28	63	13
Honley Res.	20	3	2	15	33	76	11

Reserve Div. Two	P	W	D	L	F	A	Pts
Shepley Res.	22	18	1	3	79	22	55
Cumberw'th Res.	22	16	2	4	64	33	50
Westend Res.	22	12	6	4	57	37	42
Heyside Res.	22	12	2	8	72	55	38
Uppermill A	22	10	5	7	56	50	35
Wooldale W. Res.	22	10	3	9	60	37	33
Diggle A	22	9	1	12	62	53	28
New Mill Res.	22	8	3	11	49	57	27
Mount Res.	22	7	1	14	30	85	22
Slaithwaite Res.	22	6	4	12	39	64	22
Scholes Res.	22	6	2	14	36	56	20
HV Academ. Res.	22	2	2	18	32	87	8

Reserve Div. Three	P	W	D	L	F	A	Pts
Upperthong Res.	22	14	6	2	75	36	48
Meltham Ath. B	22	15	2	5	80	46	47
KKS A'brow Res.	22	12	3	7	78	56	39
Kirkheaton Rov. A	22	12	1	9	75	61	37
Cumberworth A	22	10	5	7	70	49	35
Netherton A	22	10	5	7	62	56	35
Holmbridge Res.	22	9	3	10	79	75	30
Shelley Res.	22	9	3	10	43	58	30
Brook Mtrs Res.	22	7	3	12	54	67	24
Paddock Rg. Res.	22	7	2	13	57	64	23
Honley A	22	5	2	15	44	79	17
Cartworth M. Res.	22	3	3	16	30	100	12

Reserve Div. Four	P	W	D	L	F	A	Pts
Skel'thorpe Res.	18	13	1	4	58	34	40
YMCA Res.	18	13	0	5	76	26	39
Lindley Res.	18	12	1	5	63	42	37
Britannia Sports A	18	12	0	6	45	25	36
Meltham Ath. C	18	9	3	6	41	32	30

	P	W	D	L	F	A	Pts
Stag Res.	18	8	1	9	54	53	25
Hade Edge Res.	18	6	2	10	32	43	20
Scholes A	18	5	2	11	29	50	17
Flockton Res.	18	3	3	12	17	56	12
Mount A	18	2	1	15	25	79	7

I ZINGARI COMBINATION

Division One	P	W	D	L	F	A	Pts
Old Xaverians A	20	16	2	2	47	20	50
Mossley Hill Res.	20	15	2	3	51	26	47
Leyfield Res.	20	14	1	5	57	30	43
Aintree Villa Res.	20	9	3	8	47	46	30
Sacre Coeur Res.	20	9	2	9	53	45	29
BRNESC Res.	20	9	2	9	38	41	29
Collegiate OB Res.	20	8	3	9	52	53	27
Birchfield Res.	20	6	4	10	45	44	22
Edge Hill BC Res.	20	7	0	13	36	59	21
Stoneycroft Res.	20	4	1	15	29	55	13
Walton CFC	20	1	4	15	28	64	7

Division Two	P	W	D	L	F	A	Pts
Alder Res.	20	17	2	1	98	21	53
MANWEB	20	17	2	1	94	20	53
Beehive	20	12	4	4	60	28	40
Liv'pool Cavaliers	20	10	6	4	47	37	36
Liobians Res.	20	9	3	8	52	43	30
Essemmay Res.	20	8	3	9	39	44	27
Polish	20	7	2	11	39	54	23
Mexoc	20	7	1	12	50	63	22
Walton CFC Res.	20	4	1	15	31	71	13
Rockville W. Res.	20	4	1	15	25	86	13
Rice Lane City F.	20	2	1	17	11	79	7

ILFORD & DISTRICT LEAGUE

Premier Division	P	W	D	L	F	A	Pts
Durning	14	10	1	3	56	23	31
Cranes United	14	10	1	3	41	18	31
Forest United	14	8	2	4	33	23	26
London & Essex	14	8	0	6	28	25	24
Castle United	14	7	1	6	33	31	22
St Francis	14	5	2	7	26	32	17
FC Barolle	14	2	3	9	17	41	9
Manor Park Utd	14	0	2	12	8	49	2

London Tigers - record expunged
Puma 200 - record expunged
Titans United - record expunged

Division One	P	W	D	L	F	A	Pts
Redbridge Elite	16	13	2	1	54	20	41
Chingford Athletic	16	12	1	3	56	34	37
Clockwork	16	9	2	5	58	38	29
Midland	16	8	2	6	42	45	26
Glendale	16	7	0	9	37	39	21
Ryan A	16	6	2	8	36	47	20
Newham United A	16	4	3	9	38	50	15
Newham Warriors	16	4	2	10	27	42	14
Trelawney *-3*	16	2	0	14	30	63	3

East Ham Inter - record expunged
RIP London - record expunged
The Hammers - record expunged

Division Two	P	W	D	L	F	A	Pts
Forest Utd Res.	20	12	3	5	62	33	39
East Londoners	20	12	3	5	58	34	39
Esprit	20	10	6	4	51	25	36
St Francis Res.	20	9	5	6	45	40	32
Castle U. Res.	20	9	4	7	68	41	31
Red. Elite Res. *-3*	20	10	4	6	53	42	31
Alliance United *-1*	20	9	4	7	62	42	30
AAH Romford	20	8	3	9	54	44	27
Newham Royals	20	8	2	10	68	59	26
RYPSA	20	3	4	13	29	58	13
Phoenix Colts	20	0	2	18	22	154	2

ISLE OF WIGHT LEAGUE

Division One	P	W	D	L	F	A	Pts
West Wight	26	22	2	2	99	20	68
Oakfield	26	19	2	5	101	39	59
N'port IW Res. *-1*	26	16	6	4	79	37	53
Shanklin	26	13	6	7	38	30	45
Binstead & COB	26	11	7	8	47	53	40
Northwood St J.	26	12	2	12	58	54	38
Niton	26	11	3	12	55	61	36
St Helens Blue S.	26	10	2	14	43	64	32
Cowes Sports A	26	8	6	12	47	60	30
Carisbrooke Utd	26	8	6	12	36	54	30
Red Star Spartans	26	7	7	12	55	63	28
Brighstone	26	8	4	13	38	55	28
Sandown	26	7	4	15	51	68	25
Ventnor	26	0	3	23	17	104	3

Division Two	P	W	D	L	F	A	Pts
GKN	22	16	4	2	82	30	52
Newchurch	22	14	6	2	76	33	48
W & B Sports	22	13	3	6	49	32	42
Rookley	22	11	6	5	54	39	39
Seaview	22	10	5	7	59	42	35
Shanklin VYCC	22	8	10	4	48	30	34
Kyngs Towne	22	9	3	10	50	54	30
Yarmouth & C'bne	22	8	5	9	49	50	29
Ryde Saints	22	8	5	9	45	47	29
E. Cowes VA Res.	22	4	6	12	36	74	18
Wroxall	22	3	4	15	29	59	13
Wakes	22	0	0	22	12	99	0

Division Three	P	W	D	L	F	A	Pts
Arreton Athletic	18	13	3	2	70	33	42
Brading Town A	18	12	1	5	53	22	37
Pan Sports	18	11	2	5	61	37	35
Osborne Coburg	18	11	1	6	53	34	34
Cowes Old Boys	18	7	1	10	49	52	22
Bembridge	18	5	0	13	19	50	15
Newport Colts	18	0	0	18	15	95	0

KIDDERMINSTER & DISTRICT LEAGUE

Premier Division	P	W	D	L	F	A	Pts
Wyre Forest	24	20	2	2	95	28	62
Kings Heath OB	24	16	3	5	78	39	51
Wollescote Villa	24	15	3	6	73	45	48
Birch Coppice	24	15	2	7	76	47	47
KS Athletic	24	12	4	8	51	45	40
Old Hill -1	24	10	7	7	63	46	36
Bobbington	24	10	3	11	51	45	33
Oldswinford Harr.	24	9	2	13	44	65	29
Two Gates	24	8	2	14	58	55	26
Kinver -3	24	8	1	15	44	66	24
Areley Kings	24	6	2	16	25	75	20
Albron	24	3	7	14	34	69	16
Quarry Bank	24	3	4	17	34	101	13

Division One	P	W	D	L	F	A	Pts
Furnace Sports	20	17	3	0	80	16	54
Burlish Olympic	20	14	4	2	91	26	46
Dudley Wood Ath	20	14	3	3	81	26	45
Blackheath Libs	20	9	5	6	46	31	32
Lodgefield Park	20	9	5	6	43	33	32
Old Hill Res.	20	7	6	7	48	46	27
GDIS	20	6	8	6	38	35	26
Greyhound Inn	20	3	5	12	34	60	41
Dud. White Swan	20	3	4	13	33	76	13
Three Crowns Utd	20	3	2	15	35	78	11
Tenbury Town *-1*	20	1	3	16	21	123	5

Meta Sports - record expunged

KINGSLEY LEAGUE
(Hodgson Insurance)

	P	W	D	L	F	A	Pts
Black Torrington	16	14	0	2	73	25	42
South Petherwin	16	10	1	5	56	29	31
Woolsery Res.	16	9	2	5	60	43	29
Bridgerule	16	8	2	6	43	33	26
Holsworthy A	16	8	1	7	49	43	25
Kilkhampton Res.	16	5	2	9	32	50	17
Week St Mary Res.	16	5	1	10	38	47	16
Merton Res.	16	3	3	10	30	59	12
Hartland A	16	2	4	10	24	76	10

KINGSTON & DISTRICT LEAGUE

Premier Division	P	W	D	L	F	A	Pts
Chessington KC	18	13	2	3	38	22	41
Molesey Villa	18	12	0	6	52	27	36
SHFC London	18	11	2	5	42	30	35
Claygate Royals	18	11	0	7	33	23	33
Summerstown	18	9	4	5	39	21	31
Robin Hood FC	18	8	1	9	30	27	25
Maori Park	18	6	2	10	25	28	20
Kingston Acads	18	5	1	12	37	43	16
International	18	4	2	12	23	65	14
Wandsworth Town	18	3	2	13	20	53	11

Division One	P	W	D	L	F	A	Pts
AFC Molesey	18	14	1	3	42	14	43
O Rutlishians Res.	18	12	3	3	43	20	39
Kingston Albion	18	11	4	3	38	15	37
Hersham RBL	18	9	2	7	29	36	29
AFC West End	18	7	2	9	34	30	23
Wandsworth Cor.	18	7	2	9	29	38	23
Esher United	18	6	4	8	25	29	22
Thornton Heath	18	5	4	9	27	39	19
Westside Res.	18	3	5	10	19	41	14
Dynamo Pimlico	18	2	1	15	15	39	7

Division Two	P	W	D	L	F	A	Pts
LM United	18	18	0	0	61	22	54
Repton	18	12	2	4	58	23	38
AC Malden	18	9	5	4	47	33	32
Merton Rovers	18	10	1	7	45	30	31
Wandle	18	9	2	7	44	30	29
Esher Ath. Res.	18	6	3	9	38	61	21
Malden Manor	18	4	5	9	37	46	17
Lower Green	18	5	2	11	34	46	17
Old Rutlishians A	18	3	4	11	21	55	13
Maori Park Res.	18	2	0	16	19	58	6

Division Three	P	W	D	L	F	A	Pts
AFC Watermans	18	15	2	1	80	19	47
Oxshott Royals	18	12	2	4	46	27	38
Surrey Fire	18	10	5	3	41	22	35
Darkside	18	9	4	5	59	30	31
Double H	18	8	4	6	48	41	28
Epsom Casuals *-1*	18	7	7	4	42	33	27
Ches'gton KC Res.	18	6	1	11	34	46	19
Surbiton Eagles	18	6	0	12	25	36	18
Barnslake	18	3	0	15	10	76	9
Merton Social *-1*	18	1	1	16	12	67	3

Division Four	P	W	D	L	F	A	Pts
NPL A	18	16	0	2	74	19	48
Red Star	18	13	2	3	60	26	41
Lower Green Res.	18	13	1	4	55	27	40
Summerstown Res.	18	13	1	4	63	38	40
St Martins	18	7	2	9	41	34	23
Chessington KCA	18	7	2	9	43	40	23
AFC Hampton	18	6	3	9	40	55	21
North Sheen	18	4	4	10	35	37	16
AFC Molesey Res.	18	1	2	15	21	100	5
Merton Social Res.	18	1	1	16	13	69	4

Division Five	P	W	D	L	F	A	Pts
NPL B	14	7	5	2	47	30	26
Dynamo Kingston	14	8	0	6	50	34	24
Outcasts	14	7	3	4	35	31	24
Westside A	14	7	1	6	38	31	22
AFC Kingston	14	6	4	4	36	29	22
M. Racing Ewell	14	6	2	6	36	43	20
Hook Venturers	14	4	1	9	33	52	13
AFC W'mans Res.	14	2	2	10	16	41	8

Division Six	P	W	D	L	F	A	Pts
Old Roehamptonians	14	12	0	2	45	10	36
Epsom Cas. Res.	14	8	3	3	42	20	27
Banstead Town	14	8	2	4	56	33	26
Claygate Ryls Res.	14	8	1	5	31	24	25
Darkside Res.	14	6	4	4	42	41	22
Westside B	14	3	2	9	17	37	11
St Martins Res.	14	2	3	9	19	46	9
Stoke Rangers	14	1	1	12	20	61	4

LANCASHIRE AMATEUR LEAGUE
(Redrow)

Premier Division	P	W	D	L	F	A	Pts
Old Blackburnians	26	19	6	1	68	33	63
Old Boltonians	26	14	5	7	49	33	47
Chaddertonians	26	13	7	6	72	41	46
Rossendale Amrs	26	13	7	6	51	31	46
Little Lever SC	26	14	3	9	61	33	45
Failsw'th Dynamos	26	14	3	9	53	51	45
Roch. St Clements	26	12	6	8	48	43	42
Old Mancunians	26	9	8	9	52	48	35
Bolton Wyresdale	26	10	2	14	44	59	32
Bury GSOB	26	9	2	15	41	48	29
Horwich RMI	26	7	6	13	36	55	27
Radcliffe Town	26	6	5	15	47	54	23
Bolton Lads Club	26	6	3	17	39	83	21
Lymm *-4*	26	3	3	20	36	85	8

Division One	P	W	D	L	F	A	Pts
Howe Bridge Mills	26	20	1	5	64	25	61
Chew Moor Bk	26	19	3	4	95	29	60
Prairie United	26	18	3	5	84	44	57
Horwich Victoria	26	16	3	7	64	42	51
Mostonians	26	13	4	9	64	48	43
O B'burnians Res.	26	12	5	9	54	50	41

	P	W	D	L	F	A	Pts
Castle Hill	26	10	8	8	62	49	38
Little Lever Res.	26	11	4	11	64	66	37
Hindley Juniors	26	9	4	13	51	64	31
Broughton Ams	26	9	2	15	56	65	29
Thornleigh	26	6	5	15	45	76	23
Tyldesley United	26	6	4	16	36	65	22
Chad'tonians Res.	26	5	5	16	50	75	20
Spotland Meth.	26	1	3	22	32	123	6

Division Two	P	W	D	L	F	A	Pts
Ross'dale A Res.	26	17	5	4	83	26	56
Ainsworth	26	15	9	2	67	38	54
Hesketh Casuals	26	16	5	5	67	38	53
Bolton Ambass.	26	15	2	9	89	64	47
Radcliffe Boys	26	13	3	10	80	59	42
Old B'burnians A	26	11	7	8	54	47	40
Acc. Loyal Amtrs	26	11	4	11	69	73	37
Rochdale SC Res.	26	11	3	12	56	59	36
O'ham Hulmeians	26	9	6	11	61	66	33
Bury GSOB Res.	26	9	6	11	58	72	33
Astley Bridge	26	9	4	13	50	48	31
O Boltonians Res.	26	7	3	16	43	71	24
Roach Dynamos	26	5	2	19	38	84	17
Ladybridge *-4*	26	2	5	19	34	104	7

Division Three	P	W	D	L	F	A	Pts
Mostonians Res.	26	19	5	2	105	43	62
O M'cunians Res.	26	14	9	3	67	41	51
Ashtonians	26	14	6	6	67	36	48
Bolton Wyre. Res.	26	12	7	7	64	49	43
Broughton A Res.	26	12	5	9	58	50	41
Rossendale A. A	26	10	5	11	64	54	35
Bacup United	26	10	4	12	58	52	34
Roch. St Clem. A	26	7	10	9	52	51	31
Failsworth Res. *-4*	26	8	9	9	56	65	29
Tottington United	26	6	7	13	62	78	25
Little Lever SC A	26	7	4	15	54	88	25
Lymm Res. *-4*	26	7	6	13	55	80	23
Hesketh Res. *-4*	26	5	8	13	51	69	19
Acc. Lyl A. Res. *-4*	26	6	5	15	41	98	19

Division Four	P	W	D	L	F	A	Pts
Castle Hill Res.	22	19	1	2	90	15	58
Chew Moor B Res.	22	16	2	4	73	27	50
Bolton LC Res.	22	13	3	6	73	39	42
Radcliffe T. Res.	22	13	3	6	55	44	42
Old B'burnians B	22	11	4	7	65	43	37
Chaddertonians A	22	12	0	10	48	44	36
Horwich RMI Res.	22	8	5	9	47	62	29
Horwich Vics Res.	22	7	5	10	46	60	26
Old Boltonians A	22	6	3	13	40	75	21
Little Lever SC B	22	3	5	14	34	72	14
Hesketh Cas. A	22	3	3	16	32	71	12
Howe B Mills Res.	22	3	2	17	34	85	11

Division Five	P	W	D	L	F	A	Pts
Radcliffe B. Res.	22	15	6	1	71	28	51
Old M'cunians A	22	13	4	5	51	35	43
Old Boltonians B	22	12	4	6	71	48	40
Rossendale A. B	22	11	3	8	48	48	36
Thornleigh Res.	22	9	7	6	60	46	34
Ainsworth Res. *-4*	22	12	2	8	57	57	34
Bury GSOB A	22	9	6	7	46	43	33
Mostonians A *-4*	22	8	5	9	50	44	25
Roch. St Clem. B	22	6	5	11	36	48	23
Tottington U. Res.	22	6	3	13	55	61	21
Ashtonians Res.	22	5	3	14	33	58	18
Spotland M. Res.	22	0	4	18	33	95	4

Division Six	P	W	D	L	F	A	Pts
Lymm B	20	16	1	3	70	24	49
Oldham H. Res.	20	14	2	4	63	35	44
Broughton Ams A	20	12	5	3	73	39	41
Radcliffe Town A	20	12	1	7	60	48	37
Old Mancunians B	20	10	1	9	51	53	31
Thornleigh B	20	6	5	9	35	47	23
Hesketh C. B *-4*	20	8	2	10	49	50	22
Thornleigh A	20	4	5	11	43	62	17
Bolton W'dale A	20	4	5	11	23	50	17
Radcliffe Town B	20	3	5	12	37	65	14
Lymm A	20	3	4	13	30	61	13

Division Seven	P	W	D	L	F	A	Pts
Chaddertonians B	20	15	3	2	79	44	48
Old B'burnians C	20	14	5	1	83	36	47
Broughton Ams B	20	15	1	4	83	24	46
Rossendale A. C	20	10	6	4	60	37	36
Castle Hill A	20	9	6	5	60	41	33
Oldham Hulm. A	20	6	5	9	36	56	23
Bolton W'dale B	20	6	4	10	46	57	22
Rossendale A. D	20	5	3	12	38	71	18
Horwich RMI A	20	5	2	13	34	64	17
Bury GSOB B	20	3	3	14	23	64	12
Oldham Hulm. B	20	2	2	16	32	80	8

LANCASHIRE LEAGUE

(Lancit Haulage)

East Division	P	W	D	L	F	A	Pts
Bradford PA Res.	26	21	1	4	74	21	64
Guiseley Res.	26	20	2	4	73	29	62
Wakefield Res.	26	17	4	5	57	38	55
Farsley C. Res.	26	14	4	8	47	36	46
Ossett Alb. Res.	26	13	2	11	54	55	41
Stalybridge Res.	26	11	3	12	59	48	36
Harrogate RA Res.	26	10	4	12	55	58	34
Ossett Town Res.	26	10	3	13	39	57	33
Pontefract C. Res.	26	9	5	12	34	37	32
Woodley Sports A	26	9	4	12	52	56	31
Hyde United Res.	26	9	3	14	47	60	30
Thackley Res.	26	7	7	11	40	41	29
Harrogate T. Res.	26	4	5	17	31	63	17
Yorks Amtrs Res.	26	2	3	21	34	97	9

West Division	P	W	D	L	F	A	Pts
Fleetwood T. Res.	20	16	3	1	65	17	51
Leigh Gen. Res.	20	13	1	6	52	29	40
Barrow Res.	20	12	0	8	51	34	36
Bamber Bge Res.	20	11	2	7	48	37	35
Chorley Res.	20	10	3	7	48	27	33
Clitheroe Res.	20	9	5	6	45	28	32
Formby Res.	20	8	3	9	38	54	27
Lancaster C. Res.	20	6	4	10	33	44	22
Darwen Res.	20	4	4	12	27	63	16
Workington Res.	20	3	4	13	17	62	13
Burscough Res.	20	2	3	15	33	62	9

LANCASHIRE & CHESHIRE AMATEUR LEAGUE

Premier Division	P	W	D	L	F	A	Pts
Whalley Range	26	17	2	7	71	37	53
Rochdalians	26	14	9	3	86	47	51
Mellor	26	15	4	7	55	37	49
Old Trafford	26	13	6	7	70	49	45
Moston Brook	26	12	7	7	73	59	43
Hooley Bge Celtic	26	9	9	8	61	50	36
South Manchester	26	10	6	10	45	49	36
Old Ashtonians	26	10	5	11	56	66	35
Hazel Grove	26	9	6	11	53	55	33
Abacus Media	26	10	2	14	52	74	32
Old Stretfordians	26	7	7	12	57	70	28
Bedians	26	7	3	16	56	78	24
Newton FC	26	6	6	14	52	82	24
Norris Villa	26	4	6	16	41	75	18

Division One	P	W	D	L	F	A	Pts
Govan Athletic	26	15	7	4	62	29	52
Spurley Hey	26	17	1	8	72	45	52
Chorltonians	26	16	2	8	73	55	50
Gatley	26	13	4	9	51	51	43
Stoconians	26	11	9	6	61	43	42
Alkrington Dyn *-3*	26	13	5	8	63	49	41
Irlam Steel	26	11	7	8	52	42	40
Cheadle H. Villa *-3*	26	11	5	10	66	59	35
Eagle	26	9	5	12	51	70	32
Parrswood Celtic	26	9	4	13	46	55	31
Hollingworth OB	26	8	3	15	52	70	27
Burnage Metro	26	7	4	15	49	65	25
Newton Heath	26	7	3	16	46	69	24
Aldermere	26	5	1	20	42	84	16

Division Two	P	W	D	L	F	A	Pts
Hattersley	26	22	3	1	111	28	69
Milton	26	19	2	5	120	60	59
New East Manch.	26	15	4	7	110	74	49
Heaton Mersey	26	15	4	7	67	36	49
AFC Oldham	26	15	2	9	102	66	47
Tintwistle Athletic	26	11	5	10	65	64	38
VIP	26	11	4	11	61	64	37
Droylsden Amtrs	26	10	4	12	52	59	34
Oldham Victoria	26	9	5	12	52	73	32
Moorside Rangers	26	8	5	13	59	73	29
Manchester Rov.	26	9	2	15	57	81	29
Santos FC	26	6	5	15	49	73	23
Deans Youth	26	4	5	17	38	87	17
VC United	26	2	2	22	38	143	8

Division A	P	W	D	L	F	A	Pts
Rochdalians Res.	30	21	3	6	94	33	66
Chorltonians Res.	30	19	3	8	104	62	60
Whalley Rge Res.	30	18	5	7	107	68	59
Bedians Res.	30	16	9	5	62	42	57
Newton Hth Res.	30	17	2	11	81	70	53
Mellor Res.	30	15	7	8	79	53	52
Newton Res.	30	13	6	11	75	72	45
Hazel Grove Res.	30	13	5	12	75	68	44
Moston Bk Res.	30	13	5	12	86	85	44
O Ashtonians Res.	30	13	2	15	72	80	41
Sth Manch. Res.	30	10	3	17	41	65	33
Gatley Res.	30	7	6	17	55	89	27
Hooley Bdge Res.	30	7	6	17	52	86	27
Old Stretford. Res.	30	6	7	17	56	82	25
Burnage M. Res.	30	6	6	18	52	83	24
Stoconians Res.	30	6	5	19	54	107	23

Division B	P	W	D	L	F	A	Pts
Alkrington D. Res.	28	20	3	5	94	39	63
Deans Youth Res.	28	17	6	5	112	57	57
Old Trafford Res.	28	17	5	6	88	59	56
Irlam Steel Res.	28	16	3	9	81	61	51
Hollingworth Res.	28	15	2	11	88	65	47
Aldermere Res.	28	12	7	9	80	59	43
Chorltonians A	28	12	7	9	71	65	43
Pendlebury United	28	11	5	12	57	62	38
Spurley Hey Res.	28	10	5	13	59	84	35
Bridge Colts	28	9	3	16	54	78	30
Droylsden A. Res.	28	8	5	15	74	104	29
Cheadle HV Res.	28	9	2	17	60	90	29
Abacus Medi.Res.	28	8	4	16	40	74	28
Mellor A	28	7	5	16	38	57	26
Burnage Metro A	28	5	6	17	52	94	21

Norris Villa Res. - record expunged

Division C	P	W	D	L	F	A	Pts
Old Stretfordians A	26	19	3	4	78	45	60
Whalley Range A	26	19	2	5	90	45	59
Oldham Vics Res.	26	17	5	4	71	43	56
Moorside R. Res.	26	15	5	6	89	53	50
Milton Res.	26	13	4	9	72	60	43
Parrswood Res. *-3*	26	13	3	10	79	54	39
AFC Oldham Res.	26	11	5	10	75	69	38
Santos Res. *-3*	26	10	8	8	64	64	35
Stoconians A	26	9	6	11	50	60	33
Staly	26	8	5	13	77	70	29
Govan Ath. Res.	26	6	5	15	39	57	23
Chorltonians B	26	6	3	17	68	100	21
Denton WE Youth	26	4	3	19	40	84	15
Manc. Rov. Res.	26	1	5	20	30	118	8

Division D	P	W	D	L	F	A	Pts
Bedians A	24	19	3	2	91	34	60
Irlam Steel A	24	18	0	6	90	44	54
Old Stretford. B	24	16	2	6	85	43	50
Mellor B	24	15	3	6	73	47	48
Hooley Bridge A	24	14	3	7	74	50	45
Old Ashtonians A	24	11	2	11	63	65	35
Moston Brook A	24	9	2	13	57	73	29
Gatley A	24	8	3	13	44	59	27
Stoconians B	24	8	3	13	51	70	27
AFC Oldham A	24	7	2	15	52	69	23
Chorltonians C	24	6	5	13	55	75	23
Burnage Metro B	24	4	4	16	33	68	16
Aldermere A	24	4	2	18	33	104	14

Division E	P	W	D	L	F	A	Pts
Deans Youth A	24	20	2	2	106	35	62
Moston Brook B	24	17	2	5	80	35	53
Aldermere B	24	17	1	6	81	50	52
Newton A	24	11	6	7	62	65	39
Old Ashtonians B	24	11	4	9	84	58	37
Old Stretford. C	24	10	5	9	53	50	35
Stoconians C	24	10	4	10	73	68	34
Spurley Hey A	24	10	4	10	63	71	34
Chorltonians D	24	7	4	13	64	76	25
Bedians B	24	6	4	14	54	87	22
Whalley Range B	24	5	4	15	48	108	19
Staly Res. *-3*	24	5	3	16	52	73	15
Burnage Metro C	24	3	5	16	39	83	14

LEEDS RED TRIANGLE LEAGUE

Premier Division	P	W	D	L	F	A	Pts
Gate	24	19	3	2	149	29	60
Holton Moor	24	19	2	3	142	39	59
Wykebeck Arms U.	24	18	3	3	105	40	57
East Leeds	24	14	4	6	83	54	46

	P	W	D	L	F	A	Pts
Dewsbury Rd Soc.	24	13	2	9	109	72	41
Seacroft WMC	24	11	4	9	76	71	37
Kippax Welf. Res.	24	11	3	10	71	83	36
Churwell New Inn	24	10	4	10	80	72	34
Amaranth	24	9	2	13	79	91	29
Ekhaya	24	6	4	14	58	87	22
Merlins	24	4	2	18	48	141	14
Middleton Park	24	4	0	20	60	163	12
AFC Leeds	24	1	1	22	33	151	4

Division One	P	W	D	L	F	A	Pts
Farnley Sports	20	15	5	0	76	21	50
Bainbridge United	20	13	1	6	57	34	40
New Farnley CC	20	13	1	6	53	36	40
Leodis	20	11	4	5	44	31	37
Railway E Ardsley	20	10	1	9	54	39	31
Halfway H. Morley	20	9	3	8	56	46	30
Skinners Arms	20	9	1	10	49	45	28
Drighlington Ad.	20	7	2	11	44	43	23
Leeds Deaf	20	6	2	12	30	57	20
Squinting Cat	20	3	4	13	37	79	13
Cricketers Arms	20	1	2	17	23	92	5

LEICESTER CITY LEAGUE

Division One	P	W	D	L	F	A	Pts
South Wigston W.	12	10	0	2	43	20	30
Saffron Lnge Bar	12	8	3	1	39	13	27
Scraptoft V. WMC	12	7	3	2	40	24	24
Soar Media	12	6	1	5	31	28	19
Nautical William	12	3	1	8	30	48	10
AFC Aylestone	12	2	1	9	27	42	7
FC Rowlatts	12	0	3	9	24	59	3

Division Two	P	W	D	L	F	A	Pts
Wigston Athletic	14	10	3	1	72	18	33
Victoria	14	10	2	2	39	25	32
Scraptoft Valley A.	14	7	4	3	49	30	25
FC Cricks	14	6	6	2	42	26	24
Park End	14	6	3	5	36	45	21
Kirkland	14	2	4	8	21	37	10
Shakha	14	2	2	10	21	58	8
Cosby Victory	14	1	0	13	14	55	3

LEICESTER & DISTRICT LEAGUE

Premier Division	P	W	D	L	F	A	Pts
Desford	26	22	2	2	112	19	68
Houghton Rgrs	26	18	4	4	82	30	58
Belgrave	26	16	4	6	68	35	52
Magna	26	16	4	6	62	38	52
Glenfield Town	26	12	5	9	53	46	41
Oadby Boys Club	26	12	3	11	39	40	39
County Hall	26	10	7	9	51	51	37
Cosby United	26	11	3	12	55	71	36
Birstall RBL	26	10	4	12	58	54	34
Welby Lane Utd	26	7	6	13	48	59	27
Blaby United	26	7	4	15	44	72	25
FC Kirkland	26	6	3	17	44	84	21
Burbage Old B.	26	5	4	17	40	67	19
St Patricks	26	3	1	22	28	118	10

Division One	P	W	D	L	F	A	Pts
Kingsway Rgrs	24	20	2	2	99	20	62
Midland Syston SP	24	18	1	5	98	42	55
Mountsorrel Amrs	24	18	0	6	109	44	54
Guru Nanak Gurd.	24	16	0	8	65	38	48
Queniborough	24	13	2	9	76	42	41
Hinckley Athletic	24	12	2	10	52	50	38
Huncote	24	12	2	10	55	59	38
Glen Villa	24	9	4	11	60	53	31
Kibworth Town	24	9	4	11	64	79	31
Melton Mowbray	24	7	1	16	36	75	22
North Kilworth	24	5	2	17	27	58	17
Broughton Astley	24	4	2	18	35	95	14
Woodgate/Nfdpool	24	1	2	21	18	139	5

Division Two	P	W	D	L	F	A	Pts
Thurnby United	20	17	1	2	122	18	52
Leicester YMCA	20	17	1	2	102	33	52
Topps United	20	14	4	2	73	25	46
Newbold Jubilee	20	10	2	8	58	45	32
Thurlaston Mags	20	8	2	10	38	74	26
Leicester Tile	20	7	3	10	58	65	24
Saffron Gap	20	7	3	10	55	62	24
Sporting Sapcote	20	8	0	12	37	83	24
Oakham Imperial	20	2	7	11	24	60	13
Fleckney Athletic	20	3	4	13	24	62	13
FC Khalsa A	20	2	3	15	20	84	9

Stanton 2008 - record expunged
St Andrews Hearts - record expunged

Reserve Prem Div	P	W	D	L	F	A	Pts
Cosby Utd Res.	20	14	1	5	62	43	43
Welby Lane Res.	20	12	3	5	60	39	39
Glenfield T. Res.	20	10	5	5	52	35	35
FC Kirkland Res.	20	10	4	6	48	40	34
Belgrave Res.	20	10	1	9	52	44	31
Magna Res.	20	8	2	10	42	47	26
County Hall Res.	20	8	2	10	33	43	26
St Patricks Res.	20	7	3	10	54	62	24
GN Gurdwar Res.	20	7	2	11	34	43	23
Glen Villa Res.	20	5	4	11	26	40	19
Kibworth T. Res.	20	5	1	14	34	61	16

Reserve Div One	P	W	D	L	F	A	Pts
Birstall RBL Res.	20	13	3	4	61	26	42
Desford Res.	20	13	2	5	68	27	41
Houghton R. Res.	20	13	2	5	60	28	41
Burbage OB Res.	20	10	6	4	42	25	36
Oadby BC Res.	20	10	3	7	30	30	33
Midland SSP Res.	20	6	6	8	33	42	24
Nth Kilworth Res.	20	6	5	9	33	44	23
Huncote Res.	20	5	6	9	34	51	21
Queniboro. Res.	20	4	7	9	37	52	19
Mountsorrel Res.	20	4	3	13	32	50	15
Oakham Imp Res.	20	4	1	15	35	90	13

LINCOLN & DISTRICT LEAGUE
(W J Harrison Printers)

	P	W	D	L	F	A	Pts
Heckington United	26	24	1	1	81	12	73
Plough Skel'thorpe	26	22	1	3	106	26	67
Ivy Tavern CSA	26	18	2	6	83	37	56
Cherry Knights	26	16	3	7	88	57	51
Waddington Utd	26	12	6	8	60	64	42
AFC Victory -3	26	14	1	11	53	18	40
Fulbeck United -3	26	13	4	9	57	42	40
FC Ruston United	26	10	2	14	45	61	32
Market Rasen T.	26	7	5	14	25	55	26
Metheringham	26	7	3	16	56	71	24
Ruston Spts Res.	26	6	3	17	45	71	21
Horncastle Res. -3	26	7	3	16	37	82	21
Bracebridge Hth	26	5	3	18	34	75	18
Harby	26	1	3	22	20	119	6

LIVERPOOL CMS LEAGUE

Premier Division	P	W	D	L	F	A	Pts
Park Brown	20	18	1	1	66	23	55
Holy Name	20	15	2	3	62	38	47
King Charles	20	15	0	5	62	24	45
Rice Lane CF Res.	20	13	0	7	59	43	39
Liver Academy	20	12	2	6	41	35	38
Polonia Camps	20	9	2	9	34	37	29
Coyne	20	9	0	11	33	55	27
Credit Union	20	7	2	11	35	50	23
NSC Central	20	3	3	14	18	27	12
FC Cadwa	20	0	3	17	4	3	3
Merryweathers	20	0	3	17	6	54	3

Division One	P	W	D	L	F	A	Pts
Credit U. Wester	22	21	1	0	134	26	64
Glasshouse	22	15	1	6	59	30	46
Vagas	22	15	1	6	67	43	46
Liver Acad. Colts	22	13	2	7	62	43	41
Everton Comm.	22	13	1	8	48	48	40
Penny Lane	22	11	3	8	57	48	36
Select	22	10	2	10	47	25	32
Delagoa	22	8	3	11	42	79	27
Ashgrove	22	7	0	15	41	86	21
M'side Congaleze	22	6	2	14	38	92	20
Chatsworth	22	3	4	15	23	75	13
Kurdish Lions	22	0	0	22	2	25	0

LIVERPOOL OLD BOYS AMATEUR LEAGUE

Division One	P	W	D	L	F	A	Pts
Old Bootleians	18	14	2	2	54	21	44
Alumni	18	13	3	2	64	21	42
St Mary's Coll. OB	18	10	3	5	42	29	33
Waterloo GSOB	18	9	5	4	52	29	32
Naylorsfield -2	18	10	1	7	51	44	29
Cardinal Newman	18	8	4	6	42	30	28
Oaks Institute OB	18	7	2	9	26	41	23
FC Salle -3	18	4	3	11	33	46	12
Wavertree WDOB	18	2	2	14	14	56	8
Collegiate OB A	18	0	1	17	13	74	1

Alder A - record expunged

Division Two	P	W	D	L	F	A	Pts
Heygreen OB -5	20	17	1	2	69	24	47
Quarry Bank OB	20	13	4	3	62	44	43
Bankfield OB -2	20	12	4	4	69	33	38
Old Xaverians B	20	11	2	7	51	36	32
Alsop Old Boys	20	7	4	9	31	33	25
O Bootleians Res.	20	8	0	12	48	74	24
Old Cathinians -4	20	8	2	10	38	43	22
Bootech Old B.	20	5	4	11	35	51	19
Sacre Coeur Res.	20	5	3	12	38	55	18
Ercanil Old Boys	20	5	3	12	42	67	18
Moss. Hill Ath A -3	20	5	1	14	38	61	13

Division Three	P	W	D	L	F	A	Pts
Old Holts Res.	22	15	5	2	71	28	50
Quarry Bank Res.	22	16	2	4	74	39	50
W'loo GSOB Res.	22	15	2	4	73	46	50
Card. N'man Res.	22	12	2	8	52	41	38
O Cathinians Res.	22	9	6	7	53	48	33
Convocation	22	9	4	9	51	44	31
De La Salle OB	22	9	4	9	42	38	31
South Mersey -2	22	8	4	9	50	51	26
Gateacre -4	22	7	6	9	41	53	23
Corinthian	22	5	1	16	37	75	16
Blue Coat Old B.	22	4	3	15	28	55	15
Collegiate OB B	22	2	1	19	35	89	7

Division Four	P	W	D	L	F	A	Pts
O Cathinians A +1	22	18	1	2	102	29	56
Old Xaverians C	22	16	3	3	68	38	51
Waterloo GSOB A	22	13	5	4	92	47	44
O Bootleians A -6	22	12	6	4	54	34	36
Quarry Bank A	22	8	6	8	61	58	30
Hope Park	22	7	7	7	55	61	28
Alsop Old B. Res.	22	6	7	9	56	62	25
Richmond	22	6	4	12	55	61	22
Liobians A	22	7	1	14	62	98	22
Rhein	22	6	0	16	36	76	18
Kingsford -4	22	3	8	11	40	92	13
Essemmay A -2	22	4	2	16	45	70	12

Division Five	P	W	D	L	F	A	Pts
Roby College -3	22	21	1	0	110	29	61
Cardinal New. A	22	15	2	5	77	33	47
Old Cathinians B	22	13	2	7	61	38	41
St Mary's C. Res.	22	11	4	7	70	30	37
Old Bootleians B	22	12	1	9	61	53	37
Waterloo GSOB B	22	11	3	8	63	55	36
De La Salle Res.	22	9	3	10	42	55	30
Old Instonians	22	7	3	12	42	51	24
Business Sch. -3	22	8	3	11	58	76	24
Liobians B	22	5	5	12	48	81	20
W'tree WDOB Res.	22	3	5	14	26	74	14
Kingsford Res.	22	1	0	21	28	111	3

LONDON COMMERCIAL LEAGUE

Division One	P	W	D	L	F	A	Pts
British Airways	16	13	0	3	64	35	39
Chis. Homefields	16	11	2	3	44	27	35
HFC	16	9	1	6	48	39	28
Sporting Hackney	16	8	2	6	27	24	26
East Fulham	16	6	2	8	24	31	20
Hillingdon Irish	16	5	2	9	30	37	17
Aston Athletic	16	5	1	10	40	55	16
Roxeth	16	5	0	11	32	45	15
WLA	16	3	4	9	26	42	13

LOWESTOFT & DISTRICT LEAGUE
(Notley's)

Division One	P	W	D	L	F	A	Pts
Hearts of Oak	24	20	2	2	107	27	62
Pot Black	24	18	4	2	66	22	58
Norton Athletic	24	15	2	7	72	50	47
FC Hearts	24	14	0	10	84	68	42
Spexhall	24	11	5	8	57	41	38
Wrentham	24	11	5	8	72	62	38
Barsham	24	9	5	10	47	59	32
Kirkley/Pake. A -3	24	10	3	11	56	47	30
Waveney Res.	24	8	4	12	62	68	28
Blundeston Mags	24	8	4	12	44	66	28
Caxton Res. -3	24	5	6	13	40	64	18
Oxford Arms	24	2	2	20	29	104	8
Sole Bay Res. -6	24	2	4	18	25	83	4

Division Two	P	W	D	L	F	A	Pts
W. Hse Seltic +2	26	23	1	2	102	27	72
Ole Frank	26	19	1	6	110	47	58
Norton Ath. Res.	26	18	2	6	71	36	56

	P	W	D	L	F	A	Pts
Pakefield Re-Utd	26	16	1	9	72	61	49
Hopton White Hart	26	13	4	9	73	76	43
Crusaders	26	11	2	13	84	71	35
Bungay Town A	26	11	2	13	66	56	35
Lowestoft Int. -3	26	10	5	11	54	54	32
Ellingham	26	9	2	15	56	76	29
Oulton Bd Res. -4	26	10	2	14	64	71	28
Tudor	26	9	1	16	54	81	28
Corton A	26	8	3	15	83	89	27
Waveney Gunners	26	8	2	16	57	65	26
Oxford Arms Res.	26	2	2	22	37	173	8

Division Three	P	W	D	L	F	A	Pts
Suffolk Punch	24	21	2	1	87	23	65
Gt Yarm Town Hall	24	18	4	2	116	26	58
Harleston T. Res.	24	16	3	5	67	31	51
Lake Lothing	24	15	2	7	68	45	47
Spexhall Res.	24	12	4	8	46	44	40
Kirkley & Pake. B	24	11	1	12	65	58	34
Waveney A -3	24	10	4	10	50	47	31
Earsham -2	24	9	5	10	53	53	29
Marquis of Lorne	24	7	6	11	43	57	27
W. Horse S. Res.	24	6	2	16	35	72	20
Blund'ston Res. -3	24	5	5	14	58	81	17
Westhall	24	3	3	18	28	75	12
Factory Arms	24	2	1	21	29	133	7

LUTON DISTRICT & SOUTH BEDS LEAGUE

Premier Division	P	W	D	L	F	A	Pts
Stopsley Common	24	21	2	1	82	30	65
Offley Social	24	14	5	5	77	41	47
Christians in Spt	24	14	5	5	58	41	47
Lewsey Park	24	11	1	12	47	48	34
Luton Leagrave	24	10	2	12	49	60	32
St Josephs	24	9	2	13	51	55	29
Stopsley Park	24	8	3	13	51	67	27
Eaton Bray	24	5	1	18	31	81	16
Boater	24	4	3	17	50	73	15

Division One	P	W	D	L	F	A	Pts
Christ. in Spt Res.	21	18	0	3	63	33	54
USL Galacticos	21	15	2	4	87	27	47
Sundon Pk Rgrs	21	13	1	7	73	41	40
Farley Boys	21	11	2	8	62	32	35
AFC Slip End	21	10	3	8	60	47	33
The 61 FC A	21	5	3	13	46	90	18
Stopsley Pk Res.	21	3	2	16	32	100	11
Crown Sundon	21	2	1	18	23	76	7

MAIDSTONE & DISTRICT LEAGUE
(Express Cabs)

Premier Division	P	W	D	L	F	A	Pts
Shepway United	16	13	1	2	67	18	40
Eccles	16	12	3	1	48	15	39
Leeds SV	16	9	3	4	33	27	30
Addington	16	7	2	7	49	36	23
Hunton	16	6	4	6	18	28	22
Smarden	16	6	2	8	37	45	20
East Malling	16	4	3	9	16	32	15
Ditton United	16	2	4	10	7	38	10
Blue Eagles	16	2	0	14	15	51	6

Division One	P	W	D	L	F	A	Pts
Wateringbury Vill.	22	15	5	2	59	31	50
MPE	22	12	4	6	70	38	40
Headcorn	22	12	4	6	70	49	40
AFC Biddenden	22	12	2	8	54	47	38
Eccles Res.	22	10	5	7	71	59	35
Aylesford	22	10	4	8	48	41	34
Cobdown United	22	10	3	9	41	41	33
Sutton Saints	22	8	5	9	43	42	29
Yalding	22	7	4	11	45	56	25
West Farleigh	22	7	3	12	45	64	24
Saxon Chief	22	4	2	16	39	77	14
East Malling Res.	22	4	1	17	39	79	13

Division Two	P	W	D	L	F	A	Pts
Castle Colts	18	15	1	2	84	23	46
Three Suttons	18	12	2	4	61	35	38
Malgo Res.	18	10	2	6	49	33	32
Hunton Res.	18	10	1	7	54	33	31
RKP United	18	9	4	5	39	36	31
Lenham W. Res.	18	7	6	5	57	57	27
Maidstone Ath.	18	5	4	9	29	53	19
Wheatsheaf Celt.	18	2	6	10	30	54	12
Headcorn Res.	18	2	4	12	22	59	10
Kingshill Spitfires	18	2	2	14	25	67	8

Division Three	P	W	D	L	F	A	Pts
Regal United	20	18	0	2	114	37	54
Larkfield	20	16	2	2	72	22	50
Parkwood Jupitors	20	13	4	3	80	51	43
Malgo A	20	8	1	11	48	55	25
Thurnham United	20	6	6	8	37	42	24
Addington Res.	20	6	4	10	41	54	22
Walnut Tree Loose	20	6	3	11	37	69	21
Staplehurst/MU A	20	5	4	11	32	45	19
W. Farleigh Res.	20	5	4	11	22	50	19
Phoenix United	20	4	6	10	36	67	18
Sutton Saints Res.	20	4	4	12	41	68	16

MATLOCK & DISTRICT LEAGUE

	P	W	D	L	F	A	Pts
Ashbourne T. Res.	22	19	2	1	113	24	59
Tibshelf	22	15	5	2	68	36	50
Matlock Town Yth	22	13	2	7	74	42	41
Darley Dale Lions	22	11	5	6	71	41	38
Riddings Rovers	22	10	5	7	81	60	35
The Kings Arms	22	10	5	7	55	45	35
Shirland MW	22	10	3	9	63	55	33
Laburnum Saints	22	6	5	11	46	68	23
Hilcote United	22	6	5	11	50	73	23
Sth Wingfield Ath.	22	6	3	14	44	76	21
AFC Lea Hol'way	22	5	1	16	48	93	16
Duke William	22	0	2	20	14	109	2

MID-ESSEX LEAGUE
(Broch Group)

Premier Division	P	W	D	L	F	A	Pts
Braintree/Bocking	24	19	3	2	73	24	60
Scotia Billericay	24	17	4	3	88	34	55
Harold Wood A -3	24	18	2	4	72	33	53
Silver End United	24	16	2	6	68	32	50
Beacon Hill R. -2	24	12	4	8	56	43	42
Little Waltham -1	24	13	3	8	62	43	41
Southminster Res.	24	11	1	12	44	52	34
Ravens	24	9	4	11	47	56	31
Springfield Rouge	24	9	3	12	57	55	30
U Chelm Churches	24	7	2	15	51	77	23
Manford Way A	24	4	3	17	30	59	15
Mundon Victoria	24	2	2	20	18	71	8
Bradwell United	24	2	1	21	25	112	7

Division One	P	W	D	L	F	A	Pts
Byfleet Rangers	20	15	3	2	75	33	48
Focus Ferrers	20	14	3	3	50	22	45
Rhodesia United	20	13	1	6	63	39	40
Forest Glade	20	12	0	8	61	37	36
Sparta Basildon	20	10	1	9	63	29	31
Frenford Senior A	20	9	3	8	35	41	30
Shelley Royals	20	9	2	9	39	45	29
Marconi Athletic	20	7	1	12	53	57	22
Old C'fordians A	20	6	1	13	33	49	19
Southminster A	20	6	1	13	24	52	19
Ferrers Athletic	20	0	2	18	10	102	2

Division Two	P	W	D	L	F	A	Pts
Manford Way B	18	15	2	1	55	18	47
Scotia B'cay Res.	18	15	1	2	82	20	46
Tillingham Hotspur	18	11	2	5	51	21	35
Great Baddow	18	9	3	6	51	31	29
Harold Wood Ath B	18	7	3	8	36	41	23
Writtle Manor +2	18	5	4	9	42	58	21
Hutton A	18	6	2	10	40	55	20
Stock United	18	6	0	12	34	64	18
Boreham	18	4	2	12	37	59	14
Epping A -1	18	2	1	15	16	77	6

Division Three	P	W	D	L	F	A	Pts
Battlesbridge	24	16	4	4	72	34	52
Shenfield Holland	24	15	7	2	66	35	52
Brendans	24	14	5	5	67	42	47
St Margarets	24	14	3	7	57	31	45
City Colts +3	24	12	5	7	46	43	44
Sungate A -4	24	12	6	6	70	42	38
Wickham Ryls +2	24	10	6	8	42	40	38
E2V Technologies	24	11	2	11	50	52	35
Old Chelm'dians B	24	7	4	13	34	59	25
Runnymede -9	24	10	0	14	44	44	21
Bradwell Res. +3	24	4	5	15	28	67	14
Focus F. Res. +3	24	2	3	19	33	78	12
Crays Hill United	24	3	2	19	30	72	11

Division Four	P	W	D	L	F	A	Pts
Braintree/BU Res.	24	17	2	5	61	35	53
Ltle Waltham Res.	24	14	5	5	74	39	47
Frenford Senior B	24	13	7	4	65	49	46
Byfleet Rgrs Res.	24	13	4	7	71	47	43
Beacon Hill Res.	24	12	6	6	56	48	42
Felsted Rovers	24	11	5	8	60	32	38
Runwell Hosp. A	24	11	3	10	80	62	36
Mundon Vics Res.	24	10	5	9	57	54	35
Burnham Ramb. A	24	10	2	12	54	63	32
Springfield A	24	9	3	12	54	60	30
Battlesbridge Res.	24	7	6	11	43	51	27
Shelley Ryls Res.	24	3	1	20	31	86	10
Marconi Ath. Res.	24	1	1	22	18	98	4

Division Five	P	W	D	L	F	A	Pts
Gt Baddow Res.	24	19	3	2	120	27	60
White Hart United	24	17	5	2	71	26	56
Durning Res.	24	17	2	5	105	43	53
Tillingham H. Res.	24	17	2	5	99	42	53
Wickham R. Res.	24	15	3	6	44	21	48
Marks Farm	24	13	3	8	70	54	42
Boreham Res. -1	24	9	5	10	55	74	31
E2V Tech Res. +3	24	7	4	13	43	78	28
Beacon Hill R. A	24	5	4	15	37	64	19
Battlesbridge A	24	5	1	18	31	80	19
Silver End U. Res.	24	4	6	14	37	91	18
Utd Church Res. +2	24	3	2	19	28	87	13
Dunmow -3	24	4	2	18	31	84	8

MID-SOMERSET LEAGUE

Premier Division	P	W	D	L	F	A	Pts
Purnells Sports	16	13	1	2	76	18	40
Mells & Vobster U.	16	10	1	5	44	34	31
Wookey	16	9	2	5	40	26	29
Belrose	16	7	4	5	41	40	25
Meadow Rangers	16	7	1	8	32	29	22
Chilcompton Spts	16	5	4	7	30	36	19
Coleford Athletic	16	3	7	6	33	42	16
Chew Magna	16	4	2	10	31	45	14
Pensford -3	16	1	4	11	22	79	4

Division One	P	W	D	L	F	A	Pts
Farrington Gurney	18	13	3	2	73	30	42
Westfield Res.	18	11	4	3	70	36	37
Purnell Spts Res.	18	7	6	5	36	38	27
Glastonbury Res.	18	7	3	8	50	45	24
Oakhill	18	6	5	7	35	32	23
Stoke Rovers	18	6	5	7	27	42	23
Frome Colls Res.	18	6	3	9	35	43	21
Temple Cloud -3	18	7	1	10	51	62	19
Evercreech Rov.	18	6	1	11	38	56	19
Frome TS Res.	18	4	3	11	40	71	15

Division Two	P	W	D	L	F	A	Pts
Pilton United	18	13	2	3	58	27	41
Wells City A	18	11	5	2	46	20	38
Tunley A. Res. -3	18	11	2	5	54	43	32
Mells & V. Res. -3	18	10	1	7	43	33	28
Interhound	18	9	0	9	38	43	27
Coleford A. Res.	18	7	2	9	42	49	23
Chilcompton Res.	18	6	4	8	41	44	22
Welton Arsenal -3	18	5	4	9	32	42	16
Belrose Res.	18	4	3	11	32	55	15
Clutton Res.	18	2	1	15	25	56	7

Division Three	P	W	D	L	F	A	Pts
Wookey Res.	16	13	0	3	58	22	39
Farrington G. Res.	16	9	2	5	50	27	29
Chilcompton Utd	16	9	1	6	34	26	28
Meadow Rgrs Res.	16	7	3	6	33	29	24
Radstock Town A	16	7	1	8	36	39	22
Westfield A -6	16	6	5	5	40	36	17
Evercreech Res.	16	5	2	9	32	42	17
Shepton Mallet B	16	4	2	10	28	42	14
Stoke Rov. Res.	16	3	2	11	25	73	11

MID-SUSSEX LEAGUE
(Gray Hooper Holt LLP)

Premier Division	P	W	D	L	F	A	Pts
Old Varndeanians	24	15	3	6	50	28	48
Lindfield	24	13	5	6	71	49	44
Balcombe	24	13	5	6	63	46	44
Willingdon Athletic	24	13	4	7	44	29	43
Hassocks A +3	24	12	3	9	48	38	42
Uckfield Town Res.	24	12	5	7	45	33	41
Maresfield Village	24	11	4	9	44	44	37
Jarvis Brook	24	9	4	11	39	52	31
Forest Row -3	24	10	3	11	48	46	30
Wisdom Sports	24	8	4	12	49	51	28
E. Grinstead Utd	24	7	5	12	33	47	26
Franklands Village	24	4	5	15	33	61	17
Hartfield	24	2	4	18	22	65	10

Division One	P	W	D	L	F	A	Pts
Crawley Down A	22	14	5	3	55	29	47
Rotherfield	22	13	4	5	56	30	43
Lewes Bridgeview	22	11	5	6	57	41	38
Village of Ditchling	22	11	5	6	47	37	38
Heath Pilgrims	22	10	4	8	53	54	34
O V'deanians Res.	22	9	5	8	42	35	32
AFC Ringmer	22	10	1	11	42	49	31
Wisdom Spts Res.	22	7	6	9	43	53	27
Buxted	22	7	5	10	44	50	26
Horsted Keynes	22	6	7	9	53	62	25
Hurstpierp't Res.	22	4	5	13	33	54	17
Felbridge	22	2	4	16	22	53	10

Division Two	P	W	D	L	F	A	Pts
Roffey	18	15	2	1	75	13	47
Cuckfield Town	18	11	4	3	41	23	37
Keymer/Hassocks	18	10	3	5	44	30	33
Turners Hill	18	8	5	5	55	39	29
Ashurst Wood	18	6	7	5	37	32	25
Newick	18	6	5	7	36	52	23
Cuckfield Rangers	18	5	4	9	33	48	19
Ardingly	18	3	7	8	31	44	16
Sporting Lindfield	18	3	2	13	24	61	11
Willingdon A. Res.	18	2	3	13	22	56	9

Division Three	P	W	D	L	F	A	Pts
Dormansland Rkts	20	16	0	4	65	14	48
AFC Grinstead	20	11	4	5	49	23	37
Lindfield Res. *+3*	20	9	7	4	47	29	37
Burgess Hill Albion	20	10	5	5	34	30	35
Peacehaven Utd	20	10	2	8	46	38	32
West Hoathly	20	8	3	9	37	35	27
East Court	20	7	4	9	40	43	25
Fletching	20	7	3	10	36	54	24
E. Grinstead T. A	20	5	5	10	23	36	20
Maresfield V. Res.	20	5	4	11	31	51	19
E. Grin. U. Res. *-3*	20	3	1	16	23	78	7

Division Four	P	W	D	L	F	A	Pts
Uckfield Town A	18	15	0	3	73	27	45
Framfield/B'boys	18	11	4	3	58	23	37
Crowborough A *-3*	18	11	2	5	59	28	32
Plumpton Ath. *+3*	18	8	3	7	62	45	30
O. Varndeanians A	18	8	5	5	44	40	29
Roffey Res.	18	7	4	7	32	31	25
Cuckfield T. Res.	18	4	6	8	35	48	18
Burg. H. Alb. Res.	18	4	3	11	32	74	15
Lingfield A	18	4	2	12	28	66	14
Danehill	18	3	1	14	27	68	10

Division Five	P	W	D	L	F	A	Pts
Barcombe	20	17	2	1	71	18	53
Scaynes Hill	20	15	1	4	71	45	46
Copthorne	20	13	3	4	61	33	42
Ansty Spts & Soc.	20	10	4	6	54	41	34
Turners Hill Res.	20	9	6	5	54	39	33
Fairwarp	20	7	5	8	52	46	26
V. of Ditchling Res.	20	5	4	11	32	52	19
Rottingdean Vets	20	4	6	10	34	57	18
Newick Res.	20	5	3	12	35	65	18
Nutley	20	4	2	14	36	67	14
Ardingly Res.	20	1	4	15	33	70	7

Division Six	P	W	D	L	F	A	Pts
East Grinstead W.	20	15	1	4	65	24	46
Handcross Village	20	14	2	4	77	37	44
Wivelsfield G. Res.	20	14	1	5	70	31	43
Copthorne Rovers	20	12	4	4	57	31	40
Jarvis Brook Res.	20	10	1	9	52	48	31
Lindfield A	20	7	6	7	48	40	27
Bolney Rovers	20	8	2	10	41	50	26
Buxted Res. -3	20	8	3	9	30	38	24
Wisdom Sports A	20	4	2	14	36	80	14
Hth Pilgrims Res.	20	3	2	15	24	74	11
Fairfield	20	2	2	16	15	62	8

Division Seven	P	W	D	L	F	A	Pts
Forest Row Res.	20	16	4	0	73	21	52
Balcombe Res.	20	14	3	3	55	18	45
Dormansland Res.	20	13	6	1	61	33	45
Copthorne Res.	20	11	3	6	70	39	36
Fletching Res.	20	8	2	10	27	62	26
Maresfield Vill. A	20	8	0	12	48	48	24
Hartfield Res.	20	5	5	10	18	44	20
Horsted K. Res.	20	6	1	13	42	56	19
Felbridge Res.	20	5	2	13	27	46	17
Ashurst Wd Res.	20	5	1	14	35	56	16
Willingdon Ath. A	20	4	3	13	28	61	15

Division Eight	P	W	D	L	F	A	Pts
Vill.of Ditchling A	20	15	2	3	70	31	47
Franklands V. Res.	20	12	3	5	56	35	39
Ansty Spts/S. Res.	20	11	2	7	60	45	35
West Hoathly Res.	20	9	6	5	63	51	33
Danehill Res.	20	9	3	8	82	60	30
Rotherfield Res.	20	9	3	8	56	53	30
Halsford Lions	20	9	3	8	59	58	30
Burgess Hill Alb. A	20	8	3	9	43	52	27
Uckfield Town B	20	5	1	14	40	72	16
Cuckfield Town A	20	4	2	14	28	50	14
Scaynes Hill Res.	20	3	4	13	28	78	13

Division Nine	P	W	D	L	F	A	Pts
E. Grinstead T. B	18	11	5	2	46	25	38
Barcombe Res.	18	10	4	4	55	34	34
Framfield/B. Res.	18	11	1	6	49	35	34
Lindfield B	18	10	3	5	43	33	33
Wivelsfield G. A	18	9	2	7	63	38	29
Plumpton A. Res.	18	8	2	8	32	30	26
Cuckfield R. Res.	18	8	1	9	37	42	25
Maresfield Vill. B	18	5	2	11	35	52	17
Handcross V. Res.	18	3	4	11	22	50	13
Buxted A	18	2	2	14	31	74	8

MIDLAND AMATEUR ALLIANCE

Premier Division	P	W	D	L	F	A	Pts
FC05	24	19	3	2	95	35	60
Old Elizabethans	24	19	3	2	83	35	60
Woodborough U.	24	18	3	3	90	35	57
Southwell Amtrs	24	16	3	5	84	37	51
Nottinghamshire	24	12	4	8	59	48	40
Steelers	24	9	3	12	55	66	30
Pinxton Nth End	24	7	5	12	57	66	26
Beeston OB Ass.	24	6	4	14	53	68	22
County NALGO	24	6	4	14	39	67	22
Monty Hind OB	24	6	3	15	52	68	21
Brunts Old Boys	24	6	3	15	44	107	21
Wollaton A	24	6	1	17	54	82	19
TVFC	24	6	1	17	47	98	19

Division One	P	W	D	L	F	A	Pts
Crown Inn Selston	26	20	3	3	99	47	63
Acorn Athletic	26	17	3	6	90	51	54
Nott'mshire Res.	26	15	4	7	77	45	49
Beeston Res.	26	11	9	6	60	55	42
Radcliffe Olym. A	26	11	6	9	58	57	39
Lady Bay	26	10	7	9	62	62	37
Eaton Hall College	26	9	9	8	53	44	36
Bassingfield	26	8	9	9	71	74	33
Wollaton B	26	9	6	11	55	58	33
West Bridgford U.	26	10	3	13	58	74	33
EMTEC	26	9	1	16	65	100	28
O E'bethans Res.	26	7	6	13	56	70	27
Calverton MW A	26	4	5	17	49	77	17
Derbys Ams Res.	26	4	5	17	38	77	17

Division Two	P	W	D	L	F	A	Pts
Broadmeadows	26	20	4	2	109	43	64
Southwell A. Res.	26	20	3	3	109	34	63
Coronation	26	18	5	3	83	38	59
Nott'mshire A	26	17	6	3	82	34	57
Nuthall Athletic	26	15	4	7	80	55	49
Sherwood Colliery	26	13	5	8	61	39	44
Kirk Hallam SC	26	12	4	10	98	82	40
Chilwell Vipers	26	9	5	12	64	75	32
Tibshelf Comm.	26	7	5	14	43	76	26
Cambdge Knights	26	6	6	14	48	93	24
Town Mill	26	5	3	18	48	97	18
Old Bemrosians	26	5	2	19	45	99	17
Hickling	26	4	2	20	40	86	14
Ravenshead Rgrs	26	3	2	21	31	90	11

MIDLAND REGIONAL ALLIANCE

Premier Division	P	W	D	L	F	A	Pts
Rowsley	38	29	4	5	94	35	91
Melbourne Dyn.	38	26	7	5	103	53	85
Ilkeston Town Res.	38	25	6	7	106	40	81
Wirksworth T. *-1*	38	23	10	5	88	39	78
Dronfield Town	38	22	6	10	77	49	72
Eastwood Res. *-3*	38	23	3	12	104	61	69
Willington FC	38	22	3	13	81	72	69
Derby Rolls R Leis	38	17	6	15	82	75	57
C. Donington T. *-6*	38	18	5	15	94	71	53
Holbrook St Mich.	38	13	12	13	82	72	51
Matlock T. Res. *-4*	38	15	9	14	64	56	50
Ashover *-3*	38	15	2	21	66	83	44
Ripley	38	13	5	20	57	78	44
Borrowash Res.	38	12	6	20	48	74	42
Lg Eaton Res. *-3*	38	13	2	23	77	77	38
Allestree	38	10	3	25	44	110	33
Cromford	38	9	5	24	53	115	32
Newmount	38	7	8	23	48	84	29
Sandiacre Town	38	8	3	27	57	107	27
Belper United	38	5	5	28	39	113	20

Division One	P	W	D	L	F	A	Pts
Allenton United	30	27	3	0	139	23	84
Chellaston	30	22	1	7	86	49	67
Dronfield Res. *-1*	30	19	4	7	69	38	60
Selston	30	18	5	7	94	49	59
Swanwick PR *-3*	30	15	4	11	63	53	46
Heanor Colliers	30	14	3	13	76	73	45
Mickleover RBL	30	13	5	12	73	67	44
Matlock Sports	30	13	4	13	66	64	43
Beeston AFC *-3*	30	14	2	14	66	70	41
Pastures	30	10	6	14	50	69	36
Derbys Amtrs *-3*	30	11	5	14	56	62	35
Bargate Rovers	30	7	6	17	62	83	27
Holbrook SM Res.	30	8	3	19	44	89	27
Derby RRL Res.	30	6	7	17	42	91	25
Little Eaton	30	5	6	19	49	86	21
Woolley Moor *-1*	30	4	4	22	38	107	15

Division Two	P	W	D	L	F	A	Pts
Cotes Park	30	22	4	4	101	45	70
Findern	30	18	8	4	85	29	62
Shirland Athletic	30	19	4	7	97	53	61
Rowsley Res.	30	18	5	7	95	41	59
Melbourne D. Res.	30	17	3	10	51	46	54
Alvaston Town	30	13	8	9	79	68	47
Wirksworth Res. *-3*	30	14	4	12	68	50	43
Wirksw'th Ivanhoe	30	13	3	14	41	55	42
Belper U. Res. *-6*	30	11	10	9	39	48	37
Sandiacre T. Res.	30	10	4	16	69	77	34
Swanwick PR Res.	30	10	4	16	61	72	34
Pastures Res. *-3*	30	9	7	14	53	76	31
C. Donington Res.	30	7	7	16	50	84	28
Bargate R. Res. *-1*	30	7	4	19	43	88	24
Ltle Eaton Res. *-3*	30	6	4	20	45	81	19
Hilton Harriers	30	4	5	21	36	100	17

MINING LEAGUE
(One & All Sports)

Division One	P	W	D	L	F	A	Pts
Illogan Res. *-3*	30	26	0	4	116	40	75
Troon *-6*	30	26	0	4	150	24	72
St Buryan *-6*	30	21	2	7	99	58	59
Storm	30	17	4	9	72	51	55
Robartes Arms	30	16	6	8	65	53	54
Halsetown *-3*	30	15	2	13	75	79	44
Gulval	30	12	5	13	92	82	41
Threemilestone *-4*	30	13	5	12	78	72	40
St Ives Town Res.	30	12	4	14	78	78	40
Four Lanes *-1*	30	13	2	15	50	63	40
Redruth United	30	11	3	16	64	77	36
Trevenson United	30	8	4	18	64	78	28
Spice of Life	30	8	4	18	70	104	28
Gwinear C'town	30	7	1	22	55	119	22
Trispen	30	5	6	19	56	128	21
St Just Res.	30	5	2	23	50	128	17

Division Two	P	W	D	L	F	A	Pts
Newlyn Non Ath.	30	24	2	4	125	45	74
Chacewater Res.	30	23	2	5	115	56	71
Goonhavern	30	18	3	9	93	75	57
Illogan RBL A *-3*	30	17	5	8	80	61	53
Sennen *-1*	30	16	5	9	91	59	52
Camb. School Mines	30	15	3	12	98	66	48
Threemilestone Res.	29	13	1	15	45	64	40
Madron	29	12	3	14	84	88	39
St Agnes A *-7*	30	12	5	13	55	84	34
Mount Ambrose *-3*	30	11	3	16	58	89	33
Halsetown Res.	30	8	6	16	61	77	30
Mousehole A *-3*	30	10	3	17	70	94	30
Titans	30	8	6	16	58	80	30
Portreath Res.	30	8	5	17	52	81	29
Holman SC A	30	8	3	19	56	79	27
Crown Inn Glory	30	7	3	20	46	89	24

Division Three	P	W	D	L	F	A	Pts
West Cornwall	28	22	3	3	116	34	66
Ludgvan Res. *-3*	28	20	2	6	129	67	59
Storm Res.	28	18	4	6	93	35	48
Cornish New Boys	28	16	7	5	98	44	55
St Ives Mariners	28	17	2	9	117	59	53

St Buryan Res.	28	17	0	11	58	57	51
Pendeen Res. *-6*	28	14	3	11	69	67	39
Gulval Res.	28	12	2	14	91	74	38
Newlyn NA Res.	28	11	4	13	83	87	37
Redruth Utd Res.	28	10	4	14	75	72	34
Trevenson Res. *-2*	28	10	3	15	57	66	31
Wendron Utd C *-3*	28	8	1	19	43	120	22
Heamoor *-1*	28	6	3	19	29	108	20
Madron Res.	28	5	1	22	35	119	16
Marazion Res. *-6*	28	4	1	23	34	118	7

NORTH & MID-HERTS LEAGUE

Premier Division	P	W	D	L	F	A	Pts
Probuild	16	15	0	1	69	19	45
White Hart *-1*	16	12	2	2	58	18	37
L'don Colney A *-1*	16	7	3	6	25	32	23
Whitwell Village	16	6	3	7	45	47	21
London Road	16	6	2	8	32	40	20
Nirankari NH *-3*	16	7	1	8	34	25	19
Welwyn GC Res.	16	3	4	9	30	52	13
Sporting KFA	16	3	3	10	29	60	12
Redbourn	16	2	4	10	23	52	10

Division One Mid	P	W	D	L	F	A	Pts
Colney Athletic	14	12	2	0	64	13	38
Park Street V. A	14	9	3	2	48	17	30
Potters Bar Crus.	14	9	1	4	49	24	28
Global	14	5	2	7	30	32	17
Inn on the Green	14	5	2	7	31	47	17
Kings Sports Res.	14	3	4	7	30	51	13
Warriors XI	14	2	2	10	22	45	8
St Albans Wdrs	14	2	2	10	25	70	8

Division One North	P	W	D	L	F	A	Pts
Sporting Kandola	14	11	1	2	81	27	34
Probuild Res.	14	10	2	2	59	25	32
Baldock Letchw. A	14	8	1	5	49	30	25
St Ippolyts	14	7	2	5	46	34	23
Fairlands	14	6	2	6	44	40	20
City Hearts	14	6	2	6	50	51	20
Therfield Eagles	14	2	1	11	26	77	7
Westwell	14	0	1	13	10	81	1

NORTH BUCKS & DISTRICT LEAGUE

Premier Division	P	W	D	L	F	A	Pts
Lavendon Sports	26	22	1	3	106	31	67
Steeple Claydon	26	21	1	4	84	28	64
AFC Brickhill Rgrs	26	20	3	3	100	38	63
Grendon Rangers	26	16	3	7	70	44	51
Brackley Sports	26	16	1	9	64	43	49
Bletchley Manor	26	11	4	11	47	57	37
Deanshanger Ath.	26	11	3	12	49	49	36
Stewkley	26	10	5	11	55	68	35
Syresham	26	7	10	9	36	45	31
Thornborough Ath.	26	9	1	16	51	84	28
Southcott Village	26	6	7	13	58	63	25
Bletchley Trees	26	5	3	18	40	95	18
MK Titans	26	3	4	19	39	95	13
Wing Village	26	1	2	23	23	82	5

Intermediate Division	P	W	D	L	F	A	Pts
Sherington	24	19	2	3	74	29	59
Silverstone	24	16	4	4	68	34	52
PB Wolverton T.	24	14	4	6	77	46	46
Castlethorpe	24	12	5	7	57	45	41
Yardley Gobion	24	12	3	9	56	52	39
Abbey	24	11	3	10	52	56	36
Twyford United	24	10	4	10	50	46	34
Great Horwood	24	10	1	13	52	56	31
Workplace Wdrs	24	9	2	13	52	58	29
Great Linford	24	8	5	11	37	48	29
Brackley Spts Res.	24	8	4	12	35	41	28
Hanslope	24	3	4	17	39	84	13
Marsh Gibbon	24	1	5	18	32	86	8

Division One	P	W	D	L	F	A	Pts
Woburn Sands W.	24	19	2	3	94	34	59
Potterspury	24	18	4	2	78	41	58
PB Wolverton Res.	24	16	1	7	86	54	49
Lavendon Res.	24	15	1	8	90	54	46
E & H	24	13	4	7	62	46	43
MK Titans Res.	24	11	5	8	54	53	38
MK Wdrs Res.	24	11	4	9	52	44	37
Woughton	24	9	3	12	66	71	30
Wicken Sports	24	7	4	13	55	70	25
Sherington Res.	24	6	3	15	53	72	21
Bletch. Trees Res.	24	6	3	15	34	61	21
Steeple Clay. Res.	24	4	2	18	47	101	14
Yardley Gob. Res.	24	1	4	19	26	96	7

Division Two	P	W	D	L	F	A	Pts
Westbury	26	21	2	3	98	36	65
Heath Panthers	26	19	3	4	89	17	60
Deanshanger Res.	26	18	5	3	90	40	59
Royal British Leg.	26	15	5	6	67	34	50
Charlton	26	13	5	8	61	47	44
Grendon R. Res.	26	12	7	7	61	45	43
Great Linford Res.	26	11	4	11	42	53	37
Twyford Utd Res.	26	10	3	13	43	58	33
Stewkley Res.	26	6	9	11	49	57	27
Syresham Res.	26	7	5	14	41	64	26
Gt Horwood Res.	26	7	5	14	38	67	26
Hanslope Res.	26	4	6	16	44	93	18
Wing Village Res.	26	4	4	18	27	70	16
Marsh Gibb. Res.	26	3	1	22	23	92	10

NORTH DEVON LEAGUE
(North Devon Journal)

Premier Division	P	W	D	L	F	A	Pts
Boca Seniors	28	25	0	3	91	39	75
Appledore Res.	28	19	4	5	98	40	61
Braunton	28	17	4	7	79	43	55
Barnstaple AAC	28	16	4	8	89	48	52
North Molton	28	14	7	7	60	38	49
Combe Martin	28	14	3	11	81	68	45
Shamwickshire R.	28	10	11	7	56	50	41
Bradworthy United	28	11	6	11	60	53	39
Ilfracombe T. Res.	28	10	4	14	58	56	34
Torridgeside	28	7	7	14	62	82	28
Morwenstow Res.	28	8	3	17	50	108	27
Georgeham	28	7	4	17	48	72	25
Putford	28	5	8	15	54	76	23
Hartland	28	4	7	17	52	101	19
Dolton Rangers	28	5	4	19	39	103	19

Senior Division	P	W	D	L	F	A	Pts
Torrington	26	22	1	3	116	24	67
Braunton Res.	26	21	2	3	90	42	65
Bideford Res.	26	18	3	5	72	26	57
Shebbear United	26	13	6	7	72	46	45
Bratton Fleming	26	11	4	11	69	52	37
Sham'kshire Res.	26	9	8	9	66	70	35
Pilton Academicals	26	10	4	12	47	49	34
Northam Lions	26	9	6	11	61	65	33
B'staple AAC Res.	26	10	3	13	63	81	33
Chittlehampton	26	8	7	11	49	55	31
Kilkhampton	26	7	6	13	63	83	27
South Molton	26	8	0	18	44	71	24
Combe M. Res. *-3*	26	4	4	18	45	96	13
Clovelly	26	3	4	19	43	140	13

Int. Division One	P	W	D	L	F	A	Pts
Landkey	28	20	4	4	100	34	64
Bude Town Res.	28	19	4	5	114	48	61
Nth Molton Res.	28	18	6	4	91	36	60
Equalizers	28	16	4	8	81	49	52
Torrington Res.	28	17	1	10	69	62	52
Woolsery	28	14	8	6	87	54	50
T'gton Admirals *-3*	28	13	5	10	75	60	41
Park United	28	12	5	11	73	77	41
High Bickington	28	10	4	14	59	69	34
Braunton "A"	28	8	4	16	56	94	28
Anchor	28	7	6	15	59	89	27
Merton	28	7	4	17	57	79	25
Northam L. Res.	28	6	6	16	55	96	24
Sporting Barum	28	5	3	20	48	98	18
Hartland Res.	28	5	2	21	32	111	17

Int. Division Two	P	W	D	L	F	A	Pts
Buckland Brewer	24	15	5	4	60	30	50
Ilfracombe Town A	24	16	1	7	86	50	49
Lynton	24	14	6	4	81	35	48
Putford Res.	24	13	4	7	46	41	43
Pilton Acads Res.	24	11	5	8	70	48	38
Bradworthy Res.	24	11	3	10	69	59	36
South Molton Res.	24	11	3	10	49	50	36
North Molton A	24	11	2	11	50	59	35
Mortehoe	24	10	4	10	59	54	34
B. Fleming Res.	24	8	2	14	52	73	26
Northam Lions A	24	7	3	14	48	77	24
Torridgeside Res.	24	5	3	16	53	71	18
Chit'hampton Res.	24	1	5	18	31	107	8

NORTH EAST NORFOLK LEAGUE

Premier Division	P	W	D	L	F	A	Pts
Gimingham	22	15	3	4	62	31	48
Mundesley	22	14	5	3	61	30	47
East Ruston	22	11	5	6	62	37	38
Happisburgh	22	11	4	7	59	52	37
Corpusty	22	10	6	6	57	53	36
N Walsham T. A	22	9	4	9	61	48	31
Lyng	22	8	6	8	45	47	30
Nth Walsham OB	22	7	8	7	60	54	29
Coltishall	22	8	4	10	53	45	28
Horning	22	7	4	11	54	67	25
Hickling FC	22	2	4	16	34	69	10
Erpingham *-1*	22	1	5	16	26	101	7

Division One	P	W	D	L	F	A	Pts
Bodham	22	20	1	1	140	28	61
Runton	22	17	2	3	87	31	53
Aldborough	22	15	5	2	86	42	50
Stalham Town A	22	11	2	9	51	69	35
Corpusty Res.	22	11	0	11	60	65	33
Aylsham A	22	8	4	10	65	82	28
Briston	22	8	1	13	50	65	25
Buxton Res.	22	7	3	12	61	100	24
Nth Wal. OB Res.	22	7	2	13	75	75	23
Holt United A	22	6	2	14	42	112	20
Felmingham	22	5	3	14	47	60	18
Dilham	22	3	3	16	47	82	12

Division Two	P	W	D	L	F	A	Pts
Mundesley Res.	20	14	2	4	76	43	44
Haisbro Atheltic	20	13	3	4	78	29	42
Cawston	20	10	6	4	53	47	36
Briston Res.	20	10	5	5	71	33	35
East Ruston Res.	20	10	2	8	43	41	32
Cromer YOB	20	8	5	7	58	45	29
Blakeney FC	20	8	5	7	51	55	29
Gimingham Res.	20	7	2	11	52	66	23
Holt Colts	20	5	1	14	27	59	16
Hickling Res.	20	3	4	13	39	79	13
Aldborough Res.	20	4	1	15	33	84	13

NORTH GLOUCESTERSHIRE LEAGUE
(Sparkpak)

Premier Division	P	W	D	L	F	A	Pts
Aylburton Rovers	26	19	5	2	79	41	62
Minsterworth	26	19	3	4	98	49	60
Ruardean Hill Rg.	26	16	4	6	60	33	52
Newent Town	26	16	3	7	75	40	51
Woolaston	26	13	8	5	53	31	47
Lydney Town Res.	26	12	3	11	49	41	39
Westbury United	26	11	4	11	59	51	37
Staunton & Corse	26	6	8	12	45	57	26
Milkwall	26	7	5	14	45	71	26
Coleford United	26	7	4	15	46	68	25
Broadwell A. Res.	26	7	4	15	33	58	25
Mushet/Coalway	26	6	6	14	30	61	24
Redbrook Rovers	26	5	4	17	51	84	19
Lydbrook A. Res.	26	4	7	15	36	74	19

Division One	P	W	D	L	F	A	Pts
Huntley	22	17	3	2	83	45	54
Baker Street	22	17	2	3	71	29	53
Whitecroft	22	12	6	4	62	33	42
Ellwood Res.	22	11	5	6	53	32	38
Newnham United	22	11	3	8	62	53	36
English Bicknor	22	9	7	6	40	35	34
Rank Outsiders	22	8	2	12	42	48	26
Blakeney	22	6	6	10	55	63	24
Bream Amateurs	22	6	3	13	38	60	21
Yorkley	22	4	6	12	30	57	18
Worrall Hill	22	4	2	16	26	71	14
Lydbrook Ath. A	22	2	5	15	34	70	11

Division Two	P	W	D	L	F	A	Pts
Howle Hill	24	18	2	4	83	33	56
Sedbury United	24	18	0	6	80	47	54
Harrow Hill A	24	14	2	8	75	57	44
Mitcheldean Res.	24	12	5	7	69	42	41
Aylburton R. Res.	24	12	4	8	49	42	40
Puma	24	10	6	8	54	56	36
Woolaston Res.	24	10	3	11	38	39	33
Lydney Town A	24	10	3	11	46	63	33
Longhope	24	8	5	11	50	73	29
Newent T. Res.	24	8	4	12	53	51	28
Westbury U Res.	24	5	6	13	56	63	21
Soudley Res.	24	6	3	15	38	70	21
Ruspidge United	24	3	1	20	31	86	10

Division Three	P	W	D	L	F	A	Pts
Viney St Sw. Res.	18	14	2	2	44	16	44
Ruardean Hill Res.	18	13	4	1	51	13	43
St Briavels	18	13	2	3	50	22	41

	P	W	D	L	F	A	Pts
Staunton/C. Res.	18	8	3	7	44	24	27
Whitecroft Res.	18	7	4	7	31	29	25
Mushet & C. Res.	18	5	4	9	18	25	19
Puma Res.	18	5	3	10	25	43	18
Tidenham Res.	18	4	6	8	21	43	18
Blakeney Res.	18	4	1	13	22	44	13
Mitcheldean A	18	2	1	15	10	57	7

Division Four	P	W	D	L	F	A	Pts
White Horse	24	19	1	4	94	27	58
Coleford Utd Res.	24	18	0	6	94	41	54
Minsterworth Res.	24	16	2	6	73	35	50
Milkwall Res.	24	13	3	8	71	33	42
Yorkley Res.	24	12	4	8	67	49	40
Rk O'siders Res.	24	12	3	9	57	52	39
Redbrook R. Res.	24	13	0	11	60	66	39
Bream Amtrs Res.	24	10	4	10	53	58	34
Whitecroft A	24	8	3	13	37	60	27
Eng. Bicknor Res.	24	6	3	15	47	71	21
St Briavels Res.	24	6	1	17	30	90	19
Tidenham A	24	6	0	18	45	90	18
Puma A	24	4	2	18	26	82	14

NORTH LANCASHIRE & DISTRICT LEAGUE

(Lancaster Honda)

Premier Division	P	W	D	L	F	A	Pts
Highgrove	26	19	4	3	88	38	61
Marsh United	26	18	4	4	72	25	58
Storeys	26	17	4	5	67	34	55
Ingleton	26	17	2	7	67	37	53
Morecambe Ryls	26	14	5	7	49	45	47
Carnforth Rgrs	26	14	4	8	72	29	46
TIC Dynamos	26	13	5	8	59	33	44
Cartmel & District	26	13	5	8	50	36	44
Kirkby Lonsdale	26	8	4	14	42	67	28
Halton Rangers	26	7	3	16	42	68	24
M'cmbe Hoops -3	26	8	0	18	64	84	21
Galgate -3	26	7	2	17	42	57	20
Swarthmoor Soc.	26	2	4	20	24	83	10
Caton United	26	1	2	23	38	140	5

Division One	P	W	D	L	F	A	Pts
Bentham	26	22	1	3	81	23	67
Bowerham	26	21	0	5	71	22	63
Storeys Res.	26	17	3	6	75	35	54
Marsh Utd Res.	26	16	2	8	62	39	50
Slyne Hest (LCC)	26	12	6	8	72	47	42
Cartmel/D. Res.	26	12	5	9	50	40	41
Ingleton Res.	26	10	5	11	49	61	35
Highgrove Res.	26	9	4	13	47	56	31
More. Ryls Res.	26	9	3	14	50	58	30
College -3	26	9	5	12	40	49	29
Millhead	26	8	4	14	52	72	28
Boys Club	26	7	6	13	40	51	27
Torrisholme -3	26	3	5	18	26	85	11
Grange	26	1	3	22	33	110	6

Division Two	P	W	D	L	F	A	Pts
Bolton-le-Sands	22	17	3	2	63	19	54
Freehold	22	16	2	4	56	18	50
Overton	22	13	3	6	45	36	42
Arnside	22	10	8	4	47	29	38
K. Lonsdale Res.	22	11	1	10	51	39	34
Furness Rov. Res.	22	10	3	9	42	32	33
M'cmbe Cricket C	22	9	2	11	63	52	29
Slyne Hest Res.	22	8	5	9	27	34	29
Swarthmoor Res.	22	7	3	12	31	57	24
Westgate Wdrs	22	6	2	14	37	46	20
Caton Utd Res. -3	22	6	0	16	27	85	15
Galgate Res. -3	22	1	4	17	26	68	4

Division Three	P	W	D	L	F	A	Pts
Carnforth R. Res.	22	14	6	2	60	28	48
Allithwaite Rgrs	22	15	3	4	56	31	48
Halton Rgrs Res.	22	15	1	6	60	28	46
Squires	22	12	7	3	56	45	43
Bentham Res.	22	10	6	6	54	33	36
Gregson	22	9	4	9	44	37	31
Burton Thistle	22	6	6	10	46	48	24
Heysham	22	5	6	11	29	50	21
Boys Club Res.	22	5	4	13	26	47	19
Bolton-le-S. Res.	22	4	6	12	33	61	18
Grange Res.	22	4	5	13	37	61	17
Arnside Res.	22	4	4	14	23	55	16

Division Four	P	W	D	L	F	A	Pts
Morecambe Gold	22	15	4	3	70	29	49
Highgrove Colts	22	14	4	4	79	41	46
Moghuls	22	15	1	6	46	39	46
AFC Moorlands	22	13	4	5	65	47	43
Villa Royale	22	14	1	7	63	45	43
Millhead Res.	22	12	3	7	70	44	39
College Res.	22	12	2	8	71	58	38
M'cambe CC Res.	22	7	2	13	49	66	23
Heysham Res.	22	5	2	15	34	56	17
Ingleton A	22	4	4	14	30	63	16
Gregson Res.	22	4	2	16	32	67	14
Overton Res. -9	22	1	3	18	32	86	-3

NORTH LEICESTERSHIRE LEAGUE

Premier Division	P	W	D	L	F	A	Pts
M. Mowbray BS	18	14	3	1	70	20	45
Sileby Saints	18	14	0	4	77	33	42
Loughborough	18	11	4	3	48	30	37
Caterpillar	18	7	2	9	45	50	23
Shepshed Amtrs	18	6	5	7	25	40	23
Ingles	18	6	4	8	47	46	22
Genesis	18	6	4	8	43	44	22
Sutton Bonington	18	7	1	10	36	39	22
Woodhouse Imp.	18	3	2	13	28	68	11
Loughborough T.	18	2	3	13	35	84	9

Bagworth Colliery - record expunged
Whitwick Colliery - record expunged

Division One	P	W	D	L	F	A	Pts
Falcons	20	17	1	2	73	16	52
Markfield	20	14	4	2	66	30	46
Whitwick Wdrs	20	13	4	3	49	25	43
Asfordby Village	20	12	3	5	47	33	39
East Leake Ath.	20	10	3	7	58	43	33
Sileby Victoria	20	7	5	8	39	44	26
Charnwood Old B.	20	6	5	9	43	68	23
Kegw'th Imperial	20	5	4	11	46	49	19
S. Bon'gton Acad	20	6	1	13	39	66	19
Burton -1	20	1	4	15	29	68	6
ATI Garryson	20	1	2	17	27	74	5

Division Two	P	W	D	L	F	A	Pts
Birstall Old Boys	20	14	3	3	77	31	45
Ashby Ivanhoe A	20	14	2	4	82	29	44
Belton Villa	20	13	2	5	88	40	41
Anstey Crown	20	11	3	6	81	44	36
The Railway EWM	20	11	3	6	55	31	36
Vice Versa	20	9	3	8	55	57	30
Markfield Res.	20	9	2	9	64	45	29
Thurmaston Rgrs	20	9	1	10	56	38	28
Castle Donington	20	7	0	13	37	45	21
Loughboro. Res.	20	3	1	16	25	115	10
Shepshed A. Res.	20	0	0	20	14	159	0

Division Three	P	W	D	L	F	A	Pts
Ingles Res.	22	17	1	4	73	31	52
ATI Garryson Res.	22	15	4	3	100	41	49
Thringstone Rgrs	22	13	2	7	66	40	41
Bagworth C. Res.	22	12	2	8	74	62	38
Loughboro. Utd	22	10	6	6	59	50	36
E. Leake A. Res.	22	8	4	10	51	49	28
Woodhse I. Res.	22	8	1	13	53	88	25
Thringstone MW	22	6	4	12	34	46	22
Measham Imp.	22	6	4	12	49	71	22
Greenhill YC	22	6	4	12	38	61	22
Belgrave A	22	6	3	13	56	80	21
Sileby Sts Res. -1	22	6	3	13	38	72	20

Division Four	P	W	D	L	F	A	Pts
Whitwick W. Res.	22	16	4	2	80	26	52
M. Mow. BS Res.	22	14	6	2	67	19	48
Ferrari	22	13	4	5	68	53	43
Caterpillar Res.	22	13	3	6	64	45	42
Long Clawson	22	10	4	8	56	51	34
Markfield A	22	7	8	7	62	52	29
Genesis Res.	22	8	5	9	47	55	29
Birstall OB Res.	22	8	3	11	53	63	27
L'boro. Utd Res.	22	6	5	11	43	50	23
Sileby Vics Res.	22	5	5	12	51	68	20
S. Bonington Res.	22	3	3	16	24	63	12
L'borough Galaxy	22	3	2	17	36	106	11

NORTH NORTHUMBERLAND LEAGUE

Division One	P	W	D	L	F	A	Pts
Ashington Athletic	18	13	2	3	65	19	41
Berwick Town	18	13	1	4	59	26	37
Shilbottle Coll. W.	18	10	1	7	39	28	34
Alnmouth	18	10	2	6	59	30	32
Lowick United	18	9	2	7	44	37	32
North Sunderland	18	9	2	7	38	33	29
Rothbury	18	6	3	9	33	59	24
Bedlington T. Res.	18	8	0	10	34	34	21
Craster Rovers	18	1	3	14	19	73	9
Acklington Athletic	18	2	2	14	27	78	5

Lynemouth Miners Welfare - record expunged

Division Two	P	W	D	L	F	A	Pts
Alnwick T. Res.	20	18	1	1	87	18	55
Berwick Utd Res.	20	13	3	4	72	47	39
Lynem'th MW Res.	20	11	4	5	53	30	37
Springhill	20	10	4	6	67	38	34
Belford	20	9	3	8	48	43	30
Wooler	20	8	4	8	43	38	25
Bamburgh Castle	20	8	1	12	41	49	25
Hedgeley Rovers	20	5	4	11	32	59	22
Embleton W. Rov.	20	5	2	13	35	59	14
Rothbury Res.	20	4	2	14	23	79	14
Alnmouth United	20	3	4	13	27	66	13

Berwick Town Res. - record expunged

NORTH WEST NORFOLK LEAGUE

(Build Center)

Division One	P	W	D	L	F	A	Pts
Heacham	24	19	4	1	97	40	61
Kings Lynn A	24	16	3	5	96	27	51
Reffley Royals	24	14	4	6	83	39	46
Wiggenhall	24	14	3	7	66	33	45
West Winch	24	13	6	5	67	39	45
Lynn Docklands	24	12	4	8	59	43	40
Terrington	24	11	7	6	50	50	40
Sandringham	24	7	6	11	38	59	27
Ingoldisthorpe	24	7	3	14	46	47	24
W. Lynn S&S Res.	24	7	3	14	38	65	24
Narborough	24	5	3	16	32	63	18
Lynn Napier -3	24	6	1	17	42	94	16
Gaywood -3	24	1	1	22	13	128	1

Division Two	P	W	D	L	F	A	Pts
Pott Row	26	23	3	0	107	25	72
Docking	26	19	4	3	114	35	61
Wisbech United	26	14	5	7	64	43	47
Gt Massingham	26	13	5	8	56	41	44
Flitcham	26	11	5	10	63	59	38
Ing'isthorpe Res.	26	11	3	12	59	64	36
Marham Wdrs	26	11	3	12	56	66	36
Terrington Res.	26	11	2	13	64	72	35
Old Hunstanton -5	26	11	2	13	68	70	32
Watlington	26	8	7	11	43	57	31
Castle Rising	26	8	3	15	60	80	27
Hunstanton	26	8	3	15	35	86	27
Dersingham R. A	26	6	5	15	53	81	23
West Winch Res.	26	0	6	20	30	94	6

Division Three	P	W	D	L	F	A	Pts
Lynn Discovery	24	24	0	0	140	35	72
Barney United	24	17	3	4	92	42	54
Wiggenhall Res.	24	16	4	4	98	49	52
South Creake	24	13	3	8	69	54	42
Smithdon	24	11	2	11	63	65	35
William Burt -3	24	9	3	12	45	44	27
Heacham Res.	24	7	5	12	52	74	26
Snettisham	24	7	3	14	51	87	24
Denver Bell	24	7	3	14	50	86	24
W. Lynn Riverside	24	6	4	14	48	87	22
Walsingham	24	5	6	13	36	50	21
Burnham Mkt -3	24	7	3	14	58	99	21
Narboro. Res. -9	24	6	3	15	41	71	12

Division Four	P	W	D	L	F	A	Pts
Castle Rising Res.	20	14	2	4	71	36	44
Discovery Royals	20	13	2	5	104	36	41
Greyfriars	20	11	4	5	46	30	37
Wiggenhall A -3	20	13	0	7	63	36	36
Lynn Napier Res.	20	8	8	4	49	41	32
Watlington Res. -3	20	10	2	8	52	53	29
Dersingham R. B	20	7	1	12	28	38	22
Springwood -3	20	7	3	10	55	69	21
Snettisham Res.	20	6	3	11	39	67	21
Pentney	20	5	2	13	43	72	17
Heacham A	20	2	1	17	22	94	7

NORTHAMPTON TOWN LEAGUE

(Peter Smith Recruitment)

Premier Division	P	W	D	L	F	A	Pts
Cotton Hill	20	15	0	5	81	44	45
N'ton Harlequins	20	13	1	6	75	26	40

Team	P	W	D	L	F	A	Pts
Delapre Old Boys	20	11	3	6	57	54	36
Hitec Roofing	20	10	4	6	56	48	34
Univ. Northampton	20	10	1	9	68	45	31
Hometech	20	8	4	8	47	48	28
Airflow	20	7	5	8	46	46	26
Obelisk United	20	7	2	11	41	65	23
Thorplands Utd -3	20	7	2	11	54	75	20
Far Cotton Loco	20	5	4	11	42	52	19
Denton -3	20	2	4	14	32	96	7

Millwheel - record expunged

Division One	P	W	D	L	F	A	Pts
Ashley Rovers	20	17	1	2	78	31	52
Liberty Stars	20	14	3	3	69	30	45
Real Dragoon	20	13	1	6	57	39	40
L Buckby Ravens	20	12	1	7	92	44	37
SPA	20	12	1	7	46	33	37
N'ton Harl. Res.	20	9	3	8	57	50	30
Corby Strip M Res.	20	5	1	14	39	65	16
Northants Police	20	4	4	12	29	57	16
J King Blisworth A	20	4	2	14	24	65	14
Thorplands Res. -3	20	5	2	13	37	88	14
Univ. N'ton Res. -6	20	4	3	13	35	61	9

NOTTS AMATEUR ALLIANCE

Premier Division	P	W	D	L	F	A	Pts
Netherfield Albion	20	12	3	5	63	40	39
Grey Mare United	20	11	3	6	44	42	36
Ashland Rovers	20	10	5	5	36	34	35
Beacon -3	20	10	3	7	52	32	30
Arnold Longbow	20	8	6	6	55	48	30
Headstocks	20	8	5	7	44	33	29
FC Samba	20	9	2	9	41	39	29
Santos	20	8	4	8	37	28	28
Vernon Villa	20	7	3	10	45	52	24
Trident	20	7	2	11	56	70	23
Gedling S'bank A	20	1	2	17	23	78	5

Division One	P	W	D	L	F	A	Pts
Ashland R. Res.	22	19	1	2	117	41	58
East Valley United	22	13	3	6	65	40	42
Calverton MW B	22	13	1	8	56	39	40
Nuthall	22	11	6	5	57	42	39
Ruddington V. A	22	9	5	8	52	55	32
Kirton Brickworks	22	9	2	11	38	44	29
AFC Bridgford	22	7	5	10	43	61	26
Kimberley MWOB	22	7	2	13	44	60	23
Premium	22	6	5	11	41	59	23
Vernon Villa Res.	22	6	4	12	42	60	22
Boots Athletic A	22	7	1	14	44	63	22
Grey Goose	22	6	3	13	44	79	21

Division Two	P	W	D	L	F	A	Pts
Kashmir	20	16	1	3	78	33	49
Coopers Arms FC	20	15	4	1	83	39	49
Burton Joyce A	20	13	1	6	70	47	40
Clifton United	20	11	5	4	44	29	38
Notts Metropolis	20	7	3	10	42	49	24
Nottm Sikh Lions	20	7	3	10	51	64	24
Arnold Town A	20	6	3	11	45	54	21
Basford United A	20	6	2	12	39	58	20
Ali I	20	5	5	10	34	53	20
Netherfield A. Res.	20	5	4	11	46	55	19
Three Crowns FC	20	2	3	15	38	89	9

Division Three	P	W	D	L	F	A	Pts
Real United	22	19	2	1	94	29	59
Gedling T. Res.	22	16	1	5	89	44	49
Durham Ox	22	12	4	6	55	39	40
Clifton Utd Res.	22	10	5	7	72	49	35
Bingham Town	22	8	8	6	62	61	32
Premium A	22	9	3	10	58	55	30
Pegasus	22	9	2	11	57	85	29
Notts Met. Res.	22	7	3	12	55	78	24
Netherfield Boys	22	6	5	11	49	53	23
Nottinghamshire B	22	6	4	12	43	66	22
Sherwood Cas.	22	4	6	12	43	69	18
Harvey Hadden	22	2	5	15	42	91	11

NOTTS SENIOR LEAGUE
(Precision Training)

Senior Division	P	W	D	L	F	A	Pts
Bilboro. Pelican	32	19	9	4	82	35	66
Boots Athletic	32	20	2	10	76	40	62
Basford United	32	18	5	9	74	48	59
Wollaton	32	17	4	11	72	63	55
Magdala Amtrs	32	15	7	10	60	52	52
Cotgrave CWU	32	14	9	9	72	65	51
H'nall Rolls Leis.	32	11	11	10	55	58	44
Linby Colliery W.	32	13	4	15	55	62	43
Keyworth United	32	12	5	15	54	59	41
Caribbean Cav.	32	13	3	16	56	65	39
Kimberley MW	32	11	5	16	53	54	38
Clifton	32	11	4	17	61	73	37
Attenborough	32	10	7	15	54	70	37
Ruddington Utd	32	9	9	14	54	68	36
Gedling S'thbank	32	10	5	17	47	75	35
Notts Police	32	9	7	16	58	75	34
Awsworth Villa	32	9	6	17	57	78	33

Division One	P	W	D	L	F	A	Pts
Bulwell	28	20	2	6	110	38	62
Greenw'd M. Res.	28	15	9	4	78	39	54
Basford Utd Res.	28	15	8	5	61	33	53
Sandhurst	28	15	6	7	70	43	51
Matrixgrade	28	15	6	7	72	53	51
Bilborough P. Res.	28	15	5	8	58	34	50
Wollaton Res.	28	14	5	9	87	40	47
Gedling Sbk Res.	28	13	4	11	56	50	43
Cotgrave Res.	28	12	6	10	58	65	42
Boots Ath. Res.	28	9	9	10	56	55	36
Keyworth U. Res.	28	8	4	16	46	68	28
Kimberley MW Res.	28	6	6	16	47	82	24
Clifton Res.	28	6	5	17	47	111	23
Underwood Villa	28	6	3	19	51	92	21
Bilborough Town	28	1	2	25	26	120	5

Division Two	P	W	D	L	F	A	Pts
Calverton MW Ac.	20	15	3	2	55	28	48
Awsworth V. Res.	20	14	2	4	63	27	44
Magdala A. Res.	20	13	4	3	43	26	43
Linby CW Res.	20	11	3	6	69	37	36
Sandhurst Res.	20	9	2	9	29	42	29
Hucknall RL Res.	20	8	3	9	37	37	27
Ruddington V. Res.	20	8	3	9	48	49	27
Caribbean C. Res.	20	6	4	10	38	55	22
Bottesford	20	4	3	13	37	55	15
Attenboro. Res.	20	2	5	13	21	51	11
Keyworth U. Acad.	20	3	2	15	37	70	11

PERRY STREET & DISTRICT LEAGUE

Premier Division	P	W	D	L	F	A	Pts
Crewkerne	22	16	3	3	80	35	51
South Petherton	22	14	3	5	53	23	45
Ilminster T. Res.	22	13	1	8	49	36	40
Lyme Regis	22	11	6	5	63	31	39
Merriott Rovers	22	12	2	8	52	48	38
Combe St N. Res.	22	11	3	8	31	33	36
W. Hse Sym'bury	22	11	2	9	46	54	35
Perry Street & YH	22	6	6	10	28	45	24
Beaminster	22	6	3	13	38	54	21
Misterton	22	4	7	11	46	54	19
Farway United	22	5	0	17	26	70	15
Winsham	22	4	2	16	35	64	14

Division One	P	W	D	L	F	A	Pts
Barrington	22	18	0	4	76	24	54
Charmouth	22	16	1	5	70	34	49
Forton Rangers	22	15	1	6	63	28	46
W & Mid Chinnock	22	13	2	7	64	48	41
Lyme Regis Res.	22	12	2	8	62	47	38
Chard Rangers	22	10	3	9	49	50	33
Thorncombe	22	10	2	10	60	55	32
Pymore	22	9	1	12	43	57	28
Merriott R. Res. -5	22	7	5	10	39	59	21
Netherbury	22	7	0	15	42	69	21
Chard United	22	3	1	18	33	82	10
Chard T. Colts -3	22	1	4	17	29	77	4

Division Two	P	W	D	L	F	A	Pts
Ilminster T. Colts	22	17	4	1	76	30	55
Perry Street Res.	22	17	2	3	88	26	53
Millwey Rise	22	14	2	6	56	31	44
Shep. Beauchamp	22	12	3	7	63	35	39
Hinton St George	22	11	5	6	66	46	38
Uplyme	22	11	3	8	51	56	36
Forton R. Res. -1	22	8	2	12	52	55	25
Dowlish/Donyatt	22	5	4	13	49	60	19
Drimpton -1	22	6	2	14	43	89	19
S. Petherton Res.	22	5	3	14	54	80	18
Combe St N. A	22	5	2	15	37	79	17
WH Sym. Res. -1	22	5	0	17	37	85	14

Division Three	P	W	D	L	F	A	Pts
Norton Athletic	20	16	3	1	74	20	51
Beaminster Res.	20	14	2	4	54	22	44
Luso-Chard	20	11	5	4	69	43	38
Crewkerne Res.	20	11	2	7	48	32	35
Hawkchurch	20	9	3	8	51	52	30
Millwey Rise Res.	20	9	2	9	44	42	29
Shep. Beau. Res.	20	7	6	7	46	43	27
Chard Rgrs Res.	20	7	1	12	37	69	22
Lyme Bantams	20	4	3	13	36	63	15
Hinton SG Res. -1	20	4	3	13	31	59	14
Combe SN B -3	20	3	0	17	23	68	6

Division Four	P	W	D	L	F	A	Pts
Misterton Res.	22	18	1	3	93	34	55
Fivehead United	22	18	0	4	74	32	54
Crewkerne Rgrs	22	17	1	4	96	42	52
FC First	22	15	0	7	100	57	45
Ilminster Town A	22	11	3	8	68	54	36
Charmouth Res.	22	10	3	9	45	53	33
Barrington Res.	22	9	3	10	57	58	30
Farway Utd Res.	22	9	0	13	51	63	27
Winsham Res.	22	6	4	12	45	55	22
Thorncombe Res.	22	6	1	15	38	75	19
Chard United Res.	22	2	2	18	25	92	8
H'church Res. -1	22	1	2	19	34	111	4

PLYMOUTH & WEST DEVON COMBINATION

Premier Division	P	W	D	L	F	A	Pts
Mount Gould	22	18	1	3	70	18	55
Roborough	22	14	5	3	74	30	47
Univ. of Plymouth	22	14	5	3	67	29	47
Wessex Rangers	22	12	6	4	50	37	42
Staddiscmbe Colts	22	8	8	6	48	41	32
Tamarside -3	22	9	4	9	43	43	28
Horrabridge R. SA	22	8	4	10	32	45	28
Old Suttonians	22	7	6	9	37	40	27
Plym. Parkway A	22	8	3	11	30	43	27
Yealm G'well Rgrs	22	4	2	16	32	55	14
Vospers OV Res.	22	2	4	16	25	70	10
Lee Moor -3	22	3	2	17	37	94	8

Royal Mail MDEC - record expunged

Senior Division	P	W	D	L	F	A	Pts
Ordulph Arms	22	15	5	2	79	25	50
Utd Services Plym.	22	14	7	1	65	27	49
Western M'gage S.	22	14	1	7	52	32	43
Yelverton	22	13	3	6	77	47	42
SWEB	22	12	4	6	65	51	40
Horrabridge Res.	22	11	3	8	62	44	36
Cafe Roma	22	8	2	12	51	56	26
Univ Plym. Res. -3	22	8	4	10	59	56	25
O Suttonians Res.	22	7	3	12	52	56	24
Plymouth YMCA	22	6	1	15	49	94	19
Morley Rangers	22	4	2	16	42	86	14
Buckland Milton/C	22	2	1	19	27	106	7

Plymouth City - record expunged

Intermediate Div.	P	W	D	L	F	A	Pts
Roborough Res.	20	16	0	4	90	42	48
Chard United	20	15	3	2	71	31	48
Staddiscmbe Res.	20	11	3	6	69	54	36
Kings A. Tamerton	20	10	3	7	61	56	33
Plym. Trophyman	20	9	4	7	65	47	31
Ivybridge T. Res.	20	8	2	10	47	47	26
Chaddlew'd MOB	20	7	4	9	44	49	25
Ham Green Rov.	20	7	2	11	43	44	23
Univ. Plym'th A -3	20	7	4	9	57	60	22
Shakespeare	20	7	1	12	47	57	22
Morley Rgrs Res.	20	0	0	20	21	128	0

Porters - record expunged

PORTSMOUTH & DISTRICT LEAGUE

Premier Division	P	W	D	L	F	A	Pts
Wymering	20	17	1	2	109	25	52
Univ. Portsmouth	20	17	1	2	110	30	52
W'looville Soc. C.	20	12	2	6	59	40	38
Prospect	20	12	2	6	63	50	38
Co-op	20	12	2	6	66	54	38
Old Portmuthians	20	8	1	11	44	55	25
Hayling Billy	20	7	1	12	56	84	22
St Helena Bobs	20	6	4	10	45	75	22
Kingston Arrows	20	5	1	14	56	86	16
Horndean United	20	3	1	16	33	94	10
Segensworth	20	2	2	16	29	77	8

Division One	P	W	D	L	F	A	Pts
Portsea Comm. -2	20	16	4	0	94	24	50
Farefield Sports	20	12	4	4	46	21	40
Fleur de Lys	20	12	2	6	52	30	38

Newcome Arms	20	10	5	5	77	45	35
Denmead/P. Res.	20	10	4	6	66	57	34
AFC Ventora -1	20	10	2	8	44	43	31
Wymering Res.	20	6	3	11	32	58	21
Fleet Supp. Ltd -1	20	6	2	12	36	67	19
Southside	20	5	3	12	40	57	18
Portchester	20	5	2	13	29	61	17
Cosham Blues	20	1	3	16	29	82	6

Division Two	P	W	D	L	F	A	Pts
P'mth Kurdish Utd	22	17	2	3	82	36	53
Rovers Reunited	22	15	3	4	88	38	48
Cosham B. Res.	22	14	3	5	69	35	45
Carberry	22	13	2	7	79	33	41
Inter Solent	22	13	2	7	82	39	41
FC Southsea	22	12	3	7	65	40	39
Southsea Town	22	12	3	7	70	48	39
Westover Rgrs	22	8	2	12	61	89	26
Farefield Sp. Res.	22	6	2	14	48	60	20
Cosham Pk Rgrs	22	5	0	17	37	87	15
DBC	22	3	1	18	26	110	10
Stamshaw Spart.	22	2	1	19	32	124	7

PRESTON & DISTRICT LEAGUE

Premier Division	P	W	D	L	F	A	Pts
Longridge Town	30	24	4	2	113	21	76
Preston Wdrs	30	20	5	5	109	41	65
Southport Trinity A	30	18	4	8	72	46	58
Southport Amtrs	30	18	2	10	78	47	56
New Longton Rov.	30	14	10	6	62	43	52
B'cough Richmond	30	14	4	12	67	56	46
Hoghton W. End	30	14	4	12	50	58	46
Appley Bridge	30	11	7	12	52	59	40
Lostock St G. Res.	30	11	6	13	54	65	39
Tarleton Corries	30	11	5	14	71	61	38
Leyland St Marys	30	11	3	16	61	109	36
Croston Spts Res.	30	10	5	15	59	86	35
Leyland Red Rose	30	7	7	16	62	88	28
Baxters -3	30	8	2	20	51	94	23
Town Green	30	6	4	20	45	82	22
Eccleston/Heskin	30	5	4	21	45	95	19

Division One	P	W	D	L	F	A	Pts
Ainsdale Utd -3	22	15	3	4	39	26	45
Charnock Rich. A	22	13	2	7	50	29	41
Southport Trin. B	22	12	3	7	51	36	39
Walmer Bridge	22	12	3	7	44	40	39
CCA	22	12	2	8	51	48	38
Chipping	22	10	2	10	61	58	32
Sumners	22	9	5	8	45	47	32
Preston GSA	22	8	3	11	46	51	27
Hoole United	22	7	3	12	49	49	24
Highcross	22	7	3	12	41	48	24
Top Spinners	22	6	4	12	34	52	22
B'cough Bridge +3	22	4	1	17	34	61	16

Division Two	P	W	D	L	F	A	Pts
Walton-le-Dale	20	12	3	5	63	39	39
Mawdesley	20	10	4	6	48	38	34
AFC Mawdesley	20	11	0	9	56	44	33
Southport Am Res.	20	8	8	4	43	35	32
Farington Villa	20	9	3	8	39	37	30
Leyland RR Res.	20	8	3	9	42	51	27
Preston United	20	8	2	10	49	51	26
Preston GSA Res.	20	7	4	9	49	58	25
Newman College	20	7	3	10	35	42	24
Longridge T. Res.	20	7	2	11	42	45	23
Tarleton Cor. Res.	20	3	8	9	33	59	17

Division Three	P	W	D	L	F	A	Pts
Leyland Red R. A	20	16	2	2	103	53	50
Birkdale United	20	14	2	4	67	35	44
Deepdale	20	12	6	2	70	30	42
Wyre Villa A	20	13	2	5	82	37	41
Penwortham Town	20	10	1	9	62	61	31
Catforth	20	8	3	9	43	66	27
Leyland St M Res.	20	6	3	11	55	52	21
Hoghton WE Res.	20	6	2	12	44	66	20
Muldoons	20	5	3	12	36	72	18
Walmer Bdge Res.	20	3	3	14	31	66	12
New Longton Res.	20	1	5	14	25	80	8

Division Four	P	W	D	L	F	A	Pts
Adelphi	18	18	0	0	88	22	54
Eccleston/H. Res.	18	11	3	4	61	38	36
Penwortham STU	18	11	1	6	81	44	34
AFC Walton	18	10	4	4	73	40	34
Ribchester	18	10	2	6	73	37	32
Ribbleton/Chorley	18	8	0	10	77	68	24
Hoole United Res.	18	5	4	9	39	50	19
New Longton R. A	18	6	1	11	42	76	19
AFC Mawd'y Res.	18	1	2	15	18	78	5
Tarleton Corries A	18	1	1	16	19	118	4

REDHILL & DISTRICT LEAGUE

Premier Division	P	W	D	L	F	A	Pts
Caterham Old B.	22	14	6	2	69	29	48
RH123 Athletic	22	14	2	6	70	31	44
Brockham	22	13	5	4	62	32	44
Limpsfield Blues	22	13	5	4	54	27	44
Horley Town A	22	11	4	7	58	42	37
Smallfield	22	7	8	7	40	44	29
Chipstead A	22	8	4	10	34	58	28
Charlwood	22	8	1	13	38	49	25
Kenley	22	6	6	10	35	64	24
Frenches Athletic	22	4	7	11	30	51	19
Walton Heath	22	5	2	15	35	55	17
Tatsfield Rovers	22	2	4	16	42	85	10

Division One	P	W	D	L	F	A	Pts
AFC Woodhatch	22	18	3	1	91	19	57
Real Holmesdale	22	17	2	3	67	28	53
Tatsfield R. Res.	22	13	3	6	46	25	42
Woodland Albion	22	12	5	5	49	41	41
Reigate Hill	22	12	4	6	64	41	40
Bookham A	22	10	5	7	42	36	35
Warlingham A	22	8	6	8	58	48	30
Smallfield Res.	22	8	5	9	42	49	29
Reigate Sala	22	5	2	15	29	77	17
Reed	22	5	1	16	37	68	16
Nutfield Res.	22	2	5	15	18	64	11
Nork Social	22	1	1	20	20	67	4

Division Two	P	W	D	L	F	A	Pts
Westcott	20	16	3	1	87	30	51
Merstham A	20	15	0	5	67	38	45
S. Godstone Res.	20	12	2	6	53	34	38
Mersth. N'ton Res.	20	12	2	6	53	35	38
Bletchingley Res.	20	10	3	7	47	43	33
South Park A	20	9	4	7	40	35	31
Horley Town B	20	6	3	11	31	60	21
Charlwood Res.	20	5	3	12	43	53	18
Monotype	20	5	2	13	43	58	17
Hatch	20	4	2	14	34	90	14
W'ton N Foresters	20	4	0	16	32	54	12

Division Three	P	W	D	L	F	A	Pts
Woodcote Old B.	22	18	3	1	89	33	57
RH123 Ath. Res.	22	17	1	4	68	38	52
Racing Epsom	22	16	2	4	81	28	50
Warlingham B	22	13	1	8	54	36	40
Court Lodge	22	11	5	6	44	40	38
Overton Athletic	22	11	4	7	38	35	37
Shelton Spartans	22	9	3	10	50	56	30
Reigate Hill Res.	22	9	1	12	52	48	28
Paynes Sports	22	5	2	15	37	76	17
Reigate Priory A	22	5	0	17	36	76	15
Oxted & District A	22	4	2	16	41	82	14
Park Lane	22	1	2	19	35	77	5

Division Four	P	W	D	L	F	A	Pts
Holland Spts Res.	20	17	2	1	83	22	53
Alliance	20	13	2	5	65	27	41
Brockham Res.	20	12	4	4	85	42	40
Limpsfield B. Res.	20	12	4	4	55	35	40
AFC Redhill	20	9	2	9	52	44	29
Walton Hth Res.	20	8	5	7	33	38	29
RH123 Athletic A	20	6	4	10	49	50	22
Sagemaster	20	5	5	10	49	69	20
Park Lane Res.	20	6	2	12	25	76	20
Frenches A. Res.	20	5	3	12	33	68	18
Monotype Res.	20	0	1	19	19	77	1

Division Five	P	W	D	L	F	A	Pts
R. H'dale Res.	21	15	2	4	57	26	47
Caterham OB Res.	21	14	2	5	102	36	44
Horley	21	13	2	6	74	42	41
Court Lodge Res.	21	10	1	10	67	54	31
Merstham B	21	7	4	10	46	58	25
Westcott Res.	21	7	4	10	44	61	25
Alpine Lane	21	5	4	12	35	84	19
Reigate Priory B	21	3	1	17	22	86	10

ROCHESTER & DISTRICT LEAGUE
(MEMS Power Generation)

Premier Division	P	W	D	L	F	A	Pts
FC Quayside	22	18	3	1	65	17	57
Gillingham Green	22	17	2	3	92	17	53
Bredhurst	22	15	4	3	72	23	49
Hollands & B. Res.	22	10	6	6	46	38	36
Medway Knights	22	11	1	10	68	46	34
Lordswood Ath.	22	9	4	9	53	45	31
Medway City	22	9	2	11	47	47	29
Cannon '24	22	9	1	12	38	61	28
Greenwich Thistle	22	7	3	12	40	75	24
Cliffe Woods	22	6	2	14	55	68	20
Horsted	22	3	1	18	26	79	10
Medway Queen	22	2	3	17	21	107	9

Division One	P	W	D	L	F	A	Pts
BAE Sports & Soc.	24	18	4	2	95	32	58
Evolution	24	17	2	5	98	47	53
Park Regis	24	17	2	5	78	41	53
Upchurch	24	16	1	7	51	38	49
Stockbury Athletic	24	13	3	8	59	52	42
Luton Athletic	24	11	4	9	64	55	37
Pegasus	24	11	3	10	50	41	36
Grain Athletic	24	7	7	10	56	64	28
Medway Ports	24	6	3	15	49	62	21
Bredhurst J. Res.	24	5	5	14	31	65	20
Three Sisters	24	5	3	16	52	86	18
Cliffe Woods Res.	24	5	2	17	45	97	17
Cobras	24	4	3	17	45	93	15

Division Two	P	W	D	L	F	A	Pts
Riverside	24	19	5	0	106	35	62
Fitters United	24	16	3	5	80	36	51
Pegasus Res.	24	16	3	5	70	43	51
Breach Rovers	24	15	4	5	74	36	49
Cliffe Woods A	24	14	0	10	68	53	42
Collyers	24	12	4	8	54	45	40
Plough/Chequers	24	12	2	10	65	54	38
Strood	24	10	7	7	72	65	37
JD Decking	24	8	1	15	52	96	25
Medway Galvan.	24	6	0	18	42	82	18
Bredhurst Res.	24	4	4	16	31	75	16
Anchorians	24	5	0	19	32	42	15
Isle of Grain	24	2	1	21	27	111	7

Division Three	P	W	D	L	F	A	Pts
Minster WMC	22	15	4	3	65	30	49
Park Regis Res.	22	12	5	5	78	51	41
Coach & Horses	22	11	8	3	58	37	41
Emerald Star	22	11	4	7	48	41	37
Woodcoombe SS	22	11	2	9	59	48	35
Southern Belle	22	10	3	9	51	56	33
Outer Fenn	22	9	4	9	53	50	31
Insanity	22	10	1	11	52	56	31
Poachers	22	7	4	11	45	52	25
Kings Head	22	7	1	14	51	70	22
O'Connell's	22	6	3	13	49	73	21
Walderslade	22	2	3	17	33	78	9

Division Four	P	W	D	L	F	A	Pts
Cliffe Woods B	22	18	2	2	103	22	56
Woodcoombe Res.	22	13	4	5	61	40	43
Star Sports	22	13	3	6	51	28	42
Medway Athletic	22	10	6	6	38	31	36
General at Sea	22	11	2	9	64	46	35
W. Horse Borstal	22	10	3	9	38	51	33
Lepsons AWR	22	10	2	10	70	58	32
The Rose Inn Gill.	22	10	2	10	48	53	32
Rainham '84	22	7	6	9	46	60	27
Em. Star Classics	22	8	2	12	50	63	26
The Rising Sun	22	2	4	16	24	106	10
Valley Colts	22	1	2	19	13	48	5

Division Five	P	W	D	L	F	A	Pts
Hoo Village	24	22	1	1	142	35	67
Medway Colts	24	19	4	1	145	39	61
Real Knights	24	15	4	5	114	50	49
Sturdee	24	13	5	6	82	45	44
Slade '05	24	12	3	9	80	93	39
Riverside Res.	24	10	3	11	64	75	33
Bleakwood Rgrs	24	10	3	11	61	73	33
SCC Old Boys	24	8	3	13	40	67	27
Stockbury A. Res.	24	8	1	15	67	94	25
Bowaters	24	7	4	13	32	69	25
Sirtcom	24	5	4	15	48	93	19
AFC Phoenix	24	5	3	16	61	85	18
Medway Rovers	24	2	2	20	24	142	8

Division Six	P	W	D	L	F	A	Pts
Snodland Nomads	24	19	3	2	129	33	60
Hoo Institute	24	18	3	3	107	21	57
Medway Rams	24	15	1	8	80	49	46
Windermere Wdrs	24	13	3	8	80	77	42
Three Mariners	24	13	1	10	80	50	40
S'thern Belle Res.	24	10	4	10	64	53	34
Medway Pts Res.	24	11	1	12	69	63	34
Outer Fenn Res.	24	10	3	11	62	52	33
Beechwood '76	24	9	3	12	52	67	30
Rain. Cricketers	24	8	3	13	42	77	27
The Weston Arms	24	8	1	15	52	80	25
Invicta Colts	24	6	4	14	52	84	22
Woodcoombe A	24	1	0	23	15	178	3

ROCHDALE & DISTRICT LEAGUE
(Rochdale Online)

Premier Division	P	W	D	L	F	A	Pts
Weavers Arms *+2*	18	15	1	2	81	20	48
Stonemasons *+2*	18	13	2	3	61	38	43
Wardle *+2*	18	13	1	4	67	38	42
Asia	18	12	1	5	53	31	37
Harlequin	18	8	3	7	48	45	27
Tophams Tavern	18	4	4	10	42	80	16
Dog & Partridge *-2*	18	3	6	9	40	55	13
Fothergill/Whittles	18	3	4	11	29	61	13
Roca Juniors *-4*	18	4	3	11	40	62	11
Sudden Carling	18	2	1	15	28	60	7

SALISBURY & DISTRICT LEAGUE

Premier Division	P	W	D	L	F	A	Pts
Stockton/Codford	16	14	1	1	46	7	43
Alderbury	16	12	0	4	56	42	36
Friends Provident	16	9	1	6	48	20	28
Nomansland	16	9	0	7	42	44	27
Porton Sports	16	8	1	7	41	32	25
S Newton/Wishf'd	16	7	0	9	40	41	21
West Harnham	16	7	0	9	34	44	21
Enford	16	3	0	13	30	55	9
Whiteparish	16	1	1	14	31	83	4

Division One	P	W	D	L	F	A	Pts
Chalke Valley Res.	14	10	2	2	48	27	32
Tisbury	14	9	3	2	41	20	30
Duck Inn	14	7	5	2	37	17	26
The Five Bells	14	6	1	7	37	38	19
Winterslow	14	5	3	6	34	41	18
Greyhound (Ames)	14	5	2	7	38	32	17
Alderbury Res.	14	4	3	7	33	43	15
Langford	14	0	1	13	17	67	1

Division Two	P	W	D	L	F	A	Pts
RGV Netheravon	18	17	1	0	105	26	52
Malmesbury Arms	18	13	2	3	80	31	41
S'henge Snooker	18	12	1	5	75	41	37
Boscombe Down	18	9	3	6	48	38	30
Stockton & C. Res.	18	9	2	7	48	42	29
Woodisbury	18	8	2	8	48	42	26
Tisbury Res.	18	5	1	12	30	53	16
S Newton/W. Res.	18	4	4	10	32	65	16
Victoria Hotel	18	2	2	14	34	84	8
Beacon Sports	18	1	2	15	28	106	5

Division Three	P	W	D	L	F	A	Pts
Durrington WMC	16	10	2	4	68	29	32
Coach & Horses	16	10	1	5	74	30	31
Porton Spts Res.	16	9	2	5	54	31	29
Figheldean Rgrs	16	9	1	6	55	47	28
Alderholt A	16	8	1	7	54	46	25
Devizes Inn	16	6	4	6	44	50	22
Burgess Trees	16	6	3	7	37	55	21
Hi-Flex Sports	16	3	4	9	35	67	13
Winterslow Res.	16	1	2	13	17	83	5

SCUNTHORPE & DISTRICT LEAGUE
(Johnstone Insurance)

Division One	P	W	D	L	F	A	Pts
AFC Brumby	22	21	0	1	90	20	63
Scunthonians	22	16	3	3	68	17	51
Messingham TJ	22	16	0	6	82	39	48
BBM	22	14	1	7	62	49	43
Epworth Town	22	10	5	7	49	42	35
Swinefleet Juniors	22	9	3	10	38	57	30
Scotter United	22	8	1	13	43	57	25
Limestone Rgrs	22	8	1	13	33	54	25
Haxey Town	22	7	2	13	31	44	23
Barton United	22	6	4	12	34	47	22
Crosby Colts	22	3	3	16	32	86	12
New Holland Villa	22	2	1	19	26	76	7

Division Two	P	W	D	L	F	A	Pts
AFC Brumby Res.	26	19	4	3	75	30	61
Mallard *-3*	26	20	2	4	77	34	59
George/Dragon *+3*	26	13	8	5	63	37	50
Crosby C. Res. *+3*	26	14	3	9	70	52	48
College Wdrs	26	14	4	8	65	41	46
Epworth T. Res. *-3*	26	12	7	7	63	39	40
Sherpa	26	11	2	13	58	62	35
Barnetby United	26	10	2	14	56	77	32
Jailhouse	26	8	5	13	58	68	29
Scunth'nians Res.	26	7	3	16	62	73	24
Scotter Utd Res.	26	5	9	12	52	78	24
Barrow Wdrs	26	7	3	16	39	66	24
Swinefleet J. Res.	26	6	5	15	43	81	23
Briggensians	26	6	3	17	42	85	21

Division Three	P	W	D	L	F	A	Pts
AFC Goods Office	26	21	2	3	90	36	65
Crosby Colts Jnrs	26	20	2	4	126	51	62
Luddington	26	20	2	4	95	38	62
AFC Lebus *-1*	26	17	3	6	112	61	53
Epworth T. Colts	26	15	2	9	84	56	47
Winterton Town *+2*	26	12	4	10	57	65	42
College W. Res.	26	11	3	12	76	75	36
Revision Logistics	26	9	4	13	65	61	31
Men's Health	26	10	0	16	54	81	30
Santon	26	8	3	15	49	85	27
Broughton Albion	26	7	4	15	46	68	25
Scawby Britannia	26	8	0	18	67	85	24
Limestone R. Res.	26	4	5	17	26	74	17
Parkwood Athletic	26	3	0	23	34	145	9

SELBY & DISTRICT LEAGUE

Division One	P	W	D	L	F	A	Pts
Rileys & Fryston	18	13	2	3	68	27	41
Pollington	18	12	3	3	86	38	39
Glass- houghton	18	11	3	4	47	29	36
Yorkshire Penny	18	9	5	4	62	37	32
Pontefract Town	18	8	2	8	56	59	26
Rileys Rangers	18	7	3	8	45	55	24
Moorends	18	7	3	8	51	65	24
New Airedale	18	6	2	10	39	51	20
Garforth WMC	18	3	2	12	31	64	11
Fairburn -3	18	1	1	16	29	89	1

Division Two	P	W	D	L	F	A	Pts
Ferrybridge Ams	26	23	1	2	123	20	70
Garforth Rangers	26	19	3	4	85	27	60
Knottingley Res.	26	15	4	7	61	39	49
Willow Park	26	15	3	8	60	40	48
Sherburn WR A	26	14	3	9	64	48	45
Gt Preston Res. *-3*	26	15	2	9	73	63	44
Drax	26	13	3	10	64	62	42
Monk Fryston	26	10	4	12	64	69	34
Garforth	26	9	5	12	58	67	32
G'forth WMC Res.	26	8	1	17	31	69	25
Kellington	26	7	3	16	58	87	24
Wetherby Ath. B	26	4	5	17	31	76	17
Hensall Athletic	26	4	4	17	35	84	16
Selby RSSC Res.	26	5	1	20	27	80	16

SEVENOAKS & DISTRICT LEAGUE

Premier Division	P	W	D	L	F	A	Pts
Hildenborough Ath.	22	18	2	2	83	23	56
Sevenoaks T. A	22	17	0	5	70	31	51
Kemsing	22	12	7	3	52	32	43
A London	22	10	5	7	57	46	35
St Lawrence	22	11	1	10	46	48	34
Borough Green U.	22	9	4	9	44	41	31
Nomads	22	8	3	11	48	65	27
Halstead	22	7	3	12	55	65	24
Eynsford	22	7	3	12	45	66	24
Ightham	22	5	4	13	37	62	19
Sevenoaks Weald	22	5	3	14	36	63	18
Dunton Green	22	4	3	15	33	64	15

Division One	P	W	D	L	F	A	Pts
Ton. Bapt. Church	20	17	2	1	67	17	53
Orpington A	20	15	2	3	84	31	47
Ide Hill	20	13	0	7	67	44	39
Chipstead A	20	11	1	8	64	54	34
Wilderpark	20	10	4	6	40	51	34
Kingsdown Racers	20	9	2	9	42	41	29
Seal	20	7	4	9	52	54	25
Eynsford Res.	20	7	3	10	48	65	24
Fleetdown Utd A	20	3	3	14	34	55	12
St Lawrence Res.	20	4	0	16	36	76	12
Halstead Res.	20	3	1	16	18	64	10

Dunton Green Res. - record expunged

SHEFFIELD & HALLAMSHIRE COUNTY SENIOR LEAGUE
(Windsor Food Service)

Premier Division	P	W	D	L	F	A	Pts
Athersley Rec.	24	20	1	3	58	18	61
Wombwell Main	24	15	5	4	50	27	50
Stocksbridge Res.	24	12	6	6	46	31	42
Dearne Coll. MW	24	11	6	7	59	40	39
Handsworth	24	12	1	11	62	54	37
Oughtibridge WM	24	11	4	9	51	56	37
Dinnington T. Res.	24	8	10	6	43	32	34
Sp'wd Throstles *-3*	24	11	3	10	51	43	33
Mexborough MS	24	8	4	12	46	61	28
Penistone Church	24	8	2	14	32	49	26
Houghton Main	24	5	4	15	44	63	19
HSBC	24	4	4	16	40	67	16
Thorpe Hesley	24	3	6	15	44	85	15

Division One	P	W	D	L	F	A	Pts
Sheffield Res.	26	19	7	0	92	29	64
Millmoor Juniors	26	19	3	4	90	30	60
Caribbean Sports	26	17	4	5	60	39	55
Worsbro. Cmn *-3*	26	15	5	6	68	40	47
Sheffield Ath. *-3*	26	13	3	10	73	56	39
Outo Kumpu SS	26	11	5	10	53	56	38
Everest	26	10	6	10	51	45	36
Silkstone United	26	8	6	12	40	55	30
Wickersley OB	26	7	8	11	42	50	29
Ecclesfield Red R.	26	8	4	14	49	52	28
S. Kirkby Coll. *-3*	26	9	2	15	50	63	26
W'bro. BMW Res.	26	7	5	14	42	78	26
Frecheville CA	26	7	4	15	54	68	25
Sheffield Lane Top	26	0	2	24	28	131	2

Division Two	P	W	D	L	F	A	Pts
Aston	22	13	5	4	56	32	44
Hallam Res.	22	13	4	5	51	21	43
High Green Villa	22	12	6	4	42	16	42
Bramley S'side J.	22	10	8	4	66	33	38
Handsworth Res.	22	11	3	8	67	44	36
Penistone C. Res.	22	11	3	8	42	48	36
Parramore S. Res.	22	9	8	5	56	32	35
Athersley R. Res.	22	9	4	9	42	33	31
Thorncliffe	22	6	3	13	40	51	21
De La Salle OB	22	5	4	13	36	43	19
Sheff. Bankers *-5*	22	4	7	11	38	46	14
Phoenix S&S Res.	22	1	1	20	16	153	4

SHROPSHIRE ALLIANCE

	P	W	D	L	F	A	Pts
Technical Serv.	24	20	1	3	94	40	61
Oswestry Boys C.	24	18	1	5	84	35	55
Hanwood U. Res.	24	15	3	6	81	39	48
Weston Rhyn	24	13	1	10	50	52	40
Fountain Sports	24	12	2	10	58	48	38
Felton Lions	24	11	4	9	66	47	37
Ludlow T. Colts	24	11	4	9	55	58	37
Cockshutt	24	12	1	11	54	59	37
Prees United	24	8	2	14	36	44	26
Peacock United	24	7	5	12	37	59	26
Bayston Hill	24	7	4	13	49	69	25
Kinnerley	24	4	2	18	40	83	14
St Martins Res.	24	2	2	20	23	94	8

SOUTH DEVON LEAGUE
(Woolcombe Beer Watts Solicitors)

Premier Division	P	W	D	L	F	A	Pts
Kingskerswell & C.	24	20	1	3	71	30	61
Upton Athletic	24	17	0	7	76	30	51
Brixham Utd *-12*	24	17	4	3	61	20	43
East Allington U.	24	13	3	8	63	45	42
Galmpton Res.	24	12	0	12	46	50	36
Brixham Villa	24	9	6	9	51	39	33
Hele Rovers	24	9	6	9	45	44	33
Totnes/D. Res. *-3*	24	9	5	10	55	56	29
Kingsteignton Ath.	24	7	7	10	39	41	28
Chagford	24	8	1	15	35	56	25
Waldon Athletic *+3*	24	6	0	18	32	76	21
N. Spurs Res. *-3*	24	6	2	16	38	76	17
Riviera Spurs	24	4	3	17	34	83	15

Newton Abbot Res. - record expunged

Division One	P	W	D	L	F	A	Pts
Ashburton	26	17	5	4	79	36	56
Watts Blake & B.	26	17	2	7	68	36	53

	P	W	D	L	F	A	Pts
Abbotskerswell *-3*	26	17	3	6	101	46	51
Ipplepen Athletic	26	16	3	7	61	45	51
Staverton & L. *-3*	26	17	2	7	71	35	50
Brixham Villa Res.	26	14	5	7	55	41	47
Dartmouth Res. *-3*	26	12	7	7	63	41	40
Loddiswell	26	10	3	13	64	65	33
Galmpton Gents A	26	7	3	16	41	67	24
Upton Ath. Res. *-3*	26	8	3	15	53	86	24
Paignton Villa	26	6	3	17	45	85	21
Paignton Saints *-3*	26	6	4	16	55	95	19
Moretonh'pstd *-3*	26	5	5	16	50	80	17
Newton 66 *-3*	26	4	4	18	37	85	13

Division Two	P	W	D	L	F	A	Pts
Buckland Ath. Res.	26	19	2	5	89	27	59
Harbertonford	26	16	4	6	69	41	52
Chudleigh Athletic	26	16	3	7	66	32	51
Stoke Gab. Res.	26	17	4	5	75	37	49
K'kerswell Res. *-6*	26	14	6	6	58	46	48
Langdon *-3*	26	14	6	6	65	44	45
Newton United *+2*	25	10	4	11	67	64	36
Teign Village	25	8	9	8	49	47	33
Kingsteignton Res.	26	8	3	15	30	86	27
Brixham U Res. *-7*	26	7	6	13	43	64	20
E. Allington Res.	26	5	4	17	39	77	19
Meadowbrook *+3*	26	4	4	18	37	76	19
South Brent *-6*	26	6	3	17	48	85	15

Channings Wood - record expunged

Division Three	P	W	D	L	F	A	Pts
B'fastleigh Res. *+3*	26	20	2	4	106	31	65
Beesands Rov. *+3*	26	17	3	6	72	50	57
Hele Rov. Res. *-6*	26	18	2	6	98	60	50
Watts BB Res.	26	16	2	8	76	55	50
Dartmouth A	26	15	3	8	64	55	48
Foxhole United *-3*	26	13	2	11	65	54	38
Newton Spurs A	26	10	4	12	51	54	34
Broadhempston U.	26	9	4	13	72	61	31
Bov. Tracey Res.	26	8	6	12	59	72	30
Liverton Res. *-9*	26	12	0	14	54	67	27
Waldon Res. *-3*	26	8	4	14	52	82	25
Totnes & Dart. A	26	7	3	16	47	78	24
Ilsington Villa *-3*	26	5	1	20	45	73	13
Brixham Town *-3*	26	4	4	18	43	112	13

Division Four	P	W	D	L	F	A	Pts
Staverton Res. *+3*	26	20	3	3	122	35	66
Teignm'th Res. *-6*	26	21	4	1	127	35	61
Hookhills Utd	26	19	2	5	105	30	59
Stoke Fleming	26	18	5	3	85	30	59
Kingskerswell A	26	14	3	9	78	48	45
Bab'combe Cor. *+3*	26	13	3	10	67	53	45
Torbay Christians	26	12	4	10	53	55	40
Stoke Gabriel A	26	11	3	12	68	62	36
Malborough Utd	26	8	3	15	52	83	27
Abb'swell Res. *-3*	26	8	0	18	62	114	21
B'hempston Res.	26	4	4	18	43	106	16
Loddiswell Res.	26	5	0	21	47	138	15
Ashburton Res. *-6*	26	5	4	17	45	94	13
Ipplepen Res. *-6*	26	3	4	19	37	108	7

Division Five	P	W	D	L	F	A	Pts
Watcombe Wdrs	26	22	2	2	144	25	68
Buckland Ath. A	26	22	0	4	126	32	66
Denbury Ath. *-6*	26	22	2	2	123	25	62
Newton Utd Res.	26	14	4	8	62	72	46
Brixham Villa "A"	26	14	3	9	74	39	45
Babbacombe Res.	26	11	5	10	78	65	38
Riviera Spurs Res.	26	10	3	13	58	82	33
Marldon	26	9	4	13	56	73	31
Chudleigh Res. *-3*	26	9	3	14	70	69	27
Harb'ford Res. *-12*	26	12	3	11	58	67	27
P'ton Sts Res. *+6*	26	5	4	17	45	94	25
Paignton V. Res.	26	6	1	19	53	99	19
Newton 66 Res.	26	6	1	19	38	151	19
M'pstead Res. *-6*	26	2	1	23	31	123	1

Division Six	P	W	D	L	F	A	Pts
South Brent Res.	18	14	0	4	73	26	42
Chagford Res. *+3*	18	11	2	5	44	26	38
Watts B&B. A *-6*	18	13	1	4	62	28	34
Stoke Flem. Res.	18	9	5	4	59	51	32
Dittisham United	18	8	2	8	49	50	26
K'bridge & Kellaton	18	8	1	9	44	52	25
Marldon Res.	18	8	1	9	39	52	25
Foxhole Utd Res.	18	7	0	11	39	45	21
Denbury Ath. Res.	18	2	3	13	20	48	9
Teign V. Res. *-6*	18	2	1	15	27	78	1

SOUTH LONDON ALLIANCE

Premier Division	P	W	D	L	F	A	Pts
Blackheath Wdrs	24	17	2	5	77	44	53
Crofton Albion	24	12	6	6	62	52	42
Bexlians	24	12	5	7	41	29	41
Lewisham Athletic	24	11	6	7	54	39	39
Cray Valley Res.	24	11	3	10	53	44	36
AFC Sydenham	24	10	5	9	49	46	35
Tudor Sports Res.	24	8	8	8	37	44	32
Old Roan	24	9	3	12	55	70	30
Metrogas Res.	24	7	6	11	62	66	27
Parkhurst Rgrs	24	7	6	11	51	65	27
Wickham Wdrs	24	9	0	15	38	57	27
Drummond Ath.	24	7	5	12	45	57	26
Johnson & Phillips	24	6	5	13	40	51	23

Long Lane - record expunged

Division One	P	W	D	L	F	A	Pts
Seven Acre Spts	22	16	4	2	71	28	52
New Park	22	14	4	4	63	34	46
F'boro. OBG Res.	22	12	5	5	44	39	41
Knights Old Boys	22	12	4	6	49	35	40
Bridon Ropes Res.	22	10	6	6	44	36	36
Old Town New B.	22	10	5	7	52	46	35
NASFAT	22	9	7	6	41	33	34
Dresdner K'nwort	22	8	2	12	39	39	26
Thames Borough	22	4	6	12	34	61	18
Chislehurst Sports	22	5	2	15	42	75	17
Beaverwood	22	4	2	16	32	59	14
Elite	22	3	3	16	30	56	12

Charterhouse-in-Southwark - record expunged

Crayford Arrows - record expunged

Division Two	P	W	D	L	F	A	Pts
Bexley	24	18	4	2	61	24	58
Old Roan Res.	24	17	4	3	81	38	55
Long Lane Res.	24	14	7	3	65	34	49
Old Colfeians	24	15	4	5	57	36	49
Avery Hill College	24	10	4	10	38	52	34
Beckenham Ryls	24	9	4	11	46	57	31
Crofton Alb. Res.	24	8	5	11	51	57	29
Blackh'th W. Res.	24	7	8	9	52	59	29
Metrogas A	24	8	3	13	51	52	27
Johnson & P. Res.	24	7	3	14	36	61	24
Salmon	24	6	4	14	54	55	22
W. Bromley Albion	24	6	4	14	45	47	22
Heath	24	2	4	18	21	86	10

Division Three	P	W	D	L	F	A	Pts
Eltham Town	22	20	1	1	70	19	61
FC Hollington	22	19	2	1	95	23	59
Bridon Ropes A	22	16	2	4	84	24	50
Farnboro. OBG A	22	11	3	8	55	50	36
Bexlians Res.	22	10	1	11	50	60	31
Wickham Pk Res.	22	6	4	12	35	43	22
Valley Park Rgrs	22	7	1	14	49	66	22
Chislehurst Res.	22	6	4	12	31	48	22
Elite Res.	22	6	3	13	36	86	21
Old Roan A	22	5	5	12	37	65	20
Bexley Res.	22	6	1	15	31	55	19
AFC Wickham	22	4	5	13	37	71	17

Division Four	P	W	D	L	F	A	Pts
Crofton Albion A	22	20	1	1	84	28	61
Tudor Sports A	22	18	2	2	111	27	56
Lions Athletic	22	17	1	4	113	41	52
West Hill	22	14	2	6	111	57	44
Cray Town	22	10	4	8	64	43	34
Lewisham A. Res.	22	9	4	9	65	59	31
Seven Acre Res.	22	9	4	9	53	70	31
Crayford A. Res.	22	7	4	11	61	64	25
Dartford Town	22	6	1	15	36	65	19
Beaverwood Res.	22	4	4	14	41	93	16
Sutton Dynamo	22	3	2	17	38	121	11
Charlton A. Deaf	22	0	1	21	26	135	1

Nuxley - record expunged

Pembroke House - record expunged

SOUTH YORKSHIRE AMATEUR LEAGUE

Premier Division	P	W	D	L	F	A	Pts
Gleadless	18	14	2	2	76	24	44
Ecclesfield B. Bull	18	12	2	4	57	37	38
Jubilee Sports	18	11	4	3	65	24	37
Sheffield W. End	18	11	0	7	67	47	33
Civil Service	18	7	2	9	34	60	23
Farm Road S & S.	18	6	4	8	41	64	22
New Bohemians	18	5	3	10	35	57	18
Oxspring United	18	5	3	10	38	64	18
Furnace	18	5	2	11	39	46	17
Aston Res.	18	2	2	14	29	58	8

Division One	P	W	D	L	F	A	Pts
Boynton Sports	16	14	1	1	65	26	43
Millmoor Jnrs Res.	16	10	3	3	75	22	33
Sheffield Medics	16	10	2	4	61	32	32
Oughtibridge Res.	16	8	2	6	54	36	26
Noahs Ark	16	7	1	8	39	41	22
Shef. Bankers Res.	16	6	1	9	39	51	19
Phoenix SC Res.	16	5	0	11	45	58	15
Thurgoland Welf.	16	4	2	10	30	66	14
Bradway	16	2	0	14	26	102	6

Division Two	P	W	D	L	F	A	Pts
Surud United	12	9	2	1	40	25	29
Burngreave	12	8	3	1	44	24	27
Half Moon	12	7	1	4	49	27	22
Worsbro. Dale Dyn.	12	7	0	5	48	37	21
White Rose	12	4	0	8	24	39	12
Aviva	12	3	0	9	20	37	9
De La Salle Res.	12	1	0	11	22	58	3

SOUTHAMPTON LEAGUE
(Drew Smith Homes)

Premier Division	P	W	D	L	F	A	Pts
Bush Hill	20	18	0	2	73	18	54
Nursling	20	15	1	4	83	26	46
Solent WTL	20	12	1	7	55	40	37
AFC Solent	20	11	4	5	40	35	37
Bishopstoke WMC	20	10	2	8	59	47	32
Freemantle	20	9	2	9	53	55	29
Sporting Wessex	20	7	1	12	41	43	22
Malvern	20	6	1	13	35	50	19
Spartans	20	5	3	12	28	50	18
Capital	20	5	1	14	26	77	16
Comrades	20	2	4	14	27	79	10

AFC Target - record expunged

Senior Division	P	W	D	L	F	A	Pts
Hythe & D. Res.	22	17	2	3	62	26	53
Northend United	22	16	1	5	56	26	49
Netley CS Res. *-3*	22	14	3	5	84	37	42
Hythe Aztecs	22	11	2	9	59	48	35
AFC Redbridge	22	11	1	10	68	54	34
Comrades Res.	22	11	1	10	70	60	34
AFC Hop	22	9	5	8	40	34	32
Durley Res.	22	10	0	12	54	58	30
Michelmersh Res.	22	7	6	9	39	54	27
Burridge *-3*	22	9	2	11	42	39	26
Wellow	22	4	1	17	23	85	13
Inmar	22	0	2	20	22	98	2

Jnr Division One	P	W	D	L	F	A	Pts
Warsash Wasps	18	17	0	1	75	21	51
London Airways	18	15	0	3	74	26	45
AFC Hiltingbury	18	14	0	4	56	37	42
Sholing Sports	18	8	2	8	54	46	26
Braishfield	18	6	4	8	46	44	22
Booker Sports	18	6	2	10	34	62	20
Otterbourne A	18	6	0	12	33	56	18
WEB	18	4	1	13	26	50	13
Langley Manor	18	2	4	12	27	54	10
Priory Rovers *-6*	18	5	1	12	35	64	10

Jnr Division Two	P	W	D	L	F	A	Pts
Allbrook	20	15	3	2	76	36	48
Veracity Vipers	20	14	3	3	77	33	45
Hare & Hounds	20	12	3	5	65	39	39
Cadnam United	20	10	2	8	50	51	32
Hedge End Town	20	9	4	7	46	47	31
Nimbin United	20	8	3	9	45	43	27
BTC Southampton	20	8	1	11	37	39	25
Rownhams	20	7	3	10	39	46	24
Hythe Aztec Res.	20	6	5	9	48	57	23
Lowford	20	4	3	13	42	68	15
Test Park Rgrs	20	2	0	18	35	101	6

Jnr Division Three	P	W	D	L	F	A	Pts
Rsg Sun Colden C.	18	14	2	2	79	36	44
Forest Town FC	18	12	3	3	81	19	39
Wheatshield Wdrs	18	10	1	7	58	54	31
Compton	18	9	2	7	45	40	29
S'pton Energy	18	9	2	7	50	48	29
AFC Hilt'gbry Res.	18	9	1	8	37	40	28
Academicals	18	8	1	9	55	44	25
S & B Sports	18	7	4	7	42	46	25
Inter Northam	18	2	1	15	21	74	7
Hinkler	18	1	1	16	21	88	4

Jnr Division Four	P	W	D	L	F	A	Pts
Spartan Res.	20	17	1	2	86	21	52
AFC Grains	20	15	4	1	73	16	49
Wombles	20	12	1	7	43	24	37
Netley Marsh	20	11	2	7	63	51	35
Chamberlayne	20	10	3	7	54	54	33
Swan	20	7	3	10	52	43	24
AFC R'bdge Res.	20	8	0	12	36	63	24
Infinity *-3*	20	7	2	11	42	53	20
Capital Res.	20	6	2	12	27	59	20
Gate	20	3	3	14	27	75	12
Subway Totton	20	3	1	16	27	71	10

Jnr Division Five	P	W	D	L	F	A	Pts
Warsash W. Res.	18	14	3	1	71	13	45
Mark One	18	10	5	3	43	24	35
Wildern United	18	10	4	4	53	37	34
Priory Rov. Res.	18	9	5	4	53	25	32
AFC Stoneham A	18	8	2	8	50	43	26
Testwood	18	8	1	9	43	41	25
Lyndhurst Res.	18	6	6	6	38	29	24
Sparky Albion	18	6	3	9	28	31	21
Michelmersh A	18	3	2	13	18	72	11
Manor Wasps	18	0	1	17	11	93	1

Jnr Division Six	P	W	D	L	F	A	Pts
Warren Social	18	17	0	1	75	24	51
East Boldre	18	11	3	4	54	28	36
Eastleigh United	18	9	4	5	58	38	31
QK S'thampton A	18	10	1	7	51	37	31
Compton Res.	18	8	2	8	42	36	26
AFC Aldermoor	18	7	4	7	41	44	25
Freemantle Res.	18	8	0	10	43	46	24
Eastleigh Athletic	18	6	3	9	41	62	21
Hamble United	18	3	2	13	27	51	11
Hamble Town	18	1	1	16	31	97	4

Jnr Division Seven	P	W	D	L	F	A	Pts
Stanton	18	9	2	7	45	41	29
B. Waltham Dyn.	18	8	4	6	50	38	28
AFC Regent	18	8	3	7	50	39	27
Braishfield Res.	18	8	2	8	41	59	26
FC Winston	18	6	6	6	38	39	24
L.. Airways Res.	18	7	3	8	40	45	24
Athletico Romsey	18	5	4	9	32	35	19

SOUTHEND BOROUGH COMBINATION

Premier Division	P	W	D	L	F	A	Pts
Old Southendian	18	11	5	2	39	19	27
Southchurch HOS	18	12	2	4	49	34	26
Catholic United	18	8	5	5	53	37	21
Rochford Town	18	9	3	6	51	38	21
Ekco Thames Pk	18	8	1	9	41	41	17
Leigh Town	18	6	3	9	32	38	15
Weir Sports	18	6	3	9	37	50	15
Shoebury Town	18	6	2	10	43	47	14
Borough Rovers	18	5	4	9	32	47	14
Blackgate Gunn.	18	4	2	12	24	50	10

Division One	P	W	D	L	F	A	Pts
All Claims	22	17	1	4	87	37	35
Ekco Thames Res.	22	16	2	4	72	38	34
Corinthians	22	15	4	3	46	23	34
Emstar United	22	15	3	4	73	34	33
Thundersley Utd	22	6	9	7	63	65	21
Southend Colls	22	9	2	11	65	55	20
Zebra Sports	22	6	8	8	43	45	20
Airborne United	22	6	5	11	46	64	17
Westcliff Amateur	22	6	5	11	43	61	17
Ensign	22	6	4	12	43	59	16
BKS Sports	22	4	2	16	28	83	10
Thorpe Athletic	22	2	3	17	32	77	7

Division Two	P	W	D	L	F	A	Pts
Hullbridge S. Res.	22	15	5	2	71	34	35
Ensign Res.	22	13	5	4	81	47	31
Catholic Utd Res.	22	13	5	4	63	37	31
Cupids Co. Club	22	11	3	8	50	49	25
O S'thendian Res.	22	8	5	9	45	50	21
Ashingdon	22	6	6	10	61	62	18
Shoebury T. Res.	22	8	2	12	66	69	18
Ekco Thames A	22	7	2	13	40	64	16
Earls Hall United	22	5	5	12	41	74	15
Ltle Theatre Club	22	5	3	14	44	49	13
Leigh Town Res.	22	2	1	19	41	108	5

Division Three	P	W	D	L	F	A	Pts
Weir Sports Res.	22	16	2	4	71	34	34
White Horse Rgrs	22	15	2	5	75	25	32
Castle Point Gas	22	15	1	6	70	30	31
Ashingdon Res.	22	14	2	6	61	40	30
Cupids CC Res.	22	11	2	9	49	54	24
Trinity (S)	22	11	1	10	47	44	23
Southchurch Res.	22	7	6	9	42	43	20
Old Southendian A	22	8	4	10	37	53	20
Trackback	22	6	3	13	28	58	15
Leigh Ramblers A	22	6	3	13	29	63	15
Sthnd Colls Res.	22	4	5	13	36	53	13
Ekco Thames B	22	2	3	17	31	79	7

Division Four	P	W	D	L	F	A	Pts
Leigh Revolution	22	18	3	1	64	20	39
Corinthians Res.	22	15	1	6	64	36	31
Catholic United A	22	12	1	9	67	54	25
Earls Hall Utd Res.	22	11	3	8	53	46	25
Elmwood Old B.	22	10	4	8	64	45	24
Heathfield	22	9	4	9	50	46	22
Weir Sports A	22	7	4	11	55	66	18
S'thchurch HOS A	22	8	1	13	44	60	17
Little Theatre Res.	22	8	1	13	38	73	17
Thundersley Res.	22	7	2	13	43	60	16
Southend Colls A	22	5	5	12	38	55	15
Rayford Ath. Res.	22	7	1	14	49	68	15

Division Five	P	W	D	L	F	A	Pts
Sceptre Elite	22	22	0	0	112	18	44
FC Toro	22	17	3	2	91	31	37
Barnsford H'canes	22	16	1	5	73	28	33
Southend Trojans	22	13	3	6	68	42	29
Westcliff United	22	9	4	9	80	62	22
Rayford Athletic A	22	7	6	9	54	66	20
Weir Sports B	22	4	8	10	41	57	16
Leigh Ramblers B	22	5	5	12	41	72	15
Landwick	22	6	3	13	47	84	15
Southend Colls B	22	4	5	13	33	100	13
O. Southendian B	22	4	3	15	42	86	11
Southend Rgrs	22	2	5	15	27	63	9

SOUTHEND & DISTRICT LEAGUE
(Wickford Carpets)

Premier Division	P	W	D	L	F	A	Pts
Sporting Pitsea	14	10	3	1	57	17	33
Club Sirrus	14	9	2	3	40	21	29
Leigh United	14	9	1	4	43	20	28
Swan Mead	14	9	1	4	45	23	28
AFC Horndon	14	7	3	4	54	29	24
Rawreth Sports	14	4	0	10	13	64	12
Kg John Barmy A.	14	2	1	11	26	57	7
Sparkbridge	14	0	1	13	11	58	1

Division One	P	W	D	L	F	A	Pts
Rochford T. Res.	14	12	0	2	41	23	36
Signet United	14	9	1	4	48	27	28
Hockley Spartans	14	8	1	5	32	22	25
Sparco	14	8	0	6	32	23	24
Thundersley Rov.	14	7	1	6	36	26	22
Wickford Rangers	14	5	3	6	25	34	18
Chalkwell Park	14	2	1	11	17	52	7
White Red Eagles	14	1	1	12	19	43	4

SOUTHPORT & DISTRICT LEAGUE

	P	W	D	L	F	A	Pts
The Corrie	26	22	4	0	147	43	70
Sandy Lane	26	19	2	5	101	65	59
Christ The King OB	26	17	2	7	71	40	53
Redgate Rovers	26	16	1	9	94	61	49
Poulton Wdrs	26	15	2	9	76	59	47
Trojan Security *-3*	26	15	2	9	83	48	44
Formby Dons	26	13	5	8	67	62	44
Redwood *-3*	26	12	3	11	68	59	36
Stapleton Rovers	26	9	2	15	68	90	29
St Pauls *-3*	26	9	2	15	62	71	26
Birkdale Crown	26	7	2	17	53	72	23
Banks	26	5	2	19	49	100	17
Massams	26	5	2	19	48	110	17
Formby Athletic	26	2	1	23	39	146	7

ST EDMUNDSBURY & DISTRICT LEAGUE
(Glasswells)

Division One	P	W	D	L	F	A	Pts
Priors	18	12	4	2	62	29	40
Rising Sun FC	18	9	5	4	44	32	32
Barons	18	10	0	8	55	35	30
Lawshall Swan	18	8	5	5	51	43	29
Bartons	18	9	1	8	42	34	28
Ixworth Pykkerell	18	8	2	8	49	52	26
Bushel	18	7	4	7	34	44	25
Westbury United	18	5	5	8	47	50	20
Elephant & Castle	18	6	1	11	43	67	19
Elveden Phoenix	18	2	1	15	30	71	7

Division Two	P	W	D	L	F	A	Pts
Haughley Utd Res.	22	22	0	0	91	24	66
Barrow FC	22	14	4	4	64	30	46
Pot Black FC	22	15	0	7	67	42	45
Mildenhall United	22	13	2	7	55	38	41
RF Saints	22	12	2	8	93	56	38
Beck Row	22	8	3	11	45	61	27
Sporting '87 A	22	8	2	12	53	55	26
Black Boy	22	8	2	12	50	61	26
Bacton United A	22	8	1	13	33	60	25
Bury Rovers	22	5	4	13	49	88	19
Rising Sun Res.	22	5	1	16	48	76	16
Garboldisham	22	3	1	18	40	97	10

ST HELENS COMBINATION

Premier Division	P	W	D	L	F	A	Pts
Knowsley South	18	12	5	1	42	16	41
Penlake	18	12	4	2	64	22	40
York *+3*	18	10	4	4	41	29	37
Greenfield FC *-3*	18	11	4	3	48	26	34
Prescot Leisure	18	7	5	6	41	31	26
Rainford Nth End	18	6	4	8	33	34	22
Old Congs	18	4	2	12	29	45	14
Clock Face Miners	18	4	2	12	23	52	14
New Street	18	4	2	12	28	62	14
Pilkington A	18	2	4	12	24	56	10

Dentons Green - record expunged

Division One	P	W	D	L	F	A	Pts
Boilermakers	22	18	1	3	95	34	55
Junction	22	14	2	6	56	41	44
Prescot Leis. Res.	22	12	5	5	54	35	41
Penlake Res.	22	12	2	8	61	44	38
Rainford NE Res.	22	11	2	9	52	48	35
Bold Rangers	22	9	4	9	61	50	31
Eccleston United	22	7	6	9	47	53	27
Sidac Social Res.	22	8	3	11	46	56	27
Thatto Heath	22	6	5	11	48	67	23
Bath Springs	22	6	4	12	38	61	22
Cricketers FC	22	4	7	11	40	55	19
Brown Edge	22	3	3	16	37	91	12

STROUD & DISTRICT LEAGUE

Division One	P	W	D	L	F	A	Pts
Leonard Stanley	26	18	5	3	71	30	59
Matson	26	17	6	3	71	44	57
Tuffley Rov. Res.	26	17	4	5	74	27	55
Frampton United	26	14	7	5	67	35	49
Minchinhampton	26	12	6	8	68	62	42
Longlevens Res.	26	11	9	6	55	49	42
Abbeymead Rov.	26	11	4	11	67	62	37
Whitminster	26	11	4	11	50	54	37
Ebley Omega	26	8	11	7	55	45	35
Marshall Langston	26	6	7	13	45	53	25
K. Stanley Res. *-3*	26	8	2	16	41	73	23
Cashes Green	26	5	3	18	52	73	18
Shurdington Rov.	26	4	2	20	33	94	14
Uley	26	3	4	19	42	90	13

Division Two	P	W	D	L	F	A	Pts
Randwick	26	19	4	3	78	32	61
Hardwicke Res.	26	19	2	5	79	32	59
Tetbury Town Res.	26	17	6	3	89	42	57
Kingswood Res.	26	13	5	8	59	32	44
Dursley T. Res.	26	14	2	10	59	46	44
Horsley United	26	12	4	10	67	41	40
Gloucester CSe	26	11	5	10	45	50	38
Thornbury T. Res.	26	10	4	12	47	52	34
Whiteshill Utd *-6*	26	12	2	12	49	61	32
Wotton R. Res. *-1*	26	8	4	14	44	75	27
Tibberton United	26	6	4	16	37	72	22
Coaley Rovers	26	6	3	17	38	80	21
Longford Res.	26	4	5	17	29	76	17
Cam B'dogs Res.	26	5	1	20	33	96	16

Division Three	P	W	D	L	F	A	Pts
Stoneh'se Res. *+2*	24	17	3	4	70	35	56
Quedgeley Wdrs	24	16	5	3	71	23	53
Eastcombe	24	14	4	6	65	34	46
Ramblers Res. *+3*	24	11	3	10	51	52	39
Upton St L'nards	24	11	5	8	71	54	38
Frampton U. Res.	24	10	6	8	44	45	36
Trident	24	8	6	10	46	56	30
Wickwar Wdrs *+2*	24	7	6	11	51	55	29

	P	W	D	L	F	A	Pts
Sharpness Res.	24	8	4	12	47	67	28
B/Thrupp Res. +3	24	6	5	13	41	49	26
Berkeley Res. -8	24	10	4	10	31	53	26
M'pton RDS Res.	24	6	6	12	40	62	24
Uley Res.	24	2	3	19	24	85	9

Division Four	P	W	D	L	F	A	Pts
BA Rangers	24	20	2	2	92	27	62
Slimbridge Res.	24	19	0	5	110	36	57
AC Royals	24	16	3	5	71	33	51
Taverners Res.	24	12	4	8	71	53	40
Stonehouse T. A	24	10	5	9	58	46	35
Longlevens A	24	10	5	9	58	49	35
Glos Civil S. Res.	24	9	7	8	32	33	34
Barnwood U. Res.	24	8	7	9	44	52	31
Chalford Res.	24	8	4	12	38	58	28
Charfield Res.	24	6	4	14	36	93	22
Quedgeley W Res.	24	4	7	13	35	56	19
Alkerton Rangers	24	4	2	18	41	99	14
North Nibley	24	2	6	16	24	67	12

Division Five	P	W	D	L	F	A	Pts
Matchplay Reeves	22	16	2	4	83	34	50
Abbeymead Res.	22	15	4	3	92	36	49
Whitminster Res.	22	14	4	4	85	26	46
Didmarton	22	14	4	4	80	29	46
AFC Phoenix	22	14	3	5	96	35	45
Randwick Res.	22	10	4	8	50	48	34
Nympsfield -3	22	8	6	8	55	72	27
Arlingham	22	6	2	14	49	82	20
L'nard Stan. Res.	22	6	2	14	40	77	20
Dursley Town A	22	4	2	16	30	107	14
Victoria Celtic -3	22	5	0	17	45	92	12
Longlevens B	22	3	1	18	22	89	10

Division Six	P	W	D	L	F	A	Pts
Ramblers A	22	16	4	2	74	26	52
Glevum United	22	15	1	6	76	37	46
Ebley Omega Res.	22	14	4	4	68	30	46
Wotton Rovers A	22	12	4	6	65	50	40
Cashes G. Res.	22	10	5	7	59	62	35
Horsley Utd Res.	22	9	5	8	61	57	32
Brockworth Alb. B	22	7	6	9	49	52	27
Upton St Leo. Res.	22	8	1	13	47	61	25
Eastcombe Res.	22	5	5	12	45	70	20
Stroud Harriers	22	4	5	13	41	69	17
Cam Bulldogs A -3	22	4	6	12	37	70	15
Coaley Rov. Res.	22	3	4	15	34	73	13

Division Seven	P	W	D	L	F	A	Pts
Tredworth Tigers	20	18	1	1	122	32	55
Stroud Imperial	20	14	0	6	82	39	42
Whitminster A	20	13	1	6	50	33	40
Chipping Sodb'y B	20	12	3	5	68	38	39
Trident Res.	20	10	2	8	61	58	32
Randwick A	20	9	4	7	42	49	31
BA Rangers Res.	20	8	3	9	73	55	27
Quedgeley W. A	20	7	0	13	37	50	21
Wickwar W. Res.	20	6	1	13	42	59	19
Uley A	20	5	1	14	41	77	16
Alkerton Rg. Res.	20	0	0	20	24	152	0

Sports NSSC - record expunged

Division Eight	P	W	D	L	F	A	Pts
Bush	20	19	1	0	140	17	58
Hardwicke A	20	15	1	4	89	40	46
Sherston -3	20	13	2	5	67	48	38
Stonehouse T. B	20	11	3	6	65	55	36
Woodchester	20	11	2	7	81	58	35
North Nibley Res.	20	8	1	11	53	71	25
Shurdington Res.	20	7	0	13	40	77	21
Upton St L'nards A	20	6	1	13	56	100	19
Avonvale United A	20	4	2	14	44	75	14
Stroud Imp. Res.	20	4	2	14	44	99	14
Matchplay R. Res.	20	3	4	13	43	83	13

SUBURBAN LEAGUE

Premier Division	P	W	D	L	F	A	Pts
Basingstoke T. Res.	34	20	7	7	77	34	67
Met. Police Res.	34	20	6	8	69	50	66
Eastleigh Res.	34	18	7	9	69	48	61
Sutton Utd Res.	34	17	7	10	83	50	58
Uxbridge Res.	34	17	6	11	59	42	57
Tonbridge A. Res.	34	17	5	12	55	31	56
Tooting/Mit. Res.	34	15	11	8	67	49	56
Wealdstone Res.	34	15	8	11	57	49	53
AFC W'don Res.	34	13	10	11	56	46	49
Ashford (Mx) Res.	34	13	3	18	61	78	42
Whyteleafe Res.	34	9	13	12	51	56	40
Ash United Res.	34	10	9	15	39	62	39
Three Bridges Res.	34	10	9	15	42	67	39
Dunstable T. Res.	34	10	7	17	50	56	37
Corinthian C. Res.	34	8	10	16	53	72	34
Chalfont St P. Res.	34	10	4	20	59	88	34
Burgess Hill Res.	34	9	6	19	40	84	33
Burnham Res.	34	8	6	20	38	63	30

Northern Division	P	W	D	L	F	A	Pts
Bedfont G. Res.	32	22	6	4	83	32	72
Northwood Res.	32	21	6	5	72	32	69
Beaconsfield Res.	32	21	4	7	75	33	67
Boreham W. Res.	32	17	6	9	78	52	57
Hampton/RB Res.	32	17	6	9	69	44	57
Harefield Utd Res.	32	15	8	9	66	50	53
AFC Hayes Res.	32	14	4	14	55	56	46
Amersham T. Res.	32	13	5	14	65	70	44
Fleet Town Res.	32	13	4	15	69	61	43
Camberley T. Res.	32	11	7	14	66	61	40
Sandhurst T. Res.	32	10	9	13	66	72	39
Bedfont Res.	32	9	8	15	42	78	35
N. Greenford Res.	32	9	7	16	52	86	34
Leighton T. Res.	32	7	8	17	44	69	29
N'pt Pagnell Res.	32	7	7	18	41	70	28
Bracknell T. Res.	32	7	4	21	32	66	25
Cove Res.	32	6	7	19	32	75	25

Berkhamsted Town Res. - record expunged

Southern Division	P	W	D	L	F	A	Pts
Leatherhead Res.	34	29	2	3	103	33	89
Croydon Ath. Res.	34	23	4	7	75	46	73
Eastb'ne B. Res.	34	22	4	8	101	59	70
Merstham Res.	34	19	4	11	94	56	61
Epsom & E. Res.	34	18	4	12	77	55	58
Colliers Wood Res.	34	14	9	11	70	66	51
Godalming T. Res.	34	13	9	12	62	67	48
Crowborough Res.	34	13	8	13	73	60	47
Walton Cas. Res.	34	13	7	14	70	68	46
Horley Town Res.	34	12	9	13	68	63	45
Raynes PV Res.	34	12	6	16	51	67	42
Ches'gton/H. Res.	34	12	6	16	52	77	42
Oakwood Res.	34	12	5	17	69	75	41
Chipstead Res.	34	10	5	19	71	83	35
E. Grinst'd T. Res.	34	10	5	19	73	90	35
Cobham Res.	34	10	4	20	62	115	34
Hors. YMCA Res.	34	8	7	19	49	74	31
Molesey Res.	34	4	6	24	46	112	18

Haywards Heath Town Res. - record expunged

SURREY INTERMEDIATE LEAGUE (WEST)

Premier Division	P	W	D	L	F	A	Pts
Ripley Village	24	19	3	2	72	24	60
Spelthorne Sports	24	17	6	1	76	21	57
Virginia Water	24	13	4	7	72	36	43
Wrecclesham	24	12	6	6	66	45	42
Yateley	24	13	3	8	70	51	42
Woking & Horsell	24	13	2	9	62	53	41
Worp'don Phoenix	24	11	6	7	50	39	39
Chiddingfold	24	9	4	11	39	44	31
Old Salesians	24	8	1	15	46	69	25
Merrow	24	6	5	13	37	55	23
Shottermill & Has.	24	5	2	17	35	65	17
Godalming/FA -1	24	4	3	17	39	80	14
Shalford	24	3	1	20	22	104	10

Division One	P	W	D	L	F	A	Pts
Abbey Rangers	22	18	2	2	103	18	56
Burpham	22	18	2	2	77	19	56
University Surrey	22	14	5	3	55	17	47
Unis Old Boys	22	12	1	9	48	37	37
Pyrford -3	22	10	6	6	45	37	33
Ryl H'way OB -3	22	10	4	8	41	30	31
Cranleigh	22	10	1	11	40	44	31
Gfd City W'siders	22	8	4	10	30	48	28
Burymead	22	4	3	15	25	60	15
Hammer United	22	4	3	15	29	67	15
Ewhurst	22	4	3	15	21	72	15
Ockham	22	2	2	18	21	86	8

Reserve Prem Div	P	W	D	L	F	A	Pts
Ripley Vill. Res.	24	19	3	2	74	28	60
Spelthorne Res.	24	19	2	3	96	19	59
Wrecclesham Res.	24	17	3	4	69	26	54
Woking & H. Res.	24	13	7	4	80	41	46
Shalford Res. -3	24	12	3	9	48	51	36
Worp'don P. Res.	24	9	3	12	67	58	30
Chiddingfold Res.	24	9	3	12	46	57	30
Yateley Res.	24	9	2	13	52	61	29
Merrow Res.	24	8	3	13	42	66	27
Virginia Wtr Res.	24	6	7	11	47	62	25
O. Salesians Res.	24	6	4	14	45	64	22
G'ming/ F Res. -3	24	6	3	15	40	76	18
Shottermill Res.	24	1	1	22	23	120	4

Reserve Div One	P	W	D	L	F	A	Pts
Univ. Surrey Res.	22	19	1	2	88	28	58
Ryl Holloway Res.	22	18	1	3	81	23	55
Cranleigh Res.	22	13	4	5	59	34	43
Abbey Rgrs Res.	22	13	4	5	45	30	43
Burpham Res.	22	13	2	7	52	34	41
Pyrford Res.	22	10	0	12	45	41	30
Guildford CW Res.	22	8	1	13	39	54	25
Unis Old B. Res.	22	7	3	12	36	40	24
Burymead Res.	22	6	2	14	20	61	20
Ewhurst Res.	22	5	3	14	26	59	18
Ockham Res.	22	5	0	17	18	58	15
Hammer Utd Res.	22	3	3	16	30	77	12

SURREY SOUTH EASTERN COMB.

Int. Div One	P	W	D	L	F	A	Pts
Oxted & District	26	19	3	4	63	24	60
Wandgas Sports	26	18	2	6	64	43	56
Tadworth	26	13	7	6	56	27	46
Battersea	26	13	7	6	68	40	46
Puretown	26	13	4	9	65	55	43
Tooting Bec	26	13	2	11	59	58	41
St Andrews +2	26	10	6	10	40	48	38
Westminster C. +3	26	10	5	11	46	61	38
Old Plymouthians	26	11	3	12	42	43	36
Sporting Bahia -1	26	11	4	11	54	59	36
NPL	26	10	5	11	74	78	35
Old Bristolians	26	8	4	14	42	64	28
CS United	26	3	3	20	35	55	12
Nutfield -1	26	1	3	22	28	81	5

Int. Div Two	P	W	D	L	F	A	Pts
FC Triangle +2	20	15	3	2	38	20	50
Sutton High +3	20	10	6	4	38	27	39
South Godstone	20	10	4	6	44	30	34
Croygas Phoenix	20	11	1	8	59	46	34
Thornton Hth Rov.	20	10	3	7	49	45	33
Merton Abbey -14	20	13	4	3	60	32	29
Yourstory	20	8	3	9	44	34	27
Westside +2	20	5	5	10	28	38	22
Ashtead	20	6	3	11	38	58	21
AFC Ewell +6	20	3	3	14	37	68	18
Chess'ton/HU A +2	20	1	1	18	20	57	6

Junior Division One	P	W	D	L	F	A	Pts
Weston G. Sports	18	14	2	2	63	20	44
Trinity	18	13	3	2	55	27	42
Cheam Vill. W. -3	18	12	3	3	47	21	36
Fulham Deaf	18	11	2	5	56	33	35
Worcester Pk A +3	18	6	3	9	24	55	24
Chile Int. +3	18	5	0	13	37	38	18
NPL Res.	18	5	1	12	32	67	16
Bat'sea I. u-25s -3	18	5	3	10	43	47	15
St Andrews Res	18	4	3	11	28	57	15
Fetcham	18	3	4	11	40	60	13

Junior Division Two	P	W	D	L	F	A	Pts
Supercala	24	17	4	3	74	39	55
Norton	24	17	4	3	71	36	55
Epsom A. Res. -1	24	14	5	5	71	46	46
Shaftesbury Town	24	13	3	8	65	48	42
Wilf Kroucher	24	10	5	9	65	59	35
Cheam Vill. Res.	24	10	5	9	49	45	35
Roehampton Ath.	24	10	2	12	35	40	32
Battersea Iron. A	24	7	9	8	55	52	30
Battersea Res.	24	7	6	11	41	57	27
Crescent R. A +2	24	5	5	14	51	84	22
Destiny Acad. -5	24	7	5	12	38	53	21
Old Plym'th. Res.	24	6	3	15	46	65	21
Wandgas Sp. Res.	24	3	4	17	34	71	13

Jnr Division Three	P	W	D	L	F	A	Pts
Crescent Rov. B	22	14	5	3	74	35	47
Kerria Knights -3	22	16	2	4	68	38	47
Croy. G. u-23s -3	22	12	4	6	40	37	37
Oxted & D. Res.	22	11	3	8	49	31	36
Trinity Res. +3	22	10	2	10	50	49	35
Ashtead Res. +3	22	10	2	10	52	56	35
Mole Valley A -10	22	11	3	8	50	53	26

	P	W	D	L	F	A	Pts
Oakstead	22	7	5	10	45	53	26
Tooting B. Res. *+5*	22	5	4	13	42	56	24
Oakhill United	22	6	4	12	40	51	22
Shirley Town	22	6	2	14	36	51	20
Cheam VW. A *+3*	22	5	2	15	31	67	20

Jnr Division Four	P	W	D	L	F	A	Pts
Tadworth Res.	26	20	2	4	104	39	62
Park Boys	26	16	4	6	67	52	52
Sutton H. Res. *+3*	26	15	3	8	58	41	51
Trinity A *-3*	26	17	2	7	94	49	50
Norton Res. *+3*	26	14	4	8	68	69	49
Old Town *+3*	26	12	5	9	52	57	44
Cheam City *-18*	26	19	2	5	110	45	41
Alexander Forbes	26	11	1	14	50	66	34
Addington Ath. *+2*	26	9	3	14	53	72	32
Fetcham Res.	26	6	6	14	56	70	24
Fulham D. Res. *+6*	26	4	5	17	41	76	23
Old Plym'thians A	26	5	6	15	44	70	21
W'sterne H. A *+3*	26	5	3	18	41	85	21
Croydon G'side B	26	5	2	19	47	94	17

SWINDON & DISTRICT LEAGUE

Premier Division	P	W	D	L	F	A	Pts
Fratellos	12	7	3	2	33	19	24
Rodbourne Arms	12	6	4	2	37	23	22
Moonrakers	12	6	0	6	28	30	18
Queensfield	12	4	4	4	32	27	16
VBA Rangers	12	4	3	5	31	35	15
Bulldog	12	4	2	6	25	27	14
Bakers Arms	12	3	0	9	20	45	9

Duke of Edinburgh - record expunged

TAUNTON & DISTRICT LEAGUE
(Somtech)

Division One	P	W	D	L	F	A	Pts
Bridgwater Sports	22	14	4	4	70	20	46
Highbridge Town	22	13	5	4	49	21	44
Dulverton Town	22	11	5	6	52	44	38
Alcombe Rovers	22	11	2	9	49	41	35
Taverners	22	11	2	9	62	59	35
Locomotives *-3*	22	11	3	8	53	46	33
Middlezoy Rovers	22	9	4	9	53	39	31
Porlock	22	8	5	9	45	39	29
Wyvern	22	7	2	13	45	64	23
Marketeers	22	7	1	14	43	72	22
Cannington	22	6	2	14	36	82	20
Hulan	22	4	5	13	44	74	17

Division Two	P	W	D	L	F	A	Pts
Staplegrove	20	15	1	4	64	32	46
Nether Stowey	20	14	1	5	65	29	43
B. Lydeard Res.	20	13	2	5	69	24	41
Sampford Blues	20	13	2	5	59	32	41
Woolavington Pred.	20	11	1	8	79	35	34
T'ton Civil Service	20	11	1	8	59	29	34
Minehead Res.	20	9	4	7	50	42	31
B'water Spts Res.	20	5	4	11	42	59	19
Westonzoyland	20	4	2	14	28	56	14
Spaxton *-6*	20	4	2	14	30	92	8
Norton Fitzwarren	20	1	0	19	19	134	3

Wyvern Res. - record expunged

Division Three	P	W	D	L	F	A	Pts
Wembdon	22	18	3	1	86	28	57
Staplegrove Res.	22	13	4	5	75	45	43
Watchet T. Res.	22	12	5	5	47	31	41
White Hart Rgrs	22	11	3	8	55	42	36
Sydenham Rgrs	22	10	4	8	62	51	34
Old Inn All Stars	22	8	4	10	76	75	28
B'wtr Sports Colts	22	8	3	11	48	46	27
Williton	22	7	6	9	47	46	27
Redgate	22	7	5	10	56	61	26
Alcombe R. Res.	22	8	2	12	57	70	26
North Petherton	22	7	5	10	50	64	26
Milverton Rgrs *-3*	22	0	2	20	33	133	-1

Division Four	P	W	D	L	F	A	Pts
Appletree	22	18	2	2	89	31	56
Wembdon Saints	22	15	4	3	75	32	49
Middlezoy R. Res.	22	13	4	5	58	32	43
Exmoor Rangers	22	12	5	5	55	32	41
Highbridge T. Res.	22	12	2	8	55	40	38
W'zoyland Res.	22	10	2	10	47	52	32
Stogursey Greyhds	22	9	4	9	46	64	31
N. F'warren Res.	22	9	2	11	60	54	29
Hamilton Hawks	22	5	3	14	34	54	18

	P	W	D	L	F	A	Pts
Dulverton Res. *-3*	22	5	3	14	41	68	15
Porlock Res.	22	3	1	18	31	77	10
Staplegrove Colts	22	3	4	15	36	91	10

Dynamo Devon - record expunged

TELFORD COMBINATION

	P	W	D	L	F	A	Pts
Ketley Bank	20	14	5	1	77	32	33
Shifnal Utd Res.	20	15	2	3	81	29	32
Madeley Sports	20	14	4	2	77	30	32
Hadeley Park Alb.	20	10	5	5	77	53	25
The Warren	20	9	3	8	77	66	21
HQ Spts & Social	20	8	5	7	48	47	21
Atlas	20	6	6	8	42	47	18
Claverley *-2*	20	6	1	13	42	56	11
Much Wenlock	20	3	3	14	26	56	9
Impact Res. *-2*	20	4	2	14	37	114	8
Denso	20	2	2	16	26	80	6

TONBRIDGE & DISTRICT LEAGUE

Premier Division	P	W	D	L	F	A	Pts
Hawkenbury	18	13	3	2	79	25	42
High Brooms Cas.	18	11	0	7	45	37	33
Southborough	18	10	1	7	43	30	31
Tonbridge Inv. Res.	18	8	0	10	44	46	24
Woodlands	18	7	2	9	37	60	23
Rusthall A	18	5	2	11	34	62	17
Langton Green	18	4	2	12	39	61	14

Division One	P	W	D	L	F	A	Pts
Eden Rangers	16	11	2	3	69	21	35
Blackham/Ashurst	16	11	0	5	51	32	33
Hawkenbury Res.	16	10	2	4	46	30	32
E. Peckham Jnrs	16	9	1	6	34	26	28
Tunbdge Wells U.	16	7	2	7	46	46	23
Pembury Res.	16	6	2	8	39	49	20
Brenchley Wdrs	16	6	2	8	43	57	20
Hadlow Harrow	16	5	1	10	42	42	16
Roselands	16	1	0	15	22	89	3

Division Two	P	W	D	L	F	A	Pts
Insulators	18	15	2	1	71	18	47
Hadlow Evolution	18	14	1	3	68	14	43
Hawkenbury A	18	11	1	6	53	41	34
Tonbridge Inv. A	18	9	2	7	32	44	29
Southborough Res.	18	9	1	8	49	45	28
Paddock Wood	18	7	0	11	40	39	21
Leigh	18	6	2	10	36	45	20
Capel Sports & S.	18	6	2	10	24	37	20
Penshurst Park	18	4	1	13	40	87	13
Horsmonden Spts	18	2	2	14	24	67	8

Division Three	P	W	D	L	F	A	Pts
Rusthall B	18	15	2	1	79	28	47
AFC Valour	18	15	0	3	75	17	45
High Brooms Res.	18	13	4	1	66	27	43
Dowgate +3	18	7	1	10	42	38	25
Frant	18	7	2	9	58	68	23
Ashton Prime *-3*	18	7	2	9	43	38	20
W'dlands Res. *+3*	18	5	1	12	33	63	19
Brenchley W. Res.	18	4	3	11	33	70	15
P'dock W Res. *+2*	18	2	4	12	27	65	12
Roselands Res. *-4*	18	3	5	10	31	73	10

TROWBRIDGE & DISTRICT LEAGUE

Division One	P	W	D	L	F	A	Pts
Seend United	22	18	1	3	67	22	55
The Deverills	22	15	3	4	55	36	48
Lavington	22	12	3	7	61	47	39
Frome Town Spts	22	10	4	8	52	37	34
Freshford United	22	8	7	7	52	48	31
Blue Circle	22	9	3	10	53	57	30
Bradford United	22	8	3	11	46	45	27
Trowb'dge Town A	22	7	4	11	48	65	25
Steeple Ashton	22	7	4	11	35	53	25
Semington M'pies	22	7	4	11	47	69	25
Westbury Utd A	22	6	3	13	46	46	21
FC Northbridge	22	3	5	14	40	77	13

Division Two	P	W	D	L	F	A	Pts
St And. Winsley	18	17	1	0	78	23	52
Broughton FC	18	13	2	3	72	33	40
Bromham Res.	18	11	3	4	62	33	36
Trowbridge Wdrs	18	11	3	4	45	28	36
Bratton	18	8	3	7	37	37	27
Seend Utd Res.	18	5	3	10	36	34	17
Heytesbury	18	5	2	11	33	50	16
FC Courthouse	18	5	1	12	25	46	13
Frome Town Sp. A	18	2	2	12	20	78	8
Bradford Utd Res.	18	2	2	14	20	66	7

Division Three	P	W	D	L	F	A	Pts
Foresters	18	17	1	0	103	20	52
North Bradley	18	13	2	3	67	26	41
Calne Eagles	18	11	4	3	53	29	37
Westwood	18	9	2	7	48	46	29
Westfield	18	6	3	9	41	56	20
FC Chip'ham Y. A	18	6	3	9	38	55	20
Bratton Res.	18	6	2	10	33	50	20
The Stiffs	18	6	1	11	35	53	18
Mere Town YDT	18	5	2	11	38	57	16
Steeple Ash. Res.	18	0	2	16	35	99	2

TYNE & WEAR AMATEUR LEAGUE
(Dunsford Business Supplies)

	P	W	D	L	F	A	Pts
Gleneagles	16	13	2	1	78	19	41
Thorney Close Inn	16	12	3	1	63	14	39
Blue Bell Fulwell	16	8	5	3	50	36	29
Hebburn GHIC Ath	16	7	2	7	45	48	23
Sandhills	16	7	0	9	36	43	21
G'hd Snooker Ctre	16	4	5	7	37	57	17
Willow Pond	16	3	3	10	41	75	12
Chaplins	16	2	4	10	28	60	10
N'bottle WMC *-10*	16	2	4	10	34	60	0

TYNESIDE AMATEUR LEAGUE

Division One	P	W	D	L	F	A	Pts
Killingw'th YPC T.	28	22	1	5	82	36	67
W'laton Vulcan Inn	28	19	4	5	78	39	61
Blyth Town Res.	28	19	2	7	75	45	59
Kicks Wallsend	28	18	3	7	75	51	57
Cull. Custom Plan.	28	16	5	7	85	42	53
Newcastle City	28	14	5	9	91	61	47
Blyth Thoroton H.	28	13	4	11	63	70	43
Wardley	28	12	6	10	72	54	42
Blyth Spartans A	28	12	4	12	49	54	40
West Jesmond	28	9	4	15	44	63	31
Gosforth BG Res.	28	8	7	13	40	59	31
Wallsend T. Res.	28	7	2	19	58	103	23
Lindisfarne Ath.	28	6	3	19	41	91	21
Bellingham	28	5	3	20	44	77	18
Newc. Medicals	28	3	1	24	47	99	10

Division Two	P	W	D	L	F	A	Pts
Blakelaw Croft. L.	24	23	0	1	106	20	69
Red Star Benwell	24	19	3	2	75	21	60
New York	24	17	3	4	86	53	54
Walker Cent. Res.	24	13	3	8	79	53	42
Newc. Diggers U.	24	13	2	9	65	44	41
Blaydon House	24	11	2	11	70	64	35
Killingw'th Station	24	8	6	10	53	55	30
Newc. RVI L'side	24	9	1	14	45	49	28
Grainger Pk BC	24	7	6	11	52	69	27
Rutherford Res.	24	6	5	13	38	66	23
Gosforth BG A	24	6	2	16	40	82	20
Newc. JCB Ein. *-3*	24	6	1	17	38	85	16
Cullercoats A	24	1	0	23	36	122	3

WAKEFIELD & DISTRICT LEAGUE

Premier Division	P	W	D	L	F	A	Pts
Horb'y Cherry Tree	18	15	1	2	47	25	46
B'fd Airedale Celtic	18	12	2	4	60	35	38
Thornhill	18	12	1	5	68	33	37
Stanley	18	10	3	5	50	32	33
Ryecroft Sports	18	7	2	9	40	36	23
Snydale Athletic	18	7	2	9	29	43	23
Nostell MW A	18	6	2	10	35	46	20
Walton	18	5	4	9	24	45	19
W Bear Kexbrough	18	5	2	11	29	57	17
Crofton Sports	18	1	1	16	22	52	4

Division One	P	W	D	L	F	A	Pts
Gate Res.	24	18	5	1	81	22	59
Dodworth MW	24	18	2	4	92	38	56
Soothill -4	24	17	3	4	75	39	50
Kingstone UWMC	24	14	5	5	84	57	47
Alverthorpe WMC	24	15	1	8	76	46	46
AFC Shepherds *-4*	24	15	2	7	87	48	43
Dewsbury ROB *-1*	24	10	3	11	71	66	32
Fieldhead Hosp.	24	7	4	13	60	80	25
Old Bank WMC *-1*	24	6	5	13	48	68	22
Stanley Utd Res.	24	6	4	14	61	86	22
Royal Oak	24	4	3	17	40	92	15
Eastmoor Res. *-3*	24	3	6	15	40	86	12
Waterloo FC	24	1	1	22	35	122	4

Division Two	P	W	D	L	F	A	Pts
Royston	24	21	0	3	118	33	63
Oss. Two Brewers	24	18	4	2	77	36	58
Rose of York	24	18	0	6	94	34	54
Outwood Victoria	24	17	3	4	77	34	54
FC Wasps	24	15	3	6	66	41	48
AFC 2 Brewers -4	24	12	0	12	66	46	32
Wrenthorpe	24	8	0	16	56	93	24
AFC Cross Keys	24	6	5	13	42	75	23
Scissett -2	24	8	0	16	42	88	22
Wakefield Utd -1	24	6	3	15	44	75	20
F'stone C. Res. -5	24	6	4	14	49	60	17
Cliffe Tree	24	5	1	18	41	93	16
Plough	24	3	3	18	35	99	12

AFC Wakefield - record expunged

Division Three	P	W	D	L	F	A	Pts
Garforth Rgrs Res.	22	17	2	3	89	35	53
Morley C & SC	22	16	0	6	68	28	48
Little Bull	22	15	2	5	62	30	47
Alverthorpe Res.	22	12	4	6	57	47	40
Snydale Ath. Res.	22	11	1	10	53	60	34
Prostar	22	9	5	8	60	50	32
Horbury T. Res.	22	8	4	10	56	64	28
Thornes	22	8	3	11	51	53	27
Victoria Horbury	22	7	5	10	52	57	26
Inns of Court	22	7	3	12	40	55	24
Crofton Spts Res.	22	3	2	17	35	77	11
Scissett Res. -2	22	3	1	18	24	91	8

WARRINGTON & DISTRICTLEAGUE

(Sindh & Luqmans Cuisine)

Premier Division	P	W	D	L	F	A	Pts
Whiston Cross Holt	22	14	3	5	50	27	45
Ravenhead Knauff	22	13	3	6	53	37	42
Halebank	22	12	4	6	60	44	40
Cronton Villa	22	9	6	7	41	41	33
Runcorn Albion	22	9	5	8	49	48	32
Haydock	22	9	3	10	48	49	30
St Michaels DH	22	9	2	11	54	47	29
Vulcan	22	7	7	8	45	45	28
Beeches	22	8	4	10	41	44	28
Blackbrook	22	7	3	12	53	74	24
Moorfield	22	5	7	10	27	34	22
Halton Borough	22	3	7	12	27	58	16

Division One	P	W	D	L	F	A	Pts
Sidac Social	18	12	5	1	35	12	41
Ford Sports Res.	18	10	2	6	40	33	32
Fife Rangers	18	8	5	5	35	31	29
Burtonwood Albion	18	9	2	7	51	50	29
Windle Lbr Club	18	8	4	6	50	40	28
Orford BA	18	6	4	8	39	40	22
Rainhill Town	18	6	3	9	42	37	21
Cronton Villa Res.	18	6	2	10	32	45	20
Grange SC	18	6	1	11	34	49	19
Widnes Bayer	18	4	2	12	25	46	14

Division Two	P	W	D	L	F	A	Pts
Whiston CH Res.	20	16	2	2	56	22	50
Prescot C. Res.	20	14	3	3	75	27	45
Legion	20	12	2	6	50	29	38
Rainhill Town Res.	20	11	2	7	32	27	35
Runcorn Alb. Res.	20	8	5	7	38	39	29
Lomax	20	8	4	8	41	49	28
St Mich. DH Res.	20	8	2	10	43	51	26
Halebank Res.	20	7	4	9	32	41	25
Croft	20	8	0	12	49	52	24
Culcheth SC	20	4	2	14	37	70	14
Vulcan Res.	20	1	0	19	18	64	3

Division Three	P	W	D	L	F	A	Pts
Avon Athletic	22	16	2	4	60	32	50
Village Social	22	15	4	3	67	30	49
Spartak	22	13	1	8	47	32	40
Fife Rangers Res.	22	12	3	7	53	37	39
St Michaels DH A	22	11	2	9	40	36	35
Grappenhall Res.	22	10	4	8	51	35	34
Winwick	22	9	4	9	42	43	31
Runcorn Albion A	22	7	4	11	46	59	25
Monk Sports Res.	22	6	4	12	40	49	22
Moorfield Res.	22	6	3	13	45	54	21
Halton Boro. Res.	22	6	2	14	31	71	20
Penketh United	22	3	3	16	32	76	12

Division Four	P	W	D	L	F	A	Pts
Avon Athletic Res.	22	20	1	1	121	31	61
Widnes St Maries	22	17	3	2	76	22	54
Moore Utd Res.	22	13	4	5	76	52	43
Burtonwood Res.	22	10	4	8	40	46	34
Grange SC Res.	22	9	4	9	64	54	31
Orford BA Res.	22	9	4	9	49	57	31
Farnworth Griffin	22	8	3	11	47	70	27
Waterloo Wdrs	22	8	1	13	39	53	25
Grappenhall S. A	22	6	4	12	38	51	22
Rainhill Town A	22	4	6	12	35	59	18
Culcheth SC Res.	22	5	3	14	31	71	18
Moorfield A	22	4	1	17	26	76	13

Division Five	P	W	D	L	F	A	Pts
Villa Rainhill	20	18	1	1	107	11	55
Mosscroft	20	18	1	1	109	26	55
Smiths SDFC	20	15	1	4	80	33	46
Dragons	20	9	3	8	61	65	30
Blue Lion	20	9	2	9	49	66	29
St Michaels DH B	20	7	4	9	43	51	25
Blackbrook Res.	20	7	4	9	42	51	25
Haydock Res.	20	5	2	13	36	66	17
Halton Borough A	20	4	3	13	25	64	15
Cronton Villa A	20	4	2	14	20	55	14
Newton-le-Willows	20	2	1	17	22	106	7

WEARSIDE COMBINATION

(TWR Trade Frames)

Premier Division	P	W	D	L	F	A	Pts
Jolly Potter	20	15	2	3	74	28	47
Hendon FC	20	14	3	3	83	35	45
Colonel Prior	20	11	6	3	55	37	39
Redhouse	20	9	2	9	46	52	29
Blue House	20	8	4	8	45	50	28
Fulwell Blue Bell	20	7	5	8	48	47	26
HF S'view Plastics	20	8	2	10	32	43	26
Aquatic Sports	20	7	3	10	53	60	24
Hendon Grange	20	6	3	11	51	62	21
Eas'ton LWMC -3	20	7	2	11	39	55	20
Mountain Daisy	20	1	2	17	26	83	5

Division One	P	W	D	L	F	A	Pts
Hylton Colliery W.	20	16	1	3	88	29	49
Sporting Redh'se	20	13	4	3	81	40	43
S'hm Times Inn	20	14	1	5	75	37	43
Travellers Rest	20	11	3	6	53	37	36
The Fort	20	11	1	8	70	58	34
Sassco.co.uk	20	9	4	7	58	63	31
Cambridge Hotel	20	8	2	10	52	60	26
Usworth	20	8	0	12	58	62	24
Park View	20	5	1	14	38	67	16
Country Park Inn	20	3	3	14	45	83	12
Times Inn	20	2	0	18	40	122	6

WENSLEYDALE LEAGUE

(Wensleydale Creamery)

	P	W	D	L	F	A	Pts
Bowes	32	27	4	1	135	28	85
Richmond Acad.	32	25	3	4	120	26	78
Buck Inn Broncos	32	25	2	5	134	53	77
Colburn Town -3	32	25	4	3	147	50	76
Leyburn United	32	22	3	7	149	51	69
R'mond Mav. Res.	32	19	5	8	110	48	62
Hawes United	32	18	2	12	100	70	56
Buck Inn OB -3	32	15	4	13	89	66	46
Carperby Rovers	32	12	5	15	69	80	41
Unicorn	32	10	4	18	62	92	34
Redmire United -3	32	10	6	16	46	85	33
Spen. & Harmby	32	8	5	19	67	92	29
Reeth & Dist. AC	32	5	4	23	47	125	19
Askrigg United	32	4	4	24	31	157	16
Hawes Utd Res.	32	5	1	26	32	159	16
Richmond Ath. -6	32	5	4	23	48	125	13
K. Malzeard A -9	32	6	2	24	50	129	11

WEST HERTS LEAGUE

(Arlon Printers)

Premier Division	P	W	D	L	F	A	Pts
Hemel Hemp. Rov.	18	17	0	1	77	15	51
Martin Baker Rov.	18	10	2	6	44	29	32
Tring Athletic A	18	10	2	6	36	29	32
Kings Sports	18	10	1	7	57	44	31
SWR Garage Drs	18	8	2	8	43	35	26
St Albans North	18	8	2	8	36	38	26
Metpol Bushey A	18	7	2	9	41	57	23
Sun Postal Rovers	18	6	3	9	38	45	21
Hemel Aces	18	4	1	13	18	51	13
Oxhey Jets A	18	2	1	15	18	65	7

Division One	P	W	D	L	F	A	Pts
Inter Hemel	14	10	1	3	49	26	31
Oxhey	14	10	1	3	44	30	31
Hadley A	14	9	2	3	38	24	29
Croxley C & H	14	8	1	5	42	34	25
Metpol Bushey B	14	6	1	7	35	39	19
H. Hemp. Rv. Res.	14	4	2	8	32	33	14
Oxhey Wanderers	14	2	1	11	18	35	7
Kings Sports Res.	14	2	1	11	23	60	7

Jomarth Construction - record expunged

Division Two	P	W	D	L	F	A	Pts
Old Parmiterians A	18	14	3	1	73	31	45
Harpenden Rov. A	18	10	3	5	58	47	33
Aldenham Res.	18	10	1	7	64	43	31
L'Artista	18	8	3	7	50	43	27
Hadley B	18	7	4	7	46	38	25
Glenn Sports	18	6	4	8	48	51	22
Bovingdon A	18	7	1	10	44	49	22
Oxhey Jets B	18	6	4	8	34	48	22
Hunton Bridge	18	5	4	9	38	62	19
Potten End	18	3	1	14	28	71	10

Evergreen A - record expunged

Division Three	P	W	D	L	F	A	Pts
Hemel H. Rov. A	18	13	3	2	72	22	42
Martin Baker Res.	18	13	1	4	85	28	40
SWR Gar. D. Res.	18	11	2	5	58	31	35
Tring Athletic B	18	10	2	6	43	33	32
Maple Cross	18	8	1	9	43	65	25
Rick'worth St Geo.	18	6	6	6	27	45	24
Langleybury CC	18	6	4	8	46	41	22
Croxley C&H Res.	18	5	2	11	23	58	17
Harpenden Rov. B	18	5	0	13	34	61	15
Oxhey Res.	18	2	1	15	23	70	7

WEST SUSSEX LEAGUE

(Covers)

Premier Division	P	W	D	L	F	A	Pts
Newtown Villa	18	15	3	0	54	13	48
T D Shipley	18	13	3	2	42	16	42
Barnham	18	9	3	6	44	32	30
Univ. of Chichester	18	8	1	9	28	32	25
Cowfold	18	6	6	6	30	23	24
Upper Beeding	18	5	5	8	20	31	20
Petworth	18	6	1	11	23	41	19
Lancing United	18	5	2	11	35	45	17
East Dean	18	4	3	11	28	42	15
Wittering United	18	3	5	10	17	46	14

Predators - record expunged

Division One	P	W	D	L	F	A	Pts
Clymping Res.	18	12	3	3	53	30	39
Southwater	18	12	3	3	55	33	39
Stedham United	18	11	4	3	52	26	37
Billinshurst	18	9	4	5	41	32	31
West Chiltington	18	8	3	7	33	26	27
Angmering	18	7	4	7	43	41	25
Henfield	18	6	4	8	44	48	22
Ashington Rovers	18	6	4	8	56	61	22
Capel	18	2	3	13	36	57	9
Fittleworth	18	1	0	17	34	93	3

WESTMORLAND LEAGUE

(Bluefin)

Division One	P	W	D	L	F	A	Pts
Ambleside United	26	21	3	2	97	33	66
Wetheriggs Utd	26	21	2	3	95	36	65
Carvetii United	26	18	4	4	82	42	58
Keswick	26	15	7	4	73	39	52
Appleby	26	13	5	8	87	44	44
Kendal County	26	12	7	7	60	46	43
Penrith Rangers	26	12	5	9	78	50	41
Shap	26	10	4	12	71	66	34
Burneside	26	8	2	16	45	71	26
Sedbergh Wdrs	26	7	5	14	43	97	26
Lunesdale United	26	5	6	15	59	87	21
Coniston	26	3	10	13	43	71	19
Greystoke	26	2	5	19	43	100	11
Windermere SC	26	2	1	23	23	117	7

Division Two	P	W	D	L	F	A	Pts
Kirkoswald	22	17	5	0	70	12	56
Wetheriggs Res.	22	16	4	2	62	31	52
Kendal Celtic	22	13	5	4	56	35	44
Kendal United	22	12	4	6	52	32	40
Staveley United	22	12	3	7	67	29	39
Ibis	22	10	2	10	56	45	32

	P	W	D	L	F	A	Pts
Shap Res.	22	9	4	9	33	40	31
Kendal C. Res. *-6*	22	8	4	10	53	47	22
Keswick Res.	22	5	4	13	39	56	19
Dent	22	5	2	15	31	95	17
Ambleside Res.	22	3	1	18	26	64	10
Windermere Res.	22	1	4	17	19	78	7

Division Three	P	W	D	L	F	A	Pts
Endmoor KGR	22	17	3	2	80	22	54
Appleby Res.	22	15	5	2	78	23	50
Carvetii Utd Res.	22	16	2	4	74	33	50
Burneside Res.	22	13	1	8	58	41	40
Penrith Rgrs Res.	22	11	4	7	53	33	37
Kirkby Thore Rgrs	22	10	2	10	52	42	32
Langwathby Utd	22	8	5	9	51	34	29
Ullswater United	22	8	1	13	44	60	25
Wetheriggs Utd A	22	6	5	11	50	64	23
Sedbergh W. Res.	22	6	2	14	49	86	20
Braithwaite	22	3	1	18	29	94	10
Ibis Res.	22	3	1	18	23	109	10

Division Four	P	W	D	L	F	A	Pts
Alston Moor	22	18	2	2	99	17	56
Langwathby Res.	22	17	5	0	71	14	56
Milnethorpe Cor. A	22	16	2	4	83	29	50
Endmoor KGRRes.	22	11	3	8	69	57	36
Lunesdale Res.	22	9	4	9	63	51	31
Greystoke Res.	22	9	4	9	58	50	31
Burneside A	22	8	5	9	56	54	29
Staveley Res. *-3*	22	7	3	12	37	65	21
Esthwaite Vale	22	6	3	13	34	73	21
Coniston Res.	22	5	1	16	21	64	16
Kendal C. Res. *-6*	22	6	1	15	39	80	13
Windermere A *-3*	22	3	1	18	31	107	7

WESTON & DISTRICT LEAGUE

Division One	P	W	D	L	F	A	Pts
Cleeve West Res.	22	15	5	2	58	30	50
Portishead T. A	22	13	4	5	71	35	43
KVFC	22	12	5	5	62	40	41
Hutton FC	22	12	5	5	55	47	41
Nailsea T. Res.	22	9	3	10	33	39	30
East Worle	22	8	5	9	35	39	29
Churchill C. Res.	22	7	4	11	41	65	25
Bournville Rovers	22	7	3	12	48	51	24
Nailsea United A	22	7	3	12	45	55	24
Draycott	22	5	6	11	34	47	21
Winscombe Res.	22	5	6	11	29	48	21
St George EG Res.	22	5	5	12	33	48	20

Division Two	P	W	D	L	F	A	Pts
Weston St J. S Bar	20	16	1	3	87	34	49
Kewstoke Lions	20	15	2	3	74	35	47
Milton Crusaders	20	13	1	6	63	33	40
Clevedon Utd A	20	11	2	7	50	20	35
Locking Park	20	9	3	8	51	44	30
Portishead T. B	20	8	2	10	42	45	26
Selkirk United	20	8	1	11	43	47	25
Portishd WMC *-6*	20	8	3	9	48	50	21
Clarence Park	20	5	4	11	32	73	19
Winscombe A	20	4	2	14	32	76	14
Congresbury Res.	20	2	1	17	19	84	7

Division Three	P	W	D	L	F	A	Pts
Herons Moor Rgrs	22	18	2	2	127	42	56
Worle Res.	22	17	3	2	92	40	54
Yatton Ath. Res.	22	12	4	6	84	58	40
Westland Utd Res.	22	11	4	7	56	36	37
Wrington-R. Res.	22	10	1	11	53	64	31
Cleeve West A	22	9	3	10	43	56	30
Nailsea United B	22	8	4	10	55	58	28
Burnham U. A *-1*	22	7	3	12	40	65	23
Kewstoke L. Res.	22	6	4	12	46	79	22
Locking Villa	22	6	4	12	41	80	22
South Pk Rgrs *-1*	22	5	4	13	50	86	18
Blagdon	22	3	4	15	34	57	13

Division Four	P	W	D	L	F	A	Pts
Weston United	22	21	1	0	91	13	64
Axbridge Town	22	15	2	5	77	37	47
Wedmore	22	12	2	8	54	53	38
Cheddar A	22	11	4	7	47	38	37
Clevedon Utd B	22	11	2	9	51	44	35
Westend	22	11	1	10	47	53	34
King Alfred SC *-1*	22	10	3	9	51	55	32
Nailsea Utd Colts	22	8	4	10	64	55	28
Hutton Res.	22	8	2	12	43	71	26
Banwell Res. *-1*	22	3	6	13	32	55	14

	P	W	D	L	F	A	Pts
St George EG A	22	2	4	16	35	74	10
Draycott Res. *-3*	22	2	5	15	27	71	8

Division Five	P	W	D	L	F	A	Pts
East Worle Res.	18	14	3	1	79	29	45
Clevedon Dons	18	13	1	4	72	23	40
Berrow Res	18	10	5	3	57	29	35
KVFC Res.	18	8	2	8	47	50	26
AFC Nailsea	18	7	3	8	41	38	24
Bournville R. Res.	18	8	0	10	49	58	24
Portish'd Colts *-3*	18	7	3	8	52	46	21
Weston SJSB Res.	18	7	0	11	42	49	21
Kewstoke Lions A	18	3	1	14	26	85	10
Cheddar B *-3*	18	4	0	14	31	89	9

Division Six	P	W	D	L	F	A	Pts
Tickenham United	20	17	2	1	96	21	53
Sparta Kewstoke	20	16	2	2	85	19	50
Dynamo Dury	20	12	3	5	65	38	39
Backwell Utd A *-1*	20	11	2	7	48	44	34
Dolphin Athletic	20	9	2	9	46	43	29
St George EG B	20	6	5	9	50	50	23
Selkirk Utd Res.	20	6	2	12	33	52	20
Wedmore Res.	20	5	4	11	25	53	19
Yatton Athletic A	20	5	3	12	49	60	18
AFC Nailsea Res.	20	4	5	11	35	79	17
Athletico Wrington	20	2	4	14	22	95	10

WIGAN & DISTRICT AMATEUR LEAGUE

Premier Division	P	W	D	L	F	A	Pts
Newburgh United	24	16	6	2	67	35	54
Winstanley St Aid.	24	16	5	3	65	25	53
Highfield	24	15	5	4	70	35	50
Standish St Wilf.	24	15	4	5	68	42	49
Sterling	24	11	6	7	76	61	39
Hindley Town	24	11	3	10	77	56	36
Shevington	24	11	3	10	41	37	36
Fir Tree Rangers	24	10	5	9	61	51	35
AFC Scholes	24	7	6	11	45	63	27
Leigh Phoenix	24	5	4	15	42	64	19
Pemberton *-3*	24	7	1	16	48	77	19
Ince Central	24	2	5	17	28	70	11
Worsley Mesnes *-3*	24	3	1	20	28	100	7

Division One	P	W	D	L	F	A	Pts
Bickerstaffe	26	23	1	2	93	31	70
Downall Green U.	26	19	4	3	107	26	61
Cross Guns	26	15	7	4	68	42	52
Tyldesley	26	15	3	8	64	43	48
Gidlow Athletic OB	26	11	7	8	60	48	40
Wigan Rovers	26	11	4	11	40	48	37
Coppull Celtic	26	9	6	11	55	64	33
W'stanley SA Res.	26	9	4	13	47	67	31
Billinge A	26	8	5	13	53	72	29
Up Holland	26	6	9	11	49	57	27
Three Crowns *-6*	26	7	7	12	47	64	22
St Judes	26	5	6	15	33	48	21
Hindley Town Res.	26	5	5	16	40	63	20
Springfield *-3*	26	4	2	20	31	114	11

Division Two	P	W	D	L	F	A	Pts
Ince	24	17	4	3	89	38	55
Leigh Legion	24	18	1	5	94	44	55
Ormskir	24	15	2	7	83	58	47
Atherton Spts & S.	24	12	4	8	77	58	40
Farnworth Town	24	12	2	10	96	75	38
Bickerstaffe Res	24	10	5	9	48	45	35
Fir Tree Rgrs Res.	24	11	2	11	67	72	35
Goose Green *-3*	24	9	7	8	63	69	31
Standish Res. *-3*	24	9	6	9	61	70	30
Hindley Celtic *-3*	24	8	0	16	67	86	21
Shevington Res.	24	6	3	15	48	75	21
Wigan Rov. Res.	24	5	3	16	37	88	18
Ashton Villa	24	3	3	18	49	101	12

Tamar - record expunged

WITNEY & DISTRICT FA

Premier Division	P	W	D	L	F	A	Pts
Hailey	20	15	2	3	80	24	47
Charlbury Town	20	12	5	3	62	29	41
Brize Norton	20	9	9	2	41	21	36
Ducklington	20	11	3	6	42	35	36
Witney Royals	20	9	6	5	49	34	33
Hanborough	20	10	2	8	48	36	32
Spartan Rangers	20	9	3	8	50	33	30
Bampton Town	20	8	4	8	48	53	28
West Witney	20	4	2	14	38	51	14
Minster Lovell	20	4	2	14	22	59	14
Cassington	20	0	0	20	16	121	0

Division One	P	W	D	L	F	A	Pts
Combe	20	14	3	3	70	27	45
Kingham All B.	20	11	5	4	45	30	38
North Leigh A	20	11	4	5	50	26	37
Aston FC	20	10	4	6	30	26	34
Ducklington Res.	20	7	5	8	36	33	26
AC Finstock	20	7	4	9	44	55	25
Bampton T. Res.	20	7	3	10	35	33	24
FC Mills	20	6	6	8	34	39	24
Witney Wdrs	20	6	3	11	40	53	21
Milton FC	20	6	3	11	36	52	21
Brize Norton Res.	20	5	0	15	24	70	15

Eynsham Association A - record expunged

Division Two	P	W	D	L	F	A	Pts
FC Chequers	22	19	3	0	82	12	60
Chipping Norton	22	14	5	3	70	32	47
Hanboro. Res. *-6*	22	12	5	5	53	30	35
Wychwood Forest	22	10	5	7	50	39	35
FC Nomads	22	9	5	8	28	36	32
Tackley	22	9	4	9	35	48	31
Southrop	22	7	5	10	45	38	26
Two Rivers *+6*	22	6	2	14	38	56	26
Wootton Sports	22	7	3	12	37	55	24
West Witney Res.	22	6	5	11	37	60	23
Spartan Rgrs Res.	22	6	2	14	28	64	20
Kingham Res. *-6*	22	3	4	15	32	65	7

Division Three	P	W	D	L	F	A	Pts
Witney Ryls Res.	22	20	1	1	72	15	61
Chad Park	22	19	1	2	95	13	58
Ducklington A	22	15	3	4	76	30	48
Charlbury T. Res.	22	12	3	7	63	37	39
FC Chequers Res.	22	11	0	11	62	48	33
Aston Res.	22	10	1	11	51	52	31
Minster Lov. Res.	22	9	1	12	46	77	28
Spartan Rgrs A	22	7	4	11	36	48	25
FC Mills Res.	22	7	2	13	50	70	23
Hailey Res.	22	5	2	15	46	88	17
Milton FC Res.	22	3	3	16	23	92	12
Fieldtown	22	2	3	17	16	66	9

Division Four	P	W	D	L	F	A	Pts
Carterton A	22	18	0	4	69	28	54
Stanton Harcourt	22	16	2	4	74	24	50
Chip. Norton Res.	22	14	1	7	69	40	43
Eynsham Sports	22	14	1	7	82	56	43
Freeland A	22	14	0	8	54	45	42
FC Hollybush	22	12	0	10	53	54	36
AFC Marlborough	22	11	1	10	61	47	34
Combe Res.	22	8	2	12	51	53	26
Witney Royals A	22	7	1	14	42	88	22
Wychwood F. Res.	22	5	4	13	35	46	19
Witney Athletic	22	5	1	16	32	89	16
Brize Norton A *-3*	22	1	1	20	25	77	1

WORCESTER & DISTRICT LEAGUE

	P	W	D	L	F	A	Pts
Grovesnor Sports	18	13	2	3	64	36	41
Martley Spurs	18	12	3	3	55	29	39
Powick	18	11	3	4	74	23	36
Hallow WMC	18	7	6	5	43	35	27
VBL Sports	18	8	3	7	51	50	27
Hanley Swan	18	7	2	9	44	58	23
Univ. of Worcester	18	6	3	9	31	43	21
Upton Town	18	5	4	9	31	44	19
FC Tything *-3,-3g*	18	5	4	9	43	63	16
West Malvern	18	1	0	17	24	82	3

WORTHING & DISTRICT LEAGUE
(Ian Hart Funeral Services)

Premier Division	P	W	D	L	F	A	Pts
L & S Athletic	20	17	1	2	94	30	52
Ferring	20	15	3	2	77	26	48
Worthing Athletic	20	14	3	3	71	40	45
Sompting	20	8	6	6	46	38	30
GSK Sports	20	8	4	8	52	49	28
Fern Estates	20	8	3	9	47	43	27
Woodside/Goring	20	6	6	8	37	41	24
Shoreham RBL	20	6	2	12	60	83	20
Durrington Rafa	20	4	3	13	39	65	15
AFC Broadwater	20	3	3	14	30	82	12
Worthing Albion	20	2	4	14	28	84	10

Division One	P	W	D	L	F	A	Pts
GSK Sports Res.	24	19	2	3	113	33	59
LWS Highdown R.	24	15	2	7	71	42	47
L & S Athletic Res.	24	14	5	5	66	41	47
AC Azzurri	24	14	3	7	77	46	45

Team	P	W	D	L	F	A	Pts
TMG	24	15	0	9	76	47	45
Gor. St Theresa's	24	12	5	7	64	50	41
Northbrook	24	13	2	9	56	56	41
Ath Wenban Smith	24	11	4	9	77	64	37
Edge	24	9	1	14	46	57	28
AFC B'water Res.	24	6	3	15	64	83	21
Adur Athletic	24	6	3	15	40	95	21
Lancing United A	24	3	2	19	40	88	11
St Marys FC	24	2	2	20	21	109	8

Division Two	P	W	D	L	F	A	Pts
Ferring Res.	22	17	2	3	69	22	53
Wort. BCOB Res.	22	16	2	4	67	29	50
W. Tarring WMC	22	16	1	5	86	38	49
GSK Sports A	22	12	1	9	52	47	37
Northbrook Res.	22	10	2	10	38	47	32
Worthing Ath. Res.	22	10	0	12	47	57	30
Sompting Res.	22	8	4	10	34	48	28
LWS H'down Res.	22	8	0	14	37	58	24
Southside Ath. -3	22	7	5	10	61	57	23
Adur Athletic Res.	22	7	2	13	41	50	23
Goring ST Res.	22	6	3	13	37	56	21
Lancing United B	22	4	0	18	38	98	12

WYCOMBE & DISTRICT LEAGUE

Senior Division	P	W	D	L	F	A	Pts
AC Marlow	20	15	3	2	59	20	48
Wycombe Judo	20	13	3	4	58	17	42
Holmer Green OB	20	12	4	4	57	21	40
AFC Spartans	20	13	0	7	63	35	39
FC Titans	20	9	2	9	28	34	29
Hambleden	20	9	2	9	49	58	29
Winchmore Hill	20	8	4	8	43	44	28
Red Lion Wooburn	20	9	1	10	49	51	28
Penn/Tylers G. A	20	3	5	12	26	51	14
AFC Missenden	20	3	2	14	29	83	11
AFC Amersham	20	3	0	17	21	68	9

Premier Division	P	W	D	L	F	A	Pts
FC Leisure	26	20	2	4	73	40	62
AC Marlow Res.	26	17	2	7	75	43	53
Wycombe Athletic	26	17	1	8	74	37	52
Great Missenden	26	15	4	7	72	38	49
K Church (Amer)	26	14	6	6	79	44	48
Bucks SU Res.	26	13	3	10	71	54	42
Winchmore H Res.	26	12	4	10	63	54	40
Chinnor A	26	11	5	10	49	48	38
Wooburn Athletic	26	9	6	11	47	47	33
Stokenchurch	26	8	6	12	62	66	30
AFC Studley G.	26	9	1	16	60	86	28
Downley A. Res.	26	7	5	14	50	84	26
P. of Wales Rgrs	26	5	0	21	30	95	15
Spartak Marlow	26	2	1	23	25	94	7

YEOVIL & DISTRICT LEAGUE

Premier Division	P	W	D	L	F	A	Pts
Pen Mill	20	16	1	3	78	24	49
Normalair RSL	20	13	4	3	58	33	43
Milborne Port	20	10	3	7	49	48	33
Henstridge	20	9	5	6	53	41	32
Stoke-s-Hamdon	20	9	2	9	45	43	29
Westland Sp. Res.	20	7	5	8	44	42	26
Baltonsborough	20	6	7	7	39	41	25
Keinton Mandeville	20	7	3	10	37	54	24
Templecombe R.	20	7	2	11	30	49	23
Tor	20	5	5	10	36	41	20
Cas. Cary Res. -8	20	2	1	17	26	79	-1

YORK LEAGUE

(Leeper Hare)

Premier Division	P	W	D	L	F	A	Pts
Hamilton Panthers	28	22	3	3	92	47	69
Old Malton St M.	28	19	4	5	75	38	61
Huntington Rov.	28	16	5	7	79	51	53
Dunnington	28	16	5	7	64	37	53
Kartiers (Selby)	28	16	1	11	60	43	49
Haxby United -3	28	14	5	9	74	61	44
Wigginton Grass.	28	13	3	12	62	52	42
Dringhouses	28	9	7	12	57	60	34
York St John Univ.	28	9	6	13	48	70	33
Wilberfoss	28	8	8	12	49	52	32
Poppleton United	28	8	5	15	55	56	29
Tate & Lyle Selby	28	6	6	16	30	76	24
Copmanthorpe	28	6	5	17	44	82	23
Malton & Norton	28	4	10	14	36	68	22
Tockwith	28	6	3	19	40	72	21

Division One	P	W	D	L	F	A	Pts
Riccall United	24	16	6	2	67	32	54
Tadcaster A. Res.	24	14	5	5	60	31	47
Thorpe United	24	13	7	4	68	42	46
York Railway Inst.	24	12	4	8	74	60	40
Amotherby/Swin.	24	11	7	6	47	40	40
Ouseburn United	24	10	5	9	47	41	35
Nestle Rowntree	24	9	5	10	53	51	32
Easingwold Town	24	9	3	12	36	44	30
Bishopthorpe Utd	24	8	6	10	38	52	30
Pocklington T. Res.	24	7	7	10	37	43	28
Stamford Bridge	24	7	3	14	39	71	24
Rufforth United	24	6	4	14	31	50	22
Norwich Union FC	24	2	2	20	37	77	8

Division Two	P	W	D	L	F	A	Pts
Hemingbrough U.	22	13	6	3	73	39	45
Post Office FC	22	13	6	3	54	32	45
Heslington	22	12	4	6	58	28	40
Heworth	22	12	4	6	67	51	40
St Clements	22	12	2	8	60	44	38
Huby United	22	11	2	9	51	46	35
Rawcliffe Rgrs	22	9	5	8	72	68	32
Church Fenton WH	22	9	3	10	55	44	30
Fulford United	22	7	6	9	53	55	27
Elvington Harriers	22	5	3	14	41	62	18
Osbaldwick	22	6	0	16	45	79	18
Moor Lane	22	2	1	19	36	117	7

New Earswick - record expunged

Division Three	P	W	D	L	F	A	Pts
Terrington Glory	24	22	2	0	106	17	68
Selby RSSC	24	22	1	1	95	20	67
Strensall	24	16	2	6	86	43	50
Crayke	24	11	4	9	51	41	37
Wheldrake	24	11	4	9	58	50	37
Selby Olympia	24	9	3	12	57	77	30
Stillington	24	8	4	12	45	54	28
Civil Service	24	7	6	11	59	66	27
Barmby Moor -3	24	9	2	13	40	63	26
Melbourne	24	7	5	12	51	89	26
Bishop Wilton	24	5	2	17	42	79	17
Norton Utd FC -3	24	5	3	16	33	81	15
LNER Builders	24	3	4	17	29	72	13

Reserve Division A	P	W	D	L	F	A	Pts
Haxby Utd Res.	22	17	3	2	67	32	54
Bishopthorpe Res.	22	12	3	7	38	30	39
Cop'thorpe Res.	22	11	3	8	40	36	36
O. Malton SM Res.	22	10	5	7	63	40	35
York SJ Univ. Res.	22	10	3	9	50	45	33
Dringhouses Res.	22	9	4	9	49	62	31
Dunnington Res.	22	8	6	8	43	40	30
Huntington Res.	22	9	3	10	39	48	30
Wigginton Res. -3	22	8	7	7	54	50	28
Kartiers Res.	22	8	3	11	39	46	27
Thorpe Utd Res.	22	4	6	12	30	41	18
Heworth Res. -3	22	3	0	19	22	64	6

Reserve Division B	P	W	D	L	F	A	Pts
Hamilton P. Res.	20	13	4	3	67	22	43
Wilberfoss Res.	20	11	7	2	54	23	40
Easingwold Res.	20	11	7	2	56	25	40
Riccall Utd Res.	20	10	4	6	47	33	34
Ouseburn U. Res.	20	7	6	7	53	47	27
Poppleton Res.	20	8	2	10	47	57	26
Tockwith Res.	20	6	6	8	26	38	24
Pocklington Res.	20	6	3	11	33	45	21
Stamford B. Res.	20	6	1	13	28	53	19
York Rail. I. Res.	20	5	3	12	40	58	18
Nestle R. Res. -3	20	4	3	13	31	81	12

YORKSHIRE OLD BOYS LEAGUE

Senior Division A	P	W	D	L	F	A	Pts
Leeds Medics & D.	22	16	4	2	62	21	52
Wortley	22	14	5	3	64	24	47
Leeds Univ. Old B.	22	13	4	5	58	35	43
Trinity/All Sts COB	22	12	6	4	62	37	42
Ealandians	22	12	1	9	65	41	37
Heck'wike GSOB	22	11	3	8	48	46	36
Huddersfield Ams	22	10	0	12	42	66	30
Old Rovers	22	6	3	13	32	59	21
Yorkshire Bank	22	5	4	13	28	47	19
St Nicholas FC	22	6	2	14	30	55	17
Bramley Juniors	22	4	3	15	42	78	15
FC Headingley	22	3	5	14	32	56	11

Senior Division B	P	W	D	L	F	A	Pts
Gildersome Spurs	22	16	4	2	85	30	52
Alwoodley Old B.	22	16	3	3	76	25	51
Stanningley Old B.	22	16	3	3	65	27	51
Old Batelians	22	13	0	9	71	53	39
Shire Academics	22	11	4	7	62	49	37
Leeds M & D Res.	22	10	4	8	46	45	34
Calverley	22	6	4	12	44	58	22
Old Modernians	22	5	6	11	38	46	21
Sandal Athletic	22	6	3	13	45	61	21
St Bedes Old B.	22	6	2	14	28	74	20
Old Collegians	22	5	2	15	28	59	17
Roundhegians	22	2	5	15	23	84	11

Division One	P	W	D	L	F	A	Pts
Wheelwright OB	22	14	4	4	76	32	46
Gildersome Res.	22	13	5	4	59	46	44
Wortley Res	22	12	4	6	53	33	40
Old Thornesians	22	12	3	7	60	39	39
Leeds M & D A	22	11	6	5	52	39	39
Bainbridge	22	11	3	8	55	42	36
O Centralians Res.	22	8	7	7	60	53	31
Leeds Ind'dent	22	8	3	11	45	55	27
Leeds City Old B.	22	5	4	13	39	57	19
East Ardsley W.	22	5	3	14	47	65	18
Collingham JOB	22	4	6	12	33	71	18
Western Jnrs OB	22	4	2	16	38	85	14

Division Two	P	W	D	L	F	A	Pts
Amaranth Old B.	24	16	4	4	68	37	52
Moortown Old B.	24	14	3	7	70	40	45
Dewsbury Rgrs	24	15	2	7	91	53	44
Leeds C. OB Res.	24	13	3	8	68	59	42
E. Leeds Trin. OB	24	12	3	9	57	48	39
Agnes Stewart OB	24	11	4	9	64	54	37
O. Mod'nians Res.	24	10	4	10	47	46	34
Gildersome Sprs A	24	10	3	11	43	54	33
Bramley JOB Res.	24	8	6	10	45	43	30
Ealandians Res.	24	9	1	14	60	82	28
Trinity/ASCOB Res.	24	7	4	13	40	64	25
Huddersf'ld A Res.	24	7	3	14	50	77	24
Old Centralians A	24	3	2	19	41	87	11

Division Three	P	W	D	L	F	A	Pts
Grangefield OB	26	22	1	3	106	27	67
Alwoodley Res.	26	21	3	2	90	40	66
H'wike GSOB Res.	26	16	2	8	87	55	50
Grangefield Res.	26	15	3	8	84	53	48
Leeds Ind. Res.	26	13	3	10	66	59	42
Colton Acads Res.	26	12	5	9	54	60	38
Colton Acads	26	11	5	10	57	65	38
St Bedes OB Res.	26	11	2	13	52	55	35
Leeds M & D. B	26	11	0	15	64	71	33
O Collegians Res.	26	8	5	13	41	58	29
Wheelwright Res.	26	8	2	16	40	68	26
Old Batelians Res.	26	7	4	15	46	70	25
R'hegians Res.	26	5	1	20	45	93	16
Hudd. Amateurs A	26	3	2	21	41	99	11

Division Four	P	W	D	L	F	A	Pts
Colton Acads A	24	17	4	3	59	38	52
H'wike GSOB A	24	15	4	5	65	41	49
W'dhse Moor Meth	24	14	5	5	66	30	47
Wortley A	24	12	5	7	55	28	41
Sandal Wdrs	24	11	5	8	57	54	38
East Ardsley Res.	24	11	3	10	53	52	36
Sandal Ath. Res.	24	9	6	9	50	52	33
Bramley JOB A	24	6	11	7	33	34	29
O Modernians B	24	8	3	13	48	51	27
O Modernians A	24	6	8	10	40	52	26
Leeds City OB A	24	6	6	12	51	55	24
Old Batelians A	24	7	3	14	63	88	24
Old Centralians B	24	1	3	20	21	86	6

Division Five	P	W	D	L	F	A	Pts
Ealandians A	24	19	2	3	82	39	59
O Thorn'ians Res.	24	17	3	4	87	39	54
Wheelwright OB A	24	14	3	7	68	56	45
Old Collegians A	24	12	8	4	62	46	44
O Thornesians A	24	13	5	6	57	47	44
Alwoodley OB A	24	11	2	11	54	60	35
St Bedes OB A	24	10	3	11	62	53	33
Hudd. Amateurs B	24	10	1	13	60	65	31
Roundhegians A	24	10	1	13	50	70	31
Leeds City OB B	24	7	7	10	42	46	27
Old Modernians C	24	6	3	15	45	68	21
Old Centralians B	24	3	2	19	38	77	11
Old Collegians B	24	2	4	18	32	73	10

WELSH PREMIER LEAGUE

www.low.org.uk

Sponsored by: Principality Building Society

Founded: 1992

Recent champions:
2004: Rhyl
2005: Total Network Solutions
2006: Total Network Solutions
2007: The New Saints
2008: Llanelli

		P	W	D	L	F	A	Pts
Rhyl		**34**	**29**	**3**	**2**	**95**	**29**	**90**
Llanelli		**34**	**26**	**5**	**3**	**98**	**38**	**83**
The New Saints		**34**	**20**	**11**	**3**	**79**	**27**	**71**
Carmarthen Town		**34**	**19**	**5**	**10**	**52**	**47**	**62**
Port Talbot Town		**34**	**16**	**8**	**10**	**57**	**48**	**56**
Bangor City		**34**	**16**	**7**	**11**	**58**	**40**	**55**
Haverfordwest County		**34**	**16**	**7**	**11**	**53**	**39**	**55**
Aberystwyth Town		**34**	**12**	**10**	**12**	**51**	**50**	**46**
Gap Connah's Quay		**34**	**12**	**5**	**17**	**49**	**65**	**41**
Newtown		**34**	**10**	**10**	**14**	**46**	**54**	**40**
Technogroup Welshpool		**34**	**11**	**7**	**16**	**48**	**70**	**40**
Airbus UK Broughton		**34**	**12**	**3**	**19**	**47**	**57**	**39**
NEWI Cefn Druids		**34**	**9**	**7**	**18**	**57**	**74**	**34**
Neath Athletic		**34**	**10**	**4**	**20**	**43**	**65**	**34**
Prestatyn Town		**34**	**8**	**9**	**17**	**48**	**70**	**33**
Porthmadog		**34**	**10**	**2**	**22**	**57**	**91**	**32**
Caersws		**34**	**6**	**7**	**21**	**28**	**61**	**25**
Caernarfon Town	*-3*	**34**	**5**	**8**	**21**	**32**	**73**	**20**

	Aberystwyth Town	Airbus UK B'ghton	Bangor City	Caernarfon Town	Caersws	Carmarthen Town	Gap Connah's Q.	Haverfordwest Co.	Llanelli	NEWI Cefn Druids	Neath Athletic	Newtown	Port Talbot Town	Porthmadog	Prestatyn Town	Rhyl	Technogroup W'pl	The New Saints
Aberystwyth Town		1-0	1-2	3-1	2-2	0-3	1-1	0-3	1-1	1-1	6-2	2-0	1-1	5-2	2-1	0-1	0-2	2-2
Airbus UK Broughton	1-2		2-3	4-3	0-2	0-1	0-0	2-4	0-4	1-0	4-3	3-1	1-1	0-3	1-1	1-3	5-0	1-0
Bangor City	0-0	1-0		1-1	3-0	2-0	6-0	1-1	0-2	4-2	0-1	1-2	4-2	1-0	1-1	0-2	0-2	0-0
Caernarfon Town	1-0	0-2	0-2		2-2	1-3	0-2	0-1	0-5	4-2	1-0	0-0	2-4	0-2	1-1	0-1	2-3	0-5
Caersws	1-3	1-3	0-1	1-0		0-2	0-1	1-0	0-2	1-2	0-0	1-1	4-2	3-2	1-2	0-3	0-1	2-6
Carmarthen Town	2-1	1-0	3-1	2-1	1-1		2-0	3-0	1-4	1-0	5-2	0-0	1-1	1-0	1-0	1-2	0-1	2-3
Gap Connah's Quay	1-2	2-3	1-3	1-1	1-0	1-3		2-1	3-1	2-3	5-0	3-3	0-2	3-1	3-1	2-3	1-0	0-2
Haverfordwest County	5-1	3-0	0-2	1-1	2-0	1-1	2-0		0-1	1-1	2-0	1-0	0-1	4-2	3-1	1-3	3-1	2-2
Llanelli	3-0	3-2	4-3	3-2	3-0	5-2	4-1	2-1		1-1	2-1	3-1	2-0	5-0	6-1	0-1	4-1	1-1
NEWI Cefn Druids	2-5	0-2	1-0	0-1	3-1	1-2	6-0	0-1	0-4		3-1	2-3	1-1	2-4	3-2	2-4	3-3	0-1
Neath Athletic	0-4	3-1	0-1	2-1	0-0	2-0	0-1	1-1	0-3	1-0		3-0	2-3	3-0	2-0	2-2	3-2	1-4
Newtown	2-1	0-1	1-3	2-2	0-0	2-3	1-2	4-2	2-6	4-0	2-0		1-0	2-0	1-1	1-2	4-1	0-0
Port Talbot Town	1-1	2-1	2-1	1-0	2-0	0-0	0-2	1-2	4-6	3-2	2-0	1-2		1-3	3-1	2-2	4-0	0-0
Porthmadog	4-1	3-4	0-6	1-3	0-1	1-3	6-5	2-1	3-3	2-3	1-4	3-1	1-2		3-2	0-3	2-1	2-2
Prestatyn Town	1-0	2-1	2-2	5-0	3-2	1-2	1-1	0-1	0-1	3-3	1-0	1-0	0-3	5-2		1-4	2-2	1-4
Rhyl	0-0	1-0	4-1	4-0	3-1	3-0	2-0	2-0	5-1	3-4	4-2	3-0	2-3	2-0	7-2		7-1	2-1
Technogroup Welshpool	0-1	2-1	1-1	1-1	1-0	2-0	3-1	1-3	1-3	3-3	2-1	2-2	1-2	3-2	2-2	0-2		1-2
The New Saints	1-1	1-0	2-1	6-0	4-0	8-0	2-1	0-0	0-0	4-1	2-1	1-1	2-0	6-0	2-0	0-3	3-1	

LOOSEMORE'S SOLICITORS LEAGUE CUP GROUP STAGE

(see next page for details of the group stage)

QUARTER-FINALS

Aberystwyth Town 4 Caersws 1, **Bangor City** 3 Rhyl 1

NEWI Cefn Druids 0 **The New Saints** 2, Newtown 1 **Neath Athletic** 1 *aet* (2-4p)

SEMI-FINALS

(played over two legs)

Bangor City 1 Aberystwyth Town 2, Aberystwyth Town 2 **Bangor City** 4

Neath Athletic 2 The New Saints 0, **The New Saints** 3 Neath Athletic 0

FINAL *(April 5th at Newtown)*

The New Saints 2 Bangor City 0

LOOSEMORE'S SOLICITORS LEAGUE CUP GROUP STAGE

GROUP ONE

	P	W	D	L	F	A	Pts
Aberystwyth Town	4	1	3	0	7	3	6
Carmarthen Town	4	1	2	1	4	4	5
Haverfordwest County	4	1	1	2	3	7	4

Aberystwyth Town 1 Carmarthen Town 1
Aberystwyth Town 4 Haverfordwest County 0
Carmarthen Town 0 Haverfordwest County 1
Carmarthen Town 1 Aberystwyth Town 1
Haverfordwest County 1 Aberystwyth Town 1
Haverfordwest County 1 Carmarthen Town 2

GROUP TWO

	P	W	D	L	F	A	Pts
Neath Athletic	4	2	1	1	13	12	7
Llanelli	4	2	0	2	12	10	6
Port Talbot Town	4	1	1	2	11	14	4

Llanelli 2 Port Talbot Town 4
Llanelli 3 Neath Athletic 5
Neath Athletic 0 Llanelli 3
Neath Athletic 5 Port Talbot Town 3
Port Talbot Town 1 Llanelli 4
Port Talbot Town 3 Neath Athletic 3

GROUP THREE

	P	W	D	L	F	A	Pts
Newtown	4	2	1	1	11	4	7
NEWI Cefn Druids	4	2	1	1	7	7	7
Caernarfon Town	4	0	2	2	4	11	2

Caernarfon Town 1 NEWI Cefn Druids 1
Caernarfon Town 0 Newtown 0
NEWI Cefn Druids 0 Newtown 2
NEWI Cefn Druids 3 Caernarfon Town 2
Newtown 2 NEWI Cefn Druids 3
Newtown 7 Caernarfon Town 1

GROUP FOUR

	P	W	D	L	F	A	Pts
Caersws	4	2	2	0	13	7	8
Bangor City	4	2	1	1	10	11	7
Porthmadog	4	0	1	3	5	10	1

Bangor City 1 Caersws 6
Bangor City 3 Porthmadog 0
Caersws 1 Porthmadog 1
Caersws 3 Bangor City 3
Porthmadog 2 Bangor City 3
Porthmadog 2 Caersws 3

GROUP FIVE

	P	W	D	L	F	A	Pts
Rhyl	4	3	0	1	13	3	9
Technogroup Welshpool	4	2	0	2	7	7	6
Airbus UK Broughton	4	1	0	3	5	15	3

Airbus UK Broughton 0 Rhyl 4
Airbus UK Broughton 2 Technogroup Welshpool 0
Rhyl 1 Technogroup Welshpool 2
Rhyl 6 Airbus UK Broughton 1
Technogroup Welshpool 0 Rhyl 2
Technogroup Welshpool 5 Airbus UK Broughton 2

GROUP SIX

	P	W	D	L	F	A	Pts
The New Saints	4	3	1	0	12	6	10
Gap Connah's Quay	4	2	0	2	3	6	6
Prestatyn Town	4	0	1	3	7	10	1

Gap Connah's Quay 0 The New Saints 2
Gap Connah's Quay 2 Prestatyn Town 1
Prestatyn Town 0 Gap Connah's Quay 1
Prestatyn Town 3 The New Saints 4
The New Saints 3 Gap Connah's Quay 0
The New Saints 3 Prestatyn Town 3

WELSH PREMIER TEAMS IN EUROPE

UEFA CHAMPIONS LEAGUE

FIRST QUALIFYING ROUND

1st Leg: *(July 15th at Llanelli)*
LLANELLI 1 FK Ventspils 0 Att: 942
2nd Leg: *(July 22nd at Ventspils)*
FK Ventspils 4 LLANELLI 0 Att: 2,000

INTERTOTO CUP

FIRST ROUND

1st Leg: *(June 21st at Bohemians Dublin)*
Bohemians Dublin 5 RHYL 1 Att: 1,500
2nd Leg: *(June 28th at Rhyl)*
RHYL 2 **Bohemians Dublin** 4 Att: 1,453

UEFA CUP

FIRST QUALIFYING ROUND

1st Leg: *(July 17th at FK Suduva Marijampole)*
FK Suduva Marijampole 1 THE NEW SAINTS 0 Att: 2,500
2nd Leg: *(July 31st at Newtown)*
THE NEW SAINTS 0 **FK Suduva Marijampole** 1 Att: 879

1st Leg: *(July 17th at Wrexham)*
BANGOR CITY 1 FC Midtjylland 6 Att: 703
2nd Leg: *(July 31st at Herning)*
FC Midtjylland 4 BANGOR CITY 0 Att: 4,050

WELSH PREMIER LEAGUE CONSTITUTION 2009-10

ABERYSTWYTH TOWN
Park Avenue Stadium, Maesgogerddan, Aberystwyth, Ceredigion SY23 1PG
Tel: 01970 617939
Colours: Green, black & white
www.atfc.org.uk

AIRBUS UK BROUGHTON
The Airfield, Broughton, Chester, Cheshire CH4 0BA
Tel: 01244 528317
Colours: Blue
www.airbusfc.com

BALA TOWN
Maes Tegid Stadium, Castle Street, Bala, Gwynedd LL23 7UY
Tel: 01678 520986
Colours: Red & black
www.balatownfc.co.uk

BANGOR CITY
The Stadium, Farrar Road, Bangor, Gwynedd LL57 1LJ
Tel: 01248 355852
Colours: Blue & white
www.bangorcityfc.com

CAERSWS
Recreation Ground, Bridge Street, Caersws, Powys SY17 5DT
Tel: 01686 688753
Colours: Blue & white
www.caersws-fc.com

CARMARTHEN TOWN
Richmond Park, Priory Street, Carmarthen, Carmarthenshire SA31 1LR
Tel: 01267 222851
Colours: Old gold & black
www.carmarthentownafc.net

ELEMENTS CEFN DRUIDS
Plas Kynaston Lane, Plas Kynaston, Cefn Mawr, Wrexham, Denbighshire LL14 3AT
Tel: 01978 824332
Colours: Black & white
www.cefndruidsafc.co.uk

GAP CONNAH'S QUAY
Deeside Stadium, Kelsterton Road, Connah's Quay, Deeside CH5 4BR
Tel: 01244 831212
Colours: White & black
official.sportsnetwork.net/main/s493.htm

HAVERFORDWEST COUNTY
Bridge Meadow Stadium, Bridge Meadow Lane, Haverfordwest, Pembrokeshire SA61 2EX
Tel: 01437 769048
Colours: Royal blue
www.haverfordwestcounty.co.uk

LLANELLI
Stebonheath Park, Penallt Road, Stebonheath, Llanelli, Carmarthenshire SA15 1EY
Tel: 01554 772973
Colours: Red
www.llanelliafc.org

NEATH ATHLETIC
The Gnoll, Gnoll Park Road, Neath, West Glamorgan SA11 3BU
Tel: 01639 620177
Colours: Yellow & blue
www.neathfc.com

NEWTOWN
GF Grigg Latham Park, Park Lane, Newtown, Powys SY16 1EN
Tel: 01686 623120
Colours: Red
www.newtownafc.co.uk

PORT TALBOT TOWN
The GenQuip Stadium, Victoria Road, Aberavon, Port Talbot, West Glamorgan SA12 6AD
Tel: 01639 882465
Colours: Blue & white
www.porttalbottown.com

PORTHMADOG
Y Traeth, Porthmadog, Gwynedd LL49 9PP
Tel: 01766 514687
Colours: Red, black & white
www.porthmadogfc.com

PRESTATYN TOWN
Bastion Gardens, Bastion Road, Prestatyn, Clwyd LL19 7ES
Tel: 01745 856905
Colours: Red
www.prestatyntownfootballclub.co.uk

RHYL
Belle Vue Stadium, Grange Road, Rhyl, Denbighshire LL18 4BY
Tel: 01745 338327
Colours: White & black
www.rhylfc.com

THE NEW SAINTS
The Venue at Park Hall, Burma Road, Oswestry, Shropshire SY11 4AS
Tel: 01691 684840
Colours: Green & white
www.tnsfc.co.uk

WELSHPOOL TOWN
Maesydre Recreation Grounds, Howells Drive, Welshpool, Powys SY21 7SU
Colours: White & black
Tel: 01938 555567
www.welshpooltownfc.co.uk

N: BalaTown (P- Cymru Alliance)
UT: Caernarfon Town (R - Cymru Alliance)
EWI Cefn Druids become Elements Cefn Druids, Technogroup Welshpool become Welshpool Town

CYMRU ALLIANCE LEAGUE

www.cymru-alliance.co.uk

Sponsored by: Huws Gray

Founded: 1990

Recent champions:
2004: Airbus UK
2005: Buckley Town
2006: Glantraeth.
2007: Llangefni Town
2008: Prestatyn Town

	Bala	Buckley	Denbigh	Flint	Glantraeth	Gresford	Guilsfield	Holyhead	Lex XI	Llandudno	Llandyrnog	Llanfairpwll	Llangefni	Mold Alex	Mynydd Isa	P'rhyncoch	Ruthin
Bala Town		0-0	4-1	2-1	2-0	4-1	5-1	1-4	2-0	1-0	2-0	2-0	2-3	3-0	5-0	3-0	5-0
Buckley Town	0-6		1-0	1-2	4-3	2-0	2-1	0-4	0-2	2-1	3-2	2-2	0-4	3-2	0-4	4-2	2-1
Denbigh Town	1-1	2-0		1-4	0-0	1-0	4-2	1-2	3-0	0-2	3-0	2-2	1-1	4-4	0-2	2-1	0-1
Flint Town United	5-5	5-4	1-0		7-1	1-1	2-1	3-3	1-1	0-0	3-1	1-5	2-3	2-4	4-4	4-0	0-1
Glantraeth	0-1	0-3	1-2	1-6		1-2	1-2	1-5	3-4	1-6	3-5	4-1	0-2	1-1	0-2	1-1	1-4
Gresford Athletic	0-0	1-1	1-2	1-2	2-1		2-5	1-0	1-3	1-5	2-2	0-1	0-7	0-2	1-0	2-1	2-3
Guilsfield	0-2	1-2	3-1	1-2	1-2	3-2		1-2	1-2	0-2	3-0	1-2	0-4	2-6	4-0	1-0	2-4
Holyhead Hotspur	2-2	2-0	3-2	0-5	1-0	0-1	0-2		4-2	2-1	3-0	3-0	0-1	3-1	1-0	8-0	0-0
Lex XI	0-2	1-1	1-1	2-0	3-1	3-2	2-3	5-0		4-2	3-1	1-1	0-2	1-1	3-1	0-0	2-3
Llandudno Town	1-2	1-1	2-0	1-1	2-1	1-1	3-0	1-3	4-0		2-0	4-1	0-0	1-1	2-0	1-1	1-2
Llandyrnog United	1-3	1-2	2-1	0-2	1-1	1-0	0-4	1-2	0-2	1-3		2-6	0-1	2-2	4-5	1-3	2-3
Llanfairpwll	0-8	2-1	1-3	0-2	2-2	2-0	1-1	1-3	3-3	1-4	1-0		0-2	3-4	1-4	1-0	1-1
Llangefni Town	2-0	3-0	2-1	2-2	1-2	3-3	2-1	0-2	4-1	1-1	6-0	2-1		1-1	1-1	3-0	0-1
Mold Alexandra	0-2	1-0	3-0	1-1	2-2	2-0	1-4	2-4	5-1	2-3	2-1	1-1	1-8		4-2	0-1	1-3
Mynydd Isa	0-0	3-1	1-0	2-1	4-2	2-1	2-0	0-1	4-3	3-3	2-1	0-1	1-0	4-1		10-1	3-2
Penrhyncoch	0-2	2-1	1-1	2-5	2-1	2-0	6-1	0-2	2-1	0-1	2-1	2-2	2-3	3-2	1-4		2-1
Ruthin Town	0-2	3-2	0-0	1-4	1-2	0-1	1-0	1-2	4-2	0-4	2-0	2-1	1-0	5-2	2-3	3-1	

		P	W	D	L	F	A	Pts
Bala Town		32	23	6	3	81	23	75
Holyhead Hotspur		32	23	3	6	71	36	72
Llangefni Town		32	20	7	5	74	27	67
Mynydd Isa		32	19	4	9	73	51	61
Llandudno Town		32	16	9	7	65	33	57
Ruthin Town		32	18	3	11	56	50	57
Flint Town United	*-3*	32	16	9	7	81	52	54
Buckley Town		32	12	5	15	45	64	41
Lex XI	*-3*	32	12	7	13	58	62	40
Mold Alexandra		32	10	9	13	62	71	39
Llanfairpwll		32	9	9	14	47	67	36
Denbigh Town		32	9	8	15	40	49	35
Guilsfield		32	11	1	20	52	67	34
Penrhyncoch	*-3*	32	10	5	17	41	72	32
Gresford Athletic		32	7	6	19	32	63	27
Glantraeth		32	4	6	22	40	82	18
Llandyrnog United		32	3	3	26	33	82	12

LEAGUE CUP

PRELIMINARY ROUND
Mold Alexandra 2 **Ruthin Town** 3

FIRST ROUND
Denbigh Town 3 Penrhyncoch 0
Flint Town United 4 Glantraeth 0
Gresford Athletic 1 **Lex XI** 2
Guilsfield 1 Buckley Town 0
Holyhead Hotspur 2 Llangefni Town 1
Llanfairpwll 3 **Bala Town** 4
Mynydd Isa 2 Llandudno 3 *(Llandudno expelled)*
Ruthin Town 4 Llandyrnog United 3

QUARTER-FINALS
Denbigh Town 0 **Bala Town** 2
Guilsfield 1 Flint Town United 0 *aet*
Lex XI 6 **Holyhead Hotspur** 0 *aet (Lex expelled)*
Mynydd Isa 2 **Ruthin Town** 3

SEMI-FINALS
Bala Town 2 Ruthin Town 1 *(at Buckley Town)*
Holyhead Hot. 0 Guilsfield 0 *aet* (5-3p) *(at Mold)*

FINAL
(May 16th at Llandudno Town)
Bala Town 2 Holyhead Hotspur 0 *aet*

CYMRU ALLIANCE CONSTITUTION 2009-10

BERRIEW .... Recreation Ground, Berriew, Powys .... Non
BETHESDA ATHLETIC .... Parc Meurig Park, Bethesda, Bangor LL57 3NT .... Non
BUCKLEY TOWN .... Globe Way, Liverpool Way, Buckley CH7 3LL .... Non
CAERNARFON TOWN .... The Oval, Marcus Street, Caernarfon LL55 2HT 01286 676885/67462
DENBIGH TOWN .... Central Park, Park Street, Denbigh LL16 3DD 01745 81250
FLINT TOWN UNITED .... Cae Y Castell, March Lane, Flint CH6 5PJ 01352 73098
GLANTRAETH .... Cae Trefdraeth, Bodorgan, Anglesey LL62 5EU 01407 84040
GRESFORD ATHLETIC .... Clappers Lane, Gresford, Wrexham LL12 8RW .... Non
GUILSFIELD .... Community Centre, Guilsfield, Welshpool SY21 9ND .... Non
HOLYHEAD HOTSPUR .... The New Stadium, Kingsland, Holyhead LL65 2YE 01407 76411
LEX XI .... Stansty Park, Summerhill, Wrexham LL11 4YG 01978 26114
LLANDUDNO TOWN .... Maesdu Park, Builder Street, Llandudno LL30 1HH 01492 86094
LLANFAIRPWLL .... Maes Eilian, Llanfairpwllgwyngyll, Anglesey LL61 5YG .... Non
LLANGEFNI TOWN .... Cae Bob Parry, Talwrn Road, Llangefni LL77 7LP 01248 72499
LLANGOLLEN TOWN .... Tower Field, Dinbren Road, Llangollen LL20 8TF .... Non
MOLD ALEXANDRA .... Alyn Park, Denbigh Road, Mold CH7 1SW .... Non
PENRHYNCOCH .... Cae Baker, Penrhynchoch, Aberystwyth SY23 3XH 01970 82899
RUTHIN TOWN .... Memorial Playing Fields, Park Road, Ruthin LL15 1NB .... Non

IN: Berriew (P - Mid-Wales League), Bethesda Athletic (P - Welsh Alliance), Caernarfon Town (R - Welsh Premier League), Llangolle Town (P - Welsh National League (Wrexham Area) Premier Division)
OUT: Bala Town (P - Welsh Premier League), Llandyrnog United (R - Welsh Alliance), Mynydd Isa (W)

WELSH LEAGUE

www.welshleague.org.uk

Sponsored by:

MacWhirter

Founded: 1904

Recent champions:

2004: Llanelli

2005: Ton Pentre

2006: Goytre United

2007: Neath

2008: Goytre United

Division One		P	W	D	L	F	A	Pts
ENTO Aberaman Athletic		34	24	5	5	73	33	77
Goytre United		34	24	4	6	90	39	76
Barry Town	*-3*	34	22	7	5	63	26	70
Bettws		34	18	8	8	64	32	62
Bridgend Town		34	18	6	10	65	49	60
Cambrian & Clydach Vale		34	16	9	9	62	48	57
Afan Lido		34	15	9	10	70	49	54
Pontardawe Town		34	14	10	10	48	32	52
Ton Pentre		34	14	7	13	59	51	49
Cardiff Corinthians		34	13	7	14	51	53	46
Bryntirion Athletic		34	12	8	14	54	58	44
Dinas Powys		34	10	5	19	43	73	35
Caldicot Town		34	9	7	18	41	67	34
Caerleon		34	9	7	18	36	64	34
Taffs Well		34	8	9	17	43	58	33
Newport YMCA		34	8	4	22	41	76	28
Croesyceiliog		34	7	5	22	45	82	26
Cwmbran Town		34	3	7	24	32	90	16

	Afan L.	Barry	Bettws	B'gend	B'tirion	C'leon	Caldicot	C'brian	Cardiff	Croes.	Cwm. T	Dinas P.	ENTO	Goytre	Newp't	P'dawe	Taffs W	Ton P.
Afan Lido		0-3	3-3	4-4	2-0	4-0	1-0	0-2	4-0	5-0	1-1	4-1	0-3	0-2	7-0	0-3	3-0	2-0
Barry Town	0-2		1-1	2-1	3-0	1-0	1-2	5-2	1-2	3-0	2-0	4-1	2-0	2-1	0-2	2-0	2-0	2-0
Bettws	1-1	0-0		1-1	2-1	5-0	4-1	1-2	1-0	2-1	0-2	1-0	2-1	1-3	2-0	3-1	1-1	1-0
Bridgend Town	0-2	2-2	2-1	***D***	2-1	0-1	2-1	2-2	0-4	7-3	1-0	4-0	1-3	1-0	3-0	1-1	5-2	4-0
Bryntirion Athletic	0-1	1-1	0-4	2-4	***I***	5-1	3-0	2-2	4-2	2-1	3-1	4-2	2-3	3-3	2-2	2-1	1-1	0-3
Caerleon	2-2	1-3	0-6	1-4	0-0	***V***	1-3	1-1	0-0	2-1	5-1	0-2	1-2	1-2	0-1	0-1	1-2	0-0
Caldicot Town	3-3	1-1	2-1	0-1	3-2	1-2	***I***	0-3	2-0	1-0	1-1	2-1	0-2	1-2	1-2	0-0	2-1	0-3
Cambrian/Clydach	2-0	1-3	2-0	5-2	0-2	1-1	3-2	***S***	2-3	0-0	3-1	3-2	0-1	3-2	2-0	3-1	1-2	1-1
Cardiff Corinthians	2-2	1-3	0-1	1-1	1-2	1-0	5-1	1-2	***I***	2-2	4-0	0-3	1-2	1-1	0-3	2-1	1-3	3-0
Croesyceiliog	0-1	1-3	0-4	1-2	1-4	1-1	5-1	0-4	0-2	***O***	3-0	3-0	1-4	3-1	1-3	1-2	1-1	1-3
Cwmbran Town	2-7	0-1	0-4	1-2	0-1	1-3	1-1	1-1	0-3	2-3	***N***	0-5	1-3	0-4	4-1	2-2	1-1	0-5
Dinas Powys	1-5	1-2	0-0	2-1	0-3	0-2	1-0	0-0	1-2	3-1	3-0		0-8	2-4	3-1	1-1	1-0	2-2
ENTO Aberaman	2-1	0-0	2-1	0-1	1-1	2-0	5-1	3-0	1-1	3-3	2-0	2-1	***O***	0-2	3-2	4-0	1-0	2-1
Goytre United	2-0	3-0	1-1	2-0	4-0	3-0	3-1	2-1	5-1	3-0	4-0	3-0	5-3	***N***	5-1	0-0	4-3	3-0
Newport YMCA	1-1	0-1	0-2	2-0	1-1	2-3	2-4	5-2	1-2	0-1	0-6	1-2	1-2	1-3	***E***	0-1	0-2	1-6
Pontardawe Town	1-1	0-0	3-0	2-0	1-0	4-1	2-2	0-1	2-0	1-2	6-0	6-0	0-1	2-1	2-1		1-0	0-0
Taffs Well	5-0	0-5	0-5	0-2	4-0	2-3	0-0	1-1	0-1	4-2	0-0	1-1	1-1	2-4	1-3	1-0		1-2
Ton Pentre	3-1	0-2	1-2	0-2	1-0	0-2	3-1	1-4	2-2	6-2	5-3	3-1	0-1	5-3	1-1	0-0	2-1	

WELSH DIVISION ONE CONSTITUTION 2009-10

ABERAMAN ATHLETIC. . . . . Aberaman Park, Cardiff Road, Aberaman, Aberdare CF44 6AA 07506 680185
AFAN LIDO . . . . Marston's Stadium, Princess Margaret Way, Aberavon Beach, Port Talbot SA12 6PE 01639 892960
BARRY TOWN . . . . Jenner Park Athletic Stadium, Barry Road, Barry CF62 9BG. 01446 735858
BETTWS . . . . North Site, Bettws Road, Bettws, Bridgend CF32 8SG 07887 530804
BRIDGEND TOWN . . . . University of Glamorgan PF, Treforest Industrial Estate, Treforest, Pontypridd CF37 5UP 01443 482681
BRYNTIRION ATHLETIC . . . . Bryntirion Park, Llangewydd Road, Bryntirion, Bridgend CF31 4JU 01656 652702
CAERLEON . . . . Cold Bath Road, Caerleon, Newport NP18 1NF 01633 420074
CALDICOT TOWN. . . . . Jubilee Way, Caldicot NP26 4NA 07802 665937
CAMBRIAN & CLYDACH VALE BGC King George V New Field, Highfield Road, Clydach Vale, Tonypandy CF40 2XX 07980 558495
CARDIFF CORINTHIANS . . . . Riverside Ground, Station Road, Radyr, Cardiff CF15 8AB 02920 843407
DINAS POWYS . . . . The Murch, Sunnycroft Lane, Dinas Powys CF64 4QQ. 07852 488552
ELY RANGERS . . . . Station Road, Wenvoe, Cardiff CF5 6AG 02920 598725
GARDEN VILLAGE . . . . Stafford Common, Victoria Road, Kingsbridge, Gorseinon, Swansea SA4 3AB 01792 533188
GOYTRE UNITED . . . . Glenhafod Park, Goytre, Port Talbot SA13 2YP 01639 898983/895615
PONTARDAWE TOWN . . . . Recreation Ground, Alloy Industrial Estate, Pontardawe SA8 4HL 01792 862228
TAFFS WELL . . . . Rhiw Dda'r, Parish Road, Taffs Well, Cardiff CF15 7SA. 02920 811080
TON PENTRE . . . . Ynys Park, Sawmill Villas, Llanfoist Street, Ton Pentre CF41 7AF 01443 442625/432813
WEST END . . . . Pri Deri Park, Eigen Crescent, Mayhill, Swansea SA1 6LB 07754 537012

IN: Ely Rangers (P), Garden Village (P), West End (P)
OUT: Croesyceiliog (R), Cwmbran Town (R), Newport YMCA (R)
ENTO Aberaman Athletic become Aberaman Athletic

Division Two		P	W	D	L	F	A	Pts
West End		34	22	5	7	102	49	71
Ely Rangers		34	21	6	7	79	38	69
Garden Village		34	21	6	7	90	55	69
Penrhiwceiber Rgrs		34	21	3	10	67	39	66
Llanwern		34	17	9	8	75	46	60
Cwmbran Celtic		34	17	7	10	69	51	58
Newcastle Emlyn		34	17	7	10	72	61	58
Ammanford		34	15	10	9	73	52	55
Tredegar Town		34	13	8	13	51	55	47
UWIC		34	14	4	16	76	67	46
Grange H'quins	*-3*	34	12	8	14	53	70	41
Treharris Athletic		34	11	3	20	60	95	36
Maesteg Park		34	9	7	18	40	64	34
Llangeinor		34	9	5	20	42	71	32
Caerau Ely		34	9	3	22	46	83	30
Pentwyn Dynamo	*-4*	34	8	8	18	65	78	28
Garw	*-3*	34	6	13	15	44	69	28
Pontypridd Town		34	5	6	23	39	100	21

NATHANIAL CAR SALES LEAGUE CUP

(all teams in league)

FIRST ROUND

Barry 2 Grange Quins 1 *aet*
Bridgend 7 Newcastle E. 2
Briton F. 6 Croesyceiliog 4
Bryntirion 5 Llwydcoed 2 *aet*
Caerau Ely 0 **Porthcawl** 3
Caldicot 3 Ammanford 1
Cardiff Corinthians 2 Ely Rangers 2 *aet* (3-2p)
ENTO A'man 1 Caerleon 0
Garden V. 3 Seven Sisters 1
Garw 4 Ystradgynlais 2
Goytre 1 **Bettws** 3
Merthyr Sts 1 **Cwmaman** 4
Monmouth 1 **Cwmbran C.** 2
Newport CS 3 Llanwern 1
Newport YMCA 2 Maesteg 1
Penrhiwceiber Rangers 0 Pontardawe Town 0 *aet* (4-3p)
Pentwyn Dyn. 2 UWIC 1
Pontyclun 2 **Llantwit F.** 6
Risca Utd 0 **Dinas Powys** 3
Taffs Well 0 **Cambrian** 3
Treharris 3 **Aberbargoed** 4
Troedyrhiw 0 **Tredegar** 2

SECOND ROUND

Afan Lido 6 Bryntirion 2
AFC Porth 4 Briton Ferry 0
Bridgend 3 Aberbargoed 1
Caldicot 2 Tredegar Town 1
Cardiff C. 1 **Goytre United** 3
Cwmaman Institute 1 **Porthcawl Town** 1 *aet* (2-4p)
Cwmbran C. 5 Pontypridd 1
Cwmbran T. 3 Bettws 2 *aet*
Dinas P. 3 Newport YMCA 1
ENTO Aberaman Athletic 4 Cwmamman United 1
Garden V. 2 **Ton Pentre** 4 *aet*
Garw 1 **Newport CS** 3
Llangeinor 0 **Llansawel** 2
Penrhiwceiber Rangers 1 Llantwit Fardre 1 *aet* (4-2p)
Pentwyn 2 Barry 2 *aet* (5-4p)
West End 5 Cambrian 2 *aet*

THIRD ROUND

Bridgend 5 Dinas Powys 2
Caldicot Town 0 Cwmbran Celtic 0 *aet* (4-1p)
Cwmbran T. 3 West End 2
ENTO A'man 0 **AFC Porth** 1
Llansawel 1 **Afan Lido** 6
Penrhiwceiber Rangers 3 Newport Civil Service 2 *aet*
Porthcawl 3 Pentwyn 1
Ton Pentre 1 **Goytre United** 2

QUARTER-FINALS

AFC Porth 0 **Afan Lido** 4
Cwmbran Town 2 **Bridgend** 3
Penrhiwceiber 2 Goytre U. 1
Porthcawl 3 Caldicot Town 2

SEMI-FINALS

Afan Lido 4 Bridgend Town 1 *(at Goytre United)*
Penrhiwceiber Rangers 1 Porthcawl 0 *(at Maesteg Park)*

FINAL

(March 23rd at Maesteg Park)
Afan Lido 1 Penrhiwceiber Rangers 1 *aet* (6-5p)

	Am	Cae	Cwm	Ely	GV	Gw	Gra	Llg	Llw	Mae	New	PR	PD	Pon	TT	TA	UW	Wes
Ammanford		2-1	0-2	0-1	3-3	1-1	3-1	2-0	1-1	5-0	2-3	0-2	3-1	1-1	2-1	2-0	1-0	2-2
Caerau Ely	0-5		6-2	0-3	0-4	1-1	0-4	2-0	1-3	1-4	4-0	3-1	2-4	2-0	1-2	3-2	2-0	0-1
Cwmbran Celtic	1-4	3-0		0-3	7-5	1-1	2-0	1-0	1-1	2-1	1-2	3-0	4-1	4-0	2-1	6-0	1-0	3-5
Ely Rangers	3-1	2-1	2-3	***D***	0-1	4-0	2-1	4-0	2-0	2-1	8-1	2-0	1-1	3-0	4-2	4-0	1-0	1-0
Garden Village	1-1	2-1	2-1	3-3	***I***	3-1	7-0	3-3	1-2	1-0	4-1	2-1	1-2	2-0	2-1	1-1	2-1	3-1
Garw	1-5	2-0	0-3	0-3	1-4	***V***	2-1	5-0	2-0	2-2	1-1	1-3	1-1	1-1	0-0	1-1	0-2	1-2
Grange Harlequins	3-3	1-0	1-1	1-1	1-3	5-3	***I***	3-2	2-2	2-1	2-1	1-3	1-0	4-1	1-2	1-4	2-1	0-2
Llangeinor	2-0	2-2	0-2	1-0	3-5	2-1	1-2	***S***	0-2	1-2	0-1	0-3	2-0	1-0	1-3	2-3	1-0	3-1
Llanwern	3-2	5-0	3-1	1-1	2-3	1-1	1-1	4-1	***I***	2-0	0-0	1-3	3-1	2-2	3-2	8-1	1-3	0-4
Maesteg Park	0-2	0-1	2-2	1-0	3-2	2-0	2-2	2-2	1-3	***O***	1-3	2-0	1-2	2-3	2-0	2-1	1-1	0-2
Newcastle Emlyn	2-2	5-3	2-0	4-4	2-1	6-1	4-1	4-2	2-2	0-2	***N***	2-3	3-3	2-0	0-1	3-0	7-3	1-0
Penrhiwceiber R.	6-1	4-0	1-1	2-0	4-2	1-1	0-0	2-1	1-0	3-0	2-0		3-0	4-0	0-1	0-1	2-1	3-1
Pentwyn Dynamo	0-3	6-1	1-1	2-4	1-2	2-4	1-1	2-2	1-2	2-2	1-2	1-2	***T***	4-1	0-1	3-3	4-1	2-5
Pontypridd Town	2-2	2-5	1-3	0-3	1-6	2-2	1-2	0-1	1-5	2-0	3-0	1-3	3-2	***W***	1-1	4-2	1-5	1-3
Tredegar Town	1-1	2-1	1-1	1-1	0-2	1-1	2-4	5-1	0-1	6-0	1-5	3-1	2-4	2-0	***O***	1-0	2-2	2-2
Treharris Athletic	3-8	4-1	0-2	3-0	2-3	2-4	4-0	2-0	0-7	2-0	1-0	0-2	7-2	5-2	0-1		2-5	2-6
UWIC	0-1	1-1	2-0	5-3	2-1	2-0	3-1	1-3	3-4	0-0	1-2	5-1	2-7	6-2	5-0	8-1		5-0
West End	4-2	4-0	3-2	2-4	3-3	4-1	5-1	2-2	1-0	5-1	1-1	2-1	2-1	10-0	4-0	3-1	10-0	

WELSH DIVISION TWO CONSTITUTION 2009-10

AFC LLWYDCOED . . . . Llwydcoed Football Ground, Merthyr Road, Llwydcoed, Aberdare CF44 0UT 01685 87392
AFC PORTH . . . . Dinas Park, Dinas, Porth, Rhondda CF40 1JG 07974 25294
AMMANFORD . . . . Ammanford Recreation Ground, Manor Road, Ammanford SA18 3AP 07749 26136
CAERAU ELY . . . . Cwrt-y-Ala, Ely, Cardiff CF5 5QT 07788 58572
CARDIFF BAY HARLEQUINS. . . . . . Cardiff International Stadium, Leckwith Road, Cardiff CF11 8AZ 02920 78839
CROESYCEILIOG . . . . Woodland Road, Croesyceiliog, Cwmbran NP11 2DZ 01633 48515
CWMBRAN CELTIC . . . . Celtic Park, Henllys Way, Cwmbran NP44 7LP 07968 94789
CWMBRAN TOWN . . . . Cwmbran Stadium, Henllys Way, Cwmbran NP44 3XL 01633 62710
LLANGEINOR . . . . Llangeinor Park, Bettws Road, Llangeinor, Bridgend CF32 8NU 01656 87167
LLANWERN . . . . Newport Stadium, Spytty Park, Langland Way, Newport NP19 0PT 07762 01331
MAESTEG PARK . . . . Tudor Park, St David's Place, Maesteg, Maesteg CF34 9LR. 01656 73000
NEWCASTLE EMLYN . . . . Parc Emlyn, Lower Car Park, New Road, Newcastle Emlyn SA38 9BG 01239 71099
NEWPORT YMCA. . . . . Mendalgief Road, Newport NP20 2HF 01633 26687
PENRHIWCEIBER RANGERS. . Glasbrook, Glasbrook Terrace, Penrhiwceiber, Mountain Ash CF45 3SY. 07774 74384
PORTHCAWL TOWN . . . . Locks Lane, Porthcawl CF36 3HY. 07866 54583
TREDEGAR TOWN . . . . Tredegar Leisure Complex, Stable Lane, Tredegar NP22 4BH 01495 72355
TREHARRIS ATHLETIC WESTERN. . . Athletic Ground, Commercial Terrace, Treharris CF46 5PY 07960 07988
UWIC . . . . Cyncoed Campus, UWIC, Cyncoed Road, Cardiff CF23 6XD 02920 41677

IN: AFC Llwydcoed (P), AFC Porth (P), Croesyceiliog (R), Cwmbran Town (R), Newport YMCA (R), Porthcawl Town (P)
OUT: Ely Rangers (P), Garden Village (P), Garw (R), Pentwyn Dynamos (R), Pontypridd Town (R), West End (P)
Grange Harlequins become Cardiff Bay Harlequins, Treharris Athletic become Treharris Athletic Western

Division Three		P	W	D	L	F	A	Pts
AFC Llwydcoed		34	26	6	2	126	31	84
AFC Porth		34	25	5	4	91	33	80
Porthcawl Town		34	21	7	6	65	36	70
Cwmamman United		34	19	5	10	76	65	62
Newport Civil Service		34	19	4	11	72	52	61
Llantwit Fardre		34	17	7	10	81	42	58
Aberbargoed Buds		34	17	5	12	71	71	56
Pontyclun		34	16	5	13	80	58	53
Monmouth Town		34	14	4	16	79	64	46
Troedyrhiw		34	14	3	17	69	69	45
Briton Ferry Athletic		34	13	5	16	61	52	44
Goytre		34	11	9	14	49	50	42
Cwmaman Institute		34	9	9	16	50	59	36
Seven Sisters		34	10	5	19	39	71	35
Risca United		34	9	8	17	46	83	35
Llansawel		34	7	8	19	42	63	29
Ystradgynlais		34	4	5	25	36	119	17
Merthyr Saints	*-3*	34	4	2	28	39	154	11

RESERVES CUP

FINAL *(May 14th at Maesteg Park)*

Port Talbot Town Res. 4 Bettws Res. 1

Reserve Division East		P	W	D	L	F	A	Pt
Croesyceiliog Res.		30	24	1	5	74	37	73
Bettws Res.		30	20	3	7	64	30	63
Newport YMCA Res.		30	18	5	7	77	42	59
Cwmbran Celtic Res.		30	16	6	8	74	46	54
Cambrian & Clydach Res.	*-3*	30	16	8	6	68	33	53
Ely Rangers Res.		30	16	3	11	70	54	51
Caldicot Town Res.		30	14	5	11	75	53	47
Caerleon Res.		30	13	6	11	60	58	45
Cardiff Corinthians Res.		30	12	4	14	62	61	40
Dinas Powys Res.		30	10	5	15	50	67	35
Llantwit Fardre Res.		30	8	6	16	46	62	30
Risca United Res.		30	9	3	18	38	71	30
Newport Civil Serv. Res.	*-6*	30	10	5	15	55	70	29
Garw Res.		30	7	5	18	40	69	26
Pontyclun Res.		30	7	3	20	50	75	24
Aberbargoed Buds Res.	*-1*	30	3	6	21	34	109	14

Reserve Division West		P	W	D	L	F	A	Pt
Port Talbot Town Res.		24	20	2	2	95	31	62
Pontardawe Town Res.		24	18	3	3	93	25	57
Afan Lido Res.		24	18	3	3	63	16	57
Neath Athletic Res.		24	14	3	7	84	57	45
Ammanford Res.		24	13	3	8	52	57	42
Garden Village Res.		24	12	4	8	62	48	40
Bryntirion Athletic Res.		24	9	5	10	63	60	32
AFC Llwydcoed Res.		24	8	3	13	46	65	27
Goytre United Res.		24	6	3	15	44	72	21
Cwmamman United Res.		24	4	7	13	40	57	19
Porthcawl Town Res.	*-3*	24	5	4	15	37	77	16
Briton Ferry Athletic Res.		24	2	6	16	23	90	12
Newcastle Emlyn Res.		24	1	6	17	22	69	9

(Llansawel Res., Seven Sisters Res. - record expunged)

	Llw	Por	Abe	Bri	CI	CU	Goy	Lla	LF	Mer	Mon	New	Pon	Por	Ris	Sev	Tro	Yst
AFC Llwydcoed		1-0	5-2	2-1	2-1	5-1	4-1	5-1	5-1	15-0	4-1	6-0	0-2	4-0	14-0	1-1	5-1	9-0
AFC Porth	1-1		4-3	2-1	1-0	4-0	3-1	1-0	3-0	6-0	3-2	1-0	2-1	2-1	4-0	2-2	3-0	3-0
Aberbargoed Buds	1-2	1-1	***D***	1-0	2-2	4-2	0-2	2-1	1-6	2-0	2-1	4-1	3-2	1-3	3-3	3-0	3-1	4-1
Briton Ferry Athletic	3-4	0-3	0-2	***I***	3-2	0-1	3-3	0-2	0-2	2-0	2-3	0-0	0-1	2-0	2-0	4-1	2-1	7-0
Cwmaman Institute	2-3	0-3	3-1	1-3	***V***	2-2	0-2	2-2	0-1	2-2	4-3	0-2	1-2	0-0	3-0	1-0	3-0	4-2
Cwmamman United	0-2	3-3	1-2	2-1	2-1	***I***	2-0	2-1	4-1	3-2	3-3	2-1	2-1	2-3	2-1	5-0	3-2	8-2
Goytre	0-0	1-2	2-2	1-1	4-1	0-1	***S***	0-2	0-3	2-3	1-1	1-1	4-3	0-1	0-0	3-0	0-2	0-0
Llansawel	2-2	0-3	0-2	0-4	0-0	1-2	1-1	***I***	1-2	2-0	4-1	1-0	1-2	2-4	1-2	2-3	1-1	0-2
Llantwit Fardre	1-2	1-0	5-1	2-4	1-1	4-2	2-1	5-0	***O***	13-0	2-0	0-0	0-0	1-1	1-1	2-0	1-2	6-0
Merthyr Saints	2-8	1-7	2-4	2-3	0-3	3-5	0-4	2-5	0-7	***N***	0-5	3-4	0-9	1-4	3-1	2-0	0-0	3-2
Monmouth Town	2-3	1-2	6-0	0-2	5-0	2-0	1-2	1-1	3-1	3-2		5-0	1-1	2-0	8-1	3-4	1-2	4-0
Newport Civil S.	1-2	2-2	1-2	3-2	3-2	7-3	3-1	2-1	3-0	7-0	3-1	***T***	2-3	0-1	3-0	1-0	3-2	7-1
Pontyclun	1-2	2-3	4-1	3-3	1-2	0-4	3-2	2-2	0-3	3-2	5-0	0-1	***H***	0-4	7-1	0-0	2-1	6-1
Porthcawl Town	0-0	1-0	0-0	2-1	2-1	1-1	1-0	1-0	0-0	2-1	1-3	1-2	4-1	***R***	6-0	4-0	3-1	4-2
Risca United	1-1	3-4	1-3	2-1	2-0	0-0	0-1	2-0	1-1	6-1	2-1	0-1	2-3	3-3	***E***	1-2	2-0	2-0
Seven Sisters	0-4	2-1	4-2	1-0	0-0	4-2	0-2	1-1	0-2	5-1	2-3	2-1	0-4	0-1	1-4	***E***	2-4	0-1
Troedyrhiw	1-0	2-4	4-2	1-2	1-4	2-3	2-3	4-1	4-3	6-1	4-1	2-5	3-1	1-2	2-1	3-0		6-1
Ystradgynlais	0-3	0-8	1-5	2-2	2-2	0-1	2-4	0-3	2-1	4-0	1-2	1-2	1-5	2-4	1-1	1-2	1-1	

WELSH DIVISION THREE CONSTITUTION 2009-10

BERBARGOED BUDS . . . . Recreation Ground, Bedwellty Road, Aberbargoed CF81 9AY 07773 407902
BERTILLERY BLUEBIRDS . . . . Cwmnantygroes Field, Six Bells, Abertillery NP13 2PW 01495 213999
RITON FERRY LLANSAWEL . . . . Old Road, Briton Ferry, Neath SA11 2HA 07952 777361
ORUS STEEL. Corus Sports Ground, Margam, Port Talbot SA13 2NF 01639 882066
WMAMAN INSTITUTE. . . . . . . Canolfan Cwmaman, Glanaman Road, Cwmaman, Aberdare CF44 6HY. 07786 588890
WMAMMAN UNITED. . . . . Grenig Park, Penpound Lane, Glanaman, Ammanford SA18 1EJ. 07977 925808
ARW SBGC . . . . Blandy Park, Oxford Street, Pontycymmer, Bridgend CF32 8EG 07795 216107
OYTRE. . . . . Plough Road, Penperlleni, Pontypool NP4 0AL. 07790 419852
LANTWIT FARDRE . . . . Tonteg Park, Main Road, Tonteg, Pontypridd CF38 1ND 01443 207393
IONMOUTH TOWN . . . . Monmouth Sports Ground, Chippenham, Monmouth NP25 5EY 07990 800939
IEWPORT CIVIL SERVICE . . . . Civil Service Sports Club, Shannon Close, Bettws NP20 6LX 08457 555555
ENTWYN DYNAMOS Pentwyn Leisure Centre, Parc Coed-y-Nant, Bryn Celyn Road, Pentwyn, Cardiff CF23 7EZ 02920 549211
ONTYCLUN . . . . The Ivor Park, Cowbridge Road, Pontyclun CF72 9BS 07814 214383
ONTYPRIDD TOWN . . . . Ynysangharad Park, Pontypridd CF37 4PE 01443 486571
ISCA UNITED . . . . Ty-Isaf Park, Isaf Road, Risca, Newport NP11 6EG 07950 753629
EVEN SISTERS . . . . Welfare Ground, Dulais Road, Seven Sisters, Neath SA10 9EY 01639 700354
OUTH GOWER. . . . . South Gower Sports Club, Scurlage, Gower, Swansea SA3 1BA. 01792 390857
ROEDYRHIW . . . . The Willows Community Centre, Bridge Street, Troedyrhiw, Merthyr Tydfil CF48 4DS. 01443 692198

N: Abertillery Bluebirds (P - Gwent County League Division One), Corus Steel (P – South Wales Amateur League Division One), Garw R), Pentwyn Dynamos (R), Pontypridd Town (R), South Gower (P – Swansea Senior League Division One)

UT: AFC Llwydcoed (P), AFC Porth (P), Merthyr Saints (R - South Wales Amateur League Division One), Porthcawl Town (P), stradgynlais (R - Neath League Premier Division)

WELSH ALLIANCE

www.welshallianceleague.co.uk

Sponsored by: Design2Print

Founded: 1984

Recent champions:
2004: Rhyl Res.
2005: Bodedern
2006: Prestatyn Town
2007: Denbigh Town
2008: Bethesda Athletic

	Amlwch T.	Barmouth	Bethesda A.	Conwy Utd	Glan Conwy	Halkyn Utd	Holywell T.	Llanberis	Llandudno J.	Llanllyfni	Llanrug Utd	Llanrwst Utd	Nantlle Vale	Nefyn United	Pwllheli	Rhydymwyn	Rhyl Res.
Amlwch Town		4-6	2-14	1-9	0-12	0-5	1-7	0-5	0-6	2-3	1-5	0-6	1-1	0-3	1-1	0-5	1-4
Barmouth & Dyffryn Utd	14-1		1-4	2-0	1-3	2-1	3-0	3-0	2-2	7-0	0-2	2-1	3-2	2-2	3-1	1-4	2-2
Bethesda Athletic	2-1	5-2		6-0	1-4	10-0	5-2	6-0	3-1	5-0	1-2	2-1	10-0	6-0	3-0	4-1	3-2
Conwy United	4-0	1-3	1-5		0-4	2-1	3-1	4-1	1-2	2-1	3-1	0-3	4-2	1-0	2-4	1-1	1-4
Glan Conwy	14-0	4-3	2-5	3-2		2-3	8-0	4-0	1-2	3-1	4-3	2-2	3-0	1-0	3-3	2-2	1-0
Halkyn United	6-0	4-3	1-5	3-3	1-2		5-1	2-3	2-2	7-6	4-3	2-2	4-1	2-1	2-3	2-1	1-4
Holywell Town	10-0	1-4	0-3	2-2	2-1	1-4		2-1	3-2	8-1	1-1	0-1	4-0	2-3	1-0	0-1	4-1
Llanberis	1-0	2-2	0-6	0-2	1-3	1-2	1-3		3-3	2-1	0-1	2-3	0-0	1-1	0-4	1-3	1-0
Llandudno Junction	9-0	2-3	3-2	1-0	3-0	1-4	2-0	3-1		2-0	0-2	2-1	6-1	5-1	5-0	0-1	3-3
Llanllyfni	2-1	1-0	1-3	1-1	5-2	6-4	4-3	5-1	1-1		1-1	1-6	4-1	5-2	1-0	2-3	1-1
Llanrug United	8-0	3-1	0-9	0-3	3-1	3-1	4-1	3-3	1-4	7-1		2-0	8-0	0-2	0-2	3-4	4-3
Llanrwst United	3-2	9-1	3-6	1-0	2-0	1-2	3-2	4-3	1-0	3-1	1-1		3-2	1-3	2-0	1-3	1-0
Nantlle Vale	4-0	0-4	1-6	1-6	1-5	2-4	1-1	1-2	2-4	0-3	1-3	1-4		1-4	0-1	0-5	0-5
Nefyn United	5-1	2-1	0-1	4-2	4-2	1-0	5-1	5-2	3-1	1-0	4-3	1-3	4-1		0-0	1-1	1-1
Pwllheli	4-0	3-1	0-2	3-1	2-4	2-0	4-1	3-1	0-4	4-1	4-2	2-1	2-1	1-1		1-3	3-1
Rhydymwyn	4-0	2-2	2-2	3-2	0-6	2-0	2-0	3-0	5-2	4-0	2-3	0-0	5-1	7-1	3-2		1-2
Rhyl Res.	8-0	2-1	2-1	1-0	1-0	3-0	4-0	0-1	7-3	2-1	4-2	0-3	5-2	3-0	4-1	2-0	

		P	W	D	L	F	A	Pts
Bethesda Athletic		32	27	1	4	146	35	82
Rhydymwyn		32	20	6	6	83	44	66
Rhyl Res.		32	19	4	9	81	43	61
Llanrwst United		32	19	4	9	76	45	61
Glan Conwy		32	19	3	10	106	53	60
Llandudno Junction		32	17	5	10	86	54	56
Nefyn United		32	16	6	10	65	58	54
Llanrug United		32	16	4	12	84	66	52
Pwllheli		32	16	4	12	60	54	52
Barmouth & Dyffryn Utd		32	14	5	13	85	70	47
Halkyn United	*-3*	32	15	3	14	79	79	45
Conwy United		32	12	4	16	63	65	40
Llanllyfni		32	11	4	17	61	89	37
Holywell Town		32	10	3	19	64	80	33
Llanberis		32	7	5	20	40	82	26
Nantlle Vale		32	1	3	28	31	123	6
Amlwch Town		32	0	2	30	20	190	2

G A MORTIMERS NORMAC PRECISION COOKSON CUP

PRELIMINARY ROUND
Amlwch Town 0 **Halkyn United** 3

FIRST ROUND
Glan Conwy 7 Nefyn United 0
Halkyn United 2 **Bethesda Athletic** 3 *aet*
Holywell Town 0 **Barmouth & Dyffryn United** 1
Llanberis 2 **Llanllyfni** 2 *aet* (1-2p)
Llandudno Junction 0 **Llanrug United** 1
Llanrwst United 2 **Conwy United** 3 *(at Conwy Utd)*
Nantlle Vale 1 **Pwllheli** 7 *(at Pwllheli)*
Rhydymwyn 2 Rhyl Res. 1

QUARTER-FINALS
Bethesda Athletic 5 Llanllyfni 0
Glan Conwy 4 Barmouth & Dyffryn United 2
Pwllheli 5 Conwy United 3
Rhydymwyn 1 **Llanrug United** 5 *(at Llanrug United)*

SEMI-FINALS
Llanrug United 1 **Glan Conwy** 4
Pwllheli 1 **Bethesda Athletic** 2

FINAL
(March 26th at Llandudno Town)
Bethesda Athletic 2 Glan Conwy 0

WELSH ALLIANCE CONSTITUTION 2009-10

Club	Ground	Telephone
AMLWCH TOWN	Lon Bach, Amlwch, Anglesey LL68 9BL	Non
BARMOUTH & DYFFRYN UNITED	Wern Mynach, Park Road, Barmouth LL42 1PL	Non
BLAENAU FFESTINIOG AMATEURS	Cae Clyd, Manod, Blaenau Ffestiniog LL41 4BA	Non
CONWY UNITED	The Morfa, Penmaen Road, Conwy LL32 8HA	01492 57308
GLAN CONWY	Cae Ffwt, Llanrwst Road, Glan Conwy, Colwyn Bay LL28 5SP	None
HALKYN UNITED	Pant Newydd, Halkyn	01352 78057
HOLYWELL TOWN	Halkyn Road, Holywell CH8 7SJ	Non
LLANBERIS	Ffordd Padarn, Llanberis, Caernarfon LL55 4SU	Non
LLANDUDNO JUNCTION	The Flyover, Victoria Drive, Llandudno Junction LL31 9PG	Non
LLANDYRNOG UNITED	Swyn Y Nant, Llandyrnog, Denbigh LL16 4HB	Non
LLANRUG UNITED	Eithin Duon, Llanrug, Caernarfon LL55 4DA	01286 67754
LLANRWST UNITED	Gwydyr Park, Llanrwst LL26 0PN	Non
NANTLLE VALE	Cae Emrys, Tyn Weirglodd, Penygroes LL54 6PA	Non
NEFYN UNITED	Caer Delyn, Nefyn, Pwllheli	Non
PWLLHELI	Dwyfor Leisure Centre, Recreation Road, Pwllheli LL53 5PF	01758 61343
RHYDYMWYN	Vicarage Road, Rhydymwyn, Mold CH7 5HL	Non

IN: Blaenau Ffestiniog Amateurs (P - Gwynedd League), Llandyrnog United (R - Cymru Alliance)
OUT: Bethesda Athletic (R - Cymru Alliance), Llanllyfni (W), Rhyl Res. (S - Clwyd Reserves League)

OTHER WELSH LEAGUES 2008-09

ABERDARE VALLEY LEAGUE
(Heatwise)

Division One	P	W	D	L	F	A	Pt
Aberaman *-3*	22	18	3	1	59	24	54
Pen'ceiber Con A.	22	16	1	5	76	19	49
AFC Abercynon	22	14	3	5	73	32	45
Mackworth	22	12	5	5	65	39	41
Tynte Rovers	22	11	4	7	62	46	37
Penywaun	22	11	0	11	61	52	33
Glancynon	22	9	4	9	57	61	31
Lamb Inn *-3*	22	9	2	11	63	68	26
Cwmaman I. Res.	22	7	2	13	38	54	23
Mountain Ash Ath	22	7	2	13	51	79	23
Blaengwawr	22	2	2	18	27	108	8
Gadlys Rovers	22	0	4	18	18	68	4

Division Two	P	W	D	L	F	A	Pt
Perthcelyn United	28	26	1	1	187	33	79
Cwmbach Res.	28	19	4	5	90	56	61
P'ceiber C Res. *+6*	28	17	1	10	95	48	58
Perthcelyn Res.	28	18	1	9	100	64	55
AFC Llwydcoed A	28	15	5	8	77	50	50
The White Lion *-3*	28	15	5	8	115	64	47
Carnetown Res.	28	12	5	11	72	65	41
Mackworth Res. *-3*	28	13	4	11	83	84	40
Mountain Ash T.	28	12	3	13	69	78	39
FC Ab'cwmboi Res.	28	9	5	14	81	86	32
Plough Inn *-6*	28	11	2	15	56	88	29
Colliers Arms	28	7	6	15	55	108	27
Dinas Rock *+3*	28	4	5	19	37	114	20
Glancynon Res. *+3*	28	3	6	19	50	109	18
Gadlys Rov. Res.	28	2	1	25	33	165	7

ABERYSTWYTH & DISTRICT LEAGUE
(Cambrian Tyres)

Division One	P	W	D	L	F	A	Pt
Dolgellau AA	20	17	1	2	70	24	52
Tregaron Turfs	20	16	3	1	89	25	51
Tywyn/Bryn. Res.	20	12	0	8	66	32	36
Bont	20	9	1	10	53	50	28
Padarn United	20	7	6	7	49	40	27
Penrhyncoch Res.	20	8	3	9	36	40	27
Aberdyfi	20	8	2	10	39	50	26
Llanilar	20	7	2	11	36	56	23
UW A'wyth Res.	20	7	1	12	39	51	22
Llanrhystud	20	4	0	16	37	98	12
P'parcau Res. *-18*	20	4	3	13	32	80	-3

Division Two	P	W	D	L	F	A	Pt
Bow Street Res.	20	17	2	1	86	24	53
Machynlleth	20	14	1	5	74	39	43
UW Abery'twyth A	20	12	3	5	61	24	39
Trawsgoed	20	10	5	5	48	41	35
Talybont	20	8	5	7	64	45	29
Corris United	20	8	5	7	56	48	29
Penrhyncoch A	20	7	4	9	48	48	25
Dolgellau AA Res.	20	7	4	9	52	55	25
FC Phoenix	20	6	6	8	50	41	24
Llanon	20	1	1	18	19	128	4
Llyfrgell Gen *-3*	20	1	2	17	24	89	2

ANGLESEY LEAGUE
(Kitchen Medic)

	P	W	D	L	F	A	Pt
Pentraeth Nurs.	18	15	1	2	55	26	46
Bro Goronwy	18	14	2	2	61	19	44
Trearddur Bay U.	18	12	3	3	52	20	39
H'hd Gwelfor Ath.	18	11	1	6	47	29	34
Llanfairpwll Res.	18	9	1	8	36	32	28
Llanerchymedd	18	6	4	8	34	38	22
Llangoed & Dist.	18	5	3	10	26	49	18
Cemaes Bay	18	4	3	11	26	51	15
Llandegfan	18	2	1	15	26	73	7
Valley	18	1	3	14	24	50	6

BRIDGEND LEAGUE
(Celtic Tyres)

Division One	P	W	D	L	F	A	Pt
Llanharan	22	18	1	3	90	34	55
Caerau Boys Club	22	17	2	3	97	36	53
FC Maesteg	22	16	2	4	71	36	50
Cefn Cribwr	22	14	0	8	56	43	42
Brackla	22	13	1	8	60	43	40
Tondu Robins	22	11	3	8	48	56	36
Great Western	22	8	0	14	62	83	24
Brynna Res.	22	6	3	13	43	61	21
Llangeinor Res. *-3*	22	5	4	13	39	60	16
Bryntirion A. A *-3*	22	6	1	15	48	71	16
Gilfach Ath. Res.	22	4	3	15	30	78	15
Pencoed A. Res.	22	3	2	17	15	58	11

Division Two	P	W	D	L	F	A	Pt
Bryncae	24	20	2	2	102	29	62
Broadlands *+2*	24	18	4	2	90	25	60
Cefn Cribwr Res.	24	15	3	6	70	57	48
Lewistown Res.	24	14	3	7	99	47	45
Caerau BC Res.	24	13	1	10	51	55	40
West House *-3*	24	12	6	6	64	52	39
Gilfach Sports *-1*	24	11	5	8	86	50	37
FC Maesteg Res.	24	9	4	11	62	62	31
Llanharan Res.	24	7	2	15	49	75	23
Llanharry Res. *-6*	24	8	1	15	43	82	19
Tondu Rob. Res.	24	5	3	16	46	89	18
Gwr *-3*	24	6	0	18	42	72	15
Aberkenfig Con	24	1	0	23	38	147	3

CAERNARFON & DISTRICT LEAGUE
(Gwynedd Safeflue)

Division One	P	W	D	L	F	A	Pt
Caernarfon Wdrs	18	14	2	2	85	20	44
Bangor City Res.	18	13	5	0	84	21	44
Y Felinheli	18	11	3	4	46	32	36
Mynydd Llandegai	18	8	6	4	42	28	30
Caernarfon Boro.	18	7	5	6	43	28	26
Talysarn Celts	18	7	5	6	39	40	26
Nefyn United Res.	18	5	1	12	35	60	15
Blaenau FA Res.	18	4	3	11	32	61	15
Llanrug Utd Res.	18	2	2	14	24	62	8
Trefor	18	2	2	14	20	98	8

Division Two	P	W	D	L	F	A	Pt
Mountain Rangers	12	7	3	2	34	15	24
Waunfawr	12	6	2	4	28	34	20
Machno United	12	5	3	4	32	21	18
Pwllheli Res.	12	5	2	5	27	20	17
Penrhyndeudraeth	12	4	3	5	26	29	15
Llanystumdwy Res.	12	4	2	6	22	34	14
Barmouth/D. Res.	12	2	3	7	17	33	9

CARDIFF COMBINATION

Premier Division	P	W	D	L	F	A	Pt
Adamsdown Ath.	18	14	1	3	74	25	43
Cardiff Hibernian	18	13	2	3	86	30	41
Heath Park	18	11	3	4	58	43	36
Avenue Hotspur	18	11	2	5	51	37	35
Llaneydn Bulldogs	18	10	3	5	55	36	33
AC Central	18	5	4	9	40	49	19
South Park Ath.	18	3	5	10	25	52	14
Cathays United	18	4	1	13	25	70	13
Fairwater Hotel	18	3	3	12	22	66	12
Park Lawn	18	3	2	13	32	60	11

Division One	P	W	D	L	F	A	Pt
RAFA Boys	20	18	2	0	101	12	56
STM Sports	20	17	1	2	91	21	52
Thornhill	20	14	1	5	62	47	43
4th Home Guard	20	14	0	6	83	40	42
Roath Park Ryls	20	14	0	6	61	40	42
Cathays Cons	20	8	0	12	26	48	24
Pontprennau Puma	20	7	2	11	37	55	23
AFC Highcroft	20	4	2	14	28	77	14
AFC W'church Res.	20	4	0	16	27	70	12
BTD Stars	20	2	3	15	25	73	9
Little Blue United	20	2	1	17	23	81	7

Division Two	P	W	D	L	F	A	Pt
RAFA Boys Res.	16	11	3	2	61	33	36
Cardiff Hibs Res.	16	8	3	5	54	42	27
Avenue Hot. Res.	16	9	0	7	42	37	27
AFC Butet'n Res.	16	7	5	4	37	33	26
DUI Dragons	16	7	3	6	45	36	24
Llaneydn B. Res.	16	6	4	6	52	49	22
Park Lawn Res.	16	5	4	7	42	50	19
AC Central Res.	16	3	3	10	34	52	12
Fairwtr Hotel Res.	16	3	1	12	21	56	10

CARDIFF & DISTRICT LEAGUE
(S A Brains)

Premier Division	P	W	D	L	F	A	Pt
St Albans	22	17	3	2	73	25	54
St Patricks FC	22	14	0	8	54	41	42
Llanrumney Res.	22	13	1	8	71	44	40
Grange Ath. Res.	22	12	3	7	61	47	39
Clwb Cymric	22	10	5	7	61	41	35
Grange Cath. OB	22	9	4	9	42	44	31
Trelai	22	7	7	8	37	46	28
Fairwater Res.	22	7	5	10	59	64	26
C'diff Academical	22	7	4	11	47	48	25
Creigiau	22	6	5	11	46	56	23
Fairwater Rebels	22	6	5	11	49	67	23
Grange H. Res. *-3*	22	3	0	19	35	112	6

Division One	P	W	D	L	F	A	Pt
Cdf Cosmos Portos	22	20	2	0	96	15	62
Cwrt-y-Vil	22	18	0	4	84	40	54
Glyncoes Corries	22	13	1	8	70	47	40
Cogan Cor. Res.	22	11	4	7	58	39	37
The Villa	22	10	4	8	58	46	34
Deprtivo Centrica	22	9	2	11	51	38	29
Cardiff Rovers	22	8	4	10	41	52	28
Gwaelod-y-Garth	22	8	3	11	44	45	27
Cwlb Cymric Res.	22	7	3	12	43	60	24
Whitchurch Blues	22	6	3	13	38	76	21
Llanrumney Utd A	22	3	4	15	37	90	13
Bridgnd St Res.	22	3	2	17	35	107	11

Division Two	P	W	D	L	F	A	Pt
Canton Libs	20	16	2	2	100	21	50
St Josephs Res.	20	13	2	5	85	47	41
St Marys B'n Res	20	12	2	6	44	35	38
Cathays Tenants	20	10	6	4	50	38	36
Grange FC	20	10	3	7	65	45	33
Llanrumney U. OB	20	9	4	7	68	50	31
Cross Inn	20	6	3	11	31	77	21
Suburban Sports	20	6	2	12	36	57	20
AFC Rumney -3	20	5	4	11	41	69	16
The Villa Res.	20	2	5	13	29	75	11
Cdf Cosmos A. *-3*	20	3	3	14	22	57	9

Division Three	P	W	D	L	F	A	Pt
Pentwyn D. Res.	18	16	2	0	101	22	50
Splott Albion Res.	18	13	2	3	65	35	41
St Josephs A	18	9	3	6	58	50	30
St Albans Res.	18	7	5	6	50	60	26
Gower Sports	18	6	6	6	52	52	24
Cdf C. Portos Res.	18	5	6	7	43	62	21
Fairwater A *-3*	18	5	4	9	42	58	16
Cdf Acad. Res.	18	4	4	10	36	52	16
Sporting Llandaff	18	3	4	11	38	60	13
Tongwynlais Res.	18	3	2	13	43	77	11

Division Four	P	W	D	L	F	A	Pt
Memory Lane	12	8	3	1	46	19	27
Inter Cardiff	12	8	1	3	43	27	25
Trowbridge Old B.	12	6	4	2	34	29	22
Grange COB Res.	12	6	2	4	33	28	20
Ely Rangers A	12	4	2	6	29	41	14
St Albans Old B.	12	2	2	8	28	39	8
Fairoak Old Boys	12	1	0	11	17	47	3

CARDIGANSHIRE LEAGUE
(Costcutter)

Division One	P	W	D	L	F	A	Pt
Lampeter Town	22	19	0	3	87	20	57
New Quay	22	17	1	4	90	24	52
Cardigan Town	22	15	3	4	60	17	48
St Dogmaels	22	15	2	5	69	32	47
Maesglas	22	13	3	6	62	33	42
Aberaeron	22	11	4	7	56	39	37
Llanboidy	22	7	2	13	32	53	23
Crannog *-3*	22	7	4	11	35	48	22
Aberporth	22	6	2	14	29	47	20
Ffostrasol	22	6	2	14	25	59	20
Pencader United	22	1	2	19	16	106	5
Llanybydder	22	2	1	19	13	96	4

Division Two	P	W	D	L	F	A	Pt
Llandysul	20	16	2	2	72	31	50
Dewi Stars	20	15	2	3	64	25	47
Aberaeron Res.	20	11	3	6	62	48	36
Bargod	20	10	2	8	43	36	32
Felinfach	20	9	4	7	57	36	31
Newc. Emlyn Res.	20	10	1	9	55	54	31
New Quay Res.	20	7	2	11	50	67	23
Maesglas Res. *-3*	20	7	3	10	49	44	21
Cardigan T. Res.	20	6	3	11	36	55	21
Lampeter T. Res.	20	4	1	15	37	75	13
SDUC	20	3	1	16	25	79	10

CLWYD LEAGUE
(McKenzie Jones)

Premier Division	P	W	D	L	F	A	Pt
Prestatyn T. Res.	26	21	4	1	89	26	67
Abergele Rovers	26	20	3	3	100	28	63
Mochdre Sports	26	17	6	3	71	29	57
Greenfield	26	16	2	8	72	54	50
Flint Town U Res.	26	10	6	10	46	36	36
Penmaenmawr Ph.	26	11	3	12	56	56	36
Sychdyn	26	10	4	12	53	68	34
Rhuddlan Town	26	9	5	12	53	63	32
Llansannan	26	9	3	14	52	57	30
Llandyrnog Res.	26	7	5	14	39	55	26
Aston Park Rgrs	26	7	3	16	46	85	24
Brynford United	26	7	3	16	41	81	24
Denbigh T. Res.	26	5	8	13	32	59	23
Halkyn Utd Res.	26	3	5	18	27	80	14

Division One	P	W	D	L	F	A	Pt
Gap Con. Quay Res.	26	22	3	1	103	32	69
Llandudno T. Res.	26	21	3	2	90	25	66
L'dudno Junc. Res.	26	17	6	3	88	32	57
Shotton Steel	26	18	2	6	79	48	56
Glan Conwy Res.	26	13	6	7	78	45	45
Point of Ayr	26	9	7	10	72	66	34
Aston Pk Rgrs Res.	26	10	2	14	56	71	32
Abergele Rov. Res.	26	9	2	15	54	88	29
Cerrigydrudion	26	8	4	14	58	71	28
Betws-yn-Rhos	26	7	6	13	40	67	27
Prestatyn Town A	26	7	4	15	51	64	25
Y Glannau	26	7	2	17	42	82	23
Caerwys	26	5	5	16	54	84	20
Rhuddlan T. Res.	26	3	0	23	33	123	9

Division Two	P	W	D	L	F	A	Pt
Mostyn Dragons	22	19	1	2	76	22	58
St Asaph	22	16	3	3	80	24	51
Rhos United	22	12	3	7	65	39	39
Llannefydd	22	10	3	9	65	69	33
Meliden	22	10	2	10	59	47	32
Holywell T. Res.	22	10	2	10	54	57	32
Aston Pk Rgrs A	22	9	2	11	47	61	29
Wepre Rangers	22	8	4	10	56	63	28
Penrhyn United	22	8	4	10	54	79	28
Llanrwst Utd Res.	22	5	6	11	47	72	21
Bro Cernyw	22	4	3	15	35	71	15
Shotton S. Res.	22	3	3	16	38	72	12

EAST GWENT LEAGUE
(Surridge Sports)

Division One	P	W	D	L	F	A	Pt
Tintern	24	20	1	3	118	35	61
Monmouth Res.	24	19	2	3	96	29	59
Chepstow T. Res.	24	18	2	4	93	37	56
Undy Athletic Res.	24	15	2	7	88	39	47
Caldicot Town A	24	14	2	8	73	54	44
Sudbrook CC Res.	24	12	5	7	65	47	41
Bulwark	24	11	1	12	72	71	34
Thornwell R&We	24	8	6	10	61	58	30
Mathern Wdrs	24	7	3	14	48	66	24
Portskewett/S'bk	24	6	4	14	63	75	22
Rogiet	24	5	3	16	49	93	18
Devauden Green	24	3	4	17	38	95	13
Chepstow Athletic	24	2	1	21	21	186	7

Division Two	P	W	D	L	F	A	Pt
Chepstow Grape	20	12	5	3	66	29	41
Tippling	20	13	2	5	57	28	41
Castle	20	12	0	8	62	50	36
Chepstow Town A	20	9	5	6	57	44	32
Rockfield Res.	20	8	6	6	69	55	30
Undy Athletic A -6	20	10	4	6	56	62	28
Bulwark Res.	20	8	2	10	59	72	26
Underwood Res	20	7	4	9	55	55	25
Subrook CC A	20	7	2	11	47	48	23
Mathern Wds Res.	20	3	4	13	34	73	13
Wyesham Wdrs	20	3	2	15	37	83	11

GWENT COUNTY LEAGUE
(Welsh Autoparts)

Division One	P	W	D	L	F	A	Pt
Abertillery B'birds	30	26	1	3	96	22	79
Albion Rovers	30	25	4	1	98	27	79
Clydach Wasps	30	18	8	4	77	40	62
Undy Athletic	30	17	6	7	76	47	57
Chepstow Town	30	18	2	10	75	53	56
Coed Eva Athletic	30	15	5	10	69	49	50
Treowen Stars	30	14	6	10	67	53	48
Cwmffrwdoer Spts	30	13	6	11	86	58	45
Pentwynmawr Ath.	30	10	6	14	63	66	36
Ab'tillery Excelsior	30	10	5	15	56	67	35
Abercarn United	30	8	9	13	52	66	33
Spencer Yth/Boys	30	9	2	19	57	89	29
Blaenavon Blues	30	6	6	18	45	74	24
Cefn Fforest	30	6	5	19	41	89	23
Mardy	30	5	4	21	53	111	19
RTB Ebbw Vale	30	2	1	27	23	123	7

Division Two	P	W	D	L	F	A	Pt
Govilon	26	20	2	4	122	42	62
Lliswerry	26	17	6	3	57	26	57
Panteg	26	15	4	7	68	42	49
Rogerstone Welf.	26	12	8	6	67	59	44
Trinant	26	11	7	8	54	58	40
Tranch	26	10	9	7	55	47	39
Sudbrook Ckt C.	26	12	3	11	61	58	39
Fairfield United	26	12	2	12	54	63	38
Malpas Gladiator	26	8	7	11	52	66	31
Llanhilleth Athletic	26	7	7	12	43	51	28
Newport Corries	26	7	7	12	47	56	28
Trethomas B'birds	26	6	7	13	56	76	25
Cromwell Youth	26	4	5	17	42	91	17
Lucas Cwmbran	26	0	8	18	36	79	8

Division Three	P	W	D	L	F	A	Pt
AC Pontymister	24	20	2	2	84	27	62
PILCS	24	17	3	4	69	34	54
Llanwern RTB	24	16	2	6	79	43	50
Whiteheads	24	13	4	7	68	53	43
Rockfield Rovers	24	13	3	8	86	53	42
Abergavenny Thur	24	10	5	9	49	55	35
Villa Dino C'church	24	10	4	10	48	60	34
Underwood Social	24	9	3	12	52	51	30
Race	24	9	3	12	53	62	30
New Inn	24	7	5	12	44	58	26
Sebastopol	24	7	1	16	39	69	22
Caldicot Castle	24	5	1	18	35	74	16
Crickhowell	24	1	2	21	31	98	5

West Pontnewydd - record expunged

GWENT CENTRAL LEAGUE
(Knauf Insulation)

Premier Division	P	W	D	L	F	A	Pt
Trevethin	21	21	0	0	153	22	63
Usk Town	21	16	2	3	85	48	50
Pontypool Town	21	13	2	6	85	48	41
Pandy	21	8	4	9	65	89	28
Goytre Res. -3	21	8	0	13	48	65	21
Lower New Inn	21	5	2	14	41	99	17
Llanarth	21	4	1	16	57	94	13
Gilwern & District	21	2	3	16	31	100	9

Division One	P	W	D	L	F	A	Pt
Clydach W. Res.	24	21	1	2	115	18	64
Govilon Res.	24	18	0	6	110	38	54
Blaenavon B. Res.	24	17	3	4	83	34	54
Tranch Res.	24	17	2	5	99	43	53
Panteg Res.	24	13	1	10	72	73	40
PILCS Res.	24	12	1	11	68	62	37
Cwm'doer Res. -3	24	11	1	12	65	67	31
Fairfield U. Res. -6	24	11	2	11	53	64	29
Mardy Res.	24	9	2	13	53	66	29
New Inn Res.	24	7	3	14	60	93	24
Abergavenny Res.	24	6	3	15	41	83	21
Race Res.	24	2	1	21	29	132	7
Sebastopol Res. -3	24	0	4	20	32	109	1

Division Two	P	W	D	L	F	A	Pt
Prescoed	21	17	1	3	115	39	52
Trevethin Res.	21	16	1	4	94	49	49
Llanfoist -6	21	14	1	6	85	50	37
Clydach Wasps A	21	11	3	7	58	42	36
Usk Town Res.	21	9	2	10	62	59	29
Pontypool T. Res.	21	7	4	10	60	59	25
Llanarth Res. -3	21	2	1	18	48	137	4
Gilwern Res. -3	21	1	1	19	32	119	1

Crickhowell Res. - record expunged

GWYNEDD LEAGUE
(Teejac.com)

	P	W	D	L	F	A	Pt
Blaenau Ffestiniog	28	20	3	5	82	32	63
Holyhead H. Res.	28	16	6	6	66	41	54
Gwalchmai	28	16	5	7	54	32	53
Bethel	28	17	1	10	90	55	52
Llanystumdwy	28	16	3	9	80	56	51
Bodedern Athletic	28	14	5	9	67	48	47
Llangefni T. Res.	28	13	6	9	67	45	45
Gaerwen	28	10	8	10	56	47	38
P'thmadog Res. -6	28	13	5	10	70	62	38
Bontnewydd	28	9	5	14	39	59	32
Rhiwlas	28	9	3	16	51	73	30
Bangor Univ. -3	28	8	5	15	46	64	26
Llanfairfechan T.	28	8	1	19	56	75	25
Beaumaris Town	28	7	1	20	52	92	22
Real Llandudno	28	5	1	22	36	131	16

MERTHYR TYDFIL LEAGUE
(Working Links)

Premier Division	P	W	D	L	F	A	Pt
Bluebirds	18	14	1	3	98	29	43
Court House	18	12	3	3	49	19	39
Abercanaid	18	10	6	2	33	20	36
Pentrebach Lbr	18	10	2	6	44	35	32
Pantyscallog VJ	18	8	2	8	41	40	26
FC Martyrs	18	7	0	11	38	78	21
Aberfan SDC	18	5	4	9	37	47	19
T'harris A Western	18	5	1	12	34	54	16
Gordon Lennox	18	4	2	12	35	59	14
Caeharris Guest C.	18	4	1	13	29	57	13

Division One	P	W	D	L	F	A	Pt
Gellideg Foundation	16	13	1	2	69	30	40
Georgetown BGC	16	12	1	3	62	30	37
Baili Glas	16	11	0	5	71	38	33
Penydarren Res.	16	8	1	7	60	59	25
Troedyrhiw Res.	16	7	3	6	43	29	24
Bedlinog	16	6	3	7	42	57	21
Gurnos SC -6	16	5	3	8	49	81	12
Quar Park Rgrs	16	2	2	12	35	63	8
Cefn Coed -6	16	0	2	14	27	71	-4

Division Two	P	W	D	L	F	A	Pt
White Horse	12	10	0	2	56	15	30
Lord Raglan	12	9	1	2	52	32	28
Park View FC	12	7	1	4	71	41	22
Trelewis W. Res.	12	5	3	4	32	28	18
Llew Goch	12	5	0	7	27	42	15
FC Brunswick	12	3	0	9	32	51	9
Drovers	12	0	1	11	11	72	1

MID-WALES LEAGUE
(Spar)

	P	W	D	L	F	A	Pt
Newtown Res.	34	27	4	3	121	36	85
Berriew	34	26	3	5	71	22	81
Aberystwyth Res.	34	22	4	8	94	46	70
Carno	34	22	4	8	70	39	70
Tywyn & Bryncrug	34	16	9	9	74	56	57
Rhayader Town	34	14	13	7	67	45	55
Newb'dge-on-Wye	34	12	12	10	70	58	48
UW Aberystwyth	34	15	3	16	65	62	48
Presteigne St And.	34	12	7	15	70	87	43
Waterloo Rovers	34	13	3	18	63	80	42
Dyffryn Banw	34	11	8	15	63	65	41
Bow Street	34	11	6	17	63	88	39
New Saints Res.	34	10	5	19	62	88	35
Penparcau -24	34	16	8	10	63	47	32
Llanrhaeadr	34	6	13	15	59	83	31
Llanfyllin Town	34	6	8	20	48	95	26
Caersws Res. -3	34	5	4	25	50	97	16
Kerry	34	2	6	26	33	112	12

MID-WALES (SOUTH) LEAGUE
(Watson Associaties)

	P	W	D	L	F	A	Pt
Hay St Marys	30	26	2	2	164	27	80
Gwernyfed	30	24	2	4	132	33	74
Llandrindod Wells	30	21	5	4	95	19	68
Builth Wells	30	19	4	7	101	59	61
Rhosgoch Rgrs	30	19	2	9	90	55	59
Newcastle-on-Clun	30	16	6	8	67	40	54
Presteigne Res.	30	15	8	7	82	42	53
Sennybridge	30	13	7	10	73	61	46
Knighton Town	30	13	4	13	70	69	43
Penybont United	30	10	3	17	56	59	33
Llan'dod W. Colts	30	9	2	19	46	78	29
Radnor Valley	30	7	5	18	37	104	26
Penybont Athletic	30	7	2	21	37	110	23
St Harmon	30	4	5	21	41	106	17
Builth Wednesdays	30	5	2	23	40	130	17
Newbridge Res.	30	2	1	27	27	166	7

MONTGOMERYSHIRE & DISTRICT LEAGUE
(J T Hughes)

Division One	P	W	D	L	F	A	Pt
Llansantffraid Vill.	26	23	3	0	89	28	72
Montgomery Town	26	20	3	3	76	26	63
Llanidloes Town	26	17	2	7	67	35	53
Abermule	26	13	6	7	55	52	45
TN Saints Colts	26	12	3	11	64	53	39
Newtown Colts	26	9	6	11	47	56	33
Llangedwyn	26	9	5	12	42	54	32
Meifod *-3*	26	10	3	13	59	62	30
Four Crosses	26	8	6	12	45	56	30
Guilsfield Res.	26	8	5	13	50	54	29
Llanfair United	26	6	8	12	56	71	26
Waterloo R. Res.	26	5	6	15	35	66	21
Bettws FC	26	4	7	15	27	58	19
Bishops Castle T.	26	5	3	18	32	73	18

Division Two	P	W	D	L	F	A	Pt
T. Welshpool Res.	28	23	3	2	102	25	72
Trewern United	28	22	2	4	91	43	68
Berriew Res.	28	17	6	5	69	39	57
Defaid Du *-15*	28	21	5	2	134	44	53
Llanfechain	28	13	7	8	67	52	46
Carno Res.	28	11	4	13	57	55	37
Llanwddyn	28	11	4	13	82	90	37
Llanidloes T. Res.	28	10	5	13	52	55	35
Churchstoke	28	9	3	16	54	90	30
Trefonnen	28	8	4	16	52	68	28
Kerry Res.	28	8	3	17	47	72	27
Waterloo R. Colts	28	7	5	16	44	93	26
Llansantffraid Res.	28	7	4	17	61	96	25
Llanfair Utd Res.	28	6	7	15	34	75	25
D. Banw Res. *-3*	28	5	2	21	46	95	14

NEATH LEAGUE
(Eagle Heating & Plumbing)

Premier Division	P	W	D	L	F	A	Pt
Onllwyn	22	19	3	0	60	17	60
Giants Grave	22	18	2	2	88	25	56
Bryn Rovers	22	14	0	8	58	41	42
Cwm Wanderers	22	13	3	6	52	41	42
FC Clydach	22	12	2	8	47	41	38
Park Travellers	22	9	2	11	69	58	29
Sunnybank WMC	22	9	2	11	52	44	29
AFC Caewern	22	7	2	13	46	59	23
Ynysygerwen	22	6	4	12	47	59	22
Glynneath Town	22	6	3	13	52	81	18
CMB	22	5	2	15	34	60	17
FC Nedd	22	1	1	20	26	105	4

Division One	P	W	D	L	F	A	Pt
AFC Pontardawe	18	13	1	4	51	30	40
Ynysymeudwy Ath	18	10	3	5	56	37	33
Lonlas Youth	18	11	2	5	70	26	32
Clydach Sports	18	9	4	5	53	35	31
Cilfrew Rovers	18	8	5	5	62	34	29
Rhos	18	8	4	6	57	54	28
Bear	18	5	4	9	35	48	19
Cimla Youth	18	5	3	10	42	64	18
Harp Rovers	18	4	4	10	31	41	16
Borough	18	2	0	16	26	114	6

Division Two	P	W	D	L	F	A	Pt
Coelbren Athletic	15	12	1	2	54	20	37
Godregraig Ath.	15	11	2	2	58	37	35
Resolven	15	7	2	6	45	33	23
AFC Denticare	15	5	1	9	28	55	16
Llandarcy	15	3	1	11	39	54	10
INCO	15	3	1	11	31	56	10

Reserve Div One	P	W	D	L	F	A	Pt
Giants Grave Res.	16	14	1	1	83	14	43
Bryn Rovers Res.	16	12	1	3	73	25	37
Pk Travellers Res.	16	11	0	5	76	56	33
AFC P'dawe Res.	16	10	0	6	73	43	30
Cwmamman Res.	16	8	0	8	50	47	24
Ynysygerwen Res.	16	5	1	10	31	74	16
Cwm Wdrs Res.	16	4	1	11	40	77	13
Glynneath T. Res.	16	4	0	12	32	88	12
CMB Res.	16	1	2	13	30	64	5

Reserve Div Two	P	W	D	L	F	A	Pt
Lonlas Youth Res.	18	14	0	4	109	32	42
Resolven Res.	18	12	5	1	71	25	41
Rhos Res.	18	12	3	3	80	31	39
Sunnybank Res.	18	9	2	7	51	41	29
Clydach Spts Res.	18	9	2	7	37	38	29
AFC Caewern Res.	18	7	4	7	38	33	25
Ynysym'dwy Res.	18	7	1	10	53	57	22
Glynneath Town A	18	5	0	13	52	79	15
AFC Pont'dawe A	18	5	0	13	51	82	15
Borough Res.	18	1	1	16	19	143	4

Reserve Div Three	P	W	D	L	F	A	Pt
Bryn Rovers A	16	11	4	1	69	24	37
INCO Res.	16	11	1	4	60	32	34
Cilfrew Rov. Res.	16	10	0	6	62	47	30
Cimla Youth Res.	16	9	2	5	56	39	29
FC Clydach Res.	16	8	3	5	38	40	27
Rhos A	16	7	2	7	54	42	23
Harp Rovers Res.	16	4	3	9	36	53	15
INCO A	16	2	1	13	18	67	7
Pontarddulais Res.	16	1	2	13	20	69	5

NEWPORT & DISTRICT LEAGUE
(Ryan Transport)

Premier Division X	P	W	D	L	F	A	Pt
Marshfield	20	17	1	2	74	22	52
Pill	20	17	1	2	70	27	52
Pontnewydd Utd	20	16	1	3	72	22	49
St Julians	20	11	2	7	51	25	35
Pill Mill Hibernians	20	9	2	9	39	43	29
Shaftesbury Youth	20	6	1	13	32	46	19
Tradesmans Arms	20	5	3	12	33	52	18
Caerleon Town	20	5	3	12	36	63	18
Oakfield	20	5	3	12	31	75	18
Malpas	20	5	1	14	28	48	16
Henllys Rangers	20	4	2	14	36	79	14

Ship & Pilot - record expunged

Llanwern Sports & Social - record expunged

Premier Division Y	P	W	D	L	F	A	Pt
Albion Rov. Res.	24	20	2	2	102	34	62
Lliswerry Res.	24	18	5	1	85	25	59
Coed Eva Res.	24	16	1	7	105	46	49
C'bran Celtic Res.	24	15	2	7	91	55	47
Rogerstone Res.	24	15	1	8	80	56	46
AC P'mister Res.	24	14	2	8	76	51	44
Lucas Cwm. Res.	24	13	1	10	69	52	40
Spencer Yth Res.	24	8	3	13	58	65	27
Newport Cor. Res.	24	9	0	15	72	80	27
Trethomas Res.	24	8	0	16	44	96	24
Villa Dino Ch. Res.	24	7	2	15	47	78	23
Cromwell Res.	24	3	0	21	39	137	9
Whiteheads Res.	24	1	1	22	34	127	4

Division One	P	W	D	L	F	A	Pt
Malpas United	22	17	2	3	100	44	53
Ship & Pilot Res.	22	16	1	5	77	52	49
Graig-y-Rhacca	22	15	3	4	73	37	48
Cwmcarn Athletic	22	13	3	6	54	39	42
Pill Res.	22	13	1	8	64	35	40
Lliswerry A	22	10	3	9	59	43	33
Marshfield Res.	22	9	2	11	42	51	29
Albion Rovers A	22	7	3	12	52	71	24
Cwmbran Celtic A	22	7	3	12	49	78	24
Pontnewydd Res.	22	6	4	12	49	71	22
Malpas Res.	22	6	1	15	55	75	19
Caerleon T. Res.	22	0	0	22	24	102	0

Oakfield Res. - record expunged

NORTH GWENT LEAGUE
(Ryan Transport)

Premier Division	P	W	D	L	F	A	Pt
Fleur-de-Lys Welf.	15	13	2	0	61	18	41
Garnlydan Athletic	16	11	2	3	40	24	35
Rhymney	16	10	3	3	52	23	33
Tredegar Athletic	15	7	4	4	40	28	25
Tredegar Arms	16	7	2	7	36	41	23
Dugout	16	4	5	7	33	31	17
Pantside	16	4	3	9	35	41	15
Castle Briery Hill	16	3	2	11	28	56	11
Rassau Rangers	16	0	1	15	13	76	1

Red Lion - record expunged

Division One	P	W	D	L	F	A	Pt
Glamorgan Tap	18	16	0	2	81	29	48
Cwm	18	13	2	3	103	34	41
Nantyglo	18	13	2	3	78	25	41
Fleur-de-Lys Res.	18	12	1	5	67	33	37
The Oak	18	9	1	8	53	47	28
Brynmawr Town	18	7	4	7	73	64	25
Blaina United	18	7	2	9	45	55	23
Pontlanffraith Sptns	18	3	0	15	25	68	9
Britannia Inn	18	1	4	13	24	120	7
PFS Athletic	18	0	2	16	25	99	2

PEMBROKESHIRE LEAGUE
(Brains)

Division One	P	W	D	L	F	A	Pt
Hakin United	26	21	3	2	95	41	66
Pennar Robins *-1*	26	16	2	8	80	47	49
Goodwick United	26	14	4	8	52	38	46
Monkton Swifts	26	12	8	6	51	40	44
Clarbeston Road	26	13	3	10	80	58	42
Merlins Bridge	26	13	3	10	74	57	42
Nerberth	26	11	3	12	48	56	36
Herbrandston	26	9	6	11	46	49	33
Solva *-1*	26	10	4	12	55	62	33
Kilgetty *-1*	26	9	5	12	52	61	31
Neyland	26	8	5	13	61	72	29
Haverfordwest Res.	26	8	4	14	51	68	28
St Ishmaels	26	7	6	13	40	60	27
Carew	26	2	2	22	27	103	8

Division Two	P	W	D	L	F	A	Pt
Tenby	26	21	4	1	106	17	67
Prendergast Villa	26	20	3	3	97	28	63
Milford United	26	19	3	4	90	31	60
Saundersfoot Sp.	26	16	4	6	70	39	52
Milford Athletic *-3*	26	15	2	9	51	33	44
Johnston	26	13	3	10	61	46	42
Pembroke Boro.	26	11	2	13	51	63	35
Camrose	26	9	6	11	61	52	33
Pendine	26	10	1	15	50	88	31
Letterston	26	9	2	15	43	59	29
Angle	26	8	1	17	53	75	25
Haverfordwest CC	26	6	5	15	37	62	23
Fishguard Sports	26	3	2	21	29	86	11
Manorbier Utd *-3*	26	3	0	23	27	147	6

Division Three	P	W	D	L	F	A	Pt
Hundleton	26	21	4	1	103	34	67
St Clears	26	20	2	4	106	34	62
Hakin United Res.	26	18	4	4	72	29	58
Lamphey	26	12	3	11	80	60	39
Merlins B. Res. *-3*	26	13	3	10	65	65	39
Pennar Rob. Res.	26	11	4	11	62	67	37
Monkton Res. *-6*	26	11	4	11	54	64	31
Solva Res. *-3*	26	11	0	15	53	100	30
Boadhaven	26	8	4	14	66	76	28
Lawrenny	26	9	1	16	46	66	28
Narberth Res.	26	7	4	15	60	87	25
Hubberston *-1*	26	7	3	16	47	86	23
St Florence	26	6	4	16	58	80	22
Prendergast Res. *-1*	26	7	2	17	55	79	22

Division Four	P	W	D	L	F	A	Pt
Goodwick U. Res.	22	20	2	0	85	18	62
Herb'ston Res. *-1*	22	15	5	2	81	29	49
Milford U. Res. *-4*	22	15	4	3	76	31	45
Saundersfoot Res.	22	14	2	6	64	34	44
Milford Ath. Res.	22	10	3	9	43	41	33
Clarbeston R Res.	22	10	0	12	76	62	30
Johnston Res.	22	6	6	10	42	61	24
Camrose Res. -3	22	7	5	10	56	65	23
St Ishmaels Res.	22	5	5	12	40	60	20
Carew Res.	22	5	5	12	26	57	20
Kilgetty Res.	22	2	4	16	27	67	10
Neyland Res. -3	22	1	3	18	21	112	3

PORT TALBOT & DISTRICT LEAGUE

Premier Division	P	W	D	L	F	A	Pt
Real Bay View	18	17	0	1	89	27	51
Gwynfi United	18	10	3	5	46	39	33
Margam YC	18	10	1	7	47	44	31
Cornelly United	18	9	0	9	45	35	27
Cwmafan Welfare	18	7	4	7	39	49	25
Glynoorrwg *-3*	17	8	0	9	56	59	21
Baglan RD Res.	18	5	3	10	43	55	18
Corus Steel Res.	17	6	0	11	32	54	18
Cwmafan *-3*	18	5	3	10	40	44	15
Trefelin BGC Res.	18	4	2	12	27	58	14

Division One	P	W	D	L	F	A	Pt
Pt Tal. Town Exiles	24	21	1	2	99	29	64
Abercregan.	24	16	6	2	74	28	54
Porthcawl Athletic	24	17	2	5	79	35	53
Newton Wdrs	24	13	7	4	94	40	46
Croeserw United	24	14	3	7	70	47	45
Royal Mail PT	24	11	3	10	56	49	36
Cornelly Utd Res.	24	8	3	13	43	57	27

Team	P	W	D	L	F	A	Pt
Gwynfi Utd Res.	24	8	2	14	50	55	26
Port Talbot Tigers	24	7	1	16	51	77	22
Margam YC Res.	24	6	3	15	36	59	21
Kenfig Hill Res. -3	24	7	1	16	39	88	19
Cefn Cribbwr	24	5	1	18	46	105	16
Cornelly Utd A -6	24	5	3	16	35	103	12

RHONDDA & DISTRICT LEAGUE

	P	W	D	L	F	A	Pt
Ynyshir/Wattstown	22	19	1	2	96	25	58
Treorchy BGC	22	17	3	2	102	19	54
AFC Porth Res.	22	14	3	5	75	49	45
Trebanog Rgrs	22	13	3	6	92	50	42
Llwynypia BGC	22	13	1	8	79	39	40
Tonyrefail W. Res.	22	9	5	8	47	45	32
Tonyrefail BGC Res.	22	10	2	10	56	68	32
Lewis Merthyr	22	8	0	14	52	77	24
Cwmparc Legion	22	7	1	14	46	76	22
Max United	22	7	1	14	57	105	22
The Baglan	22	1	4	17	28	102	7
Penygraig BGC	22	1	2	19	22	97	5

Turberville Arms Res. - record expunged

SOUTH WALES AMATEUR LEAGUE
(Monnington Group)

Division One	P	W	D	L	F	A	Pt
Corus Steel	30	24	3	3	92	25	75
Caerau United	30	21	3	6	92	37	66
Rhoose	30	18	3	9	72	50	57
Baglan Red Drag.	30	17	4	9	69	49	55
Rhydyfelin	30	15	4	11	72	67	49
Splott Albion	30	15	2	13	75	53	47
Aber Valley YMCA	30	13	6	11	76	66	45
Trefelin BGC -3	30	14	5	11	75	62	44
Turberville Arms	30	13	5	12	59	56	44
Ynysddu Crus.	30	13	4	13	68	78	43
AFC Bargoed R.	30	13	3	14	65	76	42
Llantwit Major	30	12	3	15	71	74	39
Carnetown BGC -3	30	10	4	16	68	70	31
Llanharry	30	9	2	19	68	94	29
Taffs Well Res.	30	6	1	23	43	96	19
Llangynwyd Rgrs	30	1	0	29	25	137	3

Division Two	P	W	D	L	F	A	Pt
Cardiff Draconians	30	21	2	7	105	57	65
Treforest	30	18	9	3	82	37	63
Kenfig Hill	30	18	6	6	71	45	60
Trelewis Welfare	30	16	4	10	69	55	52
Blaenrhondda	30	15	3	12	63	48	48
Brynna	30	14	2	14	71	74	44
Hirwaun Welfare	30	14	1	15	82	77	43
Wyndham	30	11	7	12	58	61	40
FC Abercwmboi	30	11	6	13	61	62	39
Ton & Gelli BC	30	11	5	14	66	66	38
Graig	30	11	5	14	51	64	38
Pencoed Athletic	30	11	3	16	50	72	36
Ferndale Boys C.	30	8	7	15	60	76	31
Penarth Town -3	30	11	1	18	52	88	31
AFC Talbot Green	30	7	8	15	51	64	29
Gilfach Goch Ath.	30	8	1	21	42	88	25

SOUTH WALES SENIOR LEAGUE
(Thomas Carroll)

Division One	P	W	D	L	F	A	Pt
Fairwater	28	21	4	3	83	27	67
Penydarren BC +3	28	18	5	5	83	44	62
Grange Albion	28	19	4	5	81	36	61
Sully Sports	28	17	6	5	88	38	57
Llanrumney Utd	28	16	8	4	80	46	56
Cwm Welfare	28	15	3	10	74	45	48
St Josephs	28	13	3	12	64	54	42
Fochriw	28	10	5	13	62	62	35
Tonyrefail BGC	28	11	0	17	53	77	33
Lewistown	28	9	4	15	72	75	31
Bridgend St -6, 5g	28	10	5	13	57	73	29
Tonypandy A. +3	28	6	7	15	41	72	28
Cogan Coronation	28	7	5	16	38	61	26
St Marys Butet'n	28	3	3	22	39	116	12
Ynyshir Albion	28	3	2	23	29	123	11

Crickhowell Res. - record expunged

Division Two	P	W	D	L	F	A	Pt
St Athan +3	28	21	2	5	82	37	68
Cwmbach Ryl S.	28	20	5	3	76	34	65
Brecon Corries	28	18	4	6	80	39	58
Stanleytown	28	14	5	9	46	37	47
Lisvane/Llanishen	28	13	5	10	63	55	44
Cascade	28	11	6	11	62	66	39

Team	P	W	D	L	F	A	Pt
AFC Caerphilly	28	12	2	14	77	65	38
AFC Butetown	28	11	4	13	69	65	37
Tongwynlais	28	9	6	13	61	68	33
Hopkinstown +2	28	7	9	12	52	66	32
AFC Whitchurch	28	9	4	15	53	69	31
Cadoxton Cons +3	28	7	5	16	40	71	29
Llwynypia -4, 6g	28	10	2	16	44	81	28
Penrhiwfer -3, 3g	28	7	8	13	38	57	26
Nelson Cavaliers	28	5	5	18	42	84	20

Caerphilly Town - record expunged

SWANSEA LEAGUE
(Pic-up Spares)

Division One	P	W	D	L	F	A	Pt
Ragged School	22	15	3	4	47	25	48
South Gower	22	12	7	3	54	30	43
Port Tennant Colts	22	12	7	3	59	37	43
Cwm Press	22	11	5	6	47	35	38
Winch Wen	22	10	7	5	51	37	37
Swansea Dockers	22	11	4	7	46	43	37
Penlan Club	22	10	4	8	54	38	34
Bonymaen Colts	22	9	3	10	40	40	30
Gors -1	22	6	7	9	38	48	24
Morriston Olympic	22	5	2	15	37	61	17
Morriston T. Res.	22	2	4	16	26	65	10
Brunswick Utd -1	22	2	1	19	32	72	6

Division Two	P	W	D	L	F	A	Pt
Stanley Arms	24	23	1	0	125	22	70
West End Res.	22	16	3	3	72	26	51
Plough Colts +3	22	14	3	5	60	46	48
North End	22	13	4	5	59	39	43
Llangyfelach	22	12	5	5	51	28	41
Rockspur	22	9	2	11	44	40	29
Maltsters Sports	22	8	5	9	41	46	29
Gowerton	22	7	7	8	40	41	28
Brynawel	22	7	6	9	28	32	27
Coopers Arms	22	6	7	9	39	42	25
Carreg Wen -1	22	6	7	9	34	48	24
Treboeth United	22	5	4	13	32	57	19
St Josephs FC	22	1	3	18	29	84	6

TAFF ELY RHYMNEY VALLEY ALLIANCE

Premier Division	P	W	D	L	F	A	Pt
Penyrheol	16	13	2	1	79	23	41
AFC Tiryberth	16	8	4	4	48	34	28
Cilfynydd	16	9	1	6	47	34	28
Cefn Hengoed	16	9	1	6	53	45	28
Aber Valley Res.	16	8	0	8	52	44	24
Penrhos -1	16	7	3	6	36	33	23
Graigwen Juniors	16	4	2	10	37	42	14
Cwm Welfare Res	16	3	2	11	30	88	11
Treforest Res.	16	3	1	12	23	62	10

Division One	P	W	D	L	F	A	Pt
Pontlottyn	12	10	1	1	62	17	31
Brithdir Bluebirds	12	6	6	0	32	19	24
Junction Stars	12	6	2	4	29	24	20
Cascade Res.	12	5	1	6	27	35	16
Rhydyfelin Labour -3	12	5	2	5	33	29	14
Ponty Bridge	12	2	2	8	20	51	8
Nelson Cav. Res.	12	1	0	11	12	40	3

VALE OF GLAMORGAN LEAGUE

Premier Division	P	W	D	L	F	A	Pt
SW Flooring	20	15	2	3	73	31	47
Master Mariner	20	14	4	2	68	29	46
Barry	20	12	2	6	59	41	38
Barry Villa	20	11	3	6	70	46	36
SP Construction	20	9	3	8	57	63	30
Cadoxton Imps	20	7	5	8	44	63	26
Barry Bluebirds	20	6	5	9	52	47	23
Cardiff Airport	20	5	3	12	36	54	18
St Athan Res.	20	5	2	13	37	71	17
Sully Sports Res.	20	4	4	12	40	74	16
Llantwit Mjr Res.	20	3	5	12	35	52	14

Division One	P	W	D	L	F	A	Pt
AFC Tadross	24	19	3	2	103	35	60
Castle FC	24	17	4	3	79	43	55
Glenbrook	24	13	6	5	55	39	45
Sully Sports A	24	12	4	8	56	50	40
Colcot -1	24	11	5	8	63	42	37
Hotton Road	24	11	4	9	64	50	37
Barry Dynam	24	11	4	9	65	52	37
Knap	24	9	2	13	62	67	29
Tynewydd	24	7	5	12	42	74	26
Dockers	24	6	7	11	51	70	25
Wenvoe Exiles	24	5	6	13	45	66	21
Cadoxton Athletic	24	4	4	16	49	75	16
Pit Stop	24	2	4	18	33	104	10

Division Two	P	W	D	L	F	A	Pt
Park Villa	22	18	1	3	98	35	55
Tynewydd Res.	22	15	2	5	71	35	47
Phoenix Construc.	22	13	4	5	58	42	43
Cogan Coron. A	22	12	4	6	83	64	40
C'xton Imps Res.	22	10	3	9	65	51	33
AFC T'ross Res. -5	22	10	4	8	72	65	29
Penarth T. Res.	22	8	5	9	47	59	29
Barry Dyn. Res.	22	7	3	12	43	78	24
Park Vets -3	22	7	5	10	54	84	23
Cadoxton	22	6	4	12	55	49	22
AFC Galaxy	22	3	3	16	47	80	12
Island Marine -1	22	3	2	17	43	94	10

WELSH NATIONAL LEAGUE (WREXHAM AREA)
(Nizam-Druid)

Premier Division	P	W	D	L	F	A	Pt
Llangollen Town	28	22	4	2	89	31	70
Penycae	28	20	5	3	75	30	65
Rhos Aelwyd	28	18	6	4	77	36	60
Hawarden Rgrs	28	17	8	3	64	28	59
Coedpoeth United	28	16	5	7	77	39	53
Castell Alun Colts	28	11	6	11	52	60	39
Borras Park Alb.	28	12	2	14	53	55	38
Llay Welfare	28	9	4	15	48	68	31
Chirk AAA	28	8	6	14	47	54	30
Brickfield Rangers	28	9	3	16	55	69	30
Venture Comm.	28	6	10	12	46	54	28
Corwen Amateurs	28	7	7	14	45	63	28
Overton Rec.	28	6	9	13	40	58	27
Brymbo	28	4	6	18	39	81	18
Acrefair Youth	28	3	3	22	32	113	12

Division One	P	W	D	L	F	A	Pt
FC Cefn	22	19	1	2	88	37	58
Gwersyllt Athletic	22	15	4	3	65	29	49
Penyffordd	22	14	4	4	66	33	46
New Brighton Villa	22	14	4	4	62	31	46
Penley	22	13	2	7	70	45	41
Johnstown Youth	22	11	1	10	54	46	34
Communities First	22	9	2	11	61	45	29
Garden Village FC	22	7	7	8	38	45	28
Holt Nomads	22	4	4	14	50	74	16
Glyn Ceiriog	22	3	5	14	35	79	14
Mold Juniors	22	4	0	18	30	76	12
Llanuwchllyn	22	1	2	19	20	99	5

Reserve Division	P	W	D	L	F	A	Pt
Bala Town Res.	32	24	7	1	108	26	79
Airbus UK Res.	32	21	5	6	81	32	68
Rhos Aelwyd Res.	32	20	5	7	87	54	65
Ruthin Town Res.	32	19	3	10	78	52	60
NEWI Cefn Res.	32	16	7	9	65	35	55
Buckley T. Res.	32	17	4	11	81	59	55
Hawarden Res.	32	15	10	7	61	47	55
Gresford A. Res.	32	16	6	10	78	51	54
Lex XI Res.	32	15	3	14	75	75	48
Llangollen T. Res.	32	13	4	15	69	88	43
Borras Park Res.	32	10	7	15	66	84	37
Mynydd Isa Res.	32	10	3	19	59	73	33
Penycae Res.	32	8	8	16	54	66	32
Llay Welfare Res.	32	8	4	20	58	113	28
Chirk AAA Res.	32	7	4	21	64	92	25
Mold Alex. Res. -3	32	9	1	22	47	92	25
Brymbo Res.	32	1	5	26	30	122	8

Res./Colts Div	P	W	D	L	F	A	Pt
Castell Alun Res.	28	22	0	6	122	46	66
Coedpoeth Res.	28	19	5	4	74	42	62
Hawarden Colts	28	18	4	6	82	38	58
Penley Res.	28	13	7	8	73	55	46
Penyffordd Res.	28	13	6	9	77	69	45
Acrefair Yth Res.	28	13	5	10	85	71	44
Ruthin Town Colts	28	13	3	12	70	54	42
Glyn Ceiriog Res.	28	12	4	12	46	73	40
Borras Park Colts	28	11	3	14	53	75	36
Overton Rec Res.	28	10	5	13	54	56	35
Garden Vill. Res.	28	8	5	15	58	65	29
Johnstown Res.	28	8	5	15	54	75	29
Corwen Ams Res.	28	8	4	16	53	71	28
Brickfield R. Res.	28	7	5	16	49	91	26
Llangollen Colts	28	3	3	22	42	111	12

SCOTLAND

Compiled by Bill Mitchell with thanks to Stewart Davidson

SENIOR NON-LEAGUE REVIEW

There are four senior Leagues of 'Seniors' in Scotland's Non-League scene - South, East, Highland and North Caledonian - with The East and Highland Leagues by far the strongest.

East consists of a Premier Division and First Division (each with a dozen clubs) and Spartans were the top side with only two league defeats all season. The Cup competitions were won by four different clubs - League Runners-Up Dalbeattie Star, Whitehill Welfare, Herriot-Watt University and the resurgent Gretna 08.

In the meantime, the Highland League was won in convincing style by Cove Rovers, while they decided wisely to expand to eighteen clubs and voted in three newcomers - Turriff United, Formartine United and Strathspey Thistle.

One wonders how Fort William (losers 10-0 to Banks O'Dee at Spain Park in the Scottish Cup), Buckie Thistle and Huntly, who lost to them in competitive matches, voted.

Elsewhere, the North Caledonian was won by Golspie Sutherland, who also won the SWL Cup, while Tain Thistle should be commended for bravely completing their fixtures despite only one win from eighteen matches.

The South of Scotland League was won by returning Threave Rovers of Castle Douglas, who also won the Cree Lodge Cup, but had to take second place to Crichton in the Detroit Trophy.

Other Cup winners were St Cuthbert Wanderers (twice) Nithsdale Wanderers, Dalbeattie Star and Wigtown & Badenoch, while commendations go to Fleet Star, who still struggled but show signs of improving.

Only three Non-League clubs progressed beyond the Third Round of the Scottish Cup - Spartans, Forres Mechanics and Inverurie Loco Works - with Spartans beating Annan Athletic (away) and only losing 1-2 at Airdrie United to call into question their failure to be preferred for Scottish League membership in favour of the Dumfriesshire club.

NORTH OF SCOTLAND HIGHLAND LEAGUE

	P	W	D	L	F	A	Pts
Cove Rangers	28	22	4	2	98	26	70
Deveronvale	28	19	8	3	80	30	63
Inverurie Loco Works	28	18	3	7	72	33	57
Keith	28	18	2	8	62	35	56
Wick Acadamy	28	16	3	9	54	46	51
Buckie Thistle	28	25	3	10	60	41	48
Fraserburgh	28	13	8	7	62	47	47
Huntly	28	14	4	10	51	40	46
Forres Mechanics	28	12	7	9	64	42	43
Nairn County	28	12	5	11	44	45	41
Clachnacuddin	28	8	7	13	53	58	34
Lossiemouth	28	7	4	17	31	55	25
Rothes	28	2	3	22	24	80	9
Brora Rangers	28	2	3	22	21	91	9
Fort William	28	0	1	27	16	121	1

Highland League Cup.

Semi-Finals

Inverurie Loco Works	5-1	Nairn County
Keith	0-2	Fraserburgh

Final at Keith - 6th May 2009

Fraserburgh	1-2	Inverurie Loco Works
(McBride)		(Coull and Michie)

After extra time, 0-0 at 90 minutes.

North of Scotland Cup

Semi-Finals

Caledonian Thistle	2-0	Wick Academy
Nairn County	5-0	Rothes

Final at Clachnacuddin - 21st September 2009

Caledonian Thistle	0-2	Nairn County
		(Graham and MacLeod)

Aberdeenshire Cup

Cup Final at Inverurie - 20th Sept 2008

Keith	5-2	Huntly
(Wood 2,Fyfe 2 Lennox)		(Guild and Ewen)

Aberdeenshire Shield

Cup Final - 17th March 2009

Cove Rangers	2-0	Banks O'Dee
(Bain and Henderson)		

EAST OF SCOTLAND LEAGUE

Premier League	P	W	D	I	F	A	P
Spartans	22	16	4	2	73	26	52
Dalbeattie Star	22	14	4	4	51	26	48
Lothian Thistle	22	11	3	8	46	26	36
Edinburgh University	22	8	8	6	37	19	32
Whitehill Welfare	22	8	8	6	38	28	32
Preston Athletic	22	9	5	8	36	31	32
Herriot Watt University	22	9	3	10	33	32	30
Edinburgh City	22	8	5	9	45	34	29
Coldstream	22	8	5	9	30	30	29
Selkirk	22	8	3	11	19	55	27
Easthouses Lily	22	72		13	40	40	23
Peebles Rovers	22	10		2112		124	3

Division One

Tynecastle	22	17	3	2	58	22	54
Civil Service Strollers	22	15	1	6	48	29	48

Other positions: Stirling University 44pts, Gretna 2008 44pts, Craigroyston 39pts, Gala Fairydean 31pts, Vale of Leithen 31pts, Leith Athletic 28pts, Ormiston 20 pts, Eyemouth United 17pts, Kelso United 17pts and Hawick Royal Albert 2pts.

East of Scotland League Cup

Semi-Finals

Dalbeattie Star 2-1 Vale of Leithen

Stirling University 1-3 Preston Athletic

Final at Selkirk - 31st May 2009

Dalbeattie Star 2-0 Preston Athletic

(Sloan and Kerr)

Image Printers Cup

Semi-Finals

Edinburgh Universty 0-1 Whitehill Welfare

Gretna 2008 2-3 Edinburgh City

Final at Preston Athletic

Whitehill Welfare 3-2 Edinburgh City

(Haynes,Pryde and Gormley) (Clee and Geir)

King Cup

Semi Finals

Edinburgh City 0-1 Vale of Leithen

Kelso United 0-1 Heriot Watt Uni.

Final at Vale of Leithen

Heriot Watt University 1-0 Vale of Leithen

(Berser)

Alex Jack Cup

Semi-Finals

Gretna 2008 5-2 Kelso United

Stirling University 0-1 Tynecastle

Final at Gala - 18th January 2009

Gretna 2008 4-2 Tynecastle

(Carmichael,Nicholson, Reynard Seggie) (Allum and Aird)

SOUTH OF SCOTLAND LEAGUE

	P	W	D	L	F	A	P
Threave Rovers	26	23	1	2	125	30	70
Chrichton Royal	26	22	1	3	98	28	67
Wigtown & Badenorth	26	18	3	5	74	44	57
Stranrair Reserves	26	17	4	5	90	51	55
St Cuthbert Wanderers	26	16	1	9	70	78	49
Annan Athletic 'A'	26	15	3	8	78	44	48
Dalbeattie Star 'A'	26	10	5	11	54	53	35
Nithsdale Wanderers	26	9	3	14	52	65	30
Abbeyvale	26	7	5	14	44	64	26
Heston Rovers	26	7	1	18	33	67	22
Mid Annandale	26	5	5	16	42	89	20
Newton Stewart	26	5	4	17	47	85	19
Creetown	26	5	3	18	37	81	18
Fleet Star	26	3	1	22	32	127	10

South of Scotland Challenge Cup

Dalbeattie Star 4-1 Annon Athletic

South of Scotland League Cup

St Cuthbert Wanderers 1-0 Chrighton Royal

Haig Gordon Memorial Trophy

Nithsdale Wanderers 5-5 Creetown

Nithsdale Wanderers won 5-4 on penalties after 4-4 score at 90 minutes

Potts Cup

Wigston & Badenoch 3-1 St Cuthbert Wand.

Tweedie Cup

St Cuthbert Wanderers 2-0 Newton Stewart

Cree Lodge Cup

Threeve Rovers 6-2 Nithsdale Wanderers

Detroit Trophy (For overall best performances in 2008-2009)

(First Five Positions)

Chrichton 85 pts,Threave Rovers 79, St Cuthbert Wandrers 73, Wigtown & Badenock 72 and Stranraer 64points.

NORTH CALEDONIAN SENIORS LEAGUE

	P	W	D	L	F	A	Pts
Golspie Sutherland	18	16	1	1	82	15	49
Halkirk United	18	13	2	3	77	26	41
Galintore	18	10	2	6	47	37	32
Muir of Ord Rovers	18	9	2	7	35	38	29
Bonar Bridge	18	9	2	7	42	48	26
Thurso	18	7	4	7	33	30	25
Bunildh Thistle	18	6	2	10	26	47	20
Alness United	18	5	3	10	27	43	18
Invergordon	18	5	3	10	20	56	16
Tain Thistle	18	1	1	16	23	17	4

18th January 2009

Cup Finals

Port Services Cup

Halkirk United 1-0 Alness United

S.A.L. Cup

Golspie Sutherland 3-1 Halkirk Unoted

Football Times Cup

Halkirk United 2-0 Golspie Sutherland

Jock McKay Cup

Halkirk United 5-2 Thurso

Scottish F.A.Cup

(Main results for non-league clubs)

Third Round

Airdrie United 3-0 Cove Rangers

Clachnacuddin 0-5 Stenhousemuir

Edinburgh City 0-3 Brechin City

Elgin City 2-1 Spartans

Forres Mechanics 2-2 Dalbeattie Star

Inverurie Loco Works 4-0 Vale of Leithen

Lochee United 1-1 Ayr United

Replays

Dalbeattie Star 2-4 Forres Mechanics

(after extra time - 1-1 after 90 minutes)

Ayr United 3-1 Lochee United

Fourth Round

Airdrie United 2-1 Spartans

Forfar Athletic 6-1 Forres Mechanics

Inverurie Loco Works 0-3 Motherwell

Scottish Amateur Cup Final

Queens Park 3-1 Hurlford Thistle

S.F.A.South Regional Cup Final at Meadowbank Stadium, Edinburgh on 15th March 2009

Spartans 6-0 Edinburgh

(Archibald 2,King and three own goals!)

S.F.A.North Regional Cup Final at Deveronvale on 18th October 2008

Inverurie Loco Works 3-1 Cove Rangers

(Gauld, Milneand Smith) (Livingstone)

JUNIOR NON-LEAGUE REVIEW

A superb Junior Cup Final was just one example of a fine season with the main honours going Westward after several seasons when the East had been superior. All four semi-finalists were from the West, and some excellent ties were decided on a new home-and-home basis. The four matches were very well attended, so the experiment was a success.

Elsewhere Beith won the New Coin Automatics West of Scotland Cup by beating Auchinleck Talbot in the final (2-1) and the area's Super League was a thriller with Irvine Meadow just shading Pollok.

Cumnock and Neilston went down and are replaced from the First Division by Largs Thistle and Kilbirnie Ladeside. There was also a play-off for promotion to the Super League, which saw Lanark United beat Glenafton Athletic to send them down.

Two local Ayrshire Cups were won by Irvine Meadow with others for Girvan (South Ayrshire) and Androssan Winton Rovers (North Ayrshire). Meadow collected the 'Ardagh Glass" League Cup and Weekly Press Cup to add to their League title along with the Evening Times Cup Winners Cup - a four title haul. Other local cups were won by Kilsyth Rangers (Central League Cup) and Lanark United (Clydesdale Cup).

Over in th East, the Super League title was quite comfortably won by Bonnyrigg Rose with other divisional winners including Musselburgh Athletic (Premier), Montrose Roselea (North), St Andrews United (Central) and Armadale Thistle (South). But it was sad to see famous Tayport and Forfar West End descend.

Local Cup winners included Linlithgow Rose (Fife & Lothians), Lochee United (East of Scotland) Newtongrange Star (Dechmount East- South League Cup), Hill of Beath Hawthorn (ACA East- Central League Cup) , Forfar West End (D.J.Laing - North League Cup) Glenrothes (Redwood Leisure Cup) Carnoustie Panmore (Currie Cup), Kelty Hearts (Maloco Cup), Musselburgh Athletic (MJM Flooring Cup) and Sunnybank (GA Enginering Cup).

The latter takes us to the North Region as Sunnybank (second in the Premier Division) were a rare Example of a North Region team taking such an honour.

The Northern Premier Division title was retained by Banks O'Dee (mentioned elsewhere) with Buchanhaven Hearts winning the First Division and newcomers Inverness City topping the Second Divvision.

A special mention should be made of Cruden Bay (First Division) and Whitehills, who completed a tough fixture list.

Cup winners were Dyce (Grill League Cup and North Regional Cup), Formartine United (Morrison Cup), Hermes (McLeman Cup) and Inverness City (Elginshire League Cup).

The North Leagues are likely to be divided into two after departures to the Highland League, but even so they enjoy enthusiastic and keen support.

A Junior Club of the Season? It must be Irvine Meadow with a League title and three cups. So for once Pollok must take a second place, while it will be interesting to see whether the Ayrshire team does some Scottish Cup 'giant killing'.

WEST REGION SUPERLEAGUE

Premier Division

	P	W	D	L	F	A	Pts
Irvine Meadow	22	15	3	4	40	22	48
Pollock	22	15	1	6	50	30	46
Beith	22	13	3	6	39	32	42
Auchinleck Talbot	22	12	4	6	46	33	40
Petershill	22	10	8	4	34	22	38
Kirkintilloch Rob Roy	22	9	3	10	38	32	30
Arthurlie	22	8	4	10	39	39	28
Vale of Clyde	22	7	5	10	33	38	26
Bellshill Athletic	22	8	2	12	30	46	26
Glenafton Athletic	22	7	4	11	34	42	25
Cumnock	22	5	3	14	30	44	18
Neilston	22	2	2	18	16	47	8

Play offs to decide promotion and relegation
Glenafton Athletic 2-1 Lanark United
Larark United 2-0 Glenafron Athletic

First Division

Champions and Runners-Up

LargsThistle	26	18	4	4	53	22	58
Kilbirnie Lakeside	26	17	1	8	52	26	52

Lanark United 47 pts, Girvan 46, Clydebank 41, Maybole 38, Renfrew 38, East Kilbride Thistle 35,Annbank United 35, Kilsyth Rangers 33, Port Glasgow 32, Shotts Bon Accrd 30, Kilwinning Rangers 16 and Hurlford United 15pts. The last four clubs were relegated.

Ayrshire League

Dalry Thistle	22	13	6	3	43	18	45
Whitletts Victoria	22	13	5	4	45	20	44

The first two clubs were promoted and the rest of the remaining positions were: Lugar Boswell Thistle 40pts, Ardrossan Winton Rovers 40, Troon 39, Kello Rovers 38, Darvel 34, Irvine Victoria 33,Craigmark Burntonians 30, Muirkirk 13, Saltcoats Victoria 10 and Ardeer Thistle 9pts.

Central League

Divison One

Rutherglen Glencairn	24	19	2	3	65	30	59
Ashfeld	24	14	1	9	60	43	43

The top two clubs were promoted and the remianing clubs were: Thorniewood United 43pts, Maryhill 42, Campulslang Rangers 36, St Anthonys 31, Larkhall Thistle 30, Lesahagow 29, Val e of Leven 25, Yoker Athletic 23, Benburb 22 and Johnstone Burgh 19 pts. The bottom three clubs relegated.

Divison Two

Blantyre Victoria	20	12	2	6	43	22	38
Dunipace	20	11	4	5	49	26	37
Glasgow Perthshire	20	11	4	5	43	28	37

Top three promoted and the remaining clubs were: Carluke Rovers 32pts, Shettleston 36, Royal Albert 32, Greenock 25, Forth Wanderers 23, St Rochs 23, Newmains United 16 and Wishaw 12 pts.

WEST CUP FINALS

New Coin Automatics West of Scotland Cup
Beith 2-1 Auchinleck Talbot

Ayrshire Ardagh Glass League Cup
Irvine Meadow 3-0 Lugar Boswell Thistle

Ayrshire Weekly Press Cup
Irvine Meadow 2-1 Auchlinleck Talbot

South Ayrshire Cup
Ardrossan Winton Rovers 4-0 Irvine Victoria

Central Sectional League Cup
Arthurlie 3-2 Shotts Bon Accord

Central League Cup
Kilsyth Rangers 1-1 Pollok

Evening Times Cup Winners Cup
Irvine Meadow 1-0 Pollok

Clydesdale Cup
Lanark United 0-0 Forth Wanderers
(Lanark United won 4-2 on penalties)

EAST REGION

Super League 1	P	W	D	L	F	A	Pts
Bonnyrigg Rose	22	12	5	5	40	28	41
Camelon	22	11	2	9	44	33	35
Linlithgow	22	10	2	10	30	29	32
Whitburn	22	8	7	7	34	32	31
Kelty Hearts	22	8	6	8	39	31	30
Bo'ness United	22	8	4	10	26	38	28
Hill of Beath Hawthorn	22	9	3	10	30	32	30
Glenrothes	22	8	6	8	28	43	30
Bathgate Thistle	22	8	5	9	36	27	29
Lochlee United	22	8	5	9	30	41	29
Forfar West End	22	7	6	9	34	34	27
Tayport	22	7	5	10	26	29	26

Premier Division	P	W	D	L	F	A	Pts
Musselburgh Athletic	22	16	3	3	59	19	51
Newtongrange Star	22	16	3	3	58	19	51
Carnoustie Panmuir	22	10	5	7	48	32	35
Penicuik Athletic	22	10	5	7	48	32	35
Klnnoull	22	9	6	7	36	31	33
Arniston Rangers	22	8	6	8	26	31	30
Ballingry Rovers	22	8	3	11	34	39	27
Blairgowrie	22	7	4	11	49	52	25
Fauldhouse	22	7	4	11	36	45	25
Oakley United	22	7	3	12	32	49	24
Dundonald Bluebell	22	7	1	14	32	49	24
North End	22	4	4	14	28	58	16

North Division
Champions

Montrose Rosellea 22 18 3 1 57 12 57

Remaining clubs: Broughty Athletic 52pts, Violet 47, Lochee Harp 40, Arbroath Victoria 38, Arbroath S.C. 31, East Craigie 29, Downfield 28, Coupar Angus 24, Kirrie Thistle 18, Brechin Victoria 17 and Forfar Albion 1point.

Central Division
Champions

St Andrews 24 19 5 0 84 29 82

Remaining Clubs: Rosyth 49, Kirkcaldy Y.M. 49, Jeanfield Swifts 44, Thornton Hibs 40, Lochore Welfare 34, Bankfoot Athletic 34, Crossgates Primrose 33, Lochgelly Albert 32, Steelend Victoria 20, Scone Thistle 20, Newburgh 19 and Luncarty 7 points.

South Division
Champions

Armadale Thistle 55pts, Tranent 51pts, Sauchie 49, Broxburn Athletic 43, Edinburgh United 40,West Calder United 40, Harthill Royal 37, Dalkeith Thistle 37, Blackburn United 36, Stoneyburn 35, Haddington Athletic 32, Dunbar United 28, Pumpherston 14 and Livingston United 10pts.

CUP FINALS

Fife & Lothians Cup
Linlithgow Rose 1-0 Thornton Hibs

East of Scotland Cup
Lochee United 3-0 Glenrothes

Dechmont East - South League Cup
Camelon 1-1 Newtongrange Star
(Newtongrange won 2-1 on penalties)

ADA East -Central Leage Cup
Hill of Beath Hawthorn 1-1 Glenrothes
(Hill of Beath Hawthorn won 7-6 on penalties)

D.J.Laing East - North League Cup
Forfar West End 1-0 Lochee United

Redwood Leisure Cup
Glenrothes 2-2 Tayport
(Glenrothes won 4-2 on penalties)

Currie Cup
Carnoustie Panmore 4-1 Glenrothes

Maloco Cup
Kelty Hearts 1-0 Glenrothes

MJM Flooring Cup
Musselburgh Athletic 2-1 Linlithgow Rose

G.A.Engineering Cup
Blairgowrie 2-2 Sunnybank
(Sunnybank won 4-3 on penalties)

NORTH REGION

Premier Division	P	W	D	L	F	A	Pts
Banks O'Dee	26	17	5	4	71	30	56
Sunnybank	26	16	5	5	61	31	53
Culter	26	14	4	8	54	39	46
Dyce	26	14	4	8	38	30	46
Banchory St Teman	26	11	6	9	33	42	39
Longside	26	10	6	10	34	39	36
Hermes	26	11	3	12	46	52	36
Maud	26	10	5	11	69	51	35
East End	26	11	2	13	38	42	35
Ellon United	26	7	9	10	30	41	30
Lewis United	26	7	7	12	28	51	28
Turriff United	26	6	9	11	36	41	27
Hillhead	26	7	6	13	29	54	27
Stonehaven	26	3	5	18	29	53	14

First Division

Champions: Buchanhaven Hearts 65points. Formartine United 49pts, Strathspey Thistle 45, F.C.Stonywood 41,Hall Russell United 41, Fraserburgh United 39, Lossiemouth United 37, Forres Thistle 37, Islavale 35, Parkvale 35, Glentaner 35, Buckie Rovers 33, Dufftown 9 and Cruden Bay 6 points.

Second Division

Champions: Inverness City 53 points. New Elgin 43, Deveronside 41, Bishopmill United 38, Burghead Thistle 35, Fochabers 24, Nairn St Ninian 24, RAF Lossiemouth 18 and Whitehills 15 points.

CUP FINALS

Grill League Cup
Dyce 0-0 East End
(Dyce won 4-2 on penalties)

North Regional Cup
Dyce 4-1 Formartine United

Morrison Cup
Buckie Rovers 2-2 Formartine United
(Formartine won 5-2 on penalties)

McLeman Cup
Hermes 1-0 Banks O'Dee

Elginshire League Cup
Inverness City 3-0 Bishopsmill United

NORSCO REGIONAL CUP

Third Round
Banchory St Ternan 0 Turriff United 1
Culter 2 Dyce 4
Glentanar 2 Longside 5
Maud 0 Formartine United 2

Semi-finals
Formartine United 0 Turriff United 1
Longside 1 Dyce 3

FINAL
Friday, 16th May 2008 at Maud)
DYCE 2-0 Turriff United
Neish, Edens

ATR GROUP CUP

Semi-finals
Ellon United 4 Stonehaven 2
Sunnybank 2 East End 0

FINAL
(Friday, 30th May 2008 at Hermes)
ELLON UNITED 3-2 SUNNYBANK
McNamara, Chapman — Reid, Bartlett
Noble pen

MORRISON TROPHY

Second Round
Hall Russsell United 3 Banchory St Ternan 1
Islavale 2 Lewis United 0
Lads Club 2 Strathspey Thistle 0
FC Stoneywood 2 Glentanar 1

Semi-finals
FC Stoneywood 2 Islavale 3
Hall Russell United 4 Lads Club 1

FINAL
(Friday, 23rd May 2008 at Maud)
ISLAVALE 1-0 HALL RUSSELL UNITED
Ross

ELGINSHIRE LEAGUE CUP

Semi-finals
Burghead Thistle 1 Buckie Rovers 0
Lossie nited 0 New Elgin 1

Burghead Thistle were awarded the cup after New Elgin were disqualified from the competition and Lossiemouth failed in a petition to be reinstated.

GUERNSEY F.A.

Tel: 01481 200 443 Fax: 01481 200 451 Email: neil.laine@guernseyfa.com

Corbet Field, Grand Fort Road, St Sampson's, Guernsey GY2 4FG.

Secretary: Neil Laine. **Chairman:** Mark Le Tissier.

SURE MOBILE SENIOR COUNTY LEAGUE

DIVISION 1	P	W	D	L	F	A	GD	Pts
North	18	14	2	2	58	25	33	44
Belgraves	18	12	2	4	75	26	49	38
St Martin's	18	11	4	3	54	23	31	37
Rangers	18	9	1	8	56	54	2	28
Vale Rec	18	6	0	12	30	44	-14	18
Sylvans	18	5	3	10	31	44	-13	18
Rovers	18	0	0	18	11	99	-88	0
DIVISION 2								
St Martin's	16	12	1	3	46	20	26	37
North	16	10	3	3	45	30	15	33
Rangers	16	10	1	5	47	31	16	31
Vale Rec	16	9	1	6	50	25	25	28
Belgraves	16	9	0	7	48	40	8	27
Sylvans	16	8	1	7	24	39	-15	25
B Nomads	16	3	4	9	20	39	-19	13
Centrals	16	3	3	10	28	45	-17	12
Rovers	16	1	0	15	19	58	-39	3
DEVELOPMENT U21 LEAGUE								
North	18	15	2	1	84	15	69	47
Belgraves	18	12	0	6	53	33	20	36
St Martin's	18	9	1	8	42	40	2	28
Sylvans	18	7	3	8	33	35	-2	24
Vale Rec	18	6	3	9	33	52	-19	21
Rangers	18	6	1	11	30	51	-21	19
Rovers	18	1	4	13	18	67	-49	7

J W LOVERIDGE CUP UNDER 18S								
North	6	6	0	0	42	4	38	18
Rovers	6	4	0	2	20	13	7	12
Sylvans	6	4	0	2	16	16	0	12
Vale Rec	6	3	0	3	20	15	5	9
Belgraves	6	3	0	3	22	18	4	9
St Martins	6	1	0	5	5	15	-10	3
Rangers	6	0	0	6	0	44	-44	0
SURE MOBILE U16 DEVELOPMENT								
Rovers	18	15	1	2	120	24	96	46
North	18	14	0	4	75	23	52	42
Vale Rec	18	12	1	5	87	31	56	37
St Martin's	18	10	0	8	79	57	22	30
Belgraves	18	7	0	11	49	63	-14	21
Sylvans	18	4	0	14	40	99	-59	12
Rangers	18	0	0	18	11	164	-153	0
SURE MOBILE U14 DEVELOPMENT LEAGUE								
North	18	17	1	0	94	18	76	52
Vale Rec	18	13	1	4	76	32	44	40
Sylvans	18	12	3	3	71	36	35	39
Belgraves	18	7	2	9	44	65	-21	23
Rovers	18	5	2	11	47	66	-19	17
St Martin's	18	3	3	12	36	97	-61	12
Rangers	18	0	0	18	0	54	-54	0
SURE MOBILE WOMEN'S LEAGUE								
Sylvans	12	12	0	0	74	10	64	36
St Martin's	12	8	1	3	45	19	26	25
Rovers	12	8	0	4	45	28	17	24
Vale Rec	12	5	1	6	20	33	-13	16
Belgraves	12	4	1	7	16	37	-21	13
North	12	2	0	10	8	46	-38	6
Rangers	12	1	1	10	13	48	-35	4

JERSEY F.A.

Tel: 01534 730 433 Fax: 01534 730 434 Email: paul.creeden@jerseyfa.com

Springfield Stadium, Jarvin Road, St Helier, Jersey JE2 4LF.

Chief Executive: Paul Creeden.

COCA-COLA COMBINATION

Division One	P	W	D	L	F	A	GD	Pts
St. Paul's	16	12	3	1	58	12	46	39
Trinity	16	12	3	1	31	12	19	39
Jersey Scottish	16	9	3	4	36	18	18	30
Grouville	16	6	6	4	29	25	4	24
St Peter	16	5	4	7	32	29	3	19
St Ouen	16	5	4	7	22	30	-8	19
Rozel Rovers	16	4	2	10	22	42	-20	14
Jersey Wanderers	16	4	0	12	19	46	-27	12
Sporting Academics	16	2	1	13	22	57	-35	7

St Paul's crowned Champions after 6-0 play-off win over Trinity.

Division Two	P	W	D	L	F	A	GD	Pts
Portuguese Club	18	17	1	0	64	7	57	52
First Tower	18	9	7	2	47	19	28	34
St Clement	18	10	3	5	60	36	24	33
Magpies	18	9	2	7	34	24	10	29
Jersey Nomads	18	6	4	8	39	46	-7	22
St John	18	7	1	10	30	44	-14	22
Beeches OB	18	6	4	8	32	50	-18	22
St Brelade	18	6	3	9	22	33	-11	21
St Lawrence	18	4	5	9	26	40	-14	17
St Martin/SCF	18	0	2	16	18	73	-55	2

Division One Reserves	P	W	D	L	F	A	GD	Pts
St. Paul's	14	8	2	4	42	23	19	26
Jersey Wanderers	14	8	1	5	34	28	6	25
Jersey Scottish	14	9	1	4	30	26	4	25
Rozel Rovers	14	7	1	6	37	33	4	22
St Peter	14	6	1	7	38	30	8	19
St Ouen	14	5	3	6	28	28	0	18
Grouville	14	6	2	6	37	23	14	17
St Clement	14	1	1	12	16	71	-55	4

Division Two Reserves	P	W	D	L	F	A	GD	Pts
First Tower	18	12	3	3	71	24	47	39
Sporting Academics	18	11	4	3	72	37	35	37
Trinity	18	11	3	4	79	28	51	33
St Brelade	18	10	3	5	66	47	19	33
St Lawrence	18	8	4	6	35	41	-6	28
Magpies	18	7	6	5	46	41	5	24
St John	18	5	4	9	34	38	-4	19
Jersey Nomads	18	6	1	11	38	48	-10	19
Beeches OB	18	3	5	10	28	58	-30	14
St Martin/SCF	18	0	1	17	15	122	-107	1

Division Three (C teams)	P	W	D	L	F	A	GD	Pts
Grouville	14	11	1	2	52	18	34	34
Rozel Rovers	14	9	1	4	48	28	20	28
St Peter	14	8	0	6	35	27	8	24
St Ouen	14	7	3	4	28	20	8	24
Jersey Wanderers	14	7	2	5	35	31	4	23
Sporting Academics	14	3	2	9	24	33	-9	11
St John (-1pt)	14	3	2	9	25	51	-26	10
St Clement	14	2	1	11	28	67	-39	7

Ladies	P	W	D	L	F	A	GD	Pts
First Tower United	12	11	0	1	76	8	68	33
St Paul's	12	10	0	2	52	8	44	30
St John	12	5	1	6	38	30	8	16
Jersey Wanderers	12	2	1	9	17	68	-51	7
St Brelade	12	1	0	11	10	79	-69	3

CHANNEL ISLAND CUP FINALS

Muratti Semi Final	Alderney	0	-	5	Guernsey
Muratti Final	Guernsey	0	-	1	Jersey
Upton Park C.I. Club Championship	St. Paul's	2	-	1	Guernsey Northerners
J.F.A. Wheway Cup Final	St. Paul's	2	-	0	Grouville
J.F.A. Charity Cup	St. Paul's (won 11-10 on pens)	0	-	0*	Trinity
G.F.A. Jeremie Cup Final	Belgrave Wanderers (won on pens)	1	-	1*	St. Martin
Le Riche Cup Final	Jersey Scottish	2	-	1*	St. Paul's
Under 21 Muratti	Jersey	2	-	3*	Guernsey
Under 18 Muratti	Jersey	1	-	0	Guernsey
Under 16 Muratti	Guernsey	0	-	1	Jersey
Star Trophy School Boys	Guernsey	1	-	3	Jersey
Under 18 Portsmouth Trophy (CI Club Championship)	Guernsey Northerns	2	-	3	Jersey Wanderers
Ladies Muratti	Guernsey	0	-	1	Jersey
*AET					
J.F.A. International Triangular Tournament	Jersey	2	-	1	Gibraltar
	Gibraltar	0	-	2	Madeira
	Jersey	0	-	2	Madeira

ISLE OF MAN F.A.

Tel: 01624 615 576 Fax: 01624 615 578 Email: mike.nudd@isleofmanfa.com

PO Box 53, The Bowl, Douglas, Isle of Man IM99 1GY.

Chief Exective: Mike Nudd.

SURE MOBILE PREMIER

	P	W	D	L	F	A	Gd	Pts
St. George's	24	18	4	2	85	28	57	58
Peel	24	18	3	3	74	27	47	57
Rushden United	24	17	2	5	60	26	34	53
St Marys	24	16	3	5	62	40	22	51
DHSOB	24	16	2	6	68	43	25	50
Laxey	24	11	3	10	49	37	12	36
Gymnasium	24	7	6	11	58	70	-12	27
Ramsey	24	8	2	14	40	50	-10	26
Michael United	24	6	4	14	34	68	-34	22
Union Mills	24	6	3	15	40	76	-36	21
Corinthians	24	5	2	17	39	71	-32	17
Colby	24	5	2	17	33	73	-40	17
Ayre United	24	4	2	18	42	75	-33	14

CFS DIVISION TWO

	P	W	D	L	F	A	Gd	Pts
St Johns	26	24	1	1	133	27	106	73
Castletown	26	23	1	2	141	32	109	70
Pulrose	26	20	2	4	123	43	80	62
Marown	26	19	0	7	110	53	57	57
RYCOB	26	14	4	8	95	65	30	46
Braddan	26	14	1	11	82	72	10	43
Douglas Royal	26	12	3	11	94	79	15	39
Malew	26	11	4	11	75	70	5	37
Onchan	26	8	4	14	79	94	-15	28
Douglas & District	26	7	1	18	51	117	-66	22
Foxdale	26	5	4	17	58	99	-41	19
Police	26	5	2	19	50	136	-86	17
Northern Athletic	26	3	1	22	29	108	-79	10
Ronaldsway	26	1	4	21	47	172	-125	7

SURE MOBILE COMBINATION ONE

	P	W	D	L	F	A	Gd	Pts
Rushden	24	20	1	3	115	27	88	61
St. Georges	24	16	5	3	93	36	57	53
Peel	24	15	6	3	92	45	47	51
DHSOB	24	17	0	7	83	40	43	51
Laxey (-3pt)	24	13	4	7	92	46	46	40
St. Marys (-3)	24	12	2	10	54	63	-9	35
Ramsey	24	8	5	11	58	70	-12	29
Union Mills	24	8	4	12	37	68	-31	28
Corinthians	24	6	7	11	48	75	-27	25
Ayre	24	6	3	15	45	89	-44	21
Gymnasium (-3)	24	4	7	13	46	63	-17	16
Michael Utd (-3)	24	5	4	15	42	78	-36	16
Colby	24	2	0	22	24	129	-105	6

CFS COMBINATION TWO

	P	W	D	L	F	A	Gd	Pts
Marown	26	23	0	3	135	30	105	69
Castletown	26	22	2	2	152	37	115	68
St. Johns	26	18	2	6	102	38	64	56
Onchan	26	15	3	8	72	53	19	48
Braddan	26	14	5	7	84	47	37	47
RYCOB	26	13	3	10	86	72	14	42
Douglas Royal	26	13	2	11	73	54	19	41
Pulrose	26	12	4	10	86	81	5	40
Malew (-3)	26	11	4	11	76	76	0	34
Ronaldsway	26	8	3	15	65	102	-37	27
Douglas & District	26	6	2	18	47	105	-58	20
Police	26	6	1	19	54	127	-73	19
Foxdale	26	4	0	22	39	108	-69	12
Northern Athletic	26	1	1	24	25	166	-141	4

SURE MOBILE WOMEN'S LEAGUE

	P	W	D	L	F	A	Gd	Pts
Douglas Royal	9	9	0	0	65	5	60	27
Corinthians	9	7	1	1	80	5	75	22
Rushden United	9	7	1	1	67	3	64	22
Peel	9	6	0	3	23	25	-2	18
Gymnasium	9	5	0	4	26	16	10	15
Castletown	9	3	1	5	26	33	-7	10
Colby	8	2	0	6	10	39	-29	6
Laxey	9	1	2	6	8	36	-28	5
Michael United	8	1	0	7	2	77	-75	3
Ramsey	9	0	1	8	5	73	-68	1

the

FOOTBALL ASSOCIATION COMPETITIONS

The FA CUP e-on **Above:** Action from an F.A. Cup 3rd Qualifying round match which saw AFC Totton comfortably knock Fleet Town out, 5-2. Here we see The 'Stags' James Taylor making sure he gets to the ball before the Fleet player.

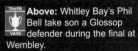

The FA VASE **Above:** Whitley Bay's Phil Bell take son a Glossop defender during the final at Wembley.

The FA TROPHY **Left:** Mark Greeves, York City, looks set to disposes Stevenage Borough's Lee Boylan in the Trophy Final. Photos: Graham Brown.

ENGLAND C

The England team and management before their International Challege Trophy final against Belgium. Photo: Keith Clayton.

ENGLAND YOUNGSTERS REACH FINAL BUT LOSE TO BELGIUM

Just when a settled and successful managerial team have settled down to look after our England teams who represent non-league football, we find our end of season four nations competition disintegrating and our Under 23 tournament quite naturally dominated by full time youngsters with Blue Square Premier clubs.

A previous manager, John Owen the ex-Altrincham centre half who, like our present successful leader Paul Fairclough had enjoyed long runs with an unbeaten side, also suffered from a lack of a competitive tournament for his full side.

It is very frustrating, especially as the youngsters are doing very well. They started last season needing a point from their game with Italy to qualify for the final of their European tournament and to warm up for this game and keep the squad together a fixture was arranged with Bosnia Herzegovina B, a very strong side indeed.

In Sarajevo the opposition turned out to be a mixture of Under 21 and full internationals and, on the night, proved far too powerful for the English lads who suffered their first defeat for eleven games. With eight new 'caps' England were losing by four goals at half time, but showing great spirit fought back with two goals before the home side pulled away again with two late strikes.

The trip away had pulled the squad closer together however, and they duly achieved an exciting 2-2 draw in Naples. England came back to equalise twice to achieve Fairclough's 'best ever England result'. Italy were certainly up for the match and it was a superb all round fighting performance which brought immense satisfaction to the management team who had put so much into this team since the competition was set up.

The goals came from Histon's Josh Simpson, who was outstanding in midfield, and his strike fourteen minutes after half time equalised Italy's goal nine minutes before the break. Italy took the lead again sixteen minutes later, but James Constable, who had a good season in front of goal, nodded in Exodus Geohaghon's long throw at the far post to take England to the final.

A fixture was arranged with Malta and a comfortable 4-0 success did no harm for morale and the spirit of the whole party which included sixteen new faces. Manager Fairclough really had a wonderful array of talent from which to make his selection for the Cup Final against Belgium, and the display in Malta was excellent with Nicky Wroe, Shaun Densmore and Lee Tomlin particularly outstanding.

The International Challenge Trophy Final was played at the end of the season at Oxford United's Kassam Stadium in front of 2,842 but after an excellent game the experienced and very skillful Belgian lads proved to be just too experienced and won with a very good goal from Capon after 64 minutes.

Hopefully in the future, our non-league footballer's' will have a full international side as well as an Under 23 squad with both enjoying competitive tournaments. I know the Representative Committee would like that but will the The Football Association hierarchy help to make it possible. We've had this problem on and off for thirty years and usually they realise the importance of even non-league players having the chance to 'Play for England'.

TW.

ENGLAND C 2008-09

No.	Date	Comp	H/A	Opponents	Att:	Result	Goalscorers
1	Sept 16	F	A	Bosnia & Herzegovina	-	L 2-6	Moore 55, Day 62
2	Nov 12	ICT	A	Italy	-	D 2-2	Simpson 58, Constable 82
3	Feb 17	F	A	Malta U21	-	**W** 4-0	Brown 6, Borg 52 (og), Densmore 56, Newton 89
4	May 19	ICT Final	H	Belgium	2,842	L 0-1	

ICT - International Challenge Trophy. F - Friendly

THE PLAYERS - 2008-09

NAME		CLUB	2008-09 CAPS	08-09 GOALS	TOTAL CAPS	TOTAL GOALS
Arnold	Nathan	Mansfield Town	1	0	1	0
Arnold	Steve	Grays Athletic	1	0	1	0
Bailey	Stephen	Grays Athletic	1	0	1	0
Bartlett	Adam	Blyth Spartans	2	0	6	0
Bostwick	Michael	Stevenage Borough	1	0	1	0
Boyes	Adam	York City	1	0	1	0
Brodie	Richard	York City	1	0	1	0
Brown	Paul	Barrow	1	1	1	1
Byrom	Joel	Northwich Victoria	1	0	1	0
Byron	Michael	Droylsden	1	0	1	0
Charles	Darius	Ebbsfleet United	1	0	1	0
Clayton	Paul	Alfreton Town	2	0	2	0
Cole	Mitchell	Stevenage Borough	2	0	12	7
Constable	James	Oxford United	2	1	3	1
Cronin	Lance	Ebbsfleet United	1	0	7	0
D'Laryea	Jonathan	Mansfield Town	2	0	2	0
Day	Matt	Oxford United	1	1	1	1
Densmore	Shaun	Altrincham	2	1	2	1
Doe	Scott	Weymouth	1	0	1	0
Fleming	Andrew	Wrexham	1	0	1	0
Foster	Luke	Oxford United	1	0	1	0
Geohaghon	Exodus	Kettering	2	0	2	0
Gleeson	Dan	Cambridge United	1	0	7	0
Harrad	Shaun	Burton Albion	2	0	10	1
Hearn	Liam	Alfreton Town	1	0	1	0
Kempson	Darren	Wrexham	0	0	0	0
Laird	Scott	Stevenage Borough	1	0	1	0
McMahon	Lewis	Gainsborough Trinity	1	0	1	0
Moore	Luke	Ebbsfleet United	1	1	1	1
Newton	Sean	Droylsden	2	1	2	1
Penn	Russell	Kidderminster Harriers	2	0	8	1
Pitman	Jon-Paul	Crawley Town	1	0	1	0
Riley	Martin	Kidderminster Harriers	1	0	1	0
Roberts	Dale	Rushden & Diamonds	1	0	1	0
Robinson	Anton	Weymouth	2	0	2	0
Shaw	Tom	Tamworth	1	0	1	0
Simpson	Josh	Histon	1	1	1	1
Smith	James	Ebbsfleet United	2	0	4	0
Stevens	Jamie	Crawley Town	1	0	1	0
Tomlin	Lee	Rushden & Diamonds	2	0	2	0
Tremarco	Carl	Wrexham	1	0	1	0
Walker	Jason	Barrow	1	0	1	0
Welsh	Ishmael	Grays Athletic	2	0	2	0
Wright	Mark	Thurrock	1	0	1	0
Wright	Jake	Tamworth	1	0	1	0
Wroe	Nicky	Torquay United	2	0	2	0

INTERNATIONAL CHALLENGE TROPHY

GROUP A	P	W	D	L	F	A	Pts	GD
ENGLAND	3	2	1	0	6	3	7	3
FINLAND	3	2	0	1	3	3	6	0
ITALY	3	1	1	1	7	6	4	1
WALES	3	0	0	3	3	7	0	-4

GROUP B	P	W	D	L	F	A	Pts	GD
BELGIUM	3	2	1	0	5	3	7	2
REPUBLIC OF IRELAND	3	2	0	1	4	2	6	2
SLOVAKIA	3	1	1	1	2	3	4	-1
NORTHERN IRELAND	3	0	0	3	1	4	0	-3

	CRONIN	DAY	M. WRIGHT	FOSTER	ROBINSON	SMITH	N. ARNOLD	D'LARYEA	BRODIE	MOORE	COLE	STEVENS	BAILEY	HARRARD	BARTLETT	KEMPSON	GLEESON	TREMARCO	J. WRIGHT	SIMPSON
	X	X	X	X	X	X	X	X	X	X	X	S	S	S	U	U				
					S	X		X			X			S	X		X	X	S	X
	U														X					
Total Appearances																				
	1	1	1	1	1	2	1	2	1	1	2	0	0	0	2	0	1	1	0	1
	0	0	0	0	1	0	0	0	0	0	0	1	1	2	0	0	0	0	1	0
	1	0	0	0	0	0	0	0	0	0	0	0	0	0	1	1	0	0	0	0

	GEOHAGHON	PENN	BOSTWICK	CONSTABLE	PITMAN	ROBERTS	DENSMORE	NEWTON	BYRON	WROE	RILEY	TOMLIN	MCMAHON	CLAYTON	WALKER	BROWN	S. ARNOLD	DOE	SHAW	BOYES	WELSH	CHARLES	
	X	X	S	X	X																		
						X	X	X	X	X	X	X	X	X	X	X	S	S	S	S	S		
	X	X		X			X	S		X		X		X							S	X	
Total Appearances																							
	2	2	0	2	1	1	2	1	1	2	1	2	1	2	1	1	0	0	0	0	0	1	**X**
	0	0	1	0	0	0	0	1	0	0	0	0	0	0	0	0	1	1	1	1	2	0	**S**
	0	0	0	0	0	0	0	0	0	0	0	0	0	0	0	0	0	0	0	0	0	0	**U**

Also Played: Byrom X(4). Laird X(4). Fleming S(4). Hearn S(4).

INTERNATIONAL CHALLENGE TROPHY FINAL

Photos by: Keith Clayton

Above: James Constable gets shields the ball from Belgium's Cabeke and the ball.

Top Right: This time it's Paul Clayton who is pressured for the ball by Cabeke backed-up by Biemans.

Right: Perfect balance! England's Andrew Fleming crosses under pressure from Cabeke.

ENGLAND'S RESULTS 1979 - 2009

BARBADOS

02.06.08	Bridgetown	2 - 0

BELGIUM

11.02.03	KV Ostend	1 - 3
04.11.03	Darlington	2 - 2
15.11.05	FC Racing Jets	2 - 0
19.05.09	Oxford United	0 - 1

BOSNIA & HERZEGOVINA

16.09.08	Grbavia Stadium	2 - 6

FINLAND UNDER-21

14.04.93	Woking	1 - 3
30.05.94	Aanekoski	0 - 2
01.06.07	FC Hakka	1 - 0
15.11.07	Helsinki	2 - 0

GIBRALTAR

27.04.82	Gibraltar	3 - 2
31.05.95	Gibraltar	3 - 2
21.05.08	Colwyn Bay	1 - 0

GRENADA

31.05.08	St. George's	1 - 1

HOLLAND

03.06.79	Stafford	1 - 0
07.06.80	Zeist	2 - 1
09.06.81	Lucca	2 - 0
03.06.82	Aberdeen	1 - 0
02.06.83	Scarborough	6 - 0
05.06.84	Palma	3 - 3
13.06.85	Vleuten	3 - 0
20.05.87	Kirkaldy	4 - 0
11.04.95	Aalsmeer	0 - 0
02.04.96	Irthlingborough	3 - 1
18.04.97	Appingedam	0 - 0
03.03.98	Crawley	2 - 1
30.03.99	Genemuiden	1 - 1
21.03.00	Northwich	1 - 0
22.03.01	Wihemina FC	3 - 0
24.04.02	Yeovil Town	1 - 0
25.03.03	BV Sparta 25	0 - 0
16.02.05	Woking	3 - 0
29.11.06	Burton Albion	4 - 1

IRAQ

27.05.04	Macclesfield	1 - 5

IRISH PREMIER LEAGUE XI

13.02.07	Glenavon FC	1 - 3

ITALY

03.06.80	Zeist	2 - 0
13.06.81	Montecatini	1 - 1
01.06.82	Aberdeen	0 - 0
31.05.83	Scarborough	2 - 0
09.06.84	Reggio Emilia	0 - 1
11.06.85	Houten	2 - 2
18.05.87	Dunfermline	1 - 2
29.01.89	La Spezia	1 - 1
25.02.90	Solerno	0 - 2
05.03.91	Kettering	0 - 0
01.03.99	Hayes	4 - 1
01.03.00	Padova	1 - 1
20.11.02	AC Cremonese	3 - 2
11.02.04	Shrewsbury	1 - 4
10.11.04	US Ivrea FC	1 - 0
15.02.06	Cambridge United	3 - 1
12.11.08	Benevento	2 - 2

MALTA UNDER-21

17.02.09	Malta	4 - 0

NORWAY UNDER-21

01.06.94	Slemmestad	1 - 2

REPUBLIC OF IRELAND

24.05.86	Kidderminster	2 - 1
26.05.86	Nuneaton	2 - 1
25.05.90	Dublin	2 - 1
27.05.90	Cork	3 - 0
27.02.96	Kidderminster	4 - 0
25.02.97	Dublin	0 - 2
16.05.02	Boston	1 - 2
20.05.03	Merthyr Tydfil	4 - 0
18.05.004	Deverondale	2 - 3
24.05.05	Cork	1 - 0
23.05.06	Eastbourne Boro'	2 - 0
22.05.07	Clachnacuddin	5 - 0

SCOTLAND

31.05.79	Stafford	5 - 1
05.06.80	Zeist	2 - 4
11.06.81	Empoli	0 - 0
05.06.82	Aberdeen	1 - 1
04.06.83	Scarborough	2 - 1
07.06.84	Modena	2 - 0
15.06.85	Harderwijk	1 - 3
23.05.87	Dunfermline	2 - 1
18.05.02	Kettering	2 - 0
24.05.03	Carmarthen Town	0 - 0
23.05.04	Deverondale	3 - 1
28.05.05	Cork	3 - 2
27.05.06	Eastbourne Boro'	2 - 0
25.05.07	Ross County	3 - 0
22.05.08	Colwyn Bay	1 - 0

USA

20.03.02	Stevenage Boro.	2 - 1
09.06.04	Charleston USA	0 - 0

WALES

27.03.84	Newtown	1 - 2
26.03.85	Telford	1 - 0
18.03.86	Merthyr Tydfil	1 - 3
17.03.87	Gloucester	2 - 2
15.03.88	Rhyl	2 - 0
21.03.89	Kidderminster	2 - 0
06.03.90	Merthyr Tydfil	0 - 0
17.05.91	Stafford	1 - 2
03.03.92	Aberystwyth	1 - 0
02.03.93	Cheltenham	2 - 1
22.02.94	Bangor	2 - 1
28.02.95	Yeovil Town	1 - 0
23.05.99	St Albans	2 - 1
16.05.00	Llanelli	1 - 1
13.02.01	Rushden & Dia.	0 - 0
14.05.02	Boston	1 - 1
22.05.03	Merthyr Tydfil	2 - 0
20.05.04	Keith FC	0 - 2
26.05.05	Cork	1 - 0
25.05.06	Eastbourne Boro'	1 - 1
27.05.07	Clachnacuddin	3 - 0
21.02.08	Exeter City	2 - 1
24.05.08	Rhyl	3 - 0

RESULTS SUMMARY 1979 - 2009	P	W	D	L	F	A
Barbados	1	1	0	0	2	0
Belgium	4	1	1	2	5	6
Bosnia & Herzegovina	1	0	0	1	2	6
Finland Under-21	4	2	0	2	4	5
Grenada	1	0	1	0	1	1
Gibraltar	3	3	0	0	7	4
Holland	19	14	5	0	40	8
Iraq	1	0	0	1	1	5
Irish Premier League XI	1	0	0	1	1	3
Italy	17	5	7	4	23	21
Malta	1	1	0	0	4	0
Norway Under-21	1	0	0	1	1	2
Republic of Ireland	12	9	0	3	28	10
Scotland	15	10	3	2	30	15
USA	2	1	1	0	2	1
Wales	23	13	6	4	32	18
TOTALS	**106**	**60**	**24**	**21**	**183**	**105**

MANAGERS 1979 - 2009

		P	W	D	L	F	A
1979	Howard Wilkinson	2	2	0	0	6	1
1980 - 1984	Keith Wright	17	9	5	3	30	16
1985 - 1988	Kevin Verity	12	7	2	3	23	15
1989 - 1996	Tony Jennings	19	10	4	5	27	18
1997	Ron Reid	2	0	1	1	0	2
1998 - 2002	John Owens	14	8	5	1	22	10
2002 -	Paul Fairclough	40	24	7	9	75	43

GOALSCORERS 1979 - 2009

13 GOALS...
Carter, Mark

7 GOALS...
Cole, Mitchell

6 GOALS...
Ashford, Noel

5 GOALS...
Davison, Jon
Williams, Colin

4 GOALS...
Culpin, Paul
D'Sane, Roscoe
Johnson, Jeff
Mackhail-Smith, Craig

3 GOALS...
Adamson, David
Guinan, Steve
Grayson,Neil
Hatch, Liam
Kirk, Jackson
Morison, Steve
Morrison, Michael
Opponents
Watkins, Dale

2 GOALS...
Alford, Carl
Barrett, Keith
Bishop, Andrew
Burgess, Andrew
Casey, Kim
Cordice, Neil
Elding, Anthony
Hayles, Barry
Hill, Kenny
Howell, David
Mutrie, Les
Patmore, Warren

2 goals continued....
Richards, Justin
Seddon, Gareth
Southam, Glen
Watson, John
Weatherstone, Simon
Whitbread, Barry

1 GOAL...
Agana, Tony
Anderson, Dale
Ashton, John
Benson, Paul
Blackburn, Chris
Boardman, Jon
Bolton, Jimmy
Boyd, George
Bradshaw, Mark
Brown, Paul
Browne, Corey
Carey-Bertram, Daniel
Carr, Michael
Cavell, Paul
Charles, Lee
Charley, Ken
Charnock, Kieran
Constable, James
Crittenden, Nick
Davies, Paul
Day, Matt
Densmore, Shaun
Drummond, Stewart
Furlong, Paul
Grant, John
Harrad, Shaun
Hine, Mark
Humphreys, Delwyn
Kennedy, John
Kerr, Scott
Kimmins,Ged
King, Simon
Leworthy, David
McDougald, Junior
Mayes, Bobby
Moore, Neil
Moore, Luke
Newton, Sean
O'Keefe, Eamon
Oli, Dennis
Penn, Russell
Pitcher, Geoff
Ricketts, Sam
Robbins, Terry
Robinson, Mark
Roddis,Nick
Rodgers, Luke
Rogers, Paul
Ryan, Tim
Sellars, Neil
Shaw, John
Sheldon, Gareth
Simpson, Josh
Sinclair, Dean
Smith, Ian
Smith, Ossie
Stansfield, Adam
Stephens,Mickey
Stott, Steve
Taylor, Steve
Thurgood, Stuart
Tubbs, Matthew
Venables, David
Way, Darren
Webb, Paul
Wilcox, Russ

MOST CAPPED PLAYER

	Club	Caps	Seasons
John Davison	Altrincham	24	1979 - 1986

FULL INTERNATIONAL HONOURS

To date three players have played for England at both Full International and Semi-Professional/England C levels.

Peter Taylor	Full: 1976	SPro: 1984	whilst at Maidstone United
Alan Smith	Full: 1988	SPro: 1982	whilst at Alvechurch
Steve Guppy	Full: 1999	SPro: 1993	whilst at Wycombe Wanderers

ENGLAND SEMI-PROFESSIONALS, NATIONAL GAME XI AND ENGLAND 'C' CAPS 1979 - 2009

KEY TO COUNTRY CODES:
Ba - Barbados B - Belgium BH - Bosnia & Herzegovina
E - Eire F - Finland G - Gibraltar Gr - Granada H - Holland
I - Italy IP - Irish Premier Lge IQ - Iraq M - Malta N - Norway
S - Scotland W - Wales US - U.S.A.

Players capped for the first time during season 2008-09 are shown in bold.

Gary Abbott (Welling) **87** v I(s), S(s), 92 W(s) 3
David Adamson (Boston Utd) **79 v** S, H **80** v I,S, H 5
Les Afful (Forest Green Rovers) **07** v H, IP 2
Tony Agana (Weymouth) **86** v E 1
Junior Agogo (Barnet) **03** v H, i (s), S 3
Danny Alcock (Stafford Rangers) **07** v IP 1
Carl Alford (Kettering T. & Rushden & Ds) **96** v E,H 2
Dale Anderson (Burton Albion) **02** v H **03** v I 2
Mark Angel (Boston United) **02** v W(s), E, S 3
Ian Arnold (Kettering Town) **95** v W(s), H 2
Jim Arnold (Stafford Rangers) **79** v S, H 2
Nathan Arnold (Mansfield Town) **09** v BH 1
Steve Arnold (Grays Athletic) **09** v M 1
Nick Ashby (Kettering & Rushden & Diamonds) 5
94 v F, N, **95** v G **96** v E, H
Noel Ashford (Enfield & Redbridge Forest.) 21
82 v G,H,S. **83 v** I,H,S, **84** W,H,S,I, **85** W,I(s), **86** E,E,
87 W(s), I,H,S. **90** v W,E **91** I(s)
John Ashton (Rushden & Diamonds) **07** v E, S, W, F 4
John Askey (Macclesfield) **90** v W 1
Ryan Austin (Burton Albion) **06** v I. **07** v H. 2
Danny Bacon (Hucknall Town) **04** v IQ 1
Carl Baker (Southport) **06** v I. **07** v F. 2
Matt Baker (Hereford United) **03** v I, S, **04** E,S,IQ,US 6
Nicky Bailey (Barnet) **05** v H, E, S, W. 4
Stephen Bailey (Grays Athletic) **09** v BH 1
Paul Bancroft (Kidderminster H.) **89** v I,W **90** I,W.E, **91** v W 6
Chris Banks (Cheltenham T.) **98** v H, 99 W 2
Keith Barrett (Enfield) **81** v H,S,I **82 v** G,I,H,S **83** v I,H,S
84 v W(s), H, S **85** I,H,S 16
Adam Bartlett (Blyth Spartans) **07** v F. **08** v G,W,Ba. **09** v I,B 6
Laurence Batty (Woking) **93** v F(s), **95** v W,H,G 4
Mark Beeney (Maidstone) **89** v I(s) 1
Paul Beesley (Chester C.) **01** v H(s) 1
Dean Bennett (Kidderminster H) **00** v W(s) 1
Paul Benson (Dagenham & Redbridge) **07** v IP. 1
Graham Benstead (Kettering) **94** v W,F,N(s) 3
Kevin Betsy (Woking) **98** v H(s) 1
Marcus Bignot (Kidderminster H) **97** v H 1
Andy Bishop (York City) **05** v I,H. **06** v B,I. 4
Neil Bishop (York City) **07** v E, W. 2
James Bittner (Exeter City) **04** v B,I 2
Chris Blackburn (Chester C. & Morecambe) **03** v I. **05** v I,H. **06** v I. 4
Shane Blackett (Dagenham & Red). **06** v E,S. 2
Greg Blundell (Northwich Victoria) **03** v H 1
Jon Boardman (Woking) **03** v I, S. **04** I,W,US 5
Jimmy Bolton (Kingstonian) **95** v G 1
Steve Book (Cheltenham Town) **99 v** I,H,W 3
Michael Bostwick (Stevenage Borough) **09** v I 1
George Boyd (Stevenage Boro') **06** v B,I,E,W,S. **07** v H. 6
Adam Boyes (York City) **09** v M 1
Lee Boylan (Canvey Island) **04** v US 1
Gary Brabin (Runcorn) **94 v** W,F,N 3
Mark Bradshaw (Halifax T.) **98** v H 1
Leon Braithwaite (Margate) **02** v US 1
John Brayford (Burton Albion) **08** v F,W,G,S,W,Gr,Ba. 7
Paul Brayson (Northwich Victoria) **07** v S. 1
Colin Brazier (Kidderminster) **87** v W 1
David Bridges (Cambridge Utd) **06** v I 1
Stewart Brighton (Bromsgrove) **94** v W 1
Richard Brodie (York City) **09** v BH 1
Steve Brooks (Cheltenham) **88** v W(s) **90** v W,E 3
Derek Brown (Woking) **94 v** F(s),N 2
Kevan Brown (Woking) **95** v W,H,G **96** v H **97** v E 5
Paul Brown (Barrow) **09** v M 1
Wayne Brown (Chester C.) **01** v W, H(s), **02** v US, H(s),W,S. 7
03 v H
Corey Browne (Dover) **94** v F(s),N(s), **95** v H(s) 3
Liam Brownhill (Witton Albion) **08** v F,W. 2
David Buchanan (Blyth) **86** v E(s),E 2
Nicki Bull (Aldershot Town) **03** v B. **04** v I, H, E. 4
Andrew Burgess (Oxford United/Rushden & Dia.) **07** v E,S,W. 8
08 v G,S,W,Gr,Ba.
Brian Butler (Northwich) **93** v F 1
Steve Butler (Maidstone) **88** v W, **89 v** I,W 3
Gary Butterworth (Rushden & Diamonds)
97 v E,H **98 v** H **99** v I,H,W **00** v I
7
Chris Byrne (Macclesfield T.) **97** v H 1
Joel Byrom (Northwich Victoria) **09** v B 1
Michael Byron (Droylsden) **09** v M 1
DJ Campbell (Yeading) **05** v E, S. 2
Paul Carden (Burton Albion) **07** v E,W. 2
Daniel Carey-Bertram (Hereford Utd) **06** v B 1
Danny Carlton (Morecambe) **04** v IQ 1
Michael Carr (Northwich) **06** v B,I,E,W,S. **07** v H.IP. 7
Mark Carter (Runcorn & Barnet) v 11
87 v W,I,H,S **88** v W, **89 v** I,W, **90** v I,E, **91** v I,W(s)
Kim Casey (Kidderminster) **86** v W,E,E(s), **87** v W,I 5
Paul Cavell (Redbridge) **92** v W **93** v F 2
Peter Cavanagh (Accrington) **04** v B,I,E 3
Jon Challinor (Aldershot Town) **04** v B,I 2
Lewis Chalmers (Altrincham/Aldershot) **07** v H,E,S,F. 10
08 v F,W,G,W,Gr,Ba.
Darius Charles (Ebbsfleet United) **09** v B 1
Lee Charles (Hayes) **99** v I(s), H(s), W(s) 3
Anthony Charles (Aldershot/Farnborough) **04** v B,I 2
Kevin Charlton (Telford) **85** v W,I 2
Ken Charlery (Boston U) **01** v H(s) 1
Kieran Charnock (Northwich) **05** v E,W. **06** v B,I,E,W,S. 11
07 v H,IP,E,W.

Andrew Clarke (Barnet) **90** v E,E 2
David Clarke (Blyth Spartans) **80** v I,S(s),H, **81** v H,S,I 14
82 v I,H,S **83** v H,S **84** v H,S,I
Gary Clayton (Burton) **86** v E 1
Paul Clayton (Alfreton Town) **09** v M,B 2
Robert Codner (Barnet) **88** v W 1
Mitchell Cole (Stevenage Borough) **07** v E,S,W,F. 12
08 v W,G,S,W,Gr,Ba. **09** v BH,I.
John Coleman (Morecambe) **93** v F(s) 1
Darren Collins (Enfield) **93** v F(s), **94** v W,F,N 4
Matt Collins (Nuneaton Borough) **04** v I 1
Andy Comyn (Hednesford T.) **98** **v** H(s), **99 v** I(s),H(s),W(s) 4
Steve Conner (Dartford, Redbridge & Dagenham & R) 5
90 v I **91** v I,W **92** v W **93** v F.
James Constable (Kidderminster & Oxford Utd) **08** v F. **09** I,B 3
David Constantine (Altrincham) **85** v I,H,S **86 v** W 4
Robbie Cooke (Kettering) **89** v W(s), **90** v I 2
Scott Cooksey (Hednesford T.) **97** v E, **98** vH(s) **01** v W(s),H 4
Alan Cordice(Wealdstone)**83** v I,H,S **84** vW,S(s), I(s),**85** I,H,S 9
Rob Cousins (Yeovil Town) **00 I** v I(s),H,W 3
Gavin Cowan (Canvey Island) **04** v B,IQ 2
Ken Cramman (Gateshead & Rushden & Diamonds) 3
96 v E **97** v E,H
Ian Craney (Altrincham & Accrington) **03** v B. **04** US. **05** I. 7
06 v B,I,E,W.
Nick Crittendon (Yeovil Town) **02** v US (s) 1
Lance Cronin (Ebbsfleet United) **07** v H,E,W,F. **08** v F,W. **09** vBH 7
Paul Cuddy (Altrincham) **87** v I,H,S 3
Paul Culpin (Nuneaton B) **84** v W, **85** v W(s) ,I,H,S 5
Jonathan D'Laryea (Mansfield Town) **09** v Bh,I. 2
Michael Danzey (Woking) **99** v I,H 2
Paul Davies (Kidderminster H.) 6
86 v W, **87** **v** W,I,S, **88** **v** W **89** v W
John Davison (Altrincham) **79** v S,H **80** v I,S, **81** **v** H,S ,I. 24
82 v G,I,H,S **83** I,H,S. **84** W,H,I,S **85** **v** I,H,S 86 **v** W,E,E.
Matt Day (Oxford United) **09** v BH 1
John Denham (Northwich Victoria) **80** v H 1
Peter Densmore (Runcorn) **88** v W **89** v I 2
Shaun Densmore (Altrincham) **09** v M,B. 2
Phil Derbyshire (Mossley) **83** v H(s) S(s) 2
Scott Doe (Weymouth) **09** v M. 1
Mick Doherty (Weymouth) **86** v W(s) 1
Neil Doherty (Kidderminster H.) **97** v E 1
Clayton Donaldson (York City) **07** v H,IP. 2
Stuart Drummond (Morecambe) **00** v I(s),H ,W **01 v** W ,H 13
02 v US, W,E(s), S **03** v H, I, W, S (s)
Roscoe D'Sane (Aldershot Town) **03** v B(s),H(s),E,W,S. **04** B,I 7
Chris Duffy (Canvey Island) **03** v B 1
Neil Durkin (Leigh RMI) **02** v H(s) 1
Lee Elam (Morecambe) **03** v H,E,W,S)s) 4
Anthony Elding (Stevenage Borough) **04** v B. **05** v I,H,E,W,S. 6
Paul Ellender (Scarborough) **01** v W(s) 1
Lee Endersby (Harrow Bor.) **96 v** H 1
Mick Farrelly (Altrincham) **87** **v** I,H,S 3
Steve Farrelly (Macclesfield & Kingstonian) 5
95 v H(s),G(s), **00** v I,H,W(s)
Trevor Finnegan (Weymouth) **81** v H,S 2
Murray Fishlock (Yeovil Town) **99** v H(s) 1
Andrew Fleming (Wrexham) **09** v B. 1
Richard Forsyth (Kidderminster) **95** v W,H,G 3
Danny Foster (Dagenham & Redbridge) **07** v E,S,F. 3
Ian Foster (Kidderminster H) **00** v W(s) 1

Exodus Geohaghon.

Luke Foster (Oxford United) **09** v BH. 1
Amos Foyewa (Woking) **04** v E,W,S 3
Barry Fuller (Stevenage Borough) **07** v IP. 1
Paul Furlong (Enfield) **90 v** I,E,E **91** v I,W 5
Mark Gardiner (Macclesfield T.) **97** v E 1
Exodus Geohaghon (Kettering Town) **09** v I,B. 2
Jerry Gill (Yeovil T.) **97** v E 1
Matt Glennon (Carlisle Utd) **05** v W,S. 2
Dan Gleeson (Cambridge Utd) **08** v F,W,G,S,Gr,Ba. **09** v I. 7
John Glover (Maidstone Utd) **85** v W,I,H,S 4
Mark Golley (Sutton Utd.)
87 v H(s),S, **88** v W, **89** v I,W, **92** v W 6
Jason Goodliffe (Hayes) **00** v I, H,W, **01** W **02** US, W,E,S. 8
Paul Gothard (Dagenham & Redb.) **97** v E(s), **99** v I(s),W(s) 3
Jeff Goulding (Fisher Athletic) **08** v W. 1
Mark Gower (Barnet) **02** v H, W, E, S(s) 4
Simon Grand (Carlisle) **05** v H. 1
John Grant (Aldershot Town) **07** v E,S,W,F. 4
Neil Grayson (Cheltenham T.) **98** v H **99** v I,H,W 4
Phil Gridelet (Hendon & Barnet) **89** v I,W, **90** v W,E,E 5
Scott Griffiths (Dagenham & Redbridge) **07** v H,IP. 2
Steve Guinan (Hereford) **04** v E,W,S,US 4
Steve Guppy (Wycombe W.) **93** v W 1
Scott Guyett (Southport) **01** v H, **03** v H,I,W,S. 5
Tim Hambley (Havant & Waterlooville) **02** v H 1
Steve Hanlon (Macclesfield) **90** v W 1
Ben Harding (Aldershot) **08** v W,G,W. 3
David Harlow (Farnborough T.) **97** v E(s),H 2
Shaun Harrad (Burton Albion) **07** v F. **08** v F,W,G,S,W,Gr,Ba. 8
09 v BH,I.
Stephen Haslam (Halifax) **05** v E,W,S. 3
Liam Hatch (Barnet) **04** v E,W,S,IQ,US. **05** H. 6
Wayne Hatswell (Chester City/Cambridge Utd) **03** v E(s),W(s).
08 v S,W,Gr,Ba. 6
Karl Hawley (Carlisle Utd) **05** v I,H. 2
Barry Hayles (Stevenage Bor.) **96** v E,H 2
Greg Heald (Barnet) **02** v H 1
Brian Healy (Morecambe) **98** v H 1
Liam Hearn (Alfreton Town) **09** v B. 1
Ronnie Henry (Stevenage Boro) **06** v S. **07** v IP. **08** v F,W. 4
Tony Hemmings (Northwich) **93** v F 1
Andy Hessenthaler (Dartford) **90** v I 1
Kenny Hill (Maidstone Utd) **80** v I,S,H 3
Mark Hine (Gateshead) **95** v W(s),H 2
Simeon Hodson (Kidderminster) **94** v W,F,N 3
Lewis Hogg (Barnet) **04** v B 1

Colin Hogarth (Guiseley) **95 v** W,H 2
Steven Holden (Kettering) **94** v W,F,N(s) **95** v H,G 5
Ricky Holmes (Chelmsford City) **08** v W. 1
Mark Hone (Welling United) **90** v I **93** v F, **94** vW(s),F(s),N 5
Gary Hooley (Frickley) **85** v W 1
Dean Hooper (Kingstonian) **98** v H 1
Keith Houghton (Blyth Spartans) **79** v S 1
Barry Howard (Altrincham) **81** v H,S,I **82** v G,I,H,S 7
Neil Howarth (Macclesfield) **95** v H(s) **97** v E 2
David Howell (Enfield) **85** v H(s),S(s) **86** v W,E **87** v W,I,H,S **88** v W, **89** v I,W **90** v I,E,E 14
Lee Howells (Cheltenham T.) **98** v H **99 v** W 2
Lee Hughes (Kidderminster Harriers) **96** v E,H **97** v E,H 4
Delwyn Humphreys (Kidderminster H.) **91** v W(s) **92** v W **94** v W,F,N **95** v W,H 7
Steve Humphries (Barnet) **87** v H(s) 1
Nicky Ironton (Enfield) **83** H(s) **84** v W 2
Jimmy Jackson (Gravesend & Northfleet) 03 v H(s) 1
Simon Jackson (Woking) **05** v I. 1
Justin Jackson (Morecambe & Rushden & Diamonds) 2
00 v W **01** v W
Kirk Jackson (Stevenage Borough) **02** v US, E,S,(Yeovil Town) **03** v E,W,S(s) 6
Shwan Jalal (Woking) **05** v H. **06** v I,E,W,S. 5
Mark Janney (Dagenham & Redbridge) **03** v H 1
Tony Jennings (Enfield) 12
79 v S,H **80** v I,S,H **81 v** H,S,I **82** v G,I,H,S
Jeff Johnson (Altrincham) **81** v S,I **82** v G,I,H,S **83** v I,H,S **84 v** H,S,I **84 v** I,H,S **86** v W(s),E,E 18
Lee Johnson (Yeovil Town) **03** v I, H(s), E, W, S 5
Paul Jones (Exeter City) **06** v I 1
Steve Jones (Leigh RMI) **01** v H 1
Tom Jones (Weymouth) **87** v W 1
Tom Jordan (Tamworth) **04** v B 1
Antone Joseph(Telford U. & Kidderm'terH.)**84** v S(s), **85** v W,I, H,S **86** v W(s), **87** W,I(s),H, **88** v W **89** v I,W **90 v** I,E,E 15
John Keeling (Purfleet) **03** v B(s) 1
Marcus Kelly (Rushden & Diamonds) **07** v IP. 1
Darran Kempson (Morecambe) **06** v E,W. 2
John Kennedy (Canvey Island) **03** v I, B, H, E, W, S. **04** IQ,US 8
Jon Kennedy (Accrington) **04** v I,IQ,US 3
Andy Kerr (Wycombe) **93** v W 1
Scott Kerr (Scarborough) **04** v E,W,S,IQ. **05** v I,H,E,W,S 9
Lance Key (Kingstonian) 03 v B 1
Ged Kimmins (Hyde Utd.) **96** v E(s),H(s) **97 v** E(s) 3
Simon King (Barnet) **05** v I,H,S. 3
Scott Laird (Stevenage Borough) **09** v B. 1

Scott Laird.

Mike Lake (Macclesfield) **89** v I 1
Martin Lancaster (Chester City) **03** vI (s)
Andy Lee (Telford U. & Witton A.) **89** I(s), **91** v I,W 3
Arran Lee-Barrett (Weymouth) **07** v H. 1
Stuart Lewis (Stevenage Borough) **08** v F. 1
David Leworthy (Farnborough & Rushden & Diamonds) **93 v** W, **94** v W **97** v E,H 4
Adam Lockwood (Yeovil Town) **02** v E **03** v I 2
Stacey Long (Gravesend & Northfleet) **07** v IP. 1
Kenny Lowe (Barnet) **91 v** I,W 2
Craig McAllister (Basingstoke Town) **03** v B 1
Martin McDonald (Macclesfield) **95** v G(s) 1
Danny McDonnell (Worcester City) **04** v W 1
Junior MacDougald (Dagenham & Redbridge) **01** v H(s) **02** W, E(s), S(s) 4
Mark McGregor (Forest Green Rovers & Nuneaton Borough) 3
00 v I(s),H(s) **01** v W(s)
Kevin McIntyre (Doncaster Rovers) **00 v** H(s)W, **01 v** W(s)H 4
John McKenna (Boston Utd) **88 v** W(s), **90** v I,E,E. 7
91 v I,W, **92** vW
Aaron McLean (Aldershot & Grays) **04** v B,I. **06** v E,W,S. 5
Lewis McMahon (Gainsborough Trinity) **09** v M. 1
David McNiven (Leigh RMI) **04** v W,S,IQ,US 4
Chris McPhee (Ebbsfleet Utd) **08** v G,S,W. 3
Craig Mackhail-Smith (Dag. & Red.) **05** v W,S. **06** v I,E,W,S. 7
07 v H.
Tamika Mkandawire (Hereford Utd) **06** v B,I. 2
Fiston Manuella (Aylesbury United) **03** v B 1
John Margerrison (Barnet) **87 v** W 1
Simon Marples (Doncaster Rovers) **00 v** I,H 2
John Martin (Stevenage Borough) **08** v G,S,W. 3
Leroy May (Stafford R.) **95 v** G(s) 1
Bobby Mayes (Redbridge) **92 v** W
Paul Mayman (Northwich Vic) **80 v** I,S 2
Stewart Mell (Burton) **85v** W 1
Neil Merrick (Weymouth) **80** v I(s),S 2
Adam Miller (Aldershot Town) **04** v I 1
Russell Milton (Dover) 94 v F,N 2
Mark Molesley (Aldershot Town) **07** v E,S,W,F. 4
Luke Moore (Ebbsfleet United) **09** v BH. 1
Neil Moore (Telford United) **02** v US (s),H, W, E,S 5
Steve Morison (Stevenage Borough) **07** v H,IP,F.
08 v G,S,W,Gr,Ba. 8
Trevor Morley (Nuneaton) **84 v** W,H,S,I **85 v** W,S(s) 6
Michael Morrison (Cambridge Utd) **07** v H.
08 v F,W,G,S,W,Gr,Ba. 8
Dean Moxey (Exeter City) **05** v H. **08** v W,S. 3
Chris Murphy (Telford United) **04** v B 1
Karl Murrphy (Woking) **04** v B,I 2
Tarkan Mustafa (Rushden & Diamonds) **01** v W,H 2
Les Mutrie (Blyth Spartans) **79 v** S,H, **80** v I,S,H 5
Mark Newson (Maidstone U) **84 v** W,H,S,I, **85 v** W 5
Doug Newton (Burton) **85** v W,H,S 3
Shaun Newton (Droylsden) **09** v M,B. 2
Paul Nicol (Kettering T) **91 v** I,W, **92** v W 3
Kevin Nicholson (Forest Green Rovers/Torquay Utd)
07 v E.S.W. **08** v G,S,W,Gr,Ba. 8
Richard Norris (Northwich Victoria) **03** v H, S, 2
Steve Norris (Telford) **88** v W(s) 1
John Nutter (Grays) **06** v E,W,S. 3
Joe O'Connor (Hednesford T.) **97 v** E,H(s) 2

Eamon O'Keefe (Mossley) **79 v** S,H 2
Erkan Okay (Histon) **08** v F. 1
Dennis Oli (Grays) **06** v B,E,W,S. **07** v H. 5
Luke Oliver (Woking) **05** v H. 1
Frank Ovard (Maidstone) **81** v H(s),S(s),I(s) 3
Andy Pape (Harrow Bor. & Enfield) **85** v W(s,)H,S. 15
86 v W(s),E, **87** v W,I,H,S **88** v W, **89** **IW**, **90** I,W,E
Brian Parker (Yeovil Town) **80 v** S 1
Warren Patmore (Yeovil Town) **99** v I,H,W, **00 v** I,H, **01** W,H 7
Gary Patterson (Kingstonian) **99** v I,H, **00** v H,W, **01 v** W,H 7
Steve Payne (Macclesfield T.) **97 v** H 1
Trevor Peake (Nuneaton Bor) **79 v** S,H 2
David Pearce (Harrow Bor) **84 v** I(s) 1
Russell Penn (Kidderminster) **08** v F,W,G,W,Gr,Ba. **09** v I,B. 8
David Perkins (Morecambe) **04** v B,I,E,S,IQ,US. **05** v I.
06 v B,I. 9
Warren Peyton (Nuneaton Borough) **02** v H(s) **03** v I 2
Brendan Phillips (Nuneaton Bor. & Kettering T.), 4
79 v S,H, **80 v** S(s),H.
Gary Philips (Barnet) **82 v** G 1
Owen Pickard (Yeovil T.) **98** v H(s) 1
Geoff Pitcher (Kingstonian) **99 v** W, **00 v** I,H,W, **01** v W,H 6
Jon-Paul Pitman (Crawley Town) **09** v I. 1
Phil Power (Macclesfield T.) **96** v E(s),H(s) 2
Ryan Price (Stafford R. & Macclesfield) **92** v W(s) **93** v W,F. 6
96 v E,H **97** v H.
Steve Prindiville **98 v** H(s) 1
Andy Proctor (Accrington Stanley) **04** v IQ 1
Marc Pullan (Crawley Town) **03** v B 1
Robert Purdie (Hereford United) **04** v I. **05** v I. 2
Wayne Purser (Barnet) **03** v I 1
Mark Quayle (Telford United) **02** v H 1
Adam Quinn (Halifax Town) **07** v H,IP,E,S,W,F. 6
Simon Read (Farnborough) **92** v W(s) 1
Matt Redmile (Barnet) **04** v E,W,S 3
Andy Reid (Altrincham) **95 v** W 1
Martin Rice (Exeter City) **07** v IP. 1
Carl Richards (Enfield) **86 v** E 1
Justin Richards (Woking) **06** v E,W,S. 3
Derek Richardson (Maidstone U) **83 v** I, **84 v** W, **86** v E 4
Ian Richardson (Dagenham & Red) **95 v** G 1
Kevin Richardson (Bromsgrove) **94** v W,F,N 3
Paul Richardson (Redbridge) **92** v W, **93 v** W, F 3
Scott Rickards (Tamworth) **03** v B. **04** B 2
Sam Ricketts (Telford) **04** v B,E,W,S 4
Adriano Rigoglioso (Morecambe) **03** v H(s) 1
Martin Riley (Kidderminster Harriers) **09** v M. 1
Anthony Rivierre (Welling United) **03** v B 1
Terry Robbins (Welling) **92 v** W, **93** v W,F, **94** v W,F,N 6
Dale Roberts (Rushden & Diamonds) **09** v M. 1
Gary Roberts (Accrington) **06** v I,E,W,S. 4
Anton Robinson (Weymouth) **09** v BH,I. 2
Mark Robinson (Hereford) **05** v E,W,S. 3
Peter Robinson (Blyth S) **83 v** I,H,S **84** W,I 85 v W 6
Ryan Robinson (Morecambe) **06** v B. 1
Nick Roddis (Woking) **01 v** H **02** US,H,W,E(s),S 6
Luke Rodgers (Shrewsbury) **04** v B,I. 2
John Rogers (Altrincham) **81 v** H,S,I **82 v** I(s),S 5
Paul Rogers (Sutton) **89** v W, **90** v I, E(2), **91** I,W 6
Colin Rose (Witton Alb.) **96 v** E(s), H 2
Kevin Rose (Kidderminster) **94 v** F(s),N 2

Russell Penn.

Michael Rose (Hereford United) **03** v I, H, E, S 4
Brian Ross (Marine) **93 v** W(s),F(s), **94** v W(s) **95 v** W,H 5
Carl Ruffer (Chester City) **01** v H(s) 1
Tim Ryan (Southport & Doncaster Rovers) **98 v** H. 14
99 v I,H,W, **00 v** I,H,W **01** v W,H **02** v US,H,W,I,S
Gareth Seddon (Hyde United) **07** v E.W. 2
Jake Sedgemore (Shrewsbury) **04** v E,W,S,IQ,US. 5
Neil Sellars (Scarboro) **81** v H,S,I **82** v G,H(s),S, **83 v** I,H,S 9
Mark Shail (Yeovil T.) **93** v W 1
John Shaw (Halifax Town) **08** v G,S,W,Gr,Ba. 5
Jon Shaw (Burton Albion) **06** v I. 1
Simon Shaw (Doncaster Rovers) **99** v I,H 2
Tom Shaw (Tamworth) **09** v M. 1
Peter Shearer (Cheltenham) **89 v** I(s) 1
Gareth Sheldon (Exeter) **04** v I,E,W,S,IQ,US. 6
Paul Shirtliff (Frickley A. & Boston U.) **86** vE,E **87** v W,I,H. 15
88 v W **89 v** I, W, **90 v** I,W,E,E, **92 v** W **93** v W,F
Paul Showler (Altrincham) **91** v I(s),W 2
Tim Sills (Kingstonian) **03** v B 1
Gordon Simmonite (Boston United) **79** v S(s,)H(s), **80** v I,S,H 5
Gary Simpson(Stafford R.) **86** v E,E, **87** v I,H,S,**90** v I,W,E,E 9
Josh Simpson (Histon) **09** v I. 1
Wayne Simpson (Stafford) **94** v F,N(s) 2
Dean Sinclair (Barnet) **05** v I,H,E,W,S. 5
Terry Skiverton (Yeovil Town) **01 v** W **02 v** US **03** v !,W, 4
Glenn Skivington (Barrow) **90** v I,W,E **91** v I,W 5
Jamie Slabber (Grays) **06** v B. 1
Adrian Smith (Kidderminster H) **00** v I(s),H(s),W 3
Alan Smith (Alvechurch) **82** v G,I,S 3
Ian Smith (Mossley) **80** v I,S,H(s) 3
James Smith (Ebbsfleet Utd) **08** v Gr,Ba. **09** v BH,I. 4
Mark Smith (Stevenage Bor.) **96** v E,H **98** v H **99** v I,H,W. 9
00 v I,H,W(s).
Ossie Smith (Runcorn) **84** v W 1
Phil Smith (Margate) **04** v B 1
Tim Smithers (Nuneaton) **85** v W(s),I **86** v W 3
Guiseppe Sole (Woking) **07** v H,IP,F. 3
Adam Sollitt (Kettering Town) **00** v I(s),H(s),W 3
Leon Solomon (Welling United) **07** v F. 1
Glen Southam (Bishop's Stort' & Dag & R.) **04** v E,W,S,IQ,US.12
05 v W,S. **06** v S. **07** v E,S,W,F.
Craig Stanley (Hereford & Morecambe) **05** v E,W. **07** v H,IP. 4
Adam Stansfield (Yeovil Town & Hereford) **02** v W (s), I, S 5
05 v E,S.
Simon Stapleton (Wycombe) **93** v W 1
Mickey Stephens (Sutton), **82** v G,S(s) **86 v** W,E,E(s) 5

Lee Tomlin.

Jamie Stevens (Crawley Town) **09** v BH. 1
Billy Stewart (Southport) **98** v H 1
Mark Stimson (Canvey Islland) **02** v US 1
Bob Stockley (Nuneaton Borough) **80** v H 1
David Stockdale (York) **05** v I. 1
Darren Stride (Burton Albion) **02** v H 1
Steve Stott (Kettering T., Rushden & Ds & Yeovil T.) **95** v W,H(s),G **96** v E,H **99** v H,W(s) 7
Ryan Sugden (Chester City) 03 v I 1
Ben Surey (Gravesend & Nflt.) **05** v I. 1
Andy Taylor (Exeter City) **05** v E,W,S. 3
James Taylor (Havant & Waterlooville) **02** v H,W, E(s),S(s) 4
Peter Taylor (Maidstone) **84** v HSI 3
Steve Taylor (Bromsgrove R.) **95** v G 1
Shaun Teale (Weymouth) **88** v W 1
Paul Terry (Dagenham & Redbridge) **03** vE (s), W(s), S 3
Stuart Terry (Altrincham) **95** v W 1
Brian Thompson(Yeovil & Maidstone) **79** v S,H **81** v H,S,I. **82** v I,H,S **83** v I,H,S **84** v W,H,S,I 15
Neil Thompson (Scarborough) **87** v W,I,H,S 4
Garry Thompson (Morecambe) **03** v I. **04** v E,W,IQ,US 5
Steve Thompson (Wycombe) **93** v W 1
Stuart Thurgood (Grays Ath.) **05** v I,H. **06** v E,W,S. 5
Kevin Todd (Berwick Rangers) **91** v W 1
Lee Tomlin (Rushden & Diamonds) **09** v M,B. 2
Mike Tomlinson (Runcorn F.C.Halton) **03** v B (s) 1
Anthony Tonkin (Yeovil Town) **02** v US 1
Simon Travis (Forest Green R & Hereford) **02 v** US, H. **05** v E. **06** v E,W,S. 6
Carl Tremarco (Wrexham) **09** v I. 1
Andy Tretton (Hereford) **04** v E,W,S,US 4
Matthew Tubbs (Salisbury City) **07** v E. **08** v F. 2
Mark Tucker (Woking) **96** v E 1
Tony Turner (Telford) **85 v** W 1
Scott Tynan (Rushden & Diamonds) **07** v S,W. **08** v S,Gr. 4
Paul Underwood (Rushden & D) **99** v I,H **00 v** I**01** v W 4
David Venables(Stevenage B)**94 v** W(s)**95 v** H,G**96 v** E,H(s) 5
Jamie Victory (Cheltenham T.) **98** vH(s) 1
Ashley Vickers (Dagenham & Redbridge) **04** v IQ 1

David Waite (Enfield) **82** v G 1
Steve Wales (Yeading) **06** v B. 1
Jason Walker (Barrow) **09** v M. 1
Paul Walker (Blyth) **86 v** W,E,E(s), **87 v** S(s) 4
Steve Walters (Northwich Victoria) **97** v H 1
Mark Ward (Northwich Victoria) **83** v S(s) 1
Steve Ward (Canvey Island) **03** v B 1
Dale Watkins (Cheltenham T.) **98** v H **99** v I(s), **00** v I,H,W 5
John Watson (Wealdstone, Scarborough & Maidstone) **79** v S(s),H **80** v I,S,H **81** v H,S,I **82** v I,H,S **83** v I,H,S **84** v W(s),H,S,I 18
Steve Watson (Farnborough Town) **02** v US(s), W(s), S 3
Liam Watson (Marine) **95** v W,H(s) 2
Paul Watts (Redbridge Forest) **89** v W **90** v I,E,E **91** v I **92** v W **93** v W,F 8
Darren Way (Yeovil Town) **03** vI (s), E, W 3
Chris Weale (Yeovil Town) **03** v I (s), H (s), E, W. 4
Simon Weatherstone (Boston United) **02** v W(s),E,S(s) 3
Paul Webb (Bromsgrove R & Kidderminster H) **93** v F **94** v W,F,N(s) **95** v W,H,G **96** v E,H **97** v E,H 11
Aaron Webster (Burton Albion) **02 v** H(s),W,S(s) **03** v I 3
Ishmael Welsh (Grays Athletic) **09** v M,B. 2
Mark West (Wycombe W) **91** v W 1
Steve West (Woking) **01** v W(s) 1
Barry Whitbread (Runcorn & Altrincham) **79 v** S,H **80** v I,S,H, **81 v** I 6
Tristram Whitman (Doncaster Rovers) **03** v W(s), S 2
Russ Wilcox (Frickley) **86** v W,E 2
Adam Wilde (Worcester City) **03** v B 1
Barry Williams (Nuneaton Borough) **99** v H(s),W 2
Colin Williams (Scarborough & Telford Utd.) **81** v H,S. **82** v I,H,S. **84** v H,S,I. **85** v I,H,S. 12
Roger Willis (Barnet) **91** v I(s) 1
Paul Wilson (Frickley Athletic) **86** v W 1
Martyn Woolford (York City) **08** v Gr,Ba. 2
Andy Woods (Scarborough) **02** v US,H(s),W,S. 4
Simon Wormull (Dover Athletic) **99** v I(s),W **02 v** W,E,S. 5
Mark Wright (Thurrock) **09** v BH. 1
Jake Wright (Tamworth) **09** v I. 1
Nicky Wroe (Torquay United) **09** v M,B. 2
Adam Yates (Morecambe) **07** v H,S,W. 3
Mark Yates (Cheltenham Town) **99** v I, W 2
Ismail Yakubu (Barnet) **04** v I,US. **05** v I,E,W,S. 6

The 128th F.A.Challenge Cup competition was again sponsored by E-on and kicked off with the First Preliminary Round on Saturday 15th August.

A record 762 clubs had been accepted for the competition and would be playing for £16.4 million prize money which was a 69% increase on the previous season. Forty three new entrants would be making local football history but realised that to reach the Wembley Final they would have to play at least thirteen ties!

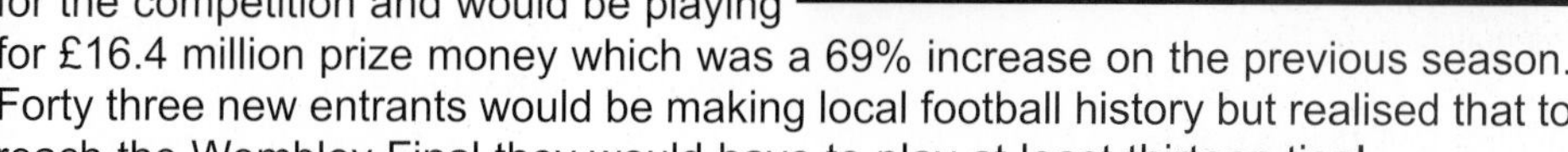

All the clubs had their own targets and those competing in the Preliminary or Qualifying Rounds would consider it very special to enjoy the excitement of the competition proper.

EASTWOOD TOWN MAKE HISTORY

Last season saw Step 4 clubs Bury Town and Curzon Ashton, plus Step 5 club Leiston from The Eastern Counties League, all featuring in The First Round Proper draw. Curzon Ashton hit the jackpot when drawn at home to Exeter City and duly won a thrilling cup tie 3-2 in front of 1,259. Bury Town lost 2-4 at Alfreton Town after leading 2-1 in front of 1,060, but little Leiston drew at home to Northern Premier League Fleetwood Town and 2,010 saw them lose the replay.

Joining Curzon Ashton in the First Round head-lines were Blyth Spartans who beat Shrewsbury Town 3-1, Droylsden who won a home replay with Darlington 1- 0, Histon who beat Swindon Town 1-0 at home and Kettering Town who drew at home to Lincoln City 1-1 but won the replay 2-1 with a last minute goal from Christie watched by 3,953. Grays Athletic also produced a brave performance forcing a replay with Carlisle United before losing 0-2 at home.

There were also some all non-league clashes. Eastwood Town didn't get a glamour tie but were at home to Brackley Town and won a tight game 2-1 to reach the Second Round Proper for the first time. Torquay United won their home match with Evesham United, Oxford United progressed at the second attempt against Dorchester Town, Kidderminster Harriers beat Cambridge United 1-0 and Barrow completed a fine replay victory against Eastbourne Borough.

HISTON BEAT LEEDS UNITED

The Second Round draw rewarded Eastwood Town with a Division Two club at home and unbeaten Wycombe Wanderers were dispatched 2-0 in front of a 1,955 'gate'. Curzon Ashton had to travel to Kidderminster where their run came to an end and Alfreton Town lost heavily at Scunthorpe.

Additional non-league departures included Fleetwood Town who were just edged out in a five goal thriller at home to Hartlepool United watched by 3,280 and Droylsden who eventually beat Chesterfield after an abandoned match and a replay before being eliminated for playing an ineligible player.

An all non-league tie gave Torquay United home advantage and a 2-0 victory over Oxford United. There were some special heroes as Blyth Spartans drew at Bournemouth and won the replay, Forest Green Rovers beat Rochdale 2-0 in front of 1,715 at the New Lawn and Barrow recorded a famous victory over Brentford , the eventual Division Two champions, while Kettering Town also hit the headlines with a televised replay victory over Notts County.

The real highlight of the Round however was enjoyed by 4,500 watching Matt Langston's goal which gave Histon a 1-0 victory over famous Leeds United which was also enjoyed by thousands live on Setanta T.V.

A NON-LEAGUE RECORD

A record eight non-league clubs were included in the F.A.Cup Third Round Draw with the Premier League clubs, and two actually had the thrill of facing opposition from the top flight. Barrow travelled to the North East and acquitted themselves excellently to score against Middlesbrough and only conceded two and Blyth Spartans held Blackburn Rovers to a single goal in a televised game at home.

Poor Eastwood Town's reward was a visit to Kettering Town of the Blue Square Premier, where they lost by the odd goal in three. Kidderminster Harriers enjoyed a West Midlands 'derby' in front of 13,653 but lost 0-2 to Coventry City and Histon eventually entertained Swansea City on a weather battered pitch but lost by the only goal of the match.

Torquay United, who only seem to play at home in the F.A.Cup brought back memories of their Football League days with a 1-0 defeat of Blackpool. But, the most thrilling tie of the day was fought out at The New Lawn where Forest Green Rovers led Derby County 2-0 and 3-2 before eventually losing 3-4 and missing out on a fund raising away replay.

It was a great week-end's football which was a credit to the eight non-league clubs and it was left to Kettering Town and Torquay United to carry the flag into The Fourth Round.

'The Gulls' were home again, this time to Coventry City, and having had the best chances throughout the afternoon, an 87th minute goal by Elliot Ward saw the Championship side through to the Fifth Round.

Live on Setanta again, Kettering Town shared in a superb cup tie with Premier Division Fulham, and with just two minutes to go and a 2-2 scoreline, it looked as if 'The Poppies 'were going to force a replay. Only tiredness and Fulham's extra quality proved too much in the dying moments of the game and two late goals saw the London club through to the next round.

A great season of non-league involvement in the F.A.Cup was highlighted by Kettering Town's great run to the Fourth Round, Histon's memorable victory over Leeds United and of course the record eight clubs competing in the Third Round proper of the famous competition.

The coverage of Setanta Television was excellent throughout the season. From the early non-league involvement to the wonderful nine hour coverage on Cup Final day. The whole competition was presented with obvious respect and an understanding of the importance the famous knock out tournament meant to so many true football people.

TW.

The Histon players run off to celebrate what was to be the winning goal in their FA Cup 2nd Round tie with League Two side Leeds United. Photo: Peter Barnes.

EXTRA PRELIMINARY ROUND

BIGGEST HOME WIN:	**8-0** Mildenhall Town v Felixstowe & Walton
BIGGEST AWAY WIN:	**4-7** Darwen v Penrith
HIGHEST ATTENDANCE:	**433** Lowestoft Town v St Ives Town
NUMBER OF GAMES:	**201 + 36** (2007-08 - 169+39)
TOTAL ATTENDANCE:	**22,258** (19,339) NB:missing 1 attendances
AVERAGE ATTENDANCE:	**94** (93) average takes into account missing 1

Home	Away	Score	Att
Bedlington Terriers	v Chester Le Street Town	1 - 0	125
Consett	v Pontefract Collieries	5 - 1	128
South Shields	v Hebburn Town	5 - 1	206
Horden Colliery Welfare	v Sunderland Nissan	1 - 3	44
Northallerton Town	v Whitley Bay	1 - 3	124
Glasshoughton Welfare	v Billingham Synthonia	2 - 2	144
Billingham Synthnia	v Glasshoughton Welfare	R 5 - 1	103
Crook Town	v North Shields	6 - 1	95
Pickering Town	v Liversedge	4 - 1	182
West Auckland Town	v Hall Road Rangers	2 - 1	60
Jarrow Roofing Boldon CA	v Spennymoor Town	2 - 1	79
Team Northumbria	v Esh Winning	4 - 1	73
West Allotment Celtic	v Sunderland Ryhope CA	2 - 1	70
Shildon	v Leeds Carnegie	3 - 0	120
Armthorpe Welfare	v Yorkshire Amateur	5 - 0	40
Marske United	v Whickham	0 - 1	73
Billingham Town	v Brandon United	2 - 2	90
Brandon United	v Billingham Town	R 1 - 2	70
Morpeth Town	v Ryton	0 - 2	61
Washington	v Stokesley SC	0 - 0	117
Stokesley SC	v Washington	R 2 - 0	148
Bishop Auckland	v Darlington Railway Athletic	3 - 2	142
(at West Auckland)			
Seaham Red Star	v Selby Town	1 - 3	75
Bridlington Town	v Guisborough Town	3 - 2	135
Norton & Stockton Ancients	v Newcastle Benfield	0 - 1	72
Silsden	v Eccleshill United	4 - 1	173
Ashington	v Thackley	1 - 0	151
(at Blyth Spartans)			
Thornaby	v Tow Law Town	0 - 3	70
Dunston Federation	v Tadcaster Albion	4 - 0	162
Cheadle Town	v Newcastle Town	1 - 4	72
Leek CSOB	v AFC Fylde	1 - 4	68
Maltby Main	v Bottesford Town	3 - 4	63
Dinnington Town	v Atherton LR	1 - 2	92
Parkgate	v Norton United	1 - 2	43
Darwen	v Penrith	4 - 7	84
Holker Old Boys	v St Helens Town	2 - 2	56
St Helens Town	v Holker Old Boys	R 1 - 0	83
Formby	v AFC Emley	3 - 1	91
Winsford United	v Nostell Miners Welfare	3 - 3	130
Nostell Miners Welfare	v Winsford United	R 3 - 0	135
Bootle	v Eccleshall	5 - 1	55
Abbey Hey	v Flixton	1 - 1	55
Flixton	v Abbey Hey	R 3 - 1*	68
Barton Town Old Boys	v Winterton Rangers	1 - 3	132
Maine Road	v Chadderton	2 - 1	76
Brodsworth Miners Welfare	v Ashton Town	2 - 1	36
Oldham Town	v Ashton Athletic	2 - 0	44
Congleton Town	v AFC Blackpool	2 - 2	92
AFC Blackpool	v Congleton Town	R 1 - 4	54
Ramsbottom United	v Hallam	2 - 0	135
Alsager Town	v Padiham	0 - 1	54
Runcorn Linnets	v Rossington Main	3 - 2	170
Colne	v Daisy Hill	4 - 1	55
Atherton Collieries	v Bacup Borough	1 - 2	42
Squires Gate	v Biddulph Victoria	3 - 1	55
AFC Wulfrunians	v Pilkington XXX	1 - 1	65
Pilkington XXX	v AFC Wulfrunians	R 2 - 1	68
Arnold Town	v Long Eaton United	1 - 2	117
(at Gedling MW)			
Tipton Town	v Teversal	2 - 0	39
Highgate United (wo)	v Brierley Hill & Withymoor		
Racing Club Warwick	v Cadbury Athletic	6 - 2	78
Westfields	v Gedling Miners Welfare	7 - 1	44
Stratford Town	v Pershore Town	2 - 0	164
Shirebrook Town	v Causeway United	3 - 2	97
Gedling Town (wo)	v Stapenhill		
New Mills	v Friar Lane & Epworth	1 - 2	184
Borrowash Victoria	v Market Drayton Town	2 - 4	52
Coventry Sphinx	v Barwell	1 - 2	124
Tividale	v Coleshill Town	1 - 3	54
Wellington WM	v Mickleover Sports	1 - 4	46
Dunkirk	v Alvechurch	1 - 4	93
Heather St Johns	v Cradley Town	0 - 3	86
Ledbury Town	v Bromyard Town	2 - 3	84
Staveley MW	v Bridgnorth Town	3 - 1	81
Goodrich	v Meir KA	1 - 1	44
Meir KA	v Goodrich	R 4 - 4*	76
(Meir won 5-4 on penalties)			
Pegasus Juniors	v Glossop North End	1 - 4	41
Rocester	v Nuneaton Griff	0 - 1	96
Southam United	v Boldmere St Michaels	3 - 1	102
Hinckley Downes	v Shawbury United	4 - 2	98
Heath Hayes	v Shifnal Town	1 - 3	120
Oadby Town	v Oldbury United	0 - 3	70
Ellesmere Rangers	v Dudley Sports	4 - 0	
Dudley Town	v Rainworth Miners Welfare	1 - 2	75
Brocton	v Lye Town	1 - 1	98
Lye Town	v Brocton	R 5 - 1	252
Gornal Athletic	v Pelsall Villa	3 - 1	26
GSA	v Coalville	1 - 3	30
Stone Dominoes	v Walsall Wood	3 - 2	37
Bolehall Swifts	v Studley	1 - 3	52
Castle Vale	v Barrow Town	0 - 2	152
Yaxley	v Lincoln Moorlands Railway	4 - 3	62
Sleaford Town	v Ely City	3 - 2	320
Haverhill Rovers	v March Town United	2 - 2	81
March Town United	v Haverhill Rovers	R 2 - 0	105
Stowmarket Town	v Ipswich Wanderers	2 - 2	87
Ipswich Wanderers	v Stowmarket Town	R 2 - 0	116
St Neots Town	v Holbeach United	7 - 1	190
Mildenhall Town	v Felixstowe & Walton United	8 - 0	166
Gorleston	v Fakenham Town	3 - 5	92
Woodbridge Town	v Newmarket Town	1 - 0	93
Diss Town	v Walsham Le Willows	1 - 2	162
Hadleigh United	v Great Yarmouth Town	0 - 1	118
Whitton United	v Cornard United	1 - 1	47
Cornard United	v Whitton United	R 3 - 3*	33
(Cornard won 4-2 on penalties)			
Leiston	v Blackstones	2 - 1	124
Long Melford	v Boston Town	2 - 5	95
Thetford Town	v Needham Market	0 - 1	206
Debenham LC	v Dereham Town	0 - 1	91
Lowestoft Town	v St Ives Town	2 - 1	433
Wisbech Town	v Norwich United	1 - 1	170
Norwich United	v Wisbech Town	R 1 - 3	114
Deeping Rangers	v Bourne Town	3 - 0	129
Wroxham	v Kirkley & Pakefield	1 - 0	194
Raunds Town	v Harwich & Parkeston	2 - 2	94
Harwich & Parkeston	v Raunds Town	R 0 - 3	131
FC Clacton	v St Margaretsbury	2 - 0	151
Rothwell Corinthians	v Langford	2 - 3	47
Erith Town	v Potton United	7 - 1	25
Clapton	v Stewarts & Lloyds Corby	0 - 3	78
Cockfosters	v Ampthill Town	0 - 1	94

Home	Away	Score	Att
Tring Athletic	v Berkhamsted Town	5 - 3	163
Desborough Town	v Saffron Walden Town	4 - 4	92
Saffron Walden Town	v Desborough Town	R 2 - 1	166
Southend Manor	v AFC Kempston Rovers	2 - 1	40
North Greenford United	v Tiptree United	0 - 1	64
Kentish Town	v Wellingborough Town	1 - 1	179
Wellingborough Town	v Kentish Town	R 2 - 0	112
Tokyngton Manor	v Biggleswade United	2 - 3	24
(at Yeading)			
Cogenhoe United	v Northampton Spencer	0 - 1	144
Stotfold	v Colney Heath	3 - 1	73
Kingsbury London Tigers	v Eton Manor	1 - 0	108
Long Buckby	v Broxbourne Borough V&E	0 - 2	50
Hanwell Town	v Wootton Blue Cross	3 - 2	39
London Colney	v Sporting Bengal United	1 - 1	74
Sporting Bengal United	v london Colney	R 1 - 0	98
Stanway Rovers	v Welwyn Garden City	4 - 0	94
Halstead Town	v London APSA	4 - 1	133
Haringey Borough	v Bedfont	1 - 3	39
Wivenhoe Town	v Barkingside	1 - 4	72
Hullbridge Sports	v Leverstock Green	2 - 1	50
Oxhey Jets	v Hertford Town	5 - 0	58
Hoddesdon Town	v Stansted	2 - 3	45
(at Welwyn Garden City)			
Wembley	v Royston Town	1 - 1	99
Royston Town	v Wembley	R 4 - 0	201
Bedfont Green	v Barking	4 - 0	55
Brimsdown Rovers	v Hatfield Town	0 - 2	223
Bowers & Pitsea	v Harefield United	1 - 2	70
Romford	v Biggleswade Town	3 - 0	146
(At Aveley)			
Daventry United	v Burnham Ramblers	0 - 0	47
Burnham Ramblers	v Daventry United	R 5 - 3	84
Selsey	v Egham Town	1 - 0	139
Three Bridges	v VCD Athletic	2 - 3	66
Mile Oak	v Bookham	3 - 0	77
Hailsham Town	v Worthing United	1 - 0	79
Ash United	v Sevenoaks Town	0 - 4	48
Westfield	v East Preston	0 - 3	61
Banstead Athletic	v Colliers Wood United	0 - 2	35
Hassocks	v Shoreham	0 - 1	72
Slade Green	v Tunbridge Wells	1 - 1	99
Tunbridge Wells	v Slade Green	R 2 - 1	112
Ringmer	v Rye United	4 - 3*	73
Pagham	v Hythe Town	1 - 5	120
Dorking	v Chessington & Hook United	2 - 1	54
Littlehampton Town	v Peacehaven & Telscombe	2 - 5	58
(at Bognor Regis Town)			
Whitehawk	v Croydon	0 - 0	73
Croydon	v Whitehawk	R 4 - 3	63
Eastbourne United Assoc	v Epsom & Ewell	2 - 4	90
Crawley Down	v Chichester City United	2 - 2	56
Chichester City United	v Crawley Down	R 3 - 1	72
Cobham	v Southwick	1 - 1	53
Southwick	v Cobham	R 1 - 3	77
Erith & Belvedere	v Lancing	4 - 0	105
Wick	v Molesey	0 - 3	82
Wealden	v East Grinstead Town	3 - 4	48
Frimley Green	v Guildford City	1 - 0	54
Faversham Town	v Horsham YMCA	0 - 2	268
Redhill	v Herne Bay	1 - 2	87
Camberley Town	v Lordswood	1 - 1	71
Lordswood	v Camberley Town	R 2 - 4	52
Sidley United	v Farnham Town	4 - 2	98
Chertsey Town	v Deal Town	2 - 2	113
Deal Town	v Chertsey Town	R 1 - 2	104
Lingfield	v Arundel	0 - 3	93

Home	Away	Score	Att
(At East Grinstead)			
Horley Town	v Raynes Park Vale	2 - 2	80
Raynes Park Vale	v Horley Town	R 3 - 1	72
Bournemouth	v Fareham Town	2 - 1	79
New Milton Town	v Amesbury Town	5 - 0	91
Westbury United	v Hamble ASSC	0 - 0	59
Hamble ASSC	v Westbury United	R 2 - 2*	62
(Westbury won 4-2 on penalties)			
Brockenhurst	v Reading Town	2 - 1	122
Aylesbury Vale	v Highworth Town	4 - 2*	66
Kidlington	v Sandhurst Town	4 - 1	58
Christchurch	v Melksham Town	2 - 1	66
(at Wimborne Town)			
Witney United	v Buckingham Town	2 - 0	133
Milton United	v Lymington Town	1 - 2	42
Hartley Wintney	v Cove	3 - 1	88
VT FC	v Newport Pagnell Town	0 - 2	32
Hungerford Town	v Marlow United	0 - 0	59
Marlow United	v Hungerford Town	R 2 - 2*	59
(Marlow won 4-2 on penalties)			
Devizes Town	v Calne Town	2 - 2	63
Calne Town	v Devizes Town	R 3 - 0	76
Downton	v Abingdon Town	2 - 0	54
Chalfont St Peter	v Ardley United	4 - 3	56
Bicester Town	v Bristol Manor Farm	1 - 0	39
Thame United	v Bitton	0 - 0	42
Bitton	v Thame United	R 3 - 0	82
Bemerton Heath Harlequins	v Almondsbury Town	1 - 4	58
Corsham Town	v Moneyfields	0 - 2	102
Shortwood United	v Henley Town	5 - 0	46
Harrow Hill	v Alresford Town	4 - 1	40
Cowes Sports	v Alton Town	4 - 3	88
Ringwood Town	v Hallen	1 - 0	48
Carterton	v Newport IoW	2 - 1	60
Flackwell Heath	v Wootton Bassett Town	1 - 1	63
Wootton Bassett Town	v Flackwell Heath	R 1 - 6	97
Wantage Town	v Brading Town	1 - 3	355
Fairford Town	v Shrivenham	4 - 1	56
Chard Town	v Street	2 - 2	41
Street	v Chard Town	R 5 - 1*	123
Elmore	v Bodmin Town	0 - 4	42
Willand Rovers	v Wadebridge Town	6 - 0	65
Welton Rovers	v Poole Town	0 - 1	107
Launceston	v Sherborne Town	3 - 0	146
Liskeard Athletic	v Larkhall Athletic	0 - 5	38
Ilfracombe Town	v Tavistock	1 - 4	81
Bideford	v Keynsham Town	4 - 2	180
Shaftesbury	v Falmouth Town	2 - 2	77
Falmouth Town	v Shaftesbury	R 4 - 2	66
Odd Down	v Bishop Sutton	2 - 1	48
Gillingham Town	v Saltash United	2 - 2	243
Saltash United	v Gillingham Town	R 2 - 4	116
Radstock Town	v Brislington	1 - 2	51
Bridport	v Barnstaple Town	2 - 1	107
(at Barnstaple Town)			
Dawlish Town	v Wimborne Town	0 - 0	114
Wimborne Town	v Dawlish Town	R 3 - 2*	273
Minehead	v Clevedon United	0 - 3	40
St Blazey	v Hamworthy United	0 - 2	85
Frome Town	v Shepton Mallet	3 - 1	169

Above: Paul Djeneralovic's free-kick evades the Clapton defender on the line to register S & L Corby's second goal.
Photo: Gordon Whittington.

Left: Action from the Desborough Town v Saffron Walden 1st Qualifying Round tie which ended in a 4-4 draw.
Photo: Peter Barnes.

Below: Worthing United's Fay fires a powerful shot at the goal past Hailsham's Reeve. Photo: Roger Turner.

PRELIMINARY ROUND

BIGGEST HOME WIN:	**7-5** Flixton v Bottesford Town (replay)
BIGGEST AWAY WIN:	**0-6** Westbury United v Fairford Town & Camberley Town v Worthing
HIGHEST ATTENDANCE:	**833** FC Halifax Town v Silsden
NUMBER OF GAMES:	**167 + 32** (165+37)
TOTAL ATTENDANCE:	**29,157** (30,417)
AVERAGE ATTENDANCE:	**147** (151)

Home	Away	Score	Att
Ashington	v Ossett Albion	2 - 1	341
Banbridge, Hogg	*Kelsey*	*(at Bedlington Terriers)*	
Team Northumbria	v Bedlington Terriers	0 - 3	83
Armthorpe Welfare	v Crook Town	1 - 1	40
Crook Town	v Armthorpe Welfare	R 3 - 0	146
Wakefield	v Stokesley SC	2 - 0	72
Turner, Howarth			
South Shields	v Selby Town	0 - 4	201
Sunderland Nissan	v Newcastle Blue Star	1 - 2	88
Hobson	*Novak (2)*		
West Allotment Celtic	v Shildon	1 - 3	100
West Auckland Town	v Durham City	0 - 5	146
	Smith, Morris, English (2), Fisher		
Bishop Auckland	v Consett	3 - 3	185
Consett	v Bishop Auckland	1 - 4	173
Goole	v Newcastle Benfield	0 - 4	181
	Hamilton (2), Chilton, Young		
Billingham Town	v Whitley Bay	0 - 4	178
FC Halifax Town	v Silsden	0 - 0	833
Silsden	v FC Halifax Town	R 1 - 3	442
Morlarty	*Scott (2), Smith*		
Whickham	v Pickering Town	0 - 2	135
Jarrow Roofing Boldon CA	v Bridlington Town	2 - 2	65
Bridlington Town	v Jarrow Roofing Boldon CA	R 2 - 1	122
Garforth Town	v Tow Law Town	1 - 0	145
Selby			
Billingham Synthonia	v Ryton	0 - 2	96
Dunston Federation	v Harrogate Railway	1 - 0	172
Dickson			
Newcastle Town	v Skelmersdale United	0 - 1	117
	Houghton		
Oldham Town	v Rossendale United	1 - 1	75
Landregan	*Whittal-Williams*		
Rossendale United	v Oldham Town	R 3 - 0	126
Turner, Williams, Eastwood			
Bootle	v Padiham	1 - 0	80
Trafford	v Stocksbridge PS	2 - 4	147
Barlow (2)	*Ring, Ward (2), Vardy*		
Congleton Town	v Squires Gate	1 - 1	136
Squires Gate	v Congleton Town	R 0 - 3	69
Penrith	v Clitheroe	1 - 3	153
Robertson	*Lomax (2), Flannery*		
Bottesford Town	v Flixton	2 - 2	72
Flixton	v Bottesford Town	R 7 - 5	68
Lancaster City	v Salford City	1 - 2	160
Foster	*Massay, Forrester*		
Norton United	v Leek Town	1 - 3	235
Dunn	*Moult, Edwards, Miller*		
Mossley	v Ramsbottom United	3 - 1	202
Blackshaw, Egan, Fish	*Morley*		
Formby	v Colne	0 - 5	59
Brigg Town	v Maine Road	2 - 2	92
Greetham, Davies	*Mack, Beckford*		
Malne Road	v Brigg Town	R 1 - 2	80
Mack	*Wood, Hope*		
Radcliffe Borough	v Winterton Rangers	1 - 2	137
Howson	*Holt, Richards*		
Warrington Town	v Nostell Miners Welfare	0 - 0	132
Nostell Miners Welfare	v Warrington Town	R 1 - 2	160
Stilgoe	*Hadland, Towey*		
Bacup Borough	v St Helens Town	3 - 1	58
Chorley	v Atherton LR	0 - 1	208
	Crewe		
AFC Fylde	v Sheffield	1 - 1	291
Walwyn	*Ingall*		
Sheffield	v AFC Fylde	R 4 - 0	285
Goddard (2), G Smith, Winter			
Woodley Sports	v Brodsworth Miners Welfare	0 - 0	52
Brodsworth Miners Welfare	v Woodley Sports	R 0 - 2	66
	Headley, Queeley		
Curzon Ashton	v Runcorn Linnets	4 - 0	138
Elliott (3), Norton			
Bamber Bridge	v Colwyn Bay	4 - 3	151
Porter (2), Steele, Mahoney	*Otley (2), Moran*		
Hinckley Downes	v Gornal Athletic	0 - 4	102
Atherstone Town	v Quorn	1 - 0	198
Barlone			
Malvern Town	v Coalville	1 - 3	92
Smith	*Dodd, Swann (2)*		
Oldbury United	v Friar Lane & Epworth	0 - 1	67
Long Eaton United	v Rushall Olympic	1 - 0	72
Alsopp			
Glapwell	v Market Drayton Town	2 - 1	104
Grayson, Burdett	*Porter*		
Ellesmere Rangers	v Bromsgrove Rovers	2 - 1	179
Loughborough Dynamo	v Tipton Town	0 - 1	125
	Yearwood		
Shirebrook Town	v Studley	1 - 3	93
Stone Dominoes	v Rainworth Miners Welfare	1 - 2	53
Nuneaton Town	v Gedling Town	1 - 0	549
Foster			
Westfields	v Stratford Town	2 - 4	77
Chasetown	v Carlton Town	5 - 0	452
Perrow (3), H Harris, Holland			
Kidsgrove Athletic	v Pilkington XXX	3 - 0	106
McCarthy, Moss, Matthews			
Highgate United	v Romulus	1 - 4	90
O'Shea	*Smith, Fagan, Brown, Mitchell*		
Sutton Coldfield Town	v Cradley Town	2 - 3	92
Owen, Moarn	*Rowe, Greaves, McDonald*		
Gresley Rovers	v Alvechurch	4 - 1	247
Saunders, Barratt, Blenkinsopp, Lock	*Edwards*		
Shepshed Dynamo	v Mickleover Sports	3 - 2	167
Benjamin, Saunders, Epps	*Law, Ashton*		
Retford United	v Barrow Town	3 - 1	205
Bray (2), Godber	*Wilson*		
Glossop North End	v Belper Town	1 - 2	247
Bailey	*Walker, Wilson*		
Meir KA	v Nuneaton Griff	1 - 0	77
Lye Town	v Southam United	1 - 2	133
Leamington	v Staveley MW	4 - 0	575
Corbett, Bellingham, Morgan, Husband			
Willenhall Town	v Bedworth United	0 - 0	106
Bedworth United	v Willenhall Townnnn	R 2 - 3*	130
Edmonds, Skoniezki	*MacKenzie, Findley, Stevenson*		
Racing Club Warwick	v Stourport Swifts	0 - 2	86
	Morris, Smith		
Coleshill Town	v Shifnal Town	2 - 3	91

Goal mouth action from the Wellingborough Town versus Kentish Town Extra Preliminary round replay. Having drawn 1-1 at Kentish Town, Wellingborough won this replay 2-0 to set up a Preliminary Round match against Croydon Athletic.
Photo: Peter Barnes.

Home	Away	Score	Att
Bromyard Town	v Barwell	1 - 5	57
Spalding United *Miller, Tager*	v Yaxley *Jacobs, Harrod, Salerno*	2 - 3	153
Soham Town Rangers	v Needham Market *Thrower, Sparkes*	0 - 2	167
Leiston *(at March Town United)*	v March Town United	3 - 1	170
Wisbech Town	v Mildenhall Town	2 - 2	208
Mildenhall Town	v Wisbech Town	R 4 - 0	213
Fakenham Town	v Boston Town	0 - 4	76
Grantham Town *Turner (2), Cann (2)*	v Woodbridge Town *Manning*	4 - 1	187
Walsham Le Willows	v Sleaford Town	1 - 2	112
Dereham Town *Miller, Terrington*	v Stamford *Pearson, Gray*	2 - 2	166
Stamford *Taylor*	v Dereham Town	R 0 - 1	209
AFC Sudbury *Blackwell*	v Lowestoft Town *Cockerill*	1 - 1	309
Lowestoft Town *(Lowestoft won 4-1 on penalties)*	v AFC Sudbury	R 2 - 2*	598
Ipswich Wanderers	v Cornard United	1 - 1	69
Cornard United	v Ipswich Wanderers	R 3 - 0	40
Great Yarmouth Town	v Wroxham	2 - 2	190
Wroxham	v Great Yarmouth Town	R 3 - 0	205
St Neots Town *Antechugru (2)*	v Lincoln United *Walters, Wilkinson (2)*	2 - 3	250
Deeping Rangers *Stevens*	v Bury Town *Read, Walker*	1 - 2	137
Brentwood Town *Holmes, Foyena*	v Erith Town *Douglas*	2 - 1	108
Dulwich Hamlet	v Broxbourne Borough V&E	1 - 1	164
Broxbourne Borough V&E *Kearney*	v Dulwich Hamlet *Simpson, Cumberbatch*	R 1 - 2	96
Great Wakering Rovers *Ansell, Jones, Gresham, Beale*	v Bedfont Green	4 - 0	78
Langford	v Arlesey Town *Osbourne*	0 - 1	161
Oxhey Jets *Omara, Arthur (2), Turner, Page*	v Ilford *Thomas (2)*	5 - 2	93
Northwood	v Metropolitan Police *George, Arrabell*	0 - 2	131
Northampton Spencer *Taylor (2)*	v Wingate & Finchley *Lees, Samuel*	2 - 2	101
Wingate & Finchley *Chase, Lees, Williams, Clarke*	v Northampton Spencer	R 4 - 0	41
Bedfont	v Tiptree United	2 - 4	83
Barton Rovers *Baker (og), Sozzo*	v Burnham Ramblers *Burrows*	2 - 1	67
Leyton *Brady, Edwards*	v Romford *Sutchley*	2 - 1	106
Ampthill Town	v Dunstable Town *Nolan, Strange, Billy, Sinclair*	0 - 4	140
Halstead Town	v Stotfold	1 - 2	103
East Thurrock United *Smith (2), Harrison, Tuohy*	v Hatfield Town *Martin Standen, Matt Standen*	4 - 2	139
FC Clacton	v Stansted	4 - 0	138
Barkingside	v Stanway Rovers	0 - 4	80
Cheshunt *Prestedge, Lewis*	v Southend Manor *Dawson*	2 - 1	192
Tilbury	v Leighton Town *Nugent, Roche*	0 - 2	57
Stewarts & Lloyds Corby *Byrne (2), Doherty*	v Corinthian Casuals *Edgehill, Bojang*	3 - 2	98
Hanwell Town	v Aveley *Elbi, Carlos, Bradbury, Skerritt, Vaughan*	0 - 5	71
Witham Town *Hearn, Love, Edwards*	v Maldon Town *McDonald (3)*	3 - 3	185
Maldon Town *Kevin Hawes*	v Witham Town *Hearn, Low, Emery (2)*	R 1 - 4	121
Waltham Forest	v Thamesmead Town *Smith*	0 - 1	38
Harefield United	v Saffron Walden Town	1 - 1	130
Saffron Walden Town	v Harefield United	R 2 - 0	209
Ware *Frendo, Horsey, Bristow, Doku*	v Sporting Bengal United	4 - 0	148

Home	Away	Score	Att
Concord Rangers	v Kingsbury London Tigers	2 - 0	128
Howard, Oakley			
Rothwell Town	v Hullbridge Sports	2 - 0	83
Burrows, Byrne			
Hillingdon Borough	v Enfield Town	3 - 1	108
Warrell, Campbell, Lyons	*Remy*		
Redbridge	v Uxbridge	1 - 3	91
Scarborough	*K Warner, D Warner, Dennison*		
Croydon Athletic	v Wellingborough Town	3 - 1	126
Waldren (2), Fontana	*Thompson*		
Tring Athletic	v Biggleswade United	1 - 2	87
AFC Hayes	v Royston Town	1 - 3	83
Osubu	*Lockett, Robins, Hammond*		
Woodford United	v Raunds Town	1 - 1	74
Stidder	*Jarvis*		
Raunds Town	v Woodford United	R 0 - 0*	129
(Raunds won 4-3 on penalties)			
Potters Bar Town	v Waltham Abbey	1 - 1	84
Makofo	*M Sontag*		
Waltham Abbey	v Potters Bar Town	R 1 - 0	131
H Elmes			
Walton Casuals	v Molesey	2 - 0	106
Weston, Lewington			
Mile Oak	v Arundel	0 - 2	93
Horsham YMCA	v Tunbridge Wells	3 - 1	112
Sevenoaks Town	v Folkestone Invicta	4 - 4	140
Elliott, Constable, Evans, Gibbons	*Jackson (2), J Everitt, Dryden*		
Folkestone Invicta	v Sevenoaks Town	R 4 - 1	194
J Everitt (2), Green, Humphrey	*Constable*		
Ashford Town	v Leatherhead	3 - 2	293
Sherwood, Hogg, Jones	*Hutchins (2)*		
Herne Bay	v Chipstead	2 - 2	210
Jones, Lawrence	*Campbell, John*		
Chipstead	v Herne Bay	R 2 - 0*	110
Oakins, Cole-Bolt			
Epsom & Ewell	v Frimley Green	2 - 1	70
Whitstable Town	v Selsey	1 - 0	153
Cory			
Camberley Town	v Worthing	0 - 6	131
	Kirkwood, Bortherton, Andrews (2), Demetriou, Elliott		
Hythe Town	v Walton & Hersham	2 - 1	209
Kingwell, Smissen	*Stone*		
Crowborough Athletic	v Ringmer	3 - 1	108
Clarke (2), Gordon	*Patel*		
East Preston	v Erith & Belvedere	1 - 2	71
Sittingbourne	v Chertsey Town	2 - 1	168
Burgess Hill Town	v Hailsham Town	2 - 0	159
Harper, Westlake			
Cobham	v Merstham	0 - 2	68
	Lock, Greenhouse		
Shoreham	v Kingstonian	1 - 3	281
Keehan	*P Williams, Traynor, Wilson-Denis*		
Chatham Town	v Dorking	2 - 2	119
Botterill, Avery	*Larence (2)*		
Dorking	v Chatham Town	R 0 - 1	88
	Davey		
East Grinstead Town	v Colliers Wood United	0 - 3	122
Raynes Park Vale	v Godalming Town	1 - 2	114
Zielenienski	*Ojukwu (2)*		
Whyteleafe	v Peacehaven & Telscombe	0 - 0	96
Peacehaven & Telscombe	v Whyteleafe	R 1 - 3	102
Smith	*McKenzie (2), McNamara*		
VCD Athletic	v Croydon	3 - 1	91
Sidley United	v Eastbourne Town	1 - 2	180
Cray Wanderers	v Chichester City United	4 - 1	134
AFC Totton	v Moneyfields	2 - 1	251
Amadu, Gosney	*Blake*		
Westbury United	v Fairford Town	0 - 6	78
Cowes Sports	v Lymington Town	4 - 0	102
Aylesbury Vale	v Burnham	1 - 1	74
Gordon	*Bird*		
Burnham	v Aylesbury Vale	R 1 - 2	112
Bird	*Roberts, Kynsey*		
Aylesbury United	v Windsor & Eton	2 - 0	214
Maynard, Hawkins			
Ringwood Town	v Marlow	2 - 2	81
Lovell, Baguely	*Nugent, Roche*		
Marlow	v Ringwood Town	R 4 - 0	92
Lane (3), Stone			
Chalfont St Peter	v Harrow Hill	2 - 1	65
Didcot Town	v Bournemouth	5 - 0	208
Bartley (2), King, Hope, Vine			
Carterton	v North Leigh	0 - 1	79
	Cooper		
Newport Pagnell Town	v Cirencester Town	1 - 0	117
Shrives			
Gosport Borough	v Hartley Wintney	5 - 0	148
Chuddy (2), Bennett, Birmingham, Sturman			
Kidlington	v Almondsbury Town	2 - 3	64
Chesham United	v Brading Town	5 - 1	332
Burnell (2), Cox (2), Obeng	*Greening*		
Fleet Town	v Brockenhurst	1 - 1	128
McClurg	*Keeping*		
Brockenhurst	v Fleet Town	R 0 - 1	130
	Field		
Bitton	v Bishops Cleeve	2 - 1	88
McLinden, Reynolds	*Tomkins*		
Witney United	v Thatcham Town	2 - 2	126
Wiggens (2)	*Ray, Asker*		
Thatcham Town	v Witney United	R 3 - 1*	134
Brown, Ray, Johnson	*Wiggins*		
Beaconsfield SYCOB	v Marlow United	1 - 0	114
Swift			
Shortwood United	v Christchurch	2 - 0	75
Abingdon United	v Slough Town	1 - 1	156
Holden	*Pritchard*		
Slough Town	v Abingdon United	R 5 - 2	211
McGonlgley, Bubb, Durrant, Platt (2)	*Brooks, Curtin*		
Andover	v Calne Town	1 - 3	134
Turvey	*D Lardner (2), Moore*		
New Milton Town	v Downton	1 - 2	59
Flackwell Heath	v Winchester City	3 - 4	72
Cannon, Mason, Moore	*Kelly, Mamoudu, Foster, King*		
Bracknell Town	v Bicester Town	3 - 0	103
Macintosh, Grant, Telemaque			
Bodmin Town	v Bridgwater Town	0 - 3	149
	Pepperell, Young, McKay		
Launceston	v Paulton Rovers	0 - 2	200
	Cousins, D Cleverley		
Clevedon United	v Taunton Town	0 - 3	119
	S Jones, Welch (2)		
Odd Down	v Wimborne Town	0 - 2	71
Street	v Bideford	3 - 3	146
Bideford	v Street	R 2 - 1	155
Cinderford Town	v Frome Town	0 - 1	109
	Lapham		
Falmouth Town	v Truro City	0 - 4	487
	Broad, Bye, Tolley (2)		
Poole Town	v Willand Rovers	2 - 1	229
Hamworthy United	v Brislington	3 - 2	80
Larkhall Athletic	v Tavistock	6 - 2	130
Bridport	v Gillingham Town	3 - 0	287
(at Gillingham)			

Above: Jon Saunders, Sidley United's 'keeper, gets an outstretched hand to a header from Eastbourne Town's No.9 Shaun Loft during this Preliminary Round tie. Photo: Roger Turner.

Left: 1st Qualifying Round action from Ashford Town's (Mx) 3-0 win over Raunds Town. Photo: Peter Barnes.

Above: Tonbridge 'keeper, Lee Worgan, collects the ball from a Dover corner in the 1st Qualifying Round. Photo: Alan Coomes.

Left: The Brentwood defenders are unable to stop Owen Beale's shot crossing the line to give Arlesey Town a 1-0 1st Q. Rnd replay win. Photo: Gordon Whittington.

FIRST QUALIFYING ROUND

BIGGEST HOME WIN:	**8-1** Hailsowen Town v Meir KA
BIGGEST AWAY WIN:	**0-6** Ashington v Durham City
	& Hillingdon Boro' v East Thurrock United
HIGHEST ATTENDANCE:	**1,784** Nantwich Town v FC United of M.
NUMBER OF GAMES:	**117 + 18** (115 + 31)
TOTAL ATTENDANCE:	**31,532** (32,994)
AVERAGE ATTENDANCE:	**234** (226)

Bedlington Terriers	v Bradford Park Avenue	0 - 1	161
	Patterson		
Selby Town	v Guiseley	0 - 4	217
	Muller, Bambrook, Brown, Burton		
Garforth Town	v Ossett Town	1 - 0	151
Kelly			
Newcastle Benfield	v Bridlington Town	1 - 1	53
Bridlington Town	v Newcastle Benfield	R 1 - 2	172
Harrison	*Marshall, Buzzeo*		
Ashington	v Durham City	0 - 6	284
	Toft (2), Ruchardson, English, Houlihan, Morris		
Whitby Town	v Dunston Federation	3 - 2	244
Brunskill, Charlton, Raw	*Preen, Sheeran*		
Consett	v North Ferriby United	4 - 4	175
Moffat, Johnson (2), Dickman	*Denton (2), Fry, Torpey*		
North Ferriby United	v Consett	R 6 - 1	135
Bradshaw, Jackson, Davidson (3), Torpey	*Moffat*		
Wakefield	v Crook Town	4 - 3	127
Barrick (2), Howarth, Marchant	*Olusola, Tait (2)*		
Ryton	v FC Halifax Town	0 - 4	384
	Stott, Morning, Gedman (2)		
Newcastle Blue Star	v Shildon	2 - 0	187
Brayson, Novak			
Pickering Town	v Whitley Bay	0 - 1	209
Congleton Town	v Prescot Cables	0 - 2	169
	Byers, Price		
Sheffield	v Colne	3 - 2	242
Winter, Goddard, Partridge	*Broderick, Cockett*		
Woodley Sports	v Rossendale United	1 - 3	66
Wild	*Eastwood (2), Turner*	*(at Abbey Hey)*	
Bacup Borough	v Cammell Laird	3 - 0	87
Cosgrove, Turner			
Brigg Town	v Stocksbridge PS	0 - 4	131
	Lonell, Fothergill (2), Sidebottom		
Clitheroe	v Leek Town	1 - 1	258
Johnson	*Miller*		
Leek Town	v Clitheroe	R 0 - 1	224
	Johnson		
Buxton	v Bootle	3 - 1	412
Knight (2), Balfe	*Dolan*		
Frickley Athletic	v Skelmersdale United	1 - 0	240
Walsh			
Nantwich Town	v FC United Of Manchester	0 - 0	1,784
FC United Of Manchester	v Nantwich Town	R 3 - 4	1,012
Carden, Self, Wilson	*Walker (3), O'Loughlin*		
Flixton	v Mossley	1 - 4	123
Hodkin	*Cook, Fish (2), Egan*		
Bamber Bridge	v Witton Albion	1 - 2	214
O'Neill	*Thompson, Willis*		
Salford City	v Atherton LR	5 - 0	118
Kay, Dwyer (2), Billingham, Depezia			
Curzon Ashton	v Leigh Genesis	1 - 0	158
Moore			
Winterton Rangers	v Warrington Town	4 - 2	100
Holt (3), Plant	*Smith, Rendell*		
Ashton United	v Kendal Town	2 - 3	118
Deegan, Robinson	*Taylor, Osman, Ashcroft*		
Marine	v Worksop Town	1 - 5	205
McMahon	*Sansay (2), Jackson, White*		
Hednesford Town	v Atherstone Town	1 - 2	416
Barnet	*Barlone, Miley*		
Shepshed Dynamo	v Stourport Swifts	7 - 0	156
Marshall (2), Benjamin (2), Saunders (2), Norris			
Friar Lane & Epworth	v Rugby Town	0 - 0	210
Rugby Town	v Friar Lane & Epworth	R 5 - 3	176
Purton, Kolodynski(2), Dykes(2)	*Gibbons, Chapman, Trevor*		
Cradley Town	v Ellesmere Rangers	2 - 2	77
	Barton, OG		
Ellesmere Rangers	v Cradley Town	3 - 1	274
Stourbridge	v Rainworth Miners Welfare	0 - 0	183
Rainworth Miners Welfare	v Stourbridge	R 1 - 3	155
Wilkinson	*Bennett, Mahon, Dyson*		
Gresley Rovers	v Chasetown	2 - 4	438
Blenkinsopp (2)	*Perrow (4)*		
Meir KA	v Halesowen Town	1 - 1	214
Miszkiel	*Rowe*		
Halesowen Town	v Meir KA	8 - 1	308
Denny(3), Rowe(2), Palmer(2), OG	*OG*		
Shifnal Town	v Long Eaton United	0 - 1	84
	Allsop		
Gornal Athletic	v Southam United	0 - 0	93
Southam United	v Gornal Athletic	R 2 - 1	153
	Meese		
Retford United	v Willenhall Town	1 - 1	220
Hindley	*Nisbett*		
Willenhall Town	v Retford United	R 1 - 3	95
McKenzie	*Godber (2), Whittington*		
Ilkeston Town	v Matlock Town	4 - 1	495
Howell, Duncum, Istead, Douglas	*Warne*		
Coalville	v Studley	2 - 1	128
Romulus	v Stratford Town	2 - 1	100
Allen, Fagan	*Jakab*		
Eastwood Town	v Kidsgrove Athletic	4 - 0	230
Smith (2), Gardner (2)			
Leamington	v Evesham United	0 - 3	712
	Lutz, Hayden, Owen		
Belper Town	v Barwell	3 - 2	120
Walker, Rushbury (2)	*Lester (2)*		
Boston United	v Glapwell	6 - 1	857
Melton, Leabon, Ryan (3), Rowan	*Burdett*		
Nuneaton Town	v Tipton Town	3 - 1	531
Nisebic, Foster, Spacey	*Edwards*		
Cambridge City	v Lowestoft Town	2 - 0	391
Calliste, Neilson			
Cornard United	v Leiston	0 - 5	50
	Girling, McGlone (3), Cunningham		
Grantham Town	v Wroxham	3 - 4	185
Stubbs, Turner, Goury-Hales	*Challen, Cook, Harley, Gilmore*		
Lincoln United	v Mildenhall Town	3 - 2	147
Walters, Good (2)	*Paynter, North*		
Bury Town	v Boston Town	3 - 1	200
Smith, Reed, Hipperson	*Mason*		
Sleaford Town	v Stamford	2 - 6	349
Stones, Siddons	*Cotton (2), Pearson (2), Harlows, Clarke*		
Needham Market	v Yaxley	2 - 2	150
Yaxley	v Needham Market	R 0 - 3	128
Boreham Wood	v Biggleswade United	3 - 0	75
Buchanan, Allinson, Archer			
Hillingdon Borough	v East Thurrock United	0 - 6	80
	Touhy (3), K Smith, M Cornhill, Holding		
Royston Town	v Hendon	2 - 4	303
OG, Robins	*Mapes (2), Guentchev, Busby*		
Ware	v Barton Rovers	1 - 1	188
Bristow	*Hayes*		
Barton Rovers	v Ware	R 1 - 2	112
O'Brien	*Frendo, Doku*		
Stewarts & Lloyds Corby	v Croydon Athletic	5 - 1	65
Burne (3), Mills, Caswell	*Clayton*		
Tiptree United	v Stanway Rovers	1 - 3	128
Billericay Town	v FC Clacton	4 - 1	337
Bricknell (2), Flack, Woods-Garness	*S Hillier*		
Oxhey Jets	v Dulwich Hamlet	1 - 5	148
Arthur	*Plummer (2), Hamici (3)*		

Hemel Hempstead	v Harrow Borough	1 - 1	199
Deeney	Walters		
Harrow Borough	v Hemel Hempstead	R 1 - 2	121
Constant	Sippetts, Edgeworth		
Thamesmead Town	v Great Wakering Rovers	2 - 1	78
Dimmock, Grant	Jones		
Metropolitan Police	v Corby Town	0 - 3	140
	Nolan, Warren, Metham		
Wingate & Finchley	v Witham Town	2 - 0	115
Street, Grant			
Stotfold	v Leighton Town	0 - 3	101
	Clifford, Hatch (2)		
Hitchin Town	v Concord Rangers	5 - 0	225
P Barnes (2), M Barnes (2), Stupple			
Leyton	v Brackley Town	2 - 4	80
Valenti, Killick	Winters, Mackey (2), Spencer		
Canvey Island	v Dunstable Town	1 - 5	312
Fanibuyan	Preston, Strange		
Raunds Town	v Ashford Town (Mx)	0 - 3	154
	S Harris (3)		
Heybridge Swifts	v Uxbridge	1 - 1	145
Clarke	Nicholls		
Uxbridge	v Heybridge Swifts	R 1 - 3	105
K Warner	OG (2), Hudgel		
Cheshunt	v Staines Town	0 - 3	236
	Thomas, Kersey, Scarlett		
Saffron Walden Town	v AFC Hornchurch	0 - 2	337
	Styles, Wall		
Harlow Town	v Aveley	5 - 1	245
Richards, Roberts, Henry (2), Adeyinka	Thomas		
Brentwood Town	v Arlesey Town	1 - 1	145
Sweeney	Osbourne		
Arlesey Town	v Brentwood	R 1 - 0	110
Beale			
Waltham Abbey	v Rothwell Town	0 - 1	143
	Flannigan		
Wealdstone	v Bedford Town	2 - 2	312
Gray, Hughes	Phillips (2)		
Bedford Town	v Wealdstone	R 1 - 1*	349
Miller	Clrake	(Bedford won 4-2 on penalties)	
Dartford	v Hastings United	3 - 2	830
Cass, Butterworth, Dafter	Adams, Radley		
Crowborough Athletic	v Walton Casuals	1 - 0	145
Crush			
Burgess Hill Town	v Epsom & Ewell	5 - 2	156
Greenfield, Beck (2), Harper, T Martin	Burns, Rodrigues		
Horsham	v Colliers Wood United	1 - 0	258
Achibald			
Horsham YMCA	v Whyteleafe	1 - 1	114
Lamont	Hudson		
Whyteleafe	v Horsham YMCA	R 2 - 0	82
Scott, McKenzie			
Folkestone Invicta	v Ramsgate	1 - 0	305
Dryden			
Erith & Belvedere	v Sittingbourne	2 - 0	133
Johnson, Smith			
Worthing	v Margate	5 - 1	338
Douglas, Kirkwood, Kennett, Pook, Akehurst	Wilson		
Godalming Town	v Arundel	1 - 1	140
Stanley	Norgate		
Arundel	v Godalming Town	R 1 - 2	123
Hockett	Ottley (2)		
Carshalton Athletic	v Eastbourne Town	4 - 1	247
Stevens, Jolly (3)	Norwood		
Kingstonian	v Ashford Town	3 - 0	401
Williams, Wilson-Denis, Hustwick			
Sutton United	v Cray Wanderers	3 - 1	325
McCallum, West, Dundas	Atkins		
Merstham	v Whitstable Town	2 - 1	130
Lock (2)	Pulman		
Hythe Town	v VCD Athletic	0 - 0	143
VCD Athletic	v Hythe Town	R 3 - 0	153
Tonbridge Angels	v Dover Athletic	1 - 2	795
Rook	Wallis, Welford		
Chipstead	v Chatham Town	1 - 0	85
Fleming			
Maidstone United	v Tooting & Mitcham United	2 - 1	355
Saunders, Bradbrook	P Vines		
Bracknell Town	v Oxford City (Tie awarded to Oxford)		
Aylesbury Vale	v Downton	2 - 0	70
Shortwood United	v Didcot Town	3 - 2	124
Davis (3)	Roach, Vine		
Farnborough	v Slough Town	1 - 0	571
Saunders			
Fleet Town	v Cowes Sports	3 - 0	141
Paterson, Anderson, Smart			
Newport Pagnell Town	v Marlow	2 - 1	148
Lynch (2)	Roche		
Aylesbury United	v Almondsbury Town	1 - 0	163
Hawkins			
Chalfont St Peter	v Gloucester City	5 - 3	145
Lough, Brosnan (2), Stretton, Hughes	Pitcher, Sysom, Sykes		
Chippenham Town	v Banbury United	2 - 0	369
Calne Town	v Bashley	0 - 5	125
	Knight, Gillespie (2), Parnell, Knowles		
Bitton	v Beaconsfield SYCOB	3 - 2	92
Reynolds (2), Cherry	Swift, Bubb		
Fairford Town	v Gosport Borough	1 - 2	81
Boucher	Lynch, Bennett		
Winchester City	v AFC Totton	0 - 3	301
North Leigh	v Chesham United	2 - 3	160
Simms, McCabe	Burnell, Cox (2)		
Thatcham Town	v Swindon Supermarine	1 - 0	103
Ascot			
Frome Town	v Bideford	1 - 1	189
Bideford	v Frome Town	R 1 - 3*	193
Paulton Rovers	v Larkhall Athletic	3 - 0	243
Claridge, Cousons, D Cleverley			
Bridgwater Town	v Mangotsfield United	1 - 3	296
Olonod	Clough (2), Page		
Hamworthy United	v Taunton Town	2 - 1	110
Thomas (2)	S Anthony		
Truro City	v Yate Town	3 - 1	556
Taylor, Walker, Watkins	Beadle		
Clevedon Town	v Bridport	4 - 1	161
Peckham, Brigham (2), Prosser	Fellows		
Wimborne Town	v Tiverton Town	0 - 1	389
	Hopkinson		
Poole Town	v Merthyr Tydfil	3 - 0	271
Gill, Austin (2)			

Victor Asombang (No.10), Walton Casuals, puts the Crowborough Athletic defence under pressure during their 1st Qualifying Round tie.
Photo: Roger Turner.

SECOND QUALIFYING ROUND

BIGGEST HOME WIN:	**5-0** Fleet Town v Newport Pagnell Town
BIGGEST AWAY WIN:	**0-5** Thurrock v Boreham Wood
HIGHEST ATTENDANCE:	**1,370** AFC Wimbledon v Bedford Town
NUMBER OF GAMES:	**80 + 22** (80 + 19)
TOTAL ATTENDANCE:	**38,648** (36,830)
AVERAGE ATTENDANCE:	**379** (372)

Nantwich Town	v FC Halifax Town	4 - 1	1091
Naggington, Blackhurst, Walker (2)	*Moore*		
Kendal Town	v Mossley	1 - 2	208
Hobson	*Blackshaw, Henry*		
Southport	v Vauxhall Motors	3 - 2	593
Robinson (2), Connolly	*Rooney (2)*		
Frickley Athletic	v Clitheroe	1 - 0	271
Jones			
North Ferriby United	v Newcastle Blue Star	1 - 4	134
Bradshaw	*Bowey, Brayson (2), Emms*		
Whitby Town	v Blyth Spartans	2 - 2	403
Garvie, Thompson	*McCabe, Dalton*		
Blyth Spartans	v Whitby Town	R 5 - 2	408
Williams, McCabe, Dale (3)	*Beadle, Huggins*		
Stocksbridge PS	v Curzon Ashton	1 - 2	150
Fothergill	*Edghill (2)*		
Wakefield	v Fleetwood Town	0 - 3	161
	Warlow, Milligan, Potts		
Droylsden	v Bradford Park Avenue	2 - 1	425
Cryam, Newton	*Rudd*		
Winterton Rangers	v Newcastle Benfield	1 - 1	116
Holt	*Young*		
Newcastle Benfield	v Winterton Rangers	R 2 - 1*	84
Young, Leighton	*Lumsden (og)*		
Durham City	v Rossendale United	4 - 0	142
Toft, Richardson (2), Johnston	*(at Eppleton CW)*		
Whitley Bay	v Hyde United	3 - 1	364
Chow, Moore, Livermore	*Lynch*		
Guiseley	v Garforth Town	2 - 2	454
Merris, Hanson	*Piper, Haywood*		
Garforth Town	v Guiseley	1 - 3	244
Kelly	*Burton, Brown, Tiani*		
Buxton	v Burscough	1 - 0	442
Wiggins-Thomas			
Prescot Cables	v Salford City	2 - 1	220
Flood, Williams	*Forrester*		
Workington	v Harrogate Town	0 - 0	413
Harrogate Town	v Workington	R 0 - 0*	305
(Harrogate won 5-4 on penalties)			
Gateshead	v Witton Albion	1 - 1	212
Harwood	*Drew*		
Witton Albion	v Gateshead	R 1 - 3	227
Willis	*Armstrong, Southern, Turnbull*		
Stalybridge Celtic	v Farsley Celtic	4 - 0	500
Ellington, Barwick, Torpey, Barlow			
Sheffield	v Bacup Borough	4 - 1	247
Goddard (2), Smith, Winter	*Fagan*		
Coalville	v Stafford Rangers	2 - 1	410
Adams, Miveld	*Wellcombe*		
Evesham United	v Nuneaton Town	2 - 2	405
Owen, Hands	*Spacey, Foster*		
Nuneaton Town	v Evesham United	R1 - 2	508
Ramsay	*Owen, Hayden*		
Lincoln United	v Eastwood Town	0 - 1	115
	Shaw		
Rugby Town	v Long Eaton United	5 - 1	223
Musgrove, Koladinski (2), King, Gearing	*Newton*		
Shepshed Dynamo	v Alfreton Town	1 - 2	374
Norris	*Fortune-West, Cusworth*		
Chasetown	v Rothwell Town	1 - 1	562
Perrow	*Flannigan*		
Rothwell Town	v Chasetown	2 - 5*	194
Snedden, Maddox	*Holland, Perrow (2), Onokah, Branch*		
Hucknall Town	v Cradley Town	3 - 0	230
Ricketts, Timons, Robertson			
Belper Town	v Redditch United	4 - 1	301
Stevenson (2), Graves, Wilson	*Storey*		
Boston United	v Stamford	2 - 1	1125
Froggatt (2)	*Clarke*		
Retford United	v Romulus	3 - 1	209
Grimes, Chappell, Godber	*Fagan*		
Stourbridge	v Brackley Town	1 - 1	199
Dyson	*Mackey*		
Brackley Town	v Stourbridge	R 1 - 0	187
Hadland			
Halesowen Town	v Gainsborough Trinity	3 - 0	502
Smith, Cornwall, Abby			
Southam United	v Atherstone Town	1 - 1	247
Friend	*Barlone*		
Atherstone Town	v Southam United	R 3 - 1*	267
Greenway (2), Storer	*Graham*		
Stewarts & Lloyds Corby	v Ilkeston Town	2 - 3	177
Caswell, Byrne	*Douglas, Adam, Morgan-Smith*		
King's Lynn	v Worksop Town	2 - 1	1080
France, Bloomfield	*Jackson*		
AFC Telford United	v Corby Town	3 - 2	1262
Fearns (3)	*Burgess, Towers*		
Worcester City	v Tamworth	0 - 1	898
	Wylde		
Hinckley United	v Solihull Moors	4 - 1	369
Platnauer, Bonner, Webster (2)	*Middleton*		
Bromley	v AFC Hornchurch	0 - 1	581
	Janney		
Thurrock	v Boreham Wood	0 - 5	90
	Allinson, Worsworth, Archer (2), Watters		
Dunstable Town	v Chipstead	2 - 3	142
Nolan (2)	*Oakins, O'Shea, Campbell*		
Folkestone Invicta	v Horsham	1 - 2	345
Wilkins	*Howard, Archibald*		
Wroxham	v Heybridge Swifts	2 - 1	223
Key, White	*Fisher (at Norwich United)*		
Burgess Hill Town	v Bognor Regis Town	0 - 0	426
Bognor Regis Town	v Burgess Hill Town	R 0 - 2	319
	Harper, Johnson		
Bedford Town	v AFC Wimbledon	2 - 2	1296
Fentle, Clark	*Main, Aiteouakrim*		
AFC Wimbledon	v Bedford Town	R 3 - 0	1370
Hatton, Davis, Kedwell			
Welling United	v Whyteleafe	1 - 1	336
Martin	*Hudson*		
Whyteleafe	v Welling United	R 2 - 0	206
Hudson, Rivers			
Bishop's Stortford	v Wingate & Finchley	3 - 2	303
Harris (3)	*Nelson*		
Hitchin Town	v Stanway Rovers	0 - 0	293
Stanway Rovers	v Hitchin Town	R 0 - 2	154
	M Barnes (2)		
St Albans City	v Harlow Town	0 - 0	404
Harlow Town	v St Albans City	R 3 - 2	299
Richards, Cousins (og), Green	*Cousins, Cohen*		
Erith & Belvedere	v Godalming Town	0 - 2	156
	Hutchings, Perkins		
Dulwich Hamlet	v Hendon	2 - 2	353
Noel, Cumberbach	*Hudson, Hunt*		
Hendon	v Dulwich Hamlet	R 2 - 1	139
Diedhiou, Hunt	*Noel*		
Merstham	v Thamesmead Town	1 - 1	137
Lock	*Smith*		
Thamesmead Town	v Merstham	R 1 - 5	102
Grant	*Francis, Locke (2), Agmel (2)*		
Leighton Town	v Crowborough Athletic	0 - 1	161
	Gordon		
Dartford	v Hampton & Richmond Borough	0 - 1	1057
	Matthews		
Staines Town	v Hayes & Yeading United	0 - 0	561
Hayes & Yeading United	v Staines Town	R 5 - 3*	348
Hendry (2), Ruby, Knight, James	*Butler (2), Onochie*		
Maidstone United	v Fisher Athletic	3 - 2	389
Paul, Pinnock, Lewis	*Beaney, Kamara*		
Bury Town	v Chelmsford City	2 - 1	698
Duffy (og), L Reed	*Minton*		

Left: AFC Wimbledon's, Jon Main, shields the ball from the Bedford Town defender during the teams 2-2 draw in the 2nd Qualifying Round. Photo: David Barnes.
Above: Hitchin Town attack the Stanway Rovers goal in their goal-less draw. Photo: Gordon Whittington.

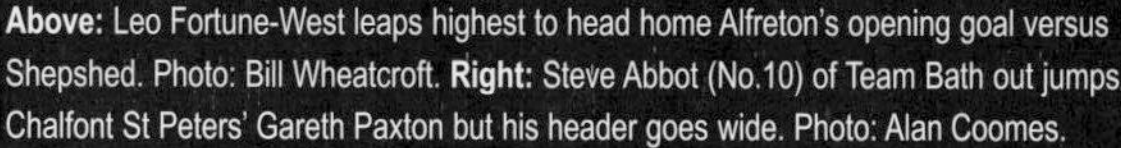

Above: Leo Fortune-West leaps highest to head home Alfreton's opening goal versus Shepshed. Photo: Bill Wheatcroft. **Right:** Steve Abbot (No.10) of Team Bath out jumps Chalfont St Peters' Gareth Paxton but his header goes wide. Photo: Alan Coomes.

Hemel Hempstead	v Ware	1 - 2	202
Dillon	*Fehmi, Burton*		
Carshalton Athletic	v Leiston	1 - 2	311
Jolly	*McGlone, Sillett*		
Sutton United	v Billericay Town	3 - 1	410
Dunn, Webb, McCallum	*Wareham*		
Cambridge City	v Worthing	1 - 1	357
Theobald	*Kirkwood*		
Worthing	v Cambridge City	R 2 - 1	267
Graverton, Pulling	*Spendlove*		
Kingstonian	v Braintree Town	4 - 0	356
Lodge (4)			
Dover Athletic	v Needham Market	3 - 1	809
Browning, Collin, Hughes	*Field*		
East Thurrock United	v VCD Athletic	3 - 0	157
Tuohy (3)			
Arlesey Town	v Ashford Town (Mx)	1 - 4	129
Francis	*Wellard, Harrison, W Harris (2)*		
Paulton Rovers	v Bitton	1 - 0	198
D Cleverley			
Fleet Town	v Newport Pagnell Town	5 - 0	191
McClurg, Field, Hamilton, Boylan, E Smith			
Poole Town	v Frome Town	1 - 3	431
Dibba	*M Salter (2), Allison*		
Bath City	v Clevedon Town	2 - 0	486
Gilroy, Cochlin			
Aylesbury United	v Mangotsfield United	4 - 1	203
Taylor, Heney, Clapham, Mealor	*Ball*		
Weston Super Mare	v Chesham United	2 - 4	281
McKeaver (2)	*Burnell, Talbot, Holgate (2), Cox*		

Eastleigh	v Farnborough	1 - 0	687
A Riviere			
AFC Totton	v Thatcham Town	2 - 1	302
Taylor, Davis	*Johnston*		
Havant & Waterlooville	v Shortwood United	2 - 2	402
Elphick, Simpemba	*Bennett, Davis*		
Shortwood United	v Havant & Waterlooville	0 - 1	310
	Holloway		
Bashley	v Maidenhead United	2 - 1	312
Gillespie, Eastham	*Newman*		
Basingstoke Town	v Hamworthy United	3 - 1	329
Beaumont (3)	*Brierley*		
Oxford City	v Tiverton Town	2 - 1	257
Faulkner, Lyon	*Wyatt*		
Aylesbury Vale	v Gosport Borough	1 - 1	136
Melisi	*Bennett*		
Gosport Borough	v Aylesbury Vale	R 4 - 0	132
Culliford, Ford, Thomas (2)			
Dorchester Town	v Newport County	2 - 2	396
Moss (2)	*Duffy, Rose*		
Newport County	v Dorchester Town	R 1 - 2	653
Reid	*Crittenden (2)*		
Chalfont St Peter	v Team Bath	0 - 1	190
	Canham		
Truro City	v Chippenham Town	1 - 1	710
Yetton	*Holly*		
Chippenham Town	v Truro City	R 4 - 2	498
Pratt (2), Harvey, White	*Walker, Martin*		

THIRD QUALIFYING ROUND

BIGGEST HOME WIN:	**5-2** AFC Totton v Fleet Town
BIGGEST AWAY WIN:	**1-6** Stalybridge Celtic v Durham City
HIGHEST ATTENDANCE:	**2,710** Dover Athletic v AFC Wimbledon
NUMBER OF GAMES:	**40 + 8** (40 +3)
TOTAL ATTENDANCE:	**26,997** (22,501)
AVERAGE ATTENDANCE:	**562** (523)

Belper Town	v Prescot Cables	4 - 1	437
Stevenson, Walker, Wilson (2)	*O'Donnel*		
Guiseley	v Sheffield	3 - 3	431
Ovington, Brown (2)	*Partridge, Outram, G Smith*		
Sheffield	v Guiseley	R 2 - 1	451
Goddard, Ingall	*Burton*		
Buxton	v Blyth Spartans	0 - 1	556
	Williams		
Curzon Ashton	v Mossley	4 - 3	492
Edghill (2), Elliott, Norton	*Challinor (2), Dignan*		
Retford United	v Newcastle Benfield	1 - 0	300
Fisher			
Droylsden	v Gateshead	3 - 2	370
Townson, Byron, Lamb	*Gate, Harwood*		
Eastwood Town	v Harrogate Town	2 - 2	401
Hume, Robinson	*Dunning (P), Dean*		
Harrogate Town	v Eastwood Town	R 0 - 2	283
	Dunning, Holmes		
Alfreton Town	v Ilkeston Town	0 - 0	820
Ilkeston Town	v Alfreton Town	R 1 - 3	848
Green	*Davidson, Law (P), Clayton*		
Stalybridge Celtic	v Durham City	1 - 6	525
Williams	*Richardson (2), Cogden (3), Toft*		
Fleetwood Town	v Frickley Athletic	2 - 0	722
Mercer, Bell			
Whitley Bay	v Nantwich Town	1 - 5	797
Chow	*Lennon (4), Griggs*		
Newcastle Blue Star	v Hucknall Town	4 - 0	290
Brayson (3), Nicholson			
Southport	v Boston United	0 - 2	792
	Leabon, Rowan		
AFC Hornchurch	v Merstham	2 - 0	473
Green (2)			
Boreham Wood	v Brackley Town	0 - 1	216
	Cracknell (P)		
Hendon	v AFC Telford United	1 - 2	377
Haule (P)	*Ferns, Moore*		
Hitchin Town	v Hinckley United	1 - 2	503
Siley (P)	*Hall (2)*		
Kingstonian	v Hayes & Yeading United	1 - 3	578
Traynor (P)	*Hendry (2) (1P), Scott (P)*		
Hampton & Richmond Borough	v Whyteleafe	2 - 0	501
Yaku, Matthews			
Tamworth	v East Thurrock United	3 - 1	608
Shaw, Pritchard, Sheldon	*Lewis*		
Wroxham	v King's Lynn	0 - 2	1022
	Defty (2)		
Leiston	v Coalville	1 - 0	418
Boardley (P)			
Dover Athletic	v AFC Wimbledon	0 - 0	2710
AFC Wimbledon	v Dover Athletic	R 2 - 0	1939
Finn, Kedwell			
Evesham United	v Chasetown	2 - 0	407
Owen, Lennon			
Halesowen Town	v Maidstone United	1 - 4	872
Denny	*Nugent, Saunders, Brackman, Seevy*		
Bishop's Stortford	v Rugby Town	2 - 1	411
Harris, Wixon (P)	*King*		
Harlow Town	v Crowborough Athletic	1 - 1	609
Richards	*Clarke*		
Crowborough Athletic	v Harlow Town	R 0 - 2	323
	Adeyinka, Green		
Bury Town	v Worthing	1 - 0	482
Barrett			
Atherstone Town	v Chipstead	1 - 1	449
Well	*Oakins*		
Chipstead	v Atherstone Town	R 3 - 0	222
Oakins (3)			
Ware	v Sutton United	1 - 2	474
Hammett	*West, Dunn*		
Havant & Waterlooville	v Godalming Town	2 - 1	462
Holloway, Booth	*Purdy*		
Horsham	v Paulton Rovers	2 - 1	297
Mingle, Sigere	*Cleverley*		
Basingstoke Town	v Bashley	2 - 2	356
Ruggles, Bryant	*Parnell, Gillespie (P)*		
Bashley	v Basingstoke Town	R 0 - 3	349
	Williamson, Bryant (2)		
Oxford City	v Chesham United	2 - 1	454
Redknap, Faulkner	*Marsaoa*		
AFC Totton	v Fleet Town	5 - 2	402
Davis (3P), Sherborne, Osman	*Field (2)*		
Ashford Town (Mx)	v Chippenham Town	1 - 0	277
S Harris			
Frome Town	v Team Bath	2 - 2	504
Salter (2)	*Abbott, Perrott*		
Team Bath	v Frome Town	R 4 - 0	438
Thomson, Arnold (2), Canham			
Burgess Hill Town	v Eastleigh	2 - 1	336
Harper (2)	*Brown*		
Dorchester Town	v Gosport Borough	1 - 0	436
Moss			
Bath City	v Aylesbury United	0 - 1	577
	Hawkins		

FOURTH QUALIFYING ROUND

BIGGEST HOME WIN:	**4-0** Forest Green Rovers v Ashford Town (Mx) (replay)
BIGGEST AWAY WIN:	**1-5** King's Lynn v Kidderminster Harriers
HIGHEST ATTENDANCE:	**3,115** Wrexham v Eastwood Town
NUMBER OF GAMES:	**32 + 8** (32 + 8)
TOTAL ATTENDANCE:	**39,954** (43,310)
AVERAGE ATTENDANCE:	**999** (1,083)

Hinckley United	v Curzon Ashton	1 - 1	555
Curzon Ashton	v Hinckley United	R 1 - 1*	519
Barker	*Franklin*		
(Curzon won 3-2 on penalties)			
Kettering Town	v Burton Albion	3 - 0	1764
Seddon, Dempstr, Potter			
Tamworth	v Barrow	0 - 4	1012
	McNulty, Brodie (2), Brown (P)		
King's Lynn	v Kidderminster Harriers	1 - 5	1460
Francis	*Barnes-Homer, Penn, Brittain, Smikle, Richards*		
Boston United	v Cambridge United	2 - 3	1956
Leabon, Ryan	*Crow, Wilmott, Blommer (og)*		
Newcastle Blue Star	v Altrincham	1 - 2	305
Snowden	*Little, Lane*		
Droylsden	v Belper Town	0 - 0	557
Belper Town	v Droylsden	R 1 - 2	568
Wilson	*McGuire, Townson*		
Durham City	v Histon	2 - 2	257
Johnstone, Calvin-Smith	*Simpson (2)*		
Histon	v Durham City	R 5 - 2	441
Midson (2),Wright (2),Simpson	*Johnstone, Cogden*		

Top left - 3Q Rnd: Alfreton's Anton Brown shields the ball from Curtis Shaw, Ilkeston. Photo: Bill Wheatcroft.
Right - 3Q Rnd: Challinor, Mossley, stretches out a leg to tackle Edghill, Curzon Ashton. Photo: Keith Clayton.
Bottom left - 4Q Rnd: Goalmouth action from the tie between Ashford Town (Mx) and Forest Green Rovers. Photo: Gordon Whittington.
Right - 4Q Rnd: Tashan Adeyinka, Harlow Town, has a powerful shot at goal as a Burgess Hill defender closes in. Photo: Roger Turner.

Retford United *Whittington*	v Alfreton Town *Fortune-West, Clayton (2)*	1 - 3	922
Northwich Victoria	v AFC Telford United *Moore (2), Brown (P)*	0 - 3	1003
Blyth Spartans *Brown, Reay, Dale*	v Sheffield *Partridge*	3 - 1	680
York City	v Mansfield Town	0 - 0	1976
Mansfield Town *Hurren*	v York City	R 1 - 0	2004
Fleetwood Town *Bell (3), Pond*	v Nantwich Town *Lennon, Carter, Walker (P)*	4 - 3	874
Wrexham	v Eastwood Town	0 - 0	3115
Eastwood Town *Todd, Holmes*	v Wrexham	R 2 - 0	860
Stevenage Borough *Cole, Laird*	v Horsham *Sigere, Farrell*	2 - 2	1051
Horsham *Carney*	v Stevenage Borough *McMahon, Willock (2), Morison*	R 1 - 4	641
Woking	v Ebbsfleet United *Moore (2P)*	2 - 2	1462
Ebbsfleet United *Ibe*	v Woking	1 - 0	869
Hampton & Richmond Borough	v Brackley Town *Green*	0 - 1	582
Oxford United *Guy, Constable*	v Hayes & Yeading United	2 - 0	2521
Maidstone United	v AFC Wimbledon *Hatton*	0 - 1	1719
Team Bath *Benison*	v Salisbury City	1 - 0	649
Dorchester Town *Crittenden*	v Bishop's Stortford	1 - 0	433
Oxford City	v Eastbourne Borough *Baker*	0 - 1	564
Ashford Town (Mx)	v Forest Green Rovers	0 - 0	337
Forest Green Rovers *Mohamed (2), Afful (2)*	v Ashford Town (Mx)	R 4 - 0	425
Evesham United *Sheppell (2)*	v Rushden & Diamonds	2 - 0	609
Bury Town *Reed (2), Bullard, Smith (P)*	v Basingstoke Town *Warner*	4 - 1	1121
Burgess Hill Town	v Harlow Town *Richards, Bunn (2)*	0 - 3	845
Grays Athletic *Elliott, Cogan (P)*	v AFC Totton	2 - 0	490
Aylesbury United	v Sutton United *Hann*	0 - 2	545
Torquay United *Thompson (2), Sills (2)*	v Chipstead *Coleman*	4 - 1	1800
Leiston *Cunningham*	v Lewes *Cox*	1 - 1	847
Lewes *Wheeler*	v Leiston *Boardley (2), Eagle*	R 1 - 3	363
Crawley Town	v Havant & Waterlooville *Simpemba (2), Watkins*	0 - 3	1253
Weymouth *Beavon*	v AFC Hornchurch *Lee, Parker*	1 - 2	904

FIRST ROUND PROPER

Home	Away	Score	Att
Colchester United	v Leyton Orient	0 - 1	4600
Havant & Waterlooville	v Brentford	1 - 3	1631
Simpemba	*Williams, MacDonald, Elder*		
Blyth Spartans	v Shrewsbury Town	3 - 1	2742
Reay (2), Leeson	*Holt*		
Sutton United	v Notts County	0 - 1	2041
	Butcher		
Torquay United	v Evesham United	2 - 0	2275
Sills (2)			
Oxford United	v Dorchester Town	0 - 0	3196
Dorchester Town	v Oxford United	R 1 - 3*	1474
Mudge	*Constable, Trainer, Odubade*		
Bury	v Gillingham	0 - 1	2161
AFC Wimbledon	v Wycombe Wanderers	1 - 4	4528
Hatton	*Harrold (3), Phillips*		
Chester City	v Millwall	0 - 3	1932
Carlisle United	v Grays Athletic	1 - 1	3921
Madine	*Stuart*		
Grays Athletic	v Carlisle United	R 0 - 2	1217
	Graham, Kavanagh		
Team Bath	v Forest Green Rovers	0 - 1	906
	Mohamed		
Eastbourne Borough	v Barrow	0 - 0	1216
Barrow	v Eastbourne Borough	R 4 - 0	2031
Brodie, Brown, Henry, Logan			
AFC Hornchurch	v Peterborough United	0 - 1	3000
	Mackail-Smith		
Yeovil Town	v Stockport County	1 - 1	3582
Stockport County	v Yeovil Town	R 5 - 0	3260
Leiston	v Fleetwood Town	0 - 0	1250
Fleetwood Town	v Leiston	R 2 - 0	2010
Bell, Warlow			
Accrington Stanley	v Tranmere Rovers	0 - 0	2126
Tranmere Rovers	v Accrington Stanley	R 1 - 0	2560
Walsall	v Scunthorpe United	1 - 3	2318
AFC Bournemouth	v Bristol Rovers	1 - 0	3935
Brighton & Hove Albion	v Hartlepool United	3 - 3	2545
Hartlepool United	v Brighton & Hove Albion	R 2 - 1	3288
Aldershot Town	v Rotherham United	1 - 1	2632
Rotherham United	v Aldershot Town	R 0 - 3	2431
Morecambe	v Grimsby Town	2 - 1	1713
Huddersfield Town	v Port Vale	3 - 4	6942
Alfreton Town	v Bury Town	4 - 2	1060
McIntosh, Fortune-West, Law, Clayton	*Johnson, Reed*		
Kidderminster Harriers	v Cambridge United	1 - 0	1717
Richards (P)			
Leicester City	v Stevenage Borough	3 - 0	7586
Dyer, Fryatt, King			
Milton Keynes Dons	v Bradford City	1 - 2	5542
Darlington	v Droylsden	0 - 0	2479
Droylsden	v Darlington	R 1 - 0	1672
Tipton			
Chesterfield	v Mansfield Town	3 - 1	6612
AFC Telford United	v Southend United	2 - 2	3631
Adams (2)	*Laurant, Christophe*		
Southend United	v AFC Telford United	R 2 - 0	4415
Francis, Walker			
Curzon Ashton	v Exeter City	3 - 2	1259
Worsley, Ogoo, Norton	*Basham, Moxey*		
Histon	v Swindon Town	1 - 0	1541
Wright			
Kettering Town	v Lincoln City	1 - 1	3314
Geohaghan	*N'Guessan*		
Lincoln City	v Kettering Town	R 1 - 2	3953
John-Lewis	*Westcarr, Christie*		
Barnet	v Rochdale	1 - 1	1782
Rochdale	v Barnet	R 3 - 2*	2339
Hereford United	v Dagenham & Redbridge	0 - 0	1825
Dagenham & Redbridge	v Hereford United	R 2 - 1	1409
Cheltenham Town	v Oldham Athletic	2 - 2	2585
Oldham Athletic	v Cheltenham Town	R 0 - 1	2552
Luton Town	v Altrincham	0 - 0	3200
Altrincham	v Luton Town	R 0 - 0*	2397
(Luton won 4-2 on penalties)			
Crewe Alexandra	v Ebbsfleet United	1 - 0	2593
Donaldson			
Eastwood Town	v Brackley Town	2 - 1	960
Cooke, Meikle	*Winters*		
Leeds United	v Northampton Town	1 - 1	9531
Northampton Town	v Leeds United	R 2 - 5	3960
Harlow Town	v Macclesfield Town	0 - 2	2149
	Brisley, Dunfield		

SECOND ROUND PROPER

Home	Away	Score	Att
Chesterfield	v Droylsden	2 - 2	5698
Ward, Lester	*Brown, Halford*		
Droylsden	v Chesterfield	R 2 - 1	2824
Newton (2) 1p	*Lester*		
tie awarded to Chesterfield after Droylsden played an ineligible player			
Peterborough United	v Tranmere Rovers	0 - 0	5980
Tranmere Rovers	v Peterborough United	R 1 - 2*	3139
Eastwood Town	v Wycombe Wanderers	2 - 0	1955
Meikle, Knox			
Notts County	v Kettering Town	1 - 1	4451
Canham	*Solkhon*		
Kettering Town	v Notts County	R 2 - 1	3019
Solkhon, Seddon	*Smith*		
Leicester City	v Dagenham & Redbridge	3 - 2	7791
Barrow	v Brentford	2 - 1	3532
Brown (P), Henny	*MacDonald*		
Bradford City	v Leyton Orient	1 - 2	5065
Southend United	v Luton Town	3 - 1	4111
Forest Green Rovers	v Rochdale	2 - 0	1715
Smith, Low			
Histon	v Leeds United	1 - 0	4103
Langston			
Scunthorpe United	v Alfreton Town	4 - 0	4249
May, Hooper (2), Togwell			
Torquay United	v Oxford United	2 - 0	2647
Benyon (2)			
Fleetwood Town	v Hartlepool United	2 - 3	3280
Bell, Warlow	*Mackay (2), Porter*		
Morecambe	v Cheltenham Town	2 - 3	1758
Gillingham	v Stockport County	0 - 0	4419
Stockport County	v Gillingham	R 1 - 2	3329
Millwall	v Aldershot Town	3 - 0	6159
Carlisle United	v Crewe Alexandra	0 - 2	2755
AFC Bournemouth	v Blyth Spartans	0 - 0	4165
Blyth Spartans	v AFC Bournemouth	R 1 - 0	4040
Dalton			
Kidderminster Harriers	v Curzon Ashton	2 - 0	2070
Moore, Creighton			
Port Vale	v Macclesfield Town	1 - 3	4684

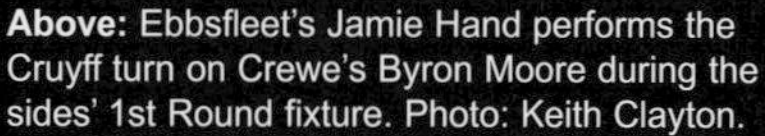

Above: Ebbsfleet's Jamie Hand performs the Cruyff turn on Crewe's Byron Moore during the sides' 1st Round fixture. Photo: Keith Clayton.

Above right: Andrew Mangan, Forest Green Rovers, and Rochdale's Rory McArdle tussle for the ball in the Blue Square Premier side's 2-0 win.

Right: Kidderminster's goal comes under attack from a Coventry City corner in this 3rd Round tie which the Championship side won 2-0. Photo: Peter Barnes.

THIRD ROUND PROPER

Home	Away	Score	Att.
Portsmouth (H)	v Bristol City	0 - 0	14446
Bristol City	v Portsmouth (H)	R 0 - 2	14302
Sheffield Wednesday	v Fulham	1 - 2	18377
Preston North End	v Liverpool	0 - 2	23046
Birmingham City	v Wolverhampton Wanderers	0 - 2	22232
West Ham United	v Barnsley	3 - 0	28869
Middlesbrough	v Barrow	2 - 1	25132
Alves (2)	*Walker 80*		
Hull City	v Newcastle United	0 - 0	20557
Newcastle United	v Hull City	R 0 - 1	31380
Hartlepool United	v Stoke City	2 - 0	5367
Chelsea	v Southend United	1 - 1	41090
Southend United	v Chelsea	R 1 - 4	11314
Manchester City	v Nottingham Forest	0 - 3	31869
Cardiff City	v Reading	2 - 0	12448
Ipswich Town	v Chesterfield	3 - 0	12524
Charlton Athletic	v Norwich City	1 - 1	12615
Norwich City	v Charlton Athletic	R 0 - 1	13997
West Bromwich Albion	v Peterborough United	1 - 1	18659
Peterborough United	v West Bromwich Albion	R 0 - 2	10735
Torquay United	v Blackpool	1 - 0	3654
Green			
Leyton Orient	v Sheffield United	1 - 4	4527
Southampton	v Manchester United	0 - 3	31901
Millwall	v Crewe Alexandra	2 - 2	5754
Crewe Alexandra	v Millwall	R 2 - 3	3060
Histon	v Swansea City	1 - 2	2821
Simpson	*Pintado, Bauza*		
Forest Green Rovers	v Derby County	3 - 4	4836
Smith, Lawless, Stonehouse	*Hulse, Albrechtsen, Green, Davies (P)*		
Queens Park Rangers	v Burnley	0 - 0	8896
Burnley	v Queens Park Rangers	R 2 - 1*	3760
Leicester City	v Crystal Palace	0 - 0	15976
Crystal Palace	v Leicester City	R 2 - 1	6023
Tottenham Hotspur	v Wigan Athletic	3 - 1	34040
Cheltenham Town	v Doncaster Rovers	0 - 0	4417
Doncaster Rovers	v Cheltenham Town	R 3 - 0	5345
Arsenal	v Plymouth Argyle	3 - 1	59424
Kettering Town	v Eastwood Town	2 - 1	5090
Westcarr, Seddon	*Robinson*		
Blyth Spartans	v Blackburn Rovers	0 - 1	3445
	Villanueva		
Macclesfield Town	v Everton	0 - 1	6008
Watford	v Scunthorpe United	1 - 0	8690
Sunderland	v Bolton Wanderers	2 - 1	20685
Coventry City	v Kidderminster Harriers	2 - 0	13652
McKenzie, Best			
Gillingham	v Aston Villa	1 - 2	10107

FOURTH ROUND PROPER

Liverpool	v Everton	1 - 1	43524
Everton	v Liverpool	R 1 - 0	37918
Manchester United	v Tottenham Hotspur	2 - 1	75014
Hull City	v Millwall	2 - 0	18639
Sunderland	v Blackburn Rovers	0 - 0	22634
Blackburn Rovers	v Sunderland	R 2 - 1	10112
Hartlepool United	v West Ham United	0 - 2	6849
Sheffield United	v Charlton Athletic	2 - 1	15957
Cardiff City	v Arsenal	0 - 0	20079
Arsenal	v Cardiff City	R 4 - 0	57237
Portsmouth (H)	v Swansea City	0 - 2	17357
Chelsea	v Ipswich Town	3 - 1	41137
Doncaster Rovers	v Aston Villa	0 - 0	13517
Aston Villa	v Doncaster Rovers	3 - 1	24203
West Bromwich Albion	v Burnley	2 - 2	18294
Burnley	v West Bromwich Albion	R 3 - 1	6835
Torquay United	v Coventry City	0 - 1	6018
	Ward		
Kettering Town	v Fulham	2 - 4	5406
Westcarr (2)	*Davies, Murphy, Johnson, Zamora*		
Watford	v Crystal Palace	4 - 3	10006
Derby County	v Nottingham Forest	1 - 1	32035
Nottingham Forest	v Derby County	R 2 - 3	29001
Wolverhampton Wanderers	v Middlesbrough	1 - 2	18013

FIFTH ROUND PROPER

Sheffield United	v Hull City	1 - 1	22283
Hull City	v Sheffield United	R 2 - 1	17239
Watford	v Chelsea	1 - 3	16851
West Ham United	v Middlesbrough	1 - 1	33658
Middlesbrough	v West Ham United	R 2 - 0	15602
Blackburn Rovers	v Coventry City	2 - 2	15053
Coventry City	v Blackburn Rovers	R 1 - 0	22793
Derby County	v Manchester United	1 - 4	32103
Swansea City	v Fulham	1 - 1	16573
Fulham	v Swansea City	R 2 - 1	12316
Everton	v Aston Villa	3 - 1	35439
Arsenal	v Burnley	3 - 0	57454

SIXTH ROUND PROPER

Coventry City	v Chelsea	0 - 2	31407
Fulham	v Manchester United	0 - 4	24662
Arsenal	v Hull City	2 - 1	55641
Everton	v Middlesbrough	2 - 1	37856

SEMI-FINALS - at Wembley Stadium

Arsenal	v Chelsea	1 - 2	88103
Manchester United	v Everton	0 - 0*	88141

(Everton win 4-2 on penalties)

THE FINAL - at Wembley Stadium

Chelsea	v Everton	2 - 1	89931

KETTERING TOWN 2 (1)

Westcarr 36, 83 (pen)

FULHAM 4 (1)

Davies 12, Murphy 77, Johnson 88, Zamora 89

KETTERING TOWN SQUAD

Harper, Eaden, Geohaghan, Dempster, Jaszczun (Potter 71), Bennett, Boucaud, Solkhon, Graham (Marna 89), Westcarr, Seddon (Beardsley 73).
Unused Subs: Wrack, Galbraith.

FULHAM SQUAD

Schwarzer, Stoor, Hangeland, Hughes, Konchesky, Davies, Andreasen, Etuhu (Murphy 69), Gera (Zamora 69), Johnson, Dempsey.
Unused Subs: Zuberbuhler, Pantsil, Nevland, Kallio, Baird.

Right: This Kettering player easily evades Zoltan Gera's challenge.

Below: It's a race to the loose ball.

Below: Craig Westcarr scores the first of his two goals.

Photos: Peter Barnes.

Right: Peterborough's Craig Mackail-Smith can only watch as AFC Hornchurch's Mark Goodfellow fires in a shot during their 1st Round tie. Photo: Alan Coomes.
Below: Action from the 1st Round match between Leicester City and Stevenage Borough. Photo: Peter Barnes.

Right: Leeds United were on the receiving end of a giant killing when Histon progressed to the 3rd Round with a 1-0 win. Photo: Peter Barnes.

Below: James Faulkner sweeps in Oxford City's winner from close range against Chesham United in the 3rd Qualifying Round. Photo: Gordon Whittington.

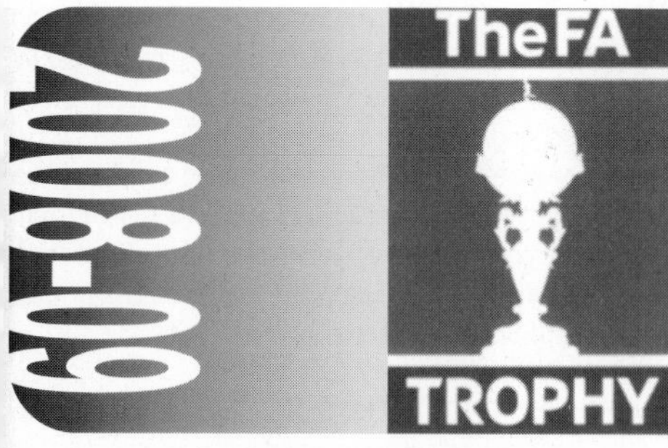

The F.A. Challenge Trophy is the national knock out competition for clubs competing in steps one to four. The Conference clubs in The Blue Square Premier are obviously the favourites but giant killing is always the ambition of those contesting the early rounds from the Divisions One of Ryman, Unibond and BGB Gas.

TRAFFORD AND LEIGHTON TOWN SCORE 15 BETWEEN THEM

Preliminary Round headlines featured Trafford's 8-1 victory over Rossendale United and Leighton Town's 7-1 success against Chipstead, with the best attendance of 347 watching Harrogate R.A. beat F.C.Halifax Town 2-1. Many clubs such as Didcot Town, Truro City and Winchester City with good F.A.Vase pedigrees featured in the very early stages of the senior competition although Didcot surprisingly lost at home to Andover.

F.A.CUP STARS EASTWOOD TOWN LOSE AT HOME

It's always been difficult for clubs who have been enjoying the headlines and excitement sparked by an F.A.Cup run in the current season to also do well in the F.A.Trophy. Last season Eastwood Town handed out Wycombe Wanderers' first defeat of the campaign before being drawn away to Kettering Town in the 3rd Round of the F.A.Cup but lost at home to Ilkeston Town in the First Qualifying Round of the Trophy!

It was strange to see Boston United also featuring in the First Qualifying Round but they made sure of progress with a fine 6-0 victory over Kidsgrove Athletic in front of 797. Sutton United, another ex-finalist of the competition, beat local rivals Tooting & Mitcham United 2-0. Truro City, enjoying their first Trophy competition, drew 3-3 at home with Chesham United in front of 511, exactly the same attendance as Sutton. However, it was F.C.United who attracted easily the biggest crowd of 1,227 for their 1-0 victory over Radcliffe Borough.

I enjoyed a visit to Bromsgrove where Rovers entertained Gloucester City and Alex Sykes scored one of his eleven penalties in City's 4-1 victory.

WINDSOR & ETON'S MICHAEL CHENNELL HITS EIGHT IN TWO TROPHY TIES

This round was notable for the high goalscoring away from home. From the thirty three games played on the Saturday, eighty one goals were scored by the visitors, including Ramsgate's 6-3 victory at Hitchin, Cammel Laird's 5-1 defeat of Leigh Genesis, Farnborough's 5-0 thrashing of Soham Town plus four each from Brackley Town, Hednesford Town and AFC Totton winning at Northwood (4-1), Stamford (4-3) and Thatcham Town (4-0) respectively.

The individual goalscoring star was Windsor & Eton's Michael Chennells, who scored four goals for the second F.A.Trophy match in succession, in his club's two away triumphs, 5-1 at Winchester City and 5-0 at Burnham.

One of the best attendances of the round (749) saw a thrilling 3-3 draw when Oxford City visited Dartford's lovely new ground and F.C.United 3-0 victory attracted 599 to Worksop while Boston United won 4-2 in front of 359 at Clitheroe.

DURHAM CITY AND SKELMERSDALE UNITED TAKE THE HONOURS

Two leading Unibond Division One North clubs had been making steady progress from The Preliminary Round and Skelmersdale United had beaten Shepshed Dynamo (H) 2-1, Sheffield F.C. (H) 1-0, Buxton (A) 1-0 and now had qualified for the Competition Proper with a 1-0 victory at Glapwell.

Durham City needed a couple of replays in their first two ties. Curzon Ashton 1-1 (H) and 2-1 (A) and Halesowen Town (H) 4-4 and (A) 1-0, Marine (A) 2-1 and 2-1 (A) at Solihull Moors.

Another case of a successful F.A.Cup side not rising to the same standards in the Trophy was Blyth Spartans who lost at home to Alfreton Town in a thrilling 3-4 game, and I was interested to watch the high flying A.F.C. Wimbledon win 3-1 at Worcester CIty, a club with a new and enthusiastic Chairman planning to help City into happier times as soon as possible.Their crowd of 895 was the largest of the day just ahead of 749 at King's Lynn where the crowd were entertained to a thrilling 3-2 victory over Stafford Rangers.

UXBRIDGE BEAT A.F.C. WIMBLEDON

The weather hit this round of The Trophy but Skelmersdale United's run came to an end at Barrow who had also enjoyed the F.A.Cup, but Durham City's run continued with a 2-0 home win over Harrogate Town.

A very local 'derby' attracted 1,332 to watch Histon beaten 2-3 by Cambridge United. Another club from the Eastern side of the country who did carry on their good F.A.Cup form in the F.A.Trophy, was Bury Town, and they had also started in the First Qualifying Round and had enjoyed their victories over Leighton Town (H)1-0, Dulwich Hamlet (A) 3-0, Hampton & Richmond Borough (A) 2-1 before the run came to an end by 1-3 at Havant & Waterlooville.

Stevenage Borough and Torquay United showed their potential with home victories over St Albans City (4-1) and Bath City (2-0) respectively, but Uxbridge, another club representing step four, had continued their fine run, which had started in The First Qualifying Round, with victories over Walton & Hersham (H) 2-1, Boreham Wood (A) 2-1 and Dorchester Town (H) 2-1 before really hitting the headlines with an exciting 2-1 home victory over the high flying AFC Wimbledon.

It was strange to see Wrexham entertaining Mansfield Town in the F.A.Trophy but 1,559 turned up to see a 2-1 home win in the biggest crowd on a very wet Saturday. While Lewes cheered themselves up in a miserable season by winning 2-1 at Team Bath, a seven goal thriller was won by Workington by a single goal at home to King's Lynn and Kettering Town won 4-1 at Cambridge City.

SWINDON'S SUPER TROPHY RUN CONTINUES

Another round badly affected by the weather saw only three ties played on the original Saturday. Durham drew at home to Southport but their run came to an end with a 1-3 result in the replay. The Unibond Division One side had proved their all round ability and character by also enjoying a good F.A.Cup run and a promotion challenge in their league.

In the other two games played Burton Albion and Torquay United (the two clubs who were to be celebrating promotion later in the season) both won their home ties.

In the postponed games, Barrow and Workington produced a memorable battle in the clash of local rivals with underdogs Workington winning 3-0. Strong Blue Square Premier clubs Wrexham, Stevenage Borough, Kidderminster Harriers and York City all won away from home but the biggest victory was gained by Swindon Supermarine at Uxbridge where they won 6-1.

My local club Tiverton Town were leading Kettering Town by a single goal with two minutes to go but conceded a very doubtful penalty. Heads dropped, but ex England international goalkeeper Steve Book saved the kick and the game went into injury time, only for Mark Cooper's fine cup side to score an excellent equaliser in the third of four extra minutes! In the replay Kettering won on penalties with the score 1-1 after extra time.

There weren't many clubs outside the Blue Square Premier left in the last sixteen but Havant & Waterlooville certainly entertained in their Second Round tie against Lewes. After a 3-3 draw in Sussex 'The Hawks' won 4-3 in the replay.

F.A.CUP 4TH ROUND HEROES KNOCKED OUT

The two clubs who had represented Non-League Football in The Fourth Round of The F.A.Cup both lost to Blue Square North clubs in this round of The F.A.Trophy. A.F.C.Telford United travelling to Rockingham Road to beat Kettering Town by a Carey-Bertram goal and Southport achieving a superb 3-0 home victory over Torquay United with goals from Steve Daly (2) and Kevin Lee.

Premier clubs did make their presence felt in three other ties however, as Wrexham won 3-1 at Workington and two home successes were registered by Forest Green Rovers who beat high scoring Hednesford Town 1-0 and holders Ebbsfleet United who finally halted little Swindon Supermarine's best ever Trophy run.

In two all Premier ties,York City won their home replay on a penalty shoot out against Kidderminster Harriers, after two 1-1 draws and Stevenage Borough gave Burton Albion every chance to concentrate on their championship bid by beating the league leaders 4-0 with top scorer Steve Morison scoring twice.

With five Blue Square Premier clubs and two from Blue Square North in the quarter final draw, one tie suffered from continued poor weather conditions until Havant & Waterlooville eventually beat Crawley Town 2-0 to give Blue Square South representation.

A.F.C. TELFORD UNITED'S THIRTEENTH CUP TIE

Blue Square North were guaranteed a semi-finalist as their representatives were drawn against each other. After 2,059 had watched a thrilling 2-2 draw at The New Bucks Head Stadium, Southport earned a home replay thanks to a late equaliser.

Stevenage Borough continued to find goalscoring relatively easy and enjoyed a 4-0 victory over Forest Green Rovers while York City beat Havant & Waterlooville 2-0 thus ensuring that The Blue Square Premier provided three semi-finalists with Wrexham and Ebbsfleet United drawing 0-0 in front of 3,028.

In the replays Ebbsfleet reached the semi-final for the second consecutive year with a 3-1 victory over Wrexham and AFC Telford qualified for the semi-finals with a 1-0 away victory, which ensured they would play at least an impressive thirteen F.A.Cup and F.A.Trophy cup ties in the season.

YORK CITY QUALIFY FOR FIRST FINAL

No one could argue that the two finalists didn't deserve their place in the Wembley Final. Stevenage Borough and York City both won their two semi-final legs and both scored four semi-final goals in doing so. York City had lost at the semi-final stage last season and having had a disappointing league campaign, a Wembley appearance was just what the club, their supporters and the town itself needed.

Stevenage Borough had won the 2007 Trophy in the first final back at Wembley and were still in contention for promotion, so would they be able to take the Trophy Final as seriously as their opponents? By the time the final was to be played, Borough could either be disappointed with a play-off failure or too excited about promotion to bother with the Trophy. How would it be?

As it was both clubs prepared for a special day at Wembley, and how they approached it would probably be reflected in the ultimate result. Steve Morison was still scoring goals for Borough although Peter Vincenti, a Channel Islander from Jersey, scored the only goal of the semi-final second leg, and York City's marksman, Richard Brodie needed to be at his match winning best if York City were to eventually triumph. **TW.**

PRELIMINARY ROUND

BIGGEST HOME WIN:	**8-1** Trafford v Rossendale United
BIGGEST AWAY WIN:	**1-5** Mossley v Stocksbridge PS and Godalming Town v Enfield Town
HIGHEST ATTENDANCE:	**347** Harrogate Railway v FC Halifax Town
NUMBER OF GAMES:	**51 + 7** (2007-08 46 +10)
TOTAL ATTENDANCE:	**7,752** (9,747)
AVERAGE ATTENDANCE:	**134** (174)

Home	Away	Score	Att
Trafford	v Rossendale United	8 - 1	121
Halligan, Grandison, Lundy (2), Barlow (4)	*Calvert*		
Retford United	v Kidsgrove Athletic	1 - 2	173
Bray	*O.G., Hurst*		
Clitheroe	v Grantham Town	4 - 1	195
Sargeson, Lomax (2), Fisher	*Gyoury-Hales*		
Brigg Town	v Willenhall Town	4 - 0	98
Borland, Lamb, Muldoon (2)			
Durham City	v Curzon Ashton	1 - 1	171
English	*Norton*		
Curzon Ashton	v Durham City	R 1 - 2	147
Worlsey	*Smith, English*		
Romulus	v Loughborough Dynamo	3 - 2	77
Brown (3)	*Gibbons, Moriera*		
Goole	v Nuneaton Town	1 - 1	253
Nuneaton Town	v Goole	R 0 - 1	258
Spalding United	v Wakefield	2 - 1	70
Wormall (2)	*Sobers*		
Lancaster City	v Leek Town	1 - 0	146
Reid			
Rushall Olympic	v Ossett Albion	2 - 1	71
Beale, Lamey	*Cooke*		
Garforth Town	v Belper Town	2 - 0	143
Kelly, Piper			
Skelmersdale United	v Shepshed Dynamo	2 - 1	164
McConville, Walker	*Robinson*		
Chorley	v Warrington Town	0 - 0	209
Warrington Town	v Chorley	R 2 - 0	128
Lamb (2)			
Woodley Sports	v Quorn	0 - 1	92
	Jenkins		
Harrogate Railway	v FC Halifax Town	2 - 1	347
Jones, Cartman	*Daniel*		
Carlton Town	v Atherstone Town	2 - 1	82
Smith, Akers	*Simmonds*		
Sheffield	v Bamber Bridge	5 - 3	242
Outram, Goddard (2), Woolley, Roney	*Howson (2), Black*		
Mossley	v Stocksbridge PS	1 - 5	191
	Vardy (3), Fothergill, Ring		
Salford City	v Gresley Rovers	2 - 0	113
Kay, Depeiaza			
Aveley	v Ilford	2 - 0	84
Vaughan, Carlos			
Waltham Forest	v AFC Sudbury	1 - 4	90
Mamoud	*Hawes (3), Bussens*		
Wingate & Finchley	v Ware	2 - 1	60
Ellis, Williams	*Berry*		
Great Wakering Rovers	v Ashford Town	5 - 3	112
Webb, Richmond (4)	*Seanla (2), Doerr*		
Northwood	v Whyteleafe	2 - 0	101
Williams (2)			
Merstham	v Arlesey Town	4 - 1	101
	Allen		
Metropolitan Police	v Waltham Abbey	0 - 0	81
Waltham Abbey	v Metropolitan Police	R 1 - 2	88
Holland	*Bowen, George*		
Kingstonian	v Whitstable Town	2 - 3	294
Williams, Traynor	*Wisker, Gess, Pulman*		
Rothwell Town	v Tilbury	2 - 2	66
Byrne (2)	*Black, Stephenson*		
Tilbury	v Rothwell Town	R 2 - 0	57
Stephenson, Kamara			
Leatherhead	v Sittingbourne	1 - 2	140
Cuff	*Akhazzan, Bradbrook*		
Leighton Town	v Chipstead	7 - 1	88
Clifford, Silvesrti (3), Hatch (3)	*Oxley*		
Bury Town	v Barton Rovers	2 - 1	214
Smith, Steward	*Hanley*		
Maldon Town	v Cheshunt	0 - 1	72
	Lewis		
Crowborough Athletic	v Eastbourne Town	3 - 0	145
Clarke (2), Gordon			
Folkestone Invicta	v Chatham Town	1 - 1	208
	O.G.		
Chatham Town	v Folkestone Invicta	R 2 - 0	154
Ascheri, Austin			
Leyton	v Dulwich Hamlet	1 - 4	83
	Cumberbatch, Plummer, Hamioi, O.G.		
Potters Bar Town	v Brentwood Town	0 - 2	84
	Stanley, Crowther		
East Thurrock United	v Thamesmead Town	2 - 1	97
Cornhill, Toumy	*Cable*		
Concord Rangers	v Woodford United	4 - 1	79
Fobi-Edusei, Heale, Ogilvile, Syrett	*Alleyne*		
Walton Casuals	v Hillingdon Borough	4 - 3	85
Carr, Ambridge, Westen, Farr	*Edwards, Joseph, Lyons*		
Godalming Town	v Enfield Town	1 - 5	169
Purdy	*Remy (2), Marshall, Deanes (2)*		
Corinthian-Casuals	v Worthing	1 - 3	110
	Benn, Demetriou (2)		
Soham Town Rangers	v Redbridge	1 - 0	128
Timson			
Burgess Hill Town	v Dunstable Town	3 - 1	170
Fogden, Harper, Lousi	*Olaleye*		
Bracknell Town	v Malvern Town	2 - 0	68
Harvey, Jack			
Aylesbury United	v Bridgwater Town	2 - 0	186
Henney, Hankins			
Didcot Town	v Andover	1 - 2	182
Bartley	*Swayne, Turvey*		
Winchester City	v Taunton Town	3 - 0	119
Roden, Williams, Richardson			
Fleet Town	v Beaconsfield SYCOB	3 - 1	98
Noakes, McClurg, Smith	*Bubb*		
Cinderford Town	v Truro City	2 - 4	116
Heath, Griffin	*Hockley, Stonebridge, Watkins (2)*		
Paulton Rovers	v Thatcham Town	1 - 1	105
Jefferies	*Johnson*		
Thatcham Town	v Paulton Rovers	R 2 - 0	110
Vine, Johnson			
Marlow	v Cirencester Town	2 - 0	117
Hadley, Simpson			

FIRST QUALIFYING ROUND

BIGGEST HOME WIN:	**6-0** Soham Tn R. v Witham Tn.
Hemel H. v AFC Hayes. Stourbridge v Salford C. Boston Utd v Kidsgrove Ath.	
BIGGEST AWAY WIN:	**0-5** Winchester City v Windsor & Eton
HIGHEST ATTENDANCE:	**1,227** FC Utd of M'chester v Radcliffe Boro'
NUMBER OF GAMES:	**72 + 14** (72 +18)
TOTAL ATTENDANCE:	**20,066** (19,969)
AVERAGE ATTENDANCE:	**233** (227)

Home	Away	Score	Att.
Romulus	v Garforth Town	1 - 1	90
	Kamara		
Garforth Town	v Romulus	R 3 - 4	78
Holthkiss, Ronan, St Juste			
Harrogate Railway	v Leigh Genesis	0 - 1	129
	Stepien		
Stourbridge	v Salford City	6 - 0	162
Canavan, Bennett, Slater, Broadhurst, Dovey, O.G.			
Rushall Olympic	v Bedworth United	0 - 0	90
Bedworth United	v Rushall Olympic	R 4 - 1	79
Lamb, Gordon, Twigger, Kinder	*Fitzpatrick*		
Witton Albion	v Worksop Town	0 - 1	219
	Sanasy		
Whitby Town	v Trafford	3 - 2	223
Scott, Beadle, Huggins	*Lundy, Barlow*		
Hednesford Town	v Quorn	3 - 1	338
Barnett, Dyer (2)	*Jenkins*		
Ashton United	v Lincoln United	2 - 1	103
Kearney, Talbot	*Wilkins*		
Matlock Town	v Warrington Town	0 - 1	242
	Rendell		
FC United of Manchester	v Radcliffe Borough	1 - 0	1227
Turner			
Brigg Town	v Marine	1 - 5	131
Muldoon	*McMahon (2), Lynch, Lawless, Arnold*		
Boston United	v Kidsgrove Athletic	6 - 0	797
Talbot (2), Rowan (2), Ryan, Millson			
Skelmersdale United	v Sheffield	1 - 0	201
Donnelly			
Guiseley	v Ossett Town	0 - 1	272
	Savory		
Glapwell	v Leamington	3 - 2	203
Kennedy, Shelley, Brayson	*Stanley (2)*		
Colwyn Bay	v Chasetown	2 - 2	268
Hopley (2)	*Birch, Smith*		
Chasetown	v Colwyn Bay	R 2 - 1	341
Holland, Smith	*Canning*		
Stocksbridge PS	v Goole	3 - 1	143
Richards, Ashley, Fothergill			
Lancaster City	v Rugby Town	3 - 3	166
Marshall, Foster, Jackson	*Stone, Koledynski, Taylor*		
Rugby Town	v Lancaster City	R 2 - 0	131
Musgrove, Taylor			
Spalding United	v North Ferriby United	0 - 0	154
North Ferriby United	v Spalding United	R 2 - 0	89
Frickley Athletic	v Nantwich Town	0 - 2	187
	Griggs, Whittaker		
Prescot Cables	v Cammell Laird	0 - 3	249
	Collins, Rimmer, O.G.		
Stamford	v Kendal Town	3 - 0	210
Watson, Cotton, Kirk			
Durham City	v Halesowen Town	4 - 4	202
Smith, Richardson, Johnston, English	*Danks (3), O.G.*		
Halesowen Town	v Durham City	R 0 - 1	311
	Richardson		
Bradford Park Avenue	v Clitheroe	1 - 2	294
	Lomax, Redhead		
Eastwood Town	v Ilkeston Town	0 - 2	504
	Istead, Honell		
Newcastle Blue Star	v Sutton Coldfield Town	2 - 2	119
Bowey, Brayson	*Quiggin, Farrell*		
Sutton Coldfield Town	v Newcastle Blue Star	R 4 - 1	55
Owen, Moran, Farrell (2)			
Buxton	v Carlton Town	5 - 3	302
	Thomas, Brady		
Concord Rangers	v Billericay Town	3 - 1	291
Heale (3)	*Bricknell*		
Uxbridge	v Walton & Hersham	2 - 1	129
Lawrence, Dyer	*Hassell*		
Walton Casuals	v Heybridge Swifts	0 - 0	83
Heybridge Swifts	v Walton Casuals	R 3 - 2*	94
Cousins (2), Brotherton	*Curr, Kigandu*		
Whitstable Town	v Brackley Town	3 - 4	170
Munday, Wisker (2)	*Pierson, Cracknell, Thorpe (2)*		
Worthing	v Merstham	2 - 0	318
Andrews, Kirkwood			
Maidstone United	v AFC Hornchurch	1 - 1	384
Pinnock	*Green*		
AFC Hornchurch	v Maidstone United	R 1 - 2	257
Wall	*Pinnock, Bradbrook*		
Crowborough Athletic	v Northwood	0 - 2	87
	Ursell (2)		
Wingate & Finchley	v Ashford Town (Mx)	1 - 1	80
	Harrison		
Ashford Town (Mx)	v Wingate & Finchley	R 2 - 4	52
Todd, Palmer	*Ellis, Samuel, Lees (2)*		
Brentwood Town	v AFC Sudbury	2 - 3	223
Flozier (2)	*Hawes (2), Rowe*		
Wealdstone	v Croydon Athletic	1 - 0	195
O'Leary			
Bedford Town	v Corby Town	1 - 2	374
Phillips	*Diggin (2)*		
Hemel Hempstead	v AFC Hayes	6 - 0	147
Yeboah, Deeney, Dillon, Sippetts, Roberts (2)			
Metropolitan Police	v Dulwich Hamlet	0 - 2	111
	Simpson, Taylor		
Soham Town Rangers	v Witham Town	6 - 0	127
Williams, Jones (2), Carter (2), Furnell			
Aveley	v Hitchin Town	1 - 2	108
Maskell			
Tilbury	v Cray Wanderers	1 - 1	67
Stowe			
Cray Wanderers	v Tilbury	R 1 - 0	78
Kinch			
Harrow Borough	v Chatham Town	2 - 1	101
Hall, Shroot	*Binks*		
Staines Town	v Dover Athletic	0 - 2	320
	Hughes, Colins		
Boreham Wood	v Burgess Hill Town	2 - 0	89
Allinson, Buchanan			
Tonbridge Angels	v Ramsgate	2 - 3	372
Rook, O.G.	*Hadden, May, Ball*		
Dartford	v Harlow Town	2 - 1	851
Flanagan, Hayes	*Taylor*		
Bury Town	v Leighton Town	1 - 0	201
Barrett			
Enfield Town	v Great Wakering Rovers	0 - 2	208
	Benjamin, Richmonds		
Cambridge City	v Canvey Island	1 - 1	312
Sharp	*Moore*		
Canvey Island	v Cambridge City	R 0 - 0*	245
(Cambridge won 4-2 on penalties)			

Right: Action from the Preliminary Round tie between Rothwell Town and Tilbury which all square. Photo: Peter Barnes.

Below: Tonbridge Angels, Gooding (No.6), heads the ball over his own crossbar to deny Ramsgate's captain, Nick Davis, from scoring in this 1st Qualifying Round match. Photo: Roger Turner.

Below: Ilkeston keeper Dan Haysted tips this Eastwood shot wide during Ilkeston's 0-2 victory in the 1st Qualifying Round. Photo: Bill Wheatcroft.

Home	Away	Score	Att
Cheshunt *Prestedge*	v East Thurrock United *Smith, Touhy*	1 - 2	125
Horsham *Farrell, Sigere, Haddon, Nwachukwu*	v Sittingbourne *Bradbrook, Brady*	4 - 2	199
Margate	v Hendon *Hunt*	0 - 1	362
Hastings United *Ramsay (2), Sawyer*	v Carshalton Athletic *Kadi*	3 - 1	320
Sutton United *Dunn, Hann*	v Tooting & Mitcham United	2 - 0	511
Tiverton Town *Villis, Walsh (3), Knighton*	v North Leigh *Cooper, Futcher*	5 - 2	344
Mangotsfield United	v Bashley *Eastham, Keeler*	0 - 2	134
Yate Town *O.G.*	v Stourport Swifts *Commen*	1 - 1	132
Stourport Swifts *Jones*	v Yate Town *Griffiths (3)*	R 1 - 3	73
Andover *Swayne (2), Jarvis*	v Gosport Borough *Birmingham (2)*	3 - 2	115
Banbury United	v Burnham *Bird*	0 - 1	217
Merthyr Tydfil *Keddle, Harris, Jones (2)*	v Bishops Cleeve *Hopkins*	4 - 1	273
Bromsgrove Rovers *Meakin-Richards*	v Gloucester City *Sykes (2), Morford (2)*	1 - 4	362
Evesham United *Fitter, Scheppel, Owen, Hay*	v Clevedon Town	4 - 0	110
Winchester City	v Windsor & Eton *Porter, Chennels (4)*	0 - 5	163
Bracknell Town *Geary, McIntosh*	v Swindon Supermarine *Edenborough, Griffin (2), Stanley*	2 - 4	102
Farnborough *Saunders, Rumbold, Charles, Barima*	v Marlow	4 - 0	348
Thatcham Town *Thomas, Asker, Vine, Johnson (2)*	v Slough Town *Pritchard, Jordan, Romeo (2)*	5 - 4	177
Truro City *Yetton (2), O.G.*	v Chesham United *Keepence, Kyriacou, Burnell*	3 - 3	511
Chesham United *Ledger, Cooper*	v Truro City *Ash*	R 2 - 1*	279
Oxford City *Jackman, Brooks (2)*	v Aylesbury United	3 - 1	299
AFC Totton *Lank, Davies, Sherbourne*	v Abingdon United *Beechers, Curtin*	3 - 2	211
Chippenham Town *Holly (2)*	v Fleet Town *Field*	2 - 1	316

SECOND QUALIFYING ROUND

BIGGEST HOME WIN:	**4-2** East Thurrock v Gloucester City
BIGGEST AWAY WIN:	**3-6** Hitchin Town v Ramsgate
HIGHEST ATTENDANCE:	**749** Dartford v Oxford City
NUMBER OF GAMES:	**36 + 5** (36 + 11)
TOTAL ATTENDANCE:	**8,922** (13,465)
AVERAGE ATTENDANCE:	**218** (286)

Home	Away	Score	Att
Worksop Town	v FC United of Manchester	0 - 3	599
	Chadwick, Kyle (2)		
Chasetown	v North Ferriby United	1 - 1	377
Onokah	*Bradshaw*		
North Ferriby United	v Chasetown	R 1 - 4	111
Bradshaw	*Holland, Parsons, Harris*		
Buxton	v Skelmersdale United	0 - 1	345
	Donnelly		
Ossett Town	v Bedworth United	1 - 0	110
Lee			
Ashton United	v Ilkeston Town	0 - 2	142
	Douglas, Cahill		
Clitheroe	v Boston United	2 - 4	359
Smith, O.G.	*W. Parker, Rowan (2), L. Parker*		
Marine	v Durham City	1 - 2	206
Cumiskey	*Cogdon, Johnston*		
Romulus	v Warrington Town	2 - 2	115
Fagan (2)	*Daniels, Toney*		
Warrington Town	v Romulus	R 3 - 1*	88
Daniels, Gaghan, Tickle	*Fagan*		
Stourbridge	v Evesham United	2 - 1	198
Broadhurst, Dovey	*Owen*		
Leigh Genesis	v Cammell Laird	1 - 5	94
Sefton	*Adamson, Jebb, Reed, Hay, Rimmer (at Chorley FC)*		
Sutton Coldfield Town	v Glapwell	2 - 3	103
Farrell, Davis	*Shelley, Grayson, Brown*		
Rugby Town	v Nantwich Town	1 - 3	238
Musgrove	*Carter (2), Walker*		
Stamford	v Hednesford Town	3 - 4	245
Coxton (3)	*Durrell, Dyer, Draper (2)*		
Stocksbridge PS	v Whitby Town	0 - 2	153
	Hackworth, Rae		
Swindon Supermarine	v Maidstone United	2 - 0	333
Cook, Taylor			
Great Wakering Rovers	v AFC Sudbury	1 - 1	130
Richmond	*O.G.*		
AFC Sudbury	v Great Wakering Rovers	R 4 - 3*	201
Revell, Heath (2), Tracey	*Johnson, Trenkel, Richmond*		
Soham Town Rangers	v Farnborough	0 - 5	188
	Scott, Gamble (3), Charles		
East Thurrock United	v Gloucester City	4 - 2	134
Cornhill, Touhy (2), Gresham	*Harris, Sykes*		
Boreham Wood	v Uxbridge	1 - 2	77
Mason	*Lawrence, Warner*		
Northwood	v Brackley Town	1 - 4	115
Gordon	*Perpetuini, Cracknell, Mackey (2)*		
Hendon	v Sutton United	1 - 2	269
Hunt	*Dundas, McCallum*	*(at Wembley FC)*	
Harrow Borough	v Hastings United	2 - 3	111
Highton, Clarke	*Adams, Franklyn, O.G.*		
Dover Athletic	v Cambridge City	2 - 3	509
Welford, Collin	*Midgley, Fuller, Calliste*		
Heybridge Swifts	v Chippenham Town	0 - 0	169
Chippenham Town	v Heybridge Swifts	R 0 - 1	223
	King		
Andover	v Merthyr Tydfil	3 - 2	180
Swayne, Jarvis, Turvey	*Shepherd (2)*		
Burnham	v Windsor & Eton	0 - 5	181
	Coyne, Chennels (4)		
Dulwich Hamlet	v Bury Town	0 - 3	245
	Reed (3)		
Dartford	v Oxford City	3 - 3	749
McDonald (3)	*Gunn, Jackman, Gardner*		
Oxford City	v Dartford	R 2 - 4	219
Saulsbury, Faulkner	*Butterworth, McDonald (2), Noble*		
Horsham	v Cray Wanderers	1 - 2	158
Sigere	*Willy, Dolby*		
Hitchin Town	v Ramsgate	3 - 6	246
Sealey, Gregson (2)	*Hadden, Royston, Laslett, May (2), Ball*		
Corby Town	v Chesham United	2 - 3	279
Diggin, Burgess	*Kyriacou, Fotheringham, Marsala*		
Yate Town	v Bashley	1 - 3	148
Griffiths	*Rowe, Gillespie (2)*		
Thatcham Town	v AFC Totton	0 - 4	138
	Richardson, Taylor (2), Dutton-Black		
Concord Rangers	v Hemel Hempstead	1 - 3	117
Heale	*Martin, Roberts, Edgeworth*		
Wealdstone	v Tiverton Town	1 - 2	220
Hicks	*Jarvis, Walsh*		
Wingate & Finchley	v Worthing	1 - 0	100

THIRD QUALIFYING ROUND

BIGGEST HOME WIN:	**6-2** Farnborough v Braintree Tn (replay)
BIGGEST AWAY WIN:	**2-4** Maidenhead Utd v Chesham Utd
HIGHEST ATTENDANCE:	**936** FC Utd of Manchester v Boston Utd
NUMBER OF GAMES:	**40 + 8** (40 + 9)
TOTAL ATTENDANCE:	**14,464** (17,959)
AVERAGE ATTENDANCE:	**301** (367)

Home	Away	Score	Att
Hinckley United	v Burscough	1 - 2	251
Webster	*Parry, Heler*		
King's Lynn	v Stafford Rangers	3 - 2	748
Weaver, Thomas, Joachim	*Palmer, Magee*		
Solihull Moors	v Durham City	1 - 2	196
Edwards	*Cogdon, Johnston*		
Ossett Town	v Fleetwood Town	3 - 1	151
Hay, Baldry, Savory	*Warlow*		
Whitby Town	v Stalybridge Celtic	0 - 3	176
	Woolliscroft, Wood, Joynes		
Redditch United	v Cammell Laird	1 - 1	200
Ayres	*Hay*		
Cammell Laird	v Redditch United	R 0 - 2	132
	Murray, Rawle		
Tamworth	v Workington	0 - 1	433
	Wright		
Warrington Town	v Nantwich Town	0 - 1	232
	Blackhurst		
FC United of Manchester	v Boston United	1 - 3	936
Dieyte	*Parker (2), Ryan*		
Vauxhall Motors	v Southport	0 - 0	287
Southport	v Vauxhall Motors	R 2 - 1	224
Gray, Kilheeney	*Noon*		
Chasetown	v Ilkeston Town	1 - 2	471
Birch	*Cahill, Howell*		
Farsley Celtic	v Droylsden	2 - 0	207
Iqbal, James			
Gainsborough Trinity	v AFC Telford United	0 - 2	441
	Fearns, Carey-Bertram		
Hyde United	v Hednesford Town	1 - 1	275
Simm	*Dyer*		
Hednesford Town	v Hyde United	R 5 - 0	263
Hall, Barnett, Dyer, Draper, O.G.			

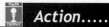

Left: High flying goal mouth action from the 2nd Qualifying Round match at Corby Town in which visitors, Chesham United, won 3-2. Photo: Peter Barnes.

Right: Cambridge City, in possession, won through to the 1st Round after a 1-0 win over visiting club Hastings United. Photo: Peter Barnes.

Blyth Spartans *Gildea, McCabe (2)*	v Alfreton Town *Clayton (2), Law, Hearn*	3 - 4	446
Stourbridge *Hines, Broadhurst (2)*	v Hucknall Town *Ricketts, Bacon*	3 - 2	176
Gateshead	v Harrogate Town *Marshall (2)*	0 - 2	236
Glapwell	v Skelmersdale United *Donnelly*	0 - 1	169
Uxbridge *Warner, Nicholls*	v Dorchester Town *Mudge*	2 - 1	110
Fisher Athletic	v Havant & Waterlooville *Collins, Elphick*	0 - 2	170
Weston Super Mare *Brown*	v AFC Sudbury *Bussens, Heath*	1 - 2	218
Team Bath *Perrott (2)*	v Windsor & Eton *Butler*	2 - 1	114
Swindon Supermarine *Stanley*	v Bromley	1 - 0	229
Braintree Town *Hawes*	v Farnborough *Burton*	1 - 1	212
Farnborough *Woozley, Gamble, Wheeler, Richardson (2)*	v Braintree Town *Hawes, Marks*	R 6 - 2	321
Basingstoke Town *Ruggles*	v Thurrock	1 - 0	202
Cambridge City *Midgley*	v Hastings United	1 - 0	302
Bath City *Jones, Simpson, Gilroy (3)*	v East Thurrock United *Bajowa*	5 - 1	359
Wingate & Finchley *Samuel*	v Sutton United *Downer*	1 - 1	149
Sutton United *Eribeene, Palmer*	v Wingate & Finchley *O'Brien, Chase*	R 2 - 2*	212

(Wingate & Finchley won 4-3 on penalties)

Maidenhead United *Surey, Baptiste*	v Chesham United *Kyriacou, Burnell, Cox (2)*	2 - 4	256
St Albans City	v Dartford	0 - 0	525
Dartford *Haworth*	v St Albans City *Quilter (St Albans won 4-2 on penalties)*	R 1 - 1*	542
Hampton & Richmond Borough *Matthews*	v Bury Town *Walker, Barrett*	1 - 2	334
Cray Wanderers	v Brackley Town *Cracknell, Maluey, Winters*	0 - 3	112
Eastleigh	v Bashley *Rowe, Allen*	0 - 2	424
Andover	v Newport County *Rose, Hughes, Reid*	0 - 3	264
Worcester City *Wilding*	v AFC Wimbledon *Aiteouakrim (2), Godfrey*	1 - 3	895
Ramsgate	v Bognor Regis Town *Jupp, McEnery*	0 - 2	247
Hayes & Yeading United *Knight (4)*	v Chelmsford City *Rainford*	4 - 1	347
Welling United *Sheringham*	v AFC Totton *Gosney*	1 - 1	309
AFC Totton *O.G.*	v Welling United *Sinclair, Smith*	R 1 - 2	232
Hemel Hempstead *Wales, Roberts, Dillon, Sippetts, Edgeworth*	v Heybridge Swifts *King*	5 - 1	168
Bishop's Stortford	v Tiverton Town	0 - 0	271
Tiverton Town *Rudge*	v Bishop's Stortford	R 1 - 0	290

FIRST ROUND PROPER

BIGGEST HOME WIN:	**5-1** Forest Green Rovers v Hemel H.
BIGGEST AWAY WIN:	**1-6** Stourbridge v Stalybridge Celtic
HIGHEST ATTENDANCE:	**1,559** Wrexham v Masnfield Town
NUMBER OF GAMES:	**32 + 3** (32 + 2)
TOTAL ATTENDANCE:	**17,258** (20,852)
AVERAGE ATTENDANCE:	**493** (613)

Home	Away	Score	Att
Altrincham	v Southport	1 - 4	609
Senior	*Duffy, Daly (2), Kilheeney*		
Durham City	v Harrogate Town	2 - 0	232
Laws, Johnston			
Northwich Victoria	v York City	0 - 2	393
	Brodie (2)		
Wrexham	v Mansfield Town	2 - 1	1559
Suffo, Brown	*O'Connor*		
Hednesford Town	v Nantwich Town	3 - 2	264
Durrell, Dyer (2)	*Whittaker, Carter*		
Burton Albion	v Farsley Celtic	1 - 1	923
Pearson	*Speight*		
Farsley Celtic	v Burton Albion	R 2 - 2*	262
Bentham, Campbell	*Banim (2)*	*(Burton won 3-2 on penalties)*	
Ilkeston Town	v Ossett Town	3 - 2	205
Istead, Howell, Douglas			
Barrow	v Skelmersdale United	2 - 1	743
Joyce, Walker			
Alfreton Town	v Redditch United	0 - 1	192
	Smith		
Kidderminster Harriers	v Burscough	3 - 2	685
Jones, Brittain, Moore	*Wade, Heler*		
Workington	v King's Lynn	4 - 3	418
Campion, McLuckie, Arnison (2)	*Graham, Frew, O.G.*		
Stourbridge	v Stalybridge Celtic	1 - 6	148
Canavan	*Barwick, Torpey, Ellington, Barlow (2), Platt*		
Boston United	v AFC Telford United	1 - 2	895
Rowan	*Jagielka, Carey-Bertram*		
Swindon Supermarine	v Eastbourne Borough	1 - 0	302
Stevenage Borough	v St Albans City	4 - 1	737
Boylan, Morison (2), Drury	*Cohen*		
Cambridge City	v Kettering Town	1 - 4	432
Haniver	*Dempster, Solkhon, Arthur, Westcarr*		
AFC Sudbury	v Oxford United	0 - 2	434
	Guy (2)		
Bashley	v Tiverton Town	2 - 2	165
Keeler, Tarr	*Hopkinson, Walsh*		
Tiverton Town	v Bashley	R 2 - 1	436
Walsh, Jarvis	*Keeler*		
Welling United	v Weymouth	2 - 0	262
Ademola, Sheringham			
Histon	v Cambridge United	2 - 3	1346
	Willmott, Rendell (2)		
Forest Green Rovers	v Hemel Hempstead	5 - 1	509
Clist, Mangan, Fowler, McDonald (2)	*Thomas*		
Bognor Regis Town	v Ebbsfleet United	0 - 2	299
	Long, O.G.		
Farnborough	v Wingate & Finchley	3 - 1	304
Charles, Wheeler, Richardson	*Grant*		
Uxbridge	v AFC Wimbledon	2 - 1	582
Dyer (2)	*Aiteouakrim*		
Hayes & Yeading United	v Grays Athletic	2 - 0	158
Havant & Waterlooville	v Bury Town	3 - 1	232
Watkins (3)	*Smith*		
Torquay United	v Bath City	2 - 0	1176
Mansell, D'sane			
Woking	v Salisbury City	1 - 2	506
Marum	*Fowler, Griffin*		
Basingstoke Town	v Brackley Town	3 - 1	221
Watkins, Hankin, Jombarti	*Mackey*		
Newport County	v Rushden & Diamonds	1 - 1	603
Reid	*Rankine*		
Rushden & Diamonds	v Newport County	R 1 - 1*	421
Smith	*Reid*	*(Rushden won 5-3 on penalties)*	
Chesham United	v Crawley Town	2 - 4	399
	Giles, Pittman, Quinn, Fletcher		
Team Bath	v Lewes	1 - 2	206
Smith	*Cullip, Standing*		

SECOND ROUND PROPER

BIGGEST HOME WIN:	**5-0** Forest Green Rovers v Redditch Utd
BIGGEST AWAY WIN:	**1-6** Uxbridge v Swindon Supermarine
HIGHEST ATTENDANCE:	**1,958** Oxford United v York City
NUMBER OF GAMES:	**16 + 3** (16 + 5)
TOTAL ATTENDANCE:	**15,051** (19,160)
AVERAGE ATTENDANCE:	**792** (912)

Home	Away	Score	Att
Lewes	v Havant & Waterlooville	3 - 3	258
Standing, Keehan, Charles	*Simpemba, Nightingale, Booth*		
Havant & Waterlooville	v Lewes	R 4 - 3	302
Walker, Simpemba, Booth, Gray	*Foreman, Minto St Aimie, O.G.*		
Ilkeston Town	v Kidderminster Harriers	3 - 5	401
Cahill (2), Newsham	*Moore, Penn, Richards, Smikle, Brittain*		
Burton Albion	v Salisbury City	3 - 0	1472
Webster (2), Goodfellow			
Basingstoke Town	v Wrexham	1 - 2	597
Jombarti	*Evans, O.G.*		
Hednesford Town	v Welling United	4 - 3	346
Durrell (3), Barnett	*Ming, Sheringham, O.G.*		
Forest Green Rovers	v Redditch United	5 - 0	441
Rigoglioso (2), Platt, Symons, O.G.			
Tiverton Town	v Kettering Town	1 - 1	604
Hopkinson	*Graham*		
Kettering Town	v Tiverton Town	R 1 - 1*	816
Westcarr	*Rudge*	*(Kettering won 4-1 on penalties)*	
Durham City	v Southport	1 - 1	387
Johnston	*Hinn*		
Southport	v Durham City	R 3 - 1	533
Daly (2), Duffy	*Toft*		
AFC Telford United	v Hayes & Yeading United	4 - 0	986
Rodgers, Carey-Bertram, Brown (2)			
Farnborough	v Stevenage Borough	0 - 2	705
	Boylan, Roberts		
Torquay United	v Rushden & Diamonds	1 - 0	1728
Hargreaves			
Ebbsfleet United	v Stalybridge Celtic	2 - 1	467
Long, Hand	*Joynes*		
Barrow	v Workington	0 - 3	1614
	McLuckie, Arnison (2)		
Uxbridge	v Swindon Supermarine	1 - 6	203
Warner	*Allen, Cook (2), Edenborough, Griffin, Hopper*		
Oxford United	v York City	1 - 2	1958
Constable	*McBreen, Brodie*		
Cambridge United	v Crawley Town	0 - 5	1233
	Whetherstone, Pittman (3), Quinn		

Above: Action from the 1st Round match between Histon and Cambridge United.

Below: Semi final 1st leg action from which Stevenage took a slender one goal advantage.

Above: There was nothing between Kettering and Tiverton who drew this 2nd Rnd replay.

Right: Goal mouth action from Steveange's 4-0 win over Forest Green Rovers in Round 4. Photos: Peter Barnes.

THIRD ROUND PROPER

NUMBER OF GAMES: **8 + 1** (8 + 2)
TOTAL ATTENDANCE: **11,724** (13,533)
AVERAGE ATTENDANCE: **1,303** (1,353)

Kettering Town	v AFC Telford United	0 - 1	1692
	Carey-Bertram		
Kidderminster Harriers	v York City	1 - 1	1113
Brittain	*Boyes*		
York City	v Kidderminster Harriers	R 1 - 1*	683
McBreen	*Richards*	*(York won 13-12 on penalties)*	
Workington	v Wrexham	1 - 3	1029
Wright	*Fairhurst, Williams (2)*		
Forest Green Rovers	v Hednesford Town	1 - 0	768
Rigoglioso			
Ebbsfleet United	v Swindon Supermarine	2 - 0	3750
Gash (2)			
Havant & Waterlooville	v Crawley Town	2 - 0	413
Watkins, Nightingale			
Southport	v Torquay United	3 - 0	980
Lee, Daly (2)			
Stevenage Borough	v Burton Albion	4 - 0	1296
Bridges, Morison (2), Cole			

QUARTER FINALS

NUMBER OF GAMES: **4 + 2** (4 + 1)
TOTAL ATTENDANCE: **10,001** (8,075)
AVERAGE ATTENDANCE: **1,667** (1,615)

Wrexham	v Ebbsfleet United	0 - 0	3028
Ebbsfleet United	v Wrexham	R 3 - 1	992
Martin, Moore, Sole	*Louis*		
Stevenage Borough	v Forest Green Rovers	4 - 0	1348
Roberts, Bridges, Morison, Drury			
AFC Telford United	v Southport	2 - 2	2059
Adams, Carey-Bertram	*Lee, Leadbetter*		
Southport	v AFC Telford United	R 0 - 1	895
	Rodgers		
York City	v Havant & Waterlooville	2 - 0	1679
McBreen (2)			

SEMI FINALS

TOTAL ATTENDANCE: **11,656** (12,738)
AVERAGE ATTENDANCE: **2,914** (3,185)

1ST LEG

Stevenage Borough	v Ebbsfleet United	3 - 2	2344
Boylan, Bridges, Morison	*Long, Barrett*		
AFC Telford United	v York City	0 - 2	2792
	Rusk, Purkiss		

2ND LEG

Ebbsfleet United	v Stevenage Borough	0 - 1	3008
	Vincenti		
York City	v AFC Telford United	2 - 1	3512
McBreen, Brodie	*Brown*		

THE FINAL

STEVENAGE BOROUGH 2 YORK CITY 0

(Blue Square Premier) (Blue Square Premier)

at Wembley Stadium Attendance 27,102

Having battled their way through the knockout competition provided by over 260 other teams, 263 and 262 in different places in the programme, these two sides found they were sharing their day with question marks about the state of the newly laid pitch following replacement of the surface used for F A Cup semi-finals three weeks previously. In this event, the 40th Trophy final and the 33rd at Wembley, despite spectators being able to see clearly the pattern of the strips of turf which had been used, the surface, the seventh attempt so far, played no part in the outcome. In fact Borough boss Graham Westley believed it rewarded good football. A shame we did not see all that much of such skill in a largely one sided game, out of which Stevenage gained some compensation for their exit from the Conference play offs at the semi final stage.

Spectators saw some glimpses of excitement but City supporters would have been disappointed that the evident gulf between the two teams prevented a more competitive occasion. Despite the razzmatazz engendered by pounding 'music' and a shrilly shrieking stadium announcer, the red carpet for anonymous individuals of "representatives of the FA and sponsors Carlsberg" who were presented to the teams, and the cavorting of Setanta staff with uninhibited access, the game itself did not contribute to the carnival atmosphere that had been attempted.

In their 'one off' purple shirts, a tribute to their archbishop, the autographed garments were later to be auctioned for charity. However it meant the Minstermen wearing Cadbury's colours for a one time Rowntree city. York were first to attack. Brodie raced down the right but his low cross was scuffed by McBreen and went wide. Borough's Murphy then opened his side's efforts but shot straight at Ingham. Pejic and Mills each had an off target effort before Morrison four times, Boylan, Drury and Bostwick's attempts to one from Brodie demonstrated the attacking superiority of Stevenage. Red flares, somehow smuggled in by York fans, could have been signs of their distress.

A mass time out for water intake after 36 minutes, while Mills received treatment, showed that it was pretty hot down there, even with the non operational roof still stuck on open after two years. Two more goal attempts for each side followed but half time arrived with no score.

The second half opened with a chance for Boylan but, with the York defence, appealing for handball, he placed it wide. A free kick then rescued Ingham as he was prevented from reaching Henry's cross. Stevenage were noticeably now pushing more men forward. Vincenti's powerful shot was diverted wide before, in the 68th minute, Roberts, up for a corner, headed down and Morison, at the second attempt, touched it home. Immediately the lead was close to double when Vincenti headed wide from Henry's cross. Parslow almost headed into his own net before a York foul led to a brief, belligerent scene, untypical of the game.

Another York booking was indicative of their frustration and disappointment in being unable to carve out goalscoring attempts and in injury time their fate was sealed with the best shot of the match. A throw in found Boylan completely unmarked to belt the ball over Ingham and that was that, apart from the stage managed jumping up and down of the victors on the hastily erected platform in front of the winner's fans, complete with detonated silver foil ticker tape, and strategically placed fizz for the compulsory spraying of team mates, all accompanied by the throbbing, very loud, electronic cacophony. Commercialism reigned.

Morison, rumoured to be off to Millwall, was announced as man of the match. Few would disagree, although Drury ran him close, for he set a fine example of endeavour and persistent effort. None of the participants could be faulted in that respect but there was certainly, and regrettably, more hype than substance to this match. **ARTHUR EVANS**

STEVENAGE BOROUGH:
Chris Day, Ronnie Henry, Michael Bostwick, Mark Roberts, Lawrie Wilson, Gary Mills, Darren Murphy, Andy Drury, Peter Vincenti (Eddie Anaclet 86th min), Lee Boylan, Steve Morison.
Subs not used: Ashley Bayes, Mark Albrighton, Dino Maamria and Calum Willock.

YORK CITY:
Michael Ingham, Ben Purkiss, David McGurk, Danny Parslow, Shaun Pejic, Levi Mackin, Mark Greaves(sub Andrew McWilliams 74th min), Simon Rusk (Simon Russell 80th min), Richard Brodie, Daniel McBreen (Onome Sodje 60th min), Adam Boyes.
Subs not used – Josh Mimms and Mark Robinson.

Referee: Michael Jones, assisted by Jake Collins and Adam Watts.
Fourth official – Robert Shoebridge.

Left: Lee Boylan, Stevenage Borough, takes the ball around York City's Shaun Pejic.
Photo: Roger Turner.

Middle left: Stevenage's Ronny Henry and York's Onome Sodje are both intent on getting to the ball first.
Photo: Keith Clayton.

Below: York City's Adam Boyes gets in a shot before Ronny Henry can get in a tackle.
Photo: Alan Coomes.

Below: York's skipper, Danny Parslow, is unable to stop Steve Morison firing in the opening goal.
Photo: Roger Turner.

PAST F.A. TROPHY FINALS

1970 MACCLESFIELD TOWN 2 (Lyons, B Fidler) TELFORD UNITED 0 Att: 28,000
Northern Premier League *Southern League*
Macclesfield: Cooke, Sievwright, Bennett, Beaumont, Collins, Roberts, Lyons, B Fidler,Young, Corfield, D Fidler.
Telford: Irvine, Harris, Croft, Flowers, Coton, Ray,Fudge, Hart, Bentley, Murray, Jagger. Ref: K Walker

1971 TELFORD UTD 3 (Owen, Bentley, Fudge) HILLINGDON BORO. 2 (Reeve, Bishop) Att: 29,500
Southern League *Southern League*
Telford: Irvine, Harris, Croft, Ray, Coton, Carr, Fudge, Owen, Bentley, Jagger ,Murray.
Hillingdon B.: Lowe, Batt, Langley, Higginson, Newcombe, Moore, Fairchild,Bishop, Reeve, Carter, Knox. Ref: D Smith

1972 STAFFORD RANGERS 3 (Williams 2, Cullerton) BARNET 0 Att: 24,000
Northern Premier League *Southern League*
Stafford R.: Aleksic, Chadwick, Clayton, Sargeant, Aston, Machin, Cullerton, Chapman,Williams, Bayley, Jones.
Barnet: McClelland, Lye, Jenkins, Ward, Embrey, King, Powell, Ferry, Flatt, Easton, Plume . Ref: P Partridge

1973 SCARBOROUGH 2 (Leask, Thompson) WIGAN ATHLETIC 1 (Rogers) aet Att:23,000
Northern Premier League *Northern Premier League*
Scarborough: Garrow, Appleton, Shoulder, Dunn, Siddle, Fagan, Donoghue, Franks,Leask (Barmby), Thompson, Hewitt.
Wigan: Reeves, Morris, Sutherland, Taylor,Jackson, Gillibrand, Clements, Oats (McCunnell), Rogers, King, Worswick. Ref: H Hackney

1974 MORECAMBE 2 (Richmond, Sutton) DARTFORD 1 (Cunningham) Att: 19,000
Northern Premier League *Southern League*
Morecambe: Coates, Pearson, Bennett, Sutton, Street, Baldwin, Done, Webber,Roberts (Galley), Kershaw, Richmond.
Dartford: Morton, Read, Payne, Carr, Burns,Binks, Light, Glozier, Robinson (Hearne), Cunningham, Halleday. Ref: B Homewood

1975 **1** MATLOCK TOWN 4 (Oxley, Dawson, T Fenoughty, N Fenoughy) SCARBOROUGH 0 Att: 21,000
Northern Premier League *Northern Premier League*
Matlock: Fell, McKay, Smith, Stuart, Dawson, Swan, Oxley, N Fenoughy, Scott, T Fenoughty, M Fenoughty.
Scarborough: Williams, Hewitt, Rettitt, Dunn, Marshall, Todd, Houghton, Woodall, Davidson, Barnby, Aveyard. Ref: K Styles

1976 SCARBOROUGH 3 (Woodall, Abbey, Marshall(p)) STAFFORD R. 2 (Jones 2) aet Att: 21,000
Northern Premier League *Northern Premier League*
Scarborough: Barnard, Jackson, Marshall, H Dunn, Ayre (Donoghue), HA Dunn, Dale,Barmby, Woodall, Abbey, Hilley.
Stafford: Arnold, Ritchie, Richards, Sargeant,Seddon, Morris, Chapman, Lowe, Jones, Hutchinson, Chadwick. Ref: R Challis

1977 SCARBOROUGH 2 (Dunn(p), Abbey) DAGENHAM 1 (Harris)
Northern Premier League *Isthmian League* Att: 21,500
Scarborough: Chapman, Smith, Marshall (Barmby), Dunn, Ayre, Deere, Aveyard,Donoghue, Woodall, Abbey, Dunn.
Dagenham: Hutley, Wellman, P Currie, Dunwell,Moore, W Currie, Harkins, Saul, Fox, Harris, Holder. Ref: G Courtney

1978 ALTRINCHAM 3 (King, Johnson, Rogers) LEATHERHEAD 1 (Cook)
Northern Premier League *Isthmian League* Att: 20,000
Altrincham: Eales, Allan, Crossley, Bailey, Owens, King, Morris, Heathcote,Johnson, Rogers, Davidson (Flaherty).
Leatherhead: Swannell, Cooper, Eaton, Davies,Reid, Malley, Cook, Salkeld, Baker, Boyle (Bailey). Ref: A Grey

1979 STAFFORD RANGERS 2 (A Wood 2) KETTERING TOWN 0
Northern Premier League *Southern League* Att: 32,000
Stafford: Arnold, F Wood, Willis, Sargeant, Seddon, Ritchie, Secker, Chapman, A Wood, Cullerton, Chadwick (Jones).
Kettering: Lane, Ashby, Lee, Eastell, Dixey,Suddards, Flannagan, Kellock, Phipps, Clayton, Evans (Hughes). Ref: D Richardson

1980 **2** DAGENHAM 2 (Duck, Maycock) MOSSLEY 1 (Smith)
Isthmian League *Northern Premier League* Att : 26,000
Dagenham: Huttley, Wellman, Scales, Dunwell, Mooore, Durrell, Maycock, Horan,Duck, Kidd, Jones (Holder).
Mossley: Fitton, Brown, Vaughan, Gorman, Salter, Polliot, Smith, Moore, Skeete, O'Connor, Keelan (Wilson). Ref: K Baker

1981 **3** BISHOP'S STORTFORD 1 (Sullivan) SUTTON UNITED 0
Isthmian League *Isthmian League* Att:22,578
Bishop's Stortford: Moore, Blackman, Brame, Smith (Worrell), Bradford, Abery, Sullivan,Knapman, Radford, Simmonds, Mitchell.
Sutton Utd.: Collyer, Rogers, Green, J Rains,T Rains, Stephens (Sunnucks), Waldon, Pritchard, Cornwell, Parsons, Dennis. Ref: J Worrall

1982
ENFIELD 1 (Taylor) ALTRINCHAM 0
Alliance Premier League *Alliance Premier League* Att:18.678
Enfield: Jacobs, Barrett, Tone, Jennings, Waite, Ironton, Ashford, Taylor,Holmes, Oliver (Flint), King. Ref: B Stevens
Altrincham: Connaughton, Crossley, Davison, Bailey, Cuddy, King (Whitbread), Allan, Heathcote, Johnson, Rogers, Howard.

Notes:

1 The only occasion three members of the same family played in the same FA Trophy Final team.
2 The first of the Amateurs from the Isthmian League to win the FA Trophy.
3 Goalkeeper Terry Moore had also won an Amateur Cup Winners Medal with Bishop's Stortford in 1974.
All games played at Wembley (old & new) unless stated.

1983 TELFORD UTD 2 (Mather 2) — NORTHWICH VICTORIA 1 (Bennett) — Att: 22,071
Alliance Premier League — *Alliance Premier League*
Telford: Charlton, Lewis, Turner, Mayman (Joseph), Walker, Easton, Barnett,Williams, Mather, Hogan, Alcock.
Northwich: Ryan, Fretwell, Murphy, Jones, Forshaw, Ward, Anderson, Abel (Bennett), Reid, Chesters, Wilson. Ref: B Hill

1984 NORTHWICH VICTORIA 1 (Chester) — BANGOR CITY 1 (Whelan) — Att: 14,200
Replay NORTHWICH VICTORIA 2 (Chesters(p), Anderson) — BANGOR CITY 1 (Lunn) — Att: 5,805 (at Stoke)
Alliance Premier League — *Alliance Premier League*
Northwich: Ryan, Fretwell, Dean, Jones, Forshaw (Power 65), Bennett, Anderson,Abel, Reid, Chesters, Wilson. Ref: J Martin
Bangor: Letheren, Cavanagh, Gray, Whelan, Banks,Lunn, Urqhart, Morris, Carter, Howat, Sutcliffe (Westwood 105) . Same in replay.

1985 WEALDSTONE 2 (Graham, Holmes) — BOSTON UNITED 1 (Cook) — Att: 20,775
Alliance Premier League — *Alliance Premier League*
Wealdstone: Iles, Perkins, Bowgett, Byatt, Davies, Greenaway, Holmes, Wainwright,Donnellan, Graham (N Cordice 89), A Cordice.
Boston: Blackwell, Casey, Ladd,Creane, O'Brien, Thommson, Laverick (Mallender 78), Simpsom, Gilbert, Lee, Cook. Ref: J Bray

1986 ALTRINCHAM 1 (Farrelly) — RUNCORN 0 — Att: 15,700
Gola League — *Gola League*
Altrincham: Wealands, Gardner, Densmore, Johnson, Farrelly, Conning, Cuddy,Davison, Reid, Ellis, Anderson. Sub: Newton.
Runcorn: McBride, Lee, Roberts,Jones, Fraser, Smith, S Crompton (A Crompton), Imrie, Carter, Mather, Carrodus. Ref: A Ward

1987 KIDDERMINSTER HARRIERS 0 — BURTON ALBION 0 — Att: 23,617
Replay KIDDERMINSTER HARRIERS 2 (Davies 2) — BURTON ALBION 1 (Groves) — Att: 15,685 (at West Brom)
Conference — *Southern League*
Kidderminster: Arnold, Barton, Boxall, Brazier (sub Hazlewood in rep), Collins (sub Pearson 90 at Wembley), Woodall, McKenzie, O'Dowd, Tuohy, Casey, Davies. sub:Jones.
Burton: New, Essex, Kamara, Vaughan, Simms, Groves, Bancroft, Land, Dorsett, Redfern, (sub Wood in replay), Gauden.
Sub: Patterson. Ref: D Shaw

1988 ENFIELD 0 — TELFORD UNITED 0 — Att: 20,161, Ref: L Dilkes
Replay ENFIELD 3 (Furlong 2, Howell) — TELFORD 2 (Biggins, Norris(p)) — Att: 6,912 (at W Brom)
Conference — *Conference*
Enfield: Pape, Cottington, Howell, Keen (sub Edmonds in rep), Sparrow (sub Hayzleden at Wembley), Lewis (sub Edmonds at Wembley), Harding, Cooper, King,Furlong, Francis.
Telford: Charlton, McGinty, Storton, Nelson, Wiggins, Mayman (sub Cunningham in rep (sub Hancock)), Sankey, Joseph, Stringer (sub Griffiths at Wembley, Griffiths in replay), Biggins, Norris.

1989 TELFORD UNITED 1 (Crawley) — MACCLESFIELD TOWN 0 — Att: 18,102
Conference — *Conference*
Telford: Charlton, Lee, Brindley, Hancock, Wiggins, Mayman, Grainger, Joseph, Nelson, Lloyd, Stringer. Subs: Crawley, Griffiths.
Macclesfield: Zelem, Roberts, Tobin, Edwards, Hardman, Askey, Lake, Hanton, Imrie, Burr, Timmons. Subs: Devonshire, Kendall.
Ref: T Holbrook

1990 BARROW 3 (Gordon 2, Cowperthwaite) — LEEK TOWN 0 — Att: 19,011
Conference — *Northern Premier League*
Barrow: McDonnell, Higgins, Chilton, Skivington, Gordon, Proctor, Doherty (Burgess), Farrell (Gilmore), Cowperthwaite, Lowe, Ferris.
Leek: Simpson, Elsby (Smith), Pearce, McMullen, Clowes, Coleman (Russell),Mellor, Somerville, Sutton, Millington, Norris Ref: T Simpson

1991 WYCOMBE W. 2 (Scott, West) — KIDDERMINSTER HARRIERS 1 (Hadley) — Att: 34,842
Conference — *Conference*
Wycombe: Granville, Crossley, Cash, Kerr, Creaser, Carroll, Ryan, Stapleton,West, Scott, Guppy (Hutchinson). Ref: J Watson
Kidderminster: Jones, Kurila, McGrath, Weir, Barnett, Forsyth, Joseph (Wilcox), Howell (Whitehouse), Hadley, Lilwall, Humphries

1992 COLCHESTER UTD* 3 (Masters, Smith, McGavin) — WITTON ALBION 1 (Lutkevitch) — Att: 27,806
Conference — *Conference*
Colchester: Barrett, Donald, Roberts, Knsella, English, Martin, Cook, Masters,McDonough (Bennett 65), McGavin, Smith. Ref: K P Barratt
Witton: Mason, Halliday, Coathup, McNeilis, Jim Connor, Anderson, Thomas, Rose, Alford, Grimshaw (Joe Connor), Lutkevitch (McCluskie)

1993 WYCOMBE W*. 4 (Cousins, Kerr, Thompson, Carroll) — RUNCORN 1 (Shaughnessy) — Att: 32,968
Conference — *Conference*
Wycombe: Hyde, Cousins, Cooper, Kerr, Crossley, Thompson (Hayrettin 65),Carroll, Ryan, Hutchinson, Scott, Guppy. Sub: Casey.
Runcorn: Williams, Bates, Robertson, Hill, Harold (Connor 62), Anderson, Brady (Parker 72), Brown, Shaughnessy, McKenna, Brabin
Ref: I J Borritt

1994 WOKING 2 (D Brown, Hay) — RUNCORN 1 (Shaw (pen)) — Att: 15,818
Conference — *Conference*
Woking: Batty, Tucker, L Wye, Berry, Brown, Clement, Brown (Rattray 32), Fielder, Steele, Hay (Puckett 46), Walker. Ref: Paul Durkin
Runcorn: Williams, Bates, Robertson, Shaw, Lee, Anderson, Thomas, Connor, McInerney (Hill 71), McKenna, Brabin. Sub: Parker

1995 WOKING 2 (Steele, Fielder) — KIDDERMINSTER HARRIERS 1 aet (Davies) — Att: 17,815
Conference — *Conference*
Woking: Batty, Tucker, L Wye, Fielder, Brown, Crumplin (Rattray 42), S Wye, Ellis, Steele, Hay (Newberry 112), Walker. (Sub: Read(gk)
Kidderminster: Rose, Hodson, Bancroft, Webb, Brindley (Cartwright 94), Forsyth, Deakin, Yates, Humphreys (Hughes 105), Davies, Purdie. Sub: Dearlove (gk) Ref: D J Gallagher

1996 MACCLESFIELD TOWN 3 (Payne, OG, Hemmings) NORTHWICH VICTORIA 1 (Williams) Att: 8,672
Conference *Conference*
Macclesfield: Price, Edey, Gardiner, Payne, Howarth(C), Sorvel, Lyons, Wood (Hulme 83), Coates, Power, Hemmings (Cavell 88).
Northwich: Greygoose, Ward, Duffy, Burgess (Simpson 87), Abel (Steele), Walters, Williams, Butler (C), Cooke, Humphries, Vicary.
Ref: M Reed

1997 WOKING 1 (Hay 112) DAGENHAM & REDBRIDGE 0 Att: 24,376
Conference *Isthmian League*
Woking: Batty, Brown, Howard, Foster, Taylor, S Wye, Thompson (sub Jones 115), Ellis, Steele (L Wye 108), Walker, Jackson (Hay 77).
Dagenham: Gothard, Culverhouse, Connor, Creaser, Jacques (sub Double 75), Davidson, Pratt (Naylor 81), Parratt, Broom, Rogers, Stimson (John 65). Ref: J Winter

1998 CHELTENHAM TOWN 1 (Eaton 74) SOUTHPORT 0 Att: 26,387
Conference *Conference*
Cheltenham: Book, Duff, Freeman, Banks, Victory, Knight (Smith 78), Howells, Bloomer, Walker (sub Milton 78), Eaton, Watkins. Sub: Wright.
Southport: Stewart, Horner, Futcher, Ryan, Farley, Kielty, Butler, Gamble, Formby (sub Whittaker 80), Thompson (sub Bollard 88), Ross. Sub: Mitten. Ref: G S Willard

1999 KINGSTONIAN 1 (Mustafa 49) FOREST GREEN ROVERS 0 Att: 20,037
Conference *Conference*
Kingstonian: Farrelly, Mustafa, Luckett, Crossley, Stewart, Harris, Patterson, Pitcher, Rattray, Leworthy (Francis 87), Akuamoah. Subs (not used): John, Corbett, Brown, Tranter
Forest Green Rovers: Shuttlewood, Hedges, Forbes, Bailey (Smart 76), Kilgour, Wigg (Cook 58), Honor (Winter 58), Drysdale, McGregor, Mehew, Sykes. Subs (not used): Perrin, Coupe Ref: A B Wilkie

2000 KINGSTONIAN 3 (Akuamoah 40, 69, Simba 75) KETTERING TOWN 2 (Vowden 55, Norman 64p) Att: 20,034
Conference *Conference*
Kingstonian: Farelly, Mustafa, Luckett, Crossley, Stewart (Saunders 77), Harris, Kadi (Leworthy 83), Pitcher, Green (Basford 86), Smiba, Akuamoah. Subs (not used): Hurst, Allan
Kettering Town: Sollit, McNamara, Adams, Perkins, Vowden, Norman (Duik 76), Fisher, Brown, Shutt, Watkins (Hudson 46), Setchell (Hopkins 81). Subs (not used): Ridgway, Wilson Ref: S W Dunn

2001 CANVEY ISLAND 1 (Chenery) FOREST GREEN ROVERS 0 at Villa Park Att: 10,007
Isthmian League *Conference*
Forest Green Rovers: Perrin, Cousins, Lockwood, Foster, Clark, Burns, Daley, Drysdale (Bennett 46), Foster (Hunt 75), Meecham, Slater. Subs (not used): Hedges, Prince, Ghent
Canvey Island: Harrison, Duffy, Chenery, Bodley, Ward, Tilson, Stimson (Tanner 83), Gregory, Vaughan (Jones 76), Parmenter. Subs (not used): Bennett, Miller, Thompson. Ref: A G Wiley

2002 YEOVIL TOWN 2 (Alford, Stansfield) STEVENAGE BOROUGH 0 at Villa Park Att: 18,809
Conference *Conference*
Yeovil Town: Weale, Lockwood, Tonkin, Skiverton, Pluck (White 51), Way, Stansfield, Johnson, Alford (Giles 86), Crittenden (Lindegaard 83), McIndoe. Subs (not used): O'Brien, Sheffield
Stevenage Borough: Wilkerson, Hamsher, Goodliffe, Trott, Fraser, Fisher, Wormull (Stirling 71), Evers (Williams 56), Jackson, Sigere (Campbell 74), Clarke. Subs (not used): Campbell, Greygoose Ref: N S Barry

2003 BURSCOUGH 2 (Martindale 25, 55) TAMWORTH 1 (Cooper 78) at Villa Park Att: 14,265
Northern Premier *Southern Premier*
Burscough: Taylor, Teale, Taylor, Macauley (White 77), Lawless, Bowen, Wright, Norman, Martindale (McHale 80), Byrne (Bluck 84), Burns. Subs (not used): McGuire (g/k) Molyneux.
Tamworth: Acton, Warner, Follett, Robinson, Walsh, Cooper, Colley, Evans (Turner 64), Rickards (Hatton 88), McGorry, Sale (Hallam 54). Subs (not used): Grocutt, Barnes (g/k). Ref: U D Rennie

2004 HEDNESFORD TOWN 3 (Maguire 28, Hines 53, Brindley 87) CANVEY ISLAND 2 (Boylan 46, Brindley 48 og) at Villa Park Att: 6,635
Southern Premier *Isthmian Premier Champions*
Hednesford Town: Young, Simkin, Hines, King, Brindley, Ryder (Barrow 59), Palmer, Anthrobus, Danks (Piearce 78), Maguire, Charie (Evans 55). Subs (not used): Evans (g/k) McGhee.
Canvey Island: Potter, Kennedy, Duffy, Chenery, Cowan, Gooden (Dobinson 89), Minton, Gregory (McDougald 80), Boylan, Midgley (Berquez 73), Ward. Subs (not used): Theobald, Harrison (g/k). Ref: M L Dean

2005 GRAYS ATHLETIC 1 (Martin 65) Pens: 6 HUCKNALL TOWN 1 (Ricketts 75) Pens: 5 at Villa Park Att: 8,116
Conference South *Conference North*
Grays Athletic: Bayes, Brennan, Nutter, Stuart, Matthews, Thurgood, Oli (Powell 80), Hopper (Carthy 120), Battersby (sub West 61), Martin, Cole. Subs (not used): Emberson, Bruce..
Hucknall Town: Smith, Asher, Barrick (Plummer 30), Hunter, Timons, Cooke, Smith (Ward 120), Palmer (Heathcote 94), Ricketts, Bacon, Todd. Subs (not used): Winder, Lindley. Ref: P Dowd

2006 GRAYS ATHLETIC 2 (Oli, Poole) WOKING 0 at Upton Park Att: 13,997
Conference *Conference*
Grays Athletic: Bayes, Sambrook, Nutter, Stuart, Hanson, Kightly (Williamson 90), Thurgood, Martin, Poole, Oli, McLean. Subs (not used): Eyre (g/k), Hooper, Olayinka, Mawer.
Woking: Jalal, Jackson, MacDonald, Nethercott (Watson 60), Hutchinson, Murray, Smith (Cockerill 60), Evans (Blackman 85), Ferguson, McAllister, Justin Richards. Subs (not used): Davis (g/k), El-Salahi. Ref: Howard Webb (Sheffield)

2007 KIDDERMINSTER HARRIERS 2 (Constable 2) STEVENAGE BOROUGH 3 (Cole, Dobson, Morrison)
Conference *Conference* Att: 53,262 (New Trophy record)
Kidderminster Harriers: Bevan, Kenna, Hurren, Creighton, Whitehead, Blackwood, Russell, Penn, Smikle (Reynolds 90), Christie (White 75) , Constable.
Subs not used: Taylor, Sedgemore, McGrath.
Stevenage Borough: Julian, Fuller, Nutter, Oliver, Gaia, Miller, Cole, Morrison, Guppy (Dobson 63), Henry, Beard.
Subs not used: Potter, Slabber, Nurse, McMahon. Ref: Chris Foy (Merseyside)

2008 EBBSFLEET UNITED 1 (McPhee) *Blue Square Premier* — TORQUAY UNITED 0 *Blue Square Premier* — Att: 40,186

Ebbsfleet United: Cronin, Hawkins, McCarthy, Smith, Opinel, McPhee, Barrett, Bostwick, Long (MacDonald 84), Moore, Akinde.
Subs not used: Eribenne, Purcell, Ricketts, Mott.

Torquay United: Rice, Mansell, Todd, Woods, Nicholson, D'Sane (Benyon 66), Hargreaves, Adams, Zebroski, Sills (Hill 88), Phillips (Stevens 46).
Subs not used: Matt Hockley and Chris Robertson. Ref: Martin Atkinson (West Riding)

Above: Chris Day, Stevenage 'keeper, out jumps Ebbfleet's Sacha Opinel during the 2nd leg of their Semi Final. Photo: Roger Turner.

Action.....

Lawrie Wilson, Stevenage, evades the tackle of York's David McGurk.
Photo: Keith Clayton.

Wembley action taken by Peter Barnes.

FIRST QUALIFYING ROUND

The first Vase matches were due to be played on the weekend 6th/7th/8th September but wild weather prevented many of the northern fixtures to be completed at the week-end. It's very early to be knocked out of your main national cup competition but Hoddesden Town, the first Vase winners in 1975, lost on a Friday evening fixture at home to Colney Heath so had the dubious honour of being the first club to be eliminated in last season's competition.

The opposition in 1975 were Epsom & Ewell and the Surrey club along with Guisborough Town, runners up in 1980, also played in the Preliminary Round but these two successfully moved on to the next round.

Up in the North East, where the bad weather forced the postponements, two very famous names from the old Amateur Cup; Crook Town and Bishop Auckland featured in this round and won their respective matches.

SECOND QUALIFYING ROUND

The biggest round of the competition covered the country with pairings linking relatively local opposition. Clubs with good Vase pedigrees such as St. Helens Town and AFC Emley both lost at home, but names to keep an eye on such as Bodmin Town, who won 4-0 at Wadebridge Town and Spennymoor Town, 4-2 winners at Tow Law Town, were obviously keen to enjoy a good Vase run.

Arnold Town are sometimes considered another 'sleeping giant' at this level, and they also impressed away from home in this round with a 6-2 win at Blaby & Whetstone Athletic, while Leiston, who were to become the most successful Vase level club in the F.A.Cup last season, beat Huntingdon Town 5-1.

It is imperative that any club with ambitions for a good run, hangs on and battles in the early rounds, as strange results often occur in front of small attendances before the competition settles down. The F.A.Vase can bring little clubs amazing publicity and can change their whole attitude to the game, but the early rounds have to be survived.

FIRST ROUND PROPER

For the clubs who have already played twice in the competition, The First Round Proper is the first important stage to underline the fact the competition is becoming tougher and more serious.

In a traditional Northern League clash, Crook Town lost 2-4 at home to Shildon and from the Eastern side of the country Leiston won 2-0 at Wroxham. But Western hope Bodmin Town lost 2-3 away to Brislington

Outstanding victories were gained by Bridlington Town 6-1 v West Allotment Celtic, Stratford Town who beat Coleshill Town 6-0 and Tiptree United who scored eight without reply against Hertford Town.

Senior clubs with exemptions would now be joining the competition, but although it was only early October, with three rounds successfully negotiated, some clubs with three Vase victories under their belt already have the confidence gained from an exciting cup run.

SECOND ROUND

The last 64 clubs in the F.A.Vase emerge from this round and clubs such as Spennymoor Town and Leiston not only have survived from the First Qualifying Round but also beat Stokesley S.C. and Debenham L.C. respectively to feature in the Third Round draw.

Holders A.F.C. Fylde drew tough opposition in Newcastle Benfield but progressed with a 1-0 victory. Two of the leaders in the Hellenic League, Almondsbury Town and Hungerford Town met in Bristol with the visitors going through 2-0 and Whitley Bay looked in good form during their 5-2 defeat of Abbey Hey.

Three other favoured clubs showed they meant business as Bideford won 4-2 at Brislington, Lowestoft Town beat Tiptree Town 2-0 and Arnold recorded another convincing victory, beating Pilkington XXX 4-0 at home.

THIRD ROUND

Two clubs hit the headlines with six goals at home. Scarborough Athletic beating Blackstones 6-1 and Biggleswade Town thrashing Wivenhoe Town 6-0. Results like these excite supporters who begin to wonder whether it could be their year and perhaps a trip to Wembley could be a real possibility.

With another home tie, AFC Fylde won 4-1 against Runcorn Linnets and Leiston and Lowestoft, also with home ties, beat Aylesbury Vale 4-1 and Harefield United 2-1 respectively.

Supporters usually prefer their clubs to meet opposition from outside their own league in the cup competitions, so ties like the Bideford v Frome Town (2-1) and Christchurch v New Milton United (3-0) probably won't have created as much interest, but the winning clubs can look forward to possible new opposition in the open Fourth Round draw.

FOURTH ROUND

The open draw was certainly best illustrated by Bideford hosting Scarborough Athletic in this round, and a 1-0 victory kept the Devon club in the competition, although I am sure the Yorkshire party will have enjoyed the week-end away finding it an exciting and worthwhile experience.

Needham Market were held to a 0-0 draw by visitors A.F.C.Fylde, and then the Eastern Club produced a superb result by beating the holders 2-1 in the replay in Lancashire.

Leiston's wonderful cup season came to an end after a long trip from east to west, where they faced Hungerford Town who won a thriller 3-2. Lowestoft attracted the day's top attendance of 759 to see them beat Witney United and Chalfont St Peter travelled all the way up to the North East where they won the tie of the round, 6-5 after extra time!

Good away victories were celebrated by Marske United of the Northern League who travelled to V.C.D. Athletic of the Wessex League and won 3-2 with Whitley Bay, another Northern 'giant,' who crossed the country to Lancashire to win 3-1. The strong clubs are emerging now and the last sixteen will provide some quality matches.

FIFTH ROUND

Only one game of the eight was played on Fifth Round Saturday because of nationwide snow storms apart from the West Country, where the unlucky Spennymoor Town were the first to lose in this round, as Bideford beat them 2-0 in Devon.

The round developed slowly and on the next Saturday an extra time win for Lowestoft Town must have thrilled the home support of 1,042 for, after trailing 1-3 to Hungerford Town, who were punished for having two players dismissed, the home side came back to win 4-3 with a hat-trick from Russell Stock.

Victories for Chalfont St Peter, Biggleswade Town and Glossop North End all brought new names to the quarter finals while Needham Market had lost in the semi-finals in the previous campaign so they had a point to prove.

Whitley Bay had the best F.A.Vase record and they also joined the last eight with a confident 2-0 home victory over Stratford Town. While the last Fifth Round tie to be completed saw Marske United achieve a fine 3-0 away win at St Ives Town and reach the Sixth Round for the second time.

QUARTER FINALS

The Quarter Finals produced three substantial home wins in front of crowds of four figures and a 1-1 draw when Needham Market entertained Chalfont St Peter, where a disappointing crowd of 579 watched both sides score in the first half of extra time. The replay in front of a similar attendance didn't produce a single goal but Chalfont St Peter celebrated after a 6-5 penalty shoot out triumph.

Glossop North End (North West Counties) were always in control against Marske United (Northern League) and thrilled their supporters with a fine 5-2 victory. Last years losing finalists Lowestoft Town (Eastern Counties) recorded an overwhelming 4-0 win over Bideford (Western League) with two more goals from Stock. Vase favourites Whitley Bay (Northern League) were also in complete command over Biggleswade Town (Spartan South Midlands) and ran out 5-2 victors.

SEMI-FINALS

With twenty goals scored in the four quarter final ties plus eleven successful penalties in the shoot out, the fans were looking forward to two entertaining semi-finals. No-one was disappointed. The first legs produced two thrillers. A 3-3 draw at Chalfont St Peter included two late goals for the visitors and the two favourites, Whitley Bay and Lowestoft Town who had been drawn together, attracted 2,907 with the home side edging their first meeting by 2-1. 'Bay' appeared to be cruising 2-0, but a late penalty for the visitors kept Lowestoft very much in contention for their home tie.

The Second leg at Glossop was watched by 1,538 and was just as tight. With a 1-1 scoreline after ninety minutes, Chalfont appeared to be on their way to Wembley, as injury time was being played, but the drama continued and a Glossop equaliser was officially credited at 120 minutes +4. So a Wembley place depended on a penalty shoot out and as the home side had reached the Semi-Finals through penalties, perhaps Chalfont St Peter were favourites. But Glossop had just 'come back from the dead' with a last minute equaliser, and it was their high spirits that may have just made the difference as the Northern club won 6-5 from the spot.

Meanwhile, an excellent 2,250 attendance at Lowestoft saw two quality cup sides continue a tight battle for the full ninety minutes. A very early goal for the home team brought the aggregate score level but Whitley Bay went ahead again just ten minutes later and kept that lead to the final whistle. Once again the F.A.Challenge Vase had produced a superb competition with plenty of drama and some 'best ever Vase runs' for a number of ambitious clubs who will probably be hoping to move on to The F.A.Trophy in the near future.

Lowestoft Town and my old club Hungerford Town have done that by qualifying for The Southern League. Hungerford had competed in every F.A.Vase competition since its conception in 1975, and everyone there will miss the competition and will always be sorry that those three semi-finals and indeed last two years good runs didn't ever bring an appearance in the final. Lowestoft, of course will feel its time to move on after enjoying a final in 2007 and last year's run to the semi-final. Good luck to them both in the F.A.Trophy.

TW.

FIRST QUALIFYING ROUND

BIGGEST HOME WIN:	**6-0** New Mills v Wolverhampton Casuals
BIGGEST AWAY WIN:	**1-7** Goodrich v Pelsall Villa
HIGHEST ATTENDANCE:	**214** Wisbech Town v Swaffham Town
NUMBER OF GAMES:	**113 + 8** (2007-08 - 82 + 5)
TOTAL ATTENDANCE:	**8,602** (5,500) NB: missing two attendances
AVERAGE ATTENDANCE:	**72** (63)

Home	Away	Score	Att
Guisborough Town	v Pontefract Collieries	5 - 0	78
Johnston, Moan, Ryan, Bythway, McPhillips			
Northallerton Town	v Marske United	0 - 1	88
	Herbet		
Spennymoor Town	v Norton & Stockton Ancients	3 - 2*	84
Clarke (2), Richards	*Mulligan, Mitchell*		
Whickham	v Stokesley SC	0 - 0*	65
Stokesley SC	v Whickham	R 4 - 1	88
Radigan, Yalcin (2), Williams			
Brandon United	v Bottesford Town	2 - 0	53
Dixon, Pritchalo			
Chester Le Street Town	v South Shields	3 - 1	95
Seaham Red Star	v Glasshoughton Welfare	4 - 1	64
Bettson (2), Winspear, Ure	*Jackson*		
Easington Colliery	v Silsden	1 - 3	28
	Hollindrae, Reilly, Packer		
Crook Town	v Billingham Synthonia	3 - 2	108
McAvoy, Olusoga, Coad	*Abel, Campbell*		
Washington	v Sunderland Nissan	1 - 2	
Ruddick	*Stephenson, Hodgson*		
Willington	v Thackley	1 - 6	27
	Fox, Matthews, Blissett, Coy (2), Shah		
Jarrow Roofing Boldon CA	v Bishop Auckland	0 - 3	62
	Parkin, Barton		
Penrith	v Atherton LR	2 - 1*	92
Robinson, Errington			
Runcorn Linnets	v Padiham	4 - 3*	191
Edwards, Morrison (2), Morris	*Bowden, Wharton (2)*		
Worsbrough Bridge Ath.	v Cheadle Town	5 - 2	40
Forgoine, Poskitt, Hirst, Wilkinson, Jackson	*Brocklehurst, Hussain*		
Flixton	v Congleton Town	0 - 2	71
	Wooley, Tulloch		
Atherton Collieries	v Chadderton	3 - 2	54
Dunne (2), Hayder	*Walters, Mooney*		
Colne	v Darwen	3 - 2*	82
Hall, Crorken, Tinker	*Wisdom, O'Neill*		
Goodrich	v Pelsall Villa	1 - 7	34
Holdcroft	*Bentley, Baggott, Griffiths, Rogers (2), Sherwood, Westley*		
Bridgnorth Town	v Stratford Town	1 - 4	46
Horler	*Byrne, Jakab (2), Gasper*		
Oadby Town	v Staveley MW	3 - 0	116
White, Conway, Lynch			
Clipstone Welfare	v Highgate United	1 - 3	38
Hood			
Cadbury Athletic	v Heather St Johns	4 - 2*	31
Bulmer, Ainge (2), Martin	*Hollis, Turville*		
Pershore Town	v Graham Street Prims	2 - 1	39
Brookes, Hooper	*Carson*		
Ellistown (w/o)	v Stapenhill (folded)		
Gedling Miners Welfare	v Norton United	1 - 2	51
Maddison	*Rutter, Dundas*		
Hinckley Downes	v Gedling Town	0 - 1	85
	Baum		
Heanor Town	v Rolls Royce Leisure	5 - 4	48
Garner (3), Mawer, Timson			
Pegasus Juniors	v Barwell	0 - 5	43
	Brassington, Potter (2), Charley, Lester		
Wednesfield	v Coventry Copsewood	2 - 0	31
Rutter, Fellows			
Bardon Hill Sports	v Holwell Sports	2 - 1	52
Malloy, Saunt	*Mooney*		
Bromyard Town	v Blackwell Miners Welfare	2 - 3*	44
Sheehan, Graham	*Bramley, Harris, Hone*		
Brocton	v Calverton Miners Welfare	2 - 2	89
Crowley, McMahon	*Marsh (2)*		
Calverton Miners Welfare	v Brocton	R 4 - 1	38
Westwood, Boulton (3)	*Thompson*		
Coleshill Town	v Bolehall Swifts	3 - 2	68
Robinson (2), O.G.	*Purvey, Llewellyn*		
Glossop North End	v Sporting Khalsa	5 - 0	202
Gorton, Kay, Bailey, Hodges, Parker			
Causeway United	v Ollerton Town	0 - 0*	82
Ollerton Town	v Causeway United	R 1 - 2	88
Wilson	*How, Jones*		
Dudley Sports	v Rainworth Miners Welfare	0 - 1	57
	Hales		
Sutton Town	v Rocester	1 - 4	44
Powell	*Beardsley, Carr, Sowter*		
New Mills	v Wolverhampton Casuals	6 - 0	204
Howard, Kmaras (3), Baine, Mather			
Shirebrook Town	v Castle Vale	2 - 3	80
Wilkinson, Watson	*Ray, Crisp (2)*		
Teversal	v Nuneaton Griff	3 - 0	48
Smith (2), Woodcock			
Newark Town	v Meir KA	3 - 1	72
	Miszkiel		
Birstall United	v Long Eaton United	2 - 4	79
Thomas, Cain	*Steadman (2), Bowles*		
GSA	v Mickleover Sports	2 - 4	35
Singh Sangha, Devlin	*Martin (2), Ashton, Fox*		
Barrow Town	v Wellington WM	3 - 0	84
Gupwell, Warner (2)			
Bartley Green	v Saffron Dynamo	3 - 1	35
Millington, Hewitt (2)			
Kimberley Town	v Gornal Athletic	0 - 2	35
	Nicholls, Brown		
Haverhill Rovers	v Ely City	1 - 0	103
Cutts			
Leiston	v Bourne Town	4 - 0	126
Lowe, Bramble, Meelone, Saker			
Lincoln Moorlands Railway	v Sleaford Town	1 - 0*	102
Jennings			
Debenham LC	v Fakenham Town	4 - 0	72
Jopling (2), Smith (2)			
Mildenhall Town	v Godmanchester Rovers	3 - 0	143
Werthmann, Scully, Ryland			
Gorleston	v Deeping Rangers	2 - 0	85
Gorham, Bell			
Wisbech Town	v Swaffham Town	5 - 0	214
Impey, Cobb (2), Cubberly (2)			
Clapton	v Thrapston Town	2 - 3	73
Gardiner (2)	*Purser, Kierle, Harrison*		
Welwyn Garden City	v Daventry Town	1 - 6	41
Gordon	*O'Grady, Berwick (3), Finlay (2)*		
London Colney	v Hatfield Town	5 - 2	89
Davey (2), Gallagher (2), O.G.	*Reade, Lawrence*		
Cranfield United	v Haringey Borough	3 - 1	51
Lawless, Wells, Reynolds	*Kalu*		
Bedfont	v Ampthill Town	2 - 1	34
Gallagher, Henry	*Mundy*		
Burnham Ramblers	v Harwich & Parkeston	3 - 1	61
Forgus, Wilson (2)	*Greenley*		
Rushden & Higham Utd	v Feltham	4 - 0	83
Woods, Gregory, Ainge, Batt			
Basildon United	v Wootton Blue Cross	2 - 1	30
	Danodio		
Hoddesdon Town	v Colney Heath	0 - 1	79
	O.G.		
Bedford	v Hullbridge Sports	1 - 2*	40
Reed	*Perry, Wackett*		
Southend Manor	v Harpenden Town	3 - 1	34
Wheatstone (2), Baldwin			
Broxbourne Boro' V&E (w/o)	v Beaumont Athletic (removed)		
Hanwell Town	v Barking	1 - 1*	76
O'Brien	*Dennis*		
Barking	v Hanwell Town	R 0 - 6	69
	Roodenburg (3), Baverstock, O'Brien		
Stansted	v Brimsdown Rovers	2 - 1	45
Spillane, Taylor	*O.G.*		
Tie awarded to Brimsdown Rovers Stansed removed for playing ineligible player.			
London APSA	v Oxhey Jets	1 - 3	20
	Gladdy, Roberts, Arthur		

Home		Away	Score	Att
Saffron Walden Town	v	Sporting Bengal United	4 - 2	121
		Hoque, Hussain		
Langford	v	Cockfosters	5 - 1	87
Pateman, Howell, Byrne, Groves (2)		*Pigden*		
Tring Athletic	v	Leverstock Green	0 - 2	128
		Camill, Parkinson		
Dorking	v	Sidley United	3 - 1	56
Boniface, Page, Donker		*Collier*		
Oakwood	v	Chertsey Town	3 - 3*	45
Bidwell, McNab, Hassard		*Pomroy (2), Johnson*		
Chertsey Town	v	Oakwood	R 3 - 2	69
Brooker (2), O'Leary		*McNab (2)*		
Hassocks	v	Three Bridges	4 - 3*	90
Hibbert, Russell (2), Amos		*Macvilan, Davis (2)*		
Southwick	v	Mile Oak	2 - 2*	60
Thomspn, Nino		*Burnett, Eaton*		
Mile Oak	v	Southwick	R 1 - 0	61
Eaton				
Bookham	v	Hailsham Town	5 - 0	78
Piercy (3), Kent, Ramsey				
Selsey	v	Holmesdale	1 - 1*	138
Dobbs		*Smith*		
Holmesdale	v	Selsey	R 2 - 3*	65
Greaves (2)		*Brown, Ridley, O.G.*		
Wick	v	Erith Town	2 - 3	52
Murfin, Scerri		*Burns (3)*		
Eastbourne United Assoc	v	Banstead Athletic	1 - 5	48
Crabb		*Wallace, Loyza, Torino (2), Terry*		
Chessington & Hook Utd	v	Steyning Town	4 - 3	59
Woods (2), Maan, Smith		*Mitchell, Rowe, Pickup*		
Epsom & Ewell	v	Colliers Wood United	4 - 2	57
Keys, White (2), Hough		*Hughes, Bedj-Broj*		
Herne Bay	v	Lingfield	1 - 2*	150
King		*Davis, Courtney*		
Peacehaven & Telscombe	v	Littlehampton Town	4 - 1	53
Jones, Cullinane, Smith, Baker		*Burgess*		
Worthing United	v	Crawley Down	0 - 2	48
		Beeston, Upton		
Malmesbury Victoria	v	Cheltenham Saracens	2 - 1	48
Soane, Alexander		*Ireland*		
Hamble ASSC	v	Harrow Hill	1 - 4	35
Constable		*Freeman, Jackson, Weyman (2)*		
Petersfield Town (w/o)	v	Tadley Calleva (withdrew)		
Downton	v	Westbury United	1 - 4	45
Hoare		*Friendship, Pearce, Yachou, Wheeler*		
Newport Pagnell Town	v	Totton & Eling	1 - 1*	
Lynch		*Lowther*		
Totton & Ellng	v	Newport Pagnell Town	R 2 - 1	60
Steer, Hardiman		*Mitten*		
Amesbury Town	v	Marlow United	6 - 3*	84
Turpin (5), Bernstsen		*Doswell, Flint, Pedley*		
Bournemouth	v	Calne Town	2 - 3	38
Saadi, King		*Lye, Lardner (2)*		
Christchurch	v	Hartley Wintney	3 - 1	64
Barnes (2), Burrows				
Highworth Town	v	Thame United	3 - 0	122
Hill, Corcoran (2)				
Longwell Green Sports	v	Shrewton United	3 - 2	71
Summers, Parnell, Always		*Foot (2)*		
Moneyfields	v	Shortwood United	0 - 1	78
		Bennett		
Alresford Town	v	Romsey Town	3 - 2*	42
Copping, Findlay, Pascual		*Donaldson*		
Ringwood Town	v	Cowes Sports	0 - 4	24
		Rayner, Pointer, Evans (2)		
Bicester Town	v	Wantage Town	1 - 5	36
Williams		*Learoyd, Keen (2), Horsell, Daley*		
Lydney Town	v	Fairford Town	1 - 5*	51
Robbins		*Walker (3), Rudd, Gill*		
Buckingham Athletic	v	Wootton Bassett Town	3 - 5*	44
Norman, Hammond, Latham		*Yeardley, Terry (3), Shand*		
Reading Town	v	Pewsey Vale	4 - 1	60
Thorne, Herridge, Clark, Cripps		*Fitzgerald*		
Blackfield & Langley	v	Corsham Town	2 - 1	51
Williams, Sommerfield		*Gingell*		
Milton United	v	Brockenhurst	2 - 1	54
Chalmers, Keyes		*Wakefield*		
Fareham Town	v	Bristol Manor Farm	0 - 3	77
		Abraham, Feltham, Stephens		
Tie awarded to Fareham Bristol M.F. removed for playing ineligible player				
Minehead	v	Launceston	1 - 2	43
Burns		*Sargent (2)*		
Newquay	v	Wadebridge Town	2 - 3*	120
Middleton, Pullen		*Cameron (2), Grills*		
Porthleven	v	St Blazey	3 - 1	96
Kemp, Young, Liddicoat		*Kanakh*		
Saltash United	v	Liskeard Athletic	3 - 1	141
Sargison, Nute, Palmer		*Brookes*		
Gillingham Town	v	Larkhall Athletic	0 - 2	136
		Bailey (2)		
Newton Abbot	v	Budleigh Salterton	2 - 0	42
Heath, Comyn				
Penryn Athletic	v	Hamworthy United	0 - 2	64
		Byerley (2)		
Bridport	v	Brislington	0 - 4	72
Ilfracombe Town	v	Wellington	3 - 7	82
Harper-Penman, Marinaro, Clunie		*Adams, Vaughan, Jeeks (3), Kingston*		
Bishop Sutton	v	Bodmin Town	1 - 3	44
Bone		*O'Hagan, Berry (2)*		
Penzance	v	Welton Rovers	0 - 1	175
		Lewis		

SECOND QUALIFYING ROUND

BIGGEST HOME WIN:	**7-0** ERITH & BELVEDERE V SIDLESHAM
BIGGEST AWAY WIN:	**0-7** YORKSHIRE AMATEURS V SHILDON
HIGHEST ATTENDANCE:	**240** BIRTLEY TOWN V SCARBOROUGH ATHLETIC (AT WASHINGTON)
NUMBER OF GAMES:	**175 + 8 INC ONE WALKOVER** (175 + 15)
TOTAL ATTENDANCE:	**12,521** (13,661) NB: MISSING 4 ATTENDANCES
AVERAGE ATTENDANCE:	**70** (72)

Home		Away	Score	Att
Horden Colliery Welfare	v	Sunderland Nissan	1 - 2	51
Atkinson		*Tattant, Appleby*		
Peterlee Town	v	Billingham Town	2 - 0	44
Howe, Liley				
Leeds Carnegie	v	Brandon United	3 - 0	58
McGory (2), Cooper				
Darlington Railway Athletic	v	Morpeth Town	0 - 3	62
		Bell, Benjamin, Campbell		
Selby Town	v	Seaham Red Star	5 - 1	124
		Winspear		
Thornaby	v	Thackley	4 - 5*	38
		Cotton, Daly, McGuiness, Bliussett, Donaldson		
Barton Town Old Boys	v	Crook Town	1 - 2*	136
McKay		*Foster, Olusoga*		
Ashington	v	North Shields	2 - 0	151
Dunn, Bainbridge				
Birtley Town	v	Scarborough Athletic	2 - 3	240
Thirkell (2)		*Phillips, Thompson, Ellis*	(at Washington)	
West Auckland Town	v	Sunderland Ryhope CA	2 - 4	45
Barnes (2)		*Owens, Jennings, Tait (2)*		
Tow Law Town	v	Spennymoor Town	2 - 4	152
McGoire, Eccles		*Ruddy, Clarke (3)*		
Esh Winning	v	Team Northumbria	2 - 1	45
Coates, Martin		*Hall*		
Hall Road Rangers	v	Ryton	1 - 4	68
Palmer		*Walton (2), McBryde, Reay*		
Armthorpe Welfare	v	Guisborough Town	3 - 6	40
Sibenge, Jones (2)		*O'Riordan, Storr (2), Onions (3)*		
Yorkshire Amateur	v	Shildon	0 - 7	80
		Byrne, Chapman (3), Watling (3)		
West Allotment Celtic	v	Silsden	2 - 1*	99
Eccleshill United	v	Bedlington Terriers	0 - 1	53
		Dodsworth		
Marske United	v	Bishop Auckland	4 - 1	129
Newton (2), Skelton, Kasonali		*Moss*		
Stokesley SC	v	Chester Le Street Town	3 - 2*	88
Hamilton, Yalcin, Williams		*Gardner, Draper*		
Hebburn Town	v	Tadcaster Albion	1 - 2*	47
Urwin		*Bonarious, Dowling*		
Runcorn Linnets	v	Bacup Borough	4 - 0	134

Above: Ampthill 'keeper, Diego Vasquez, makes another fine save this time to deny Bedfont's Russell Miner during this 1st Qualifying Round tie.
Photo: Gordon Whittington.

Above right: Gornal's Jeff Hill (9) lifts his shot over Kimberley keeper Mark Rawson but the effort is cleared by the onrushing defender.
Photo: Bill Wheatcroft.

Above: Northampton Spencer's No.10. opens the scoring against Hullbridge Sports in the 2nd Qualifying Round. Photo: Peter Barnes.

Left: Ringmer's Ryan McMillan (left) powers his header just wide of the Lordswood goal during this 2nd Qualifying Round match.
Photo: Alan Coomes.

Home		Away	Score	Att
Young (2), Courtney, O.G.				
Abbey Hey	v	Parkgate	2 - 1	50
Heffernan (2)		*Lopes*		
St Helens Town	v	Ashton Athletic	1 - 2	51
Mitchell		*Court, Evans*		
Nostell Miners Welfare	v	Poulton Victoria	2 - 1	64
Watts, Bedford		*Burrows*		
AFC Blackpool	v	Squires Gate	1 - 2*	100
Ashall		*Taylor, Bartlett*		
Rossington Main	v	Daisy Hill	2 - 0	50
Holmes (2)				
Holker Old Boys	v	Colne	2 - 2*	47
Hargreaves, Bamber		*Hall, Longley*		
Colne	v	Holker Old Boys	R 5 - 0	55
Tinker, Cruz, Croken (2), Threlfall				
Worsbrough Bridge Athletic	v	Ramsbottom United	1 - 3	52
Garside		*Dawson, Jones, Stephenson*		
Penrith	v	Dinnington Town	2 - 0	75
Robertson, Reed				
Hallam	v	Winsford United	3 - 2	58
Patterson, Ward, Tevendale		*Riley, Mason*		
Congleton Town	v	Maltby Main	3 - 0	102
Bostock, Baker, Smith				
Brodsworth Miners Welfare	v	Ashton Town	3 - 0	45
Fell, Craig, Wilkin				
AFC Emley	v	Oldham Town	2 - 6	123
Kenworthy (2)		*Hughes, Scanlon, Melia (2), Phillips (2)*		
Atherton Collieries	v	Bootle	0 - 3	47
		Hay, Dolan, McDonald		
Cradley Town	v	Warstone Wanderers	1 - 1*	42
Cole		*Griffiths (Warstone won 2-1 on penalties)*		
Pilkington XXX	v	Cadbury Athletic	2 - 1	46
King, Nash		*Ainge*		
Pelsall Villa	v	Castle Vale	0 - 2	
		Gardiner, Andrews		
Anstey Nomads	v	Shifnal Town	0 - 1	127
		Jevons		
Greenwood Meadows	v	Dosthill Colts	0 - 3	39
		Politt (2), McCall		
Stone Dominoes	v	Tividale	4 - 1	38
Scheuber, Rabie, Brown, Curley		*Joshua*		
New Mills	v	Ellistown	3 - 2	170
Howard, Giggs, Mather		*Miller, O'Callaghan*		
Dunkirk	v	Heath Hayes	4 - 0	43
Baker, Brady (2), Bascombe				
Kirby Muxloe SC	v	Wednesfield	1 - 0	56
Varrell				
Bewdley Town	v	Long Eaton United	1 - 3	134
Hart		*Steadman, Gamble, Piliero*		
Barwell	v	AFC Wulfrunians	2 - 0	67
Radford	v	Leek CSOB	0 - 2	68
		Fox (2)		

Home		Away	Score	Att
Bartley Green		St Andrews SC	1 - 1	38
Draper		*Nayzel*		
St Andrews SC		Bartley Green	R 2 - 3	50
Robinson, Mee		*Jacques, Millington (2)*		
Calverton Miners Welfare		Glossop North End	1 - 4	51
Boulton		*Bailey, Whelan, Hodges, Hind*		
Coleshill Town		Ibstock United	4 - 3	58
Dance, Robinson, Porter, Kitching		*J.Lewis, R.Lewis (2)*		
Darlaston Town		Oadby Town	3 - 0	90
Frost, Johns, Nicholls				
Newark Town		Gornal Athletic	3 - 3*	81
Dobb, Self, Wilford		*Meese, Brown, Hill*		
Gornal Athletic		Neawark Town	R 0 - 1	
		Ellison		
Mickleover Sports		Biddulph Victoria	1 - 2	71
Ashton		*Smith, Everall*		
Blaby & Whetstone Athletic		Arnold Town	2 - 6	83
Asman, Matthews		*Hall, Wilkins, Warton, Carruthers (3)*		
Friar Lane & Epworth		Coalville	0 - 2	91
		Dodd, Adams		
Stratford Town		Gedling Town	3 - 1	133
Crawford, Jakob (2)		*Gill*		
Norton United		Heanor Town	2 - 3	46
Talbot, Rutter		*Garner, Needham, Maher*		
Dudley Town		Southam United	2 - 0*	39
Ashton, Kinch				
Ellesmere Rangers		Borrowash Victoria	1 - 3	79
Webb		*Mottershead, North (2)*		
Rainworth Miners Welfare		Walsall Wood	2 - 0	70
Naylor (2)				
Westfields		Blackwell Miners Welfare	4 - 0	41
Hill, Davis (3)				
Bardon Hill Sports		Teversal	1 - 3	42
Pollard		*Woodcock, Orton, Lyall*		
Pershore Town		Rothley Imperial	2 - 3	47
Cannon, Taffe		*Bryant, Ejiofor, Box*		
Loughborough University		Ledbury Town	2 - 0	68
Miller (2)			*(at Ledbury)*	
Barrow Town		Lye Town	1 - 2	73
Warner		*Morris, Billingham*		
Holbrook Miners Welfare		Eccleshall	1 - 1*	45
O.G.		*Marren*		
Eccleshall		Holbrook Miners Welfare	R 1 - 0	73
Spence				
Racing Club Warwick		Rocester	3 - 1	55
Crawford, Ramsey, Plant		*Bagley*		
Oldbury United		Highgate United	1 - 2	45
Hemus		*Gummery (2)*		
Radcliffe Olympic		Alvechurch	3 - 4	50
Westcarr (2), Korol		*Gittings, Ball, Rogers, McKeon*		
Causeway United (w/o)		Brierley Hill & Withymoor		
Leiston		Huntingdon Town	5 - 1	138
Rowe, Hedd, McElone, Saker, Bramble		*Nevill*		
Felixstowe & Walton Utd		Whitton United	4 - 3	101
Bloomfield, Frost, Edwards, Claydon		*Thompson, Wright, Curtis*		
Cornard United		Eynesbury Rovers	3 - 1	20
Clarke (2), Lawson		*Randell*		
Walsham Le Willows		Wisbech Town	2 - 4	112
Holder, Cusack		*Ablett, Smith (2), King*		
St Neots Town		Great Yarmouth Town	1 - 0	235
Cole				
Woodbridge Town		Yaxley	0 - 1	87
		Parrott		
Holbeach United		Gorleston	2 - 1	99
Cartwright, Orrey		*Maddison*		
Lincoln Moorlands Railway		Diss Town	1 - 5	49
Hanson		*Foley, Wilson, McKail, Hayes, Deacon*		
Haverhill Rovers		Long Melford	0 - 1	102
Newmarket Town		March Town United	3 - 0	73
Grainger, Sannoh, Shaw				
Debenham LC		Stowmarket Town	1 - 0	104
Turley				
Kirkley & Pakefield		Norwich United	1 - 0	161
Cole				
Ipswich Wanderers		Hadleigh United	0 - 6	92
		Laws, Barber, Payne, Fleming (2) Dennett		
Mildenhall Town		Thetford Town	2 - 0	141
Scully, O.G.				
Thrapston Town		Burnham Ramblers	2 - 1	71
Harrison, Morgan		*Wilson*		
North Greenford United		Sport London E Benfica	0 - 3	39
		Dyalo (2), Nascimento		
Saffron Walden Town		Biggleswade United	0 - 1	138
		Stocker		
Potton United		Bugbrooke St Michael	5 - 0	34
Goodall, Fisk, Hamilton, Billington, McMurrough				
Halstead Town		Hanwell Town	4 - 1	130
Daly, Bryan, Turner (2)		*O.G.*		
Southend Manor		Royston Town	2 - 3	85
Flynn, Msiska		*Hammond (2), Robins*	*(at Royston)*	
London Colney		Daventry Town	0 - 4	43
		Berwick, Finlay (2), Gordon		
AFC Kempston Rovers		Kentish Town	1 - 3	45
Field		*Donoghue, Doyle, Essaighi*		
Langford		Cogenhoe United	1 - 2	98
Waller		*Cassidy, McGowan*		
Wellingborough Town		Cranfield United	6 - 0	113
Parkinson (2), Thompson (2), Mitchell, O.G.				
Rushden & Higham Utd		Daventry United	0 - 1	43
		Sawro		
Oxhey Jets		Northampton Sileby Rangers	3 - 1	43
Roberts, Arthur, Turner		*Giles*		
Bedfont		Codicote	2 - 3	35
Bakali, Henry		*Teale, Smith, Jones*		
Crawley Green		Leverstock Green	2 - 3	65
Freeman, Singleton		*Hammond, Sears, Davis*		
FC Clacton		Tokyngton Manor	6 - 2	102
Gibson, Smith (2), White, Hillier, Waters		*Watson, Reynards*		
Bedfont Green		Rothwell Corinthians	6 - 1	26
Barrie-Bates, Barrance, Henry (3), Hart		*White*		
St Margaretsbury		Colney Heath	5 - 1	54
Barker, Draper, Tobin, Angelini, O.G.		*Howard*		
Stewarts & Lloyds Corby		Enfield	1 - 0	
Byrne				
Tiptree United		Broxbourne Borough V&E	3 - 2	65
Ward, English, Townrow		*Odamo, Wade*		
Wembley		Basildon United	0 - 4	57
		Collins, Robinson (2), Arrate		
Kingsbury London Tigers		Raunds Town	1 - 2	27
Beysne		*Spaughton, Jarvis*		
Northampton Spencer		Hullbridge Sports	2 - 0	54
Surridge, Hancock				
Brimsdown Rovers		Eton Manor	0 - 1	55
		Hayles		
Dorking		Selsey	3 - 5*	61
Page, Cassidy, Bennett		*Dobbs, Morey, Brown, Ridley, Woolf*		
East Grinstead Town		Lancing	2 - 1*	67
		Partridge		
Faversham Town		Tunbridge Wells	0 - 1	132
		Tate		
Badshot Lea		Pagham	4 - 3	54
Griffiths (3), Smith		*Forden (2), Towers*		
Egham Town		Crawley Down	4 - 2	68
Loveridge, Muldowney (2) White		*Tidey, White*		
Lingfield		Horley Town	1 - 2	58
Jones		*Marquis, Tomlinson*		
Hassocks		Chertsey Town	2 - 3*	110
Laing		*Moody, Johnson, Cooper*		
Slade Green		Redhill	1 - 3	59
May		*Ansell, Dennis, Reid*		
Lordswood		Ringmer	4 - 0	35
Osborne, Dodsworth, Bridges (2)				
Wealden		Mile Oak	0 - 5	35
		Martin (2), Skinner, Eaton, Patterson		
Erith Town		Rye United	3 - 4	52
Cassius, Burns (2)		*Richardson, Price (2), Woodley*		
Erith & Belvedere		Sidlesham	7 - 0	86
Thorogood, Pursglove (4), Smith, Budek				

Home	Away	Score	Att
Bookham	v Frimley Green	3 - 3*	68
Piercy (2), Woodward	*Shannon, Peters (2)*		
Frimley Green	v Bookham	R 4 - 1	41
Peters (2), Shannon, Wilsher	*Oliver*		
Ash United	v Sevenoaks Town	1 - 0	63
Mukabaa			
Croydon	v Haywards Heath Town	4 - 0	53
Waters, White, Hines, Kirby			
South Park	v Shoreham	1 - 2*	70
Ward	*Annis, Callaghan*		
Raynes Park Vale	v Chessington & Hook United	1 - 2	62
Ellard			
St Francis Rangers	v Westfield	4 - 3*	42
Jeremiah, Gault (2), Palmer	*Daltry, Tusov, Malone*		
Farnham Town	v Peacehaven & Telscombe	1 - 3	35
Harding	*Clarke, Mitchell, Watton*		
Newhaven	v Banstead Athletic	1 - 3	94
Holmes	*Torino, Terry, Corbett*		
Chichester City United	v Seaford	4 - 0	38
Huntley, Vassello, Temple (2)			
Saltdean United	v Epsom & Ewell	0 - 1	71
	McLaughlin		
Deal Town	v Cobham	0 - 3	104
	Andrews (2), Wilson		
Andover New Street	v Totton & Eling	0 - 1	31
	Steer		
Farnborough North End	v Bemerton Heath Harlequins	0 - 2	44
	Lilley, Price		
Abingdon Town	v Flackwell Heath	1 - 2	55
Brooks	*Mason, Ramsey*		
Hallen	v Reading Town	1 - 3	52
Brimson	*Lewis, Clark, O.G.*		
Wantage Town	v Binfield	1 - 2	46
	Williams, McClurg		
Holyport	v Sandhurst Town	0 - 2	92
	Wilson, Corbett		
Christchurch	v Petersfield Town	2 - 0	93
Keates, Osbourne			
Ardley United	v Harrow Hill	2 - 3	42
Stidder, Beckett	*Freeman, Weyman (2)*		
Henley Town	v Wootton Bassett Town	0 - 6	26
	Oram, Yeardley, Terry (3), Ritchie		
Hayling United	v Carterton	1 - 0	132
Murphy			
Shortwood United	v Devizes Town	4 - 0	57
Coates, Davis (2), Allard			
Milton United	v Clanfield (Oxon)	2 - 2*	39
Jones, Ingram			
Clanfield (Oxon)	v Milton United	R 1 - 1*	70
Court	*Keyes*	*(Clanfield won 4-2 on penalties)*	
Aylesbury Vale	v Alton Town	3 - 1	47
Corbould, Melisi (2)	*Rayner*		
Fairford Town	v Hook Norton	1 - 1*	38
Walker	*Standen*		
Hook Norton	v Fairford Town	R 3 - 1	54
Johnson (2), Moulder	*Rudd*		
Warminster Town	v Laverstock & Ford	2 - 1	101
Reamey, Welch	*Crook*		
Highworth Town	v New Milton Town	1 - 2	
Cole	*Woolner, Allen*		
Amesbury Town	v Melksham Town	0 - 2	105
	Auckland, Beasley		
Kidlington	v Chalfont Wasps	2 - 1*	68
Flanagan, Lovegrove	*Thompson*		
Cowes Sports	v Calne Town	1 - 3*	102
Pointer	*Armstrong (2), Lardner*		
Blackfield & Langley	v Longwell Green Sports	0 - 1	53
	Mountfield		
Buckingham Town	v AFC Wallingford	4 - 0	59
Hart, Mills. McCormick (2)			
Westbury United	v Malmesbury Victoria	2 - 2*	51
Smith, Pearce	*Hemsley, Webb*		
Malnesbury Victoria	v Westbury United	R 3 - 1	53
Gee, Charlton, Coles	*Pearce*		
United Services Portsmouth	v Brading Town	2 - 4*	78
Collis, Robinson	*Greening (3), Armstrong*	*(at Brading)*	
Fareham Town	v Alresford Town	2 - 1	87
Stone, Wilson	*Findlay*		
Wadebridge Town	v Bodmin Town	0 - 4	170
	O'Hagan, Hobbs (2), Ovens		
Shaftesbury	v Shepton Mallet	3 - 1	75
Chant, Ellis, Gale	*Francis*		
Tavistock	v Wellington	2 - 0	
Honey (2)			
Radstock Town	v Hamworthy United	1 - 4	79
Sarr	*Byerley (30, Claremont*		
Welton Rovers	v Cullompton Rangers	0 - 2	63
	Williams, Dawson		
Street	v Falmouth Town	6 - 2	72
Pearse (2), Pople (2), O.G. (2)	*Hawke, Drummond*		
Barnstaple Town	v Newton Abbot	3 - 1	102
Layland, Squire (2)	*Comyn*		
Porthleven	v Buckland Athletic	4 - 3	104
Young, Robertson, Burchill (2)			
Launceston	v Keynsham Town	3 - 1	98
Sargent (2), O.G.	*Bernard*		
Odd Down	v Brislington	0 - 2	35
	Guibarra (2)		
Saltash United	v Portishead Town	6 - 1	116
Clark (2), Thorne (3), O.G.	*Holder*		
Clevedon United	v Elmore	1 - 0*	19
Norris			
Chard Town	v Sherborne Town	1 - 2*	103
	Parkinson, Cunningham		
Larkhall Athletic	v Plymouth Parkway	2 - 1	80
Bailey, Highmore	*Wright*		

FIRST ROUND PROPER

BIGGEST HOME WIN:	**10-1** Ryton v Guisborough Town
BIGGEST AWAY WIN:	**1-6** Flackwell Heath v Hook Norton
HIGHEST ATTENDANCE:	**490** New Mills v Glossop North End
NUMBER OF GAMES:	**102 + 11** (104 + 4)
TOTAL ATTENDANCE:	**10,302** (9,024)
AVERAGE ATTENDANCE:	**92** (84)

Home	Away	Score	Att
Esh Winning	v Scarborough Athletic	1 - 2	241
Coates	*Gray*		
Guisborough Town	v Ryton	1 - 1*	72
McPhillips	*McBride*		
Ryton	v Guisborough Town	R 10 - 1	89
Patterson, Burrell (2), Walton (3), Reay (2), Dobby, McKenna	*McPhillips*		
Crook Town	v Shildon	2 - 4	184
Kokes (2)	*Byrne (2), Chapman (2)*		
Bedlington Terriers	v Stokesley SC	1 - 1*	74
Shanoran			
Stokesley SC	v Bedlington Terriers	R 3 - 1*	182
Hendum, Yalcin, Williams	*Bell*		
Winterton Rangers	v Selby Town	2 - 1	81
Clarke, Archer	*Gorman*		
Sunderland Nissan	v Morpeth Town	0 - 0*	37
Morpeth Town	v Sunderland Nissan	R 3 - 4*	48
Grant, Benjamin, Campbell	*Tarrant (2), Banks (2)*		
Thackley	v Liversedge	3 - 0	80
Coy, Shah (2)			
Ashington	v Leeds Carnegie	3 - 1	117
Hogg, Bainbridge (2)	*Elliott*		
Sunderland Ryhope CA	v Marske United	1 - 2	84
Jennings	*Swalwell (2)*		
Tadcaster Albion	v Spennymoor Town	1 - 5	88
James	*Beasley, Clarke (2), Irvine, Ainsley*		
Bridlington Town	v West Allotment Celtic	6 - 1	154
Fleming, Chilaka (3), Palmer (2)	*Dawson*		
Newcastle Benfield	v Peterlee Town	4 - 1	46
Young (2), Chilton (2)	*Snaith*		
Ashton Athletic	v Nostell Miners Welfare	4 - 4*	45
Ryder, Lawton, Gallanders, Sherlock	*Watts, Stephens, Nichols, Rushton*		
Nostell Miners Welfare	v Ashton Athletic	R 3 - 1	91
Bedford, Stephens, Nicholas	*Ryder*		
Oldham Town	v Congleton Town	1 - 0	50
Scanlon			
Alsager Town	v Hallam	2 - 2*	52
McCarthy, Clarke	*Patterson, Land*		

Home	Away	Score	Att
Hallam	v Alsager Town	R 1 - 3	60
Bates	*Duckworth (2), Clarke*		
Colne	v Abbey Hey	2 - 3	69
Howarth, Tinker	*Monde-Leke, Mullholland, Doherty*		
Maine Road	v Runcorn Linnets	3 - 3*	125
Mason, Mack, Rothel	*Morrison, Courtney, Whyte*		
Runcorn Linnets	v Maine Road	R 2 - 1*	148
Courtney, Morris	*Mack*		
Bootle	v Ramsbottom United	2 - 1*	73
McDonald, Hickey	*Stephenson*		
Rossington Main	v Brodsworth Miners Welfare	1 - 4	110
Fraser	*Cooper, Wilkin (2), Fell*		
Penrith	v Squires Gate	2 - 1	60
Brown, Paul	*Ryan*		
Borrowash Victoria	v Arnold Town	1 - 3	82
Spencer	*Wilkins, Carruthers (2)*		
Kirby Muxloe SC	v Pilkington XXX	1 - 3	69
Aston	*Coyne, Johnston, Hill*		
Dosthill Colts	v Loughborough University	2 - 1	34
McCall, Yonwin	*Miller*		
Castle Vale	v Stone Dominoes	1 - 2	26
Smith	*McKinney, McGuire*		
Coalville	v Newark Town	4 - 0	119
San, Adams (2), Saunders			
Market Drayton Town	v Teversal	3 - 0	60
Rogers (3)			
Darlaston Town	v Eccleshall	3 - 1	53
Follows (2)	*Oxley*		
Warstone Wanderers	v Long Eaton United	0 - 4	30
	Mushambi (2), Sutton (2)		
Alvechurch	v Causeway United	1 - 3*	72
Ball	*How, Busby (2)*		
Bartley Green	v Barwell	1 - 2	50
Manning	*McPhee, Julien*		
Dudley Town	v Rothley Imperial	2 - 0	60
Ashton (2)			
Racing Club Warwick	v Heanor Town	1 - 2*	53
Crawford	*Timson, Wells*		
Newcastle Town	v Highgate United	5 - 0	73
Bourne, Minor, Budrys, Kinsey, Johnson			
Westfields	v Lye Town	2 - 1	47
Thomas (2)	*Greenaway*		
Leek CSOB	v Boldmere St Michaels	1 - 2	29
Tarr	*McNaught, Mason*		
New Mills	v Glossop North End	1 - 4	490
Howard	*Allen, Bailey, Hamilton, Hind*		
Shifnal Town	v Biddulph Victoria	0 - 1	51
	Mould		
Rainworth Miners Welfare	v Dunkirk	1 - 3	58
Naylor	*Brady (2), Smith*		
Stratford Town	v Coleshill Town	6 - 0	143
Byrne, Blair, Jakob, Brookes (2), Gasper			
Cornard United	v Wisbech Town	2 - 0	40
Price, Aves			
Hadleigh United	v Debenham LC	0 - 1	134
	Turley		
Dereham Town	v Newmarket Town	4 - 2	131
Beaumont (2), Howell, Atkins	*Salmons, Thurlbourne*		
Holbeach United	v Felixstowe & Walton United	1 - 1*	84
Nimmo	*O.G.*		
Felixstowe & W. Utd	v Holbeach United	R 0 - 1	126
	Warfield		
Wroxham	v Leiston	0 - 2	141
	Cunningham, Sillett		
Mildenhall Town	v Diss Town	4 - 2	195
Spriggs, Harris, Paynter, Scully	*Deacon, Partridge*		
Yaxley	v Kirkley & Pakefield	4 - 4*	81
Palmer, Harrold (2), Hailstone	*Blois, Highfield, Stone, Stokeld*		
Kirkley & Pakefield	v Yaxley	R 5 - 1	162
De Coteau, Fox (2), Blake, Henderson	*Barrick*		
Long Melford	v St Neots Town	0 - 2	126
	Bannister, Steele		
Kentish Town	v Thrapston Town	5 - 2	44
Donoghue, Butler, Hiller (2), O.G.	*Morgan, Morris*		
Cogenhoe United	v Codicote	6 - 0	68
Ashton, Cross (3), Frost (2)			
Eton Manor	v Sport London E Benfica	1 - 2	15
Jjunju	*Dyalo, Nascimento*		
Halstead Town	v Raunds Town	2 - 4	129
Rowell, Newman	*Russell, Davis, Spaughton, Atkins*		
Leverstock Green	v Northampton Spencer	2 - 3	70
Cahill, Armstrong	*Richardson (2), Surridge*		
Biggleswade United	v Desborough Town	3 - 0	48
Biggleswade Town	v Berkhamsted Town	2 - 0	105
Flack, Redford			
Potton United	v Wivenhoe Town	1 - 3	38
Woodhead	*Sargent, England, Ide*		
Daventry Town	v Daventry United	2 - 0	181
Berwick (2)			
Stewarts & Lloyds Corby	v Oxhey Jets	3 - 0	55
Forbes, Caswell, Djeneralovic			
FC Clacton	v Bedfont Green	4 - 1	102
Waters (2), White, Hillier	*Barrie-Bates*		
Basildon United	v Stotfold	4 - 1	67
King, Lee, Robinson (2)	*Rennie*		
Barkingside	v Bowers & Pitsea	2 - 2*	56
Lewis (2)	*Birkett, John*		
Bowers & Pitsea	v Barkingside	R 0 - 2	91
	Lewis, O.G.		
Royston Town	v Wellingborough Town	1 - 3*	140
Young	*Urquart, Thompson (2)*		
Tiptree United	v Hertford Town	8 - 0	76
Watson, Wraight, Coleman, Arlick, English (3), Noble			
St Margaretsbury	v Romford	1 - 2	93
O'Brien	*Turner, Mbala*		
Chessington & Hook Utd	v Shoreham	0 - 3	75
	O'Brien (2), Boddy		
Banstead Athletic	v Erith & Belvedere	2 - 1	35
Terry (2)	*Thorogood*		
East Preston	v Whitehawk	0 - 2	47
	Francis, Gunn		
Molesey	v Badshot Lea	2 - 1	65
Baxter (2)	*White*		
Hythe Town	v Egham Town	0 - 3	118
	Foulser, White (2)		
Frimley Green	v Redhill	2 - 1	35
Peters, Moffatt	*Murphy*		
East Grinstead Town	v Rye United	4 - 2	57
	Price, Smith		
Guildford City	v Selsey	1 - 3	83
Sheppard	*Hinshelwood, Brown, Britton*		
Chichester City United	v Epsom & Ewell	2 - 0	42
Vassello, Temple			
Horsham YMCA	v Peacehaven & Telscombe	1 - 4	79
Lalley	*Saunders, Millis, Watton, Bunch*		
Horley Town	v Croydon	2 - 4	70
Weller, Tomlinson	*Waters, Dabrowa, Wood, Wordsworth*		
Arundel	v Chertsey Town	1 - 0	75
Huckett			
Mile Oak	v Cobham	1 - 0	64
Pulling			
Lordswood	v St Francis Rangers	1 - 5	43
Bridges	*Wood, Jeremiah (2), Palmer (2)*		
Tunbridge Wells	v Ash United	4 - 1	128
Russell, Cable (2), Lord	*Smith*		
Melksham Town	v New Milton Town	0 - 1*	75
	Byers		
Longwell Green Sports	v Clanfield (Oxon)	0 - 1	67
	Benson		
Newport IoW	v Witney United	0 - 1	147
	Thompson		
Almondsbury Town	v Reading Town	1 - 0	65
Fareham Town	v Binfield	1 - 1*	104
Wilson	*McClurg*		
Binfield	v Fareham Town	R 3 - 2	123
Williams, Sargent, Withers	*Middleton, Wilson*		
Aylesbury Vale	v Harrow Hill	5 - 1	127
Roberts, Iannong, Melisi, Usmani (2)	*Weyman*		
Bemerton Heath Harlequins	v Shortwood United	3 - 0	71
Sanger, Price, Palmer			
Chalfont St Peter	v Totton & Eling	5 - 2	50
Hedley, Hughes (3), Bunce	*Edwicker, Hardiman*		

Above: Lewis Taylor of Herne Bay sees his shot blocked by Louis Perkins (No.4) of Lingfield in the 1st Qualifying Round.
Photo: Alan Coomes.

Left: Action from the 1st Qualifying Round match between Rushden & Higham United and Feltham (stripes).
Photo: Peter Barnes.

Home	Away	Score	Att
Buckingham Town	v Malmesbury Victoria	2 - 0	89
VT FC *Hunt (4), Bowers, Wigley*	v Calne Town *Armstrong*	6 - 1	109
Sandhurst Town *Williams, Corbett*	v Warminster Town *Welch*	2 - 1	54
Cove *Johnston*	v Christchurch *Osborne, Rideout*	1 - 2	53
Hayling United *Kirby, Lindsey (2)*	v Brading Town	3 - 0	70
Wootton Bassett Town *Terry, Moulton, Tearle*	v Kidlington *Williams, Flanagan*	3 - 2	96
Flackwell Heath *Masen*	v Hook Norton *Pearman, Johnson (3), Keenan, Standen*	1 - 6	40
Porthleven *Davies*	v Larkhall Athletic *Collier, Bailey*	1 - 2	81
Frome Town *Cheesman, Caslake*	v Tavistock *Honey*	2 - 1*	141
Street	v Clevedon United *Woodland, King*	2 - 2*	70
Clevedon United *McCall, Bartnikowski*	v Street	R 2 - 4	37
Sherborne Town *Cunningham (2)*	v Saltash United *Manley, Coulton, Lewis, Farnham*	2 - 4	95
Barnstaple Town *Squire*	v Hamworthy United *Byerley, Clark*	1 - 2	102
Shaftesbury	v Wimborne Town *Joyce (2), Gibbons*	0 - 3	135
Cullompton Rangers	v Willand Rovers *Raily*	0 - 1*	472
Brislington *Church (3)*	v Bodmin Town *Flynn, Gilbert*	3 - 2	172
Dawlish Town *Vickary, Lynch, Stevens, Bushin (2)*	v Launceston *Andrew*	5 - 1	68

SECOND ROUND PROPER

BIGGEST HOME WIN:	**5-1** STEWARTS & LLOYDS CORBY V HEANOR TN.
BIGGEST AWAY WIN:	**2-6** KENTISH TOWN V BIGGLESWADE TOWN
HIGHEST ATTENDANCE:	**664** SCARBOROUGH ATHLETIC V SUNDERLAND N.
NUMBER OF GAMES:	**64 + 6** (64 + 9)
TOTAL ATTENDANCE:	**9,571** (8,817) NB: MISSING SIX ATTENDANCES
AVERAGE ATTENDANCE:	**150** (121)

Home	Away	Score	Att.
Spennymoor Town	v Stokesley SC	2 - 1	155
Lawther (2)			
Alsager Town	v Runcorn Linnets	1 - 1*	166
Jones	*Whyte*		
Runcorn Linnets	v Alsager Town	R 2 - 2*	
Whyte, Morrison	*Williams, Whitney (Runcorn won 5-4 on penalties)*		
Bootle	v Oldham Town	5 - 3	101
Coulton, Fowler (2), Hickey, Tosney	*Phillips, Buxton (2)*		
Winterton Rangers	v Ashington	3 - 1*	107
Watson, Holt, Clarke	*Bainbridge*		
Consett	v Marske United	0 - 1	161
	Newton		
Ryton	v Nostell Miners Welfare	2 - 2*	62
Pell, Walton	*Denton, Nicholas*		
Nostell Miners Welfare	v Ryton	R 4 - 1	106
Bedford, Marchant, Stephens, Rushton			
Bridlington Town	v Penrith	0 - 2	191
	Robinson (2)		
AFC Fylde	v Newcastle Benfield	1 - 0	437
Booth			
Scarborough Athletic	v Sunderland Nissan	3 - 2*	664
Medcalf (2), Hogg	*Tarrant, Hodgson*		
Whitley Bay	v Abbey Hey	5 - 2*	294
Coulson, Moore, Kerr, Robinson (2)	*Maloney, Nevins*		
Brodsworth Miners Welfare	v Pickering Town	0 - 2	73
	Salt		
Formby	v Dunston Federation	0 - 4	70
	Young, Brown, Sheeran, Wells		
Thackley	v Shildon	0 - 1	131
	Byrne		
Dosthill Colts	v Coalville	2 - 5	149
Yonwin, Boggild	*Haynes, Attwood, Swan, Adams, Waldrum*		
Arnold Town	v Pilkington XXX	4 - 0	88
Wilkins, Mitchell (2), Holden	*(at Dunkirk FC)*		
Stone Dominoes	v Coventry Sphinx	1 - 0	72
Curley			
Glossop North End	v Biddulph Victoria	4 - 0	210
Allen, Parker (2), Hodges			
Blackstones	v Dunkirk	2 - 0	72
Scother, Stead			
Shawbury United	v Westfields	2 - 2*	87
Westfields	v Shawbury United	R 2 - 2*	93
Noon, Hill	*Lee (2) (Westfields won 5-4 on penalties)*		
Market Drayton Town	v Newcastle Town	2 - 1	161
Ryan, Ellis	*Kinsey*		
Daventry Town	v Dudley Town	3 - 1	111
Burke, Cullen, O.G.	*Tasker*		
Stratford Town	v Causeway United	4 - 2	207
Robinson (2), Jakab, Rawlings	*Cox (2)*		
Tipton Town	v Boldmere St Michaels	1 - 0	52
Jones			
Stewarts & Lloyds Corby	v Heanor Town	5 - 1	55
Caswell (2), Byrne (3)	*Wells*		
Darlaston Town	v Long Eaton United	0 - 3	36
	Holmes (2), Sutton		
Boston Town	v Cogenhoe United	1 - 2	
Kennedy	*Ashby*		
Barwell	v Studley	3 - 3*	78
Castle, Green, McPhee	*Curtis, Bailey, Styles*		
Studley	v Barwell	R 2 - 2*	76
Ruck, Pountney	*Spencer, Charley (Barwell won 4-3 on penalties)*		
Sport London E Benfica	v St Neots Town	0 - 5	154
	Knight, Okechukwu, Rogers, Kenneford, Steele		
Wellingborough Town	v Long Buckby	0 - 3	
	Dunkley (2), Foster		
FC Clacton	v Basildon United	4 - 0	202
Hillier, Dunkley, Waters (2)			
St Ives Town	v Romford	2 - 1	451
McDougald, Kennett	*Gammons*		
Lowestoft Town	v Tiptree United	2 - 0	539
Cockrill, Godbold			
Kirkley & Pakefield	v Dereham Town	0 - 1	191
	Garner		
Raunds Town	v Holbeach United	1 - 2	
Taylor	*Nimmo, Allen*		
Leiston	v Debenham LC	1 - 0	250
Lowe			
VCD Athletic	v Mildenhall Town	2 - 1	118
Huggins, Bradshaw	*Robinson*		
Harefield United	v Barkingside	2 - 1	188
Lloyd, Buckle	*Jones*		
Needham Market	v Northampton Spencer	1 - 0	175
Bexfield			
Wivenhoe Town	v Cornard United	3 - 0	235
Young, Campana, Underwood			
Kentish Town	v Biggleswade Town	2 - 6	48
Donoghue (2)	*Webster, Weeden (2), Cooper, Lamarcraft, Bensaud*		
Biggleswade United	v Stanway Rovers	0 - 3	61
	Newson (2), Callander		
Chalfont St Peter	v Clanfield (Oxon)	2 - 0	46
Molesey	v St Francis Rangers	3 - 0	121
Baxter (2), O'Leary			
Frimley Green	v Binfield	1 - 0	98
Rapley			
Banstead Athletic	v Arundel	1 - 2*	
Hollingsworth	*Huckett, Nieagbour*		
Aylesbury Vale	v East Grinstead Town	4 - 0	46
Roberts, Kynsey, Wright, Vsmani			
Sandhurst Town	v Witney United	1 - 2	68
Vickery	*Wickens, Thompson*		
Christchurch	v Tunbridge Wells	1 - 0	138
Burrows			
Chichester City United	v Shoreham	0 - 4*	114
	Callaghan (2), Kane, Annis		
Croydon	v Mile Oak	3 - 0	111
Atkins, Savage, Mohammed			
Selsey	v Whitehawk	2 - 0	144
Britton, Horly			
Hook Norton	v VT FC	1 - 1*	115
Standen	*Bright*		
VT FC	v Hook Horton	R 4 - 0	93
Brewster, Ashford, Sales (2)			
Egham Town	v Buckingham Town	0 - 1	
	Max-Abant		
Hayling United	v New Milton Town	2 - 4	175
	Pidgley, Allen, Cox, Sampays		
Camberley Town	v Peacehaven & Telscombe	4 - 3	99
Cornell (2), Johnson, Muir	*Saunders, Bunch, Mitchell*		
Larkhall Athletic	v Lymington Town	4 - 1	135
Burns, Cooper, Highmore (2)	*Ritchie*		
Bitton	v Poole Town	4 - 2	147
Cherry, Meaker, Reynolds (2)	*Walker, Austin*		
Wimborne Town	v Wootton Bassett Town	4 - 0	342
James, Stokoe, Joyce (2)			
Dawlish Town	v Street	3 - 4	73
Fisher, Lynch, Fenner	*Cox, Clifford-Jones, Bisgrove, Cushing*		
Shrivenham	v Hamworthy United	2 - 2*	74
Cox, Silvanus	*Walker, Byerley*		
Hamworthy United	v Shrivenham	R 4 - 1	126
Dovell, Cherrett, Byerley, Cannie	*Scarff*		
Willand Rovers	v Bemerton Heath Harlequins	2 - 1*	128
Croft, Steele			
Almondsbury Town	v Hungerford Town	0 - 2	90
	Macklin, Fila		
Brislington	v Bideford	2 - 4	58
Bryant, Hiroli	*Downing, Wood, Laight, Gough*		
Frome Town	v Saltash United	4 - 1	153
Crowley, Duggan (2), Russell	*Madden*		

Top R1: Marc Schulz (No.11) has his header blocked by the Pilkington defenders.
Photo: Bill Wheatcroft.

Middle R1: A fortuitous own goal in Kentish Town's favour against Thrapston Town.
Photo: Gordon Whittington.

Bottom R2: Everyone watches as this effort comes back off the bar during this Raunds Town v Holbeach United match. Photo: Peter Barnes.

THIRD ROUND PROPER

BIGGEST HOME WIN:	**7-0** MARSKE UNITED V PICKERING TOWN
BIGGEST AWAY WIN:	**1-4** ARUNDEL V COGENHOE UNITED
HIGHEST ATTENDANCE:	**842** LOWESTOFT TOWN V HAREFIELD UNITED
NUMBER OF GAMES:	**32 + 4** (32 + 2)
TOTAL ATTENDANCE:	**4,341** (4,341) NB: MISSING TWO ATTENDANCES
AVERAGE ATTENDANCE:	**195** (128)

Home	Away	Score	Att
Glossop North End *Bailey, Hamilton*	v Winterton Rangers *Render*	2 - 1	236
Barwell	v Coalville *Jarvis*	0 - 1	108
Market Drayton Town *Davies*	v Arnold Town *Wilkins*	1 - 1*	149
Arnold Town	v Market Drayton Town *Carvey, Rogers*	R 0 - 2 *(at Carlton Town)*	116
Spennymoor Town *Beasley, Gott, Gordon*	v Shildon *Moore, Watling*	3 - 2	
Marske United *Swalwell, Wesson, Cochrane, Newton, Thompson, Gamble, Bradley*	v Pickering Town	7 - 0	265
Penrith	v Whitley Bay *Reay*	0 - 1*	145
Long Eaton United	v Bootle *Fowler*	0 - 1	
Scarborough Athletic *Blott (3), Gray (3)*	v Blackstones *Scother*	6 - 1	583
AFC Fylde (H) *Thompson, Booth, Horsfall, Allen*	v Runcorn Linnets *Morrison*	4 - 1	413
Stratford Town	v Westfields *Hill*	1 - 1*	219
Westfields	v Stratford Town *Jakab*	R 0 - 1	71
Tipton Town	v Dunston Federation *Bulford, Wells (2)*	0 - 3	120
Stone Dominoes *Brown*	v Nostell Miners Welfare	1 - 0	78
Long Buckby *Lee*	v St Ives Town *Fielding, McDougald*	1 - 2*	180
Needham Market *Parker, Smy, Evans, Thrower*	v St Neots Town *Rocco, Hall, Dyett*	4 - 3	219
Stanway Rovers *Callander*	v Shoreham	1 - 0	100
Leiston *Lowe (3), Sillett*	v Aylesbury Vale *Roberts*	4 - 1	165
Lowestoft Town *Woodrow, King*	v Harefield United *Buckle*	2 - 1	842
Croydon *Waters, Aabrowa, Gnaly*	v Camberley Town	3 - 1	102
Stewarts & Lloyds Corby *Logan, Mills*	v Daventry Town *Greatrey*	2 - 1	44
FC Clacton *Heighway, Hillier, Waters, Coyle*	v Holbeach United *Nimmo (2), Keeble*	4 - 3*	188
Arundel	v Cogenhoe United *Frost (3), Holman*	1 - 4	126
Biggleswade Town *Morgan, Kilroy, Lamacroft, Redford (3)*	v Wivenhoe Town	6 - 0	192
Dereham Town *Beaumont, Howell (2)*	v Molesey *Baxter*	3 - 1*	204
Selsey	v Chalfont St Peter *Lewis, Strutton*	0 - 2	265
Frimley Green *Peters*	v VCD Athletic *Huggins*	1 - 1*	93
VCD Athletic *Ward, Penny, Huggins, Hassett*	v Frimley Green	R 4 - 0	75
Larkhall Athletic *Gilbert, Bailey (2)*	v Wimborne Town *Joyce*	3 - 1	163
VT FC *Spinney*	v Willand Rovers	1 - 0*	155
Witney United *Wickens, Thompson*	v Buckingham Town *Redsull*	2 - 1	236
Hamworthy United *Byerley*	v Hungerford Town *Clark, Saunders, Rusher*	1 - 3	150
Christchurch *Cook, Burrows (2)*	v New Milton Town	3 - 0	168
Street	v Bitton	0 - 0*	132
Bitton *Reynolds, O.G.*	v Street *Palmer*	R 2 - 1*	95
Bideford *Down, Wood*	v Frome Town *Rawlins*	2 - 1	236

FOURTH ROUND PROPER

BIGGEST HOME WIN:	**4-0** CHRISTCHURCH V FC CLACTON
BIGGEST AWAY WIN:	**5-6** DUNSTON FEDERATION V CHALFONT ST. P.
HIGHEST ATTENDANCE:	**759** LOWESTOFT TOWN V WITNEY UNITED
NUMBER OF GAMES:	**16 + 3** (16 + 1)
TOTAL ATTENDANCE:	**6,919** (5,858)
AVERAGE ATTENDANCE:	**364** (345)

Home	Away	Score	Att
Bitton *Reynolds, Welling*	v Cogenhoe United *Frost*	2 - 1	230
VCD Athletic *Rice, Duckworth*	v Marske United *Wesson, Cochrane, Skelton*	2 - 3	203
Biggleswade Town *Kilroy, O.G.*	v Croydon *Atkins*	2 - 1	430
St Ives Town	v Stanway Rovers	0 - 0*	598
Stanway Rovers	v St Ives Town	R 0 - 2	321
Market Drayton Town *Horler, Ward*	v VT FC *Sales*	2 - 1	264
Coalville *Brown*	v Spennymoor Town *Ward*	1 - 1*	340
Spennymoor Town *Ruddy*	v Coalville *Jarvis* *(Spennymoor won 5-4 on penalties)*	R 1 - 1*	302
Needham Market	v AFC Fylde (H)	0 - 0*	320
AFC Fylde (H) *Palmer*	v Needham Market *Denniss, Thrower (P)*	R 1 - 2	457
Christchurch *Barnes (2), Rideout (2)*	v FC Clacton	4 - 0	252
Stratford Town *Niblett, Blair, Faulds*	v Stone Dominoes *Brown (2)*	3 - 2	336
Bideford *Barker*	v Scarborough Athletic	1 - 0	570
Larkhall Athletic *Jeffrey, Bailey*	v Dereham Town *Beaumont, Howell, Atkins, Barrett*	2 - 4	235
Hungerford Town *Scott (2), Fila*	v Leiston *Ward, Rowe*	3 - 2*	265
Bootle *Fowler*	v Whitley Bay *Chow, Robinson, Reid*	1 - 3	272
Dunston Federation *Wells, Dixon, Sheeran, Bulford, Preen*	v Chalfont St Peter *Carroll, Hughes, Strutton, Swaysland, Louth, Stack*	5 - 6*	372
Glossop North End *Hodges (2)*	v Stewarts & Lloyds Corby *Edwards*	2 - 1	393
Lowestoft Town *Godbold*	v Witney United	1 - 0	759

FIFTH ROUND PROPER

NUMBER OF GAMES:	**8** (8+2)
TOTAL ATTENDANCE:	**4,679** (6,273)
AVERAGE ATTENDANCE:	**585** (627)

Home	Away	Score	Att
St Ives Town	v Marske United *Wilson, Thompson, Swales*	0 - 3	464
Lowestoft Town *Cockrill, Stock (3)*	v Hungerford Town *Fila, Concannon, Macklin*	4 - 3	1042
Chalfont St Peter *Lewis (2), Bronson, Louth*	v Christchurch	4 - 0	323
Biggleswade Town *Redford (2), Cooper, Weeden*	v Market Drayton Town *Ward, O.G.*	4 - 2	718
Bitton	v Glossop North End *Morris, Hodges*	0 - 2	443
Bideford *Barker, Hawkings*	v Spennymoor Town	2 - 0	461
Whitley Bay *Chow, Fawcett*	v Stratford Town	2 - 0	779
Needham Market *Parker, Sparkes*	v Dereham Town *Barrett*	2 - 1	449

Top left R4: Jamie Clarke fires in a shot for Spennymoor Town against Coalville Town. Photo: Bill Wheatcroft.

Top right R5: Paul McMullen nets for Market Drayton Town to equalise, however Biggleswade Town went on to win 4-2. Photo: Gordon Whittington.

Middle left R5: Action from the St Ives Town v Marske Town tie which Marske won 0-3. Photo: Peter Barnes.

Above SF 1 Leg: Glossop North End and Chalfont St Peters' players battle for the ball, whilst **left** Darren Hamilton shoots at the Chalfont goal. Photos: Eric Marsh and Roger Turner respectively.

QUARTER-FINALS

NUMBER OF GAMES: **4 + 1** (4+1)
TOTAL ATTENDANCE: **5,218** (4,106)
AVERAGE ATTENDANCE: **1,044** (821)

Whitley Bay	v Biggleswade Town	5 - 2	1286
Coulson (2), Bell, Kerr (P), Chow	*Redford, Webster*		
Lowestoft Town	v Bideford	4 - 0	1725
Stock (2), McGee, Woodlow			
Needham Market	v Chalfont St Peter	1 - 1*	579
Smith	*Lewis*		
Chalfont St Peter	v Needham Market	R 0 - 0*	508
Chalfont won 6-5 on penalties			
Glossop North End	v Marske United	5 - 2	1120
Hodges, Bailey (2), Kay, Hind	*Thompson (2)*		

SEMI-FINALS

TOTAL ATTENDANCE: **7,971** (6,588)
AVERAGE ATTENDANCE: **1,993** (1,647)

1ST LEG

Chalfont St Peter	v Glossop North End	3 - 3	1185
Strutton, Carroll, Brosnan	*Gorton, Hodges, Bailey*		
Whitley Bay	v Lowestoft Town	2 - 1	2947
Chow, Kerr (P)	*McGee*		

2ND LEG

Glossop North End	v Chalfont St Peter	2 - 2	1589
Bailey, Lugsden	*Lewis, Stratton*		
Glossop won 6-5 on penalties			
Lowestoft Town	v Whitley Bay	1 - 1	2250
Cockrill	*Ryan*		

THE FINAL

GLOSSOP NORTH END 0 WHITLEY BAY 2

(North West Counties Premier Division) (Northern Division One)

at Wembley Stadium Attendance 12,212

Same score as the Trophy Final the day before but a more competitive and entertaining contest all round. The Wembley hype was similar with the loud, pulsating bass on high although the announcer was slightly less hysterical. There was more ammunition in the crowd figures for those who wish to hold Trophy and Vase finals on the same day and when you consider the staffing costs involved in using this magnificent stadium there appears no economic sense in separating them. Rumours that next year they will indeed be played on the same day were said to be circling the FA members present. We will see.

Only the lowest tier of three was really in use and then just mainly one length of the stadium, Whitley Bay supporters having a slight numerical majority. With both sides normally wearing blue there was a preponderance of that colour in spectator apparel. On the pitch Glossop were all in white, Bay in blue and white striped shirts, blue shirts and socks.

Again it was dry overhead with occasional bursts of sunshine. As Whitley supporters were to the east they benefited from the warmth of the sinking sun while Glossop's were curtained in the relative shadows, a parallel extended to the supporters' hopes of victory as the minutes ticked away and the disparity between sunny and shaded end became even more apparent.

Support at the Vase always feels more family orientated. The fans are closer to the players in daily living, often relatives or neighbours who consequently meet in their routine experiences. Less money and smaller attendances also make for closer working and more inter-socialising. There is certainly a welcome absence amongst supporters of the aping of the professional game's unpleasant side and usually, but admittedly not always, far less hostility or fear of physical confrontation. This was shown particularly poignantly at the end of the trophy presentations when both teams went, unrehearsed, to each other's supporters, to applaud and be applauded in a warm show of comradeship and respect. No bookings in the entire match underlined this very evident sportsmanship.

Glossop went into the match with no substitute keeper. The 17 year old Gotham, who had made a significant contribution to their reaching Wembley, particularly in the semi final penalty shoot out, was injured so his place went to Cooper, the other Glossop keeper being cup tied. Bay lined up as anticipated. How pleasing it was to see two teams listed on the team sheets in traditional order of positions with no player numbers higher than 18 and most between 1 and 11.

On another similarly trivial note I wondered why the previous day the clubs had been allowed two personnel in the technical area for the Trophy and yet only one each for the Vase. Have I missed a regulation somewhere?

The first scoring attempt was made by the Hillmen. Rick Bailey's shot hit a defender and so trickled into Burke's grasp. Glossop were also first to gain a corner but the clearance led to a Bay attack and their first corner, followed by one of Picton's prodigious throw ins. Johnston's fantastic shot from just inside the opponent's half saw a back pedalling Cooper just manage to tip it over before, at the Bay end, a terrific drive from Allen smashed against the angle. It was enervating stuff.

Hodges then broke down the right but Burke plucked his cross safely before onrushing heads could mean danger. Back to the other end and the first score – Chow dribbled infield past three defenders, slid the ball through to Kerr who was able to look up before driving fiercely between Cooper and the post.

An injury to Glossop's Bailey allowed a drink break, which even the ref participated in. Rejuvenated, Bailey jinked down the right but could not find a recipient for his ground pass. Hodges then broke into the opposition area and found Morris whose shot was blocked. The ball, quickly transferred to the other goalmouth, reached Chow who found himself surprisingly clear. His shot was touched by Cooper's left hand but insufficiently to prevent it finding the net. This was Chow's fortieth score of the season and came in injury time.

Two up, the North Easterners had a happy break while Cooper spent time honing his skills, even though he had not been to blame for either goal. One goal difference would, most believed, have been surmountable but two down must have looked like some of the challenging peaks amongst which the Glossopians dwell.

Two early Chow surges, a shot deflected over and another dangerous surge halted by Yates falling on the ball, leading to penalty appeals, augured more trouble for the Hillmen. They responded with immediate goal attempts from Hamilton, Gorton and Hodges, none of which troubled Burke. Bay were next to show. Cooper's foot blocked a Johnston shot, Chow headed against the bar and Moore's shot was turned round by Cooper diving to his left. Chow and Ryan both headed over from corners. A Hodges lob promised for Glossop but landed on, rather than in, the net. Burke dropped a Hodges' cross, sub Tom Bailey's shot was blocked and three successive Glossop corners raised their hopes. Penalty appeals were waved aside as a Hodges shot was blocked, Balfe fired over and Hodges dribble ended with a tame shot straight at Burke.

Neutrals willed a Glossop score to increase the tension but Morris' shot drifted wide after being set up by Hodges and Tom Bailey and exhausted players were soon sinking to the turf, which had produced no controversy, as Mr Friend's whistle brought an end to the match but not the very excited celebrations at one end and appreciative applause at the other. So ended another splendid advert for Vase football, with Bay's industrious Kerr judged man of the match.

ARTHUR EVANS

GLOSSOP NORTH END:
Matt Cooper, Dave Young, Jamie Kay, Kelvin Lugsden, Danny Yates, Jay Gorton, Rick Bailey (Sam Hind 57th min), Dave Morris, Nick Allen (Mark Balfe 65th min), Darren Hamilton (Tom Bailey 72nd min), Dave Hodges.
Subs not used: Rick Whelan and Martin Parker.

WHITLEY BAY:
Terry Burke, Mark Taylor, Lee Picton, Craig McFarlane (Chris Fawcett 60th min), David Coulson, Leon Ryan, Chris Moore, Damon Robson, Lee Kerr, Paul Chow (Paul Robinson 73rd min), Adam Johnston (Phil Bell 60th min).
Subs not used: Rob McLean and Darren Reay.
Referee: Kevin Friend, assistants David Coote and Robert Madley. Fourth official, Graham Scott.

Right: Adam Johnston (Whitley Bay) takes on a Glossop defender. Photo: Keith Clayton.

Below: Hamilton (Glossop) does an over-head kick under pressure from Coulson (Whitley Bay). Photo: Keith Clayton.

Below right: Lee Picton and Paul Chow hold the F.A. Vase aloft. Photo: Eric Marsh.

Bottom: The Whitley Bay squad celebrate their victory in front of the fans. Photo: Alan Coomes.

PAST F.A. VASE FINALS

1975 **HODDESDON TOWN 2 *(Spartan Sth Mids)*** **EPSOM & EWELL 1 *(Surrey Senior)*** **Att: 9,500**
Sedgwick 2 **Wales** **Ref: Mr R Toseland**
Hoddesdon: Galvin, Green, Hickey, Maybury, Stevenson, Wilson, Bishop, Picking, Sedgwick, Nathan, Schofield
Epsom & Ewell: Page, Bennett, Webb, Wales, Worby, Jones, O'Connell, Walker, Tuite, Eales, Lee

1976 **BILLERICAY TOWN 1 *(Essex Senior)*** **STAMFORD 0 (aet) *(United Counties)*** **Att: 11,848**
Aslett **Ref: Mr A Robinson**
Billericay: Griffiths, Payne, Foreman, Pullin, Bone, Coughlan, Geddes, Aslett, Clayden, Scott, Smith
Stamford: Johnson, Kwiatowski, Marchant, Crawford, Downs, Hird, Barnes, Walpole, Smith, Russell, Broadbent

1977 **BILLERICAY TOWN 1 *(Essex Senior)*** **SHEFFIELD 1 (aet) *(Yorkshire)*** **Att: 14,000**
Clayden **Coughlan og** **Ref: Mr J Worrall**
Billericay: Griffiths, Payne, Bone, Coughlan, Pullin, Scott, Wakefield, Aslett, Clayden,Woodhouse, McQueen. Sub: Whettell
Sheffield: Wing, Gilbody, Lodge, Hardisty, Watts, Skelton, Kay, Travis, Pugh, Thornhill,Haynes. Sub: Strutt
Replay **BILLERICAY TOWN 2** **SHEFFIELD 1** **Att: 3,482**
Aslett, Woodhouse **Thornhill** **at Nottingham Forest**
Billericay: Griffiths, Payne, Pullin, Whettell, Bone, McQueen, Woodhouse, Aslett, Clayden, Scott, Wakefield
Sheffield: Wing, Gilbody, Lodge, Strutt, Watts, Skelton, Kay, Travis, Pugh, Thornhill, Haynes

1978 **NEWCASTLE BLUE STAR 2 *(Wearside)*** **BARTON ROVERS 1 *(South Midlands)*** **Att: 16,858**
Dunn, Crumplin **Smith** **Ref: Mr T Morris**
Newcastle: Halbert, Feenan, Thompson, Davidson, S Dixon, Beynon, Storey, P Dixon, Crumplin, Callaghan, Dunn. Sub: Diamond
Barton Rovers: Blackwell, Stephens, Crossley, Evans, Harris, Dollimore, Dunn, Harnaman, Fossey, Turner, Smith. Sub: Cox

1979 **BILLERICAY TOWN 4 *(Athenian)*** **ALMONDSBURY GREENWAY 1 *(Glos. Co)*** **Att: 17,500**
Young 3, Clayden **Price** **Ref: Mr C Steel**
Billericay: Norris, Blackaller, Bingham, Whettell, Bone, Reeves, Pullin, Scott, Clayden,Young, Groom. Sub: Carrigan
Almondsbury: Hamilton, Bowers, Scarrett, Sulllivan, Tudor, Wookey, Bowers, Shehean, Kerr,Butt, Price. Sub: Kilbaine

1980 **STAMFORD 2 *(United Counties)*** **GUISBOROUGH TOWN 0 *(Northern)*** **Att: 11,500**
Alexander, McGowan **Ref: Neil Midgeley**
Stamford: Johnson, Kwiatkowski, Ladd, McGowan, Bliszczak I, Mackin, Broadhurst, Hall,Czarnecki, Potter, Alexander. Sub: Bliszczak S
Guisborough: Cutter, Scott, Thornton, Angus, Maltby, Percy, Skelton, Coleman, McElvaney,Sills, Dilworth. Sub: Harrison

1981 **WHICKHAM 3 *(Wearside)*** **WILLENHALL 2 (aet) *(West Midlands)*** **Att: 12,000**
Scott, Williamson, Peck og **Smith, Stringer** **Ref: Mr R Lewis**
Whickham: Thompson, Scott, Knox, Williamson, Cook, Ward, Carroll, Diamond, Cawthra,Robertson, Turnbull. Sub: Alton
Willenhall: Newton, White, Darris, Woodall, Heath, Fox, Peck, Price, Matthews, Smith,Stringer. Sub: Trevor

1982 **FOREST GREEN ROVERS 3 *(Hellenic)*** **RAINWORTH M.W 0 *(Notts Alliance)*** **Att: 12,500**
Leitch 2, Norman **Ref: Mr K Walmsey**
Forest Green: Moss, Norman, Day, Turner, Higgins, Jenkins, Guest, Burns, Millard, Leitch, Doughty. Sub: Dangerfield
Rainworth M.W: Watson, Hallam, Hodgson, Slater, Sterland, Oliver, Knowles, Raine, Radzi, Reah, Comerford. Sub: Robinson

1983 **V.S. RUGBY 1 *(West Midlands)*** **HALESOWEN TOWN 0 *(West Midlands)*** **Att: 13,700**
Crawley **Ref: Mr B Daniels**
VS Rugby: Burton, McGinty, Harrison, Preston, Knox, Evans, ingram, Setchell, Owen,Beecham, Crawley. Sub: Haskins
Halesowen Town: Coldicott, Penn, Edmonds, Lacey, Randall, Shilvock, Hazelwood, Moss, Woodhouse,P Joinson, L Joinson. Sub: Smith

1984 **STANSTED 3 *(Essex Senior)*** **STAMFORD 2 *(United Counties)*** **Att: 8,125**
Holt, Gillard, Reading **Waddicore, Allen** **Ref: Mr T Bune**
Stanstead: Coe, Williams, Hilton, Simpson, Cooper, Reading, Callanan, Holt, Reevs,Doyle, Gillard. Sub: Williams
Stamford: Parslow, Smitheringate, Blades, McIlwain, Lyon, Mackin, Genovese, Waddicore,Allen, Robson, Beech. Sub: Chapman

1985 **HALESOWEN TOWN 3 *(West Midlands)*** **FLEETWOOD TOWN 1 *(N W Counties)*** **Att: 16,715**
L Joinson 2, Moss **Moran** **Ref: Mr C Downey**
Halesowen: Coldicott, Penn, Sherwood, Warner, Randle, Heath, Hazlewood, Moss (Smith),Woodhouse, P Joinson, L Joinson
Fleetwood Town: Dobson, Moran, Hadgraft, Strachan, Robinson, Milligan, Hall, Trainor, Taylor(Whitehouse), Cain, Kennerley

1986 **HALESOWEN TOWN 3 *(West Midlands)*** **SOUTHALL 0 *(Isthmian 2 South)*** **Att: 18,340**
Moss 2, L Joinson **Ref: Mr D Scott**
Halesowen: Pemberton, Moore, Lacey, Randle (Rhodes), Sherwood, Heath, Penn, Woodhouse, PJoinson, L Joinson, Moss
Southall: Mackenzie, James, McGovern, Croad, Holland, Powell (Richmond), Pierre,Richardson, Sweales, Ferdinand, Rowe

1987 **ST. HELENS 3 *(N W Counties)*** **WARRINGTON TOWN 2 *(N W Counties)*** **Att: 4,254**
Layhe 2, Rigby **Reid, Cook** **Ref: Mr T Mills**
St Helens: Johnson, Benson, Lowe, Bendon, Wilson, McComb, Collins (Gledhill), O'Neill,Cummins, Lay, Rigby. Sub: Deakin
Warrington: O'Brien. Copeland, Hunter, Gratton, Whalley, Reid, Brownville (Woodyer), Cook,Kinsey, Looker (Hill), Hughes

1988 **COLNE DYNAMOES 1 *(N W Counties)*** **EMLEY 0 *(Northern Counties East)*** **Att: 15,000**
Anderson **Ref: Mr A Seville**
Colne Dynamoes: Mason, McFafyen, Westwell, Bentley, Dunn, Roscoe, Rodaway, Whitehead (Burke),Diamond, Anderson, Wood (Coates)
Emley: Dennis, Fielding, Mellor, Codd, Hirst (Burrows), Gartland (Cook), Carmody,Green, Bramald, Devine, Francis

1989 **TAMWORTH 1 *(West Midlands)*** **SUDBURY TOWN 1 (aet) *(Eastern)*** **Att: 26,487**
Devaney **Hubbick** **Ref: Mr C Downey**
Tamworth: Bedford, Lockett, Atkins, Cartwright, McCormack, Myers, Finn, Devaney, Moores,Gordon, Stanton. Subs: Rathbone, Heaton
Sudbury Town: Garnham, Henry, G Barker, Boyland, Thorpe, Klug, D Barker, Barton, Oldfield,Smith, Hubbick. Subs: Money, Hunt
REPLAY **TAMWORTH 3** **SUDBURY TOWN 0** **Att: 11,201**
Stanton 2, Moores **at Peterborough**
Tamworth: Bedford, Lockett, Atkins, Cartwright, Finn, Myers, George, Devaney, Moores,Gordon, Stanton. Sub: Heaton
Sudbury Town: Garnham, Henry, G Barker, Boyland, Thorpe, Klug, D Barker, Barton, Oldfield,Smith, Hubbick. Subs: Money, Hunt

1990 **YEADING 0 *(Isthmian 2 South)*** **BRIDLINGTON TOWN 0 (aet) *(N Co East)*** **Att: 7,932**
Ref: Mr R Groves
Yeading: Mackenzie, Wickens, Turner, Whiskey (McCarthy), Croad, Denton, Matthews, James(Charles), Sweates, Impey, Cordery
Bridlington: Taylor, Pugh, Freeman, McNeill, Warburton, Brentano, Wilkes (Hall), Noteman,Gauden, Whiteman, Brattan (Brown)

Replay **YEADING 1** **BRIDLINGTON TOWN 0** **Att: 5,000**
Sweales **at Leeds Utd FC**
Yeading: Mackenzie, Wickens, Turner, Whiskey, Croad (McCarthy), Schwartz, Matthews,James, Sweates, Impey (Welsh), Cordery
Bridlington: Taylor, Pugh, Freeman, McNeill, Warburton, Brentano, Wilkes (Brown), Noteman,Gauden (Downing), Whiteman, Brattan

1991 **GRESLEY ROVERS 4 *(West Midlands)*** **GUISELEY 4 (aet) *(Northern Co East)*** **Att: 11,314**
Rathbone, Smith 2, Stokes **Tennison 2, Walling, A Roberts** **Ref: Mr C Trussell**
Gresley: Aston, Barry, Elliott (Adcock), Denby, Land, Astley, Stokes, K Smith, Acklam,Rathbone, Lovell (Weston)
Guiseley: Maxted, Bottomley, Hogarth, Tetley, Morgan, McKenzie, Atkinson (Annan),Tennison, Walling, A Roberts, B Roberts

Replay **GUISELEY 3** **GRESLEY ROVERS 1** **Att: 7,585**
Tennison, Walling, Atkinson **Astley** **at Bramall Lane**
Guiseley: Maxted, Annan, Hogarth, Tetley, Morgan, McKenzie (Bottomley), Atkinson,Tennison (Noteman), Walling, A Roberts, B Roberts
Gresley: Aston, Barry, Elliott, Denby, Land, Astley, Stokes (Weston), K Smith, Acklam, Rathbone, Lovell (Adcock)

1992 **WIMBORNE TOWN 5 *(Wessex)*** **GUISELEY 3 *(Northern Premier Div 1)*** **Att: 10,772**
Richardson, Sturgess 2, Killick 2 **Noteman 2, Colville** **Ref: Mr M J Bodenham**
Wimborne: Leonard, Langdown, Wilkins, Beacham, Allan, Taplin, Ames, Richardson, Bridle,Killick, Sturgess (Lovell), Lynn
Guiseley: Maxted, Atkinson, Hogarth, Tetley (Wilson), Morgan, Brockie, A Roberts,Tennison, Noteman (Colville), Annan, W Roberts

1993 **BRIDLINGTON TOWN 1 *(NPL Div 1)*** **TIVERTON TOWN 0 *(Western)*** **Att: 9,061**
Radford **Ref: Mr R A Hart**
Bridlington: Taylor, Brentano, McKenzie, Harvey, Bottomley, Woodcock, Grocock, A Roberts, Jones, Radford (Tyrell), Parkinson. Sub: Swailes
Tiverton Town: Nott, J Smith, N Saunders, M Saunders, Short (Scott), Steele, Annunziata, KSmith, Everett, Daly, Hynds (Rogers)

1994 **DISS TOWN 2 *(Eastern)*** **TAUNTON TOWN 1 *(Western)*** **Att: 13,450**
Gibbs (p), Mendham **Fowler** **Ref: Mr K. Morton**
Diss Town: Woodcock, Carter, Wolsey (Musgrave), Casey (Bugg), Hartle, Smith, Barth, Mendham, Miles, Warne, Gibbs
Taunton Town: Maloy, Morris, Walsh, Ewens, Graddon, Palfrey, West (Hendry), Fowler, Durham, Perrett (Ward), Jarvis

1995 **ARLESEY TOWN 2 *(South Midlands)*** **OXFORD CITY 1 *(Ryman 2)*** **Att: 13,670**
Palma, Gyalog **S Fontaine** **Ref: Mr G S Willard**
Arlesey: Young, Cardines, Bambrick, Palma (Ward), Hull, Gonsalves, Gyalog, Cox, Kane,O'Keefe, Marshall (Nicholls). Sub: Dodwell
Oxford: Fleet, Brown (Fisher), Hume, Shepherd, Muttock, Hamilton (Kemp), Thomas, Spittle, Sherwood, S Fontaine, C Fontaine. Sub: Torres

1996 **BRIGG TOWN 3 *(N Co East)*** **CLITHEROE 0 *(N W Counties)*** **Att: 7,340**
Stead 2, Roach **Ref: Mr S J Lodge**
Brigg: Gawthorpe, Thompson, Rogers, Greaves (Clay), Buckley (Mail), Elston, C Stead, McLean, N Stead (McNally), Flounders, Roach
Clitheroe: Nash, Lampkin, Rowbotham (Otley), Baron, Westwell, Rovine, Butcher, Taylor (Smith), Grimshaw, Darbyshire, Hill (Dunn)

1997 **WHITBY TOWN 3 *(Northern)*** **NORTH FERRIBY UTD. 0 *(N Co East)*** **Att: 11,098**
Williams, Logan, Toman **Ref: Graham Poll**
North Ferriby: Sharp, Deacey, Smith, Brentano, Walmsley, M Smith, Harrison (Horne), Phillips (Milner), France (Newman), Flounders, Tennison
Whitby Town: Campbell, Williams, Logan, Goodchild, Pearson, Cook, Goodrick (Borthwick), Hodgson, Robinson, Toman (Pyle), Pitman (Hall)

1998 **TIVERTON TOWN 1 *(Western)*** **TOW LAW TOWN 0 *(Northern)*** **Att: 13,139**
Varley **Ref: M A Riley**
Tiverton: Edwards, Felton, Saunders, Tatterton, Smith J, Conning, Nancekivell (Rogers), Smith K (Varley), Everett, Daly, Leonard (Waters)
Tow Law: Dawson, Pickering, Darwent, Bailey, Hague, Moan, Johnson, Nelson, Suddick, Laidler (Bennett), Robinson.

1999 **TIVERTON TOWN 1 *(Western)*** **BEDLINGTON TERRIERS 0 *(Northern)*** **Att: 13, 878**
Rogers 88 **Ref: W. C. Burns**
Bedlington Terriers: O'Connor, Bowes, Pike, Boon (Renforth), Melrose, Teasdale, Cross, Middleton (Ludlow), Gibb, Milner, Bond. Subs: Pearson, Cameron, Gowans
Tiverton Town: Edwards, Fallon, Saunders, Tatterton, Tallon, Conning (Rogers), Nancekivell (Pears), Varley, Everett, Daly, Leonard. Subs: Tucker, Hynds, Grimshaw

2000 **DEAL TOWN 1 *(Kent)*** **CHIPPENHAM TOWN 0 *(Western)*** **Att: 20,000**
Graham 87 **Ref: E. K. Wolstenholme**
Deal Town: Tucker, Kempster, Best, Ash, Martin, Seager, Monteith, Graham, Lovell, Marshall, Ribbens. Subs: Roberts, Warden, Turner
Chippenham Town: Jones, James, Andrews, Murphy, Burns, Woods, Brown, Charity, Tweddle, Collier, Godley. Subs: Tiley, Cutler

2001 **TAUNTON TOWN 2 *(Western)*** **BERKHAMPSTED TOWN 1 *(Isthmian 2)*** **(at Villa Park)** **Att: 8,439**
Fields 41, Laight 45 **Lowe 71** **Ref: E. K. Wolstenholme**
Taunton Town: Draper, Down, Chapman, West, Hawkings, Kelly, Fields (Groves), Laight, Cann (Tallon), Bastow, Lynch (Hapgood). Subs: Ayres, Parker
Berkhampsted Town: O'Connor, Mullins, Lowe, Aldridge, Coleman, Brockett, Yates, Adebowale, Richardson, Smith, Nightingale. Subs: Ringsell, Hall, Knight, Franklin, Osborne

2002 **WHITLEY BAY 1 *(Northern)*** **TIPTREE UNITED 0 *(Eastern)*** **(at Villa Park)** **Att: 4742**
Chandler 97 **Ref: A Kaye**
Whitley Bay: Caffrey, Sunderland, Walmsley, Dixon (Neil), Chandler, Walton, Fenwick (Cuggy). Subs: Cook, Livermore
Tiptree United: Haygreen, Battell, Wall, Houghton, Fish, Streetley (Gillespie), Wareham (Snow), Daly, Barefield, Aransibia (Parnell), Brady. Subs: Powell, Ford.

2003 **A.F.C SUDBURY 1 *(Eastern Counties)*** **BRIGG TOWN 2 *(Northern Co.East)*** **(at Upton Park)** **Att: 6,634**
Raynor 30 **Housham 2, Carter 68** **Ref: M Fletcher**
AFC Sudbury:- Greygoose, Head (Norfolk 63), Spearing, Tracey, Bishop, Anderson (Owen 73), Rayner, Gardiner (Banya 79), Bennett, Claydon, Betson. Subs (not used) Taylor, Hyde.
Brigg Town:- Steer, Raspin, Rowland, Thompson, Blanchard, Stones, Stead (Thompson 41), Housham, Borman (Drayton 87), Roach, Carter. Subs (not used) Nevis, Gawthorpe.

2004 **A.F.C SUDBURY 0 *(Eastern Counties)*** **WINCHESTER CITY 2 *(Wessex)*** **(at St Andrews)** **Att: 5,080**
Forbes 19, Smith 73 (pen) **Ref: P Crossley**
AFC Sudbury:- Greygoose, Head, Wardley, Girling, Tracey, Norfolk, Owen (Banya 62), Hyde (Calver 57), Bennett, Claydon, Betson (Francis 73n). Subs (not used) - Rayner, Nower.
Winchester City:- Arthur, Dyke (Tate 83), Bicknell, Redwood, Goss, Blake, Webber, Green, Mancey, Forbes (Rogers 70), Smith (Green 90). Subs (not used) - Lang and Rastall.

2005 **A.F.C SUDBURY 2 *(Eastern Counties)*** **DIDCOT TOWN 3 *(Hellenic)*** **(at White Hart Lane)** **Att: 8,662**
Wardley, Calver (pen) **Beavon (2), Wardley (og)** **Ref: R Beeby**
AFC Sudbury:- Greygoose, Girling, Wardley, Bennett, Hyde (Hayes 78), Owen (Norfolk 65), Claydon (Banya 59), Head, Calver, Betson, Terry Rayner. Subs (not used) – Howlett, Nower.
Didcot Town:- Webb, Goodall, Heapy, Campbell, Green, Parrott, Hannigan, Ward, Concannon (Jones 88), Beavon (Bianchini 90), Powell. Subs (not used) – Cooper, Allen, Spurrett.

2006 **HILLINGDON BOROUGH 1 *(Spartan S.Mids P.)*** **NANTWICH TOWN 3 *(NWC 1)*** **(at St Andrews)** **Att: 3,286**
Nelson **Kinsey (2), Scheuber**
Hillingdon Borough:- Brown, Rundell (Fenton 80),Kidson, Phillips, Croft, Lawrence, Duncan (Nelson 46), Tilbury, Hibbs, Wharton (Lyons 38). Subs (not used): O'Grady, White.
Nantwich Town:- Hackney, A.Taylor, T.Taylor, Smith, Davis, Donnelly, Beasley, Scheuber (Parkinson 69), Kinsey (Marrow 69), Blake (Scarlett 86) and Griggs. Subs (not used): O'Connor and Read.

2007 **AFC TOTTON 1 *(Wessex Division 1)*** **TRURO 3 *(Western Division1)*** **Att: 27,754 (New Vase record)**
Potter **Wills (2), Broad** **Ref: P Joslin**
AFC Totton: Brunnschweiler, Reacord, Troon (Stevens 60), Potter (Gregory 82), Bottomley, Austen, Roden, Gosney, Hamodu (Goss 89), Osman, Byres. Subs not used: Zammit, McCormack.
Truro City: Stevenson, Ash, Power, Smith, Martin (Pope 84), Broad, Wills, Gosling, Yetton, Watkins, Walker (Ludlam 90). Subs not used: Butcher, Routledge, Reski.

2007 **AFC TOTTON 1** ***(Wessex Division 1)*** **TRURO 3** ***(Western Division1)*** **Att: 27,754 (New Vase record)**
Potter **Wills (2), Broad** **Ref: P Joslin**

AFC Totton: Brunnschweiler, Reacord, Troon (Stevens 60), Potter (Gregory 82), Bottomley, Austen, Roden, Gosney, Hamodu (Goss 89), Osman, Byres. Subs not used: Zammit, McCormack.

Truro City: Stevenson, Ash, Power, Smith, Martin (Pope 84), Broad, Wills, Gosling, Yetton, Watkins, Walker (Ludlam 90). Subs not used: Butcher, Routledge, Reski.

2008 **KIRKHAM & WESHAM 2** ***(North West Co. Div.2)*** **LOWESTOFT TOWN 1** ***(Eastern Co. Premier)*** **Att: 19,537**
Walwyn (2) **Thompson (og)** **Ref: A D'Urso**

Kirkham and Wesham: Summerfield, Jackson (Walwyn 79), Keefe (Allen 55), Thompson, Shaw, Eastwood, Clark, Blackwell, Wane, Paterson (Sheppard 90), Smith. Subs not used: Moffat and Abbott

Lowestoft Town: Reynolds, Poppy, Potter, Woodrow, Saunders, Plaskett (McGee 79), Godbold, Darren Cockrill (Dale Cockrill 46), Stock, Hough, King (Hunn 55). Subs not used: McKenna and Rix.

All Finals at Wembley unless otherwise shown

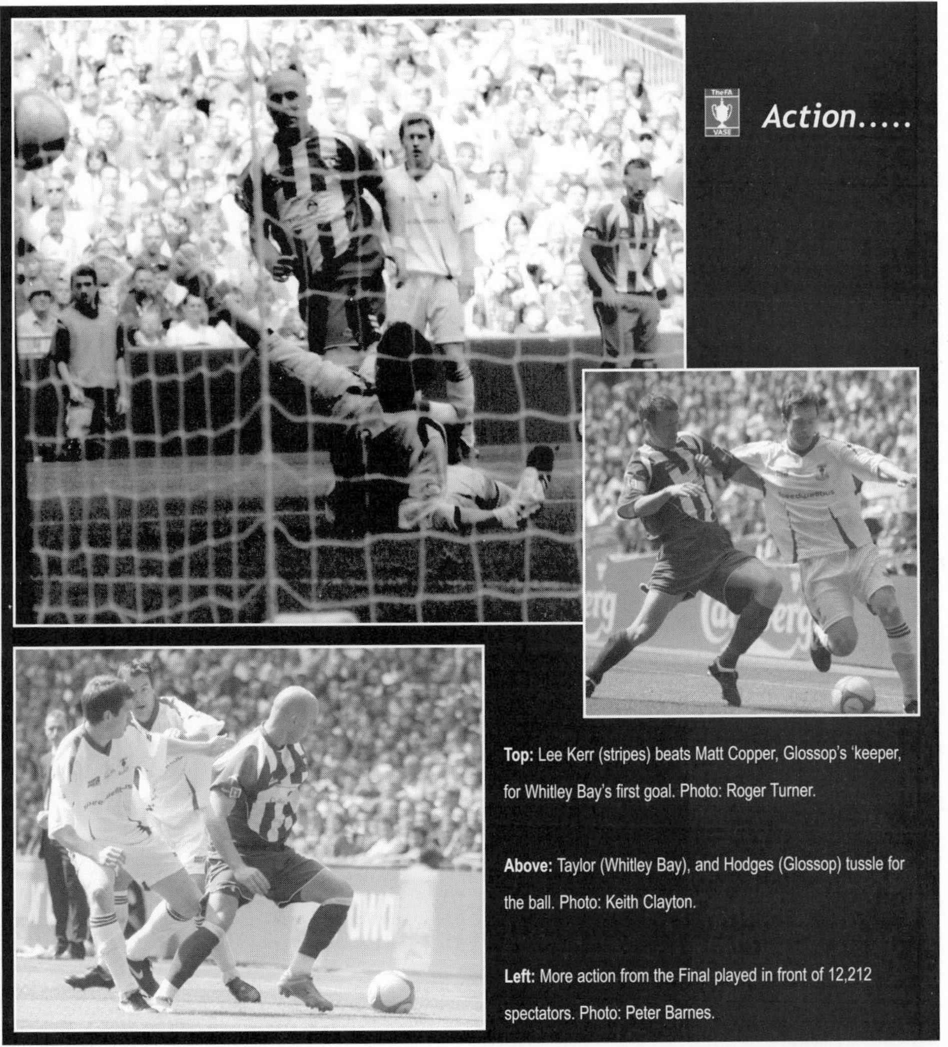

Top: Lee Kerr (stripes) beats Matt Copper, Glossop's 'keeper, for Whitley Bay's first goal. Photo: Roger Turner.

Above: Taylor (Whitley Bay), and Hodges (Glossop) tussle for the ball. Photo: Keith Clayton.

Left: More action from the Final played in front of 12,212 spectators. Photo: Peter Barnes.

QUALITY HOTEL HEATHROW

- Easy access to Wembley, Twickenham and Central London
- Close to M25, M4, M40
- Heathrow Airport 15 mins - shuttle bus service
- 128 comfortable ensuite rooms
- Restaurant, Bar, Room service
- Mini Gym
- WiFi available throughout hotel\internet kiosk in lobby

London Road, Slough
Berkshire SL3 8QB
Email: info@qualityheathrow.com

or visit
www.qualityheathrow.com

PRELIMINARY ROUND

Bromyard Town	v	Rugby Town	4 - 3
Walsall Wood	v	Coventry Sphinx	2 - 5
Redditch United	v	Pelsall Villa	2 - 1
Wednesfield	v	Ellesmere Rangers	2 - 6
Mile Oak	v	Tonbridge Angels	1 - 5
Hebburn Town	v	Dunston Federation	2 - 5
Radstock Town	v	Team Bath	1 - 2
Colne	v	AFC Blackpool	4 - 0
Portishead	v	Bath City	2 - 3
Ringmer	v	Margate	3 - 5
Leigh Genesis	v	Nantwich Town	0 - 2
Ilford	v	Ware	1 - 4
Vauxhall Motors	v	Woodley Sports	3 - 2
Gateshead	v	West Allotment Celtic	3 - 2
Loughborough Dynamo	v	Grantham Town	10 - 0
Gornal Athletic	v	Pershore Town	3 - 0
Newmarket Town	v	Histon	0 - 5
Soham Town Rangers	v	Leiston	1 - 0
Walsham Le Willows	v	Ipswich Wanderers	3 - 0
Wroxham	v	Great Yarmouth Town	0 - 2
(Tie awarded to Wroxham)			
Diss Town	v	Stowmarket Town	1 - 3
Yaxley	v	AFC Kempston Rovers	1 - 3
Dunstable Town	v	Daventry Town	5 - 1
Cheshunt	v	Boreham Wood	0 - 6
St Albans City	v	Romford	8 - 1
Chatham Town	v	Horley Town	1 - 0
Hassocks	v	Walton & Hersham	3 - 0
Godalming Town	v	Three Bridges	2 - 2
Pagham	v	Molesey	2 - 0
Alton Town	v	Marlow	1 - 3
Sherborne Town	v	Havant & Waterlooville	1 - 5
Prudhoe Town	v	Whitley Bay	1 - 6
Seaham Red Star	v	Walker Central	1 - 2
Norton United	v	Stone Dominoes	5 - 0
Chipstead	v	Haywards Heath Town	4 - 1
Carshalton Athletic	v	Oakwood	4 - 5
Merthyr Tydfil	v	Chard Town	1 - 0
Horsham YMCA	v	Kingstonian	1 - 9
Wallsend BC	v	Ryton	13 - 0
Stalybridge Celtic	v	Wrexham	2 - 3
Kings Lynn	v	Woodbridge Town	1 - 4
Cammell Laird	v	Altrincham	5 - 1
Liversedge	v	Stocksbridge Park Steels	2 - 1
Silsden AFC	v	FC Halifax Town	4 - 3
Farsley Celtic	v	Hall Road Rangers	0 - 1
Sheffield	v	Bradford (Park Avenue)	6 - 1
Blaby & Whetstone Athletic	v	New Mills	2 - 0
Oadby Town	v	Alfreton Town	2 - 1
Rainworth MW	v	Long Eaton United	0 - 2
Stafford Rangers	v	Newcastle Town	4 - 0
Dosthill Colts	v	Lye Town	4 - 2
Malvern Town	v	Burton Albion	3 - 1
Highgate United	v	Nuneaton Griff	4 - 2
Hednesford Town	v	Bedworth United	3 - 2
AFC Telford United	v	Bewdley Town	3 - 1
Long Melford	v	Debenham LC	1 - 3
Mildenhall Town	v	Cornard United	1 - 4
Arlesey Town	v	Sileby Rangers	0 - 8
St Margaretsbury	v	Hullbridge Sports	4 - 1
Waltham Abbey	v	Tring Athletic	2 - 1
Canvey Island	v	AFC Hornchurch	2 - 1
Hoddesdon Town	v	FC Clacton	4 - 0
Royston Town	v	Thurrock	0 - 4
Harefield United	v	Wingate & Finchley	4 - 1
Hampton & Richmond Borough	v	Dulwich Hamlet	5 - 0
Welling United	v	Wealdstone	1 - 4
Northwood	v	Redbridge	2 - 4
Hanwell Town	v	AFC Wimbledon	2 - 4
Ashford Town (Middx)	v	Haringey Borough	2 - 1
Deal Town	v	Lewes	0 - 5
Faversham Town	v	VCD Athletic	4 - 4
Tooting & Mitcham United	v	Worthing	1 - 1
Wokingham Town & Emmbrook	v	AFC Wallingford	3 - 0
Cove	v	Fleet Town	1 - 3
Farnborough	v	Maidenhead United	2 - 4
Sandhurst Town	v	Carterton	0 - 1
Henley Town	v	Aylesbury United	5 - 1
Brackley Town	v	Bugbrooke St Michaels	4 - 3
Kettering Town	v	Rothwell Corinthians	1 - 2
Bishop's Stortford	v	Tiptree United	3 - 1
Grays Athletic	v	Colney Heath	2 - 4
Ebbsfleet United	v	Redhill	14 - 0
Westfield	v	Epsom & Ewell	0 - 3
Mansfield Town	v	Bourne Town	13 - 0
Rushden & Diamonds	v	Raunds Town	5 - 0
Binfield	v	Beaconsfield SYCOB	2 - 5
Teversal	v	Mickleover Sports	2 - 5
Bury Town	v	Kirkley & Pakefield	5 - 0
Corinthian Casuals	v	North Greenford United	0 - 2
Reading Town	v	Kidlington	1 - 3
Forest Green Rovers	v	Mangotsfield United	3 - 2
York City	v	Sunderland RCA	5 - 0
Rocester	v	Sutton Coldfield Town	1 - 2
Eastbourne Borough	v	Folkestone Invicta	3 - 2
Lincoln United	v	Holwell Sports	2 - 0
Bromsgrove Rovers	v	Tipton Town	3 - 1
March Town United	v	Whitton United	0 - 4
Welwyn Garden City	v	Billericay Town	1 - 3
Halstead Town	v	Southend Manor	0 - 4
Kentish Town	v	Uxbridge	2 - 1
Chesham United	v	Thatcham Town	2 - 1
Newport County	v	Brislington	10 - 0
Bitton AFC	v	Torquay United	1 - 1
Stourport Swifts	v	Willenhall Town	3 - 1
Stourbridge	v	Racing Club Warwick	4 - 0
Burgess Hill Town	v	Bisley	6 - 1
Chalfont St Peter	v	Burnham	3 - 1
Weston Super Mare	v	Cheltenham Saracens	2 - 3

FIRST ROUND QUALIFYING

AFC Totton	v	Salisbury City	2 - 3
Chalfont St Peter	v	Andover	3 - 0
Cammell Laird	v	Southport	2 - 2
Formby	v	Vauxhall Motors	5 - 0
Margate	v	Hastings United	2 - 3
Gateshead	v	Guisborough Town	5 - 0
Colne	v	Bootle	2 - 1
Long Eaton United	v	Carlton Town	1 - 5
Mickleover Sports	v	Arnold Town	4 - 0
Rolls Royce Leisure	v	Retford United	0 - 2
Glossop North End	v	Hinckley United	2 - 4
Coventry Sphinx	v	Norton United	5 - 2
Stafford Rangers	v	Ellesmere Rangers	1 - 2
Sutton Coldfield Town	v	Chasetown	2 - 1
Fakenham Town	v	Bury Town	0 - 5
Soham Town Rangers	v	Dereham Town	2 - 1
Cornard United	v	Lowestoft Town	1 - 4
AFC Kempston Rovers	v	Wellingborough Town	2 - 3
Bowers & Pitsea	v	Witham Town	2 - 3
Colney Heath	v	Chelmsford City	3 - 1
Thamesmead Town	v	Redbridge	2 - 1
Cockfosters	v	Wealdstone	2 - 1
Ramsgate	v	Dover Athletic	2 - 3
Maidstone United	v	Dartford	1 - 0
Chatham Town	v	Sittingbourne	12 - 2
Oakwood	v	Horsham	4 - 3
Kidlington	v	Chesham United	3 - 2
Didcot Town	v	Bracknell Town	2 - 1
Carterton	v	Windsor & Eton	0 - 1
VT	v	Havant & Waterlooville	1 - 2
Forest Green Rovers	v	Elmore	4 - 0
Tiverton Town	v	Newport County	2 - 3
Merthyr Tydfil	v	Yate Town	3 - 4
York City	v	Whitley Bay	5 - 0
Ashton Athletic	v	Burscough	1 - 3
FCV Reds	v	Stewarts & Lloyds	2 - 1
Boreham Wood	v	Brentwood Town	3 - 2
Ebbsfleet United	v	East Grinstead Town	3 - 1
Chipstead	v	Croydon	2 - 1
Rye United	v	Tonbridge Angels	0 - 6
Cobham	v	Burgess Hill Town	0 - 8
Thame United	v	Wokingham Town & Emmbrook	4 - 0
Wallsend BC	v	Dunston Federation	2 - 1

Padiham	v	Fleetwood Town	0 - 1
Congleton Town	v	Curzon Ashton	0 - 0, 4 - 5p
Chorley	v	Marine	0 - 2
Sheffield	v	Garforth Town	0 - 1
Silsden AFC	v	Yorkshire Amateur	1 - 4
North Ferriby United	v	Wakefield	2 - 3
Loughborough Dynamo	v	Mansfield Town	0 - 9
Deeping Rangers	v	Lincoln United	0 - 2
Gresley Rovers	v	Boston United	1 - 3
Malvern Town	v	Solihull Moors	1 - 6
Hednesford Town	v	Redditch United	2 - 0
Highgate United	v	Worcester City	2 - 5
Whitton United	v	Walsham Le Willows	1 - 3
Debenham LC	v	Needham Market	2 - 0
Stowmarket Town	v	Woodbridge Town	0 - 5
Cambridge United	v	Felixstowe & Walton United	8 - 2
Stotfold	v	Brackley Town	5 - 0
Cogenhoe United	v	Dunstable Town	4 - 3
Braintree Town	v	St Albans City	0 - 6
Canvey Island	v	Leverstock Green	1 - 3
Hoddesdon Town	v	Hitchin Town	3 - 1
Billericay Town	v	Waltham Abbey	0 - 1
Ware	v	Hemel Hempstead Town	2 - 4
Wivenhoe Town	v	St Margaretsbury	1 - 4
Southend Manor	v	Maldon Town	2 - 3
Hampton & Richmond Borough	v	AFC Wimbledon	3 - 2
Ashford Town (Middx)	v	Harefield United	6 - 2
Leyton	v	Fisher Athletic	0 - 3
North Greenford United	v	Hayes & Yeading United	1 - 6
Croydon Athletic	v	Enfield Town	2 - 2, 4 - 2p
Faversham Town	v	Lewes	2 - 4
Sutton United	v	Pagham	5 - 0
Three Bridges	v	Shoreham	2 - 0
Kingstonian	v	Colliers Wood United	5 - 4
Fleet Town	v	Oxford United	0 - 8
Maidenhead United	v	Oxford City	6 - 0
Henley Town	v	Banbury United	3 - 3, 8 - 9p
Marlow	v	Basingstoke Town	1 - 3
Poole Town	v	Gosport Borough	2 - 3
Bournemouth	v	Moneyfields	1 - 2
Dorchester Town	v	Shaftesbury	3 - 1
Northwich Victoria	v	Wrexham	0 - 7
Lancaster City	v	Daisy Hill	1 - 3
Barwell	v	Staveley MW	2 - 4
Oadby Town	v	Rothley Imperial	4 - 1
Matlock Town	v	Stamford AFC	1 - 2
Blaby & Whetstone Athletic	v	Birstall United	7 - 3
Sileby Rangers	v	Thrapston Town	12 - 0
Merstham	v	Lordswood	1 - 3
Epsom & Ewell	v	Hassocks	5 - 0
Chertsey Town	v	Woking	0 - 3
Christchurch	v	Weymouth	0 - 1
Cheltenham Saracens	v	Westbury United	5 - 0
Cirencester Town	v	Paulton Rovers	7 - 0
Salford City	v	Nantwich Town	4 - 5
Hall Road Rangers	v	Ossett Town	4 - 0
Wroxham	v	Histon	1 - 7
Rothwell Town	v	Cranfield United	1 - 3
Rushden & Diamonds	v	Leighton Town	9 - 2
Bromley	v	South Park	6 - 1
Winchester City	v	Eastleigh	0 - 2
Bridgwater Town	v	Torquay United	0 - 2
Bath City	v	Wootton Bassett Town	5 - 1
Chester-Le-Street Town	v	Walker Central	4 - 5
Eastbourne Borough	v	Lingfield	7 - 0
Workington	v	Ashton Town AFC	1 - 2
Selby Town	v	Eccleshill United	1 - 4
Glasshoughton Welfare	v	Liversedge	1 - 2
Ossett Albion	v	Thackley	1 - 4
Bromsgrove Rovers	v	Alvechurch	3 - 1
Wellington	v	Gornal Athletic	2 - 1
AFC Telford United	v	Stourport Swifts	5 - 2
Thurrock	v	Burnham Ramblers	4 - 0
Kentish Town	v	Staines Town	1 - 2
Camberley Town	v	Worthing	1 - 5
Aylesbury Vale	v	Newport Pagnell Town	1 - 2
Stourbridge	v	Nuneaton Town	3 - 1
Bromyard Town	v	Stratford Town	3 - 5
Boldmere St Michaels	v	Dosthill Colts	2 - 0
Rothwell Corinthians	v	Northampton Spencer	3 - 4
Stevenage Borough	v	Bishop's Stortford	7 - 2
Bishop's Cleeve	v	Team Bath	1 - 3
Warrington Town	v	Prescot Cables	2 - 1
Bashley	v	Hamworthy United	2 - 3
Guiseley AFC	v	Worksop Town	1 - 2

SECOND ROUND QUALIFYING

Daisy Hill	v	Formby	0 - 5
Walker Central	v	Wallsend BC	3 - 2
Hastings United	v	Eastbourne Borough	1 - 6
Gateshead	v	York City	0 - 1
Colne	v	Cammell Laird	2 - 3
Mickleover Sports	v	Retford United	2 - 0
Carlton Town	v	Boston United	0 - 5
Coventry Sphinx	v	Ellesmere Rangers	3 - 2
Stotfold	v	Northampton Spencer	1 - 3
Hemel Hempstead Town	v	Waltham Abbey	2 - 1
Cockfosters	v	Thamesmead Town	3 - 5
Maidstone United	v	Lordswood	1 - 0
Whyteleafe	v	Dover Athletic	2 - 5
Didcot Town	v	Beaconsfield SYCOB	3 - 3, 8 - 7p
Leverstock Green	v	Maldon Town	1 - 2
Chipstead	v	Chatham Town	0 - 1
Warrington Town	v	Nantwich Town	0 - 3
Wakefield	v	Garforth Town	4 - 3
Liversedge	v	Hall Road Rangers	3 - 0
Worksop Town	v	Eccleshill United	3 - 0
Shirebrook Town	v	Lincoln United	4 - 3
Hinckley United	v	Staveley MW	3 - 1
Bromsgrove Rovers	v	Boldmere St Michaels	2 - 3
Stratford Town	v	Sutton Coldfield Town	1 - 3
Lowestoft Town	v	Walsham Le Willows	1 - 4
Debenham LC	v	Cambridge United	0 - 4
Histon	v	Soham Town Rangers	2 - 1
Wellingborough Town	v	FCV Reds	0 - 2
Hoddesdon Town	v	Stevenage Borough	3 - 5
Colney Heath	v	Boreham Wood	0 - 2
Ashford Town (Middx)	v	Fisher Athletic	3 - 1
Three Bridges	v	Woking	1 - 2
Maidenhead United	v	Thame United	1 - 4
Windsor & Eton	v	Buckingham Town	0 - 6
Banbury United	v	Kidlington	4 - 2
Salisbury City	v	Dorchester Town	9 - 1
Eastleigh	v	Gosport Borough	5 - 4
Bath City	v	Cirencester Town	0 - 2
Ashton Town AFC	v	Fleetwood Town	1 - 4
Curzon Ashton	v	Burscough	2 - 1
Oadby Town	v	Blaby & Whetstone Athletic	3 - 3
Ebbsfleet United	v	Tonbridge Angels	2 - 1
Epsom & Ewell	v	Kingstonian	1 - 1
Team Bath	v	Torquay United	3 - 4
Solihull Moors	v	Wellington	18 - 0
Hednesford Town	v	AFC Telford United	3 - 3
Woodbridge Town	v	Bury Town	3 - 5
Sileby Rangers	v	Rushden & Diamonds	2 - 3
Cogenhoe United	v	Cranfield United	3 - 0
Witham Town	v	St Margaretsbury	3 - 2
Bromley	v	Lewes	2 - 3
Oakwood	v	Burgess Hill Town	0 - 3
Oxford United	v	Basingstoke Town	2 - 3
Yorkshire Amateur	v	Thackley	4 - 2
Stamford AFC	v	Mansfield Town	2 - 6
Thurrock	v	St Albans City	3 - 2
Hayes & Yeading United	v	Hampton & Richmond Borough	2 - 0
Worthing	v	Sutton United	0 - 4
Chalfont St Peter	v	Newport Pagnell Town	0 - 3
Havant & Waterlooville	v	Hamworthy United	3 - 1
Newport County	v	Yate Town	4 - 0
Worcester City	v	Stourbridge	3 - 4
Staines Town	v	Croydon Athletic	1 - 1, 3 - 5p
Weymouth	v	Moneyfields	4 - 1
Cheltenham Saracens	v	Forest Green Rovers	1 - 3
Marine	v	Wrexham	2 - 4

THIRD ROUND QUALIFYING

Cammell Laird	v	Curzon Ashton	0 - 4
Formby	v	Fleetwood Town	2 - 3
Coventry Sphinx	v	Sutton Coldfield Town	3 - 2
Walsham Le Willows	v	Histon	1 - 5
FCV Reds	v	Cogenhoe United	2 - 1
Croydon Athletic	v	Thamesmead Town	6 - 2
Chatham Town	v	Eastbourne Borough	0 - 2
Maidstone United	v	Dover Athletic	0 - 6
Nantwich Town	v	Wrexham	1 - 0
Newport Pagnell Town	v	Basingstoke Town	1 - 4
Wakefield	v	Liversedge	2 - 1

Oadby Town	v	Boston United	2 - 2, 5 - 3p
Hednesford Town	v	Stourbridge	4 - 0
Solihull Moors	v	Boldmere St Michaels	3 - 0
Hayes & Yeading United	v	Ashford Town (Middx)	2 - 1
Woking	v	Sutton United	3 - 1
Didcot Town	v	Buckingham Town	3 - 1
Salisbury City	v	Eastleigh	1 - 5
Cirencester Town	v	Torquay United	5 - 2
Cambridge United	v	Bury Town	3 - 0
Boreham Wood	v	Maldon Town	4 - 2
Ebbsfleet United	v	Lewes	2 - 4
Shirebrook Town	v	Hinckley United	0 - 2
Rushden & Diamonds	v	Northampton Spencer	7 - 0
Witham Town	v	Thurrock	1 - 5
Stevenage Borough	v	Hemel Hempstead Town	2 - 1
Forest Green Rovers	v	Newport County	3 - 4
York City	v	Walker Central	8 - 0
Mickleover Sports	v	Mansfield Town	0 - 7
Yorkshire Amateur	v	Worksop Town	0 - 1
Burgess Hill Town	v	Kingstonian	4 - 3
Thame United	v	Banbury United	1 - 2
Weymouth	v	Havant & Waterlooville	1 - 2

FIRST ROUND PROPER

Walsall	v	Hednesford Town	5 - 3
AFC Bournemouth	v	Bristol Rovers	0 - 1
Didcot Town	v	Cirencester Town	2 - 2, 1 - 4p
Nantwich Town	v	Curzon Ashton	5 - 0
Brighton & Hove Albion	v	Dover Athletic	5 - 1
Accrington Stanley	v	Wakefield	3 - 1
Rushden & Diamonds	v	Northampton Town	1 - 2
Banbury United	v	Dagenham & Redbridge	1 - 2
Basingstoke Town	v	Barnet	0 - 2
Woking	v	Exeter City	1 - 2
Solihull Moors	v	FCV Reds	2 - 0
Cambridge United	v	Colchester United	4 - 1
Rochdale	v	Huddersfield Town	1 - 0
Bury	v	Crewe Alexandra	0 - 2
Fleetwood Town	v	Oldham Athletic	0 - 3
Shrewsbury Town	v	Chesterfield	2 - 0
Mansfield Town	v	Peterborough United	3 - 2
Southend United	v	Brentford	3 - 3, 8 - 9p
Oadby Town	v	Hinckley United	2 - 1
Gillingham	v	Eastbourne Borough	3 - 0
Cheltenham Town	v	Newport County	5 - 1
Swindon Town	v	Eastleigh	4 - 1
Grimsby Town	v	Lincoln City	0 - 1
Bradford City	v	Scunthorpe United	1 - 0
Hartlepool United	v	Carlisle United	1 - 4
Chester City	v	Leeds United AFC	0 - 2
Macclesfield Town	v	Morecambe	4 - 1
Worksop Town	v	Rotherham United	0 - 3
Stevenage Borough	v	Thurrock	2 - 3
Lewes	v	Histon	2 - 0
Hayes & Yeading United	v	Croydon Athletic	1 - 2
Aldershot Town	v	Havant & Waterlooville	1 - 4
Boreham Wood	v	Leyton Orient	0 - 5
Burgess Hill Town	v	Wycombe Wanderers	0 - 2
Leicester City	v	Port Vale	2 - 1
Millwall	v	Luton Town	2 - 0
Coventry Sphinx	v	Milton Keynes Dons	2 - 3
Darlington	v	Tranmere Rovers	2 - 3
York City	v	Stockport County	2 - 3
Yeovil Town	v	Hereford United	4 - 1

SECOND ROUND PROPER

Bristol Rovers	v	Brighton & Hove Albion	3 - 1
Leicester City	v	Milton Keynes Dons	3 - 1
Stockport County	v	Crewe Alexandra	3 - 3, 2 - 4p
Yeovil Town	v	Cirencester Town	1 - 2
Lewes	v	Croydon Athletic	3 - 0
Brentford	v	Thurrock	6 - 2
Oadby Town	v	Leeds United AFC	0 - 3
Solihull Moors	v	Tranmere Rovers	0 - 2
Lincoln City	v	Mansfield Town	3 - 1
Shrewsbury Town	v	Bradford City	2 - 0
Cheltenham Town	v	Gillingham	0 - 1
Nantwich Town	v	Macclesfield Town	2 - 1
Swindon Town	v	Exeter City	3 - 0
Wycombe Wanderers	v	Leyton Orient	1 - 2
Barnet	v	Havant & Waterlooville	3 - 1
Accrington Stanley	v	Carlisle United	0 - 3
Walsall	v	Rochdale	4 - 3*
Millwall	v	Dagenham & Redbridge	5 - 1
Oldham Athletic	v	Rotherham United	2 - 0
Cambridge United	v	Northampton Town	0 - 2

THIRD ROUND PROPER

Everton	v	Nantwich Town	2 - 0
Burnley	v	West Bromwich Albion	3 - 1
Sheffield Wednesday	v	Millwall	1 - 3
Carlisle United	v	Crewe Alexandra	1 - 3
Northampton Town	v	Tranmere Rovers	0 - 3
Aston Villa	v	Arsenal	2 - 3
Southampton	v	Derby County	3 - 1*
Queens Park Rangers	v	Bristol City	5 - 3*
Leicester City	v	Wolverhampton Wanderers	2 - 3
Barnet	v	Bristol Rovers	1 - 2
Leyton Orient	v	Watford	0 - 4
Barnsley	v	Walsall	2 - 3
Newcastle United	v	Oldham Athletic	2 - 1
Lewes	v	Hull City	1 - 2
Birmingham City	v	Lincoln City	2 - 1
Reading	v	Preston North End	0 - 1
Sunderland AFC	v	Cirencester Town	2 - 1
Cardiff City	v	Blackpool	3 - 0
Portsmouth	v	Gillingham	2 - 1
Norwich City	v	Wigan Athletic	1 - 0
Coventry City	v	Stoke City	2 - 3
Swansea City	v	Manchester City (H)	0 - 3
Swindon Town	v	Crystal Palace	1 - 5
Tottenham Hotspur	v	Sheffield United	3 - 0
Leeds United AFC	v	Liverpool	1 - 2
Ipswich Town	v	Shrewsbury Town	1 - 0
Plymouth Argyle	v	Fulham	2 - 1
Charlton Athletic	v	Blackburn Rovers	2 - 1
Nottingham Forest	v	West Ham United	3 - 1
Brentford	v	Middlesbrough	1 - 2
Bolton Wanderers	v	Doncaster Rovers	2 - 0
Manchester United	v	Chelsea	2 - 3

FOURTH ROUND PROPER

Ipswich Town	v	Crystal Palace	4 - 2
Bristol Rovers	v	Liverpool	2 - 2, 2 - 4p
Queens Park Rangers	v	Newcastle United	1 - 3
Chelsea	v	Walsall	5 - 1
Burnley	v	Everton	1 - 3
Charlton Athletic	v	Tottenham Hotspur	0 - 3
Portsmouth	v	Manchester City (H)	0 - 1
Arsenal	v	Wolverhampton Wanderers	3 - 1
Preston North End	v	Sunderland AFC	0 - 1
Southampton	v	Watford	0 - 1
Plymouth Argyle	v	Millwall	3 - 2
Bolton Wanderers	v	Hull City	4 - 0
Middlesbrough	v	Nottingham Forest	1 - 2
Cardiff City	v	Tranmere Rovers	0 - 0, 5 - 4p
Birmingham City	v	Crewe Alexandra	3 - 2
Norwich City	v	Stoke City	1 - 1, 4 - 2p

FIFTH ROUND PROPER

Ipswich Town	v	Watford	2 - 3
Plymouth Argyle	v	Tottenham Hotspur	0 - 3
Cardiff City	v	Birmingham City	0 - 2
Liverpool	v	Chelsea	1 - 0
Everton	v	Norwich City	1 - 1, 1 - 3 p
Manchester City (H)	v	Newcastle United	4 - 2
Sunderland AFC	v	Arsenal	0 - 4
Nottingham Forest	v	Bolton Wanderers	0 - 1

QUARTER FINALS

Birmingham City	v	Watford	1 - 0
Manchester City (H)	v	Norwich City	1 - 0
Tottenham Hotspur	v	Arsenal	1 - 3
Liverpool	v	Bolton Wanderers	4 - 2

SEMI FINALS - Home & Away

Home		Away	1st Leg	2nd Leg
Liverpool	v	Birmingham City	3 - 1	3 - 0
Arsenal	v	Manchester City (H)	4 - 1	2 - 1

THE FINAL

Home		Away	1st Leg	2nd Leg
Arsenal	v	Liverpool	4 - 1	2 - 1

F.A. COUNTY YOUTH CUP

FIRST ROUND

Jersey FA	v	Kent FA	0-2
North Riding FA	v	Lincolnshire FA	1-5
Sheffield & Hallamshire FA	v	Cheshire FA	0-2
Westmorland FA	v	Cumberland FA	3-1
Nottinghamshire FA	v	Staffordshire FA	3-0
Somerset FA	v	Amateur Football Alliance	3-4
London FA	v	Herefordshire FA	4-1
Surrey FA	v	Oxfordshire FA	2-2*, 4-5p
Essex FA	v	Devon FA	2-1
Dorset FA	v	Guernsey FA	2-1
Northamptonshire FA	v	Huntingdonshire FA	1-2
Hertfordshire FA	v	Worcestershire FA	2-3
Berks & Bucks FA	v	Cornwall FA	4-5
Durham FA	v	Derbyshire FA	6-0
Liverpool FA	v	Manchester FA	2-1

SECOND ROUND

Essex FA	v	Middlesex FA	0-3
London FA	v	Bedfordshire FA	3-0
East Riding FA	v	Liverpool FA	1-2
Lincolnshire FA	v	Leicestershire & Rutland FA	0-2
Westmorland FA	v	Lancashire FA	1-2
Shropshire FA	v	Birmingham FA	1-5
Wiltshire FA	v	Amateur Football Alliance	2-1
Dorset FA	v	Kent FA	0-4
Sussex FA	v	Oxfordshire FA	1-4
Norfolk FA	v	Hampshire FA	1-2
Nottinghamshire FA	v	Isle of Man FA	0-3
Cornwall FA	v	Worcestershire FA	4-5
Huntingdonshire FA	v	**Suffolk FA (H)**	0-6
Durham FA	v	Cheshire FA	5-4
Cambridgeshire FA	v	Gloucestershire FA	5-1
West Riding FA	v	Northumberland FA	5-0

THIRD ROUND

Worcestershire FA	v	**Suffolk FA (H)**	0-1
Oxfordshire FA	v	Kent FA	0-5
Hampshire FA	v	Wiltshire FA	3-5
Durham FA	v	Liverpool FA	2-3
Leicestershire & Rutland FA	v	West Riding FA	2-1
Lancashire FA	v	Cambridgeshire FA	1-7
Birmingham FA	v	Middlesex FA	3-2
Isle of Man FA	v	London FA	2-1

Tie abandoned after 87 mins due to injured player, 2-3 tie awarded to Durham - Liverpool removed.

FOURTH ROUND

Kent FA	v	Durham FA	2-1
Suffolk FA (H)	v	Isle of Man FA	1-2
Birmingham FA	v	Leicestershire & Rutland FA	1-0
Cambridgeshire FA	v	Wiltshire FA	1-4

SEMI FINALS

Isle of Man FA	v	Kent FA	2-2* 3-4p
Birmingham FA	v	Wiltshire FA	2-1

THE FINAL

Kent FA	v	Birmingham FA

LAST TEN FINALS

1999	Durham FA	v	Sussex FA	1-0
2000	Birmingham FA	v	Surrey FA	2-1
2001	Northamptonshire FA	v	Birmingham FA	3-0
2002	Birmingham FA	v	Durham FA	2-1
2003	Northumberland FA	v	Liverpool FA	1-0
2004	Durham FA	v	North Riding FA	4-0
2005	Suffolk FA	v	Hampshire FA	2-1
2006	Bedfordshie FA	v	Durham FA	3-2
2007	West Riding FA	v	Suffolk FA	1-1*, 4-3p
2008	Suffolk FA	v	Cambridgeshire FA	2-1

F.A. SUNDAY CUP

PRELIMINARY ROUND

Sporting Dynamo	v	Scots Grey	0-13
Sandy (Sunday)	v	Gossoms End	3-0
Cube	v	Shelford Falcons	3-4
Bedfont Sunday	v	Battersea Ironsides	3-0

FIRST ROUND

Heywood Irish Centre	v	Home & Bargain	2-2
Brow	v	Swanfield	2-3
Bolton Woods	v	Allerton	3-3
Dock	v	Crossflatts	2-0
Barry's	v	Hartlepool Lion Hillcarter	3-5
BRNESC	v	Rawdon	3-3
Queens Park	v	Pocklington Town	4-0
Canada	v	Hartlepool Athletic Rugby	2-0
Hessle Rangers	v	Western Approaches	0-2
Dawdon Colliery Welfare	v	Dengo United	4-0
Hartlepool Rovers Quoit	v	Ford Motors	0-2
Murton Victoria	v	Sandon Dock	3-2
Halton Moor	v	Paddock	0-2
Beverley United	v	Lobster	2-3
Sunderland RCA Barnes	v	Lee Jones	4-0
Nicosia	v	Oyster Martyrs	4-7
Shankhouse United	v	Thornhill Lees	2-3
Queensbury	v	Witton Park Rose & Crown	0-5
West Lee	v	Obiter Fabs 4	2-3
Elland AFC	v	Seaburn	1-0
Tower	v	Royal Standard	2-0
JOB	v	The View	2-4
Silsden (Sunday)	v	Jolly Miller	2-0
Fforde Grene Brazil	v	Seymour KFCA	2-1
Grey Horse (Failsworth)	v	Sandstone	2-3
Warstones Wanderers (Sunday)	v	Leicester Polska	5-1
Belt Road	v	Bartley Green Sunday	2-2
Harp 2003	v	Keresley RFC	6-1
Bulls Head (Dawley Bank)	v	Grosvenor Park	4-1
Victoria	v	Travellers	1-2
Kingshurst Sporting Club	v	Scots Grey	1-2
Magnet Tavern	v	Grafham	8-0
Springfield Lions	v	Wisbech St Mary	1-2
Hawkins Sports	v	Birstall Stamford	3-6
Duke Of Rutland	v	Plough Barfly's	2-0
61 (Sunday)	v	Sandy (Sunday)	3-3
Hammer	v	Celtic SC (Luton)	1-4
AC Sportsman & Ravensborough	v	Shelford Falcons	0-1
Risden Wood	v	AFC Black Swan OB	3-0
London Maccabi Lions	v	Bury Park Saracens	3-1
Belstone	v	Luton Old Boys (Sunday)	3-0
St Josephs South Oxhey	v	Moat	1-2
Partizan	v	Club Lewsey	0-6
Enfield Rangers	v	Greengate	3-1
Brantham Athletic (Sunday)	v	FC Houghton Centre	9-2
Loughton Nu Bar	v	St Josephs (Luton)	3-4
CB Hounslow United (Sunday)	v	Brixton United	1-3
Wycombe Town	v	Bedfont Sunday	3-1
Broadfields United	v	Sutton Athletic	3-2
Sunbury Athletic	v	Kerria Sports	2-3
Hanham Sunday	v	Bucks SU	3-1
Ashton	v	Richfield Rovers	2-1
Seven Allstars	v	Lebeq Tavern Courage	1-2
Rapid Moorfields	v	Bristol Athletic	1-0
Ajax LA	v	Brook	1-0
Whitenap	v	Bournemouth Electric	0-1
Lakeside Athletic	v	Poole Borough	5-1
Totton Town	v	Knighton Arms	2-4
Britannia	v	Poulton Royal	2-0
St Margarets	v	Crawley Green (Sunday)	3-0

SECOND ROUND

Hetton Lyons Cricket Club (H)	v	Lobster	3-2
Bartley Green Sunday	v	Bulls Head (Dawley Bank)	1-2
Birstall Stamford	v	Scots Grey	4-4, 3-4p
Brixton United	v	Broadfields United	1-3
Coundon Conservative	v	Murton Victoria	2-0
Magnet Tavern	v	Travellers	4-0
Swanfield	v	BRNESC	3-3, 3-4p
Bolton Woods	v	Britannia	2-1
Paddock	v	Queens Park	2-2, 0-2p
Hartlepool Lion Hillcarter	v	Canada	1-2
Western Approaches	v	Heywood Irish Centre	2-3
Dawdon Colliery Welfare	v	Sunderland RCA Barnes	1-2
Dock	v	Thornhill Lees	1-2
Elland AFC	v	Sandstone	1-3
Tower	v	Fforde Grene Brazil	3-6
Ford Motors	v	Oyster Martyrs	1-3
Witton Park Rose & Crown	v	The View	1-0
Obiter Fabs 4	v	Silsden (Sunday)	1-2
Warstones Wanderers (Sunday)	v	Harp 2003	2-1
Wisbech St Mary	v	St Margarets	2-6
Duke Of Rutland	v	London Maccabi Lions	0-2
Heyford United	v	Club Lewsey	0-4
61 (Sunday)	v	Belstone	0-0, 3-4p
Enfield Rangers	v	Celtic SC (Luton)	3-1
Shelford Falcons	v	Moat	4-1
Risden Wood	v	Stanbridge & Tilsworth	2-4
Brantham Athletic (Sunday)	v	St Josephs (Luton)	2-1
Kerria Sports	v	Wycombe Town	3-5
Lebeq Tavern Courage	v	Rapid Moorfields	6-1
Hanham Sunday	v	Ashton	3-2
Bournemouth Electric	v	Ajax LA	5-1
Knighton Arms	v	Lakeside Athletic	2-3

THIRD ROUND

Bolton Woods	v	Queens Park	0-5
Thornhill Lees	v	**Hetton Lyons Cricket Club (H)**	1-8
Fforde Grene Brazil	v	Sandstone	3-1
Canada	v	BRNESC	7-0
Sunderland RCA Barnes	v	Heywood Irish Centre	0-4
Witton Park Rose & Crown	v	Silsden (Sunday)	4-2
Stanbridge & Tilsworth	v	London Maccabi Lions	3-1
Magnet Tavern	v	Warstones Wanderers (Sunday)	6-1
Scots Grey	v	St Margarets	6-2
Oyster Martyrs	v	Coundon Conservative	3-1
Bulls Head (Dawley Bank)	v	Shelford Falcons	5-2
Club Lewsey	v	Brantham Athletic (Sunday)	3-3, 7-6p
Enfield Rangers	v	Belstone	2-2, 7-6p
Hanham Sunday	v	Wycombe Town	1-2
Lebeq Tavern Courage	v	Broadfields United	7-2
Lakeside Athletic	v	Bournemouth Electric	5-1

FOURTH ROUND

Bulls Head (Dawley Bank)	v	Heywood Irish Centre	0-4
Wycombe Town	v	Club Lewsey	4-1
Stanbridge & Tilsworth	v	Enfield Rangers	5-0
Magnet Tavern	v	Oyster Martyrs	1-2
Queens Park	v	Fforde Grene Brazil	2-5
Scots Grey	v	**Hetton Lyons Cricket Club (H)**	1-0
Canada	v	Witton Park Rose & Crown	2-5
Lakeside Athletic	v	Lebeq Tavern Courage	1-0

QUARTER FINALS

Fforde Grene Brazil	v	Stanbridge & Tilsworth	2-1
Scots Grey	v	Heywood Irish Centre	3-1
Oyster Martyrs	v	Witton Park Rose & Crown	1-0
Wycombe Town	v	Lakeside Athletic	1-1

SEMI FINALS

Scots Grey	v	Lakeside Athletic	1-0
Fforde Grene Brazil	v	Oyster Martyrs	2-3

THE FINAL - played at Anfield

Oyster Martyrs	v	Scots Grey	3-4*
Latham 35, Rooney 57, Lipson 120		Bignall 16, Staples 90+2, Jefferies 98 (p), 118	

F.A. NATIONAL LEAGUE SYSTEMS CUP

The National League Systems Cup is limited to leagues at Step 7 of the National League System and other leagues as decided by the Football Association. The winning league then represents England in the UEFA Regions Cup.

PRELIMINARY ROUND - MAR'09

Reading Football League	v	Middlesex County League	4 - 1
Midland Football Combination (D1)	v	West Yorkshire Football League	1 - 0
Brighton Hove & District League	v	Dorset Premier League	0 - 3
Nottinghamshire Senior League	v	Teesside Football League	0 - 1
Northampton Town League	v	Hampshire Premier League	2 - 1
Guernsey Senior County League	v	Kent County League	6 - 0
Isle of Man League	v	Manchester Football League	1 - 0
Jersey Football Combination	v	Spartan South Mids Lge (D2)	2 - 0
Wearside League	v	Cambridgeshire County League	1 - 2
Mid Sussex League	v	Bedfordshire Football League	0 - 4
Northamptonshire Combination	v	Peterborough & District League	2 - 1
Cumberland County League	v	Yorkshire Old Boys League	4 - 5

FIRST ROUND - SEPTEMBER'09

Dorset Premier League	v	Sussex County League (Div.3)	19/09
Southern Amateur Football League (H)	v	Gloucestershire County League	19/09
Humber Premier League	v	West Cheshire League	26/09
Lancashire & Cheshire Amateur League	v	Anglian Combination	26/09
Cheshire Football League	v	Yorkshire Old Boys League	26/09
Lancashire & Cheshire Amateur League	v	Birmingham & District Amateur League	26/09
Northamptonshire Combination	v	West Riding County Amateur League	26/09
Teesside Football League	v	Cambridgeshire County League	26/09
Northern Football Alliance	v	Liverpool County Premier League	26/09
Midland Football Combination (Div 1)	v	Isle of Man League	26/09
Bedfordshire Football League	v	Amateur Football Combination	26/09
Worthing & District League	v	Essex Olympian League	26/09
Hertfordshire Senior County League	v	Essex & Suffolk Border League	26/09
Wiltshire Football League	v	Jersey Football Combination	26/09
Northampton Town League	v	Guernsey Senior County League	26/09
Somerset County League	v	Reading Football League	26/09

UEFA REGIONS' CUP

INTERMEDIARY ROUND

GROUP 2	P	W	D	L	F	A	Pts
Region 1 (Rep.Ireland)	3	1	2	0	7	3	5
CR Piemonte Valle D'Aosta (Italy)	3	1	2	0	5	3	5
Southern Amateur League (England)	**3**	**1**	**2**	**0**	**3**	**0**	**5**
East of Scotland (Scotland)	3	0	0	3	2	11	0

England	v	Rep. Ireland	0-0
Italy	v	Scotland	3-1
England Ewen 4, 71, Stavri 22	v	Scotland	3-0
Rep. Ireland	v	Italy	2-2
Italy	v	England	0-0
Scotland	v	Rep. Ireland	1-5

Despite a better goal difference than the Italians, UEFA's raking system placed England in third. Republic of Ireland's, Region 1, qualified for the 2008/09 UEFA Regions' Cup.

PRELIMINARY ROUND

Newcastle Medics LFC	v	Prudhoe Youth Club LFC	1 - 4
Tynedale Ladies	v	St Francis 2000 Ladies	0 - 9
Teesside Athletic LFC	v	East Durham United LFC	2 - 4
Wigan LFC	v	Morecambe Ladies	4 - 1
Keighley Ladies AFC	v	Kirklees LFC	4 - 1
Heather St Johns LFC	v	Oadby & Wigston Girls & Ladies	1 - 0
Friar Lane & Epworth LFC	v	Huncote Sports & Social LFC	9 - 0
Hereford Phoenix Ladies	v	Tipton Town Ladies	14 - 0
Fairfield Villa LFC	v	Stoke City LFC	0 - 3
Horley Town LFC	v	Bisley Ladies	3 - 2
MK Wanderers LFC	v	Salisbury City LFC	3 - 1
Cheltenham Town Ladies	v	Newbury Ladies & Girls	5 - 0
Oadby Town Women	v	Clifton Ladies	1 - 6
Long Eaton United LFC	v	Loughborough Foxes LFC	0 - 4
Lancaster City WFC	v	Wigan Athletic Ladies	0 - 9
Guiseley Ladies AFC	v	Sheffield United Community LFC	3 - 2
Sheffield Ladies	v	Barnsley LFC	1 - 3
Welbeck Welfare Ladies	v	Marlborough Rovers LFC	14 - 1
Worcester City WFC	v	Pegasus Ladies	2 - 3
Ferndale Ladies	v	Leamington Lions LFC	2 - 5
Cambridge University LFC	v	Histon Hornets LFC	1 - 0
Swanton United Ladies	v	Hethersett Athletic LFC	0 - 5
Peterborough LFC	v	Peterborough Azure LFC	2 - 2
Woodbridge Town LFC	v	Thorpe United LFC	7 - 0
Haverhill Rovers LFC	v	West Lynn LFC	0 - 5
Leighton Linslade Ladies	v	Bedford Ladies	0 - 6
Arlesey Town Ladies	v	Daventry Town LFC	8 - 2
Leighton United LFC	v	Kingsthorpe Ladies & Girls	6 - 2
Kettering Town LFC	v	Woodford United LFC	11 - 0
St Martins LFC	v	AFC Kempston Rovers LFC	4 - 3
Sandy Ladies	v	Brackley Sports LFC	5 - 0
Raunds Town LFC	v	Flitwick Eagles Ladies	3 - 1
Hemel Hempstead Town LFC	v	Billericay LFC	5 - 2
Tempest LFC	v	Runwell & Rayleigh Raiders LFC	2 - 2
Braintree Town LFC	v	Tring Athletic LFC	2 - 0
Great Berry Ladies	v	Royston Town LFC	5 - 7
Hutton Ladies	v	Hawkwell Athletic Ladies	1 - 2
Hoddesdon Owls LFC	v	Dagenham & Redbridge LFC	0 - 2
West Bergholt LFC	v	Barking LFC	1 - 2
Old Actonians LFC	v	The Comets LFC	7 - 0
Panthers LFC	v	Denham United LFC	5 - 3
London Corinthians LFC	v	Aylesford LFC	4 - 0
Crawley Wasps LFC	v	Crowborough Athletic LFC	1 - 3
Ramsgate LFC	v	Deal Town Ladies	0 - 4
Seahaven Harriers Ladies & Girls	v	Haywards Heath Town LFC	0 - 2
Rottingdean Village LFC	v	Eastbourne Town LFC	0 - 1
Eastleigh Ladies	v	Aldershot Town LFC	0 - 5
Abbey Rangers LFC	v	Shanklin LFC	0 - 18
Chichester City Utd LFC	v	Merstham Ladies	4 - 2
Littlehampton T. Devils & Ladies	v	Wandgas LFC	1 - 3
Stoke Lane Athletic LFC	v	Swindon Supermarine Ladies	4 - 3
Reading Girls	v	Brize Norton LFC	4 - 0
Alphington LFC	v	Frome Town LFC	1 - 7
Poole Town LFC	v	Weymouth Ladies	0 - 5
Maidenhead Utd Ladies	v	Chalfont St Peter LFC	5 - 1
West Bridgford LFC	v	West Bridgford Colts LFC	2 - 4
Hitchin Hearts LFC	v	Runwell Hospital LFC	6 - 0

FIRST ROUND QUALIFYING

Accrington Stanley Ladies	v	Middleton Colts LFC	1 - 5
Walsall LFC	v	Leamington Lions LFC	0 - 4
Lumley Ladies	v	East Durham United LFC	2 - 2, 3 - 2p
Whitley Bay Women	v	Boldon Ladies	12 - 0
St Francis 2000 Ladies	v	York City LFC	1 - 3
Forest Hall Women's YPC	v	Gateshead Cleveland Hall LFC	2 - 1
Prudhoe Youth Club LFC	v	Blyth Spartans LFC	0 - 5
Spennymoor Town LFC	v	North Shields Ladies	4 - 1
Darlington RA LFC	v	Birtley Town Ladies	5 - 3
Windscale LFC	v	Wigan Athletic Ladies	1 - 6
Winsford Ladies	v	Preston Rangers WFC	3 - 4
Bury Girls & Ladies	v	Whitehaven Ladies	4 - 1
Warrington Town LFC	v	Sefton Peronni LFC	3 - 3, 3 - 4p
Liverpool Feds LFC	v	Chester City LFC	2 - 1
Wigan LFC	v	Bolton Wanderers LFC	6 - 1
Penrith AFC Ladies	v	Wirral LFC	3 - 1
Winterton Rangers LFC_	v	Guiseley Ladies AFC	2 - 12
Barnsley LFC	v	Keighley Ladies AFC	5 - 0
Sheffield United Ladies	v	Huddersfield Town LFC	0 - 1
Ossett Albion LFC	v	Dearne & District Ladies	4 - 1
Hinckley United Ladies	v	Friar Lane & Epworth LFC	2 - 7
Clifton Ladies	v	Harborough Town Ladies 2007	5 - 0
Linby LFC	v	Sandiacre Town LFC	0 - 10
Mansfield Town LFC	v	Loughborough Foxes LFC	4 - 2
Heather St Johns LFC	v	Gedling Town Ladies	2 - 4
Loughborough Dynamo WFC	v	Rolls Royce Leisure LFC	1 - 2
Buxton LFC	v	West Bridgford Colts LFC	4 - 0
Studley WFC	v	Hereford Phoenix Ladies	2 - 1
Birmingham Athletic LFC	v	Wednesfield LFC	9 - 0
Stafford Town Ladies	v	Redditch United Women's	6 - 2
Stoke City LFC	v	Bourne United LFC	4 - 0
Pegasus Ladies	v	Lichfield Diamonds LFC	0 - 3
Tamworth Lionesses	v	Stourport Swifts LFC	5 - 3
Stratford Town LFC	v	Dudley United LFC	0 - 3
Woodbridge Town LFC	v	Cambridge University LFC	9 - 0
Peterborough LFC	v	Hethersett Athletic LFC	1 - 0
Cambridge United WFC	v	West Lynn LFC	1 - 2
Huntingdon Town Ladies	v	March Town United LFC	5 - 0
Kettering Town LFC	v	Bedford Ladies	0 - 1
Leighton United LFC	v	Arlesey Town Ladies	1 - 5
Sandy Ladies	v	St Martins LFC	1 - 2

Corby S&L LFC	v	Raunds Town LFC	4 - 2
Dagenham & Redbridge LFC	v	Hemel Hempstead Town LFC	3 - 3, 4 - 3p
Braintree Town LFC	v	Brentwood Town LFC	2 - 5
Sherrardswood Ladies	v	Saffron Walden Town LFC	1 - 7
Sawbridgeworth Town LFC	v	C&K Basildon LFC	2 - 4
Garston LFC	v	Runwell & Rayleigh Raiders LFC	12 - 0
Hitchin Hearts LFC	v	Hannakins Ladies	2 - 4
Barking LFC	v	London Colney LFC	2 - 1
Battersea LFC	v	Panthers LFC	0 - 2
Brentford WFC	v	One Wish Ladies	21 - 0
Regents Park Rangers LFC	v	Wingate & Finchley LFC	2 - 1
Uxbridge United Ladies	v	Haringey Borough LFC	0 - 15
Old Actonians LFC	v	Hampton LFC	6 - 0
AFC Wimbledon Ladies	v	Joybabe LFC	5 - 0
Haywards Heath Town LFC	v	London Corinthians LFC	1 - 2
Deal Town Ladies	v	Crowborough Athletic LFC	4 - 3
Ebbsfleet United LFC	v	Eastbourne Town LFC	3 - 2
Maidstone Town LFC	v	Canterbury City LFC	2 - 1
Chichester City United LFC	v	Aldershot Town LFC	1 - 5
Shanklin LFC	v	Horley Town LFC	1 - 1, 2 - 3p
Andover New Street LFC	v	Wandgas LFC	3 - 1
Southampton Saints WFC	v	Havant & Waterlooville LFC	0 - 2
Oxford United LFC	v	Swindon Spitfires WFC	0 - 1
Aylesbury United LFC	v	Maidenhead United Ladies	0 - 11
Tetbury Town LFC	v	Bitton Ladies	3 - 2
Oldland Abbotonians LFC	v	Wycombe Wanderers LFC	0 - 1
Reading Girls	v	MK Wanderers LFC	2 - 6
Woodley Saints LFC	v	Slough LFC	3 - 2
Stony Stratford Town LFC	v	Launton LFC	0 - 4
Marlow Ladies	v	Bracknell Town LFC	1 - 7
Banbury United LFC	v	Newent Town Ladies	4 - 0
Chippenham Town Ladies	v	Henley Town LFC	1 - 0
Stoke Lane Athletic LFC	v	Cheltenham Town Ladies	3 - 6
Cullompton Rangers LFC	v	Frome Town LFC	1 - 2
Launceston LFC	v	Weymouth Ladies	2 - 2, 3 - 1p
Ilminster Town LFC	v	Purbeck Ladies	5 - 2
Larkhall Athletic LFC	v	Keynsham Town Development LFC	4 - 0
Hawkwell Athletic Ladies	v	Royston Town LFC	2 - 6
Hampstead WFC	v	Tower Hamlets WFC	3 - 4

SECOND ROUND QUALIFYING

York City LFC	v	Lumley Ladies	4 - 0
Whitley Bay Women	v	Norton & Stockton Ancients LFC	3 - 0
Blyth Spartans LFC	v	Forest Hall Women's YPC	11 - 0
Darlington RA LFC	v	Spennymoor Town LFC	8 - 1
Sefton Peronni LFC	v	Wigan Athletic Ladies	0 - 1
Bury Girls & Ladies	v	Preston Rangers WFC	9 - 2
Wigan LFC	v	Liverpool Feds LFC	1 - 7
Penrith AFC Ladies	v	Middleton Colts LFC	2 - 1
Huddersfield Town LFC	v	Ossett Albion LFC	2 - 4
Barnsley LFC	v	Guiseley Ladies AFC	2 - 3
Welbeck Welfare Ladies	v	Friar Lane & Epworth LFC	3 - 5
Sandiacre Town LFC	v	Clifton Ladies	3 - 2
Gedling Town Ladies	v	Mansfield Town LFC	2 - 5
Buxton LFC	v	Rolls Royce Leisure LFC	1 - 4
Stoke City LFC	v	Studley WFC	3 - 0
Stafford Town Ladies	v	Birmingham Athletic LFC	5 - 2
Lichfield Diamonds LFC	v	Leamington Lions LFC	1 - 0
Dudley United LFC	v	Tamworth Lionesses	3 - 1
West Lynn LFC	v	Huntingdon Town Ladies	7 - 0
Peterborough LFC	v	Woodbridge Town LFC	2 - 2
St Martins LFC	v	Corby S&L LFC	1 - 2
Arlesey Town Ladies	v	Bedford Ladies	1 - 4
C&K Basildon LFC	v	Dagenham & Redbridge LFC	2 - 5
Saffron Walden Town LFC	v	Brentwood Town LFC	1 - 4
Hannakins Ladies	v	Garston LFC	0 - 3
Royston Town LFC	v	Barking LFC	1 - 2
Regents Park Rangers LFC	v	Panthers LFC	0 - 3
Brentford WFC	v	Tower Hamlets WFC	0 - 5
Old Actonians LFC	v	Haringey Borough LFC	1 - 4
AFC Wimbledon Ladies	v	Manford Way Ladies	7 - 0
Ebbsfleet United LFC	v	Maidstone Town LFC	1 - 0
Deal Town Ladies	v	London Corinthians LFC	2 - 4
Andover New Street LFC	v	Havant & Waterlooville LFC	1 - 6
Horley Town LFC	v	Aldershot Town LFC	5 - 1
Maidenhead Utd Ladies	v	Tetbury Town LFC	6 - 0
Cheltenham Town Ladies	v	Launton LFC	3 - 1
Bracknell Town LFC	v	Chippenham Town Ladies	4 - 0
Chinnor Ladies	v	Banbury United LFC	3 - 1
Swindon Spitfires WFC	v	MK Wanderers LFC	3 - 2
Woodley Saints LFC	v	Wycombe Wanderers LFC	0 - 4
Ilminster Town LFC	v	Larkhall Athletic LFC	3 - 6
Launceston LFC	v	Frome Town LFC	1 - 4

THIRD ROUND QUALIFYING

Haringey Borough LFC	v	AFC Wimbledon Ladies	2 - 3
Garston LFC	v	Barking LFC	0 - 2
Blyth Spartans LFC	v	Darlington RA LFC	6 - 10
Whitley Bay Women	v	York City LFC	0 - 2
Liverpool Feds LFC	v	Penrith AFC Ladies	4 - 0
Bury Girls & Ladies	v	Wigan Athletic Ladies	3 - 1
Guiseley Ladies AFC	v	Ossett Albion LFC	4 - 2
Mansfield Town LFC	v	Rolls Royce Leisure LFC	2 - 1
Sandiacre Town LFC	v	Friar Lane & Epworth LFC	7 - 0
Lichfield Diamonds LFC	v	Dudley United LFC	1 - 1, 4 - 3p
Stafford Town Ladies	v	Stoke City LFC	1 -3
Peterborough LFC	v	West Lynn LFC	4 - 1
Bedford Ladies	v	Corby S&L LFC	4 - 0
Brentwood Town LFC	v	Dagenham & Redbridge LFC	0 - 1
London Corinthians LFC	v	Ebbsfleet United LFC	1 - 5
Horley Town LFC	v	Havant & Waterlooville LFC	0 - 5
Swindon Spitfires WFC	v	Bracknell Town LFC	0 - 8
Maidenhead Utd Ladies	v	Chinnor Ladies	7 - 3
Wycombe Wanderers LFC	v	Cheltenham Town Ladies	3 - 3, 3 - 4p
Frome Town LFC	v	Larkhall Athletic LFC	1 - 0
Tower Hamlets WFC	v	Panthers LFC	2 - 1

FIRST ROUND PROPER

Leeds City Vixens LFC	v	Crewe Alexandra LFC	4 - 0
Guiseley Ladies AFC	v	Peterlee Town LFC	4 - 1
Morley Spurs LFC	v	Blackpool Wren Rovers LFC	2 - 4
Derby County LFC	v	Mansfield Town LFC	4 - 0
Leafield Athletic LFC	v	West Bromwich Albion WFC	3 - 3, 5 - 4p
Norwich City Ladies	v	AFC Wimbledon Ladies	1 - 0
Bedford Town Bells LFC	v	Reading Royals LFC	2 - 0
West Auckland Town LFC	v	Middlesbrough LFC	0 - 2
Liverpool Feds LFC	v	Salford SV Ladies	4 - 2
Bury Girls & Ladies	v	Rochdale AFC Ladies	3 - 5
Stockport County LFC	v	Bradford City LFC	0 - 1
Scunthorpe United LFC	v	Darlington RA LFC	1 - 2
Stoke City LFC	v	Peterborough LFC	6 - 2
Coventry City LFC	v	Copsewood (Coventry) LFC	3 - 2
Lichfield Diamonds LFC	v	Leicester City Ladies	3 - 4
Loughborough Students LFC	v	Sandiacre Town LFC	3 - 2
Cambridge City LFC	v	Wolverhampton Wanderers WFC	0 - 4
Lewes LFC	v	Tower Hamlets WFC	9 - 0
Ebbsfleet United LFC	v	Wellingborough Diamonds LFC	1 - 3
Enfield Town LFC	v	Queens Park Rangers LFC	3 - 0

Dagenham & Redbridge LFC	v	Luton Town Ladies	2 - 3
Tottenham Hotspur LFC	v	Oxford City LFC	3 - 1
Welwyn Garden City LFC	v	Chesham United LFC	0 - 2
Northampton Town LFC	v	Bedford Ladies	4 - 1
Maidenhead United Ladies	v	Swindon Town LFC	0 - 1
Frome Town LFC	v	Forest Green Rovers LFC	2 - 4
TNS & Shrewsbury T. WFC	v	Bracknell Town LFC	5 - 0
Yeovil Town LFC	v	Plymouth Argyle LFC	2 - 8
AFC Team Bath Ladies	v	Weston St Johns LFC	2 - 0

SECOND ROUND PROPER

Lewes LFC	v	Bedford Town Bells LFC	6 - 0
Blackpool Wren Rovers LFC	v	Rochdale AFC Ladies	3 - 1
Swindon Town LFC	v	Luton Town Ladies	2 - 6
Enfield Town LFC	v	Norwich City Ladies	1 - 0
Wellingborough Diamonds LFC	v	Leicester City Ladies	6 - 1
Leafield Athletic LFC	v	Wolverhampton Wanderers WFC	0 - 3
Stoke City LFC	v	Loughborough Students LFC	1 - 2
Guiseley Ladies AFC	v	Derby County LFC	0 - 2
York City LFC	v	Liverpool Feds LFC	2 - 1
Leeds City Vixens LFC	v	Bradford City LFC	6 - 4
Middlesbrough LFC	v	Darlington RA LFC	3 - 2
TNS & Shrewsbury T. WFC	v	Coventry City LFC	2 - 2, 1 - 4p
Tottenham Hotspur LFC	v	Northampton Town LFC	1 - 4
Havant & Waterlooville LFC	v	Chesham United LFC	1 - 2
Forest Green Rovers LFC	v	Cheltenham Town Ladies	2 - 0
AFC Team Bath Ladies	v	Plymouth Argyle LFC	0 - 6

THIRD ROUND PROPER

Manchester City LFC	v	Newcastle United WFC	3 - 3
Aston Villa LFC	v	Wolverhampton Wanderers WFC	4 - 1
Enfield Town LFC	v	Colchester United LFC	0 - 1
Charlton Athletic LFC	v	Ipswich Town WFC	2 - 1
Crystal Palace LFC	v	Reading Women	4 - 3
Leeds City Vixens LFC	v	Sunderland WFC	1 - 6
Rotherham United LFC	v	York City LFC	2 - 1
Tranmere Rovers LFC	v	Middlesbrough LFC	1 - 3
Wellingborough Diamonds LFC	v	Derby County LFC	1 - 5
Northampton Town LFC	v	Barnet Ladies	0 - 5
Plymouth Argyle LFC	v	Forest Green Rovers LFC	0 - 2
Truro City Ladies	v	Portsmouth LFC	0 - 4
Curzon Ashton LFC	v	Blackpool Wren Rovers LFC	5 - 0
Cardiff City LFC	v	Keynsham Town LFC	1 - 1, 4 - 3p
Sheffield Wednesday LFC	v	Preston North End WFC	4 - 5
Loughborough Students LFC	v	Ooh Lincoln Ladies	0 - 2
Leicester CityW	v	Coventry City LFC	3 - 1
Brighton & Hove Albion WFC	v	Luton Town Ladies	0 - 1
Millwall Lionesses LFC	v	West Ham United LFC	2 - 0
Lewes LFC	v	Chesham United LFC	3 - 3, 3 - 2p

FOURTH ROUND PROPER

Watford LFC	v	Bristol Academy LFC	1 - 3
Crystal Palace LFC	v	Aston Villa LFC	1 - 2
Charlton Athletic LFC	v	Birmingham City LFC	0 - 6
Barnet Ladies	v	Portsmouth LFC	2 - 1
Blackburn Rovers LFC	v	Luton Town Ladies	3 - 0
Everton LFC	v	WFC Fulham	4 - 0
Arsenal LFC (H)	v	Colchester United LFC	7 - 0
Manchester City LFC	v	Preston North End WFC	4 - 3
Leeds Carnegie Ladies	v	Forest Green Rovers LFC	7 - 0
Doncaster Rovers Belles LFC	v	Millwall Lionesses LFC	0 - 1
Ooh Lincoln Ladies	v	Curzon Ashton LFC	0 - 1
Derby County LFC	v	Lewes LFC	3 - 3, 4 - 3p
Nottingham Forest LFC	v	Liverpool LFC	0 - 1
Sunderland WFC	v	Cardiff City LFC	4 - 1
Leicester CityW	v	Middlesbrough LFC	2 - 4
Chelsea LFC	v	Rotherham United LFC	9 - 1

FIFTH ROUND PROPER

Bristol Academy LFC	v	Birmingham City LFC	2 - 2
Millwall Lionesses LFC	v	Blackburn Rovers LFC	0 - 1
Derby County LFC	v	Chelsea LFC	0 - 2
Aston Villa LFC	v	Leeds Carnegie Ladies	0 - 3
Sunderland WFC	v	Barnet Ladies	5 - 0
Manchester City LFC	v	Everton LFC	0 - 4
Ooh Lincoln Ladies	v	Nottingham Forest LFC	3 - 1
Middlesbrough LFC	v	**Arsenal LFC (H)**	0 - 4

SIXTH ROUND PROPER

Arsenal LFC (H)	v	Leeds Carnegie Ladies	3 - 1
Sunderland WFC	v	Bristol Academy LFC	4 - 2
Chelsea LFC	v	Ooh Lincoln Ladies	3 - 1
Blackburn Rovers LFC	v	Everton LFC	0 - 2

SEMI-FINALS

Arsenal LFC (H)	v	Everton LFC	3-1
Yankey 24, Ludlow 31		Dowie 54	
Sunderland WFC	v	Chelsea LFC	3-0
Guttridge 72, Williams 80,90			

THE FINAL

ARSENAL LFC (H) 2	1 SUNDERLAND WFC
Chapman 33, Little 90+2	McDougall 90+5

ARSENAL LFC (H)

Byrne
Bassett
Grant C
Flaherty
Fahey
Davison
Ludlow
Chapman
Yankey
Little
Grant S

SUBSTITUTES
Lander 62 mins for Grant S
Ross 82 mins for Davison
White 90 mins for Bassett

SUNDERLAND WFC

Alderson
Bronze (MOTM)
Greenwell
Bannon
Halliday
Staniforth
McDougall
Nobbs
Williams
Gutteridge
Stokes

SUBSTITUTES
Devine 62 mins for Williams
Danby 83 mins for Gutteridge

Played at Pride Park, Derby County FC - Att: 23,291

F.A. FUTSAL LEAGUE

DEFENDING NATIONAL CHAMPIONS - HELVECIA FC

NORTH	P	W	D	L	F	A	Pts
Middlesbrough Futsal Club	9	6	2	1	50	36	20
Sheffield & Hallamshire	10	6	0	4	57	35	18
Loughborough University	9	6	0	3	54	47	18
Manchester Futsal Club	10	5	1	4	37	31	16
Sheffield FC Futsal Club	9	3	2	4	50	54	11
Grimsby YMCA	10	2	1	7	60	81	7
Futsal Club Barsa	9	2	0	7	43	67	6

Results: 08 Feb 2008 - 26 July 2009

Futsal Club Barsa	v	Manchester Futsal Club	2-5
Sheffield FC Futsal Club	v	Middlesbrough Futsal Club	5-5
Grimsby YMCA	v	Sheffield & Hallamshire	2-8
Middlesbrough FC	v	Loughborough University	7-5
Sheffield & Hallamshire	v	Futsal Club Barsa	14-3
Manchester Futsal Club	v	Sheffield FC Futsal Club	1-5
Loughborough University	v	Grimsby YMCA	13-4
Sheffield & Hallamshire	v	Middlesbrough Futsal Club	3-5
Sheffield FC Futsal Club	v	Futsal Club Barsa	6-5
Manchester Futsal Club	v	Grimsby YMCA	7-4
Loughborough University	v	Sheffield FC Futsal Club	7-6
Futsal Club Barsa	v	Middlesbrough Futsal Club	1-4
Sheffield FC Futsal Club	v	Grimsby YMCA	4-9
Manchester Futsal Club	v	Middlesbrough Futsal Club	3-3
Sheffield & Hallamshire	v	Loughborough University	6-1
Sheffield & Hallamshire	v	Manchester Futsal Club	3-2
Grimsby YMCA	v	Middlesbrough Futsal Club	4-9
Futsal Club Barsa	v	Loughborough University	4-10
Manchester Futsal Club	v	Futsal Club Barsa	6-2
Middlesbrough FC	v	Sheffield FC Futsal Club	6-2
Sheffield & Hallamshire	v	Grimsby YMCA	2-5
Grimsby YMCA	v	Futsal Club Barsa	7-9
Loughborough University	v	Manchester Futsal Club	4-2
Sheffield & Hallamshire	v	Sheffield FC Futsal	8-6
Grimsby YMCA	v	Sheffield FC Futsal	10-10
Loughborough University	v	Sheffield & Hallamshire	2-8
Middlesbrough FC	v	Manchester Futsal Club	2-5
Futsal Club Barsa	v	Grimsby YMCA	10-7
Manchester Futsal Club	v	Loughborough University	3-4
Sheffield FC Futsal	v	Sheffield & Hallamshire	6-3
Middlesbrough FC	v	Grimsby YMCA	9-8
Manchester Futsal FC	v	Sheffield & Hallamshire	3-2
Loughborough University	v	Futsal Club Barsa	8-7

SOUTH	P	W	D	L	F	A	Pts
FC White Bear	10	7	1	2	82	43	22
Helvecia FC	8	7	0	1	93	35	21
Genesis	9	6	2	1	66	45	20
Kickers	10	5	3	2	48	34	18
London United FC	7	2	2	3	34	37	8
FC Enfield	9	2	2	5	55	73	8
FC Baltic	9	2	1	6	46	62	7
Vaughans	8	2	0	6	35	45	6
Deportivo QM FC	10	1	1	8	33	118	4

Results: 08 Feb 2008 - 26 July 2009

Kickers	v	FC Baltic	8-2
Genesis	v	Deportivo QM FC	16-6
FC Enfield	v	FC White Bear	9-8
Helvecia FC	v	FC Enfield	16-7
FC Baltic	v	Genesis	7-7
Deportivo QM FC	v	Kickers	0-4
Helvecia	v	Kickers	7-6
Deportivo QM FC	v	Vaughans	4-13
FC White Bear	v	Genesis	6-4
Helvecia FC	v	FC Baltic	10-8
Deportivo QM FC	v	FC White Bear	4-17
Kickers	v	Vaughans	4-2
Kickers	v	FC White Bear	4-4
Vaughans	v	FC Baltic	6-9
Genesis	v	London United FC	7-7
FC Enfield	v	Deportivo QM FC	11-11
Deportivo QM FC	v	Helvecia FC	1-35
FC White Bear	v	London United FC	5-8
Genesis	v	Vaughans	8-6
FC Enfield	v	Kickers	5-5
Vaughans	v	FC Enfield	5-2
FC Baltic	v	Deportivo QM FC	4-6
London United FC	v	FC White Bear	4-6
Genesis	v	Kickers	8-5
FC Enfield	v	FC Baltic	5-7
Kickers	v	London United FC	3-3
Vaughans	v	FC White Bear	3-10
Genesis	v	Helvecia FC	6-5
Vaughans	v	Kickers	0-4
FC White Bear	v	Deportivo QM FC	9-0
London United FC	v	FC Enfield	4-8
FC Baltic	v	Helvecia FC	4-9
FC Baltic	v	FC White Bear	2-6
Helvecia FC	v	Vaughans	4-0
FC Enfield	v	Genesis	3-6
Deportivo QM FC	v	London United FC	1-5
Helvecia FC	v	London United FC	7-3
FC Baltic	v	Kickers	3-5
FC White Bear	v	FC Enfield	11-5
Deportivo QM FC	v	Genesis	0-4

MIDLANDS	P	W	D	L	F	A	Pts
Hartpury College	7	6	0	1	47	25	18
Tranmere Victoria	8	5	1	2	47	30	16
Team Bath	9	4	0	5	34	43	12
Birmingham Tigers	8	3	0	5	38	42	9
The New Saints FC	8	3	0	5	33	50	9
Team United Birmingham	8	2	1	5	36	45	7

Results: 08 Feb 2008 - 26 July 2009

Team Utd Birmingham	v	Birmingham Tigers	6-4
The New Saints FC	v	Team Bath	6-4
Hartpury College	v	Tranmere Victoria	3-6
Team Utd Birmingham	v	The New Saints FC	7-3
Birmingham Tigers	v	Hartpury College	1-4
Team Bath	v	Tranmere Victoria	5-3
Team Bath	v	Birmingham Tigers	7-6
Team Utd Birmingham	v	Hartpury College	7-11
The New Saints FC	v	Tranmere Victoria	2-10
Tranmere Victoria	v	Team Utd Birmingham	7-4
Team Bath	v	Hartpury College	3-5
Birmingham Tigers	v	The New Saints FC	5-10
Team Utd Birmingham	v	Team Bath	2-3
Birmingham Tigers	v	Tranmere Victoria	7-4
The News Saints FC	v	Hartpury College	4-10
Birmingham Tigers	v	Team utd Birmingham	HW (5-0HT)
Team Bath	v	The New Saints FC	6-3
The New Saints FC	v	Team Utd Birmingham	5-3
Hartpury College	v	Birmingham Tigers	7-4
Tranmere Victoria	v	Team Bath	5-2
Tranmere Victoria	v	The New Saints FC	HW (HT5-0)
Birmingham Tigers	v	Team Bath	6-4
Team Utd Birmingham	v	Tranmere Victoria	7-7
Hartpury College	v	Team Bath	7-0

F.A. FUTSAL NATIONAL CUP

GROUP A	P	W	D	L	F	A	Pts
Team Bath	3	3	0	0	17	3	9
London United	3	2	0	1	11	4	6
Middlesbrough FC	3	1	0	2	11	9	3
Worcester University	3	0	0	3	2	25	0

Middlesbrough FC	v	Worcester University	9-0
Team Bath	v	London United	3-0
Middlesbrough FC	v	Team Bath	1-6
Worcester University	v	London United	0-8
Middlesbrough FC	v	London United	1-3
Worcester University	v	Team Bath	2-8

GROUP B	P	W	D	L	F	A	Pts
Helvecia FC	3	3	0	0	21	2	9
Loughborough Students	3	2	0	1	10	10	6
Sheffield & Hallamshire FC	3	0	1	2	7	16	1
FC Lietuva	3	0	1	2	5	15	1

Helvecia FC	v	Sheffield & Hallamshire	7-1
Loughborough Students	v	FC Lietuva	5-0
Helvecia FC	v	Loughborough Students	8-0
Sheffield & Hallamshire	v	FC Lietuva	4-4
Helvecia FC	v	FC Lietuva	6-1
Sheffield & Hallamshire	v	Loughborough Students	2-5

GROUP C	P	W	D	L	F	A	Pts
FC White Bear	3	2	1	0	8	5	7
Kickers	3	1	2	0	6	5	5
Hartpury College	3	1	0	2	11	12	3
Dengo United	3	0	1	2	8	11	1

Dengo United	v	FC White Bear	1-3
Hartpury College	v	Kickers	2-3
Hartpury College	v	Dengo United	7-6
Kickers	v	FC White Bear	2-2
Hartpury College	v	FC White Bear	2-3
Kickers	v	Dengo United	1-1

GROUP D	P	W	D	L	F	A	Pts
Genesis FC	3	3	0	0	19	7	9
Tranmere Victoria	3	1	1	1	10	10	4
Leeds Met Carnegie (M)	3	1	0	2	9	17	3
Streetly	3	0	1	2	7	11	1

Leeds Met Carnegie (M)	v	Tranmere Victoria	2-5
Streetly	v	Genesis FC	2-4
Leeds Met Carnegie (M)	v	Streetly	4-2
Tranmere Victoria	v	Genesis FC	2-5
Leeds Met Carnegie (M)	v	Genesis FC	3-10
Tranmere Victoria	v	Streetly	3-3

QUARTER-FINALS

Team Bath	v	Tranmere Victoria	1-3
Helvecia FC	v	Kickers	8-2
FC White Bear	v	Loughborough Students	3-4
Genesis FC	v	London United	1-3

SEMI FINALS

Tranmere Victoria	v	Helvecia FC	1-4
Loughborough Students	v	London United	2-1

THE FINAL

Helvecia FC	v	Loughborough Students	2-1

Hartpury College beat Sheffield & Hallamshire, 4-0 to win the Plate.

COUNTY FOOTBALL ASSOCIATIONS

BEDFORDSHIRE F.A.

Tel: 01582 565 111 Fax: 01582 565 222

Email: peter.brown@bedfordshirefa.com

Century House, Skimpot Road,

Dunstable, Bedfordshire LU5 4JU

Chief Executive: Peter D Brown.

BERKS & BUCKS F.A.

Tel: 01367 242 099 Fax: 01367 242 158

Email: brian.moore@berks-bucksfa.com

15a London Street, Faringdon,

Oxon SN7 7HD

Chief Executive: Brian Moore

BIRMINGHAM COUNTY F.A.

Tel: 0121 357 4278 Fax: 0121 358 1661

Email: info@birminghamfa.com

Ray Hall Lane, Great Barr, Birmingham

B43 6JF

Secretary: David Shelton

CAMBRIDGESHIRE F.A.

Tel: 01223 209 020 Fax: 01223 209 030

Email: info@cambridgeshirefa.com

Bridge Road, Impington, Cambridgeshire

CB24 9PH

Chief Executive: Roger Pawley

CHESHIRE F.A.

Tel: 01606 871 166 Fax: 01606 871 292

Email: info@cheshirefa.com

Hartford House, Hartford Moss Rec. Centre,

Winnington, Northwich CW8 4BG

Chief Executive: Maureen Dunford

CORNWALL F.A.

Tel: 01726 74080 Fax: 01726 76174

Email: secretary@cornwallfa.com

1 High Cross Street, St Austell, Cornwall

PL25 4AB

Secretary: Barry Cudmore

CUMBERLAND F.A.

Tel: 01900 872 310 Fax: 01900 61647

Email: info@cumberlandfa.com

17 Oxford Street, Workington, Cumbria,

CA14 2AL

Chief Executive: Geoff Turrell.

DERBYSHIRE F.A.

Tel: 01332 361 422 Fax: 01332 360 130

Email: info@derbyshirefa.com

Units 8-9 Stadium Business Court,

Millennium Way, Pride Park, Derby DE24 8HP

Chief Executive: Keith Compton.

DEVON F.A.

Tel: 01626 332 077 Fax: 01626 336 814

Email: info@devonfa.com

County Headquarters, Coach Road,

Newton Abbot, Devon TQ12 1EJ

Chief Executive: Paul Morrison.

DORSET F.A.

Tel: 01202 682 375 Fax: 01202 666 577

Email: sue.hough@dorsetfa.com

County Ground, Blandford Close,

Hamworthy, Poole BH15 4BF

Chief Executive: Sue Hough.

DURHAM F.A.

Tel: 0191 387 2929 Fax: 0191 387 2919

Email: info@durhamfa.com

'Codeslaw', Riverside South,

Chester le Street, Co.Durham DH3 3SJ

Secretary: John Topping.

EAST RIDING F.A.

Tel: 01482 221 158 Fax: 01482 221 169

Email: info@eastridingfa.com

Roy West Centre, 220 Inglemire Lane,

Hull HU6 7TS

Chief Executive: Dennis R Johnson.

ESSEX F.A.

Tel: 01245 393 079 Fax: 01245 393 089

Email: info@essexfa.com

The County Office, Springfield Lyons Approach,

Springfield, Chelmsford CM2 5LB

Chief Executive: Phil Sammons.

GLOUCESTERSHIRE F.A.

Tel: 01454 615 888 Fax: 01454 618 088

Email: info@gloucestershirefa.com

Oaklands Park, Almondsbury, Bristol

BS32 4AG

Chief Executive: David Neale.

HAMPSHIRE F.A.

Tel: 01256 853 000 Fax: 01256 357 973

Email: info@hampshirefa.com

Winklebury Football Complex,

Winklebury Way, Basingstoke RG23 8BF

Chief Executive: Neil Cassar.

HEREFORDSHIRE F.A.

Tel: 01432 342 179 Fax: 01432 279 265

Email: info@herefordshirefa.com

County Ground Offices,

Widemarsh Common, Hereford HR4 9NA

Chief Executive: Jim Lambert.

HERTFORDSHIRE F.A.

Tel: 01462 677 622 Fax: 01462 677 624

Email: secretary@hertfordshirefa.com

County Ground, Baldock Road, Letchworth,

Herts SG6 2EN

Chief Executive: Nick Perchard.

HUNTINGDONSHIRE F.A.

Tel: 01480 414 422 Fax: 01480 447 489

Email: info@huntsfa.com

Cromwell Chambers, 8 St Johns Street,

Huntingdon, Cambs PE29 3DD

Secretary: Mark Frost.

KENT F.A.

Tel: 01634 843 824 Fax: 01634 815 369

Email: info@kentfa.com

69 Maidstone Road, Chatham, Kent

ME4 6DT

Chief Executive: Keith Masters.

LANCASHIRE F.A.

Tel: 01772 624 000 Fax: 01772 624 700

Email: secretary@lancashirefa.com

The County Ground, Thurston Road, Leyland

PR25 2LF

Chief Executive: David Burgess.

LEICESTERSHIRE & RUTLAND F.A.

Tel: 0116 286 7828 Fax: 0116 286 4858

Email: info@leicestershirefa.com

Holmes Park, Dog & Gun Lane, Whetstone

LE8 6FA

Chief Executive: Laurence Jones.

LINCOLNSHIRE F.A.

Tel: 0844 967 0708 Fax: 0844 967 0709

Email: john.griffin@lincolnshirefa.com

4 Henley Way, Doddington Road, Lincoln

LN6 3QR

Secretary: John Griffin.

LIVERPOOL F.A.

Tel: 0151 523 4488 Fax: 0151 523 4477

Email: info@liverpoolfa.com

Liverpool Soccer Centre, Walton Hall Park,

Walton Hall Avenue, Liverpool L4 9XP

Secretary: David Pugh.

LONDON F.A.

Tel: 0870 774 3010 Fax: 020 7610 8370

Email: info@londonfa.com

11 Hurlingham Business Park, Sulivan Road,

Fulham, London SW6 3DU

Secretary: David Fowkes.

Chairman: Tony Sharples.

MANCHESTER F.A.

Tel: 0161 604 7620 Fax: 0161 604 7622

Email: info@manchesterfa.com

Salford Sports Village, Littleton Road,

Lower Kersal, Slaford, Manchester M7 3NQ

Chief Executive: Roger Reade

Chairman: Frank Hannah.

MIDDLESEX F.A.

Tel: 020 8515 1919 Fax: 020 8515 1910

Email: info@middlesexfa.com

39 Roxborough Road, Harrow, Middlesex

HA1 1NS

Chief Executive: Peter Clayton.

NORFOLK F.A.

Tel: 01603 704 050 Fax: 01603 704 059

Email: info@norfolkfa.com

11 Meridian Way, Thorpe St Andrew, Norwich

NF7 0TA

Chief Executive: Shaun Turner.

NORTH RIDING F.A.

Tel: 01642 717 770 Fax: 01642 717 776

Email: info@northridingfa.com

Broughton Road, Stokesley, Middlesbrough

TS9 5NY

Chief Executive: Tom Radigan.

NORTHAMPTONSHIRE F.A.

Tel: 01604 670 741 Fax: 01604 670 742

Email: info@northamptonshirefa.com

9 Duncan Close, Redhouse Square,

Moulton Park, Northampton NN3 6WL

Chief Executive: David Payne.

NORTHUMBERLAND F.A.

Tel: 0191 270 0700

Email: rowland.maughan@northumberlandfa.com

Whitley Park, Whitley Road,

Newscastle upon Tyne NE12 9FA

Chief Executive: Rowland E Maughan.

NOTTINGHAMSHIRE F.A.

Tel: 0115 983 7400 Fax: 0115 946 1977

Email: info@nottnghamshirefa.com

Unit 6b, Chetwynd Business Park,

Chilwell, Nottinghamshire NG9 6RZ

Chief Executive: Elaine Oram.

OXFORDSHIRE F.A.

Tel: 01993 778 586 Fax: 01993 772 191

Email: info@oxfordshirefa.com

PO Box 62, Witney, Oxon

OX28 1HA

Secretary: Ian Mason.

SHEFFIELD & HALLAMSHIRE F.A.

Tel: 0114 241 4999 Fax: 0114 241 4990

Email: info@sheffieldfa.com

Clegg House, 69 Cornish Place, Cornish St.,

Sheffield S6 3AF

Chief Executive: James Hope-Gill.

SHROPSHIRE F.A.

Tel: 01743 362 769 Fax: 01743 270 494

Email: secretary@shropshirefa.com

The New Stadium, Oteley Road,

Shrewsbury, Shropshire SY2 6ST

Chief Executive: David Rowe.

SOMERSET F.A.

Tel: 01761 410 280 Fax: 01761 410 477

Email: info@somersetfa.com

30 North Road, Midsomer Norton, Radstock,

Somerset BA3 2QD

Chief Executive: Jon Pike.

STAFFORDSHIRE F.A.

Tel: 01785 256 994 Fax: 01785 279 837

Email: secretary@staffordshirefa.com

Unit F, Dyson Court, Staffordshire Tech. Pk,

Beaconside, Stafford ST18 0LQ

Chief Executive: Brian Adshead.

SUFFOLK F.A.

Tel: 01449 616 606 Fax: 01449 616 607

Email: info@suffolkfa.com

The Buntings, Cedars Park, Stowmarket,

Suffolk IP14 5GZ

Chief Executive: Martin Head.

SURREY F.A.

Tel: 01372 373 543 Fax: 01372 361 310

Email: info@surreyfa.com

Connaught House, 36 Bridge Street,

Leatherhead, Surrey KT22 8BZ

Secretary: Ray Ward.

SUSSEX F.A.

Tel: 01903 753 547 Fax: 01903 761 608

Email: info@sussexfa.com

Culver Road, Lancing, West Sussex

BN15 9AX

Chief Executive: Ken Benham.

WEST RIDING F.A.

Tel: 0113 282 1222 Fax: 0113 282 1525

Email: info@wrcfa.com

Fleet Lane, Woodlesford, Leeds

LS26 8NX

Chief Executive: Roy Carter.

WESTMORLANDS F.A.

Tel: 01539 730 946 Fax: 01539 740 567

Email: info@westmorlandfa.com

Unit 1, Riverside Business Park, Natland Rd,

Kendal, Cumbria LA9 7SX

Chief Executive: Peter Ducksbury.

WILTSHIRE F.A.

Tel: 01793 486 047 Fax: 01793 692 699

Email: mike.benson@wiltshirefa.com

Units 2/3 Dorcan Business Village, Dorcan,

Swindon, Wiltshire SN3 5HY

Secretary: Mike Benson.

Chairman: Richard Gardiner.

WORCESTERSHIRE F.A.

Tel: 01905 827 137 Fax: 01905 798 963

Email: info@worcestershirefa.com

Craftsman House, De Salis Drive,

Hampton Lovett Ind.Est., Droitwich WR9 0QE

Secretary: Mervyn Leggett.

Chairman: Roy Northall.

London FA Junior Cup Winners
Summerstown
Photo: Gordon Whittington

Bedfordshire Senior Trophy Winners
61 FC (Luton)
3-1 winners over AFC Kempston Rovers.
Photo: Gordon Whittington

MISCELLANEOUS CUPS 2008-09

AMATEUR FOOTBALL ALLIANCE SENIOR CUP

FIRST ROUND

Albanian 2 **Old Actonians Association** 4
HSBC (w/o) v Bethwin Mens (scr.)
St Albans Rangers 2 **Ibis** 6
Old Buckwellians 0 **Weirside Rangers** 8
Old Foresters 2 Old Malvernians 1
Old Brentwoods 1 **Economicals** 2
Egbertians 1 **Kew Association** 5
Kings Old Boys 0 **Honourable Artillery Company** 2
Old Westminster Citizens 2 **Old Parmiterians** 5
BB Eagles 3 Southgate Olympic 0
Wood Green Old Boys 2 Old Finchleians 1
Old Dorkinians 2 **Old Kolsassians** 5
East Barnet Old Grammarians 3 **Old Uffingtonians** 4
Old Manorians 2 **Brent** 3
Merton 2 Carshalton 0
Bank of England 2 William Fitt 1
Fulham Compton Old Boys 2 Old Chigwellians 0
Mill Hill Village 2 **Latymer Old Boys** 4
Old Tiffinians 6 Old Latymerians 1
Old Lyonian 2 **Old Elizabethans** 4
Norsemen 3 Old Paulines A 2
Parkfield 0 **Civil Service** 2
Sinjuns Grammarians 1 **Southgate County** 2
Polytechnic 8 Hale End Athletic 0
Lloyds TSB Bank 5 **Old Bromleians** 5 *aet* (3-4p)
Glyn Old Boys 2 **Enfield Old Grammarians** 4

SECOND ROUND

Latymer Old Boys 0 **Old Suttonians** 2
Old Carthusians 1 **Old Parmiterians** 5
Old Edmontonians 1 **Alexandra Park** 3
Old Actonians Association 5 Old Esthameians 2
West Wickham (w/o) v Hampstead Heathens (scr.)
Old Salesians 6 South Bank Cuaco 2
Weirside Rangers 2 **Leyton County OB** 2 *aet* (3-4p)
Mill Hill County Old Boys 3 Old Guildfordians 2
Old Hamptonians 0 **Old Ignatians** 2
Old Salvatorians 1 **Old Minchendenians** 3
Broomfield 3 Old Thorntonians 1
Old Challoners 1 Centymca 0
Polytechnic 4 Alleyn Old Boys 1
Old Parkonians 0 **Crouch End Vampires** 2
Old Bromleians 0 **Nottsborough** 8
Old Owens 3 **Old Aloysians** 4
Bealonians 4 Old Salopians 0
Old Cholmeleians 2 Brent 1
Kew Association 1 **Old Meadonians** 2
Old Stationers 0 **Fulham Compton Old Boys** 3
Old Wilsonians 4 HSBC1
Wake Green Amateur 3 Ibis 1
Wandsworth Borough 1 **Old Elizabethans** 3
Winchmore Hill 6 Enfield Old Grammarians 1
BB Eagles 1 **Old Belgravians** 4
Honourable Artillery Company 0 **UCL Academicals** 1
Old Isleworthians 4 Old Foresters 3
Southgate County 1 **Norsemen** 4
Bank of England 1 **Wood Green Old Boys** 2
Old Kolsassians 1 **Civil Service** 3
Old Tiffinians 2 **Merton** 6
Old Uffingtonians 4 Economicals 3

THIRD ROUND

Old Suttonians 1 **Merton** 3
Old Parmiterians (w/o) v Old Elizabethans (scr.)
Broomfield 3 West Wickham 2
Wake Green Amateur (w/o) v Old Isleworthians (scr.)
Bealonians 1 Old Aloysians 0
Leyton County Old Boys 3 Old Challoners 2
Winchmore Hill 10 Old Ignatians 0
Norsemen 4 Old Uffingtonians 2
Civil Service 1 Old Cholmeleians 1 *aet* (5-4p)
Polytechnic 5 Wood Green Old Boys 0
Old Salesians 2 **UCL Academicals** 3
Old Belgravians 0 **Old Meadonians** 3
Fulham Compton Old Boys 0 **Crouch End Vampires** 2
Old Actonians Association 4 Alexandra Park 2
Old Minchendenians 6 Mill Hill County Old Boys 3
Old Wilsonians 0 **Nottsborough** 2

FOURTH ROUND

Old Parmiterians 6 Leyton County Old Boys 0
Merton 1 **Crouch End Vampires** 1 *aet* (3-5p)
Civil Service 3 Wake Green Amateur 1
Broomfield 1 **Nottsborough** 2
Old Minchendenians 1 **Norsemen** 3
Old Actonians Association 0 **UCL Academicals** 1
Old Meadonians 1 **Winchmore Hill** 5
Polytechnic 1 Bealonians 1 *aet* (3-1p)

QUARTER-FINALS

Norsemen 1 **Old Parmiterians** 2
Polytechnic 2 Crouch End Vampires 1
Winchmore Hill 3 UCL Academicals 0
Civil Service 0 **Nottsborough** 2

SEMI-FINALS

Winchmore Hill 0 **Polytechnic** 0 *aet* (3-5p)
Nottsborough 3 Old Parmiterians 1

FINAL

(April 4th at Bank of England)
Nottsborough 1 Polytechnic 0

AXMINSTER HOSPITAL CUP

FIRST ROUND

Budleigh Salterton 6 Exmouth Amateurs 1
Ilminster Town 1 Crewkerne 0
Bickleigh 3 **Chard Town** 4
Combe St Nicholas 1 Seaton Town 0
Cullompton Rangers 4 Millwey Rise 0
East Budleigh 0 **Feniton** 1 *(at Budleigh Salterton)*
Axminster Town (w/o) v Sidbury United (scr.)

QUARTER-FINALS

Feniton 1 **Budleigh Salterton** 5 *(at Budleigh Salterton)*
Cullompton Rangers 3 Combe St Nicholas 2
Axminster Town 0 **Exmouth Town** 2
Chard Town 0 **Ilminster Town** 4 *(at Ilminster Town)*

SEMI-FINALS

Budleigh Salterton 2 Exmouth Town 1
Ilminster Town 1 **Cullompton Rangers** 2

FINAL

(May 31st at Axminster Town)
Budleigh Salterton 2 Cullompton Rangers 1

BEDFORDSHIRE PREMIER CUP

(July 30th at Stotfold)
Stotfold 0 **Luton Town** 1

BEDFORDSHIRE SENIOR CUP

FIRST ROUND

Barton Rovers 4 Langford 1
Stotfold 3 **Dunstable Town** 5 *aet*

QUARTER-FINALS

Dunstable Town 0 Leighton Town 0 *aet* (4-3p)
Arlesey Town 4 Barton Rovers 2
Biggleswade Town 4 Bedford Town 1
Potton United 3 **Biggleswade United** 4

SEMI-FINALS

Biggleswade Town (w/o) v Arlesey Town (scr.)
Biggleswade United 0 **Dunstable Town** 1

FINAL

(May 7th at Luton Town)
Dunstable Town 1 Biggleswade Town 1 *aet* (6-5p)

BEDFORDSHIRE SENIOR TROPHY

FIRST ROUND

AFC Dunstable 4 Blunham 2
AFC Kempston Rovers 3 Wootton Blue Cross 1
AFC Kempston Town 4 Ickwell & Old Warden 1
Bedford 4 Arlesey Athletic 4 *aet* (4-3p)

Bedford Sports Athletic 4 Sandy 1
Brache Sparta 5 Wilshamstead 1
Campton 3 Meltis Corinthians 0
Kent Athletic 3 Henlow 0
Oakley Sports 2 Caldecote 1
Renhold United 2 Caddington 1
The 61 FC (Luton) 6 Crawley Green 1
Totternhoe 3 Dunton 2

SECOND ROUND

AFC Kempston Rovers 2 AFC Kempston Town 1
Ampthill Town 2 **Campton** 5 *aet*
Cranfield United 3 Kent Athletic 2
Oakley Sports 4 Brache Sparta 0
Renhold United 3 **The 61 FC (Luton)** 5
Riseley Sports 3 Bedford Sports Athletic 1
Sharnbrook 1 **AFC Dunstable** 3
Totternhoe 2 Bedford 1

QUARTER-FINALS

AFC Dunstable 0 **AFC Kempston Rovers** 1
Campton 1 **Oakley Sports** 2
Cranfield United 4 Totternhoe 3
The 61 FC (Luton) 4 Riseley Sports 0

SEMI-FINALS

Cranfield United 0 **AFC Kempston Rovers** 5
Oakley Sports 1 **The 61 FC (Luton)** 6

FINAL

(April 4th at Biggleswade Town)
AFC Kempston Rovers 1 **The 61 FC (Luton)** 3

BERKS & BUCKS SENIOR CUP

SECOND ROUND

Maidenhead United 2 Burnham 0
Beaconsfield SYCOB 1 **Marlow** 4
Thatcham Town 1 **Didcot Town** 2
Abingdon United 1 **Windsor & Eton** 2 *aet*
Bracknell Town 1 Milton Keynes Dons 0

QUARTER-FINALS

Bracknell Town 1 **Maidenhead United** 2
Windsor & Eton 8 Chesham United 1
Marlow 1 Slough Town 0
Wycombe Wanderers 4 Didcot Town 1 *(at Didcot Town)*

SEMI-FINALS

Maidenhead United 0 **Windsor & Eton** 1
Wycombe Wanderers 0 **Marlow** 1 *(at Marlow)*

FINAL

(May 4th at Milton Keynes Dons)
Windsor & Eton 1 Marlow 0

BERKS & BUCKS SENIOR TROPHY

FIRST ROUND

Flackwell Heath 3 Milton United 1
Abingdon Town 1 **Marlow United** 2
Hungerford Town 4 Holmer Green 2
Reading Town 4 Shrivenham 2
Chalfont Wasps 5 Wantage Town 2 *(at Wantage)*
Aylesbury Vale 4 Chalfont St Peter 1 *(at Chalfont)*

QUARTER-FINALS

Hungerford Town 1 **Newport Pagnell Town** 2
Marlow United 0 **Flackwell Heath** 1
Sandhurst Town 0 **Reading Town** 1
Aylesbury Vale 2 Chalfont Wasps 2 *aet* (3-1p)

SEMI-FINALS

Newport Pagnell Town 4 Aylesbury Vale 2
Reading Town 4 Flackwell Heath 2 *aet*

FINAL

(April 28th at Abingdon United)
Newport Pagnell Town 0 **Reading Town** 2

BIRMINGHAM SENIOR CUP

FIRST ROUND

Sutton Coldfield Town 1 Redditch United 0
Rugby Town 3 Racing Club Warwick 2 *aet*

SECOND ROUND

Hednesford Town 3 Alvechurch 2
Oldbury United 0 **Walsall** 3
Boldmere St Michaels 0 **Burton Albion** 1
Nuneaton Town 2 **Wolverhampton Wanderers** 3
Studley 0 **Leamington** 1
Willenhall Town 6 Romulus 1
Tipton Town 2 **Birmingham City** 3
Stratford Town 2 Causeway United 0
Tamworth 2 Banbury United 0
Bedworth United 1 **Sutton Coldfield Town** 2
Atherstone Town 2 Halesowen Town 0
Coventry Sphinx 0 **Bromsgrove Rovers** 1
Highgate United 1 **West Bromwich Albion** 4
Rushall Olympic 3 Coleshill Town 1
Solihull Moors 3 Rugby Town 2
Stourbridge 3 Cradley Town 0

THIRD ROUND

Sutton Coldfield Town 3 **Burton Albion** 6
Stratford Town 2 **Tamworth** 3 *aet*
Leamington 1 **Bromsgrove Rovers** 2
Rushall Olympic 3 West Bromwich Albion 2 *aet*
Solihull Moors 1 Walsall 0
Willenhall Town 3 Birmingham City 0
Stourbridge 4 Wolverhampton Wanderers 3 *aet*
Atherstone Town 0 **Hednesford Town** 2

QUARTER-FINALS

Solihull Moors 1 **Rushall Olympic** 3
Tamworth 2 Burton Albion 1
Bromsgrove Rovers 0 **Stourbridge** 2
Hednesford Town 2 Willenhall Town 1

SEMI-FINALS

Tamworth 0 **Stourbridge** 0 *aet* (3-4p)
Hednesford Town 1 Rushall Olympic 0

FINAL

(April 22nd at Burton Albion)
Stourbridge 0 **Hednesford Town** 2

BIRMINGHAM FLOODLIGHT CUP

FIRST ROUND

Wednesfield 1 **Goodrich** 2
Darlaston Town 2 Oldbury Athletic 0
Massey-Ferguson 3 Bustleholme 1
Pilkington XXX 1 **Lye Town** 3
Bolehall Swifts 2 Boldmere St Michaels 1
Cadbury Athletic 4 Tividale 0
Dudley Sports 2 Gornal Athletic 0
Castle Vale 4 Nuneaton Griff 1

SECOND ROUND

Bartley Green 0 **Darlaston Town** 3
Coton Green 1 **Dudley Town** 2
Dudley Sports 1 AFC Wulfrunians 0
Lye Town 2 **Cadbury Athletic** 4
Coventry Copsewood 1 **Southam United** 2
Goodrich 1 **Continental Star** 4
Knowle 2 Bolehall Swifts 1
Massey-Ferguson 2 **Castle Vale** 3

QUARTER-FINALS

Dudley Town 2 Knowle 1
Continental Star 0 **Dudley Sports** 2
Cadbury Athletic 1 **Darlaston Town** 4 *(at Darlaston)*
Southam United 2 Castle Vale 1

SEMI-FINALS

Dudley Sports 0 **Darlaston Town** 4
Southam United 3 Dudley Town 0

FINAL

(March 3rd at Solihull Moors)
Southam United 3 Darlaston Town 1

BOLTON HOSPITAL CUP

FIRST ROUND

Eagley 3 Breightmet United 1
Ramsbottom United 2 Bolton County 1
Atherton LR 6 Stoneclough 2
Tempest United 1 **Turton** 4

SEMI-FINALS

Eagley 2 Turton 1 *(at Atherton LR)*
Atherton LR 1 Ramsbottom United 0
(at Atherton Collieries)

FINAL

(May 26th at Bolton Wanderers)
Atherton LR 2 **Eagley** 3

BRIGHTON CHARITY CUP

FIRST ROUND

Chichester City United 4 Rustington 1

SECOND ROUND

Mile Oak 2 **Ringmer** 4
Shoreham 3 Peacehaven & Telscombe 0
Pagham 1 **Horsham** 3
Seaford Town 1 St Francis Rangers 1 *aet* (5-3p)
Whitehawk 3 Steyning Town 0
Wick 2 Storrington 0 *aet*
Worthing United 2 **Southwick** 3
East Preston 0 **Chichester City United** 1

QUARTER-FINALS

Wick 0 **Horsham** 3
Seaford Town 1 Ringmer 0
Chichester City United 3 Southwick 3 *aet* (3-2p)
Whitehawk 1 **Shoreham** 3 *aet*

SEMI-FINALS

Shoreham 3 Horsham 2 *aet*
Seaford Town 0 **Chichester City United** 2

FINAL

Shoreham v Chichester City United
(cancelled due to Chichester City United standing trial)

BUCKINGHAMSHIRE COUNTY CUP

FIRST ROUND

Buckingham Athletic 1 **Long Buckby** 3
Ampthill Town 5 **Stony Stratford Town** 7 *aet*
Wootton Blue Cross 0 **Olney Town** 3
Bicester Town 1 Brackley Town 1 *aet* (4-2p)

QUARTER-FINALS

Long Buckby (scr.) v **Bicester Town** (w/o)
Banbury United 6 Winslow United 1
Olney Town 0 **Leighton Town** 7
Stony Stratford Town 2 **Buckingham Town** 2 *aet* (2-4p)

SEMI-FINALS

(played over two legs)

Banbury United 2 Bicester Town 0, Bicester Town 0 **Banbury United** 4
Buckingham Town 1 Leighton Town 1, **Leighton Town** 3 Buckingham Town 2 *aet*

FINAL

(May 4th at Buckingham Town)

Banbury United 4 Leighton Town 2

CAMBRIDGESHIRE PROFESSIONAL CUP

(July 29th at Cambridge City)

Cambridge City 1 Histon 1 (4-3p)

CAMBRIDGESHIRE INVITATION CUP

(Sponsor: Ridgeons)

PRELIMINARY ROUND

Mildenhall Town 3 Hundon 0 *aet*
Newmarket Town 2 Waterbeach 1
Wisbech Town 2 **CRC** 3
Ely City 2 Great Shelford 0 *aet*

QUARTER-FINALS

March Town United 1 **CRC** 3 *aet*
Mildenhall Town 2 Newmarket Town 0
Histon 1 **Cambridge City** 1 *aet* (5-6p)
Soham Town Rangers 2 **Ely City** 3

SEMI-FINALS

Mildenhall Town 1 **CRC** 3
Cambridge City 3 Ely City 2 *aet*

FINAL

(April 21th at Cambridge United)

CRC 0 **Cambridge City** 1

CLIFF BULLEN CAMBRIDGESHIRE CHALLENGE CUP

PRELIMINARY ROUND

Comberton United 6 Swavesey Institute 1
Girton United 0 **Hardwick** 0 *aet* (6-7p)
Haddenham Rovers 4 Whittlesford United 5
Linton Granta 0 **Castle Camps** 4

FIRST ROUND

Cambridge University Press 6 Castle Camps 3
Comberton United 1 RHS United 0
Fordham 2 **Sawston United** 3
Foxton 2 Histon A 1
Great Chesterford 0 **Soham Town Rangers Res.** 1
Great Shelford 5 Leverington Sports 0
Hardwick 2 Over Sports 1
Littleport Town 3 Cottenham United 1
March Town United Res. 3 Saffron Crocus 1
Milton 1 **Chatteris Town** 2
Outwell Swifts 3 Cherry Hinton 1
Whittlesey United 11 Soham United 0
Whittlesford United 1 **Fulbourn Institute** 3
Wimblington 0 **Waterbeach** 1
Wisbech Town Res. 2 **West Wratting** 4
Ely City Res. 3 Parson Drove 1

SECOND ROUND

Cambridge University Press 5 Whittlesey United 0
Comberton United 4 Littleport Town 2
Foxton 2 March Town United Res. 1 *aet*
Fulbourn Institute 4 Ely City Res. 1
Great Shelford 6 Waterbeach 2
Soham Town Rangers Res. 1 **Hardwick** 3
West Wratting 5 Sawston United 2
Outwell Swifts 0 **Chatteris Town** 0 *aet* (0-3p)

QUARTER-FINALS

Great Shelford 2 **West Wratting** 3
Foxton 3 **Cambridge University Press** 5
Fulbourn Institute 4 Hardwick 2
Chatteris Town 2 Comberton United 1

SEMI-FINALS

West Wratting 1 **Folbourn Institute** 3
Canmbridge University Press 3 Chatteris Town 1

FINAL

(May 18th at Cambridge City)

Fulbourn Institute 2 Cambridge University Press 1

CAPITAL COUNTIES FEEDER LEAGUES TROPHY

(Sponsor: Anagram Records)

FIRST ROUND

Aston Clinton 1 **Tring Corinthians** 2
Baldock Town Letchworth 1 London Lions 0
Bedmond Sports & Social 0 **Brache Sparta** 5
Bethnal Green United 3 Mill End Sports 1
Broadfields United 0 **Canning Town** 3
Buntingford Town 3 **Bovingdon** 5
Epping 3 Hertford Heath 2
Evergreen 1 **Hanworth Villa** 2
Knebworth 1 **Lemsford** 5
Metropolitan Police Bushey 1 **Manford Way** 3
Padbury United 3 Knaphill 0
Sandridge Rovers 0 **Winslow United** 5
Standon & Puckeridge 1 **Wormley Rovers** 4
Takeley 4 Frenford Senior 1

SECOND ROUND

Baldock Town Letchworth 4 Bovingdon 2
Brache Sparta 1 **Park Street Village** 6
Canning Town 0 **Takeley** 2
Hanworth Villa 1 Bethnal Green United 0
White Ensign 4 Tring Corinthians 3
Epping 3 Lemsford 2
Winslow United 3 Manford Way 1
Wormley Rovers 1 **Padbury United** 3

QUARTER-FINALS

Padbury United 4 White Ensign 3 *aet*
Takeley 0 Hanworth Villa 1 *(Hanworth Villa expelled)*
Park Street Village 1 Baldock Town Letchworth 0
Epping 0 **Winslow United** 1

SEMI-FINALS

Padbury United 1 **Park Street Village** 2
Winslow United 0 **Takeley** 1

FINAL

(May 10th at HCFA, Letchworth)

Takeley 2 Park Street Village 2 *aet* (3-1p)

CHESHIRE SENIOR CUP

FIRST ROUND

Altrincham 4 Vauxhall Motors 2
Hyde United 0 **Congleton Town** 1
Alsager Town 0 **Stalybridge Celtic** 1
Cammell Laird 1 **Warrington Town** 2
Winsford United 1 **Runcorn Linnets** 3
Cheadle Town 2 **Witton Albion** 5
Woodley Sports 4 Northwich Victoria 1

QUARTER FINALS

Nantwich Town 5 Warrington Town 0
Stalybridge Celtic 0 **Altrincham** 2
Witton Albion 2 Congleton Town 1
Runcorn Linnets 2 **Woodley Sports** 3 *aet*

SEMI-FINALS

Altrincham 4 Witton Albion 0
Nantwich Town 2 Woodley Sports 1

FINAL *(March 23rd at Witton Albion)*

Altrincham 3 Nantwich Town 0

CORNWALL SENIOR CUP

PRELIMINARY ROUND

Padstow United 2 **St Dominick** 3
Perranporth 4 St Day 0
Perranwell 7 Nanpean Rovers 1
Polperro 1 **Roche** 2 *aet*
Portreath 2 St Just 0
Probus 1 Mullion 0
RNAS Culdrose 2 **Helston Athletic** 3
St Columb Major 1 **St Agnes** 3
St Ives Town 2 Lanreath 0
St Stephens Borough 8 Biscovey 1

FIRST ROUND

Illogan RBL 1 St Ives Town 0 *aet*
Morwenstow 2 **Perranporth** 3 *aet*
Perranwell 5 Holmans Sports Club 0
Probus 5 Ludgvan 0
Roche 0 **Helston Athletic** 1
St Agnes 2 **St Dominick** 3
St Stephens Borough 3 Portreath 2
Sticker 4 St Stephen 1

SECOND ROUND

Bodmin Town 1 **Truro City** 3
Hayle 0 **Perranporth** 5
Helston Athletic 1 **Saltash United** 8
Illogan RBL 2 Foxhole Stars 1
Penryn Athletic 2 Godolphin Atlantic 1
Porthleven 2 Penzance 0
Probus 0 **Dobwalls** 6
St Dominick 1 **Newquay** 3
St Stephens Borough 3 St Blazey 2
Sticker 2 Bude Town 1
Torpoint Athletic 3 Camelford 2
Falmouth Town 4 Wendron United 2 *aet*
Callington Town 3 Mousehole 0
Launceston 1 **Perranwell** 2
Millbrook 1 Liskeard Athletic 0
Wadebridge Town 2 **St Austell** 6

THIRD ROUND

Illogan RBL 1 **Truro City** 3
Penryn Athletic 4 Falmouth Town 1
Perranporth 4 Newquay 0
Perranwell 2 Sticker 1
Porthleven 3 Millbrook 0
St Austell 4 Torpoint Athletic 0
St Stephens Borough 1 **Callington Town** 5
Saltash United 7 Dobwalls 0

QUARTER-FINALS

Penryn Athletic 3 Truro City 2
Porthleven 1 **St Austell** 2
Saltash United 4 Perranwell 2
Callington Town 0 **Perranporth** 0 *aet*
Replay: **Perranporth** 2 Callington Town 0

SEMI-FINALS

Perranporth 0 **St Austell** 2 *(at Newquay)*
enryn Athletic 0 **Saltash United** 3 *(at Wadebridge Town)*

FINAL

(April 13th at St. Blazey)

St Austell 3 Saltash United 2

DURNING LAWRENCE CORNWALL CHARITY CUP

FIRST ROUND

Penryn Athletic 5 Mousehole 1
Penzance 5 Camelford 0
Dobwalls 1 **Porthleven** 3
Godolphin Atlantic 1 Wendron United 0
Hayle 4 Foxhole Stars 2
Newquay 4 Callington Town 2
Truro City Res. 4 **St Austell** 7

QUARTER-FINAL

St Austell 4 Newquay 1
Penryn Athletic 1 **Penzance** 5
Porthleven 3 Hayle 2
Godolphin Atlantic 4 Millbrook 1

SEMI-FINAL

Penzance 1 St Austell 0 *(at Porthleven)*
Godolphin Atlantic 1 **Porthleven** 2 *(at Truro City)*

FINAL *(May 12th at Penryn Athletic)*

Penzance 3 Porthleven 0

CUMBERLAND SENIOR CUP

FIRST ROUND

Greystoke 6 Bransty 2
Kirkoswald 5 Silloth 4
Northbank Carlisle (w/o) v Salterbeck (scr.)
Parton 1 **Longtown** 7
Penrith A (scr.) v **Penrith Rangers** (w/o)
St Bees 3 **Langwathby** 4
Wetheriggs United 3 Wigton Harriers 0

SECOND ROUND

Braithwaite 1 **Langwathby** 3
Carlisle City 2 **Aspatria** 3
Cockermouth (w/o) v Whitehaven Miners Social (scr.)
Gillford Park 2 Northbank Carlisle 1
Harraby Catholic Club 6 Alston Moor Sports Club 0
Hearts of Liddlesdale 2 **Longtown** 4
Mirehouse 6 Greystoke 0
Netherall 4 Keswick 1
Penrith Rangers 4 **Cleator Moor Celtic** 5
St Margaret Marys 1 **Frizington White Star** 3
Wigton Athletic 1 **Wetheriggs United** 4
Windscale 1 Kirkoswald 0

THIRD ROUND

Penrith Town 2 Gillford Park 0
Aspatria 1 **Wetheriggs United** 4
Frizington White Star 1 **Workington** 7
Harraby Catholic Club 2 Netherall 1 *aet*
Mirehouse 3 Longtown 1
Whitehaven Amateurs 5 Cockermouth 3 *aet*
Windscale 3 Langwathby 1
Cleator Moor Celtic 1 **Carlisle United** 4

QUARTER-FINALS

Carlisle United 3 Whitehaven Amateurs 0
Harraby Catholic Club 4 Windscale 1 *(at Windscale)*
Penrith Town 6 Wetheriggs United 0
Mirehouse 1 **Workington** 3

SEMI-FINALS

Harraby Catholic Club 0 **Penrith Town** 1
Workington 1 Carlisle United 0 *aet*

FINAL

(April 22nd at Carlisle United)

Workington 2 Penrith Town 0

DERBYSHIRE SENIOR CUP

(Sponsor: Cawarden)

FIRST ROUND

Graham Street Prims 6 Pinxton 3
Heanor Town 2 Blackwell Miners Welfare 1 *aet*
Holbrook Miners Welfare 2 Borrowash Victoria 1
Mickleover Sports 3 Staveley Miners Welfare 0
Glossop North End 3 New Mills 1

SECOND ROUND
Bolsover Town (scr.) v **Shirebrook Town** (w/o)
Belper Town 8 Parkhouse 1
Long Eaton United 1 **Mickleover Sports** 7
Matlock Town 3 Glapwell 1
Glossop North End 6 Graham Street Prims 1
Holbrook Miners Welfare 0 **Buxton** 4
Gresley Rovers 1 **Alfreton Town** 4
Heanor Town 1 **Ilkeston Town** 3
QUARTER FINALS
Belper Town 1 **Shirebrook Town** 4
Glossop North End 0 **Matlock Town** 1
Buxton 3 Alfreton Town 1
Mickleover Sports 2 Ilkeston Town 1 *(at Ilkeston Town)*
SEMI-FINALS
Buxton 1 Mickleover Sports 0
Matlock Town 1 Shirebrook Town 0
FINAL *(May 5th at Chesterfield)*
Buxton 1 Matlock Town 0

DEVON ST LUKES BOWL
(Sponsor: Westinsure)
FIRST ROUND
Holsworthy 3 Newton Abbot Spurs 2
Newton Abbot (scr.) v **Plymouth Parkway** (w/o)
Elburton Villa 2 Buckland Athletic 0
(at Buckland Athletic)
Elmore 5 Dartmouth 2 *aet*
Ilfracombe Town 1 **Dawlish Town** 2
Tavistock 2 **Ivybridge Town** 4
SECOND ROUND
Plymouth Parkway 1 **Exeter City** 2
Witheridge 0 **Tiverton Town** 3 *(at Tiverton Town)*
Barnstaple Town 2 Plymouth Argyle 1
Holsworthy 1 **Willand Rovers** 3
Dawlish Town 1 Clyst Rovers 0
Elmore 4 Elburton Villa 3
Cullompton Rangers 0 **Torquay United** 2
Ivybridge Town 3 Bideford 2 *aet (at Tavistock)*
QUARTER-FINALS
Elmore 1 Torquay United 0
Dawlish Town 5 Willand Rovers 3
Ivybridge Town 0 **Tiverton Town** 5 *(at Tiverton Town)*
Barnstaple Town 0 **Exeter City** 7
SEMI-FINALS
Elmore 0 **Exeter City** 6
Tiverton Town 5 Dawlish Town 0
FINAL
(May 7th at Tiverton Town)
Tiverton Town 0 **Exeter City** 2

DORSET SENIOR CUP
FIRST ROUND
Shaftesbury 4 Poole Borough 1
Holt United 4 Verwood Town 0
Portland United 4 Sturminster Marshall 2
Bridport 3 Cobham Sports 2
SECOND ROUND
Bridport (w/o) v Cranborne (scr.)
Dorchester Town 4 Blandford United 0
Swanage Town & Herston 0 **Poole Town** 5
Wimborne Town 5 Hamworthy Recreation 0
Chickerell United 3 Shaftesbury 0
Holt United 1 **Sherborne Town** 3
Portland United 0 **Hamworthy United** 2
Sturminster Newton United 0 **Gillingham Town** 1
QUARTER-FINALS
Dochester Town 2 Bridport 0
Wimborne Town 6 Gillingham Town 1
Hamworthy United 0 **Poole Town** 2
Chickerell United 0 **Sherborne Town** 2
SEMI-FINALS
Wimborne Town 2 **Poole Town** 3 *(at Hamworthy United)*
Dorchester Town 3 Sherborne Town 1 *(at Weymouth)*
FINAL
(April 7th at Weymouth)
Poole Town 2 Dorchester Town 0 *aet*

DURHAM CHALLENGE CUP
(Sponsor: Newton Moor)
PRELIMINARY ROUND
Darlington Railway Athletic 4 Belford House 1
Esh Winning 6 Silksworth CC 1
South Shields 2 Bishop Auckland 1
Washington 0 **Hebburn Town** 1
West Auckland Town 2 Annfield Plain 1
Brandon United 2 **Crook Town** 3
East Durham United 3 Willington 0
Peterlee Town 6 Seaham Red Star 2
Boldon Community Association 1 Ryhope Colliery Welfare 0
Jarrow 2 Sunderland Ryhope CA 1
Newton Aycliffe 1 Hartlepool 0
South Shields Harton & Westoe 0 **Coxhoe Athletic** 1
FIRST ROUND
Billingham Town 0 **Darlington** 5
Durham City 10 Boldon Community Association 0
Jarrow Roofing Boldon CA 3 Spennymoor Town 2
South Shields 4 Whickham 1
Tow Law Town 3 Esh Winning 2
Billingham Synthonia 4 Jarrow 2
Consett 5 Newton Aycliffe 1
Easington Colliery 3 Crook Town 1
Hartlepool United 1 **Ryton** 2
Hebburn Town 1 **West Auckland Town** 4
Horden Colliery Welfare 1 **Norton & Stockton Ancients** 2
Peterlee Town 0 **Shildon** 4
Coxhoe Athletic 2 **Darlington Railway Athletic** 4
Wolviston 0 **Birtley Town** 4
Dunston Federation 1 Sunderland Nissan 0 *(at Nissan)*
East Durham United 2 **Chester-le-Street Town** 6
SECOND ROUND
Billingham Synthonia 5 Easington Colliery 0
Dunton Federation 3 Jarrow Roofing Boldon CA 1
West Auckland Town 2 Chester-le-Street Town 1
Birtley Town 4 South Shields 3 *(at South Shields)*
Darlington Railway Athletic 0 **Durham City** 1
Norton & Stockton Ancients 1 **Tow Law Town** 3
Shildon 3 Ryton 1
Darlington (scr.) v **Consett** (w/o)
QUARTER-FINALS
Tow Law Town 2 **Billingham Synthonia** 3
Consett 2 West Auckland Town 1
Shildon 6 Birtley Town 2
Dunston Federation 0 **Durham City** 1 *aet (at Durham City)*
SEMI-FINALS
Billingham Synthonia 3 Shildon 0
Consett 1 **Durham City** 2
FINAL *(April 13th at West Auckland Town)*
Durham City 0 **Billingham Synthonia** 1

EAST RIDING SENIOR CUP
FIRST ROUND
Hedon Rangers 4 Reckitts 2
Pocklington Town 2 Easington United 1
SECOND ROUND
Bridlington Town 10 St Andrews Police Club 0
Chalk Lane 4 Westella & Willerby Res. 0
Hutton Cranswick United 2 Hornsea Town 1
Pocklington Town 5 Hedon Rangers 3
Sculcoates Amateurs 2 Hull City 2 *aet* (4-3p)
Westella & Willerby 2 Malet Lambert YC 0
North Ferriby United 7 Beverley Town 1
Hall Road Rangers 11 Hessle Rangers 0
QUARTER-FINALS
Sculcoates Amateurs 2 **Chalk Lane** 3
Westella & Willerby 3 Hutton Cranswick United 1
Hall Road Rangers 1 **Bridlington Town** 3
Pocklington Town 0 N**orth Ferriby United** 4
SEMI-FINALS
North Ferriby 1 Westella & W. 1 *aet* (7-6p) *(at Pocklington)*
Bridlington Town 5 Chalk Lane 1 *(at Hall Road Rangers)*
FINAL *(April 27th at Hull City)*
North Ferriby United 3 Bridlington Town 1

ESSEX SENIOR CUP

FIRST ROUND

Harwich & Parkeston 4 Hullbridge Sports 1
Stansted 2 **Romford** 1 *(Stansted expelled)*
Takeley 3 London APSA 0
Tiptree United 4 Mauritius Sports Association 1
FC Clacton 8 Clapton 1

SECOND ROUND

Wivenhoe Town 3 Bowers & Pitsea 0
Takeley 1 **Halstead Town** 4
Barking 3 Tiptree United 3 *aet* (5-4p)
Basildon United 2 **Burnham Ramblers** 4 *aet*
FC Clacton 2 Harwich & Parkeston 1
Eton Manor 1 **Stanway Rovers** 6
Saffron Walden Town 1 **Romford** 1 *aet* (4-5p)
Southend Manor 4 Barkingside 2

THIRD ROUND

Braintree Town 1 **Brentwood Town** 3
Tilbury 2 **Canvey Island** 3
Wivenhoe Town 5 Thurrock 0
Chelmsford City 7 Southend Manor 1
Southend United 2 **Redbridge** 3
Burnham Ramblers 0 **Romford** 1
Concord Rangers 2 East Thurrock United 1
Grays Athletic 7 Maldon Town 0
Waltham Abbey 1 **FC Clacton** 4
Witham Town 2 Ilford 0
Waltham Forest 3 Stanway Rovers 2 *aet*
Dagenham & Redbridge 7 Halstead Town 0
Heybridge Swifts 2 Barking 0
Colchester United 2 Aveley 1
Great Wakering Rovers 1 **AFC Hornchurch** 3
Harlow Town 0 **Billericay Town** 5

FOURTH ROUND

Brentwood Town 0 **Chelmsford City** 2
Colchester United 6 Romford 1
Dagenham & Redbridge 5 Witham Town 1
AFC Hornchurch 3 Billericay Town 2 *aet*
Concord Rangers 3 Heybridge Swifts 0
FC Clacton 4 Wivenhoe Town 0
Waltham Forest 1 **Redbridge** 2
Grays Athletic 2 **Canvey Island** 3 *aet*

QUARTER-FINALS

Chelmsford City 2 Dagenham & Redbridge 0
FC Clacton 1 **Concord Rangers** 2
Colchester United 6 AFC Hornchurch 0
Redbridge 2 Canvey Island 0 *(at Thurrock)*

SEMI-FINALS

Chelmsford City 2 Colchester United 1
Redbridge 1 **Concord Rangers** 2

FINAL

(March 31st at Dagenham & Redbridge)
Chelmsford City 2 Concord Rangers 0

GLOUCESTERSHIRE SENIOR CUP

FIRST ROUND

Yate Town 3 Bishop's Cleeve 2
Cinderford Town 0 **Mangotsfield United** 1

QUARTER-FINALS

Cheltenham Town 4 Forest Green Rovers 0
Mangotsfield United 1 **Gloucester City** 3
Cirencester Town 1 **Bristol City** 4
Yate Town 3 Bristol Rovers 2

SEMI-FINALS

Bristol City 2 Cheltenham Town 1
Gloucester City 2 Yate Town 2 *aet* (3-2p)

FINAL

(May 6th at Bristol City)
Bristol City 5 Gloucester City 1

GLOUCESTERSHIRE CHALLENGE TROPHY

FIRST ROUND

Winterbourne United 2 Taverners 0
Patchway Town 0 **Bristol Manor Farm** 3
(at Bristol Manor Farm)
AXA 2 **Almondsbury Town** 4
Longwell Green Sports 1 Hardwicke 0

SECOND-ROUND

Bishops Cleeve Res. 1 **Winterbourne United** 2
Fairford Town 6 Cirencester United 0
Shortwood United 7 Thornbury Town 1
Almondsbury 1 **Harrow Hill** 3
Lydney Town 3 Highridge United 0
Slimbridge 2 Hallen 1
Cadbury Heath 2 DRG Stapleton 0
Chipping Sodbury Town 1 **Henbury** 7
Hanham Athletic 0 **Ellwood** 2
Oldland Abbotonians 6 Kings Stanley 1
Roman Glass St George 1 **Bitton** 5
Shirehampton 1 **Berkeley Town** 2
Tytherington Rocks 0 **Bristol Manor Farm** 6
Cheltenham Saracens 6 Tuffley Rovers 1
Yate Town Res. 4 **Almondsbury Town** 6
Longwell Green Sports 3 B & W Avonside 0

THIRD ROUND

Almondsbury Town 1 **Slimbridge** 1 *aet* (3-4p)
Harrow Hill 2 Oldland Abbotonians 1
Lydney Town 4 Winterbourne United 2
Fairford Town 0 **Longwell Green Sports** 2
Cadbury Heath 3 Henbury 2
Bristol Manor Farm 3 Berkeley Town 1
Shortwood United 3 Ellwood 0
Bitton 7 Cheltenham Saracens 0

QUARTER-FINALS

Harrow Hill 0 **Bitton** 3
Cadbury Heath 0 **Longwell Green Sports** 2
Slimbridge 4 Lydney Town 0
Shortwood United 2 Bristol Manor Farm 2 *aet* (5-3p)

SEMI-FINALS

Longwell Green Sports 1 **Slimbridge** 2
Bitton 3 Shortwood United 3 *aet* (5-3p)

FINAL

(April 30th at Almondsbury Town)
Bitton 1 **Slimbridge** 2

GWENT SENIOR CUP

PRELIMINARY ROUND

Croesyceiliog 2 **Tredegar Town** 4
Goytre 1 Newport YMCA 0
Monmouth Town 3 **Cwmbran Town** 4 *(at Cwmbran Town)*
Newport Civil Service (w/o) v Aberbargoed Buds (scr.)

QUARTER FINALS

Cwmbran Celtic 2 Risca United 0
Cwmbran Town 1 **Newport County** 4
Tredegar Town 2 **Newport Civil Service** 3
Goytre 1 **Caldicot Town** 1 *aet* (2-4p)

SEMI-FINALS

Newport Civil Service 1 Newport County 0
Caldicot Town 0 **Cwmbran Celtic** 0 *aet* (4-5p)

FINAL

(May 16th at Abergavenny Thursdays)
Newport Civil Service 4 Cwmbran Celtic 3

HAMPSHIRE SENIOR CUP

FIRST ROUND

Tadley Calleva 0 **VTFC** 4
Alton Town 2 **Alresford Town** 4
Bournemouth 2 **Brockenhurst** 3
Cove 1 **Newport IOW** 2
Fareham Town 4 Whitchurch United 0
Hamble ASSC 3 AFC Portchester 1
Hartley Wintney 3 Fawley 2 *aet*
Hythe & Dibden 0 **Cowes Sports** 2
Ringwood Town 4 New Milton Town 2
East Cowes Victoria Athletic 1 **Romsey Town** 2
Moneyfields 6 Brading Town 1
Stockbridge 0 **Blackfield & Langley** 2
Andover New Street 2 **Totton & Eling** 3

SECOND ROUND

Winchester City 0 **Bashley** 2
Eastleigh 7 Fleet Spurs 0
Ringwood Town 1 **Farnborough** 5 *aet*

AFC Totton 1 **Hayling United** 2
Alresford Town 2 **Aldershot Town** 3
Andover 6 Newport IOW 3
Brockenhurst 3 Romsey Town 2 *aet*
Cowes Sports 1 **United Services Portsmouth** 3
Gosport Borough 4 Moneyfields 1
Hamble ASSC 0 **Basingstoke Town** 4
Lymington Town 5 Hartley Wintney 4 *aet*
Petersfield Town 4 Horndean 1
Christchurch 0 **Totton & Eling** 1
Farnborough North End 2 **Blackfield & Langley** 4 *aet*
VTFC 5 Havant & Waterlooville 2
Fleet Town 6 Fareham Town 1

THIRD ROUND

Eastleigh 6 Totton & Eling 0
Lymington Town 1 **Fleet Town** 4 *aet*
Basingstoke Town 2 Aldershot Town 1
Blackfield & Langley 1 **VTFC** 3
Brockenhurst 2 Hayling United 0
Gosport Borough 0 **Farnborough** 2
Petersfield Town 0 **Andover** 7
United Services Portsmouth 0 **Bashley** 7

QUARTER-FINALS

Andover 2 **Eastleigh** 1 *(Andover expelled)*
Brockenhurst 2 Farnborough 1 *aet*
VTFC 4 Basingstoke Town 2 *aet*
Fleet Town 2 Bashley 1 *aet*

SEMI-FINALS

Brockenhurst 0 **VTFC** 5
Fleet Town 2 Eastleigh 0

FINAL

(April 30th at Southampton)
Fleet Town 1 VTFC 0

HAMPSHIRE RUSSELL COTES CUP

FIRST ROUND

Ringwood Town 2 Petersfield Town 0
Blackfield & Langley 0 **New Milton Town** 2
Newport IOW 3 **Fleet Town** 4
Moneyfields 1 **Christchurch** 2 *(at Christchurch)*

SECOND ROUND

Gosport Borough 1 Totton & Eling 0
Bemerton Heath Harlequins 3 Amesbury Town 2
Farnborough North End 1 **Brockenhurst** 2
New Milton Town 0 **Hayling United** 3
Hythe & Dibden 4 AFC Portchester 2
Andover 4 Andover New Street 0
Hamble ASSC 3 Ringwood Town 1 *aet*
Fleet Town 8 Christchurch 2

QUARTER-FINALS

Brockenhurst 1 **Bemerton Heath Harlequins** 2 *aet*
Hamble ASSC 1 **Andover** 9
Hythe & Dibden 1 **Hayling United** 1 *aet* (3-4p)
Fleet Town 8 Gosport Borough 0

SEMI-FINALS

Andover 0 **Fleet Town** 1
Hayling United 4 Bemerton Heath Harlequins 1

FINAL

(May 5th at Fleet Town)
Fleet Town 3 Hayling United 1

HEREFORDSHIRE SENIOR CUP

FIRST ROUND

Westfields 4 Ledbury Town 1
Pegasus Juniors 1 **Hereford United** 4

SEMI-FINALS

Bromyard Town 2 Wellington 1
Westfields 1 Hereford United 1 *aet* (3-2p)

FINAL

(May 5th at Pegasus Juniors)
Westfields 3 Bromyard Town 0

HEREFORDSHIRE CHALLENGE CUP

FIRST ROUND

Ewyas Harold 9 Kington Town 2
Hinton 3 Hereford Lads Club 1
Leominster Town 2 Ross Town 1
Wooferton 6 Fownhope 2
Pegasus Juniors 8 Bromyard Town 0
Sutton United 1 **Westfields** 2

QUARTER-FINALS

Hinton 2 **Wellington** 4
Ledbury Town 6 Ewyas Harold 0
Woofferton 5 Leominster Town 0
Westfields 6 Pegasus Juniors 4

SEMI-FINALS

Wellington 5 Woofferton 0
Westfields 4 Ledbury Town 0

FINAL *(April 13th at Hereford United)*
Westfields 2 **Wellington** 2 *aet* (2-3p)

HERTFORDSHIRE SENIOR CUP

FIRST ROUND

St Albans City 3 Barnet 0
Hemel Hempstead Town 3 **Bishop's Stortford** 3 *aet* (3-4p)
Hertford Town 2 Colney Heath 0
Leverstock Green 4 Potters Bar Town 1
Broxbourne Borough V & E 1 **Hitchin Town** 2
Welwyn Garden City 1 Cockfosters 0

SECOND ROUND

Sawbridgeworth Town 1 **Boreham Wood** 3
Cheshunt 3 Hitchin Town 2
Leverstock Green 3 Watford 0
St Margaretsbury 2 **St Albans City** 4
Tring Athletic 1 **Hertford Town** 2
Oxhey Jets 3 Welwyn Garden City 1
Ware 4 Bishop's Stortford 1
Berkhamsted Town (scr.) v **Stevenage Borough** (w/o)

QUARTER-FINALS

Stevenage Borough 4 Hertford Town 2 *aet*
Boreham Wood 1 **Leverstock Green** 3
Cheshunt 3 Ware 0
St Albans City 0 **Oxhey Jets** 3

SEMI-FINALS

Cheshunt 2 Oxhey Jets 1
Stevenage Borough 1 Leverstock Green 0

FINAL

(April 8th at HCFA, Letchworth)
Stevenage Borough 2 Cheshunt 1

HERTFORDSHIRE CHARITY CUP

FIRST ROUND

Ware 4 Bishop's Stortford 0
Hitchin Town 1 **St Albans City** 4
Potters Bar Town 0 **Berkhamsted Town** 3
Hemel Hempstead Town 2 Cheshunt 1

SEMI-FINALS

Berkhamsted Town 2 **Ware** 3
Hemel Hempstead Town 10 St Albans City 0

FINAL

(February 17th at HCFA, Letchworth)
Hemel Hempstead Town 2 Ware 1

HERTFORDSHIRE SENIOR CENTENARY TROPHY

FIRST ROUND

Baldock Town 1 **Kings Langley** 4
Bedmond Sports & Social 0 **Hatfield Town** 11
Bovingdon 2 Royston Town 0
London Colney 1 **Codicote** 2
Park Street Village 3 Sun Postal Sports 3 *aet* (4-3p)
Standon & Puckeridge 1 **Metrpolitan Police Bushey** 3
Wormley Rovers 6 Buntingford Town 2

SECOND ROUND

Bovingdon 4 **Hatfield Town** 4 *aet* (3-4p)
Hertford Heath 3 Sandridge Rovers 0
Hoddesdon Town 2 Lemsford 0 *aet*
Kings Langley 1 **London Lions** 2
Knebworth 1 **Evergreen** 7
Metropolitan Police Bushey 1 **Harpenden Town** 3
Park Street Village 4 Codicote 1
Wormley Rovers 2 Mill End Sports 1

QUARTER-FINALS
Evergreen 0 **Park Street Village** 1
Harpenden Town 2 **Hoddesdon Town** 4
Hertford Heath 2 **Hatfield Town** 5 *aet*
London Lions 0 Wormley Rovers 0 *aet* (4-1p)
SEMI-FINALS
Hoddesdon Town 3 London Lions 2 *aet*
Park Street Village 1 **Hatfield Town** 2 *aet*
FINAL
(March 25th at at HCFA, Letchworth)
Hoddesdon Town 1 Hatfield Town 1 *aet* (5-3p)

HERTFORDSHIRE CHARITY SHIELD

FIRST ROUND
Harpenden Town 1 **Hoddesdon Town** 3
Kings Langley 1 St Margaretsbury 0
Leverstock Green 4 **Royston Town** 5
Oxhey Jets 5 Welwyn Garden City 0
Hertford Town 2 **Tring Athletic** 4
London Colney 1 **Colney Heath** 2
Sawbridgeworth Town 1 **Broxbourne Borough V & E** 2
Hatfield Town 2 **Sun Postal Sports** 5 *(at Hertford Town)*
QUARTER-FINALS
Hoddesdon Town 0 **Broxbourne Borough V & E** 2
Oxhey Jets 2 **Royston Town** 4 *aet*
Colney Heath 3 **Tring Athletic** 4 *aet*
Sun Postal Sports 1 **Kings Langley** 3
SEMI-FINALS
Broxbourne Borough V & E 3 Kings Langley 2
Royston Town 5 Tring Athletic 4
FINAL
(May 12th at HCFA, Letchworth)
Broxbourne Borough V & E 4 Royston Town 1

HINCHINGBROOKE CUP

PRELIMINARY ROUND
St Ives Town 3 Potton United 1
Eynesbury Rovers 1 **AFC Kempston Rovers** 2
Huntingdon Town 0 **Rushden & Higham United** 1
Stotfold 2 Yaxley 1
Northampton Spencer 0 **St Neots Town** 2 *(at St Neots)*
Biggleswade United 1 **Cranfield United** 2
FIRST ROUND
Bourne Town 1 Rothwell Corinthians 0
AFC Kempston Rovers 3 **St Ives Town** 3 *aet* (5-6p)
Cranfield United 2 Arlesey Athletic 0
Deeping Rangers 3 **Langford** 4
Godmanchester Rovers 2 Wootton Blue Cross 1
Thrapston Town 1 **St Neots Town** 2
Rushden & Higham United 2 Biggleswade Town 1
Blackstones 1 **Stotfold** 6
QUARTER-FINALS
Bourne Town 0 **Rushden & Higham United** 0 *aet* (6-7p)
Godmanchester Rovers 0 **St Ives Town** 1 *aet*
St Neots Town 3 Langford 2
Stotfold (w/o) v Cranfield United (scr.)
SEMI-FINALS
Rushden & Higham United 0 **St Ives Town** 1
St Neots Town 3 Stotfold 0
FINAL
(May 18th at Huntingdon Town)
St Ives Town 2 **St Neots Town** 3

HUNTINGDONSHIRE PREMIER CUP

(Sponsor: NPower)
FIRST ROUND
St Ives Town (w/o) Stotfold (.scr)
Eaton Socon 1 **St Neots Town** 3 *(at St Neots Town)*
Ramsey Town 3 Eynesbury Rovers 1
Godmanchester Rovers 3 Potton United 1 *aet*
Biggleswade United 3 Huntingdon Town 0
Yaxley 0 Ely City 6 ***(Ely City expelled)***
Langford 3 Needingworth United 1
Wootton Blue Cross 2 **Biggleswade Town** 3 *(at Biggleswade Town)*
QUARTER-FINALS
Ramsey Town 1 Biggleswade United 0
Godmanchester Rovers 0 **St Ives Town** 1
Yaxley (w/o) v Biggleswade Town (scr.)
Langford 2 St Neots Town 0
SEMI-FINALS
Yaxley 1 **Ramsey Town** 2
St Ives Town 2 Langford 1
FINAL
(May 20th at Huntingdon Town)
St Ives Town 3 Ramsey Town 1

HUNTINGDONSHIRE SENIOR CUP

FIRST ROUND
AFC Fletton 5 Eaton Socon 2
Somersham Town 1 Brampton 1 *aet* (5-4p)
SECOND ROUND
Alconbury 1 **AFC Fletton** 3
Eynesbury Rovers 6 Warboys Town 0
Godmanchester Rovers 0 **Huntingdon Town** 3
Hemingfords United 6 Great Paxton 1
Needingworth United 0 **St Ives Town** 4
Ramsey Town 2 Yaxley 1 *aet*
Somersham Town 5 **Stilton United** 6 *aet*
St Neots Town 6 Bluntisham Town 1
QUARTER-FINALS
AFC Fletton 3 Stilton United 2
Eynesbury Rovers 2 St Neots Town 0
Hemingfords United 3 Huntingdon Town 2
Ramsey Town 0 **St Ives Town** 2
SEMI-FINALS
St Ives Town 3 Eynesbury Rovers 2
Hemingfords United 0 **AFC Fletton** 3
FINAL
(May 4th at Yaxley)
St Ives Town 3 AFC Fletton 0

KENT SENIOR CUP

FIRST ROUND
Cray Wanderers 1 **Ramsgate** 2
Welling United 3 Sittingbourne 2
Thamesmead Town 3 Ashford Town 1
Chatham Town 0 **Folkestone Invicta** 6
Ebbsfleet United 1 Dover Athletic 0
Maidstone United 2 Margate 1
Whitstable Town 1 Tonbridge Angels 1 *aet* (5-4p)
Bromley 4 Dartford 2
QUARTER-FINALS
Welling United 7 Folkestone Invicta 1
Maidstone United 0 **Bromley** 2
Ramsgate 3 Thamesmead Town 2 *aet*
Whitstable Town 2 Ebbsfleet United 1
SEMI-FINALS
Bromley 2 **Whitstable Town** 3
Welling United 3 Ramsgate 1
FINAL
(March 16th at Welling United)
Welling United 6 Whitstable Town 1

KENT SENIOR TROPHY

(Sponsor: Umbro)
FIRST ROUND
Greenwich Borough 1 **Sevenoaks Town** 2
Holmesdale 2 Hythe Town 1
Lordswood 2 Milton & Fulston United 1
VCD Athletic 1 Bearsted 0
West Wickham 4 Norton Sports 0
SECOND ROUND
Deal Town 2 Holmesdale 1
Slade Green 1 **Tunbridge Wells** 7
Beckenham Town 0 **West Wickham** 1
Erith Town 1 **Herne Bay** 3
Faversham Town 2 **Orpington** 3
Sevenoaks Town 3 Croydon 2
VCD Athletic 4 Crockenhill 0
Erith & Belvedere 3 Lordswood 1
QUARTER-FINALS
Sevenoaks Town 1 **West Wickham** 2
Deal Town 2 Tunbridge Wells 0

Herne Bay 2 **VCD Athletic** 7 *aet*
Orpington 0 **Erith & Belvedere** 2
SEMI-FINAL
Deal Town 1 **Erith & Belvedere** 1 *aet* (5-6p)
VCD Athletic 2 West Wickham 0
FINAL
(April 19th at Welling United)
VCD Athletic 3 Erith & Belvedere 2 *aet*

KENT INTERMEDIATE CHALLENGE SHIELD

FIRST ROUND
AFC Sheppey 0 **Coney Hall** 2
APM Mears 1 **Stansfeld O & B Club** 2
Bly Spartans 4 Lydd Town 0
Bromley Green 6 Kennington 4 *aet*
Canterbury City 3 Belvedere 1
Greenways 0 **Fleet Leisure** 5
Guru Nanak 0 **Cray Valley PM** 3
Hollands & Blair 4 Phoenix Sports 3 *aet*
New Romney 7 Westerham 5 *aet*
Oakwood 2 Hawkhurst United 0
Rusthall 3 Tudor Sports 2
Sheerness East 3 Chipstead 2
Staplehurst & Monarchs United 0 **Tonbridge Invicta** 1
Sutton Athletic 3 Farnborough Old Boys Guild 2
University of Kent 1 Snodland 0
SECOND-ROUND
Bromley Green 7 New Romney 0
Canterbury City 3 Otford United 2
Coney Hall 3 Tonbridge Invicta 1
Cray Valley Paper Mills 3 Sheerness East 0
Fleet Leisure 2 **Bly Spartans** 4
Hollands & Blairs 6 University of Kent 1
Rusthall 6 Oakwood 1
Stansfeld O & B Club 3 Sutton Athletic 0
QUARTER-FINALS
Bly Spartans 1 **Stansfeld O & B Club** 2
Coney Hall 3 **Cray Valley Paper Mills** 5 *aet*
Hollands & Blairs 2 Canterbury City 1
Rusthall 2 Bromley Green 1
SEMI-FINALS
Hollands & Blairs 3 Stansfeld O & B Club 1
Rusthall 1 Cray Valley Paper Mills 1 *aet* (4-3p)
FINAL
(April 4th at Tunbridge Wells FC)
Hollands & Blairs 2 Rusthall 1

LANCASHIRE TROPHY

(Sponsor: United Co-operatives)
FIRST ROUND
Ashton Athletic 2 AFC Blackpool 1
Atherton LR 1 **Bacup Borough** 3
Bamber Bridge 0 **Marine** 2
Chorley 1 **Skelmersdale United** 3
Holker Old Boys 0 **AFC Fylde** 3
Lancaster City 2 Darwen 1
Squires Gate 3 **Radcliffe Borough** 3 *aet* (3-4p)
Padiham 2 **Kendal Town** 7
Nelson 1 **Colne** 2
Rossendale United 2 Clitheroe 1
Atherton Colleries 0 **Leigh Genesis** 3
Daisy Hill 0 **Ramsbottom United** 2
SECOND ROUND
Lancaster City 1 **Colne** 2
Skelmersdale United 4 AFC Fylde 1
Leigh Genesis 2 **Radcliffe Borough** 3
(at Radcliffe Borough)
Barrow 3 **Burscough** 3 *aet* (1-3p)
Rossendale United 1 **Southport** 3
Fleetwood Town 4 Bacup Borough 1
Ramsbottom United 5 Ashton Athletic 3 *aet*
Kendal Town 3 Marine 2
QUARTER-FINALS
Burscough 3 Colne 1
Skelmersdale United 5 Ramsbottom United 1
Fleetwood Town 1 **Radcliffe Borough** 2
Southport 1 **Kendal Town** 4
SEMI-FINALS
Kendal Town 1 **Radcliffe Borough** 2
Skelmersdale United 2 Burscough 0
FINAL
(March 31st at LCFA, Leyland)
Skelmersdale United 2 Radcliffe Borough 1

LEICESTERSHIRE CHALLENGE CUP

(Sponsor: Westerby Homes)
FIRST ROUND
Bardon Hill Sports 2 **Barrow Town** 5 *aet*
Ibstock United 1 **Barwell** 3
St Andrews SC 4 Kirby Muxloe SC 0
SECOND ROUND
Coalville Town 4 Friar Lane & Epworth 0
Hinckley Downes 2 **Loughborough Dynamo** 3
Quorn 7 Blaby & Whetstone Athletic 2
Barrow Town 6 Ellistown 1
Barwell 4 St Andrews SC 1
Heather St John 2 Holwell Sports 1
Loughborough University 3 Oadby Town 2
Hinckley United 2 **Shepshed Dynamo** 3 *aet*
QUARTER-FINALS
Barrow Town 0 **Barwell** 1
Coalville Town 3 Heather St John 1
Quorn 2 Loughborough University 1
Shepshed Dynamo 4 Loughborough Dynamo 2
SEMI-FINALS
(both at LCFA, Blaby)
Quorn 1 Shepshed Dynamo 0
Barwell 3 Coalville Town 2
FINAL *(May 12th at Leicester City)*
Quorn 0 **Barwell** 2

LINCOLNSHIRE SENIOR CUP

SEMI-FINAL
Grimsby Town 1 Lincoln City 0
FINAL
(April 2nd at Scunthorpe United)
Scunthorpe United 4 Grimsby Town 0

LINCOLNSHIRE SHIELD

FIRST ROUND
Spalding United 0 **Boston United** 2
Stamford 4 Gainsborough Trinity 3
Grantham Town 2 Brigg Town 1
SEMI-FINAL
Grantham Town 0 **Stamford** 1
Boston United 2 Lincoln United 0
FINAL *(December 3rd at Boston United)*
Boston United 1 **Stamford** 4

LINCOLNSHIRE TROPHY

FIRST ROUND
Blackstones 3 Appleby Frodingham 2
Sleaford Town 7 Harrowby United 2
Bottesford Town 1 **Boston Town** 7
Holbeach United 2 Bourne Town 1
Lincoln Moorlands Railway 2 Barton Town Old Boys 1
Grimsby Borough 2 Nettleham 1
QUARTER-FINALS
Deeping Rangers 1 **Boston Town** 3
Sleaford Town 2 Holbeach United 1
Grimsby Borough 1 **Lincoln Moorlands Railway** 3
Winterton Rangers 3 Blackstones 1
SEMI-FINALS
Boston Town 4 Lincoln Moorlands Railway 0
Sleaford Town 0 **Winterton Rangers** 1
FINAL *(April 21st at Lincoln City)*
Boston Town 2 Winterton Rangers 0

LIVERPOOL SENIOR CUP

FIRST ROUND
AFC Liverpool 1 **Waterloo Dock** 6
Aigburth People's Hall 1 **Bootle** 5 *(at Bootle)*

Prescot Cables 3 Cammell Laird 2
East Villa 6 St Helens Town 3 *aet*
Skelmersdale United 0 **Formby** 3
Ashton Town 1 **Warrington Town** 6
SECOND ROUND
Bootle 0 **Formby** 1
Warrington Town 1 **Burscough** 6
Waterloo Dock 2 East Villa 1 *aet (at LCFA, Wavertree)*
Marine 3 Prescot Cables 1
QUARTER-FINALS
Burscough 4 Everton Res. 1
Waterloo Dock 6 Tranmere Rovers Res. 5 *aet (at Bootle)*
Formby 0 **Liverpool Res.** 3
Marine 1 **Southport** 5
SEMI-FINALS
Burscough 0 **Waterloo Dock** 3
Southport 0 **Liverpool Res.** 3 *aet*
FINAL *(April 27th at Marine)*
Liverpool Res. 1 Waterloo Dock 0

LONDON SENIOR CUP
FIRST ROUND
Beckenham Town (w/o) v Barkingside (scr.)
Croydon 3 Kingbury London Tigers 0
AFC Wimbledon 0 **Erith Town** 3
Cockfosters 5 Haringey Borough 0
Hoddesdon Town 3 **Erith & Belvedere** 4 *aet*
VCD Athletic 2 **Welling United** 3
Lewisham Borough (Community) 1 Brimsdown Rovers 0
Mauritius Sports Association 4 Barking 1
Colliers Wood United 4 Clapton 2
Thamesmead Town 1 Hanwell Town 0
SECOND ROUND
Welling United 2 Mauritius Sports Association 1
Croydon 2 **Erith & Belvedere** 3
Wingate & Finchley 3 Corinthian Casuals 0
Lewisham Borough (Community) 2 Erith Town 1
Kingstonian 6 Leyton 0
Beckenham Town 2 **Dulwich Hamlet** 3
Thamesmead Town 0 **Redbridge** 2 *aet*
Colliers Wood United 2 **Cockfosters** 4
THIRD ROUND
Bromley 2 **Hendon** 2 *aet* (5-6p)
Fisher Athletic 3 Lewisham Borough (Community) 0
Redbridge 0 **Tooting & Mitcham United** 6 *(at Tooting)*
Harrow Borough 1 Metropolitan Police 0
Dulwich Hamlet 0 **Erith & Belvedere** 1
Kingstonian 2 **Wingate & Finchley** 1
Cray Wanderers 3 Cockfosters 0
Croydon Athletic 0 Welling Utd 1 *aet (Welling expelled)*
QUARTER FINALS
Fisher Athletic 2 **Harrow Borough** 2 *aet* (4-5p)
Erith & Belvedere 0 **Hendon** 4
Croydon Athletic 3 Kingstonian 1
Tooting & Mitcham United 5 Cray Wanderers 1
SEMI-FINALS
Harrow Borough 0 **Croydon Athletic** 5
Tooting & Mitcham United 0 **Hendon** 4
FINAL
(April 29th at AFC Wimbledon)
Hendon 2 Croydon Athletic 2 *aet* (3-1p)

MANCHESTER PREMIER CUP
FIRST ROUND
Droylsden 2 Irlam 1
Maine Road 6 Flixton 1
Mossley 3 Chadderton 0
Oldham Town 3 Abbey Hey 1
Radcliffe Borough 0 **Trafford** 1
Salford City 1 **Ashton United** 2
Glossop North End 1 **Curzon Ashton** 2
New Mills 4 Hyde United 2 *aet*
QUARTER-FINALS
Ashton United 2 **New Mills** 3 *(at New Mills)*
Trafford 1 **Droylsden** 5
Maine Road 2 **Mossley** 4 *aet*
Oldham Town 1 **Curzon Ashton** 4 *aet*
SEMI-FINALS
Curzon Ashton 0 **Droylsden** 1
Mossley 2 New Mills 1
FINAL
(April 29th at Oldham Athletic)
Droylsden 2 Mossley 1

MIDDLESEX SENIOR CUP
FIRST ROUND
Ashford Town (Middx) 2 North Greenford United 1
Enfield Town 2 Wingate & Finchley 1
Hillingdon Borough 2 **Hayes & Yeading United** 8
Staines Town 5 Enfield 0
Wembley 5 Tokyngton Manor 2 *aet*
SECOND ROUND
AFC Hayes 6 Uxbridge 0
Hampton & Richmond Borough 1 Northwood 0
Hanwell Town 2 **Ashford Town (Middx)** 3
Harefield United 1 Hayes & Yeading United 0 *aet*
Harrow Borough 6 Enfield Town 2 *aet*
Hendon 3 Bedfont Green 0 *(at Wembley)*
Bedfont 0 **Staines Town** 4
Wealdstone 3 Wembley 0
QUARTER-FINALS
Staines Town 1 **Ashford Town (Middx)** 2
Hendon 1 Harrow Borough 1 *aet* (2-1p)
Wealdstone 1 Hampton & Richmond Borough 0
Harefield United 2 **AFC Hayes** 4
SEMI-FINALS
Ashford Town (Middx) 1 **AFC Hayes** 4
Hendon 4 Wealdstone 3
FINAL
(April 13th Northwood)
Hendon 0 **AFC Hayes** 2

MIDDLESEX CHARITY CUP
FIRST ROUND
Bedfont 3 Hanwell Town 1
(Competition abandoned due to inclement weather)

MIDDLESEX PREMIER CUP
FIRST ROUND
Enfield Town Res. 4 AFC Hayes Res. 2 *aet*
SECOND ROUND
Ashford Town (Middx) Res. 1 **Staines Lammas** 3
Bedfont Res. 0 **Sport London E Benfica** 2
Wealdstone Res. 4 CB Hounslow United 0
Harrow Borough Res. 2 **Uxbridge Res.** 2 *aet* (3-4p)
North Greenford United Res. 3 **Rayners Lane** 4
Enfield Town Res. 1 **Park View** 4
Northwood Res. 0 **Hanworth Villa** 5
Harefield United Res. 2 **Hayes & Yeading United Res.** 4 *aet*
QUARTER-FINALS
Sport London E Benfica (w/o) v Park View (scr.)
Rayners Lane 1 **Hayes & Yeading United Res.** 6 *(at Harrow Borough)*
Wealdstone Res. 2 Hanworth Villa 1
Staines Lammas 1 Uxbridge Res. 1 *aet* (3-1p) *(at Uxbridge)*
SEMI-FINALS
Sport London E Benfica 0 **Staines Lammas** 1 *aet*
Wealdstone Res. 2 Hayes & Yeading United Res. 1
FINAL
(March 25th at Ashford Town (Middx))
Staines Lammas 0 **Wealdstone Res.** 4

NORFOLK SENIOR CUP
FIRST ROUND
Caister United 1 **Horsford United** 5
Gayton United 3 Wells Town 0
St Andrews 0 **Mattishall** 5
SECOND ROUND
Long Stratton 2 **Horsford United** 4
Mattishall 0 **Attleborough Town** 2
Scole United 1 **Gayton United** 4
Stalham Town 2 Wymondham Town 0

THIRD ROUND
Attleborough Town 1 **Hindringham** 2
Cromer Town 3 Acle United 3 *aet*
Replay: **Acle United** 3 Cromer Town 1
Dersingham Rovers 0 **Great Yarmouth Town** 3
Fakenham Town 3 Stalham Town 2
Gayton United 1 **Gorleston** 2
Hempnall 1 **Loddon United** 2
Holt United 2 Watton United 1
North Walsham Town 3 Horsford United 2
Sheringham 0 Blofield United 0 *aet*
Replay: Blofield United 2 **Sheringham** 6
Sprowston Athletic 2 AFC Norwich 0
Swaffham Town 1 **Thetford Town** 3
Diss Town 1 Downham Town 1 *aet*
Replay: Downham Town 1 **Diss Town** 2
FOURTH ROUND
Gorleston 5 North Walsham Town 1
Wroxham 3 Sprowston Athletic 0
Dereham Town 4 Diss Town 2
Sheringham 1 **Thetford Town** 3 *aet*
Great Yarmouth Town 1 **Acle United** 2 *aet*
Holt United 2 Hindringham 0
Fakenham Town 1 **Loddon United** 5
Norwich United 1 King's Lynn Res. 1 *aet*
Replay: **King's Lynn Res.** 1 Norwich United 0
QUARTER-FINALS
Acle United 0 **Wroxham** 5
Dereham Town 5 Thetford Town 3
Holt United 0 **Gorleston** 5
King's Lynn Res. 2 Loddon United 0 *(at Loddon United)*
SEMI-FINALS
King's Lynn Res. 6 Gorleston 1 *(at Gorleston)*
Dereham Town 1 **Wroxham** 2
FINAL *(April 15th at Norwich City)*
Wroxham 1 **King's Lynn Res.** 3

NORTH RIDING SENIOR CUP

FIRST PRELIMINARY ROUND
Fishburn Park 0 **Nunthorpe Athletic** 0 *aet* (6-7p)
Scarborough Town 1 **Grangetown Boys Club** 2
Teesside Athletic 2 Kirkbymoorside 0
SECOND PRELIMINARY ROUND
Pickering Town 1 **Whitby Town** 1 *aet* (3-4p)
Grangetown Boys Club 1 **Marske United** 1 *aet* (3-4p)
(at Marske United)
Thornaby 1 **Northallerton Town** 3 *(at Northallerton Town)*
Guisborough Town 1 **Guisborough Town HC** 1 *aet* (4-5p)
Stokesley Sports Club 4 Scarborough Athletic 3
Nunthorpe Athletic 1 **Teesside Athletic** 1 *aet* (3-4p)
QUARTER-FINALS
Guisborough Town HC 0 **Marske United** 3
Northallerton Town 1 **Teesside Athletic** 2
Stokesley Sports Club 3 York City 0
Middlesbrough 5 Whitby Town 0
SEMI-FINAL
Stokesley Sports Club 3 Teesside Athletic 2
Middlesbrough 2 Marske United 0 *(at Marske United)*
FINAL
(May 13th at Stokeseley Sports Club)
Middlesbrough 2 Stokesley Sports Club 0

NORTHAMPTONSHIRE SENIOR CUP

(Sponsor: Hillier)
FIRST ROUND
Rushden & Diamonds 2 Rothwell Town 0 *(at Rothwell)*
Corby Town 3 **Long Buckby** 2 *(Corby Town expelled)*
Brackley Town 6 Northampton Spencer 0
Desborough Town 5 Raunds Town 4 *aet*
Wellingborough Town 0 **Daventry Town** 1
Woodford United 1 **Stewarts & Lloyds Corby** 4
Cogenhoe United 0 **Kettering Town** 2
QUARTER-FINALS
Brackley Town 4 Stewarts & Lloyds Corby 1
Daventry Town 5 Kettering Town 1
Long Buckby 3 Desborough Town 2
Rushden & Diamonds 1 Rothwell Corinthians 0
SEMI-FINALS
Rushden & Diamonds 1 **Long Buckby** 2
Brackley Town 6 Daventry Town 1
FINAL
(April 28th at Brackley Town)
Brackley Town 0 **Long Buckby** 2

NORTHUMBERLAND SENIOR CUP

FIRST ROUND
Heaton Stannington 2 **Blyth Spartans** 4
Prudhoe Town 1 **Newcastle United Res.** 6
Ashington 3 Morpeth Town 1
Team Northumbria 3 Heddon 2 *aet*
Bedlington Terriers 3 Shankhouse 1
Newcastle Benfield 3 Whitley Bay 2
Walker Central 1 West Allotment Celtic 0
North Shields 0 **Newcastle Blue Star** 3
QUARTER-FINALS
Newcastle United Res. 5 Team Northumbria 0
Ashington 3 Bedlington Terriers 0
Newcastle Blue Star 2 Blyth Spartans 1
Walker Central 0 **Newcastle Benfield** 4
SEMI-FINALS
Ashington 2 Newcastle Blue Star 1
Newcastle United Res. 2 Newcastle Benfield 1
FINAL
(May 12th at Newcastle United)
Newcastle United Res. 4 Ashington 0

NORTHUMBERLAND BENEVOLENT BOWL

FIRST ROUND
Alnwick Town (w/o) v Westerhope JG (scr.)
Berwick United 4 Red Row Welfare 1
Blyth Town 5 Ponteland United 2
Gosforth Bohemian Garnett 1 **Ashington Colliers** 2
Newcastle University 0 **Whitley Bay A** 1
Seaton Delaval Amateurs 2 **Percy Main Amateurs** 3
Stocksfield 2 **Cramlington Town** 3
Wark 0 **Wallington** 5
QUARTER-FINALS
Alnwick Town 0 **Whitley Bay A** 2
Ashington Colliers 3 Wallington 2
Berwick United 1 **Blyth Town** 6
Cramlington Town 1 **Percy Main Amateurs** 2
SEMI-FINALS
Ashington Colliers 1 **Percy Main Amateurs** 2
Blyth Town 2 Whitley Bay A 0
FINAL
(April 17th at West Allotment Celtic)
Percy Main Amateurs 0 **Blyth Town** 2

NOTTINGHAMSHIRE SENIOR CUP

FIRST ROUND
Basford United 2 **Calverton Miners Welfare** 3
Blidworth Welfare 2 Bilborough Pelican 1
Clipstone Welfare 1 Boots Athletic 1 *aet* (3-2p)
Forest Town 7 Thoresby Colliery Welfare 0
Kimberley Town 2 Rolls Royce Leisure 1
Notts Police 2 Keyworth United 1
Radcliffe Olympic 3 Caribbean Cavaliers 1
Sutton Town 1 **Newark Flowserve** 1 *aet* (2-3p)
Wollaton 4 Attenborough 2
Radford 0 **Hucknall Rolls Leisure** 1
Teversal 1 **Greenwood Meadows** 1 *aet* (2-4p)
Dunkirk 1 Newark Town 0
SECOND ROUND
Blidworth Welfare 1 **Radcliffe Olympic** 3
Greenwood Meadows 2 **Dunkirk** 3
Kimberley Town 0 **Forest Town** 2
Newark Flowserve 1 **Hucknall Rolls Leisure** 3
Notts Police 1 **Calverton Miners Welfare** 4
Wollaton 2 Clipstone Welfare 0
THIRD ROUND
Dunkirk 0 **Hucknall Town** 1 *(Hucknall expelled)*
Ollerton Town 1 **Rainworth Miners Welfare** 2

Wollaton 2 **Arnold Town** 3 *(at Redford)*
Hucknall Rolls Leisure 0 **Carlton Town** 4
Southwell City 1 **Eastwood Town** 7
Forest Town 3 Radcliffe Olympic 0
Calverton Miners Welfare 0 **Retford United** 4
Gedling Town 3 Gedling Miners Welfare 1
QUARTER-FINALS
Carlton Town 3 Forest Town 0
Retford United 1 Dunkirk 0
Gedling Town 1 **Arnold Town** 2
Rainworth Miners Welfare 0 **Eastwood Town** 1
SEMI-FINALS
Eastwood Town 3 Carlton Town 1
Retford United 4 Arnold Town 0
FINAL *(May 7th at Notts County)*
Retford United 2 Eastwood Town 1

OXFORDSHIRE SENIOR CUP

FIRST ROUND
Clanfield 6 Bletchington 0
Bicester Town 0 **Thame United** 1
Chadlington 2 **Horspath** 4
Easington Sports (scr.) **Garsington** (w/o)
Enstone Sports 2 **Rover Cowley** 3
Eynsham Association 1 **Stonesfield Sports** 2
Headington Amateurs 1 **Ardley United** 4
Woodcote & Stoke Row 2 Marston Saints 1
Adderbury Park 0 **Carterton** 1
SECOND ROUND
Hook Norton 4 Ardley United 0
Horspath 0 **Carterton** 3
Kidlington 3 Stonesfield Sports 0
Launton Sports 1 **Clanfield** 7
Oxford University Press 2 **Henley Town** 2 *aet* (3-5p)
Rover Cowley 0 **Garsington** 2
Thame United 0 **Chinnor** 2
Woodcote & Stoke Row 0 **Old Woodstock Town** 4
THIRD ROUND
Clanfield 6 Chinnor 0
Henley Town 2 **Hook Norton** 3 *aet*
Old Woodstock Town 5 Carterton 4
Garsington 2 Kidlington 1
QUARTER-FINALS
North Leigh 6 Clanfield 0 *(at Clanfield)*
Hook Norton 1 **Banbury United** 2 *aet*
Old Woodstock Town 1 **Oxford United** 3 *aet*
Oxford City 8 Garsington 0
SEMI-FINALS
Banbury United 3 Oxford City 2 *aet*
North Leigh 0 **Oxford United** 3 *(at Oxford City)*
FINAL *(April 21st at Oxford United)*
Oxford United 2 Banbury United 1

SHEFFIELD & HALLAMSHIRE SENIOR CUP

FIRST ROUND
Dinnington Town 2 Athersley Recreation 0
Parkgate 4 Phoenix Sports & Social 2
Rossington Main 3 Harworth Colliery Institute 0
Worsbough Bridge MW 2 Yorkshire Main 2 *aet* (4-2p)
AFC Emley 2 Frecheville CA 1
Handsworth 4 Maltby Main 2
South Kirkby Colliery 0 **Hemsworth Miners Welfare** 2
Nostell Miners Welfare 1 **Kinsley Boys** 2
rodsworth Miners Welfare 2 Mexborough Main Street 0
Penistone Church 0 **Bentley Colliery** 3
Parramore Sports 4 Mexborough Pocket 0
SECOND ROUND
Hemsworth Miners Welfare 2 Dinnington Town 1
Kinsley Boys 0 **Frickley Athletic** 5 *(at Frickley Athletic)*
Stocksbridge Park Steels 3 Sheffield 0
AFC Emley 3 **Worsbrough Bridge MW** 6
Brodsworth Miners Welfare 3 Parkgate 1
Handsworth 3 Parramore Sports 1
Worksop Town 1 Rossington Main 0
Hallam 6 Bentley Colliery 2
QUARTER-FINALS
Stocksbridge Park Steels 1 Frickley Athletc 0
Worsbrough Bridge MW 1 **Hemsworth Miners Welfare** 2
Brodsworth Miners Welfare 5 Hallam 0
Worksop Town 2 Handsworth 1
SEMI-FINALS
Stocksbridge Park Steels 3 Worksop Town 1
Brodsworth Miners Welfare 3 Hemsworth Miners Welfare 2
FINAL
(April 29th at Sheffield Wednesday)
Stocksbridge Park Steels 3 Brodsworth Miners Welfare 0

SHROPSHIRE SENIOR CUP

FIRST ROUND
Bridgnorth Town 1 Shifnal Town 0
SEMI-FINAL
Shrewsbury Town 3 Market Drayton Town 2
AFC Telford United 3 Bridgnorth Town 0
FINAL
(July 18th at Shrewsbury Town)
Shrewsbury Town 1 **AFC Telford United** 1 (1-4p)

SOMERSET PREMIER CUP

FIRST ROUND
Weston-super-Mare 5 Taunton Town 2
Bridgwater Town 5 Team Bath 3
Clevedon Town 3 **Portishead Town** 3 *aet* (3-4p)
Radstock Town 1 **Welton Rovers** 4
Minehead Town 0 **Shepton Mallet** 1
Chard Town 1 **Bristol Manor Farm** 2
Yeovil Town 4 Wellington Town 0
Street 2 **Bath City** 3
Frome Town 2 Odd Down 1
SECOND ROUND
Clevedon United 5 Bishop Sutton 0
Paulton Rovers 2 Larkhall Athletic 0
Bridgwater Town 4 Shepton Mallet 1
Keynsham Town 0 **Portishead Town** 2 *aet*
Weston-super-Mare 1 **Brislington** 3
Bitton 1 **Bristol Manor Farm** 1 *aet* (4-5p)
Frome Town 3 Bath City 1
Welton Rovers 2 Yeovil Town 1
QUARTER-FINALS
Bridgwater Town 5 Portishead Town 1
Brislington 0 Bristol Manor Farm 0 *aet* (6-5p)
Clevedon United 1 **Paulton Rovers** 3
Frome Town 0 Welton Rovers 0 *aet* (5-4p)
SEMI-FINALS
Bridgwater Town 3 **Paulton Rovers** 5 *aet*
Brislington 0 **Frome Town** 1 *aet*
FINAL
(May 7th at Welton Rovers)
Paulton Rovers 1 **Frome Town** 3

SOUTH MIDLANDS FLOODLIGHT CUP

FIRST ROUND
Cockfosters 1 **Hertford Town** 4
Royston Town 3 Cheshunt 0
Hoddesdon Town 3 **Wormley Rovers** 5
Oxhey Jets 4 Stansted 0
Sawbridgeworth Town 2 Bedford 2 *aet* (4-2p)
Biggleswade Town 7 Arlesey Athletic 1
Potton United 0 **St Margaretsbury** 2
QUARTER-FINALS
Sawbridgeworth Town 2 **Oxhey Jets** 5
Hertford Town 2 St Margaretsbury 2 *aet* (4-2p)
Wormley Rovers 3 Biggleswade Town 0
Royston Town 3 Broxbourne Borough V & E 1
SEMI-FINALS
Hertford Town 0 **Royston Town** 2
Wormley Rovers 2 **Oxhey Jets** 6
FINAL
(May 15th at Oxhey Jets)
Oxhey Jets 1 **Royston Town** 2

SOUTH WALES SENIOR CUP

FIRST ROUND

AFC Caerphilly 3 **Caerau United** 6
Blaenrhondda 3 Ferndale Boys Club 1
Grange Albion 3 St Athan 1
Hirwaun Welfare 6 Treforest 4
Llanharry 8 Aber Valley YMCA 5
Penydarren Boys Club 5 Cadoxton Cons 1
Splott Albion 4 Cwmbach Royal Stars 0
St Marys Butetown 5 Wyndham 1
Turberville Arms 2 Ynyshir Albion 0

SECOND ROUND

Cwm Welfare 6 AFC Bargoed Redz 1
Grange Albion 4 Hopkinstown 0
Lewistown 2 **Caerau United** 3 *aet*
Llanbradach Social 4 Stanleytown 3
Llanrumney United 4 Blaenrhondda 2
Rhoose 2 AFC Whitchurch 1
Rhydyfelin 2 Carnetown BGC 1
Splott Albion 3 **Sully Sports** 4 *aet*
St Josephs 2 Brecon Corinthians 0
Brynna 7 Tongwynlais 4 *aet*
Corus Steel 5 FC Abercwmboi 0
Hirwaun Welfare 5 Bridgend Street 2
Penrhiwfer 0 **Llanharry** 2
Penydarren Boys Club 4 AFC Talbot Green 3
Turberville Arms 2 Llangynwyd Rangers 1
St Marys Butetown 1 **Trelewis Welfare** 2

THIRD ROUND

Corus Steels 4 Grange Albion 0
Brynna 3 St Josephs 0
Cwm Welfare 6 Llanharry 0
Hirwaun Welfare 6 **Rhoose** 6 *aet* (4-5p)
Llanbradach Social 1 **Caerau United** 8
Penydarren Boys Club 4 Rhydyfelin 1
Sully Sports 3 **Llanrumney United** 4
Trelewis Welfare 0 **Turberville Arms** 1

QUARTER-FINALS

Brynna 1 **Llanrumney United** 5 *aet*
Penydarren Boys Club 7 Cwm Welfare 0
Rhoose 0 **Corus Steel** 3
Turberville Arms 2 **Caerau United** 3

SEMI-FINALS

Llamrumney United 0 **Penydarren Boys Club** 3
Caerau United 4 Corus Steel 0

FINAL

(May 12th at ENTO Aberaman Athletic)
Penydarren Boys Club 1 Caerau United 0

SOUTHERN COMBINATION CUP

FIRST ROUND

Sandhurst Town 3 Feltham 1
Westfield 2 Horsley 1
Hanworth Villa 4 Knaphill 2
Chertsey Town 2 Reading Town 0

SECOND ROUND

Dorking 0 **Bedfont** 2
Cove 2 Frimley Green 1
Virginia Water 3 **Merstham** 3 *aet* (0-3p) *(at Merstham)*
Guildford City 0 **Sandhurst Town** 1
Hanworth Villa 1 **Cobham** 5 *aet*
Chessington & Hook United 4 Westfield 1 *aet*
Chertsey Town 1 **Staines Lammas** 2
Ashford Town (Middx) (scr.) v **Chipstead** (w/o)

QUARTER-FINALS

Chessington & Hook United 4 Cobham 1
Bedfont (w/o) Chipstead (scr.)
Staines Lammas 0 **Sandhurst Town** 3
(at Ashford Town (Middx))
Cove 3 Merstham 2

SEMI-FINALS

Bedfont 2 **Chessington & Hook United** 3
Cove 3 Sandhurst Town 2

FINAL

(May 9th at Cove)
Cove 4 Chessington & Hook United 1

STAFFORDSHIRE SENIOR CUP

FIRST ROUND

Leek Town 1 **Stafford Rangers** 4
Kidsgrove Athletic (w/o) v Burton Albion (scr.)
Newcastle Town 1 Tamworth 0
Hednesford Town 4 Rushall Olympic 1
Chasetown 2 Biddulph Victoria 0

QUARTER-FINALS

Newcastle Town 0 **Port Vale** 2
Kidsgrove Athletic 3 Rocester 2 *aet*
Chasetown 2 Stoke City 0
Hednesford Town 1 **Stafford Rangers** 2

SEMI-FINALS

Chasetown 1 **Kidsgrove Athletic** 2
Stafford Rangers 3 Port Vale 2

FINAL

(April 22nd at Port Vale)
Stafford Rangers 2 **Kidsgrove Athletic** 2 *aet* (3-4p)

STAFFORDSHIRE VASE

FIRST ROUND

Shenstone Pathfinder 1 **Hanley Town** 4

SECOND ROUND

Norton 1 **Riverway** 3
Audley & District 1 **Brocton** 4
Ball Haye Green 5 Eccleshall AFC 0
Barlaston 0 **Bloxwich United** 3
Bilston Town 4 Sporting Khalsa 3
Brereton Social 3 **Walsall Wood** 4
Burntwood Town 1 **Redgate Clayton** 6
Eccleshall 3 Foley 1
Florence 2 **Abbey Hulton United** 3
Goldenhill Wanderers 3 **Warstone Wanderers** 4 *aet*
Hanley Town 2 Stone Dominoes 1
Heath Hayes 2 Pelsall Villa 0
Meir KA 2 Bilbrook 0
Norton United 1 Wolverhampton Casuals 0
Stafford Town 3 Leek CSOB 2
Wolstanton United 3 Heath Town Rangers 2

THIRD ROUND

Brocton 1 **Heath Hayes** 4
Riverway 2 Warstone Wanderers 0
Stafford Town 5 Bilston Town 0
Bloxwich United 1 Meir KA 0
Ball Haye Green 3 Redgate Clayton 0
Eccleshall 0 **Wolstanton United** 2
Norton United 1 Hanley Town 2 *(Hanley Town expelled*
Walsall Wood 2 Abbey Hulton United 1 *aet*

QUARTER-FINALS

Bloxwich United 3 Riverway 1
Ball Haye Green 2 Stafford Town 0
Heath Hayes 5 Wolstanton United 4
Norton United 2 Walsall Wood 0

SEMI-FINALS

Ball Haye Green 3 Bloxwich United 0
Heath Hayes 2 Norton United 2 *aet* (3-1p)

FINAL *(March 30th at Stafford Rangers)*
Ball Haye Green 1 **Heath Hayes** 2 *aet*

SUFFOLK PREMIER CUP

(Sponsor: LB Group)

FIRST ROUND

Bury Town 2 **Needham Market** 2 *aet* (3-4p)
Newmarket Town 1 **Leiston** 2
Whitton United 3 **Lowestoft Town** 4
Kirkley & Pakefield 1 **Mildenhall Town** 2
Walsham-le-Willows 3 Haverhill Rovers 2
Woodbridge Town 2 **AFC Sudbury** 3

QUARTER-FINALS

Felixstowe & Walton United 0 **Lowestoft Town** 3
Mildenhall Town 1 **AFC Sudbury** 2
Leiston 0 **Ipswich Town** 3
Needham Market 2 Walsham-le-Willows 1

SEMI-FINALS
owestoft Town 2 AFC Sudbury 1 *(at Woodbridge Town)*
eedham Market 1 Ipswich Town 0 *(at Needham Market)*
FINAL *(April 28th at Ipswich Town)*
Lowestoft Town 3 Needham Market 2

SUFFOLK SENIOR CUP

(Sponsor: Touchline Sports)
FIRST ROUND
Brandon Town 0 **Leiston St Margarets** 3
Bungay Town 1 **Grundisburgh** 3
Capel Plough 5 Woodbridge Athletic 4
Cornard United 1 Stowupland Falcons 0
Corton 3 Ipswich Wanderers 1
East Bergholt United 3 Hundon 2
Felixstowe United 2 **Lakenheath** 3
Framlingham Town 3 **Ransomes Sports** 3 *aet* (2-4p)
Ipswich Athletic 0 **Debenham Leisure Centre** 3
Long Melford 0 **Beccles Town** 3
Sole Bay 3 **Melton St Audrys** 8
St Johns 3 Coplestonians 0
Stonham Aspal 0 **Brantham Athletic** 4
Crane Sports 3 Hadleigh United 2
Stowmarket Town 2 Team Bury 1
Wickhambrook (scr.) v **Westerfield United** (w/o)
SECOND ROUND
Cornard United 0 **Capel Plough** 1
Debenham Leisure Centre 4 **Lakenheath** 5
East Bergholt United 1 **Brantham Athletic** 3
Grundisburgh 3 Melton St Audrys 1
Leiston St Margarets 2 Stowmarket Town 0
St Johns 0 **Crane Sports** 1 *aet*
Beccles Town 5 Westerfield United 0
Corton 2 Ransomes Sports 1
QUARTER-FINALS
Brantham Athletic 2 **Corton** 4 *aet*
Grundisburgh 0 **Crane Sports** 1 *aet*
Capel Plough 1 **Beccles Town** 2
Lakenheath 1 **Leiston St Margarets** 2
SEMI-FINALS
Beccles Town 1 Leiston St Margarets 0
Corton 1 **Crane Sports** 3
FINAL
(March 31st at Ipswich Town)
Beccles Town 1 Crane Sports 0

SURREY SENIOR CUP

FIRST ROUND
Ash United 2 **Redhill** 2 *aet* (4-5p)
Badshot Lea 1 **Chertsey Town** 3
Epsom & Ewell 1 Horley Town 0
hessington & Hook United 2 Egham Town 2 *aet* (6-5p)
Lingfield 2 Raynes Park Vale 0
Molesey 1 Guildford City 0
SECOND ROUND
Banstead Athletic 0 **Ashford Town (Middx)** 5
Kingstonian 1 Chipstead 0
Beckenham Town 2 **Metropolitan Police** 4
Godalming Town 0 **Corinthian Casuals** 2
Molesey 2 **Merstham** 2 *aet* (2-4p)
Whyteleafe 3 Crystal Palace 2
Cobham 1 **Leatherhead** 2
Croydon 0 **Woking** 2
Walton Casuals 2 Lingfield 0
ookham 2 Carshalton Athletic 1 *(at Carshalton Athletic)*
Chertsey Town 3 Colliers Wood United 2
AFC Wimbledon 1 Tooting & Mitcham United 0
Dorking 2 Walton & Hersham 1
Sutton United 2 **Epsom & Ewell** 3
Chessington & Hook United 1 **Redhill** 3 *(at Redhill)*
Dulwich Hamlet 2 Camberley Town 1
THIRD ROUND
Walton Casuals 0 **Kingstonian** 3
Ashford Town (Middx) 2 Metropolitan Police 1
Bookham 4 **Chertsey Town** 6
Corinthian Casuals 3 Dorking 1 *aet*
Epsom & Ewell 3 Redhill 0
Merstham 2 Whyteleafe 1 *aet*
Woking 4 Leatherhead 0
AFC Wimbledon 0 **Dulwich Hamlet** 1 *aet*
QUARTER-FINALS
Merstham 3 Chertsey Town 0
Epsom & Ewell 2 Corinthian Casuals 1
Ashford Town (Middx) 2 Kingstonian 1
Dulwich Hamlet 0 **Woking** 1
SEMI-FINALS
Ashford Town (Middx) 4 Epsom & Ewell 1
Merstham 0 **Woking** 2
FINAL *(May 5th at Metropolitan Police)*
Woking 2 **Ashford Town (Middx)** 3

SUSSEX SENIOR CUP

FIRST ROUND
Seaford Town 0 **Shoreham** 2
Rustington 0 **Chichester City United** 1
Crawley Down 2 East Grinstead Town 2
Replay: East Grinstead T. 0 **Crawley Down** 0 *aet* (3-4p)
Midhurst & Easebourne Utd 3 **Peacehaven & Telscombe** 4 *aet*
Oakwood 3 Rye United 2
Worthing United 1 **Littlehampton Town** 3
Eastbourne United Association 5 Mile Oak 5 *aet*
Replay: **Mile Oak** 2 Eastbourne United Association 1
Bexhill United 0 **Hassocks** 5
Loxwood 0 **Hailsham Town** 1
Selsey 1 Southwick 0
Storrington 0 **St Francis Rangers** 2
Westfield 4 Steyning Town 2 *aet*
Ringmer 4 Pagham 0
Sidley United 1 **Lancing** 4
Wealden 3 Sidlesham 0
SECOND ROUND
Crawley Town 0 **Brighton & Hove Albion** 1
Eastbourne Borough 4 Mile Oak 3
Lancing 2 **Three Bridges** 3
Eastbourne Town 1 **Arundel** 4
St Francis Rangers 0 **Horsham YMCA** 3
Whitehawk 1 **Chichester City United** 2
Crawley Down 0 **Worthing** 3
Ringmer 1 **Horsham** 2
Wick 1 **Lewes** 5
Hassocks 2 **Bognor Regis Town** 5 *aet (Bognor expelled)*
Selsey 3 Peacehaven & Telscombe 1
Littlehampton Town 1 **East Preston** 3
Wealden 0 **Hailsham Town** 4
Burgess Hill Town 0 **Hastings United** 1
(at Hastings United)
Oakwood 2 **Crowborough Athletic** 5 *aet*
Shoreham 3 Westfield 3 *aet*
Replay: Westfield 1 **Shoreham** 1 *aet* (2-3p)
THIRD ROUND
Worthing 0 **Eastbourne Borough** 2
Hailsham Town 1 **Brighton & Hove Albion** 3
Crowborough Athletic 3 Arundel 3 *aet*
Replay: Arundel 4 **Crowborough Athletic** 5 *aet*
Selsey 0 **Lewes** 1 *aet*
Horsham 2 Three Bridges 1
Hastings United 2 **Horsham YMCA** 5
Shoreham 2 East Preston 1
Hassocks 1 Chichester City United 0
QUARTER-FINALS
Hassocks 0 **Shoreham** 1
Eastbourne Borough 11 Crowborough Athletic 1
Horsham 3 Lewes 1
Brighton & Hove Albion 2 Horsham YMCA 0
(at Horsham YMCA)
SEMI-FINAL
Brighton & Hove Albion 4 Horsham 1 *(at Worthing)*
Shoreham 2 **Eastbourne Borough** 2 *aet* (3-5p)
(at Three Bridges)
FINAL
(May 4th at Eastbourne Borough)
Eastbourne Borough 1 Brighton & Hove Albion 0 *aet*

SUSSEX RUR CHARITY CUP

(Sponsor: Principal)

FIRST ROUND

Chichester City United 1 **Wick** 2
Shoreham 4 Rye United 3 *aet*
Worthing United 1 **Lancing** 5
St Francis Rangers 2 Seaford Town 1
Storrington 2 **Wealden** 3
Bexhill United 0 **Lingfield** 5

SECOND ROUND

Selsey 2 Arundel 0
Redhill 0 **Steyning Town** 0 *aet* (6-5p)
East Preston 1 **Rustington** 0 *(East Preston expelled)*
Southwick 1 **Pagham** 5
Loxwood 3 Sidlesham 0
Eastbourne United Association 4 Whitehawk 2
Ringmer 2 Sidley United 1
Hailsham Town 3 East Grinstead Town 1
Horsham YMCA 1 **Shoreham** 2
Mile Oak 6 Wick 3 *aet*
Lancing 3 **Littlehampton Town** 5
Peacehaven & Telscombe 0 **Crawley Down** 1
Oakwood 1 **St Francis Rangers** 3
Hassocks 2 Midhurst & Easebourne Utd 1
Three Bridges 11 Wealden 0
Lingfield 3 Westfield 0

THIRD ROUND

Rustington 3 Ringmer 0
Redhill 1 Shoreham 0
Loxwood 1 Pagham 2 *(Pagham expelled)*
Littlehampton Town 1 **Eastbourne United Association** 6
Mile Oak 0 **Hassocks** 1 *aet*
Selsey 2 Crawley Down 1
St Francis Rangers 4 Hailsham Town 2
Lingfield 1 **Three Bridges** 2 *(at Three Bridges)*

QUARTER-FINALS

Loxwood 3 Selsey 1
Eastbourne United Association 6 Redhill 0
Rustington 3 St Francis Rangers 2 *aet*
Hassocks 1 **Three Bridges** 4

SEMI-FINALS

Loxwood 0 **Rustington** 1 *(at Arundel)*
Three Bridges 0 **Eastbourne United Association** 1 *(at Ringmer)*

FINAL

(April 29th at Lancing)
Eastbourne United Association 4 Rustington 1 *aet*

WALSALL SENIOR CUP

FIRST ROUND

Dudley Town 2 Wednesfield 1
Bolehall Swifts 2 Romulus 1 *aet*
Cradley Town 3 Pelsall Villa 0
Wolverhampton Casuals 0 **Oldbury United** 1
Continental Star 1 **Gornal Athletic** 2
Walsall Wood 0 **Shifnal Town** 1

SECOND ROUND

Gornal Athletic 0 **Heath Hayes** 2
Oldbury United 2 Bolehall Swifts 1 *aet*
Shifnal Town 0 **Rushall Olympic** 2
Tividale 1 **Biddulph Victoria** 1 *aet* (6-7p)
Cradley Town 1 **Boldmere St Michaels** 4
Goodrich 2 Lye Town 1
Chasetown 2 Dudley Town 0
Darlaston Town 0 **Tipton Town** 2

QUARTER-FINALS

Boldmere St Michaels 1 Oldbury United 0
Rushall Olympic 1 Chasetown 1 *aet* (4-2p)
Goodrich 1 Biddulph Victoria 0
Tipton Town 3 Heath Hayes 0

SEMI-FINALS

Goodrich 0 **Rushall Olympic** 6
Tipton Town 4 Boldmere St Michaels 2

FINAL

(May 12th at Walsall)
Tipton Town 1 **Rushall Olympic** 2

WELSH CUP

PRELIMINARY ROUND

AFC Llwydcoed 4 Ystradgynlais 2
Aberbargoed Buds 3 **Cwmaman Institute** 4
Bethesda Athletic 7 Corwen Amateurs 0
Borras Park Albion 2 **Brickfield Rangers** 3
Bow Street 4 Overton Recreation 2
Briton Ferry Athletic 2 Troedyrhiw 1
Carno 1 **Tredegar Town** 3 *(at Tredegar Town)*
Castle Alun Colts 4 Presteigne St Andrews 0
Cwmamman United 4 Llansawel 2
Glyn Ceiriog 0 **Coedpoeth United** 6
Goytre 1 **Newport Civil Service** 3
Holywell Town 1 **Nefyn United** 2
Kerry 0 **Llanberis** 2
Llanllyfni 4 Llanfyllin Town 2
Llanrug United 5 Llanrhaedr 1
Llantwit Fardre 0 **AFC Porth** 2
Merthyr Saints 0 **Pontyclun** 9
Porthcawl Town 2 Monmouth Town 1
Rhayader Town 2 **Pwllheli** 4
Risca United 2 Seven Sisters 2 *aet* (3-2p)
Tywyn & Bryncrug 2 Newbridge-on-Wye 0
Venture Community 2 Dyffryn Banw 1

FIRST ROUND

AFC Llwydcoed 3 Porthcawl Town 0
Afan Lido 3 Cwmamman United 0
Berriew 0 **Llangollen Town** 1
Bettws 1 **Taffs Well** 1 *aet* (3-4p)
Brickfield Rangers 4 Nefyn United 3
Briton Ferry Athletic 3 AFC Porth 1
Brymbo 0 **Mold Alexandra** 8
Buckley Town 6 Penycae 3
Caerau Ely 1 **Pentwyn Dynamos** 2 *aet*
Caerleon 1 **Goytre United** 4
Caldicot Town 0 **Ammanford** 1
Cambrian & Clydach Vale BGC 4 Newcastle Emlyn 1
Cardiff Corinthians 3 Ely Rangers 0
Castell Alun Colts 1 Llandyrnog United 0
Conwy United 2 **Penrhyncoch** 3 *aet*
Croesyceiliog 0 **Maesteg Park** 3
Cwmbran Celtic 3 Garw 1
Denbigh Town 4 Llanllyfni 1
ENTO Aberaman Athletic 2 Barry Town 1
Flint Town United 4 Rhos Aelwyd 3
Glan Conwy 2 Llanrwst United 1 *aet*
Glantraeth 1 **Bala Town** 6
Grange Harlequins 1 **Newport Civil Service** 5 *aet* *(at Newport Civil Service)*
Guilsfield 2 Ruthin Town 0
Halkyn United 4 Coedpoeth United 2 *aet*
Hawarden Rangers 0 **Llanfairpwll** 2
Llanberis 2 **Bow Street** 3
Llandudno Junction 4 Penparcau 2
Llangefni Town 3 Llandudno Town 1
Llangeinor 0 **Dinas Powys** 2
Llanrug United 0 **Pwllheli** 2
Llanwern 3 Ton Pentre 0
Llay Welfare 8 Amlwch Town 1
Mynydd Isa 3 **Holyhead Hotspur** 3 *aet* (5-6p)
Newport YMCA 3 Cwmaman Institute 2
Penrhiwceiber Rangers 1 **Pontypridd Town** 1 *aet* (3-4p
Pontyclun 0 **Bridgend Town** 0 *aet* (1-3p)
Risca United 2 Pontardawe Town 0
Rhydymwyn (w/o) v Cefn United (scr.)
Tredegar Town 0 **Gresford Athletic** 1
Treharris Athletic 1 **Bryntirion Athletic** 9
Tywyn & Bryncrug 4 Bethesda Athletic 1
UWIC 1 **Cwmbran Town** 3
Venture Community 1 **Lex XI** 2
West End 2 **Garden Village** 3
Nantlle Vale 1 **Chirk AAA** 4

SECOND ROUND

Carmarthen Town 6 Bow Street 1
Llanelli 4 Neath Athletic 0
Port Talbot Town 1 ENTO Aberaman Athletic 0

Aberystwyth Town 2 Afan Lido 2 *aet* (3-2p)
Airbus UK Broughton 2 Welshpool Town 1
Bala Town 3 **Prestatyn Town** 3 *aet* (4-5p)
Bangor City 1 GAP Connah's Quay 0
Brickfield Rangers 3 **Buckley Town** 4
Bridgend Town 3 Cwmbran Town 1
Bryntirion Athletic 1 **Cardiff Corinthians** 2
Denbigh Town 4 Chirk AAA 1
Dinas Powys 0 **Briton Ferry Athletic** 1 *aet*
Flint Town United 4 Mold Alexandra 0
Garden Village 2 Risca United 0
Gresford Athletic 4 Rhydymwyn 1
Holyhead Hotspur 2 Llay Welfare 1
Lex XI 2 Glan Conwy 1
Llandudno Junction 0 **Pwllheli** 2
Llangefni Town 3 Llanfairpwll 0
Llangollen Town 1 **Tywyn & Bryncrug** 2
NEWI Cefn Druids 4 Halkyn United 2
Newport Civil Service 0 **Caersws** 1
Newport YMCA 3 Cwmbran Celtic 2
Penrhyncoch 3 Maesteg Park 2 *aet*
Pentwyn Dynamos 1 Ammanford Town 0
Pontypridd Town 1 **Haverfordwest County** 4
Porthmadog 5 Caernarfon Town 3
Rhyl 8 Castell Alun Colts 0
Taffs Well 0 **Goytre United** 2
The New Saints 4 Guilsfield Athletic 2
Llanwern 1 **AFC Llwydcoed** 6
Cambrian & Clydach Vale BGC 0 **Newtown** 1

THIRD ROUND

Buckley Town 1 **Airbus UK Broughton** 5
AFC Llwydcoed 1 Flint Town United 0
Bangor City 4 Garden Village 0
Bridgend Town 1 Llangefni Town 0
Caersws 0 **Aberystwyth Town** 3
Cardiff Corinthians 0 **Goytre United** 6
Gresford Athletic 2 **Prestatyn Town** 3 *aet*
Holyhead Hotspur 2 Pentwyn Dynamos 1
Lex XI 2 Porthmadog 0
NEWI Cefn Druids 1 Newtown 0
Newport YMCA 2 Briton Ferry Athletic 1
Port Talbot Town 7 Denbigh Town 0
Pwllheli 0 **Carmarthen Town** 6
Rhyl 4 Haverfordwest County 0
The New Saints 7 Penrhyncoch 1
Tywyn & Bryncrug 0 **Llanelli** 3

FOURTH ROUND

Airbus UK Broughton 2 NEWI Cefn Druids 1
Port Talbot Town 2 Llanelli 1
AFC Llwydcoed 0 **Aberystwyth Town** 3
Bangor City 1 Rhyl 1 *aet* (4-2p)
Bridgend Town 4 Lex XI 0
Holyhead Hotspur 1 **Newport YMCA** 1 *aet* (5-6p)
Prestatyn Town 5 Goytre United 3 *aet*
The New Saints 2 **Carmarthen Town** 3

QUARTER-FINALS

Aberystwyth Town 5 Prestatyn Town 1
Airbus UK Broughton 0 **Bangor City** 5
Carmarthen Town 1 Port Talbot Town 1 *aet* (4-1p)
Newport YMCA 0 **Bridgend Town** 1

SEMI-FINALS

Bangor City 2 Bridgend Town 1 *(at Aberystwyth Town)*
Aberystwyth Town 3 Carmarthen Town 2 *aet*
(at Haverfordwest County)

FINAL

(May 4th at Llanelli Scarlets)
Bangor City 2 Aberystwyth Town 0

WELSH TROPHY

FIRST ROUND

Blaengwawr Inn (scr.) v **Turberville Arms** (w/o)
Llanystumdwy (w/o) v Knighton Town (scr.)
Abercarn United 2 Trefelin BGC 2 *aet* (4-2p)
Amlwch Town 2 **Carno** 5
Coed Eva Athletic 9 Aberfan 2
Ferndale Boys Club 8 FC Brunswick 4
Glan Conwy 11 Newbridge-on-Wye 1
Glyn Ceiriog 4 **Y Felinheli** 5
Hirwaun Welfare 3 Panteg 0
Johnstown Youth 3 Kerry 2
Llangollen Town 0 **Hawarden Rangers** 3
Llanidloes Town (w/o) v Nantlle Vale (scr.)
Llanrumney United 4 Graig 2
Llansantffraid Village 2 **Pwllheli** 3
Maltsters Sports 3 AFC Whitchurch 1
Overton Recreation 1 **Llanrhaedr** 3
Pentwynmawr Athletic 2 Abertillery Excelsior 0
RTB Ebbw Vale 2 **Barry** 3
Seren Goch 1 **Llanharry** 8
Trelewis Welfare 0 **AFC Bargoed Redz** 1
Tywyn & Bryncrug 1 **Montgomery Town** 2

SECOND ROUND

Llanystumdwy (w/o) v Cefn United (scr.)
AFC Bargoed Redz 3 Nelson Cavaliers 2
Abercarn United 4 Carnetown 0
Blaenrhondda 2 **Clydach Wasps** 3
Brymbo 0 **Berriew** 4
Coed Eva Athletic 1 **Corus Steel** 2
Coedpoeth United 1 **Borras Park Albion** 3
Cogan Coronation 4 Turberville Arms 2
Corwen Amateurs 4 Llanrug United 2
Ferndale Boys Club 1 **Blaenavon Blues** 2 *aet*
Glan Conwy 7 Llanrhaedr 2
Hirwaun Welfare 5 Ton & Gelli Boys Club 2
Llanberis 1 **Brickfield Rangers** 3
Llandudno Junction 2 **Hawarden Rangers** 3
Llanfyllin Town 0 **Rhayader Town** 2
Llanidloes Town 0 **Nefyn United** 2
Llanrumney United 1 Bonymaen Colts 0
Llanrwst United 6 Montgomery Town 5 *aet*
Maltsters Sports 4 **Llandrindod Wells** 6 *aet*
Penamenmawr Phoenix 2 **Venture Comm.** 2 *aet* (3-4p)
Pentwynmawr Athletic 2 Baglan Red Dragon 1
Penycae 4 Four Crosses 1
Presteigne St Andrews 4 Llay Welfare 3 *aet*
Ragged School 9 Mardy 1
Rhos Aelwyd 3 Holywell Town 1
Rhydymwyn 2 Carno 1
STM Sports 1 **Kenfig Hill** 2
South Gower 4 Cwmbach Royal Stars 1
Sully Sports 4 Llanharry 1
Y Felinheli 3 Pwllheli 1
Ynysddu Crusaders 3 Barry 2
Johnstown Youth 0 **Chirk AAA** 5

THIRD ROUND

AFC Bargoed Redz 3 Sully Sports 2
Berriew 4 Chirk AAA 1 *aet*
Blaenavon Blues 3 Hirwaun Welfare 3 *aet* (4-3p)
Brickfield Rangers 2 **Penycae** 3
Cogan Coronation 3 Ynysddu Crusaders 2
Corus Steel 3 Abercarn United 2
Glan Conwy 12 Borras Park Albion 1
Kenfig Hill 2 Llanrumney United 0
Llandrinodod Wells 1 **Clydach Wasps** 2
Llanystumdwy 0 **Hawarden Rangers** 4
Nefyn United 1 Rhos Aelwyd 0
Pentwynmawr Athletic 11 Rhayader Town 1
Presteigne St Andrews 6 Corwen Amateurs 3
Ragged School 3 South Gower 2
Rhydymwyn 1 Llanrwst United 0 *aet*
Venture Community 2 **Y Felinheli** 3

FOURTH ROUND

AFC Bargoed Redz 2 Clydach Wasps 1
Cogan Coronation 1 **Corus Steel** 1 *aet* (5-6p)
Nefyn United 3 Berriew 1
Pentwynmawr Athletic 2 **Blaenavon Blues** 2 *aet* (3-4p)
Penycae 2 Hawarden Rangers 1
Presteigne St Andrews 1 **Glan Conwy** 3
Ragged School 3 Kenfig Hill 1
Y Felinheli 1 **Rhydymwyn** 5 *(at Rhydymwyn)*

QUARTER-FINALS

Glan Conwy 1 **Ragged School** 1 *aet* (7-8p)
Nefyn United 2 AFC Bargoed Redz 1 *aet*

Penycae 4 Blaenavon Blues 1
Rhydymwyn 0 **Corus Steel** 1
SEMI-FINALS
Corus Steel 2 **Ragged School** 2 *aet* (2-4p) *(at Llanelli)*
Nefyn United 2 **Penycae** 3*(at Rhyl)*
FINAL
(April 11th at Newtown)
Penycae 0 **Ragged School** 1

WEST RIDING COUNTY CUP

(Sponsor: Group Response Security)
FIRST ROUND
Harrogate Railway Athletic 2 **Garforth Town** 3
Eccleshill United 1 **Brighouse Town** 2
Glasshoughton Welfare 2 **Yorkshire Amateur** 3
Liversedge 4 Askern Villa 2
Ossett Albion 8 Tadcaster Albion 3
Thackley 0 **Pontefract Collieries** 2
Wakefield 2 FC Halifax Town 1
Silsden 4 Leeds Carnegie 0
SECOND ROUND
Pontefract Collieries 1 **Brighouse Town** 7
Selby Town 0 **Bradford Park Avenue** 4
Harrogate Town 0 **Armthorpe Welfare** 2
Liversedge 3 **Garforth Town** 4
Yorkshire Amateur 3 Goole 2 *aet*
Guiseley 3 **Ossett Town** 4
Wakefield 0 **Farsley Celtic** 1
Silsden 1 **Ossett Albion** 3
QUARTER-FINALS
Ossett Albion 4 Farsley Celtic 2
Ossett Town 1 **Garforth Town** 2
Yorkshire Amateur 1 **Armthorpe Welfare** 2
Bradford Park Avenue 4 Brighouse Town 1
SEMI-FINALS
Garforth Town 3 Ossett Albion 1
Bradford Park Avenue 4 Armthorpe Welfare 2
FINAL
(April 8th at WRCFA, Woodlesford)
Garforth Town 1 Bradford Park Avenue 1 *aet* (5-4p)

WESTMORLAND SENIOR CUP

(Sponsor: Sportsguard)
FIRST ROUND
Appleby 5 Arnside 0
Burton Thistle 2 **Sedbergh Wanderers** 3
Endmoor KGR 7 Staveley United 2
Greystoke 8 Braithwaite 0
Kendal Celtic 2 Burneside 1
Kendal County 3 Carvetii United 2
Kirkoswald 2 Ibis 1
Lunesdale United 8 Kirkby Lonsdale 2
Penrith Rangers 4 Coniston 3
Shap 1 Kendal United 0
SECOND ROUND
Appleby 4 Alston Moor Sports Club 0
Endmoor KGR 0 **Penrith Rangers** 6
Greystoke 4 Shap 2
Kendal Celtic 0 **Milnthorpe Corinthians** 2
Kendal County 2 **Keswick** 4
Lunesdale United 6 Sedbergh Wanderers 1
Wetheriggs United 2 Ambleside United 1
Windermere SC 1 **Kirkoswald** 4
QUARTER-FINALS
Appleby 4 Greystoke 1
Keswick 3 Milnthorpe Corinthians 1
Kirkoswald 1 **Penrith Rangers** 2
Wetheriggs United 9 Lunesdale United 0
SEMI-FINALS
Penrith Rangers 2 Appleby 0
Wetheriggs United 0 **Keswick** 2
FINAL
(April 18th at Kendal Town)
Penrith Rangers 2 **Keswick** 3

WILTSHIRE PREMIER SHIELD

FIRST ROUND
(played over two legs)
Chippenham Town 0 Swindon Town 1
Swindon Town 1 Chippenham Town 2 *aet* (5-3p)
Swindon Supermarine 3 Salisbury City 2
Salisbury City 3 Swindon Supermarine 1
FINAL
(April 29th at Salisbury City)
Salisbury City 3 Swindon Town 1

WILTSHIRE SENIOR CUP

FIRST ROUND
Amesbury Town 3 Malmesbury Victoria 0
FC Chippenham Youth 3 **Downton** 5
Marlborough Town 0 **Wootton Bassett Town** 1
Pewsey Vale 2 **Shrewton United** 3
Purton 2 **Warminster Town** 3
Trowbridge Town 1 **Bromham** 2
Westbury United 6 Cricklade Town 0
Westside United 0 **New College Swindon** 8 *(at New College Swindon)*
SECOND ROUND
Calne Town 3 Shrewton United 2
Westbury United 2 **Highworth Town** 4
Wootton Bassett Town 6 Bromham 0
Bemerton Heath Harlequins 1 Bradford Town 0
Downton 4 **Corsham Town** 4 *aet* (4-5p)
Melksham Town 5 Amesbury Town 0
Warminster Town 3 Devizes Town 2
Laverstock & Ford 2 New College Swindon 1
QUARTER-FINALS
Bemerton Heath Harlequins 0 **Highworth Town** 3
Warminster Town 3 Calne Town 2
Wootton Bassett Town 2 Corsham Town 1
Laverstock & Ford 2 **Melksham Town** 3
SEMI-FINALS
Warminster Town 2 Wootton Bassett Town 1
(at Melksham Town)
Highworth Town 2 Melksham Town 1
(at Highworth Town)
FINAL
(April 22nd at Chippenham Town)
Warminster Town 1 **Highworth Town** 2 *aet*

WORCESTERSHIRE SENIOR CUP

FIRST ROUND
Malvern Town 2 **Stourbridge** 4 *aet*
QUARTER-FINALS
Stourbridge 0 **Kidderminster Harriers** 3
Worcester City 0 **Redditch United** 1
Bromsgrove Rovers 1 **Evesham United** 3
Halesowen Town 5 Stourport Swifts 0
SEMI-FINALS
Evesham United 4 Halesowen Town 0
Kidderminster Harriers 3 Redditch United 0
FINAL
(August 3rd at Worcester City)
Evesham United 1 Kidderminster Harriers 0

WORCESTERSHIRE SENIOR URN

FIRST ROUND
Bewdley Town 5 Pershore Town 4
Bromsgrove Rovers Res. 0 **Alvechurch** 3
Lye Town 3 GSA Sports 0
Dudley Sports 1 **Studley** 2 *aet*
SEMI-FINALS
Studley 2 Lye Town 2 *aet* (5-4p)
Bewdley Town 4 Alvechurch 1
FINAL
(April 20th at Kidderminster Harriers)
Studley 3 Bewdley Town 2

OTHER CUP FINALS 2008-09

A F A INTERMEDIATE CUP
(March 28th at Old Parkonians)
Bealonians 4 Chertsey O Salesians 3

ALFRED SPAREY CUP
(May 17th at Presteigne St Andrews)
Gwernyfed 6 Hay St Marys Res. 0

ANCASTER CUP
(May 22nd at Deeping Rangers)
Deeping Rangers Res. 4
Sleaford Town Res. 2 *aet*

BARRITT CUP
(May 2nd at Bangor City)
Rhyl Res. 1 **Llandudno Junction** 3

BATTLE OF BRITAIN CHARITY CUP
(Sept 17th at Blaby & Whetstone)
Anstey Nomads 6 Barrow Town 0

BEDFORDSHIRE INT. CUP
(April 14th at Langford)
Stotfold Res. 2 Dunstable T. Res. 1

BEDFORDSHIRE JUNIOR CUP
(April 21st at Potton United)
Great Barford 1 Potton Wanderers 0

BIRMINGHAM VASE
(April 6th at Solihull Moors)
AFC Wombourne United 3
Warley Development 2 *aet*

BIRMINGHAM JUNIOR CUP
(March 28th at BCFA, Great Barr)
Shirley Athletic 3 Silhill 1 *aet*

BRADFORD SENIOR CUP CUP
(May 6th at Bradford City)
Thackley 2 **Albion Sports** 4

BUCKINGHAM JUNIOR CHARITY CUP
(March 19th at Buckingham Town)
Brackley Sports 2 Steeple Claydon 1

CAMBRIDGESHIRE JUNIOR INVITATION CUP
(April 29th at Histon)
Coates Ath. 1 West Wratting Res. 0

CAMBRIDGESHIRE LOWER JUNIOR CUP
(April 30th at March Town United)
Wisbech St Mary A 1 **RHS Utd Res.** 2

CENTRAL WALES CUP
(May 25th at Rhayader Town)
Hay St Marys 0 **Newtown Res.** 3

CEREDIGION CUP
(May 4th at Newcastle Emlyn)
New Quay 5 Lampeter Town 1

CHESHIRE AMATEUR CUP
(April 17th at Vauxhall Motors)
West Kirby 2 Poulton Victoria 1

CHESTER SENIOR CUP
(April 22nd at Christleton)
Upton Athletic Association 0
Chester Nomads 3

COALVILLE CHARITY CUP
(April 14th at Heather St John)
Ellistown 1 Heather St Johns 0

CORNWALL JUNIOR CUP
(April 13th at St Blazey)
St Dennis 1 Falmouth Athletic 1
REPLAY
(April 22nd at St Blazey)
St Dennis 5 Falmouth Athletic 2

COVENTRY EVENING TELEGRAPH CUP
(April 7th at Coventry City)
Nuneaton Griff 1 Coventry
Copsewood 1 *aet* (4-3p)

COVENTRY CHARITY CUP
(March 11th at Coventry City)
Alvis 2 Stockingford AA 1

DERBYSHIRE DIV. CUP NORTH
(April 21st at Matlock Town)
Whaley Bridge Ath. 4 Dronfield T. 3

DERBYSHIRE DIV. CUP SOUTH
(April 9th at Long Eaton United)
Ilkeston Town Res. 4 Chellaston 1

DERBYSHIRE JUNIOR CUP NORTH
(April 23rd at Tideswell United)
Dronfield T. Res. 0 **Chapel T. Res.** 2

DERBYSHIRE JUNIOR CUP SOUTH
(March 26th at Long Eaton United)
Findern 1 The Seal Inn 0

DEVON PREMIER CUP
(April 23rd at Tiverton Town)
Bovey Tracey 0 **Boca Seniors** 1

DEVON SENIOR CUP
(April 29th at Newton Abbot)
Lifton 0 **Buckland Athletic Res.** 1

DEVON INTERMEDIATE CUP
(April 9th at Newton Abbot)
Babbacombe Corries 2 **Lamerton** 5

DORSET TROPHY
(April 14th at Dorchester Town)
Parley Sports 1 Bridport Res. 0

DORSET INTERMEDIATE CUP
(April 21st at Shaftesbury)
Stalbridge 1 **Kingston Lacy** 5

DORSET JUNIOR CUP
(April 9th at Bridport)
Dorchester Sports 2 **Thorncombe** 5

DORSET MINOR CUP
(April 2nd at Hamworthy United)
Screw It Carpentry 3
Branksome Celtic 2

ESSEX PREMIER CUP
(April 15th at Billericay Town)
Holland 1 Maldon St Marys 0

ESSEX JUNIOR CUP
(April 1st at Great Wakering Rovers)
Alemite Ath. 5 Gas Rec. Res. 2 *aet*

ESSEX JUNIOR TROPHY
(March 25th at Billericay Town)
Emstar United 3 Sheering United 0

EVESHAM JUNIOR HOSPITAL CUP
(May 9th at Littleton)
Littleton 3 Bretforton Old Boys 2

GOLDLINE TROPHY
(April 6th at Bolton Wanderers)
Atherton LR 2 Stoneclough 1

GOLESWORTHY CUP
(May 20th at Ottery St Mary)
Colaton Raleigh 0 **Sidbury Utd A** 4

GRANDISSON CUP
(May 19th Ottery St Mary)
Colyton 0 Sidbury
United Res. 0 *aet* (5-4p)

HALIFAX & DISTRICT CUP
(April 29th at FC Halifax Town)
Brighouse Town 1 **Ovenden West Riding** 2 *aet*

HAMPSHIRE INTERMEDIATE CUP
(April 29th at Christchurch)
West Wight 3 Netley Central Sports 0

HASTINGS SENIOR CUP
(April 8th at Sidley United)
Hastings United 3 Rye United 0

HERTFORDSHIRE INT. CUP
(March 31st at HCFA, Letchworth)
Bishop's Stortford Swifts 3
London Colney Res. 0

HERTFORDSHIRE JUNIOR CUP
(April 10th at HCFA, Letchworth)
White Hart (NH) 0 **Hemel Hempstead Rovers** 0 *aet* (3-4p)

HUDDERSFIELD CUP
(April 20th at Huddersfield Town)
Storthes Hall 2 Meltham Athletic 1

HUNTINGDONSHIRE SCOTT GATTY CUP
(March 25th at Eynesbury Rovers)
St Neots Town Res. 2
Huntingdon Town Res. 0

HUNTINGDONSHIRE BENEVOLENT CUP
(April 22nd at Huntingdon Town)
St Neots Town Res. 2
Eynesbury Rovers Res. 0

HUNTINGDONSHIRE JUNIOR CUP
(April 15th at Somersham Town)
Godmanchester Rovers Res. 3
Somersham Town Res. 3 *aet* (2-4p)

J W HUNT CUP
(May 11th at Wolverhampton Wanderers)
Bloxwich Utd 1 AFC Wulfrunians 0

KEIGHLEY & DISTRICT CUP
(April 17th at Silsden)
Crosshills 2 Steeton 1

KENT SENIOR CUP 2007-08
(July 26th at Bromley)
Cray Wanderers 0 **Ebbsfleet Utd** 4

KENT INTERMEDIATE CUP
(April 29th at Tonbridge Angels)
Tonbridge Angels Res. 3
Erith & Belvedere Res. 0

LANCASHIRE AMATEUR SHIELD
(March 23rd at LCFA, Leyland)
Gregorians 1 Rochdale
Sacred Heart 1 *aet* (4-3p)

LANCASHIRE AMATEUR CUP
(March 9th at LCFA, Leyland)
Preston Wanderers 3
Chew Brook Sports Club 2

LEEDS & DISTRICT CUP
(April 15th at Yorkshire Amateur)
Whitkirk Wanderers 3 Leeds
Medics & Dentists 2 *aet*

LEICESTERSHIRE SENIOR CUP
(May 5th at LCFA, Holmes Park)
Leics Constabulary 0 **Quorn Res.** 1

LEICESTERSHIRE JUNIOR CUP
(April 13th at LCFA, Holmes Park)
Kirby Muxloe Res. 2 Desford 1 aet

LEICESTERSHIRE JUNIOR VASE
(April 7th at LCFA, Holmes Park)
Wigston Athletic 3 Desford Res. 1

LINCOLNSHIRE JUNIOR CUP
(May 2nd at Brigg Town)
Swineshead Inst. 3 AFC Brumby 1

LIVERPOOL CHALLENGE CUP
(May 12th at LCFA, Walton Hall Ave.
Waterloo Dock 2 Aigburth PH 1

LIVERPOOL INTERMEDIATE CUP
(April 21st at LCFA, Walton Hall Ave.)
Alumni 0 **Mosscroft** 2

LIVERPOOL JUNIOR CUP
(May 6th at LCFA, Walton Hall Ave.)
Eagle Sports 2 **Knowsley South** 3

LONDON INTERMEDIATE CUP
(April 18th at Metropolitan Police)
Thamesmead Town Res. 1 **Tooting & Mitcham United Res.** 2

LONDON JUNIOR CUP
(April 4th at Kingsbury London Tigers)
Newham Borough (SECP) 0
Summertown 1

LONDON OLD BOYS SENIOR CUP
(April 22nd at Potters Bar Town)
Old Aloysians 1 **UCL Academicals** 3

MANCHESTER CHALLENGE TROPHY
(February 11th at MCFA, Branthingham Road)
AVRO 2 Curzon Ashton Res. 0

MANCHESTER AMATEUR CUP
(April 7th at MCFA, Branthingham Rd)
Old Stretfordians 0 Heywood St
James 0 *aet* (3-2p)

MIDDLESEX CHARITY CUP 2007-08
(August 12th at Hayes & Yeading Utd)
Enfield Town 4 Hillingdon Boro. 1 *aet*

MIDDLESEX INTERMEDIATE CUP
(April 1st at Harrow Borough)
British Airways 1 Southall 0

MIDDLESEX JUNIOR CUP
(April 8th at North Greenford United)
Grosvenor House 2 Supreme Ath. 1

MIDDLESEX JUNIOR TROPHY
(April 22nd at Hanwell Town)
Indian Gymkhana Res. 2
GSK Leisure Club 3

MID-CHESHIRE SENIOR CUP
(April 6th at Witton Albion)
Witton Albion 2 Congleton Town 0

MORRISON BELL CUP
(May 21st at Ottery St Mary)
Royal Marines 4 Clyst Valley 2

NORFOLK JUNIOR CUP
(March 24th at Norwich City)
Norwich St Johns 1 King's Lynn A 1
aet (4-3p)

NORFOLK PRIMARY CUP
(April 24th at King's Lynn)
Docking Rangers 2 Pott Row 1

NORTH BEDS CHARITY CUP
(May 6th at Biggleswade Town)
Langford 1 **Stotfold** 5

NORTH CAMBRIDGESHIRE JUNIOR CUP
(April 15th at March Town United)
Coates Athletic 3 Guyhirn 1

NORTH EAST WALES CUP
(May 12th at Wrexham)
Lex XI 2 Mynydd Isa 2 *aet* (4-3p)

NORTH HAMPSHIRE INTERMEDIATE CUP
(April 14th at Alresford Town)
FC Censo 4 Twyford 0

NORTH RIDING COUNTY CUP
(March 4th at Stokesley Sports Club)
Fishburn Park 0
Grangetown Boys Club 4

NORTH RIDING CHALLENGE CUP
(April 15th at Stokesley Sports Club)
Whinney Banks YCC 2
Thirsk Falcons 1 *aet*

NORTH WALES COAST CUP
(May 16th at Flint Town United)
Llandudno Town 1
Gap Connah's Quay 0

NORTH WALES COAST INTERMEDIATE CUP
(May 2nd at Llandudno Town)
Greenfield 2 Gwalchmai 1

NORTH WALES COAST JUNIOR CUP
(May 9th at Denbigh Town)
St Asaph 1 **Trearddur Bay** 2

NORTHAMPTONSHIRE JUNIOR CUP
(April 15th at Rushden & Diamonds)
Bugbrooke St Michaels 1
Peterborough Northern Star 3

NORTHAMPTONSHIRE LOWER JUNIOR CUP
(March 26th at Raunds Town)
Weldon United Res. 0 **Northampton ON Chenecks Res.** 5

NORTHUMBERLAND MINOR CUP
(May 1st at Whitley Park, Benton)
Blakelaw Crofters Lodge 2
Wallsend Town 1

NOTTS INTERMEDIATE CUP
(April 22nd at Hucknall Town)
Carlton Town Res. 2 Linby CW 0

NOTTS JUNIOR CUP
(May 14th at Rainworth MW)
Ashland Rovers Res. 2 **White Lion** 3

NOTTS MINOR CUP
(May 12th at Dunkirk)
Bassingfield 2 **Calverton Miners Welfare Res.** 3 *aet*

OXFORDSHIRE CHARITY CUP
(April 18th at Enstone Sports)
Hailey 0 **Garsington** 3

OXFORDSHIRE INT. CUP
(April 20th at Oxford City)
Kidlington Res. 1 **North Leigh Res.** 2

OXFORDSHIRE JUNIOR SHIELD
(April 25th at Witney United)
Benson 2 Spartan Rangers 1

POWELL CHARITY CUP
(May 3rd at Wem Town)
Whitchurch Alport 0 **Instones** 1

RADNORSHIRE CUP
(April 13th at Llandrindod Wells)
Knighton 3 Gwernyfed 3 *aet* (3-0p)

ROBERTSBRIDGE CHARITY CUP
(May 5th at Robertsbridge)
St Leonards Social 1
Hooe Sports 1 *aet* (4-1p)

ROLLESTON CHARITY CUP
(May 4th at LCFA, Holmes Park)
Anstey Nomads 7 Hinckley United 1

RUNCORN CHALLENGE CUP
(April 17th at Pavilions, Runcorn)
Helsby 2 Runcorn Albion 1

SEATON CHALLENGE CUP
(May 23rd at Seaton Town)
Seaton T. 2 **B. Salterton Res.** 5 *aet*

SHEFFIELD & HALLAMSHIRE CHALLENGE CUP
(April 22nd at Doncaster Rovers)
Hall Green United 2 Kirkburton 1

SHEFFIELD & HALLAMSHIRE JUNIOR CUP
(April 15th at Stocksbridge PS)
HSBC 1 **Telecom Sports** 6

SHROPSHIRE JUNIOR CUP
(April 16th at Shrewsbury Town)
Ludlow Res. 0 **Ellesmere R. Res.** 3

SLOUGH TOWN SENIOR CUP
(April 10th at Burnham)
Wraysbury 1 Orchard Park Rgrs 0

SMEDLEY CROOKE MEMORIAL CHARITY CUP
(April 30th at Bromsgrove Rovers)
Boldmere SM Res. 5 Fairfield Villa 1

SOMERSET SENIOR CUP
(May 4th at Paulton Rovers)
Westland Spts 2 **Bridgwater Res.** 3

SOMERSET JUNIOR CUP
(April 15th at Bishop Sutton)
Fry Club Old Boys 0 **Purnell Sports** 5

SOMERSET INTERMEDIATE CUP
(May 5th at Cheddar)
Weston St Johns Sportsbar 1
Bishops Lydeard Res. 1 *aet* (3-1p)

SOMERSET MAVIS TATE CUP
(May 6th at Shepton Mallet)
Weston St Johns Sportsbar 1
Bishops Lydeard Res. 1 *aet* (3-1p)

SOUTHAMPTON SENIOR CUP
(April 28th at Southampton)
Nursling 0 **Team Solent** 2

SOUTHAMPTON JUNIOR A CUP
(April 13th at Sporting BTC)
Upham 2 AFC Hiltingbury 0

SOUTHAMPTON JUNIOR B CUP
(April 13th at Sporting BTC)
Warsash Wasp Res. 2
Spartans Res. 3 *aet*

SOUTH MIDLANDS RESERVES FLOODLIGHT CUP
(May 20th at Stotfold)
Stotfold Res. 1 Stansted Res. 0

SOUTH WALES INTERMEDIATE CUP
(May 7th at Taffs Well)
Llanharan 2 **Penrhiwceiber Con Athletic** 4

STAFFORDSHIRE VASE
(April 6th at Eccleshall)
Penkridge Town 1 **Manor Inne** 2

STAFFORDSHIRE PRESIDENT'S CUP
(March 16th at Norton United)
Ball Green Y&A 5 Wolstanton Res. 4

SUFFOLK JUNIOR CUP
(May 6th at Ipswich Town)
Achilles 5 Old Newton United 2 *aet*

SUFFOLK RESERVES CUP
(May 7th at Leiston)
Lowestoft Town Res. 2
Grundisburgh Res. 1

SURREY PREMIER CUP
(April 15th at Leatherhead)
Met Police Res. 2 Farleigh Rovers 1

SURREY INTERMEDIATE CUP
(May 6th at Sutton United)
Battersea Ironsides 3 Bletchingley 1

SURREY JUNIOR CUP
(May 13th at Walton Casuals)
Summertown 0 **Horley Town Res.** 4

SUSSEX INTERMEDIATE CUP
(April 21st at Lancing)
Forest 1 Bosham 0

SUSSEX JUNIOR CUP
(March 24th at Lancing)
AFC Ringmer 1 **Fishbourne** 2

VERNON WENTWORTH CUP
(May 6th at Worthing)
Clymping 2 St Francis Rgrs Res. 1

WAKEFIELD & DISTRICT CUP
(April 8th at Wakefield)
Altofts 2 Nostell Miners Welfare 1

WEST RIDING CHALLENGE CUP
(May 1st at WRCFA, Woodlesford)
Meltham Athletic 0 **Ovenden WR** 1

WEST RIDING CHALL. TROPHY
(April 27th at WRCFA, Woodlesford)
Whitkirk Wanderers Res. 3
Storthes Hall Res. 0

WESTMORLAND BENEVOLENT TROPHY
(April 8th at Kendal Town)
Ambleside United 4
Wetheriggs United 1

WESTMORLAND JUNIOR CUP
(April 15th at Kendal Town)
Wetheriggs United Res. 1 **Ibis** 2 *aet*

WHARFEDALE CUP
(April 13th at Guiseley)
Baildon Trinity Athletic 2 Pool 1

WIRRAL SENIOR CUP
(May 2nd at Vauxhall Motors)
Newton 2 **Cammell Laird Res.** 3 *aet*

WIRRAL AMATEUR CUP
(April 13th at Ashville)
Willaston 2 FC Pensby 1

WORCESTER NURSING CUP
(April 22nd at Worcester City)
Archdale 3 Martley Spurs 0

WORCESTERSHIRE JUNIOR CUP
(April 8th at Worcester City)
Fairfield Villa 3 Wyre Forest 1

WORCESTERSHIRE MINOR CUP
(April 17th at Pershore Town)
Broadway United 1 Upton Town 0

WYCOMBE SENIOR CUP
(May 11th at Burnham)
Burnham 1 Chalfont St Peter 0 *aet*

WYCOMBE JUNIOR CUP
(April 21st at Holmer Green)
Chalfont Wasps Res. 2
AC Marlow Res. 0

YMCA CUP
(May 30th at South Molton)
North Molton Res. 4
Chittlehampton 0

WWW.NLNEWSDESK.CO.UK

AMATEUR FOOTBALL ALLIANCE

President: J R Wilson
Chief Executive Officer: Mike Brown, Unit 3, 7 Wenlock Road, London N1 7SL
Tel: 0844 980 8207
Website: www.amateur-fa.com :: **Email:** mike.brown@amateur-fa.com

AMATEUR FOOTBALL ALLIANCE REPRESENTATIVE TEAM

Southern Counties Championship 2008-09 Season

Winners: Amateur Football Alliance

SENIOR TEAM MATCH RESULTS

AFA v Oxford University -	(H)	W 7-3 (Friendly)
AFA v Royal Navy -	(H)	W 2-0
AFA v Sussex FA -	(A)	W 3-1
AFA v Army FA -	(A)	W 2-1
AFA v Middlesex FA -	(H)	W 3-1
AFA v London FA -	(A)	W 7-2
AFA v RAF FA -	(A)	L 2-0 (Friendly)

UNDER 18 MATCH RESULTS 2008-9

AFA v Someset FA -	(A)	W 4-3 (FA Youth Cup)
AFA v Sussex FA -	(H)	L 6-0
AFA v Wiltshire FA -	(A)	L 2-1 (FA Youth Cup)
AFA v Kent FA -	(A)	L 4-1
AFA v London FA -	(A)	W 2-0
AFA v Royal Navy FA -	(H)	L 4-1
AFA v Middlesex FA -	(A)	L 3-1
AFA v Surrey FA –	(H)	L 2-1

UNDER 16 MATCH RESULTS 2008-9

AFA v Surrey FA -	(H)	L 2-0
AFA v Sussex FA -	(H)	D 2-2
AFA v Kent FA -	(H)	W 2-1
AFA v Middlesex FA -	(H)	W 2-1
AFA v London FA -	(A)	D 2-2

AMATEUR FOOTBALL ALLIANCE CUPS

Senior	Nottsborough	1	v	0	Polytechnic
Senior Middlesex/Essex	Albanian	4	v	2	Winchmore Hill
Senior Kent/Surrey	West Wickham	1	v	0	Nottsborough
Intermediate	Bealonians	4	v	3	Chertsey Old Salesians
Intermediate Middlesex/Essex	Old Salvatorians	2	v	4	Old Actonians
Intermediate Kent/Surrey	Hon Artillery Co	2	v	1	Nottsborough
Junior	Old Actonians	1	v	2	Winchmore Hill
Minor	Old Kingsburians	6	v	0	Winchmore Hill
Senior Novets	Civil Service	4	v	1	Old Westminster Citizens
Junior Novets	Crouch End Vampires	1	v	4	Old Actonians
Intermediate Novets	Polytechnic	4	v	2	West Wickham
Closed Veterans	Old Aloyisans	0	v	3	Old Meadonians
Open Veterans	Old Meadonians	1	v	2	Malden
Womens'	Flamingoes	12	v	0	Bethwin
Youth U'18 Saturday	Enfield Community	0	v	4	Bealonians
Youth U'17 Saturday	West Essex Colts	2	v	3	Southerk Tigers
Youth U'16 Saturday	Whitewebbs Eagles	2	v	3	Springfield
Youth U'15 Saturday	Ilford Colts	0	v	1	Independent
Youth U'14 Saturday	Providence House	8	v	0	Bealonians
Youth U'13 Saturday	Independent	2	v	0	West Essex Colts
Youth U'12 Saturday	Young Guns	2	v	4	Providence House
Youth U'11 Saturday	Kodak	3	v	1	West Essex Colts
Youth U'18 Sunday	Muswell Hill	3	v	0	Broomfield PL
Youth U'17 Sunday	Wakthan Abbey	2	v	0	Norsemen
Youth U'16 Sunday	Norsemen	4	v	0	Bealonians
Youth U'15 Sunday	Southgate Adelaide	2	v	0	Welling United
Youth U'14 Sunday	Waltham Abbey	1	v	2	Southgate Adelaide
Youth U'13 Sunday	Chase Side	3	v	2	Broomfield PL
Youth U'12 Sunday	Alexandra Park	2	v	5	Chase Side
Youth U'11 Sunday	West Essex Colts	2	v	1	Alexandra Park
Girls U'16	Lea Valley Girls	3	v	2	Westside Girls
Girls U'14	Lea Valley Girls	6	v	1	Potters Bar Girls

AMATEUR FOOTBALL COMBINATION

PREMIER DIVISION	P	W	D	L	F	A	GD	Pts
Bealonians	18	13	1	4	42	19	23	40
Old Aloysians	18	10	3	5	35	25	10	33
Honorable Artillery Company	18	9	3	6	36	35	1	30
Old Hamptonians	18	7	5	6	33	25	8	26
Albanian	18	7	5	6	32	32	0	26
Old Meadonians	18	7	3	8	38	33	5	24
Parkfield	18	7	3	8	32	42	-10	24
Old Parmiterians	18	5	4	9	34	39	-5	19
Old Salvatorians	18	6	4	8	31	37	-6	18
UCL Academicals	18	3	1	14	24	50	-26	10

LONDON OLD BOYS SENIOR CUP

UCL Academicals 3 Old Aloysians 1

SOUTHERN AMATEUR FOOTBALL LEAGUE

SENIOR DIVISION 1	P	W	D	L	F	A	GD	Pts
Nottsborough	20	13	5	2	49	15	+34	44
Winchmore Hill	20	11	4	5	33	17	+16	37
Old Salesians	20	9	6	5	35	24	+11	33
Old Owens	20	9	5	6	34	26	+8	32
West Wickham	20	9	4	7	27	24	+3	31
Polytechnic	20	8	6	6	34	35	-1	30
Old Wilsonians	20	8	5	7	32	29	+3	29
Weirside Rangers	20	5	7	8	29	31	-2	22
Old Actonians Association	20	5	6	9	32	41	-9	21
Old Esthameians	20	4	2	14	25	55	-30	14
Alleyn Old Boys	20	2	4	14	21	54	-33	10

LONDON LEGAL LEAGUE

DIVISION 1	P	W	D	L	F	A	GD	Pts
Slaughter & May	18	14	2	2			36	44
Financial Services Authority	18	11	4	3			15	37
Clifford Chance	18	11	3	4			12	36
Ashurst	18	11	2	5			15	35
Linklaters	18	8	4	6			20	28
Watson Farley Williams	18	7	4	7			5	25
Freshfields Bruckhaus Deringer	18	6	4	8			-11	22
Nabarro	18	4	3	11			-12	14
Allen & Overy	18	2	3	13			-35	7
Dechert	18	1	1	16			-45	4

CHALLENGE CUP FINAL

Linklaters 2 Financila Services Authority 1

WEAVERS CUP FINAL

Watson Farley and Williams 2 Ashurst 0

ARTHURIAN LEAGUE

PREMIER DIVISION	P	W	D	L	F	A	GD	Pts
Old Carthusians	18	13	3	2	51	20	31	42
Old Harrovians	18	12	1	5	51	42	9	37
Old Brentwoods	18	9	1	8	32	30	2	28
Old Cholmeleians	18	8	3	7	33	34	-1	27
Old King's (Wimbledon)	18	7	4	7	32	34	-2	25
Old Westminsters	18	6	6	6	33	30	3	24
Lancing Old Boys	18	5	4	9	31	37	-6	19
Old Foresters	18	6	2	10	34	35	-1	17
Old Etonians	18	4	4	10	31	41	-10	16
Old Malvernians	18	3	6	9	23	48	-25	15

ARTHUR DUNN CUP

Old Carthusian 1 Lancing Old Boys 1
(Old Carthusians won 5-4 on penalties)

LONDON UNIVERSITY
INTER COLLEGIATE LEAGUE MENS

DIVISION 1	P	W	D	L	F	A	GD	Pts
Royal Holloway	12	9	2	1	44	20	24	29
London School of Economics	12	9	1	2	30	11	19	28
Royal Free & Uni. Coll. Medical School	11	8	2	1	31	16	15	26
University College London	12	7	1	4	24	15	9	22
University College London	12	7	0	5	50	26	24	21
Queen Mary, Uni. of London	11	6	2	3	24	23	1	20
School of Oriental & African Studies	12	7	1	4	29	19	10	19*
St Barts & the Royal London	11	5	0	6	28	21	7	15
Royal Holloway Res	12	3	1	8	10	31	-21	10
Imperial College Res	12	3	0	9	12	36	-24	9
Imperial College	10	2	2	6	19	26	-7	8
London School of Economics 3rd	12	2	1	9	15	42	-27	7
London School of Economics Res	11	0	1	10	15	45	-30	1

LONDON UNIVERSITY
INTER COLLEGIATE LEAGUE WOMENS

DIVISION 1	P	W	D	L	F	A	GD	Pts
University College London Women's 1s ULU	10	7	2	1	54	15	39	23
Royal Holloway, University of London Women's 1s ULU	10	6	4	0	36	7	29	22
King's College London Medical Schools Women's 1s ULU	10	6	2	2	63	26	37	20
Queen Mary, University of London Women's 1s ULU	10	3	1	6	19	43	-24	10
Royal Veterinary College Women's 1s ULU	10	2	1	7	15	46	-31	7
Goldsmiths, University of London Women's 1s ULU	10	1	0	9	12	62	-50	-3*

ARMED FORCES FOOTBALL

INTER SERVICES CUP

MEN'S COMPETITION

	P	W	D	L	F	A	Pts
Royal Air Force	2	1	1	0	2	1	4
Royal Navy	2	1	0	1	2	2	3
Army	2	0	1	1	2	3	1

Inter Service Champions 2007/08: Royal Air Force

Inter Service Champions 2006/07: Army

Inter Service Champions 2005/06: Army

Inter Service Champions 2004/05: Army

Inter Service Champions 2003/04: Royal Navy

WOMEN'S COMPETITION

	P	W	D	L	F	A	Pts
Royal Air Force	2	1	1	0	4	2	4
Army	2	0	2	0	2	2	2
Royal Navy	2	0	1	1	2	4	1

Inter Service Champions 2007/08: Army

Inter Service Champions 2006/07: Army

Inter Service Champions 2005/06: Royal Air force

Inter Service Champions 2004/05: Army

Inter Service Champions 2003/04: Army

3 (UK) Div HQ & Sig Regt captain steps up to lift the Army F.A. Cup. Photo: Eric Marsh.

ROYAL AIR FORCE - SENIOR MENS RESULTS 2008-09

Date	Opponents	Venue	Competition	Result
Oct 22	M.o.D.	RAF Uxbridge	Friendly	W 7-1
Nov 12	English Police	RAF Uxbridge	Friendly	D 1-1
Dec 3	Farnborough	Farnborough FC	Friendly	L 1-2
Dec 10	Prison Service	Leicester	Friendly	W 3-1
Jan 11-16	Elgin City	Pre Inter-Services	Friendly	W 1-0
	Aberdeen	training camp	Friendly	L 0-6
	Lossiemouth	at RAF Kinloss	Friendly	W 4-0
Jan 28	Amateur FA	RAF Uxbridge	Friendly	W 2-0
Feb 12	Fire Service	RAF Uxbridge	Friendly	W 4-1
Feb 22 - Mar 1	RAF Cyprus	Pre Inter-Serivces	Friendly	W 4-0
	Combined Services Cyprus	training camp Cyprus	Friendly	W 2-0
Mar 4	Royal Navy	RAF Uxbridge	Inter-Services	W 1-0
Mar 18	Army	Aldershot	Inter-Services	D 1-1
Apr 8	Royal Netherlands Air Force	RAF Uxbridge	Presidents Cup	W 5-0

ROYAL NAVY - SENIOR MENS RESULTS 2008-09

Date	Opponents	Venue	Competition	Result
Oct 22	South Down Academy FC	Portsmouth	Friendly	D 1-1
Nov 12	AFA	London	SC Cup	L 0-2
Nov 26	London FA	Portsmouth	SC Cup	D 1-1
Dec 4	Fire Service	Portsmouth	Friendly	W 5-0
Dec 10	Sussex FA	Portsmouth	SC Cup	W 2-1
Jan 21	Prison Service	Portsmouth	Friendly	L 1-2
Jan 28	Havant & Waterlooville FC	Portsmouth	Friendly	D 1-1
Feb 18	United Services Portsmouth	Portsmouth	Friendly	W 5-2
Mar 4	Royal Air Force	RAF Uxbridge	Inter-Services	L 0-1
Mar 11	Army	Portsmouth	Inter-Services	W 2-1

NAVY CUP (from the Quarter Final Stages)

QUARTER FINALS

Hms Sultan	v	FPGRM	1-3
Hms Collingwood	v	Hms Excellent	3-1
Hms Seahawk	v	Hms Drake	3-0
40 Cdo Rm	v	Brnc Dartmouth	5-0

SEMI FINALS

Hms Collingwood	v	FPGRM	2-4
40 Cdo Rm	v	Hms Seahawk	1-6

FINAL

Hms Seahawk	v	FPGRM	0-3

BRITISH UNIVERSITIES FOOTBALL

MEN'S CHAMPIONSHIP FINAL

UWE HARTPURY (H)	1	1	LOUGHBOROUGH
Davies 115	11 pens	12 pens	*Mpi 104*

UWE Hartpury

1 Richard Thomas
2 Lee Molyneaux (C)
3 Ben Pugh
4 James Baldwin
5 Russell Courtney
6 Marc Richards
7 Steve Davies
8 Alex Allard
9 Marcus Palmer
10 Sean Seavill
11 Isaac Shaze

SUBSTITUTES
Jamie Powell
Beng Ngwa
Mike Symons
Jon Else
Alex Hards

Loughborough

1 David Coombes
2 James Aldred
3 Ben Harvey
4 Omar Takriti
5 Adam Steventon
6 Luke Horrocks (C)
7 Matt Aldred
8 Liam Green
9 Mikel Suarez
10 Bradley Pritchard
11 Steve Blenkinsopp

SUBSTITUTES
Charlie Mpi
Rob Edmands
Daniel Sleath
Anthony Moulds
Rob Webb

PREMIER LEAGUE FINAL STANDINGS

NORTH		SOUTH
LOUGHBOROUGH	1	BRIGHTON
BIRMINGHAM	2	BATH
LEEDS MET	3	SWANSEA
LEEDS	4	BRUNEL WEST LONDON
NORTHUMBRIA	5	EXETER
LINCOLN	6	UWE HARTPURY

TIER ONE FINAL STANDINGS

NORTHERN		WESTERN
EDGE HILL	1	BATH 2
HULL	2	BOURNEMOUTH
MANCHESTER	3	CARDIFF
MMU CHESHIRE	4	PLYMOUTH
SUNDERLAND	5	SOUTHAMPTON
YORK ST JOHN	6	WEST OF ENGLAND

MIDLANDS		SOUTH EASTERN
NOTTINGHAM	1	CHICHESTER
NOTTINGHAM 2	2	ESSEX
NOTTINGHAM TRENT	3	HERFORDSHIRE
OXFORD	4	KENT
WARWICK	5	READING
WORCESTER	6	ST MARYS

WOMEN'S CHAMPIONSHIP FINAL

LEEDS MET CARNEGIE	3	0	NORTHUMBRIA
Heckler 62, 72, Lee 88			

PREMIER LEAGUE FINAL STANDINGS

NORTH		SOUTH
LOUGHBOROUGH	1	BATH
BIRMINGHAM	2	BRIGHTON
LEEDS MET	3	BRUNEL WEST LONDON
MANCHESTER	4	EXETER
NORTHUMBRIA	5	HERTFORDSHIRE
MMU CHESHIRE	6	UWIC

ENGLISH SCHOOLS' FOOTBALL ASSOCIATION

4, Parker Court, Staffordshire Technology Park, Beaconside, Stafford ST18 0WP
Tel : 01785 785970; website :www..esfa.co.uk

Chief Executive
John Read (john.read@schoolsfa.com)

Competitions Manager
Mike Spinks (mike.spinks@schoolsfa.com)

Non-League Directory Publicity
Mike Simmonds (0115 9313299)
m.simmonds31@btinternet.com

Photos : RWT Photography (01733 204445)
(r.windle@tiscali.co.uk))

THE INTERNATIONAL SEASON

THE CARNEGIE CENTENARY SCHOOLS' SHIELD (UNDER 18)

FINAL TABLE 2008-09	P	W	D	L	F	A	Pts
England	4	3	0	1	6	1	9
Northern Ireland	4	3	0	1	6	3	9
Republic of Ireland	4	2	1	1	6	3	7
Wales	4	1	0	3	2	9	3
Scotland	4	0	1	3	2	2	6

England Results

Opponents	Venue	Result		England Goalscorers
Wales	Boston United F.C.	**W**	**3-0**	Watson (2), Libby
Northern Ireland	Macclesfield Town F.C.	L	0-1	
Scotland	St. Mirrren F.C.	**W**	**2-0**	Morgan, Carter
Republic of Ireland	Waterford F.C.	**W**	**1-0**	Baptista

Friendly International:
England Schools 2 France Under 18s 4 At Wembley Stadium

ENGLAND SCHOOLS' F.A UNDER 18 INTERNATIONAL SQUAD 2008-2009
Back Row: Tom Chapman, Matthew Tasker, Steven Norris, Jamie Libby, Tom Pass, David Wheeler, Joe Villiers.
Middle Row: Jacob Batista, Taylor Morgan, Michael Scott, Joe Clayton, Simon Johnson, Robert Carter.
Front Row: David Knight, Nick Hancock, Danny Watson, Matthew Whitehead, James Norwood. Inset : James Ellis.

SCHOOLS' CUP COMPETITIONS

U11 SMALL SCHOOLS SOCCER SEVENS
SATURDAY 13th JUNE 2009, WEMBLEY STADIUM

NORTH LEVERTON (BASSETLAW PSFA)	2	THE BRITISH (WOTTON UNDER EDGE PSFA)	1

Referee:Dominic Gregory (Hampshire)
Goalscorers: Owen Gamble (2, North Leverton), Cameron Pring (British)

U11 INTER-ASSOCIATION 7-A-SIDE TROPHY
SATURDAY 13th JUNE 2009, WEMBLEY STADIUM

SOLIHULL PSFA	2	SOUTHAMPTON	1

Referee: Neil Hair (Cambridgeshire)
Goalscorers: Bailey Ralph (2, Solihull), Matthew Worthington (Southampton)

U11 SCHOOLS 7-A-SIDE CUP (BOYS)
SATURDAY 13th JUNE 2009, WEMBLEY STADIUM

HAREWOOD (GLOUCESTER PSFA)	3	MANOR FARM (HIGH WYCOMBE PSFA)	1

Referee: Richard Callus (Leicestershire)
Goalscorers: Karnell Chambers (2, Harewood), Will Hayward (Harewood), James Outten (Manor Farm)

U11 SCHOOLS 7-A-SIDE CUP (GIRLS)
SATURDAY 13th JUNE 2009, WEMBLEY STADIUM

ABBEY ROAD (RUSHCLIFFE PSFA)	0	ST PAUL'S (HIGH WYCOMBE PSFA)	0

Referee: George Lock (Essex)

U12 INDOOR 5-A-SIDE CUP FINAL (BOYS)
MONDAY 09 MARCH 2009, JJB SOCCERDOME, PRIDE PARK, DERBY

ST THOMAS THE APOSTLE (SOUTH LONDON SFA)	4	SOUTH HUNSLEY (EAST RIDING SFA)	3

Referee: Chris Ward (Nottinghamshire)
Goalscorers: Kaswayne Williams (3, St Thomas), Kyle Grant (St Thomas), Will Annan (South Hunsley), Eddie Rogerson (2, South Hunsley),

U12 INDOOR 5-A-SIDE CUP FINAL (GIRLS)
MONDAY 09 MARCH 2009, JJB SOCCERDOME, PRIDE PARK, DERBY

MAIDEN ERLEGH (READING SFA)	5	TRINITY (NOTTINGHAM SFA)	0

Referee: Peter Kenworthy (Nottinghamshire)
Goalscorers: Jade Bradley (4, Maiden Erlegh), Rachel Newborough (Maiden Erlegh)

U12 BOYS SCHOOLS CUP FINAL
SPONSORED BY MATCH! & DANONE
TUESDAY 19 MAY 2009, GOODISON PARK, EVERTON FC

ARCHBISHOP BECK (LIVERPOOL SFA)	2	RICHARD CHALLONER (KINGSTON SFA)	1

Referee: Graham Lawler (Greater Manchester)
Goalscorers: Rhys Hardacre (Archbishop Beck), Brian Lee (Archbishop Beck), Jack Watret (Richard Challoner)

U13 GIRLS MINUTE MAID SCHOOLS CUP FINAL
TUESDAY 19 MAY 2009, KEEPMOAT STADIUM, DONCASTER ROVERS FC

HABERDASHER'S ASKE'S (BLACKHEATH SFA)	1	SOUTH HOLDERNESS (EAST RIDING SFA)	0

Referee: Helen Fulcher (Lincolnshire)
Goalscorers: Gemma Porter (Haberdasher's)

U13 BOYS MINUTE MAID SCHOOLS CUP FINAL
TUESDAY 19 MAY 2009, KEEPMOAT STADIUM, DONCASTER ROVERS FC

WEST BRIDGFORD (SOUTH NOTTS SFA)	2	QUEENS (WATFORD SFA)	1

Referee: Kevin Gray (Nottinghamshire)
Assistants: Peter Kenworthy (Nottinghamshire) and Keith Goulding (Nottinghamshire)
Fourth Official: Des Coulson (North Yorkshire)
Goalscorers:Joe Harbottle (West Bridgford), Pierce Bramley (West Bridgford), Nathan Osaji (Queens)

U13 INTER ASSOCIATION TROPHY FINAL
SUNDAY 17 MAY 2009, ST JAMES' PARK, NEWCASTLE UNITED FC

GATESHEAD SFA	3	NORTHAMPTON SFA	1

Referee: Eddie Ilderton (Northumberland)
Goalscorers:Connor Halpin (Gateshead), Jake Avilez (2, Gateshead), Ivan Toney (Northampton)

U14 BOYS PREMIER LEAGUE SCHOOLS CUP FINAL
SATURDAY 28 MARCH 2009, OLD TRAFFORD, MANCHESTER UNITED FC

AUDENSHAW (TAMESIDE SFA)	2	FOREST (EAST BERKSHIRE SFA)	1

Referee: Mike Jones (Cheshire)
Goalscorers:Dean Partington (Audenshaw), Niall Maher (Audenshaw), Valdy Simeon (Forest)

U15 INTER ASSOCIATION TROPHY FINAL
MONDAY 11 MAY 2009, EDGLEY PARK, STOCKPORT COUNTY FC

STOCKPORT SFA	2	WARRINGTON SFA	1

Referee: Mike Youds (Merseyside)
Goalscorers:Josh Harrison (Stockport), Nick Barber (Stockport), Joe Guest (Warrington)

U15 BOYS SCHOOLS CUP FINAL
THURSDAY 14 MAY 2009, BRAMALL LANE, SHEFFIELD UNITED FC

WALBOTTLE (NEWCASTLE UPON TYNE SFA)	1	RIDGEWAY (PLYMOUTH SFA)	0

Referee: Gary Brittain (Nottinghamshire)
Goalscorers: Liam McNamara (Walbottle)

U15 GIRLS SCHOOLS CUP FINAL
WEDNESDAY 06 MAY 2009, ST JAMES' PARK, EXETER CITY FC

TIDEWAY (BRIGHTON & HOVE SFA)	2	FALLIBROOME (MACCLESFIELD SFA)	1

Referee: Ray Brown (Cornwall)
Goalscorers:Antonia Rigby (Tideway), Holly Kelley (Tideway), Helen Moyes (Fallibroome)

U16 BOYS INTER COUNTY TROPHY FINAL
MONDAY 27 APRIL 2009, NEW DEN, MILLWALL FC

GREATER MANCHESTER CSFA	3	ESSEX CSFA	1

Referee: Mike Barnes (Inner London)
Goalscorers: Matthew Chadwick (Greater Manchester), James Torkowski (Greater Manchester), Leroy Chintenger (Greater Manchester), Senol Demirbala (Essex),

U16 GIRLS RAF SCHOOLS CUP FINAL
TUESDAY 05 MAY 2009, CITY OF MANCHESTER STADIUM, MANCHESTER CITY FC

ST WILFRID'S (BLACKBURN & DARWEN SFA)	2	WINSTON CHURCHILL (WOKING SFA)	1

Referee: Sgt J Boyle (RAF Benson)
Goalscorers:Megan Searson (St Wilfrid's), Jessica Clegg (St Wilfrid's), Emma Lawrence (Winston Churchill)

U16 BOYS RAF SCHOOLS CUP FINAL
TUESDAY 05 MAY 2009, CITY OF MANCHESTER STADIUM, MANCHESTER CITY FC

WRIGHT ROBINSON (MANCHESTER SFA)	4	HOWARD OF EFFINGHAM (GUILDFORD SFA)	1

Referee: Trevor Kettle (Berkshire)
Goalscorers: Jordan Thompson (Wright Robinson), Kaide Moreland (2, Wright Robinson), Josh Oguntayo (Wright Robinson), Josh Gallagher (Howard of Effingham)

U16 INTER COUNTY GIRLS TROPHY FINAL
THURSDAY 02 APRIL 2009, SINCIL BANK, LINCOLN CITY FC

WEST YORKSHIRE CSFA	1	MIDDLESEX CSFA	0

Referee: Keith Goulding (Nottinghamshire)
Goalscorers: Faye Birkby (West Yorkshire)

U18 BOYS INTER COUNTY TROPHY FINAL
WEDNESDAY 29 APRIL 2009, KENILWORTH ROAD, LUTON TOWN FC

NORTHUMBERLAND CSFA	4	HAMPSHIRE CSFA	0

Referee: Tony Schneider (Inner London)
Goalscorers: Steven Forster (Northumberland), Daniel Hindmarsh (3, Northumberland)

U18 SCHOOLS FINAL TROPHY FOR GIRLS
THURSDAY 07 MAY 2009, CARROW ROAD, NORWICH CITY FC

FILTON COLLEGE (BRISTOL & S GLOUCESTERSHIRE SFA)	9	MANCHESTER COLLEGE (MANCHESTER SFA)	0

Referee: Neil Hair (Cambridgeshire)
Goalscorers: Sharla Passariella (4, Filton), Emma Plewa (2, Filton), Sam Thomsit, Sophie Wyatt (Filton), Jade Scammell (Filton)

U18 SCHOOLS FINAL TROPHY FOR BOYS
TUESDAY 06 MAY 2009, THE EBB STADIUM, ALDERSHOT TOWN FC

ST BEDE'S (SOUTH EAST SUSSEX SFA)	5	CARRE'S GRAMMAR (KESTEVEN SFA)	2

Referee: Paul Armstrong (Berkshire)
Goalscorers:Bradley Bant (St Bede's), James Norwood (2, St Bede's), Dan Gorringe (St Bede's), Moritz Diemer (St Bede's)

WOMEN'S FOOTBALL

NATIONAL DIVISION 2008-09

		P	W	D	L	F	A	Pts
1.	**Arsenal**	**22**	**20**	**1**	**1**	**89**	**14**	**61**
2.	Everton	22	20	1	1	68	10	61
3.	Chelsea	22	16	2	4	55	23	50
4.	Doncaster Rovers Belles	22	9	6	7	43	36	33
5.	Birmingham City	22	10	3	9	39	43	33
6.	Leeds Carnegie	22	8	4	10	32	40	28
7.	Watford	22	7	4	11	31	40	25
8.	Bristol Academy	22	5	8	9	39	49	23
9.	Blackburn Rovers	22	5	3	14	27	52	18
10.	Nottingham Forest	22	5	2	15	25	59	17
11.	Liverpool	22	4	4	14	28	63	16
12.	WFC Fulham	22	1	6	15	17	64	9

NORTHERN DIVISION 2008-09

		P	W	D	L	F	A	Pts
1.	**Sunderland**	**22**	**17**	**2**	**3**	**95**	**16**	**53**
2.	OOH Lincoln	22	16	4	2	79	15	52
3.	Manchester City	22	13	4	5	42	22	43
4.	Newcastle United	22	12	5	5	58	28	41
5.	Leicester City	22	12	4	6	54	33	40
6.	Reading	22	9	6	7	43	31	33
7.	Aston Villa	22	10	2	10	49	50	32
8.	Preston North End	22	7	3	12	37	51	24
9.	Sheffield Wednesday	22	6	0	16	37	72	18
10.	Curzon Ashton	22	4	4	14	35	70	16
11.	Tranmere Rovers	22	4	2	16	28	76	14
12.	Rotherham United	22	3	2	17	17	110	11

SOUTHERN DIVISION 2008-09

		P	W	D	L	F	A	Pts
1.	**Millwall Lionesses**	**22**	**17**	**3**	**2**	**61**	**14**	**54**
2.	Barnet	22	11	7	4	58	33	40
3.	West Ham United	22	10	9	3	41	20	39
4.	Charlton Athletic	22	10	6	6	37	28	36
5.	Portsmouth	22	9	6	7	50	36	33
6.	Colchester United	22	8	6	8	37	41	30
7.	Cardiff City	22	8	5	9	40	38	29
8.	Keynsham Town	22	8	3	11	34	49	27
9.	Crystal Palace	22	5	8	9	31	43	23
10.	Brighton & Hove Albion	22	5	5	12	28	44	20
11.	Ipswich Town	22	5	3	14	19	64	18
12.	Truro City	22	3	5	14	32	58	14

NATIONAL DIVISION 2009-10	NORTHERN DIVISION 2009-10	SOUTHERN DIVISION 2009-10
Arsenal	Aston Villa	Barnet
Birmingham City	Curzon Ashton	Brighton & Hove Albion
Blackburn Rovers	Derby County	Cardiff City
Bristol Academy	Leeds City Vixens	Charlton Athletic
Chelsea	Leicester City	Colchester United
Doncaster Rovers Belles	Liverpool	Crystal Palace
Everton	Luton Town	Keynsham Town
Leeds Carnegie	Manchester City	Portsmouth
Millwall Lionesses	Newcastle United	Queens Park Rangers
Nottingham Forest	OHH Lincoln	Reading
Sunderland	Preston North End	WFC Fulham
Watford	Sheffield Wednesday	West Ham United

LEAGUE CUP

FIRST ROUND

Sunderland	v	Sheffield Wednesday	4-1
Colchester United	v	Portsmouth	5-6
Newcastle United	v	Preston North End	1-2
Reading	v	Barnet	0-2

SECOND ROUND

Nottingham Forest	v	Liverpool	4-2
Tranmere Rovers	v	Doncaster Rovers Belles	1-6
OOH Lincoln	v	Sunderland	3-1
Watford	v	Crystal Palace	3-0
Blackburn Rovers	v	Rotherham United	7-2
West Ham United	v	Portsmouth	1-2
Preston North End	v	Cuzon Ashton	5-3
Brighton & H.A.	v	Truro City	3-2
Chelsea	v	Barnet	4-0
Leeds Carnegie	v	Manchester City	1-0
Cardiff City	v	WFC Fulham	1-2
Bristol Academy	v	Keynsham Town	3-0
Millwall Lionesses	v	Ipswich Town	7-1
Leicester City	v	Aston Villa	6-2
Arsenal	v	Charlton Athletic	6-2
Everton (H)	v	Birmingham City	2-1

THIRD ROUND

Nottingham Forest	v	Doncaster Rovers Belles	0-4
OOH Lincoln	v	Watford	2-3
Blackburn Rovers	v	Portsmouth	3-4
Preston North End	v	Brighton & H.A.	1-0
Chelsea	v	Leeds Carnegie	3-2
WFC Fulham	v	Bristol Academy	4-2
Millwall Lionesses	v	Leciester City	1-3
Arsenal	v	Everton (H)	3-1

QUARTER-FINALS

Doncaster Rovers Belles	v	Watford	3-0
Portsmouth	v	Preston North End	0-1
Chelsea	v	WFC Fulham	3-0
Leicester City	v	Arsenal	0-7

SEMI-FINALS

Doncaster Rovers Belles	v	Preston North End	3-1
Chelsea	v	Arsenal	0-4

THE FINAL

Doncaster Rovers Belles	v	Arsenal	0-5

ENGLAND SENIOR TEAM - 2008/09

	Date	Opponents	H/A	Comp	Result		Goalscorers	Att
1	Jul 17	Germany	A	Friendly	L	0-3	-	9,195
2	Sept 28	Czech Rep.	A	Euro Qual.	**W**	**5-1**	Westwood 61, K.Smith 79,86, Carney 81, J.Scott 86	1,054
3	Oct 02	Spain	A	Euro Qual.	D	2-2	Carney 55, K. Smith 77	
4	Feb 09	Finland	N	Friendly	D	2-2		
5	11	Finland	N	Friendly	**W**	**4-1**		
6	Mar 05	South Africa	N	Cyprus Cup	**W**	**6-0**	Williams 18, Sanderson 19, K.Smith 42, Houghton 54, Chapman 87, 90+1	
7	07	France	N	Cyprus Cup	D	2-2	Carney 28, Stoney 75	
8	10	Scotland	N	Cyprus Cup	**W**	**3-0**	Aluko 40, Westwood 66, Clarke 83	
9	12	Canada	N	Cyprus Cup	**W**	**3-1**	Sanderson 32, K.Smith 40, Williams 45+1	
10	Apr 23	Norway	H	Friendly	**W**	**3-0**	Williams 18,81, Johnson 39	4,468
11	Jul 16	Iceland	H	Friendly	L	0-2		4,170
12	22	Denmark	H	Friendly	**W**	**1-0**	Handley 87	4,177
13	Aug 25	Italy	N	Euro Grp C				
14	28	Russia	N	Euro Grp C				
15	31	Sweden	N	Euro Grp C				

	BROWN	ALEX SCOTT	STONEY	F. WILLIAMS	WHITE	ASANTE	CARNEY	JILL SCOTT	SANDERSON	KELLY SMITH	YANKEY	JOHNSON	SUE SMITH	WESTWOOD	UNITT	ALUKO	CHAMBERLAIN	BASSETT	BUET	HOUGHTON	CHAPMAN	CLARKE	YORSTON	HANDLEY	R.WILLIAMS	TELFORD	DAVISON	HICKMOTT	DOWIE	SUSI	BARDSLEY	
1	X	X	X	X	X	X	X	X	X	X	X	S	S	S																		1
2	X	X	X	X		X	X	X	X	X	X	X	S	S	S	U	U	U	U													2
3	X	X	X	X	U	X	X	X	U	X	X	X	S	S	U	X	U	U														3
4																																4
5																																5
6	U	X	X	X		X	X	X	X	X	S		X	S	U	S	X		S	X	S	S	U									6
7	X	S	X	X		X	X	X	U	X	U	X	X	X	U	S	U		U	X	S	U	U									7
8	U	X	U	U		U	U	U	S	U	X	X	U	X	X	X	X		X	U	X	X	X									8
9	X	X	X	X		X	X	X	X	X	U	U	X	U	U	S	U		U	X	U	U	U									9
10	X	X	X	X		X	X	X		X	U	X	X	U	U	X	U	U	U		S	S	U	U	U	U	U	U				10
11					X			X	U		X	U	U	X	X	X	X	X	X		U	X	X	U	S	S	S	U	U	S		11
12		X	X	X	U	X	X	X	X		U	X	X	S	U		U	U			X	U		S	U			U	U		X	12
13																																13
14																																14
15																																15
Total Appearances																																
	6	8	8	8	2	8	8	9	5	7	5	6	5	3	2	4	3	1	2	3	2	2	2	0	0	0	0	0	0	0	1	**X**
	0	1	0	0	0	0	0	0	1	0	1	1	3	5	1	3	0	0	1	0	3	2	0	1	1	1	1	0	0	1	0	**S**
	2	0	1	1	2	1	1	1	3	1	4	2	2	2	6	1	6	4	4	1	2	3	4	2	2	1	1	3	2	0	0	**U**

X - STARTED. S - PLAYING SUBSTITUTE. U - UNUSED SUBSTITUTE.

EURO QUALIFYING TABLE - GROUP 1

		P	W	D	L	F	A	Pts
1.	**ENGLAND**	**8**	**6**	**2**	**0**	**24**	**4**	**20**
2.	SPAIN	8	5	2	1	24	7	17
3.	CZECH REPUBLIC	8	4	2	2	18	14	14
4.	BELARUS	8	1	1	6	10	27	4
5.	NORTHERN IRELAND	8	0	1	7	2	26	1

EURO CHAMPIONSHIPS - GROUP C

		P	W	D	L	F	A	Pts
1.	SWEDEN	0	0	0	0	0	0	0
2.	**ENGLAND**	**0**	**0**	**0**	**0**	**0**	**0**	**0**
3.	RUSSIA	0	0	0	0	0	0	0
4.	ITALY	0	0	0	0	0	0	0

HELLENIC LEAGUE PROGRAMME OF THE YEAR AWARDS 2008/2009

For the fourth year of judging, Brian King (Hellenic League Secretary) provided most of the programmes (writes BERNARD DENNIS). Letters were sent to Pegasus Juniors and Marlow United, who responded in order to make it a 100% contest for the first time in four years.

In the Premier Division, Witney United, as last year, produced the best programme, with second place going to Kidlington with the most improved issue, rising from 15th in 2007/8.

Division One East's top three places went to the same teams as last season, but in a different order. Binfield were top (2nd last year), Rayners Lane second (3rd) and last year's winners Bisley were third. It is sad to report that my own village team, Englefield Green, were awarded the wooden spoon. Having made four reserve team appearances for them in season 1952/3, it is somewhat embarrassing to state that they produced a far better programme then than they do now. But it does prove that when I am judging, I do not give away any favours !

Division One West saw Wootton Bassett Town and Tytherington Rocks feature in the top three yet again. It gets boring - why can't they get promoted so that we can see how well they would do with a Premier Programme ?

PREMIER DIVISION

1	Witney United	211
2	Kidlington	182
3	Bicester Town	177
4	Old Woodstock T.	174
5	Hook Norton	169
6	Harrow Hill	167
7	Ardley United	158
8	Wantage Town	156
9	Reading Town	150
=	Abingdon Town	150
11	Highworth Town	149
12	Chalfont Wasps	146
13	Fairford Town	133
=	Almondbury Town	133
15	Carterton Town	130
=	Hungerford Town	130
17	Flackwell Heath	120
18	Marlow United	113
19	Shrivenham	111
20	Pegasus Juniors	107
21	Milton United	101
22	Shortwood United	21

DIVISION ONE EAST

1	Binfield	194
2	Rayners Lane	177
3	Bisley	165
4	Launton Sports	160
5	Prestwood	150
6	Henley Town	149
7	Kintbury Rangers	142
8	Holyport	141
9	Finchampstead	140
10	Eton Wick	136
11	Thame United	117
12	Wokingham & E.	113
13	Penn & Tylers G.	104
14	Chinnor	87
15	Newbury	86
16	South Kilburn	85
17	Ascot United	83
18	Englefield Green	80

DIVISION ONE WEST

1	Wootton Bassett	289
2	Tytherington Rocks	207
3	Headington Amats.	206
4	Purton	167
5	Trowbridge Town	158
6	Cirencester United	152
7	Winterbourne Utd	145
8	Lydney Town	144
9	Easington Sports	141
10	Malmesbury Vics	139
11	Cricklade Town	132
12	Hardwicke	119
13	Oxford C. Nomads	114
14	Letcombe	113
15	Cheltenham Saracens	104
16	Clanfield	88
17	Pewsey Vale	75

Stuart Latham has judged the programmes (to hand) in the **SPARTAN SOUTH MIDLANDS LEAGUE**. The overall winner was First Division Hoddesdon Town, whose programme Stuart judged to "contain numerous items that are included in every programme which I am aware of, but its still an excellent production as ever." There were two programmes judged from Division Two, Padbury United (168) and Aston Clinton (92). Division One was topped by Stuart's own programme, Chalfont St Peter, by a substantial margin.

SPARTAN MIDLAND LGE. PREMIER DIVISION

1	Chalfont St Peter	368
2	Cockfosters	296
3	Broxbourne Bor.	239
4	Hanwell Town	216
5	Tring Athletic	210
6	Kentish Town	175
7	Aylesbury Vale	171
8	Biggleswade Utd	158
9	Harefield United	147
10	Haringey Borough	144
11	Langford	136
12	Welwyn Garden C	116
13	Hertford Town	78

DIVISION ONE

1	Hoddesdon Town	421
2	Crawley Green	341
3	Royston Town	199
4	Sun Postal Sports	169
5	Bedford	142
6	Winslow United	122
7	Bedford Town Res	121

BLUE SQUARE SOUTH & SOUTHERN LEAGUE SOUTH & WEST DIVISION, PROGRAMME OF THE YEAR AWARDS 2008/2009 by Mark Smith

BLUE SQUARE SOUTH

1	Chelmsford City	506
2	AFC Wimbledon	439
3	Newport County	382
4	Braintree Town	341
5	Bishop's Stortford	331
6	Team Bath	327
7	Worcester City	275
8	Hampton & Richmond	271
9	Eastleigh	270
10	Hayes & Yeading	261
11	Maidenhead Utd	260
12	Bromley	259
13	Havant & Waterlooville	251
14	Welling United	246
15	St Albans City	245
16	Weston-sup-Mare	243
17	Basingstoke Town	239
18	Thurrock	233
19	Bognor Regis T	229
20	Bath City	228
21	Dorchester Town	227
22	Fisher Athletic	182

There are three outstanding programmes in the Blue Square South this season which I'm fairly certain would not look out of place in League Two (or above!).

The top two this season, Chelmsford City and AFC Wimbledon, were both members of the Isthmian Premier last season and have continued their excellent work this season in Blue Square South, both on and off the field. Both programmes are packed full of information and photographs and are exceptionally well presented. They are a credit to their clubs and

the programme editors, Mandy Smith (Chelmsford) and David Charles (AFC Wimbledon) have to be commended for their efforts. In third place is the issue from Newport County. This programme has, in my view, some of the most original content and the pages on the visiting club are a delight to read. It only finished third purely and simply because there are considerably more pages of content in the top two programmes. Braintree Town's colourful issue finished fourth, whilst the extremely informative Bishop's Stortford programme (which again has some original articles and some excellent historical content) finished fifth.

Havant & Waterlooville having finished 2nd last season, dropped back to 13th (which is where they came in 2006/7 season), but many of the issues in the mid-table grouping produced a programme which showed little discernable difference from last season's effort. The exception to this is the issue from St Albans City which last season was inexcusably poor in terms of content and value for money (and finished 22nd), but this year has improved considerably.

Stranded at the bottom end of the table is Fisher Athletic which, given their considerable financial difficulties this season, is somewhat understandable. Editor Joe Arif has still managed to produce a reasonable effort but containing just 16 pages which meant that it was the only programme in the division not to reach 200 points.

This year's winner in the BGB Southern League South & West Division is Abingdon United and their programme editor, Bill Fletcher, has again excelled and this issue is deservedly one of the best non-league programmes in the country. This is a programme that might lack a little quality in its presentation, but makes up for it with the huge quantity of reading material provided.

The runners-up are Windsor & Eton who continue to produce consistently good programmes and this is another issue that is packed with information, and credit must go to the editors Michael Gegg and Dan Gomm.

Winchester City finished in third place with a very well presented programme, whilst league newcomers

Truro City finished fourth. The fact that the top three earned well over 300 points was testimony to the quality of each issue.

Slough Town finished fifth this time around but their professionally printed, glossy programme contains many original and interesting contributions of great interest.

At the bottom, AFC Hayes finished last, fifty points adrift of their nearest rival but, as always, a programme is better than no programme!

I would like to take this opportunity to thank Dave Smithson of the Windsor & Eton FC Club Shop for yet again obtaining the majority of the programmes surveyed and without whose help the divisional results would be incomplete.

BGB SOUTH & WEST DIVISION

1	Abingdon United	383
2	Windsor & Eton	346
3	Winchester City	333
4	Truro City	281
5	Slough Town	268
6	Bracknell Town	264
7	Bridgwater Town	239
8	Beaconsfield SYCOB	237
9	Uxbridge	232
10	Taunton Town	230
11	Bishop's Cleeve	217
12	Paulton Rovers	208
13	Andover	191
14	Cirencester Town	182
15	Thatcham Town	181
16	Burnham	164
17	AFC Totton	150
18	Didcot Town	145
19	North Leigh	142
20	Cinderford Town	134
21	Gosport Borough	128
22	AFC Hayes	78

SUSSEX COUNTY LEAGUE PROGRAMME OF THE YEAR AWARDS 2008/2009
by Bernard Dennis

Probably the best County in the country for Non-League football - not just regarding programmes but in its setup - well organised with lots of dedicated and friendly people involved. 52 teams in three divisions and names Divisions 1, 2 and 3 without the silly use of the word "Premier". Just like the good old days of the Football League. This season, I received a programme from all Division One and Two clubs, and seven out of fifteen from Division Three - this was due to the efforts of my four helpers.

Alan Barnes, Secretary at Littlehampton for the fourth year - always enthusiastic about this competition. Phil McAndrew who assisted last year. Richard Milburn, programme editor at Rustington who was somewhat distressed that his club failed to win Division Three having to be runners up to the improved Southwick issue.

Richard Wilson, a resident of Battle and a Portsmouth fan who is not attached to any Sussex club - but when Portsmouth are away he ground-hops Sussex clubs and collects one per club.

No substantial changes or surprises with the programme placings but it was pleasing to gain some entries from Division three, with a great effort from Ifield Edwards.

DIVISION ONE

1	Hassocks	225
2	Ringmer	195
3	Horsham YMCA	191
4	Eastbourne U.A.	178
5	East Grinstead T.	157
6	Redhill	147
7	Arundel	141
8	Selsey	140
9	Three Bridges	136
10	Chichester C.U.	129
11	St Francis R.	125
12	Hailsham Town	122
13	Shoreham	121
14	Whitehawk	116
15	Oakwood	114
16	Wick	109
17	Lingfield	103
18	Pagham	96
19	Worthing United	94
20	East Preston	68

DIVISION TWO

1	Southwick	261
2	Rustington	242
3	Littlehampton	214
4	Mile Oak R.	206
5	Crawley Down	193
6	Lancing	173
7	Seaford	172
8	Loxwood	122
9	Steyning Town	118
10	Rye United	113
11	Peacehavenm & T	108
12	Westfield	92
13	Sidley United	84
14	Bexhill United	80
15	Sidlesham	77
16	Midhurst & Ease.	64
17	Wealden	63
18	Storrington	57

DIVISION THREE

1	Ifield Edwards	190
2	Little Common A.	136
3	Uckfield T.	130
4	Pease Pottage V	110
5	Rottingdean	104
6	Hurstpierpoint	102
7	Clymping	70

COMBINED COUNTIES LEAGUE, won by Molesey of the Premier League with 250 points, ahead of Badshot Lea with 178. Division One was won by Feltham with 179, South Park were second with 77 and C.B. Hounslow United third on 68.

Always a poor response from this League and this season must be the worst. Surprising, because it has ten teams from the former Isthmian League who were demoted with the re-structuring of a few seasons ago and who at that time produced excellent programmes.

Even more disappointing is Knaphill who produced last season one of the best ever Step 6 programmes, and this season could not be bothered to submit one for judging despite three requests.

There were only two entries from the ESSEX SENIOR LEAGUE, won by Basildon United with 177 points, ahead of Barking with 168. Only two entrants - same as last year with Basildon winning again if you can call it a contest ?

There was only one programme submitted from the DORSET COUNTY PREMIER LEAGUE, from an approach to 15 League teams, although I am now advised that most do not produce a programme. The winner, therefore, is Hamworthy Recreation with 161 marks.

Next month - Wessex League, Western League, South West Peninsula League, Combined Counties League, Essex Senior League, Kent League and Kent County League

BGB SOUTHERN PREMIER		
1	Banbury United.	362
2	Farnborough	318
3	Cambridge City	272
4	Gloucester City	227
5	Mangotsfield Utd	215
6	Halesowen Town	.213
7	Hitchin Town	212
8	Chippenham Town	200
9	Tiverton Town	199
10	Rugby Town	191
11	Stourbridge	190
12	Clevedon Town	185
13	Corby Town	183
14	Oxford City	180
15	Bedford Town	179
16	Swindon S'marine	175
17	Bashley	167
18	Hemel Hempstead.	165
19	Merthyr Tydfil	160
20	Yate Town	158
21	Brackley Town	145
22	Evesham United	134

BGB SOUTHERN LEAGUE PREMIER DIVISION, PROGRAMME OF THE YEAR AWARDS 2008/2009

Not an entirely easy task, although the top three were really out on their own **(writes BOB SMALE)**. My main problem was deciding if Banbury would hold on to their crown, when pushed by the high gloss and high colour production from Farnborough and the "2007/08 Conference South's 'Programme of the season"of Cambridge City.

Although not scoring quite so highly as last season, Banbury's had so much content and knowing the effort that has to be put into ANY programme, then David Shadbolt and the team had worked so hard on this. Both Farnborough and Cambridge City can also feel very proud of their efforts. I felt that Farnborough's was a little pricey and on a personal note, I was not too keen on the slightly larger size, but I gave points accordingly.

In fact, all the basics were in each programme and in the end, it came down to just the little extras between one and another. For those who were unfortunate to be at the bottom, I know the efforts that they put in, but they were let down by quality of paper and printing.

Bashley were unlucky inasmuch as their programme was the first of the season, and they also used the same cover shot as last season. Evesham's printing of the teams on the back cover suffered as the print rubbed off very easily.

WESTERN LEAGUE PREMIER		
1	Willand R.	252
2	Barnstaple T.	199
3	Corsham Town	191
4	Frome Town	166
5	Sherborne Town	162
6	Chard Town	157
7	Dawlish Town	155
DIVISION ONE		
1	Larkhall Athletic	150

In my three previous years of judging I had not received a single issue from **THE WESTERN LEAGUE,** so eight has to be an improvement **(writes BERNARD DENNIS).** The Willand programme is very good, but there must be some more out there, somewhere !

THE SOUTH WEST PENINSULA LEAGUE

Premier (1) Buckland Athletic 364, (2) Cullompton Rangers 224. Division One East (1) Okehampton Athletic 157 (2) Budleigh Salterton 125. Division One West (1) St Austell 117 (2) Dobwalls 62

The poorest League response – six received from three leagues with 56 clubs – and for the first time all were approached individually by letter. In the Premier, the same two teams again sent in excellent programmes with Buckland Athletic again winning with a 139 points increase. This programme would rate over half way up in the Blue Square Conference Premier table with improved paper quality, colour and photos, and more interesting articles, and it only costs £1 whereas £2.50 is the Conference price. It is also a far better programme than six of the Coca Cola League Two issues which I have seen.

WESSEX PREMIER

(1) Poole Town 346 ; (2) Bournemouth 337 ; (3) Alresford Town 113 ; (4) Alton Town 108
Only four programmes submitted this year against ten in 2007/08. The same two clubs attained first and second placed with a considerable increase in points.

WESSEX DIVISION ONE

(1) Ringwood Town 195 ; (2) Amersbury Town 162 ; (3) Verwood Town 127

This is the first time we have seen a Ringwood programme and it was a pleasure to meet the editor, Ian Claxton, who came to my premises with a quantity of 2007/8 and 2008/9 surplus issues for my own stock. This was done in exchange for 1000 of my surplus as he intends to open a programme shop at their ground and I am always keen to promote such a project. Too many Non League clubs over the past few years have closed their shops due to lack of interest, or the inability to find volunteers to staff them. I hope it is a success and that he returns, as promised, for more stock for next season and to also distribute to neighbouring clubs.

KENT LEAGUE PREMIER DIVISION
(1) Herne Bay 229 ; (2) Norton Sports 199 ; (3) Hythe Town 178 ; (4) Faversham 171 ; (5) Erith & Belvedere 168 ; (6) Deal Town 159

KENT COUNTY LEAGUE
(1) Rusthall 187 ; (2) Orpington 184 ; (3) Lewisham Borough 128 ; (4) Standsfeld Oxford & Bermondsey 108
This is a new league with four submission – hopefully more next year as the top two were quite interesting.

NON-LEAGUE PUBLICATIONS

I get the impression that more and more mature football enthusiasts are watching less live top class football, maybe for the reasons discussed in my editorial, and prefer to catch up with the stars through television while enjoying the friendliness of the non-league family at local clubs.

To keep up to date with our level of the game, the weekly **'Non-League Paper'** has proved invaluable and is hopefully now safely established and there are some excellent magazines such as the ones listed below. **T.W.**

The wonderful quarterly magazine **'Groundtastic'** (80 pages) gives a comprehensive review of all grounds old and new.
(email: editors@groundtastic.co.uk and website: www.groundtastic.co.uk).
Editors: Vince Taylor & Paul Claydon

'Non League Digest' (60 pages) gives a very thorough monthly round-up of features including all aspects of the game that interest groundhoppers.
(email: steveking@nonleaguedigest.com and website: www.nonleaguedigest.com .
Editor: Steve KIng.

'Non League Retrospect' The National Game History magazine (46 pages) is packed with fascinating historical facts and features.
(email: enquiries@3-2books.co.uk and website: www.3-2books.com)
Editors: Fred Hawthorn and Ronald Price.

The Football Traveller is a weekly publication giving you up to date details of fixtures from over a hundred competitions plus news and features on programmes and travel around the country.
(email: berrytft@googlemail.com and website: www.thefootballtraveller.co.uk)
Editor: Bill Berry.

Soccer History Magazine (56 pages) is a quarterly publication covering all aspects of the history of the game.
Website: www.soccer-history.co.uk

INDEX OF CLUBS

(For clubs at Step 5 and below, the page number refers to the club's 2008-09 league table)

4th Home Guard 1023
66 Star United 991
A & G Auto Repairs 993
A & N Evans 996
A London 1007
AAH Romford 998
Abacus Media 999
Abba Athletic 986
Abbey 1003
Abbey Fields 991
Abbey Hey 776
Abbey Hulton United 952
Abbey Rangers 1010
Abbeymead Rovers 1009
Abbotskerswell 1008
Aber Valley YMCA 1026
Aberaeron 1023
Aberaman 1023
Aberbargoed Buds 1021
Abercanaid 1024
Abercarn United 1024
Abercregan 1025
Aberdyfi 1023
Aberfan SDC 1024
Aberford Albion 983
Abergavenny Thursdays 1024
Abergele Rovers 1024
Aberkenfig Con 1023
Abermule 1025
Aberporth 1023
Abertillery Bluebirds 1024
Abertillery Excelsior 1024
Aberystwyth Town 1015
Abingdon Town 737
Abingdon United 588
Abington United 902
ABK Sports 986
AC Azzurri 1013
AC Central 1023
AC Finstock 1013
AC Malden 998
AC Marlow 1014
AC Matravers 969
AC Meadowcroft 986
AC Olympia 990
AC Pontymister 1024
AC Royals 1010
Academicals 1008
Accrington Loyal 986
Accrington Loyal Amateurs 999
Accrington Town 986
Aces SSJ 986
Achilles 955
Acklam Steelworks 979
Acklington Athletic 1004
Acle United 893
Acocks Green 987
Acorn Athletic 1002
Acrefair Youth 1026
Adamsdown Athletic 1023
Adderbury Park 942
Addingham 996
Addington 1001
Addington Athletic 1011
Addlestone Town 996
Adelphi 1006
Adur Athletic 1014
AEI Rugby 991
AEK Boco 989
Afan Lido 1019
AFC Abbey Rodbourne 966
AFC Abercynon 1023
AFC Aldermaston 864
AFC Aldermoor 1009
AFC Amersham 1014
AFC Aylestone 1000
AFC Bargoed Redz 1026
AFC Bebington Athletic 961
AFC Bedfont Green 996
AFC Berg 986
AFC Biddenden 1001
AFC Blackpool 777
AFC Bluebridge 969
AFC Bourne 996
AFC Bransgore 988
AFC Brickhill Rgrs 1003
AFC Bridgford 1005
AFC Broadwater 1013
AFC Bromley 990
AFC Brumby 1007
AFC Burton 988
AFC Butetown 1026
AFC Butetown Res 1023
AFC Caerphilly 1026
AFC Caewern 1025
AFC Castrol 966
AFC Chilworth 996
AFC Corinthians 946
AFC Cross Keys 1012
AFC Crossleys 996
AFC Crowley 956
AFC Crown & Anchor 996
AFC Denticare 1025
AFC Dunstable 824
AFC Emley 789
AFC Ewell 1010
AFC Fletton 944
AFC Friendship 995
AFC Froyle 986
AFC Fylde 470
AFC Galaxy 1026
AFC Gomshall 996
AFC Goods Office 1007
AFC Grains 1009
AFC Grinstead 1002
AFC Guildford 996
AFC Hampton 998
AFC Hatfield Town 918
AFC Hayes 586
AFC Hayes Harriers 987
AFC Heathfield 990
AFC Heathrow 934
AFC Hersham 996
AFC Highcliffe 988
AFC Highcroft 1023
AFC Hiltingbury 1008
AFC Hop 1008
AFC Hornchurch 614
AFC Horndon 1009
AFC Hoxne 956
AFC Hull 994
AFC Humber 994
AFC Informa 991
AFC Internazionale 763
AFC Kempston Rov. 852
AFC Kempston Town 898
AFC Kings 994
AFC Kingston 998
AFC Lea Holloway 1001
AFC Lebus 1007
AFC Leeds 1000
AFC Liverpool 777
AFC Llwydcoed 1021
AFC Llwynypia 1026
AFC Louth 993
AFC Malt Shovel 994
AFC Marlborough 1013
AFC Mawdesley 1006
AFC Meadway 987
AFC Missenden 1014
AFC Molesey 998
AFC Moorlands 1004
AFC Mottingham 989
AFC Nailsea 1013
AFC Norwich 893
AFC Oldham 999
AFC Padiham 992
AFC Parkstone 988
AFC Phoenix (Glos) 1010
AFC Phoenix (Kent) 1006
AFC Piper 994
AFC Pontardawe 1025
AFC Portchester 864
AFC Porth 1021
AFC Preston 994
AFC Redbridge 1008
AFC Redhill 1006
AFC Regent 1009
AFC Ringmer 1002
AFC Rovers 994
AFC Rumney 1023
AFC Scholes 1013
AFC Sevenoaks 922
AFC Shepherds Arms 1011
AFC Sheppey 920
AFC Sidford 992
AFC Slip End 1001
AFC Solent 1008
AFC Somers 987
AFC Spartans (Bristol) 989
AFC Spartans (Wycombe) 1014
AFC Stanley 988
AFC Stoneham 916
AFC Studley Green 1012
AFC Sudbury 564
AFC Sydenham 1008
AFC Tadross 1026
AFC Talbot Green 1026
AFC Target 1008
AFC Telford United 173
AFC Tiryberth 1026
AFC Titans 956
AFC Totton 587
AFC Two Brewers 1012
AFC Valour 1011
AFC Ventora 1006
AFC Victory 1000
AFC Wakefield 1012
AFC Wallingford 935
AFC Walton 1006
AFC Watermans 998
AFC Welsh Tavern 995
AFC West End 998
AFC West Hull 994
AFC Whitchurch 1026
AFC Wickham 1008
AFC Wimbledon 27
AFC Woburn Arms 996
AFC Wombourne United 878
AFC Woodhatch 1006
AFC Wulfrunians 876
AFC Wymington 938
AG Athletic 987
Agnes Stewart Old Boys 1014
AIB 988
Aigburth People's Hall 928
Aimbry 997
Ainsdale United 1006
Ainsworth 999
Aintree Villa 960
Airborne United 1009
Airbus UK Broughton 1015
Airflow 1005
Ajax United 987
Albany Athletic 929
Albany Athletic FC 988
Albion (GY) 996
Albion Mills 956
Albion Rovers 1024
Albion Sports 981
Albron 998
Albury 987
Alcombe Rovers 1011
Alconbury 944
Aldborough 1003
Aldborough United 994
Aldeburgh Town 956
Aldenham 1012
Alder 929
Alderbury 1007
Alderholt 988
Aldermere 999
Aldershot Spartans 986
Alemite Athletic 987
Alexander Forbes 1011
Alexandra Hotel 988
Alford 993
Alfreton Town 179
Ali I 1005
Alkerton Rangers 1010
Alkrington Dynamoes 999
All Claims 1009
Allbrook 1008
Allenburys Sports 918
Allendale 969
Allendon Sports 994
Allenton United 1002
Allestree 1002
Alliance 1006
Alliance United 998
Allied Rec 995
Allithwaite Rangers 1004
Almondsbury 881
Almondsbury Town 737
Alnmouth 1004
Alnmouth United 1004
Alnwick Town 939
Alphington 814
Alpine Lane 1006
Alresford Colne Rangers 908
Alresford Town 863
Alsager Town 776
Alsop Old Boys 1000
Alston Moor 1013
Altarnun 993
Altofts 984
Alton Town 863
Alton United 986
Altrincham 33
Alumni 1000
Alvaston Town 1002
Alvechurch 769
Alverthorpe WMC 1011
Alveston 762
Alvis 991
Alwoodley Old Boys 1014
Amaranth 1000
Amaranth Old Boys 1014
Ambergate 994
Amble 941
Amble United 941
Ambleside Sports 991
Ambleside United 1012
American Express 988
Amersham Town 823
Amesbury Town 864
Amlwch Town 1022
Ammanford 1020
Amory Argyle 992
Amotherby 987
Amotherby & Swinton 1014
Ampito 988
Ampleforth 987
Ampthill Town 823
AMU 934
Ancaster Rovers 995
Anchor 1003
Anchorians 1006
Andover 589
Andover New Street 864
Andoversford 990
Angle 1025
Anglian Windows 895
Angmering 1012
Angus Village 929
Anlaby Park 994
Anlaby United 987
Annfield Plain 958
Anstey Crown 1004
Anstey Nomads 926
Anstey Town 927
Ansty Sports & Social 1002
APM Mears 920
Apperley & Tewkesbury Dynamos 990
Appleby 1012
Appleby Frodingham 789
Appledore 814
Appletree 1011
Appley Bridge 1006
Aquatic Sports 1012
Archdale 762
Arches 995
Ardingly 1002
Ardington & Lockinge 935
Ardleigh United 991
Ardley United 737
Ardsley Celtic 980
Areley Kings 998
Arlesey Athletic 823
Arlesey Town 565
Arlingham 1010
Armthorpe Welfare 788
Arncott 986
Arnold Longbow 1005
Arnold Town 788
Arnside 1004
Arreton Athletic 998
Arundel 836
Ascot United 738
Asfordby Amateurs 926
Asfordby Village 1004
Ash 990
Ash Green 995
Ash United 703
Ashbourne Town 994
Ashbourne United 953
Ashbrooke Belford House 958
Ashburton 1007
Ashby Ivanhoe 926
Ashdon Villa 902
Ashford Borough 990
Ashford Town 680
Ashford Town (Middx) 616
Ashgrove 1000
Ashingdon 1009
Ashington 800
Ashington Athletic 1004
Ashington Colliers 939
Ashington Rovers 1012
Ashland Rovers 1005
Ashley Rovers 1005
Ashover 1002
Ashridge Park 946
Ashtead 1010
Ashton Athletic 776
Ashton Keynes 991
Ashton Lions 991
Ashton Old Boys 989
Ashton Prime 1011
Ashton Rangers 989
Ashton Town 777
Ashton United 430
Ashton United FC 989
Ashton Villa 1013
Ashtonians 999
Ashurst Wood 1002
Ashville 961
Asia 1007
Asianos 995
Askam United 965
Askern Villa 789
Askrigg United 1012
Aspatria 992
Astley Bridge 999
Aston (Birmingham) 987
Aston (Sheffield) 1007
Aston Athletic 1000
Aston Clinton 824
Aston FC 1013
Aston Labs 987
Aston Park 986
Aston Park Rangers 1024
Athersley Recreation 1007
Atherstone Town 566
Atherton Collieries 776
Atherton LR 776
Atherton Sports & Social 1013
Atherton Town 931
Athletic Sparkhill 987
Athletico 994
Athletico Dorchester 969
Athletico Romsey 1009
Athletico Wenban Smith 1014
Athletico Wrington 1013
ATI Garryson 1004
Atlantic 986
Atlas 1011
Attenborough 1005
Attleborough Snooker 992
Attleborough Town 894
Audley & District 952
Autopaints Brighton 988
Aveley 618
Avenue Hotspur 1023
Avery Hill College 1008
Aviva 1008
Avon Athletic 1012
Avondale Rangers 987
Avonmouth 989
Avonmouth United 989
Avonvale United 991
AVRO 931
Awliscombe United 992
Awsworth Villa 1005
AXA 914
AXA FC 991
Axbridge Town 1013
Axminster Town 814
Axmouth United 992
Aylburton Rovers 1003
Aylesbury Dynamos 986
Aylesbury Park Rangers 986
Aylesbury United 567
Aylesbury Vale 822
Aylesford 1001
Aylestone Park 926
Aylsham 896
AZ 82 995
B & W Avonside 914
BA Rangers 1010

Babbacombe Corries 1008
BAC/EE Springfield 965
Backwell United 948
Bacton United 956
Bacup Borough 776
Bacup CC 993
Bacup United 999
Badshot Lea 703
BAE Sports & Social 1006
Bagby & Balk 987
Baglan Red Dragon 1026
Bagshot 986
Bagworth Colliery 1004
Baildon Trinity Athletic 985
Baileys 986
Baili Glas 1024
Bainbridge 1014
Bainbridge United 1000
Baker Street 1003
Bakers Arms 1011
Bakewell Town 997
Bala Town 1018
Balcombe 1001
Balderton Old Boys 995
Baldock Cannon 997
Baldock Town Letchchworth 917
Ball Haye Green 952
Balsall & Berkswell 991
Balsalorna 987
Balsham 902
Baltonsborough 1014
Bamber Bridge 471
Bamburgh Castle 1004
Bamford 997
Bampton 992
Bampton Town 1013
Banbury Galaxy 986
Banbury United 520
Bancroft 994
Bangor City 1015
Bangor University 1024
Bank Top 988
Bankfield 929
Bankfield Old Boys 1000
Banks 1009
Banstead Athletic 703
Banstead Town 998
Banwell 951
Barcombe 1002
Bardon Hill Sports 715
Bardsey 983
Bardwell 986
Barford United 986
Bargate Rovers 1002
Bargod 1023
Barking 730
Barking Borough 995
Barking Borough Seniors 995
Barkingside 730
Barkston & Syston 995
Barlaston 952
Barlestone St Giles 927
Barmby Moor 1014
Barmouth & Dyffryn Utd 1022
Barn Elms 934
Barnehurst 989
Barnet Wood 990
Barnetby United 1007
Barney United 1004
Barnham 1012
Barnoldby 993
Barnoldswick Barons 992
Barnoldswick Town 963
Barnsford Hurricanes 1009
Barnslake 998
Barnstaple AAC 1003
Barnstaple Town 880
Barnston 912
Barnton 905
Barnwood United 995
Barons 1009
Barrington (Cambs) 902
Barrington (Somerset) 1005
Barrow 39
Barrow Athletic 991
Barrow Celtic 995
Barrow FC 1009
Barrow Island 995
Barrow Town 715
Barrow Wanderers 995
Barrow Wanderers 1007
Barrowby 995
Barrowford Celtic 993
Barry 1026
Barry Bluebirds 1026
Barry Dynamo 1026
Barry Town 1019
Barry Villa 1026
Barsham 1000
Bartestree 997
Bartley Green 761
Barton 902
Barton Mills 902
Barton Rovers 568
Barton Rovers FC 947
Barton Royal Oak 990
Barton Town Old Boys 789
Barton United 1007
Barton United 953
Barton United FC 990
Bartons 1009
Barwell 769
Barwick 985
Basford United 1005
Bashley 522
Basildon Town 912
Basildon United 730
Basingstoke Labour Club 986
Basingstoke Town 297
Baslow 997
Bassingbourn 902
Bassingfield 1002
Baston 995
Bath Arsenal 987
Bath City 303
Bath Rangers 987
Bath Spa University 987
Bath Springs 1009
Battersea 1010
Battersea Ironsides 957
Battle Baptists 994
Battle Rangers 994
Battlesbridge 1001
Battyeford Airedale Celtic 1011
Baughurst 986
Bawdeswell 990
Baxters 1006
Bay Athletic 980
Bay Horse Kilham 993
Bayston Hill 1007
BBM 1007
BCS Bardwell 943
Beacon 1005
Beacon Hill Rovers 1001
Beacon Knights 992
Beacon Sports 1007
Beaconsfield SYCOB 569
BEADS 978
Beaminster 1005
Bean 995
Bear 1025
Bearsted 919
Bearwood Athletic 987
Beaumaris Town 1024
Beaumont Athletic 910
Beaverwood 1008
Bebington Rovers 987
Beccles Caxton 895
Beccles Town 893
Beck Row 1009
Beckenham Royals 1008
Beckenham Town 755
Beckwithshaw Saints 996
Bective Wanderers 938
Bedale 978
Bedale Town 996
Bedfont 703
Bedfont Green 590
Bedfont Green Soc. North 996
Bedfont Green Soc. South 996
Bedfont Sports 933
Bedfont Town 934
Bedford 823
Bedford Sports Ath. 898
Bedford Town 524
Bedgrove Dynamos 986
Bedgrove United 986
Bedians 999
Bedlington Terriers 800
Bedlinog 1024
Bedmond Spts & Soc. 917
Bedwell Rangers 918
Bedworth Ex-Service 991
Bedworth United 570
Bee Hotel 987
Beeches 1012
Beechfield United 932
Beechwood '76 1007
Beehive 998
Beer Albion 992
Beesands Rovers 1008
Beeston AFC 1002
Beeston Old Boys Assoc. 1002
Beeston St Anthony's 983
Beetley 990
Bekesbourne Sports 990
Belford 1004
Belgrave 1000
Bellingham 1011
Belmore United 990
Belper Town 492
Belper United 1002
Belrose 1001
Belthorn Dog Inn 988
Belton Villa 1004
Belvedere 921
Bembridge 998
Bemerton Heath Quins 863
Bendix 989
Benfield Chemfica 941
Benfleet 910
Bengeo Trinity 997
Benhall St Mary 956
Benson 935
Benson Lions 936
Bentham 1004
Bentley 879
Bentley Colliery 904
Bentley Heath United 987
Benwick Athletic 945
Bere Alston United 970
Bere Regis 969
Berinsfield CA 947
Berinsfield CA Res 947
Berkeley Town 914
Berkhamsted Sports 986
Berkhamsted Town 822
Berks County Sports 946
Bermuda WMC 992
Berriew 1025
Berrow 951
Berrow Res 1013
Berry Brow 997
Berry Brow Liberal 997
Berwick Town 1004
Berwick United 940
Bethel 1024
Bethesda Athletic 1022
Bethnal Green United 933
Betteshanger Welfare 920
Bettws 1019
Bettws FC 1025
Betws-yn-Rhos 1024
Beulah Baptists 994
Beverley Town 973
Beverley Town Juniors 994
Bewdley Town 876
Bexhill AAC 994
Bexhill United 837
Bexley 1008
Bexlians 1008
Bibury 991
Bicester Town 737
Bickerstaffe 1013
Bickerstaffe Res 1013
Bickleigh 992
Biddulph Victoria 769
Bideford 880
Bideford Old Boys 989
Bierton 986
Biggin Hill 990
Biggleswade Town 571
Biggleswade United 822
Bilborough Pelican 1005
Bilborough Town 1005
Bilbrook 878
Bildeston Rangers 956
Billericay Town 620
Billinge 905
Billingham Kader 979
Billingham Synthonia 800
Billingham Town 800
Billinghay Athletic 988
Billinshurst 1012
Bilston Town 878
Bilton Social 992
Binfield 738
Bingham Town 1005
Bingley Town 992
Binstead & COB 998
Birch Coppice 998
Birch Coppice Bullets 987
Birchanger 987
Birchfield 928
Birkdale Crown 1009
Birkdale United 1006
Birmigham Citadel 987
Birstall Old Boys 1004
Birstall RBL 1000
Birstall United 926
Birtley Town 801
Biscovey 970
Bishop Auckland 800
Bishop Sutton 880
Bishop Waltham Dynamo 1009
Bishop Wilton 1014
Bishop's Stortford Swifts 911
Bishops Castle Town 1025
Bishop's Caundle 969
Bishops Cleeve 591
Bishops Itchington 986
Bishops Lydeard 948
Bishop's Stortford 309
Bishopstoke WMC 1008
Bishopthorpe United 1014
Bisley Sports 738
Bisterne Rangers 988
Bisterne United 988
Bitton 880
BKS Sports 1009
Blaby & Whetstone Ath. 926
Blaby United 1000
Black Boy 1009
Black Country Rangers 879
Black Horse 986
Black Horse Stanton 990
Black Torrington 998
Blackbrook 1012
Blackburn Leisure 994
Blackburn Olympic 988
Blackburn United 988
Blackfield & Langley 864
Blackgate Gunners 1009
Blackham & Ashurst 1011
Blackheath Liberals 998
Blackheath Town 878
Blackheath United 923
Blackheath Wdrs 1008
Blackpool Wren Rovers 963
Blacksmiths Arms 990
Blackstones 851
Blackwell Miners Welfare 715
Blacon Youth Club 960
Blaenau Ffestiniog Ams 1024
Blaenavon Blues 1024
Blaengwawr 1023
Blaenrhondda 1026
Blagdon 1013
Blaina United 1025
Blakelaw Crofters Lodge 1011
Blakeney 1003
Blakeney FC 1003
Blandford United 907
Blaydon House 1011
Blazing Rag 997
Bleakwood Rangers 1006
Blean 990
Bletchingley 992
Bletchington 942
Bletchley Manor 1003
Bletchley Town 824
Bletchley Trees 1003
Blewbury 935
Blidworth Welfare 903
Blofield United 893
Bloxham 986
Bloxwich United 876
Blue Bell Fulwell 1011
Blue Chip 898
Blue Circle 1011
Blue Coat Old Boys 1000
Blue Eagles 1001
Blue House 1012
Blue Lion 1012
Blue Marlin 934
Blue Star 988
Bluebirds 1024
Blueline 930
Blundeston Magpies 1000
Blunham 898
Blunsdon United 966
Bluntisham Rangers 901
Bly Spartans 919
Blyth Spartans 185
Blyth Thoroton Hotel 1011
Blyth Town 939
Boadhaven 1025
Boarhound 993
Boater 1001
Bobbington 998
Boca Seniors 1003
Bodedern Athletic 1024
Bodham 1003
Bodicote Sports 986
Bodmin Town 813
Bognor Regis Town 622
Boilermakers 1009
Bold Rangers 1009
Boldmere Falcons 987
Boldmere St Michaels 769
Boldon Community Assoc. 958
Bolehall Swifts 761
Bolney Rovers 1002
Bolsover Town 904
Bolton Ambassadors 999
Bolton County 965
Bolton Lads Club 998
Bolton Wyresdale 998
Bolton-le-Sands 1004
Bont 1023
Bontnewydd 1024
Bonymaen Colts 1026
Booker Sports 1008
Bookham 703
Boosbeck St Aidans 994
Boosbeck United 994
Bootech Old Boys 1000
Bootle 777
Bootle FC 995
Boots Athletic 1005
Borden Village 922
Border Wanderers 992
Boreham 1001
Boreham Wood 624
Borough 1025
Borough Green 1007
Borough Green Utd 1007
Borough Rovers 1009
Borough United 923
Boroughbridge 983
Borras Park Albion 1026
Borras Park Albion Colts 1026
Borrowash Victoria 715
Borrowdale United 993
BOSC 986
Boscastle 993
Boscombe Down 1007
Bosham 838
Bosnian Sports Club 987
Boston Spartans 985
Boston Town 851
Boston Town Old Boys 988
Boston United 432
Botley 936
Botley Village 972
Bottesford 1005
Bottesford Town 789
Bottisham Sports 902
Boughton Athletic 991
Bourne Town 851
Bournemouth 863
Bournemouth Electric 988
Bournemouth Hospital 988
Bournemouth Univ. 916
Bournemouth UST 988
Bournville Rovers 1013
Bourton & Frankton 991
Bourton Rovers 995
Bovey Tracey 814
Bovingdon 917
Bow AAC 992
Bow Street 1025
Bowaters 1006
Bowerham 1004
Bowers & Pitsea 730
Bowes 1012
Bowling Green 988
Boxford Rovers 991
Boxted Lodgers 909
Boynton Sports 1008
Boys Brigade OB 988
Boys Club 1004
Bracebridge Heath 1000
Brache Sparta 823
Brackla 1023
Brackley Sports 1003
Brackley Town 526
Bracknell Town 592
Bradenham Wdrs 896
Bradfield Rovers 909
Bradford Park Avenue 434
Bradford Town 881
Bradford United 1011
Brading Town 863
Bradley 992
Bradley Stoke Town 989
Bradninch 992

Bradway 1008
Bradwell 997
Bradwell United 1001
Bradworthy United 1003
Brafferton Rangers 996
Braintree & Bocking Utd 1001
Braintree Town 315
Braishfield 1008
Braithwaite 1013
Bramford Road Old Boys 955
Bramford United 956
Bramham 996
Bramhope 996
Bramley Juniors 1014
Bramley Sunnyside Juniors 1007
Bramley United 986
Brampton 900
Brampton FC 997
Brampton Park 994
Brandesburton 974
Brandon British Legion 993
Brandon Town 893
Brandon TT Sports 989
Brandon United 801
Branksome Celtic 988
Bransgore United 988
Bransholme Athletic 974
Bransty Rangers 992
Brantham Athletic 718
Bratton 1011
Bratton Fleming 1003
Braughing Rovers 997
Braunton 1003
Brazil 989
Breach Rovers 1006
Bream Amateurs 1003
Breckland Wanderers 990
Brecon Corinthians 1026
Bredhurst 1006
Bredhurst Juniors 922
Bredon 995
Breightmet United 931
Brenchley Wanderers 1011
Brendans 1001
Brentham 934
Brentwood Town 658
Brereton Social 762
Brereton Town 953
Brickfield Rangers 1026
Bridge Colts 999
Bridge Inn 986
Bridgend Street 1026
Bridgend Town 1019
Bridgerule 998
Bridgham United 990
Bridgnorth Town 769
Bridgwater Sports 1011
Bridgwater Sports Colts 1011
Bridgwater Town 593
Bridlington Excelsior 993
Bridlington Rovers 993
Bridlington Seabirds 993
Bridlington Spts Club 974
Bridlington Tigers 993
Bridlington Town 788
Bridon 995
Bridon Ropes 921
Bridport 881
Brigg Town 493
Briggensians 1007
Brighouse Old Boys 985
Brighouse Town 789
Brighstone 998
Brightlingsea Regent 908
Brighton Electricity 988
Brighton North End 988
Brimscombe & Thrupp 995
Brimsdown Rovers 822
Brimsham Green 989
Brinklow 991
Brislington 880
Brislington Cricketers 989
Bristol Athletic 989
Bristol County 989
Bristol Manor Farm 880
Bristol North West 989
Bristol Telephones 989
Briston 1003
Britannia 986
Britannia Inn 1025
Britannia Old Boys 987
Britannia Sports 997
Brithdir Bluebirds 1026
British Airways 1000
Briton Ferry Athletic 1021
Brixham Town 1008
Brixham United 1007
Brixham Villa 1007
Brixworth All Saints 937
Brize Norton 1013
Brize Norton A -3 1013
BRNESC 929
Bro Cernyw 1024
Bro Goronwy 1023
Broad Plain House 989
Broad Walk 989
Broadbridge Heath 838
Broadclyst Social Club 992
Broadfield 992
Broadfields United 933
Broadheath Central 906
Broadhempston Utd 1008
Broadlands 1023
Broadmayne 969
Broadmeadows 1002
Broadway United 990
Broadwell Amateurs 995
Brockenhurst 863
Brockham 1006
Brockworth Albion 995
Brocton 761
Brodsworth Welfare 788
Bromham 966
Bromleians Sports 921
Bromley 321
Bromley Green 919
Bromsgrove Rovers 572
Bromsgrove Town 987
Bromyard Town 876
Bronte Wanderers 982
Bronze Social 961
Brook Motors 997
Brooklands 986
Brooklands/Jaguar 991
Broomfield 912
Broseley Juniors 976
Brotton Railway Arms 994
Broughton 972
Broughton & N. Newington 943
Broughton Albion 1007
Broughton Amateurs 999
Broughton Astley 1000
Broughton FC 1011
Brown Clee 977
Brown Edge 1009
Broxbourne Badgers 997
Brunswick United 1026
Brunts Old Boys 1002
Brymbo 1026
Bryn Rovers 1025
Brynawel 1026
Bryncae 1023
Brynford United 1024
Brynmawr Town 1025
Brynna 1026
Bryntirion Athletic 1019
BSM08 988
BT 987
BT Trimley 955
BTC Southampton 1008
BTD Stars 1023
Buck Inn Broncos 1012
Buck Inn Old Boys 1012
Buckden 902
Buckfastleigh Rangers 814
Buckhurst Hill 911
Buckingham Athletic 823
Buckingham Town 852
Buckland Athletic 813
Buckland Brewer 1003
Buckland Milton & Crapstone 1005
Buckley Town 1018
Buckminster United 995
Bucknell 997
Bucks CC 986
Bucks Students Union 824
Buddies II 996
Bude Town 971
Budleigh Salterton 814
Bugbrooke St Mich. 852
Builth Wednesdays 1025
Builth Wells 1025
Bulkington S & S 991
Bulldog 1011
Bulwark 1024
Bulwell 1005
Bulwell Town 904
Bungay Town 894
Buntingford Town 917
Buntingford Wdrs 997
Bunwell 990
Burbage Old Boys 1000
Bures United 909
Burgess Hill Albion 1002
Burgess Hill Town 681
Burgess Trees 1007
Burgess-Hodgson 990
Burgh 993
Burghill 997
Burley 988
Burley Trojans 996
Burlish Olympic 998
Burnage Metro 999
Burneside 1012
Burngreave 1008
Burnham 573
Burnham Market 1004
Burnham Ramblers 730
Burnham United 948
Burnley Belvedere 965
Burnley Boys Club 993
Burnley GSOB 993
Burnley Road Bowling 986
Burnley United 963
Burntwood Town 762
Burpham 1010
Burridge 1008
Burscough 436
Burscough Bridge 1006
Burscough Richmond 1006
Burton 1004
Burton Agnes 993
Burton Park Wdrs 852
Burton Thistle 1004
Burton United 938
Burtonwood Albion 1012
Burwash 994
Burwell Swifts 902
Bury Amateurs 932
Bury GSOB 998
Bury Rovers 1009
Bury Town 574
Burymead 1010
Bush 1010
Bush Hill 1008
Bushel 1009
Bushey Rangers 918
Business School 1000
Bustleholme 876
Bustleholme Athletic 987
Butcher 986
Buxted 1002
Buxton 438
Buxton Christians 997
Buxton FC 897
Buxworth 997
Byfleet 996
Byfleet Rangers 1001
Byrons Wanderers 966
C & G 990
Cabin End 988
Cable & Wireless 987
Cadbury Athletic 761
Cadbury Heath 881
Caddington 824
Cadnam United 1008
Cadoxton 1026
Cadoxton Athletic 1026
Cadoxton Cons 1026
Cadoxton Imps 1026
Caeharris Guest Club 1024
Caerau Boys Clib 1023
Caerau Ely 1020
Caerau United 1026
Caerleon 1019
Caerleon Town 1025
Caernarfon Borough 1023
Caernarfon Town 1015
Caernarfon Wdrs 1023
Caerphilly Town 1026
Caersws 1015
Caerwys 1024
Cafe Roma 1005
Caister 894
Caldecote 898
Calder 996
Caldicot Castle 1024
Caldicot Town 1019
Callington Town 815
Calne Eagles 1011
Calne Town 880
Calver 997
Calverley 1014
Calverton Miners Welfare 903
Cam Bulldogs 995
Camberley Town 703
Camborne Park 995
Camborne School of Mines 1002
Cambourne Rovers 902
Cambrian & Clydach Vale BGC 1019
Cambridge Ambassadors 902
Cambridge Athletic 902
Cambridge City 528
Cambridge Community Church 902
Cambridge Hotel 1012
Cambridge Knights 1002
Cambridge United 45
Cambridge Univ. Press 899
Camden United 902
Camelford 815
Cammell Laird 494
Campion 980
Campton 898
Camrose 1025
Canberra 993
Canning Town 910
Cannington 1011
Cannon 24 1006
Canterbury City 920
Canton Libs 1023
Canvey Island 626
Capel 1012
Capel Plough 955
Capel Sports & Social 1011
Capenhurst Villa 961
Capital 1008
Carberry 1006
Carborundum 1009
Cardiff Academical 1023
Cardiff Airport 1026
Cardiff Corinthians 1019
Cardiff Cosmos Athletic 1023
Cardiff Cosmos Portos 1023
Cardiff Draconians 1026
Cardiff Hibernian 1023
Cardiff Rovers 1023
Cardigan Town 1023
Cardinal Newman 1000
Carew 1025
Carharrack 995
Caribbean Cavaliers 1005
Caribbean Sports 1007
Carisbrooke United 998
Carleton Rovers 992
Carlin How 994
Carlisle City 939
Carlton Athletic 983
Carlton Town 495
Carmarthen Town 1015
Carmel United 989
Carnetown BGC 1026
Carnforth Rangers 1004
Carno 1025
Carpathians 996
Carperby Rovers 1012
Carreg Wen 1026
Carshalton Athletic 628
Carterton 737
Cartmel & District 1004
Cartwheel Sports 989
Cartworth Moor 997
Carvetii United 1012
Cascade 1026
Cashes Green 1009
Cassington 1013
Castell Alun Colts 1026
Castle (Essex) 991
Castle (Gwent) 1024
Castle Acre Swifts 990
Castle Briery Hill 1025
Castle Camps 900
Castle Cary 948
Castle Colts 1001
Castle Combe 966
Castle Donington 1004
Castle Donington Town 1002
Castle FC 1026
Castle Hill 999
Castle Point Gas 1009
Castle Rising 1004
Castle United 998
Castle Vale 761
Castle Vale JKS 762
Castlethorpe 1003
Castor & Ailsworth 945
Castrol Social 960
Caterham Old Boys 1006
Caterpillar 1004
Catfield 995
Catford Exiles 990
Catforth 1006
Cathays Cons 1023
Cathays Tenants 1023
Cathays United 1023
Catholic United 1009
Caton United 1004
Catsfield 994
Catterick 969
Catterick Village 996
Causeway United 769
Cawston 1003
Caythorpe 995
CB Hounslow United 704
CB Hounslow United Social 934
CCA 1006
CCK 988
Cefn Coed 1024
Cefn Cribbwr 1025
Cefn Cribwr 1023
Cefn Fforest 1024
Cefn Hengoed 1026
Cemaes Bay 1023
Central Park 987
Cerrigydrudion 1024
Cestrian Alex 991
CGB Humbertherm 975
Chacewater 995
Chad Park 1013
Chadderton 777
Chaddertonians 998
Chaddlewood Miners Old Boys 1005
Chadlington 942
Chagford 1007
Chagos Island 992
Chailey 988
Chalfont St Peter 822
Chalfont Wasps 737
Chalford 995
Chalk Lane 973
Chalke Valley 966
Chalkwell Park 1009
Challow United 936
Chalvey (WMC) Spts 908
Chamberlayne 1009
Channings Wood 1008
Chapel Swifts 993
Chapel Town 931
Chaplins 1011
Chard Rangers 1005
Chard Town 880
Chard Town Colts 1005
Chard United (Devon) 1005
Chard United (Somerset) 1005
Charfield 995
Charing 990
Charlbury Town 1013
Charlton 1003
Charlton Athletic Community 923
Charlton Athletic Deaf 1008
Charlton Kings 991
Charlton Rovers 990
Charlton United 943
Charlwood 1006
Charmouth 1005
Charnock Richard 963
Charnwood Old Boys 1004
Charterhouse-in-Southwark 1008
Chartham Sports Club 990
Chasetown 496
Chatburn 992
Chatham Town 682
Chatsworth 1000
Chatteris Fen Tigers 902
Chatteris Town 901
Cheadle Hulme Villa 999
Cheadle Town 777
Cheadle Town Old Boys 954
Cheam City 1011
Cheam Village Warriors 1010
Cheddar 948
Chellaston 1002
Chelmsford City 327
Chelmsley Town 763
Cheltenham Civil Service 995
Cheltenham Saracens 739
Chepstow Athletic 1024
Chepstow Grape 1024
Chepstow Town 1024
Cheriton Fitzpaine 992
Cherry Bees 988
Cherry Hinton 900

Cherry Knights 1000
Cherry Tree 991
Chertsey Town 703
Chesham United 575
Cheshire Lines 928
Cheshunt 659
Chessington & Hook United 703
Chessington KC 998
Chessington KCA 998
Chester 996
Chester City 51
Chester Nomads 961
Chesterfield Town 991
Chester-le-Street T. 800
Chesterton 953
Chew Magna 1001
Chew Moor Brook 998
Chew Valley Seniors 986
Chichester City Utd 836
Chickerell United 907
Chiddingfold 1010
Chilcompton Sports 1001
Chilcompton United 1001
Child Okeford 969
Childrey 936
Chile International 1010
Chilham 990
Chilwell Vipers 1002
Chingford Athletic 998
Chinley 997
Chinnor 738
Chippenham Town 530
Chipperfield Corinthians 918
Chipping 1006
Chipping Norton Town 1013
Chipping Sodbury Town 914
Chipstead (Kent) 921
Chipstead (Surrey) 683
Chirk AAA 1026
Chiseldon 966
Chislehurst 923
Chislehurst Dynamoes 990
Chislehurst Sports 1008
Chiswick Homefields 1000
Chittlehampton 1003
Chobham 704
Chopwell Officials Club 940
Chorley 472
Chorley Saints 991
Chorltonians 999
CHQ United 991
Christ The King 991
Christ The King Old Boys 1009
Christchurch 863
Christian Club Woking 996
Christians in Sport 1001
Christleton 960
Chudleigh Athletic 1008
Church Fenton White Horse 1014
Church Kirk Rangers 986
Church Lawford 991
Church Stretton Town 977
Church Town 986
Church Warsop Welf. 904
Churchdown Panthers 990
Churchill Club 949
Churchstoke 1025
Churwell Lions 984
Churwell New Inn 1000
Cilfrew Rovers 1025
Cilfynydd 1026
Cimla Youth 1025
Cinderford Town 594
Cinque Port 991
Cinque Ports 994
Cirencester Town 595
Cirencester United 739
City Bar 991
City Colts 1001
City Hearts 1003
City Life 902
City of Norwich SOBU 897
Civil Service 1008
Civil Service Larkhall 986
Clacton United 909
Clanfield (Hants) 916
Clanfield (Oxon) 739
Clapton 730
Clarbeston Road 1025
Clarence Park 1013
Claughton Hotel 987
Claverley 1011
Claydon 955
Claygate Royals 998
Cleator Moor Celtic 958
Clee Hill United 976
Cleethorpes Town 973
Cleeve West Town 948
Cleevonians 991
Clements '83 764
Clevedon Dons 1013
Clevedon Town 532
Clevedon United 881
Cliffe 994
Cliffe Tree 1012
Cliffe Woods 1006
Clifford 996
Clifton (Beds) 898
Clifton (Lancs) 988
Clifton (Notts) 1005
Clifton United 1005
Clipston 938
Clipstone Welfare 903
Clitheroe 473
Clitheroe RBL 993
Clock Face Miners 1009
Clockwork 998
Clovelly 1003
Clowne Miners Welf. 991
Clowne Rovers 991
Club AZ 905
Club Sirrus 1009
Clubmoor Farmers 930
Clutton 950
Clwb Cymric 1023
Clydach Sports 1025
Clydach Wasps 1024
Clymping 838
Clyst Rovers 813
Clyst Valley 992
CMB 1025
Coach & Horses 1006
Coach & Horses FC 997
Coaley Rovers 1009
Coalpit Heath 989
Coalville Town 769
Coates Athletic 945
Cobdown United 1001
Cobham 703
Cobham Sports 907
Cobham United 996
Coble Ennis Square 979
Cobras 1006
Cockermouth 992
Cockers 990
Cockfield United 955
Cockfosters 822
Cockshutt 1007
Coddenham 956
Codicote 917
Coed Eva Athletic 1024
Coedpoeth United 1026
Coelbren Athletic 1025
Cogan Coronation 1026
Cogenhoe United 851
Coggeshall Town 908
Colaton Raleigh 992
Colburn Town 1012
Colchester Athletic 991
Colchester Hotspurs 991
Colcot 1026
Cold Ashby Rovers 938
Colden Common 916
Coldham United 902
Coleford Athletic 1001
Coleford United 1003
Coleshill Town 769
Coleshill United 935
Colkirk 990
College 1004
College Wanderers 1007
Collegiate Old Boys 929
Collier Row Seniors 994
Colliers Arms 1023
Colliers Wood United 703
Collingham Juniors Old Boys 1014
Collycroft Sports 991
Collyers 1006
Colne 776
Colne Engaine 991
Colne United 993
Colney Athletic 1003
Colney Heath 822
Colonel Prior 1012
Colsterworth United 995
Coltishall 1003
Colton Academicals 1014
Colwyn Bay 474
Colyton 992
Combe 1013
Combe Martin 1003
Combe St Nicholas 951
Comberton United 900
Communities First 1026
Compton 1008
Compton FC 947
Comrades 1008
Concord Rangers 660
Coney Hall 919
Congleton Athletic 953
Congleton Town 776
Congleton Vale 952
Congresbury 951
Coningsby 988
Coniston 1012
Cononley Sports 992
Consett 800
Consett u-21s 993
Constantine 995
Continental Star 761
Convocation 1000
Conwy United 1022
Cookham Dean 946
Co-op 1005
Coopers Arms 1026
Coopers Arms FC 1005
Copland 934
Coplestonians 955
Copley United 996
Copmanthorpe 1014
Copperas Hill 929
Coppull Celtic 1013
Coppull United 963
Copsewood (Cov.) 991
Copthorne 1002
Copthorne Rovers 1002
Corby Danesholme Vikings 938
Corby Eagles 938
Corby Everards 938
Corby Hearth 938
Corby Kingfisher Ath. 938
Corby Locomotives 938
Corby Madisons 937
Corby Pegasus 937
Corby Phoenix 938
Corby Strip Mills 938
Corby Talisman 938
Corby Town 191
Corfe Castle 969
Corinium Sports 991
Corinthian 1000
Corinthian Casuals 684
Corinthian Sports 989
Corinthians 1009
Cornard United 718
Cornelly United 1025
Corner Bar 994
Cornforth United 993
Cornish New Boys 1002
Coronation 1002
Corpusty 1003
Corris United 1023
Corsair 987
Corsham Town 880
Corton 894
Corus Steel 1026
Corwen Amateurs 1026
Cosby United 1000
Cosby Victory 1000
Cosham Blues 1006
Cosham Park Rgrs 1006
Cosmopolitans 987
Cotes Park 1002
Cotgrave Colliery Welfare United 1005
Coton Green 761
Cottenham United 899
Cottered 997
Cottesmore Amateurs 926
Cotton Hill 1004
Coulby Newham 979
Coulsdon United 704
Coundon Court Old Boys 991
Countess Wear Dynamoes 992
Counting House 1009
Country Park Inn 1012
County Hall 1000
County Hall Rangers 997
County NALGO 1002
Coupland Insulation 989
Court House 1024
Court Lodge 1006
Courtmoor 986
Cove 703
Coventry Amateurs 764
Coventry Colliery 991
Coventry Copsewood 761
Coventry Sphinx 769
Coventry University 991
Coversure Athletic 988
Cowes Old Boys 998
Cowes Sports 863
Cowfold 1012
Cowling 992
Coxhoe Athletic 958
Coyne 1000
CPA Holy Name 987
CPA Holy Name Res 987
Cradley Town 769
Crag Road United 981
Craggs Farm 995
Cramlington Town 939
Cranborne 907
Cranbrook Town 994
Crane Sports 955
Cranes United 998
Cranfield United 823
Cranleigh 1010
Crannog 1023
Craster Rovers 1004
Craven Arms Town 977
Crawley Down 837
Crawley Green 823
Crawley Town 55
Cray Town 1008
Cray Valley Paper Mills 919
Cray Wanderers 630
Crayford Arrows 1008
Crayke 1014
Crays Hill United 1001
CRC 717
Credit Union 1000
Credit Union Wester 1000
Crediton United 814
Creech St Michael 951
Creigiau 1023
Crescent 992
Crescent Rovers 704
Cresconians 987
Crew Club Sports 988
Crewe 906
Crewkerne 1005
Crewkerne Rangers 1005
Crick Athletic 938
Cricketers 991
Cricketers Arms 1000
Cricketers FC 1009
Crickhowell 1024
Cricklade Town 739
Cringlewood Athletic 986
Crockenhill 921
Croeserw United 1025
Croesyceiliog 1019
Croft 1012
Crofton Albion 1008
Crofton Sports 1011
Cromer Town 893
Cromer YOB 1003
Cromford 1002
Cromwell Inn 986
Cromwell Youth 1024
Cronton Villa 1012
Crook Town 801
Crookham Krakatoa 986
Crooklands Casuals 964
Cropredy 986
Crosby Colts 1007
Crosby Colts Juniors 1007
Crosfields-Rylands 905
Cross Guns 1013
Cross Inn 1023
Crosscourt United 989
Crosshills 964
Crossway 991
Crossways 969
Croston Sports 964
Crowborough Athletic 611
Crowhurst 994
Crowhurst Res 994
Crowland Town 944
Crowmarsh Gifford 935
Crown 994
Crown Inn 990
Crown Inn Glory 1002
Crown Inn Selston 1002
Crown Parkway 989
Crown Rovers 986
Crown Sundon 1001
Crowthorne Sports 947
Croxley C & H 1012
Croxley Guild 918
Croxton 995
Croydon 755
Croydon Athletic 685
Croydon Greenside 957
Croygas Phoenix 1010
Crusaders (Birmingham) 987
Crusaders (Hants) 972
Crusaders (Suffolk) 1001
CS United 1010
CSV United 938
CTK Southside 989
Cuckfield Rangers 1002
Cuckfield Town 1002
Cuffley 918
Culcheth SC 1012
Cullercoats 940
Cullercoats Custom Planet 1011
Cullompton Rangers 813
Culm United 992
Culverstone United 995
Cumberworth 997
Cupids Country Club 1009
Cury 995
Curzon Ashton 475
Cutters Friday 948
Cwm 1025
Cwm Press 1026
Cwm Wanderers 1025
Cwm Welfare 1026
Cwm Welfare Res 1026
Cwmafan 1025
Cwmafan Welfare 1025
Cwmaman Institute 1021
Cwmamman United 1021
Cwmbach Royal Stars 1026
Cwmbran Celtic 1020
Cwmbran Town 1019
Cwmcarn Athletic 1025
Cwmffrwdoer Sports 1024
Cwmparc Legion 1026
Cwrt-y-Vil 1023
Dainite Sports 938
Dairy Maid 986
Daisy Hill 777
Dalehead United 902
Dalton Athletic 996
Dalton Crusaders 997
Dalton United 963
Danehill 1002
Darkside 998
Darlaston Town 876
Darley Dale Lions 1001
Darlington Cleveland Bridge 978
Darlington Railway Athletic 801
Darlington Rugby Club 978
Dartford 632
Dartford Town 1008
Dartmouth 813
Darwen 777
Daten 906
Daventry Drayton Grange 938
Daventry Town 851
Daventry United 852
Dawley Bank 976
Dawley Wanderers 977
Dawlish Town 880
Dawlish United 992
DBC 1006
De La Salle Old Boys 1007
De La Salle Old Boys FC 1000
Deal Town 755
Deans Youth 999
Deanshanger Athletic 1003
Dearne Colliery MW 1007
Debden 900
Debden Sports 918
Debenham Leisure Centre 718
Deddington Town 986
Dedham Old Boys 908
Deepdale 1006
Deeping Rangers 851
Deeping Sports 944
Deer Park Old Boys 987
Defaid Du 1025
Delagoa 1000
Delapre Old Boys 1005
Denbigh Town 1018
Denbury Athletic 1008
Denholme United 996
Denmead & Purbrook 972
Dennington United 956
Denso 1011
Dent 1013
Denton 1005
Denton Town 906
Denton West End Youth 999
Dentons Green 1009
Denver Bell 1004

Deprtivo Centrica 1023
Derby Deaf 994
Derby Rolls Royce Leisure 1002
Derby Singh Brothers 995
Derbyshire Amateurs 1002
Dereham Posties 990
Dereham Town 717
Dersingham Rovers 893
Desborough Town 851
Desford 1000
Desi 987
Destiny Academy 1010
Devauden Green 1024
De-Veys 989
Devizes Inn 1007
Devizes Town 880
Dewi Stars 1023
Dewsbury Rangers 1014
Dewsbury Rangers Old Boys 1011
Dewsbury Road Social 1000
Dewsbury Town Old Boys 997
Dickleburgh 990
Didcot Casuals 935
Didcot Town 534
Didmarton 1010
Diggle 997
Dilham 1003
Dinas Powys 1019
Dinas Rock 1023
Dinnington Town 788
Discovery Royals 1004
Diss Town 718
Dittisham United 1008
Ditton United 1001
DJST 996
Dobwalls 815
Dockers 1026
Docking 1004
Doddington United 945
Dodworth Miners Welfare 1011
Dog & Partridge 1007
Dogtown Odd Down 986
Dolgellau AA 1023
Dolphin Athletic 1013
Dolton Rangers 1003
Donhead United 969
Donington 993
Dorchester Sports 969
Dorchester Town 333
Dorchester Town Rovers 969
Dore Valley 997
Dorking 704
Dorking Wanderers 838
Dormansland Rockets 1002
Dorset Knob 988
Dosthill Boys 987
Dosthill Colts 762
Double H 998
Dove Holes 997
Dover Athletic 339
Dowgate 1011
Dowlish & Donyatt 1005
Down Ampney 991
Downall Green Utd 1013
Downham Town 718
Downley Albion 986
Downton 864
Dowty Dynamos 990
Dragons 1012
Drax 1007
Draycott 1013
Drayton 935
Drayton Village 986
Dresdner Kleinwort 1008
DRG Stapleton 914
Driffield Evening Institute 993
Driffield Rangers 993
Driffield Star 993
Driffield Wanderers 993
Drighlington Adwalton 1000
Drimpton 1005
Dringhouses 1014
Droitwich Spa 762
Dronfield Town 1002
Dronfield Woodhouse 997
Drovers 1024
Droylsden 195
Droylsden Amateurs 999
Drummond Athletic 1008
Drywall Athletic 996
Duck Inn 1007
Ducklington 1013
Duckmanton Community 991
Duddon United 991
Dudley Hill Athletic 982
Dudley Hill Rangers 981
Dudley Sports 876
Dudley Town 876
Dudley United 878
Dudley White Swan 998
Dudley Wood Athletic 998
Dugout 1025
DUI Dragons 1023
Duke of Edinburgh 1011
Duke of Wellington 994
Duke of York 986
Duke William 1001
Dukinfield Town 932
Dullingham 902
Dulverton Town 1011
Dulwich Hamlet 686
Dulwich Town 990
Duncombe Park 987
Dundry Athletic 950
Dunkeswell Rovers 992
Dunkirk 715
Dunlop 991
Dunmow 1001
Dunmow Rhodes 987
Dunnington 1014
Dunsfold 996
Dunstable Town 516
Dunston Federation 800
Dunton 898
Dunton & Broughton Rangers 927
Dunton Green 1007
Durham City 440
Durham Garden House 993
Durham Ox 1005
Durley 972
Durning 998
Durrington Rafa 1013
Durrington WMC 1007
Dursley Town 995
Duxford United 902
Dyffryn Banw 1025
Dynamo Devon 1011
Dynamo Dury 1013
Dynamo Kingston 998
Dynamo Pimlico 998
Dynamoes 982
E & H 1003
E2V Technologies 1001
Eagle 999
Eagle House Elite 989
Eagle Sports 906
Eagley 963
Ealandians 1014
Earby Town 992
Earith United 902
Earl Grey 995
Earl Shilton Albion 927
Earls Barton United 938
Earls Colne 908
Earls Hall United 1009
Earlswood Town 762
Earsham 1001
Easington Colliery 958
Easington Lane WMC 1012
Easington Sports 739
Easington United 973
Easington United Casuals 994
Easingwold Town 1014
East Allington United 1007
East Ardsley Wdrs 1014
East Bergholt United 955
East Boldre 1009
East Budleigh 992
East Court 1002
East Cowes Victoria Athletic 864
East Dean 1012
East Drayton 995
East Durham United 958
East End Park WMC 984
East Fulham 1000
East Grinstead Mavericks 1002
East Grinstead Town 836
East Grinstead United 1001
East Grinstead Wanderers 1002
East Ham Inter 998
East Harling 896
East Hendred 935
East Leake Athletic 1004
East Leeds 999
East Leeds Trinity Old Boys 1014
East Lodge 972
East Londoners 998
East Malling 1001
East Manchester 931
East Peckham Juniors 1011
East Preston 836
East Ruston 1003
East Thurrock United 661
East Valley United 1005
East Villa 928
East Worle 1013
Eastbourne Athletic 994
Eastbourne Borough 61
Eastbourne Dynamos 994
Eastbourne Fishermen 994
Eastbourne Galaxy 994
Eastbourne Town 687
Eastbourne United Association 836
Eastcliff 991
Eastcombe 1009
Eastcote 993
Eastleigh 343
Eastleigh Athletic 1009
Eastleigh United 1009
Eastmoor 981
Easton 897
Easton United 969
Eastrington Village 994
Eastville, Midville & NL 988
Eastwood Town 201
Eaton Bray 1001
Eaton Hall College 1002
Eaton Socon 899
Ebbsfleet United 67
Ebchester 993
Ebley Omega 1009
Eccles 1001
Ecclesfield Black Bull 1008
Ecclesfield Red Rose 1007
Eccleshall 777
Eccleshall AFC 952
Eccleshill United 788
Eccleston & Heskin 1006
Eccleston United 1009
Edale 997
Eddie Beedle 994
Eden Grove 989
Eden Rangers 1011
Edenfield 986
Edgbaston United 987
Edgcumbe 993
Edge 1014
Edge Hill BCOB 929
Egerton 986
Egham Cricket Club 996
Egham Town 703
Ekco Thames Park 1009
Ekhaya 1000
Elburton Villa 813
Elephant & Castle 1009
Eli Lilly 930
Elite 1008
Elizabeth Allen Old Boys 997
Elland Allstars 996
Elland United 996
Ellesmere Port 960
Ellesmere Rangers 876
Ellingham 1001
Ellistown 715
Ellwood 914
Elm Grove 957
Elmbridge Old Boys 990
Elmdon Heath 987
Elmhurst 986
Elmore 881
Elmswell 956
Elmwood Old Boys 1009
Elstead 996
Elstow Abbey 898
Elsworth Sports 902
Eltham Palace 923
Eltham Town 1008
Elton Vale 931
Elveden Phoenix 1009
Elvington Harriers 1014
Ely City 717
Ely Crusaders 902
Ely Rangers 1020
Embleton Whinstone Rovers 1004
Embsay 992
Emerald Star 1006
Emerald Star Classics 1006
Emersons Green 989
Emmanuel 996
Emneth Spartans 902
Emstar United 1009
EMTEC 1002
Endmoor KGR 1013
Endsleigh 990
Enfield 730
Enfield FC 993
Enfield Town 662
Enford 1007
Engineers 996
Englefield Green Rovers 738
English Bicknor 1003
Ensign 1009
Enstone Sports 942
ENTO Aberaman Athletic 1019
Enty 988
Enville Athletic 763
Epping 910
Epsom & Ewell 703
Epsom Athletic 957
Epsom Casuals 998
Epsom Eagles 957
Epworth Town 1007
Equalizers 1003
Ercanil Old Boys 1000
Erin Go Bragh 987
Erith & Belvedere 755
Erith '147 923
Erith Town 755
Erpingham 1003
Esh Winning 801
Esher Athletic 957
Esher United 998
Esprit 998
Essemay Old Boys 929
Esthwaite Vale 1013
Estover Park 902
Eton Manor 730
Eton Wick 738
E-Trade Deaconsfield 997
Ettingshall Park Farm 879
Euro Dagenham 994
Europeans 990
Eutectic 934
Euxton Villa 963
Evercreech Rovers 1001
Everest 1007
Evergreen 917
Eversley 957
Everton Community 1000
Evesham United 536
Evington 927
Evolution 1006
Ewhurst 1010
Ewyas Harold 996
Ex-Blues 990
Exeter Civil Service 814
Exmoor Rangers 1011
Exmouth Amateurs 992
Exmouth Arms 992
Exmouth Town 814
Exning Athletic 902
Eyam 997
Eye Sports & Social 945
Eynesbury Rovers 852
Eynsford 1007
Eynsham Association 942
Eynsham Sports 1013
Faces 910
Factory Arms 1001
Failsworth Dynamos 998
Fair Oak 972
Fairburn 1007
Fairfield 1002
Fairfield Park Rangers 987
Fairfield United 1024
Fairfield Villa 762
Fairford Leys 986
Fairford Town 737
Fairlands 1003
Fairoak Old Boys 1023
Fairwarp 1002
Fairwater 1026
Fairwater Hotel 1023
Fairwater Rebels 1023
Fakenham Town 718
Falcons (Glos) 990
Falcons (Leics) 1004
Falmer Falcons 988
Falmouth Albion 995
Falmouth Athletic 995
Falmouth Town 813
Far Cotton Loco 1005
Farefield Sports 1005
Fareham Town 863
Faringdon Town 935
Farington Villa 1006
Farleigh Rovers 704
Farley Boys 1001
Farm Road Spts & S.I 1008
Farnborough 538
Farnborough North End 864
Farnborough Old Boys Guild 921
Farnham Town 704
Farnham United 986
Farnley 982
Farnley Sports 1000
Farnley Terriers 997
Farnworth Griffin 1012
Farnworth Town 1013
Farrington Gurney 1001
Farsley Celtic 205
Farway United 1005
Faversham Town 755
Fawley 864
FC Abercwmboi 1026
FC Assyria 934
FC Barolle 998
FC Barometrics 990
FC Beaconsfield 993
FC Brunswick 1024
FC Burghclere 986
FC Cadwa 1000
FC Cefn 1026
FC Censo 986
FC Chequers 1013
FC Chippenham Youth 966
FC Clacton 718
FC Clydach 1025
FC Courthouse 1011
FC Cricks 1000
FC Deportivo Galicia 933
FC Dynamo 927
FC Electrics 990
FC First 1005
FC Halifax Town 476
FC Headingley 1014
FC Hearts 1000
FC Hodnet 977
FC Hollington 1008
FC Hollybush 1013
FC Khalsa 927
FC Kirkland 1000
FC Leisure 1014
FC Maesteg 1023
FC Martyrs 1024
FC Mills 1013
FC Naranja 986
FC Nedd 1025
FC Nomads 1013
FC Northbridge 1011
FC Pensby 962
FC Phoenix 1023
FC Polonia 969
FC Quayside 1006
FC Ridings 994
FC Romania 995
FC Rowlatts 1000
FC Ruston United 1000
FC Salle 1000
FC Samba 1005
FC Shepperton 996
FC Southsea 1006
FC Stone 995
FC Team 934
FC Titans 1014
FC Toro 1009
FC Triangle 1010
FC Tything 1013
FC United of Manchester 442
FC Village 987
FC Von Essen 987
FC Wasps 1012
FC Windowman 969
FC Winston 1009
FC Woodlands 991
FC05 1002
FCC XI 991
Featherstone 953
Featherstone Colliery 984
Feckenham 763
Feering United 991
Feildens Arms 988
Felbridge 1002
Felinfach 1023
Felixstowe & Walton United 717
Felixstowe United 955
Felmingham 1003
Felsted Rovers 1001
Feltham 704
Felton Lions 1007
Fenay Bridge 997
Fencing Centre 988
Feniscowles & Pleasington 993
Feniton 992

Fenny Compton 986
Fens Hotel Stranton 996
Fenstanton 902
Fern Estates 1013
Ferndale Boys Club 1026
Ferndown Sports 969
Ferndown Town 988
Fernley 986
Ferrari 1004
Ferrers Athletic 1001
Ferring 1013
Ferrybridge Amateurs 1007
Fetcham 1010
Ffostrasol 1023
FG Galaxy 992
Field Sports & Social 983
Fieldhead Hospital 1011
Fieldtown 1013
FIFA Standard 988
Fife Rangers 1012
Figheldean Rangers 1007
Figleaves 902
Filliongley 991
Filton Athletic 989
Finchampstead 738
Findern 1002
Findern Sports 994
Finedon Volta 938
Finlay Rovers 990
Finmere 986
Fintan 991
Fir Tree Rangers 1013
Fishburn Park 978
Fisher Athletic 25
Fishguard Sports 1025
Fishponds Old Boys 989
Fishtoft 988
Fitters United 1006
Fittleworth 1012
Fivehead United 1005
Fives Athletic 932
Flackwell Heath 737
Flagship 1009
Flamborough 993
Flamengo 987
Flanders 994
Fleckney Athletic 1000
Fleet Leisure 919
Fleet Spurs 864
Fleet Spurs Vets 986
Fleet Support Ltd 1006
Fleet Town 688
Fleetdown United 923
Fleetlands 916
Fleetway Printers 995
Fleetwood Hesketh 964
Fleetwood Town 211
Fletching 1002
Fleur de Lys 1005
Fleur-de-Lys Welfare 1025
Flight Refuelling 969
Flint Town United 1018
Flitcham 1004
Flitwick Town 898
Flixton 776
Flockton 997
Florence 952
Fochriw 1026
FOCUS 962
Focus Ferrers 1001
Foley 952
Folkestone Invicta 689
Folkstone Lanterns 990
Folly Lane BCOB 991
Follygate & Inwardleigh 992
Ford Motors 928
Fordham 899
Fordingbridge Turks 988
Forest 838
Forest Glade 1001
Forest Green Rovers 73
Forest Hall 941
Forest Hill Park 923
Forest Row 1001
Forest Town 903
Forest Town FC 1008
Forest United 998
Foresters 1011
Foresters Athletic 993
Formby 776
Formby Athletic 1009
Formby Dons 1009
Forton Rangers 1005
Fosdyke 988
Fothergill & Whittles 1007
Foulsham 897
Fountain Sports 1007
Four Crosses 1025
Four Lanes 1002
Four Marks 972
Fowey United 993
Fowlmere 902
Fownhope 996
Fox Inn 994
Foxash Social 909
Foxhole Stars 815
Foxhole United 1008
Foxton 900
Framfield & Blackboys United 1002
Framlingham Town 955
Frampton Athletic 989
Frampton United 1009
Franklands Village 1001
Frant 1011
Fratellos 1011
Frecheville CA 1007
Freckleton 963
Freehold 1004
Freeland 943
Freemantle 1008
Freethorpe 897
Freiston 988
Frenches Athletic 1006
Frenford Senior 910
Frensham RBL 986
Freshford Sports 987
Freshford United 1011
Friar Lane & Epworth 769
Frickley Athletic 444
Friends Provident 1007
Frilsham & Yattendon 946
Frimley 986
Frimley Green 704
Frimley Select 986
Friskney 988
Fritwell 943
Frizington White Star 992
Frodsham United 991
Frodsham Vets 991
Frogpool-Cusgarne 995
Frome Collegians 950
Frome Town 596
Frome Town Sports 1011
Frontiers 987
Fry Club 949
Fry Club Old Boys 986
Fulbeck United 1000
Fulbourn Institute 899
Fulbourn Sports & Social Club 902
Fulford United 1014
Fulham Deaf 1010
Full Measure 993
Fulwell Blue Bell 1012
Fulwood Amateurs 963
Furnace 1008
Furnace Green Rovers 992
Furnace Sports 998
Furness Athletic 995
Furness Cavaliers 965
Furness Rovers 964
Furness Vale 997
Future 987
Gadlys Rovers 1023
Gaerwen 1024
Gainsborough Trinity 217
Gala Wilton 995
Galgate 1004
Galleywood 910
Galmpton United & Torbay Gentlemen 814
Gamesley 905
Gamlingay United 902
Gap Connah's Quay 1015
Garboldisham 1009
Garden Village 1020
Garden Village FC 1026
Garforth 1007
Garforth Rangers 1007
Garforth Town 477
Garforth WMC 1007
Gargrave 992
Garnlydan Athletic 1025
Garsington 942
Garstang 963
Garswood United 905
Garw 1020
Gas Recreation 908
Gate (Hants) 1009
Gate (West Yorks) 999
Gateacre 1000
Gateshead 79
Gateshead Rutherford 940
Gateshead Snooker Centre 1011
Gatley 999
Gayton United 894
Gaywood 1004
GDIS 998
Gedling Miners Welfare 715
Gedling Southbank 1005
Gedling Town 715
Gedney Hill 945
Gellideg Foundation 1024
General at Sea 1006
Genesis 1004
Gentil Knight 990
Geoff Wednesday 994
George & Dragon 1007
Georgeham 1003
Georgetown BGC 1024
Giants Grave 1025
Gidlow Athletic Old Boys 1013
Gilberdyke 994
Gildersome Spurs Old Boys 1014
Gilfach Athletic 1023
Gilfach Goch Athletic 1026
Gilfach Sports 1023
Gillamoor 987
Gillens Arms 996
Gillford Park 939
Gillingham Green 1006
Gillingham Town 881
Gilwern & District 1024
Gimingham 1003
Girton United 900
GKN 998
Glamorgan Tap 1025
Glan Conwy 1022
Glancynon 1023
Glantraeth 1018
Glapwell 497
Glasshoughton 1007
Glasshoughton Welfare 789
Glasshouse 1000
Glastonbury Town 948
Gleadless 1008
Glemsford & Cavedish United 909
Glen Villa 1000
Glenbrook 1026
Glendale 998
Gleneagles 1011
Glenfield Town 1000
Glenn Sports 1012
Glenside 5 Old Boys 989
Glevum United 1010
Global 1003
Globe Bullough Park 986
Glory Farm 986
Glossop North End 776
Gloucester City 223
Gloucester Civil Service 1009
Gloucester Elmleaze 990
Glyn Ceiriog 1026
Glyncoes Corries 1023
Glynneath Town 1025
Glynoorrwg 1025
Godalming & Farncombe Athletic 1010
Godalming Town 690
Godalming United 996
Godmanchester Rovers 718
Godolphin Atlantic 815
Godregraig Athletic 1025
Goffs Oak 997
Golborne Sports 906
Golcar United 980
Golden Farm 991
Golden Fleece 993
Golden Hill Sports 989
Goldenhill Wanderers 952
Goldsborough 994
Golfers Arms 995
Goodrich 876
Goodshaw United 993
Goodwick United 1025
Goodwin 994
Goole 498
Goole Goods Office 994
Goonhavern 1002
Goose Green United 1013
Gordon Lennox 1024
Goring St Theresa's 1014
Goring United 947
Gorleston 718
Gorleston Wanderers 996
Gornal Athletic 876
Gors 1026
Gosfield United 909
Gosforth Bohemians Garnett 940
Gosport Borough 597
Govan Athletic 999
Govilon 1024
Gower Sports 1023
Gowerton 1026
Goytre 1021
Goytre United 1019
Graham Street Prims 715
Graig 1026
Graigwen Juniors 1026
Graig-y-Rhacca 1025
Grain Athletic 1006
Grainger Park Boys Club 1011
Grainthorpe 993
Granby Rovers 969
Grange 1004
Grange Albion 1026
Grange Athletic 961
Grange Catholic Old Boys 1023
Grange FC 1023
Grange Harlequins 1020
Grange Inn 990
Grange Moor 997
Grange Park 934
Grange SC 1012
Grangefield Old Boys 1014
Grangetown Boys Club 978
Grangetown YCC 979
Gransden Chequers 902
Grantham Squash Club 995
Grantham Town 499
Grappenhall Sports 906
Grassington United 992
Grays Athletic 85
Great Ayton United 979
Great Baddow 1001
Great Barford 898
Great Barr 987
Great Bentley 908
Great Blakenham 956
Great Bradfords 909
Great Chesterford 901
Great Chishill 902
Great Cressingham 990
Great Doddington 938
Great Horwood 1003
Great Linford 1003
Great Massingham 1004
Great Milton 986
Great Missenden 1014
Great Paxton 900
Great Preston 985
Great Shelford 899
Great Wakering Rovers 663
Great Western 1023
Great Western FC 987
Great Yarmouth Peelers 996
Great Yarmouth Town 718
Great Yarmouth Town Hall 1001
Great Yarmouth United 996
Greenalls Padgate St Oswalds 905
Greenbury United 997
Greenfield 1024
Greenfield FC 1009
Greenhill 763
Greenhill YC 1004
Greenmeadow 966
Greens United 934
Greenways 921
Greenwich Borough 755
Greenwich Thistle 1006
Greenwood Meadows 715
Greenwood Rovers 996
Greetland 996
Gregorians 931
Gregson 1004
Grendon Rangers 1003
Gresford Athletic 1018
Gresley 715
Gressenhall 990
Gretton 938
Grey Goose 1005
Grey Mare United 1005
Greyfriars 1004
Greyfriars Athletic 989
Greyhound (Amesbury) 1007
Greyhound Inn 998
Greyhounders 995
Greystoke 1012
Griffin 988
Grimsby Borough 789
Grindleford 997
Grindleton 992
Grosvenor House 934
Grove Rangers 935
Grove United 1009
Grovesnor Sports 1013
Grundisburgh 955
GSA Sports 761
GSK Sports 1013
GSK Ulverston Rangers 965
Guestling Rangers 994
Guildford City 703
Guildford City Weysiders 1010
Guildford Park 996
Guilsfield 1018
Guisborough Quoit 978
Guisborough Town 801
Guisborough Town HC 958
Guiseley 446
Guiseley Red Lion 996
Gulval 1002
Gunnislake 993
Gunton 995
Gurnos SC 1024
Guru Nanak 920
Guru Nanak Gurdwar (GNG) 1000
Guyhirn 945
Gwaelod-y-Garth 1023
Gwalchmai 1024
Gwernyfed 1025
Gwersyllt Athletic 1026
Gwinear Churchtown 1002
Gwr 1023
Gwynfi United 1025
GY International 995
Haddenham Rovers 901
Haddenham United 986
Hade Edge 997
Hadeley Park Albion 1011
Hadleigh United 718
Hadley 824
Hadlow Evolution 1011
Hadlow Harrow 1011
Hadlow Rovers 1007
Hagbourne United 936
Hailey 1013
Hailsham Town 836
Haisbro Atheltic 1003
Hakin United 1025
Hale 962
Hale Leys United 986
Hale Rovers 986
Halebank 1012
Halesowen Lighthouse 987
Halesowen Town 540
Halesworth Town 956
Halewood Town 930
Half Moon 1008
Halfway House Celtic 991
Halfway House Morley 1000
Halifax Athletic 996
Halifax Irish Centre 996
Halifax Irish Club 980
Halkyn United 1022
Hall Green United 980
Hall Road Rangers 788
Hallam 788
Hallen 880
Hallow WMC 1013
Halls 923
Halsetown 1002
Halsford Lions 1002
Halstead 1007
Halstead Town 718
Haltemprice 994
Haltemprice Rangers 994
Halton 960
Halton Borough 1012
Halton Rangers 1004
Halwill 992
Ham Green Rovers 1005
Hamble ASSC 863
Hamble Club 916
Hamble Town 1009
Hamble United 1009
Hambleden 1014
Hambledon 996
Hambrook 989
Hamilton Hawks 1011
Hamilton Panthers 1014
Hammer United 1010
Hampsthwaite United 996
Hampton 764
Hampton & Richmond Borough 349
Hampton Park Rangers 997
Hamworthy Recreaion 907
Hamworthy United 863
Hanborough 1013
Handcross Village 1002
Handley Sports 969
Handsworth 1007

Handsworth Athletic 987
Handsworth GSOB 987
Hanham Athletic 914
Hanham Athletic Colts 989
Hanley Swan 1013
Hanley Town 952
Hannakins Farm 911
Hanney United 936
Hanover 988
Hanslope 1003
Hanwell Town 822
Hanwood United 879
Hanworth 934
Hanworth Villa 704
Happisburgh 1003
Hapton 986
Harbertonford 1008
Harborne Athletic 987
Harborough Town 937
Harbour View Developments 969
Harby 1000
Hardly Athletic 991
Hardwick 900
Hardwicke 739
Hare & Hounds 1008
Harefield United 822
Haringey Borough 822
Harlequin 1007
Harleston Town 897
Harleys 991
Harlow Hill 996
Harlow Link 997
Harlow Town 664
Harold Park 995
Harold Styans 996
Harold Wood Athletic 910
Harp Rovers 1025
Harpenden Rovers 918
Harpenden Town 823
Harpole 937
Harpur Hill 997
Harraby Catholic Club 939
Harrington United 988
Harrogate Railway Athletic 478
Harrogate Town 227
Harrow Borough 634
Harrow Hill 737
Harrow St Mary's 934
Harrowby United 903
Harston 902
Hartcliffe 989
Hartcliffe Community Centre 989
Hartfield 1001
Hartland 1003
Hartlepool 958
Hartlepool Coz 996
Hartlepool St Francis 993
Hartlepool Town 993
Hartley Wintney 703
Hartshead 984
Hartshill 991
Harvest Pet Products 996
Harvey Hadden 1005
Harwell International 935
Harwell Village 935
Harwich & Parkeston 717
Harwich Rangers 991
Harworth Colliery 995
Harworth Colliery Institute 903
Harworth Colliery Juniors 995
Haslingden St Mary's 963
Haslingfield 902
Hassocks 836
Hastings Elite 994
Hastings Rangers 994
Hastings United 636
Hatch 1006
Hatfield Heath 987
Hatfield Main 903
Hatfield Peverel 908
Hatfield Town 823
Hatherleigh Town 992
Hatherley Rangers 995
Hathern 927
Hathersage 997
Hattersley 999
Haughley United 955
Haughmond 976
Havant & Waterlooville 355
Havelock Inn 988
Haverfordwest CC 1025
Haverfordwest County 1015
Haverhill Rovers 717
Haverigg United 995
Hawarden Rangers 1026
Hawarden Rangers Colts 1026
Hawcoat Park 964
Hawes United 1012
Hawkchurch 1005
Hawkenbury 1011
Hawkes Mill Sports 991
Hawkhurst United 921
Hawkins Sports 953
Haxby United 1014
Haxey Town 1007
Hay St Marys 1025
Haydock 1012
Haydon United 986
Hayes & Yeading United 91
Hayes Gate 933
Hayes United 933
Hayfield 997
Hayle 815
Hayling Billy 1005
Hayling United 863
Haywards Heath Town 838
Haywards Heath United 1002
Hazel Grove 999
Heacham 1004
Headcorn 1001
Headington Amateurs 739
Headland Level Six 996
Headley Athletic 986
Headley United 916
Headstocks 1005
Healing Hotspurs 993
Heamoor 1002
Heanor Colliers 1002
Heanor Town 715
Hearts of Liddesdale 992
Hearts of Oak 1000
Heath 1008
Heath Hayes 761
Heath Panthers 1003
Heath Park 1023
Heath Pilgrims 1002
Heath Rangers 1002
Heath Rovers 987
Heath Town Rangers 876
Heather St John 761
Heathfield 1009
Heathfield FC 990
Heathfield Hotspurs 994
Heathpark 986
Heaton Mersey 999
Heaton Moor Phoenix 986
Heaton Stannington 939
Heavitree Social United 992
Hebburn GHI Computers Athletic 1011
Hebburn Reyrolle 940
Hebburn Town 801
Hebden Royd Red Star 996
Heckington Millers 995
Heckington United 1000
Heckmondwike GSOB 1014
Heckmondwike Town 981
Heddon 939
Hedge End Rangers 972
Hedge End Town 1008
Hedgeley Rovers 1004
Hedinghams United 909
Hednesford Town 542
Hedon Rangers 973
Hedon Rangers Juniors 994
Hedon United 994
Hele Rovers 1007
Helions Bumpstead 901
Hellesdon 895
Hellifield Sports 992
Helperby United 996
Helsby 961
Helston Athletic 967
Hemel Aces 1012
Hemel Hempstead Rovers 1012
Hemel Hempstead Town 544
Hemingbrough United 1014
Hemingfords United 900
Hempnall 893
Hempstead United 902
Hemsby 897
Hemsworth Miners Welfare 789
Hemyock 992
Henbury 914
Hendon 638
Hendon FC 1012
Hendon Grange 1012
Henfield 1012
Hengrove Athletic 881
Henley Athletic 956
Henley Forest 764
Henley Town 738
Henleys Electric 988
Henllys Rangers 1025
Henlow 898
Hensall Athletic 1007
Henstridge 1014
Hepworth United 997
Herbrandston 1025
Hereford Civil Service 997
Hereford Lads Club 996
Hereford Lads Club Colts 997
Herne Bay 755
Herne Bay Athletic 990
Herongate Athletic 911
Herons Moor Rangers 1013
Herriard Sports 986
Hersham 996
Hersham RBL 998
Herstmonceux 994
Hertford Celtic 997
Hertford Heath 997
Hertford Town 822
Hertfordshire Rangers 987
Hesketh Bank 964
Hesketh Casuals 999
Heslington 1014
Hessle Rangers 973
Hessle Sporting Club 974
Heswall 960
Hethersett Athletic 990
Heworth 1014
Hexham 941
Heybridge Swifts 665
Heyford Athletic 937
Heyford United 986
Heygreen Old Boys 1000
Heysham 1004
Heyside 997
Heytesbury 1011
Heywood Irish Centre 997
Heywood St James 932
HF Seaview Plastics 1012
HFC 1000
HG Aerospace 994
Hickling 1002
Hickling FC 1003
Hi-Flex Sports 1007
High Bickington 1003
High Brooms Casuals 1011
High Green Villa 1007
High Lane 993
Highbridge Town 1011
Highcross 1006
Highfield 1013
Highfield Athletic 991
Highfield Rangers 926
Highfield Rovers 990
Highgate United 769
Highgrove 1004
Highgrove Colts 1004
Highmoor/IBIS 946
Highridge United 914
Highworth Town 737
Hikers BHA 988
Hilcote United 1001
Hildenborough Athletic 1007
Hillfields Old Boys 989
Hillingdon 934
Hillingdon Abbots Seniors 934
Hillingdon Borough 610
Hillingdon Irish 1000
Hillmorton 938
Hilltop 934
Hilton Harriers 1002
Hinckley Athletic 1000
Hinckley Downes 715
Hinckley United 233
Hindhead Athletic 986
Hindley Celtic 1013
Hindley Juniors 999
Hindley Town 1013
Hindolveston 990
Hindringham 893
Hindsford 931
Hingham Athletic 990
Hinkler 1008
Hinksey 943
Hinton (Herefordshire) 996
Hinton (Herts) 918
Hinton St George 1005
Hirwaun Welfare 1026
Histon 97
Hitchin Town 576
Hitchin Town Arena 918
Hitec Roofing 1005
Hockley Spartans 1009
Hoddesdon Town 823
Hodgsons 994
Hoghton West End 1006
Holbeach Bank 988
Holbeach St Marks 988
Holbeach United 851
Holbrook Miners Welfare 715
Holbrook St Michaels 1002
Hole I'Th Wall 988
Holker Old Boys 777
Holland 909
Holland Sports 957
Hollands & Blair 919
Hollington United 994
Hollingworth Old Boys 999
Hollins Grove Con Club 988
Hollinwood 931
Hollybush United 994
Holmans Sports Club 967
Holmbridge 997
Holmbury St Mary 996
Holme Lacy 997
Holme Rovers 994
Holmefield Arms 991
Holmer 997
Holmer Green 822
Holmer Green Old Boys 1014
Holmesdale 755
Holmfield 996
Holsworthy 813
Holt Colts 1003
Holt JCB 953
Holt Nomads 1026
Holt United (Dorset) 907
Holt United (Norfolk) 893
Holton Moor 999
Holton-le-Clay 993
Holwell Sports 715
Holy Name 1000
Holyhead Gwelfor Athletic 1023
Holyhead Hotspur 1018
Holyport 738
Holywell Bay & Cubert 993
Holywell Town 1022
Hometech 1005
Honiton Town 992
Honley 997
Hoo Institute 1007
Hoo Village 1006
Hooe Sports 994
Hook 986
Hook Athletic 986
Hook Norton 737
Hook Venturers 998
Hookhills United 1008
Hoole Rangers 991
Hoole United 1006
Hooley Bridge Celtic 999
Hop Pocket 991
Hope Park 1000
Hopflower 991
Hopkinstown 1026
Hopton White Hart 1001
Horbury Cherry Tree 1011
Horbury Town 984
Horden Colliery Welfare 801
Hordens 988
Horley 1006
Horley Town 703
Horley Wanderers 992
Horncastle Town 975
Horndean 863
Horndean United 1005
Horning 1003
Hornsea Town 973
Hornton 986
Horrabridge Rangers SA 1005
Horse & Groom 969
Horseed 934
Horsford United 894
Horsham 640
Horsham YMCA 691
Horsley 957
Horsley United 1009
Horsmonden Sports 1011
Horspath 942
Horsted 1006
Horsted Keynes 1002
Horton 992
Horton Kirby 995
Horwich RMI 998
Horwich Victoria 998
Hotton Road 1026
Houghton Main 1007
Houghton Rangers 1000
Hounslow Wanderers 934
Hoveton Wherrymen 897
Howden Amateurs 994
Howden Clough 983
Howden Town 994
Howe Bridge Mills 998
Howle Hill 1003
HQ Sports & Social 1011
HSBC 1007
Hub 991
Hubberston 1025
Huby United 1014
Hucknall Rolls Leisure 1005
Hucknall Town 448
Huddersfield Amateurs 1014
Hulan 1011
Hull Athletic 994
Hullbridge Sports 730
Huncote 1000
Hundleton 1025
Hundon 899
Hungerford Town 598
Hunslet 985
Hunstanton 1004
Hunsworth 981
Hunters Bar 997
Huntingdon Town 852
Huntingdon United RGE 902
Huntington Rovers 1014
Huntley 1003
Hunton 1001
Hunton Bridge 1012
Hurst (Berks) 946
Hurst (Sussex) 994
Hurst Green 993
Hurstpierpoint 838
Hutton 911
Hutton Cranswick United 904
Hutton FC 1013
HV Academicals 997
Hyde United 239
Hykeham Town 975
Hylton Colliery Welfare 1012
Hythe & Dibden 864
Hythe Aztecs 1008
Hythe Town 755
Ibis 1012
Ibstock United 715
Icklesham Casuals 994
Ickwell & Old Warden 898
Ide Hill 1007
Ifield Edwards 838
Ightham 1007
Ilderton Athletic 990
Ilford 666
Ilfracombe Town 880
Ilkeston Town 245
Ilkley Town 984
Illogan RBL 967
Ilminster Town 949
Ilminster Town Colts 1005
Ilsington Villa 1008
Immingham Bluestone 996
Impact Squad 989
Impact United 977
Imperial (Lancs) 991
Imperial (Somerset) 950
Imperial College Old Boys 934
Imperial Saints 989
Ince 1013
Ince Central 1013
INCO 1025
Indian Gymkhana 933
Infinity 1009
Ingles 1004
Ingleside 989
Ingleton 1004
Ingoldisthorpe 1004
Inmar 1008
Inn on the Green 1003
Inns of Court 1012
Insanity 1006
Insulators 1011
Intel 966
Inter 997
Inter Cardiff 1023
Inter Charter 974
Inter Hemel 1012
Inter Mytchett Crusaders 986
Inter Northam 1008
Inter Quinton 987
Inter Solent 1006
Inter The Bloomfield 989
Inter Vaughans 987
Interhound 1001
International 998
International Allstars 991
Invicta Colts 1007

Ipplepen Athletic 1008
Ipswich Athletic 955
Ipswich Exiles 956
Ipswich Postals 956
Ipswich United 956
Ipswich Wanderers 718
Irchester United 852
Ireti Athletic 997
Irlam 777
Irlam Steel 999
Iron Tugboat City 990
Island Marine 1026
Isle of Grain 1006
Isleham United 902
Islington 988
Islip United 938
Iver Heath Rovers 993
Ivy Tavern CSA 1000
Ivybridge Town 813
Ixworth Pykkerell 1009
Jaguar-Daimler 991
Jailhouse 1007
James King Blisworth 938
Jarrow 958
Jarrow Roofing
Boldon CA 801
Jarvis Brook 1001
JD Decking 1006
JE Yardley 987
John Bull United 956
John Rose 987
Johnson & Phillips 1008
Johnston 1025
Johnstown Youth 1026
Jolly Potter 1012
Jomarth Construction 1012
Joydens Wood 995
JP Morgan 988
Jubilee Sports 1008
Jubilee Winshill 990
Junction 1009
Junction FC 996
Junction Stars 1026
Junior All Stars 934
Junior Club Tackleway 994
Juno United 993
Juva 995
Kaleef 990
Kangaroos 969
Kartel Sports 986
Kartiers (Selby) 1014
Kashmir 1005
KC 966
KEA 986
Keelby United 993
Keens Park Rangers 996
Kegworth Imperial 1004
Keighley Shamrocks 981
Keinton Mandeville 1014
Kellingley Welfare 984
Kellington 1007
Kelma 991
Kelsall 991
Kelvedon Hatch 910
Kempston 898
Kempston Athletic 898
Kempston Hammers Sp. 898
Kemsing 1007
Kendal Celtic 1012
Kendal County 1012
Kendal Town 450
Kendal United 1012
Kenfig Hill 1026
Kenilworth Town KH 764
Kenilworth Wardens 991
Kenley 1006
Kennington 920
Kennington United 942
Kensington Dragons 934
Kent Athletic 824
Kentisbeare 992
Kentish Town 822
Kerria Knights 1010
Kerry 1025
Keswick 1012
Ketley Bank 1011
Kettering Ise Lodge 938
Kettering Nomads 938
Kettering Orchard Park 938
Kettering Park Rovers 938
Kettering Town 103
Kettering Town Galaxy 938
Ketton 945
Kewstoke Lions 1013
Keymer & Hassocks 1002
Keynsham Town 881
Keyworth United 1005
Keyworth United
Academy 1005
Kibworth Town 1000
Kicks Wallsend 1011
Kidderminster Harriers 109
Kidlington 737
Kidlington Old Boys 943
Kidsgrove Athletic 500
Kidsgrove Carpets 953
Kilgetty 1025
Kilkhampton 1003
Killinghall Nomads 996
Killingworth Station 1011
Killingworth YPC 940
Killingworth YPC Town 1011
Kimberley Miners
Welfare 1005
Kimberley Miners
Welfare Old Boys 1005
Kimberley Town 903
Kimpton Rovers 918
King Alfred SC 1013
King Charles 1000
King George 986
King John Barmy Army 1009
King's Sutton 986
Kingburn Athletic 974
Kingham All Blacks 1013
Kings 990
Kings AFC 898
Kings Arms Tamerton 1005
Kings Church
(Amersham) 1014
Kings Cliffe United 945
Kings Head 1006
Kings Heath Old Boys 998
Kings Langley 823
King's Lynn 452
Kings Sports 1012
Kings Stanley 914
Kingsbridge & Kellaton 1008
Kingsbury London
Tigers 822
Kingsdown Racers 1007
Kingsford 1000
Kingshill Spitfires 1001
Kingshill Sports 991
Kingshurst Phoenix 987
Kingskerswell
& Chelston 1007
Kingsley United 929
Kingsteignton Athletic 1007
Kingston 996
Kingston Academicals 998
Kingston Albion 998
Kingston Arrows 1005
Kingston Lacy 969
Kingstone 997
Kingstone United WMC 1011
Kingstonian 642
Kingsway Rangers 1000
Kingswood 995
Kington Town 996
Kinnerley 1007
Kinnersley 974
Kinsley Boys 903
Kintbury Rangers 738
Kinver 998
Kippax Athletic 984
Kirby Athletic 991
Kirby Muxloe SC 715
Kirk Deighton Rangers 996
Kirk Hallam Social Club 1002
Kirkburton 980
Kirkby Lonsdale 1004
Kirkby Malzeard 996
Kirkby Thore Rangers 1013
Kirkby Town 904
Kirkby United 995
Kirkbymoorside 958
Kirkdale United 987
Kirkheaton Rovers 997
Kirkland 1000
Kirkley & Pakefield 717
Kirkoswald 1012
Kirton Brickworks 1005
Kirton Town 988
Kislingbury 937
Kiveton Park 904
KKS Ashbrow 997
KMLC 966
Knap 1026
Knaphill 704
Knaresborough Celtic 996
Knaresborough Town 983
Knebworth 917
Knighton Town 1025
Knights Old Boys 1008
Knowle 761
Knowle Reds 989
Knowle United 989
Knowles Arms 988
Knowsley South 1009
Knutsford 905
Kodak (Harrow) 933
KS Athletic 998
Kurdish Lions 1000
KVFC 1013
Kydds Athletic 991
Kyngs Towne 998
Kynoch 987
L & S Athletic 1013
L'Artista 1012
Laburnum Saints 1001
Lacon Arms 996
Lady Bay 1002
Ladybridge 999
Lake Lothing 1001
Lakenheath 899
Lamb Inn 1023
Lamb Inn FC 997
Lambourn Sports 935
Lamerton 993
Lampeter Town 1023
Lamphey 1025
Lancaster City 479
Lancing 837
Lancing United 1012
Lancs Constabulary 965
Landkey 1003
Landwick 1009
Lane End 986
Lanes End 922
Langdon 1008
Langdon FC 992
Langford 822
Langford FC 1007
Langford Rovers 949
Langho 993
Langley Manor 1008
Langley Rangers 987
Langleybury Cricket
Club 1012
Langtoft 993
Langtoft United 945
Langton Green 1011
Langwathby United 1013
Lanivet 993
Lanner 995
Lanreath 970
Lapford 992
Larkfield 1001
Larkfield & New Hythe
Wanderers 922
Larkhall Athletic 881
L'Artista 1012
Latter-Day Saints 990
Launceston 813
Launceston United 993
Launton Sports 738
Lavendon Sports 1003
Laverstock & Ford 863
Lavington 1011
Lawford Lads 909
Lawrence Rovers 989
Lawrence Weston 989
Lawrenny 1025
Lawshall Swan 1009
Lealholm 994
Leamington 546
Leamington Hibernian 763
Leatherhead 692
Lebeq United 989
Leckhampton Rovers 991
Ledbury Town 876
Ledbury Town Colts 997
Lee Moor 1005
Leeds Carnegie 789
Leeds City 983
Leeds City Old Boys 1014
Leeds Deaf 1000
Leeds Independent 1014
Leeds Medics
& Dentists 1014
Leeds SV 1001
Leeds University
Old Boys 1014
Leek CSOB 777
Leek Town 501
Legal & General 988
Legion 1012
Leicester Tile 1000
Leicester YMCA 1000
Leics Constabulary 926
Leigh 1011
Leigh Athletic 931
Leigh Genesis 480
Leigh Legion 1013
Leigh Phoenix 1013
Leigh Ramblers 911
Leigh Revolution 1009
Leigh Town 1009
Leigh United 1009
Leighton Town 577
Leighton United 898
Leintwardine 997
Leiston 717
Leiston St Margarets 955
Leisure Sports Orchard 930
Lemsford 917
Leodis 1000
Leominster Town 996
Leonard Stanley 1009
Lepsons AWR 1006
Lepton Highlanders 997
Lesters Elite 990
Letchworth Garden
City Eagles 918
Letcombe 739
Letef Select 986
Letterston 1025
Leven Members Club 994
Leverington Sports 944
Leverstock Green 822
Lewes 361
Lewes Bridgeview 1002
Lewis Ashley Services 994
Lewis Merthyr 1026
Lewisham Athletic 1008
Lewisham
Borough (Community) 919
Lewistown 1026
Lewsey Park 1001
Lex XI 1018
Lexden Rovers 991
Leyburn United 1012
Leyfield 929
Leyland Red Rose 1006
Leyland St Marys 1006
Leyton 667
Leytonstone United 911
Liberty Stars 1005
Lichfield City 764
Lidlington United Sports 898
Lifton 971
Lightwater United 996
Limestone Rangers 1007
Limpsfield Blues 1006
Linby Colliery Welfare 1005
Lincoln Moorlands
Railway 788
Lincoln United 502
Lindfield 1001
Lindisfarne Athletic 1011
Lindley 997
Lindley Liberal 997
Linear United 947
Linford Wanderers 911
Lingdale 994
Lingdale United 994
Lingfield 836
Linotype & Cheadle HN 905
Linthwaite Athletic 997
Linton Granta 901
Liobians 930
Lions Athletic 1008
Liphook United 957
Liskeard Athletic 813
Liss Athletic 916
Lisvane/Llanishen 1026
Litlington Athletic 902
Little Blue United 1023
Little Brit Inn 988
Little Bull 1012
Little Common 838
Little Downham Swifts 902
Little Driffield 993
Little Eaton 1002
Little Lever SC 998
Little Oakley 908
Little Stoke 989
Little Thatch 989
Little Theatre Club 1009
Little Waltham 1001
Littlebourne 990
Littlehampton Town 837
Littleport Town 899
Littleton 762
Littletown 981
Liver Academy 1000
Liver Academy Colts 1000
Liverpool Cavaliers 998
Liversedge 788
Liversedge u-19s 982
Liverton United 814
Lizard Argyle 995
Llanarth 1024
Llanberis 1022
Llanboidy 1023
Llanbradach Social 1026
Llandarcy 1025
Llandegfan 1023
Llandrindod Wells 1025
Llandrindod Wells Colts 1025
Llandudno Junction 1022
Llandudno Town 1018
Llandyrnog United 1018
Llandysul 1023
Llanelli 1015
Llanerchymedd 1023
Llaneydn Bulldogs 1023
Llanfair United 1025
Llanfairfechan Town 1024
Llanfairpwll 1018
Llanfechain 1025
Llanfoist 1024
Llanfyllin Town 1025
Llangedwyn 1025
Llangefni Town 1018
Llangeinor 1020
Llangoed & District 1023
Llangollen Town 1026
Llangollen Town Colts 1026
Llangyfelach 1026
Llangynwyd Rangers 1026
Llanharran 1023
Llanharry 1026
Llanhilleth Athletic 1024
Llanidloes Town 1025
Llanilar 1023
Llanllyfni 1022
Llannefydd 1024
Llanon 1023
Llanrhaeadr 1025
Llanrhystud 1023
Llanrug United 1022
Llanrumney United 1026
Llanrumney United
Old Boys 1023
Llanrwst United 1022
Llansannan 1024
Llansantffraid Village 1025
Llansawel 1021
Llantwit Fardre 1021
Llantwit Major 1026
Llanuwchllyn 1026
Llanwddyn 1025
Llanwern 1020
Llanwern RTB 1024
Llanwern Sports
& Social 1025
Llanybydder 1023
Llanystumdwy 1024
Llay Welfare 1026
Llew Goch 1024
Lliswerry 1024
Llwynypia BGC 1026
Llyfrgell Gen 1023
LM United 998
LNER Builders 1014
Loass 994
Locking Park 1013
Locking Villa 1013
Lockleaze 989
Locks Heath 916
Locomotives 1011
Loddiswell 1008
Loddon United 893
Lode 902
Lodge Bar 991
Lodgefield Park 998
Loftus Athletic 994
Lomax 1012
London & Essex 998
London Airways 1008
London APSA 730
London Colney 823
London Lions 917
London Road 1003
London Tigers 998
London United
Football Academy 934
Long Ashton 951
Long Buckby 851
Long Buckby Ravens 1005
Long Clawson 1004
Long Crendon 943
Long Eaton United 788
Long Lane 1008
Long Lee Juniors 992
Long Marston 986
Long Melford 718
Long Riston 974
Long Stratton 894
Long Sutton Athletic 945
Long Wittenham Athletic 936
Longford 995
Longhope 1003

Longlevens 995
Longridge Town 1006
Longstanton 902
Longton Harriers 953
Longtown 992
Longwell Green Sports 881
Lonlas Youth 1025
Looe Town 993
Lord Harrowby 995
Lord Nelson Beverley 994
Lord Raglan 1024
Lords XI 992
Lordswood 755
Lordswood Athletic 1006
Lostock Gralam 906
Lostock St Gerards 964
Loughborough 1004
Loughborough Dynamo 503
Loughborough Galaxy 1004
Loughborough Town 1004
Loughborough United 1004
Loughborough University 761
Loughton 987
Louth Mariners 993
Louth Old Boys 993
Louth Town 904
Louth United 975
Lower Green 998
Lower Hopton 980
Lower New Inn 1024
Lower Stratton 966
Lower Street 987
Lowestoft International 1000
Lowestoft Town 668
Lowford 1008
Lowick United 1004
Loxwood 837
LPOSSA 934
Lucas Cwmbran 1024
Lucas Sports 928
Luddendenfoot 996
Luddington 1007
Ludford 993
Ludgershall 986
Ludgershall Sports 972
Ludgvan 967
Ludlow Town 876
Ludlow Town Colts 1007
Ludwig Leisure Basingstoke 916
Lullingstone Castle 995
Lunesdale United 1012
Luso-Chard 1005
Luton Athletic 1006
Luton Leagrave 1001
Luton Town 115
Lutterworth Athletic 927
Lutterworth Town 927
LWS Highdown Rovers 1013
Lydbrook Athletic 995
Lydd Town 920
Lydney Town 739
Lye Town 876
Lyme Bantams 1005
Lyme Regis 1005
Lymington Town 863
Lymm 998
Lympstone 992
Lyndhurst 916
Lynemouth Miners Welfare 1004
Lyng 1003
Lynn Discovery 1004
Lynn Docklands 1004
Lynn Napier 1004
Lynton & Lynmouth 1003
Lytchett Red Triangle 969
Lytham Town 965
M & B Club 910
Mablethorpe 993
Machno United 1023
Machynlleth 1023
Mackets Grenadier 929
Mackworth 1023
Made for Ever 989
Madeley Sports 1011
Madron 1002
Maesglas 1023
Maesteg Park 1020
Magdala Amateurs 1005
Magham Down 994
Maghull 960
Magna 1000
Magpies 988
Mahal 879
Maiden Newton & Cattistock 969
Maidenbower Village 992
Maidenhead Town 993
Maidenhead United 367
Maidstone Athletic 1001
Maidstone United 644
Maine Road 776
Maiwand 934
Maker-with-Rame 993
Malborough United 1008
Malden Manor 998
Maldon St Marys 912
Maldon Town 669
Malet Lambert YC 973
Malgo 922
Mallaby 961
Mallard 1007
Malmesbury Arms 1007
Malmesbury Victoria 739
Malpas (Cheshire) 906
Malpas (Gwent) 1025
Malpas Gladiator 1024
Malpas United 1025
Malremo Rangers 987
Maltby Main 788
Malton & Norton 1014
Maltsters Sports 1026
Malvern 1008
Malvern Town 516
Manby 993
Manchester Juniors 932
Manchester Rovers 999
Manchester Wanderers 987
Mandeville 986
Manea United 945
Manford Way 910
Mangotsfield United 599
Mangrove 997
Manor Athletic 962
Manor Inne 953
Manor Park United 998
Manor Wasps 1009
Manorbier United 1025
Mansfield Road 943
Mansfield Town 121
MANWEB 998
Maori Park 998
Maple Cross 1012
Maple Leaf Rovers 987
Marabese Ceramics 898
Marazion Blues 995
March Rangers 902
March Town United 718
Marcham 935
Marconi Athletic 1001
Mardy 1024
Mareham United 988
Maresfield Village 1001
Margam YC 1025
Margate 646
Marham Wanderers 1004
Marine 454
Mark One 1009
Market Drayton Town 504
Market Rasen Town 1000
Market Weighton United 994
Marketeers 1011
Markfield 1004
Marks Farm 1001
Markyate 824
Marlborough Town 966
Marldon 1008
Marlingford 897
Marlow 578
Marlow United 737
Marquis of Lorne 1001
Marrowbone & Cleaver 993
Marsden 980
Marsh Gibbon 1003
Marsh Leys 898
Marsh Rangers 933
Marsh United 1004
Marshall Langston 1009
Marshalls 962
Marshalls Sports 995
Marshfield 1025
Marske United 801
Marston Saints 942
Marston Shelton Rovers 898
Marston Social 898
Marstons 990
Martham 896
Martin Baker Rovers 1012
Martin's Nest 996
Martley Spurs 1013
Mary Dendy 993
Masham 996
Mason & Gerald Martin 996
Massams 1009
Massey-Ferguson 761
Master Mariner 1026
Matchplay Reeves 1010
Mathern Wanderers 1024
Matlock Sports 1002
Matlock Town 456
Matlock Town Youth 1001
Matrixgrade 1005
Matson 1009
Mattersey 995
Mattishall 894
Mauritius Sports Association 730
Mawdesley 1006
Mawgan 995
Mawnan 995
Max United 1026
Maxlocal 988
Mayfield 994
Maypole 987
MBCS 991
Meadow Rangers 1001
Meadowbrook Athletic 1008
Measham Imperial 1004
Medbourne 937
Medway Athletic 1006
Medway City 1006
Medway Colts 1006
Medway Galvanising 1006
Medway Knights 1006
Medway Ports 1006
Medway Queen 1006
Medway Rams 1007
Medway Rovers 1006
Meifod 1025
Meir KA 761
Melbourn 902
Melbourne 1014
Melbourne Dynamo 1002
Melbourne Sports 994
Meliden 1024
Meliora Cogito 987
Melksham Town 880
Mellor 999
Mells & Vobster United 1001
Meltham Athletic 980
Meltis Albion 898
Meltis Corinthians 898
Melton Mowbray 1000
Melton Mowbray BS 1004
Melton St Audrys 955
Memory Lane 1023
Men's Health 1007
Mendip United 988
Mendlesham 955
Meole Brace 977
Meopham 995
Mepal Sports 902
Meppershall 898
Meppershall Jurassic 898
Mere Town 969
Mere Town YDT 1011
Meriden Athletic 987
Meridian Sports 923
Merlins 1000
Merlins Bridge 1025
Mermaid 993
Merriott Rovers 1005
Merrow 1010
Merryweathers 1000
Mersea Island 908
Mersey Royal 962
Merseyside Congaleze 1000
Merstham 693
Merstham Newton 992
Merthyr Saints 1021
Merthyr Tydfil 548
Merton 1003
Merton Abbey 1010
Merton Rovers 998
Merton Social 998
Messingham Trinity Juniors 1007
Met Office 992
Meta Sports 998
Metheringham 1000
Methwold Rovers 990
Metpol Chigwell NE 912
Metrogas 921
Metropolitan Police 694
Metropolitan Police Bushey 917
Mevagissey 993
Mexborough Main Street 1007
Mexoc 998
Michelmersh & Timsbury 972
Mickleover RBL 1002
Mickleover Sports 505
Middleton Cheney 943
Middleton Park 1000
Middleton Rovers 993
Middlewich Town 905
Middlezoy Rovers 1011
Midgley United 996
Midhurst & Easebourne United 837
Midland 998
Midland Syston St Peters 1000
Midway 988
Midway FC 990
Milborne Port 1014
Milborne Sports 969
Mildenhall Town 717
Mildenhall United 1009
Mile Oak 837
Mile Oak Rovers 762
Milford & Witley 957
Milford Athletic 1025
Milford United 1025
Milkwall 1003
Mill End Sports 917
Mill Hill 993
Mill Hill St Peters 965
Millbrook 815
Millhead 1004
Millmead 996
Millmoor Juniors 1007
Millom 964
Millwey Rise 1005
Millwheel 1005
Milnthorpe Corinthians 964
Milton & Fulston United 919
Milton (Cambs) 901
Milton (Manchester) 999
Milton (Northants) 937
Milton Crusaders 1013
Milton FC 1013
Milton United 737
Milverton Rangers 1011
Minchinhampton RDS 1009
Minehead Town 881
Miners Rangers 989
Minety 966
Minster 990
Minster Lovell 1013
Minster WMC 1006
Minsterworth 1003
Mirehouse 992
Misterton 1005
Mistley United 909
Mitcheldean 995
Mixenden United 996
MK Titans 1003
MK United 995
MK Wanderers 824
Mochdre Sports 1024
Moghuls 1004
Mold Alexandra 1018
Mold Juniors 1026
Moldgreen 997
Moldgreen Conservative 997
Mole Valley SCR 704
Molescroft Rangers 994
Molesey 703
Molesey Villa 998
Moneyfields 863
Moneysupermarket.com 991
Monk Fryston 1007
Monk Sports 906
Monkton Swifts 1025
Monmouth Town 1021
Monotype 1006
Montgomery Town 1025
Monton Amateurs 932
Montpelier View 988
Montpelier Villa 988
Monty Hind Old Boys 1002
Monument Eagles 990
Moonrakers 1011
Moor Lane 1014
Moore United 906
Moorends 1007
Moorfield 1012
Moorside Rangers 999
Moortown Old Boys 1014
Morchard Bishop 992
Morda United 976
Morecambe Cricket Club 1004
Morecambe Gold 1004
Morecambe Hoops 1004
Morecambe Royals 1004
Moredon Cheney 966
Moreton (Cheshire) 987
Moreton (Dorset) 969
Moreton Rangers 990
Moretonhampstead 1008
Morley C & SC 1012
Morley Rangers 1005
Morley Town 982
Morley Village 896
Morpeth Town 800
Morriston Olympic 1026
Mortehoe 1003
Mortimer 946
Morton 995
Morton Amateurs 995
Morwenstow 970
Mosscroft 1012
Mossley 481
Mossley Hill Athletic 961
Moston Brook 999
Mostonians 998
Mostyn Dragons 1024
Motor Racing Club Ewell 998
Mott MacDonald 902
Mottisfont 972
Moulton 937
Moulton Harrox 944
Mount 997
Mount Ambrose 1002
Mount Gould 1005
Mount Nod Highway 991
Mount St Mary's 985
Mountain Ash Athletic 1023
Mountain Ash Town 1023
Mountain Daisy 1012
Mountain Rangers 1023
Mountfield United 994
Mountnessing Boca 910
Mountsorrel Amateurs 1000
Mousehole 815
Mousehole Reserves 995
MPE 1001
Mploy 988
MRF 996
Much Hadham 997
Much Wenlock 1011
Mudeford Mens Club 988
Mulbarton Wanderers 990
Mulberry Bush 898
Muldoons 1006
Mullion 967
Mundesley 1003
Mundford 896
Mundon Victoria 1001
Mursley United 824
Murton 939
Mushet & Coalway United 1003
My Generation Sports 934
Mynydd Isa 1018
Mynydd Llandegai 1023
Mytchett Rangers 996
Nabs Head 988
Nafferton 993
Nafferton Old Boys 993
Nags Head 991
Nailsea Town 949
Nailsea United 948
Nailsea United Colts 1013
Nanpean Rovers 971
Nantlle Vale 1022
Nantwich Town 458
Nantyglo 1025
Narborough 1004
Narborough & Littlethorpe 927
NASFAT 1008
Nautical William 1000
Nayland Rangers 991
Naylorsfield 1000
Neath Athletic 1015
Necton SSC 897
Needham Market 717
Needham Market Vets 956
Needingworth United 899
Nefyn United 1022
Nelson 776
Nelson Cavaliers 1026
Nelson Tigers 994
NELTC 928
Nerberth 1025
Nestle Rowntree 1014
Neston Legion 987
Nether Stowey 1011
Netherbury 1005
Netherfield Albion 1005
Netherfield Boys 1005
Netherhall 992
Netherseal Saint Peters 990
Netherton 997
Netherton United 945
Netley Central Sports 972
Netley Marsh 1009
Nettleham 903
New Airedale 1007

New Bohemians 1008
New Bradwell St Peter 823
New Brighton 960
New Brighton Villa 1026
New College Swindon 966
New Earswick 1014
New East Manchester 999
New Farnley CC 1000
New Field 991
New Haw Wanderers 996
New Holland Villa 1007
New Inn 1024
New Longton Rovers 1006
New Marske Sports Club 958
New Mill 997
New Mills 776
New Milton Eagles 988
New Milton Linnets 988
New Milton Town 863
New Park 1008
New Quay 1023
New Romney 920
New Street 1009
New Windsor Old Boys 993
New York 1011
Newark Flowserve 904
Newark Town 903
Newbold Jubilee 1000
Newbottle WMC 1011
Newbridge 987
Newbridge-on-Wye 1025
Newburgh United 1013
Newbury 738
Newcastle Benfield 800
Newcastle British Telecom 941
Newcastle City 1011
Newcastle Diggers United 1011
Newcastle East End Rail Club 940
Newcastle Emlyn 1020
Newcastle JCB Eindhoven 1011
Newcastle Medicals 1011
Newcastle RVI Lochside 1011
Newcastle Town 776
Newcastle University 939
Newcastle-on-Clun 1025
Newchurch 998
Newcome Arms 1006
Newent Town 1003
Newhall United 762
Newham Borough 994
Newham Borough (SECP) 933
Newham Royals 998
Newham United 912
Newham Warriors 998
Newhaven 838
Newhaven White Hart 988
NEWI Cefn Druids 1015
Newick 1002
Newlyn Non Athletico 1002
Newman College 1006
Newmarket Inn 993
Newmarket Town 718
Newmarket White Lion 902
Newmount 1002
Newnham United 1003
Newport Civil Service 1021
Newport Colts 998
Newport Corinthians 1024
Newport County 373
Newport County Borough 976
Newport IOW 863
Newport Pagnell Town 851
Newport Veterans 902
Newport YMCA 1019
Newquay 815
Newsome WMC 997
Newton 960
Newton '66 1008
Newton Abbot 813
Newton Abbot Spurs 813
Newton Aycliffe 958
Newton Bears 991
Newton FC 990
Newton FC 999
Newton Flotman 897
Newton Heath 999
Newton Heath & Stroud 995
Newton St Cyres 992
Newton United 1008
Newton Wanderers 1025
Newton-le-Willows 1012
Newtown (Devon) 992
Newtown (Wales) 1015
Newtown Colts 1025
Newtown Henley 947
Newtown Villa 1012
Neyland 1025
Nicholas Wanderers 988
Nimbin United 1008
Ninfield United 994
Nirankari North Herts 1003
Niton 998
NK Aces 995
Noahs Ark 1008
Nomads 1007
Nomansland 1007
Norcross & Warbreck 964
Norfolk & Chance 996
Nork Social 1006
Normalair RSL 1014
Normandy 986
Norris Villa 999
North Bradley 1011
North Burton 993
North Cave 974
North Elmham 990
North End 1026
North Ferriby Athletic 974
North Ferriby United 460
North Greenford United 703
North Greenford United Social 934
North Kensington 934
North Kilworth 1000
North Leigh 600
North Molton 1003
North Mymms 918
North Newbald 994
North Nibley 1010
North Ormesby Sports 978
North Oxford 943
North Petherton 1011
North Sea United 988
North Sheen 998
North Shields 801
North Shields Athletic 941
North Skelton Bulls Head 994
North Somercotes 993
North Sunderland 1004
North Tawton 992
North Thoresby 993
North Walsham
Old Boys 1003
North Walsham Town 893
North Weald 987
North Wingfield United 991
Northallerton Town 800
Northam Lions 1003
Northampton Harlequins 1004
Northampton ON Chenecks 852
Northampton Sileby Rangers 852
Northampton Spencer 851
Northants Police 1005
Northbank Carlisle 940
Northbrook 1014
Northend United 1008
Northenden Victoria 986
Northfield Town 762
Northiam 994
Northleach Town 990
Northowram 996
Northway 990
Northwich Victoria 249
Northwold S&SC 990
Northwood 670
Northwood St Johns 998
Northwoood Town 953
Nortoft United 988
Norton & Stockton Ancients 801
Norton (Staffs) 952
Norton (Surrey) 1010
Norton Athletic 1005
Norton Athletic FC 1000
Norton FC 1011
Norton Fitzwarren 1011
Norton Sports 755
Norton United 777
Norton United FC 1014
Norwich CEYMS 895
Norwich St Johns 895
Norwich Union FC 1014
Norwich United 717
Nostell Miners Welfare 788
Nottingham Sikh Lions 1005
Nottinghamshire 1002
Notts Metropolis 1005
Notts Police 1005
NPL 1010
NSC Central 1000
Number One Pub 996
Nuneaton Griff 761
Nuneaton Griff & Coton 991
Nuneaton Town 550
Nunsthorpe Tavern 996
Nunthorpe Athletic 978
Nursling 1008
Nutfield 1010
Nuthall 1005
Nuthall Athletic 1002
Nutley 1002
Nuxley 1008
NWCA & Shylet Tigers 987
Nympsfield 1010
O & G United 988
O'Connell's 1006
Oadby Boys Club 1000
Oadby Town 769
Oak 992
Oakengates Athletic 977
Oakfield (Gwent) 1025
Oakfield (IOW) 998
Oakfield (Kent) 995
Oakham Imperial 1000
Oakhill 1001
Oakhill United 1011
Oakland 989
Oakley Athletic 986
Oakley Sports 898
Oakley United 943
Oakridge 991
Oaks Institute Old Boys 1000
Oaksey 991
Oakstead 1011
Oakwood (Devon) 992
Oakwood (Kent) 920
Oakwood (Sussex) 836
Oakworth 992
Oatlands 996
Obelisk United 1005
Ockham 1010
Odd Down 881
Official Club Speed 1009
Offley Social 1001
Offwell Rangers 992
Okeford United 969
Okehampton Argyle 814
Old Altrinchamians 932
Old Ashtonians 999
Old Bank WMC 1011
Old Barkabbeyans 994
Old Basing 986
Old Batelians 1014
Old Bemrosians 1002
Old Bexleians 923
Old Blackburnians 998
Old Boars 1007
Old Boltonians 998
Old Bootleians 1000
Old Bradwell United 824
Old Bristolians 1010
Old Cathinians 1000
Old Centralians 984
Old Chelmsfordians 911
Old Colfeians 1008
Old Collegians 1014
Old Congs 1009
Old Cothamians 989
Old Doningtonians 988
Old Elizabethans 1002
Old Georgians 989
Old Headingley 984
Old Hill 998
Old Holts 930
Old Hunstanton 1004
Old Inn All Stars 1011
Old Instonians 1000
Old Leake 988
Old Malton St Marys 1014
Old Mancunians 998
Old Modernians 1014
Old Newton United 955
Old Nortonians 987
Old Oakmeadians 988
Old Parmiterians 918
Old Plymouthians 1010
Old Portmuthians 1005
Old Roan 1008
Old Roehamptonians 998
Old Rovers 1014
Old Rutlishians 957
Old Salesians 1010
Old Sodbury 989
Old Southendian 1009
Old Street 987
Old Stretfordians 999
Old Suttonians 1005
Old Thornesians 1014
Old Town 1011
Old Town Athletic 994
Old Town New Boys 1008
Old Trafford 999
Old Varndeanians 1001
Old Windsor 993
Old Woodstock Town 737
Old Wulfrunians 987
Old Xaverians 928
Old York '06 986
Oldbury Athletic 761
Oldbury Crusaders 989
Oldbury United 769
Oldfield Sports 986
Oldham Hulmeians 999
Oldham Town 777
Oldham Victoria 999
Oldland Abbotonians 881
Oldswinford Harriers 998
Ole Frank 1000
Ollerton Town 903
Olney Town 852
Olveston United 989
Ongar Town 910
Onllwyn 1025
OPK 923
Oracle Components 997
Orb360 988
Orchard Park Rangers 993
Orcop Juniors 997
Ordulph Arms 1005
Orford BA 1012
Orington 994
Orleton Colts 997
Ormskir 1013
Orpington 919
Orwell 902
Osbaldwick 1014
Osborne Coburg 998
Ossett Albion 482
Ossett Common Rovers 984
Ossett Town 462
Ossett Two Brewers 1012
Oswaldtwistle St Mary's 993
Oswestry Boys Club 1007
Otford United 920
Otley Rovers 996
Otley Town 983
Otterbourne 916
Otterton 992
Ottery St Mary 814
Oughtibridge WMSC 1007
Oulton Broad & Notleys 895
Oundle Town 944
Ouseburn United 1014
Outcasts 998
Outer Fenn 1006
Outo Kumpu Sports & Social 1007
Outwell Swifts 901
Outwood Victoria 1012
Oval Sports 987
Ovenden West Riding 980
Over Sports 899
Overseal Saint Matthews 990
Overthorpe Sports 980
Overton 1004
Overton Athletic 1006
Overton Recreation 1026
Overton United 916
Oving 986
Ovingdean 988
Owermoigne 969
Owton Manor SC 996
Oxenhope Recreation 985
Oxford Arms 1000
Oxford City 552
Oxford City Nomads 739
Oxford United 127
Oxford University Press 942
Oxhey 1012
Oxhey Jets 822
Oxhey Wanderers 1012
Oxshott Royals 998
Oxspring United 1008
Oxted & District 1010
Oyster 991
P & IC United 986
Padarn United 1023
Padbury United 824
Paddock Rangers 997
Paddock Wood 1011
Padiham 777
Padstow United 970
Page Celtic 928
Pagham 836
Paignton Saints 1008
Paignton Villa 1008
Pakefield Re-United 1001
Pan Sports 998
Pandy 1024
Pannal Sports 996
Panteg 1024
Pantside 1025
Pantyscallog Village Juniors 1024
Paperclip 996
Papworth 902
Park Athletic 994
Park Boys 1011
Park Brown 1000
Park End 1000
Park Lane 1006
Park Lawn 1023
Park Regis 1006
Park Road Old Boys 988
Park Street Village 917
Park Travellers 1025
Park United (Berks) 946
Park United (Devon) 1003
Park United (Lincs) 988
Park Vets 1026
Park View (Middx) 933
Park View (Wearside) 1012
Park View FC 1024
Park Villa 1026
Parkfield Amateurs 987
Parkfield BA 987
Parkgate 788
Parkgate FC 991
Parkhouse 904
Parkhurst Rangers 1008
Parkside 945
Parkside United 956
Parkside Wanderers 988
Parkwood Athletic 1007
Parkwood Jupitors 1001
Parley Sports 969
Parramore Sports 904
Parrswood Celtic 999
Parson Drove 944
Parson Street Old Boys 989
Parton United 992
Pastures 1002
Patchway Town 914
Pateley Bridge 996
Pathfinder 987
Paull Wanderers 994
Paulsgrove 916
Paulton Rovers 601
Paynes Sports 1006
PB Wolverton Town 1003
Peacehaven & Telscombe 837
Peacehaven Good Companions 988
Peacehaven United 1002
Peacock Celtic 995
Peacock United 1007
Peak Dale 997
Pease Pottage Village 838
Peasedown Athletic 949
Peasmarsh & Iden 994
Pebsham Sibex 994
Peche Hill Select 994
Peel Park 993
Pegasus (Lancs) 1006
Pegasus (Notts) 1005
Pegasus Juniors 737
Pegasus Juniors Colts 997
Pelly House 987
Pelsall Villa 876
Pemberton 1013
Pembroke 966
Pembroke Borough 1025
Pembroke House 1008
Pembury 922
Pen Mill 1014
Penarth Town 1026
Pencader United 1023
Pencoed Athletic 1026
Pencombe 997
Pendeeen Rovers 995
Pendine 1025
Pendle Athletic 992
Pendle Forest Sports Club 993
Pendle Renegades 992
Pendlebury United 999
Penistone Church 1007
Penketh United 1012
Penkridge Town 879
Penlake 1009
Penlan Club 1026
Penley 1026

Penmaenmawr
Phoenix 1024
Penn & Tylers Green 738
Penn Croft 878
Pennar Robins 1025
Pennington 931
Pennington St Marks 988
Penny Lane 1000
Penparcau 1025
Penrhiwceiber Con
Athletic 1023
Penrhiwceiber
Rangers 1020
Penrhiwfer 1026
Penrhos 1026
Penrhyn United 1024
Penrhyncoch 1018
Penrhyndeudraeth 1023
Penrith Rangers 1012
Penrith Town 800
Penryn Athletic 815
Pensford 1001
Penshurst Park 1011
Pensilva 993
Pentney 1004
Pentraeth Nurseries 1023
Pentrebach Labour 1024
Pentwyn Dynamo 1020
Pentwynmawr Athletic 1024
Penwortham St
Theresas United 1006
Penwortham Town 1006
Penybont Athletic 1025
Penybont United 1025
Penycae 1026
Penydarren Boys Club 1026
Penyffordd 1026
Penygraig BGC 1026
Penyrheol 1026
Penywaun 1023
Penzance 815
Percy Main Amateurs 940
Perranporth 967
Perranwell 967
Perry Street &
Yonder Hill 1005
Perrywood 763
Pershore Town 761
Perthcelyn United 1023
Peterborough
Northern Star 852
Peterborough Rovers 945
Peterborough Sports 944
Peterlee Town 939
Petersfield Town 864
Petworth 1012
Peugeot 991
Pewsey Vale 739
Pfizer Athletic 990
PFS Athletic 1025
Phoenix 988
Phoenix Club 992
Phoenix Colts 998
Phoenix Construction 1026
Phoenix Sports 919
Phoenix Sports & S. 904
Phoenix United
(Birmingham) 987
Phoenix United (Glos) 990
Phoenix United (Kent) 1001
Phoenix United FC 992
PHS United 988
Pickering Town 788
Piddlehinton United 969
Piddletrenthide United 969
PILCS 1024
Pilkington 905
Pilkington XXX 761
Pill 1025
Pill Mill Hibernians 1025
Pilton Academicals 1003
Pilton United 1001
Pinchbeck United 944
Pinefleet Wolfreton 974
Pinewoods 930
Pinhoe 992
Pinxton 903
Pinxton North End 1002
Pirbright Sports 996
Pit Stop 1026
Pitstone & Ivinghoe 824
PK Construction 993
Platinium 995
Platt United 922
Plexus Networking 994
Plough 1012
Plough & Chequers
Sports 1006
Plough Colts 1026
Plough Inn 1023
Plough Skellingthorpe 1000
Plumpton Athletic 1002
Plymouth City 1005
Plymouth Parkway 813
Plymouth Trophyman 1005
Plymouth YMCA 1005
Plymstock United 815
Poachers 1006
Pocklington Town 973
Point of Ayr 1024
Pointon 988
Pointon Colts 995
Polegate Town 994
Polish 998
Pollington 1007
Polonia Camps 1000
Polperro 971
Polska PGL 997
Pontardawe Town 1019
Pontefract Collieries 789
Pontefract Sports
& Social 984
Pontefract Town 1007
Ponteland United 939
Pontlanffraith Spartans 1025
Pontlottyn 1026
Pontnewydd United 1025
Pontprennau Puma 1023
Ponty Bridge 1026
Pontyclun 1021
Pontypool Town 1024
Pontypridd Town 1020
Pool 983
Poole Borough 907
Poole Town 863
Poppleton United 1014
Poringland Wanderers 895
Porlock 1011
Port Talbot Tigers 1025
Port Talbot Town 1015
Port Talbot Town Exiles 1025
Port Tennant Colts 1026
Portcastrian 988
Portchester 1006
Porters 1005
Porthcawl Athletic 1025
Porthcawl Town 1021
Porthleven 815
Porthleven Rangers 995
Porthmadog 1015
Portishead Town 881
Portishead WMC 1013
Portland United 907
Porton Sports 1007
Portreath 967
Portsea Community 1005
Portskewett &
Sudbrook 1024
Portslade Athletic 988
Portsmouth Kurdish
United 1006
Portville Warriors 989
Post Office 990
Post Office FC 1014
Pot Black 1000
Pot Black FC 1009
Pott Row 1004
Potten End 1012
Potter Street 910
Potters 1007
Potters Bar Crusaders 1003
Potters Bar Town 671
Potters Green 991
Potterspury 1003
Potton United 851
Potton Wanderers 898
Poulton 991
Poulton Town 963
Poulton Victoria 960
Poulton Wanderers 1009
Poundbury 969
Powerleague 945
Powick 1013
Poynton 906
Poynton Kings 993
Poynton Nomads 993
Prairie United 998
Predators 1012
Prees United 1007
Premier 922
Premier FC 2008 987
Premium 1005
Prendergast Villa 1025
Prescoed 1024
Prescot Cables 483
Prescot Leisure 1009
Prestatyn Town 1015
Prestbury Rovers 990
Presteigne St Andrews 1025
Preston GSA 1006
Preston United 1006
Preston Wanderers 1006
Prestwich Heys 931
Prestwood 738
Prince Albert Canterbury 990
Prince of Wales 988
Prince of Wales
Rangers 1014
Priors 1009
Priory 992
Priory Rovers 1008
Pro Pak 987
Probuild 1003
Probus 970
Prospect 1005
Prostar 1012
Prostar Windows 996
Prudhoe Town 801
Pucklechurch Sports 989
Puddletown 969
Puma 1003
Puma 2000 998
Punjab United 938
Punjab United FC 995
Punnetts Town 994
Puretown 1010
Purnells Sports 1001
Purton 739
Putford 1003
Pwllheli 1022
Pymoor 902
Pymore 1005
Pyrford 1010
Q Ball 994
QK Southampton 916
Quaddy Rangers 994
Quainton 986
Quar Park Rangers 1024
Quarry Bank 998
Quarry Bank Old Boys 1000
Quedgeley Wanderers 1009
Queen Eleanor
Great Houghton 938
Queens 997
Queens Park Athletic 988
Queensfield 1011
Quendon Athletic 987
Queniborough 1000
Quorn 506
R & B Sports 986
Rabson Rovers 946
Race 1024
Racing Club Warwick 769
Racing Epsom 1006
Radcliffe Borough 484
Radcliffe Boys 999
Radcliffe Olympic 903
Radcliffe Town 998
Radford 715
Radius 1007
Radnor Valley 1025
Radstock 947
Radstock Town 880
RAFA Boys 1023
Ragged School 1026
Raglan 996
Railway 997
Railway East Ardsley 1000
Railway Vets 991
Raine 994
Rainford North End 1009
Rainham '84 1006
Rainham Cricketers 1007
Rainham WMC 994
Rainhill Town 1012
Rainworth Miners
Welfare 789
Ramblers 995
Rampton Hospital 995
Ramsbottom Town 986
Ramsbottom United 776
Ramsbury 966
Ramsden 912
Ramsey Town 944
Ramsgate 695
Randwick 1009
Rangers 986
Rangers Breaks 991
Rangeworthy 989
Rank Outsiders 1003
Ransomes Sports 955
Rassau Rangers 1025
Ratby Sports 926
Raunds Town 851
Ravenhead Knauff 1012
Ravens 1001
Ravenscliffe 992
Ravenshead Rangers 1002
Ravenstone 927
Rawcliffe Rangers 1014
Rawdon Old Boys 982
Rawreth Sports 1009
Rawtenstall 993
Rayleigh Town 911
Rayners Lane 738
Raynes Park Vale 703
Read United 993
Reading Town 737
Reading YMCA 946
Real Bay View 1025
Real Brunswick 988
Real Dragoon 1005
Real Fairford 991
Real Holmesdale 1006
Real Hydraquip 992
Real Knights 1006
Real Llandudno 1024
Real Man of Kent 995
Real Medina 990
Real Medina Youth 990
Real Ravensdale 991
Real Riverside 987
Real Southwick 988
Real Tek 986
Real United 1005
Reckitts 973
Red Arrow Sports 990
Red Dwarf 987
Red Lion (Gwent) 1025
Red Lion (Sussex) 994
Red Lion (Wooburn) 1014
Red Lion Bourne 995
Red Lion FC 997
Red Lion Horninglow 990
Red Row Welfare 940
Red Rum 928
Red Star 998
Red Star Benwell 1011
Red Star Galaxy 987
Red Star Spartans 998
Redbourn 1003
Redbridge 672
Redbridge Elite 998
Redbrook Rovers 1003
Redcar Rugby Club 979
Redcliffe United 989
Redditch United 255
Redgate 1011
Redgate Clayton 952
Redgate Rovers 930
Redgrave Rangers 897
Redhill 836
Redhill Rangers 988
Redhouse 1012
Redlynch &
Woodfalls United 988
Redmire United 1012
Redruth United 1002
Redwood 1009
Reed 1006
Reedham 995
Reepham Town 895
Reeth & District
Athletic Club 1012
Reffley Royals 1004
Regal United 1001
Reigate Hill 1006
Reigate Priory 957
Reigate Sala 1006
REME Arborfield 946
REMYCA United 929
Renhold United 898
Renhold Village 898
Renishaw Social Club 991
Repton 998
Reservado RU 986
Resolution 987
Resolven 1025
Retford United 464
Revision Logistics 1007
RF Saints 1009
RGV Netheravon 1007
RH123 Athletic 1006
Rhayader Town 1025
Rhein 1000
Rhiwlas 1024
Rhoden Inn 988
Rhodesia United 1001
Rhoose 1026
Rhos 1025
Rhos Aelwyd 1026
Rhos United 1024
Rhosgoch Rangers 1025
RHP Newark 995
RHS United 901
Rhuddlan Town 1024
Rhydyfelin 1026
Rhydyfelin Labour 1026
Rhydymwyn 1022
Rhyl 1015
Rhymney 1025
Ribbleton & Chorley 1006
Ribchester 1006
Ricardo 988
Riccall United 1014
Rice Lane City Farm 998
Richmond 1000
Richmond Academy 1012
Richmond Athletic 1012
Richmond Mavericks 978
Richmond Raith
Rovers Jacobs 962
Richmond Town 978
Rickmansworth
St George 1012
Riddings Rovers 1001
Ridings High 989
Rileys & Fryston 1007
Rileys MBM 996
Rileys Rangers 1007
Rimington 993
Ringmer 836
Ringstead Rangers 938
Ringwood Athletic 988
Ringwood Town 864
Ringwood United 988
RIP London 998
Ripley 1002
Ripley Village 1010
Ripon City 983
Ripon Red Arrows 996
Risborough Rangers 824
Risca United 1021
Riseley Sports 898
Rishton United 988
Rising Sun 987
Rising Sun Colden
Common 1008
Rising Sun FC 1009
Ristee Towers 938
Riverhead 1007
Riverside 1006
Riverway 878
Riviera Spurs 1007
RKP United 1001
RMSC Athletic 1000
RNAS Culdrose 967
Roach Dynamos 999
Roade 937
Roath Park Royals 1023
Robartes Arms 1002
Robertsbridge United 994
Robin Hood 991
Robin Hood Athletic 984
Robin Hood FC 998
Roborough 1005
Roby College Old Boys 1000
Roca Juniors 1007
Rocester 769
Rochdale Sacred Heart 931
Rochdale St Clements 998
Rochdale Town 777
Rochdalians 999
Roche 971
Rochford Town 1009
Rock Rovers 993
Rock-a-Nore 994
Rockbeare Rockets 992
Rockbourne 988
Rockfield Rovers 1024
Rockland United 990
Rockspur 1026
Rockville Wallasey 930
Rodbourne Arms 1011
Roehampton Athletic 1010
Roffey 1002
Rogerstone Welfare 1024
Rogiet 1024
Rolls Royce 992
Rolls Royce Leisure 903
Roma 928
Roman Glass St George 881
Romford 673
Romsey Town 863
Romulus 579
Rookley 998
Roos 994
Ropery Inn 995
Rose & Crown (Bucks) 986
Rose & Crown (Lancs) 986
Rose & Crown Driffield 993
Rose of York 1012
Rosedale 987
Roselands 1011
Ross Town 996

Rossendale Amateurs 998
Rossendale United 485
Rossington Main 789
Rosudgeon-Kenneggy 995
Rothbury 1004
Rotherfield 1002
Rotherhithe 989
Rothley Imperial 926
Rothwell Athletic 983
Rothwell Corinthians 851
Rothwell Town (Northants) 580
Rothwell Town (West Yorks) 985
Rottingdean Dynamos 988
Rottingdean Village 838
Roundhegians 1014
Rover Cowley 942
Rovers Reunited 1006
Rowfant Village 992
Rowhedge 909
Rownhams 1008
Rowsley 1002
Roxeth 1000
Royal British Legion 1003
Royal Dolphins 997
Royal Heath Rangers 987
Royal Holloway Old Boys 1010
Royal Mail 946
Royal Mail MDEC 1005
Royal Mail Port Talbot 1025
Royal Marines 814
Royal Oak 1011
Royal Oak Kempston 898
Roydon 911
Roydon Spartans 997
Royston 1012
Royston Town 823
Royton Town 931
RS Beltinge 990
RSG 991
RTB Ebbw Vale 1024
Ruan Minor 995
Ruardean Hill Rangers 1003
Rubery 987
Ruddington United 1005
Rufforth United 1014
Rugby 992
Rugby Town 554
Rugeley Rangers 954
Runcorn Albion 1012
Runcorn Linnets 776
Runcorn Town 960
Running Horse 993
Runnymede 1001
Runton 1003
Runwell Hospital 912
Rush Green 995
Rushall Olympic 507
Rushden & Diamonds 133
Rushden & Higham United 852
Ruskington Rovers 995
Ruspidge United 1003
Rusthall 919
Rustington 837
Ruston Sports 975
Ruthin Town 1018
Ruthin Town Colts 1026
Rutland Rangers 944
Ryan 911
Ryburn United 996
Ryde Saints 998
Rye United 837
Ryecroft Sports 1011
Ryhope Colliery Welfare 958
RYPSA 998
Ryton 800
S & B Sports 1008
Sabden 993
Sacre Coeur Former Pupils 929
Saffron 898
Saffron Crocus 901
Saffron Dynamo 926
Saffron Gap 1000
Saffron Lounge Bar 1000
Saffron Rangers 902
Saffron Walden Town 718
Saga Sports & Social 922
Sagemaster 1006
Saham Toney 990
Sale Amateurs 986
Sale Rovers 986
Salem 996
Salford AFC 986
Salford City 486
Salford Victoria 932
Salisbury City 139
Salmon 1008
Saltash United 813
Saltdean Sharks 988
Saltdean United 838
Salterbeck 992
Saltford 949
Salts 981
Salvation Army 956
Salvation Army (Harlow) 987
Sampford Blues 1011
Sampford Peverell 992
Samuels 993
Sandal Athletic 1014
Sandal Wanderers 1014
Sandbach United 952
Sandersons Removals 996
Sandford 992
Sandgate 934
Sandhills 1011
Sandhurst (Notts) 1005
Sandhurst (Sussex) 994
Sandhurst Devels 946
Sandhurst Sports 986
Sandhurst Town 703
Sandiacre Town 1002
Sandon Royals 911
Sandown 998
Sandridge Rovers 917
Sandringham 1004
Sandy 898
Sandy Lane (Lancs) 1009
Sandy Lane (West Yorks) 985
Santon 1007
Santos 1005
Santos FC 999
Saracens 997
Sarratt 918
Sassco.co.uk 1012
Saughall Thursday 991
Saundersfoot Sports 1025
Sawbridgeworth Town 730
Sawston Rovers 902
Sawston United 901
Sawtry 945
Saxilby Athletic 995
Saxmundham Sports 956
Saxon Chief 1001
Saxton Rovers 935
SC Electrical 994
Scamblesby 993
Scarborough Athletic 789
Scarborough Town 979
Scawby Britannia 1007
Scaynes Hill 1002
SCC Old Boys 1006
Sceptre Elite 1009
Scholes 997
Scissett 1012
Scole United 894
Scotia Billericay 1001
Scotter United 1007
Scraptoft Valley Athletic 1000
Scraptoft Valley WMC 1000
Screw-It Carpentry 988
Sculcoates Amateurs 973
Scunthonians 1007
SDO 995
SDUC 1023
Sea Mills Park 989
Seacroft WMC 1000
Seaford Town 837
Seaham Kitchen Magic 993
Seaham Red Star 800
Seaham The Times Inn 1012
Seal 1007
Seaton 996
Seaton Burn 940
Seaton Delaval Amateurs 939
Seaton Town 992
Seaview 998
Sebastopol 1024
Sedbergh Wanderers 1012
Sedbury United 1003
Sedlescombe 994
Seend United 1011
Sefton Park 989
Segensworth 1005
Selby Olympia 1014
Selby RSSC 1014
Selby Town 788
Select 1000
Selkirk United 1013
Selly Oak Legend 987
Selsey 836
Selston 1002
Semington Magpies 1011
Sennen 1002
Sennybridge 1025
Sentinels 990
Settle United 992
Seven Acre Sports 1008
Seven Sisters 1021
Sevenoaks Town 755
Sevenoaks Weald 1007
Severn Beach 989
Seymour United 989
SFC 954
Shaftesbury 969
Shaftesbury (Cheshire) 987
Shaftesbury (Dorset) 864
Shaftesbury Crusade 989
Shaftesbury Town 1010
Shaftesbury Youth 1025
Shakespeare 1005
Shakha 1000
Shalford 1010
Shalford Youth 996
Shamrock 988
Shamwickshire Rovers 1003
Shankhouse 939
Shanklin 998
Shanklin VYCC 998
Shap 1012
Sharnbrook 898
Sharpness 995
Sharsted 990
Shawbury United 876
Shebbear United 1003
Sheering 987
Sheerness East 919
Sheerwater 704
Sheffield 508
Sheffield Athletic 1007
Sheffield Bankers 1007
Sheffield Lane Top 1007
Sheffield Medics 1008
Sheffield West End 1008
Shelf United 996
Shelfield Rangers 987
Shell Corringham 911
Shelley 997
Shelley Royals 1001
Shelton Athletic 990
Shelton Spartans 1006
Shenfield Association 912
Shenfield Holland 1001
Shenstone Pathfinder 878
Shepley 997
Shepperton FB 996
Shepshed Amateurs 1004
Shepshed Dynamo 509
Shepton Beauchamp 1005
Shepton Mallet 881
Shepway United 1001
Sherborne Harriers 991
Sherborne St John 986
Sherborne Town 880
Sherburn White Rose 983
Shere Punjab 987
Sherfield 986
Sheridans 987
Sheringham 893
Sherington 1003
Sherpa 1007
Sherston 1010
Sherwood 996
Sherwood Casuals 1005
Sherwood Colliery 1002
Shevington 1013
SHFC London 998
Shifnal Town 769
Shifnal United 976
Shilbottle Colliery Welfare 1004
Shildon 800
Shildon Railway 993
Shilton 991
Shinfield 946
Ship & Pilot 1025
Shipdham 990
Shipston Excelsior 764
Shipton Oliffe 990
Shiptonthorpe United 994
Shire Academics 1014
Shirebrook Town 788
Shirehampton 948
Shireway Sports 989
Shirland Athletic 1002
Shirland Miners Welfare 1001
Shirley Athletic 987
Shirley Town (Birmingham) 763
Shirley Town (Surrey) 1011
Shobdon 997
Shoebury Town 1009
Sholing Sports 1008
Shoreham 836
Shoreham RBL 1013
Shortwood United 737
Shotley 956
Shottermill & Haslemere 1010
Shotton Steel 1024
Shrewton United 881
Shrivenham 737
Shropham United 990
Shrublands 996
Shurdington Rovers 1009
Sidac Social 1012
Sidbury United 992
Siddal Athletic 996
Siddington 990
Sidlesham 837
Sidley United 837
Sidmouth Town 992
Signet United 1009
Sileby Saints 1004
Sileby Town 927
Sileby Victoria 1004
Silhill 987
Silkstone United 1007
Silksworth CC 958
Silloth 992
Silsden 776
Silsden White Star 992
Silver End United 1001
Silverstone 1003
Silverton 992
Simonside Social Club 993
Singh Sabha Barking 995
Sinnington 987
Sirtcom 1006
Sittingbourne 696
Sizewell Associates 956
Skegness Town 975
Skegness WMC 988
Skelmanthorpe 997
Skelmersdale United 487
Skidby Millers 994
Skillington 995
Skinners Arms 1000
Skippers 994
Skipton LMS 992
Skipton Town 992
Skirlaugh 994
SKS Blyskawica 966
Sky Blues 995
Slade '05 1006
Slade Farm United 943
Slade Green 755
Slaithwaite United 997
Sleaford Town 851
Slimbridge 914
Slingsby 987
Sloane 934
Slough Heating 993
Slough Town 581
Slyne with Hest (LCC) 1004
Smallfield 1006
Smarden 1001
Smiffys 995
Smithdon 1004
Smiths Athletic 995
Smiths SDFC 1012
Snaresbrook 995
Snettisham 1004
Snodland 919
Snodland Nomads 1007
Snowdown Colliery Welfare 990
Snydale Athletic 1011
Soar Media 1000
Soham Town Rangers 582
Soham United 901
Sole Bay 894
Solent WTL 1008
Solihull Moors 261
Solva 1025
Somerford Sports 988
Somersham 956
Somersham Town 900
Sompting 1013
Sonning 947
Sonning Sports 947
Sony 1009
Soothill 1011
Soudley 995
Souldern 986
Soundwell Victoria 989
South Acton 934
South Bank St Peters 979
South Bradford 981
South Brent 1008
South Bristol Central 989
South Cave United 994
South Cerney 991
South Coast Demolition 988
South Creake 1004
South East Athletic 989
South Farnborough 986
South Gloucestershire (Hambrook) 989
South Godstone 1010
South Gower 1026
South Holderness 994
South Kilburn 738
South Kirkby Colliery 1007
South Liverpool 928
South Manchester 999
South Mersey 1000
South Milford 985
South Molton 1003
South Newton & Wishford 1007
South Park 704
South Park Athletic 1023
South Park Rangers 1013
South Petherton 1005
South Petherwin 998
South Sefton Borough 928
South Shields 800
South Shields Harton & Westoe 958
South Shields United 941
South Walsham 897
South Wigston Wanderers 1000
South Wingfield Athletic 1001
South Yarmouth 996
South Zeal United 992
Southall 933
Southam United 761
Southampton Energy 1008
Southborough 1011
Southbourne 988
Southchurch Hall Old Scholars 1009
Southcott Village RA 1003
Southend Collegians 1009
Southend Manor 730
Southend Rangers 1009
Southend Trojans 1009
Southern Belle 1006
Southern Rangers Old Boys 988
Southmead Athletic 989
Southmead Community Sports 989
Southminster St Leonards 912
Southport 267
Southport Amateurs 1006
Southport Trinity 961
Southrop 1013
Southsea Town 1006
Southside (Glos) 990
Southside (Hants) 1006
Southside Athletic 1014
Southwater 1012
Southwell Amateurs 1002
Southwell City 903
Southwick 837
Sovereign Sports 997
Sowerby Bridge 996
Sowerby United 996
SP Construction 1026
SPA 1005
Spa Athletic 996
Spalding Harriers 988
Spalding Town 988
Spalding United 510
Sparco 1009
Sparkbridge 1009
Sparky Albion 1009
Sparta Basildon 1001
Sparta Kewstoke 1013
Sparta Royals 986
Spartak 1012
Spartak Chorley 991
Spartak Marlow 1014
Spartan Rangers 1013
Spartans 1008
Spaxton 1011
Speke 928
Spelthorne Sports 1010
Spencer Youth & Boys 1024
Spencers Wood 947
Spennithorne & Harmby 1012
Spennymoor Town 800

Spexhall 1000
Spice of Life 1002
Spiders 993
Spilsby Town 988
Splitz United 990
Splott Albion 1026
Sporle 990
Sport London E Benfica 823
Sporting 87 956
Sporting Athletic 988
Sporting Aztecs 987
Sporting Bahia 1010
Sporting Barum 1003
Sporting Bengal United 755
Sporting BTC 916
Sporting Club (GNP) 991
Sporting Crawley 992
Sporting Devils 992
Sporting Hackney 1000
Sporting Kandola 1003
Sporting KFA 1003
Sporting Khalsa 878
Sporting Lindfield 1002
Sporting Llandaff 1023
Sporting Pitsea 1009
Sporting Redhouse 1012
Sporting Sapcote 1000
Sporting Wessex 1008
Sports NSSC 1010
Sportsco 987
Sportsman 988
Sportzcoach United 986
Spotland Methodists 999
Spratton 938
Spring Bank Tigers 994
Springfield (Essex) 912
Springfield (Lancs) 1013
Springfield Rouge 1001
Springhead 997
Springhead 931
Springhill 1004
Springwood 1004
Springwood Throstles Davy 1007
Sproughton Sports 956
Sprowston Athletic 893
Sprowston Wanderers 895
Spurley Hey 999
Squinting Cat 1000
Squires 1004
Squires Gate 776
SRCC 947
SSPIO 945
St Agnes 967
St Albans 1023
St Albans City 379
St Albans North 1012
St Albans Old Boys 1023
St Albans Wanderers 1003
St Aldhelms 989
St Aloysius 928
St Andrews (London) 1010
St Andrews (Norfolk) 894
St Andrews Hearts 1000
St Andrews Police Club 973
St Andrews Res 1010
St Andrews SC 715
St Andrews Winsley 1011
St Annes 987
St Annes Town 989
St Asaph 1024
St Athan 1026
St Austell 815
St Bedes Old Boys 1014
St Bees 992
St Blazey 987
St Briavels 1003
St Buryan 1002
St Clears 1025
St Cleer 993
St Clements 1014
St Clements Hospital 956
St Columb Major 971
St Day 967
St Dennis 993
St Dogmaels 1023
St Dominick 971
St Dominics 930
St Edmunds 65 955
St Florence 1025
St Francis (Birmingham) 987
St Francis (Essex) 998
St Francis Flyers 992
St Francis Rangers 836
St George Easton-in-Gordano 949
St George Rangers 989
St Georges Warriors 987
St Harmon 1025
St Helena Bobs 1005
St Helens 994
St Helens Blue Star 998
St Helens Town 776
St Ippolyts 1003
St Ishmaels 1025
St Ives 991
St Ives Mariners 1002
St Ives Rangers 902
St Ives Town (Cambs) 851
St Ives Town (Cornwall) 967
St James 996
St Johns 955
St Johns Arsenal Deaf 934
St Johns FC 986
St Josephs 1026
St Josephs (Beds) 1001
St Josephs FC 1026
St Judes 1013
St Julians 1025
St Just 967
St Keverne 995
St Lawrence 1007
St Leonards Social 994
St Margaret Marys 992
St Margarets (Essex) 1001
St Margarets (Kent) 990
St Margaretsbury 822
St Marks CA 990
St Martins (Devon) 992
St Martins (Shropshire) 976
St Martins (Surrey) 998
St Mary's College Old Boys 1000
St Marys 989
St Mary's 988
St Marys Butetown 1026
St Mary's College 979
St Marys FC 1014
St Mawgan 993
St Merryn 993
St Michaels DH 1012
St Neots Town 851
St Newlyn East 971
St Nicholas 989
St Nicholas FC 1014
St Osyth 909
St Pancras 989
St Patricks 1000
St Patricks FC 1023
St Pauls (Birmingham) 987
St Pauls (Lancs) 1009
St Peters 918
St Philips Marsh Adult School 989
St Stephen 970
St Stephens 990
St Stephens Borough 971
St Teath 993
St Werburghs 962
Stacksteads St Josephs 993
Staddiscombe Colts 1005
Stafford Rangers 273
Stafford Town 878
Stag 997
Stags Head 995
Staines Lammas 704
Staines Town 385
Stainland United 996
Staithes Athletic 994
Staks 994
Stalbridge 969
Stalham Town 894
Staly 999
Stalybridge Celtic 279
Stambridge United 912
Stamford 511
Stamford Belvedere 944
Stamford Bridge 1014
Stamshaw Spartans 1006
Stand Athletic 932
Standians 932
Standish St Wilfrids 1013
Standon & Puckeridge 917
Stanford-in-the-Vale 936
Stanion United 937
Stanley 1011
Stanley Common 994
Stanley United 985
Stanleytown 1026
Stanningley Old Boys 1014
Stansfeld O & B Club 919
Stansted 730
Stanton (Hants) 1009
Stanton (Suffolk) 955
Stanton 2008 1000
Stanton Harcourt 1013
Stanway Rovers 717
Stanwick Rovers 938
Staplegrove 1011
Staplegrove Colts 1011
Staplehurst & Monarchs United 920
Stapleton Rovers 1009
Star 995
Star Sports 1006
Staunton & Corse 1003
Staveley Miners Welfare 789
Staveley United 1012
Staverton & Landscove 1008
Staverton Park Rangers 938
Stedfast United 934
Stedham United 1012
Steelers 1002
Steeple Ashton 1011
Steeple Aston 986
Steeple Bumpstead 902
Steeple Claydon 1003
Steeple Morden 902
Steeton 981
Sterling 1013
Stevenage Borough 145
Steventon 935
Stevington 898
Stewartby Village 898
Stewarts & Lloyds Corby 851
Stewkley 1003
Steyning Town 837
Sticker 970
Stickland United 969
Stillington 1014
Stilton United 945
Stirling Castle 993
Stithians 995
STM Sports 1023
Stobswood Welfare 941
Stock United 1001
Stockbridge 864
Stockbury Athletic 1006
Stockingford AA 762
Stockingford AA Pavilion 991
Stockport Georgians 931
Stocksbridge Park Steels 465
Stocksfield 940
Stockton 991
Stockton & Codford 1007
Stockwood Green Robinsons 949
Stockwood Wanderers 989
Stoconians 999
Stogursey Greyhounds 1011
Stoke Fleming 1008
Stoke Fleming Res 1008
Stoke Gabriel 814
Stoke Gifford United 989
Stoke Prior 997
Stoke Rangers 998
Stoke Rovers 1001
Stoke-by-Nayland 991
Stokenchurch 1014
Stokesley Sports Club 801
Stoke-sub-Hamdon 1014
Stone Club & Institute 995
Stone Dominoes 777
Stone Magnets 986
Stone Old Alleynians 879
Stoneclough 963
Stoneham Park 988
Stonehenge Snooker 1007
Stonehouse Town 995
Stonemasons 1007
Stones 992
Stonesfield Sports 942
Stonewall 934
Stoney Middleton 997
Stoneycroft 929
Stonham Aspal 955
Stony Stratford Town 823
Stopsley Common 1001
Stopsley Park 1001
Storeys 1004
Storm 1002
Storrington 837
Storthes Hall 980
Stotfold 851
Stothert & Pitt 987
Stourbridge 556
Stourpaine 969
Stourport Swifts 583
Stourvale 988
Stowmarket Town 718
Stowupland Falcons 955
Stradbroke United 956
Stratford Town 769
Stratton United FC 991
Street 880
Strensall 1014
Stretham Hotspurs 902
Stretton Eagles 952
Stretton Spartans 990
Stretton Village 995
Strood 1006
Stroud Harriers 1010
Stroud Imperial 1010
Studley 769
Stump Cross 996
Sturdee 1006
Sturminster Newton United 907
Sturminster Marshall 907
Sturry 990
Styal 905
Suburban Sports 1023
Subway Totton 1009
Sudbrook Cricket Club 1024
Sudbury Athletic 909
Sudbury Park 994
Sudden Carling 1007
Suffolk Punch 1001
Sully Sports 1026
Summerstown 998
Sumner Street 1009
Sumners 1006
Sun Inn Wheatley 995
Sun Postal Rovers 1012
Sun Postal Sports 823
Sunderland Nissan 800
Sunderland Ryhope CA 801
Sunderland South 993
Sundon Park Rangers 1001
Sungate 912
Sunnybank WMC 1025
Supercala 1010
Supercue 902
Surbiton Eagles 998
Surrey Athletic 996
Surrey Fire 998
Surud United 1008
Sutterton 988
Sutton 993
Sutton Athletic 921
Sutton Bonington 1004
Sutton Bonington Academicals 1004
Sutton Bridge United 945
Sutton Coldfield Town 584
Sutton Colts 993
Sutton Courtenay 935
Sutton Dynamo 1008
Sutton Fields Rangers 994
Sutton High 1010
Sutton Park 994
Sutton Saints 1001
Sutton Town 903
Sutton United (Birmingham) 987
Sutton United (Cambs) 902
Sutton United (Surrey) 648
Sutton United FC 996
Sutton Veterans 993
Sutton Way Villa 991
Suttoners Civil 988
SW Flooring 1026
Swaffham Town 718
Swale United 922
Swalecliffe 990
Swan 1009
Swan & Mitre 990
Swan Mead 1009
Swan Valley 995
Swanage Town & Herston 907
Swanley Oaks 1007
Swansea Dockers 1026
Swanton Morley 990
Swanwick Pentrich Road 1002
Swarthmoor Social Club 1004
Swavesey Institute 901
Sway 988
SWEB 1005
Swillington Saints 985
Swindon Irons 966
Swindon NALGO 966
Swindon Supermarine 558
Swinefleet Juniors 1007
Swineshead Institute 988
Swiss Cottage 994
SWR Garage Doors 1012
Sychdyn 1024
Sydenham Rangers 1011
Sydney Street WMC 986
Syngenta SC 997
Syresham 1003
T D Shipley 1012
Tacket Street BBOB 956
Tackley 1013
Tacolneston 990
Tadcaster Albion 789
Tadcaster Magnet Sports 985
Tadley Calleva 864
Tadworth 1010
Taffs Well 1019
Takeley 730
Talbot Athletic 954
Talbot Knowle 989
Talybont 1023
Talysarn Celts 1023
Tamar 1013
Tamarside 1005
Tamworth 151
Taplow United 946
Tarleton Corinthians 1006
Tarporley Victoria 906
Tarvin Athletic 991
Tate & Lyle Selby 1014
Tatsfield Rovers 1006
Tattingstone United 956
Taunton Blackbrook 948
Taunton Civil Service 1011
Taunton Town 602
Taverners (Glos) 914
Taverners (Somerset) 1011
Tavistock 813
TC Sports 989
Team Bath 25
Team Bury 908
Team Northumbria 801
Team Solent 916
Teamstats.net 988
Technical Services 1007
Technogroup Welshpool 1015
Tedburn St Mary 992
Teesside Athletic 958
Teign Village 1008
Teignmouth 814
Telford Juniors 976
Telford Town 976
Tempest United 964
Temple Cloud 1001
Templecombe Rovers 1014
Tenbury Town 998
Tenbury United 879
Tenby 1025
Tenterden Town 922
Terrington 1004
Terrington Glory 1014
Test Park Rangers 1008
Testwood 1009
Tetbury Town 995
Tetford 993
Tetney Rovers 993
Teversal 789
Tewkesbury Rovers 990
Tewkesbury Town 990
Teyfant Athletic 989
Thackley 788
Thame Town 986
Thame United 738
Thames Borough 1008
Thamesmead Town 674
Thatcham Town 603
Thatto Heath 1009
Thaxted Rangers 902
The 61 FC (Luton) 824
The Baglan 1026
The Balti House 969
The Beeches 991
The Coach & Horses 1007
The Corrie 1009
The Courts 994
The Crown 987
The Dart 990
The Deverills 1011
The Elms 990
The Five Bells 1007
The Fort 1012
The Hammers 998
The Hassocks Hornets 1002
The Hop Leaf 947
The Kings Arms 1001
The Lair 994
The New Saints 1015
The New Saints Colts 1025
The Oak 1025
The Old Prince of Orange 995
The Prince of Wales 990
The Railway EWM 1004
The Rising Eagles 995
The Rising Sun 1006
The Rose Inn Gillingham 1006
The Running Horses 990

The Seal Inn 990
The Stiffs 1011
The Swan 990
The Swan FC 986
The Tavern 986
The Three Mariners 1007
The Two Sawyers 990
The Villa 1023
The Vine 902
The Wanderers 934
The Warren 1011
The Weston Arms 1007
The White Lion 1023
The Wilberforce Wanderers 934
The Wilton 994
The Windmill 988
Theale 947
Theddlethorpe 993
Therfield Eagles 1003
Thetford Athletic 990
Thetford Rovers 896
Thetford Town 718
Thimblemill REC 762
Thirsk Falcons 996
Thoresby Colliery Welfare 904
Thorley Park 987
Thornaby 801
Thornaby Dubliners 978
Thornborough Athletic 1003
Thornbury Town 914
Thorncliffe 1007
Thorncombe 1005
Thorne Colliery 904
Thornes 1012
Thorney 945
Thorney Close Inn 1011
Thornhill (Wales) 1023
Thornhill (West Yorks) 1011
Thornleigh 999
Thornley 993
Thornton Cleveleys 965
Thornton Dale 987
Thornton Heath 998
Thornton Heath Rovers 1010
Thornwell Red & White 1024
Thorpe Athletic 1009
Thorpe Hesley 1007
Thorpe Rovers 896
Thorpe United 1014
Thorpe Village 896
Thorplands United 1005
Thorverton 992
Thrapston 938
Thrapston Town 852
Three Bridges 836
Three Crowns 1013
Three Crowns FC 1005
Three Crowns United 998
Three Gables Colts 995
Three Sisters 1006
Three Suttons 1001
Three Tuns Galacticos 898
Threemilestone SC 1002
Thringstone Miners Welfare 1004
Thringstone Rangers 1004
Thrissell Nomads 989
Thundersley Rovers 1009
Thundersley United 1009
Thundridge United 997
Thurgoland Welfare 1008
Thurlaston Magpies 1000
Thurmaston Rangers 1004
Thurmaston Town 926
Thurnby Rangers 926
Thurnby United 1000
Thurnham United 1001
Thurrock 389
Thurston 955
Thurton & Ashby 990
Tibberton United 1009
Tibshelf 1001
Tibshelf Community 1002
TIC Dynamos 1004
Ticehurst 994
Tickenham United 1013
Tidenham 995
Tideswell United 997
Tilbury 675
Tillingham Hotspur 1001
Tilly Rangers 989
Times Inn 1012
Timperley Wanderers 986
Timsbury Athletic 948
Tintern 1024
Tintinhull 969
Tintwistle Athletic 999
Tintwistle Villa 997
Tippling 1024
Tipton St John 992
Tipton Town 769
Tiptree Heath 908
Tiptree United 717
Tisbury 1007
Titans 1002
Titans United 998
Tiverton Town 560
Tividale 876
Tivoli Rovers 990
TMG 1014
Toby 994
Tockwith 1014
Todmorden Borough 965
Toftwood Rangers 990
Tokyngton Manor 823
Tollesbury 991
Ton & Gelli Boys Club 1026
Ton Pentre 1019
Tonbridge Angels 650
Tonbridge Baptist Church 1007
Tonbridge Invicta 921
Tonbridge Saracens 1007
Tondu Robins 1023
Tongham 957
Tongwynlais 1026
Tonypandy Albion 1026
Tonyrefail BGC 1026
Tooting & Mitcham United 652
Tooting Bec 1010
Top Spinners 1006
Tophams Tavern 1007
Topps United 1000
Topsham Town 992
Tor 1014
Torbay Christians 1008
Toros 997
Torpoint Athletic 813
Torridgeside 1003
Torrington 1003
Torrington Admirals 1003
Torrisholme 1004
Total Sign Solutions 994
Totley Sports 997
Totnes & Dartington SC 814
Totterdown Port of Bristol 989
Totterdown United 989
Totternhoe 824
Tottington United 999
Totton & Eling 864
Tow Law Town 800
Tower 987
Town Green 1006
Town Mill 1002
Trackback 1009
Trades & Labour Club 994
Tradesmans Arms 1025
Trafford 488
Trafford United 986
Tramway 996
Tranch 1024
Travaux 994
Travellers Rest 1012
Trawden Celtic 992
Trawsgoed 1023
Trearddur Bay United 1023
Trebanog Rangers 1026
Treboeth United 1026
Tredegar Arms 1025
Tredegar Athletic 1025
Tredegar Town 1020
Tredworth Tigers 1010
Trefelin BGC 1026
Trefonnen 1025
Trefor 1023
Treforest 1026
Tregaron Turfs 1023
Treharris Athletic 1020
Treharris Athletic Western 1024
Trelai 1023
Trelawney 998
Trelewis Welfare 1026
Treorchy BGC 1026
Treowen Stars 1024
Trethomas Bluebirds 1024
Trevenson United 1002
Trevethin 1024
Trewern United 1025
Trident (Glos) 1009
Trident (Notts) 1005
Trimley Red Devils 956
Trimpell-Slyne 964
Trinant 1024
Tring Athletic 822
Tring Corinthians 824
Trinidad 988
Trinity 1010
Trinity (S) 1009
Trinity Old Boys 1014
Trispen 1002
Triumph Athletic 991
Troedyrhiw 1021
Trojan Security 1009
Troon 1002
Trowbridge House 986
Trowbridge Old Boys 1023
Trowbridge Town 739
Trowbridge Wanderers 1011
Truro City 562
Trysull 879
Tuakana 988
Tudor 1001
Tudor Sports 921
Tuffley Rovers 914
Tunbridge Wells 755
Tunbridge Wells United 1011
Tunley Athletic 950
Tunstall Town 954
Turberville Arms 1026
Turners Hill 1002
Turnpike Sports 947
Turton 963
TVFC 1002
Two Gates 998
Two Rivers 1013
Twyford 972
Twyford & Ruscombe 947
Twyford United 1003
Twynham Rangers 988
Tydd St Mary 988
Tydd United 902
Tyersal 981
Tyldesley 1013
Tyldesley United 999
Tyndalls Park Rangers 989
Tynemouth United 941
Tynewydd 1026
Tynte Rovers 1023
Tytherington Rocks 739
Tywardreath RBL 993
Tywyn & Bryncrug 1025
UAU Exeter 992
Uberlube 991
Uckfield Town 838
UEA 897
Uffington United 936
Ufford Sports 956
Uley 1009
Ullswater United 1013
Ultrachem TKO 995
Underwood Social Club 1024
Underwood Villa 1005
Undy Athletic 1024
Unicorn 1012
Union Rovers 987
Unis Old Boys 1010
United Chelmsford Churches 1001
United Services 1002
United Services Plymouth 1005
United Services Portsmouth 864
Unitor 987
Unity 946
Universal Plastering 988
Universal Windows 987
University of Bath 986
University of Chichester 1012
University of Essex 908
University of Exeter 814
University of Greenwich 990
University of Kent 920
University of Northampton 1005
University of Plymouth 1005
University of Portsmouth 1005
University of Surrey 1010
University of Worcester 1013
Up Holland 1013
Upchurch 1006
Uplowman Athletic 992
Uplyme 1005
Upminster 912
Upottery 992
Upper Beeding 1012
Uppermill 997
Upperthong 997
Uppingham Town 944
Upton 987
Upton Athletic 1007
Upton Athletic Association 960
Upton St Leonards 1009
Upton Town 1013
Upwey & Broadwey 969
Urban Athletic 987
USA 990
Usk Town 1024
USL Galacticos 1001
Usworth 1012
UW Aberystwyth 1025
UWIC 1020
Uxbridge 604
Uxbridge Town 934
Vagas 1000
Valley 1023
Valley Colts 1006
Valley Park Rangers 1008
Vauxhall Motors 285
VBA Rangers 1011
VBL Sports 1013
VC United 999
VCD Athletic 676
Ventnor 998
Venture Community 1026
Ventus & Yeadon Celtic 981
Veracity Vipers 1008
Vernon Villa 1005
Verwood Town 864
Vicars X Doves 991
Vice Versa 1004
Vickerstown CC 963
Victoria 1000
Victoria Baptists 994
Victoria Celtic 1010
Victoria Horbury 1012
Victoria Hotel 1007
Viewpoint 995
Viking Raiders 994
Villa Dino Christchurch 1024
Villa Rainhill 1012
Villa Royale 1004
Village 987
Village of Ditchling 1002
Village Social 1012
Viney St Swithins 995
VIP 999
VIP Communications 994
Virginia Water 1010
Vista 988
Volunteer Arms 996
Vospers Oak Villa 815
VTFC 605
Vulcan 1012
W & B Sports 998
Waddington 992
Waddington United 1000
Wadebridge Town 813
Wadham Lodge 994
Wadhurst United 994
Wadsworth United 996
Waggon & Horses 991
Wainfleet United 988
Wake Green Amateurs 987
Wakefield 489
Wakefield City 981
Wakefield United 1012
Wakes 998
Walderslade 1006
Waldon Athletic 1007
Walgrave Amber 938
Walker Central 939
Walker Scott 988
Walkford 988
Wallington 940
Wallington New Foresters 1006
Wallisdown Conservative 988
Wallsend Boys Club 941
Wallsend Town 941
Walmer Bridge 1006
Walney Island 965
Walnut Tree (Loose) 1001
Walsall Phoenix 987
Walsall Wood 761
Walsham-le-Willows 717
Walshaw Sports Club 931
Walsingham 1004
Walsoken United 902
Waltham 993
Waltham Abbey 654
Waltham Forest 677
Waltham Tea Gardens 993
Walton 1011
Walton & Hersham 697
Walton Casuals 698
Walton CFC 998
Walton Court Wanderers 986
Walton Heath 1006
Walton-le-Dale 1006
Wanderers 989
Wandgas Sports 1010
Wandle 998
Wandsworth Corinthians 998
Wandsworth Town (Kingston) 998
Wantage Town 737
Warborough & Shillingford 935
Warboys Town 945
Warbreck 929
Wardle 1007
Wardley 1011
Ware 678
Ware Lions Old Boys 997
Wareham Rangers 969
Wargrave 947
Wark 939
Warley Development 878
Warley Rangers 996
Warlingham 704
Warminster Town 864
Warmley Saints 989
Warren 934
Warren Social 1009
Warrington Town 490
Warriors XI 1003
Warsash Wasps 1008
Warstone Wanderers 878
Washington 801
Watchet Town 948
Watcombe Wanderers 1008
Waterbeach 899
Waterhayes 954
Wateringbury Village 1001
Waterloo 994
Waterloo Dock 928
Waterloo FC 1011
Waterloo GSOB 1000
Waterloo Rovers 1025
Waterloo Rovers Colts 1025
Waterloo Wanderers 1012
Waterlooville Social Club 1005
Waterside 956
Watlington 1004
Watlington Town 943
Watton United 893
Watton-at-Stone 997
Watts Blake & Bearne 1007
Waunfawr 1023
Waveney 897
Waveney Gunners 1001
Wavertree WDOB 1000
Wawne Ferry 994
Wealden 837
Wealdstone 656
Weavers Arms 1007
Weavers Old Boys 938
WEB 1008
Wedmore 1013
Wednesbury Town 878
Wednesfield 876
Weedon 938
Weeley Athletic 908
Weir Sports 1009
Welbeck Welfare 904
Welby Lane United 1000
Weldon United 937
Welford Victoria 938
Welling Park 990
Welling United 395
Wellingborough Old Grammarians 938
Wellingborough Raffertys 938
Wellingborough Ranelagh 938
Wellingborough Rising Sun 938
Wellingborough Saxons 938
Wellingborough Town 851
Wellingborough WMC 938
Wellington (Herefordshire) 876
Wellington (Lancs) 986
Wellington Amateurs 878
Wellington Colts 997
Wellington Town 880
Wellow 1008
Wells City 881
Wells Town 894
Welly Old Boys 986

Welton Arsenal 1001
Welton Rovers 880
Welwyn Garden City 822
Wem Town 976
Wembdon 1011
Wembdon Saints 1011
Wembley 703
Wendling 990
Wendover 986
Wendron United 815
Wenhaston United 955
Wenvoe Exiles 1026
Weobley 997
Wepre Rangers 1024
Werrington Town 945
WESA 986
Wessex Rangers 1005
Wessex Wanderers 989
West & Middle Chinnock 1005
West Allotment Celtic 800
West Auckland Town 800
West Bergholt 908
West Bridgford United 1002
West Bromley Albion 1008
West Byfleet Albion 996
West Chiltington 1012
West Cornwall 1002
West Didsbury & Chorlton 932
West End 1020
West End FC 990
West Essex 995
West Farleigh 1001
West Green 995
West Haddon 938
West Hagley 987
West Harnham 1007
West Hill 1008
West Hoathly 1002
West Horton 982
West House 1023
West Hull Amateurs 994
West Jesmond 1011
West Kirby 960
West London Saracens 934
West Lynn Riverside 1004
West Lynn SSC 895
West Malvern 1013
West Meter 991
West Midlands Police 762
West Midlands Travel 987
West Pontnewydd 1024
West Reading 947
West Row Gunners 901
West Side Rangers 934
West Tarring WMC 1014
West Wight 998
West Winch 1004
West Witney 1013
West Wratting 900
Westbrook YMCA 996
Westbury 1003
Westbury United (Glos) 1003
Westbury United (Suffolk) 1009
Westbury United (Wilts) 881
Westcliff Amateur 1009
Westcliff United 1009
Westcott 1006
Westella & Willerby 904
Westend 1013
Westend FC 997
Westerfield United 955
Westerham 921
Westerhope JG 940
Westerleigh Sports 989
Western Juniors Old Boys 1014
Western Mortgage Services 1005
Westexe Rovers 992
Westfield 987
Westfield (Somerset) 950
Westfield (Surrey) 704
Westfield (Sussex) 837
Westfield (Wilts) 1011
Westfields 769
Westgate Wanderers 1004
Westhall 1001
Westhamians 911
Westland Sports 907
Westland United 949
Westmill 997
Westminster Casuals 1010
Weston 997
Weston Green Sports 1010
Weston Rhyn 1007
Weston St Johns Sports Bar 1013
Weston United 1013
Weston Youth 987
Westoning Recreation Club 898
Weston-super-Mare 401
Westonzoyland 1011
Westover Bournemouth 988
Westover Rangers 1006
Westover Spartans 969
Westside (Surrey) 1010
Westside (Wilts) 966
Westside Rangers 988
Westwell 1003
Westwood 1011
Westwood United 946
Wetherby Athletic 983
Wetheriggs United 1012
Wey Valley 986
Weybrook Wanderers 996
Weymouth 407
Weymouth Sports 969
Weymouth Wanderers 969
WFC Clitheroe 992
Whaddon United 990
Whaley Bridge 997
Whaley Thorns 991
Whalley Range 999
Whatton United 995
Wheatley '04 943
Wheatley Hill SC 993
Wheatsheaf 994
Wheatsheaf Celtic 1001
Wheatshield Wanderers 1008
Wheelwright Old Boys 1014
Wheldrake 1014
Whickham 801
Whinney Banks YCC 979
Whinney Hill 965
Whiston Cross Holt 1012
Whitby Town 466
Whitchurch 989
Whitchurch Alport 906
Whitchurch Blues 1023
Whitchurch Res 989
Whitchurch United 864
White Bear Kexbrough 1011
White Ensign 910
White Hart 1003
White Hart Rangers 1011
White Hart United 1001
White Horse (Glos) 1004
White Horse (Wales) 1024
White Horse Borstal 1006
White Horse Rangers 1009
White Horse Celtic 1000
White Horse Symondsbury 1005
White Knight 994
White Lion 995
White Notley 908
White Red Eagles 1009
White Roding 987
White Rose 1008
Whitecroft 1003
Whitefield Norpol 937
Whitehall 991
Whitehaven Amateurs 801
Whitehaven Miners Welfare 992
Whitehawk 836
Whiteheads 1024
Whitehill 993
Whiteparish 1007
Whiteshill United 1009
Whitkirk Wanderers 983
Whitley Bay 800
Whitley Bay Town 941
Whitminster 1009
Whitnash 991
Whitstable Town 699
Whittington Brenstar 990
Whittle 991
Whittlesey United 944
Whittlesford United 900
Whitton United 717
Whitwell Village 1003
Whitwick Colliery 1004
Whitwick Wanderers 1004
Whitworths 852
Whyteleafe 700
Wibsey 980
Wick (Bristol) 988
Wick (Sussex) 836
Wicken Amateurs 902
Wicken Sports 1003
Wickersley Old Boys 1007
Wickford Rangers 1009
Wickham Market 955
Wickham Park 923
Wickham Royals 1001
Wickham Wanderers 1008
Wickhambrook 899
Wickwar Wanderers 1009
Wideopen & District 941
Widnes Bayer 1012
Widnes St Maries 1012
Wigan Robin Park 777
Wigan Rovers 1013
Wiggenhall 1004
Wigginton Grasshoppers 1014
Wigston Athletic 1000
Wigton Athletic 992
Wigton Harriers 992
Wigton Moor 996
Wilbarston 938
Wilberfoss 1014
Wilbraham 902
Wilby 938
Wildern United 1009
Wilderpark 1007
Wilf Kroucher 1010
Willand Rovers 880
Willaston 961
Willaston Nomads 991
Willenhall Town 512
Willerby Holiday Homes 994
Willesden Constantine 933
William Burt 1004
Willingdon Athletic 1001
Willington 958
Willington FC 1002
Willington Quay Saints 941
Willis 955
Williton 1011
Willow Park 1007
Willow Pond 1011
Wilmslow Albion 932
Wilmslow Sports 993
Wilsden Juniors 992
Wilshamstead 898
Wilton Town 966
Wimblington 944
Wimborne Town 863
Wimpole 991
Wincanton Town 907
Winch Wen 1026
Winchcombe Town 995
Winchester Castle 916
Winchester City 517
Winchmore Hill 1014
Windermere SC 1012
Windermere Wanderers 1007
Windle Labour Club 1012
Windlesham 996
Windscale 958
Windsor & Eton 606
Windsor Great Park 993
Winford PH 989
Wing Village 1003
Wingate & Finchley 679
Wingham 990
Wingrave 986
Wingspan 992
Winkleigh 992
Winlaton Vulcan Inn 1011
Winnershe Rangers 947
Winscombe 948
Winsford United 776
Winsham 1005
Winslow United 823
Winstanley St Aidans 1013
Winterbourne United 739
Winterslow 1007
Winterthur 986
Winterton Rangers 788
Winterton Town 1007
Winwick 1012
Wirksworth Ivanhoe 1002
Wirksworth Town 1002
Wirral Wanderers 987
Wisbech Fen Stars 902
Wisbech St Mary 902
Wisbech Town 717
Wisbech United 1004
Wisdom Sports 1001
Witchampton United 969
Witchford 902
Witham Town 610
Witheridge 813
Witherley United 991
Withernsea 974
Witney Athletic 1013
Witney Royals 1013
Witney United 737
Witney Wanderers 1013
Wittering United 1012
Witton Albion 513
Witton Inn 988
Wivenhoe Town 717
WLA 1000
Woburn 898
Woburn Sands Wanderers 1003
Wodson Park 997
Woking 413
Woking & Horsell 1010
Wokingham & Emmbrook 738
Wollaston Victoria 938
Wollaton 1005
Wollescote Villa 998
Wolstanton United 952
Wolston 992
WolverhamptonCasuals 876
Wolverhampton Utd 878
Wolviston 958
Wombles 1009
Wombwell Main 1007
Wooburn Athletic 1014
Wood Wanderers 987
Woodborough United 1002
Woodbridge Athletic 955
Woodbridge Town 717
Woodbury 992
Woodchester 1010
Woodcoombe Sports & Social 1006
Woodcote & Stoke Row 946
Woodcote Old Boys 1006
Woodford United 585
Woodgate & Newfoundpool WMC 1000
Woodhall Spa United 988
Woodhouse Hill WMC 984
Woodhouse Imperial 1004
Woodhouse Moor Methodists 1014
Woodisbury 1007
Woodland Albion 1006
Woodlands 1011
Woodlands Athletic 995
Woodlands WMC 991
Woodley 905
Woodley Sports 491
Woodley Town 946
Woodman 993
Woodmancote 990
Woodmans Hall 990
Woodmansterne Hyde 957
Woodnesborough 990
Woodside & Goring 1013
Woodstock Park 922
Woofferton 996
Wookey 1001
Wool RBL 969
Woolaston 1003
Woolavington Predators 1011
Wooldale Wanderers 997
Wooler 1004
Woolley Moor United 1002
Woolpack 993
Woolsery 1003
Woolverstone United 956
Wootton & Dry Sandford 935
Wootton Bassett Town 739
Wootton Blue Cross 852
Wootton Sports 1013
Wootton St George 938
Worcester City 420
Worcester City Academy 763
Worcester Park 704
Workington 291
Workplace Wanderers 1003
Worksop Town 468
Worle 949
Wormingford Wanderers 991
Wormley Rovers 917
Worplesdon Phoenix 1010
Worrall Hill 1003
Worsbrough Bridge MW 789
Worsbrough Common 1007
Worsbrough Dale Dynamos 1008
Worsley Mesnes 1013
Worsthorne 993
Worth Avenue 988
Worth Park Rangers 992
Worthing 701
Worthing Albion 1013
Worthing Athletic 1013
Worthing United 836
Wortley 1014
Wortley Res 1014
Wortwell 895
Wotton Rovers 995
Woughton 1003
Wrangle United 988
Wraysbury 957
Wrecclesham 1010
Wrens Nest 879
Wrentham 1000
Wrenthorpe 1012
Wrexham 157
Wrightchoice CSA 947
Wrington-Redhill 951
Writtle 912
Writtle Manor 1001
Wrockwardine Wood 977
Wroot 995
Wroughton 966
Wroxall 998
Wroxeter Rovers 977
Wroxham 717
Wroxton Sports 986
Wulfrun Invicta 987
Wyberton 988
Wychwood Forest 1013
Wycombe Athletic 1014
Wycombe Judo 1014
Wyesham Wanderers 1024
Wyke Regis Social Club 969
Wyke Wanderers 985
Wykebeck Arms United 999
Wymering 1005
Wymondham Town 894
Wyndham 1026
Wyre Forest 998
Wyre Villa 964
Wyrley Juniors 879
Wythenshawe Amateur 931
Wythenshawe Town 932
Wyvern 1011
Y Felinheli 1023
Y Glannau 1024
Yalding 1001
Yardley Ex-Services 987
Yardley Gobion 1003
Yardley United 938
Yarmouth & Calbourne 998
Yarnton 943
Yate Town 607
Yateley 1010
Yateley Green 986
Yatton Athletic 951
Yaxham 990
Yaxley 851
Yealm Goosewell Rangers 1005
Yelverton 1005
YMCA 997
Ynysddu Crusaders 1026
Ynyshir Albion 1026
Ynyshir/Wattstown BYC 1026
Ynysygerwen 1025
Ynysymeudwy Athletic 1025
York 1009
York City 163
York Civil Service 1014
York Railway Institute 1014
York St John University 1014
Yorkley 1003
Yorkshire Amateur 789
Yorkshire Bank 1014
Yorkshire Main 903
Yorkshire Penny 1007
Youlgrave United 997
Yourstory 1010
Ystradgynlais 1021
Zebra Sports 1009

Editors
Tony Williams
(Tel: 01823 490 684)
Email: t.williams320@btinternet.com
James Wright
6 Harp Chase, Taunton, Somerset TA1 3RY
(Tel: 07786 636659 Fax: 0800 048 8641)
Email: james@nlnewsdesk.co.uk

Published by Tony Williams Publications Ltd
(Tel/Fax: 01548 531 339)
Email: twpublications@mcsolutions.org.uk